COMICS VALUES ANNUAL:
The Comic Books Price Guide

by Alex G. Malloy

Edited by Stuart W. Wells III

features editor: Robert J. Sodaro

Antique Trader Books
A Division of Landmark Specialty Publications
Norfolk, Virginia

Designed by Stuart W. Wells III
Design Coordinator: Chris Decker

Cover art by Bryan Hitch and Paul Neary
Stormwatch is ® and © Aegis Entertainment, Inc.
dba Wildstorm Productions 1998
All rights reserved.

Manufactured in the United States of America

ISBN: 0-930625-15-3
ISSN: 1062-4503

To order additional copies of this book or to
obtain a free catalog, please contact:

Antique Trader Publications
P.O. Box 1050
Dubuque, Iowa 52004
1-800-334-7165

CONTENTS

THE CONTINUING SAGA

By Alex G. Malloy

In the immortal words of Baseball legend Yogi Berra, "It's not over 'til it's over." Which is pretty much how you can describe the ongoing, but always interesting, story of comics. Just when you think the status is going to remain quo, someone like Jim Lee pulls one out of left field and sells his company (WildStorm), to DC, (as he apparently did the first week of September), lock, stock, and creator-owned imprint publishing rights.

Who could possibly have seen that one coming? Having done that, you've got to wonder what he's going to do next. One can imagine him—a couple of years hence—vocally splitting from DC (as he and the rest of the Image founders once did from Marvel), with a completely new coterie of creative talent to found, yet another, publishing consortium. However, one can also see him successfully managing the full-scale, complete and seamless melding of his characters from the WildStorm universe with those of the DC Cosmos, switching over to the corporate side, moving up the company ladder, eventually rising up to take over as publisher as Jenette Kahn's hand-picked successor.

One never knows, does one...?

And that's the beauty of this crazy, mixed-up business, one never does know (unless, of course he's Lamont Cranston, and even he might be hard pressed to fully fathom it all).

As for the rest of our annual walkabout through this beloved industry of ours, what would any year-end round-up be without a discussion concerning the status of the once mighty House of Ideas, Marvel Comics. How far have the mighty fallen. Once the cock of the walk, The House that Jack Built is still in a mighty fight for its collective life, as it struggles to pull itself out of the quagmire of Chapter 11 bankruptcy.

For all its ins and outs, the corporate in-fighting between Ronald O. Perlman and Carl C. Icahn (the two financiers who were struggling to control Marvel) comes across like the boardroom version of a continuity-wide slugfest between the forces of good and the forces of evil. Of course, both sides declared themselves to be on the side of angels—in the real world, no one ever refers to themselves as the Brotherhood of Evil Bankers; ah well, more's the pity. Needless to say, the NYSE suspended trading of Marvel stock in April (the stock was hardly worth anything at that point).

At any rate, back in February, ToyBiz put forth a reorganization plan which seems to have been adopted, so perhaps by this time next year all of this will be past history, and ToyBiz will have taken over the company. Can this mean more toy tie-ins (as if that could happen), or more comics based on toys (again, as if).

In the meantime Marvel is still contemplating a line of theme restaurants, the first of which opened in January '98 at the Universal Studios in California. There are also several Marvel-inspired rides currently under construction at the MGM Theme park in Orlando Florida. Marvel has gotten its very interactive and interesting Web site off the ground (www.marvelzone.com), plus it is accessible through AOL. All this while Joseph Calamari attempts to steer the comicbook division back into the black.

Still, on the plus side, not only was Heroes Reborn a rousing success, but the follow-up story-trail, Heroes Return, is likewise being grudgingly embraced. Further, Marvel is catching some good buzz for their new (as of this writing) foray back to the future. Then, of course, there is the current round of retro-revisionism that is about to occur when John Byrne not only takes over Spider-Man, but sling-shots him back to the beginning (a la his run on Superman).

Perhaps this time he can bring the wall-crawling wonder into the present day without the baggage of a clone (and wouldn't this be a good time to correct the mistake of Gwen Stacy's death as well)...one can only hope.

As for the rest of the pack, if all else fails, one just needs to watch Rob Liefeld—always a favorite, and entertaining, lightning rod of ours. It is probably only a matter of time before he launches (yet another), firestorm of controversy and ire within the industry. Why, just a year ago he severed his ties from the rest of his Image co-founders (as we discussed in this space last year), and founded Awesome Entertainment. Well, the bloom is already off that rose as mid-way through this year he suspended publication of the entire line.

On the up side for Liefeld, it was widely reported that he was paid a cool million for a script to a new character of his called The Mark, which is being developed into a big-budget Hollywood movie. He followed this up with an announcement that he wants to direct this flick, as well as others. Will he turn out to be the next Lucas or the next Allen Smithie? Who knows, but knowing Liefeld, it doesn't really matter what happens, or what people say, he will continue to wind up on top, and not care one wit what people say about him.

Following on the heels of Awesome's announcement, came a similar one from Acclaim. It seems that the new revamp that they attempted with their comicbook line didn't take either, and that entire division was also shut down around mid-year. Of course there were claims that a few of the comics already in production would continue, but again, who's to tell?

There were reports of Crusade Comics going under this spring, and this just in. Apparently Topps is closing the doors of its comicbook division sometime before the end of the year. However, amid all of the reports of doom and gloom, there is still hope, as there is talk of John Carbonaro re-launching his T.H.U.N.D.E.R. Agents again sometime in the coming year (there is a brief history of the Agents included in this volume).

DC Comics is also experiencing the same kinds of upheavals that have plagued the industry for the past couple of years, and save for their recent purchase of WildStorm (which everyone is still denying at this writing), the news for them seems fairly grim. We reserve the right not to like the purchase of WildStorm (if, indeed it was purchased, which it probably was), as we still are stinging over how DC's relationship with Milestone eventually played out. Still, this could be a good thing.

On the Movie front, what would a year be without a comicbook movie? This year we were treated to Wesley Snipes as Blade, which was #1 at the box office for two or three weeks towards the Fall of '98. Unfortunately, Marvel backed away from the movie prior to it's opening, due to the "R" rating, excess of blood and gore, and violence. A bad move, as it is a very hot flick. But that's not all, as Marv Wolfman sued Marvel for $35 million as he claims that he was a freelancer when he created Blade and Deacon Frost (the bad guy of the film), and never signed a work-for-hire agreement, nor gave Marvel permission to use the characters in a movie. Can't we all just get along guys?

Men In Black, already a certified hit in the theater, came to home video and to Burger King in the form of a Kid Meal toy tie-in set. Dark Horse, always one for a movie tie-in, licensed Robert A. Heinlein's *Starship Trooper* as a comic. Too bad that the movie proved to be as horrid as it was. Still their take on the comic was far better than the movie (if not as good as the Heinlein novel itself). Dark Horse canceled, and then resurrected Ghost, the last survivor of its Comics Greatest World characters. (The reborn Ghost has yet to surface, but we have our eye out for it.)

The most recent set of numbers for comics are still looking dismal, and back issue sales are still in the cellar, but there is a growing buzz in the industry about numerous fan favs, and fans are ever hopeful that...next year...this will all be over and we'll be back on top again. We here at CVA certainly hope so, and while we are reticent to go so far as saying everything will turn around and be roses again, we do believe that we are seeing the light at the end of the long hard tunnel. Meet us back here next year, and we'll have this chat once again.

As this is the age of cyberinformation, anyone who wants to learn more about this issue's topics and/or subjects, has a computer and is hooked up to the Web, can do so by accessing the Internet:

Warren Ellis can be found at www.warrenellis.com

Ellis, StormWatch, The Authority, Wetworks, and WildStorm can be found at www.wildstorm.com

Ellis and *Transmetropolitan* can be found at www.dc.com and the DC areas of AOL and www.warnerbros.com.

John Carbonaro and the T.H.U.N.D.E.R. Agents can be found at www.thunder.com.

Special thanks this year to Warren Ellis, Whilce Portacio, John Carbonaro, Cave Comics and Flamingo Street Book Shop; and to Harry Rinker and Allan Miller for guidance and talent in making this annual possible.

THE RESPLENDENT SOUND OF T.H.U.N.D.E.R.!

by Robert J. Sodaro

Sired in the Mid-'60s by One of the Most-Beloved Creators in the Industry, the T.H.U.N.D.E.R. Agents are the Superteam that Categorically Refuses to Stay Dead!

In some respects, the T.H.U.N.D.E.R. Agents have lived a most charmed life, as they have risen Phoenix-like from the grave of cancellation more times and appeared under more corporate banners and logos than any group of superheroes has any right to expect. However—on the other side of the coin—there seems to be some sort of black cloud constantly hovering their collective heads as they have never been able to make it past issue #20 in any of their many incarnations over the years.

Born in 1965, they sprang—Prometheus-like from the fertile and creative mind of Wally Wood, and—by all rights—they should be as well-known today as their Marvel Comics brethren who came into existence just a few short years earlier. Unfortunately, the breaks just didn't go their way, and the team (in fact the entire comicbook line), just didn't make it to the end of the decade. Still, the Agents themselves just wouldn't give up the ghost, and have (sometimes just barely), continued to maintain a comicbook presence to the current day. A touch over 10 years after their initial series was canceled, ownership, as well as the

T.H.U.N.D.E.R. Agent © JC Comics

rights to publish them (including their original adventures), were sold by Tower Publishing to John Carbonaro's JC Productions.

This began a nearly 20-year effort on the part of Carbonaro to bring (and keep), the Agents back in the public's eye. After a couple of false starts; a copyright-infringement lawsuit (that included two or three lines of faux-T.H.U.N.D.E.R. Agents comics); and far too many abortive efforts and "almost" deals that fell through to delineate here, Carbonaro is (yes!), once again preparing to bring his adopted children back into print.

Lightning Strikes the First Time

The T.H.U.N.D.E.R. Agents are the creation of Wally Wood, who developed them for Tower Comics in 1965 at the dawning of the Silver Age of comics. Perhaps he was inspired by Stan Lee's success over at Marvel, or the first "re-launch" of the DC universe, but whatever the reason, Tower (an existing magazine publisher), determined that it was interested in developing its own line of superheroes.

Instead of beginning slowly, and building up the characters over time, Tower jumped right into the fire with both feet, and gave us *T.H.U.N.D.E.R. Agents* #1 in November 1965. In that first issue, we were introduced to not only T.H.U.N.D.E.R. (The Higher United Nations Defense Enforcement Reserves[1]), but the three Agents that formed the originally team; Dynamo (their nominal leader), NoMan, and Menthor, as well as the T.H.U.N.D.E.R. Squad. The Squad was a non-superpowered, para-military strike force that supported and backed-up the Agents. The Squad was comprised of Guy Gilbert (Squad leader), Egghead (who went K.I.A. in issue #2), Kathryn "Kitten" Kane, John "Dynamite" Adkins (who was later unsuccessfully groomed to become Dynamo's replacement), and William "Weed" Wylie. There was also a faceless, unnamed legion of UN-sponsored soldiers who would come in to mop up after the Agents and Squad were finished with their work.

Although the Squad members had no superpowers, they each had their own specialty (Gilbert was a Major and Medal of Honor winner, Egghead was a genius at strategy, Kitten an M.I.T. scientist, Dynamite an underwater demolitions expert, and Weed was an escape artist). As stated, the higher-ups at T.H.U.N.D.E.R. attempted to groom Dynamite as Dynamo's replacement, but he proved to be not quite up to the task. The Brass had better luck with Gilbert who went on to become the superpowered Lightning.

Two things that made the T.H.U.N.D.E.R. Agents different from virtually every group of heroes that preceeded them (and many of those that followed), were 1) the team worked for the United Nations and 2) their powers cost them

---

[1] *To learn more about the Modern Age's UN-sponsored superteam StormWatch, read CVA's interview with Warren Ellis, in this issue.*

T.H.U.N.D.E.R. Agent © JC Comics

dearly. Even then, in the unwritten cannons of comics, there were essentially three scenarios as to how people acquired their powers and become superheroes, they were either born with them (Thor, Aquaman), acquired them by accident (Spider-Man, Flash), built some device that granted them power (Iron Man, Hawkman), or trained to be the best at what they did (Captain America, Batman, Daredevil)[2]. In the case of the Agents, each of them received their abilities by donning a bit of clothing or other device (Dynamo had his belt, Lightning his costume, Menthor his helmet, and NoMan his android body and invisibility cape).

All of these devices had maximum lock-out times where they would automatically shut down and require time to recharge. For Dynamo, it was 25 minutes, with an emergency five-minute back-up. NoMan's invisibility cape would shut down after 10 minutes. Still, it was Lightning that would suffer the most, for every time he used his super-speed, it shaved time off his life span. Hence whenever he went into action he was literally killing himself. Menthor "suffered" the least. His helmet actually brought the innate goodness of its wearer, eventually turning the double agent John J. Janus (Menthor), from a potential traitor, to a loyal agent.

For this he paid the ultimate price, however, and died in action protecting the Agents from the Warlords (#7). This marked perhaps the first time in comics that

---

[2] *Yes, we know, Captain America was initially augmented by Dr. Erskin's Super Soldier Formula, Batman had a passel of way-cool toys, and DD was not only enhanced by exposure to radiation, but had that way-cool Billy club of his. Still, all three needed to train every day, and relied mostly on their innate physical and mental abilities in their superheroing, as opposed to Superman who's powers were simply the result of being exposed to the peculiar radiation effects of our yellow sun, or Spidey who received his by virtue of the bite of an irradiated arachnid.*

major character died in action. Interestingly enough, this scenario was virtually identical to what occurred a couple of years earlier in *Avengers* #9 where Wonder Man joined the Avengers with the intention of betraying them, only to reform at the last minute and die while saving their lives[3].

Weather Patterns

Not ones to miss a trick, Tower quickly followed up its team book with a couple of titles where the team was broken out into solo stories. *Dynamo* and *NoMan* debuted shortly after *Thunder Agents* #1. Unfortunately neither title lasted long (*Dynamo* went four issues, and *NoMan* went two). A related title was *U.N.D.E.R.S.E.A. Agent*, which lasted 6 issues (a seventh U.N.D.E.R.S.E.A. Agent tale appeared in *T.H.U.N.D.E.R. Agents* #16.)

U.N.D.E.R.S.E.A. Agent stared another UN agent (also non-powered, like the T.H.U.N.D.E.R. Squad), named (what else), Davy Jones. Recruited from the Navy, Jones went to work for the United Nations Department of Experiment and Research Systems Established at Atlantis. Though Jones never met anyone from T.H.U.N.D.E.R., and there were no common characters in the two series, it can only be assumed, that—had the two titles continued—they would have eventually crossed paths.

Another pair of Tower books were *Fight the Enemy* (3 issues), a WW II anthology title; and *Tippy Teen* (an Archie-like book that lasted 28 issues, including a Special Collector's Edition)[4]. Still, in spite of what seems like a fairly solid line-up of comics for the mid-to-late '60, Tower wound up pulling the plug on the entire division in '69 (*T.H.U.N.D.E.R. Agents* went to issue #20). While this could have very well have been the last chapter in the story of Len Brown[5] (Dynamo), and his friends, it proved to be merely the first chapter in what has turned out to be a long and strange trip indeed.

The Coming Storm

In 1981, fan-turned-pro John Carbonaro acquired the rights to Wally Wood's best-loved children. He subsequently produced one B&W, magazine-sized issue

---

[3] *While Wonder Man also died at the end of his story (also while redeeming himself, he was introduced in that story, and it wasn't until several years later revived and re-cast into a hero. Menthor was created in **Thunder Agents** #1, and died in issue #7. His character and persona were later revived by Carbonaro.)*

[4] *Tippy Teen #1 was reprinted in **Vicki** #1 by Atlas/Seaboard. It is unknown if subsequent issues (2-4), of **Vicki** reprinted additional issues of **Tippy Teen**, or why Atlas would have acquired Tippy, but left the T.H.U.N.D.E.R. Agents behind.*

[5] *As a complete aside, Dynamo's character was named for the real-life Len Brown, an editor at Topps.*

on his own, before striking an arrangement with Archie comics to continue the series. Under the arrangement with Archie, Carbonaro continued to produce and package the Agents under the JC Comics label, while Archie acted as printer and distributor. The JC/Archie T.H.U.N.D.E.R. comics were produced in color, and standard comic-book sized. Unfortunately, due to a convoluted set of incidents, that arrangement didn't last very long (two issues of *T.H.U.N.D.E.R. Agents*, plus three issues reprinting from the original Tower series). A third, original T.H.U.N.D.E.R. Agents story appeared under Archie's Red Circle logo in *Blue Ribbon Comics* #12, an anthology title.

Shortly after this, Carbonaro met up with David Singer, which would send him down a long, tortured path, and all but kill the Agents as a viable set of characters. Singer, a self-professed fan of the Agents who imagined himself a junior-grade Stan Lee, managed to ingratiate himself with Carbonaro, first presenting himself as a partner in Carbonaro's publishing company, and then as his legal representative (Singer had a law degree, but had not yet passed the Bar). Utilizing his inside knowledge of the dealings between Carbonaro and Tower, Singer attempted to assume ownership of the agents, first by presenting himself as Carbonaro's legal representative, and—when this failed—claimed that the Agents existed in the Public Domain and attempted to wrest the Agents away from Carbonaro.

Apparently, Tower (which published magazines, but had no experience in publishing licensed characters), had inadvertently left the copyright notice off several copies of the various comics they published. Singer used this loophole to attempt to declare that the Agents had fallen into the Public Domain, and that anyone could publish them. He went so far as to issue a press release to this effect where he boldly proclaimed that "All God's Children" could publish the Agents, and then proceeded to do so under the Deluxe Comics banner, without Carbonaro.

T.H.U.N.D.E.R. Agent © JC Comics

Knowing that Tower's copyright and trademark on the Agents were valid and legal. Carbonaro sued Singer for copyright infringement in 1984, beginning what turned out to be a protracted, and nasty legal battle that lasted three years, and rocked the industry. In 1987, Carbonaro proved victorious and regained control of his beloved Agents. (He has also firmly established his ownership over the copyright and trademark of the Agents, and has been issued papers to that effect by the Copyright and Trademark offices of the U.S.) As part of the suit he acquired all of the T.H.U.N.D.E.R. material that Singer had published. At the time of Carbonaro's victory over Singer, Deluxe had long-since gone out of business, due mostly to Singer's own ineptness, lack of business acumen, shady dealings, and failure to pay his creators either on time, or what he had promised them. (Not to mention, Carbonaro had enjoined the major distributors from handling the Deluxe comics by naming them in his suit, thus severing the company's cash flow and access to the marketplace.)

The long legal battle over *The T.H.U.N.D.E.R. Agents* ultimately asserted three things: 1) Tower Comics' original copyright and trademarks on *The T.H.U.N.D.E.R. Agents* were valid and legally binding; 2) Carbonaro was now the legitimate and legal holder of those rights; and 3) Deluxe Comics was in violation of Federal Copyright and Trademark laws. Carbonaro's resounding victory over Deluxe resulted in a settlement which included cash, plus Deluxe surrendering all story and art copyrights, as well as all back-stock to Carbonaro.

At long last, Carbonaro was vindicated.

Stormy Weather Ahead

While his legal troubles were largely behind him, Carbonaro now began a decade-long search for a new home for the Agents. By his own accounting, Carbonaro spoke with virtually every major, and numerous minor, comicbook publishers in his quest to get the Agents back into print (including, but not limited to Marvel, (Marvel's Epic line), DC, Image (Extreme and WildStorm), Dark Horse, Comico, Apple (with whom he actually struck an agreement, but never managed to publish), and others. He also had discussions with a number of production houses and creators in an effort to generate either a movie, or animated TV series (Batfilms, Marv Wolfman, etc.), all to no avail.

In 1994, he finally struck a deal with George Caragonne and his company, Constant Developments, Inc. (CDI), to begin production of new T.H.U.N.D.E.R. Agents stories. Shortly after announcing his deal with Carbonaro, Caragonne hooked up with *Penthouse* magazine where he began to produce a line of Adult comic magazines for the company. In addition to the Adult comics, Caragonne launched *Omni Comics*, which, in issue #3, included the first chapter of what was to be a four-issue T.H.U.N.D.E.R. Agents story. (This story was supposed to appear as a standard, stand-alone T.H.U.N.D.E.R. Agent comic, but—again for convoluted reasons—never did.) Unfortunately, tragedy struck again. Caragonne was dismissed from Penthouse and, despondent, took his own life.

Without Caragonne to head up the comicbook division, Penthouse scaled back its operation, and canceled most of its line (including *Omni Comics*). Once again the Agents were without a home, and fell into the limbo of non-publishing.

Echoes of T.H.U.N.D.E.R. (Future)

Never one to admit, acknowledge, (or even spell), defeat, Carbonaro soldiered on. He has "re-acquired" publishing rights back from Penthouse, as well as the existing (Omni) T.H.U.N.D.E.R. artwork, and is currently in the process of re-(re)-launching the series. This time out he is doing it on his own, and not relying on others to helm the series that he has held close to his vest for over a decade. Carbonaro ("Carbs" as he is affectionately known to his friends), has long held the faith that—given half a chance—the T.H.U.N.D.E.R. Agents can make a solid go of it, and turn into the money-making franchise that it was always meant to be.

One can only hope he is right.

A (Partial) T.H.U.N.D.E.R. Agents Publishing History

TOWER:
Thunder Agents
1–20   1965–69   Even though the title was clearly an acronym on the cover, this comics is usually listed without the periods.
Dynamo
1–4   1966–67   Solo Dynamo stories
NoMan
1–2   1966–67   Solo NoMan stories
Undersea Agent
1–6   1966–67   Even though the title was clearly an acronym on the cover, this comics is usually listed without the periods.

JC Publications:
JCP Features
1   1981   B&W, magazine-sized comic with new T.H.U.N.D.E.R. Agents stories.

JC Comics: (Distributed by Archie)
T.H.U.N.D.E.R. Agents
1–2   1983–84   New T.H.U.N.D.E.R. Agents stories (continuing from the B&W magazine).
Hall of Fame Featuring the T.H.U.N.D.E.R. Agents
1–3   1983   Reprints Tower T.H.U.N.D.E.R. Agents stories from issues 1-3.

Red Circle: (Archie Comics)
Blue Ribbon Comics
12   1984   Continues new T.H.U.N.D.E.R. Agents story from JC Comics *T.H.U.N.D.E.R. Agents* #2

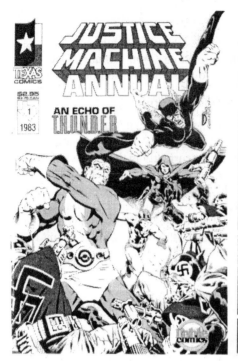

Justice Machine Ann.#1 and Wally Wood's T.H.U.N.D.E.R Agents #2 comics

Texas Comics:

The Justice Machine

Ann.1   1984   Agents appeared by themselves in a back-up story plus as guest stars—along with first appearance of the Elementals—with the Justice Machine in main story.

Deluxe Comics:

Wally Wood's T.H.U.N.D.E.R. Agents

1–5   1984–86   Not considered part of the official cannon. Owned by Carbonaro as part of the settlement from his copyright infringement lawsuit against Deluxe.

Tales of Thunder

1   1985   Not considered part of the official cannon. Owned by Carbonaro as part of the settlement from his copyright infringement lawsuit against Deluxe.

Penthouse:

Omni

3   1995   Carbonaro-authorized story, part of the official cannon.

Additional T.H.U.N.D.E.R. Stories

In addition to the above, there was a ***T.H.U.N.D.E.R. Agents*** series containing original stories which was published in England. This series was officially licensed by Tower prior to the sale of the characters to Carbonaro. It is unknown how many issues of this comic were published, or in what year(s) it was published, only one copy of a single issue is known to exist.

A single issue of a T.H.U.N.D.E.R. Agent comic was published by Solson in the '80s. This story was officially licensed by Carbonaro. The story was a future, alternative time-line which included all of the Agents, and may or may not be considered part of the official cannon. NoMan appeared on the cover.

There was also (at least three) comics that parodied the Agents. Two of them— *The Inferior Five* #1 (DC, 1972), and *Not brand Echh* #2 (Marvel, 1973)—that did so while Tower was still publishing. The third (*Boris the Bear*, Dark Horse, mid-to late '80s), did so while Carbonaro owned them. Dark Horse was served with a "cease and desist" notice from Carbonaro, and refrained from future parodies.

There was at least one issue of *Thunder Bunny* in which the Agents appeared, which received the tacit approval from Carbonaro (albeit later). Others publishers (Americomics, Maximum Comics), announced comics staring their version of the T.H.U.N.D.E.R. Agents (when the Agents were thought to exist in the Public Domain), but never delivered due to either notice from Carbonaro detailing his ownership (Americomics), or the company's own inability to produce such books (Maximum Comics announced a T.H.U.N.D.E.R. Agents comic, but no proof exists as to whether or not it ever managed to actually publish the comic).

# # #

*Robert J. Sodaro —a freelance writer living in the wilds of lower Connecticut—is **still** very nearly famous, even after some 20 years as a professional writer.*

NOT YER DADDY'S FUNNYBOOKS
An Electronic Interview with Warren Ellis

Conducted By
Robert J. Sodaro

It is fair to say that Warren Ellis isn't yer average funnybook writer. The books on which he works tend to be edgier, grittier and often, simply askew from what we've come to expect from funnybook writers. It is been postulated by some that this is so, because he is...well...British. Still, this isn't completely true, as there are numerous British funnybook writers who's work isn't any near as "odd" as Ellis's. Too, bad, because, in this four-color world of over-steroid, testosterone-enhanced, slap-dash, MTV, fast-food-take-out, burger-and-fries times of larger-than-life longjohn-wearing, towel-around-the-neck, angst-ridden era of heroes and villains, Warren Ellis is a long, refreshing breath of crisp, clean, mountain air.

His characters do things that you don't expect them to do, because they don't live in a two-dimensional, four-color world of good guys and bad guys. They live in a more realistic, highly politicized world of shadow and light, where people live and die. In short, these ain't yer daddy's funnybooks boy-o. This he-ya is, if not the real world, then at least as close an approximation of it as yer ever gonna find in a funnybook populated by folks who wear their underwear on the outside (Madonna not withstanding).

For anyone who was there at the time and paying attention this was never more evident than in issue #40 of **StormWatch** *when Ellis had Weatherman, Henry Bendix, send the StormWatch Red team to Gamorra Island for a police action where the character Rose Tattoo was ordered to cold-bloodedly kill an equal number of Gamorran civilians (233), in retaliation for an act of aggression precipitated by Island Patriarch, Kaizen Gamorra, against a British airliner. In one fell swoop, and with all the decisiveness of a surgeon swiftly and cleanly carving out a cancerous tumor to save a life, Ellis informed the world in no uncertain terms that the rules of superhero engagement were not only different, but from this point forward nothing would ever (indeed,* **could** *ever), be the same again.*

As stated. These ain't yer daddy's funnybooks no mo' (no mo').

****

(Unavoidable aside: Due to the fact that Ellis lives in England, and the interviewer lives in the States, the following interview was conducted via-e-mail (a first for this writer). The interviewer, the editors, and CVA would like to thank Mr. Ellis for his indulgence in granting this interview as he had not only just returned from holiday, but at the time of the interview was working under tight deadlines (both his and ours), as well as caring for his daughter and his sick girlfriend. Thanks ever so much Warren...now please, go back to work, 'cause we love you so much that we don't want you to be missing any deadlines on our account...the Editors.)

****

Bob: Your work on WildStorm's *StormWatch* is a very different spin on superhero/team comics, (more totalitarian, if you will), why do you feel that is?

Warren Ellis: It was a reading imposed by the group's original concept, as generated by Jim Lee and Brandon Choi. StormWatch were, make no mistake, soldiers. They were the superhuman enforcers of a United Nations far more aggressive, proactive and generally more adolescent than our own

Transmetropolitan #8 © DC Comics written by Warren Ellis

Bob: Do you believe that it has to do with the fact that, being British/non-American, you view comics/superteams different than we do?

Warren: If my take on superheroes has any difference at all to it, it's because I grew up with *2000AD*, not superhero comics.

Bob: Tell us a little bit about *Transmetropolitan*, and how it is different/the same as your superhero work.

Warren: *Transmetropolitan* is the story of Spider Jerusalem, one-time famous journalist, forced by horrible legal pressures to resume his work in the City, a vast future metropolis of indeterminate size and location. It's the place he hates the most and, ironically, the only place he can write. *Transmet* is a science fiction book; Probably the thing I like most about science fiction is its use as a tool to explore present-day culture. I and my collaborator, the excellent artist Darick Robertson, tend to use *Transmetropolitan* to slice away at every aspect of current urban life that appeals to us and see what we find. It's a future-time extrapolation/exploration of late 20th Century life, as viewed through the bleary eyes of Spider Jerusalem, Outlaw Journalist. Since its launch, it's won the Best New Comic (International), gong at the British National Comics Week Awards, several Internet-based awards (including the Don Thompson Memorial award for best new comic).

Bob: Which type of work do you prefer? Superhero books, or non-superhero books?

Warren: Non-superhero books, hands down. Don't get me wrong, I've enjoyed *StormWatch* a great deal, but the superhero subgenre is only the tiniest walk in the available landscape of auctorial pursuit. My great love in writing is to be able to talk about the world outside, the strangeness and beauty of real life. Superhero comics are not the best vehicle for that kind of work.

Bob: What other types of projects do you have in the works (about which you can talk)?

Warren: So far; I take over DC Vertigo's grand old horror title *Hellblazer* with #134. *Planetary*, created and produced by myself and artist John Cassaday with color artist Laura Depuy, launches early next year ('99) from WildStorm. *The Authority*, mentioned below. *Station*, a three-issue miniseries I'm writing for Roland Mann's Silverline Comics.

Bob: What makes *StormWatch* different/the same from other superteam books/groups (besides it being only the second team of superheroes to ever work for the UN the other being the T.H.U.N.D.E.R. Agents)

Warren: What makes StormWatch different from, say, The Avengers or the JLA, is that StormWatch is a vast organization developed entirely to back up five superhuman officers. That, to me, was one of the things that made StormWatch interesting; it was the Justice League as re-imagined by Tom Clancy. StormWatch nominally operates in the "real world", and, again, that differs the work it has to take place in something reasonably like the shady, unpleasant and tangled political life and structure we live under today. Most superhero team books seek to revive an Age of Chivalry, or create for themselves an Age of Heroism. StormWatch, by contrast, had to sit foursquare in the Age of Expediency.

Bob: Do you think that you'd ever be interested/allowed/able to do a cross-over with the T.H.U.N.D.E.R. Agents?

Warren: I'm really not aware of the T.H.U.N.D.E.R Agents...I'm not a great student of superhero comics.

Bob: When you took over the writing of *StormWatch* with issue #37, you very dramatically altered the way the team operated. Why was that? Was this due to your own personal world-view, or more of a "been-there/done-that" attitude towards superteams?

Warren: StormWatch had to live up to its own origins; it was either going to be a strong political superhero work, or it was going to be just like everything else. And if it was going to be just like everything else, then why bother doing it at all? Therefore, I went in with a big stick and got rid of everything that didn't pertain to those essential themes.

Bob: Your recent *Change or Die* storyline dealt with themes of superheroes in the "real" world, and seemed to echo some of the sentiments and themes of Allan Moore's *Watchmen*, was that by accident, or design?

Warren: Accident. I felt, and still feel, that Alan & Dave and Tom & I were pursuing different themes and effects.

StormWatch #44 and StormWatch (2nd series #1)
© Aegis Entertainment, Inc., written by Warren Ellis

Bob: I make this comparison due mostly to the appearance of characters who were so obviously modeled after long-standing characters (Superman, Batman, etc.), do you see this in that work and do it on purpose, or am I reading too much into what you did with that story?

Warren: No, I performed that modeling on purpose. The High was Superman and Captain Marvel strained through their progenitors, Doc Savage, Wylie's *Gladiator*. Wylie's character questioned his place in the world, and the early Superman was surprisingly politicized. The High came out of the conflation of the two. Smoke was essentially Chow Yun Fat as The Shadow, a utopianist with guns. The other characters were generated similarly, for one specific effect to present the original characters of comics and the weird pulp thrillers (their direct ancestors), as political beings as well as iconic figures.

Bob: You followed *Change or Die* up with *A Finer World* where you created new characters again modeled on the character archetypes you created for *Change or Die*, you are obviously going somewhere specific, can you tell us where? (Either generally, or specifically?)

Warren: It was the beginning of reminding people, and myself, what these characters are supposed to be achieving in our fictions. They're not supposed to be swamped in soap opera, pissed away on cheap and bloodless "deaths," lost in multi-part storylines that affect nothing and mean nothing. They're supposed to be entertaining us. They're supposed to be showing us how to be great. They're supposed to be striving for a finer world.

Bob: What does the future hold for A) StormWatch? B) You? C) Comicbooks?

Warren: A) Doom and mutation. B) Assassination. C) Doom and mutation. *StormWatch* is mutating, next year, into *The Authority*, a team book that addresses some different themes and concerns than I could comfortably reach in the former book. *The Authority* will be what I'm calling a "widescreen" superhero comic; Bryan Hitch and myself making the superhero team concept go properly nuts. For myself, the future is diversification; I'm currently involved in computer games, novels and other media, and I intend to explore that as well as continuing my comics career. I don't plan on writing superhero comics for too many more years. Comics need to mutate, and they need to do it now. Formats and content need to begin changing, both to support the dying direct-sales comic store, and to breach other retail avenues such as newsstands, bookstores and record stores. The 32-page floppy comic pamphlet needs to have its importance lessened; as far as I can see, survival lies in trade-paperback collections, original graphic novels, and 128-page "supermanga" packages like Viz's *Pulp*; but I'm just a comic book writer from England, and so I know nothing.

Bob: Are there any comicbooks and/or characters that you'd like to write or revive?

Warren: No, sorry.

Bob: What comics and/or characters do you regularly follow?

Warren: I regularly purchase *Preacher*, *The Invisibles*, *Berlin*, *Acme Novelty Library*, *Channel Zero*, *Spirit: the New Adventures* and pretty much anything by Alan Moore, Will Eisner, Frank Miller, Moebius, Bryan Talbot, and Steven Grant. Mark Millar's very good, and I also always buy *Pulp*.

Bob: Since it just occurred prior to this interview, would you care to offer us any views on the recent sale of WildStorm to DC?

Warren: So long as the working practices long established at WildStorm remain unchanged, and as long as my many friends at WildStorm remain unmolested, and as long as the deal buys Jim and everyone there what they wanted...then I'm reasonably happy.

Bob: Given what happened with Milestone (an independent comicbook company distributed by DC), do you think that WildStorm can/will survive as a separate entity under the ownership of DC?

Warren: Provided that DC remain adult about the situation (which is very different to Milestone), and remember exactly why they wanted to buy WildStorm in the first place, then everything will be fine.

GETTING WET
WITH WHILCE PORTACIO

At Long-Last, an Unpublished Interview with One of the "Image Seven" is
Actually Going to See the Light of Day

Conducted By
Robert J. Sodaro

(Editor's Note: This interview, was originally conducted in 1994, on the eve
of the publication of Whilce Portacio's *Wetworks*. Due to reasons far too
convoluted and complex, it never saw the light of day. In the spirit of
historical accuracy and completeness, *CVA* presents it here, for the very first
time.)

They made comicbook history with their announcement. Seven of the hottest
stars of the Marvel Bullpen of the late 1980s/early 1990s announced that they had
had enough of work-for-hire, and wanted to strut their stuff on their own. They
took their walk, formed Image, and began to craft their own pantheon of heroes.
Youngblood, *Spawn*, *WildC.A.T.s*, *Cyberforce*, *Shadowhawk*, *The Savage
Dragon*, and of course *Wetworks*. But then—as life is so often wont to do—it
threw a great big monkey wrench into the works, and the unexpected happened.
A personal tragedy in the family of Whilce Portacio (one of the mystical Seven),
other obligations, over-extension of personal commitments, etc. As it all began to
pile up, Portacio fell further and further behind, and finally his book was removed
from the Image publishing schedule.

It was at this point that the rumor mill kicked into high gear, and it was
announced that Portacio was fired from the Image board (the founding seven
members—a report that Portacio denies ever hearing, or actually ever happened.)
Finally, nearly a year after it was initially announced, his comic *Wetworks*, was
"acquired" by Jim Lee's WildStorm Studios and was finally released. (Portacio
who was always more interested in the creative end of the business, was happy
to let Lee handle all the business end of things, leaving him free to concentrate
on his art.), With its release, *Wetworks* proved to be one of the most eagerly-
awaited comics of the mid-'90s. Shortly after the initial production of his comic,
Portacio took a break from his work to chat with us about Image, *Wetworks*, and
his own place in the industry.

Wetworks, drawn by Whilce Portacio © Aegis Entertainment, Inc.

(We Now Return You to 1994, and Whilce Portacio)

Bob: Let's take it from the top. You're back. *Wetworks* is probably one of the most highly-anticipated comics in the past couple of years. It was suppose to come out, and what was the problem with that? You said you had some family problems and you wouldn't be able to do it, is that correct?

Whilce Portacio: That was the beginning of it.

Bob: I don't want to pry into your personal life, but could you talk a little about this?

Whilce: Well, my sister passed away. It hit me a lot harder than I thought it would. So, I actually, for my own personal reasons, and the relationship I had with her, I couldn't get myself to work. It was just reminding me of her. That went on for like four months. What I did was for the whole four months was just locked myself in a room and made this videotape of her. That's a personal thing. Now that was approximately four or five months. There was another personal thing that happened, and that added on to her, two or three months. What that adds on, because that happened at the exact time that Image was getting so much flack for the promptness of their books. The quote un-quote "regulations" started coming down. At first, when I tried to get back into the fold, prior to that, you solicited a book, and you did a book. Then the new rule came in where you had to finish at least one of the books, finish an issue before you could solicit it. By the time I got finished with the first issue, other regulations came in. Finish two books before you can solicit. By the time we've come up to this point, this it's about November of last year. The rule then became, because we're still getting all this flack, to finish the whole mini-series before you could even think about soliciting a book. What that also brings about is that, imagine after the six or seven months I put myself away, coming back and now I had to add on, after weeks, three more months, one month for each book. The money is getting scarce. So I had to do all these other jobs, and I had to be practical at the same time. I had to do odd jobs here and there just to make the bills.

Bob: That was my next question. How are you paying bills in this time?

Whilce: Exactly, so it became a point of—okay do I want to take the time to do these jobs and then get right back to *Wetworks* and try to get that done as fast as I can? By that time we had pulled off of solicitation, and it was taking a while. It was a choice between...this has always been my first book, and at the beginning I was the last person to sign on, I was the last person on the docket in terms of the book coming out, and I wanted it that way. That way it gave me the longest lead time so that I could do the book. You obviously always want to do the best your first book. So at this point it became a matter of whether I just wanted to do the book, and get it out there, because I knew people wanted to see it, or did I want to stick to my original...my pride...from the beginning I wanted to be the best I could at this point. Instead of just rushing into getting it done, I took the time to get it done. We're finally at this point, and all of the issues have been finished about a month and-a-half, or two months ago. Or, three months ago.

Bob: The first issue comes out when?

Whilce: My book has been solicited for the first week of every month. The first month will be July. I'll be in Chicago for the con the week before. I believe our plan is to actually release the book at that time.

Bob: You did a special ashcan didn't you?

Whilce: That was pretty much, me and Joe Krook had become friends. He always wanted to help me keep the book in the public eye. It wasn't an ashcan per say.

Bob: I haven't seen it. Was it just pages from the book?

Whilce: At that point in time, I had finished the first issue, I was working on the second issue, Scott had inked a little bit. I let him see copies of what I had. He decided to put together a couple of pages. I had these character write-ups of all the team members. He put that in there too. It was mostly, really a preview as to what was happening. From a marketing standpoint, I remember back when, on *Spider-Man*, he was coming up with the new *Spider-Man*, and I remember for months beyond that, and it's the same with *Dark Knight*, months beyond that, before that, every now and then, as I said, I'd see little things trickled in every now and then, see the work in progress, see what was going to be out in six months or so. It just kept the interest. I had no problem with him doing whatever he wanted.

Bob: Can you give me a little background on what *Wetworks* is all about?

Whilce: Actually, it's interesting. You try to make good of whatever situation you get into. That's actually one of the best things about this long process. This long delay is all my fault, but I had all this time, I've had so much time to think about the series. I have to admit that originally when we first started the series, we're our own people as Image, and I had to come up with something. I've always been interested in military groups, so I wanted to do a little military group. Brandon Choi was interested in the same thing, so we decided to get together. I think the *Terminator* stuff was on the board at the time. It was actually pretty much the concept in the beginning. As it got going, who are these guys going to be fighting? Why are they fighting? How did they get their suits? It's now to the point where it's this huge, story I want to tell. It's

Wetworks, drawn by Whilce Portacio © Aegis Entertainment, Inc.

gotten to the point now, where we've conceived it in three parts. The first part is the origin, from these well-trained military operative humans to invisible humans. They have suits now, and they're comparable to weaponry. Then I wanted to take it from a point where...okay that was the original concept...okay so they get these suits. Are they just Christmas presents? Are they just something they bought? Are they real? Then we started to get into the fact that, hey what if these suits were actually some kind of a life form? What kind of effect will these suits have on the humans? What kind of effect will the humans have on the suits? So, we started thinking about it. There's a second phase that I'm working on right now.

Bob: You mean a second trilogy?

Whilce: Yeah. I decided to do six issues as a second phase. It's symbiotic. We don't have a title for it yet. For me, I think it's the most interesting phase. I mean, obviously what we're working for is the superhero thing. That is what our fans expect out of it. That's our bread and butter. But for me, always, the basic superhero...as it has been defined lately...the basic superhero thing has never really appealed to me too much. It's been able to get my interest because, let's be frank, a lot of it is mostly just flash. It's cool. But there seems to be this undercurrent of, well, if you keep these guys really cool, grab their interest, and we keep them mysterious, maybe we can hang on to them. But, I've never subscribed to that, because like I said, I'd be grabbed in too, but after a while I'd fall off, because these people didn't become real to me. What I decided to do here was, let's start with them as humans, as in the first issue, and let's go to a point...an then decided to go up to nine issues...where in the ninth issue, they actually become these quote/unquote superheroes. So they become these super-powered beings.

Bob: You're saying the second series. Is it a second limited series? Are you going to be continuing the numbering?

Whilce: The numbering will continue. What I'll do is have the first issue *Wetworks*, labeled the origin, and the second part four-to-nine *Wetworks*, but labeled.

Bob: There'll be a subtitle for it?

Whilce: Yeah.

Bob: It will essentially be a second story?

Whilce: Right. It won't be a second book. And then a third book, and a fourth. But it will be set up into subchapters, since we've got it all worked out so much, my hope is that with the mini-series, and the second series, even I decide not to do the quote/unquote superhero series, because we've got everything ground out, and with the first book I'm working on right now, and all these clues and details and stuff, there are so many stories that can be told prior to the mini-series, or in between the mini-series and the second series, there'll be about six months between issue three and four. Little bits of time lapses in between issues. Later on I can come back and, or later on if other people are interested they can come in and do these other substories as part of the whole thing.

Bob: There's been a certain amount of criticism of some of the Image books, in that whether it's real or imagined, or even justifiable, that this is another knock-off of the X-Men. A lot of the Image group books, look like just another version of the X-Men. How would you respond to that?

Whilce: I can't respond for the gang. I can only respond to what I'm doing with my book on that. It's not something you can shirk off. The X-Men, and the X-Books, were a couple of years of my life. They were a couple of years of my formative life as a comic book artist and writer. They obviously had an impact on me. That's actually one of the reasons I'm doing the series that I'm doing. The mini-series and the middle-series, were they come together is a transformation from them as human beings to the quote/unquote superheroes. The transformation from them as normal humans to the mutant superhero stage. The reason I wanted to do that, is just like in the X-Men, because Chris Claremont had written them so real, as real as we can get in comics, that no matter who came on, whether it was Jim, or myself, or whether it was Marc Silvestri, they came on board after that, and you see with each new artist and now writer the characters, or the theme itself, actually take a turn with different people, but the book still stays the book. Bishop, who I created, he's still Bishop. I think one of the reasons is because of what Chris has written for that. Because there was that time period, it was Marc, Jim and myself, that the one constant factor was Chris and the writing. Keeping the characters reacting consistently.

Bob: Do you think that because Chris spent 17 or 18 years on the *X-Men*, in a very real sense, the *X-Men* have defined what superhero team books are today? So it doesn't matter whether or not you actually drew the books. It's that if somebody is going to create a team superhero team, it's going to look like the *X-Men* to us, simply because we've been reading 18 years of Chris' *X-Men*? They were the number-one selling book for most of that time. That's the kind of thing people want, so that's what we're going to give them.

Whilce: Right, right, right. Take an extreme case where, let's say, I was born in the Philippines. Let's say I never immigrated to the United States when I was two-years-old. I just came to the states this year, right now. But over there, I was drawing comics, illustrating, but I'd never seen an *X-Men* comicbook. I came over here, get a job with Image, and start doing something. They let me create what I want to create. You can't say that just because they did it, and did it so well, Chris and whoever was working with them at the time, if I came up with mutants, that I stole it from Chris. The mutant idea is not a...

Bob: It's not new to Chris.

Whilce: Yeah, it's just that he did it well, and he did it first. For instance, when Neal Adams came on the scene, he took the whole field, artistically, by storm. Everybody wanted to be him. He introduced illustrative techniques. He introduced real anatomy and stuff like that. Real shading and stuff. That wasn't new. That was new in the comics field, but he was an illustrator before that. There were some comicbook illustrators that were even better than him.

Bob: Even Steranko who took comics in a whole new direction, and then everybody followed Steranko for a number of years, with what he was doing.

Whilce: You take it to these extremes. The extreme point now where Neal Adams has been out of the main market for a long time, that you have Grinberg or some other people that draw similar to him, that came from his school actually. To a lot of people, it's the first time they've seen that style. But, Grinberg didn't originate the style. Neal Adams didn't originate the style, but he did originate the style in comics. No matter what we do, I think we will get that, if you want to call it flack, we will receive a lot of that flack. What I'm hoping is to take the uniqueness of what my concept is, and to really lay it out there. The uniqueness of my book, is the humans, the military operatives. The get the suits so they can be very mobile and invisible. But, is that it? Does that have no affect on them? The suits themselves are in some sense life forms. They have the power, and they have the knowledge to affect the body. Think about them in terms of the suits are these highly curious scientists, they latch on to you, they latch on to a host, they learn everything they can about that host, they affect what they can

Wetworks #12
© *Aegis Entertainment, Inc.*

of the host. For instance, one extreme example, is Dozer, this big, muscle-bound, body-building guy, who has always been body building, and his brain as a body builder is filled with all this information on nutrition, muscle growth, and how to effect growth, and stuff like that. What the suits do is take his knowledge, take his chemistry, his body, and in six months he is now this 400 pound mass of muscle. But, since you can't grow from calcium, you can grow bone strength, and tendons, and stuff like that, and he has no knowledge of that. The host does instigate that. What you have now is this immobile mass of muscle, because of gravity, just ready to fall off his skeleton. That's one little thing, in the fourth issue. If they let him out into gravity, his body would just fall off of him. The question there is, how does he overcome that? Or, does he overcome that? Does he die? He obviously will overcome that, and whether it will be an exoskeleton? or a totally symbiotic relationship, where the gold suits meld with his muscles and it becomes 50/50. Whatever, he becomes a superhero at the end. I'm hoping by the ninth issue he'll become this superhero, but I'm hoping from the mini-series, that you see him to the ninth issue that you see him with his particular problem. How the suits affects him, and what they're going to do about it. If he survives that and then becomes a superhero. You'll get to know him. You'll be able to walk in his shoes, be a part of him. He'll have a history for you. When the series goes on, whether I take it or not, or whether somebody else takes it, like in the *X-Men*, it's been laid down there. It's there. Because I'm going through a prolonged origin series, I'm hoping the characters will become more real. For solid reasons, the Dozer situation. These changes happen, and changes will happen to other people. They'll have to overcome their own individual problems. I'm hoping that at the ninth issue point, people will be concentrating more on Dozer and his particular problems.

Bob: Who's going to be writing the series? Are you writing it?

Whilce: Brandon Choi and I are writing the whole series together. It's give and take. We both have goals for all the little different points in the series. Where we want to go, who the protagonists are, what are the underlying scores. It's mostly just the battle of how to actually execute them. He'll have his theories and, I'll have my theories, I'll lay my theory out, then he'll lay his theory out. I'll change them, then I'll give them to him and he'll change it. It will finally come out.

Bob: You said that you might not be writing it after the ninth issue?

Whilce: That's very possible.

Bob: Would you continue to draw it? Would you let somebody else write it and continue to plot it? Or is that just too far off for you to think about it at this time?

ADVANCE PROMOTIONAL ASHCAN III of III   085 /500

Wetworks, drawn by Whilce Portacio © Aegis Entertainment, Inc.

Whilce: No, I'm thinking ahead. Originally it started out as just this little concept of, let's just have fun and draw books. It grew into something else. There is so much inter-layered in what we have, I'm not even sure if we're going to be able to bring it all out. There are so many other characters and ideas that Brandon and I actually want to do.

Bob: With these characters or with other characters?

Whilce: With these characters and other characters. All our ideas may not be encompassed. The world has become so big and complicated. It's like you find out something, and you go, 'Oh wow.' It's because of that, now, who made it that way? So then, you build up this history on who this person is. Then you ask the question, 'Why did this person make it that way?' Then you build up a history from there. What I'm saying is there are all these other characters, back-stories and histories that may never come out in *Wetworks*, because you have to focus on one point of view. Those ideas are so strong, and we feel so much about it, we'll want to do them anyway. I'm seeing six more months from now that I'll be wanting to try some other stuff, and do some other things. That's why I'm working so closely with the source, the source book. I'm actually writing the whole source book myself, and working so closely with Brandon on getting the mini-series done, and laying everything out, and introducing everything out there, even if I leave after the ninth issue, there will be a huge bible. Not only that, we have a huge database in my computer, and the computer at the studio.

Bob: There is a possibility, if you left the book, you would leave writing and drawing it, and then just go on to another thing? You'd still presumably have creative input into it, but the series would continue with some other artist, and some other writer.

Whilce: Think of it this way. The whole *Star Trek* and *The Next Generation*. Everybody talks about Gene Roddenberry's bible. Okay, yeah, a lot of people would love to have these huge battles between the Romulans and the Federation, but that's never going to happen because Gene Roddenberry made up that bible. We will have relative calm and peace in the universe. Sure, you might have some cool ideas about the origins of the Klingons on something like that, but if it doesn't mesh with Roddenberry's version in his bible, you can't do it. We're going to lay out this huge, huge bible, which the visual elements will be the mini-series, the second series, and the source books. Their will be this huge bible underneath that the writers will have to defer to. We'll map out in history everything that happens, and everything that will happen. It's just up to, if we have a new team, it's up to that team to decide exactly how it happens.

Bob: On a slightly different subject, you were bounced out of Image at some point, because of your lateness with the book. But were you still considered one of the owners of Image or not?

Whilce: Image is a unique concept. There is an Image office, but there really is no physical Image. That is the uniqueness of our situation. For instance, it got together because seven guys wanted to do their own things. They didn't want to be corporate people anymore. They didn't want to be owned by a company.

Bob: No, I understand. Image isn't a publisher, in a traditional sense. There are five or six studios that exist, and each of you guys publish stuff under the Image umbrella, but you're essentially doing your own thing. You interact with each other only in that you're all doing it together and you're all in the same boat. It's more of a confederation than a united publishing front.

Whilce: Right. And because of that, for instance all this talk about my quote/unquote status, in the quote/unquote fold, none of that has reached myself. I actually read that about all that stuff. I like the way you put it. Technically, that can be the point, and that might be the point. None of it has actually reached me. Personally, we've never really been...look at my personal history with the whole thing. I came on board and I attended a lot of their meetings, and I attended a lot of their earlier meetings. A lot of those meetings had nothing to do with me at that point, because I was still just at the point of figuring out what I'm going to do. What book I'm going to do. All the meetings were practical meeting about cover prices, where we were going to get them printed, where we were going to go for distribution. That stuff didn't pertain to me yet, because I had nothing coming out yet. After a while I stopped going to the meetings. Not to say I didn't want to have anything to do with the guys. Why go to the meeting where sure I might have an opinion, but Rob's book is out, Jim's book is out, Todd's book is out, Eric's book is just about to come out. They're going to have their opinions, and since their books are out, their opinions are going to have to sway at that point in time. Whether I have an opinion, whether it might be the right opinion, it doesn't pertain to me yet because my book isn't out. Who knows, I might have gotten run over the next day, and it might have been a good point.

Bob: Do these guys still vote on stuff? Like a majority vote passes a measure? How does that all work?

Whilce: We have meetings every now and then, but I personally haven't been to a meeting in a long time. Image has gotten to the point right now where it is a lot of individual companies. It's big now.

Bob: Yeah, it is.

Whilce: Things happen on their own now a lot of times. Like I said, earlier there were a lot of meetings, and they were all practical meetings. Are we

Wetworks, drawn by Whilce Portacio © Aegis Entertainment, Inc.

going to go to this con? Do we need to advertise? Do enough people know about us? The right people? The right things? All that stuff is already there. For instance Rob's decision to retire for a little while, or whatever you want to call it, and come back. Most of the decisions and things people have to think about now are just getting the book to them in time. Just getting the books out on time, and making them. We've always been seen as the cutting edge so, trying to find that next cutting edge level.

Bob: You've joined Jim in his WildStorm studios. You're now part of that. Have you thought of forming your own studio, or do you think you'll be staying with Jim for a while?

Whilce: Look and Jim and my personal history together. Even before the X-Books, we were working together at Homage studios. Homage was around for quite a while. We've always worked here in San Diego. We've always worked in the same building. As his company grew, and his stuff came out, my stuff was being formed, and my stuff was getting ready to go out, because for years and years we've been here working together, and almost all the studios now are set up so everything is done in house. Homage studios is a place where from the concept of the book all the way down to outputting the color files.

Bob: Yeah, I've spoken with Jim and with Mark. I'm up on how Homage has been running.

WE: It's a complete, almost independent house. The uniqueness to what that situation is about, is that for as long as we've been into Image, Jim has grown to be quite a businessman. With *Wetworks* and *WildC.A.T.s.* It was always going to be the case we would be working, just because of our relationship, we've been working with the same people. You obviously want to work with people you feel are the best, and who you have the best relationship with. It was always going to be a case where we would be working. We've been working with the same people. Gus Williams, Joe Chido, Ben and the guys in the preparation department. Even little points of secretaries. My two sisters have worked in the studios. My other sister is still working there, and actually formed most of the divisions in the studio. By brother-in-law is part of the other side of the studio. It's always been intimate and personal. When it came to the point *Wetworks* was going to come out, the intention of forming my company, Jim and I are close friends, and working with the same people. If we had these two separate companies, at some point in time, there would have to be some kind of a split. I'm not just saying a split between Jim and myself, I mean a split between resources. That's not very advantageous to either of us. Sure, I might feel that my book is going to be better than Jim's and when my company gets going, I'll be able to take away all his people that I've been working with. Or he'll be able to take away all the people and make sure they don't work for me. It became not are only option, but hey, it's the obvious thing to do. One, we don't split our resources. Two, because we're two parts of the market. We can become one whole part. As we talked more and more about it, it became more advantageous. And for me personally. Jim is a phenomenal businessman. I'm not a push over, but I have no particular love for business.

Bob: I can understand that.

WE: For me one of the biggest appeals was that he had this corporate division already going. By joining up with him, since I already had a personal relationship with the corporate division of his company, I could just step in and say, 'Go ahead and do what you want. I know you. I trust you.'

Bob: So, essentially WildStorm is Jim's studio, and you're working in Jim's studio for all intents and purposes?

WE: Yeah.

Bob: It's not so much that's he's your boss, as much as however you divide up who decides what. I want this computer over there. No, I want it by the window.

WE: Because it's taken me so long to get started, that company is already been set up. WildStorm is already set up. It's not I think the computer looks better over there. Now it's mostly just artistic right now. The company is running so well now. For instance, 'Jim, I think it would be a much more solid character if you did this.' Then Jim goes, 'Well that sounds stupid to me. I'm not going to do it.' Jim comes to me and says, 'Wouldn't it be cool if Dozer was purple, and Bloodqueen was green?' 'Jim, nah.' Whatever project we're working at. Since we're now together, and I can have *WildC.A.T.s* come into *Wetworks* anytime, and have *Wetworks* come into *WildC.A.T.s* anytime. Our common handshake rule is, whatever I'm working on at the time, just as long as I don't mess up anything that happened in the past, I have full control over it. Whatever he's working on, he makes all the decisions there. *Wetworks* is mine, and *WildC.A.T.s* is his.

Bob: So, pretty much you're going to be staying with *Wetworks* up until issue nine, and then after that anything is possible?

WE: Yeah, like the release says, a couple of properties Jim has come up with, with Brandon, which are just concepts at this point. Jim has been so busy with all the other deals. He's created so many books now. That was one of the appeals for me personally. I could come into it, and just like the release says, I'm creative director. I can actually come in and take those properties, and make them whatever I want to make them.

Bob: Anything else? Any message or anything you want to let the fans out there know about you and about *Wetworks*? Any misperception or misconception they still may have?

WE: My biggest problem might be the fact that my conception so far, they might have a conception on how the book should be. Or how they would like to see the book, or what they think they know of the book. I just would like people to look at the book as itself, as it happens. It might go along the lines of the way you want it or how you feel it might go, but I think I can guarantee it will be a solid book. It will not just happen. There's a lot more to what you will see, and if you read between the lines, you'll see what will happen.

Bob: Okay, sounds good.

WE: It's not just what you see on the surface. *Wetworks* gets the suits, and there's a reason why they get the suits. A good reason. They can be good with the suits, they're conducive. You'll find out...we haven't decided exactly where you find that out yet.

Bob: What about licensing? Anything in the works like trading cards, toys? Any animation deals going? Or is it still too early for that?

WE: The point we're at right now, which is one of the advantages of getting together with Jim, is that he can come in and say, 'Why don't you take a look at this copy.' It carries more weight, as opposed to just myself coming in and saying, 'Excuse me, I'm good.' For the comics market out there, you could say *Wetworks* is going to have an idea, a strong idea of what it is, what it looks like, and what it's going to be. CVS and those people they have no idea. We're at the point of basically making it real. We have a sculpture in house now, doing some sculptures. I'm actually trying my hand at doing some sculptures. My sculptures won't be...his sculptures will be fully finished sculptures with the gold and everything. Stuff that we can say, 'Dozer is a big guy and has a huge gun, and this is what he looks like.' 'Oh, wow.' The vision represented. What sculptures I'm doing, because we hope they really get into the computer bit, and the gaming bit, with the new video systems and things like that. What I'm doing is, my sculptures will be digitized and put into computers. We have a couple poster systems and stuff like that. We're going to do a couple of animation types. Fully, three computer animation stuff. Regardless of whether we get the fully finished sculptures that we have out there, or the animation stuff that we can show them, we're at the point of coordinating.

Bob: What about trading cards?

WE: I did a *Wetworks* portion in the WildStorm set.

Bob: When is the WildStorm set due out?

CVA Page xxxviii

WE: I have no idea. Let me just say, I did my pieces three months ago.

Bob: How many *Wetworks* pieces are there?

WE: 17 members and one team card

P.S. *All of this is history now. Portacio stayed with the book for a time, then returned to the Philippines, and the book was taken over by other creators. The characters continued to fight the vampire nation until recently when they became operatives for I.O. these days it seems as if the book is being pulled closer into the WildStorm universe (especially with the current storyline involving StormWatch).*

Still, given the current state of affairs at WildStorm, who's to say what the future will bring? Not us, not just yet.

CVA GRADING GUIDE

In David Brin's science fiction–fantasy novel, *The Practice Effect*, things improve with use. You start with a crudely made tool and keep using it until it becomes a fine instrument. If our world worked that way, you could read your golden age comics as often as you liked and they would just get better looking each time. Unfortunately, our world does not work that way, and reading your comics (along with just about everything else) causes comics to deteriorate.

Even if you could protect your comics from external light, heat, cold, moisture, pressure and everything else, you couldn't protect them from their own paper. Most comic books were printed on pulp paper, which has a high acid content. This means that the paper slowly turns brittle with age, no matter what you do to it, short of special museum-style preservation.

Very old, well-preserved comics are coveted collector's items. In most cases, people did not save their comic books for future generations. They read them and discarded them. Comic books were considered harmless ephemera for children. When these children outgrew their comics, their parents often threw them away. If everybody kept all of their comics, comics would not be valuable because everybody would have them scattered about the house!

The value of any comic depends on scarcity, popularity and condition. Scarcity increases with age and popularity depends on the whim of the public — only condition automatically decreases with age. Newer comics are generally available in near-mint condition, so newer comics in lesser condition have little collector potential. However, older comics are scarce, so they are still collectible in less than near-mint condition, but the value is obviously less. This is a basic tenet of all collectibles. A car is more valuable with its original paint. A baseball card is more valuable if it has not been marred by bicycle spokes. Coke bottles, stamps, coins, and toys in good condition are all more valuable than their abused counterparts. Comic books are no exception.

New comic book collectors should learn how to assess the prospective value of a comic in order to protect themselves from being fleeced by unscrupulous dealers or hucksters. Yet, a majority of dealers, especially store owners, can be considered reliable judges of comic grade. Because comic retail may be their primary source of income, certain dealers are particularly adept at noticing comic book imperfections, especially in issues they intend to purchase. As such, hobbyists and collectors must understand that dealers need to make a minimum profit on their investments. Buying collectible comics entails certain risks. Therefore, dealers must scrutinize a comic to determine if the particular book will stand a chance of resale. Well-preserved comics are invariably more desirable to dealers because they are more desirable to collectors.

There are eight standard comic grades: mint, near mint, very fine, fine, very good, good, fair, and poor. Clearly, these eight grades could be split into even finer categories when haggling over an exceptionally rare or coveted Golden Age comic. In most cases, however, comic books can be evaluated using these eight standard grades. The values listed in *Comics Values Annual* are all for comics in "Near Mint" condition. The grading/price chart given at the back of this book should be used to adjust this price for comics in different grades.

Mint

Finding new comics in true mint condition can be difficult. Finding old comics in mint condition is almost impossible. Mint condition comics usually fetch prices higher than price guide listings. Mint comics can sell for 120% or more of *Comics Values Annual* listed prices. The reason for this is the strict criteria reserved for mint comics.

Mint comics are perfect comics and allow no room for imperfections. Pages and covers must be free of discoloration, wear, and wrinkles. A mint comic is one that looks like it just rolled off the press. Staples and spine must meet perfectly without cover "rollover." The cover must be crisp, bright, and trimmed perfectly. The staples must not be rusted and the cover should not have any visible creases.

The interior pages of a mint comic are equally crisp and new. A mint comic must not show any signs of age or decay. Because of the paper stock used on many older comics, acid and oxygen cause interior pages to yellow and flake. It is much harder to find pre-1970 mint comics because of inferior storage techniques and materials. In the early days of collecting, few people anticipated that the very boxes and bags in which they stored their comics were contributing to decay. Acid from bags, backing boards, and boxes ate away at many comics.

Near Mint

A near mint comic and a mint comic are close siblings, with their differences slight, even to an experienced eye. Most of the new comics on the shelf of the local comic shop are in near mint condition. These are comics that have been handled gingerly to preserve the original luster of the book.

Near mint comics are bright, clean copies with no major or minor defects. Slight stress lines near the staples and perhaps a very minor printing defect are permissible. Corners must still be sharp and devoid of creases. Interior pages of newsprint stock should show almost no discernible yellowing. Near mint comics usually trade for 100% of the suggested *Comics Values Annual* listed prices.

Very Fine

A very fine comic is one that is routinely found on the shelves and back issue bins of most good direct market comic shops. This grade comic has few defects, none of them major. Stress around the staples of a very fine comic are visible but not yet radical enough to create wrinkles. Both the cover and interior pages should still be crisp and sharp, devoid of flaking and creases. Interior pages may be slightly yellowed from age.

Most high-quality older comics graded as very fine can obtain 80-90% of *Comics Values Annual* listed prices. Newer comics graded as very fine get about 70-85% because many near mint copies probably exist. Despite that, very fine comics are desirable for most collectors.

Fine

Fine comics are often issues that may have been stored carefully under a bed or on a shelf by a meticulous collector. This grade of comic is also very desirable because it shows little wear and retains much of its original sharpness. The cover may be slightly off center from rollover. The cover retains less of its original gloss and may even possess a chip or wrinkle. The comers should be sharp but may also have a slight crease. Yellowing begins to creep into the interior pages of a comic graded as fine.

Fine comics are respectable additions to collections and sell for about 40-60% of the listed prices.

Very Good

A very good comic may have been an issue passed around or read frequently. This grade is the common condition of older books. Its cover will probably have lost some luster and may have two or three creases around the staples or edges. The corners of the book may begin to show the beginnings of minor rounding and chipping, but it is by no means a damaged or defaced comic. Comics in very good condition sell for about 30-40% of *Comics Values Annual* listed prices.

Good

A good comic is one that has been well read and is beginning to show its age. Although both front and back covers are still attached, a good grade comic may have a number of serious wrinkles and chips. The corners and edges of this grade comic may show clear signs of rounding and flaking. There should be no major tears in a good comic nor should any pages be clipped out or missing. Interior pages may be fairly yellowed and brittle. Good comics sell for about 15-25% of the *Comics Values Annual* listed prices.

Fair

A fair comic is one that has definitely seen better days and has considerably limited resale value for most collectors. This comic may be soiled and damaged on the cover and interior. Fair comics should be completely intact and may only be useful as a comic to lend to friends. Fair comics sell for about 10-20% of the *Comics Values Annual* listed prices.

Poor

Comics in poor condition are generally unsuitable for collecting or reading because they range from damaged to unrecognizable. Poor comics may have been water damaged, attacked by a small child, or worse, perhaps, gnawed on by the family pet! Interior and exterior pages may be cut apart or missing entirely. A poor comic sells for about 5-15% of the *Comics Values Annual* listed price.

Sniffing Out Grades

Despite everything that is mentioned about comic grading, the process remains relative to the situation. A comic that seems to be in very good condition may actually be a restored copy. A restored copy is generally considered to be in between the grade it was previous to restoration and the grade it has become. Many collectors avoid restored comics entirely.

Each collector builds his collection around what he believes is important. Some want every issue of a particular series or company. Others want every issue of a favorite artist or writer. Because of this, many collectors will purchase lower-grade comics to fill out a series or to try out a new series. Mint and near mint comics are usually much more desirable to hard-core collectors. Hobbyists and readers may find the effort and cost of collecting only high-grade comics financially prohibitive.

Getting artists or writers to autograph comics has also become a source of major dispute. Some collectors enjoy signed comics and others consider those very comics defaced! The current trends indicate that most collectors do enjoy signed comics. A signature does not usually change the grade of the comic.

As mentioned, comic grading is a subjective process that must be agreed upon by the buyer and seller. Buyers will often be quick to note minor defects in order to negotiate a better price. Sellers are sometimes selectively blind to their comic's defects. *Comics Values Annual: 1999* provides this grading guide as a protection for both parties.

Name	Abbr
Abel, Jack	**JA**
Abell, Dusty	DAb
Abnett, Dan	DAn
Abrams, Paul	PlA
Adams, Art	AAd
Adams, Neal	NA
Addeo, Stephen	StA
Adkins, Dan	DA
Adlard, Charlie	CAd
Albano, John	JAo
Albrecht, Jeff	JAl
Alcala, Alfredo	AA
Alcazar, Vincent	VAz
Alexander, Chris	CAx
Alibaster, Jo	JoA
Allred, Michael	MiA
Alstaetter, Karl	KlA
Althorp, Brian	BAp
Amaro, Gary	GyA
Amendola, Sal	Sal
Ammerman, David	DvA
Anderson, Bill	BAn
Anderson, Brent	BA
Anderson, Murphy	MA
Andriola, Alfred	AlA
Andru, Ross	RA
Aparo, Jim	JAp
Aragones, Sergio	SA
Arcudi, John	JAr
Artis, Tom	TAr
Ashe, Edd	EA
Augustyn, Brian	BAu
Austin, Terry	TA
Avison, Al	AAv
Ayers, Dick	DAy
Bachalo, Chris	**CBa**
Badger, Mark	MBg
Bagley, Mark	MBa
Baikie, Jim	JBa
Bailey, Bernard	BBa
Bair, Michael	MlB
Baker, Kyle	KB
Baker, Matt	MB
Balent, Jim	JBa
Banks, Darryl	DBk
Barks, Carl	CB
Baron, Mike	MBn
Barr, Mike	MiB
Barras, John	DBs
Barreiro, Mike	MkB
Barreto, Ed	EB
Barry, Dan	DBa
Batista, Chris	CsB
Battlefield, D.	DB
Beatty, John	JhB
Beatty, Terry	TBe
Beauvais, Denis	DB
Beeston, John	JBe
Belardinelli, M.	MBe
Bell, Bob Boze	BBB
Bell, George	GBl
Bell, Julie	JuB
Benefiel, Scott	ScB
Benes, Ed	EBe
Benitez, Joe	JBz
Benjamin, Ryan	RBn
Bennett, Joe	JoB
Bennett, Richard	RiB
Benson, Scott	StB
Berger, Charles	ChB
Bernado, Ramon	RBe
Bernstein, Robert	RbB
Bierbaum, Mary	MBm
Bierbaum, Tom	TBm
Biggs, Geoffrey	GB
Binder, Jack	JaB
Bingham, Jerry	JBi
Birch, JJ	JJB
Biro, Charles	CBi
Bisley, Simon	SBs
Bissette, Stephen	SBi
Blaisdell, Tex	TeB
Blasco, Jesus	JBl
Blevins, Bret	BBl
Blum, Alex	AB
Bode, Vaughn	VB
Bogdanove, Jon	JBg
Bolland, Brian	BB
Bolle, Frank	FBe
Boller, David	DdB
Bolton, John	JBo
Bond, Philip	PBd
Booth, Brett	BBh
Boring, Wayne	WB
Bossart, William	WmB
Boxell, Tim	TB
Bradstreet, Tim	TBd
Braithwaite, Doug	DBw
Brasfield, Craig	CrB
Braun, Russell	RsB
Breeding, Brett	BBr
Brereton, Daniel	DlB
Brewster, Ann	ABr
Breyfogle, Norm	NBy
Bridwell, E. Nelson	ENB
Briefer, Dick	DBr
Bright, Mark	MBr
Brigman, June	JBr
Broderick, Pat	PB
Brodsky, Allyn	AyB
Broom, John	JBm
Broome, Matt	MtB
Brothers, Hernandez	HB
Brown, Bob	BbB
Browne, Dick	DkB
Brunner, Frank	FB
Bryant, Rick	RkB
Buckingham, Mark	MBu
Buckler, Rich	RB
Budget, Greg	GBu
Bugro, Carl	CBu
Bulanadi, Danny	DBl
Burchett, Rick	RBr
Burgard, Tim	TmB
Burke, Fred	FBk
Burns, John	JBn
Burns, Robert	RBu
Burroughs, W.	WBu
Buscema, John	JB
Buscema, Sal	SB
Busiek, Kurt	KBk
Butler, Jeff	JBt
Butler, Steve	SBt
Buzz	Buzz
Byrd, Mitch	MBy
Byrne, John	JBy
Calafiore, Jim	**JCf**
Caldes, Charles	CCa
Callahan, Jim	JiC
Calnan, John	JCa
Cameron, Don	DCn
Cameron, Lou	LC
Campbell, Eddie	ECa
Campbell, J. Scott	JSC
Campbell, Stan	StC
Campenella, Robert	RbC
Campos, Marc	MCa
Capullo, Greg	GCa
Cardy, Nick	NC
Carey, Mike	MCy
Cariello, Sergio	SCi
Carlin, Mike	MCr
Carpenter, Brent D	BDC
Carralero, Ricky	RCl
Carrasco, Dario	DoC
Carter, Joe	JCt
Case, Richard	RCa
Casey, Joe	JoC
Castellaneta, Dan	DaC
Castellini, Claudio	CCt
Castrillo, Anthony	ACa
Chadwick, Paul	PC
Chan, Ernie	ECh
Chang, Bernard	BCh
Charest, Travis	TC
Chase, Bobbie	BCe
Chaykin, Howard	HC
Check, Sid	SC
Chen, Mike	MCh
Chen, Sean	SCh
Chestney, Lillian	LCh
Chiarello, Mark	MCo
Chichester, D.G.	DGC
Chiodo, Joe	JCh
Choi, Brandon	BCi
Chriscross	Ccs
Christopher, Tom	TmC
Chua, Ernie	Chu
Chun, Anthony	ACh
Churchhill, Ian	IaC
Cirocco, Frank	FC
Citron, Sam	SmC
Claremont, Chris	CCl
Clark, Mike	MCl
Clark, Scott	ScC
Cockrum, Dave	DC
Cohn, Gary	GCh
Coker, Tomm	TCk
Colan, Gene	GC
Colby, Simon	SCy
Cole, Jack	JCo
Cole, Leonard B.	LbC
Colletta, Vince	ViC
Collins, Max Allan	MCn
Collins, Mike	MC
Collins, Nancy	NyC
Colon, Ernie	EC
Conner, Amanda	ACo
Conway, Gerry	GyC
Cooper, Dave	DvC
Cooper, John	JCp
Corben, Richard	RCo
Costanza, Peter	PrC
Cowan, Denys	DCw
Cox, Jeromy	JCx
Craig, Johnny	JCr
Crandall, Reed	RC
Crespo, Steve	SCr
Crilley, Mark	MCi
Crumb, Robert	RCr
Cruz, E. R.	ERC
Cruz, Jerry	JCz
Cruz, Roger	RCz
Culdera, Chuck	CCu
Cullins, Paris	PCu
Currie, Andrew	ACe
Damaggio, Rodolfo	RDm
Daniel, Tony	**TnD**
Danner, Paul	PuD
Darrow, Geof	GfD
David, Peter	PDd
Davis, Alan	AD
Davis, Dan	DDv
Davis, Guy	GyD
Davis, Jack	JDa
Davis, Malcolm	MDa
Davison, Al	ADv
Day, Dan	Day
Day, Gene	GD
DeFalco, Tom	TDF
Deitch, Kim	KDe
Delano, Jamie	JaD
DeLaRosa, Sam	SDR
Delgado, Richard	DRd
Dell, John	JhD
DeMatteis, J. M.	JMD
DeMulder, Kim	KDM
Deodato, Jr., Mike	MD2
Derenick, Tom	TDr
DeZago, Todd	TDz
DeZuniga, M.	MDb
DeZuniga, Tony	TD
Diaz, Paco	PaD
Dillin, Dick	DD
Dillon, Glyn	GlD
Dillon, Steve	SDi
Dini, Paul	PDi
Ditko, Steve	SD
Dixon, Chuck	CDi
Dixon, John	JDx
Dobbyn, Nigel	ND
Dodson, Terry	TyD
Doherty, Peter	PD
Dominguez, Luis	LDz
Doran, Colleen	CDo
Dorey, Mike	MDo
Dorkin, Evan	EDo
Dorman, Dave	DvD
Doucet, Julie	JDo
Drake, Stan	SDr
Dresser, Larry	LDr
Dringenberg, Mike	MDr
Drucker, Mort	MD
DuBerkr, Randy	RDB
Duffy, Jo	JDy
Dumm, Gary	GDu
Dunn, Ben	BDn
Duranona, Leo	LDu
Duursema, Jan	JD
Dwyer, Kieron	KD
Eastman, Kevin	**KEa**
Eaton, Scott	SEa
Edginton, Ian	IEd
Edlund, Ben	BEd
Egeland, Marty	MEg
Eisner, Will	WE

Name	Abbr	Name	Abbr	Name	Abbr	Name	Abbr
Elder, Bill	BE	Gibson, Ian	IG	Hernandez, Jaime	JHr	Keown, Dale	DK
Eldred, Tim	TEl	Giella, Joe	JoG	Herrera,Ben	BHr	Kerschl, Karl	KlK
Elias, Lee	LE	Giffen, Keith	KG	Hester, Phil	PhH	Kesel, Babara	BKs
Elliot, D.	DE	Gilbert, Michael T.	MGi	Hewlett, Jamie	JHw	Kesel, Karl	KK
Ellis, Warren	WEl	Giordano, Dick	DG	Hibbard, E.E.	EHi	Kieth, Sam	SK
Ellison, Harlan	HaE	Glanzman, Sam	SG	Hicklenton, John	JHk	King, Hannibal	HbK
Emberlin, Randy	RyE	Golden, Michael	MGo	Higgins, Graham	GHi	Kinsler, Everett R.	EK
Englehart, Steve	SEt	Gonzalez, Jorge	JGz	Higgins, John	JHi	Kirby, Jack	JK
Ennis, Garth	GEn	Goodman, Till	TGo	Higgins, Michael	MHi	Kisniro, Yukito	YuK
Epting, Steve	SEp	Goodwin, Archie	AGw	Hitch, Bryan	BHi	Kitson, Barry	BKi
Erskine, Gary	GEr	Gordon, Al	AG	Hobbs, Bill	BlH	Kobasic, Kevin	KoK
Erwin, Steve	StE	Gottfredson, Floyd	FG	Hoberg, Rick	RHo	Kolins, Scott	ScK
Esposito, Mike	ME	Gould, Chester	ChG	Hoffer, Mike	MkH	Krause, Peter	PKr
Estes, John	JEs	Grant, Alan	AlG	Hogarth, Burne	BHg	Krenkel, Roy	RKu
Estrada, Ric	RE	Grant, Steve	StG	Holcomb, Art	AHo	Krigstein, Bernie	BK
Evans, George	GE	Grau, Peter	PGr	Holdredge, John	JHo	Kristiansen, Teddy H.	TKr
Everett, Bill	BEv	Gray, Mick	MGy	Hoover, Dave	DHv	Kruse, Brandon	BKr
Ewins, Brett	BEw	Green, Dan	DGr	Hopgood, Kevin	KHd	Kubert, Adam	AKu
Ezquerra, Carlos	CE	Green, Randy	RGr	Horie, Richard	RHe	Kubert, Andy	NKu
Fabry, Glenn	**GF**	Greene, Sid	SGe	Hotz, Kyle	KHt	Kubert, Joe	JKu
Fago, Al	AFa	Grell, Mike	MGr	Howarth, Matt	MHo	Kupperberg, Paul	PuK
Farmer, Mark	MFm	Griffith, Bill	BG	Howell, Rich	RHo	Kurtzman, Harvey	HK
Fegredo, Duncan	DFg	Griffiths, Martin	MGs	Hudnall, James	JHl	Kwitney, Alisa	AaK
Feldstein, Al	AF	Grindberg, Tom	TGb	Hughes, Adam	AH	LaBan, Terry	TLa
Ferry, Pascual	PFe	Gross, Daerick	DkG	Hund, Dave	DeH	**Lago, Ray**	**RyL**
Fine, Lou	LF	Gross, Peter	PrG	Hunt, Chad	CH	Laird, Peter	PLa
Fingeroth, Danny	DFr	Grossman, R.	RGs	**Immonen, Stuart**	**SI**	Lanning, Andy	ALa
Finnocchiaro, Sal	SF	Gruenwald, Mark	MGu	Infantino, Carmine	CI	Lansdale, Joe	JLd
Fleisher, Michael	MFl	Grummett, Tom	TG	Ingles, Graham	GrI	Lapham, Dave	DL
Fleming, Robert	RFl	Guardineer, Frank	FG	Iorio, Medio	MI	Lark, Michael	MLr
Flemming, Homer	HFl	Guay, Rebecca	RGu	Isherwood, Geoff	GI	Larkin, Bob	BLr
Foreman, Dick	DiF	Guice, Jackson	JG	Ivie, Larry	LI	LaRocque, Greg	GrL
Forte, John	JF	Guichet, Yvel	YG	Ivy, Chris	CIv	Larroca, Salvador	SvL
Forton, Gerald	GFo	Guinan, Paul	PGn	Jackson, Julius	JJn	Larsen, Erik	EL
Fosco, Frank	FFo	Gulacy, Paul	PG	Janke, Dennis	DJa	Lash, Batton	BLs
Foster, Alan Dean	ADF	Gustovich, Mike	MG	Janson, Klaus	KJ	Lashley, Ken	KeL
Fox, Gardner	GaF	**Ha, Gene**	**GeH**	Javinen, Kirk	KJa	Lavery, Jim	JLv
Fox, Gill	GFx	Haley, Matt	MHy	Jenkins, Paul	PJe	Lawlis, Dan	DLw
Fox, Matt	MF	Hall, Bob	BH	Jenney, Robert	RJ	Lawrence, Terral	TLw
Fraga, Dan	DaF	Halsted, Ted	TeH	Jensen, Dennis	DJ	Lawson, Jim	JmL
Franchesco	Fso	Hama, Larry	LHa	Jimenez, Leonardo	LJi	Layton, Bob	BL
Frank, Gary	GFr	Hamilton, Tim	TH	Jimminiz, Phil	PJ	Leach, Garry	GL
Frazetta, Frank	FF	Hamner, Cully	CHm	Johnson, Dave	DvJ	Leach, Rick	RkL
Freeman, John	JFr	Hampton, Bo	BHa	Johnson, Jeff	JJ	Lee, Elaine	ELe
Freeman, Simon	SFr	Hampton, Scott	SHp	Johnson, Paul	PuJ	Lee, Jae	JaL
Frenz, Ron	RF	Hanna, Scott	SHa	Johnson, Todd	TJn	Lee, Jim	JLe
Friedman, Michael Jan	MFr	Hannigan, Ed	EH	Jones, Casey	CJ	Lee, Patrick	PtL
Friedrich, Mike	MkF	Hanson, Neil	NHa	Jones, Gerard	GJ	Lee, Scott	ScL
Frolechlich, A.	AgF	Harras, Bob	BHs	Jones, J.B.	JJo	Lee, Stan	StL
Fry III, James	JFy	Harris, N. Steven	NSH	Jones, Jeff	JeJ	Leeke, Mike	MLe
Fujitani(Fuje), Bob	BF	Harris, Tim	THa	Jones, Kelley	KJo	Leialoha, Steve	SL
Furman, Simon	SFu	Harris, Tony	TyH	Jones, Malcolm	MJ	Leon, John Paul	JPL
Gaiman, Neil	**NGa**	Harrison, Lou	LuH	Jones, R.A.	RAJ	Leonardi, Rick	RL
Galan, Manny	MaG	Harrison, Simon	SHn	Jones, Robert	RJn	Levins, Rik	RLe
Gallant, Shannon	ShG	Hart, Ernest	EhH	Jurgens, Dan	DJu	Lieber, Larry	LLi
Gammill, Kerry	KGa	Hartsoe, Everette	EHr	Jusko, Joe	JJu	Liefeld, Rob	RLd
Garcia, Dave	DaG	Hathaway, Kurt	KtH	**Kaluta, Mike**	**MK**	Lightle, Steve	SLi
Garner, Alex	AGo	Hawkins, Matt	MHw	Kamen, Jack	JKa	Lim, Ron	RLm
Garney, Ron	RG	Hayes, Drew	DHa	Kaminski, Len	LKa	Linsner, Joseph M.	JLi
Garzon, Carlos	CG	Haynes, Hugh	HH	Kane & Romita	K&R	Livingstone, R.	RLv
Gascoine, Phil	PGa	Hazlewood, Douglas	DHz	Kane, Bob	Bka	Lloyd, David	DvL
Gaughan, Jack	JGa	Heath, Russ	RH	Kane, Gil	GK	Lobdell, Scott	SLo
Gecko, Gabe	GG	Hebbard, Robert	RtH	Kanigher, Bob	BbK	Locke, Vince	VcL
Geggan	Ggn	Heck, Don	DH	Kaniuga, Trent	TKn	Loeb, Jeph	JLb
Gerard, Ruben	RGd	Heisler, Mike	MHs	Karounos, Paris T.	PaK	Lopez, Jose	JL
Gerber, Steve	SvG	Hempel, Mark	MaH	Katz, Jack	JKz	Lopresti, Aaron	AaL
Giacoia, Frank	FrG	Henry, Flint	FH	Kavanagh, Terry	TKa	Louapre, Dave	DLp
Giarrano, Vince	VGi	Herman, Jack	JH	Kelly, Walt	WK	Lowe, John	Low
Gibbons, Dave	DGb	Hernandez, Gilbert	GHe	Kennedy, Cam	CK	Lubbers, Bob	BLb

Name	Abbr.
Lustbader, Eric Van	ELu
Luzniak, Greg	GLz
Lyle, Tom	TL
Macchio, Ralph	**RMc**
Mack, David	DMk
Mackie, Howard	HMe
Madan, Dev	DeM
Madureira, Joe	JMd
Maggin, Elliot S.	ESM
Maguire, Kevin	KM
Magyar, Rick	RM
Mahlstedt, Larry	LMa
Mahnke, Doug	DoM
Mandrake, Tom	TMd
Maneely, Joe	JMn
Manley, Mike	MM
Mann, Roland	RMn
Mann, Roland	Man
Manning, Russ	RsM
Marais, Raymond	RdM
Mariotte, Jeff	JMi
Maroto, Esteban	EM
Marrinan, Chris	ChM
Marrs, Lee	LMr
Martin, Gary	GyM
Martin, Joe	JMt
Martinbrough, Shawn	SMa
Martinez, Henry	HMz
Martinez, Roy Allan	RMr
Marz, Ron	RMz
Marzan, Jose	JMz
Mason, Tom	TMs
Massengill, Nathan	NMa
Matsuda, Jeff	JMs
Mattsson, Steve	SMt
Maus, Bill	BMs
Mayer, Sheldon	ShM
Mayerik, Val	VMk
Mazzucchelli, David	DM
McCarthy, Brendon	BMy
McCloud, Scott	SMI
McCorkindale, B	BMC
McCraw, Tom	TMw
McCrea, John	JMC
McDaniel, Scott	SMc
McDaniel, Walter	WMc
McDonnell, Luke	LMc
McDuffie, Dwayne	DMD
McFarlane, Todd	TM
McGregor, Don	DMG
McKean, Dave	DMc
McKeever, Ted	TMK
McKenna, Mike	MkK
McKie, Angus	AMK
McKone, Mike	MMK
McLaughlin, Frank	FMc
McLaughlin, Sean	SML
McLeod, Bob	BMc
McMahon, M.	MMc
McManus, Shawn	SwM
McWilliams, Al	AMc
Medina, Angel	AMe
Medley, Linda	LiM
Mercadoocasio, Harvey	HMo
Meskin, Mort	MMe
Messner-Loebs, Bill	BML
Michelinie, David	DvM
Miehm, Grant	GtM
Mighten, Duke	DMn
Mignola, Michael	MMi
Miki, Danny	DaM
Milgrom, Al	AM
Millar, Mark	MMr
Miller, Frank	FM
Miller, Mike S.	MsM
Miller, Steve	SM
Milligan, Peter	PrM
Mills, Pat	PMs
Minor, Jason	JnM
Mitchel, Barry	BM
Moder, Lee	LMd
Moebius	Moe
Moeller, Chris	CsM
Moench, Doug	DgM
Montano, Steve	SeM
Mooney, Jim	JM
Moore, Alan	AMo
Moore, Jeff	JMr
Moore, Jerome	JeM
Moore, John Francis	JFM
Moore, Terry	TMr
Morales, Rags	RgM
Moretti, Mark	MMo
Morgan, Tom	TMo
Morisi, Pete	PMo
Morosco, Vincent	VMo
Morrison, Grant	GMo
Morrow, Gray	GM
Mortimer, Win	WMo
Motter, Dean	DMt
Moy, Jeffrey	JMy
Murray, Brian	BrM
Musial, Joe	JoM
Muth, Jon J.	JMu
Mychaels, Marat	MMy
Naifeh, Ted	**TNa**
Napolitano, Nick	NNa
Napton, Bob	BNa
Nauck, Todd	TNu
Neary, Paul	PNe
Nebres, Rudy	RN
Nelson	Nel
Netzer, Mike	MN
Newton, Don	DN
Nguyen, Hoang	HNg
Nichols, Art	ANi
Nicieza, Fabian	FaN
Nino, Alex	AN
Nocenti, Ann	ANo
Nocon, Cedric	CNn
Nodell, Martin	MnN
Nolan, Graham	GN
Nord, Cary	CNr
Norem, Earl	EN
Nostrand, Howard	HN
Novick, Irv	IN
Nowlan, Kevin	KN
Nutman, Philip	PNu
O'Barr, James	JOb
O'Neil, Denny	DON
O'Neill, Kevin	**KON**
Olbrich, Dave	**DO**
Olivetti, Ariel	AOl
Olliffe, Patrick	PO
One, Dark	DOe
Ordway, Jerry	JOy
Orlando, Joe	JO
Ortiz, Jose	JOt
Oskner, Bob	BO
Ostrander, John	JOs
Owen, James	JOn
Ozkan, Tayyar	TOz
Pace, Richard	RPc
Pacella, Mark	**MPa**
Pacheco, Carlos	CPa
Palais, Rudy	RP
Palmer, Tom	TP
Palmiotti, Jimmy	JP
Pamai, Gene	GPi
Panalign, Noly	NPl
Paniccia, Mark	MPc
Panosian, Dan	DPs
Parkhouse, Annie	APh
Parkhouse, Steve	SvP
Parobeck, Mike	MeP
Pascoe, James	JmP
Pasko, Martin	MPk
Patterson, Bruce	BrP
Pearson, Jason	JPn
Pelletier, Paul	PaP
Pence, Eric	ErP
Pennington, Mark	MPn
Pensa, Shea Anton	SAP
Perez, George	GP
Perham, James	JPh
Perlin, Don	DP
Perryman, Edmund	EP
Peterson, Brandon	BPe
Peterson, Jonathan	JPe
Petrucha, Stefan	SPr
Peyer, Tom	TPe
Phillips, Joe	JoP
Phillips, Scott	SPl
Phillips, Sean	SeP
Pini, Richard	RPi
Pini, Wendy	WP
Platt, Stephen	SPa
Pleece, Warren	WaP
Ploog, Mike	MP
Plunkett, Kilian	KPl
Pollack, Rachel	RaP
Pollard, Keith	KP
Pollina, Adam	AdP
Pope, Paul	PPo
Porch, David	DPo
Portacio, Whilce	WPo
Porter, Howard	HPo
Post, Howard	HwP
Potts, Carl	CP
Powell, Bob	BP
Power, Dermot	DPw
Pratt, George	GgP
Priest, Christopher	CPr
Prosser, Jerry	JeP
Pugh, Steve	StP
Pulido, Brian	BnP
Queen, Randy	RQu
Quesada, Joe	**JQ**
Quinn, David	DQ
Quinones, Peter	PQ
Raab, Ben	**BRa**
Raboy, Mac	MRa
Ramos, Humberto	HuR
Ramos, Rodney	RyR
Randall, Ron	RoR
Raney, Tom	TR
Rankin, Rich	RRa
Rapmund, Norm	NRd
Raymond, Alex	AR
Redondo, Nestor	NR
Reed, David	DvR
Reeves-Stevens, Judith	JRv
Reinhold, Bill	BR
Richards, Ted	TR
Richardson, Mike	MRi
Ricketts, Mark	MRc
Rico, Don	DRi
Ridgeway, John	JRy
Rieber, John Ney	JNR
Riley, John	JnR
Riply	Rip
Robbins, Frank	FR
Robbins, Trina	TrR
Robertson, Darrick	DaR
Robinson, James	JeR
Rodier, Denis	DRo
Rogers, Marshall	MR
Romita, John	JR
Romita, John Jr.	JR2
Rosenberger, J.	JRo
Ross, Alex	AxR
Ross, David	DR
Ross, John	JRs
Ross, Luke	LRs
Roth, Werner	WR
Royle, Jim	JRl
Royle, John	JRe
Rozum, John	JRz
Rubi, Melvin	MvR
Rubinstein, Joe	JRu
Rude, Steve	SR
Ruffner, Sean	SRf
Russell, P. Craig	CR
Russell, Vince	VRu
Ryan, Matt	MRy
Ryan, Paul	PR
Ryder, Tom	TmR
Sakai, Stan	SS
Sale, Tim	TSe
Salmons, Tony	TSa
Saltares, Javier	JS
Sanders, Jim III	JS3
Sasso, Mark	MSo
Saviuk, Alex	AS
Schaffenberger, Kurt	KS
Schane, Tristan	TnS
Schiller, Fred	FdS
Schmitz, Mark	MaS
Schultz, Mark	MSh
Scoffield, Sean	SSc
Scott, Jeffery	JSc
Scott, Trevor	TvS
Seagle, Steven T.	SSe
Sears, Bart	BS
Sekowsky, Mike	MSy
Semeiks, Val	VS
Senior, Geoff	GSr
Serpe, Jerry	JyS
Severin, John	JSe
Shamray, Gerry	GSh
Shanower, Eric	EiS
Sharp, Liam	LSh
Shaw, Sean	SSh
Sherman, Jim	JSh
Shoemaker, Terry	TSr
Shooter, Jim	JiS

Shum, Howard .... HSm	Stevens, Dave .... DSt	Van Fleet, John .... JVF	Williamson, Skip .... SWi
Shuster, Joe .... JoS	Stiles, Steve .... SvS	Vancata, Brad .... BVa	Willingham, Bill .... BWg
Sibal, Jonathan ...... JSb	Story, Karl .... KlS	Vance, Steve .... SVa	Willis, Damon .... DaW
Siegel & Shuster ..... S&S	Stout, William .... WiS	VanHook, Kevin ..... KVH	Wilshire, Mary .... MW
Sienkiewicz, Bill .... BSz	Stradley, Randy ...... RSd	Vargas, Vagner VV	Wilson, Colin .... CWi
Silvestri, Eric .... EcS	Strazewski, Len .... LeS	Veitch, Rick .... RV	Wilson, Gahan .... GW
Silvestri, Mark .... MS	Stroman, Larry .... LSn	Velez, Ivan, Jr. IV	Wilson, Keith S. ...... KSW
Sim, Dave .... DS	Sullivan, Lee .... LS	Velluto, Sal .... SaV	Woch, Stan .... SnW
Simon & Kirby .... S&K	Sutton, Tom .... TS	Vess, Charles CV	Woggin, Bill .... BWo
Simon, Joe .... JSm	Swan, Curt .... CS	Vey, Al .... AV	Wojtkiewicz, Chuck ..... Woj
Simonson, Louise ...... LSi	Sweetman, Dan .... DSw	Vigil, Tim .... TV	Wolf, Chance .... CWf
Simonson, Walt .... WS	**Taggart, Tom .... TTg**	Vokes, Neil .... NV	Wolfe, Joseph .... JWf
Simpson, Don .... DSs	Takenaga, Francis .... FTa	Von Eeden, Trevor .... TVE	Wolfman, Marv .... MWn
Simpson, Howard ..... HSn	Takezaki, Tony .... ToT	Vosburg, Mike .... MV	Wolverton, Basil ...... BW
Simpson, Will .... WSm	Talbot, Bryan .... BT	**Wagner, Matt .... MWg**	Wood, Bob .... BoW
Sinnott, Joe .... JSt	Tallarico, Tony .... TyT	Wagner,Ron .... RoW	Wood, Teri Sue ...... TWo
Skroce, Steve .... SSr	Tan, Billy .... BTn	Waid, Mark .... MWa	Wood, Wally .... WW
Smith, Andy .... ASm	Tanaka, Masashi ...... MTk	Walker, Kevin .... KeW	Woodring, Jim .... JWo
Smith, Barry W. ...... BWS	Tanghal, Romeo ...... RT	Waltrip, Jason .... JWp	Wormer, Kirk Van ..... KWo
Smith, Beau .... BSt	Tappin, Steve .... SeT	Waltrip, John .... JWt	Wright, Greg .... GWt
Smith, Cam .... CaS	Taylor, David .... DTy	Ward, Bill .... BWa	Wrightson, Berni ...... BWr
Smith, Jeff .... JSi	Taylor, R.G. .... RGT	Warner, Chris .... CW	Wyman, M.C. .... MCW
Smith, John .... JnS	Templeton, Ty .... TTn	Warren, Adam .... AWa	**Yaep, Chap .... CYp**
Smith, Malcolm .... MSt	Teney, Tom .... TmT	Washington 3, Robert .. 3RW	Yeates, Tom .... TY
Smith, Paul .... PS	Tenney, Mark .... MaT	Watkiss, John .... JWk	Yeowell, Steve .... SY
Smith, Robin .... RSm	Texeira, Mark .... MT	Weeks, Lee .... LW	**Zabel, Joe .... JZe**
Smith, Ron .... RS	Thibert, Art .... ATi	Wein, Len .... LWn	Zachary, Dean .... DZ
Snejbjerg, Peter ...... PSj	Thomas, Dann .... DTs	Weinstein, Howard ..... HWe	Zaffino, Jorge .... JZ
Sniegoski, Tom .... TSg	Thomas, Roy .... RTs	Welch, Larry .... LyW	Zeck, Mike .... MZ
Spark .... Spk	Thomason, Derek ..... DeT	Wendel, Andrew ...... AdW	Zick, Bruce .... BZ
Sparling, Jack .... JkS	Thompson, Jill .... JlT	Wenzel, David .... DWe	Zulli, Michael .... MZi
Spiegelman, Art ...... ASp	Thorne, Frank .... FT	Weringo, Mike .... MeW	Zyskowski, Joseph ..... JZy
Spiegle, Dan .... DSp	Tinker, Ron .... RnT	West, Kevin .... KWe	Zyskowski, Steven ..... SZ
Spinks, Frank .... FrS	Torres, Angelo .... AT	Weston, Chris .... CWn	
Springer, Frank ...... FS	Toth, Alex .... ATh	Wheatley, Mark ...... MkW	
Sprouse, Chris .... CSp	Totleben, John .... JTo	Whitney, Ogden ...... OW	
St.Pierre, Joe .... JPi	Trimpe, Herb .... HT	Wiacek, Bob .... BWi	
Starlin, Jim .... JSn	Truman, Timothy .... TT	Wiesenfeld, Aron ..... AWs	
Starr, Leonard .... LSt	Truog, Chas .... ChT	Wildey, Doug .... DW	
Staton, Joe .... JSon	Tucci, Bill .... BiT	Wildman, Andrew ...... Wld	
Steacy, Ken .... KSy	Turner, Dwayne .... DT	Williams, Anthony ..... AWi	
Steffan, Dan .... DnS	Tuska, George .... GT	Williams, David ...... DdW	
Stelfreeze, Brian .... BSf	**Ulm, Chris .... CU**	Williams, J.H. .... JWi	
Stephenson, Eric ...... ErS	**Vachss, Andrew ..... AVs**	Williams, Keith .... KWi	
Steranko, Jim .... JSo	Vado, Dan .... DVa	Williams, Kent .... KW	
Stern, Roger .... RSt	Valentino, Jim .... JV	Williams, Scott .... SW	
Stern, Steve .... SSt	Vallejo, Boris .... BV	Williamson, Al .... AW	

GENERAL ABBREVIATIONS FOR COMICS LISTINGS

Adaptation	Adapt.	Giant Size	G-Size	Photographic cover	Ph(c)
Anniversary	Anniv.	Golden Age	G.A.	Plotter	(pl)
Annual	Ann.#	Graphic Album	GAm	Prestige Format	PF
Appearance of	A:	Graphic Novel	GNv	Preview	Prev.
Artist	(a)	Hardcover	HC	Reprinted issue	rep.
Art & Plot	(a&pl)	Idenity Revealed	IR:	Retold	rtd.
Art & Script	(a&s)	Inks by	(i)	Return/Revival of	R:
Back-Up Story	BU:	Introduction of	I:	Silver Age	S.A.
Beginning of	B:	Joins of	J:	Scripted/Written By	(s)
Birth	b:	King Size	K-Size	Script & inks	(s&i)
Cameo by	C:	Leaving of	L:	Softcover	SC
Cover	(c)	New Costume	N:	Special	Spec.
Cover and Script	(c&s)	New Listing	★	Team Up	T.U.
Crossover with	x-over	No issue Number	N#	Trade Paperback	TPB
Death/Destruction of	D:	Origin of	O:	Versus	V:
Edition	Ed.	Painted Cover	P(c)	Wedding of	W:
Ending of	E:	Part	pt.	With	w/
Features	F:	Pencils by	(p)	Without	w/o

Abbr.	Name	Abbr.	Name	Abbr.	Name	Abbr.	Name
3RW	Robert Washington 3	BDC	Brent D Carpenter	CCu	Chuck Culdera	DgM	Doug Moench
AA	Alfredo Alcala	BDn	Ben Dunn	CDi	Chuck Dixon	DGr	Dan Green
AAd	Art Adams	BE	Bill Elder	CDo	Colleen Doran	DH	Don Heck
AaK	Alisa Kwitney	BEd	Ben Edlund	CE	Carlos Ezquerra	DHa	Drew Hayes
AaL	Aaron Lopresti	BEv	Bill Everett	CG	Carlos Garzon	DHv	Dave Hoover
AAv	Al Avison	BEw	Brett Ewins	CH	Chad Hunt	DHz	Douglas Hazlewood
AB	Alex Blum	BF	Bob Fujitani(Fuje)	ChB	Charles Berger	DiF	Dick Foreman
ABr	Ann Brewster	BG	Bill Griffith	ChG	Chester Gould	DJ	Dennis Jensen
ACa	Anthony Castrillo	BH	Bob Hall	ChM	Chris Marrinan	DJa	Dennis Janke
ACe	Andrew Currie	BHa	Bo Hampton	CHm	Cully Hamner	DJu	Dan Jurgens
ACh	Anthony Chun	BHg	Burne Hogarth	ChT	Chas Truog	DK	Dale Keown
ACo	Amanda Conner	BHi	Bryan Hitch	Chu	Ernie Chua	DkB	Dick Browne
AD	Alan Davis	BHr	Ben Herrera	CI	Carmine Infantino	DkG	Daerick Gross
ADF	Alan Dean Foster	BHs	Bob Harras	CIv	Chris Ivy	DL	Dave Lapham
AdP	Adam Pollina	BiT	Bill Tucci	CJ	Casey Jones	DlB	Daniel Brereton
ADv	Al Davison	BK	Bernie Krigstein	CK	Cam Kennedy	DLp	Dave Louapre
AdW	Andrew Wendel	Bka	Bob Kane	CNn	Cedric Nocon	DLw	Dan Lawlis
AF	Al Feldstein	BKi	Barry Kitson	CNr	Cary Nord	DM	David Mazzucchelli
AFa	Al Fago	BKr	Brandon Kruse	CP	Carl Potts	DMc	Dave McKean
AG	Al Gordon	BKs	Babara Kesel	CPa	Carlos Pacheco	DMD	Dwayne McDuffie
AgF	A. Frolechlich	BL	Bob Layton	CPr	Christopher Priest	DMG	Don McGregor
AGo	Alex Garner	BLb	Bob Lubbers	CR	P. Craig Russell	DMk	David Mack
AGw	Archie Goodwin	BlH	Bill Hobbs	CrB	Craig Brasfield	DMn	Duke Mighten
AH	Adam Hughes	BLr	Bob Larkin	CS	Curt Swan	DMt	Dean Motter
AHo	Art Holcomb	BLs	Batton Lash	CsB	Chris Batista	DN	Don Newton
AIA	Alfred Andriola	BM	Barry Mitchel	CsM	Chris Moeller	DnS	Dan Steffan
AKu	Adam Kubert	BMc	Bob McLeod	CSp	Chris Sprouse	DO	Dave Olbrich
ALa	Andy Lanning	BMC	B. McCorkindale	CU	Chris Ulm	DoC	Dario Carrasco
AIG	Alan Grant	BML	Bill Messner-Loebs	CV	Charles Vess	DOe	Dark One
AM	Al Milgrom	BMs	Bill Maus	CW	Chris Warner	DoM	Doug Mahnke
AMc	Al McWilliams	BMy	Brendon McCarthy	CWf	Chance Wolf	DON	O'Neil, Denny
AMe	Angel Medina	BNa	Bob Napton	CWi	Colin Wilson	DP	Don Perlin
AMK	Angus McKie	BnP	Brian Pulido	CWn	Chris Weston	DPo	Porch, David
AMo	Alan Moore	BO	Bob Oskner	CYp	Chap Yaep	DPs	Dan Panosian
AN	Alex Nino	BoW	Bob Wood	**DA**	**Dan Adkins**	DPw	Power, Dermot
ANi	Art Nichols	BP	Bob Powell	DAb	Dusty Abell	DQ	David Quinn
ANo	Ann Nocenti	BPe	Brandon Peterson	DaC	Dan Castellaneta	DR	Ross, David
AOl	Ariel Olivetti	BR	Bill Reinhold	DaF	Dan Fraga	DRd	Richard Delgado
APh	Annie Parkhouse	BRa	Ben Raab	DaG	Dave Garcia	DRi	Don Rico
AR	Alex Raymond	BrM	Brian Murray	DaM	Danny Miki	DRo	Denis Rodier
AS	Alex Saviuk	BrP	Bruce Patterson	DAn	Dan Abnett	DS	Dave Sim
ASm	Andy Smith	BS	Bart Sears	DaR	Darrick Robertson	DSp	Dan Spiegle
ASp	Art Spiegelman	BSf	Brian Stelfreeze	DaW	Damon Willis	DSs	Don Simpson
AT	Angelo Torres	BSt	Beau Smith	Day	Dan Day	DSt	Dave Stevens
ATh	Alex Toth	BSz	Bill Sienkiewicz	DAy	Dick Ayers	DSw	Dan Sweetman
ATi	Art Thibert	BT	Bryan Talbot	DB	D. Battlefield	DT	Dwayne Turner
AV	Al Vey	BTn	Billy Tan	DB	Denis Beauvais	DTs	Dann Thomas
AVs	Andrew Vachss	Buzz	Buzz	DBa	Dan Barry	DTy	David Taylor
AW	Al Williamson	BV	Boris Vallejo	DBk	Darryl Banks	DvA	David Ammerman
AWa	Adam Warren	BVa	Brad Vancata	DBl	Danny Bulanadi	DVa	Dan Vado
AWi	Anthony Williams	BW	Basil Wolverton	DBr	Dick Briefer	DvC	Dave Cooper
AWs	Aron Wiesenfeld	BWa	Bill Ward	DBs	John Barras	DvD	Dave Dorman
AxR	Alex Ross	BWg	Bill Willingham	DBw	Doug Braithwaite	DvJ	Dave Johnson
AyB	Allyn Brodsky	BWi	Bob Wiacek	DC	Dave Cockrum	DvL	David Lloyd
BA	**Brent Anderson**	BWo	Bill Woggin	DCn	Don Cameron	DvM	David Michelinie
BAn	Bill Anderson	BWr	Berni Wrightson	DCw	Denys Cowan	DvR	David Reed
BAp	Brian Althorp	BWS	Barry Windsor-Smith	DD	Dick Dillin	DW	Doug Wildey
BAu	Brian Augustyn	BZ	Bruce Zick	DdB	David Boller	DWe	David Wenzel
BB	Brian Bolland	**CAd**	**Charlie Adlard**	DDv	Dan Davis	DZ	Dean Zachary
BBa	Bernard Bailey	CaS	Cam Smith	DdW	David Williams	**EA**	**Edd Ashe**
BbB	Bob Brown	CAx	Chris Alexander	DE	D. Elliot	EB	Ed Barreto
BBB	Bob Boze Bell	CB	Carl Barks	DeH	Dave Hund	EBe	Ed Benes
BBh	Brett Booth	CBa	Chris Bachalo	DeM	Dev Madan	EC	Ernie Colon
BbK	Bob Kanigher	CBi	Charles Biro	DeT	Derek Thomason	ECa	Eddie Campbell
BBl	Bret Blevins	CBu	Carl Bugro	DFg	Duncan Fegredo	ECh	Ernie Chan
BBr	Brett Breeding	CCa	Charles Caldes	DFr	Danny Fingeroth	EcS	Eric Silvestri
BCe	Bobbie Chase	CCl	Chris Claremont	DG	Dick Giordano	EDo	Evan Dorkin
BCh	Bernard Chang	Ccs	Chriscross	DGb	Dave Gibbons	EH	Ed Hannigan
BCi	Brandon Choi	CCt	Claudio Castellini	DGC	D.G. Chichester	EhH	Ernest Hart

EHi .... E.E. Hibbard	Grl .... Graham Ingles	JDo .... Julie Doucet	JoP .... Joe Phillips
EHr ...... Everette Hartsoe	GrL ...... Greg LaRocque	JDx .... John Dixon	JoS .... Joe Shuster
EiS .... Eric Shanower	GSh ...... Gerry Shamray	JDy .... Jo Duffy	JOs .... John Ostrander
EK .... Everett R. Kinsler	GSr .... Geoff Senior	JeJ .... Jeff Jones	JOt .... Jose Ortiz
EL .... Erik Larsen	GT .... George Tuska	JeM .... Jerome Moore	JOy .... Jerry Ordway
ELe .... Elaine Lee	GtM .... Grant Miehm	JeP .... Jerry Prosser	JP .... Jimmy Palmiotti
ELu .... Eric Van Lustbader	GW .... Gahan Wilson	JeR ..... James Robinson	JPe ... Jonathan Peterson
EM .... Esteban Maroto	GWt .... Greg Wright	JEs .... John Estes	JPh .... James Perham
EN .... Earl Norem	GyA ...... Gary Amaro	JF .... John Forte	JPi .... Joe St.Pierre
ENB .... E. Nelson Bridwell	GyC ...... Gerry Conway	JFM .... John Francis Moore	JPL ...... John Paul Leon
EP ..... Edmund Perryman	GyD .... Guy Davis	JFr .... John Freeman	JPn ...... Jason Pearson
ERC .... E.R. Cruz	GyM ...... Gary Martin	JFy .... James Fry III	JQ .... Joe Quesada
ErP .... Eric Pence	**HaE ...... Harlan Ellison**	JG .... Jackson Guice	JR .... John Romita
ErS ...... Eric Stephenson	HB .... Hernandez Brothers	JGa ...... Jack Gaughan	JR2 ..... John Romita, Jr.
ESM ..... Elliot S. Maggin	HbK ...... Hannibal King	JGz ...... Jorge Gonzalez	JRe .... John Royle
FaN ...... Fabian Nicieza	HC ...... Howard Chaykin	JH .... Jack Herman	JRl .... Jim Royle
FB .... Frank Brunner	HFl ...... Homer Flemming	JhB .... John Beatty	JRo ..... J. Rosenberger
FBe .... Frank Bolle	HH .... Hugh Haynes	JhD .... John Dell	JRs .... John Ross
FBk .... Fred Burke	HK ...... Harvey Kurtzman	JHi .... John Higgins	JRu ...... Joe Rubinstein
FC .... Frank Cirocco	HMe ..... Howard Mackie	JHk ..... John Hicklenton	JRv . Judith Reeves-Stevens
FdS .... Fred Schiller	HMo . Harvey Mercadoocasio	JHl ..... James Hudnall	JRy ...... John Ridgeway
FF .... Frank Frazetta	HMz ...... Henry Martinez	JHo ...... John Holdredge	JRz .... John Rozum
FFo .... Frank Fosco	HN ...... Howard Nostrand	JHr ..... Jaime Hernandez	JS ...... Javier Saltares
FG ..... Frank Guardineer	HNg ..... Hoang Nguyen	JHw ..... Jamie Hewlett	JS3 ...... Jim Sanders III
FG ..... Floyd Gottfredson	HPo ...... Howard Porter	JiC .... Jim Callahan	JSb ...... Jonathan Sibal
FH .... Flint Henry	HSm ...... Howard Shum	JiS .... Jim Shooter	JSc ...... Jeffery Scott
FM .... Frank Miller	HSn ..... Howard Simpson	JJ .... Jeff Johnson	JSC ... J. Scott Campbell
FMc ..... Frank McLaughlin	HT .... Herb Trimpe	JJB .... JJ Birch	JSe ...... John Severin
FR .... Frank Robbins	HuR ..... Humberto Ramos	JJn ...... Julius Jackson	JSh ...... Jim Sherman
FrG ...... Frank Giacoia	HWe ..... Howard Weinstein	JJo .... J.B. Jones	JSi .... Jeff Smith
FrS .... Frank Spinks	HwP ...... Howard Post	JJu .... Joe Jusko	JSm .... Joe Simon
FS .... Frank Springer	**IaC .... Ian Churchhill**	JK .... Jack Kirby	JSn .... Jim Starlin
Fso .... Franchesco	IEd .... Ian Edginton	JKa ...... Jack Kamen	JSo ...... Jim Steranko
FT .... Frank Thorne	IG .... Ian Gibson	JkS ..... Jack Sparling	JSon .... Jim Staton
FTa ...... Francis Takenaga	IN .... Irv Novick	JKu .... Joe Kubert	JSt .... Joe Sinnott
GaF .... Gardner Fox	IV .... Ivan Velez, Jr.	JKz .... Jack Katz	JTo ..... John Totleben
GB .... Geoffrey Biggs	**JA .... Jack Abel**	JL .... Jose Lopez	JuB .... Julie Bell
GBl .... George Bell	JaB ...... Jack Binder	JLb .... Jeph Loeb	JV .... Jim Valentino
GBu .... Greg Budget	JaD ...... Jamie Delano	JLd ...... Joe Lansdale	JVF ..... John Van Fleet
GC .... Gene Colan	JaL .... Jae Lee	JLe .... Jim Lee	JWf ...... Joseph Wolfe
GCa .... Greg Capullo	JAl ...... Jeff Albrecht	JLi ..... Joseph M. Linsner	JWi ...... J.H. Williams
GCh .... Gary Cohn	JAo ...... John Albano	JlT ...... Jill Thompson	JWk ...... John Watkiss
GD .... Gene Day	JAp .... Jim Aparo	JLv .... Jim Lavery	JWo ...... Jim Woodring
GDu .... Gary Dumm	JAr ...... Jim Arcudi	JM .... Jim Mooney	JWp ...... Jason Waltrip
GE .... George Evans	JB ...... John Buscema	JMC ...... John McCrea	JWt ...... John Waltrip
GeH .... Gene Ha	JBa ...... Jim Baikie	JMd ..... Joe Madureira	JyS .... Jerry Serpe
GEn ...... Garth Ennis	JBa ...... Jim Balent	JMD .... J.M. DeMatteis	JZ .... Jorge Zaffino
GEr .... Gary Erskine	JBe ...... John Beeston	JMi ...... Jeff Mariotte	JZe .... Joe Zabel
GF .... Glenn Fabry	JBg ..... Jon Bogdanove	JmL ...... Jim Lawson	JZy ..... Joseph Zyskowski
GfD .... Geof Darrow	JBi ..... Jerry Bingham	JMn ..... Joe Maneely	**K&R ..... Kane & Romita**
GFo .... Gerald Forton	JBl ...... Jesus Blasco	JmP ..... James Pascoe	KB .... Kyle Baker
GFr .... Gary Frank	JBm ...... John Broom	JMr ...... Jeff Moore	KBk .... Kurt Busiek
GFx .... Gill Fox	JBn .... John Burns	JMs ...... Jeff Matsuda	KD .... Kieron Dwyer
GG .... Gabe Gecko	JBo ...... John Bolton	JMt ...... Joe Martin	KDe .... Kim Deitch
Ggn .... Geggan	JBr ...... June Brigman	JMu ..... Jon J. Muth	KDM ..... Kim DeMulder
GgP .... George Pratt	JBt .... Jeff Butler	JMy ...... Jeffrey Moy	KEa ..... Kevin Eastman
GHe .... Gilbert Hernandez	JBy ...... John Byrne	JMz ...... Jose Marzan	KeL ...... Ken Lashley
GHi ...... Graham Higgins	JBz ...... Joe Benitez	JnM ...... Jason Minor	KeW ...... Kevin Walker
GI ...... Geoff Isherwood	JCa ...... John Calnan	JnR ...... John Riley	KG .... Keith Giffen
GJ .... Gerard Jones	JCf ...... Jim Calafiore	JNR ..... John Ney Rieber	KGa ...... Kerry Gammill
GK .... Gil Kane	JCh ...... Joe Chiodo	JnS ...... John Smith	KHd ..... Kevin Hopgood
GL .... Garry Leach	JCo .... Jack Cole	JO ...... Joe Orlando	KHt .... Kyle Hotz
GlD .... Glyn Dillon	JCp ...... John Cooper	JoA ...... Jo Alibaster	KJ .... Klaus Janson
GLz ...... Greg Luzniak	JCr ...... Johnny Craig	JoB ...... Joe Bennett	KJa ...... Kirk Javinen
GM .... Gray Morrow	JCt .... Joe Carter	JoC .... Joe Casey	KJo ...... Kelley Jones
GMo ...... Grant Morrison	JCx ...... Jeromy Cox	JOb ...... James O'Barr	KK .... Karl Kesel
GN .... Graham Nolan	JCz .... Jerry Cruz	JoG ...... Joe Giella	KIA ..... Karl Alstaetter
GP .... George Perez	JD ...... Jan Duursema	JoM ...... Joe Musial	KIK ...... Karl Kerschl
GPi .... Gene Pamai	JDa .... Jack Davis	JOn ...... James Owen	KIS .... Karl Story

KM .... Kevin Maguire	MCy .... Mike Carey	MTk ..... Masashi Tanaka	RbC .... Robert Campenella
KN .... Kevin Nowlan	MD .... Mort Drucker	MV .... Mike Vosburg	RBe .... Ramon Bernado
KoK .... Kevin Kobasic	MD2 .... Mike Deodato, Jr.	MvR .... Melvin Rubi	RBn .... Ryan Benjamin
KON .... Kevin O'Neill	MDa ...... Malcolm Davis	MW ...... Mary Wilshire	RBr .... Rick Burchett
KP .... Keith Pollard	MDb ...... M. DeZuniga	MWa .... Mark Waid	RBu .... Robert Burns
KPl .... Kilian Plunkett	MDo .... Mike Dorey	MWg ...... Matt Wagner	RC .... Reed Crandall
KS ..... Kurt Schaffenberger	MDr ..... Mike Dringenberg	MWn ...... Marv Wolfman	RCa .... Richard Case
KSW ..... Keith S. Wilson	ME ...... Mike Esposito	MZ .... Mike Zeck	RCl .... Ricky Carralero
KSy .... Ken Steacy	MEg ...... Marty Egeland	MZi .... Michael Zulli	RCo .... Richard Corben
KtH ...... Kurt Hathaway	MeP ...... Mike Parobeck	**NA** .... **Neal Adams**	RCr .... Robert Crumb
KVH ...... Kevin VanHook	MeW ...... Mike Weringo	NBy ...... Norm Breyfogle	RCz .... Roger Cruz
KW .... Kent Williams	MF .... Matt Fox	NC .... Nick Cardy	RDB .... Randy DuBerkr
KWe .... Kevin West	MFl ..... Michael Fleisher	ND ...... Nigel Dobbyn	RdM .... Raymond Marais
KWi .... Keith Williams	MFm ...... Mark Farmer	Nel .... Nelson	RDm .... Rodolfo Damaggio
KWo ... Kirk Van Wormer	MFr .. Michael Jan Friedman	NGa .... Neil Gaiman	RE .... Ric Estrada
LbC ...... **Leonard B. Cole**	MG ...... Mike Gustovich	NHa .... Neil Hanson	RF .... Ron Frenz
LC .... Lou Cameron	MGi ..... Michael T. Gilbert	NKu .... Andy Kubert	RFl .... Robert Fleming
LCh ...... Lillian Chestney	MGo ...... Michael Golden	NMa .... Nathan Massengill	RG .... Ron Garney
LDr ...... Larry Dresser	MGr .... Mike Grell	NNa .... Nick Napolitano	RGd .... Ruben Gerard
LDu ...... Leo Duranona	MGs ...... Martin Griffiths	NPl ...... Noly Panalign	RgM .... Rags Morales
LDz ..... Luis Dominguez	MGu ..... Mark Gruenwald	NR ...... Nestor Redondo	RGr .... Randy Green
LE .... Lee Elias	MGy .... Mick Gray	NRd ...... Norm Rapmund	RGs .... R. Grossman
LeS .... Len Strazewski	MHi ...... Michael Higgins	NSH .... N. Steven Harris	RGT .... R.G. Taylor
LF .... Lou Fine	MHo ...... Matt Howarth	NV ...... Neil Vokes	RGu .... Rebecca Guay
LHa .... Larry Hama	MHs ...... Mike Heisler	NyC ...... Nancy Collins	RH .... Russ Heath
LI .... Larry Ivie	MHw ...... Matt Hawkins	**OW** ...... **Ogden Whitney**	RHe .... Richard Horie
LiM .... Linda Medley	MHy .... Matt Haley	**PaD** .... **Paco Diaz**	RHo .... Rick Hoberg
LJi ...... Leonardo Jimenez	MI .... Medio Iorio	PaK ..... Paris T. Karounos	RHo .... Rich Howell
LKa ...... Len Kaminski	MiA ...... Michael Allred	PaP ...... Paul Pelletier	RiB .... Richard Bennett
LLi .... Larry Lieber	MiB .... Mike Barr	PB .... Pat Broderick	Rip .... Riply
LMa ...... Larry Mahlstedt	MJ .... Malcolm Jones	PBd .... Philip Bond	RJ .... Robert Jenney
LMc ...... Luke McDonnell	MK .... Mike Kaluta	PC .... Paul Chadwick	RJn .... Robert Jones
LMd .... Lee Moder	MkB ...... Mike Barreiro	PCu .... Paris Cullins	RkB .... Rick Bryant
LMr .... Lee Marrs	MkF ...... Mike Friedrich	PD .... Peter Doherty	RkL .... Rick Leach
Low ...... John Lowe	MkH .... Mike Hoffer	PDd ...... Peter David	RKu .... Roy Krenkel
LRs .... Luke Ross	MkK ...... Mike McKenna	PDi .... Paul Dini	RL .... Rick Leonardi
LS .... Lee Sullivan	MkW ...... Mark Wheatley	PFe ...... Pascual Ferry	RLd .... Rob Liefeld
LSh .... Liam Sharp	MlB .... Michael Bair	PG .... Paul Gulacy	RLe .... Rik Levins
LSi ...... Louise Simonson	MLe .... Mike Leeke	PGa ...... Phil Gascoine	RLm .... Ron Lim
LSn .... Larry Stroman	MLr .... Michael Lark	PGn ...... Paul Guinan	RLv .... R. Livingstone
LSt .... Leonard Starr	MM .... Mike Manley	PGr .... Peter Grau	RM .... Rick Magyar
LuH .... Lou Harrison	MMc ...... M. McMahon	PhH .... Phil Hester	RMc .... Ralph Macchio
LW .... Lee Weeks	MMe ...... Mort Meskin	PJ .... Phil Jimminiz	RMn .... Roland Mann
LWn .... Len Wein	MMi ... Michael Mignola	PJe .... Paul Jenkins	RMr .... Roy Allan Martinez
LyW .... Larry Welch	MMK ...... Mike McKone	PKr ...... Peter Krause	RMz .... Ron Marz
MA .... **Murphy Anderson**	MMo ...... Mark Moretti	PlA .... Paul Abrams	RN .... Rudy Nebres
MaG .... Manny Galan	MMr .... Mark Millar	PLa .... Peter Laird	RnT .... Ron Tinker
MaH ...... Mark Hempel	MMy .... Marat Mychaels	PMo ...... Pete Morisi	RoR .... Ron Randall
Man ...... Roland Mann	MN .... Mike Netzer	PMs .... Pat Mills	RoW .... on Wagner
MaS .... Mark Schmitz	MnN .... Martin Nodell	PNe .... Paul Neary	RP .... Rudy Palais
MaT ..... Mark Tenney	Moe .... Moebius	PNu .... Philip Nutman	RPc .... Richard Pace
MB .... Matt Baker	MP .... Mike Ploog	PO .... Patrick Olliffe	RPi .... Richard Pini
MBa .... Mark Bagley	MPa ...... Mark Pacella	PPo .... Paul Pope	RQu .... Randy Queen
MBe ..... M. Belardinelli	MPc ...... Mark Paniccia	PQ ...... Peter Quinones	RRa .... Rich Rankin
MBg .... Mark Badger	MPk ...... Martin Pasko	PR .... Paul Ryan	RS .... Ron Smith
MBm ..... Mary Bierbaum	MPn ...... Mark Pennington	PrC ...... Peter Costanza	RsB .... Russell Braun
MBn .... Mike Baron	MR .... Marshall Rogers	PrG .... Peter Gross	RSd .... Randy Stradley
MBr .... Mark Bright	MRa ...... Mac Raboy	PrM .... Peter Milligan	RsM .... Russ Manning
MBu .... Mark Buckingham	MRc ...... Mark Ricketts	PS .... Paul Smith	RSm .... Robin Smith
MBy ...... Mitch Byrd	MRi ...... Mike Richardson	PSj ...... Peter Snejbjerg	RSt .... Roger Stern
MC .... Mike Collins	MRy .... Matt Ryan	PtL ...... Patrick Lee	RT .... Romeo Tanghal
MCa ...... Marc Campos	MS .... Mark Silvestri	PuD .... Paul Danner	RtH .... Robert Hebbard
MCh .... Mike Chen	MSh ...... Mark Schultz	PuJ .... Paul Johnson	RTs .... Roy Thomas
MCi .... Mark Crilley	MsM ...... Mike S. Miller	PuK ...... Paul Kupperberg	RV .... Rick Veitch
MCl .... Mike Clark	MSo ...... Mark Sasso	**RA** .... **Ross Andru**	RyE .... Randy Emberlin
MCn ... Max Allan Collins	MSt ...... Malcolm Smith	RAJ .... R.A. Jones	RyL .... Ray Lago
MCo ...... Mark Chiarello	MSy ...... Mike Sekowsky	RaP ...... Rachel Pollack	RyR .... Rodney Ramos
MCr .... Mike Carlin	MT .... Mark Texeira	RB .... Rich Buckler	**S&K** ...... **Simon & Kirby**
MCW .... M.C. Wyman	MtB .... Matt Broome	RbB ...... Robert Bernstein	S&S ...... Siegel & Shuster

SA . . . . Sergio Aragones	SML . . . . . Sean McLaughlin	TG . . . . Tom Grummett	TyD . . . . Terry Dodson
Sal . . . . Sal Amendola	SMt . . . . Steve Mattsson	TGb . . . . Tom Grindberg	TyH . . . . Tony Harris
SAP . . . . Shea Anton Pensa	SnW . . . . Stan Woch	TGo . . . . Till Goodman	TyT . . . . Tony Tallarico
SaV . . . . Sal Velluto	SPa . . . . Stephen Platt	TH . . . . Tim Hamilton	**VAz . . . . . . Vincent Alcazar**
SB . . . . Sal Buscema	Spk . . . . Spark	THa . . . . Tim Harris	VB . . . . Vaughn Bode
SBi . . . . . . Stephen Bissette	SPl . . . . Scott Phillips	TJn . . . . Todd Johnson	VcL . . . . Vince Locke
SBs . . . . Simon Bisley	SPr . . . . . . Stefan Petrucha	TKa . . . . . . Terry Kavanagh	VGi . . . . . . Vince Giarrano
SBt . . . . Steve Butler	SR . . . . Steve Rude	TKn . . . . . . Trent Kaniuga	ViC . . . . . . Vince Colletta
SC . . . . Sid Check	SRf . . . . Sean Ruffner	TKr . . . Teddy H. Kristiansen	VMk . . . . Val Mayerik
ScB . . . . Scott Benefiel	SS . . . . Stan Sakai	TL . . . . Tom Lyle	VMo . . . . . . Vincent Morosco
ScC . . . . Scott Clark	SSc . . . . . . Sean Scoffield	TLa . . . . Terry LaBan	VRu . . . . . . Vince Russell
SCh . . . . Sean Chen	SSe . . . . . Steven T. Seagle	TLw . . . . . . Terral Lawrence	VS . . . . Val Semeiks
SCi . . . . . . Sergio Cariello	SSh . . . . . . Sean Shaw	TM . . . . . . Todd McFarlane	VV . . . . Vagner Vargas
ScK . . . . Scott Kolins	SSr . . . . . . Steve Skroce	TmB . . . . Tim Burgard	**WaP . . . . . Warren Pleece**
ScL . . . . Scott Lee	SSt . . . . Steve Stern	TmC . . . . . Tom Christopher	WB . . . . Wayne Boring
SCr . . . . . . Steve Crespo	StA . . . . Stephen Addeo	TMd . . . . . . Tom Mandrake	WBu . . . . W. Burroughs
SCy . . . . Simon Colby	StB . . . . . . Scott Benson	TMK . . . . . Ted McKeever	WE . . . . Will Eisner
SD . . . . Steve Ditko	StC . . . . . . Stan Campbell	TMo . . . . . . Tom Morgan	WEl . . . . . . Warren Ellis
SDi . . . . Steve Dillon	StE . . . . Steve Erwin	TmR . . . . Tom Ryder	WiS . . . . . . William Stout
SDr . . . . Stan Drake	StG . . . . . . Steve Grant	TMr . . . . . . Terry Moore	WK . . . . Walt Kelly
SDR . . . . . Sam DeLaRosa	StL . . . . Stan Lee	TMs . . . . . . Tom Mason	Wld . . . . . Andrew Wildman
SEa . . . . Scott Eaton	StP . . . . Steve Pugh	TmT . . . . Tom Teney	WmB . . . . William Bossart
SeM . . . . . Steve Montano	SVa . . . . . . Steve Vance	TMw . . . . . Tom McCraw	WMc . . . . . Walter McDaniel
SeP . . . . Sean Phillips	SvG . . . . . . Steve Gerber	TNa . . . . Ted Naifeh	WMo . . . . . . Win Mortimer
SEp . . . . . . Steve Epting	SvL . . . . . Salvador Larroca	TnD . . . . . . Tony Daniel	Woj . . . . Chuck Wojtkiewicz
SeT . . . . . . Steve Tappin	SvP . . . . . Steve Parkhouse	TnS . . . . . Tristan Schane	WP . . . . Wendy Pini
SEt . . . . . Steve Englehart	SvS . . . . . . Steve Stiles	TNu . . . . . . Todd Nauck	WPo . . . . . Whilce Portacio
SF . . . . . . Sal Finnocchiaro	SW . . . . . . Scott Williams	ToT . . . . . . Tony Takezaki	WR . . . . Werner Roth
SFr . . . . . . Simon Freeman	SWi . . . . . Skip Williamson	TOz . . . . . . Tayyar Ozkan	WS . . . . . Walt Simonson
SFu . . . . . . Simon Furman	SwM . . . . Shawn McManus	TP . . . . Tom Palmer	WSm . . . . . Will Simpson
SG . . . . . . Sam Glanzman	SY . . . . . . Steve Yeowell	TPe . . . . . . Tom Peyer	WW . . . . Wally Wood
SGe . . . . Sid Greene	SZ . . . . Steven Zyskowski	TR . . . . Tom Raney	**YG . . . . Yvel Guichet**
SHa . . . . Scott Hanna	**TA . . . . Terry Austin**	TR . . . . . . Ted Richards	YuK . . . . Yukito Kisniro
ShG . . . . . Shannon Gallant	TAr . . . . Tom Artis	TrR . . . . Trina Robbins	
ShM . . . . . Sheldon Mayer	TB . . . . Tim Boxell	TS . . . . Tom Sutton	
SHn . . . . Simon Harrison	TBd . . . . . . Tim Bradstreet	TSa . . . . . . Tony Salmons	
SHp . . . . . . Scott Hampton	TBe . . . . . . Terry Beatty	TSe . . . . Tim Sale	
SI . . . . Stuart Immonen	TBm . . . . . Tom Bierbaum	TSg . . . . . Tom Sniegoski	
SK . . . . Sam Kieth	TC . . . . . . Travis Charest	TSr . . . . . Terry Shoemaker	
SL . . . . Steve Leialoha	TCk . . . . . . Tomm Coker	TT . . . . Timothy Truman	
SLi . . . . Steve Lightle	TD . . . . . . Tony DeZuniga	TTg . . . . . . Tom Taggart	
SLo . . . . Scott Lobdell	TDF . . . . . . Tom DeFalco	TTn . . . . . . Ty Templeton	
SM . . . . Steve Miller	TDr . . . . . . Tom Derenick	TV . . . . Tim Vigil	
SMa . . . Shawn Martinbrough	TDz . . . . . . Todd DeZago	TVE . . . . Trevor Von Eeden	
SmC . . . . Sam Citron	TeB . . . . . . Tex Blaisdell	TvS . . . . Trevor Scott	
SMc . . . . . . Scott McDaniel	TeH . . . . . . Ted Halsted	TWo . . . . . Teri Sue Wood	
SMl . . . . Scott McCloud	TEl . . . . Tim Eldred	TY . . . . Tom Yeates	

GENERAL ABBREVIATIONS FOR COMICS LISTINGS

A: . . . . Appearance of	GAm . . . . . . Graphic Album	Prev. . . . . Preview
(a) . . . . Artist	GNv . . . . Graphic Novel	pt. . . . . Part
Adapt. . . . . Adaptation	G-Size . . . . Giant Size	rep. . . . . Reprinted issue
Anniv. . . . . Anniversary	HC . . . . Hardcover	R: . . . . Return/Revival of
Ann.# . . . . Annual	I: . . . . Introduction of	rtd. . . . . Retold
(a&pl) . . . . Art & Plot	(i) . . . . Inks by	(s) . . . . . Scripted/Written By
(a&s) . . . . Art & Script	IR: . . . . . . Idenity Revealed	S.A. . . . . Silver Age
B: . . . . Beginning of	J: . . . . Joins of	SC . . . . Softcover
b: . . . . Birth	K-Size . . . . King Size	(s&i) . . . . . . Script & inks
BU: . . . . Back-Up Story	L: . . . . Leaving of	Spec. . . . . Special
C: . . . . Cameo by	N: . . . . New Costume	TPB . . . . . Trade Paperback
(c) . . . . Cover	N# . . . . . . No issue Number	T.U. . . . . Team Up
(c&s) . . . Cover and Script	O: . . . . Origin of	V: . . . . Versus
D: . . . . . Death/Destruction of	P(c) . . . . . . Painted Cover	W: . . . . Wedding of
Ed. . . . . Edition	(p) . . . . Pencils by	w/ . . . . With
E: . . . . Ending of	PF . . . . Prestige Format	w/o . . . . Without
F: . . . . Features	Ph(c) . . . . Photographic cover	x-over . . . . . Crossover with
G.A. . . . . Golden Age	(pl) . . . . Plotter	

DC COMICS

ABSOLUTE VERTIGO
1995
Ashcan: Invisibles, other samples 12.00

Action Comics #13 © DC Comics, Inc.

ACTION
June, 1938
1 JoS,I&O:Superman;Rescues Evelyn
Curry from electric chair 185,000.00
2 JoS,V:Emil Norvell 22,000.00
3 JoS,V:Thorton Blakely . . . 13,000.00
4 JoS,V:Coach Randall . . . 8,000.00
5 JoS,Emergency of
Vallegho Dam 7,500.00
6 JoS,I:Jimmy Olsen,
V:Nick Williams 7,500.00
7 JoS,V:Derek Niles 12,000.00
8 JoS,V:Gimpy 6,200.00
9 JoS,A:Det.Captain Reilly . . 6,000.00
10 JoS,Superman fights
for prison reform 9,000.00
11 JoS,Disguised as
Homer Ramsey 3,000.00
12 JoS,Crusade against
reckless drivers 3,000.00
13 JoS,I:Ultra Humanite 5,000.00
14 JoS,BKa,V:Ultra Humanite,
B:Clip Carson 2,800.00
15 JoS,BKa,Superman in
Kidtown 4,200.00
16 JoS,BKa,Crusade against
Gambling 2,200.00
17 JoS,BKa,V:Ultra Humanite 3,500.00
18 JoS,BKa,V:Mr.Hamilton
O:Three Aces 2,200.00
19 JoS,BKa,V:Ultra Humanite
B:Superman (c) 3,000.00
20 JoS,BKa,V:Ultra Humanite 2,800.00
21 JoS,BKa,V:Ultra Humanite 2,000.00
22 JoS,BKa,War between Toran
and Galonia 1,900.00
23 JoS,BKa,SMo,I:Lex Luthor 6,000.00
24 JoS,BKa,BBa,SMo,FG,Meets
Peter Carnahan 1,800.00
25 JoS,BKa,BBa,SMo,V:Medini 1,800.00
26 JoS,BKa,V:Clarence Cobalt 1,800.00
27 JoS,BKa,V:Mr & Mrs.Tweed 1,500.00
28 JoS,BKa,JBu,V:Strongarm
Bandit 1,500.00
29 JoS,BKa,V:Martin 1,800.00
30 JoS,BKa,V:Zolar 1,500.00
31 JoS,BKa,JBu,V:Baron
Munsdorf 900.00
32 JoS,BKa,JBu,I:Krypto Ray Gun
V:Mr.Preston 1,000.00
33 JoS,BKa,JBu,V:Brett Hall,
O:Mr. America 1,000.00
34 JoS,BKa,V:Jim Laurg 900.00
35 JoS,BKa,V:Brock Walter . . . 900.00
36 JoS,BKa,V:StuartPemberton 800.00
37 JoS,BKa,V:Commissioner
Kennedy, O:Congo Bill 800.00
38 JoS,BKa,V:Harold Morton . . 800.00
39 JoS,BKa,Meets Britt Bryson 800.00
40 JoS,BKa,Meets Nancy
Thorgenson 800.00
41 JoS,BKa,V:Ralph Cowan,
E:Clip Carson 750.00
42 V:Lex Luthor,I&O:Vigilante 1,300.00
43 V:Dutch O'Leary,Nazi(c) . . . 800.00
44 V:Prof. Steffens,Nazi(c) . . . 800.00
45 V:Count Von Henzel,
I:Stuff,Nazi(c) 800.00
46 V:The Domino 750.00
47 V:Lex Luthor—1st app. w/super
powers,I:Powerstone 800.00
48 V:The Top 750.00
49 I:Puzzler 850.00
50 Meets Stan Doborak 800.00
51 I:Prankster 850.00
52 V:Emperor of America 900.00
53 JBu,V:Night-Owl 700.00
54 JBu,Meets Stanley
Finchcomb 600.00
55 JBu,V:Cartoonist Al Hatt . . . 600.00
56 V:Emil Loring 600.00
57 V:Prankster 600.00
58 JBu,V:Adonis 600.00
59 I:Susie Thompkins,Lois
Lane's niece 550.00
60 JBu,Lois Lane-Superwoman! 600.00
61 JBu,Meets Craig Shaw 550.00
62 JBu,V:Admiral Von Storff . . 550.00
63 JBu,V:Professor Praline . . . 550.00
64 I:Toyman 600.00
65 JBu,V:Truman Treadwell . . . 500.00
66 JBu,V:Mr.Annister 500.00
67 JBu,Superman School for
Officer's Training 500.00
68 A:Susie Thompkins 500.00
69 V:Prankster 500.00
70 JBu,V:Thinker 500.00
71 Superman Valentine's
Day Special 450.00
72 V:Mr. Sniggle 450.00
73 V:Lucius Spruce 450.00
74 Meets Adelbert Dribble 450.00
75 V:Johnny Aesop 450.00
76 A Voyage with Destiny 450.00
77 V:Prankster 450.00
78 The Chef of Bohemia 450.00
79 JBu,A:J. Wilbur Wolfingham 450.00
80 A:Mr. Mxyzptlk (2nd App) . . 750.00
81 Meets John Nicholas 500.00
82 JBu,V:Water Sprite 450.00
83 I:Hocus and Pocus 450.00
84 JBu,V:Dapper Gang 450.00
85 JBu,V:Toyman 450.00
86 JBu,V:Wizard of Wokit 450.00
87 V:Truck Hijackers 450.00
88 A:Hocus and Pocus 450.00
89 V:Slippery Andy 450.00
90 JBu,V:Horace Rikker and the
Amphi-Bandits 450.00
91 JBu,V:Davey Jones 425.00
92 JBu,V:Nowmie Norman 425.00
93 Superman Christmas story . 425.00
94 JBu,V:Bullwer 'Bull' Rylie . . 425.00
95 V:Prankster 425.00
96 V:Mr. Twister 425.00
97 A:Hocus and Pocus 425.00
98 V:Mr. Mxyzptlk, A:Susie
Thompkins 425.00

Action Comics #95 © DC Comics, Inc.

99 V:Keith Langwell 425.00
100 I:InspectorErskineHawkins 1,000.00
101 V:Specs Dour,A-Bomb(c) . 900.00
102 V:Mr. Mxyzptlk 425.00
103 V:Emperor Quexo 425.00
104 V:Prankster 425.00
105 Superman Christmas story 425.00
106 Clark Kent becomes Baron
Edgestream 425.00
107 JBu,A:J.Wilbur Wolfingham 425.00
108 JBu,V:Vince Vincent 425.00
109 V:Prankster 425.00
110 A:Susie Thompkins 425.00
111 Cameras in the Clouds . . . 425.00
112 V:Mr. Mxyzptlk 425.00
113 Just an Ordinary Guy 425.00
114 V:Mike Chesney 425.00
115 Meets Arthur Parrish 425.00
116 A:J. Wilbur Wolfingham . . . 425.00
117 Superman Christmas story 425.00
118 The Execution of Clark Kent 425.00
119 Meets Jim Banning 425.00
120 V:Mike Foss 425.00
121 V:William Sharp 425.00
122 V:Charley Carson 425.00

All comics prices listed are for *Near Mint* condition.   CVA Page 1

123 V:Skid Russell 425.00	163 Meets Susan Semple 350.00	230 V:Bart Wellins 225.00
124 Superman becomes	164 Meets Stefan Andriessen . 350.00	231 Sir Jimmy Olsen, Knight of
radioactive 450.00	165 V:Crime Czar 350.00	Metropolis 225.00
125 V:Lex Luthor 450.00	166 V:Lex Luthor 350.00	232 Meets Johnny Kirk 225.00
126 V:Chameleon 425.00	167 V:Prof. Nero 350.00	233 V:Torm 225.00
127 JKu,Superman on Truth or	168 O:Olaf 350.00	234 Meets Golto 225.00
Consequences 500.00	169 Caveman Clark Kent! 350.00	235 B:Congo Bill,
128 V:'Aces' Deucey 425.00	170 V:Mad Artist of Metropolis . 350.00	B:Tommy Tomorrow 225.00
129 Meets Gob-Gob 425.00	171 The Secrets of Superman . 350.00	236 A:Lex Luthor 225.00
130 V:Captain Kidder 425.00	172 Lois Lane..Witch! 350.00	237 V:Nebula Gang 225.00
131 V:Lex Luthor 425.00	173 V:Dragon Lang 350.00	238 I:King Krypton,the Gorilla . 225.00
132 Superman meets George	174 V:Miracle Twine Gang . . . 350.00	239 'Superman's New Face' . . 225.00
Washington 425.00	175 V:John Vinden 350.00	240 V:Superman Sphinx 225.00
133 V:Emma Blotz 425.00	176 V:Billion Dollar Marvin	241 WB,A:Batman,Fortress of
134 V:Paul Strong 425.00	Gang 350.00	Solitude (Fort Superman) . . 200.00
135 V:John Morton 425.00	177 V:General 350.00	242 I&O:Brainiac 1,200.00
136 Superman Show-Off! 425.00	178 V:Prof. Sands 350.00	243 Lady and the Lion 200.00
137 Meets Percival Winter . . . 425.00	179 Superman in Mapleville . . 350.00	244 CS,A:Vul-Kor,Lya-La 200.00
138 Meets Herbert Hinkle . . . 425.00	180 V:Syndicate of Five 300.00	245 WB,V:Kak-Kul 200.00
139 Clark Kent...Daredevil! . . . 425.00	181 V:Diamond Dave Delaney . 300.00	246 WB,A:Krypton Island 200.00
140 Superman becomes Hermit 425.00	182 The Return from Planet	247 WB,Superman Lost Parents 200.00
141 V:Lex Luthor 425.00	Krypton 300.00	248 B&I:Congorilla 200.00
142 V:Dan the Dip 425.00	183 V:Lex Luthor 300.00	249 AP,A:Lex Luthor 200.00
143 Dates Nikki Larve 425.00	184 Meets Donald Whitmore . . 300.00	250 WB,'The Eye of Metropolis' 200.00
	185 V:Issah Pendleton 300.00	
	186 The Haunted Superman . . 300.00	
	187 V:Silver 300.00	
	188 V:Cushions Raymond gang 300.00	
	189 Meets Mr.&Mrs. John	
	Vandeveir 300.00	
	190 V:Mr. Mxyzptlk 300.00	
	191 V:Vic Vordan 300.00	
	192 Meets Vic Vordan 300.00	
	193 V:Beetles Brogan 300.00	
	194 V:Maln 300.00	
	195 V:Tiger Woman 300.00	
	196 Superman becomes Mental	
	Man 300.00	
	197 V:Stanley Stark 300.00	
	198 The Six Lives of Lois Lane 300.00	
	199 V:Lex Luthor 300.00	
	200 V:Morwatha 300.00	
	201 V:Benny the Brute 300.00	
	202 Lois Lane's X-Ray Vision . 300.00	

Action Comics #247 © DC Comics, Inc.

144 O:Clark Kent reporting for	203 Meets Pietro Paresca 300.00	
Daily Planet 450.00	204 Meets Sam Spulby 300.00	
145 Meets Merton Gloop 425.00	205 Sergeant Superman 300.00	
146 V:Luthor 425.00	206 Imaginary story featuring	
147 V:'Cheeks' Ross 425.00	Lois Lane 300.00	
148 Superman, Indian Chief . . 425.00	207 Four Superman Medals! . . 300.00	
149 The Courtship on Krypton! . 425.00	208 V:Mr. Mxyzptlk 300.00	

Action Comics #280 © DC Comics, Inc.

209 V:'Doc' Winters 300.00	251 AP,E:Tommy Tomorrow . . 200.00
210 V:Lex Luthor,I:Superman	252 I&O:Supergirl 1,500.00
Land 300.00	253 B:Supergirl 400.00
211 Superman Spectaculars . . 275.00	254 I:Adult Bizarro 300.00
212 V:Thorne Varden 275.00	255 I:Bizarro Lois 200.00
213 V:Paul Paxton 275.00	256 'Superman of the Future' . 125.00
214 Superman,Sup.Destroyer! . 275.00	257 WB,JM,V:Lex Luthor 125.00
215 I:Superman of 2956 . . . . . 275.00	258 A:Cosmic Man 125.00
216 A:Jor-El 275.00	259 A:Lex Luthor,Superboy . . 125.00
217 Meets Mr&Mrs.Roger Bliss 275.00	260 A:Mighty Maid 125.00
218 V:Super-Ape from Krypton . 275.00	261 I:Streaky,E:Congorilla . . . 125.00
219 V:Art Shaler 275.00	262 A:Bizarro 110.00
220 The Interplanetary	263 O:Bizarro World 125.00
Olympics 275.00	264 V:Bizarro 100.00
221 V:Jay Vorrell 225.00	265 A:Hyper-Man 100.00
222 The Duplicate Superman . 225.00	266 A:Streaky,Krypto 100.00
223 A:Jor-El 225.00	267 JM,3rd A:Legion,I:Invisible
224 I:Superman Island 225.00	Kid 400.00
225 The Death of Superman . . 250.00	268 WB,A:Hercules 125.00
226 V:Lex Luthor 225.00	269 A:Jerro 125.00
227 The Man with the Triple	270 CS,JM,A:Batman 135.00
X-Ray Eyes 225.00	271 A:Lex Luthor 125.00
228 A:Superman Museum 225.00	272 A:Aquaman 125.00
229 V:Dr. John Haley 225.00	

Additional entries (lower left column):

150 V:Morko 425.00	
151 V:Mr.Mxyzptlk,Lex Luthor	
and Prankster 425.00	
152 I:Metropolis Shutterbug	
Society 425.00	
153 V:Kingpin 425.00	
154 V:Harry Reed 425.00	
155 V:Andrew Arvin 425.00	
156 Lois Lane becomes Super-	
woman,V:Lex Luthor 425.00	
157 V:Joe Striker 425.00	
158 V:Kane Korrell	
O:Superman (retold) 900.00	
159 Meets Oswald Whimple . . 400.00	
160 I:Minerva Kent 400.00	
161 Meets Antara 400.00	
162 V:'IT!' 350.00	

273 A:Mr.Mxyzptlk	125.00
274 A:Superwoman	125.00
275 WB,JM,V:Braimiac	125.00
276 JM,6th A:Legion,I:Brainiac 5,	
Triplicate Girl,Bouncing Boy	175.00
277 CS,JM,V:Lex Luthor	100.00
278 CS,Perry White Becomes	
Master Man	100.00
279 JM,V:Hercules,Samson	100.00
280 CS,JM,V:Braniac,	
A:Congorilla	100.00
281 JM,A:Krypto	100.00
282 JM,V:Mxyzptlk	100.00
283 CS,JM,A:Legion of Super	
Outlaws	125.00
284 A:Krypto,Jerro	100.00
285 JM,Supergirl Existence Revealed,	
C:Legion (12th app.)	125.00
286 CS,JM,V:Lex Luthor	65.00
287 JM,A:Legion	65.00
288 JM,A:Mon-El	65.00
289 JM,A:Adult Legion	65.00
290 JM,C:Phantom Girl	65.00
291 JM,V:Mxyzptlk	60.00
292 JM,I:Superhorse	65.00
293 JM,O:Comet-Superhorse	100.00
294 JM,V:Lex Luthor	60.00
295 CS,JM,O:Lex Luthor	65.00
296 V:Super Ants	60.00
297 CS,JM,A:Mon-El	60.00
298 CS,JM,V:Lex Luthor	60.00
299 O:Superman Robots	60.00
300 JM,A:Mxyzptlk	60.00
301 CS(c),JM,O:Superhorse	30.00
302 CS(c),JM,O:Superhorse	30.00
303 CS(c),Red Kryptonite story	25.00
304 CS,JM,I&O:Black Flame	35.00
305 CS(c),O:Supergirl	25.00
306 JM,C:Mon-El,Brainiac 5	25.00
307 CS,JM,A:Saturn Girl	25.00
308 CS(c),V:Hercules	25.00
309 CS,A:Batman,JFK,Legion	30.00
310 CS,JM,I:Jewel Kryptonite	25.00
311 CS,JM,O:Superhorse	25.00
312 CS,JM,V:Metallo-Superman	25.00
313 JM,A:Supergirl,Lex Luthor,	
Batman	25.00
314 JM,A:Justice League	25.00
315 JM,V:Zigi,Zag	25.00
316 JM,A:Zigi,Zag,Zyra	25.00
317 JM,V:Lex Luthor	25.00
318 CS,JM,A:Brainiac	25.00
319 CS,JM,A:Legion,V:L.Luthor	25.00
320 CS,JM,V:Atlas,Hercules	25.00
321 CS,JM,A:Superhorse	25.00
322 JM,'Coward of Steel'	25.00
323 JM,A:Superhorse	25.00
324 JM,A:Abdul	25.00
325 CS(c),A:Lex Luthor	25.00
326 CS,JM,V:Legion of Super	
Creatures	25.00
327 CS,JM,C:Brainiac	25.00
328 JM,Hands of Doom	25.00
329 JM,V:Drang	25.00
330 CS,JM,Krypto	25.00
331 CS,V:Dr.Supernatural	25.00
332 CS,A:Brainiac	25.00
333 CS(c),A:Lex Luthor	25.00
334 JM(c),A:Lex Luthor,80pgs	40.00
335 CS,V:Lex Luthor	20.00
336 CS,O:Akvar	20.00
337 CS,V:Tiger Gang	20.00
338 CS,JM,V:Muto	20.00
339 CS,V:Muto,Brainiac	20.00
340 JM,I:Parasite	20.00

341 CS,V:Vakox,A:Batman	15.00
342 WB,JM,V:Brainiac	15.00
343 WB,V:Eterno	15.00
344 WB,JM,A:Batman	15.00
345 CS(c),A:Allen Funt	15.00
346 WB,JM	15.00
347 CS(c),A:Supergirl, 80pgs.	30.00
348 WB,JM,V:Acid Master	15.00
349 WB,JM,V:Dr.Kryptonite	15.00
350 A:JLA	15.00
351 WB,I:Zha-Vam	15.00
352 WB,V:Zha-Vam	15.00
353 WB,JM,V:Zha-Vam	15.00
354 JM,A:Captain Incredible	15.00
355 WB,JM,V:Lex Luthor	15.00
356 WB,JM,V:Jr. Annihilitor	15.00
357 WB,JM,V:Annihilitor	15.00
358 NA(c),CS,JM,A:Superboy	15.00
359 NA(c),CS,KS,C:Batman	15.00
360 CS(c),A:Supergirl, 80pgs.	40.00
361 NA(c),A:Parasite	12.00
362 RA,KS,V:Lex Luthor	12.00
363 RA,KS,V:Lex Luthor	12.00
364 RA,KS,V:Lex Luthor	12.00

Action Comics #315 © DC Comics, Inc.

365 A:Legion & J.L.A.	12.00
366 RA,KS,A:J.L.A.	12.00
367 NA(c),CS,KS,A:Supergirl	12.00
368 CS,KS,V:Mxyzptlk	12.00
369 CS,KS,Superman's Greatest	
Blunder	12.00
370 NA(c),CS,KS	12.00
371 NA(c),CS,KS	12.00
372 NA(c),CS,KS	12.00
373 A:Supergirl,(giant size)	25.00
374 NA(c),CS,KS,V:Super Thief	11.00
375 CS,KS,The Big Forget	11.00
376 CS,KS,E:Supergirl	11.00
377 CS,KS,B:Legion	11.00
378 CS,KS,V:Marauder	11.00
379 CS,JA,MA,V:Eliminator	11.00
380 KS,Confessions of Superman	11.00
381 CS,Dictators of Earth	11.00
382 CS,Clark Kent-Magician	11.00
383 CS,The Killer Costume	11.00
384 CS,The Forbidden Costume	11.00
385 CS,The Mortal Superman	11.00
386 CS,Home For Old Supermen	11.00

387 CS,A:Legion,Even	
Supermen Die	11.00
388 CS,A:Legion,Puzzle of	
The Wild Word	11.00
389 A:Legion,The Kid Who	
Struck Out Superman	11.00
390 CS,'Self-Destruct Superman'	11.00
391 CS,Punishment of	
Superman's Son	11.00
392 CS,E:Legion	11.00
393 CS,MA,RA,A:Super Houdini	11.00
394 CS,MA	11.00
395 CS,MA,A:Althera	11.00
396 CS,MA	11.00
397 CS,MA,Imaginary Story	11.00
398 NA(c),CS,MA,I:Morgan Edge	11.00
399 NA(c),CS,MA,A:Superbaby	11.00
400 NA(c),CS,MA,Kandor Story	20.00
401 CS,MA,V:Indians	10.00
402 NA(c),CS,MA,V:Indians	10.00
403 CS,MA,Vigilante rep.	10.00
404 CS,MA,Aquaman rep	10.00
405 CS,MA,Vigilante rep.	10.00
406 CS,MA,Atom & Flash rep.	10.00
407 CS,MA,V:Lex Luthor	10.00
408 CS,MA,Atom rep.	10.00
409 CS,MA,T.Tommorrow rep.	10.00
410 CS,MA,T.Tommorrow rep.	10.00
411 CS,MA,O:Eclipso rep.	10.00
412 CS,MA,Eclipso rep.	10.00
413 CS,MA,V:Brainiac	10.00
414 CS,MA,B:Metamorpho	10.00
415 CS,MA,V:Metropolis Monster	10.00
416 CS,MA	10.00
417 CS,MA,V:Luthor	10.00
418 CS,MA,V:Luthor,	
E:Metamorpho	10.00
419 CS,MA,CI,DG,I:HumanTarget	11.00
420 CS,MA,DG,V:Towbee	9.00
421 CS,MA,B:Green Arrow	10.00
422 CS,DG,O:Human Target	9.00
423 CS,MA,DG,A:Lex Luthor	9.00
424 CS,MA,Green Arrow	10.00
425 CS,DD,NA,DG,B:Atom	17.00
426 CS,MA,Green Arrow	7.00
427 CS,MA,DD,DG,Atom	7.00
428 CS,MA,DG,Luthor	7.00
429 CS,BO,DG,C:JLA	7.00
430 CS,MA,DD,DG,Atom	7.00
431 CS,MA,Green Arrow	7.00
432 CS,MA,DG,Toyman	7.00
433 CS,BO,DD,DG,A:Atom	7.00
434 CS,DD,Green Arrow	7.00
435 FM(c),CS,DD,DG,Atom	7.00
436 CS,DD,Green Arrow	7.00
437 CS,DG,Green Arrow	
(100 page giant)	20.00
438 CS,BO,DD,Atom	7.00
439 CS,BO,DD,Atom	7.00
440 1st MGr Green Arrow	9.00
441 CS,BO,MGr,A:Green Arrow,	
Flash,R:Krypto	6.00
442 CS,MS,MGr,Atom	3.50
443 CS,A:JLA(100 pg.giant)	20.00
444 MGr,Green Arrow	4.50
445 MGr,Green Arrow	4.50
446 MGr,Green Arrow	4.50
447 CS,BO,RB,KJ,Atom	3.50
448 CS,BO,DD,JL,Atom	3.50
449 CS,BO	3.50
450 MGr,Green Arrow	4.00
451 MGr,Green Arrow	4.00
452 CS,MGr,Green Arrow	4.00
453 CS,Atom	3.50
454 CS,E:Atom	3.50

DC COMICS

455 CS,Green Arrow 4.00	A:Air Wave 2.50	586 JBy,DG,Legends,V:New
456 CS,MGr,Green Arrow 4.00	526 JSon,AS,V:Neutron 2.50	Gods,Darkseid 2.50
457 CS,MGr,Green Arrow 4.00	527 CS,AS,I:Satanis,A:Aquaman 3.00	587 JBy,DG,Demon 2.50
458 CS,MGr,I:Black Rock 4.00	528 CS,AS,V:Brainiac,A:Aq'man . 2.50	588 JBy,DG,Hawkman 2.50
459 CS,BO,Blackrock 3.50	529 GP(c),CS,DA,AS,A:Aquaman,	589 JBy,DG,Gr.Lant.Corp. 2.50
460 CS,I:Karb-Brak 3.50	V:Brainiac 2.50	590 JBy,DG,Metal Men 2.50
461 CS,V:Karb-Brak 3.50	530 CS,DA,Brainiac 2.50	591 JBy,V:Superboy,A:Legion . . 2.50
462 CS,V:Karb-Brak 3.50	531 JSon,FMc,AS,A:Atom 2.50	592 JBy,Big Barda 2.50
463 CS,V:Karb-Brak 3.50	532 CS,C:New Teen Titans 2.50	593 JBy,Mr. Miracle 2.50
464 CS,KS,V:Pile-Driver 3.50	533 CS,V:The. 2.50	594 JBy,A:Booster Gold 2.50
465 CS,FMc,Luthor 3.50	534 CS,AS,V:Satanis,A:Air Wave . 2.50	595 JBy,A:M.Manhunter,
466 NA(c),CS,V:Luthor 3.50	535 GK(c),JSon,AS,	I:Silver Banshee 2.50
467 CS,V:Mzyzptlk 3.50	A:Omega Men 2.50	596 JBy,A:Spectre,Millenium . . . 2.50
468 NA(c),CS,FMc,V:Terra-Man . 3.50	536 JSon,AS,FMc,A:Omega Men . 2.50	597 JBy,L.Starr(i),Lois V:Lana . . 2.50
469 CS,TerraMan 3.50	537 IN,CS,AS,V:Satanis	598 JBy,TyT,I:Checkmate 3.50
470 CS,Flash Green Lantern . . . 3.50	A:Aquaman 2.50	599 RA,JBy(i),A:MetalMen,
471 CS,V:Phantom Zone Female . 3.50	538 IN,AS,FMc,V:Satanis,	BonusBook 2.50
472 CS,V:Faora Hu-Ul 3.50	A:Aquaman 2.50	600 JBy,GP,KS,JOy,DG,CS,MA,
473 NA(c),CS,Phantom Zone	539 KG(c),GK,AS,DA,A:Flash,	MMi,A:Wonder Woman;
Villians 3.50	Atom,Aquaman 2.50	Man-Bat,V:Darkseid 6.00
474 KS,V:Doctor Light 3.50	540 GK,AS,V:Satanis 2.50	
475 KS,V:Karb-Brak,A:Vartox . . 3.50	541 GK,V:Satanis 2.50	
476 KS,V:Vartox 3.50	542 AS,V:Vandal Savage 2.50	
477 CS,DD,Land Lords of Earth . . 3.50	543 CS,V:Vandal Savage 2.50	
478 CS,Earth's Last 3.50	544 CS,MA,GK,GP,45th Anniv.	
479 CS 3.50	D:Ardora,Lexor 3.50	
480 CS,A:JLA,V:Amazo 3.50	545 GK,Brainiac 2.50	
481 CS,A:JLA,V:Amazo 3.50	546 GK,A:JLA,New Teen Titans . 2.50	
482 CS,Amazo 3.50	547 GK(c),CS 2.50	
483 CS,Amazo,JLA 3.50	548 GK(c),AS,Phantom Zone . . . 2.50	
484 CS,W:Earth 2 Superman	549 GK(c),AS 2.50	
& Lois Lane 3.75	550 AS(c),GT 2.50	*Action Comics #606 © DC Comics, Inc.*
485 NA(c),CS,rep.Superman#233 4.00	551 GK,Starfire becomes	
486 GT,KS,V:Lex Luthor 3.50	Red Star 2.50	**Becomes:**
487 CS,AS,O:Atom 4.00	552 GK,Forgotten Heroes	**ACTION WEEKLY**
488 CS,AS,A:Air Wave 3.50	(inc.Animal Man) 6.00	**1988–89**
489 CS,AS,A:JLA,Atom 3.50	553 GK,Forgotten Heroes(inc.	601 GK,DSp,CS,DJu,TD,
490 CS,Brainiac 3.50	Animal Man) 6.00	B:Superman,Gr.Lantern,
491 CS,A:Hawkman 3.50	554 GK(a&c) 2.00	Blackhawk,Deadman,Secret
492 CS,'Superman's After Life' . 3.50	555 CS,A:Parasite (X-over	Six,Wilddog 2.00
493 CS,A:UFO 3.50	Supergirl #20) 2.00	602 GP(c),GK,DSp,CS,DJu,TD . . 1.75
494 CS 3.50	556 CS,KS,C:Batman 2.00	603 GK,CS,DsP,DJu,TD 1.75
495 CS 3.50	557 CS,Terra-man 2.00	604 GK,DSp,CS,DJu,TD 1.75
496 CS,A:Kandor 3.50	558 KS 2.00	605 NKu/AKu(c),GK,DSp,CS,
497 CS 3.50	559 KS,AS 2.00	DJu,TD 1.75
498 CS,Vartox 3.50	560 AS,KG,BO,A:Ambush Bug . . 2.00	606 DSp,CS,DJu,TD 1.75
499 CS,Vartox 3.50	561 KS,WB,Toyman 2.00	607 SLi(c),TD,DSp,CS,DJu 1.75
500 CS,Superman's Life Story	562 KS,Queen Bee 2.00	608 DSp,CS,DJu,TD,E:Blackhawk 1.75
A:Legion 6.00	563 AS,KG,BO,A:Ambush Bug . . 2.00	609 BB(c),DSp,DJu,TD,CS,
501 KS 2.50	564 AS,V:Master Jailer 2.00	E:Wild Dog,B:Black Canary . . 1.75
502 CS,A:Supergirl,Gal.Golem . . 2.50	565 KG,BO,A:Ambush Bug 2.00	610 KB,DJu,CS,DSp,TD,CS
503 CS,'A Save in Time' 2.50	566 BO(i),MR 2.00	A:Phantom Stranger 2.00
504 CS,'The Power and Choice' . 2.50	567 KS,AS,PB 2.00	611 AN(c),DJu,DSp,CS,BKi,TD,
505 CS 2.50	568 CS,AW,AN 2.00	BKi,B:Catwoman 3.00
506 CS 2.50	569 IN 2.00	612 PG(c),DSp,CS,BKi,TD,
507 CS,A:Jonathan Kent 2.50	570 KS 2.00	E:Secret Six,Deadman 2.50
508 CS,A:Jonathan Kent 2.50	571 BB(c),AS,A:Thresh 222 . . . . 2.00	613 MK(c),BKi,CS,MA,TGr,
509 CS,JSn,DG 2.75	572 WB,BO 2.00	Nightwing,B:Phantom Stranger 2.50
510 CS,Luthor 2.50	573 KS,BO,AS 2.00	614 TG,CS,Phantom Stranger
511 CS,AS,V:Terraman,	574 KS 2.00	
A:Air Wave 2.50	575 KS,V:Intellax 2.00	
512 CS,RT,V:Luthor,A:Air Wave . 2.50	576 KS,Earth's Sister Planet . . . 2.00	
513 CS,RT,V:Krell,A:Air Wave . . 2.50	577 KG,BO,V:Caitiff 2.00	
514 CS,RT,V:Brainiac,A:Atom . . 2.50	578 KS,Parasite 2.00	
515 CS,AS,A:Atom 2.50	579 KG,BO,Asterix Parody 2.00	
516 CS,AS,V:Luthor,A:Atom . . . 2.50	580 GK(c),KS,Superman's Failure 2.00	
517 CS,DH,A:Aquaman 2.50	581 DCw(c),KS,Superman	
518 CS,DH,A:Aquaman 2.50	Requires Legal aid 2.00	
519 CS,DH,A:Aquaman 2.50	582 AS,KS,Superman's Parents	
520 CS,DH,A:Aquaman 2.50	Alive 2.00	
521 CS,AS,I:Vixen,A:Atom 2.50	583 CS,KS,AMo(s),Last Pre	
522 CS,AS,A:Atom 2.50	Crisis Superman 8.00	
523 CS,AS,A:Atom 2.50	584 JBy,DG,A:NewTeenTitans,	
524 CS,AS,A:Atom 2.50	I:Modern Age Superman. . . . 3.00	
525 JSon,FMc,AS,I:Neutron	585 JBy,DG,Phantom Stranger . . 2.50	

E:Catwoman 2.50
615 MMi(c),CS,MA,BKi,TGr,
    Blackhawk,B:Wild Dog 1.75
616 ATh(c),CS,MA,E:Bl.Canary . . 1.75
617 CS,MA,JO,A:Ph.Stranger . . . 1.75
618 JBg(c),CS,MA,JKo,TD,
    B:Deadman,E:Nightwing 1.75
619 CS,MA,FS,FMc,KJo,TD,FMc,
    B:Sinister Six. 1.75
620 CS,MA,FS,FMc,KJo,TD 1.75
621 JO(c),CS,MA,FS,FMc,KJo,
    TD,MBr,E:Deadman 1.75
622 RF(c),MBr,TL,CS,MA,FS,
    FMc,A:Starman,E:Wild
    Dog,Blackhawk 1.75
623 MBr,TD,CS,MA,FS,FMc,JL,
    JKo,A:Ph.Stranger,
    B:Deadman,Shazam 1.75
624 AD(c),MBr,FS,FMc,CS,MA,
    TD,B:Black Canary 1.75
625 MBr,FS,FMc,CS,MA,
    TD,FMc 1.50
626 MBr,FS,FMc,CS,MA,JKo,TD,
    E:Shazam,Deadman 1.50
627 GK(c),MBr,RT,FS,FMc,CS,
    MA,TMd,B:Nightwing,Speedy . 1.75
628 TY(c),MBr,RT,TMd,CS,MA,
    FS,FMc,B:Blackhawk 1.50
629 CS,MA,MBr,RT,FS,FMc,TMd . 1.50
630 CS,MA,MBr,RT,FS,FMc,TMd,
    E:Secret Six 1.50
631 JS(c),CS,MA,MBr,RT,TMd,
    B:Phantom Stranger 1.50
632 TGr(c),CS,MA,MBr,RT,TMd . . 1.50
633 CS,MA,MBr,RT,TMd 1.50
634 CS,MA,MBr,RT,TMd,E:Ph.Stranger,
    Nightwing/Speedy,Bl.hawk . . . 1.50
635 CS,MA,MBr,RT,EB,E:Black
    Canary,Green Lantern 1.50
636 DG(c),CS,MA,NKu,MPa,FMc,
    B:Demon,Wild Dog,Ph.Lady,
    Speedy,A:Phantom Stranger . . 1.75
637 CS,MA,KS,FMc,MPa,
    B:Hero Hotline 1.50
638 JK(c),CS,MA,KS,FMc,MPa . . 1.50
639 CS,MA,KS,FMc,MPa 1.50
640 CS,KS,MA,FS,FMc,MPa,
    E:Speedy,Hero Hotline 1.50
641 CS,MA,JL,DG,MPa,E:Demon,
    Phant.Lady,Superman,Wild Dog,
    A:Ph.Stranger,Hum.Target . . . 1.75
642 GK,SD,ATi,CS,JAp,JM,CI,KN,
    Green Lantern,Superman 1.50
Becomes:

ACTION COMICS
1989–97
643 B:RSt(s),GP,BBr,V:Intergang . 2.50
644 GP,BBr,V:Matrix 2.00
645 GP,BBr,I:Maxima 2.00
646 KG,V:Alien Creature,
    A:Brainiac 2.50
647 GP,KGa,BBr,V:Brainiac 2.00
648 GP,KGa,BBr,V:Brainiac 2.00
649 GP,KGa,BBr,V:Brainiac 2.00
650 JOy,BBr,CS,BMc,GP,KGa,
    ATi,DJu,A:JLA,C:Lobo 3.00
651 GP,KGa,BBr,Day of Krypton
    Man #3,V:Maxima 3.00
652 GP,KGa,BBr,Day of Krypton
    Man #6,V:Eradicator 3.00
653 BMc,BBr,D:Amanda 2.00
654 BMc,BBr,A:Batman Pt.3 . . . . 2.50
655 BMc,BBr,V:Morrisson,Ma
    Kent's Photo Album 2.00
656 BMc,BBr,Soul Search #1,

V:Blaze 2.00
657 KGa,BBr,V:Toyman 2.00
658 CS,Sinbad Contract #3 . . . . . 2.00
659 BMc,BBr,K.Krimson
    Kryptonite #3 . . . . 3.50
660 BMc,BBr,D:Lex Luthor 3.00
661 BMc,BBr,A:Plastic Man 2.00
662 JOy,JM,TG,BMc,V:Silver
    Banshee,Clark tells
    Lois his identity 4.00
662a 2nd printing 2.00
663 BMc,Time & Time Again,pt.2,
    A:JSA,Legion 2.00
664 BMc,Time & Time Again,pt.5 . 2.00
665 TG,V:Baron Sunday 2.00
666 EH,Red Glass Trilogy,pt.3 . . . 2.00
667 JOy,JM,TG,ATi,DJu,Revenge
    of the Krypton Man,pt.4 . . . . . 2.25
668 BMc,Luthor confirmed dead . 2.00
669 BMc,V:Intergang,A:Thorn . . . 2.00
670 BMc,A:Waverider,JLA,JLE . . 2.00
671 KD,Blackout,pt.2 . . . . 2.00
672 BMc,Superman Meets Lex
    Luthor II 2.00

Action Comics #706 © DC Comics, Inc.

673 BMc,V:Hellgramite 2.00
674 BMc,Panic in the Sky (Prologue)
    R:Supergirl(Matrix) 3.50
675 BMc,Panic in the Sky #4,
    V:Brainiac 3.00
676 B:KK(s),JG,A:Supergirl,Lex
    Luthor II 2.00
677 JG,Supergirl V:Superman . . . 2.00
678 JG,O:Lex Luthor II 2.00
679 JG,I:Shellshock 2.00
680 JG,Blaze/Satanus War,pt.2 . . 2.00
681 JG,V:Hellgramite 2.00
682 DAb,TA,V:Hi-Tech 2.00
683 JG,I:Jackal,C:Doomsday 3.00
683a 2nd printing 1.50
684 JG,Doomsday Pt.4. . . . . 4.00
684a 2nd printing 2.00
685 JG,Funeral for a Friend#2 . . . 3.00
686 JG,Funeral for a Friend#6 . . . 3.00
687 JG,Reign of Superman #1,Direct
    Sales,Die-Cut(c),Mini-Poster,
    F:Last Son of Krypton 2.50
687a newsstand Ed. 2.00
688 JG,V:Guy Gardner 3.00

689 JG,V:Man of Steel,A:Superboy,
    Supergirl,R:Real Superman . . . 3.50
690 JG,Cyborg Vs. Superboy . . . 2.50
691 JG,A:All Supermen,V:Cyborg
    Superman,Mongul 3.00
692 JG,A:Superboy,Man of Steel . 2.00
693 JG,A:Last Son of Krypton . . . 2.00
694 JG,Spilled Blood#2,V:Hi-Tech 2.00
695 JG,Foil(c),I:Cauldron,A:Lobo . 3.00
695a Newsstand Ed. 2.00
696 JG,V:Alien,C:Doomsday 2.50
697 JG,Bizarro's World#3,
    V:Bizarro 2.00
698 JG,A:Lex Luthor 2.00
699 JG,A:Project Cadmus 2.00
700 JG,Fall of Metropolis#1 . . . . . 3.00
700a Platinum Edition 15.00
701 JG,Fall of Metropolis#5,
    V:Luthor 2.00
702 JG,DvM,B:DyM(s),R:Bloodsport1.75
703 JG,DvM,Zero Hour 1.75
704 JG,DvM,Eradicator 1.50
705 JG,DvM,Supes real? 1.50
706 JG,DvM,A:Supergirl 1.50
707 JG,DvM,V:Shado Dragon 1.50
708 JG,DvM,R:Deathtrap 1.50
709 JG,DvM,A:Guy Gardner,
    Warrior 1.50
710 JG,DvM,Death of Clark Kent,pt.3
    [new Miraweb format begins] . . 2.25
711 JG,DvM,Death of Clark
    Kent,pt.7 . . . . 2.25
712 Rescue Jimmy Olsen 2.25
713 . . . . 2.25
714 R:The Joker 2.25
715 DvM,DaR,V:Parasite 2.25
716 DvM,DaR,Trial of Superman . 2.25
717 DvM,DaR,Trial of Superman . 2.25
718 DvM,DRO,mystery of Demolitia 2.25
719 DvM,DRo 2.25
720 DvM,DRo,Lois ends
    engagement 3.00
721 DvM,DRo,lottery fever 2.25
722 DvM,DaR,Tornados in
    Smallville 2.25
723 V:Brainiac 2.25
724 V:S.T.A.R.labs monster 2.25
725 Tolos 2.25
726 DvM(s),TMo,DRo,Krisis of the
    Krimson Kryptonite follow-up . . 2.25
727 DvM(s),TMo,DRo,brutal weather
    in Metropolis, Final Night tie-in 2.25
728 DvM(s),TG,DRo, Some
    Honeymoon! 2.25
729 DvM(s),TG,DRo, in Fortress of
    Solitude 2.25
730 DvM(s),TG,Ro, ... 2.25
731 DvM(s),TG,DRo, R:Cauldron . 2.25
732 DvM(s),TG,DRo, Atomic Skull
    rampages through Metropolis . 2.25
733 DvM(s),TG,DRo, V:Matallo,
    A:Ray 2.25
734 DvM(s),TG,DRo, Superman &
    Atom in Kandor 2.25
735 DvM(s),TG,DRo, V:Savior . . 2.25
736 DvM(s),TG,DRo 2.25
737 MWa(s),TG,DRo, Luthor gets
    day in court 2.00
738 SI,JMz,Lois sent to Australia . 2.00
739 SI,JMz,Superman imprisoned 2.00
740 SI,JMz,Lucy Lane disappears 2.00
741 SI,JMz,V:C.O.M.P.U.T.O. . . . 2.00
742 SI,JMz 2.00
743 SI,JMz,F:Slam Bradley 2.00

744 SI,JMz,Millennium Giants
   x-over 2.00
745 SI,JMz,The Prankster 2.00
746 SI,JMz,The Prankster,pt.2 . . . . 2.00
747 SI,JMz,The Prankster,pt.3 . . . 2.00
748 SI,JMz,Dominus Theory 2.00
Ann.#1 AAd,DG,A:Batman 8.00
Ann.#2 MMi,CS,GP,JOy,DJu,BBr,
   V:Mongul 4.00
Ann.#3 TG,Armageddon X-over . . 3.00
Ann.#4 Eclipso,A:Captain
   Marvel 3.00
Ann.#5 MZ(c),Bloodlines, I:Loose
   Cannon 3.00
Ann.#6 Elseworlds,JBy(a&S) 3.00
Ann.#7 Year One Annual 4.00
Ann.#8 DvM,"Legends of the Dead
   Earth" 3.00
Ann.#9 DvM,VGi,BBr,Pulp Heroes 4.00
Archives, Vol. 1 S&S rep. 50.00
Archives, Vol. 2 S&S rep 50.00
Gold.Ann.rep.#1 . . . . 1.50
#0 Peer Pressure,pt.4 (1994) 2.00

ADAM STRANGE
1990
1 NKu,A.Strange on Rann 5.00
2 NKu,Wanted:Adam Strange . . . 4.50
3 NKu,final issue 4.50

ADVANCED
DUNGEONS & DRAGONS
1988–91
1 JD,I:Onyx,Priam,Timoth,
   Cybriana,Vajra,Luna 6.00
2 JD,V:Imgig Zu,I:Conner 4.00
3 JD,V:Imgig Zu 5.00
4 JD,V:Imgig Zu,I:Kyriani 4.00
5 JD,Spirit of Myrrth I 4.00
6 JD,Spirit of Myrrth II 4.00
7 JD,Spirit of Myrrth III 3.00
8 JD,Spirit of Myrrth IV 3.00
9 JD,Catspawn Quartet I 3.00
10 JD,Catspawn Quartet II 3.00
11 JD,Catspawn Quartet III 3.00
12 JD,Catspawn Quartet IV 3.00
13 JD,Spell Games I 3.00
14 JD,Spell Games II 3.00
15 JD,Spell Games III 3.00
16 JD,Spell Games IV 3.00
17 JD,RM,Kyriani's Story I 3.00
18 JD,RM,Kyriani's Story II 3.00
19 JD,RM,Luna I 3.00
20 JD,RM,Luna II 3.00
21 JD,RM,Luna III 3.00
22 JD,RM,Luna IV 3.00
23 TMd,RM,Siege Dragons I 3.00
24 Scavengers 2.50
25 JD,RM,Centaur Village 2.00
26 JD,Timoth the Centaur 2.00
27 JD,Kyriani,Dragons Eye #1 . . . 2.00
28 JD,Dragons Eye #2 . . . . 2.00
29 JD,RM,Dragons Eye #3 . . . . . 2.00
30 JD,RM,Carril's Killer
   Revealed 2.00
31 TMd,Onyx'Father,pt.1 . . . . . . 2.00
32 TMd,Onyx'Father,pt.2 . . . . . . 2.00
33 JD,Waterdeep,pt.1 . . . . 2.00
34 JD,Waterdeep,pt.2 . . . . 2.00
35 JD,RM,Waterdeep,pt.3 . . . . . 2.00
36 JD,RM,final issue 2.00
Ann.#1 JD,RM,Tmd 4.00

Adventure Comics #41
© DC Comics, Inc.

ADVENTURE COMICS
Nov. 1938–83
[Prev: New Comics]
32 CF(c) 3,200.00
33 . . . . 1,500.00
34 FG(c) 1,500.00
35 FG(c) 1,500.00
36 Giant Snake(c) 1,500.00
37 Rampaging Elephant(c) . . 1,500.00
38 Tiger(c) 1,500.00
39 Male Bondage(c) 1,600.00
40 CF(c),1st app. Sandman . 35,000.00
41 Killer Shark(c) 4,000.00
42 CF,Sandman(c) 5,000.00
43 CF(c) 2,500.00
44 CF,Sandman(c) 5,000.00
45 FG(c) 2,500.00
46 CF,Sandman(c) 3,700.00
47 Sandman (c) 3,500.00
48 1st app.& B:Hourman . . 22,000.00
49 . . . . 1,900.00
50 Hourman(c) 1,800.00
51 BBa(c),Sandman(c) 2,400.00
52 BBa(c),Hourman(c) 1,800.00
53 BBa(c),1st app. Minuteman 1,500.00
54 BBa(c),Hourman(c) 1,500.00
55 BBa(c),same 1,500.00
56 BBa(c),same 1,500.00
57 BBa(c),same 1,500.00
58 BBa(c),same 1,500.00
59 BBa(c),same 1,500.00
60 Sandman(c) 2,400.00
61 CF(c),JBu,Starman(c) . . 12,000.00
62 JBu(c),JBu,Starman(c) . . . 1,400.00
63 JBu(c),JBu,same 1,400.00
64 JBu(c),JBu,same 1,400.00
65 JBu(c),JBu,same 1,400.00
66 JBu(c),JBu,O:Shining Knight,
   Starman(c) 1,800.00
67 JBu(c),JBu,O:Mist 1,400.00
68 JBu(c),JBu,same 1,400.00
69 JBu(c),JBu,1st app. Sandy,
   Starman(c) 1,500.00
70 JBu(c),JBu,Starman(c) . . . 1,400.00
71 JBu(c),JBu,same 1,300.00
72 JBu(c),S&K,JBu,Sandman 11,000.00

73 S&K(c),S&K,I:Manhunter . 12,000.00
74 S&K(c),S&K,You can't Escape
   your Fate-The Sandman . . 1,500.00
75 S&K(c),S&K,Sandman and
   Sandy Battle Thor in
   'Villian from Valhalla' 1,500.00
76 S&K(c),Sandman(c),S&K . 1,500.00
77 S&K,(c),S&K,same 1,500.00
78 S&K(c),S&K,same 1,500.00
79 S&K(c),S&K,Manhunter in
   'Cobras of the Deep' 1,500.00
80 S&K(c),Sandman(c),S&K . 1,500.00
81 S&K(c),MMe,S&K,same . . 1,000.00
82 S&K(c),S&K,Sandman
   X-Mas story 1,000.00
83 S&K(c),S&K,Sandman
   Boxing(c),E:Hourman 1,000.00
84 S&K(c),S&K 1,000.00
85 S&K(c),S&K,Sandman in
   'The Amazing Dreams of
   Gentleman Jack' 1,000.00
86 S&K(c),Sandman(c) 1,000.00
87 S&K(c),same 1,000.00
88 S&K(c),same 1,000.00
89 S&K(c),same 1,000.00
90 S&K(c),same 1,000.00
91 S&K(c),JK 850.00
92 S&K(c) 750.00
93 S&K(c),Sandman in 'Sleep
   for Sale' 750.00
94 S&K(c),Sandman(c) 750.00
95 S&K(c),same 750.00
96 S&K(c),same 750.00
97 S&K(c),same 750.00
98 JK(c),Sandman in 'Hero
   of Dreams' 750.00
99 JK(c) 750.00
100 . . . . 1,000.00
101 S&K(c) 750.00
102 S&K(c) 750.00
103 B:Superboy stories,(c),BU:
   Johnny Quick,Aquaman,Shining
   Knight,Green Arrow . . 2,500.00
104 S&S,ToyTown USA 800.00
105 S&S,Palace of Fantasy . . 550.00
106 S&S,Weather Hurricane . . 550.00
107 S&S,The Sky is the Limit . 550.00
108 S&S,Proof of the Proverbs 550.00
109 S&S,You Can't Lose 550.00
110 S&S,The Farmer Takes
   it Easy 550.00
111 S&S,The Whiz Quiz Club . 550.00
112 S&S,Super Safety First . . . 550.00
113 S&S,The 33rd Christmas . 500.00
114 S&S,Superboy Spells
   Danger 500.00
115 S&S,The Adventure of
   Jaguar Boy 500.00
116 S&S,JBu,Superboy Toy
   Tester 500.00
117 S&S,JBu,Miracle Plane . . 500.00
118 S&S,JBu,The Quiz Biz
   Broadcast 500.00
119 WMo,JBu,Superboy
   Meets Girls 500.00
120 S&S,JBu,A:Perry White;
   I:Ringmaster 525.00
121 S&S,Great Hobby Contest 450.00
122 S&S,Superboy-Super-
   Magician 450.00
123 S&S,Lesson For a Bully . . 450.00
124 S&S,Barbed Wire Boys
   Town 450.00
125 S&S,The Weight Before
   Christmas 450.00

126 S&S,Superboy:Crime
Fighting Poet 450.00
127 MMe,O:Shining Knight;
Super Bellboy 450.00
128 WMo,How Clark Kent Met
Lois Lane' 450.00
129 WMo,Pupils of the Past . . 450.00
130 WMo,Superboy Super
Salesman 450.00
131 WMo,The Million Dollar
Athlete 400.00
132 WMo,Superboy Super
Cowboy 400.00
133 WMo,Superboy's Report
Card 400.00
134 WMo,Silver Gloves Sellout 400.00
135 WMo,The Most Amazing
of All Boys 400.00
136 WMo,My Pal Superboy . . . 400.00
137 WMo,Treasure of Tondimo 400.00
138 WMo,Around the World in
Eighty Minutes 400.00
139 WMo,Telegraph Boy 400.00
140 Journey to the Moon 400.00
141 WMo,When Superboy Lost
His Powers 400.00

Adventure Comics #74
© DC Comics, Inc.

142 WMo,The Man Who Walked
With Trouble 450.00
143 WMo,The Superboy Savings
Bank,A:Wooden Head Jones 450.00
144 WMo,The Way to Stop
Superboy 450.00
145 WMo,Holiday Hijackers . . . 450.00
146 The Substitute Superboy . . 450.00
147 Clark Kent,Orphan 450.00
148 Superboy Meets Mummies 450.00
149 Fake Superboys 450.00
150 FF,Superboy's Initiation . . 500.00
151 FF,No Hunting(c) 500.00
152 Superboy Hunts For a Job 425.00
153 FF,Clark Kent,Boy Hobo . . 500.00
154 The Carnival Boat Crimes . 325.00
155 FF,Superboy-Hollywood
Actor 425.00
156 The Flying Peril 325.00
157 FF,The Worst Boy in
Smallville 400.00
158 The Impossible Task 325.00
159 FF,Superboy Millionaire? . 400.00

160 Superboy's Phoney Father 325.00
161 FF 400.00
162 'The Super-Coach of
Smallville High!' 325.00
163 FF,'Superboy's Phoney
Father' 400.00
164 Discovers the Secret of
a Lost Indian Tribe! 325.00
165 'Superboy's School for
Stunt Men!' 325.00
166 'The Town That Stole
Superboy' 325.00
167 'Lana Lang, Super-Girl!' . . 325.00
168 'The Boy Who Out Smarted
Superboy' 325.00
169 'Clark Kent's Private
Butler' 325.00
170 'Lana Lang's Big Crush' . . 300.00
171 'Superboy's Toughest
Tasks!' 300.00
172 'Laws that Backfired' 300.00
173 'Superboy's School of
Hard Knocks' 300.00
174 'The New Lana Lang!' 300.00
175 'Duel of the Superboys' . . . 300.00
176 'Superboy's New Parents!' . 300.00
177 'Hot-Rod Chariot Race!' . . 300.00
178 'Boy in the Lead Mask' . . . 300.00
179 'The World's Whackiest
Inventors' 300.00
180 Grand Prize o/t Underworld 300.00
181 'Mask for a Hero' 300.00
182 The Super Hick from
Smallville' 275.00
183 'Superboy and Cleopatra' . 275.00
184 'The Shutterbugs of
Smallville' 275.00
185 'The Mythical Monster' . . . 275.00
186 . . . . 275.00
187 '25th Century Superboy' . . 275.00
188 'The Bull Fighter from
Smallville' 275.00
189 Girl of Steel(Lana Lang) . . 275.00
190 The Two Clark Kents 275.00
191 . . . . 275.00
192 'The Coronation of
Queen Lana Lang' 275.00
193 'Superboy's Lost Costume' 275.00
194 'Super-Charged Superboy' 275.00
195 'Lana Lang's Romance
on Mars!' 275.00
196 'Superboy vs. King Gorilla' 275.00
197 V:Juvenile Gangs 275.00
198 'The Super-Carnival
from Space' 275.00
199 'Superboy meets Superlad' 275.00
200 'Superboy and the Apes!' . 450.00
201 'Safari in Smallville!' 300.00
202 'Superboy City, U.S.A.' . . . 300.00
203 'Uncle Superboy!' 325.00
204 'The Super-Brat of
Smallville' 300.00
205 'The Journey of the
Second Superboy!' 300.00
206 'The Impossible Creatures' 300.00
207 'Smallville's Worst
Athlete' 300.00
208 'Rip Van Winkle of
Smallville?' 300.00
209 'Superboy Week!' 300.00
210 I:Krypto,'The Superdog
from Krypton' 3,000.00
211 'Superboy's Most
Amazing Dream!' 250.00
212 'Superboy's Robot Twin' . . 250.00

213 'The Junior Jury of
Smallville!' 250.00
214 A:Krypto 500.00
215 'The Super-Hobby of
Superboy' 250.00
216 'The Wizard City' 250.00
217 'Superboy's Farewell
to Smallville' 250.00
218 'The Two World's of
Superboy' 250.00
219 The Rip Van Wrinkle of
Smallville 250.00
220 The Greatest Show on Earth
A:Krypto 250.00
221 'The Babe of Steel' 225.00
222 'Superboy's Repeat
Performance' 225.00
223 'Hercules Junior' 225.00
224 'Pa Kent Superman' 225.00
225 'The Bird with
Super-Powers' 225.00
226 'Superboy's Super Rival!' . 225.00
227 'Good Samaritan of
Smallville' 225.00
228 'Clark Kent's Body Guard' . 225.00
229 . . . . 225.00

Adventure Comics #326
© DC Comics, Inc.

230 'The Secret of the
Flying Horse' 225.00
231 'The Super-Feats of
Super-Baby!' 225.00
232 'The House where
Superboy was Born' 225.00
233 'Joe Smith, Man of Steel!' . 225.00
234 'The 1,001 Rides of
Superboy!' 225.00
235 'The Confessions of
Superboy!' 225.00
236 'Clark Kent's Super-Dad!' . 225.00
237 Robot War of Smallville! . . 225.00
238 'The Secret Past of
Superboy's Father' 225.00
239 'The Super-Tricks of
the Dog of Steel' 225.00
240 'The Super Teacher
From Krypton' 225.00

DC COMICS

241 'The Super-Outlaw of Smallville' 225.00	303 I:Matter Eater Lad 90.00	344 CS,Super Stalag,pt.1. . . . . . 25.00
242 'The Kid From Krypton' . . . 225.00	304 D:Lightning Lad 90.00	345 CS,Super Stalag,pt.2 . . . . . 25.00
243 'The Super Toys From Krypton' 225.00	305 A:Chameleon Boy 90.00	346 CS,I&J:Karate Kid,Princess Projectra,I:Nemesis Kid 25.00
244 'The Poorest Family in Smallville' 225.00	306 I:Legion of Sub.Heroes . . . 80.00	347 CS,Legion 15.00
245 'The Mystery of Monster X' 225.00	307 I:Element Lad 90.00	348 I:Dr.Regulus 18.00
246 'The Girl Who Trapped Superboy!' 225.00	308 I:Light Lass 90.00	349 CS,I:Rond Vidar 15.00
247 I&O:Legion 4,500.00	309 I:Legion of Super Monsters . 80.00	350 CS,I:White Witch 18.00
248 Green Arrow 175.00	310 A:Mxyzptlk 80.00	351 CS,R:Star Boy 15.00
249 CS,Green Arrow 175.00	311 CS,V:Legion of Substitue Heroes 70.00	352 CS,I:Fatal Fire 15.00
250 JK,Green Arrow 175.00	312 R:Lightning Lad 80.00	353 CS,D:Ferro Lad 20.00
251 JK,Green Arrow 175.00	313 CS,J:Supergirl 70.00	354 CS,Adult Legion 12.00
252 JK,Green Arrow 175.00	314 A:Hitler 70.00	355 CS,J:Insect Queen 12.00
253 JK,1st Superboy & Robin T.U 250.00	315 A:Legion of Substitute Heroes 70.00	356 CS,Five Legion Orphans . . . 10.00
254 JK,Green Arrow 185.00	316 O:Legion 60.00	357 CS,I:Controller 10.00
255 JK,Green Arrow 185.00	317 I&J:Dreamgirl 60.00	358 I:Hunter 10.00
256 JK,O:Green Arrow 600.00	318 Legion 60.00	359 CS,Outlawed Legion,pt.1 . . 10.00
257 CS,LE,A:Hercules,Samson 150.00	319 Legion 60.00	360 CS,Outlawed Legion,pt.2 . . 10.00
258 LE,Aquaman,Superboy . . . 150.00	320 A:Dev-Em 60.00	361 I:Dominators (30th century) . 12.00
259 I:Crimson Archer 150.00	321 I:Time Trapper 75.00	362 I:Dr.Mantis Morto 10.00
260 1st S.A. O:Aquaman 625.00	322 JF,A:Legion of Super Pets . 50.00	363 V:Dr.Mantis Morlo 10.00
261 GA,A:Lois Lane 125.00	323 JF,BU:Kypto 50.00	364 A:Legion of Super Pets 10.00
262 O:Speedy 125.00	324 JF,I:Legion of Super Outlaws 50.00	365 CS,I:Shadow Lass, V:Fatal Five 10.00
263 GA,Aquaman,Superboy . . . 125.00	325 JF,V:Lex Luthor 50.00	366 CS,J:Shadow Lass 10.00
264 GA,A:Robin Hood 125.00	326 BU:Superboy 50.00	367 N:Legion H.Q.,I:Dark Circle . 12.00
265 GA,Aquaman,Superboy . . . 125.00		368 CS 10.00
266 GA,I:Aquagirl 125.00		369 CS,JAb,I:Mordru 12.00
267 N:Legion(2nd app.) 800.00		370 CS,JAb,V:Mordru 10.00
268 I:Aquaboy 125.00		371 CS,JAb,I:Chemical King . . . 12.00
269 I:Aqualad,E:Green Arrow . 225.00		372 CS,JAb,J:Timber Wolf, Chemical King 12.00
270 2nd A:Aqualad,B:Congorilla 125.00		373 I:Tornado Twins 10.00
271 O:Lex Luthor rtd 250.00		374 WM,I:Black Mace 10.00
272 I:Human Flying Fish 110.00		375 I:Wanderers 10.00
273 Aquaman,Superboy 110.00		376 Execution of Cham.Boy . . . 10.00
274 Aquaman,Superboy 110.00		377 Heroes for Hire 10.00
275 O:Superman/Batman T.U. rtd 200.00		378 Twelve Hours to Live 10.00
276 Superboy,3rd A:Metallo . . . 100.00		379 Burial In Space 10.00
277 Aquaman,Superboy 100.00		380 The Amazing Space Odyssey of the Legion,E:Legion 10.00
278 Aquaman,Superboy 100.00		381 The Supergirl Gang C:Batgirl,B:Supergirl 35.00
279 CS,Aquaman,Superboy . . . 100.00		382 NA(c),The Superteams Split Up,A:Superman 5.00
280 CS,A:Lori Lemaris 100.00		383 NA(c),Please Stop my Funeral, A:Superman,Comet,Streaky . . 6.00
281 Aquaman,Superboy E:Congorilla 100.00		384 KS,The Heroine Haters, A:Superman 5.00
282 5th A:Legion,I:Starboy . . . 200.00		385 Supergirl's Big Sister 5.00
283 I:Phantom Zone 175.00		386 The Beast That Loved Supergirl 5.00
284 CS,JM,Aquaman,Superboy 100.00		387 Wolfgirl of Stanhope; A:Superman;V:Lex Luthor 5.00
285 WB,B:Bizarro World 150.00		388 Kindergarten Criminal; V:Luthor,Brainiac 5.00
286 I:Bizarro Mxyzptlk 150.00		389 A:Supergirl's Parents, V:Brainiac 5.00
287 I:Dev-Em,Bizarro Perry White, Jimmy Olsen 100.00		390 Linda Danvers Superstar (80 page giant) 15.00
288 A:Dev-Em 100.00		391 The Super Cheat;A:Comet . . 4.50
289 Superboy 90.00	327 I&J:Timber Wolf 50.00	392 Supergirls Lost Costume . . . 4.50
290 8th A:Legion,O&J:Sunboy, I:Brainiac 5 . . . . 175.00	328 Legion 50.00	393 KS,Unwanted Supergirl 4.50
291 A:Lex Luthor 75.00	329 I:Legion of Super Bizarros . . 50.00	394 KS,Heartbreak Prison 4.50
292 Superboy,I:Bizarro Lucy Lane, Lana Lang 75.00	330 Legion 50.00	395 Heroine in Haunted House . . 4.50
293 CS,O&I:Marv-El,I:Bizarro Luthor 125.00	331 Legion 35.00	396 Mystery o/t Super Orphan . . 4.50
294 I:Bizarro M.Monroe,JFK . . 125.00	332 Legion 35.00	397 Now Comes Zod,N:Supergirl, V:Luthor 4.50
295 I:Bizarro Titano 75.00	333 Legion 35.00	398 Maid of Doom,A:Superman, Streaky,Krypto,Comet 4.50
296 A:Ben Franklin,George Washington 75.00	334 Legion 35.00	399 CI,Johnny Dee,Hero Bum . . 4.50
297 Lana Lang Superboy Sister . 75.00	335 Legion 35.00	400 MSy,35th Anniv.,Return of the Black Flame 5.00
298 The Fat Superboy 75.00	336 Legion 35.00	401 MSy,JAb,The Frightened Supergirl,V:Lex Luthor 6.00
299 I:Gold Kryptonite 75.00	337 Legion 35.00	
300 B:Legion,J:Mon-El, E:Bizarro World 400.00	338 Legion 35.00	
301 CS,O:Bouncing Boy 125.00	339 Legion 35.00	
302 CS,Legion 90.00	340 I:Computo 35.00	
	341 CS,D:Triplicate Girl (becomes Duo Damsel) 26.00	
	342 CS,Star Boy expelled 25.00	
	343 CS,V:Lords of Luck 25.00	

Adventure Comics #420
© DC Comics, Inc.

402 MSy,JAb,TD,I:Starfire,
    Dr.Kangle 6.00
403 68 page giant 15.00
404 MSy,JAb,V:Starfire 5.00
405 V:Starfire,Dr.Kangle 5.00
406 MSy,JAb,Suspicion 5.00
407 MSy,JAb,Suspicion Confirmed
    N:Supergirl 5.00
408 The Face at the Window 5.00
409 MSy,DG,Legion rep. 5.00
410 N:Supergirl 5.00
411 CI,N:Supergirl 5.00
412 rep.Strange Adventures #180
    (I:Animal Man). 7.00
413 GM,JKu,rep.Hawkman 2.25
414 Animal Man rep. 4.00
415 BO,GM,CI,Animal Man rep. . . 3.00
416 CI,All women issue,giantsize . 5.00
417 GM,inc.rep.Adventure #161,
    Frazetta art. 3.00
418 ATh,Black Canary 3.00
419 ATh,Black Canary 3.00
420 Animal Man rep. 3.50
421 MSy,Supergirl 3.00

Adventure Comics #442
© DC Comics, Inc.

422 MSy,Supergirl 3.00
423 MSy,Supergirl 3.00
424 MSy,E:Supergirl,A:JLA 3.00
425 AN,ATh,I:Captain Fear 6.00
426 MSy,DG,JAp,Vigilante 3.00
427 TD 3.25
428 TD,I:Black Orchid 15.00
429 TD,AN,Black Orchid 8.00
430 A:Black Orchid 8.00
431 JAp,ATh,B:Spectre 10.00
432 JAp,AN,A:Spectre,Capt.Fear . 8.00
433 JAp,AN 8.00
434 JAp 8.00
435 MGr(1st work),JAp,Aquaman . 8.00
436 JAp,MGr,Aquaman 8.00
437 JAp,MGr,Aquaman 8.00
438 JAp,HC,DD,7 Soldiers 8.00
439 JAp 8.00
440 JAp,O:New Spectre 8.00
441 JAp,B:Aquaman 2.50
442 JAp,A:Aquaman 2.50
443 JAp 2.50
444 JAp 2.50
445 JAp,RE,JSon,Creeper 2.50

446 JAp,RE,JSon,Creeper 2.50
447 JAp,RE,JSon,Creeper 2.50
448 JAp,Aquaman 2.50
449 JAp,MN,TA,Jonn J'onz 2.00
450 JAp,MN,TA,Supergirl 2.00
451 JAp,MN,TA,Hawkman 2.00
452 JAp,Aquaman 2.00
453 MA,CP,JRu,B:Superboy
    & Aqualad 2.00
454 CP,DG,A:Kryptonite Kid . . . 2.00
455 CP,DG,A:Kryptonite Kid
    E:Aqualad 2.00
456 JSon,JA 2.00
457 JSon,JA,JO,B:Eclipso 4.00
458 JSon,JAp,JO,BL,E:Superboy
    & Eclipso 3.50
459 IN,FMc,JAp,JSon,DN,JA,A:Wond.
    Woman,New Gods,Green Lantern,
    Flash,Deadman,(giant size) . . 8.00
460 IN,FMc,JAp,DN,DA,JSon,JA,
    D:Darkseid 8.00
461 IN,FMc,JAp,JSon,DN,JA,
    B:JSA & Aquaman 5.00
462 IN,FMc,DH,JL,DG,JA,
    D:Earth 2,Batman 5.00
463 DH,JL,JSon,FMc 3.00
464 DH,JAp,JSon,DN,DA,
    Deadman 3.50
465 DN,JSon,DG,JL 3.00
466 MN,JL,JSon,DN,DA 3.00
467 JSon,SD,RT,I:Starman
    B:Plastic Man 8.00
468 SD,JSon 2.00
469 SD,JSon,O:Starman 2.00
470 SD,JSon,O:Starman 2.00
471 SD,JSon,I:Brickface 2.00
472 SD,RT,JSon 2.00
473 SD,RT,JSon 2.00
474 SD,RT,JSon 2.00
475 BB(c),SD,RT,JSon,DG,
    B:Aquaman 2.00
476 SD,RT,JSon,DG 2.00
477 SD,RT,JSon,DG 2.00
478 SD,RT,JSon,DG 2.00
479 CI,DG,JSon,Dial H For Hero,
    E:Starman and Aquaman 2.00
480 CI,DJ,B:Dial H for Hero 2.00
481 CI,DJ 2.00
482 CI,DJ,DH 2.00
483 CI,DJ,DH 2.00
484 GP(c),CI,DJ,DH 2.00
485 GP(c),CI,DJ 2.00
486 GP(c),DH,RT,TVE 2.00
487 CI,DJ,DH 2.00
488 CI,DJ,TVE 2.00
489 CI,FMc,TVE 2.00
490 GP(c),CI,E:Dial H for Hero . . 2.00
491 KG(c),DigestSize,DN,
    Shazam,rep.other material . . . 2.00
492 KG(c),DN,E:Shazam 2.00
493 KG(c),GT,B:Challengers of
    the Unknown,reprints 2.00
494 KG(c),GT,Challengers,
    reprints 2.00
495 ATh,reprints,Challengers . . . 2.50
496 GK(c),ATh,reprints,
    Challengers 2.50
497 ATh,DA,reps.,E:Challengers . 2.50
498 GK(c),reprints,Rep.Legion . . 2.00
499 GK(c),reprints,Rep 2.00
500 KG(c),Legion reprints,Rep . . 3.00
501 reprints,Rep 2.00
502 reprints,Rep 2.00
503 reprints,final issue 2.00
Giant #1, 80 page, 7 tales (1998) . 5.00

ADVENTURES IN
THE DC UNIVERSE
1997–98

1 F:New JLA 2.00
2 F:The Flash,Catwoman 2.00
3 Wonder Woman vs. Cheetah;
    Poison Ivy vs. Batman 2.00
4 F:Green Lantern vs. Glorious
    Godfrey; Mister Miracle 2.00
5 F:Martian Manhunter, all alien
    issue 2.00
6 F:Ocean Master, Power Girl . . 2.00
7 SVa(s),F:Shazam Family 2.00
8 SVa(s),F:Blue Beetle &
    Booster Gold 2.00
9 SVa(s),F:Flash,V:Grodd,Cipher 2.00
10 SVa(s),Legion month 2.00
11 SVa(s),F:Green Lantern &
    Wonder Woman 2.00
12 SVa(s) 2.00
13 SVa(s),A:Martian Manhunter . . 2.00
14 SVa(s),Flash races Superboy . 2.00
15 SVa(s),Shazam,Aquaman . . . 2.00
16 SVa(s),F:Green Lantern 2.00
17 SVa(s),F:Batman, Creeper . . . 2.00
18 SVa(s),F:JLA 2.00
19 F:Catwoman, Wonder Woman . 2.00
Ann.#1 magic amulets,5 stories . . 4.00

Adventures of Alan Ladd #5
© DC Comics, Inc.

ADVENTURES OF
ALAN LADD
1949–51

1 Ph(c) 750.00
2 Ph(c) 400.00
3 Ph(c) 300.00
4 Ph(c) 300.00
5 Ph(c),inc.Destination Danger . 225.00
6 Ph(c) 225.00
7 . . . . 225.00
8 Grand Duchess takes over . 225.00
9 Deadlien in Rapula 225.00

ADVENTURES OF
BOB HOPE
1951–68

1 Ph(c) 1,200.00

2 Ph(c)	600.00
3 Ph(c)	325.00
4 Ph(c)	300.00
5 thru 10	@275.00
11 thru 20	@150.00
21 thru 40	@100.00
41 thru 90	@75.00
91 thru 93	@25.00
94 C:Aquaman	30.00
95 thru 105	@22.00
106 thru 109 NA	@45.00

ADVENTURES OF DEAN MARTIN AND JERRY LEWIS
1952–57

1	600.00
2	300.00
3 thru 10	@150.00
11 thru 20	@100.00
21 thru 40	@75.00
Becomes:	

ADVENTURES OF JERRY LEWIS
1957–71

41 thru 55	@50.00
56 thru 69	@35.00
70 thru 87	@25.00
88 A:Bob Hope	30.00
89 thru 91	@20.00
92 C:Superman	30.00
93 thru 96	@20.00
97 A:Batman & Joker	35.00
98 thru 100	@20.00
101 thru 104 NA	@35.00
105 A:Superman	25.00
106 thru 111	@10.00
112 A:Flash	20.00
113 thru 116	@10.00
117 A:Wonder Woman	15.00
118 thru 124	@8.00

ADVENTURES OF FORD FAIRLANE
1990

1 DH,DG	1.50
2 thru 4 DH	@1.50

ADVENTURES OF THE OUTSIDERS
(see BATMAN & THE OUTSIDERS)

ADVENTURES OF OZZIE AND HARRIET
1949–50

1 Ph(c)	650.00
2	350.00
3 thru 5	@300.00

ADVENTURES OF REX, THE WONDERDOG
1952–59

1 ATh	800.00
2 ATh	400.00
3 ATh	300.00
4	250.00
5	250.00
6 thru 11	@150.00
12 thru 20	@100.00
21 thru 46	@75.00

ADVENTURES OF SUPERBOY
(See: SUPERBOY)

ADVENTURES OF SUPERMAN
(See: SUPERMAN)

AGENT LIBERTY SPECIAL
1992

1 DAb,O:Agent Liberty	2.00

ALIEN NATION
1988

1 JBi,movie adaption	2.50

All-American Comics #26
© DC Comics, Inc.

ALL-AMERICAN COMICS
1939–48

1 B:Hop Harrigan,Scribbly,Mutt&Jeff, Red,White&Blue,Bobby Thatcher, Skippy,Daiseybelle,Mystery Men of Mars,Toonerville	5,500.00
2 B:Ripley's Believe it or Not	1,500.00
3 Hop Harrigan (c)	1,200.00
4 Flag(c)	1,200.00
5 B:The American Way	1,200.00
6 ShM(c),Fredric Marchin in 'The American Way'	950.00
7 E:Bobby Thatcher,C.H. Claudy's 'A Thousand Years in a Minute'	900.00
8 B:Ultra Man	1,400.00
9	900.00
10 ShM(c),E:The American Way, Santa-X-Mas(c)	850.00
11 Ultra Man(c)	850.00
12 E:Toonerville Folks	850.00
13 'The Infra Red Des'Royers'	850.00
14	850.00
15 E:Tippie and Reg'lar Fellars	850.00
16 O&1st App:Green Lantern, B:Lantern(c)	62,000.00
17 SMo(c)	12,500.00
18 SMo(c)	8,500.00
19 SMo(c),O&I: Atom, E:Ultra	

Man	12,000.00
20 I:Atom's costume,Hunkle becomes Red Tornado	3,500.00
21 E:Wiley of West Point & Skippy	2,000.00
22	1,800.00
23 E:Daieybelle	1,800.00
24 E:Ripley's Believe it or Not	2,500.00
25 O&I:Dr. Mid-Nite	8,200.00
26 O&I:Sargon the Sorcerer	3,000.00
27 I:Doiby Dickles	3,200.00
28	1,200.00
29 ShM(c)	1,200.00
30 ShM(c)	1,200.00
31 Adventures of the underfed orphans	1,200.00
32	900.00
33	900.00
34	900.00
35 Doiby discovers Lantern's ID	900.00
36	900.00
37	900.00
38	900.00
39	900.00
40	900.00
41	800.00
42	800.00
43	800.00
44 'I Accuse the Green Lantern!	800.00
45	800.00
46	800.00
47 Hop Harrigan meets the Enemy,(c)	800.00
48	800.00
49	800.00
50 E:Sargon	800.00
51 'Murder Under the Stars'	700.00
52	700.00
53 Green Lantern delivers the Mail	700.00
54	700.00
55 'The Riddle of the Runaway Trolley'	700.00
56 V:Elegant Esmond	700.00
57 V:The Melancholy Men	700.00
58	700.00
59 'The Story of the Man Who Couldn't Tell The Truth'	700.00
60	700.00
61 O:Soloman Grundy,'Fighters Never Quit'	3,500.00
62 'Da Distrik Attorney'	650.00
63	650.00
64 'A Bag of Assorted Nuts!'	650.00
65 'The Man Who Lost Wednesday'	650.00
66 'The Soles of Manhattan!'	650.00
67 V:King Shark	650.00
68 Meets Napoleon&Joe Safeen	650.00
69 'Backwards Man!'	650.00
70 JKu,I:Maximillian O'Leary, V:Colley, the Leprechaun	650.00
71 E:Red,White&Blue,'The Human Bomb'	550.00
72 B:Black Pirate	550.00
73 B:Winkey,Blinky&Noddy, 'Mountain Music Mayhem'	550.00
74	550.00
75	550.00
76 'Spring Time for Doiby'	550.00
77 Hop Harrigan(c)	550.00
78	550.00
79 Mutt & Jeff	550.00
80	550.00
81	550.00

---

82 . . . . 550.00	
83 Mutt & Jeff 550.00	
84 'The Adventure of the Man	
with Two Faces' 550.00	
85 . . . . 550.00	
86 V:Crime of the Month Club . 550.00	
87 'The Strange Case of	
Professor Nobody' 550.00	
88 'Canvas of Crime' 550.00	
89 O:Harlequin 650.00	
90 O:Icicle 650.00	
91 'Wedding of the Harlequin' . 650.00	
92 'The Icicle goes South' 650.00	
93 'The Double Crossing Decoy' 650.00	
94 A:Harlequin 650.00	
95 'The Unmasking of the	
Harlequin' 650.00	
96 ATh(c),'Solve the Mystery	
of the Emerald Necklaces!' . 650.00	
97 ATh(c),'The Country Fair	
Crimes' 650.00	
98 ATh,ATh(c),'End of Sports!' . 650.00	
99 ATh,ATh(c),E:Hop Harrigan 650.00	
100 ATh,I:Johnny Thunder . . 1,300.00	
101 ATh,ATh(c),E:Mutt & Jeff 1,000.00	
102 ATh,ATh(c),E:GrnLantern 1,600.00	

Becomes:

ALL-AMERICAN WESTERN
1948–52

103 A:Johnny Thunder,'The City	
Without Guns,'All Johnny	
Thunder stories 350.00	
104 ATh(c),'Unseen Allies' 350.00	
105 ATh(c),'Hidden Guns' 200.00	
106 ATh(c),'Snow Mountain	
Ambush' 150.00	
107 ATh(c),'Cheyenne Justice' . 200.00	
108 ATh(c),'Vengeance of	
the Silver Bullet' 150.00	
109 ATh(c),'Secret of	
Crazy River' 150.00	
110 ATh(c),'Ambush at	
Scarecrow Hills' 150.00	
111 ATh(c),'Gun-Shy Sheriff' . . 150.00	
112 ATh(c),'Double Danger' . . . 150.00	
113 ATh(c),'Johnny Thunder	
Indian Chief' 175.00	
114 ATh(c),'The End of	
Johnny Thunder' 150.00	
115 ATh(c),'Cheyenne Mystery' 150.00	
116 ATh(c),'Buffalo Raiders	
of the Mesa' 150.00	
117 ATh(c),V:Black Lightnin . . . 125.00	
118 ATh(c),'Challenge of	
the Aztecs' 125.00	
119 GK(c),'The Vanishing	
Gold Mine' 125.00	
120 GK(c),'Ambush at	
Painted Mountain' 125.00	
121 ATh(c),'The Unmasking of	
Johnny Thunder' 125.00	
122 ATh(c),'The Real	
Johnny Thunder' 125.00	
123 GK(c),'Johnny Thunder's	
Strange Rival' 125.00	
124 ATh(c),'The Iron Horse's	
Last Run' 125.00	
125 ATh(c),'Johnny Thunder's	
Last Roundup' 125.00	
126 ATh(c),'Phantoms of the	
Desert' 125.00	

Becomes:

ALL-AMERICAN MEN OF WAR
1952–66

127 (0) 700.00	
128 (1) 500.00	
2 JGr(c),Killer Bait 400.00	
3 Pied Piper of Pyong-Yang . . 400.00	
4 JGr(c),The Hills of Hate 400.00	
5 One Second to Zero 300.00	
6 IN(c),Jungle Killers 300.00	
7 IN(c),Beach to Hold 300.00	
8 IN(c),Sgt. Storm Cloud 300.00	
9 . . . . 300.00	
10 . . . . 300.00	
11 JGr(c),Dragon's Teeth 300.00	
12 . . . . 250.00	
13 JGr(c),Lost Patrol 250.00	
14 IN(c),Pigeon Boss 250.00	
15 JGr(c),Flying Roadblock . . . 250.00	
16 JGr(c),The Flying Jeep 250.00	
17 JGr(c),Booby Trap Ridge . . 250.00	
18 JKu(c),The Ballad of	
Battling Bells 250.00	
19 JGr(c),IN,Torpedo Track . . . 175.00	
20 JGr(c),JKu,Lifenet to	
Beach Road 175.00	
21 JGr(c),IN,RH,The	
Coldest War 175.00	
22 JGr(c),IN,JKu,Snipers Nest . 175.00	
23 JGr(c),The Silent War 175.00	
24 JGr(c),The Thin Line 175.00	
25 JGr(c),IN,For Rent-One	
Foxhole 175.00	
26 . . . . 175.00	
27 JGr(c),RH,Fighting Pigeon . 175.00	
28 JGr(c),RA,JKu,Medal	
for A Dog 175.00	
29 IN(c),JKu,Battle Bridges . . . 200.00	
30 JGr(c),RH,Frogman Hunt . . 175.00	
31 JGr(c),Battle Seat 200.00	
32 JGr(c),RH,Battle Station . . . 200.00	
33 JGr(c),IN,Sky Ambush 175.00	
34 JGr(c),JKu,No Man's Alley . 175.00	
35 JGr(c),IN, Battle Call 150.00	
36 JGr(c),JKu,Battle Window . . 150.00	
37 JGr(c),JKu,The Big Stretch . 150.00	
38 JGr(c),RH,JKu,The	
Floating Sentinel 150.00	
39 JGr(c),JKu,The Four Faces	
of Sgt. Fay 150.00	
40 JGr(c),IN,Walking Helmet . . 150.00	
41 JKu(c),RH,JKu,The 50-50 War 100.00	
42 JGr(c),JKu,Battle Arm 100.00	
43 JGr(c),JKu,Command Post . 100.00	
44 JKu(c),The Flying Frogman . 100.00	
45 JGr(c),RH,Combat Waterboy 100.00	
46 JGr(c),IN,RH,Tank Busters . 100.00	
47 JGr(c),JKu,MD,Battle Freight 100.00	
48 JGr(c),JKu,MD,Roadblock . . 100.00	
49 JGr(c),Walking Target 100.00	
50 IN,RH,Bodyguard For A Sub 100.00	
51 JGr(c),RH,Bomber's Moon . . 75.00	
52 JKu(c),RH,MD,Back	
Seat Driver 75.00	
53 JKu(c),JKu,Night Attack . . . 75.00	
54 JKu(c),IN,Diary of a	
Fighter Pilot 75.00	
55 JKu(c),RH,Split-Second Target 75.00	
56 JKu,IN,RH,Frogman Jinx . . . 75.00	
57 Pick-Up for Easy Co. 75.00	
58 JGr(c),RH,MD,A Piece of Sky 75.00	
59 JGr(c),JKu,The Hand of War . 75.00	
60 JGr(c),The Time Table 75.00	

All-American Western #116
© DC Comics, Inc.

61 JGr(c),IN,MD,Blind Target . . . 75.00	
62 JGr(c),RH,RA,No(c) 75.00	
63 JGr(c),JKu,Frogman Carrier . 75.00	
64 JKu(c),JKu,RH,The Other	
Man's War 75.00	
65 JGr(c),JKu,MD,Same	
Old Sarge 75.00	
66 JGr(c),The Walking Fort 75.00	
67 JGr(c),RH,A:Gunner&Sarge,	
The Cover Man 250.00	
68 JKu(c),Gunner&Sarge,	
The Man & The Gun 75.00	
69 JKu(c),A:Tank Killer,	
Bazooka Hill 75.00	
70 JKu(c),IN,Pigeon	
Without Wings 75.00	
71 JGr(c),A:Tank Killer,Target	
For An Ammo Boy 75.00	
72 JGr(c),A:Tank Killer,T.N.T.	
Broom 75.00	
73 JGr(c),JKu,No Detour 75.00	
74 The Minute Commandos 75.00	
75 JKu(c),Sink That Flattop 75.00	
76 JKu(c),A:Tank Killer,	
Just One More Tank 75.00	
77 JKu(c),IN,MD,Big Fish-	
little Fish 75.00	
78 JGr(c),Tin Hat for an	
Iron Man 75.00	
79 JKu(c),RA,Showdown Soldier 75.00	
80 JGr(c),RA,The Medal Men . . 75.00	
81 JGr(c),IN,Ghost Ship of	
Two Wars 60.00	
82 IN(c),B:Johnny Cloud,	
The Flying Chief 60.00	
83 IN(c),Fighting Blind 60.00	
84 IN(c),Death Dive 60.00	
85 RH(c),Battle Eagle 60.00	
86 JGr(c),Top-Gun Ace 60.00	
87 JGr(c),Broken Ace 60.00	
88 JGr(c),The Ace of Vengeance 60.00	
89 JGr(c),The Star Jockey 60.00	
90 JGr(c),Wingmate of Doom . . 60.00	
91 RH(c),Two Missions To Doom 60.00	
92 JGr(c),The Battle Hawk 60.00	
93 RH(c),The Silent Death 60.00	
94 RH(c),Be Brave-Be Silent . . . 60.00	
95 RH(c),Second Sight	

All-American Men of War #13
© DC Comics, Inc.

All-Flash #7 © DC Comics, Inc.

ALL FUNNY COMICS
1943–48
1 Genius Jones	375.00
2 same	150.00
3 same	100.00
4 same	100.00
5 thru 10	@100.00
11 Genius Jones	75.00
12 same	50.00
13 same	75.00
14	60.00
15	75.00
16 A:DC Superheroes	200.00
17 thru 23	@75.00

ALL-STAR COMICS
Summer, 1940–51
1 B:Flash,Hawkman,Hourman, Sandman,Spectre,Red White & Blue	12,000.00
2 B:Green Lantern and Johnny Thunder	5,000.00
3 First meeting of Justice Society with Flash as Chairman	35,000.00
4 First mission of JSA	4,500.00
5 V:Mr. X,I:Hawkgirl	4,000.00
6 Flash leaves	2,900.00

All-Star Comics #5 © DC Comics, Inc.

7 Green Lantern becomes Chairman, L:Hourman, C:Superman, Batman & Flash	3,000.00
8 I:Wonder Women;Starman and Dr. Mid-Nite join,Hawkman becomes chairman	25,000.00
9 JSA in Latin America	2,400.00
10 C:Flash & Green Lantern, JSA Time Travel story	2,300.00
11 Wonder Women joins; I:Justice Battalion	2,200.00
12 V:Black Dragon society	2,200.00
13 V:Hitler	2,000.00
14 JSA in occupied Europe	2,000.00
15 I:Brain Wave,A:JSA's Girl Friends	2,000.00
16 Propaganda/relevance issue	1,600.00
17 V:Brain Wave	1,600.00
18 I:King Bee	1,700.00
19 Hunt for Hawkman	1,600.00
20 I:Monster	1,600.00

For a Pilot	60.00
96 RH(c),The Last Flight of Lt. Moon	60.00
97 IN(c),A 'Target' Called Johnny	60.00
98 The Time-Bomb Ace	60.00
99 IN(c),The Empty Cockpit	60.00
100 RH(c),Battle o/t Sky Chiefs	60.00
101 RH(c),Death Ship of Three Wars	25.00
102 JKu(c),Blind Eagle-Hungry Hawk	25.00
103 IN(c),Battle Ship-Battle Heart	25.00
104 JKu(c),The Last Target	25.00
105 IN(c),Killer Horse-Ship	25.00
106 IN(c),Death Song For A Battle Hawk	25.00
107 IN(c),Flame in the Sky	25.00
108 IN(c),Death-Dive of the Aces	25.00
109 IN(c),The Killer Slot	25.00
110 RH(c),The Co-Pilot was Death	25.00
111 RH(c),E:Johnny Cloud, Tag-You're Dead	25.00
112 RH(c),B:Balloon Buster,Lt. Steve Savage-Balloon Buster	25.00
113 JKu(c),The Ace of Sudden Death	25.00
114 JKu(c),The Ace Who Died Twice	25.00
115 IN(c),A:Johnny Cloud, Deliver One Enemy Ace-Handle With Care	25.00
116 JKu(c),A:Baloon Buster, Circle of Death	25.00
117 Sept.–Oct., 1966	25.00

ALL-FLASH
1941–47
1 EHi,O:Flash,I:The Monocle	13,000.00
2 EHi,The Adventure of Roy Revenge	2,400.00
3 EHi,The Adventure of Misplaced Faces	1,300.00
4 EHi,Tale of the Time Capsule	1,200.00

5 EHi,The Case of the Patsy Colt! Last Quarterly	900.00
6 EHi,The Ray that Changed Men's Souls	750.00
7 EHi,Adventures of a Writers Fantasy, House of Horrors	750.00
8 EHi,Formula to Fairyland!	750.00
9 EHi,Adventure of the Stolen Telescope	750.00
10 EHi,Case of the Curious Cat	750.00
11 EHi,Troubles come in Doubles	650.00
12 EHi,Tumble INN to Trouble, Becomes Quarterly on orders from War Production Board O:The Thinker	650.00
13 EHi,I:The King	650.00
14 EHi,I:Winky,Blinky & Noddy Green Lantern (c)	750.00
15 EHi,Secrets of a Stranger	550.00
16 EHi,A:The Sinister	550.00
17 Tales of the Three Wishes	500.00
18 A:Winlky,Blinky&Noddy B:Mutt & Jeff reprints	500.00
19 No Rest at the Rest Home	500.00
20 A:Winky, Blinky & Noddy	500.00
21 I:Turtle	450.00
22 The Money Doubler,E:Mutt & Jeff reprints	450.00
23 The Bad Men of Bar Nothing	450.00
24 I:Worry Wart,3 Court Clowns Get Caught	450.00
25 I:Slapsy Simmons, Flash Jitterbugs	450.00
26 I:The Chef,The Boss,Shrimp Coogan,A:Winky, Blinky & Noddy	500.00
27 A:The Thinker,Gangplank Gus story	450.00
28 A:Shrimp Coogan,Winky, Blinky & Noddy	450.00
29 The Thousand-Year Old Terror, A:Winky,Blinky & Noddy	450.00
30 The Vanishing Snowman	450.00
31 A:Black Hat,The Planet of Sport	450.00
32 I:Fiddler,A:Thinker	650.00

21 Time travel story 1,500.00
22 Sandman and Dr. Fate leave,
   I:Conscience, Good Fairy . 1,500.00
23 I:Psycho-Pirate 1,500.00
24 Propaganda/relevance issue,
   A:Conscience&Wildcat,Mr.Terrific;
   L:Starman & Spectre; Flash
   & Green Lantern return ... 1,500.00
25 JSA whodunit issue 1,300.00
26 V:Metal Men from Jupiter . 1,300.00
27 Handicap issue,A:Wildcat . 1,300.00
28 Ancient curse comes to life 1,100.00
29 I:Landor from 25th century 1,100.00
30 V:Brain Wave 1,100.00
31 V:Zor 1,100.00
32 V:Psycho-Pirate 1,100.00
33 V:Soloman Grundy,A:Doiby
   Dickles, Last appearance
   Thunderbolt 2,300.00
34 I:Wizard 1,000.00
35 I:Per Degaton 1,000.00
36 A:Superman and Batman . 2,300.00
37 I:Injustice Society of
   the World 1,300.00

All-Star Comics #42 © DC Comics, Inc.

38 V:Villians of History,
   A:Black Canary 1,500.00
39 JSA in magic world,
   Johnny Thunder leaves ... 1,000.00
40 A:Black Canary,Junior Justice
   Society of America 1,000.00
41 Black Canary joins,A:Harlequin,
   V:Injustice Society
   of the World 1,000.00
42 I:Alchemist 900.00
43 V:Interdimensional gold men 900.00
44 I:Evil Star 900.00
45 Crooks develop stellar
   JSA powers 850.00
46 Comedy issue 850.00
47 V:Billy the Kid 850.00
48 Time Travel story 850.00
49 V:Comet-being invaders ... 850.00
50 V:College classmate of Flash 900.00
51 V:Diamond men from center
   of the Earth 850.00
52 JSA disappears from
   Earth for years 850.00
53 Time Travel issue 850.00
54 Circus issue 850.00

55 JSA fly to Jupiter 850.00
56 V:Chameleons from
   31st Century 850.00
57 I:Key 1,100.00
Becomes:

ALL STAR WESTERN
April-May 1951

58 Trigger Twins 300.00
59 .... 150.00
60 .... 150.00
61 thru 64 ATh 125.00
65 .... 125.00
66 .... 125.00
67 GK,B:Johnny Thunder 150.00
68 thru 81 .... @75.00
82 thru 98 .... @60.00
99 FF 75.00
100 .... 60.00
101 thru 104 .... @45.00
105 O:JSA, March, 1987 ... 45.00
106 and 107 .... @45.00
108 O:Johnny Thunder 125.00
109 thru 116 .... @45.00
117 CI,O:Super-Chief 60.00
118 .... 45.00
119 .... 40.00

ALL-STAR COMICS
1976–78

58 RE,WW,R:JSA,I:Power Girl ... 5.00
59 RE,WW,Brain Wave 4.50
60 KG,WW,I:Vulcan 4.50
61 KG,WW,V:Vulcan 4.50
62 KG,WW,A:E-2 Superman 4.50
63 KG,WW,A:E-2 Superman,
   Solomon Grundy 4.50
64 WW,Shining Knight 4.50
65 KG,WW,E-2 Superman,
   Vandal Savage 4.50
66 JSon,BL,Injustice Society ... 4.50
67 JSon,BL 4.50
68 JSon,BL 4.50
69 JSon,BL,A:E-2 Superman,
   Starman,Dr.Mid-Nite 4.50
70 JSon,BL,Huntress 4.50
71 JSon,BL 4.00
72 JSon,A:Golden.Age Huntress . 4.00
73 JSon 4.00
74 JSon 4.00

ALL STAR SQUADRON
1981–87

1 RB,JOy,JSa,I:Degaton 2.00
2 RB,JOy,Robotman 1.50
3 RB,JOy,Robotman 1.50
4 RB,JOy,Robotman 1.50
5 RB/JOy,I:Firebrand(Dannette) . 1.50
6 JOy,Hawkgirl 1.50
7 JOy,Hawkgirl 1.50
8 DH/JOy,A:Steel 1.50
9 DH/JOy,A:Steel 1.50
10 JOy,V:Binary Brotherhood . 1.50
11 JOy,V:Binary Brotherhood ... 1.50
12 JOy,R:Dr.Hastor O:Hawkman . 1.50
13 JOy,photo(c) 1.50
14 JOy,JLA crossover 1.50
15 JOy,JLA crossover 1.50
16 I&D:Nuclear 1.50
17 Trial of Robotman 1.50
18 V:Thor 1.50
19 V:Brainwave 1.50
20 JOy,V:Brainwave 1.50
21 JOy,I:Cyclotron (1st JOy
   Superman) 1.75

22 JOy,V:Deathbolt,Cyclotron ... 1.50
23 JOy,I:Amazing-Man 1.50
24 JOy,I:Brainwave,Jr.. .... 2.00
25 JOy,I:Infinity Inc. 2.00
26 JOy,Infinity Inc. 2.00
27 Spectre 1.50
28 JOy,Spectre 1.50
29 JOy,retold story 1.50
30 V:Black Dragons 1.50
31 All-Star gathering 1.50
32 O:Freedom Fighters 1.50
33 Freedom Fighters,I:Tsunami .. 1.50
34 Freedom Fighters 1.50
35 RB,Shazam family 1.50
36 Shazam family 1.50
37 A:Shazam Family 1.50
38 V:The Real American 1.50
39 V:The Real American 1.50
40 D:The Real American 1.50
41 O:Starman 1.50
42 V:Tsunami,Kung 1.50
43 V:Tsunami,Kung 1.50
44 I:Night & Fog 1.50
45 I:Zyklon 1.50

*All-Star Squadron #58
© DC Comics, Inc.*

46 V:Baron Blitzkrieg 1.50
47 TM,O:Dr.Fate 3.50
48 A:Blackhawk 1.50
49 A:Dr.Occult 1.50
50 Crisis 2.00
51 AA,Crisis 1.50
52 Crisis 1.50
53 Crisis,A:The Dummy 1.50
54 Crisis,V:The Dummy 1.50
55 Crisis,V:Anti-Monitor 1.50
56 Crisis 1.50
57 A:Dr.Occult 1.50
58 I:Mekanique 1.50
59 A:Mekanique,Spectre 1.50
60 Crisis 1942, conclusion ... 1.50
61 O:Liberty Belle 1.50
62 O:The Shining Knight 1.50
63 O:Robotman 1.50
64 WB/TD,V:Funny Face 1.50
65 DH/TD,O:Johnny Quick 1.50
66 TD,O:Tarantula 1.50
67 TD,Last Issue,O:JSA 1.50
Ann.#1 JOy,O:G.A.,Atom 1.50

All comics prices listed are for *Near Mint* condition.

Ann.#2 JOy,Infinity Inc. 1.50
Ann.#3 WB,JOy,KG,GP,DN 1.50

ALL STAR WESTERN
(see WEIRD WESTERN TALES)

ALPHA CENTURION
1996
Spec.#1 . . . . 3.00

AMBER:
THE GUNS OF AVALON
Aug. 1996
1 (of 3) adapt. of Roger Zelazny
classic 6.95
2 and 3 conclusion . . . . @6.95

AMBUSH BUG
1985
1 KG,I:Cheeks 1.25
2 KG thru 4 . . . . @1.00
AMBUSH BUG: STOCKING STUFFER 1986
1 KG,R:Cheeks 1.25
AMBUSH BUG: NOTHING SPECIAL 1992
1 KG,A:Sandman,Death 2.50

AMERICA vs.
JUSTICE SOCIETY
Jan.–April, 1985
1 AA,R,Thomas Script 2.00
2 AA 1.50
3 AA 1.50
4 AA, ... 1.50

AMERICAN FREAK: A
TALE OF THE UN-MEN
Vertigo 1994
1 B:DLp,(s),VcL,R:Un-Men 2.25
2 VcL,A:Crassus 2.25
3 VcL,A:Scylla 2.25
4 VcL,A:Scylla 2.25
5 VcL,Final Issue 2.25

AMETHYST
[Limited Series] 1983–84
[PRINCESS OF GEMWORLD]
1 Origin 1.25
2 thru 7 EC . . . . @1.00
8 EC,O:Gemworld 1.00
9 thru 12 EC . . . . @1.00
Spec.#1 KG 1.25
[Regular Series]
1985–86
1 thru 12 EC . . . . @1.00
13 EC,Crisis,A:Dr.Fate 1.00
14 EC 1.00
15 EC,Castle Amethyst Destroyed 1.00
16 EC 1.00
Spec.#1 EM 1.25
[Mini-Series]
1987–88
1 EM 1.25
2 EM 1.25
3 EM 1.25
4 EM,O:Mordru 1.25

ANARKY
March 1997
1 AIG(s),NBy,JRu,Anarky vs.
Etrigan 2.50
2 AIG(s),NBy,JRu,V:Darkseid . . . 2.50

3 AIG(s),NBy,JRu,A:Batman 2.50
4 AIG(s),NBy,JRu,A:Batman,concl. 2.50

ANGEL & THE APE
1991
1 Apes of Wrath,pt.1 . . . . 1.00
2 Apes of Wrath,pt.2,
A:G.Gardner 1.00
3 Apes of Wrath,pt.3,
A: Inferior Five 1.00
4 Apes of Wrath,pt.4,
A: Inferior Five, final issue 1.00

Anima #12 © DC Comics, Inc.

ANIMA
Vertigo 1994–95
1 R:Anima 2.00
2 V:Scarecrow 2.00
3 V:Scarecrow 2.00
4 A:Nameless one 2.00
5 CI,V:Arkana 2.00
6 CI,V:Arkana 2.00
7 Zero Hour 2.00
8 Nameless One 2.00
9 Superboy & Nameless One . . . 2.00
10 A:Superboy 2.00
11 V:Nameless One 2.00
12 A:Hawkman,V:Shrike 2.00
13 A:Hawkman,Shrike 2.00
14 Return to Gotham City 2.00
15 V:Psychic Vampire, final issue 2.25

ANIMAL ANTICS
1946–49
1 . . . . 275.00
2 . . . . 150.00
3 thru 10 . . . . @90.00
11 thru 23 . . . . @65.00

ANIMAL-MAN
1988–95
1 BB(c),B:GMo(s),ChT,DHz,
B:Animal Rights,I:Dr.Myers . . . 7.00
2 BB(c),ChT,DHz,A:Superman . . 5.00
3 BB(c),ChT,DHz,A:B'wana Beast 3.00
4 BB(c),ChT,DHz,V:B'wana Beast,
E:Animal Rights 3.00

5 BB(c),ChT,DHz,
I&D:Crafty Coyote 3.50
6 BB(c),ChT,DHz,A:Hawkman . . . 3.00
7 BB(c),ChT,DHz,D:Red Mask . . 3.00
8 BB(c),ChT,DHz,V:Mirror Master 3.00
9 BB(c),DHz,TG,A:Martian
Manhunter 3.00
10 BB(c),ChT,DHz,A:Vixen,
B:O:Animal Man 3.00
11 BB(c),ChT,DHz,I:Hamed Ali,
Tabu,A:Vixen 3.00
12 BB(c),D:Hamed Ali,A:Vixen,
B'wanaBeast 3.00
13 BB(c),I:Dominic Mndawe,R:B'wana
Beast,Apartheid 3.00
14 BB(c),TG,SeM,A:Future Animal
Man,I:Lennox 3.00
15 BB(c),ChT,DHz,A:Dolphin 3.00
16 BB(c),ChT,DHz,A:JLA. 3.00
17 BB(c),ChT,DHz,A:Mirr.Master . . 3.00
18 BB(c),ChT,DHz,A:Lennox 3.00
19 BB(c),ChT,DHz,D:Ellen,
Cliff,Maxine 3.00
20 BB(c),ChT,DHz,I:Bug-Man . . . 3.00
21 BB(c),ChT,DHz,N&V:Bug-Man 3.00
22 BB(c),PCu,SeM,A:Rip Hunter . 3.00
23 BB(c),A:Phantom Stranger . . . 2.50
24 BB(c),V:Psycho Pirate 2.50
25 BB(c),ChT,MFm,I:Comic
Book Limbo 2.50
26 BB(c),E:GMo(s),ChT,MFm,
A:Grant Morrison 2.50
27 BB(c),B:PMi(s),ChT,MFm 2.50
28 BB(c),ChT,MFm,I:Nowhere Man,
I&D:Front Page 2.50
29 ChT,SDi,V:National Man 2.50
30 BB(c),ChT,MFm,V:Angel Mob . 2.50
31 BB(c),ChT,MFm 2.50
32 BB(c),E:PMi(s),ChT,MFm 2.50
33 BB(c),B:TV(s),SDi,A:Travis
Cody 2.50
34 BB(c),SDi,Requiem 2.50
35 BB(c),SDi,V:Radioactive Dogs . 2.50
36 BB(c),SDi,A:Mr.Rainbow 2.50
37 BB(c),SDi,Animal/Lizard Man . 2.50
38 BB(c),SDi,A:Mr.Rainbow 2.00
39 BB(c),TMd,SDi,Wolfpack in
San Diego 2.00
40 BB(c),SDi,War of the Gods
x-over 2.00
41 BB(c),SDi,V:Star Labs
Renegades,I:Winky 2.00
42 BB(c),SDi,V:Star Labs
Renegades 2.00
43 BB(c),SDi,I:Tristess,A:Vixen . . 2.00
44 BB(c),SDi,A:Vixen 2.00
45 BB(c),StP,SDi,I:L.Decker 2.00
46 BB(c),SDi,I:Frank Baker 2.00
47 BB(c),SDi,I:Shining Man,
(B'wana Beast) 2.00
48 BB(c),SDi,V:Antagon 2.00
49 BB(c),SDi,V:Antagon 2.00
50 BB(c),E:TV(s),SDi,I:Metaman . 3.50
51 BB(c),B:JaD(s),StP,B:Flesh
and Blood 2.50
52 BB(c),StP,Homecoming 2.50
53 BB(c),StP,Flesh and Blood . . . 2.50
54 BB(c),StP,Flesh and Blood . . . 2.50
55 BB(c),StP,Flesh and Blood . . . 2.50
56 BB(c),StP,E:Flesh and Blood,
Double-sized 3.00
Vertigo
57 BB(c),StP,B:Recreation,
Ellen in NY 2.50
58 BB(c),StP,Wild Side 2.50

Animal Man #37 © DC Comics, Inc.

59 BB(c),RsB,GHi(i),Wild Town	2.50
60 RsB,GHi(i),Wild life	2.50
61 BB(c),StP,Tooth and Claw#1	2.50
62 BB(c),StP,Tooth and Claw#2	2.50
63 BB(c),V:Leviathan	2.50
64 DIB(i),WSm,DnS(i), Breath of God	2.50
65 RDB(c),WSm, Perfumed Garden	2.25
66 A:Kindred Spirit	2.25
67 StP,Mysterious Ways #1	2.25
68 StP,Mysterious Ways #2	2.25
69 Animal Man's Family	2.25
70 GgP(c),StP	2.25
71 GgP(c),StP,Maxine Alive?	2.25
72 StP	2.25
73 StP,Power Life Church	2.25
74 StP,Power Life Church	2.25
75 StP,Power Life Church	2.25
76 StP,Pilgrimage problems	2.00
77 Cliff shot	2.00
78 StP,Animal Man poisoned	2.00
79 New Direction	2.00
80 New Direction	2.00
81 Wild Type,pt.1	2.00
82 Wild Type,pt.2	2.00
83 Wild Type,pt.3	2.00
84 F:Maxine,SupernaturalDreams	2.00
85 Animal Mundi,pt.1	2.25
86 Animal Mundi,pt.2	2.25
87 Animal Mundi,pt.3	2.25
88 Morphogenetic Fields	2.25
89 final issue	2.25
Ann.#1 BB(c),JaD,TS(i),RIB(i), Children Crusade,F:Maxine	4.25
TPB Rep.#1 thru #10	19.95

ANIMANIACS
Warner Bros./DC May 1995

1 F:Yakko,Wakko,Dot	1.50
2 Health Spa	1.50
3 Travel back in time	1.50
4	1.50
5	1.50
6 V:Cleopatra	1.50
7 Scratchinsniff Replaced	1.50
8 Disputin win Newton	1.50

9 thru 12	@1.50
13 thru 17	@1.75
18 visit to France	1.75
19 "The Y Files"	1.75
20 "Rebels Just Because"	1.75
21 x-mas issue,A:Santa	1.75
22	1.75
23 F:Hellow Nurse	1.75
24 F:The Goodfeathers,A:Pinky and the Brain	1.75
25 F:Slappy Squirrel	1.75
26 "Haunted House of Pancakes"	1.75
27 "Plane for Keeps"	1.75
28 "Science Issue"	1.75
29 "The Return of Hello Nurse, Agent of H.U.B.B.A."	1.75
30 "Electro-Walter and Dyna-Squirrel"	1.75
31 Nastina LeCreep	2.00
32 "Lifestiles of the Old & Cranky"	2.00
33 "The Long Lost Warner"	2.00
34 Minerxa, Warrior Princess	2.00
35	2.00
36 Generation Gap	2.00
37 F:Brain	2.00
38 special all-cute issue	2.00
39 Arnold Nobel	2.00
40 Slappy Squirrel	2.00
41 Slappy's Mother Goose	2.00
Christmas Spec.	1.50

ANTHRO
1968–69

1 HwP	35.00
2 HwP	22.00
3 thru 5 HwP	@22.00
6 HwP,WW(c&a)	22.00

Aquaman #61 © DC Comics, Inc.

AQUAMAN
[1st Regular Series] 1962–78

1 NC,I:Quisp	600.00
2 NC,V:Captain Sykes	250.00
3 NC,Aquaman from Atlantis	150.00
4 NC,A:Quisp	90.00
5 NC,The Haunted Sea	85.00
6 NC,A:Quisp	75.00
7 NC,Sea Beasts of Atlantis	75.00

8 NC,Plot to Steal the Seas	75.00
9 NC,V:King Neptune	75.00
10 NC,A:Quisp	75.00
11 I: Mera	60.00
12 NC,The Cosmic Gladiators	55.00
13 NC,Invasion of the Giant Reptiles	55.00
14 NC,AquamanSecretPowers	55.00
15 NC,Menace of the Man-Fish	55.00
16 NC,Duel of the Sea Queens	50.00
17 NC,Man Who Vanquished Aquaman	50.00
18 W:Aquaman & Mera	52.00
19 NC,Atlanteans for Sale	45.00
20 NC,Sea King's DoubleDoom	45.00
21 NC,I:Fisherman	35.00
22 NC,The Trap of the Sinister Sea Nymphs	35.00
23 NC,I:Aquababy	35.00
24 NC,O:Black Manta	32.00
25 NC,Revolt of Aquaboy	32.00
26 NC,I:O.G.R.E.	32.00
27 NC,Battle of the Rival Aquamen'	32.00
28 NC,Hail Aquababy,King of Atlantis	32.00
29 I:Ocean Master	30.00
30 NC,C:JLA	25.00
31 NC,V:O.G.R.E.	25.00
32 NC,V:Tryton	25.00
33 NC,I:Aquagirl	45.00
34 NC,I:Aquabeast	25.00
35 I:Black Manta	25.00
36 NC,What Seeks the Awesome Threesome?	25.00
37 I:Scavenger	25.00
38 NC,I:Liquidator	25.00
39 NC,How to Kill a Sea King	25.00
40 JAp,Sorcerers from the Sea	22.00
41 JAp,Quest for Mera,pt.1	14.00
42 JAp,Quest for Mera,pt.2	14.00
43 JAp,Quest for Mera,pt.3	14.00
44 JAp,Quest for Mera,pt.4	14.00
45 JAp,Quest for Mera,pt.5	14.00
46 JAp,Quest for Mera concl.	14.00
47 JAp,Revolution in Atlantis #1 rep.Adventure #268	12.00
48 JAp,Revolution in Atlantis #2 rep.Adventure #260	17.00
49 JAp,As the Seas Die	12.00
50 JAp,NA,A:Deadman	25.00
51 JAp,NA,A:Deadman	25.00
52 JAp,NA,A:Deadman	25.00
53 JAp,Is California Sinking?	8.00
54 JAp,Crime Wave	8.00
55 JAp,Return of the Alien	8.00
56 JAp,I&O:Crusader (1970)	8.00
57 JAp,V:Black Manta (1977)	8.00
58 JAp,O:Aquaman rtd	9.00
59 JAp,V:Scavenger	8.00
60 DN,V:Scavenger	8.00
61 DN,BMc,A:Batman	8.00
62 DN,A:Ocean Master	7.00
63 DN,V:Ocean Master, final issue	7.00

[2nd Regular Series] 1991–92

1 Poseidonis Under Attack, C:J'onn J'onzz,Blue Beetle	2.25
2 V:Oumland	2.00
3 I:Iqula	2.00
4 V:Iqula,A:Queequeg	1.50
5 A:Aqualad,Titans,M.Manhunter, R:Manta	1.50
6 V: Manta	1.50
7 R:Mera	1.50

Aquaman (2nd Series) #9
© DC Comics, Inc.

8 A:Batman,V:NKV Demon 1.50
9 Eco-Wars#1,A:Sea Devils 1.50
10 Eco-Wars#2,A:Sea Devils 1.50
11 V:Gigantic Dinosaur 1.50
12 A:Iaula 1.50
13 V:The Scavenger 1.50
14 V:The Scavenger 1.50
[3rd Regular Series] 1994–97
0 B:PDd(s),Paternal secret 2.00
1 PDd(s),R:Aqualad,I:Charybdis . 2.50
2 V:Charybdis 4.00
3 B:PDd(s),Superboy 2.00
4 B:PDd(s),Lobo 2.00
5 New Costume 2.00
6 V:The Deep Six 2.00
7 Kako's Metamorphosis 2.00
8 V:Corona and Naiad 2.00
9 JSP(c&a),V:Deadline,A:Koryak . 1.75
10 A:Green Lantern,Koryak 1.75
11 R:Mera 1.75
12 F:Mera 1.75
13 V:Thanatos 1.75
14 PDd,V:Major Disaster,Underworld
Unleashed tie-in 1.75
15 PDd,V:Tiamat 1.75
16 PDd,A:Justice League 1.75
17 PDd,V:underwater gargoyles . . 1.75
18 . . . . 1.75
19 PDd,V:Ocean Master 1.75
20 PDd,V:Ocean Master 1.75
21 PDd,JCf,A:Dolphin,
V:ThiernaNaOge 1.75
22 PDd(s) 1.75
23 PDd(s),I:Deep Blue (Neptune
Perkins) 1.75
24 PDd(s),A:Neptune Perkins . . . 1.75
25 PDd(s),MEg,HSm,Atlantis united,
Aquaman king? 1.75
26 PDd(s),MEg,HSm,Oceans
threatened, Final Night tie-in . 1.75
27 PDd(s),MEg,HSm,V:Demon
Gate, dolphin killer 1.75
28 PDd(s),JCf,JP,A:J'Onn J'Onzz 1.75
29 PDd(s),MEg,HSm, ... 1.75
30 PDd(s),MEg,HSm,"The Pit" . . . 1.75
31 PDd(s),V:The Shark, mind-

controlled aquatic army 1.75
32 PDd(s),A:Swamp Thing 1.75
33 PDd(s),Aquaman's dark powers
affect him physically 1.75
34 PDd(s),V:Triton 1.75
35 PDd(s),JCf,I:Gamesman,
A:Animal Man 1.75
36 PDd(s),JCf,R:Poseidonis,
Tempest,Vulko 1.75
37 PDd,JCf,Genesis,V:Darkseid . . 2.00
38 PDd,JCf,capitalism 2.00
39 PDd,JCf,Perkins Family Reunion2.00
40 PDd,JCf,Dr. Polaris 2.00
41 PDd,JCf,BSf,F:Power Girl 2.00
42 PDd,JCf 2.00
43 PDd,JCf,Millennium Giants,
pt.2 x-over, A:Superman Red . 2.00
44 PDd,JCf,F:Golden Age Flash,
Sentinel 2.00
45 PDd,JCf,V:Triton 2.00
46 PDd,JCf,news of Mera 2.00
47 DAn,Shadows on Water,pt.1 . . 2.00
48 DAn,Shadows on Water,pt.2 . . 2.00
49 DAn,ALa,JCf,V:Tempest 2.00
Ann.#1 Year One Annual, V:Triton,
A:Superman,Mera 3.50
Ann.#2 Legends o/t Dead Earth . 2.95
Ann.#3 Pulp Heroes (Hard Boiled) 3.95
Ann.#4 PDa, Ghosts 3.00

AQUAMAN
[1st Limited Series] 1986
1 V:Ocean Master 5.00
2 V:Ocean Master 3.00
3 V:Ocean Master 3.00
4 V:Ocean Master 3.00
[2nd Limited Series] 1989
1 CS,Atlantis Under Siege 3.00
2 CS,V:Invaders 1.75
3 CS,Mera turned Psychotic 1.50
4 CS,Poseidonis Under Siege . . . 1.50
5 CS,Last Stand,final issue 1.50
Spec#1 MPa,Legend o/Aquaman . 2.00

AQUAMAN: TIME & TIDE
1993–94
1 PDd(s),O:Aquaman 2.50
2 and 3 PDd(s),O:Aquaman
contd. . . . . @2.00
4 PDd(s),O:Aquaman,final issue. 1.75
TPB rep.#1–4 . . . . 9.95

ARAK
1981–85
1 EC,O:Ara 1.50
2 EC 1.00
3 EC,I:Valda 1.00
4 thru 10 EC . . . . @1.00
11 EC,AA 1.00
12 EC,AA,I:Satyricus 1.00
13 thru 19 AA . . . . @1.00
20 AA,O:Angelica 1.00
21 thru 23 AA 1.00
24 Double size 1.50
25 thru 30 . . . . @1.00
31 D Arak,becomes shaman 1.00
32 thru 48 . . . . @1.00
49 Cl/TD 1.00
50 TD 1.25
Ann.#1 . . . . 1.00

ARCANA: THE BOOKS
OF MAGIC
Vertigo 1994
Ann.#1 JBo(c),JNR(s),PrG,Children's
Crusade,R:Tim Hunter,
A:Free Country 6.00

Argus #1 © DC Comics, Inc.

ARGUS
[Mini-Series] 1995
1 R:Argus,I:Raver 1.50
2 Blinded by metahuman hitmen . 1.75
3 Spy Satellite 1.75
4 The Watcher 1.75
5 Data Highways 1.75
6 Restored Sight 1.75

ARION,
LORD OF ATLANTIS
1982–85
1 JDu 1.50
2 JDu 1.00
3 JDu 1.00
4 JDu,O:Arion 1.00
5 JDu 1.00
6 JDu 1.00
7 thru 12 . . . . @1.00
13 JDu 1.00
14 JDu 1.00
15 JDu 1.00
16 thru 35 . . . . @1.00
Spec. 1.25

ARION THE IMMORTAL
1 RWi,R:Arion 1.75
2 RWi,V:Garffon 1.50
3 RWi,V:Garn Daanuth 1.50
4 RWi,V:Garn Daanuth 1.50
5 RWi,Darkworlet 1.50
6 RWi,MG,A:Power Girl 1.50

ARMAGEDDON 2001
May 1991
1 DJu,DG,I&O:Waverider 4.00
1a 2nd printing 2.00
1b 3rd printing (silver) 1.75

2 DJu,ATi,Monarch revealed as Hawk,
D:Dove,L:Capt Atom(JLE) 2.00
Spec.#1 MR 1.75

ARMAGEDDON 2001 ARMAGEDDON: THE ALIEN AGENDA
1991–92
1 DJu,JOy,A:Monarch,Capt.Atom 1.75
2 V:Ancient Romans 1.25
3 JRu(i),The Old West 1.25
4 DG,GP,V:Nazi's,last issue 1.25

ARMAGEDDON: INFERNO
1992
1 TMd,LMc,A:Creeper,Batman,
Firestorm 1.75
2 AAd,LMc,WS,I:Abraxis,A:Lobo . 1.50
3 AAd,WS,LMc,TMd,MN,R:Justice
Society 1.50
4 AAd,WS,LMc,TMd,MN,DG,
V:Abraxis,A:Justice Society ... 1.50

ARSENAL
Aug., 1998
1 (of 4) F:Black Canary 2.50

ARTEMIS: REQUIEM
1996
1 BML(s) (of 6) 1.75
2 thru 6 BML(s),EBe, ... @1.75

ATARI FORCE
1984–85
1 JL,I:TempestDart 1.50
2 JL 1.00
3 JL 1.00
4 RA/JL/JO 1.00
5 RA/JL/JO 1.00
6 thru 12 JL .... @1.00
13 KG 1.00
14 thru 21 EB .... @1.00

ATLANTIS CHRONICLES
1990
1 EM,Atlantis 50,000 years ago . 3.50
2 EM,Atlantis Sunk 3.25
3 EM,Twin Cities of Poseidonis
& Tritonis 3.25
4 EM,King Orin's Daughter
Cora Assumes Throne 3.25
5 EM,Orin vs. Shalako 3.25
6 EM,Contact with Surface
Dwellers 3.25
7 EM,Queen Atlanna gives Birth to
son(Aquaman)48 pg.final issue 3.25

ATOM, THE
1962–68
1 MA,GK,I:Plant Master 750.00
2 MA,GK,V:Plant Master 325.00
3 MA,GK,I:Chronos 225.00
4 MA,GK,Snapper Carr 150.00
5 MA,GK 150.00
6 MA,GK 150.00
7 MA,GK,1st Atom & Hawkman
team-up 250.00
8 MA,GK,A:JLA,V:Doctor Light 125.00
9 MA,GK 125.00
10 MA,GK 125.00
11 MA,GK 100.00

12 MA,GK 100.00
13 MA,GK 100.00
14 MA,GK 100.00
15 MA,GK 100.00
16 MA,GK 75.00
17 MA,GK 75.00
18 MA,GK 75.00
19 MA,GK,A:Zatanna 75.00
20 MA,GK 75.00
21 MA,GK 50.00
22 MA,GK 50.00
23 MA,GK 50.00
24 MA,GK,V:Jason Woodrue ... 50.00
25 MA,GK 50.00
26 GK 45.00
27 GK 45.00
28 GK 45.00
29 GK,A:E-2 Atom,Thinker. ... 150.00
30 GK 50.00
31 GK,A:Hawkman 45.00
32 GK 45.00
33 GK 45.00
34 GK,V:Big Head 45.00
35 GK 45.00
36 GK,A:Golden Age Atom 65.00
37 GK,I:Major Mynah 45.00
38 "Sinister stopover Earth" 45.00
Becomes:

ATOM & HAWKMAN
1968–69
39 MA, V:Tekla 50.00
40 DD,JKu,MA 40.00
41 DD,JKu,MA 40.00
42 MA,V:Brama 40.00
43 MA,I:Gentleman Ghost 40.00
44 DD 40.00
45 DD 40.00

ATOM SPECIAL
1 SDi,V:Chronos (1993) 3.00
2 Zero Hour Atom (1994) 3.00

AVATAR
1991
1 A:Midnight & Allies 8.00
2 Search for Tablets 6.00
3 V:Cyric, Myrkul, final issue 6.00

AZRAEL
1994
1 I:New Azrael,Brian Bryan 6.00
2 A:Batman,New Azrael 4.50
3 V:Order of St. Dumas 3.50
4 The System 3.00
5 BKi(c&a),R:Ra's al Ghul,Talia
[new Miraweb format begins] .. 3.00
6 BKi(c&a),Ra's al Ghul,Talia ... 2.50
7 Sister Lily's Transformation 2.50
8 System Secret 2.25
9 Jean Paul Vanishes 2.25
10 DON,BKi,JmP,F:Neron,
Underworld Unleashed tie-in .. 2.00
11 DON,BKi,JmP,A:Batman 2.00
12 DON,BKi,JmP,Azrael looks
for Shondra 2.00
13 DON,BKi,Demon Time,pt.1 ... 2.00
14 DON,BKi,Demon Time,pt.2 ... 2.00
15 DON,BKi,Contagion,pt.5 .... 2.00
16 DON,BKi,Contagion,pt.10 .... 2.00
17 DON,BKi,JmP,A:Dr.Orchid ... 2.00
18 DON,BKi,JmP,A:Dr.Orchid ... 2.00
19 DON(s) 2.00
20 DON(s) 2.00
21 DON(s) 2.00

Azrael #20 © DC Comics, Inc.

22 DON(s),BKi,JmP,"Angel in
Hiding," pt.2 (of 3) 2.00
23 DON(s),BKi,JmP,"Angel in
Hiding," pt.3 .... 2.00
24 DON(s),BKi,JmP,The Order's
return 2.00
25 DON(s),BKi,JmP,V:Brother
Rollo 2.00
26 .... 2.00
27 DON(s),BKi,JmP,"Angel Insane,
"pt.1 .... 2.00
28 DON(s),BKi,JmP,Joker, Riddler
& Two-Face escape from
Arkham Asylum 2.00
29 DON(s),DBw,JmP, F:Rä's Al
Ghül, pt.1 .... 2.00
30 DON(s),DBw,JmP, F:Rä's Al
Ghül, pt.2 .... 2.00
31 DON(s),JmP "Angel and the
Monster Maker" pt.1 (of 3) ... 2.00
32 DON(s),JmP "Angel and the
Monster Maker" pt.2 .... 2.00
33 DON(s),JmP "Angel and the
Monster Maker" pt.3 concl. ... 2.00
34 DON(s),JmP,Genesis,
a parademon 2.00
35 DON(s),JmP,F:Hitman 2.00
36 DON,JmP,Return of Bane,pt.1 2.00
37 DON,JmP,Return of Bane,pt.2 2.00
38 DON,JmP,Return of Bane,pt.3 2.00
39 DON,JmP 2.00
40 DON,JmP,Cataclysm,pt.4,x-over 3.00
41 DON,JmP,A:Devil Latour 2.00
42 DON,JmP,Madame Kalypso .. 2.00
43 DON,JmP,Lilhy,Brian Bryan .. 2.00
44 DON,JmP,Luc & Lilhy disappear 2.00
45 DON,JmP,V:Deathstroke,
A:Calibax 2.00
46 DON(s),JmP,V:Calibax 2.25
Ann.#1 Year One Annual 4.00
Ann.#2 Legends o/t Dead Earth . . 3.00
Ann.#3 Pulp Heroes (Hard Boiled) 4.00

AZRAEL/ASH
March 1997
1 one-shot DON(s),JQ,V:Surtr,
A:Batman, x-over 4.95

AZRAEL PLUS
Oct. 1996
1 one-shot, DON(s),VGi,F:Vic
Sage, The Question 2.95

AZTEK:
THE ULTIMATE MAN
1996–97
1 GMo&MMr(s),NSH,I:Aztek &
Synth 2.50
2 GMo&MMr(s),NSH,A:Green
Lantern 2.00
3 GMo&MMr(s),NSH,V:Doll-Face 2.00
4 GMo&MMr(s),NSH,I:Lizard King,
Vanity 2.00
5 GMo&MMr(s),NSH,O:Aztek,
V:Lizard King 2.00
6 GMo&MMr(s),NSH,V:Vanity,
A: Joker 2.00
7 GMo&MMr(s),NSH,A:Batman . . 2.00
8 GMo&MMr(s),NSH,return to Brotherhood of Zuetzatcoatl,A:Raptor . 2.00
9 GMo&MMr(s),NSH,V:Parasite,
A:Superman 2.00
10 GMo&MMr(s),NSH,A:Justice
League, final issue 5.00

BABYLON 5
1995
1 From TV series 16.00
2 From TV series 11.00
3 Mysterious Assassin 8.00
4 V:Mysterious Assassin 8.00
5 Shadows of the Present,pt.1 . . 8.00
6 Shadows of the Present,pt.2 . . 8.00
7 Shadows of the Present,pt.3 . . 7.00
8 Laser-Mirror Starweb,pt.1 . . . . 7.00
9 Laser-Mirror Starweb,pt.2 . . . . 7.00
10 Laser-Mirror-Starweb,pt.3 . . . . 7.00
11 final issue 7.00

BABYLON 5:
IN VALEN'S NAME
Jan., 1998
1 (of 3) PDd, from TV series 2.50
2 PDd 2.50
3 PDd 2.50

BATGIRL
1988
Spec.#1 V: Cormorant,I:Slash . . . 8.00

BATGIRL ADVENTURES
Dec. 1997
1-shot RBr,V:Poison Ivy,A:Harley
Quinn 3.00

BATMAN
Spring, 1940
1 I:Joker,Cat(Catwoman),
V:Hugo Strange 65,000.00
2 V:Joker/Catwoman team . 12,000.00
3 V:Catwoman 7,000.00
4 V:Joker 6,000.00
5 V:Joker 4,500.00
6 V:'Clock Maker' 3,700.00
7 V:Joker 3,500.00
8 V:Joker 3,500.00
9 V:Joker 3,500.00
10 V:Catwoman 3,500.00
11 V:Joker,Penguin 5,500.00
12 V:Joker 2,200.00

13 V:Joker 2,300.00
14 V:Penguin;Propaganda sty 2,500.00
15 V:Catwoman 2,100.00
16 I:Alfred,V:Joker 4,500.00
17 V:Penguin 1,500.00
18 V:Tweedledum &
Tweedledee 1,800.00
19 V:Joker 1,500.00
20 V:Joker 1,500.00
21 V:Penguin 1,100.00
22 V:Catwoman,Cavalier . . . 1,100.00
23 V:Joker 1,600.00
24 I:Carter Nichols, V:Tweedledum
& Tweedledee 1,200.00
25 V:Joker/Penguin team . . . 1,600.00
26 V:Cavalier 1,100.00
27 V:Penguin 1,100.00
28 V:Joker 1,200.00
29 V:Scuttler 1,100.00
30 V:Penguin,I:Ally Babble . . 1,100.00
31 I:Punch and Judy 900.00
32 O:Robin,V:Joker 950.00
33 V:Penguin,Jackall 1,000.00
34 A:Ally Babble 900.00

Batman #15 © DC Comics, Inc.

35 V:Catwoman 900.00
36 V:Penguin,A:King Arthur . . . 900.00
37 V:Joker 900.00
38 V:Penguin 900.00
39 V:Catwoman,Christmas Story 900.00
40 V:Joker 1,100.00
41 V:Penguin 700.00
42 V:Catwoman 700.00
43 V:Penguin 700.00
44 V:Joker,A:Carter Nichols,Meets
ancester Silas Wayne 1,100.00
45 V:Catwoman 700.00
46 V:Joker,A:Carter Nichols,
Leonardo Da Vinci 650.00
47 O:Batman,V:Catwoman . . 2,600.00
48 V:Penguin, Bat-Cave story . 800.00
49 I:Mad Hatter & Vicki Vale . 1,300.00
50 V:Two-Face,A:Vicki Vale . . . 700.00
51 V:Penguin 650.00
52 V:Joker 700.00
53 V:Joker 700.00
54 V:'The Treasure Hunter' . . . 650.00
55 V:Joker 700.00
56 V:Penguin 650.00

57 V:Joker 700.00
58 V:Penguin 650.00
59 I:Deadshot 650.00
60 V:'Shark' Marlin 650.00
61 V:Penguin 800.00
62 O:Catwoman,I:Knight
& Squire 850.00
63 V:Joker 600.00
64 V:Killer Moth 600.00
65 I:Wingman,V:Catwoman . . . 625.00
66 V:Joker 625.00
67 V:Joker 625.00
68 V:Two-Face,Alfred story . . . 550.00
69 I:King of the Cats,
A:Catwoman 600.00
70 V:Penguin 550.00
71 V:Mr. Cipher 550.00
72 'The Jungle Batman' 550.00
73 V:Joker,A:Vicki Vale 650.00
74 V:Joker 550.00
75 I:The Gorilla Boss 550.00
76 V:Penguin 550.00
77 'The Crime Predictor' 550.00
78 'The Manhunter from Mars' . 650.00
79 A:Vicki Vale 550.00
80 V:Joker 550.00
81 V:Two-Face 550.00
82 'The Flying Batman' 450.00
83 V:'Fish' Frye 450.00
84 V:Catwoman 500.00
85 V:Joker 450.00
86 V:Joker 450.00
87 V:Joker 450.00
88 V:Mr. Mystery 450.00
89 I:Aunt Agatha 450.00
90 I:Batboy 350.00
91 V:Blinky Grosset 350.00
92 I:Ace, the Bat-Hound 350.00
93 'The Caveman Batman' . . . 500.00
94 Alfred has Amnesia 350.00
95 'The Bat-Train' 350.00
96 'Batman's College Days' . . . 350.00
97 V:Joker 350.00
98 A:Carter Nichols,Jules Verne 350.00
99 V:Penguin,A:Carter Nichols,
Bat Masterson 350.00
100 'Great Batman Contest' . . 2,000.00
101 'The Great Bat-Cape Hunt' 400.00
102 V:Mayne Mallok 375.00
103 A:Ace, the Bat-Hound 375.00
104 V:Devoe 375.00
105 A:Batwoman 450.00
106 V:Keene Harper gang 350.00
107 V:Daredevils 350.00
108 Bat-cave story 350.00
109 'The 1,000 Inventions
of Batman' 350.00
110 V:Joker 375.00
111 . . . . 300.00
112 I:Signalman 300.00
113 I:Fatman 300.00
114 . . . . 300.00
115 . . . . 300.00
116 . . . . 300.00
117 . . . . 300.00
118 . . . . 300.00
119 . . . . 300.00
120 . . . . 300.00
121 I:Mr.Freeze 350.00
122 . . . . 210.00
123 A:Joker 200.00
124 "Mystery Seed from Space" 200.00
125 . . . . 200.00
126 . . . . 200.00
127 A:Superman & Joker 225.00

Batman #56 © DC Comics, Inc.

128	200.00
129 O:Robin(Retold)	265.00
130	200.00
131 I:2nd Batman	150.00
132 'Lair of the Sea-Fox'	150.00
133	150.00
134	150.00
135	150.00
136 A:Joker,Bat-Mite	175.00
137 V:Mr.Marvel,The Brand	150.00
138 A:Bat-Mite	150.00
139 I:Old Batgirl	165.00
140 A:Joker	165.00
141 V:Clockmaster	150.00
142 Batman robot story	150.00
143 A:Bathound	150.00
144 A:Joker,Bat-Mite,Bat-Girl	150.00
145 V:Mr.50,Joker	165.00
146 A:Bat-Mite,Joker	125.00
147 Batman becomes Bat-Baby	125.00
148 A:Joker	150.00
149 V:Maestro	125.00
150 V:Biff Warner,Jack Pine	125.00
151 V:Harris Boys	100.00
152 A:Joker	110.00
153 Other Dimension story	100.00
154 V:Dr. Dorn	100.00
155 1st S.A. Penguin	450.00
156 V:Gorilla Gang	100.00
157 V:Mirror Man	100.00
158 A:Bathound,Bat-Mite	100.00
159 A:Joker,Clayface	110.00
160 V:Bart Cullen	100.00
161 A:Bat-Mite	100.00
162 F:Robin	100.00
163 A:Joker	100.00
164 CI,A:Mystery Analysts,new Batmobile	90.00
165 V:The Mutated Man	90.00
166 Escape story	90.00
167 V:Karabi & Hydra, the Crime Cartel	90.00
168 V:Mr. Mammoth	90.00
169 A:Penguin	125.00
170 V:Getaway Genius	90.00
171 CI,1st S.A. Riddler	450.00
172 V:Flower Gang	65.00
173 V:Elwood Pearson	65.00

174 V:Big Game Hunter	65.00
175 V:Eddie Repp	65.00
176 Giant rep.A:Joker,Catwom.	75.00
177 BK,A:Elongated Man,Atom	65.00
178 CI	65.00
179 CI,2nd Riddler(Silver)	135.00
180 BK,A:Death-Man	65.00
181 CI,I:Poison Ivy	90.00
182 A:Joker,(giant size rep).	65.00
183 CI,A:Poison Ivy	75.00
184 CI,Mystery of the Missing Manhunters	60.00
185 Giant rep.	65.00
186 A:Joker	50.00
187 Giant rep.A:Joker	65.00
188 CI,A:Eraser	35.00
189 CI,A:Scarecrow	55.00
190 CI,A:Penguin	45.00
191 CI,The Day Batman Soldout	35.00
192 CI,The Crystal ball that betrayed Batman	35.00
193 Giant rep.	45.00
194 MSy,BK,A:Blockbuster,Mystery Analysts of Gotham City	35.00
195 CI	35.00
196 BK,Psychic Super-Sleuth	35.00
197 MSy,A:Bat Girl,Catwoman	75.00
198 A:Joker,Penguin,Catwoman, O:Batman rtd,(G-Size rep)	75.00
199 CI,'Peril o/t Poison Rings'	35.00
200 NA(c),O:rtd,A:Joker,Pengiun, Scarecrow	160.00
201 A:Batman Villians	30.00
202 BU:Robin	18.00
203 NA(c),(giant size)	25.00
204 FR(s),IN,JG	16.00
205 FR(s),IN,JG	16.00
206 FR(s),IN,JG	16.00
207 FR(s),IN,JG	16.00
208 GK,new O:Batman, A:Catwoman	35.00
209 FR(s),IN,JG	18.00
210 A:Catwoman	20.00
211 FR(s),IN,JG	18.00
212 FR(s),IN,JG	18.00
213 RA,30th Anniv.Batman,new O: Robin,rep.O:Alfred,Joker	60.00
214 IN,A:Batgirl	15.00
215 IN,DG	15.00
216 IN,DG,I:DaphnePennyworth	15.00
217 NA(c)	16.00
218 NA(c),giant	35.00
219 NA,IN,DG,Batman Xmas	35.00
220 NA(c),IN	15.00
221 IN,DG	15.00
222 IN,Rock'n Roll story	30.00
223 NA(c),giant	30.00
224 NA(c)	14.00
225 NA(c),IN,DG	14.00
226 IN,DG I:10-Eyed Man	14.00
227 IN,DG,A:Daphne Pennyworth	14.00
228 giant Deadly Traps rep.	30.00
229 IN	14.00
230 NA(c),Robin	14.00
231 F:Ten-Eyed Man	14.00
232 DON(s),NA,DG, I:Ras al Ghul	75.00
233 giant Bruce Wayne iss.	30.00
234 NA,DG,IN,1stS.A.Two-Face	110.00
235 CI,V:Spook	13.00
236 NA	20.00
237 NA	40.00
238 NA,JC,JKu,giant	25.00
239 NA,RB	14.00

Batman #132 © DC Comics, Inc.

240 NA(c),RB,giant,R-Ghul	14.00
241 IN,DG,RB,A:Kid Flash	15.00
242 RB,MK	15.00
243 NA,DG,Ras al Ghul	28.00
244 NA,Ras al Ghul	28.00
245 NA,IN,DG,FMc,Ras al Ghul	28.00
246	15.00
247 Deadly New Year	15.00
248	15.00
249 'Citidel of Crime'	15.00
250 IN,DG	15.00
251 NA,V:Joker	45.00
252	15.00
253 AN,DG,A:Shadow	15.00
254 NA,GK,B:100 page issues	20.00
255 GK,CI,NA,DG,I:CrazyQuilt	35.00
256 Catwoman	18.00
257 IN,DG,V:Penguin	18.00
258 IN,DG	18.00
259 GK,IN,DG,A:Shadow	18.00
260 IN,DG,Joker	40.00
261 CI,GK,E:100 page issues	20.00
262 A:Scarecrow	15.00
263 DG(i),A:Riddler	12.00
264 DON(s),DG,A:Devil Dayre	8.00
265 RB,BWr	9.00
266 DG,Catwoman(old Costume)	10.00
267 DG	8.00
268 DON(s),IN,TeB,V:Sheikh	8.00
269 A:Riddler	9.00
270 B:DvR(s)	8.00
271 IN,FMc	8.00
272 JL	8.00
273 V:Underworld Olympics/76	8.00
274	8.00
275	8.00
276	8.00
277	8.00
278	8.00
279 A:Riddler	9.00
280	8.00
281	8.00
282	8.00
283 V:Camouflage	8.00
284 JA,R:Dr.Tzin Tzin	8.00
285	8.00
286 V:Joker	12.00
287 BWi,MGr,Penguin	8.00

288 BWi,MGr,Penguin	8.00
289 MGr, V:Skull	8.00
290 MGr,V:Skull Dagger	8.00
291 B:Underworld Olympics #1,	
A:Catwoman	8.00
292 A:Riddler	8.00
293 A:Superman & Luthor	8.00
294 E:DvR(s),E:Underworld	
Olympics,A:Joker	9.00
295 GyC(s),MGo,JyS,V:Hamton	8.00
296 B:DvR(s),V:Scarecrow	8.00
297 RB,Mad Hatter	8.00
298 JCA,DG,V:Baxter Bains	8.00
299 DG	8.00
300 WS,DG,A:Batman E-2,	
Robin E-2	14.00
301 JCa,TeB	10.00
302 JCa,DG,V:Human Dynamo	10.00
303 JCa,DG	10.00
304 E:DvR(s),V:Spook	10.00
305 GyC,JCa,DeH,V:Thanatos	11.00
306 JCa,DeH,DN,V:Black Spider	11.00
307 B:LWn(s),JCa,DG,	
I:Limehouse Jack	11.00
308 JCa,DG,V:Mr.Freeze	11.00
309 E:LWn(s),JCa,FMc,	
V:Blockbuster	11.00
310 IN,DG,A:Gentleman Ghost	11.00
311 SEt,FMc,IN,Batgirl,	
V:Dr.Phosphorus	11.00
312 WS,DG,Calenderman	11.00
313 IN,FMc,VTwo-Face	11.00
314 IN,FMc,V:Two-Face	11.00
315 IN,FMc,V:Kiteman	11.00
316 IN,FMc,F:Robin,	
V:Crazy Quilt	11.00
317 IN,FMc,V:Riddler	12.00
318 IN,I:Fire Bug	11.00
319 JKu(c),IN,DG,A:Gentleman	
Ghost,E:Catwoman	11.00
320 BWr(c)	11.00
321 DG,WS,A:Joker,Catwoman	12.00
322 V:Cap.Boomerang,Catwoman	11.00
323 IN,A:Catwoman	11.00
324 IN,A:Catwoman	11.00
325	11.00
326 A:Catwoman	11.00
327 IN,A:Proffessor.Milo	11.00
328 A:Two-Face	11.00
329 IN,A:Two-Face	11.00
330	11.00
331 DN,FMc,V:Electrocutioner	11.00
332 IN,DN,Ras al Ghul.1st solo	
Catwoman story	12.00
333 IN,DN,A:Catwoman,	
Ras al Ghul	10.00
334 FMc,Ras al Ghul,Catwoman	10.00
335 IN,FMc,Catwoman,Ras al	
Ghul	10.00
336 JL,FMc,Loser Villains	10.00
337 DN,V:Snow Man	10.00
338 DN,Deathsport	10.00
339 A:Poison Ivy	10.00
340 GCA,Mole	10.00
341 A:Man Bat	10.00
342 V:Man Bat	10.00
343 GC,KJ,I:The Dagger	10.00
344 GC,KJ,Poison Ivy	10.00
345 I:New Dr.Death,A:Catwoman	10.00
346 DN,V:Two Face	10.00
347 A:Alfred	10.00
348 GC,KJ,Man-Bat,A:Catwoman	10.00
349 GC,AA,A:Catwoman	10.00
350 GC,TD,A:Catwoman	10.00
351 GC,TD,A:Catwoman	10.00

352 Col Blimp	10.00
353 JL,DN,DA,A:Joker	11.00
354 DN,AA,V:HugoStrange,A:	
Catwoman	10.00
355 DN,AA:A:Catwoman	10.00
356 DG,DN, Hugo Strange	10.00
357 DN,AA,I:Jason Todd	11.00
358 A:King Croc	10.00
359 DG,O:King Croc,Joker	11.00
360 I:Savage Skull	10.00
361 DN,Man-Bat,I:Harvey Bullock	10.00
362 V:Riddler	10.00
363 V:Nocturna	10.00
364 DN,AA,J.Todd 1st full solo	
story (cont'd Detective #531)	10.00
365 DN,AA,C:Joker	10.00
366 DN,AA,Joker,J.Todd in	
Robin Costume	15.00
367 DN,AA,Poisonlvy	9.00
368 DN,AA,I:2nd Robin	
(Jason Todd)	12.00
369 DN,AA,I:Dr.Fang,V:Deadshot	7.00
370 DN,AA	7.00
371 DN,AA,V:Catman	4.50

Batman #476 © DC Comics, Inc.

372 DN,AA,A:Dr.Fang	4.00
373 DN,AA,V:Scarecrow	4.00
374 GC,AA,V:Penguin	5.00
375 GC,AA,V:Dr.Freeze	4.00
376 DN,Halloween issue	4.00
377 DN,AA,V:Nocturna	4.00
378 V:Mad Hatter	4.00
379 V:Mad Hatter	4.00
380 AA,V:Nocturna	4.00
381 V:Batman	4.00
382 A:Catwoman	4.50
383 GC	4.00
384 V:Calender Man	4.00
385 V:Calender Man	4.00
386 I:Black Mask	4.00
387 V:Black Mask	4.00
388 V:Capt.Boomerang & Mirror	
Master	4.00
389 V:Nocturna,Catwoman	4.50
390 V:Nocturna,Catwoman	4.50
391 V:Nocturna,Catwoman	4.50
392 A:Catwoman	4.50
393 PG,V:Cossack	3.50
394 PG,V:Cossack	3.50

395 V:Film Freak	3.50
396 V:Film Freak	3.50
397 V:Two-Face,Catwoman	4.00
398 V:Two-Face,Catwoman	4.00
399 HaE(s),Two-Face	3.50
400 BSz,AAd,GP,BB,A:Joker	20.00
401 JBy(c),TVE,Legends,	
A:Magpie	3.50
402 JSn,Fake Batman	3.50
403 DCw,Batcave discovered	3.50
404 DM,FM(s),B:Year 1,I:Modern	
Age Catwoman	12.00
405 FM,DM,Year 1	8.00
406 FM,DM,Year 1	8.00
407 FM,DM,E:Year 1	8.00
408 CW,V:Joker,	
new O:Jason Todd	5.00
408a 2nd printing	1.00
409 DG,RA,V:Crime School	4.00
409a 2nd printing	1.00
410 DC,Jason Todd	4.00
411 DC,DH,V:Two Face	3.00
412 DC,DH,I:Mime	3.00
413 DC,DH	3.00
414 JAp,Slasher	3.00
415 JAp,Millenium Week #2	3.00
416 JAp,1st Batman/Nightwing	
T.U.	3.00
417 JAp,B:10 Nights,I:KGBeast	9.00
418 JAp,V:KGBeast	8.00
419 JAp,V:KGBeast	8.00
420 JAp,E:10 Nights,D:KGBeast	8.00
421 DG	3.50
422 MBr,V:Dumpster Slayer	3.00
423 TM(c),DC,Who is Batman	4.00
424 MBr,Robin	3.00
425 MBr,Gordon Kidnapped	3.00
426 JAp,B:Death in the Family,	
V:Joker	10.00
427 JAp,V:Joker	9.00
428 JAp,D:2nd Robin	7.00
429 JAp,A:Superman,	
E:Death in the Family	5.00
430 JAp,JSn,V:Madman	4.00
431 JAp,Murder Investigation	2.75
432 JAp	2.75
433 JBy,JAp,Many Deaths of the	
Batman #1	4.00
434 JBy,JAp,Many Deaths #2	3.00
435 JBy,Many Deaths #3	3.00
436 PB,B:Year#3,A:Nightwing,I:Tim	
Drake as child	6.00
436a 2ndPrint(green DC logo)	2.00
437 PB,year#3	3.00
438 PB,year#3	2.50
439 PB,year#3	2.50
440 JAp,Lonely Place of Dying #1,	
A:Tim Drake (face not shown)	3.00
441 JAp,Lonely Place Dying	3.00
442 JAp,I:3rd Robin(Tim Drake)	5.00
443 JAp,I:Crimesmith	2.00
444 JAp,V:Crimesmith	2.00
445 JAp,I:K.G.Beast Demon	2.00
446 JAp,V:K.G.Beast Demon	2.00
447 JAp,D:K.G.Beast Demon	2.00
448 JAp,A:Penguin#1	2.50
449 MBr,A:Penguin#3	2.50
450 JAp,I:Joker II	2.00
451 JAp,V:Joker II	2.00
452 KD,Dark Knight Dark City#1	2.00
453 KD,Dark Knight Dark City#2	2.00
454 KD,Dark Knight Dark City#3	2.00
455 Identity Crisis#1,	
A:Scarecrow	2.50
456 IdentityCrisis#2	3.00

457 V:Scarecrow,A:Robin,
New Costume 5.00
457a 2nd printing 2.00
458 R:Sarah Essen 2.00
459 A:Sarah Essen 2.00
460 Sisters in Arms,pt.1
A:Catwoman 3.00
461 Sisters in Arms,pt.2
Catwoman V:Sarah.Essen . . . 3.00
462 Batman in San Francisco . . . 1.75
463 Death Valley 1.75
464 V:Two-Hearts 1.75
465 Batman/Robin T.U. 3.00
466 Robin Trapped 2.00
467 Shadowbox #1(sequel to
Robin Mini-Series) 2.50
468 Shadowbox #2 . . . . 2.00
469 Shadowbox #3 . . . . 2.00
470 War of the Gods x-over 1.75
471 V:Killer Croc 1.75
472 The Idiot Root,pt.1 . . . . 1.75
473 The Idiot Root,pt.3 . . . . 1.75
474 Destroyer,pt.1 (LOTDK#27) . . 2.25
475 R:Scarface,A:VickiVale 1.75
476 A:Scarface 1.75
477 Ph(c),Gotham Tale,pt.1 . . . . 1.75
478 Ph(c),Gotham Tale,pt.2 . . . . 1.75
479 TMd,I:Pagan 1.75
480 JAp,To the father I never
knew 1.75
481 JAp,V:Maxie Zeus 1.75
482 JAp,V:Maxie Zeus 1.75
483 JAp,I:Crash & Burn 1.75
484 JAp,R:Black Mask 1.75
485 TGr,V:Black Mask 1.75
486 JAp,I:Metalhead 1.75
487 JAp,V:Headhunter 1.75
488 JAp,N:Azrael 7.00
489 JAp,Bane vs Killer Croc,
I:Azrael as Batman 6.00
489a 2nd Printing 2.00
490 JAp,Bane vs.Riddler 7.00
490a 2nd Printing 1.75
490b 3rd Printing 1.50
491 JAp,V:Joker,A:Bane 4.00
491a 2nd Printing 1.50
492 B:DgM(s),NB,Knightfall#1,
V:Mad Hatter,A:Bane 5.00
492a Platinum Ed. 7.00
492b 2nd Printing 1.50
493 NB,Knightfall,#3,Mr.Zsasz . . . 3.00
494 JAp,TMd,Knightfall #5,A:Bane,
V:Cornelius,Stirk,Joker 2.50
495 NB,Knightfall#7,V:Poison
Ivy,A:Bane 2.50
496 JAp,JRu,Knightfall#9,V:Joker,
Scarecrow,A:Bane 2.50
497 JAp,DG,Knightfall#11,V:Bane,
Batman gets back broken 4.00
497a 2nd Printing 1.75
498 JAp,JRu,Knightfall#15,A:Bane,
Catwoman,Azrael Becomes
Batman 2.50
499 JAp,SHa,Knightfall#17,
A:Bane,Catwoman 2.50
500 JQ(c),JAp,MM,Die Cut(c),
Direct Market,Knightfall#19,
V:Bane,N:Batman 3.00
500a KJo(c),Newstand Ed. 2.50
501 MM,I:Mekros 2.00
502 MM,V:Mekros 2.00
503 MM,V:Catwoman 2.00
504 MM,V:Catwoman 2.00
505 MM,V:Canibal 2.00
506 KJo(c),MM,A:Ballistic 2.00

507 KJo(c),MM,A:Ballistic 2.00
508 KJo(c),MM,V:Abattior 2.00
509 KJo(c),MM,KnightsEnd#1,
A:Shiva 3.00
510 KJo(c),MM,Knights End #7,
V:Azrael 2.00
511 Zero Hour, A:Batgirl 2.00
512 Killer Croc sewer battles 2.00
513 Two-Face and convicts 2.00
514 Identity Crisis 2.00
515 KJo,Return of Bruce Wayne,
Troika,pt.1 . . . . 2.00
515 Collector's Edition 3.50
516 V:The Sleeper 2.00
517 V:The Sleeper 2.00
518 V:The Black Spider 2.00
519 KJo,V:The Black Spider
[new Miraweb format begins] . . 2.00
520 EB,A:James Gordon 2.00
521 R:Killer Croc 2.00
522 R:Scarecrow 2.00
523 V:Scarecrow 2.00
524 DgM,KJo,V:Scarecrow 2.00
525 DgM,KJo,Underworld
Unleashed tie-in 2.00

Batman #480 © DC Comics, Inc.

526 DgM,A:Alfred,Nightwing,Robin 2.00
527 DgM,V:Two-Face,I:Schism . . 2.00
528 . . . . 2.00
529 DgM,KJo,Contagion,pt.6 . . . . 2.50
530 DgM,KJo,The Aztec
Connection,pt.1 . . . . 2.50
530a collector's edition 2.50
531 DgM,KJo,The Aztec
Connection,pt.2 . . . . 2.00
531a collectors edition 2.50
532 DgM(s),KJo,"The Aztec Connection," pt.3, A:Deadman 2.00
532a card stock cover 2.50
533 DgM(s),KJo,Legacy prelude . 2.00
534 DgM(s),KJo,Legacy, pt.5 . . . . 2.00
535 DgM(s),KJo,JhB,I:The Ogre,
double size 3.50
535a Collector's edition,
gatefold cover 4.00
536 DgM(s),KJo,JhB,V:Man-Bat,
Final Night tie-in 2.00
537 DgM(s),KJo,JhB,A:Man-Bat,
pt.2 . . . . 2.00

538 DgM(s),KJo,JhB,A:Man-Bat,
pt.3 . . . . 2.00
539 . . . . 2.00
540 DgM(s),KJo,JhB,Spectre,pt.1 . 2.00
541 DgM(s),KJo,JhB,Spectre,pt.2 . 2.00
542 DgM(s),KJo,JhB,V:Faceless,
pt. 1 . . . . 2.00
543 DgM(s),KJo,JhB,pt. 2 . . . . . . 2.00
544 DgM(s),KJo,JhB, F:Joker,pt.1 2.00
545 DgM(s),KJo, F:Joker, Demon,
pt.2 . . . . 2.00
546 DgM(s),KJo,JhB,F:Joker,
Demon, pt.3 concl. 2.00
547 DgM,KJo,JhB,Genesis tie-in . 2.00
548 DgM(s),KJo,JhB,V:Penguin, pt.1 2.00
549 DgM(s),KJo,JhB,V:Penguin, pt.2 2.00
550 DgM,KJo,JhB,I:Chase 3.00
550a deluxe, with file card inserts 3.50
551 DgM,KJo,JhB,F:Ragman 3.00
552 DgM, ... 2.00
553 DgM,KJo,SB,Cataclysm
x-over, pt.3 . . . . 3.00
554 DgM,KJo,SB,Cataclysm, ... 3.00
555 DGm,JhB,SB,BSf,Aftershock . 2.00
556 DGm,NBy,BSf,Aftershock . . . 2.00
557 DGm,VGi,SB,BSf,F:Ballistic . . 2.00
558 DGm,JAp,SB,doubts 2.00
559 DgM(s),BH,SB,Aftershock . . . 2.00
Ann.#1 CS 450.00
Ann.#2 . . . . 250.00
Ann.#3 A:Joker 200.00
Ann.#4 . . . . 100.00
Ann.#5 . . . . 100.00
Ann.#6 . . . . 80.00
Ann.#7 . . . . 80.00
Ann.#8 TVE,A:Ras al Ghul . . . 8.00
Ann.#9 JOy,AN,PS 7.00
Ann.#10 DCw,DG,V:HugoStrange 7.00
Ann.#11 JBy(c),AMo(s),V:Penguin 8.00
Ann.#12 RA,V:Killer 5.00
Ann.#13 A:Two-Face 6.00
Ann.#14 O:Two-Face 4.00
Ann.#15 Armageddon,pt.3 . . . . 6.00
Ann.#15a 2nd printing(silver) . . . 2.50
Ann.#16 SK(c),Eclipso,V:Joker . . . 3.00
Ann.#17 EB,Bloodline#8,
I:Decimator 3.00
Ann.#18 Elseworld Story 3.50
Ann.#19 Year One, O:Scarecrow . 4.00
Ann.#20 Legends o/t Dead Earth . 2.95
Ann.#21 Pulp Heroes (Weird
Mystery) DgM(s) 3.95
Ann.#22 BWr(c) Ghosts 3.00
Specials & 1-shots
Spec.#0 (1994) 3.00
Spec.#1 MGo,I:Wrath 4.00
Giant #1, seven tales, 80pg (1998) 5.00
Batman: Arkham Asylum — Tales
of Madness, AIG, Cataclysm
tie-in (1998) 3.00
Batman: Batgirl, JBa,RBr,
Girlfrenzy (1998) 2.00
Batman: Blackgate, CDi(s), JSon,
in Blackgate prison (1996) . . . 4.50
Batman: Blackgate — Isle of Men, DgM,
JAp,BSf,BSz,Cataclysm (1998) 3.00
Batman Dark Knight Gallery (1995) 3.50
Batman: Death of Innocents, DON(s),
JSt, BSz, Land mine victims
(1996) 4.00
Batman Gallery,collection of past
(c),posters,pin-ups,JQ(c) (1992) 4.00
Batman: Gotham By Gaslight,MMi,
V:Jack the Ripper 6.00
Batman: The Killing Joke,BB,AMo(s),

O:Joker,Batgirl paralyzed (1988)8.00
2nd thru 6th Printings . . . . . @5.00
Batman: Mitefall, V:Bane Mite (1995)495
Batman: Penguin Triumphant (1992)5.00
Batman: Plus (1997) 3.00
Batman Record Comic (1996) . . . 1.00
Batman/Riddler: The Riddle
Factory (1995) 4.95
Secret Files #1 SMc(c) inc.
O:Batman (1997) 6.00
Batman: Seduction of the Gun,
V:Illegal Gun Control (1992) . . 3.00
Batman/Two-Face: Crime and
Punishment (1995) 4.95
2nd printing (1998) 3.00
Two-Face Strikes Twice #1 . . . . . 5.25
Two-Face Strikes Twice #2 . . . . . 5.25
Batman: Vengeance of Bane,
GN,I:Bane (1992) 30.00
2nd Printing 5.00
Batman: Vengeance of Bane II
(1995) 3.95
Batman Villains Secret Files,
AIG,CDi,RMz,BB,F:Greatest Foes
(1998) 5.00
Elseworld 1-shots
Batman: The Blue, The Grey, and
The Bat, JL (1992) 5.95
Batman: Brotherhood of the Bat
(1995) 5.95
Batman: Dark Allegiances (1996) . 5.95
Batman: Holy Terror (1991) 6.50
Batman: In Darkest Knight
MiB(s),JBi (1994) 5.50
Batman Knightgallery (1995) 3.50
Batman: Masque, MGr, in turn of
the century Gotham 7.00
Batman: Master of the Future,EB,
Sequel to Goth.by Gaslight
(1991) 6.00
Batman: Scar of the Bat (1996) . . 5.00
Graphic Novels
The Abduction 6.00
Batman A lonely Place of Dying
(1990) rep. Batman #440–442
& New Titans #60–61 . . . . . 4.00
Batman: Blind Justice, rep. Detective
Comics #598–#600 (1992) . . . 7.50
Batman: Castle of the Bat,
(Elseworlds) 5.95
Batman: Dark Joker, KJo 12.00
Many Deaths of the Batman;
rep. #433–#435 (1992) 3.95
Batman: Full Circle AD,
A:Reaper (1992) 7.00
Batman: I, Joker, BH, Elseworlds,
in 2083 (1998) 4.95
The Scottish Connection 6.00
Batman: Ten Knights of the Beast,
rep. #417–#420 (1994) 5.95
Batman: The Ultimate Evil:
1 Novel adaptation (of 2) 5.95
2 Novel adaptation, rep. 5.95
Hard Covers & Trade Paperbacks
Batman Archives Vol.3 . . . . 39.95
HC Archives, Vol. 4, rep. 50.00
Batman: Arkham Asylum,DMc
HC (1989) 28.00
TPB 15.00
Birth of the Demon, O:Ras al
Ghul (1992)
HC 25.00
TPB (1993) 13.00
Batman: Bloodstorm,KJo,V:Joker,
Vampires, (sequel to Red Rain)

HC 24.95
TPB 12.95
Bride of the Demon, TGr, V:Rā's al Ghūl
HC 21.00
TPB 13.00
Batman: Dark Knight Dynasty,
three elseworlds stories
HC (1998) 25.00
Batman: A Death in the Family,
rep. Batman #426-429 (1988)
TPB 8.00
2nd printing 5.00
3rd printing 4.00
Batman: Digital Justice (1990)
HC 26.00
Batman: Faces (1995)
TPB 10.00
Batman: Gothic, rept. Legends of the
Dark Knight #6–#10 (1992)
TPB 13.00
New printing 13.00
Greatest Batman Stories
HC 35.00
TPB 16.00

Batman Annual #2 © DC Comics, Inc.

Greatest Batman Stories, Vol. 2
TPB 17.00
Greatest Joker Stories
HC 20.00
TPB 15.00
Batman: Knight's End, rep. Batman
#509–#510, Shadow of the Bat
#29–#30, Detective #676–#677,
Legends #62–#63, Catwoman #12,
Robin #8–#9
TPB 14.95
Knightfall rep. #1–#11
TPB 12.95
Knightfall rep. #12-#19
TPB 12.95
Batman: The Last Angel, F:Catwoman
V:Aztec bat-god (1994)
TPB 12.95
Batman: The Last Arkham
TPB 12.95
Legacy, sequel to Contagion, rep. (1996)
TPB 18.00
Batman: Night Cries,SHa 30.00
Batman: Prodigal, rep,
TPB 15.00

Batman: Son of the Demon,JBi (1987)
HC 55.00
TPB 17.00
2nd thru 4th printings . . . . . @8.95
Batman: Tales of the Demon (1991)
TPB 20.00
Batman: Year One Rep. Batman
#404–#407 (1998)
HC 16.00
TPB 14.00
2nd Printing 10.00
3rd Printing 10.00
Batman: Four of a Kind, from
Year One annuals (1998)
TPB 15.00
Year Two (1990) rep. Detective
Comics #575–#578
TPB 10.00
Movies
TPB The Movies, (all 4) (1997) . 20.00
Batman, JOy, Movie adaptation . . 3.00
Perfect Bound 6.00
Batman Returns, SE,JL Movie
Adaption, ... 6.00
Newsstand Format 4.00
Batman: Mask of the Phantasm,
animated movie adapt. 5.25
Newstand Ed. 3.25
Batman Forever, Movie Adaptation 5.95
Newsstand version 3.95
Batman and Robin, DON(s), Movie
Adaptation (1997) 3.95
Collector's edition, ... 5.95
GN Batman: Bane, BSz(c) movie
tie-in (1997) 4.95
GN Batman: Batgirl, BSz(c) movie
tie-in (1997) 4.95
GN Batman: Mr. Freeze, BSz(c)
movie tie-in (1997) 4.95
GN Batman: Poison Ivy, BSz(c)
movie tie-in (1997) 4.95
X-overs
GN Batman & Superman Adventures:
World's Finest (1997) adaptation
of animated adventures, 64pg . 7.00
Batman/Captain America (DC/Marvel
1996) Elseworlds 6.00
Batman/Deadman, Death and
Glory, JeR(s),JEs (1996)
HC 25.00
TPB 12.95
Batman/Demon (1996) 5.00
Batman/Dracula:Red Rain KJo,MJ,
Batman becomes Vampire,
HC Elseworlds Story (1991) . 35.00
SC (1992) 12.00
Batman/Green Arrow: The Poison
Tomorrow,MN,JRu,V:Poison
Ivy (1992) 6.25
Batman/Houdini: The Devil's
Workshop (1993) 6.50
Batman: Huntress/Spoiler—Blunt
Trauma, CDi,Cataclysm (1988) 3.00
Batman/Judge Dredd: Judgement on
Gotham,SBs,V:Scarecrow, Judge
Death (1991) 9.00
Batman/Judge Dredd: Vendetta in
Gotham, AIG(s),V:Ventriliquist
(1993) 5.25
Batman/Judge Dredd: The Ultimate
Riddle (1995) 5.00
Batman/Phantom Stranger, AIG(s),
Lemurian artifact (1997) 5.00
Batman/Punisher: Lake of Fire,
DON(s),BKi,A:Punisher,V:Jigsaw

(DC/Marvel 1994) 5.25
Batman/Spawn: War Devil, DgM,CDi,
  AlG(s), KJ,V:Croatoan (1994) . 6.00
Batman/Spider-Man (1997) 5.00
Batman vs. The Incredible Hulk
  (DC/Marvel 1995) 4.00

Batman Adventures #7
© DC Comics, Inc.

BATMAN ADVENTURES
1992–95
(Based on TV cartoon series)

1 MeP,V:Penguin 5.00
2 MeP,V:Catwoman 4.00
3 MeP,V:Joker 3.00
4 MeP,V:Scarecrow 3.00
5 MeP,V:Scarecrow 3.00
6 MeP,A:Robin 3.00
7 MeP,V:Killer Croc,w/card 6.00
8 MeP,Larceny my Sweet 2.50
9 MeP,V:Two Face 2.50
10 MeP,V:Riddler 3.00
11 MeP,V:Man-Bat 2.00
12 MeP,F:Batgirl 2.00
13 MeP,V:Talia 2.00
14 MeP,F:Robin 2.00
15 MeP,F:Commissioner Gordon . 2.00
16 MeP,V:Joker 2.00
17 MeP,V:Talia 2.00
18 MeP,R:Batgirl 1.75
19 MeP,V:Scarecrow 1.75
20 MeP,V:Mastermind,Mr.Nice,
  Perfessor 1.75
21 MeP,V:Man-Bat,Tygrus 1.75
22 MeP,V:Two-Face 1.75
23 MEP,V:Poison Ivy 1.75
24 MeP,I:Kyodi Ken 1.75
25 MeP,dbl.size,Superman 2.50
26 MeP,A:Robin,Batgirl 1.75
27 MeP,I:Doppleganger 1.75
28 Joker 1.75
29 A:Talia 1.50
30 O:Mastermind, Mr. Nice 1.50
31 I:Anarcky 1.50
32 Criminals dressed as
  Napoleonic Soldiers 1.75
33 Bruce and date mugged 1.75
34 V:Dr. Hugo Strange 1.75

35 A:Catwoman 1.75
36 V:Joker, Final issue 1.75
Ann.#1 Roxy Rocket 3.00
Ann.#2 JBa,BBl,DG,TG,SHa,BKi,MM,
  GN,JRu,V:Demon,Ra's al
  Ghul,Etrigan 3.50
Holiday Special 2.95
Spec. Mad Love 3.95
TPB Collected Adventures #1 . . . 5.95
TPB Collected Adventures #2 . . . 5.95

BATMAN ADVENTURES:
THE LOST YEARS
Nov. 1997

1 (of 5) BHa,TBe,Batgirl 2.00
2 BHa, TBe,Dick Grayson quits . . 2.00
3 . . . . 2.00
4 BHa,TBe,F:Tim Drake 2.00
5 BHa,TBe,Tim Drake new Robin 2.00

Batman and the Outsiders #24
© DC Comics, Inc.

BATMAN AND
THE OUTSIDERS
Aug., 1983

1 B:MiB(s),JAp,O:Outsiders,
  O:Geo Force 3.00
2 JAp,V:Baron Bedlam 2.50
3 JAp,V:Agent Orange 2.00
4 JAp,V:Fearsome Five 2.00
5 JAp,A:New Teen Titans 2.50
6 JAp,V:Cryonic Man 1.50
7 JAp,V:Cryonic Man 1.50
8 JAp,A:Phantom Stranger 1.50
9 JAp,I:Master of Disaster 1.50
10 JAp,A:Master of Disaster 1.50
11 JAp,V:Takeo 1.50
12 JAp,DG,O:Katana 1.50
13 JAp,Day,O:Batman 1.50
14 BWg,Olympics,V:Maxi Zeus . . 1.50
15 TVE,Olympics,V:Maxi Zeus . . 1.50
16 JAp,L:Halo 1.50
17 JAp,V:Ahk-Ton 1.50
18 JAp,V:Ahk-Ton 1.50
19 JAp,A:Superman 1.50
20 JAp,V:Syonide,R:Halo 1.50
21 TVE,JeM,Solo Stories 1.50

22 AD,O:Halo,I:Aurakles 1.50
23 AD,O:Halo,V:Aurakles 1.50
24 AD,C:Kobra 1.50
25 AD,V:Kobra 1.50
26 AD 1.50
27 AD,V:Kobra 1.50
28 AD,I:Lia Briggs(Looker) 1.50
29 AD,V:Metamorpho 1.50
30 AD,C:Looker 1.50
31 AD,I&J:Looker 1.50
32 AD,L:Batman 1.50
Ann.#1 JA N:Geo-Force,
  I:Force of July 1.75
Ann.#2 V:Tremayne,W:Metamorpho
  & Sapphire Stagg 1.50
Becomes:

ADVENTURES OF
THE OUTSIDERS
May, 1986

33 AD,V:Baron Bedlam 1.50
34 AD,Masters of Disaster 1.50
35 AD,V:Adolph Hitler 1.50
36 AD,A:Masters of Disaster 1.50
37 . . . . 1.50
38 . . . . 1.50
39 thru 47 JAp,reprints
  Outsiders #1-#9 . . . . @1.50

BATMAN AND ROBIN
ADVENTURES, THE
Nov. 1995

1 TTn 2.00
2 TTn,V:Two-Face 1.75
3 TTn,V:The Riddler 1.75
4 TTn,V:The Penguin 1.75
5 TTn 1.75
6 TTn,Robin Fired? 1.75
7 TTn,V:Scarface 1.75
8 TTn(s) 1.75
9 TTn(s),F:Batgirl & Talia 1.75
10 TTn(s),F:Rä's Al Ghül 1.75
11 TTn(s),Alfred & Robin look
  for monster in Batcave 1.75
12 TTn(s),BKr,RBr, sequel to
  "Bane" TV episode 1.75
13 TTn(s),BKr,RBr,V:Scarecrow . . 1.75
14 TTn(s),BKr,RBr,young criminal
  turns to Batman for help 1.75
15 TTn(s) 1.75
16 TTn(s),V:Catman,A:Catwoman 1.75
17 PDi&TTn(s),JSon,RBr,Mad
  Hatter dies in Arkham 1.75
18 TTn(s),BKr,TBe,A:Joker,
  Harley Quinn 1.75
19 TTn(s),BKr,TBe,The Huntress . 1.75
20 TTn(s),BKr,TBe, office pool . . . 1.75
21 TTn(s),JSon,Riddler kidnaps
  Commissioner Gordon 1.75
22 TTn(s),BKr,TBe,V:Two-Face . . 1.75
23 TTn(s),TBe,V:Killer Croc 1.75
24 TTn(c),F:Poison Ivy 1.75
25 TTn,TBe,final issue, 48pg 3.00
Ann.#1 PDi(s),TTn, sequel to
  Batman: Mask of the Phantasm 3.00
Ann.#2 JSon,TBe,V:Hypnotist . . . 4.00
Sub-Zero one-shot, F:Mr. Freeze,
  Nora, 64pg. 3.95

BATMAN:
BANE OF THE DEMON
Feb., 1998

1 (of 4) CDi,GN,TP, Bane &
  Ra's al Ghul 2.00

DC COMICS

DC COMICS

2 CDi,GN,TP,Talia 2.00
3 CDi,GN,TP,the Lazarus Pit . . . 2.00
4 CDi,GN,TP,Bane imprisoned . . 2.00

BATMAN BLACK & WHITE
1996
1 JLe(c) numerous artists (of 4) . 6.00
2 thru 4 . . . . @5.00
HC 40.00

BATMAN CHRONICLES
1995
1 CDi,LW,BSz, multiple stories . . 3.50
2 V:Feedback 3.00
3 All villains issue 3.00
4 F:Hitman 10.00
5 Oracle, Year One story 3.00
6 Rā's Al Ghūl 3.00
7 JOy,LW, woman on death row . 3.00
8 Talia goes to Gotham to
  eliminate Batman 3.00
9 CDi(s),F:Batgirl, Mr. Freeze,
  Poison Ivy 3.00
10 BSn, anthology 3.00
11 CDi,JFM, Elseworlds stories . . 3.00
12 Cataclysm x-over 3.00
13 F:GCPD 3.00
14 SB(c),F:Alfred,Huntress 3.00
Gallery #1, Pin-ups 3.50
GN The Gauntlet 4.95

BATMAN: THE CULT
1988
1 JSn,BWr,V:Deacon Blackfire . . 9.00
2 JSn,BWr,V:Deacon Blackfire . . 7.00
3 JSn,BWr,V:Deacon Blackfire . . 7.00
4 JSn,BWr,V:Deacon Blackfire . . 6.00
TPB Rep.#1-#4 . . . . 14.95

BATMAN: THE DARK KNIGHT RETURNS
1986
1 FM,KJ,V:Two-Face 20.00
1a 2nd printing 5.00
1b 3rd printing 3.00
2 FM,KJ,V:Sons of the Batman . . 9.00
2a 2nd printing 3.00
2b 3rd printing 2.50
3 FM,KJ,D:Joker 7.00
3a 2nd printing 3.00
4 FM,KJ,Batman vs.Superman,
  A:Green Arrow,D:Alfred 5.00
HC 50.00
Paperback book 20.00
Warner paperback 17.00
HC,sign/num. 270.00
2nd-8th printing 12.95
TPB 10th Anniv. Spec, 224 pg. . 14.95

BATMAN FAMILY
Sept.–Oct., 1975
1 MGr,NA(rep.) Batgirl &
  Robin begins,giant 10.00
2 V:Clue Master 5.50
3 Batgirl & Robin reveal ID 5.50
4 . . . . 5.50
5 . . . . 5.50
6 Joker Daughter 7.00
7 CS,A:Sportsmaster,
  G.A.Huntress 4.00
8 First solo Robin story,
  C:Joker's Daughter 4.00
9 Joker's Daughter 7.00

10 R:B'woman,1st solo Batgirl sty 5.00
11 MR,Man-Bat begins 6.00
12 MR 6.00
13 MR,DN,BWi 6.00
14 HC/JRu,Man-Bat 7.00
15 MGo,Man-Bat 5.00
16 MGo,Man-Bat 5.00
17 JA,DH,MG,Batman, B:Huntress
  A:Demon,MK(c),A:Catwoman . 7.00
18 MGo,JSon,BL,Huntress,BM . . 5.00
19 MGo,JSon,BL,Huntress,BM . . 5.00
20 MGo,JSon,DH,A:Ragman,
  ElongatedMan, Oct.–Nov.,1978 6.00

Batman: GCPD #4 © DC Comics, Inc.

BATMAN: GCPD
[Mini-Series] Aug. 1996
1 CDi(s),JAp,BSz 2.25
2 CDi(s),JAp,BSz 2.25
3 CDi(s), JAp,BSz,F:Montoya,
  Kitch & Bullock 2.25
4 CDi(s), JAp,BSz, finale 2.25

BATMAN: GORDON'S LAW
October 1996
1 CDi(s),KJ,Gordon looks for
  bad cops 2.00
2 CDi(s),KJ,Gordon combats
  corruption 2.00
3 CDi(s),KJ, ... 2.00
4 (of 4) CDi(s),KJ, concl. 2.00

BATMAN: GORDON OF GOTHAM
April 1998
1 (of 4) DON,DG,KJ,F:Jim Gordon 2.00
2 DON,DG,KJ,Cuchulain 2.00
3 DON,DG,KJ,break-in 2.00
4 DON,DG,KJ,past revealed . . . 2.00

BATMAN: GOTHAM ADVENTURES
April 1998
1 TTn,RBr,TBe,F:Joker 3.00
2 TTn,RBr,TBe,F:Two-Face 2.00

3 TTn,RBr,TBe,V:Scarecrow . . . 2.00
4 TTn,RBr,TBe,A:Catwoman 2.00
5 RBr,TBe,TTn,A:Mr.Freeze 2.00

BATMAN: GOTHAM NIGHTS
1 Gotham City Mini-series 2.00
2 Lives of Gotham Citizens 2.00
3 Lives of Gotham Citizens 2.00
4 Lives of Gotham Citizens 2.00

BATMAN: GOTHAM NIGHTS II
1995
1 Sequel to Gotham Nights 1.95
2 F:Carmine Sansone 1.95
3 Fire 1.95
4 JQ(c) Decisions 1.95

BATMAN: JAZZ
[Mini-Series] 1995
1 I:Blue Byrd 2.50
2 V:Brotherhood of Bop 2.50
3 F:Blue Byrd 2.50

BATMAN: LEGENDS OF THE DARK KNIGHT 1989
1 EH,Shaman of Gotham,pt.1,
  Yellow(c) 5.00
1a Blue,Orange or Pink(c) 5.00
2 EH,Shaman of Gotham,pt.2 . . . 3.00
3 EH,Shaman of Gotham,pt.3 . . . 3.00
4 EH,Shaman of Gotham,pt.4 . . . 3.00
5 EH,Shaman of Gotham,pt.5 . . . 3.00
6 KJ,Gothic,pt.1 . . . . 3.00
7 KJ,Gothic,pt.2 . . . . 2.50
8 KJ,Gothic,pt.3 . . . . 2.50
9 KJ,Gothic,pt.4 . . . . 2.50
10 KJ,Gothic,pt.5 . . . . 2.50
11 PG,TA,Prey,pt.1 . . . . 6.00
12 PG,TA,Prey,pt.2 . . . . 5.00
13 PG,TA,Prey,pt.3 . . . . 5.00
14 PG,TA,Prey,pt.4 . . . . 5.00
15 PG,TA,Prey,pt.5 . . . . 4.00
16 TVE,Venom,pt.1 . . . . 5.00
17 TVE,JL,Venom,pt.2 . . . . 5.00
18 TVE,JL,Venom,pt.3 . . . . 5.00
19 TVE,JL,Venom,pt.4 . . . . 5.00
20 TVE,JL,Venom,pt.5 . . . . 5.00
21 BS,Faith,pt.1 . . . . 2.50
22 BS,Faith,pt.2 . . . . 2.50
23 BS,Faith,pt.3 . . . . 2.50
24 GK,Flyer,pt.1 . . . . 2.50
25 GK,Flyer,pt.2 . . . . 2.50
26 GK,Flyer,pt.3 . . . . 2.50
27 Destroyer,pt.2 (Batman#474) . 3.00
28 MWg,Faces,pt.1,V:Two-Face . 4.00
29 MWg,Faces,pt.2,V:Two-Face . 4.00
30 MWg,Faces,pt.3,V:Two-Face . 4.00
31 BA,Family 2.50
32 Blades,pt.1 . . . . 2.50
33 Blades,pt.2 . . . . 2.50
34 Blades,pt.3 . . . . 2.50
35 BHa,Destiny Pt.1 . . . . 2.50
36 BHa,Destiny Pt.2 . . . . 2.50
37 I:Mercy,V:The Cossack 2.50
38 KON,R:Bat-Mite 2.50
39 BT,Mask#1 . . . . 2.50
40 BT,Mask#2 . . . . 2.50
41 Sunset 2.25
42 CR,Hothouse #1 . . . . 2.25
43 CR,Hothouse #2,V:Poison Ivy . 2.25
44 SMc,Turf #1 . . . . 2.25

45 Turf#2 . . . . 2.25
46 RH,A:Catwoman,V:Catman . . . 2.50
47 RH,A:Catwoman,V:Catman . . . 2.50
48 RH,A:Catwoman,V:Catman . . . 2.50
49 RH,A:Catwoman,V:Catman . . . 2.50
50 BBl,JLe,KN,KM,WS,MZ,BB,
   V:Joker 6.00
51 JKu,A:Ragman 2.25
52 Tao #1,V:Dragon 2.25
53 Tao #2,V:Dragon 2.25
54 MMi 2.00
55 B:Watchtower 2.00
56 CDi(s),V:Battle Guards 2.00
57 CDi(s),E:Watchtower 2.00
58 Storm 2.50
59 DON(s),RoW,B:Qarry 2.50
60 RoW,V:Asp 2.50
61 RoW,V:Asp 2.50
62 RoW,KnightsEnd#4,A:Shiva,
   Nightwing 3.50
63 Knights End #10,V:Azrael 2.00
64 CBa 2.00
65 Joker 2.00
66 Joker 2.00

Batman: Legends of the Dark
Knight #18 © DC Comics, Inc.

67 Going Sane,pt.3 . . . . 2.00
68 Going Sane,pt.4 . . . . 2.00
69 Criminals,pt.1 . . . . 2.00
70 Criminals,pt.2 . . . . 2.00
71 Werewolf,pt.1 . . . . 2.00
72 JWk(c&a),Werewolf,pt.2
   [new Miraweb format begins] . . 2.00
73 JWk(c&a),Werewolf,pt.3 . . . . . 2.00
74 Engins,pt.1 . . . . 2.00
75 Engins,pt.2 . . . . 2.00
76 The Sleeping,pt.1 . . . . 2.00
77 The Sleeping,pt.2 . . . . 2.00
78 The Sleeping,pt.3 . . . . 2.00
79 Favorite Things 2.00
80 Idols,pt.1 . . . . 2.00
81 Idols,pt.2 . . . . 2.00
82 Idols, climax 2.00
83 new villain 2.00
84 WEl(s) 2.00
85 JeR(s) 2.00
86 DgM,JWi,MGy,Conspiracy,pt.1 2.00
87 DgM,JWi,MGy,Conspiracy,pt.2 2.00
88 DgM,JWi,MGy,Conspiracy,pt.3 2.00

89 AlG(s),"Clay," pt. 1 . . . . 2.00
90 AlG(s),"Clay," pt. 2 . . . . 2.00
91 "Freakout," pt.1 . . . . 2.00
92 GEn(s),WSm,"Freakout," pt.2 . 2.00
93 GEn(s),WSm,"Freakout," pt.3 . 2.00
94 MGi(s),Saul Fisher's story . . . 2.00
95 DAn&Ala(s),AWi,ALa,"Dirty
   Tricks" pt.1 . . . . 2.00
96 DAn&Ala(s),AWi,ALa,"Dirty
   Tricks" pt.2 . . . . 2.00
97 DAn&Ala(s),AWi,ALa,"Dirty
   Tricks" concl. 2.00
98 PJe(s),SeP,"Steps," pt.1 . . . . 2.00
99 PJe(s),SeP,"Steps," pt.2 . . . . 2.00
100 DON,JRo,F:Robin, 64pg. . . . 4.00
101 CE,KN(c)100 years in future . 2.00
102 JRo,PuJ,"Spook," pt.1 . . . . . 2.00
103 JRo,PuJ,"Spook," pt.2 . . . . . 2.00
104 JRo,PuJ,"Spook," pt.3 . . . . . 2.00
105 TVE,JRu,"Duty," pt.1 . . . . . . 2.00
106 TVE,JRu,"Duty," pt.2 . . . . . . 2.00
107 LMr,"Stalking," pt.1 . . . . 2.00
108 LMr,"Stalking," pt.2 . . . . 2.00
109 SEt,DAb,Primal Riddle,pt.1 . . 2.00
110 SEt,DAb,Primal Riddle,pt.2 . . 2.00
111 SEt,DAb,Primal Riddle,pt.3 . . 2.00
Ann.#1 JAp,KG,DSp,TL,JRu,
   MGo,JQ,'Duel',C:Joker 5.50
Ann.#2 MN,LMc,W:Gordn&Essen . 4.00
Ann.#3 MM,I:Cardinal Sin 3.75
Ann.#4 JSon(c),Elseworlds Story . 3.75
Ann.#5 CDi(s)Year One Annuals,
   O:Man-Bat 3.95
Ann.#6 Legends o/t Dead Earth . 2.95
Ann.#7 Pulp Heroes (War) 3.95
Halloween Spec.I 6.95
Halloween Spec.II 4.95
Ghosts, Halloween Special 4.95
TPB Shaman rep.#1-#5 (1993) . 12.95
TPB Batman: Gothic, rep. #6-#10
   (1992) 12.95
TPB Prey, rep.Legends of the Dark
   Knight #11–#15 (1992) 12.95
TPB Batman: Venom, TVE, rep.
   #16–#20 (1993) 9.95
TPB Collected Legends of the Dark
   Knight,BB(c),rep.#32–#34,#38,
   #42-#43 (1994) 12.95
TPB Other Realms 13.00

BATMAN:
THE LONG HALLOWEEN
October 1996

1 (of 13) JLb,TSe,Who is Holiday?
   F: usual suspects 11.00
2 JLb(s),TSe,V:Holiday,A:Solomon
   Grundy 8.00
3 JLb,TSe, ... 9.00
4 JLb(s),TSe,"New Year's Eve" . . 9.00
5 JLb(s),TSe,F:Poison Ivy, Search
   for Holiday 5.00
6 JLb(s),TSe,F:Poison Ivy,
   Catwoman 5.00
7 JLb(s),TSe,V:The Riddler 4.00
8 JLb(s),TSe,V:Scarecrow 4.00
9 JLb(s),TSe,A:Holiday,Scarecrow 4.00
10 JLb(s),TSe,V:Scarecrow,Mad
   Hatter 4.00
11 JLb(s),TSe,V:Holiday 3.50
12 JLb(s),TSe,Harvey Dent 3.50
13 JLb(s),TSe,concl.,48pg. 5.00
TPB Haunted Knight, rep. Fears,
   Madness & Ghosts 12.95

BATMAN: MAN-BAT
1995

1 R:Man-Bat, painted series . . . 5.00
2 F:Marilyn Muno 5.00
3 JBo,Elseworlds story, concl. . . 5.00
TPB rep. mini-series 14.95

BATMAN: RUN,
RIDDLER RUN
1992

1 MBg,Batman V:Riddler 5.50
2 MBg,Batman V:Riddler 5.25
3 MBg,V:Perfect Securities 5.25

BATMAN/SPIDER-MAN
Aug., 1997

GN JMD,GN,KK,V:Kingpin &
   Ra's al Ghul 5.00

BATMAN: SHADOW OF
THE BAT
1992–97

1 NB,Last Arkham Pt.1 . . . . 3.50
1a Collector set,w/posters,pop-up 5.50
2 NB,Last Arkham Pt.2 . . . . 3.00
3 NB,Last Arkham Pt.3 . . . . 3.00
4 NB,Last Arkham Pt.4 . . . . 3.00
5 NB,A:Black Spider 2.50
6 NB,I:Chancer 2.50
7 Misfits Pt.1 . . . . 2.50
8 Misfits Pt.2 . . . . 2.50
9 Misfits Pt.3 . . . . 2.50
10 MC,V:Mad Thane of Gotham . 2.00
11 V:Kadaver 2.00
12 V:Kadaver,A:Human Flea 2.00
13 NB,'The Nobody' 2.00
14 NB,Gotham Freaks#1 . . . . . . 2.00
15 NB,Gotham Freaks#2 . . . . . . 2.00
16 BBl,MM,A:Anarchy,Scarecrow . 2.00
17 BBl,V:Scarecrow 2.00
18 BBl,A:Anarchy,Scarecrow 2.00
19 BBl,Knightquest:The Crusade,pt.2,
   V:Gotham criminals 2.00
20 VGi,Knightquest:The Crusade,
   V:Tally Man 2.00
21 BBl,Knightquest:The Search,
   V:Mr.Asp 2.00
22 BBl,Knightquest:The Search,
   In London 2.00
23 BBl,Knightquest:The Search . . 2.00
24 BBl,Knightquest:The Crusade . 2.00
25 BSf(c),BBl,Knightquest: Crusade,
   A:Joe Public,V:Corrosive Man . 2.00
26 BSf(c),BBl,Knightquest: Crusade,
   V:Clayface 2.00
27 BSf(c),BBl,Knightquest: Crusade,
   I:Clayface Baby 2.00
28 BSf(c),BBl 2.00
29 BBl,BSf(c),BBl,KnightsEnd#2,
   A:Nightwing 3.50
30 BSf(c),BBl,KnightsEnd#8,
   V:Azrael 2.25
31 Zero Hour, V:Butler 2.00
32 Ventriloquist,Two-Face 2.00
33 Two-Face 2.00
34 V:Tally Man 2.00
35 BKi,Return of Bruce Wayne,
   Troika,pt.2 . . . . 2.00
35a Collectors Edition 2.95
36 Black Canary 2.00
37 Joker Hunt 2.00
38 V:The Joker 2.00
39 BSf(c),R:Solomon Grundy

[new Miraweb format begins] . . 2.00
40 BSf(c), F:Anarky 2.00
41 Explosive Dirigible 2.00
42 . . . . 2.00
43 Secret of the Universe,pt1 . . . 2.00
44 AIG,BSz(c) Secret of the
    Universe,pt.3 . . . . 2.00
45 AIG,BSz(c) 100 year old corpse 2.00
46 AIG,BSz(c) V:Cornelius Stirk . . 2.00
47 AIG,BSz(c) V:Cornelius Stirk . . 2.00
48 AIG 2.00
49 AIG,Contagion,pt.7 . . . . 2.00
50 AIG,Nightmare on Gotham,pt.1 2.00
51 AIG,DTy, Nightmare on
    Gotham,pt.2 (of 3) 2.00
52 AIG(s),"Nightmare on Gotham,"
    pt.3 . . . . 2.00
53 AIG(s),Legacy, prelude 2.00
54 AIG(s),Legacy, pt. 4, x-over . . 2.00
55 AIG(s),RBr,KJ,Bruce Wayne a
    murderer? A:Nightwing 2.00
56 AIG(s),DTy,SnW,"Leaves of
    Grass,pt.1,V:Poison Ivy 2.00
57 AIG(s),DTy,SnW,"Leaves of
    Grass,pt.2 . . . . 2.00
58 AIG(s),DTy,SnW,"Leaves of
    Grass,pt.3 . . . . 2.00
59 AIG(s),DTy,SnW,"Killer,
    Killer," pt.1 . . . . 2.00
60 AIG(s),DTy,SnW,"Killer,
    Killer," pt.2 . . . . 2.00
61 AIG(s),JAp,SnW,night of
    second chances 2.00
62 AIG(s),DTy,SnW,Two-Face,pt.1 2.00
63 AIG(s),DTy,SnW,Two-Face,pt.2 2.00
64 AIG(s),DTy,SnW,A:Jason Blood 2.00
65 AIG(s),NBy,JRu, A:Oracle,pt.1 2.00
66 AIG(s),NBy,JRu, V:Thinker,
    Cheat, pt.2 . . . . 2.00
67 AIG(s),NBy,SnW,CsM,V:Thinker,
    Cheat, pt.3, concl. 2.00
68 AIG(s),JAp,SnW,annual killer . 2.00
69 AIG(s),MBu,WF,CsM,
    The Spirit of 2000, pt. 1 . . . . . 2.00
70 AIG(s),MBu,WF,CsM, pt.2 . . . . 2.00
71 AIG(s),MBu,WF,CsM,detective 2.00
72 AIG(s),MBu,WF 2.00
73 AIG(s),MBu,WF,Cataclysm
    x-over,pt.1 . . . . 3.00
74 AIG(s),MBu,WF,Cataclysm
    cont. 2.00
75 AIG(s),MBu,WF,Aftershock . . . 3.00
76 AIG(s),MBu,WF,Aftershock . . . 2.00
77 AIG(s),MBu,WF,quake-torn . . . 2.00
78 AIG(s),MBu,Aftershock 2.00
79 AIG(s),MBu,V:Mad Hatter,
    Narcosis 2.00
Ann.#1 TVE,DG,Bloodlines#3,
    I:Joe Public 3.75
Ann.#2 Elseworlds story 3.95
Ann.#3 Year One Annual 3.95
Ann.#4 Legends of the Dead
    Earth 2.95
Ann.#5 AIG(s), Pulp Heroes 4.00

BATMAN: SWORD OF AZRAEL
1992–93
1 JQ,KN,I:Azrael 10.00
2 JQ,KN,A:Azrael 7.00
3 JQ,KN,V:Biis,A:Azrael 5.00
4 JQ,KN,V:Biis,A:Azrael 5.00
TPB rep.#1-#4 . . . . 11.00
TPB Platinum 25.00

BATMAN/GRENDEL: DEVIL'S MASQUE & DEVIL'S RIDDLE
1 MWg,Batman meets Grendel . . 5.25
2 MWg,Batman Vs. Grendel 5.25

Batman vs. Predator #3
© DC Comics, Inc.

BATMAN vs. PREDATOR
DC/Dark Horse 1991–92
1 NKu,AKu,inc.8 trading cards
    bound in (Prestige) 5.00
1a Newsstand 4.00
2 NKu,AKu,Inc. pinups (prestige) 4.00
2a Newsstand 3.00
3 NKu,AKu,conclusion,inc.
    8 trading cards (Prestige) 4.00
3a Newsstand 3.00
TPB,rep.#1-#3 . . . . 5.95

BATMAN vs. PREDATOR II BLOODMATCH
1994–95
1 R:Predators 2.75
2 A:Huntress 2.50
3 Assassins 2.50
4 V:Head Hunters 2.50
TPB Rep.#1-#4 . . . . 6.95

BATMAN/PREDATOR III: BLOOD TIES
DC/Dark Horse (, 1997)
1 (of 4) CDi,RDm,RbC, vs. pair
    of Predators 2.00
2 CDi,RDm,RbC, pt.2 . . . . 2.00
3 CDi,RDm,RbC, pt.3 . . . . 2.00
4 CDi,RDm,RbC, concl. 2.00
TPB rep. 8.00

BATMAN/WILDCAT
Feb. 1997
1 (of 3) CDi&BSt(s),SCi,ATi,
    Batman and Robin discover
    Secret Ring of combat 2.25
2 CDi&BSt(s),SCi,V:KGBeast,
    Willis Danko 2.25

3 CDi&BSt(s),SCi, Batman vs.
    Wildcat, concl. 2.25

BATTLE CLASSICS
Sept.–Oct., 1978
1 JKu, reprints 1.50

BEAUTIFUL STORIES FOR UGLY CHILDREN
Piranha Press 1989–91
1 thru 11 . . . . @2.00
12 thru 14 . . . . @2.50
15 Blood Day 2.50
16 thru 23 . . . . @2.50

BEOWOLF
April-May, 1975
1 thru 5 . . . . @1.00
6 Feb.–March, 1976 . . . . 1.00

BEST OF THE BRAVE & THE BOLD
1 JL(c),NA,rep.B&B #85. . . . . . 2.50
2 JL(c),NA,rep.B&B #81 . . . . . . 2.50
3 JL(c),NA,rep.B&B #82 . . . . . . 2.50
4 JL(c),NA,rep.B&B #80 . . . . . . 2.50
5 JL(c),NA,rep.B&B #93 . . . . . . 2.50
6 JL(c),NA,rep.B&B #83 . . . . . . 2.50

BEWARE THE CREEPER
1968–69
1 . . . . 12.00
2 thru 6 . . . . @7.50

BIG ALL-AMERICAN COMIC BOOK
Dec., 1944
1 JKu 11,000.00

BIG BOOK OF FUN COMICS
Spring, 1936
1 . . . . 12,000.00

BIG BOOK OF CONSPIRACIES, THE
DC/Paradox Press B&W 1995
TPB 12.95

BIG BOOK OF DEATH, THE
DC/Paradox Press B&W 1994
TPB 12.95

BIG BOOK OF HOAXES, THE
DC/Paradox Press B&W 1996
TPB 14.95

BIG BOOK OF LITTLE CRIMINALS, THE
DC/Paradox Press B&W 1996
TPB 14.95

BIG BOOK OF LOSERS, THE
DC/Paradox Press B&W
TPB by Paul Kirchner 14.95

BIG BOOK OF MARTYRS
DC/Paradox Aug., 1997
TPB 15.00

BIG BOOK OF SCANDAL
Oct., 1997
TPB 15.00

BIG BOOK OF THUGS, THE
DC/Paradox B&W Oct. 1996
TPB 14.95

BIG BOOK OF THE UNEXPLAINED
DC/Paradox B&W April 1997
GN DgM(s),strange phenomena . 14.95

BIG BOOK OF URBAN LEGENDS, THE
DC/Paradox B&W 1994
TPB 12.95

BIG BOOK OF WEIRDOS, THE
DC/Paradox Press B&W 1995
TPB 12.95

BIG BOOK OF THE WEIRD WILD WEST
July 1998
TPB 15.00

BIRDS OF PREY: BATGIRL
Dec., 1997
1 CDi,Batgirl & Black Canary 3.00

BIRDS OF PREY: MANHUNT
1996
1 CDi(s),MHy,F:Black Canary,
  Oracle 2.00
2 CDi(s),MHy,V,Archer Braun,
  A:Catwoman 2.00
3 CDi(s),MHy,V:Catwoman,
  Huntress 2.00
4 CDi(s),MHy,V:Lady Shiva 2.00

BIRDS OF PREY: REVOLUTION
one-shot CDi(s),BMc 2.95

BIRDS OF PREY: THE RAVENS
May 1998
1-shot, CDi,Girlfrenzy 2.00

BIRDS OF PREY: WOLVES
Aug., 1997
1-shot CDi,DG,F:Oracle & Black
  Canary 3.00

BLACK CANARY
[Limited Series] 1991–92
1 TVE/DG,New Wings,pt.1 . . . . . 2.25
2 TVE/DG,New Wings,pt.2 . . . . . 2.00

Black Canary #1 © DC Comics, Inc.

3 TVE/DG,New Wings,pt.3 . . . . . 2.00
4 TVE/DG,New Wings,pt.4,Conc . 2.00
[Regular Series] 1993
1 TVE,Hero Worship,pt.1 . . . . . . 2.25
2 TVE,Hero Worship,pt.2 . . . . . . 2.00
3 TVE,Hero Worship,pt.3 . . . . . . 2.00
4 TVE,V:Whorrsman 2.00
5 . . . . 2.00
6 Blynde Woman's Bluff 2.00
7 TVE,V:Maniacal Killer 2.00
8 . . . . 1.75
9 A:Huntress 1.75
10 TVE,A:Nightwing,Huntress . . 1.75
11 TVE,A:Nightwing 1.75
12 final issue 1.75

BLACK CANARY/ORACLE: BIRDS OF PREY
1996
1-shot DDi, double size 3.95

BLACK CONDOR
1992–93
1 I&O:Black Condor 1.25
2 V:Sky Pirate 1.25
3 V:Sky Pirate 1.25
4 V:The Shark 1.25
5 V:Mind Force 1.25
6 V:Mind Force 1.25
7 Forest Fire 1.25
8 MG,In Jail 1.25
9 A:The Ray 1.25
10 . . . . 1.25
11 O:Black Condor 1.25

BLACKHAWK
Prev: Golden Age
1957–1984
108 DD,CCu,DD&CCu(c),The
  Threat from the Abyss
  A:Blaisie 450.00
109 DD,CCu,DD&CCu(c),The
  Avalance Kid 125.00
110 DD,CCu,DD&CCu(c),Mystery
  of Tigress Island 125.00
111 DD,CCu,DD&CCu(c),Menace

of the Machines 125.00
112 DD,CCu,DD(c),The Doomed
  Dog Fight 125.00
113 DD,CCu,CCu(c),Volunteers
  of Doom 125.00
114 DD,CCu,DD&CCu(c),Gladiators
  of Blackhawk Island 125.00
115 DD,CCu,DD&CCu(c),The
  Tyrant's Return 125.00
116 DD,CCu,DD&CCu(c),Prisoners
  of the Black Island 125.00
117 DD,CCu,DD&CCu(c),Menace
  of the Dragon Boat 125.00
118 DD,CCu,DD&SMo(c),FF,The
  Bandit With 1,000 Nets . . . 135.00
119 DD,CCu,DD&SMo(c),
  V:Chief Blackhawk 75.00
120 DD,CCu,DD&SMo(c),The
  Challenge of the Wizard 75.00
121 DD,CCu,DD&CCu(c),Secret
  Weapon of the Archer 75.00
122 DD,CCu,DD&CCu(c),The
  Movie That Backfired 75.00
123 DD,CCu,DD&CCu(c),The
  Underseas Gold Fort 75.00
124 DD,CCu,DD&CCu(c),Thieves
  With A Thousand Faces 75.00
125 DD,CCu,DD&CCu(c),Secrets
  o/t Blackhawk Time Capsule . 75.00
126 DD,CCu,DD&CCu(c),Secret
  of the Glass Fort 75.00
127 DD,CCu,DD&CCu(c),Blackie-
  The Winged Sky Fighter 75.00
128 DD,CCu,DD&CCu(c),The
  Vengeful Bowman 75.00
129 DD,CCu,DD&CCu(c),The
  Cavemen From 3,000 B.C. . . 75.00
130 DD,CCu,DD&SMo(c),The
  Mystery Missle From Space . 75.00
131 DD,CCu,DD&CCu(c),The
  Return of the Rocketeers . . . 60.00
132 DD,CCu,DD&CCu(c),Raid
  of the Rocketeers 60.00
133 DD,CCu,DD&CCu(c),Human
  Dynamo 60.00
134 DD,CC,DD&CC(c),The
  Sinister Snowman 60.00
135 DD,CCu,DD&CCu(c),The
  Underworld Supermarket . . . 60.00
136 DD,CCu,DD&CCu(c),The
  Menace of the Smoke-Master 60.00
137 DD,CCu,DD&CCu(c),The
  Weapons That Backfired 60.00
138 DD,CCu,DD&SMo(c),The
  Menace of the Blob 60.00
139 DD,CCu,DD&CCu(c),The
  Secret Blackhawk 60.00
140 DD,CCu,DD&CCu(c),The
  Space Age Marauders 60.00
141 DD,CCu,DD&CCu(c),Crimes
  of the Captive Masterminds . . 50.00
142 DD,CCu,DD&CCu(c),Alien
  Blackhawk Chief 50.00
143 DD,SMo,DD&CCu(c),Lady
  Blackhawk's Rival 50.00
144 DD,CCu,DD&CCu(c),The
  Underworld Sportsmen 50.00
145 DD,CCu,DD&CCu(c),The
  Deadly Lensman 50.00
146 DD,CCu,DD&CCu(c),The
  Fantastic Fables of Blackhawk 50.00
147 DD,SMo,DD&CCu(c),The
  Blackhawk Movie Queen 50.00
148 DD,CCu,DD&CCu(c),Four
  Dooms For The Blackhawks . 50.00

DC COMICS

149 DD,CCu,DD&CCu(c),Masks of Doom 50.00	
150 DD,CCu,DD&SMo(c), Blackhawk Mascot from Space 35.00	
151 DD,CCu,DD&CCu(c),Lost City 35.00	
152 DD,CCu,DD&SMo(c),Noah's Ark From Space 35.00	
153 DD,CCu,DD&SMo(c), Boomerang Master 35.00	
154 DD,CCu,DD&SMo(c),The Beast Time Forgot 35.00	
155 DD,CCu,DD&SMo(c),Killer Shark's Land Armada 35.00	
156 DD,CCu,DD&SMo(c),Peril of the Plutonian Raider 35.00	
157 DD,CCu,DD&SMo(c),Secret of the Blackhawk Sphinx 35.00	
158 DD,CCu,DD&SMo(c),Bandit Birds From Space 35.00	
159 DD,CCu,DD&SMo(c),Master of the Puppet Men 35.00	
160 DD,CCu,DD&CCu(c),The Phantom Spy 35.00	
161 DD,SMo,DD&SMo(c),Lady Blackhawk's Crime Chief ... 35.00	
162 DD,CCu,DD&CCu(c),The Invisible Blackhawk 35.00	
163 DD,CCu,DD&SMo(c), Fisherman of Crime 35.00	
164 DD,O:Blackhawk retold 40.00	
165 DD,V:League of Anti Blackhawks 30.00	
166 DD,A:Lady Blackhawk 30.00	
167 DD,The Blackhawk Bandits . 30.00	
168 DD,Blackhawk Time Travelers 25.00	
169 DD,Sinister Hunts of Mr. Safari 25.00	
170 DD,A:Lady Blackhawk,V:Killer Shark 25.00	
171 DD,Secret of Alien Island .. 25.00	
172 DD,Challenge of the GasMaster . 20.00	
173 DD,The Super Jungle Man . 20.00	
174 DD,Andre's Impossible World 20.00	
175 DD,The Creature with Blackhawk's Brain 20.00	
176 DD,Stone Age Blackhawks . 15.00	
177 DD,Town that time Forgot .. 15.00	
178 DD,Return of the Scorpions 15.00	
179 DD,Invisible Dr.Dunbar ... 14.00	
180 DD,Son of Blackhawk 15.00	
181 DD,I:Tom Thumb Blackhawk 10.00	
182 DD,A:Lady Blackhawk 10.00	
183 DD,V:Killer Shark 10.00	
184 DD,Island of Super Monkeys 10.00	
185 DD,Last 7 days of the Blackhawks 10.00	
186 DD,A:Lady Blackhawk 10.00	
187 DD,V:Porcupine 11.00	
188 DD,A:Lady Blackhawk 11.00	
189 DD:O:rtd 11.00	
190 DD,FantasticHumanStarfish 12.00	
191 DD,A:Lady Blackhawk 10.00	
192 DD,V:King Condor 9.00	
193 DD,The Jailer's Revenge ... 9.00	
194 DD,The Outlaw Blackhawk .. 9.00	
195 DD,A:Tom Thumb Blackhawk 9.00	
196 DD,Blackhawk WWII Combat Diary story 9.00	
197 DD:new look 9.00	
198 DD:O:rtd 11.00	
199 DD,Attack with the Mummy	

Insects 10.00	
200 DD,A:Lady Blackhawk, I:Queen Killer Shark 10.00	
201 DD,Blackhawk Detached Diary Story,F:Hendrickson 10.00	
202 DD,Combat Diary,F:Andre .. 10.00	
203 DD:O:Chop-Chop 10.00	
204 DD,A:Queen Killer Shark .. 10.00	
205 DD,Combat Diary story 10.00	
206 DD,Combat Diary, F:Olaf .. 10.00	
207 DD,Blackhawk Devil Dolls .. 10.00	
208 DD,Detached service diary F:Chuck 10.00	
209 DD,V:King Condor 10.00	
210 DD,Danger..Blackhawk Bait rep.Blackhawk #139. .... 6.00	
211 DD,GC,Detached service diary 7.00	
212 DD,Combat Diary, F:Chop-Chop 7.00	
213 DD,Blackhawk goes Hollywood 7.00	
214 DD,Team of Traitors 7.00	
215 DD,Detached service diary F:Olaf 7.00	

Blackhawk 1st Series #225
© DC Comics, Inc.

216 DD,A:Queen Killer Shark ... 7.00	
217 DD,Detached service diary F:Stanislaus 7.00	
218 DD,7 against Planet Peril ... 7.00	
219 DD,El Blackhawk Peligroso .. 7.00	
220 DD,The Revolt of the Assembled Man 7.00	
221 DD,Detach service diary F:Hendrickson 6.00	
222 DD,The Man from E=MC2 .. 6.00	
223 DD,V:Mr.Quick CHange 6.00	
224 DD,Combat Diary, F:Stanislaus 6.00	
225 DD,A:Queen Killer Shark .. 6.00	
226 DD,Secret Monster of Blackhawk Island 6.00	
227 DD,Detached Service diary F:Chop-Chop 6.00	
228 DD (1st art on JLA characters) Blackhawks become super-heroes, Junk-Heap heroes #1(C:JLA) . 6.00	
229 DD,Junk-Heap Heroes #2	

(C:JLA) 6.00	
230 DD,Junk-Heap Heroes concl. (C:JLA) 6.00	
231 DD,A:Lady Blackhawk 6.00	
232 DD,A:Lady Blackhawk 6.00	
233 DD,Too Late,The Leaper ... 6.00	
234 DD,The Terrible Twins 6.00	
235 DD,A Coffin for a Blackhawk 6.00	
236 DD,Melt,Mutant, Melt 6.00	
237 DD,Magnificent 7 Assassins . 6.00	
238 DD,Walking Booby-Traps ... 6.00	
239 DD,The Killer That Time Forgot 6.00	
240 DD,He Who Must Die 6.00	
241 DD,A Blackhawk a Day ... 6.00	
242 Blackhawks back in blue & black costumes 6.00	
243 Mission Incredible (1968) ... 6.00	
244 GE,new costumes,Blackhawks become mercenaries (1976) .. 2.00	
245 GE,Death's Double Deal 2.00	
246 RE,GE,Death's Deadly Dawn 2.00	
247 RE,AM,Operation:Over Kill .. 2.00	
248 JSh,Vengeance is Mine!.. Sayeth the Cyborg 2.00	
249 RE,GE,V:Sky-Skull 2.00	
250 RE,GE,FS,D:Chuck(1977) ... 2.00	
251 DSp,Back to WWII(1982) ... 2.00	
252 thru 258 DSp .... @2.00	
259 .... 2.00	
260 HC,ATh 2.00	
261 thru 271 DSp .... @2.00	
272 .... 2.00	
273 DSp 2.00	
274 DSp 2.00	

[2nd Series]

1 HC Mini-series,Blackhawk accused of communism 3.50	
2 HC,visits Soviet Union 3.00	
3 HC,Atom Bomb threat to N.Y. . 3.00	

[3rd Series]

1 All in color for a Crime,pt.1 I:The Real Lady Blackhawk ... 1.50	
2 All in color for a Crime,pt.2 .. 1.50	
3 Agent Rescue Attempt in Rome 1.50	
4 Blackhawk's girlfriend murdered 1.50	
5 I:Circus Organization 1.50	
6 Blackhawks on false mission .. 1.50	
7 V:Circus A:Suicide Squad, rep. 1st Blackhawk story 2.50	
8 Project: Assimilation 1.50	
9 V:Grundfest 1.50	
10 Blackhawks Attacked 1.50	
11 Master plan revealed 1.50	
12 Raid on BlackhawkAirwaysHQ 1.75	
13 Team Member Accused of .. 1.75	
14 Blackhawk test pilots 1.75	
15 Plans for independence 1.75	
16 Independence, final issue 1.75	
Ann.#1 Hawks in Albania 2.95	
Spec.#1 Assassination of JFK to Saigon,1975 .... 3.50	

BLACK HOOD
Impact 1991–92

1 O:Black Hood 1.25	
2 Nick Cray becomes Black Hood 1.00	
3 New Year's Eve,A:Creeptures . 1.00	
4 Nate Cray become Black Hood, Dr.M.Harvey becomes Ozone . 1.00	
5 E:Nate Cray as Black Hood V:Ozone 1.00	
6 New Black Hood 1.00	

7 History of Seaside City 1.25
8 V:Hit Coffee 1.25
9 V:Hit Coffee 1.25
10 Slime of Your Life #1 .... 1.25
11 Slime of Your Life #2 .... 1.25
12 Final Issue 1.25
Ann#1 Earthquest,w/trading card . 2.50

BLACK LAMB, THE
DC/Helix Sept. 1996
1 TT,Vampire saga 2.50
2 TT,war between werewolf clans 2.50
3 TT,O:Black Lamb,V:Lykaon ... 2.50
4 TT thru 6 .... @2.50

BLACK LIGHTNING
1977–78
1 TVE/FS,I&O:Black Lightning .. 2.50
2 TVE/FS,A:Talia 2.00
3 TVE,I:Tobias Whale 2.00
4 TVE,A:Jimmy Olsen 2.00
5 TVE,A:Superman 2.00
6 TVE,I:Syonide 2.00
7 TVE,V:Syonide 2.00
8 TVE,V:Tobias Whale 2.00
9 TVE,V:Annihilist 2.00
10 TVE,V:Trickster 2.00
11 TVE,BU:The Ray 2.50
[2nd Series] 1995–96
1 He's Back 2.00
2 V:Painkiller 2.00
3 V:Painkiller 2.00
4 V:Painkiller,Royal Family 2.00
5 Flashbacks of Past 2.00
6 V:Gangbuster 2.25
7 V:Gangbuster 2.25
8 V:Tobias Whale 2.25
9 I&V:Demolition 2.25
10 Jefferson Pierce becomes Black
    Lightning full time 2.25
11 Hunt for Sick Nick 2.25
12 V:Sick Nick's death squad ... 2.25
13 final issue 2.25

BLACK MASK
1993–94
1 I:Black Mask 5.00
2 V:Underworld 5.00
3 V:Valentine 5.00

BLACK ORCHID
1993–95
1 DMc,O:Black Orchid,
    A:Batman,Luthor,Poison Ivy .. 6.00
2 DMc,O:cont,Arkham Asylum .. 7.00
3 DMc,A:SwampThing,conc. 6.00
TPB rep. #1 thru #3 .... 20.00
Vertigo
1 DMc(c),B:DiF(s),JIT,SnW,I:Sherilyn
    Somers,I:Logos,F:Walt Brody . 2.50
1a Platinum Ed. 12.00
2 JIT,SnW,Uprooting,V:Logos ... 2.25
3 JIT,SnW,Tainted Zone,
    V:Fungus 2.25
4 JIT,SnW,I:Nick & Orthia 2.25
5 DMc(c),JIT,SnW,
    A:Swamp Thing 2.25
6 JIT,BMc(i),God in the Cage ... 2.25
7 JIT,RGu,SnW,
    Upon the Threshold 2.25
8 DMc(c),RGu,A:Silent People .. 2.25
9 DMc(c),RGu 2.25
10 DMc(c),RGu 2.25

11 DMc(c),RGu,In Tennessee ... 2.25
12 DMc(c),RGu 2.25
13 DMc(c),RGu,F:Walt Brody ... 2.25
14 DMc(c),RGu,Black Annis 2.00
15 DMc(c),RGu,Kobolds 2.00
16 DMc(c),RGu,Suzy,Junkin 2.00
17 Twisted Season,pt.1 .... 2.00
18 Twisted Season,pt.2 .... 2.00
19 Twisted Season,pt.3 .... 2.00
20 Twisted Season,pt.4 .... 2.00
21 Twisted Season,pt.5 .... 2.00
22 Twisted Season,pt.6, final iss. . 2.25
Ann.#1 DMc(c),DiF(s),GyA,JnM,F:Suzy,
    Childrens Crusade,BU:retells
    Adventure Comics#430 ...... 4.25

BLASTERS SPECIAL
1989
1 A:Snapper Carr, Spider Guild . 2.00

BLOOD: A TALE
DC/Vertigo Sept. 1996
[Mini-series,
re-release of Marvel Epic]
1 JMD(s),KW, quest for truth
    begins 2.95
2 JMD(s),KW, Blood falls in love . 2.95
3 JMD(s),KW, companion dies .. 2.95
4 JMD(s),KW, finale 2.95

BLOOD & SHADOWS
(Vertigo) 1996
1 .... 5.95
2 Journal of Justice Jones 5.95
3 Chet Daley flung into
    21st century 5.95
4 V:God of the Razor, finale 5.95

BLOODBATH
1993
1 A:Superman 3.75
2 A:New Heroes 3.75

BLOODPACK
[Mini-Series] 1995
1 I:Blood Pack, V:Demolition ... 1.50
2 A:Superboy 1.50
3 Loira's Corpse 1.50
4 Real Heroes Final Issue 1.50

BLOOD SYNDICATE
(Milestone) 1993–96
1 I:Blood Syndicate,Rob Chaplick,
    Dir.Mark.Ed.,w/B puzzle piece,
    Skybox card,Poster 3.50
1a Newstand Ed. 2.00
2 I:Boogieman,Tech-9 Vs.
    Holocaust 1.75
3 V:S.Y.S.T.E.M.,I:Mom,D:Tech-9 1.75
4 V:S.Y.S.T.E.M. 1.75
5 I:John Wing,Kwai,Demon Fox . 1.75
6 V:John Wing 1.75
7 I:Edmund,Cornelia 1.75
8 V:Demon Fox 1.75
9 O:Blood Syndicate,I:Templo .. 1.75
10 WS(c),Ccs,Shadow War,I:Iota,
    Sideshow,Rainsaw,Slag,Ash,
    Bad Betty,Oro 2.25
11 IV(s),Ccs,A:Aquamaria 1.75
12 IV(s),Ccs,V:Dinosaur 1.75
13 IV(s),Ccs,B:Roach War 1.75
14 IV(s),Ccs,V:Roaches 1.75

Blood Syndicate #8 © DC Comics, Inc.

15 IV(s),Ccs,E:Roach War 1.75
16 IV(s),Ccs,Worlds Collide#6,
    A:Superman 1.75
17 Ccs,Worlds Collide#13,V:Rift .. 1.75
18 Ccs,V:S.Y.S.T.E.M. 1.75
19 .... 1.75
20 .... 1.75
21 .... 1.75
22 .... 1.75
23 F:Boogieman 1.75
24 L:Third Rail,Brickhouse 1.75
25 R:Tech-9 .... 2.95
26 Return of the Dead 1.75
27 R:Masquerade 1.75
28 Tech-9 takes control 2.50
29 Reader's Choice 1.00
30 Long Hot Summer 2.50
31 V:New Threat 2.50
32 MC(c),V:Soulbreaker 2.50
33 Kwai returns to paris Island ... 1.00
34 Visit to Kwen Lun 2.50
35 final issue 3.50

BLOODY MARY
DC/Helix Aug. 1996
1 (of 4) GEn(s),CE, near-
    future war 2.25
2 thru 4 GEn(s),CE, near-future
    war, concl. .... @2.25

BLOODY MARY:
LADY LIBERTY
DC/Helix July 1996
1 (of 4) GEn(s),CE, ... 2.50
2 GEn(s),CE,V:Achilles Seagal .. 2.50
3 GEn(s),CE,V:Vatman 2.50
4 GEn(s),CE,V:Vatman, concl. .. 2.50

BLUE BEETLE
1986–88
1 O:Blue Beetle 1.50
2 V:Fire Fist 1.00
3 V:Madmen 1.00
4 V:Doctor Alchemy 1.00
5 A:Question 1.00
6 V:Question 1.00

Blue Beetle #3 © DC Comics, Inc.

7 A:Question	1.00
8 A:Chronos	1.00
9 A:Chronos	1.00
10 Legends, V:Chronos	1.00
11 A:New Teen Titans	1.00
12 A:New Teen Titans	1.00
13 A:New Teen Titans	1.00
14 Pago Island,I:Catalyst	1.00
15 RA:V:Carapax	1.00
16 RA,Chicago Murders	1.00
17 R:Dan Garrett/Blue Beetle	1.00
18 D:Dan Garrett	1.00
19 RA,R:Dr. Cyber	1.00
20 RA,Millennium,A:JLI	1.00
21 RA,A:Mr.Miracle, Millennium tie in	1.00
22 RA,Prehistoric Chicago	1.00
23 DH,V:The Madmen	1.00
24 DH,final issue	1.00

BLUE DEVIL
1984–86

1 O:Blue Devil	2.00
2	1.50
3 A:Superman	1.50
4 A:JLA	1.50
5	1.50
6 EC,I:Bolt	1.00
7 KG	1.00
8 GV	1.00
9 thru 16	@1.00
17 Crisis	1.25
18 Crisis	1.25
19	1.00
20 RM,Halloween	1.00
21 RM,I:Roadmaster	1.00
22 RM,A:Jorj & Lehni	1.00
23 A:Jorj & Lehni	1.00
24 V:Blue Devil Toys	1.00
25 Mary Frances Cassidy	1.00
26 Special Baseball issue	1.00
27 Godfrey Goose	1.00
28 real live fan guest star	1.00
29	1.00
30 Double sized	1.25
31 BSz,V:Seraph	1.25
Ann.#1	1.50

BOB, THE GALACTIC BUM
[Mini-Series] 1995

1 A:Lobo	2.00
2 Planet Gnulp,A:Lobo	2.00
3 V:Khunds	2.00
4 Rando's Coronation	2.00

BOGIE MAN, THE
DC/Paradox/Pocket (April 1998)

TPB 6"x8" AIG,b&w	14.00

BOMBA, THE JUNGLE BOY
1967–68

1 CI,MA,I:Bomba	15.00
2 thru 7	@10.00

BOOK OF FATE, THE

1 KG(s),RoW,BR,	2.25
2 KG(s),RoW,BR,"The Chaos-Order War," pt.1 (of 4)	2.25
3 KG(s),RoW,BR,"The Chaos-Order War," pt.2	2.25
4 KG(s),RoW,BR,"The Chaos-Order War," pt.3, A:Two-Face	2.25
5 KG(s),RoW,BR,"The Chaos-Order War," pt.4	2.25
6 KG(s),RoW,BR,Convergence," pt.1 x-over	2.25
7 KG(s),RoW,BR, Signs, pt.1	2.25
8 KG(s),RoW,BR, Signs, pt.2	2.25
9 KG,AIG,BR,Signs, pt.3	2.50
10 KG,AIG,BR,Signs,pt.4	2.50
11 KG,AIG, in a Swiss Jail	2.50
12 AIG,KG,F:Lobo, final issue	2.50

BOOKS OF FAERIE, THE
DC/Vertigo Jan. 1997

1 PrG,F:Titania and Auberon	2.50
2 PrG,	2.50
3 (of 3) PrG	2.50
TPB	15.00

BOOKS OF FAERIE, THE: AUBERON'S TALE
DC/Vertigo (June 1998)

1 (of 3) PrG,VcL,F:Early life of King Auberon	2.50
2 PrG,VcL, early life	2.50
3 PrG,VcL, early life, concl.	2.50

BOOKS OF MAGIC
[Limited Series] 1990–91

1 B:NGa(s),JBo,F:Phantom Stranger, A:J.Constantine,Tim Hunter, Doctor Occult,Mister E	12.00
2 SHp,F:J.Constantine,A:Spectre, Dr.Fate,Demon,Zatanna	12.00
3 CV,F:Doctor Occult, A:Sandman	10.00
4 E:NGa(s),PuJ,F:Mr.E,A:Death	10.00
TPB rep.#1-#4	20.00

[Regular Series]
Vertigo 1994–97

1 MkB,B:Bindings,R:Tim Hunter	5.00
1a Platinum Edition	9.00
2 CV(c),MkB,V:Manticore	4.00
3 CV(c),MkB,E:Bindings	4.00
4 CV(c),MkB,A:Death	5.00
5 CV(c),I:Khara	3.00
6 Sacrifices,pt.I	3.00

7 Sacrifices,pt.II	3.00
8 Tim vs. evil Tim	3.00
9 Artificial Heart,pt.1	2.50
10 Artificial Heart,pt.2	2.50
11 Artificial Heart,pt.3	2.50
12 Small Glass Worlds,pt.1	2.50
13 Small Glass Worlds,pt.2	2.50
14 CV(c),A:The Wobbly	2.50
15 Hell and Back,pt.1	2.50
16 Hall and Back,pt.2	2.50
17 Playgrounds,pt.1	2.50
18 JNR,PrG,Playgrounds,cont.	2.50
19 JNR,PrG,Playgrounds,concl.	2.50
20 Barabatos gives the orders	2.50
21 JNR,PrG,Molly seeks Mayra	2.50
22	2.50
23 JNR,V:Margraves Strafenkinder	2.50
24 JNR,PrG,F:Molly vs. Amadan	2.50
25 JNR,PrG,Death and the Endless	2.50
26 JNR,PrG,Rites of Passage, pt.1	2.50
27 JNR,PrG,Rites of Passage, pt.2	2.50
28 JNR,PrG,Rites of Passage, pt.3, Cupid & Psyche	2.50
29 JNR,PrG,"Rite of Passage"	2.50
30 JNR,PrG,"Rite of Passage"	2.50
31 JNR,PrG,"Rite of Passage"	2.50
32 JNR(s),PSj,"Rites of Passage"	2.50
33 JNR(s),PSj,"Rites of Passage"	2.50
34 JNR(s),PSj,"Rites of Passage"	2.50
35 JNR(s),PrG,"Rites of Passage"	2.50
36 JNR,"Rites of Passage" cont	2.50
37 JNR,"Rites of Passage" cont.	2.50
38 JNR,"Rites of Passage" concl.	2.50
39 PrG, at Sphinx casino	2.50
40 JNR(s),F:Tim & Molly	2.50
41 JNR(s),V:Gargoyles	2.50
42 JNR(s),JIT,magical havok	2.50
43 JNR(s),PrG,F:The Wobbly	2.50
44 JNR(s),goodbye to Zatanna	2.50
45 JNR(s) Slave of Heavens, pt.1	2.50
46 JNR(s) Slave of Heavens, pt.2	2.50
47 JNR(s) Slave of Heavens, pt.3	2.50
48 JNR(s) Slave of Heavens, pt.4	2.50
49 JNR(s) Slave of Heavens, pt.5	2.50
50 JNR(s) Slave of Heavens, pt.6	2.50
51 PrG,MK,an Opener	2.50
52 PrG,MK,Homecoming	2.50
Ann.#2 JNR(s) Minotaur	4.00
TPB Rep. #5-#13 & Rave #1	12.95
TPB Reckonings, 192pg. rep. #14-#20	12.95
TPB rep mini-series	20.00
TPB Bindings, GyA,PrG,WK	13.00
TPB Transformations PrG,MK	13.00

BOOSTER GOLD
1986–88

1 DJ,V:Blackguard	2.00
2 DJ,V:Minddancer	1.50
3 DJ,V:Minddancer	1.50
4 DJ,V:Minddancer	1.50
5 DJ,V:Fascinator	1.50
6 DJ,A:Superman	1.00
7 DJ,A:Superman	1.00
8 DJ,A:Braniac 5,Cham.Boy, Ultra Boy,pt.1	1.25
9 DJ,A:Braniac 5,Cham.Boy, Ultra Boy,pt.2	1.25
10 DJ,V:1000	1.00
11 DJ,V:Shockwave	1.00
12 DJ,Booster Weakening	1.00
13 DJ,I:Rip Hunter(modern)	1.00
14 DJ,Rip Hunter	1.00
15 DJ,Rip Hunter	1.00
16 DJ,Boosters new company	1.00

Booster Gold #24 © DC Comics, Inc.

17 DJ,A:Cheshire & Hawk 1.00
18 DJ,V:Broderick 1.00
19 DJ,V:Rainbow Raider 1.00
20 DJ,V:Rainbow Raider 1.00
21 DJ,Goldstar captured by aliens . 1.00
22 DJ,A:J.L.I.,D:Goldstar 1.00
23 DJ,A:Superman & Luthor 1.25
24 DJ,Millenium 1.00
25 DJ,last issue 1.00

BOY COMMANDOS
Winter, 1942–43
1 S&K,O:Liberty Belle;Sandman
  & Newsboy Legion 4,500.00
2 S&K 1,200.00
3 S&K 800.00
4 . . . . 600.00
5 . . . . 600.00
6 S&K 550.00
7 S&K 400.00
8 S&K 400.00
9 . . . . 400.00
10 S&K 400.00
11 Infinity(c) 400.00
12 thru 16 . . . . @200.00
17 Science Fiction(c) 225.00
18 . . . . 200.00
19 . . . . 200.00
20 . . . . 225.00
21 . . . . 150.00
22 . . . . 150.00
23 S&K,S&K,(c) 175.00
24 . . . . 160.00
25 . . . . 160.00
26 Science Fiction(c) 200.00
27 . . . . 150.00
28 . . . . 150.00
29 S&K story 160.00
30 Baseball Storm 150.00
31 . . . . 150.00
32 A:Dale Evans(c) 160.00
33 . . . . 150.00
34 I:Wolf 150.00
35 . . . . 150.00
36 Nov.–Dec., 1949 . . . . 225.00

BRAVE AND THE BOLD
Aug.–Sept., 1955
1 JKu,RH,IN,I:VikingPrince,Golden
  Gladiator,Silent Knight . . . 2,800.00
2 F:Viking Prince 1,200.00
3 F:Viking Prince 650.00
4 F:Viking Prince 650.00
5 B:Robin Hood 700.00
6 JKu,F:Robin Hood,E:Golden
  Gladiator 450.00
7 JKu,F:Robin Hood 450.00
8 JKu,F:Robin Hood 450.00
9 JKu,F:Robin Hood 450.00
10 JKu,F:Robin Hood 450.00
11 JKu,F:Viking Prince 350.00
12 JKu,F:Viking Prince 350.00
13 JKu,F:Viking Prince 350.00
14 JKu,F:Viking Prince 325.00
15 JKu,F:Viking Prince 325.00
16 JKu,F:Viking Prince 325.00
17 JKu,F:Viking Prince 325.00
18 JKu,F:Viking Prince 325.00
19 JKu,F:Viking Prince 325.00
20 JKu,F:Viking Prince 325.00
21 JKu,F:Viking Prince 325.00
22 JKu,F:Viking Prince 325.00
23 JKu,O:Viking Prince 450.00
24 JKu,E:Viking Prince,Silent
  Knight 325.00
25 RA,I&B:Suicide Squad 400.00
26 F:Suicide Squad 350.00
27 Creature of Ghost Lake . . . 325.00
28 I:Justice League of
  America,O:Snapper Carr . . 5,000.00
29 F:Justice League 2,400.00
30 F:Justice League 2,000.00
31 F:Cave Carson 350.00
32 F:Cave Carson 250.00
33 F:Cave Carson 250.00
34 JKu,I&O:S.A. Hawkman . . 2,000.00
35 JKu:F:Hawkman 500.00
36 JKu:F:Hawkman 500.00
37 F:Suicide Squad 400.00
38 F:Suicide Squad 225.00
39 F:Suicide Squad 225.00
40 JKu,F:Cave Carson 150.00
41 F:Cave Carson 150.00
42 JKu,F:Hawkman 300.00
43 JKu,O:Hawkman 350.00
44 JKu,F:Hawkman 250.00
45 CI,F:Strange Sports 75.00
46 CI,F:Strange Sports 75.00
47 CI,F:Strange Sports 75.00
48 CI,F:Strange Sports 75.00
49 CI,F:Strange Sports 75.00
50 F:GreenArrow & JonnJ'onzz 175.00
51 F:Aquaman & Hawkman . . . 250.00
52 JKu,F:Sgt.Rock 150.00
53 ATh,F:Atom & Flash 75.00
54 I&O:Teen Titans 275.00
55 F:Metal Man & Atom 50.00
56 F:Flash & J'onn J'onzz 50.00
57 I&O:Metamorpho 150.00
58 F:Metamorpho 75.00
59 F:Batman & Green Lantern . 100.00
60 A:Teen Titans,I:Wonder Girl 100.00
61 MA,O:Starman,BlackCanary 125.00
62 MA,O:Starman,BlackCanary 125.00
63 F:Supergirl&WonderWoman . 40.00
64 F:Batman,V:Eclipso 60.00
65 DG,FMc,F:Flash & Doom
  Patrol 25.00
66 F:Metamorpho & Metal Men . 25.00
67 CI,F:Batman & Flash 50.00
68 F:Batman,Metamorpho,Joker,

Brave and the Bold #106
© DC Comics, Inc.

  Riddler,Penguin 65.00
69 F:Batman & Green Lantern . . 32.00
70 F:Batman & Hawkman 32.00
71 F:Batman & Green Arrow . . . 32.00
72 CI,F:Spectre & Flash 40.00
73 F:Aquaman & Atom 30.00
74 B:Batman T.U.,A:Metal Men . 30.00
75 F:Spectre 30.00
76 F:Plastic Man 30.00
77 F:Atom 30.00
78 F:Wonder Woman 30.00
79 NA,F:Deadman 60.00
80 NA,DG,F:Creeper 45.00
81 NA,F:Flash 45.00
82 NA,F:Aquaman,O:Ocean
  Master 45.00
83 NA,F:Teen Titans 50.00
84 NA,F:Sgt.Rock 45.00
85 NA,F:Green Arrow 45.00
86 NA,F:Deadman 45.00
87 F:Wonder Woman 25.00
88 F:Wildcat 25.00
89 RA,F:Phantom Stranger 25.00
90 F:Adam Strange 25.00
91 F:Black Canary 25.00
92 F:Bat Squad 25.00
93 NA,House of Mystery 45.00
94 NC,F:Teen Titans 18.00
95 F:Plastic Man 15.00
96 F:Sgt.Rock 15.00
97 NC(i),F:Wildcat 15.00
98 JAp,F:Phantom Stranger . . . 15.00
99 NC,F:Flash 15.00
100 NA,F:Green Arrow 40.00
101 JA,F:Metamorpho 10.00
102 NA,JA,F:Teen Titans 12.00
103 FMc,F:Metal Men 7.00
104 JAp,F:Deadman 7.00
105 JAp,F:Wonder Woman 7.00
106 JAp,F:Green Arrow 7.00
107 JAp,F:Black Canary 7.00
108 JAp,F:Sgt.Rock 7.00
109 JAp,F:Demon 7.00
110 JAp,F:Wildcat 7.00
111 JAp,F:Joker 12.50

112 JAp,F:Mr.Miracle. 15.00
113 JAp,F:Metal Men 15.00
114 JAp,F:Aquaman 15.00
115 JAp,O:Viking Prince 15.00
116 JAp,F:Spectre 15.00
117 JAp,F:Sgt.Rock 15.00
118 JAp,F:Wildcat,V:Joker 16.00
119 JAp,F:Man-Bat 6.00
120 JAp,F:Kamandi 6.00
121 JAp,F:Metal Men 6.00
122 JAp,F:Swamp Thing 6.00
123 JAp,F:Plastic Man 6.00
124 JAp,F:Sgt.Rock 6.00
125 JAp,F:Flash 6.00
126 JAp,F:Aquaman 6.00
127 JAp,F:Wildcat 6.00
128 JAp,F:Mr.Miracle 6.00
129 F:Green Arrow,V:Joker 13.00
130 F:Green Arrow,V:Joker 13.00
131 JAp,F:WonderWoman,
    A:Catwoman 8.00
132 JAp,F:King Fu Foom 5.00
133 JAp,F:Deadman 5.00
134 JAp,F:Green Lantern 5.00
135 JAp,F:Metal Men 5.00
136 JAp,F:Metal Men,Green Arr. . 5.00
137 F:Demon 5.00
138 JAp,F:Mr.Miracle 5.00
139 JAp,F:Hawkman 5.00
140 JAp,F:Wonder Woman. 5.00
141 JAp,F:Bl.Canary,A:Joker . . . 12.00
142 JAp,F:Aquaman 4.00
143 O:Human Target 4.00
144 JAp,F:Green Arrow 4.00
145 JAp,F:Phantom Stranger 4.00
146 JAp,F:E-2 Batman 4.00
147 JAp,A:Supergirl 4.00
148 JSon,JAp,F:Plastic Man 4.00
149 JAp,F:Teen Titans 4.50
150 JAp,F:Superman 4.00
151 JAp,F:Flash 4.50
152 JAp,F:Atom 4.00
153 DN,F:Red Tornado 4.00
154 JAp,F:Metamorpho 4.00
155 JAp,F:Green Lantern 4.00
156 DN,F:Dr.Fate 4.00
157 JAp,F:Kamandi 4.00
158 JAp,F:Wonder Woman 4.00
159 JAp,A:Ras al Ghul 4.00
160 JAp,F:Supergirl 4.00
161 JAp,F:Adam Strange 4.00
162 JAp,F:Sgt.Rock 4.00
163 DG,F:Black Lightning 4.00
164 JL,F:Hawkman 4.00
165 DN,F:Man-bat 4.00
166 DG,TA,DSp,F:Black Canary
    A:Penguin,I:Nemesis 4.00
167 DC,DA,F:Blackhawk 4.00
168 JAp,DSp,F:Green Arrow 4.25
169 JAp,DSp,F:Zatanna 4.00
170 JA,F:Nemesis 4.00
171 JL,DSp,V:Scalphunter 4.00
172 CI,F:Firestorm 4.00
173 JAp,F:Guardians 4.00
174 JAp,F:Green Lantern 4.00
175 JAp,A:Lois Lane 4.00
176 JAp,F:Swamp Thing 4.00
177 JAp,F:Elongated Man 4.00
178 JAp,F:Creeper 4.00
179 EC,F:Legion o/Superheroes . 4.00
180 JAp,F:Spectre,Nemesis 4.00
181 JAp,F:Hawk & Dove 4.00
182 JAp,F:E-2 Robin 4.00
183 CI,V:Riddler 4.50
184 JAp,A:Catwoman 5.00

Brave and the Bold #129
© DC Comics, Inc.

185 F:Green Arrow 4.25
186 JAp,F:Hawkman 4.00
187 JAp,F:Metal Men 4.00
188 JAp,F:Rose & Thorn 4.00
189 JAp,A:Thorn 4.00
190 JAp,F:Adam Strange 4.00
191 JAp,V:Joker,Penguin 9.00
192 JAp,F:Superboy 4.00
193 JAp,D:Nemesis 4.00
194 CI,F:Flash 4.00
195 JA,I:Vampire 4.00
196 JAp,F:Ragman 4.00
197 JSon,W:Earth II Batman &
    Catwoman 5.00
198 F:Karate Kid 4.00
199 RA,F:Spectre 4.00
200 DGb,JAp,A:Earth-2 Batman,I:
    Outsiders (GeoForce,Katana,Halo),
    E:Batman T.U.,final issue . . . 12.00

[Limited Series]

1 SAP,Green Arrow/Butcher T.U. . 2.00
2 SAP,A:Black Canary,Question . 2.00
3 SAP,Green Arrow/Butcher 2.00
4 SAP,GA on Trial;A:Black
    Canary 2.00
5 SAP,V:Native Canadians,I.R.A. 2.00

BREATHTAKER
1990

1 I:Breathtaker(Chase Darrow) . . 6.00
2 Chase Darrow captured 6.00
3 O:Breathtaker 6.00
4 V:The Man, final issue 4.95

BRAINBANX
DC/Helix Jan. 1997

1 ELe(s),"Down Upon the
    Darkness" 2.50
2 ELe(s),Anna flees to the Sheol 2.50
3 Ele(s),Anna stranded 2.50
4 ELe(s),Anna & Logan 2.50
5 ELe(s),"To Enter the Kingdom" 2.50
6 (of 6) 2.50

BROTHER POWER, THE GEEK
Sept.–Oct., 1968

1 . . . . 25.00
2 Nov.–Dec., 1968 . . . . 20.00

Bugs Bunny #2 © DC Comics

BUGS BUNNY
1990

1 A:Bugs,Daffy,Search for Fudd
    Statues 1.00
2 Search for Statues cont.
    V:WitchHazel 1.00
3 Bugs&Co.in outer space, final . 1.50

BUTCHER, THE
[Limited Series] 1990

1 MB,I:John Butcher 3.50
2 MB,in San Francisco 3.00
3 MB,V:Corporation 3.00
4 MB,A:Green Arrow 2.50
5 MB,A:Corvus,final issue 2.25

BUZZY
1944–58

1 . . . . 165.00
2 . . . . 75.00
3 thru 5 . . . . @40.00
6 thru 10 . . . . @35.00
11 thru 15 . . . . @25.00
16 thru 25 . . . . @25.00
26 thru 35 . . . . @20.00
36 thru 45 . . . . @15.00
46 thru 77 . . . . @15.00

CAMELOT 3000
Dec., 1982

1 BB,O:Arthur,Merlin 3.50
2 BB,A:Morgan LeFay 3.00
3 BB,J:New Knights 3.00
4 BB,V:McAllister 3.00
5 BB,O:Morgan Le Fay 3.00
6 BB,TA,W:Arthur 3.00
7 BB,TA,R:Isolde 3.00
8 BB,TA,D:Sir Kay 3.00
9 BB,TA,L:Sir Percival 3.00
10 BB,TA,V:Morgan Le Fay 3.00

11 BB,TA,V:Morgan Le Fay 3.00
12 BB,TA,D:Arthur 3.00

CAPTAIN ACTION
[Based on toy] Oct.–Nov., 1968
1 WW,I:Captain Action,Action
  Boy,A:Superman 90.00
2 GK,WW, V:Krellik 40.00
3 GK,I:Dr.Evil 40.00
4 GK,A:Dr.Evil 40.00
5 GK,WW,A:Matthew Blackwell,
  last issue 40.00

CAPTAIN ATOM
March, 1987
1 PB,O:Captain Atom 2.50
2 PB,C:Batman 2.00
3 PB,O:Captain Atom 1.75
4 PB,A:Firestorm 1.75
5 PB,A:Firestorm 1.75
6 PB,Dr.Spectro 1.75
7 R:Plastique 1.75
8 PB,Capt.Atom/Plastique 1.75
9 V:Bolt 1.75
10 PB,A:JLI 2.00
11 PB,A:Firestorm 1.50
12 PB,I:Major Force 1.50
13 PB,Christmas issue 1.50
14 PB,A:Nightshade 1.50
15 PB,Dr.Spectro, Major Force . . 1.50
16 PB,A:JLI,V:Red Tornado 1.75
17 V:Red Tornado;A:Swamp
  Thing,JLI 1.75
18 PB,A:Major Force 1.50
19 PB,Drug War 1.50
20 FMc,BlueBeetle 1.50
21 PB,A:Plastique,Nightshade . . . 1.50
22 PB,A:MaxLord,Nightshade,
  Plastique 1.50
23 PB,V:The Ghost 1.50
24 PB,Invasion X-over 1.50
25 PB,Invvasion X-over 1.50
26 A:JLA,Top Secret,pt.1 . . . . . . 1.75
27 A:JLA,Top Secret,pt.2 . . . . . . 1.75
28 V:Ghost, Top Secret,pt.3 . . . . 1.50
29 RT,Captain Atom cleared
  (new direction) 1.50
30 Janus Directive #11,V:Black
  Manta 1.50
31 RT,Capt.Atom's Powers,
  A:Rocket Red 1.50
32 Loses Powers 1.50
33 A:Batman 2.00
34 C:JLE 1.50
35 RT,Secret o/t Silver Shield,
  A:Major Force 1.50
36 RT,Las Vegas Battle,A:Major
  Force 1.50
37 I:New Atomic Skull 1.25
38 RT,A:Red Tornado,
  Black Racer 1.25
39 RT,A:Red Tornado 1.25
40 RT,V:Kobra 1.25
41 RT,A:Black Racer,
  Red Tornado 1.25
42 RT,A:Phantom Stranger,Red
  Tornado,Black Racer,
  Death from Sandman 1.25
43 RT,V:Nekron 1.25
44 RT,V:Plastique 1.25
45 RT,A:The Ghost,I:Ironfire 1.25
46 RT,A:Superman 1.25
47 RT,A:SupermanV:Ghost 1.25
48 RT,R:Red Tornado 1.25
49 RT,Plastique on trial 1.25

50 RT,V:The Ghost,DoubleSize . . 2.50
51 RT 1.25
52 RT,Terror on RTE.91' 1.25
53 RT,A:Aquaman 1.25
54 RT,A:Rasputin,Shadowstorm . . 1.25
55 RT,Inside Quantum Field 1.25
56 RT,Quantum Field cont. 1.25
57 RT,V:ShadowStorm,
  Quantum.Field 1.25
Ann.#1 I:Maj.Force 1.50
Ann.#2 A:RocketRed,Maj.Force . . 1.50

CAPTAIN CARROT
March, 1982
1 RA,A:Superman,Starro 1.25
2 AA 1.00
3 thru 19 . . . . @1.00
20 A:Changeling,Nov., 1983 . . . . 1.00

CAPTAIN STORM
May-June, 1964
1 IN(c),Killer Hunt 35.00
2 IN(c),First Shot-Last Shot . . . 20.00
3 JKu,Death of a PT Boat 20.00
4 IN(c),First Command-Last
  Command 20.00
5 IN(c), Killer Torpedo 20.00
6 JKu,IN(c),Medals For An Ocean20.00
7 IN(c),A Bullet For The General 20.00
8 IN(c),Death of a Sub 20.00
9 IN(c),Sink That Flattop 20.00
10 IN(c),Only The Last Man Lives 20.00
11 IN(c),Ride a Hot Torpedo . . . 20.00
12 JKu(c),T.N.T. Tea Party Abroad
  PT 47 . . . . 20.00
13 JKu,Yankee Banzai 20.00
14 RH(c),Sink Capt. Storm 20.00
15 IN(c),My Enemy-My Friend . . 20.00
16 IN(c),Battle of the Stinging
  Mosquito 20.00
17 IN(c),First Shot for a
  Dead Man 20.00
18 March-April, 1967 . . . . 20.00

CARTOON NETWORK PRESENTS
Warner Bros./DC June 1997
1: Dexter's Laboratory 1.75
2: Space Ghost coast-to-coast . . . 1.75
3 Cartoon All-Stars 2.00
4 Dial 'M' for Monkey 2.00
5 Birdman 2.00
6 Cow and Chicken 2.00
7 Wacky Racers 2.00
8 . . . . 2.00
9 Toonami 2.00
10 Cow and Chicken 2.00
11 Wacky Races 2.00
12 Cartoon All-Stars 2.00
13 Toonami 2.00
14 Cow and Chicken 2.00

CATWOMAN
[Limited Series] 1989
1 O:Catwoman 8.00
2 Catwoman'sSister kidnapped . . 6.00
3 Battle 4.00
4 Final,V:Batman 4.00
[Regular Series] 1993–97
0 JBa,O:Catwoman 1.50
1 B:JDy(s),JBa,DG,A:Bane 6.00
2 JBa,DG,A:Bane 3.00
3 JBa,DG,at Santa Prisca 2.75

Catwoman #2 © DC Comics, Inc.

4 JBa,DG, Bane's Secret 2.50
5 JBa,V:Ninjas 2.25
6 JBa,A:Batman 2.25
7 JBa,A:Batman 2.25
8 JBa,V:Zephyr 2.25
9 JBa,V:Zephyr 2.25
10 JBa,V:Arms Dealer 2.25
11 JBa 2.25
12 JBa,Knights End #6,A:Batman . 5.00
13 JBa,Knights End,Aftermath#2 . 2.00
14 JBa,Zero Hour 2.00
15 JBa,new path 2.00
16 JBa,Island forterss 2.00
17 . . . . 2.00
18 . . . . 2.00
19 Amazonia 2.00
20 Hollywood 2.00
21 JBa(c&a)V:Movie Monster
  [new Miraweb format begins] . . 2.00
22 JBa(c&a) Family Ties,pt.1 . . . 2.00
23 Family Ties,pt.2 . . . . 2.00
24 . . . . 2.00
25 A:Robin,Psyba-Rats 2.50
26 AlG,JBa,The Secret of the
  Universe,pt.2 (of 3) 2.00
27 CDi,Underworld Unleashed tie-in2.00
28 CDi,Catwoman enlists help . . . 2.00
29 CDi,A:Penguin 2.00
30 . . . . 2.00
31 . . . . 3.00
32 CDi,JBa,Contagion,pt.9 . . . . . 3.00
33 CDi,JBa,Hellhound,pt.1 . . . . . 2.00
34 CDi,JBa,Hellbound,pt.2 (of 3) . 2.00
35 CDi,JBa 2.50
36 CDi,JBa, Legacy, pt.2 x-over . . 2.00
37 CDi,JBa, Panara, the Leopard
  Woman 2.00
38 DgM(s),JBa,MPn,"Catwoman,
  Year One," pt.1 (of 3) 2.00
39 DgM(s),JBa,MPn,"Catwoman,
  Year One," pt. 2 . . . . 2.00
40 DgM(s),JBa,MPn,"Catwoman,
  Year One," pt. 3 . . . . 2.00
41 DgM(s),JBa,I:MorelandMcShane2.00
42 DgM(s),JBa,"Red Fang and
  Claw," pt.1 . . . . 2.00
43 DgM(s),JBa,"Red Fang and
  Claw," pt.2 . . . . 2.00

DC COMICS

44 DgM(s),JBa,"Red Fang and Claw," pt.3 . . . . 2.00
45 DgM(s),JBa,"Nine Deaths of the Cat" 2.00
46 DgM(s),JBa,F:Two Face, pt.1 . 2.00
47 DgM(s),JBa,F:Two Face, pt.2 . 2.00
48 DgM(s),JBa,V:Morella, pt.1 . . 2.00
49 DgM(s),JBa,V:Morella, pt. 2 . . 2.00
50 DgM(s),JBa,V:Cybercat 3.00
50a metallic cover, collectors ed. . 3.00
51 DgM(s),JBa,F:Huntress,pt.1 . . 2.00
52 DgM(s),JBa,F:Huntress,pt.2 . . 2.00
53 DgM(s),JBa,F:identity learned . 2.00
54 JBa,improving security 2.00
55 JBa, ... 2.00
56 JBa,Cataclysm x-over,pt.6 . . . 2.00
57 JBa,Cataclysm, V:Poison Ivy . . 2.00
58 JBa,F:Scarecrow, pt.1 . . . . . . 2.00
59 JBa,F:Scarecrow, pt.2 . . . . . . 2.00
60 JBa,F:Scarecrow, pt.3 . . . . . . 2.00
61 JBa,Bank robbery 2.00
62 JBa,A:Nemesis 2.00
Ann.#1 Elseworlds Story,A:Ra's Al Ghul 2.95
Ann.#2 JBa(c&a) Year One Annuals, Young Selina Kyle 3.95
Ann.#3 Legends o/t Dead Earth . 2.95
Ann.#4 Pulp Heroes (Macabre) . . 3.95
TPB The Catfile, rep.#15–#19 . . 10.00

CATWOMAN DEFIANT
1 TGr,DG,V:Mr.Handsome 6.00

CATWOMAN PLUS
Sept., 1997
1 LKa,AWi,ALa, F:Screamqueen . 3.00

CATWOMAN/WILDCAT
June 1998
1 (of 4) CDi,TP,SCi,BSf, V:Claw Hammer 2.50
2 CDi,BSt,TP,SCi,BSf 2.50
3 CDi,BSt,TP,SCi,BSf, ... 2.50

CENTURIONS
June, 1987
1 DH,V:Doc Terror 1.00
2 DH,O:Centurions 1.00
3 DH,V:Doc Terror 1.00
4 DH,Sept., 1987 . . . . 1.00

CHAIN GANG WAR
1993–94
1 I:Chain Gang 2.50
2 V:8-Ball 1.75
3 C:Deathstroke 1.75
4 C:Deathstroke 1.75
5 Embossed(c),A:Deathstroke . . 2.50
6 A:Deathstroke,Batman 1.75
7 V:Crooked Man 1.75
8 B:Crooked Man 1.75
9 V:Crooked Man 1.75
10 A:Deathstroke,C:Batman 1.75
11 A:Batman 1.75
12 E:Crooked Man,D:Chain Gang, Final Issue 1.75

CHALLENGERS OF THE UNKNOWN
1958–78
1 JK&JK(c),The Man Who Tampered With Infinity . . . 2,200.00
2 JK&JK(c),The Monster Maker 800.00

3 JK&JK(c),The Secret of the Sorcerer's Mirror 700.00
4 JK,WW,JK(c),The Wizard of Time 550.00
5 JK,WW&JK(c),The Riddle of the Star-Stone 550.00
6 JK,WW,JK(c),Captives of the Space Circus 550.00
7 JK,WW,JK(c),The Isle of No Return 550.00
8 JK,WW,JK&WW(c),The Prisoners of the Robot Planet 550.00
9 The Plot To Destroy Earth . . 250.00
10 The Four Faces of Doom . . 250.00
11 The Creatures From The Forbidden World 175.00
12 The Three Clues To Sorcery 175.00
13 The Prisoner of the Tiny Space Ball 175.00
14 O: Multi Man 175.00
15 Lady Giant and the Beast . . 175.00
16 Prisoners of the Mirage World 150.00
17 The Secret of the Space Capsules 150.00

Challengers of the Unknown #52
© DC Comics, Inc.

18 Menace of Mystery Island . . 150.00
19 The Alien Who Stole a Planet 150.00
20 Multi-Man Strikes Back 150.00
21 Weird World That Didn't Exist 150.00
22 The Thing In Challenger Mountain 150.00
23 The Island In The Sky 90.00
24 The Challengers Die At Dawn 90.00
25 Captives of the Alien Hunter . 90.00
26 Death Crowns The Challenge King 90.00
27 Master of the Volcano Men . . 90.00
28 The Riddle of the Faceless Man 90.00
29 Four Roads to Doomsday . . . 90.00
30 Multi-Man...Villain Turned Hero 90.00
31 O:Challengers 90.00
32 One Challenger Must Die . . . 40.00
33 Challengers Meet Their Master 40.00
34 Beachhead, USA 40.00
35 War Against The Moon Beast 40.00
36 Giant In Challenger Mountain 40.00

37 Triple Terror of Mr. Dimension 40.00
38 Menace the Challengers Made 40.00
39 Phantom of the Fair 40.00
40 Super-Powers of the Challengers 40.00
41 The Challenger Who Quit . . . 20.00
42 The League of Challenger-Haters 20.00
43 New look begins 20.00
44 The Curse of the Evil Eye . . . 20.00
45 Queen of the Challenger-Haters 20.00
46 Strange Schemes of the Gargoyle 20.00
47 The Sinister Sponge 20.00
48 A:Doom Patrol 20.00
49 Tyrant Who Owned the World 20.00
50 Final Hours for the Challengers 20.00
51 A:Sea Devil 20.00
52 Two Are Dead - Two To Go . 20.00
53 Who is the Traitor Among Us? 20.00
54 War of the Sub-Humans 20.00
55 D:Red Ryan 20.00
56 License To Kill 20.00
57 Kook And The Kilowatt Killer . 20.00
58 Live Till Tomorrow 20.00
59 Seekeenakee - The Petrified Giant 20.00
60 R:Red Ryan 20.00
61 Robot Hounds of Chang 20.00
62 Legion of the Weird 20.00
63 None Shall Escape the Walking Evil 20.00
64 JKu(c),Invitation to a Hanging 20.00
65 The Devil's Circus 10.00
66 JKu(c),Rendezvous With Revenge 10.00
67 NA(c),The Dream Killers 10.00
68 NA(c),One of Us is a Madman 10.00
69 JKu(c),I:Corinna 10.00
70 NA(c),Scream of Yesterdays . 10.00
71 NC(c),When Evil Calls 10.00
72 NA(c),A Plague of Darkness . 10.00
73 NC(c),Curse of the Killer Time Forgot 10.00
74 GT&NA(c),A:Deadman 22.00
75 JK(c),Ultivac Is Loose 7.00
76 JKu(c),The Traitorous Challenger 7.00
77 JK(c),Menace of the Ancient Vials 7.00
78 JK(c),The Island of No Return . 5.00
79 JKu(c),The Monster Maker . . . 5.00
80 NC(c),The Day The Earth Blew Up 5.00
81 MN&NA(c),Multi-Man's Master Plan 5.00
82 MN&NA(c),Swamp Thing 5.00
83 Seven Doorways to Destiny . . 5.00
84 To Save A Monster 5.00
85 The Creature From The End Of Time 5.00
86 The War At Time's End 5.00
87 final issue, July, 1978 . . . . 5.00

CHALLENGERS OF THE UNKNOWN
1991
1 BB(c) In The Spotlight 1.75
2 . . . . 1.75
3 Challengers 'Split Up' 1.75
4 'Separate Ways' 1.75
5 Moffat 1.75
6 GK(c),Challengers reunited . . . 1.75

7 AAd(c),June pregnant 1.75
8 final issue 1.75

CHALLENGERS OF THE UNKNOWN

1 StG(s),JPL 2.25
2 StG(s),LKa,JPL,SMa,Zombies . 2.25
3 StG(s),JPL,death of Challenger 2.25
4 StG&LKa(s),JPL,SMa,
   O:Challengers 2.25
5 StG&LKa(s)JPL,SMa, V:The
   Fearslayer 2.25
6 StG(s),JPL,SMa,"Convergence"
   pt. 3 x-over 2.25
7 StG(s),JPL,"Past Perfect"
   pt.1 (of 3) 2.25
8 StG(s),JPL,"Past Perfect" pt.2 . 2.25
9 StG(s),JPL,"Past Perfect"pt.3 . . 2.25
10 StG(s),JIT,F:Brenda Ruskin . . . 2.25
11 StG(s),JPL,in Gothan, pt.1 . . . 2.25
12 StG(s),JPL,in Gothan, pt.2 . . . . 2.25
13 StG(s),F:Marlon Corbett 2.25
14 . . . . 2.25
15 StG(s),JPL,Millennium Giants
   pt. 3, x-over 2.50
16 StG(s),JPL,MZ, original Chalis 2.50
17 StG(s),JPL,disappearances . . 2.50
18 StG(s),DRo,MZ, final issue . . . 2.50

CHASE
Dec., 1997

1 JWi,MGy,from Batman #550 . . 2.50
2 JWi,MGy 2.50
3 JWi,MGy,Rocket Reds 2.50
4 JWi,MGy,F:Teen Titans 2.50
5 JWi,MGy,flashback story 2.50
6 JWi,MGy,Chase's past 2.50
7 JWi,Shadowing the Bat,pt.1 . . . 2.50
8 JWi,Shadowing the Bat,pt.2 . . . 2.50
9 JWi,MBr,MGy,A:Green Lantern 2.50

CHECKMATE
April, 1988

1 From Vigilante & Action Comics 3.00
2 Chicago Bombings cont. 2.00
3 V:Terrorist Right 1.50
4 V:Crime Lords Abroad,B.U.Story
   'Training of a Knight' begins . . 1.50
5 Renegade nation of Quarac . . . 1.50
6 Secret Arms Deal 1.50
7 Checkmate Invades Quarac . . . 1.50
8 Consequences-Quarac Invasion 1.50
9 Checkmate's security in doubt . 1.50
10 V:Counterfeiting Ring 1.50
11 Invasion X-over 1.50
12 Invasion Aftermath extra 1.50
13 CommanderH.Stein's vacation 1.50
14 R:Blackthorn 1.50
15 Janus Directive #1 . . . . 1.50
16 Janus Directive #3 . . . . 1.50
17 Janus Directive #6 . . . . 1.50
18 Janus Directive #9 . . . . 1.50
19 Reorganization of Group 1.50
20 'Shadow of Bishop'
   A:Peacemaker,pt.1 . . . . 1.50
21 Peacemaker behind Iron
   Curtain,pt.2 . . . . 1.50
22 Mystery of Bishop Cont.,pt.3 . 1.50
23 European Scientists
   Suicides,pt.4 . . . . 1.50
24 Bishop Mystery cont.,pt.5 . . . . 1.50
25 Bishop's Identity Revealed . . . 1.50
26 Mazarin kidnaps H.Stein's kids 1.50
27 Stein rescue attempt,I:Cypher . 1.50

28 A:Cypher, Bishop-Robots 1.50
29 A:Cypher,Blackthorn 1.50
30 Irish Knight W.O'Donnell/British
   Knight L.Hawkins team-up 1.50
31 V:Cypher International 2.00
32 V:Cypher International 2.00
33 final issue (32 pages) 2.00

CHIAROSCURO: THE PRIVATE LIVES OF LEONARDO DaVINCI
Vertigo 1995–96

1 Biographical, Adult 2.50
2 Two of Da Vinci Sisters 2.50
3 . . . . 2.50
4 F:Salari 2.95
5 Crazy Leonardo 2.95
6 Salai schemes,O:Mona Lisa . . 2.95
7 V:Borgia & Machiavelli 2.95
8 daVinci returns to Florence . . . 2.95
9 . . . . 2.95
10 finale 2.95

CHILDREN'S CRUSADE
Vertigo 1993–94

1 NGa(s),CBa,MkB(i),F:Rowland,
   Payne (From Sandman) 4.75
2 NGa(s),AaK(s),JaD(s),PSj,A:Tim
   Hunter,Suzy,Maxine,final issue 4.50

CHRISTMAS WITH THE SUPER-HEROES
1988–89

1 JBy(c) 2.95
2 PC,GM,JBy,NKu,DG A:Batman
   Superman,Deadman,(last
   Supergirl appearance) 2.95

CHRONOS
Jan., 1998

1 JFM,PGn,SL,Time Travel 2.50
2 JFM,PGn,SL 2.50
3 JFM,PGn,SL, in 1873 . . . . 2.50
4 JFM,PGn,SL,in Chronopolis . . . 2.50
5 JFM,PGn,DHz,SL,WalkerGabriel 2.50
6 JFM,PGn,Tattooed man 2.50
7 JFM,PGn,DRo,SL,Star City . . . 2.50
8 JFM,PGn,DRo,SL,
   V:Metrognomes 2.50

CINDER & ASHE
March, 1988

1 JL,I:Cinder & Ashe 2.00
2 JL,Viet Nam Flashbacks 2.00
3 JL,Truth About Lacey revealed 2.00
4 JL,final issue, June, 1988 . . . . 2.00

CLASH
1991

1 AKu,I:Joe McLash(b/w) 4.95
2 AKu,Panja-Rise to Power 4.95
3 AKu,V:Archons,conclusion 4.95

CLAW THE UNCONQUERED
May-June, 1975

1 . . . . 3.50
2 . . . . 2.50
3 Nudity panel 2.50
4 . . . . 3.00
5 . . . . 2.50

6 . . . . 2.50
7 . . . . 2.50
8 KG 2.50
9 KG/BL,Origin 2.50
10 KG 2.50
11 KG 2.50
12 KG/BL,Aug.–Sept., 1978 . . . . 2.50

The Comet #5 © DC Comics, Inc.

COMET, THE
Impact 1991–92

1 TL,I&O:Comet I:Applejack, Victoria
   Johnson, Ben Lee 1.50
2 TL,A:Applejack,Lance Perry . . . 1.25
3 TL,V:Anti-nuclear terrorists . . . 1.25
4 TL,I&V:Black Hood,I:Inferno . . . 1.25
5 V:Cyborg Soldier 1.25
6 TL,I:The Hangman 1.25
7 'Press Problems' 1.25
8 TL,Comet ID discovered 1.25
9 TL,'Bad Judgment' 1.25
10 Fly/Comet T.U.,V:Dolphus 1.25
11 V:Inferno 1.25
12 V:Inferno 1.25
13 O:Comet's Powers 1.25
14 O:Comet's Powers Pt.2 . . . . . 1.25
15 Rob finds his mother 1.25
16 V:Aliens 1.25
17 "Shocking Truth" 1.25
18 Last Issue 1.25
Ann.#1 Earthquest,w/trading card . 1.75

COMIC CAVALCADE
1942–43

1 Green Lantern, Flash,
   Wildcat, Wonder Woman,
   Black Pirate 8,500.00
2 ShM,B:Mutt & Jeff 1,800.00
3 ShM,B:HotHarrigan,Sorcerer 1,300.00
4 Gay Ghost, A:Scribby,
   A:Red Tornado 1,200.00
5 Green Lantern, Flash
   Wonder Woman 1,100.00
6 Flash, Wonder Woman
   Green Lantern 900.00
7 A:Red Tornado, E:Scribby . . 900.00
8 Flash, Wonder Woman
   Green Lantern 900.00

DC COMICS

9 Flash, Wonder Woman
Green Lantern 900.00
10 Flash, Wonder Woman
Green Lantern 900.00
11 Flash, Wonder Woman
Green Lantern 700.00
12 E:Red, White & Blue 700.00
13 A:Solomon Grundy 1,100.00
14 Flash, Wonder Woman,
Green Lantern 700.00
15 B:Johnny Peril 700.00
16 Flash, Wonder Woman,
Green Lantern 700.00
17 Flash, Wonder Woman,
Green Lantern 700.00
18 Flash, Wonder Woman,
Green Lantern 700.00
19 Flash, Wonder Woman,
Green Lantern 700.00
20 Flash, Wonder Woman,
Green Lantern 700.00
21 Flash, Wonder Woman,
Green Lantern 700.00
22 A:Atom 700.00
23 A:Atom 700.00
24 A:Solomon Grundy 800.00
25 A:Black Canary 600.00
26 ATh, E:Mutt & Jeff 600.00
27 ATh,ATh(c) 600.00
28 ATh E:Flash, Wonder Woman
Green Lantern 600.00
29 E:Johnny Peril 650.00
30 RG,B:Fox & Crow 350.00
31 thru 39 RG . . . . @175.00
40 RG,ShM 150.00
41 thru 49 RG,ShM . . . . . . @125.00
50 thru 62 RG,ShM . . . . . . @150.00
63 RG,ShM, July 1954 . . . . . 250.00

CONGO BILL
Aug.–Sept., 1954
1 . . . . 700.00
2 . . . . 550.00
3 thru 6 . . . . 500.00
7 Aug.–Sept.,1955 . . . . . . @500.00

CONGORILLA
1992–93
1 R:Congo Bill 2.00
2 BB(c),V:Congo Bill 1.75
3 BB(c),V:Congo Bill 1.75
4 BB(c),V:Congo Bill 1.75

CONQUEROR OF THE BARREN EARTH
1985
1 thru 4 . . . . @1.00

COOL WORLD
1992
1 Prequel to Movie 1.75
2 Movie Adapt. 1.75
3 Movie Adapt. 1.75
4 . . . . 1.75

COPS
1988–89
1 PB,O:Cops,double-size 2.00
2 PB,V:Big Boss 1.50
3 PB,RT,V:Dr.Bad Vibes 1.25
4 BS,A:Sheriff Sundown 1.25
5 PB,Blitz the Robo-Dog 1.25
6 PB,A:Ms.Demeaner 1.25

7 PB,A:Tramplor 1.25
8 PB,V:BigBoss & Ally 1.25
9 PB,Cops Trapped 1.25
10 PB,Dr.Bad Vibes becomes
Dr.Goodvibes 1.25
11 PB,V:Big Boss 1.25
12 PB,V:Dr.Badvibe's T.H.U.G.S . 1.25
13 Berserko/Ms.Demeanor
marriage proposal 1.25
14 A:Buttons McBoom-Boom . . . 1.25
15 Cops vs. Crooks, final issue . . 1.25

COSMIC BOY
Dec., 1986
1 KG,EC,Legends tie-in 2.00
2 KG,EC,'Is History Destiny' . . . 1.25
3 KG,EC,'Past,Present,Future' . . 1.25
4 KG,EC,Legends 1.25

COSMIC ODYSSEY
1988
1 MMi,A:Superman,Batman,John
Stewart,Starfire,J'onnJ'onzz,
NewGods,Demon,JSn story . . 5.00
2 MMi,'Disaster'(low dist) 6.00
3 MMi,Return to New Genesis . . 4.00
4 MMi,A:Dr.Fate, final 4.00

CREEPER, THE
Oct., 1997
1 LKa,SMa,SB,R:Creeper 2.50
2 LKa,SMa,SB,A:Dr. Skolos . . . 2.50
3 LKa,SMa,SB,V:Proteus 2.50
4 LKa,SMa,SB 2.50
5 LKa,SMa,SB, new job 2.50
6 LKa,SMa,SB, strange meals . . 2.50
7 LKa,SMa,SB,F:Joker, pt.1 . . . 2.50
8 LKa,SMa,SB,F:Joker, pt.2 . . . 2.50
9 DAn,ALa,All-star issue 2.50
10 LKa,SB,Jack Ryder 2.50
11 LKa,SB,SMa,Creeper splits
again 2.50

CRIMSON AVENGER
1988
1 Mini-series 1.00
2 V:Black Cross 1.00
3 'V:Killers of the Dark Cross' . . . 1.00
4 'V:Dark Cross,final issue 1.00

CRISIS ON INFINITE EARTHS
April, 1985
1 B:MWn(s),GP,DG,I:Pariah,I&O:Alex
Luthor,D:Crime Syndicate 7.00
2 GP,DG,V:Psycho Pirate,
A:Joker,Batman 6.00
3 GP,DG,D:Losers 5.00
4 GP,D:Monitor,I:2nd Dr.Light . . 5.00
5 GP,JOy,I:Anti-Monitor 5.00
6 GP,JOy,I:2nd Wildcat,A:Fawcett,
Quality & Charlton heroes . . . 5.00
7 GP,JOy,DG,D:Supergirl 7.00
8 GP,JOy,D:1st Flash 9.00
9 GP,JOy,D:Aquagirl 4.00
10 GP,JOy,D:Psimon,A:Spectre . 4.00
11 GP,JOy,D:Angle Man 5.00
12 E:MWn(s),GP,JOy,D:Huntress,Kole,
Kid Flash becomes 2nd Flash,
D:Earth 2 . . . . 5.00

CRUCIBLE
Impact 1993
1 JQ,F:The Comet 1.25
2 JQ,A:Black Hood,Comet 1.50
3 JQ,Comet Vs.Black Hood . . . 1.50.
4 JQ,V:Tomorrow Men 1.50
5 JQ,Black Hod vs Shield 1.25
6 JQ,V:The Crucible 1.25

Crusaders #7 © DC Comics, Inc.

CRUSADERS
Impact May, 1992
1 DJu(c),I:Crusaders,inc Trading
cards 1.25
2 V:Kalathar 1.00
3 V:Kalathar 1.00
4 Crusaders form as group 1.00
5 V:Cyber-Punks 1.25
6 V:Cyborg Villains 1.25
7 Woj,Low,F:Fireball 1.25
8 Last Issue 1.25

CYBERELLA
DC/Helix Sept. 1996
1 HC(s),DCn, ... 2.25
2 HC(s),DCn,Secret history
revealed 2.25
3 HC(s),DCn,Sunny goes on
rampage 2.25
4 HC(s),DCn,Attack on MacroCorp 2.25
5 HC(s),DCn,V:Army of
Necronauts 2.25
6 HC(s),DCn, ... 2.25
7 HC(s),DCn,Trip to Hell 2.25
8 HC(s),DCn,V:BTIII, concl. 2.50
9 DCn, The Informers 2.25
10 HC(s),DCn,Wuvzums,
Digitina,pt.1 . . . . 2.25
11 HC(s),DCn,Wuvzums,pt.2 . . . 2.25
12 HC(s),final issue 2.50

DALE EVANS COMICS
1948–52
1 Ph(c),ATh,B:Sierra Smith . . . 800.00
2 Ph(c),ATh 400.00
3 ATh 225.00
4 thru 11 . . . . @200.00

DAMAGE
1994–96
1 I:Damage,V:Metallo	2.00
2 V:Symbolix	2.00
3 V:Troll	2.00
4 V:Troll	2.00
5 A:New Titans,V:Baron	2.25
6 Zero Hour,A:New Titans	2.25
7 Trial	2.00
8 Fragments,pt.1	2.00
9 Fragments,pt.2	2.00
10 Fragments,pt.3	2.00
11 Fragments,pt.4	2.00
12 Fragments,pt.5	2.00
13 Picking Up The Pieces,pt.1	2.25
14 Picking Up The Pieces,pt.2 A:The Ray	2.25
15 Picking Up the Pieces,pt.3	2.25
16	2.25
17 V:Bounty	2.25
18 Underworld Unleashed tie-in	2.25
19 Underworld Unleashed tie-in	2.25
20 final issue	2.25

DANGER TRAIL
July-Aug., 1950
1 CI,Ath,I:King For A Day	850.00
2 ATh	600.00
3 ATh	900.00
4 ATh	500.00
5 March-April, 1951	500.00

DANGER TRAIL
1 thru 4 CI,FMc,F:King Faraday V:Cobra	2.00

DARK MANSION OF FORBIDDEN LOVE, THE
Sept.–Oct., 1971
1	6.00
2 and 4 March-April, 1972	@3.50

DARKSEID VS. GALACTUS THE HUNGER
1 Orion vs. Silver Surfer	4.95
GN JBy,in Apokolips	6.00

DARKSTARS
1992–96
0 History	2.00
1 TC(c),LSn,I:Darkstars	3.50
2 TC(c),LSn,F:Ferin Colos	2.50
3 LSn,J:Mo,Flint,V:Evil Star	2.00
4 TC,V:Evilstar	3.00
5 TC,A:Hawkman,Hawkwoman	3.00
6 TC,A:Hawkman	2.50
7 TC,V:K'llash	2.00
8 F:Ferris Colos	2.00
9 Colos vs K'lassh	2.00
10 V:Con Artists	2.00
11 TC,Trinity#4,A:Green Lantern, L.E.G.I.O.N.	2.00
12 TC(c),Trinity#7,A:Green Lantern, L.E.G.I.O.N.	2.00
13 TC(c),V:Alien Underworld	2.00
14 I:Annihilator	2.00
15 V:Annihilator	2.00
16 V:Annihilator	2.00
17 Murders	2.00
18 B:Eve of Destruction	2.00
19 A:Flash	2.00
20 E:Eve of Destruction	2.00
21 A:John Stewart,Donna Troy	2.00
22 A:Controllers	2.25
23 Donna Troy is new Darkstar	2.25
24 Zero Hour,V:HalJordan,Entropy	2.25
25 Stewart	2.25
26 Alien criminals	2.25
27 and 28	@2.00
29 V:Alien Syndicate	2.00
30 A:Green Lantern	2.00
31 V:Darkseid	2.25
32 Crimelord/Syndicate War,pt.3, A:New Titans,Supergirl, Deathstroke	2.25
33 V:Jeddigan	2.25
34	2.25
35 A:Flash	2.25
36 MkF,MC,A:Flash	2.25
37 MkF,MC,Colos vs. Warrior	2.25
38 final issue	2.25

DC CHALLENGE
Nov., 1985
1 GC,Batman	2.50
2 Superman	1.50
3 CI,Adam Strange	1.50
4 GK/KJ,Aquaman	1.50
5 DGb,Dr.Fate,Capt.Marvel	1.50
6 Dr. 13	1.50
7 Gorilla Grodd	1.50
8 DG,Outsiders, New Gods	1.50
9 New Teen Titans,JLA	1.50
10 CS,New Teen Titans,JLA	1.50
11 KG,Outsiders	1.50
12 DCw,TMd,DSp,New Teen Titans, Oct., 1986	2.50

DC COMICS PRESENTS
July-Aug., 1978
[all have Superman]
1 JL,DA,F:Flash	5.00
2 JL,DA,F:Flash	4.00
3 JL,F:Adam Strange	4.00
4 JL,F:Metal Men,A:Mr.IQ	4.00
5 MA,F:Aquaman	4.00
6 CS,F:Green Lantern	4.00
7 DD,F:Red Tornado	4.00
8 MA,F:Swamp Thing	4.00
9 JSon,JA,RH,F:Wonder Woman	4.00
10 JSon,JA,F:Sgt.Rock	4.00
11 JSon,F:Hawkman	3.00
12 RB,DG,F:Mr.Miracle	4.00
13 DD,DG,F:Legion	4.00
14 DD,DG,F:Superboy	3.00
15 JSon,F:Atom,C:Batman	3.00
16 JSon,F:Black Lightning	3.00
17 JL,F:Firestorm	3.00
18 DD,F:Zatanna	3.00
19 JSon,F:Batgirl	3.50
20 JL,F:Green Arrow	2.50
21 JSon,JSa,F:Elongated Man	2.50
22 DD,FMc,F:Captain Comet	2.50
23 JSon,F:Dr.Fate	2.50
24 JL,F:Deadman	2.50
25 DD,FMc,F:Phantom Stranger	2.50
26 GP,DG,JSn,I:New Teen Titans, Cyborg,Raven,Starfire A:Green Lantern	12.00
27 JSn,RT,I:Mongul	4.00
28 JSn,RT,GK,F:Mongul	3.50
29 JSn,RT,AS,F:Spectre	3.50
30 CS,AS,F:Black Canary	3.00
31 JL,DG,AS,F:Robin	3.00
32 KS,AS,F:Wonder Woman	3.00
33 RB,DG,AS,F:Captain Marvel	3.00

DC Comics Presents #20
© DC Comics, Inc.

34 RB,DG,F:Marvel Family	3.00
35 CS,GK,F:Man-bat	3.00
36 JSn,F:Starman	3.50
37 JSn,AS,F:Hawkgirl	3.00
38 GP(c),DH,AS,DG,D:Crimson Avenger,F:Flash	3.00
39 JSon,AS,F:PlasticMan,Toyman	3.00
40 IN,FMc,AS,F:Metamorpho	3.00
41 JL,FMc,GC,RT,I:New Wonder Woman,A:Joker	8.00
42 IN,FMc,F:Unknown Soldier	3.00
43 BB(c),CS,F:Legion	3.00
44 IN,FMc,F:Dial H for Hero	3.50
45 RB,F:Firestorm	3.00
46 AS,I:Global Guardians	3.00
47 CS,I:Masters of Universe	5.00
48 GK(c),AA,IN,FMc,F:Aquaman	3.00
49 RB,F:Shazam!,V:Black Adam	3.00
50 KS,CS,F:Clark Kent	3.00
51 AS,FMc,CS,F:Atom,Masters of the Universe	3.00
52 KG,F:Doom Patrol, I:Ambush Bug	3.00
53 CS,TD,RA,DG,I:Atari Force	3.00
54 DN,DA,F:Gr.Arrow,Bl.Canary	3.00
55 AS,F:Air Wave,A:Superboy	3.00
56 GK(c),F:Power Girl	3.00
57 AS,FMc,F:Atomic Knights	3.00
58 GK(c),AS,F:Robin,Elongated Man	3.00
59 KG,KS,F:Ambush Bug	3.00
60 GK(c),IN,TD,F:Guardians	3.00
61 GP,F:Omac	3.00
62 GK(c),IN,F:Freedom Fighters	3.00
63 AS,EC,F:Amethyst	3.00
64 GK(c),AS,FMc,F:Kamandi	3.00
65 GM,F:Madame Xanadu	3.00
66 JKu,F:Demon	3.00
67 CS,MA,F:Santa Claus	3.00
68 GK(c),CS,MA,F:Vixen	3.00
69 IN,DJ,F:Blackhawk	3.00
70 AS,TD,F:Metal Men	3.00
71 CS,F:Bizarro	3.00
72 AS,DG,F:Phant.Stranger,Joker	5.00
73 CI,F:Flash	3.00
74 AS,RT,F:Hawkman	3.00
75 TMd,F:Arion	3.00

76 EB,F:Wonder Woman	3.00
77 CS,F:Forgotten Heroes	5.00
78 CS,F:Forgotten Villains	5.00
79 CS,AW,F:Legion	3.00
80 CS,F:Clark Kent	3.00
81 KG,BO,F:Ambush Bug	3.00
82 KJ,F:Adam Strange	3.00
83 IN,F:Batman/Outsiders	3.00
84 JK,ATh,MA,F:Challengers	3.00
85 RV,AW,AMo(s), F:Swamp Thing	7.00
86 Crisis,F:Supergirl	3.00
87 CS,AW,Crisis,I:Earth Prime Superboy	3.00
88 KG,Crisis,F:Creeper	3.00
89 MMi(c),AS,F:Omega Men	3.00
90 DCw,F:Firestorm,Capt.Atom	3.00
91 CS,F:Captain Comet	3.00
92 CS,F:Vigilante	3.00
93 JSn(c),AS,KS,F:Elastic Four	3.00
94 GP(c),TMd,DH,Crisis,F:Lady Quark,Pariah,Harbinger	3.00
95 MA(i),F:Hawkman	3.00
96 JSon,KS,F:Blue Devil	3.00
97 RV,F:Phantom Zone Villians, final issue,double-sized	3.00
Ann.#1,RB,F:Earth 2 Superman	3.00
Ann.#2 GK(c),KP,I:Superwoman	2.00
Ann.#3 GK,F:Captain Marvel	2.00
Ann.#4 EB,JOy,F:Superwoman	2.00

DC/MARVEL: ALL ACCESS
October 1996
sequel to DC Versus Marvel

1 (of 4) RMz(s),JG,JRu, crossover crisis again, 48pg	4.00
2 RMz(s),JG,JRu,F:Jubilee,Robin, Daredevil,Two-Face	3.00
3 RMz(s),JG,JRu,F:Doctor Strange, X-Men	3.00
4 RMz(s),JG,JRu,48pg	3.50

DC/MARVEL CROSSOVER CLASSICS
TPB, rep. all x-overs	17.95

DC GRAPHIC NOVEL
Nov., 1983

1 JL,Star Raiders	8.00
2 Warlords	8.00
3 EC,Medusa Chain	8.00
4 JK,Hunger Dogs	15.00
5 Me and Joe Priest	8.00
6 Space Clusters	8.00

DC SCIENCE FICTION GRAPHIC NOVEL
1985–87

1 KG,Hell on Earth	7.00
2 Nightwings	7.00
3 Frost and Fire	7.00
4 Merchants of Venus	7.00
5 Metalzoic	7.00
6 MR,Demon-Glass Hand	7.00
7 Sandkings	7.00

DC SPECIAL
Oct.–Dec., 1968
[All reprint]

1 CI,F:Flash,Batman,Adam Strange, (#1 thru #21 reps)	35.00
2 F:Teen Titans	40.00

3 GA,F:Black Canary	35.00
4 Mystery	20.00
5 JKu,F:Viking Prince/Sgt.Rock	20.00
6 Wild Frontier	20.00
7 F:Strange Sports	20.00
8 Wanted	20.00
9	20.00
10 LAW	20.00
11 NA,BWr,F:Monsters	20.00
12 JKu,F:Viking Prince	20.00
13 F:Strange Sports	20.00
14 Wanted,F:Penguin/Joker	22.00
15 GA,F:Plastic Man	22.00
16 F:Super Heroes & Gorillas	10.00
17 F:Green Lantern	10.00
18 Earth Shaking Stories	10.00
19 F:War Against Gianta	10.00
20 Green Lantern	10.00
21 F:War Against Monsters	10.00
22 Three Musketeers	10.00
23 Three Musketeers	10.00
24 Three Musketeers	10.00
25 Three Musketeers	10.00
26 F:Enemy Ace(rep)	10.00
27 RB,JR,F:Captain Comet	10.00
28 DN,DA,Earth disasters	10.00
29 JSon,BL,O:JSA	10.00

DC SPECIAL SERIES
Sept., 1977

1 MN,DD,IN,FMc,JSon,JA,BMc, JRu,F:Batman,Flash,Green Lantern,Atom,Aquaman	5.00
2 BWr(c),BWr,F:Swamp Thing rep.	5.00
3 JKu(c),F:Sgt.Rock	5.00
4 AN,RT,Unexpected Annual	5.00
5 CS,F:Superman	5.00
6 BMc(i),Secret Society Vs.JLA	5.00
7 AN,F:Ghosts	5.00
8 RE,DG,F:Brave&Bold,Deadman	5.00
9 SD,RH,DAy,F:Wonder Woman	5.00
10 JSon,MN,DN,TA,Secret Origins, O:Dr.Fate	5.00
11 JL,KS,MA,IN,WW,AS,F:Flash	5.00
12 MK(c),RT,RH,TS,Secrets of Haunted House	5.00
13 JKu(c),RT,SBi,RE,F:Sgt.Rock	5.00
14 BWr(c),F:Swamp Thing rep.	5.00
15 MN,JRu,MR,DG,MGo, F:Batman	7.00
16 RH,D:Jonah Hex	20.00
17 F:Swamp Thing rep.	5.00
18 JK(c),digest,F:Sgt.Rock rep.	5.00
19 digest,Secret Origins O:Wonder Woman	5.00
20 BWr(c),F:Swamp Thing rep.	5.00
21 FM,JL,DG,RT,DA,F:Batman, Legion	15.00
22 JKu(c),F:G.I.Combat	5.00
23 digest size,F:Flash	5.00
24 F:Worlds Finest	5.00
25 F:Superman II,Photo Album	5.00
26 RA,F:Superman's Fortress	9.00
27 JL,DG,F:Batman vs.Hulk	14.00

DC SUPER-STARS
1976–78

1 F:Teen Titans rep.	7.00
2 F:DC Super-Stars of Space	5.00
3 CS,F:Superman,Legion	5.00
4 DC,MA,F:Super-Stars of Space	5.00
5 CI,F:Flash rep.	5.00
6 MA,F:Super-Stars of Space	5.00
7 F:Aquaman rep.	5.00
8 CI,MA,F:Adam Strange	7.00

DC Super-Stars #7 © DC Comics, Inc.

9 F:Superman rep.	5.00
10 DD,FMc,F:Superhero Baseball Special,A:Joker	7.00
11 GM,Super-Stars of Magic	5.00
12 CS,MA,F:Superboy	5.00
13 SA	5.00
14 RB,BL,JA,JRu,Secret Origins	5.00
15 JKu(c),RB,RT(i),War Heroes	5.00
16 DN,BL,I:Star Hunters	5.00
17 JSon,MGr,BL,I&O:Huntress,O:Gr. Arrow,D:EarthII Catwoman	7.00
18 RT,DG,BL,F:Deadman,Phantom Stranger	7.00

DC UNIVERSE HOLIDAY BASH
1-shot, yuletide tales	3.95
Holiday Bash II, GN stories, 64pg.	4.00

DC UNIVERSE: TRINITY
1993

1 TC,GeH,BKi,F:Darkstars,Green Lantern,L.E.G.I.O.N.,V:Triarch	3.50
2 BKi,SHa,F:Darkstars,Green Lantern, L.E.G.I.O.N.,V:Triarch	3.50

DC VS. MARVEL
1996

1 RMz	5.50
1 2nd printing	4.00
2 & 3 see Marvel	
4 PDa	5.00

DEAD CORPS(E)
DC/Helix (July 1998)

1 StP, C.J.Rataan	2.50
2 StP, CJ becomes an expired	2.50

DEADMAN
May, 1985

1 CI,NA,rep	3.00
2 NA,rep.	3.00
3 NA,rep.	2.50
4 NA,rep.	2.50
5 NA,rep.	2.50
6 NA,rep.	2.50

Deadman #3 © DC Comics, Inc.

7 NA,rep.Nov., 1985. . . . . 2.50

[Mini-Series] 1986
1 JL,A:Batman 2.50
2 JL,V:Sensei,A:Batman 2.00
3 JL,D:Sensei 2.00
4 JL,V:Jonah, final issue 2.00

DEADMAN: EXORCISM
[Limited-Series] 1992
1 KJo,A:Phantom Stranger 5.25
2 KJo,A:Phantom Stranger 5.25

DEADMAN: LOST SOULS
TPB Mike Baron, Kelly Jones . . 19.95

DEADMAN: LOVE AFTER DEATH
1989–90
1 KJo,Circus of Monsters 4.25
2 KJo,Circus of Monsters 4.25

DEADSHOT
1988–89
1 LMc,From Suicide Squad 2.00
2 LMc,Search for Son 2.00
3 LMc,V:Pantha 1.50
4 LMc,final issue 1.50

DEATH GALLERY
Vertigo
1 DMc(c),NGa Death Sketch
Various Pinups 3.50

DEATH: THE HIGH COST OF LIVING
Vertigo 1993
1 B:NGa(s),CBa,MBu(i),Death
becomes Human,A:Hettie 9.00
1a Platinum Ed. 18.00
2 CBa,MBu(i),V:Eremite,A:Hettie . 4.50
3 E:NGa(s),CBa,MBu(i),V:Eremite,
A:Hettie 3.50
3a Error Copy 7.00
HC 19.95
TPB w/Tori Amos Intro 12.95

DEATH: THE TIME OF YOUR LIFE
Vertigo 1995
1 NGa,MBu,four-issue miniseries 2.95
2 NGa,MBu,F:Foxglove 2.95
3 NGa,MBu,conclusion 2.95
HC NGa(s),rep. #1–#4 . . . . 19.95

DEATHSTROKE: THE TERMINATOR
1991–94
1 MZ(c),(from New Teen Titans)
SE,I:2nd Ravager 4.00
1a Second Printing,Gold 3.00
2 MZ(c),SE,Quraci Agents 3.50
3 SE,V:Ravager 3.00
4 SE,D:2ndRavager(Jackel) 3.00
5 Winter Green Rescue Attempt . 3.00
6 MZ(c),SE,B:City of Assassins,
A:Batman 3.00
7 MZ(c),SE,A:Batman 2.50
8 MZ(c),SE,A:Batman 2.00
9 MZ(c),SE,E:City of Assassins,
A:Batman,I:2nd Vigilante 2.00
10 MZ(c),ANi,GP,A:2nd Vigilante . 2.00
11 MZ(c),ANi,GP,A:2nd Vigilante . 2.00
12 MGo,Short Stories re:Slade . . 2.00
13 SE,V:Gr.Lant.,Flash,Aquaman . 2.00
14 ANi,Total Chaos#1,A:New Titans,
Team Titans,V:Nightwing 2.00
15 ANi,Total Chaos#4,A:New Titans,
Team Titans,I:Sweet Lili 2.00
16 ANi,Total Chaos#7 . . . . 2.00
17 SE,Titans Sell-Out #2
A:Brotherhood of Evil 2.00
18 SE,V:Cheshire,R:Speedy . 2.00
19 SE,V:Broth.of Evil,A:Speedy . 2.00
20 SE,MZ(c),V:Checkmate 2.00
21 SE,MZ(c),A:Checkmate 2.00
22 MZ(c),Quality of Mercy#1 . . . . 2.00
23 MZ(c),Quality of Mercy#2 . . . . 2.00
24 MZ(c),V:The Black Dome 2.00
25 MZ(c),V:The Black Dome 2.00
26 MZ(c),SE,in Kenya 2.00
27 MZ(c),SE,B:World Tour,
in Germany 2.00
28 MZ(c),SE,in France 2.00
29 KM(c),SE,in Hong Kong 2.00
30 SE,A:Vigilante 2.00
31 SE,in Milwaukie 2.00
32 SE,in Africa 2.00
33 SE,I:Fleur de Lis 2.00
34 SE,E:World Tour 2.00
35 V:Mercenaries 2.00
36 V:British General 2.00
37 V:Assassin 2.00
38 A:Vigilante 2.25
39 A:Vigilante 2.25
40 Wedding in Red 2.25
Ann.#1 Eclipso,A:Vigilante 3.75
Ann.#2 SE,I:Gunfire 4.00
Ann.#3 Elseworlds Story 4.25
TPB Full Circle rep#1–#4,
New Titans#70 . . . . 12.95
Becomes:

DEATHSTROKE: THE HUNTED
1994–95
0 Slade 2.50
41 Bronze Tiger 2.25
42 Wounded 2.25
43 . . . . 2.00
44 . . . . 2.00

45 A:New Titans 2.00
Becomes:

DEATHSTROKE
1995–96
46 Checkmate,Wintergreen 2.00
47 I:New Vigilante 2.00
48 Crimelord/Syndicate War,pt.1 . 2.25
49 Crimelord/Syndicate War,pt.4
A:Supergirl, New Titans, Hawkman
Blood Pack 2.25
50 A:Titans,Outsiders,Steel 3.50
51 No Fate or Future,pt.1 . . . . . . 2.25
52 No Fate or Future,pt.2 . . . . . . 2.25
53 The Borgia Plague,pt.1 . . . . . 2.25
54 The Borgia Plague,pt.2 . . . . . 2.25
55 MWn,Rebirth? 2.25
56 MWn,Night of the Karrion,pt.2 . 2.25
57 . . . . 2.25
58 MWn,V:The Joker 2.25
59 MWn,F:Hellriders 2.25
60 MWn,final issue 2.25

DEATHWISH
1994–95
1 New mini-series 1.75
2 F:Rahme 2.50
3 . . . . 2.50
4 V:Boots 2.50

DEMOLITION MAN
1993–94
1 thru 4 Movie Adapt 1.75

Demon 2nd Series #18
© DC Comics, Inc.

DEMON
[1st Regular Series] 1972–74
1 JK,I:Demon 15.00
2 JK 7.00
3 JK 6.00
4 JK 6.00
5 JK 6.00
6 JK 5.00
7 JK 5.00
8 JK 5.00
9 JK 5.00

10 JK 5.00
11 JK 5.00
12 JK 5.00
13 JK 5.00
14 JK 5.00
15 JK 5.00
16 JK 5.00

[Limited Series] 1987

1 MWg,B:Jason Blood's Case . . . 2.00
2 MWg,Fight to Save Gotham . . . 2.00
3 MWg,Fight to Save Gotham . . . 2.00
4 MWg,final issue 2.00

[2nd Regular Series] 1990–95

0 Relationships 2.00
1 VS,A:Etrigan (32 pages) 3.00
2 VS,V:TheCrone 2.50
3 VS,A:Batman 2.25
4 VS,A:Batman 2.25
5 VS,ThePit 2.25
6 VS,In Hell 2.25
7 VS,Etrigan-King of Hell 2.25
8 VS,Klarion the Witch Boy 2.25
9 VS,Jason Leaves Gotham 2.25
10 VS,A:PhantomStranger 2.25
11 VS,A:Klarion,C:Lobo 2.50
12 VS,Etrigan Vs. Lobo 2.50
13 VS,Etrigan Vs. Lobo 2.50
14 VS,V:Odd Squad,A:Lobo 2.50
15 VS,Etrigan Vs.Lobo 2.50
16 VS,Etrigan & Jason Blood
   switch bodies 2.00
17 VS, War of the Gods x-over . . 2.00
18 VS,V:Wotan,A:Scape Goat . . . 2.00
19 VS,O:Demon,Demon/Lobo
   pin-up 3.00
20 VS,V:Golden Knight 2.00
21 VS,Etrigan/Jason,
   A:Lobo,Glenda 2.00
22 MWg,V:Mojo & Hayden 2.25
23 VS,A:Robin 2.00
24 VS,A:Robin 2.00
25 VS,V:Gideon Ryme 2.00
26 VS,B:America Rules 2.00
27 VS,A:Superman 2.00
28 VS,A:Superman 2.00
29 VS,E:America Rules 2.00
30 R:Asteroth 2.00
31 VS(c),A:Lobo 2.00
32 VS(c),A:Lobo,W.Woman 2.00
33 VS(c),A:Lobo,V:Asteroth 2.00
34 A:Lobo 2.00
35 A:Lobo,V:Belial 2.00
36 A:Lobo,V:Belial 2.00
37 A:Lobo,Morax 2.00
38 A:Lobo,Morax 2.00
39 A:Lobo 2.00
40 New Direction,B:GEn(s) 3.50
41 V:Mad Bishop 2.50
42 V:Demons 2.25
43 A:Hitman 10.00
44 V:Gotho-Demon,A:Hitman . . . 15.00
45 V:Gotho-Demon,A:Hitman . . . 15.00
46 R:Haunted Tank 2.50
47 V:Zombie Nazis 2.00
48 A:Haunted Tank,V:Zombie
   Nazis 2.00
49 b:Demon's Son,A:Joe Gun . . . 2.00
50 GEn(s) 3.00
51 GEn(s),Son & Lovers 2.25
52 Etrigan & son–Hitman 4.00
53 Glenda & child–Hitman 4.00
54 Suffer the Children 2.00
55 Rebellion 2.00
56 F:Etrigan 2.00
57 Last Stand 2.00

58 Last issue 2.00
Ann.#1 Eclipso,V:Klarion 3.25
Ann.#2 I:Hitman 15.00

DESTINY: A CHRONICLE OF DEATHS FORETOLD
DC/Vertigo (Sept. 1997)

1 (of 3) F:Destiny of the Endless . 6.00
2 Destiny of the Endless, pt.2 . . . 6.00
3 Destiny of the Endless, pt.3 . . . 6.00

Detective Comics #43
© DC Comics, Inc.

DETECTIVE COMICS
March, 1937

1 I:Slam Bradley 65,000.00
2 JoS 15,000.00
3 JoS 10,000.00
4 JoS 6,500.00
5 JoS 6,000.00
6 JoS 4,500.00
7 JoS 4,500.00
8 JoS,Mr. Chang(c) 7,000.00
9 JoS 4,500.00
10 . . . . 4,500.00
11 . . . . 3,500.00
12 . . . . 3,500.00
13 . . . . 3,500.00
14 . . . . 3,500.00
15 . . . . 3,500.00
16 . . . . 3,500.00
17 I:Fu Manchu 3,500.00
18 Fu Manchu(c) 5,000.00
19 . . . . 3,000.00
20 I:Crimson Avenger 5,500.00
21 . . . . 3,000.00
22 . . . . 3,500.00
23 . . . . 3,000.00
24 . . . . 3,000.00
25 . . . . 3,000.00
26 . . . . 3,000.00
27 BK,I:Batman 165,000.00
28 BK,V:Frenchy Blake 15,000.00
29 BK,I:Doctor Death 25,000.00
30 BK,V:Dr. Death 5,000.00
31 BK,I:Monk 25,000.00
32 BK,V:Monk 5,000.00
33 O:Batman,V:Scarlet Horde 35,000.00

34 V:Due D'Orterre 4,000.00
35 V:Sheldon Lenox 7,500.00
36 I:Hugo Strange 5,500.00
37 V:Count Grutt, last
   Batman solo 5,000.00
38 I:Robin, the Boy Wonder . 30,000.00
39 V:Green Dragon 4,800.00
40 I:Clayface (Basil Karlo) . . . 6,000.00
41 V:Graves 2,800.00
42 V:Pierre Antal 1,800.00
43 V:Harliss Greer 1,800.00
44 Robin Dream Story 1,800.00
45 V:Joker 2,800.00
46 V:Hugo Strange 1,600.00
47 Meets Harvey Midas 1,600.00
48 Meets Henry Lewis 1,600.00
49 V:Clayface 1,600.00
50 V:Three Devils 1,600.00
51 V:Mindy Gang 1,200.00
52 V:Loo Chung 1,200.00
53 V:Toothy Hare gang 1,200.00
54 V:Hook Morgan 1,200.00
55 V:Dr. Death 1,200.00
56 V:Mad Mack 1,200.00
57 Meet Richard Sneed 1,200.00
58 I:Penguin 3,300.00
59 V:Penguin 1,400.00
60 V:Joker,I:Air Wave 1,400.00
61 The Three Racketeers . . 1,200.00
62 V:Joker 1,800.00
63 I:Mr. Baffle 1,200.00
64 I:Boy Commandos,V:Joker 3,300.00
65 Meet Tom Bolton 2,400.00
66 I:Two-Face 2,700.00
67 V:Penguin 1,700.00
68 V:Two-Face 1,400.00
69 V:Joker 1,400.00
70 Meet the Amazing Carlo . . . 900.00
71 V:Joker 1,000.00
72 V:Larry the Judge 800.00
73 V:Scarecrow 900.00
74 I:Tweedledum & Tweedledee 800.00
75 V:Robber Baron 800.00
76 V:Joker 1,300.00
77 V:Dr. Matthew Thorne 900.00
78 V:Baron Von Luger 900.00
79 'Destiny's' Auction 900.00
80 V:Two-Face 1,000.00
81 I:Cavalier 750.00
82 V:Blackee Blondeen 750.00
83 V:Dr. Goodwin 775.00
84 V:Ivan Krafft 750.00
85 V:Joker 900.00
86 V:Gentleman Jim Jewell . . . 700.00
87 V:Penguin 750.00
88 V:Big Hearted John 700.00
89 V:Cavalier 700.00
90 V:Capt. Ben 700.00
91 V:Joker 900.00
92 V:Braing Bulow 600.00
93 V:'Tiger' Ragland 600.00
94 V:Lefty Goran 600.00
95 V:The Blaze 600.00
96 F:Alfred 600.00
97 V:Nick Petri 600.00
98 Meets Casper Thurbridge . . 600.00
99 V:Penguin 900.00
100 V:Digger 950.00
101 V:Joe Bart 600.00
102 V:Joker 850.00
103 Meet Dean Gray 600.00
104 V:Fat Frank gang 600.00
105 V:Simon Gurlan 600.00
106 V:Todd Torrey 600.00
107 V:Bugs Scarpis 600.00

Detective Comics #55
© DC Comics, Inc.

108 Meet Ed Gregory	600.00
109 V:Joker	750.00
110 V:Prof. Moriarty	600.00
111 'Coaltown, USA'	600.00
112 'Case Without A Crime'	600.00
113 V:Blackhand	600.00
114 V:Joker	750.00
115 V:Basil Grimes	600.00
116 A:Carter Nichols, Robin Hood	600.00
117 'Steeplejack's Slowdown'	600.00
118 V:Joker	750.00
119 V:Wiley Derek	600.00
120 V:Penguin	1,300.00
121 F:Commissioner Gordon	600.00
122 V:Catwoman	950.00
123 V:Shiner	600.00
124 V:Joker	700.00
125 V:Thinker	575.00
126 V:Penguin	575.00
127 V:Dr. Agar	575.00
128 V:Joker	700.00
129 V:Diamond Dan mob	575.00
130	575.00
131 V:'Trigger Joe'	450.00
132 V:Human Key	450.00
133 Meets Arthur Loom	450.00
134 V:Penguin	475.00
135 A:Baron Frankenstein, Carter Nichols	450.00
136 A:Carter Nichols	450.00
137 V:Joker	550.00
138 V:Joker,O:Robotman	900.00
139 V:Nick Bailey	450.00
140 I:Riddler	4,000.00
141 V:'Blackie' Nason	500.00
142 V:Riddler	900.00
143 V:Pied Piper	525.00
144 A:Kay Kyser (radio personality)	525.00
145 V:Yellow Mask mob	525.00
146 V:J.J. Jason	525.00
147 V:Tiger Shark	525.00
148 V:Prof. Zero	525.00
149 V:Joker	800.00
150 V:Dr. Paul Visio	525.00
151 I&O:Pow Wow Smith	550.00

152 V:Goblin	550.00
153 V:Slits Danton	550.00
154 V:Hatch Marlin	550.00
155 A:Vicki Vale	550.00
156 'The Batmobile of 1950'	550.00
157 V:Bart Gillis	500.00
158 V:Dr. Doom	500.00
159 V:T. Worthington Chubb	500.00
160 V:Globe-Trotter	500.00
161 V:Bill Waters	525.00
162 Batman on railroad	525.00
163 V:Slippery Jim Elgin	525.00
164 Bat-signal story	525.00
165 'The Strange Costumes of Batman'	525.00
166 Meets John Gillen	525.00
167 A:Carter Nichols, Cleopatra	525.00
168 O:Joker	3,200.00
169 V:'Squint' Tolmar	525.00
170 Batman teams with Navy and Coast Guard	525.00
171 V:Penguin	700.00
172 V:Paul Gregorian	500.00
173 V:Killer Moth	500.00
174 V:Dagger	500.00
175 V:Kangaroo Kiley	500.00
176 V:Mr. Velvet	500.00
177 Bat-Cave story	400.00
178 V:Baron Swane	400.00
179 'Mayor Bruce Wayne'	400.00
180 V:Joker	425.00
181 V:Human Magnet	400.00
182 V:Maestro Dorn	400.00
183 V:John Cook	400.00
184 I:Firefly(Garfield Lynns)	400.00
185 'Secret's of Batman's Utility Belt'	400.00
186 'The Flying Bat-Cave'	400.00
187 V:Two-Face	425.00
188 V:William Milden	400.00
189 V:Styx	400.00
190 Meets Dr. Sampson, O:Batman	575.00
191 V:Executioner	375.00
192 V: Nails Riley	375.00
193 V:Joker	425.00
194 V:Sammy Sabre	375.00
195 Meets Hugo Marmon	375.00
196 V:Frank Lumardi	375.00
197 V:Wrecker	375.00
198 Batman in Scotland	375.00
199 V:Jack Baker	375.00
200 V:Brand Keldon	500.00
201 Meet Human Target	375.00
202 V:Jolly Roger	375.00
203 V:Catwoman	400.00
204 V:Odo Neral	375.00
205 O:Bat-Cave	525.00
206 V:Trapper	375.00
207 Meets Merko the Great	375.00
208 V:Groff	375.00
209 V:Inventor	375.00
210 V:'Brain' Hobson	375.00
211 V:Catwoman	375.00
212 Meets Jonathan Bard	375.00
213 V:Mirror-Man	450.00
214 'The Batman Encyclopedia'	350.00
215 I:Ranger, Legionairy, Gaucho & Musketeer,A:Knight & Squire (See World's Finest 89)	350.00
216 A:Brane Taylor	350.00
217 Meets Barney Barrows	350.00
218 V:Dr. Richard Marston	350.00
219 V:Marty Mantee	350.00
220 A:Roger Bacon, historical	

Detective Comics #147
© DC Comics, Inc.

scientist/philosopher	350.00
221 V:Paul King	350.00
222 V:'Big Jim' Jarrell	350.00
223 V:'Blast' Varner	350.00
224	350.00
225 I&O:Martian Manhunter (J'onn J'onzz)	5,000.00
226 O:Robin's costume, A:J'onn J'onzz	1,200.00
227 A:Roy Raymond, J'onn J'onzz	450.00
228 A:Roy Raymond, J'onnJ'onz	425.00
229 A:Roy Raymond, J'onnJ'onz	425.00
230 A:Martian Manhunter,I:Mad Hatter	500.00
231 A:Batman,Jr.,Roy Raymond J'onn J'onzz	325.00
232 A:J'onn J'onzz	300.00
233 I&O:Batwoman	1,200.00
234 V:Jay Caird	300.00
235 O:Batman's Costume	550.00
236 V:Wallace Walby	350.00
237 F:Robin	300.00
238 V:Checkmate(villain)	300.00
239 Batman robot story	300.00
240 V:Burt Weaver	300.00
241 The Rainbow Batman	300.00
242 Batcave story	250.00
243 V:Jay Vanney	250.00
244 O:Batarang	250.00
245 F:Comm.Gordon	250.00
246	250.00
247 I:Professor Milo	250.00
248	250.00
249 V:Collector	250.00
250 V:John Stannor	250.00
251 V:Brand Ballard	225.00
252 Batman in a movie	225.00
253 I:Terrible Trio	225.00
254 A:Bathound	225.00
255 V:Fingers Nolan	225.00
256 Batman outer-space story	225.00
257 Batman sci-fi story	225.00
258 Batman robot story	225.00
259 I:Calendar Man	225.00

All comics prices listed are for *Near Mint* condition.

DC COMICS

Detective Comics #389
© DC Comics, Inc.

260 Batman outer space story . 225.00
261 I:Dr. Double X 200.00
262 V:Jackal-Head 200.00
263 V:The Professor 200.00
264 . . . . 200.00
265 O:Batman retold 300.00
266 V:Astro 200.00
267 I&O:Bat-Mite 225.00
268 A:"Big Joe" Foster 200.00
269 V:Director 200.00
270 Batman sci-fi story 210.00
271 V:Crimson Knight,O:Martian
   Manhunter(retold) 210.00
272 V:Crystal Creature 210.00
273 A:Dragon Society 150.00
274 V:Nails Lewin 150.00
275 A:Zebra-Man 150.00
276 A:Batmite 150.00
277 Batman Monster story 150.00
278 A:Professor Simms 150.00
279 Batman robot story 150.00
280 A:Atomic Man 150.00
281 Batman robot story 125.00
282 Batman sci-fi story 125.00
283 V:Phantom of Gotham City 125.00
284 V:Hal Durgan 125.00
285 V:Harbin 125.00
286 A:Batwoman 125.00
287 A:Bathound 125.00
288 V:Multicreature 125.00
289 A:Bat-Mite 125.00
290 Batman's robot story 125.00
291 Batman sci-fi story 125.00
292 Last Roy Raymond 125.00
293 A:Aquaman,J'onnJ'onzz . . 125.00
294 V:Elemental Men,
   A:Aquaman 125.00
295 A:Aquaman 125.00
296 A:Aquaman 125.00
297 A:Aquaman 125.00
298 I:Clayface(Matt Hagen) . . 250.00
299 Batman sci-fi stories 90.00
300 I:Mr.Polka-dot,E:Aquaman . 100.00
301 A:J'onnJ'onzz 90.00
302 A:J'onnJ'onnz 80.00
303 A:J'onnJ'onnz 80.00
304 A:Clayface,J'onnJ'onz 80.00

305 Batman sci-fi story 80.00
306 A:J'onnJ'onnz 80.00
307 A:J'onnJ'onnz 80.00
308 A:J'onnJ'onnz 80.00
309 A:J'onnJ'onnz 80.00
310 A:Bat-Mite,J'onnJ'onnz . . . 80.00
311 I:Cat-Man,Zook 90.00
312 A:Clayface,J'onnJ'onnz . . . 70.00
313 A:J'onnJ'onnz 70.00
314 A:J'onnJ'onnz 70.00
315 I:Jungle Man 70.00
316 A:Dr.DoubleX,J'onnJ'onz . . 70.00
317 A:J'onnJ'onnz 70.00
318 A:Cat-Man,J'onnJ'onnz . . . 70.00
319 A:J'onnJ'onnz 70.00
320 A:Vicki Vale 70.00
321 I:Terrible Trio 75.00
322 A:J'onnJ'onnz 65.00
323 I:Zodiac Master,
   A:J'onn J'onnz 65.00
324 A:Mad Hatter,J'onnJ'onnz . . 65.00
325 A:Cat-Man,J'onnJ'onnz . . . 65.00
326 Batman sci-fi story 65.00
327 CI,25th ann,symbol change 125.00
328 D:Alfred,I:WayneFoundation 125.00
329 A:Elongated Man 65.00
330 "Fallen Idol of Gotham" . . . 65.00
331 A:Elongated Man 65.00
332 A:Joker 50.00
333 A:Gorla 50.00
334 . . . . 50.00
335 . . . . 50.00
336 . . . . 50.00
337 "Deep Freeze Menace 50.00
338 . . . . 50.00
339 . . . . 50.00
340 . . . . 50.00
341 A:Joker 60.00
342 . . . . 50.00
343 BK,CI,Elongated Man 50.00
344 . . . . 50.00
345 CI,I:Blockbuster 50.00
346 . . . . 50.00
347 CI,Elongated Man 50.00
348 Elongated Man 50.00
349 BK(c),CI,Blockbuster 50.00
350 Elongated Man 50.00
351 CI,A:Elongated Man,
   I:Cluemaster 50.00
352 BK,Elongated Man 50.00
353 . . . . 50.00
354 BK,Elongated Man,I:Dr.
   Tzin-Tzin 50.00
355 CI,Elongated Man 50.00
356 BK,Outsider,Alfred 50.00
357 . . . . 50.00
358 BK,Elongated Man 50.00
359 I:new Batgirl 100.00
360 . . . . 50.00
361 CI 50.00
362 CI,Elongated Man 50.00
363 CI,Elongated Man 50.00
364 BK,Elongated Man 50.00
365 A:Joker 60.00
366 Elongated Man 50.00
367 Elongated Man 50.00
368 BK,Elongated Man 50.00
369 CA,Elongated Man,
   Catwoman 60.00
370 BK,Elongated Man 55.00
371 BK,Elongated Man 50.00
372 BK,Elongated Man 35.00
373 BK,Elongated Man 35.00
374 BK,Elongated Man 35.00
375 CI,Elongated Man 35.00

Detective Comics #422
© DC Comics, Inc.

376 . . . . 35.00
377 MA,Elongated Man,
   V:Riddler 35.00
378 Elongated Man 35.00
379 CI,Elongated Man 35.00
380 Elongated Man 35.00
381 GaF,Marital Bliss Miss 35.00
382 FR(s),BbB,JoG,GaF(s),SGe 35.00
383 FR(s),BbB,JoG,GaF(s),SGe 35.00
384 FR(s),BbB,JoG,GaF(s),SGe,
   BU:Batgirl 35.00
385 E:FR(s),BbB,JoG,NA(c),GK,MA,
   MkF,BU:Batgirl 35.00
386 BbK,MkF,BbB,JoG,
   BU:Batgirl 35.00
387 RA,rep.Detective #27 . . . . 75.00
388 JBr(s),BbB,JoG,
   GK,MA,FR(s) 50.00
389 FR(s),BbB,JoG,GK,MA . . . 35.00
390 FR(s),BbB,JoG,GK,MA,
   A:Masquerader 35.00
391 FR(s),NA(c),BbB,
   JoG,GK,MA 20.00
392 FR(s),BbB,JoG,I:Jason Bard 20.00
393 FR(s),BbB,JoG,GK,MA . . . 20.00
394 FR(s),BbB,JoG,GK,MA . . . 20.00
395 FR(s),NA,DG,GK,MA 30.00
396 FR(s),BbB,JoG,GK,MA . . . 20.00
397 DON(s),NA,DG,GK,MA . . . 30.00
398 FR(s),BbB,JoG,GK,ViC . . . 20.00
399 NA(c),DON(s),BbB,JoG,
   GK,ViC,Robin 22.00
400 FR(s),NA,DG,GK,I:Man-Bat . 60.00
401 NA(c),FR(s),JoG,
   BbB,JoG,GK,ViC 14.00
402 FR(s),NA,DG,V:Man-Bat . . . 30.00
403 FR(s),BbB,JoG,NA(c),GK,ViC,
   BU:Robin 20.00
404 NA,GC,GK,A:Enemy Ace . . 30.00
405 IN,GK,I:League of Assassins 20.00
406 DON(s),BbB,FrG 20.00
407 FR(s),NA,DG,V:Man-bat . . . 30.00
408 MWn(s),LWn(s),NA,DG,
   V:DrTzin Tzin 30.00
409 B:FR(s),BbB,FrG,DH,DG . . . 20.00
410 DON(s),FR(s),NA,DG,DH . . 30.00
411 NA(c),DON(s),BbB,DG,DH . 18.00

412 NA(c),BbB,DG,DH	18.00
413 NA(c),BbB,DG,DH	18.00
414 DON(s),IN,DG,DH	18.00
415 BbB,DG,DH	18.00
416 DH	18.00
417 BbB,DG,DH,BU:Batgirl	18.00
418 DON(s),DH,IN,DG,A:Creeper	18.00
419 DON(s),DH	18.00
420 DH	18.00
421 DON(s),BbB,DG,DH,A:Batgirl	15.00
422 BbB,DG,DH,Batgirl	15.00
423 BbB,DG,DH	15.00
424 BbB,DG,DH,Batgirl	15.00
425 BWr(c),DON(s),IN,DG,DH	15.00
426 LWn(s),DG,A:Elongated Man	15.00
427 IN,DG,DH,BU:Batgirl	15.00
428 BbB,DG,ENB(s),DD,JoG, BU:Hawkman	15.00
429 DG,JoG,V:Man-Bat	15.00
430 BbB,NC,ENS(s),DG, A:Elongated Man	15.00
431 DON(s),IN,MA	15.00
432 MA,A:Atom	15.00
433 DD,DG,MA	15.00
434 IN,DG,ENB(s),RB,DG	15.00
435 E:FR(s),DG,IN	15.00
436 MA,(i),DG,A:Elongated Man	15.00
437 JA,WS,I:Manhunter	20.00
438 JA,WS,Manhunter	30.00
439 DG,WS,O:Manhunter,Kid Eternity rep.	30.00
440 JAp,WS	30.00
441 HC,WS	20.00
442 ATh,WS	30.00
443 WS,D:Manhunter	30.00
444 JAp,B:Bat-Murderer, A:Ra's Al Ghul	30.00
445 JAp,MGr,A:Talia	30.00
446 JAp,last giant	9.00
447 DG(i),A:Creeper	8.00
448 DG(i),E:Bat-Murderer, A:Creeper,Ra's Al Ghul	8.00
449 'Midnight Rustler in Gotham'	9.00
450 WS	10.00
451	8.00
452	8.00
453	8.00
454	8.00
455 MGr,A:Hawkman,V:Vampire	7.50
456 V:Ulysses Vulcan	7.50
457 O:Batman rtd	10.00
458 A:Man Bat	7.50
459 A:Man Bat	7.50
460	7.50
461 V:Capt.Stingaree	7.50
462 V:Capt.Stingaree,A:Flash	7.50
463 MGr,Atom,I:Calc.,Bl.Spider	7.50
464 MGr,TA,BlackCanary	7.50
465 TA,Elongated Man	7.50
466 MR,TA,V:Signalman	15.00
467 MR,TA	15.00
468 MR,TA,A:JLA	15.00
469 WS,I:Dr.Phosphorus	7.50
470 WS,AM,V:Dr.Phosphorus	7.50
471 MR,TA,A:Hugo Strange	15.00
472 MR,TA,A:Hugo Strange	15.00
473 MR,TA,R:Deadshot	15.00
474 MR,TA,A:Penguin, N:Deadshot	16.00
475 MR,TA,A:Joker	28.00
476 MR,TA,A:Joker	28.00
477 MR,DG,rep.NA	20.00
478 MR,DG,I:3rd Clayface	15.00
479 MR,DG,A:3rd Clayface	15.00
480 DN,MA	8.00

Detective Comics #468
© DC Comics, Inc.

481 JSt,CR,DN,DA,MR, A:ManBat	15.00
482 HC,MGo,DG,A:Demon	8.00
483 DN,DA,SD,A:Demon, 40 Anniv.	12.00
484 DN,DA,Demon,O:1st Robin	6.00
485 DN,DA,D:Batwoman,A:Demon A:Ras al Ghul	5.00
486 DN,DA,DG,I:Odd Man, V:Scarecrow	5.00
487 DN,DA,A:Ras Al Ghul	5.00
488 DN,V:Spook,Catwoman	6.50
489 IN,DH,DN,DA,Ras Al Ghul	5.00
490 DN,DA,PB,FMc,A:Black Lightning;A:Ras Al Ghul	5.00
491 DN,DA,PB,FMc,A:Black Lightning;V:Maxie Zeus	5.00
492 DN,DA,A:Penguin	6.50
493 DN,DA,A:Riddler	6.00
494 DN,DA,V:Crime Doctor	5.00
495 DN,DA,V:Crime Doctor	5.00
496 DN,DA,V:Clayface I	5.00
497 DN,DA	5.00
498 DN,DA,V:Blockbuster	5.00
499 DN,DA,V:Blockbuster	5.00
500 DG,CI,WS,TY,JKu,Dead- man,Hawkman,Robin	12.00
501 DN,DA	5.00
502 DN,DA	5.00
503 DN,DA,Batgirl,Robin, V:Scarecrow	5.00
504 DN,DA,Joker	7.00
505 DN,DA	5.00
506 DN,DA	5.00
507 DN,DA	5.00
508 DN,DA,V:Catwoman	7.00
509 DN,DA,V:Catman,Catwoman	7.00
510 DN,DA,V:Madhatter	5.00
511 DN,DA,I:Mirage	5.00
512 GC,45th Anniv.	5.00
513 V:Two-Face	6.50
514	5.00
515	5.00
516	5.00
517	5.00
518 V:Deadshot	5.00
519	5.00

520 A:Hugo Strange,Catwoman	6.00
521 IN,TVE,A:Catwoman,B:BU:Green Arrow	6.50
522 D:Snowman	5.00
523 V:Solomon Grundy	5.00
524 2nd A:J.Todd	6.00
525 J.Todd	5.00
526 DN,AA,A:Joker,Catwoman 500th A:Batman	20.00
527 V:Man Bat	4.00
528 Green Arrow,Ozone	4.00
529 I:Night Slayer,Nocturna	4.00
530 V:Nocturna	4.00
531 GC,AA,Chimera,J.Todd (see Batman #364)	4.00
532 GC,Joker	7.00
533	4.00
534 GC,A:Gr.Arrow,V:Poisonlvy	4.00
535 GC,A:Gr.Arrow,V:Crazy Quitt 2nd A:New Robin	6.00
536 GC,A:Gr.Arrow,V:Deadshot	4.00
537 GC,A:Gr.Arrow	4.00
538 GC,A:Gr.Arrow,V:Catman	4.00
539 GC,A:Gr.Arrow	4.00
540 GC,A:Gr.Arrow,V:Scarecrow	4.00
541 GC,A:Gr.Arrow,V:Penguin	5.50
542 GC,A:Gr.Arrow	4.00
543 GC,A:Gr.Arrow,V:Nightslayer	4.00
544 GC,A:Gr.Arrow,V:Nightslayer Nocturna	4.00
545	4.00
546	4.00
547	4.00
548 PB	4.00
549 PB,KJ,AMo(s),Gr.Arrow	4.50
550 KJ,AMo(s),Gr.Arrow	4.50
551 PB,V:Calendar Man	4.00
552 V:Black Mask	4.00
553 V:Black Mask	4.00
554 KJ,N:Black Canary	4.00
555 GC,DD,GreenArrow	4.00
556 GC,Gr.Arrow,V:Nightslayer	4.00
557 V:Nightslayer	4.00
558 GC,Green Arrow	4.00
559 GC,Green Arrow	4.00
560 GC,A:Green Arrow	4.00
561	4.00
562 GC,V:Film Freak	4.00
563 V:Two Face	4.00
564 V:Two Face	4.00
565 GC,A:Catwoman	5.50
566 GC,Joker	6.00
567 GC,HarlanEllison	5.00
568 KJ,Legends tie-in,A:Penguin	5.50
569 AD,V:Joker	7.00
570 AD,EvilCatwoman,A:Joker	7.00
571 AD,V:Scarecrow	5.00
572 AD,CI,A:Elongated Man,Sherlock Holmes,SlamBradley,50thAnn	5.00
573 AD,V:Mad Hatter	5.00
574 AD,End old J.Todd/Robin sty	5.00
575 AD,Year 2,pt.1,I:Reaper	15.00
576 TM,AA,Year 2,pt.2, R:Joe Chill	12.00
577 TM,AA,Year 2,pt.3,V:Reaper	12.00
578 TM,AA,Year 2,pt.4, D:Joe Chill	12.00
579 I:NewCrimeDoctor	3.00
580 V:Two Face	3.00
581 V:Two Face	3.00
582 Millenium X-over	3.00
583 I:Ventriloquist	3.00
584 V:Ventriloquist	3.00
585 I:Rat Catcher	3.00
586 V:Rat Catcher	3.00

Detective Comics #532
© DC Comics, Inc.

587 NB,V:Corrosive Man 3.00
588 NB,V:Corrosive Man 3.00
589 Bonus Book #5 .... 4.00
590 NB,V:Hassan 3.00
591 NB,V:Rollo 3.00
592 V:Psychic Vampire 3.00
593 NB,V:Stirh 3.00
594 NB,A:Mr.Potato 3.00
595 IN,bonus book #11 .... 3.00
596 V:Sladek 3.00
597 V:Sladek 3.00
598 DCw,BSz,Blind Justice #1 ... 7.00
599 DCw,BSz,Blind Justice #2 ... 4.00
600 DCw,BSz,Blind Justice #3,
    50th Anniv.(double size) 5.00
601 NB,I:Tulpa 3.00
602 NB,A:Jason Blood 2.50
603 NB,A:Demon 2.50
604 NB,MudPack #1,V:Clayface,
    poster insert 2.50
605 NB,MudPack #2,V:Clayface . 2.50
606 NB,MudPack #3,V:Clayface . 2.50
607 NB,MudPack #4,V:Clayface,
    poster insert 2.50
608 NB,I:Anarky 2.00
609 NB,V:Anarky 2.00
610 NB,V:Penguin 3.00
611 NB,V:Catwoman,Catman .. 3.00
612 NB,A:Vicki Vale 1.75
613 Search for Poisoner 1.75
614 V:Street Demons 1.75
615 NB,Return Penguin #2 (see
    Batman #448-#449) 2.75
616 NB 1.75
617 A:Joker 1.75
618 NB,DG,A:Tim Drake 1.75
619 NB,V:Moneyspider 1.75
620 NB,V:Obeah,Man 1.75
621 NB,SM,Obeah,Man 1.75
622 Demon Within,pt.1 .... 2.00
623 Demon Within,pt.2 .... 2.00
624 Demon Within,pt.3 .... 2.00
625 JAp,I:Abattior 1.75
626 JAp,A:Electrocutioner 1.75
627 600th issue w/Batman,rep.
    Detective #27. .... 4.00
628 JAp,A:Abattoir 1.75

629 JAp,'The Hungry Grass' 1.75
630 JAp,I:Stiletto 1.75
631 JAp,V:Neo-Nazi Gangs 1.75
632 JAp,V:Creature 1.75
633 TMd,Fake Batman? 1.75
634 'The Third Man' 1.75
635 Video Game,pt.1 .... 1.75
636 Video Game,pt.2 .... 1.75
637 Video Game,pt.3 .... 1.75
638 JAp,Walking Time Bomb 1.75
639 JAp,The Idiot Root,pt.2 ..... 1.75
640 JAp,The Idiot Root,pt.4 ..... 1.75
641 JAp,Destroyer,pt.3
    (see LOTDK#27) 2.00
642 JAp,Faces,pt.2 .... 1.75
643 JAp,'Librarian of Souls' 1.75
644 TL,Electric City,pt.1
    A:Electrocutioner 1.75
645 TL,Electric City,pt.2 .... 1.75
646 TL,Electric City,pt.3 .... 1.75
647 TL,V:Cluemaster 1.75
648 MWg(c),TL,V:Cluemaster ... 1.75
649 MWg(c),TL,V:Cluemaster ... 1.75
650 TL,A:Harold,Ace 1.75
651 TL,'A Bullet for Bullock' 1.75
652 GN,R:Huntress 1.75
653 GN,A:Huntress 1.75
654 MN,The General,pt.1 ...... 1.75
655 MN,The General,pt.2 ...... 2.00
656 MN,The General,pt.3,C:Bane . 6.00
657 MN,A:Azrael,I:Cypher 10.00
658 MN,A:Azrael 8.00
659 MN,Knightfall#2,
    V:Ventriloquist,A:Bane 7.50
660 Knightfall#4,Bane Vs.
    Killer Croc 5.00
661 GN,Knightfall#6,V:Firefly,
    Joker,A:Bane 4.00
662 GN,Knightfall#8,V:Firefly,
    Joker,A:Huntress,Bane 3.50
663 GN,Knightfall#10,V:Trogg,
    Zombie,Bird,A:Bane 3.00
664 GN,Knightfall#12,A:Azrael .. 3.00
665 GN,Knightfall#16,A:Azrael .. 3.00
666 GN,SHa,A:Azrael,Trogg,
    Zombie,Bird 2.25
667 GN,SHa,Knightquest:Crusade,
    V:Trigger Twins 2.00
668 GN,SHa,Knightquest:Crusade,
    Robin locked out of Batcave .. 2.00
669 GN,SHa,Knightquest:Crusade,
    V:Trigger Twins 2.00
670 GN,SHa,Knightquest:Crusade,
    F:Rene Montoya 2.00
671 GN,SHa,V:Joker 2.00
672 KJ(c),GN,SHa,Knightquest:
    Crusade,V:Joker 2.00
673 KJ(c),GN,SHa,Knightquest:
    Crusade,V:Joker 2.00
674 KJ(c),GN,SHa,Knightquest:
    Crusade 2.00
675 Foil(c),KJ(c),GN,SHa,Knightquest:
    Crusade,V:Gunhawk,foil(c) .. 3.25
675a Newsstand ed. 1.75
675b Platinum edition 20.00
676 KJ(c),GN,SHa,Knights End #3,
    A:Nightwing 4.00
677 KJ(c),GN,SHa,Knights End #9
    V:Azrael 3.00
678 GN,SHa,Zero Hour 2.00
679 Ratcatcher 2.00
680 Batman,Two-Face 1.75
681 CDi,GN,KJ,Jean-Paul Valley . 1.75
682 CDi,GN,SHa,Return of Bruce
    Wayne,Troika,pt.3 .... 1.75

Detective Comics #675
© DC Comics, Inc.

682a Collector's Edition 2.50
683 R:Penguin,I:Actuary 1.75
684 Daylight Heist 1.75
685 Chinatown War 1.75
686 V:King Snake,Lynx 2.00
687 CDi,SHa,V:River Pirate 2.00
688 V:Captian Fear 2.00
689 F:Black Mask,Firefly 2.00
690 F:Black Mask,Firefly 2.00
691 V:Spellbinder 2.00
692 CDi,SHa,Underworld
    Unleashed tie-in 2.00
693 CDi,SHa,V:Poison Ivy
    & Agent Orange 2.00
694 CDi,find plant-killer 2.00
695 CDi 3.00
696 CDi,GN,SHa,Contagion,pt.8 . 3.00
697 CDi,GN,SHa,pt.1 (of 3)
    V:Lock-up 2.00
698 CDi(s),A:Two-Face 2.00
699 CDi(s), ... 2.00
700 double size, Legacy, pt.1
    x-over, R:Bane 3.50
700a cardstock cover 5.00
701 Legacy, pt. 6 x-over, V:Bane . 2.00
702 CDi(s),GN,SHa,Legacy
    aftermath 2.00
703 CDi(s),GN,SHa, riots in Gotham
    City, Final Night tie-in 2.00
704 CDi(s),GN,TP,V:Al Gabone .. 2.00
705 CDi(s),GN,Riddler & Cluemaster
    clash 2.00
706 CDi(s),GN 2.00
707 CDi(s),GN,Riddler/Cluemaster
    concl. 2.00
708 CDi(s),GN,BSz,F:Deathstroke,
    R:Gunhawk, pt.1 (of 3) 2.00
709 CDi(s),GN,BSz,F:Deathstroke,
    Gunhawk,pt.2 .... 2.00
710 CDi(s),GN,BSz,F:Deathstroke,
    Gunhawk,pt.3 .... 2.00
711 CDi(s),GN,CaS,Bruce Wayne
    fights crime 2.00
712 CDi(s),GN,I:Gearhead 2.00
713 CDi(s),GN,V:Gearhead,pt.2 . . 2.00
714 CDi(s),GN,F:Martian Manhunte2.00
715 CDi(s),GN,F:Martian Manhunter

pt.2 . . . . 2.00
716 CDi,JAp,SNw,BSf, ... 2.00
717 CDi,GN,BSf,V:Gearhead,pt.1 . 2.00
718 CDi,GN,BSf,V:Gearhead,pt.2 . 2.00
719 . . . . 2.00
720 CDi,GN,KJ,Cataclysm
x-over,pt.5 . . . . 2.00
721 CDi,GN,KJ,Cataclysm 2.00
722 CDi,JAp,BSf,Aftershock 2.00
723 CDi,BSz,Brotherhood of
the Fist x-over, pt.2 . . . . 2.00
724 CDi,JAp,BSf,F:Nightwing . . . 2.00
725 CDi,TP,BSf,Aftershock 2.00
726 CDi(s),BSf,V:Joker 2.00
Ann.#1 KJ,TD,A:Question,Talia,
V:Penguin 6.00
Ann.#2 VS,A:Harvey Harris 6.00
Ann.#3 DJu,DG,Batman in Japan . 2.50
Ann.#4 Armageddon,pt.10 . . . . . 3.00
Ann.#5 SK(c),TMd,Eclipso,V:The
Ventriloquist,Joker 3.00
Ann.#6 JBa,I:Geist 2.75
Ann.#7 CDi,Elseworlds Story 3.25
Ann.#8 CDi,KD(c) Year One Annual
O:The Riddler 3.95
Ann.#9 Legends o/t Dead Earth . . 2.95
Ann.#10 Pulp Heroes (War) CDi(s),
SB,KJ 3.95

DETENTION COMICS
Aug. 1996
one-shot DON(s) 64pg, 3 stories . 3.50

DHAMPIRE: STILLBORN
DC/Vertigo Sept. 1996
GN Nancy A. Collins adaptation . . 5.95

Doc Savage (2nd Series) #1
© *DC Comics, Inc.*

DOC SAVAGE
1987–88
1 AKu/NKu,D:Orig. Doc Savage . 3.00
2 AKu/NKu,V:Nazi's 2.50
3 AKu/NKu,V:Nazi's 2.50
4 AKu/NKu,V:Heinz 2.50
[2nd Series] 1988–90
1 'Five in the Sky'(painted cov.) . 3.00

2 Chip Lost in Himalayas 2.25
3 Doc declares war on USSR . . . 2.25
4 DocSavage/Russian team-up . . 2.25
5 V:The Erisians 2.25
6 U.S.,USSR,China Alliance
vs. Erisians 2.25
7 Mind Molder,pt.1, I:Pat Savage 2.25
8 . . . . 2.25
9 In Hidalgo 2.25
10 V:Forces of the Golden God . . 2.25
11 Sunlight Rising,pt.1 . . . . 2.25
12 Sunlight Rising,pt.2 . . . . 2.25
13 Sunlight Rising,pt.3 . . . . 2.25
14 Sunlight Rising,pt.4 . . . . 2.25
15 SeaBaron #1 . . . . 2.25
16 EB,Shadow & Doc Savage . . . 2.25
17 EB,Shadow & Doc Savage . . . 2.25
18 EB,Shadow/DocSavage conc. . 2.25
19 All new 1930's story 2.25
20 V:Airlord & his Black Zepplin . 2.25
21 Airlord (30's story conc.) 2.25
22 Doc Savages Past,pt.1 . . . . . 2.25
23 Doc Savages Past,pt.2 . . . . . 2.25
24 Doc Savages Past,pt.3 (final) . 2.25
Ann.#1 1956 Olympic Games . . . 4.50

DOCTOR FATE
July, 1987
1 KG,V:Lords of Chaos 2.50
2 KG,New Dr. Fate 2.50
3 KG,A:JLI 2.50
4 KG,V:Lords of Chaos Champion 2.50
[2nd Series] 1988–92
1 New Dr.Fate,V:Demons 2.50
2 A:Andrew Bennett(I,Vampire) . . 2.00
3 A:Andrew Bennett(I,Vampire) . . 2.00
4 V:I,Vampire 2.00
5 Dr.Fate & I,Vampire in Europe . 2.00
6 A:Petey 2.00
7 Petey returns home dimension . 2.00
8 Linda become Dr.Fate again . . 2.00
9 Eric's Mother's Ghost,
A:Deadman 2.00
10 Death of Innocence,pt.1 . . . . . 2.00
11 Return of Darkseid, Death of
Innocence,pt.2 . . . . 2.00
12 Two Dr.Fates Vs.Darkseid,
Death of Innocence,pt.3 . . . . . 2.00
13 Linda in the Astral Realm,
Death of Innocence,pt.4 . . . . . 2.00
14 Kent & Petey vs. Wotan 2.00
15 V:Wotan,A:JLI 2.00
16 Flashback-novice Dr.Fate 1.75
17 Eric's Journey thru afterlife . . . 1.75
18 Search for Eric 1.75
19 A:Dr.Benjamine Stoner, Lords of
Chaos, Phantom Stranger,
Search for Eric continued 1.75
20 V:Lords of Chaos,Dr.Stoner,
A:Phantom Stranger 1.75
21 V:Chaos,A:PhantomStranger . . 1.75
22 A:Chaos and Order 1.75
23 Spirits of Kent & Inza Nelson . 1.75
24 L:Dr.Fate Characters 1.75
25 I:New Dr. Fate 1.75
26 Dr.Fate vs. Orig.Dr.Fate 1.75
27 New York Crime 1.75
28 'Diabolism' 1.75
29 Kent Nelson 1.75
30 'Resurrection' 1.75
31 'Resurrection' contd. 1.75
32 War of the Gods x-over 1.75
33 War of the Gods x-over 1.75
34 A:T'Gilian 1.75
35 Kent Nelson in N.Y. 1.75

36 Search For Inza,A:Shat-Ru . . . 1.75
37 Fate Helmet Powers revealed . 1.75
38 'The Spirit Motor,'Flashback . . 1.75
39 U.S.Senate Hearing 1.75
40 A:Wonder Woman 1.75
41 O:Chaos and Order,last issue . 1.75
Ann.#1 TS,R:Eric's dead mother . 2.95

DOME, THE: GROUND ZERO
DC/Helix (July 1998)
1-shot DGb,AMK 8.00

DOOM FORCE
Spec.#1 MMi(c),RCa,WS,PCu,KSy,
I:Doom Force 2.75

DOOM PATROL
[1st series]
(see MY GREATEST ADVENTURE)

DOOM PATROL
[2nd Regular Series]
Oct., 1987
1 SLi,R:Doom Patrol,plus Who's Who
background of team, I:Kalki . . . 3.50
2 SLi,V:Kalki 1.75
3 SLi,I:Lodestone 1.75
4 SLi,I:Karma 1.75
5 SLi,R:Chief 1.75
6 B:PuK(s),EL,GyM(i),
I:Scott Fischer 2.00
7 EL,GyM(i),V:Shrapnel 1.75
8 EL,GyM(i),V:Shrapnel 1.75
9 E:PuK(s),EL,GyM(i),V:Garguax,
& Bonus Book 1.75
10 EL,A:Superman 2.00
11 EL,R:Garguax 1.75
12 EL,A:Garguax 1.75
13 EL,A:Power Girl 1.75
14 EL,A:Power Girl 1.75
15 EL,Animal-Veg-.Mineral Man . . 1.75
16 V:GenImmotus,Animal-Veg.-
Mineral Man 1.75
17 D:Celsius,A:Aquaman & Sea
Devils, Invasion tie-in 3.00
18 Invasion 1.50
19 B:GMo(s),New Direction,
I:Crazy Jane 5.00
20 I:Rebis(new Negative-Being),
A:CrazyJane,Scissormen 4.00
21 V:Scissormen 3.50
22 City of Bone,V:Scissormen . . . 3.50
23 A:RedJack,Lodestone kidnap . 3.50
24 V:Red Jack 3.50
25 Secrets of New Doom Patrol . . 3.50
26 I:Brotherhood of Dada 3.00
27 V:Brotherhood of Dada 3.00
28 Trapped in nightmare,V:Dada . 3.00
29 Trapped in painting,
A:Superman 3.00
30 SBs(c),V:Brotherhood of Dada 3.00
31 SBs(c),A:The Pale Police 3.00
32 SBs(c),V:Cult of
Unwritten Book 3.00
33 SBs(c),V:Cult,A:Anti-God
the DeCreator 3.00
34 SBs(c),Robotman vs. his brain,
R:The Brain & Mr.Mallah 3.00
35 SBs(c),A:Men from
N.O.W.H.E.R.E. 3.00
36 SBs(c),V:Men from
N.O.W.H.E.R.E. 3.25

Doom Patrol #14 © DC Comics, Inc.

37 SBs(c),Rhea Jones Story 2.50
38 SBs(c),V:Aliens 2.50
39 SBs(c),V:Aliens 2.50
40 SBs(c),Aliens 2.50
41 SBs(c),Aliens 2.50
42 O:Flex Mentallo 2.50
43 SBs(c),V:N.O.W.H.E.R.E. ... 2.50
44 SBs(c),V:N.O.W.H.E.R.E. ... 2.50
45 .... 2.50
46 SBs(c),RCa,MkK,A:Crazy Jane,
  Dr.Silence 2.50
47 Scarlet Harlot (Crazy Jane) ... 2.50
48 V:Mr.Evans 2.50
49 TTg(c),RCa,MGb,I:Mr.Nobody . 2.50
50 SBs(c),V:Brotherhood of Dada
  & bonus artists portfolio ... 3.00
51 SBs(c),Mr.Nobody Runs for
  President 2.50
52 SBs(c),Mr.Nobody saga conc . 2.50
53 SBs(c),Parody Issue,A:Phantom
  Stranger,Hellblazer,Mr.E 2.50
54 Rebis'Transformation 2.50
55 SBs(c),V:Crazy Jane,
  Candle Maker 2.50
56 SBs(c),RCa,V:Candle Maker . 2.50
57 SBs(c),RCa,V:Candle Maker,
  O:Team,Double-sized 3.00
58 SBs(c),V:Candle Maker 2.25
59 TTg(c),RCa,SnW(i),A:Candlemaker
  D:Larry Trainor 2.25
60 JHw(c),RCa,SnW(i),
  V:Candlemaker,A:Magnus 2.25
61 TTg(c),RCa,SnW(i),A:Magnus
  D:Candlemaker 2.25
62 DFg(c),RCa,SnW(i),
  V:Nanomachines 2.25
63 E:GMo(s),RCa,R:Crazy Jane,
  V:Keysmiths,BU:Sliding from the
  Wreckage 2.25
Vertigo 1993
64 BB(c),B:RaP(s),RCa,SnW(i),
  B:Sliding from the Wreckage,
  R:Niles Caulder 2.25
65 TTg(c),RCa,SnW(i),Nannos ... 2.25
66 RCa,E:Sliding from the
  Wreckage 2.25
67 TTg(c),LiM,GHi(i),New HQ,I:Charlie,
  George,Marion,V:Wild Girl 2.25

68 TTg(c),LiM,GHi(i),I:Indentity
  Addict 2.25
69 TTg(c),LiM,GHi(i),V:Identity
  Addict 2.25
70 TTg(c),SEa,TS(i),I:Coagula,
  V:Codpiece 2.25
71 TTg(c),LiM,TS(i),Fox & Crow .. 2.25
72 TTg(c),LiM,TS(i),Fox vs Crow . 2.25
73 LiM,GPi(i),Head's Nightmare . 2.25
74 LiM,TS(i),Bootleg Steele 2.25
75 BB(c),TMK,Teiresias Wars#1,
  Double size 2.25
76 Teiresias Wars#2 .... 2.25
77 BB(c),TMK,N:Cliff 2.25
78 BB(c),V:Tower of Babel 2.25
79 BB(c),E:Teiresias Wars 2.25
80 V:Yapping Dogs 2.25
81 B:Masquerade 2.25
82 E:Masquerade 2.25
83 False Memory 2.00
84 The Healers 2.00
85 Charlie the Doll 2.00
86 Imagine Ari's Friends 2.00
87 KB(c),Imagine Ari's
  Friends,pt.4,final issue 2.00
Ann.#1 A:Lex Luthor 2.00
Ann.#2 RaP(s),MkW,Children's
  Crusade,F:Dorothy,A:Maxine .. 4.25
Doom Patrol/Suicide Squad #1 EL,
  D:Mr.104,Thinker,Psi,Weasel . 2.50
TPB Crawling From the Wreckage,
  SBs(c),rep.#19-#25 .... 19.95

DOOMSDAY
Ann.#1 Year One annuals 3.95

DOORWAY TO NIGHTMARE
1978
1 I:Madame Xanadu 1.00
2 .... 1.00
3 .... 1.00
4 JCr 1.00
5 .... 1.00

DOUBLE ACTION COMICS
Jan., 1940
2 Pre-Hero DC 10,000.00

DRAGONLANCE
1988–91
1 Krynn's Companion's advent... 3.50
2 Vandar&Riva vs.Riba's brother 3.50
3 V:Takhesis,Queen of Darkness 3.00
4 V:Lord Soth & Kitiara 3.00
5 V:Queen of Darkness 3.00
6 Gnatch vs. Kalthanan 3.00
7 Raistlin's Evil contd. 3.00
8 Raistlin's Evil concl. 2.00
9 Journey to land o/t Minotaurs
  A:Tanis, Kitiara 2.00
10 Blood Sea,'Arena of Istar' .. 2.00
11 Cataclysm of Krynn Revealed
  'Arena of Istar' contd. 2.00
12 Horak vs.Koraf, Arena contd. . 2.00
13 Test of High Sorcery #1 ..... 2.00
14 Test of High Sorcery #2 ..... 2.00
15 Test of High Sorcery #3 ..... 2.00
16 Test of High Sorcery #4 ..... 2.00
17 Winter'sKnight:DragonkillPt.1 . 2.00
18 Winter'sKnight:DragonkillPt.1 . 2.00
19 Winter'sKnight:DragonkillPt.1 . 2.00

Dragonlance #28 © DC Comics, Inc.

20 Winter'sKnight:Dragonkill.1 . 2.00
21 Move to New World 2.00
22 Taladas,pt.1,A:Myrella 2.00
23 Taladas,pt.2,Riva vs. Dragon . 2.00
24 Taladas,pt.3,V:Minotaur Lord . 2.00
25 Taladas,pt.4,V:Axantheas 2.00
26 Rune Discovery,V:Agents
  of Eristem 2.00
27 V:Agents of Eristem 2.00
28 Riva continued. 2.00
29 Riva continued 2.00
30 Dwarf War,pt.1 .... 1.75
31 Dwarf War,pt.2 .... 1.75
32 Dwarf War,pt.3 .... 1.75
33 Dwarf War,pt.4 .... 1.75
34 conc., last issue 1.75
Ann.#1 Myrella of the Robed
  Wizards 2.95

DREAMING, THE
DC/Vertigo June 1996
1 TLa(s),PSj,"The Goldie
  Factor,"pt.1 .... 2.50
2 TLa(s),PSj,"The Goldie
  Factor,"pt.2 .... 2.50
3 TLa(s),PSj,"The Goldie
  Factor,"pt.3 .... 2.50
4 SvP,"The Lost Boy," pt.1 (of 4) 2.50
5 SvP,"The Lost Boy," pt.2 .... 2.50
6 SvP,"The Lost Boy," pt.3 .... 2.50
7 SvP,"The Lost Boy," pt.4 .... 2.50
8 AaK(s),MZi, visitor from Cain's
  past 2.50
9 BT(s),PD,TOz,"Weird Romance,"
  pt.1 (of 4) 2.50
10 BT(s),PD,TOz,"Weird Romance,"
  pt.2 .... 2.50
11 BT(s),PD,TOz,"Weird Romance,"
  pt.3 .... 2.50
12 BT(s),PD,TOz,"Weird Romance,"
  pt.4 .... 2.50
13 TLa,JIT,"Coyote's Kiss," pt. 1 . 2.50
14 TLa,JIT,"Coyote's Kiss," pt. 2 . 2.50
15 .... 2.50
16 GyA,F:Nuala 2.50
17 PD,DMc,Souvenirs, pt.1 ..... 2.50
18 PD,DMc,Souvenirs, pt.2 .... 2.50

19 PD,DMc,Souvenirs, pt.3	2.50
20 ADv, The Dark Rose, pt.1	2.50
21 ADv, The Dark Rose, pt.2	2.50
22 The Unkindness of One, pt.1	2.50
23 The Unkindness of One, pt.2	2.50
24 The Unkindness of One, pt.3	2.50
25 My Life as a Man	2.50
26 Restitution	2.50
27 Caretaker Cain	2.50
28 victims of famous fires	2.50
29 PSj,DMc,Abel'sHouse ofSecrets	2.50
TPB Beyond the Shores of Night	20.00
GN Trial and Error	6.00

DYNAMIC CLASSICS
Sept.-Oct. 1978

1 Rep. Detective 395 & 438	3.00

ECLIPSO
1992–94

1 BS,MPn,V:South American Drug Dealers	2.50
2 BS,MPn,A:Bruce Gordon	2.00
3 BS,MPn,R:Amanda Waller	2.00
4 BS,A:Creeper,Cave Carson	2.00
5 A:Creeper,Cave Carson	2.00
6 LMc,V:Bruce Gordon	2.00
7 London,1891	2.00
8 A:Sherlock Holmes	1.50
9 I:Johnny Peril	1.50
10 CDo,V:Darkseid	1.50
11 A:Creeper,Peacemaker,Steel	1.50
12 V:Shadow Fighters	1.50
13 D:Manhunter,Commander Steel, Major Victory,Peacemaker, Wildcat,Dr.Midnight,Creeper	1.75
14 A:JLA	1.50
15 A:Amanda Waller	1.50
16 V:US Army	1.50
17 A:Amanda Waller,Martian Manhunter,Wonder Woman,Flash, Bloodwynd,Booster Gold	1.75
18 A:Spectre,JLA,final issue	2.00
Ann.#1 I:Prism	2.50

ECLIPSO: THE DARKNESS WITHIN
1992

1 BS,Direct w/purple diamond, A:Superman,Creeper	4.00
1a BS,Newstand w/out diamond	3.00
2 BS,MPn,DC heroes V:Eclipso, D:Starman	3.00

EGYPT
1995–96

1 College Experiments	2.50
2 College Experiments	2.50
3 New York Haunt	2.50
4 V:Seth,Isis	2.50
5 V: The Priests	2.50
6	2.50
7 finale	2.50

80 PAGE GIANTS
Aug., 1964

1 Superman	500.00
2 Jimmy Olsen	300.00
3 Lois Lane	200.00
4 Golden Age-Flash	225.00
5 Batman	225.00
6 Superman	200.00
7 JKu&JKu(c),Sgt. Rock's Prize	

Battle Tales	200.00
8 Secret Origins,O:JLA,Aquaman, Robin,Atom, Superman	400.00
9 Flash	175.00
10 Superboy	175.00
11 Superman,A:Lex Luthor	175.00
12 Batman	175.00
13 Jimmy Olsen	175.00
14 Lois Lane	175.00
15 Superman & Batman	175.00
16 JLA #39	75.00
17 Batman #176	40.00
18 Superman #183	18.00
19 Our Army at War #164	10.00
20 Action #334	16.00
21 Flash #160	30.00
22 Superboy #129	7.00
23 Superman #187	13.00
24 Batman #182	26.00
25 Jimmy Olsen #95	10.00
26 Lois Lane #68	10.00
27 Batman #185	35.00
28 World's Finest #161	11.00
29 JLA #48	16.00
30 Batman #187	35.00
31 Superman #193	13.00
32 Our Army at War #177	8.00
33 Action #347	11.00
34 Flash #169	30.00
35 Superboy #138	6.00
36 Superman #197	12.00
37 Batman #193	16.00
38 Jimmy Olsen #104	5.00
39 Lois Lane #77	6.00
40 World's Finest #170	10.00
41 JLA #58	12.00
42 Superman #202	12.00
43 Batman #198	24.00
44 Our Army at War #190	5.00
45 Action #360	8.00
46 Flash #178	18.00
47 Superboy #147	7.00
48 Superman #207	12.00
49 Batman #203	14.00
50 Jimmy Olsen #113	5.00
51 Lois Lane #86	6.00
52 World's Finest #179	6.00
53 JLA #67	8.00
54 Superman #212	12.00
55 Batman #208	13.00
56 Our Army at War #203	5.00
57 Action #373	8.00
58 Flash #187	13.00
59 Superboy #156	6.00
60 Superman #217	10.00
61 Batman #213	35.00
62 Jimmy Olsen #122	5.00
63 Lois Lane #95	5.00
64 World's Finest #188	6.00
65 JLA #76	7.00
66 Superman #222	10.00
67 Batman #218	13.00
68 Our Army at War #216	5.00
69 Adventure #390	6.00
70 Flash #196	12.00
71 Superboy #165	6.00
72 Superman #227	10.00
73 Batman #223	14.00
74 Jimmy Olsen #131	5.00
75 Lois Lane #104	4.00
76 World's Finest #197	5.00
77 JLA #85	6.00
78 Superman #232	10.00
79 Batman #228	12.00
80 Our Army at War #229	5.00

81 Adventure #403	6.00
82 Flash #205	9.00
83 Superboy #174	5.00
84 Superman #239	10.00
85 Batman #233	12.00
86 Jimmy Olsen #140	5.00
87 Lois Lane #113	4.00
88 World's Finest #206	5.00
89 JLA #93	6.00

El Diablo #6 © DC Comics, Inc.

EL DIABLO
1989–91

1 I:El Diablo, double-size	2.50
2 V:Crime Lord Benny Contreras	2.00
3 'Day of the Dead' Celebration	2.00
4 Storm #1	2.25
5 Storm #2	2.25
6 Storm #3	2.25
7 Storm #4	2.25
8 V:Car-Theft Ring	2.00
9 V:Crime Lord of Dos Rios	2.00
10 The Franchise #1	2.00
11 The Franchise #2	2.00
12 A:Greg Sanders (golden age)	2.00
13 The River #1	2.00
14 The River #2	2.00
15 The River #3	2.00
16 Final Issue	2.00

ELECTRIC WARRIOR
1986–87

1 SF series,I:Electric Warriors	2.50
2 'Bloodstalker Mode'	2.00
3 Rogue Warrior vs. Z-Primes	2.00
4 Primmies vs. Electric Warriors	2.00
5 Lek 0-03 Rebels	2.00
6 Lek 0-03 vs. Masters	1.75
7 Lek'sFate,Derek Two-Shadows	1.75
8 Derek Two-Shadows Betrayed	1.75
9 Fate of Derek Two-Shadows	1.75
10 Two-Shadows as one	1.75
11 Rebellion	1.75
12 Rebellion continued	1.75
13 V:Prime One	1.75
14 Mutants Join Rebellion	1.75
15 Invaders Arrival	1.75
16 Unified Warriors vs. Invaders	1.75

All comics prices listed are for *Near Mint* condition. **CVA Page 47**

DC COMICS

17 V:Terrans, O:Electric Warriors . 1.75
18 Origin continued, final issue . . 1.75

ELONGATED MAN
1992
1 A:Copperhead 1.00
2 Modora,A:Flash,I:Sonar 1.00
3 A:Flash,V:Wurst Gang 1.00

ELSEWORLD'S FINEST
DC/Elseworlds (Aug, 1997)
1 (of 2) JFM,KD,F:Bruce Wayne
and Clark Kent, ... 5.00
2 JFM,KD,concl. 5.00

ELVIRA
1986–87
1 DSp,BB(c) 3.25
2 thru 9 . . . . @1.00
10 . . . . 2.00
11 DSt(c)Find Cain 2.50

ENIGMA
Vertigo 1993
1 B:PrM(s),DFg,I:Enigma,Michael
Smith,V:The Head 3.00
2 DFg,I:The Truth 3.00
3 DFg,V:The Truth,I:Envelope Girl,
Titus Bird 3.00
4 DFg,D:The Truth,I:Interior
League 3.00
5 DFg,I:Enigma's Mother 3.00
6 DFg,V:Envelope Girl 3.00
7 DFg,V:Enigma's Mother,D:Envelope
Girl,O:Enigma 3.00
8 E:PrM(s),DFg,final issue 3.00
TPB Rep. #1–#8 . . . . 19.95

ERADICATOR
1996
1 IV,Low, ... 1.75
2 IV,Low, ... 1.75
3 IV,Low,"Reign of the Superman"
concl.A:Superboy 1.75

ESSENTIAL VERTIGO: SWAMP THING
DC/Vertigo Sept. 1996
B&W reprints
1 AMo(s), rep. Saga of
the Swamp Thing #21. . . . . . . 2.50
2 thru 11 AMo(s), rep. Saga of
the Swamp Thing #22–#31. @2.00
12 AMo(s) rep. Saga Ann. #2 . . . 2.00
13 AMo(s) rep. Saga #32–#42 . @2.00
24 AMo,Windfall, final issue 2.25

ESSENTIAL VERTIGO: THE SANDMAN
DC/Vertigo 1996
3 NGa(s),SK,MDr,rep. 2.00
4 NGa(s),SK,MDr,rep. F:Etrigan
the Demon 2.00
5 NGa(s),SK,MJ,F:Morpheus,
John Dee 2.00
6 NGa(s),SK,MJ,V:Dr. Destiny . . 2.00
7 . . . . 2.00
8 NGa(s),MDr,MJ,"The Sound
of Her Wings" 2.00
9 NGa(s),MDr,MJ,"The Doll's
House" F:Nada 2.00
10 NGa(s),MDr,MJ,"The Doll's

House" 2.00
11 NGa(s),MDr,RT 2.00
12 NGa(s),CBa,MJ,"The Doll's
House," pt.3 . . . . 2.00
13 NGa,rep. "Doll's House," pt.4 . 2.00
14 NGa,rep. "Doll's House," pt.5 . 2.00
15 NGa,rep. "Doll's House," pt.6 . 2.00
16 NGa,rep. "Lost Hearts" 2.00
17 NGa,rep. "Dream Country" . . . 2.00
18 NGa,"Dream of a Thousand
Cats" 2.00
19 NGa,rep.Sandman #19 . . . . . 2.00
20 NGa,rep.Sandman #20 . . . . . 2.00
21 NGa,rep.Sandman #21 . . . . . 2.00
22 NGa,rep.Season of Mists pt.1 . 2.00
23 NGa,rep.Season of Mists pt.2 . 2.00
24 NGa,rep.Season of Mists pt.3 . 2.00
25 NGa,rep.Season of Mists pt.4 . 2.00
26 NGa,rep.Season of Mists pt.5 . 2.00
27 NGa,rep.Season of Mists,pt.6 . 2.25

EXTREME JUSTICE
1995–96
O New Group 1.50
1 V:Captain Atom 1.50
2 V:War Cyborgs 1.50
3 V:Synge 1.50
4 R:Firestorm the Nuclear Man . . 1.50
5 Firestorm & Elementals 1.75
6 Monarch,Captain Atom, Booster
Gold, Maxima 1.75
7 F:Monarch,Captain Atom 1.75
8 . . . . 1.75
9 F:Firestorm 1.75
10 Underworld Unleashed tie-in . . 1.75
11 Underworld Unleashed tie-in . . 1.75
12 Monarch's scheme revealed . . 1.75
13 Monarch vs. Captain Atom . . . 1.75
14 . . . . 1.75
15 TMo,V:The Slavemaster from
the Stars 1.75
16 TMo,V:Legion of Doom 1.75
17 TMo,V:Legion of Doom 1.75

EXTREMIST
Vertigo 1993
1 B:PrM(s),TMK,I:The Order,
Extremist(Judy Tanner) 2.50
1a Platinum Ed. 12.00
2 TMK,D:Extremist(Jack Tanner) . 2.25
3 TMK,V:Patrick 2.25
4 E:PrM(s),TMK,D:Tony Murphy . 2.25

FACE, THE
GN DFg,PrM 4.95

FAMILY MAN
Paradox 1995
1 I:Family Man 4.95
2 V:Brother Charles 4.95
3 Escape 4.95

FAREWELL MOONSHADOW
DC/Vertigo
GN JMD(s),JMu, prose & pictures 7.95

FATE
1994–96
1 Dr. Fate 2.50
2 Nabu,Astral plane 2.25
3 Bloodstain 2.00
4 Decisions 2.00

5 Judged by Enclave 2.00
6 V:Grimoire 2.00
7 V:Dark Agent 2.00
8 V:Dark Agent 2.25
9 Tries to change his destiny . . . 2.25
10 A:Zatanna 2.25
11 . . . . 2.25
12 A:Sentinel 2.25
13 V:Blaze 2.25
14 LKa,ALa,AWi,Underworld
Unleashed tie-in 2.25
15 LKa,ALa,AWi,V:Charnelle 2.25
16 LKa,ALa,AWi,canibal drug-cult 2.25
17 LKa,ALa,AWi 2.25
18 LKa,ALa,AWi,V:Charnelle 2.25
19 LKa,ALa,AWi,V:men in black . . 2.25

FAULT LINES
DC/Vertigo March 1997
Mini-series
1 LMr(s),F:Tracey Farrand 2.50
2 LMr(s) 2.50
3 LMr(s) 2.50
4 LMr(s) 2.50
5 (of 6) LMr(s) 2.50
6 LMrs(s) concl. 2.00

Fighting American #6 © DC Comics, Inc.

FIGHTING AMERICAN
1994
1 GrL,R:Fighting American 1.75
2 GrL,Media Circus 1.75
3 GrL,I&V:Gross Nation Product,
Def Iffit 1.75
4 GrL,V:Gross Nation Product,
Def Iffit 1.75
5 GrL,PhorOptor 1.75
6 Final Issue 1.75

FINAL NIGHT, THE
Sept. 1996
[Cross-Over Series]
1 KK(s),SI,JMz, Alien crash lands
on Earth 2.00
2 KK(s),SI,JMz, Earth's sun
extinguished 2.00
3 KK(s),SI,JMz, Attempts to stave
off inevitable 2.00

4 KK(s),SI,JMz, Can they save the
world, and at what price? 2.00
TPB rep. 13.00

FIREBRAND
1995
1 SaV,Alex Sanchez becomes
Firebrand 1.75
2 SaV 1.75
3 SaV,Generation Prime case
climax 1.75
4 SaV,Young gang member 1.75
5 SaV,V;serial killer(s) 1.75
6 BAu,SaV 1.75
7 .... 1.75
8 .... 1.75
9 final issue 1.75

FIRESTORM
March, 1978
1 AM,JRu,I&O:Firestorm 4.00
2 AM,BMc,A:Superman 3.00
3 AM,I:Killer Froat 3.00
4 AM,BMc,I:Hyena 3.00
5 AM,BMc,Hyena 3.00

FIRESTORM, THE NUCLEAR MAN
(see FURY OF FIRESTORM)

FIRST ISSUE SPECIAL
April, 1975
1 JK,Atlas 6.00
2 Green Team 7.00
3 Metamorpho 5.00
4 Lady Cop 5.00
5 JK,Manhunter 6.00
6 JK,Dingbats 5.00
7 SD,Creeper 5.00
8 MGr,Warlord 15.00
9 WS,Dr.Fate 7.00
10 Outsiders(not Batman team) . . 5.00
11 NR,AM Code:Assassin 5.00
12 new Starman 5.00
13 return of New Gods 8.00

FLASH COMICS
Jan., 1940
1 SMo,SMo(c),O:Flash,Hawkman,The
Whip & Johnny Thunder,B:Cliff
Cornwall,Minute Movies . 60,000.00
2 B:Rod Rain 6,000.00
3 SMo,SMo(c),B:The King .. 4,500.00
4 SMo,SMo(c),F:The Whip . 3,500.00
5 SMo,SMo(c),F:The King .. 3,000.00
6 F:Flash 4,000.00
7 Hawkman(c) 3,400.00
8 Male bondage(c) 2,200.00
9 Hawkman(c) 2,200.00
10 SMo,SMo(c),Flash(c) ... 2,200.00
11 SMo,SMo(c) 1,500.00
12 SMo,SMo(c),B:Les Watts . 1,500.00
13 SMo,SMo(c) 1,400.00
14 SMo,SMo(c) 1,500.00
15 SMo,SMo(c) 1,400.00
16 SMo,SMo(c) 1,400.00
17 SMo,SMo(c),E:CliffCornwall 1,400.00
18 SMo,SMo(c) 1,400.00
19 SMo,SMo(c) 1,400.00
20 SMo,SMo(c) 1,400.00
21 SMo(c) 1,200.00
22 SMo,SMo(c) 1,200.00
23 SMo,SMo(c) 1,200.00

Flash #11 © DC Comics, Inc.

24 SMo,SMo(c),Flash V:Spider-
Men of Mars,A:Hawkgirl .. 1,500.00
25 SMo,SMo(c) 900.00
26 SMo,SMo(c) 900.00
27 SMo,SMo(c) 900.00
28 SMo,SMo(c),Flash goes
to Hollywood 900.00
29 SMo,SMo(c) 900.00
30 SMo,SMo(c),Flash in'Adventure
of the Curiosity Ray!' 900.00
31 SMo,SMo(c),Hawkman(c) .. 800.00
32 SMo,SM(c),Flash in'Adventure
of the Fictious Villians' 800.00
33 SMo,SMo(c) 800.00
34 SMo,SMo(c),Flash in 'The
Robbers of the Round Table' 800.00
35 SMo,SMo(c) 800.00
36 SMo,SMo(c),F:Flash, The Mystery
of the Doll Who Walks Like
a Man' 800.00
37 SMo,SMo(c) 800.00
38 SMo,SMo(c) 800.00
39 SMo,SMo(c) 800.00
40 SMo,SMo(c),F:Flash, Man Who
Could Read Man's Souls! .. 800.00
41 SMo,SMo(c) 700.00
42 SMo,SMo(c),Flash V:The
Gangsters Baby! 700.00
43 SMo,SMo(c) 700.00
44 SMo,SMo(c),Flash V:The
Liars Club 700.00
45 SMo,SMo(c),F:Hawkman,Big
Butch Makes Hall of Fame . 700.00
46 SMo,SMo(c) 700.00
47 SMo,SMo(c),Hawkman in Crime
Canned for the Duration ... 700.00
48 SMo,SMo(c) 700.00
49 SMo,SMo(c) 700.00
50 SMo,SMo(c),Hawkman, Tale
of the 1,000 Dollar Bill 700.00
51 SMo,SMo(c) 600.00
52 SMo,SMo(c),Flash, Machine
that Thinks Like a Man 600.00
53 SMo,SMo(c),Hawkman, Simple
Simon Met the Hawkman . 600.00
54 SMo,SMo(c),Flash, Mysterious
Bottle from the Sea 600.00
55 SMo,SMo(c),Hawkman, Riddle of

the Stolen Statuette! 600.00
56 SMo,SMo(c) 600.00
57 SMo,SMo(c),Hawkman, Adventure
of the Gangster & the Ghost 600.00
58 SMo,SMo(c),'Merman meets
the Flash' 600.00
59 SMo,SMo(c),Hawkman
V:Pied Piper 600.00
60 SMo,SMo(c),Flash
V:The Wind Master 600.00
61 SMo,SMo(c),Hawkman
V:The Beanstalk 600.00
62 JKu,Flash in 'High Jinks
on the Rinks' 750.00
63 JKu(c),Hawkman in 'The
Tale of the Mystic Urn' 600.00
64 .... 600.00
65 JKu(c),Hawkman in 'Return
of the Simple Simon' 600.00
66 .... 600.00
67 JKu(c) 600.00
68 Flash in 'The Radio that
Ran Wild' 600.00
69 .... 600.00
70 JKu(c) 600.00
71 JKu(c),Hawkman in 'Battle
of the Birdmen' 600.00
72 JKu 600.00
73 JKu(c) 600.00
74 JKu(c) 600.00
75 JKu(c),Hawkman in 'Magic
at the Mardi Gras' 600.00
76 A:Worry Wart 600.00
77 Hawkman in 'The Case of
the Curious Casket' 600.00
78 .... 600.00
79 Hawkman in 'The Battle
of the Birds' 600.00
80 Flash in 'The Story of
the Boy Genius' 600.00
81 JKu(c),Hawkman's Voyage
to Venus 600.00
82 A:Walter Jordan 600.00
83 JKu,JKu(c),Hawkman in
'Destined for Disaster' 600.00
84 Flash V:'The Changeling' .. 600.00
85 JKu,JKu(c),Hawkman in
Hollywood 600.00
86 JKu,1st Black Canary,Flash
V:Stone Age Menace 2,000.00
87 Hawkman meets the Foil .. 900.00
88 JKu,Flash in 'The Case
of the Vanished Year!' 900.00
89 I:The Thorn 900.00
90 Flash in 'Nine Empty
Uniforms' 900.00
91 Hawkman V:The Phantom
Menace 1,000.00
92 1st full-length Black
Canary story 2,500.00
93 Flash V:Violin of Villainy . 1,000.00
94 JKu(c) 1,000.00
95 .... 1,000.00
96 .... 1,000.00
97 Flash in 'The Dream
that Didn't Vanish' 1,000.00
98 JKu(c),Hawkman in
'Crime Costume!' 1,000.00
99 Flash in 'The Star Prize
of the Year' 1,000.00
100 Hawkman in 'The Human
-Fly Bandits!' 2,400.00
101 .... 2,000.00
102 Hawkman in 'The Flying
Darkness' 2,000.00

All comics prices listed are for *Near Mint* condition.

Flash Comics #91 © DC Comics, Inc.

103	2,400.00

104 JKu,Hawkman in 'Flaming
  Darkness' Feb., 1949 .... 6,000.00

FLASH
Feb.–March, 1959

105 CI,O:Flash,I:Mirror
  Master 5,500.00
106 CI,I&O:Gorilla Grodd,
  O:Pied Piper 1,500.00
107 CI,A:Grodd 800.00
108 CI,A:Grodd 700.00
109 CI,A:Mirror Master 500.00
110 CI,MA,I:Kid Flash,
  Weather Wizard 1,350.00
111 CI,A:Kid Flash,The Invasion
  Of the Cloud Creatures ... 350.00
112 CI,I&O:Elongated Man,
  A:Kid Flash 450.00
113 CI,I&O:Trickster 375.00
114 CI,A:Captain Cold 275.00
115 CI,A:Grodd 250.00
116 CI,A:Kid Flash,The Man
  Who Stole Central City 250.00
117 CI,MA,I:Capt.Boomerang . 300.00
118 CI,MA 200.00
119 CI,W:Elongated Man 200.00
120 CI,A:Kid Flash,Land of
  Golden Giants 200.00
121 CI,A:Trickster 175.00
122 CI,I&O:The Top 175.00
123 I:Earth 2,R:G.A.Flash ... 1,100.00
124 CI,A:Capt.Boomerang 150.00
125 CI,A:Kid Flash,The
  Conquerors of Time 135.00
126 CI,A:Mirror Master 135.00
127 CI,A:Grodd 135.00
128 CI,O:Abra Kadabra 135.00
129 CI,A:Capt.Cold,Trickster,A:Gold.
  Age Flash,C:JLA (flashback) 300.00
130 CI,A:Mirror Master,
  Weather Wizard 135.00
131 CI,A:Green Lantern 125.00
132 CI,A:Daphne Dean 125.00
133 CI,A:Abra Kadabra 125.00
134 CI,A:Captain Cold 125.00
135 CI,N:Kid Flash 125.00
136 CI,A:Mirror Master 125.00
137 CI,Vandal Savage,R:JSA,

A:G.A.Flash 450.00
138 CI,A:Pied Piper 125.00
139 CI,I&O:Prof.Zoom(Reverse
  Flash) 150.00
140 CI,O:Heat Wave 120.00
141 CI,A:Top 100.00
142 CI,A:Trickster 100.00
143 CI,A:Green Lantern 100.00
144 CI,A:Man Missile,Kid Flash 100.00
145 CI,A:Weather Wizard 100.00
146 CI,A:Mirror Master 100.00
147 CI,A:Mr.Element,A:Reverse
  Flash 100.00
148 CI,A:Capt.Boomerang ... 100.00
149 CI,A:Abra Kadabra 100.00
150 CI,A:Captain Cold 100.00
151 CI,A:Earth II Flash,
  The Shade 125.00
152 CI,V:Trickster 75.00
153 CI,A:Mr.Element,Rev.Flash . 75.00
154 CI,The Day Flash Ran Away
  with Himself 75.00
155 CI,A:MirrorMaster,Capt.Cold,Top
  Capt. Boomerang,Grodd 75.00
156 CI,A:Kid Flash,The Super Hero
  who Betrayed the World 75.00
157 CI,A:Doralla Kon,The Top .. 75.00
158 CI,V:The Breakaway Bandit
  A:The Justice League 75.00
159 CI,A:Kid Flash 75.00
160 CI,giant 100.00
161 CI,A:Mirror Master 65.00
162 CI,Who Haunts the Corridor
  of Chills 65.00
163 CI,A:Abra kadabra 65.00
164 CI,V:Pied Piper,A:KidFLash . 65.00
165 CI,W:Flash,Iris West 70.00
166 CI,A:Captain Cold 65.00
167 CI,O:Flash,I:Mopee 65.00
168 CI,A:Green Lantern 65.00
169 CI,O:Flash rtd,giant 100.00
170 CI,A:Abra Kadabra,
  G.A.Flash 65.00
171 CI,A:Dexter Myles,Justice
  League,Atom;V:Dr Light 60.00
172 CI,A:Grodd 60.00
173 CI,A:Kid Flash,EarthII Flash
  V:Golden Man 60.00
174 CI,A:Mirror Master,Top
  Captain Cold 60.00
175 2nd Superman/Flash race,
  C:Justice League o/America 150.00
176 giant-size 60.00
177 RA,V:The Trickster 60.00
178 CI,(giant size) 80.00
179 RA,Fact or Fiction 60.00
180 RA,V:Baron Katana 60.00
181 RA,V;Baron Katana 40.00
182 A:Abra Kadabra 40.00
183 RA,V:The Frog 40.00
184 RA,V:Dr Yom 40.00
185 RA,Threat of the High Rise
  Buildings 40.00
186 RA,A:Sargon 40.00
187 CI,AbraKadabra,giant 60.00
188 A:Mirror Master 40.00
189 JKu(c),RA,A:Kid Flash ... 40.00
190 JKu(c),RA,A:Dexter Myles . 40.00
191 JKu(c),RA,A:Green Lantern . 40.00
192 RA;V:Captain Vulcan 40.00
193 A:Captain Cold 40.00
194 .... 40.00
195 GK,MA 40.00
196 CI,giant 60.00
197 GK 40.00

Flash Comics #200 © DC Comics, Inc.

198 GK 40.00
199 GK 40.00
200 IN,MA 40.00
201 IN,MA,A:G.A. Flash 20.00
202 IN,MA,A:Kid Flash 20.00
203 IN 20.00
204 .... 20.00
205 giant 40.00
206 A:Mirror Master 20.00
207 .... 20.00
208 .... 20.00
209 A:Capt.Boomerang,Grodd
  Trickster 20.00
210 CI 20.00
211 O:Flash 20.00
212 A:Abra Kadabra 20.00
213 CI 20.00
214 CI,rep.Showcase #37
  (O:Metal Men),giant size.. 25.00
215 IN,FMc,rep.Showcase #14 . 25.00
216 A:Mr.Element 20.00
217 NA,A:Gr.Lant.Gr.Arrow 22.00
218 NA,A:Gr.Lant.Gr.Arrow 22.00
219 NA,L:Greeen Arrow 22.00
220 IN,DG,A:KidFlash,Gr.Lantern 15.00
221 IN 15.00
222 IN 15.00
223 DG,Green Lantern 15.00
224 IN,DG,A:Green Lantern 15.00
225 IN,DG,A:Gr.Lant,Rev.Flash . 11.00
226 NA,A:Capt. Cold 15.00
227 IN,FMc,DG,Capt.Boomerang,
  Green Lantern 9.00
228 IN 9.00
229 IN,FMc,A:Green Arrow,
  V:Rag Doll (giant size) 20.00
230 A:VandalSavage,Dr.Alchemy . 9.00
231 FMc 9.00
232 giant 20.00
233 giant 20.00
234 V:Reverse Flash 5.00
235 .... 4.00
236 MGr 4.00
237 IN,FMc,MGr,A:Prof Zoom,
  Green Lantern 4.50
238 MGr 4.00
239 .... 4.00
240 MGr 4.00

241 A:Mirror Master	4.00
242 MGr,D:Top	4.00
243 IN,FMc,MGr,TA,O:Top, A:Green Lantern	4.00
244 IN,FMc,A:Rogue's Gallery	4.00
245 IN,FMc,DD,TA,I:PlantMaster	4.00
246 IN,FMc,DD,TA,I:PlantMaster	4.00
247	4.00
248 FMc,IN,I:Master	4.00
249 FMc,IN,V:Master	4.00
250 IN,FMc,I:Golden Glider	4.00
251 FMc,IN,V:Golden Glider	3.50
252 FMc,IN,I:Molder	3.50
253 FMc,IN,V:Molder	3.50
254 FMc	3.50
255 FMc,A:MirrorMaster	3.50
256 FMc,V:Top	3.50
257 FMc,A:Green Glider	3.50
258 FMc,A:Black Hand	3.50
259 FMc,IN	3.50
260 FMc,IN	3.50
261 FMc,IN,V:Golden Glider	3.50
262 FMc,IN,V:Golden Glider	3.50
263 FMc,IN,V:Golden Glider	3.50
264 FMc,IN,V:Golden Glider	3.50
265 FMc,IN	3.50
266 FMc,IN,V:Heat Wave	3.50
267 FMc,IN,V:Heat Wave	3.50
268 FMc,IN,A:E2 Flash	3.50
269 FMc,IN,A:Kid Flash	3.50
270 FMc,IN,V:Clown	3.50
271 RB,V:Clown	3.50
272 RB,V:Clown	3.50
273 RB	3.50
274 RB	3.50
275 AS,D:Iris West,PCP story	4.00
276 AS,A:JLA	3.50
277 AS,FMc,A:JLA, V:MirrorMaster	3.50
278 A:Captain.Boomerang & Heatwave	3.50
279 A:Captain.Boomerang & Heatwave	3.50
280 DH	3.50
281 DH,V:Reverse Flash	4.00
282 DH,V:Reverse Flash	4.00
283 DH,V:Reverse Flash	4.00
284 DH,Flash's life story I:Limbo Lord	3.50
285 DH,V:Trickster	3.50
286 DH,I:Rainbow Raider	3.50
287 DH,V:Dr.Alchemy	3.50
288 DH,V:Dr.Alchemy	3.50
289 DH,GP,1st GP DC art; V:Dr. Alchemy;B:B.U.Firestorm	8.00
290 GP	3.00
291 GP,DH,V:Sabretooth	3.00
292 GP,DH,V:Mirror Master	3.00
293 GP,DH,V:Pied Piper	3.00
294 GP,DH,V:Grodd	3.00
295 CI,JSn,V:Grodd	3.00
296 JSn,A:Elongated Man	3.00
297 CI,A:Captain Cold	3.00
298 CI,V:Shade,Rainbowraider	3.00
299 CI,V:Shade,Rainbowraider	3.00
300 A:New Teen Titans	5.00
301 CI,A:Firestorm	3.00
302 CI,V:Golden Glider	3.00
303 CI,V:Golden Glider	3.00
304 CI,PB,I:Col.Computron;E:B.U. Firestorm	3.00
305 KG,CI,A:G.A.Flash,B:Dr.Fate	4.00
306 CI,KG,V:Mirror Master	4.00
307 CI,KG,V:Pied Piper	3.00
308 CI,KG	3.00

309 CI,KG	4.00
310 CI,KG,V:Capt.Boomerang	3.00
311 CI,KG,V:Capt.Boomerang	3.00
312 CI,A:Heatwave	3.00
313 KG,A:Psylon,E:Dr.Fate	3.00
314 CI,I:Eradicator	3.00
315 CI,V:Gold Face	3.00
316 CI,V:Gold Face	3.00
317 CI,V:Gold Face	3.00
318 CI,DGb,V:Eradicator;B: B.U.Creeper	3.00
319 CI,DGb,V:Eradicator	3.00
320 CI,V:Eradicator	3.00
321 CI,D:Eradicator	3.00
322 CI,V:Reverse Flash	3.00
323 CI,V:Reverse Flash;E: B.U.Creeper	3.00
324 CI,D:Reverse Flash	4.00
325 CI,A:Rogues Gallery	3.00
326 CI,A:Weather Wizard	3.00
327 CI,A:JLA,G.Grodd	3.00
328 CI	3.00
329 CI,A:J.L.A.,G.Grodd	3.00
330 CI,FMc,V:G.Grodd	3.00
331 CI,FMc,V:G.Grodd	3.00
332 CI,FMc,V:Rainbow Raider	3.00
333 CI,FMc,V:Pied Piper	3.00
334 CI,FMc,V:Pied Piper	3.00
335 CI,FMc,V:Pied Piper	3.00
336 CI,FMc,V:Pied Piper	3.00
337 CI,FMc,V:Pied Piper	3.00
338 CI,FMc,I:Big Sir	3.00
339 CI,FMc,A:Big Sir	3.00
340 CI,FMc,Trial,A:Big Sir	3.00
341 CI,FMc,Trial,A:Big Sir	3.00
342 CI,FMc,Trial,V:RogueGallery	3.00
343 CI,FMc,Trial,A:GoldFace	3.00
344 CI,O:Kid Flash,Trial	3.00
345 CI,A:Kid Flash,Trial	3.00
346 CI,FMc,Trial,V:AbraKadabra	3.00
347 CI,FMc,Trial,V:AbraKadabra	3.00
348 CI,FMc,Trial,V:AbraKadabra	3.00
349 CI,FMc,Trial,V:AbraKadabra	3.00
350 CI,FMc,Trial,V:AbraKadabra	7.00
Ann.#1 O:ElongatedMan, G.Grodd	325.00

FLASH

[2nd Series] Oct., 1985

1 JG,Legends,C:Vandal Savage	8.00
2 JG,V:Vandal Savage	5.00
3 JG,I:Kilgore	4.00
4 JG,A:Cyborg	3.00
5 JG,V:Speed Demon	3.00
6 JG,V:Speed Demon	3.00
7 JG,V:Red Trinity	3.00
8 JG,V:BlueTrinity,Millenium	3.00
9 JG,I:Chunk,Millenium	3.00
10 V:Chunk,Chunks World	2.50
11 Return to Earth	2.50
12 Velocity 9	2.50
13 Vandal Savage,V:Velocity 9 Adicts	2.50
14 V:Vandal Savage	2.50
15 A:Velocity 9 Junkies	2.50
16 C:V.Savage,SpeedMcGeePt.1	2.50
17 GLa,Speed McGee,pt.2	2.50
18 GLa,SpeedMcGeePt.3, V:V.Savage	2.25
19 JM:+bonus book,R:Rogue Gallery,O:Blue/Red Trinity	2.25
20 A:Durlan	2.25
21 A:Manhunter,Invasion x-over	2.25
22 A:Manhunter,Invasion x-over	2.25
23 V:Abrakadabra	2.25

Flash Comics (2nd Series) #12
© DC Comics, Inc.

24 GLa,FlashRegainsSpeed, A:L.Lane	2.25
25 GLa,Search for Flash	2.25
26 GLa,I:Porcupine Man	2.25
27 GLa,Porcupine Man as Flash	2.25
28 GLa,A:Golden Glider, Capt.Cold	2.25
29 A:New Phantom Lady	2.25
30 GLa,Turtle Saga,pt.1	2.25
31 GLa,Turtle Saga,pt.2	2.00
32 GLa,Turtle Saga,pt.3, R:G.A.Turtle	2.00
33 GLa,Turtle Saga,pt.4	2.00
34 GLa,Turtle Saga,pt.5	2.00
35 GLa,Turtle Saga,pt.6, D:G.A.Turtle	2.00
36 GLa,V:Cult	2.00
37 GLa,V:Cult	2.00
38 GLa,V:Cult	2.00
39 GLa,V:Cult	2.00
40 GLa,A:Dr.Alchemy	2.00
41 GLa,A:Dr.Alchemy	2.00
42 GLa,MechanicalTroubles	2.00
43 GLa,V:Kilgore	2.00
44 GLa,V:Velocity	2.00
45 V:Gorilla Grod	2.00
46 V:Gorilla Grod	2.00
47 V:Gorilla Grod	2.00
48	2.00
49 A:Vandal Savage	2.00
50 N:Flash (double sz)V:Savage	5.00
51 I:Proletariat	2.00
52 I.R.S. Mission	1.75
53 A:Superman,Race to Save Jimmy Olsen	1.75
54 Terrorist Airline Attack	1.75
55 War of the Gods x-over	1.75
56 The Way of a Will,pt.1	1.75
57 The Way of a Will,pt.2	1.75
58 Meta Gene-activated Homeless	1.75
59 The Last Resort	1.75
60 Love Song of the Chunk	1.75
61 Wally's Mother's Wedding Day	1.75
62 GLa,Year 1,pt.1	2.25
63 GLa,Year 1,pt.2	1.75
64 GLa,Year 1,pt.3	1.75
65 GLa,Year 1,pt.4	1.75

66 A:Aq'man,V:Marine Marauder . 1.75
67 GLa,V:Abra Kadabra 1.75
68 GLa,V:Abra Kadabra 1.75
69 GLa,Gorilla Warfare#2 . . . . . . 1.75
70 Gorilla Warfare#4 . . . . 1.75
71 GLa,V:Dr.Alchemy 1.75
72 GLa,V:Dr.Alchemy,C:Barry
   Allen 2.50
73 GLa,Xmas Issue,R:Barry Allen . 4.50
74 GLa,A:Barry Allen? 3.00
75 GLa,A:Reverse Flash,V:Mob
   Violence 3.50
76 GLa,A:Reverse Flash 2.25
77 GLa,G.A.Flash vs
   Reverse Flash 2.25
78 GLa,V:Reverse Flash 2.25
79 GLa,V:Reverse Flash,48 pgs. . . 3.25
80 AD(c),V:Frances Kane 3.00
80a Newstand Ed 2.00
81 AD(c) 2.00
82 AD(c),A:Nightwing 2.00
83 AD(c),A:Nightwing,Starfire . . . 2.00
84 AD(c),I:Razer 2.00
85 AD(c),V:Razer 2.00
86 AD(c),A:Argus 2.00
86 V:Santa Claus 2.00
87 Chrismas issue 2.00
88 . . . . 2.00
89 On Trial 2.00
90 On Trial#2 . . . . 2.00
91 Out of Time 2.00
92 I:3rd Flash 12.00
93 A:Impulse 5.00
94 Zero Hour 5.00
95 Terminal Velocity,pt.1 . . . . . . 4.00
96 Terminal Velocity,pt.2 . . . . . . 4.00
97 Terminal Velocity,pt.3 . . . . . . 2.00
98 Terminal Velocity,pt.4 . . . . . . 2.00
99 Terminal Velocity,pt.5 . . . . . . 2.00
100 I:New Flash 5.00
100a Collector's Edition 2.50
101 Velocity Aftermath 1.50
102 V:Mongul 1.75
103 Supernatural threat from
   Linda's Past Secret 1.75
104 Exorcise Demons 1.75
105 . . . . 1.75
106 R:Magenta 1.75
107 MWa,Underworld Unleashed
   tie-in 1.75
108 MWa,Dead Heat,pt.1 . . . . . . 1.75
109 MWa,Dead Heat,pt.2 . . . . . . 1.75
110 MWa,Dead Heat,pt.4 . . . . . . 1.75
111 MWa,Dead Heat,pt.6 . . . . . . 1.75
112 MWa,New Flash in town 1.75
113 MWa,F:Linda 1.75
114 MWa,V:Chillblaine 1.75
115 thru 117 . . . . @1.75
118 MWa&BAu(s),Flash returns
   from the future 1.75
119 MWa&BAu(s),PR,Final Night
   tie-in 1.75
120 MWa&BAu(s),PR,"Presidential
   Race," pt.1 . . . . 1.75
121 MWa&BAu(s),PR,"Presidential
   Race," pt.2 . . . . 1.75
122 MWa&BAu(s),PR, ... 1.75
123 MWa&BAu(s),PR,Flash moves
   to Santa Marta 1.75
124 MWa&BAu(s),PR,Wally doesn't
   know reality from illusion . . . 1.75
125 MWa&BAu(s),PR,California,
   V:Major Disaster 1.75
126 MWa&BAu(s),PR,V:Major
   Disaster 1.75

127 MWa&Bau(s),PR,"Hell to Pay,"
   pt. 1 (of 3) 1.75
128 MWa&BAu(s),PR,"Hell to Pay"
   pt. 2, A:JLA 1.75
129 MWa&BAu(s),PR,"Hell to Pay"
   pt. 3, concl. 1.75
130 GMo&MMr(s),PR,new menace 1.75
131 GMo&MMr(s),PR,V:The Suit . 1.75
132 GMo&MMr(s),PR,V:The Suit . 2.00
133 GMo&MMr(s),PR,V:Mirror
   Master 2.00
134 GMo&MMr(s),PR,V:Weather
   Wizard & Captain Cold 2.00
135 GMo&MMr(s), ... 2.00
136 GMo&MMr(s),PR,Human
   Race,pt.1 . . . . 2.00
137 GMo&MMr(s),PR,Human
   Race,pt.2 . . . . 2.00
138 GMo&MMr(s),PR,Human
   Race,pt.3 . . . . 2.00
139 MMr(s),Clv,Black Flash,pt.1 . 2.00
140 MMr(s),Clv,Black Flash,pt.2 . 2.00
141 MMr(s),Clv,Black Flash,pt.3 . 2.00
142 MWa&BAu(s),Clv,SLi,wedding of
   Wally West & Linda Park 2.00
Ann.#1 JG,The Deathtouch 4.00
Ann.#2 A:Wally's Father 3.00
Ann.#3 Roots 2.50
Ann.#4 Armageddon,pt7 . . . . 2.50
Ann.#5 TC(1st Full Work),Eclipso,
   V:Rogue's Gallery 8.00
Ann.#6 Bloodlines#4,I:Argus 2.75
Ann.#7 Elseworlds story 2.95
Ann.#8 Year One story 3.00
Ann.#9 Legends o/t Dead Earth . . 2.95
Ann.#10 Pulp Heroes (Romance) . 3.95
Ann.#11 BAu,BWr, Ghosts 3.00
Spec #1,IN,DG,CI,50th Anniv.,
   Three Flash's 4.50
T.V. Spec.#1,JS,w/episode guide . 4.25
TPB Terminal Velocity 12.95
TPB The Life Story of the Flash . 13.00
TPB The Return of Barry Allen . 13.00
Spec #1 GN Secret Files 5.00
Archives #1 Hardcover 50.00
Giant #1 MWa,80-page (1998) . . 5.00
Secret Files #1 MWa,BAu,PRy,
   O:Flash family 5.00

THE FLASH PLUS
Nov. 1996
1 MWa(s),F:Wally West, Dick
   Grayson 2.95

FLASH GORDON
1988
1 DJu,I:New Flash Gordon 2.00
2 DJu,A:Lion-Men,Shark-Men . . . 1.75
3 DJu,V:Shark-Men 1.50
4 DJu,Dale Kidnapped by Voltan   1.50
5 DJu,Alliance Against Ming 1.50
6 DJu,Arctic City 1.50
7 DJu,Alliance vs. Ming 1.50
8 DJu,Alliance vs. Ming 1.50
9 DJu,V:Ming, final issue 1.50

FLINTSTONES AND
THE JETSONS, THE
Warner Bros./DC
1 Ancestors and Descendents meet 1.75
2 Dino wins a contest, Bay
   Watchdog 1.75
3 Mr. Spacely a baby 2.00
4 cavewomen 2.00

5 21st century house party 2.00
6 Thanksgiving Feast 2.00
7 CDi, Spy Who Grounded Me . . 2.00
8 . . . . 2.00
9 I, Rosey 2.00
10 Beast of Bedrock 2.00
11 Mr. Spacely, time travel 2.00
12 Animal appliances on strike . . 2.00
13 F:Astro 2.00
14 Flintstone Files, UFOs 2.00
15 Mr. Spacely, most powerful being
   in the universe 2.00

The Fly #9 © DC Comics, Inc.

FLY, THE
Impact 1991–92
1 I&O:Fly I:Arachnus,Chromium . 1.50
2 V:Chromium 1.25
3 O:Arachnus, I:Lt.Walker Odell . 1.00
4 A:Black Hood, V:Arachnus . . . 1.00
5 V:Arachnus 1.00
6 I:Blackjack 1.00
7 Oceanworld,V:Dolphus 1.00
8 A:Comet,Dolphus 1.00
9 F:Fireball, with trading card . . . 1.00
10 V:General Mechanix 1.00
11 Suicide Issue 1.25
12 V:Agent from WEB 1.25
13 I:Tremor 1.25
14 and 15 V:Domino . . . . @1.25
16 V:Arachnus 1.25
17 Final Issue 1.25
Ann.#1 Earthquest,pt.4,w/card . . . 2.25

FORBIDDEN TALES
OF DARK MANSION
May–June, 1972
5 thru 15 Feb.–March, 1974 . . @1.50

FOREVER PEOPLE, THE
1971–72
1 I:Forever People,A:Superman,
   A:Darkseid 50.00
2 A:Darkseid 30.00
3 A:Darkseid 30.00
4 A:Darkseid 30.00
5 . . . . 25.00
6 thru 11 . . . . @12.50

FOREVER PEOPLE
1988
1 Return of Forever People 1.50
2 'Return of Earth of Yesterday' . 1.25
3 A:Mark Moonrider 1.25
4 The Dark controlls M.Moonrider 1.25
5 R:MotherBox,Infinity Man 1.25
6 Donny's Fate, final issue 1.25

FORGOTTEN REALMS
1989–91
1 A:RealmsMaster,PriamAgrivar . 4.00
2 Mystic Hand of Vaprak,
    A:Ogre Mage 3.00
3 Mystic Hand of Vaprak contd. . 2.75
4 Ogre Mage vs.Omen the Wizard 2.75
5 Dragon Reach #1 .... 2.75
6 Dragon Reach #2 .... 2.50
7 Dragon Reach #3 .... 2.50
8 Dragon Reach #4 .... 2.50
9 V:Giant Squid 2.50
10 'Head Cheese' 2.50
11 Triangles #1 .... 2.50
12 Triangles #2 .... 2.50
13 Triangles #3 .... 2.50
14 A:Lich Viranton the Mage ... 2.00
15 Avatar Comics tie-in 2.00
16 Mad Gods and Paladins,pt.1 .. 2.00
17 Mad Gods and Paladins,pt.2 .. 2.00
18 Mad Gods and Paladins,pt.3 .. 2.00
19 Mad Gods and Paladins,pt.4 .. 2.00
20 Realms Master Crew captured 2.00
21 Catewere Tribe 2.00
22 V:The Akri 1.75
23 A:Sandusk the Leprechaun ... 1.75
24 'Everybody wants to rule
    the realms' 1.75
25 The Wake, final issue 1.75
Ann.#1 V:Advanced D&D crew .. 2.95

FOUR STAR BATTLE TALES
1973
1 thru 5 .... @1.50

FOUR STAR SPECTACULAR
March-April, 1976
1 .... 1.50
2 thru 6 .... @1.25

FOURTH WORLD GALLERY
1-shot pin-up collection (1996) .. 3.50

FOX AND THE CROW
Dec.–Jan., 1951
1 .... 750.00
2 .... 400.00
3 .... 250.00
4 .... 250.00
5 .... 250.00
6 thru 10 .... @175.00
11 thru 20 .... @125.00
21 thru 40 .... @125.00
41 thru 60 .... @50.00
61 thru 80 .... @35.00
81 thru 94 .... @25.00
95 .... 30.00
96 thru 99 .... @15.00
100 .... 18.00
101 thru 108 .... @15.00

Becomes:

STANLEY & HIS MONSTER
109 thru 112 Oct.Nov.,1968 .. @10.00

FREEDOM FIGHTERS
March-April, 1976
1 Freedom Fighters go to Earth 1 1.50
2 .... 1.25
3 .... 1.25
4 .... 1.25
5 A:Wonder Woman 1.25
6 .... 1.25
7 .... 1.25
8 .... 1.25
9 .... 1.25
10 O:Doll Man 1.25
11 O:Ray 1.25
12 O:Firebrand 1.25
13 O:Black Condor 1.25
14 A:Batgirl 1.25
15 O:Phantom Lady 1.25

From Beyond The Unknown #10
© DC Comics, Inc.

FROM BEYOND THE UNKNOWN
Oct.–Nov., 1969
1 JKu,CI 70.00
2 MA(c),CI,ATh 18.00
3 NA(c),CI 15.00
4 MA(c),CI 15.00
5 MA(c),CI 15.00
6 NA(c),I:Glen Merrit 18.00
7 CI,JKu(c) 15.00
8 NA(c),CI 18.00
9 NA(c),CI 18.00
10 MA(c),CI 15.00
11 MA(c),CI 12.00
12 JKu(c),CI 15.00
13 JKu(c),CI,WW 20.00
14 JKu(c),CI 15.00
15 MA(c),CI 12.00
16 MA(c),CI 12.00
17 MA(c),CI 12.00
18 MK(c),CI 10.00
19 MK(c),CI 10.00

20 .... 10.00
21 .... 10.00
22 MA(c) 12.00
23 CI,Space Museum 10.00
24 CI 10.00

FUNNY STOCKING STUFFER
March, 1985
1 .... 1.00

FUNNY STUFF
Summer, 1944
1 B:3 Mousketeer Terrific
    Whatzit 650.00
2 .... 350.00
3 .... 200.00
4 .... 175.00
5 .... 175.00
6 thru 10 .... @150.00
11 thru 20 .... @125.00
21 .... 75.00
22 C:Superman 300.00
23 thru 30 .... @75.00
31 thru 78 .... @50.00
79 July-Aug., 1954 ...... 50.00

FURY OF FIRESTORM
June, 1982
1 PB,I:Black Bison 3.00
2 PB,V:Black Bison 2.00
3 PB,V:Pied Piper, Killer Frost . 2.00
4 PB,A:JLA,Killer Frost 2.00
5 PB,V:Pied Piper 2.00
6 V:Pied Piper 2.00
7 I:Plastique 2.00
8 V:Typhoon 2.00
9 V:Typhoon 2.00
10 V:Hyena 2.00
11 V:Hyena 2.00
12 PB,V:Hyena 2.00
13 .... 2.00
14 PB,I:Enforcer,A:Multiplex .. 2.00
15 V:Multiplex 2.00
16 V:Multiplex 2.00
17 I:2000 Committee,Firehawk .. 2.00
18 I:Tokamak,A:Multiplex 2.00
19 GC,V:Goldenrod 2.00
20 A:Killer Frost 2.00
21 D:Killer Frost 2.50
22 O:Firestorm 2.50
23 I:Bug & Byte 2.00
24 I:Blue Devil,Bug & Byte 2.50
25 I:Silver Deer 2.00
26 V:Black Bison 2.00
27 V:Black Bison 2.00
28 I:Slipknot 2.00
29 I:2000 C'tee,I:Breathtaker .. 2.00
30 V:2000 Committee 2.00
31 V:2000 Committee 2.00
32 Phantom Stranger 2.00
33 A:Plastique 2.00
34 I:Killer Frost 2 .... 2.00
35 V:K.Frost/Plastique,I:Weasel .. 2.00
36 V:Killer Frost & Plastique ... 2.00
37 .... 2.00
38 V:Weasel 2.00
39 V:Weasel 2.00
40 .... 2.00
41 Crisis 2.00
42 Crisis,A:Firehawk 2.00
43 V:Typhoon 2.00
44 V:Typhoon 2.00
45 V:Multiplex 2.00

Firestorm, The Nuclear Man #78
© DC Comics, Inc.

46 A:Blue Devil	2.00
47 A:Blue Devil	2.00
48 I:Moonbow	2.00
49 V:Moonbow	2.00
50 W:Ed Raymond	2.00
51 A:King Crusher	2.00
52 A:King Crusher	2.00
53 V:Steel Shadow	2.00
54 I:Lava	2.00
55 Legends,V:World's Luckiest Man	2.00
56 Legends,A:Hawk	2.00
57	2.00
58 I:Parasite II	2.00
59	2.00
60 Secret behind Hugo's accident	2.00
61 V:Typhoon	2.00
61a Superman Logo	55.00
62 A:Russian 'Firestorm'	2.00
63 A:Capt.Atom	2.00
64 A:Suicide Squad	2.00
Ann.#1 EC,A:Firehawk, V:Tokamak	2.25
Ann.#2	2.25
Ann.#3	2.25
Ann.#4 KG,CS,GC,DG	2.25

Becomes:

FIRESTORM, THE NUCLEAR MAN
Nov., 1987

65 A:New Firestorm	2.00
66 A:Green Lantern	2.00
67 Millenium, Week 1	2.00
68 Millenium	2.00
69 V:Zuggernaut,Stalnivolk USA	2.00
70 V:Flying Dutchman	2.00
71 Trapped in the Timestream	2.00
72 V:Zuggernaut	2.00
73 V:Stalnivolk & Zuggernaut	2.00
74 Quest for Martin Stein	2.00
75 Return of Martin Stein	2.00
76 Firestorm & Firehawk vs Brimstone	2.00
77 Firestorm & Firehawk in Africa	2.00
78 'Exile From Eden',pt.1	2.00
79 'Exile From Eden',pt.2	2.00

80 A:Power Girl,Starman,Invasion x-over	2.00
81 A:Soyuz,Invasion aftermath	2.00
82 Invasion Aftermath	2.00
83 V:Svarozhich	2.00
84	2.00
85 Soul of Fire,N:Firestorm	2.00
86 TMd,Janus Directive #7	2.00
87 TMd	2.00
88 TMd,E:Air Wave B:Maser	2.00
89 TMd,V:Firehawk,Vandermeer Steel	2.00
90 TMd,Elemental War #1	2.00
91 TMd,Elemental War #2	2.00
92 TMd,Elemental War #3	2.00
93 TMd,Elemental War concl.	2.00
94 TMd,A:Killer Frost	2.00
95 TMd,V:Captains of Industry	2.00
96 TMd,A:Shango,African God & Obatala,Lord o/t White Cloth	2.00
97 TMd,A:Obatala,V:Shango	2.00
98 TMd,A:Masar	2.00
99 TMd,A:Brimstone,PlasmaGiant	2.00
100 TMd,AM,V:Brimstone (Firestorm back-up story) final issue	3.00
Ann.#5 JLI,Suicide Squad I:New Firestorm	2.50

GAMMARAUDERS
1989

1 I:Animal-Warrior Bioborgs	2.00
2 V:The Slugnoids	2.00
3 V:Slugnoids,I:Squawk the Penguinoid	2.00
4 V:Slugnoids	1.50
5 V:Bioborg/Podnoid	1.50
6 Slash vs.Sassin,A:RadicalDebs	1.50
7 Jok findsSword that was broken	2.00
8 Jok's search for KirkwardDerby	2.00
9 Jok the Congressman	2.00
10 The Big Nada, final issue	2.00

GANG BUSTERS
1947–58

1	650.00
2	300.00
3	200.00
4	200.00
5	200.00
6	200.00
7	200.00
8	200.00
9 Ph(c)	150.00
10 Ph(c)	150.00
11 Ph(c)	125.00
12 Ph(c)	125.00
13 Ph(c)	125.00
14 Ph(c),FF	275.00
15	100.00
16	100.00
17	275.00
18	100.00
19	100.00
20	100.00
21 thru 25	@90.00
26 JK	90.00
27 thru 40	@75.00
41 thru 44	@60.00
45 Comics Code	60.00
46 thru 50	60.00
51 MD	60.00
52 thru 67	@60.00

GANGLAND
April 1998

1 (of 4) crime anthology	3.00
2 Platinum Nights	3.00
3 Gang Buff	3.00
4 conclusion	3.00

GEMINI BLOOD
DC/Helix

1	2.25
2	2.25
3 Royal Caste	2.50
4 V:Shraddhan	2.25
5 WSi(c),V:Rolk	2.25
6	2.50
7 BSz, Gillian's secret revealed	2.50
8 Loothka	2.50
9 Nick captured by Loothka, final issue	2.50

GENESIS
Aug., 1997

1 (of 4) JBy,RoW,JRu,AD,MFm, Marvel x-over	2.00
2 JBy,RoW,JRu,AD,MFm,x-over	2.00
3 JBy,RoW,JRu,AD,MFm,x-over	2.00
4 JBy,RoW,JRu,AD,MFm,concl.	2.00

GHOSTDANCING
Vertigo 1995
[Mini-Series]

1 I:Snake,Ghost Dancing	2.00
2 Secrets	2.00
3 I:Father Craft	2.50
4 Coyote prisoner	2.50
5 F:Snot Boy	2.50

Ghosts #75 © DC Comics, Inc.

GHOSTS
Sept.–Oct., 1971

1 JAp,NC(c),Death's Bridegroom!	50.00
2 WW,NC(c),Mission Supernatural	30.00
3 TD,NC(c),Death is my Mother	25.00
4 GT,NC(c),The Crimson Claw	25.00
5 NC(c),Death, The Pale Horseman	25.00

DC COMICS

6 NC(c),A Specter Poured
  The Potion 20.00
7 MK(c),Death's Finger Points . 20.00
8 NC(c),The Cadaver In
  The Clock 20.00
9 AA,NC(c),The Last Ride
  Of Rosie The Wrecker 20.00
10 NC(c),A Specter Stalks Saigon 20.00
11 NC(c),The Devils Lake 15.00
12 NC(c),The Macabre Mummy
  Of Takhem-Ahtem 15.00
13 NC(c),Hell Is One Mile High . 15.00
14 NC(c),The Bride Wore
  A Shroud 15.00
15 AA,NC(c),The Ghost That
  Wouldn't Die 15.00
16 NC(c),Death's Grinning Face 15.00
17 NC(c),Death Held the
  Lantern High 15.00
18 AA,NC(c),Graveyard of
  Vengeance 15.00
19 AA,NC(c),The Dead Live On . 15.00
20 NC(c),The Haunting Hussar
  Of West Point 15.00
21 NC(c),The Ghost In The
  Devil's Chair 10.00
22 NC(c),The Haunted Horns
  Of Death 10.00
23 NC(c),Dead Is My Darling! .. 10.00
24 AA,NC(c),You Too, Will Die . 10.00
25 AA,NC(c),Three Skulls On
  The Zambezi 10.00
26 DP,NC(c),The Freaky Phantom
  Of Watkins Glen 10.00
27 NC(c),Conversation With
  A Corpse 10.00
28 DP,NC(c),Flight Of The
  Lost Phantom 10.00
29 NC(c),The Haunted Lady
  Of Death 10.00
30 NC(c),The Fangs of
  the Phantom 10.00
31 NC(c),Blood On The Moon .. 10.00
32 NC(c),Phantom Laughed Last 10.00
33 NC(c),The Hangman of
  Haunted Island 10.00
34 NC(c),Wrath of the Ghost Apes 10.00
35 NC(c),Feud with a Phantom . 10.00
36 NC(c),The Boy Who Returned
  From The Gave 10.00
37 LD(c),Fear On Ice 10.00
38 LD(c),Specter In The Surf ... 10.00
39 LD(c),The Haunting Hitchhiker 10.00
40 LD(c),The Nightmare That
  Haunted The World 15.00
41 LD(c),Ship of Specters 15.00
42 LD(c),The Spectral Sentries . 15.00
43 LD(c),3 Corpses On A Rope . 15.00
44 LD(c),The Case of the
  Murdering Specters 15.00
45 LD(c),Bray of the
  Phantom Beast 15.00
46 LD(c),The World's Most
  Famous Phantom 15.00
47 LD(c),Wrath of the
  Restless Specters 15.00
48 DP,LD(c),The Phantom Head 15.00
49 The Ghost in the Cellar ... 15.00
50 Home Is Where The Grave Is 15.00
51 The Ghost Who Would Not Die 15.00
52 LD(c),The Thunderhead
  Phantom 15.00
53 LD(c),Whose Spirit Invades Me 15.00
54 LD(c),The Deadly Dreams
  Of Ernie Caruso 15.00

55 LD(c),The House That Was
  Built For Haunting 15.00
56 LD(c),The Triumph Of The
  Teen-Age Phantom 15.00
57 LD(c),The Flaming Phantoms
  of Oradour 15.00
58 LD(c),The Corpse in the Closet 15.00
59 LD(c),That Demon Within Me 15.00
60 LD(c),The Spectral Smile
  of Death 8.00
61 LD(c),When Will I Die Again .. 8.00
62 LD(c),The Phantom Hoaxer! .. 8.00
63 LD(c),The Burning Bride 8.00
64 LD(c),Dead Men Do Tell Tales 8.00
65 LD(c),The Imprisoned Phantom 8.00
66 LD(c),Conversation With A
  Corpse 8.00
67 LD(c),The Spectral Sword 8.00
68 LD(c),The Phantom of the
  Class of '76 .... 5.00
69 LD(c),The Haunted Gondola .. 5.00
70 LD(c),Haunted Honeymoon .. 5.00
71 LD(c),The Ghost Nobody Knew 5.00
72 LD(c),The Ghost of
  Washington Monument ... 5.00
73 LD(c),The Specter Of The
  Haunted Highway 5.00
74 LD(c),The Gem That Haunted
  the World! 5.00
75 LD(c),The Legend Of The
  Lottie Lowry 5.00
76 LD(c),Two Ghosts of
  Death Row 5.00
77 LD(c),Ghost, Where Do
  You Hide? 5.00
78 LD(c),The World's Most
  Famous Phantom 5.00
79 LD(c),Lure of the Specter 5.00
80 JO(c),The Winged Specter .. 5.00
81 LD(c),Unburied Phantom ... 5.00
82 LD(c),The Ghost Who
  Wouldn't Die 5.00
83 LD(c),Escape From the Haunt
  of the Amazon Specter 5.00
84 LD(c),Torment of the
  Phantom Face 5.00
85 LD(c),The Fiery Phantom
  of Faracutin 5.00
86 LD(c),The Ghostly Garden ... 5.00
87 LD(c),The Phantom Freak ... 5.00
88 LD(c),Harem In Hell 5.00
89 JKu(c),Came The Specter
  Shrouded In Seaweed 5.00
90 The Ghost Galleon 5.00
91 LD(c),The Haunted Wheelchair 5.00
92 DH(c),Double Vision 5.00
93 MK(c),The Flaming Phantoms
  of Nightmare Alley 5.00
94 LD(c),Great Caesar's Ghost . 5.00
95 All The Stage Is A Haunt ... 5.00
96 DH(c),Dread of the
  Deadly Domestic 5.00
97 JAp(c),A Very Special Spirit
  A:Spectre 8.00
98 JAp(c),The Death of a Ghost
  A:Spectre 8.00
99 EC(c),Till Death Do Us Join
  A:Spectre 8.00
100 EC&DG(c),The Phantom's
  Final Debt 3.00
101 MK(c),The Haunted Hospital . 3.00
102 RB&DG(c),The Fine Art
  Of Haunting 3.00
103 RB&DG(c),Visions and
  Vengeance 3.00

104 LD(c),The First Ghost 3.00
105 JKu(c) 3.00
106 JKu(c) 3.00
107 JKu(c) 3.00
108 JKu(c) 3.00
109 EC(c) 3.00
110 EC&DG(c) 3.00
111 JKu(c) 3.00
112 May, 1982 .... 3.00

G.I.Combat #167 © DC Comics, Inc.

G.I. COMBAT
Jan., 1957
Prev: Golden Age
44 RH,JKu,The Eagle and
  the Wolves 450.00
45 RH,JKu,Fireworks Hill 250.00
46 JKu,The Long Walk
  To Wansan 200.00
47 RH, The Walking Weapon . 200.00
48 No Fence For A Jet 200.00
49 Frying Pan Seat 200.00
50 Foxhole Pilot 200.00
51 RH,The Walking Grenade .. 150.00
52 Jku,JKu(c),Call For A Tank . 150.00
53 JKu,The Paper Trap 150.00
54 RH,JKu,Sky Tank 150.00
55 Call For A Gunner 150.00
56 JKu,JKu(c),The D.I.-And the
  Sand Fleas 150.00
57 RH,Live Wire For Easy 150.00
58 JKu(c),Flying Saddle 150.00
59 JKu,Hot Corner 150.00
60 RH,Bazooka Crossroads ... 150.00
61 JKu(c),The Big Run 100.00
62 RH,JKu,Drop An Inch 100.00
63 MD,JKu(c),Last Stand 100.00
64 MD,RH,JKu,JKu(c),The
  Silent Jet 100.00
65 JKu,Battle Parade 100.00
66 MD,The Eagle of Easy
  Company 100.00
67 JKu(c),I:Tank Killer 125.00
68 JKu,RH,The Rock 100.00
69 JKu,RH,The Steel Ribbon .. 100.00
70 JKu,Bull's-Eye Bridge 100.00
71 MD,JKu,Last Stand 80.00
72 MD,JKu(c),Ground Fire 80.00

All comics prices listed are for *Near Mint* condition.

73 RH,JKu(c),Window War 80.00
74 RH,A Flag For Joey 80.00
75 RH,Dogtag Hill 80.00
76 MD,RH,JKu,Bazooka For
    A Mouse 80.00
77 RH,JKu,H-Hour For A Gunner 80.00
78 MD,RH,JKu,Who Cares
    About The Infantry 80.00
79 JKu,RH,Big Gun-Little Gun .. 80.00
80 JKu,RH(c),Flying Horsemen . 80.00
81 Jump For Glory 90.00
82 IN,Get Off My Back 90.00
83 Too Tired To Fight 90.00
84 JKu(c),Dog Company
    Is Holding 80.00
85 IN,JKu(c),The T.N.T. Trio ... 80.00
86 JKu,RH(c),Not Return 80.00
87 RH(c),I:Haunted Tank 350.00
88 RH,JKu(c),Haunted Tank Vs.
    Ghost Tank 75.00
89 JA,RH,IN,Tank With Wings .. 75.00
90 JA,IN,RH,Tank Raiders 75.00
91 IN,RH,The Tank and the Turtle 75.00
92 JA,IN,The Tank of Doom ... 75.00
93 RH(c),JA,No-Return Mission . 75.00
94 IN,RH(c),Haunted Tank Vs.
    The Killer Tank 75.00
95 JA,RH(c),The Ghost of
    the Haunted Tank 75.00
96 JA,RH(c),The Lonesome Tank 75.00
97 IN,RH(c),The Decoy Tank .. 75.00
98 JA,RH(c),Trap of Dragon's
    Teeth 75.00
99 JA,JKu,RH(c),Battle of the
    Thirsty Tanks 75.00
100 JA,JKu,Return of the
    Ghost Tank 75.00
101 JA,The Haunted Tank Vs.
    Attila's Battle Tiger 60.00
102 JKu(c),Haunted Tank
    Battle Window 60.00
103 JKu,JA,RH(c),Rabbit Punch
    For A Tiger 60.00
104 JA,JKu,RH(c),Blind
    Man's Radar 60.00
105 JA,JKu(c),Time Bomb Tank . 60.00
106 JA,JKu(c),Two-Sided War .. 60.00
107 JKu(c),The Ghost Pipers ... 60.00
108 JKu(c),The Wounded
    Won't Wait,I:Sgt.Rock 60.00
109 JKu(c),Battle of the Tank
    Graveyard 60.00
110 IN,JKu(c),Choose Your War 60.00
111 JA,JKu(c),Death Trap 60.00
112 JA,JKu(c),Ghost Ace 40.00
113 JKu,RH(c),Tank Fight In
    Death Town 40.00
114 JA,RH(c),O:Haunted Tank .. 75.00
115 JA,RH(c),MedalsForMayhem 30.00
116 IN,JA,JKu(c),Battle Cry
    For A Dead Man 30.00
117 JA,RH,JKu(c),Tank In
    The Ice Box 30.00
118 IN,JA,RH(c),My Buddy-
    My Enemy 30.00
119 IN,RH(c),Target For
    A Firing Squad 30.00
120 IN,JA,RH(c),Pull ATiger'sTail 30.00
121 RH(c),Battle of Two Wars .. 30.00
122 JA,JKu(c),Who Dies Next? . 30.00
123 IN,RH(c),The Target of Terro 30.00
124 IN,RH(c),Scratch That Tank 30.00
125 RH(c),Stay Alive-Until Dark . 30.00
126 JA,RH(c),Tank Umbrella .. 30.00
127 JA,JKu(c),Mission-Sudden

Death 30.00
128 RH(c),The Ghost of
    the Haunted Tank 30.00
129 JA,RH(c),Hold That Town
    For A Dead Man 30.00
130 RH(c),Battle of the Generals 30.00
131 JKu&RH(c),Devil For Dinner 30.00
132 JA,JKu(c),The Executioner . 30.00
133 JKu(c),Operation:Death Trap 30.00
134 MD,JKu(c),Desert Holocaust 30.00
135 GE,JKu(c),Death is the Joker 30.00
136 JKu(c),Kill Now-Pay Later .. 30.00
137 JKu(c),We Can't See 30.00
138 JKu(c),I:The Losers 35.00
139 JKu(c),Corner of Hell 30.00
140 RH,MD,JKu(c),The LastTank 30.00
141 MD,JKu(c),Let Me Live..
    Let Me Die 7.00
142 RH,JKu(c),Checkpoint-Death . 7.00
143 RH,JKu(c),The Iron Horseman 7.00
144 RH,MD,JKu(c),Every
    Man A Fort 7.00
145 MD,JKu(c),Sand,Sun
    and Death 7.00

G.I. Combat #288 © DC Comics, Inc.

146 JKu(c),Move the World 7.00
147 JKu(c),Rebel Tank 7.00
148 IN,JKu(c),The Gold-Plated
    General 7.00
149 JKu(c),Leave The
    Fighting To Us 7.00
150 JKu(c),The Death of the
    Haunted Tank 7.00
151 JKu(c),A Strong Right Arm . 7.00
152 JKu(c),Decoy Tank 7.00
153 JKu(c),The Armored Ark 7.00
154 JKu(c),Battle Prize 7.00
155 JKu(c),The Long Journey .. 7.00
156 JKu(c),Beyond Hell 7.00
157 JKu(c),The Fountain 7.00
158 What Price War 7.00
159 JKu(c),Mission Dead End ... 7.00
160 JKu(c),Battle Ghost 7.00
161 JKu(c),The Day of the Goth . 7.00
162 JKu(c),The Final Victor 7.00
163 A Crew Divided 7.00
164 Siren Song 7.00
165 JKu(c),Truce,Pathfinder 7.00
166 Enemy From Yesterday 7.00

167 JKu(c),The Finish Line 7.00
168 NA(c),The Breaking Point ... 7.00
169 WS(c),The Death of the
    Haunted Tank 7.00
170 Chain of Vengeance 7.00
171 JKu(c),The Man Who
    Killed Jeb Stuart 7.00
172 RH(c),At The Mercy of
    My Foes 7.00
173 JKu(c),The Final Crash 7.00
174 JKu(c),Vow To A Dead Foe . 7.00
175 JKu(c),The Captive Tank ... 7.00
176 JKu(c),A Star Can Cry 7.00
177 JKu(c),The Tank That
    Missed D-Day 7.00
178 JKu(c),A Tank Is Born 7.00
179 JKu(c),One Last Charge 7.00
180 JKu(c),The Saints Go
    Riding On 7.00
181 JKu(c),The Kidnapped Tank . 7.00
182 JKu(c),Combat Clock 7.00
183 JKu(c),6 Stallions To
    Hell- And Back 7.00
184 JKu(c),Battlefield Bundle 7.00
185 JKu(c),No Taps For A Tank . 7.00
186 JKu(c),Souvenir
    From A Headhunter 7.00
187 JKu(c),The General
    Died Twice 7.00
188 The Devil's Pipers 7.00
189 The Gunner is a Gorilla 7.00
190 The Tiger and The Terrier ... 7.00
191 Decoy For Death 7.00
192 The General Has Two Faces 7.00
193 JKu(c),The War That
    Had To Wait 7.00
194 GE(c),Blitzkrieg Brain 7.00
195 JKu(c),The War That
    Time Forgot 7.00
196 JKu(c),Dead Men Patrol ... 7.00
197 JKu(c),Battle Ark 7.00
198 JKu(c),The Devil
    Rides A Panzer 7.00
199 JKu(c),A Medal From A Ghost 7.00
200 JKu(c),The Tank That Died .. 7.00
201 NA&RH(c),The Rocking
    Chair Soldiers 3.50
202 NA&RH(c),Walking Wounded
    Don't Cry 3.50
203 JKu(c),To Trap A Tiger 3.50
204 JKu(c),A Winter In Hell 3.50
205 JKu(c),A Gift From
    The Emperor 3.50
206 JKu(c),A Tomb For A Tank .. 3.50
207 JKu(c),Foxhole for a Sherman 3.50
208 JKu(c),Sink That Tank 3.50
209 JKu(c),Ring Of Blood 3.50
210 JKu(c),Tankers Also Bleed .. 3.50
211 JKu(c),A Nice Day For Killing 3.50
212 JKu(c),Clay Pigeon Crew .. 3.50
213 JKu(c),Back Door To War .. 3.50
214 JKu(c),The Tanker Who
    Couldn't Die 3.50
215 JKu(c),Last Stand For Losers 3.50
216 JKu(c),Ghost Squadron 3.50
217 JKu(c), The Pigeon Spies .. 3.50
218 JKu(c), 48 Hours to Die 3.50
219 thru 288 .... @3.50

GILGAMESH II
1989

1 JSn,O:Gilgamesh 5.00
2 JSn,V:Nightshadow 4.50
3 JSn,V:Robotic Ninja 4.50
4 JSn,final issue 4.00

DC COMICS

GODDESS
Vertigo 1995–96
[Mini-Series]
1 I:Rosie Nolan	4.00
2 Rosie arrested	4.00
3 I:Jenny	4.00
4 CIA Chase	4.00
5 V:Agent Hooks	4.00
6 V:Harry Hooks	4.00
7 Mudhawks Past	4.00
8 finale	4.00

GOLDEN AGE
Elseworld 1993–94
1 PS,F:JSA,All-Star Squadron	8.00
2 PS,I:Dynaman	7.00
3 PS,IR:Mr. Terrific is Ultra-Humanite	7.00
4 PS,D:Dynaman,Mr. Terrific	6.00

GON
DC/Paradox 1996
Book 1	6.00
Book 2 Gon Again!	6.00
Book 3 Here Today,Gon Tomorrow	6.00
Book 4 Going, Going, Gon	6.00
TPB Gon Swimmin'	7.00
TPB Color Spectacular	6.00
TPB Gon Wild rep. books 3 & 4	10.00

GREATEST STORIES EVER TOLD
Greatest Superman Stories Ever Told:	
HC	75.00
SC	15.95
Greatest Batman Stories Ever Told:	
HC	60.00
SC	16.00
Vol.#2 Catwoman & Penguin	16.95
Greatest Joker Stories Ever Told:	
HC	45.00
SC BBo(c)	15.00
Greatest Flash Stories Ever Told:	
HC	30.00
SC	15.00
Greatest Golden Age Stories Ever Told:	
HC	25.00
SC	15.00
Greatest Fifties Stories Ever Told:	
HC	30.00
SC	15.00
Greatest Team-Up Stories Ever Told:	
HC	25.00
SC	15.00

GREEN ARROW
[Limited Series] 1983
1 TVE,DG,O:Green Arrow	5.00
2 TVE,DG,A:Vertigo	3.50
3 TVE,DG,A:Vertigo	3.50
4 TVE,DG,A:Black Canary	3.50

[Regular Series] 1988–97
1 EH,DG,V:Muncie	5.00
2 EH,DG,V:Muncie	4.00
3 EH,DG,FMc,V:Fyres	4.00
4 EH,DG,FMc,V:Fryes	4.00
5 EH,DG,FMc,Gauntlet	4.00
6 EH,DG,FMc,Gauntlet	4.00
7 EB,DG,A:Black Canary	4.00
8 DG,Alaska	3.50
9 EH,DG,FMc,R:Shado	3.50
10 EH,DG,FMc,A:Shado	3.50
11 EH,DG,FMc,A:Shado	3.50
12 EH,DG,FMc,A:Shado	3.00
13 DJu,DG,FMc,Moving Target	3.00
14 EH,DG,FMc	3.00
15 EH,DG,FMc,Seattle And Die	3.00
16 EH,DG,FMc,Seattle And Die	3.00
17 DJu,DG,FMc,The Horse Man	2.50
18 DJu,DG,FMc,The Horse Man	2.50
19 EH,DG,FMc,A:Hal Jordan	2.50
20 EH,DG,FMc,A:Hal Jordan	2.50
21 DJu,DG,B:Blood of Dragon, A:Shado	2.50
22 DJu,DG,A:Shado	2.50
23 DJu,DG,A:Shado	2.50
24 DJu,DG,E:Blood of Dragon	2.50
25 TVE,Witch Hunt #1	2.25
26 Witch Hunt #2	2.25
27 DJu,DG,FMc,R:Warlord	2.25
28 DJu,DG,FMc,A:Warlord	2.25
29 DJu,DG,FMc,Coyote Tears	2.25
30 DJu,DG,FMc,Coyote Tears	2.25
31 FMc,V:Drug Dealers	2.25
32 FMc,V:Drug Dealers	2.25
33 DJu,FMc,Psychology Issue	2.25
34 DJu,DG,A:Fryes,Arrested	2.25

Green Arrow #73 © DC Comics, Inc.

35 B:Black Arrow Saga,A:Shade	2.25
36 Black Arrow Saga,A:Shade	2.25
37 Black Arrow Saga,A:Shade	2.25
38 E:Black Arrow Saga,A:Shade	2.25
39 DCw,Leaves Seattle	2.25
40 MGr,Spirit Quest,A: Indian Shaman	2.25
41 DCw,I.R.A.	2.25
42 DCw,I.R.A.	2.25
43 DCw,I.R.A.	2.25
44 DCw,Rock'n'Runes,pt.1	2.25
45 Rock'n'Runes,pt.2	2.25
46 DCw,Africa	2.25
47 DCw,V:Trappers	2.25
48 DCw,V:Trappers	2.25
49 V:Trappers	2.25
50 MGr(c),50th Anniv.,R:Seattle	3.00
51 Tanetti's Murder,pt.1	2.00
52 Tanetti's Murder,pt.2	2.00
53 The List,pt.1,A:Fyres	2.00
54 The List,pt.2,A:Fyres	2.00
55 Longbow Hunters tie-in	2.00
56 A:Lt. Cameron	2.00
57 And Not A Drop to Drink,pt.1	2.00
58 And Not A Drop to Drink,pt.2	2.00
59 Predator,pt.1	2.00
60 Predator,pt.2	2.00
61 FS,F:Draft Dodgers	2.00
62 FS	2.00
63 FS,B:Hunt for Red Dragon	2.00
64 FS,Hunt for Red Dragon	2.00
65 MGr(c),Hunt for Red Dragon	2.00
66 MGr(c),E:Hunt for Red Dragon	2.00
67 MGr(c),FS,V:Rockband Killer	2.00
68 MGr(c),FS,BumRap	2.00
69 MGr(c),Reunion Tour #1	2.00
70 Reunion Tour #2	2.00
71 Wild in the Streets #1	2.00
72 MGr(c),Wild in the Streets#2	2.00
73 MGr(c),F:Vietnam Vet	2.00
74 SAP,MGr(c),V:Sniper	2.00
75 MGr(c),A:Speedy Shado, Black Canary	3.00
76 MGr(c),R:Eddie Fyers	2.00
77 MGr(c),A:Eddie Fyers	2.00
78 MGr(c),V:CIA	2.00
79 MGr(c),V:CIA	2.00
80 MGr(c),E:MGr(s),V:CIA	2.00
81 B:CDi(s),JAp,V:Shrapnel, Nuklon	2.00
82 JAp,I:Rival	2.00
83 JAp,V:Yakuza	2.00
84 E:CDi(s),JAp,In Las Vegas	2.00
85 AlG(s),JAp,A:Deathstroke	2.00
86 DgM(s),JAp,A:Catwoman	2.00
87 JAp,V:Factory Owner	2.00
88 JAp,A:M.Manhunter,Bl.Beetle	2.00
89 JAp,A:Anarky	2.25
90 Zero Hour	2.25
91 Hitman	2.25
92 Partner attacked	2.25
93 Secrets of Red File	2.25
94 I:Camo Rouge	2.25
95 V:Camo Rouge	2.25
96 I:Slyfox,A:Hal Jordan	2.00
97 Where Angels Fear to Tread,pt.2	2.25
98 Where Angels Fear to Tread,pt.3, A:Arsenal	2.25
99 Where Angels Fear to Tread	2.25
100	4.00
101 A:Superman,Black Canary	5.00
102 CDi,RbC,Underworld Unleashed tie-in	2.25
103 CDi,RbC,Underworld Unleashed tie-in	2.25
104 CDi,RbC,A:Green Lantern	2.25
105 CDi,RbC,A:Robin	2.25
106	2.25
107 CDi,RbC,protects child-king	2.25
108 CDi,A:Thorn	2.25
109 CDi,JAp,BSz,in Metropolis	2.25
110 CDi(s),RbC,I:Hatchet, Green Lantern x-over	2.25
111 CDi(s),RbC,I:Hatchet, Green Lantern x-over	2.25
112 CDi(s),RbC	2.25
113 CDi(s),RbC,In the Mongolian wastes	2.25
114 CDi(s),RbC,airplane downed, Final Night tie-in	2.25
115 CDi(s),RbC,"The Iron Death," pt.1	2.25
116 CDi(s),RbC,"The Iron Death," pt.2	2.25
117 CDi(s),RbC,"The Iron Death," pt.3, concl.	2.25
118 CDi(s),DBw,RbC,"Endangered	

Species" pt.1 . . . . 2.25
119 CDi(s),DBw,RbC,"Endangered
　Species" pt.2 . . . . 2.25
120 CDi(s),RbC,at grandfather's
　ranch 2.25
121 CDi(s),RbC,V:The Silver
　Monkey 2.25
122 CDi(s),RbC, at Idaho ranch . . 2.25
123 CDi(s),JAp,KJ,"The
　Stormbringers" concl. 2.25
124 CDi(s),RbC,V:Milo Armitage . 2.25
125 CDi(s),DBw,Green Lantern
　x-over,pt.1, 48pg 3.50
126 CDi(s),DBw,x-over, pt.3 . . . . 2.50
127 CDi(s),DBw,to San Francisco 2.50
128 CDi(s),DWb,Russian Mob . . . 2.50
129 CDi,DBw,Jansen prisoner,pt.2 2.50
130 CDi,DBw, ... 2.50
131 CDi,DBw,F:Crackshot 2.50
132 CDi,DBw,Eddie Fyers returns 2.50
133 CDi,DBw,Eddie Fyers pt.2 . . 2.50
134 CDi,DBw,Brotherhood of
　the Fist x-over,pt.1 . . . . 2.50
135 CDi,DBw,Brotherhood of the
　Fist x-over, concl. 2.50
136 CDi,DBw,Green Pastures,pt.1 2.50
137 CDi(s),DBw,A:Superman . . . 2.50
Ann.#1 A:Question,FablesII . . . 3.50
Ann.#2 EH,DG,FMc,A:Question . . 3.00
Ann.#3 A:Question 2.50
Ann.#4 'The Black Alchemist' . . 3.25
Ann.#5 TVE,FS,Eclipso,Batman . . 3.25
Ann.#6 JBa(c),I:Hook 3.50
Ann.#7 CDi, Year One 3.95
Spec. #0 Return 2.00

GREEN ARROW LONGBOW HUNTERS
Aug., 1987
1 MGr,N:GreenArrow,I:Shado . . . 5.00
1a 2nd printing 2.50
2 MGr,'Shadow' Revealed 4.00
2a 2nd printing 2.50
3 MGr,Tracking Snow 4.00
TPB, rep. #1-#3 . . . . 12.95

GREEN ARROW: THE WONDER YEARS
1993
1 MGr,GM,B:New O:Green Arrow 2.50
2 MGr,GM,I:Brianna Stone 2.00
3 MGr,GM,A:Brianna Stone . . . 2.00
4 MGr,GM,Conclusion 2.00

GREEN CANDLES
1995
1 Paradox Mystery,F:John Halting 5.95
2 F:John Halting 5.95
3 finale 5.95
TPB B&W rep. #1–#3 . . . . 9.95

GREEN LANTERN
Autumn, 1941
1 O:Green Lantern, V:Master of
　Light, Arson in the Slums 27,000.00
2 V:Baldy,Tycoon's Legacy . 6,000.00
3 War cover 4,000.00
4 Doiby and Green Lantern
　join the Army 3,000.00
5 V:Nazis and Black
　Prophet,A:General Prophet 2,000.00
6 V:Nordo & Hordes of War Hungy
　Henchmen,Exhile of Exiles,

A:Shiloh 1,500.00
7 The Wizard of Odds 1,700.00
8 The Lady and Her Jewels,
　A:Hop Harrigan 1,500.00
9 V:The Whistler, The School
　for Vandals 1,500.00
10 V:Vandal Savage,The Man Who
　Wanted the World,O:Vandal
　Savage 1,400.00
11 The Distardly Designs of
　Doiby Dickles' Pals 1,100.00
12 O:The Gambler 1,100.00
13 A:Angela Van Enters . . . 1,100.00
14 Case of the Crooked Cook 1,100.00
15 V:Albert Zero, One...Two...
　Three...Stop Thinking . . . 1,100.00
16 V:The Lizard 1,100.00
17 V:Kid Triangle, Reward for
　Green Lantern 1,100.00
18 V:The Dandy, The Connoisseur of
　crime,X-mas(c) 1,200.00
19 V:Harpies, Sing a Song of
　Disaster A:Fate 1,000.00
20 A:Gambler 1,000.00
21 V:The Woodman,The Good
　Humor Man 1,000.00
22 A:Dapper Dan Crocker . . . 1,000.00
23 Doiby Dickles Movie
　Ajax Pictures 1,000.00
24 A:Mike Mattson,OnceA Cop 1,000.00
25 The Diamond Magnet 1,000.00
26 The Scourge of the Sea . . 1,000.00
27 V:Sky Pirate 1,000.00
28 The Tricks of the
　Sports Master 1,000.00
29 Meets the Challange of
　the Harlequin 1,000.00
30 I:Streak the Wonder Dog . 1,000.00
31 The Terror of the Talismans 900.00
32 The Case of the
　Astonishing Juggler 900.00
33 Crime goes West 900.00
34 Streak meets the Princess . 900.00
35 V:The Three-in-One Criminal 900.00
36 The Mystery of the
　Missing Messenger 1,000.00
37 A:Sargon 1,000.00
38 DoublePlay,May-June,1949 1,000.00

GREEN LANTERN
1960–72, 1976–86
1 GK,O:Green Lantern 2,700.00
2 GK,I:Qward,Pieface 800.00
3 GK,V:Qward 450.00
4 GK,Secret of GL Mask 350.00
5 GK,I:Hector Hammond . . . 350.00
6 GK,I:Tomar-Re 350.00
7 GK,I&O:Sinestro 300.00
8 GK,1st Story in 5700 A.D. . . 300.00
9 GK,A:Sinestro 300.00
10 GK,O:Green Lantern's Oath 300.00
11 GK,V:Sinestro 175.00
12 GK,Sinestro,I:Dr.Polaris . . 175.00
13 GK,A:Flash,Sinestro 200.00
14 GK,I&O:Sonar,1st Jordan
　Brothers story 175.00
15 GK,Zero Hour story 165.00
16 GK,MA,I:Star Saphire,
　O:Abin Sur 175.00
17 GK,V:Sinestro 165.00
18 GK 165.00
19 GK,A:Sonar 165.00
20 GK,A:Flash 175.00
21 GK,O:Dr.Polaris 150.00
22 GK,A:Hector Hammond,Jordan

Brothers story 150.00
23 GK,I:Tattooed Man 150.00
24 GK,O:Shark 150.00
25 GK,V:Sonar,HectorHammond 150.00
26 GK,A:Star Sapphire 150.00
27 GK 150.00
28 GK,I:Goldface 150.00
29 GK,I:Black Hand 160.00
30 GK,I:Katma Tui 150.00
31 GK,Jordan brothers story . . 120.00
32 GK 120.00
33 GK,V:Dr. Light 120.00
34 GK,V:Hector Hammond . . . 120.00
35 GK,I:Aerialist 120.00
36 GK 120.00
37 GK,I:Evil Star 120.00
38 GK,A:Tomar-Re 120.00
39 GK,V:Black Hand 120.00
40 GK,O:Guardians,A:Golden
　Age Green Lantern 550.00
41 GK,A:Star Sapphire 75.00
42 GK,A:Zatanna 75.00
43 GK,A:Major Disaster 75.00
44 GK,A:Evil Star 75.00

Green Lantern #10 © DC Comics, Inc.

45 GK,I:Prince Peril,A:Golden
　Age Green Lantern 125.00
46 GK,V:Dr.Polaris 75.00
47 GK,5700 A.D. V:Dr.Polaris . . 75.00
48 GK,I:Goldface 75.00
49 GK,I:Dazzler 75.00
50 GK,V:Thraxon the Powerful . 75.00
51 GK,Green Lantern's Evil
　Alter-ego 55.00
52 GK,A:Golden Age Green
　Lantern Sinestro 100.00
53 GK,CI,Jordon brothers story . 55.00
54 GK,Menace in the Iron Lung . 55.00
55 GK,Cosmic Enemy #1 . . . . 55.00
56 GK 55.00
57 GK,V:Major Disaster 55.00
58 GK,Perils of the Powerless
　Green Lantern 55.00
59 GK,I:Guy Gardner(imaginary
　story) 225.00
60 GK,I:Lamplighter 50.00
61 GK,A:Gold.Age Gr.Lantern . 55.00
62 Steel Small,Rob Big 50.00
63 NA(c),This is the Way the

World Ends	50.00
64 MSy,We Vow Death to Green	
Lantern	50.00
65 MSy,Dry up and Die	50.00
66 MSy,5700 AD story	50.00
67 DD,The First Green Lantern .	50.00
68 GK,I Wonder where the	
Yellow Went?	50.00
69 GK,WW,If Earth Fails the	
Test.. It Means War	50.00
70 GK,A Funny Thing Happened	
on the way to Earth	50.00
71 GK,DD,MA,Jordan brothers ..	25.00
72 GK,Phantom o/t SpaceOpera	25.00
73 GK,MA,A:Star Sapphire,	
Sinestro	25.00
74 GK,MA,A:Star Sapphire,	
Sinestro	25.00
75 GK,Qward	25.00
76 NA,Gr.Lantern & Gr.Arrow	
team-up begins	200.00
77 NA,Journey to Desolation ..	60.00
78 NA,A:Black Canary,A Kind of	
Loving..A Way to Death	60.00
79 NA,DA,A:Black Canary,Ulysses	
Star is Still Alive	50.00
80 NA,DG,Even an Immortal	
can die	50.00
81 NA,DG,A:Black Canary,Death	
be my Destiny	40.00
82 NA,DG,A:Black Canary,	
V:Sinestro,(BWr 1 page)	40.00
83 NA,DG,A:BlackCanary,Gr.Lantern	
reveals I.D. to Carol Ferris .	40.00
84 NA,BWr,V:Black Hand	40.00
85 NA,Speedy on Drugs,pt.1,	
rep.Green Lantern #1	60.00
86 NA,DG,Speedy on Drugs,pt.2,	
ATh(rep)Golden Age G.L. ...	60.00
87 NA,DG,I:John Stewart,	
2nd Guy Gardner app.	35.00
88 all reprints...............	10.00
89 NA,And Through Him Save	
the World	27.00
90 MGr,New Gr.Lantern rings ..	10.00
91 MGr,V:Sinestro	6.00
92 MGr,V:Sinestro	6.00
93 MGr,TA,War against the	
World Builders	5.00
94 MGr,TA,DG,Green Arrow	
Assassin,pt.1	5.00
95 MGr,Gr.Arrow Assassin,pt.2 ..	5.00
96 MGr,A:Katma Tui	5.00
97 MGr,V:Mocker	5.00
98 MGr,V:Mocker	5.00
99 MGr,V:Mocker	5.00
100 MGr,AS,I:Air Wave	9.00
101 MGr,A:Green Arrow	5.50
102 AS,A:Green Arrow	4.50
103 AS,Earth-Asylum for an Alien	3.50
104 AS,A:Air Wave	5.00
105 AS,Thunder Doom	5.00
106 MGr,Panic..In High Places	
& Low	5.00
107 AS,Green Lantern Corp.story	5.00
108 MGr,BU:G.A.Green Lantern,	
V:Replikon	6.00
109 MGr,Replicon#2,GA.GL.#2 .	5.00
110 MGr,GA.GL.#3	5.00
111 AS,O:Green Lantern,	
A:G.A.Green Lantern	6.00
112 AS,O&A:G.A. Green Lantern .	8.00
113 AS,Christmas story	4.00
114 AS,I:Crumbler	4.00
115 AS,V:Crumbler	4.00

116 Guy Gardner as Gr.Lantern .	26.00
117 JSon,I:KariLimbo,V:Prof.Ojo .	4.00
118 AS,V:Prof.Ojo	4.00
119 AS,G.L.& G.A.solo storys ...	3.50
120 DH,A:Kari,V:El Espectro ...	3.50
121 DH,V:El Espectro	3.50
122 DH,A:Guy Gardner,Superman	6.00
123 JSon,DG,E:Green Lantern/Green	
Arrow T.U..A:G.Gardner,	
V:Sinestro	7.00
124 JSon,V:Sinestro	3.50
125 JSon,FMc,V:Sinestro	3.50
126 JSon,FMc,V:Shark	3.50
127 JSon,FMc,V:Goldface	3.50
128 JSon,V:Goldface	3.50
129 JSon,V:Star Sapphire	3.50
130 JSon,FMc,A:Sonar,B:Tales of the	
Green Lantern Corps	3.00
131 JSon,AS,V:Evil Star	3.00
132 JSon,AS,E:Tales of GL Corps	
B:B.U.Adam Strange	3.00
133 JSon,V:Dr.Polaris	2.50
134 JSon,V:Dr.Polaris	2.50
135 JSon,V:Dr.Polaris	2.50

Green Lantern #12 © DC Comics, Inc.

136 JSon,A:Space Ranger,	
Adam Strange	2.50
137 JSon,CI,MA,I:Citadel,A:Space	
Ranger,A.Strange	2.50
138 JSon,A&O:Eclipso	4.00
139 JSon,V:Eclipso	3.00
140 JSon,I:Congressman Block	
Adam Strange	2.50
141 JSon,I:OmegaMen	6.00
142 JSon,A:OmegaMen	4.00
143 JSon,A:OmegaMen	4.00
144 JSon,D:Tattooed Man,Adam	
Strange	2.50
145 JSon,V:Goldface	2.50
146 JSon,CI,V:Goldface	
E:B.U.Adam Strange	2.50
147 JSon,CI,V:Goldface	2.50
148 JSon,DN,DA,V:Quardians ...	2.50
149 JSon,A:GL.Corps	2.50
150 JSon,anniversary	3.50
151 JSon,GL.Exiled in space ...	2.50
152 JSon,CI,GL Exile #2	2.50
153 JSon,CI,Gr.Lantern Exile #3 .	2.50
154 JSon,Gr.Lantern Exile #4 ...	2.50

155 JSon,Gr.Lantern Exile #5 ...	2.50
156 GK,Gr.Lantern Exile #6	2.50
157 KP,IN,Gr.Lantern Exile #7 ...	2.50
158 KP,IN,Gr.Lantern Exile #8 ...	2.50
159 KP,Gr.Lantern Exile #9	2.50
160 KP,Gr.Lantern Exile #10 ...	2.50
161 KP,A:Omega Men,Exile #11 .	2.50
162 KP,Gr.Lantern Exile #12 ...	2.50
163 KP,Gr.Lantern Exile #13 ...	2.50
164 KP,A:Myrwhidden,Exile #14 .	2.50
165 KP,A:John Stewart & Gr.Arrow	
Green Lantern Exile #15	2.00
166 GT,FMc,DGi,Exile #16	2.00
167 GT,FMc,G.L.Exile #17	2.00
168 GT,FMc,G.L. Exile #18	2.00
169 Green Lantern Exile #19 ...	2.00
170 GT,MSy,GreenLanternCorps .	2.00
171 ATh,TA,DGb,Green Lantern	
Exile #20	2.00
172 DGb,E:Gr.Lant.Exile	2.00
173 DGb,I:Javelin,A:Congressman	
Bloch	2.00
174 DGb,V:Javelin	2.00
175 DGb,A:Flash	2.25
176 DGb,V:The Shark	2.00
177 DGb,rep. Gr.Lant #128	2.00
178 DGb,A:Monitor,V:Demolition	
Team	2.00
179 DGb,I:Predator	2.00
180 DGb,A:JLA	2.00
181 DGi,Hal Jordan quits as GL .	2.75
182 DGi,John Stewart taks over	
V:Major Disaster	2.50
183 DGi,V:Major Disaster	2.50
184 DGb,Rep. Gr.Lant. #59	3.50
185 DGi,DH,V:Eclipso	4.00
186 DGi,V:Eclipso	4.00
187 BWi,John Stewart meets	
Katma Tui	2.25
188 JSon,C:GrArrow,V:Sonar,John	
Stewart reveals I.D. to world ..	3.50
189 JSon,V:Sonar	2.00
190 JSon,A:Green Arrow/Black	
Canary,Guy Gardner	2.00
191 JSon,IR:Predator is Star	
Sapphire	2.00
192 JSon,O:Star Sapphire	2.00
193 JSon,V:Replikon,	
A:G.Gardner	2.50
194 JSon,Crisis,R:G.Gardner ...	5.00
195 JSon,Guy Gardner as Green	
Lantern,develops attitude ...	10.00
196 JSon,V:Shark,Hal Jordan	
regains ring	3.00
197 JSon,V:Shark,Sonar,	
Goldface	3.00
198 JSon,D:Tomar-Re, Hal returns as	
Green Lantern,(double size) .	3.00
199 JSon,V:Star Sapphire	2.00
200 JSon,final Gr.Lantern issue .	2.50

Becomes:

GREEN LANTERN CORPS
1986–88

201 JSon,I:NewGr.LantCorps,V:Star	
Sapphire, Sonar, Dr.Polaris ...	2.00
202 JSon,set up headquarters ...	2.00
203 JSon,tribute to Disney ...	2.00
204 JSon,Arisia reaches puberty ..	2.00
205 JSon,V:Black Hand	2.00
206 JSon,V:Black Hand	2.00
207 JSon, Legneds crossover ...	2.00
208 JSon,I:Rocket Red Brigade,	
Green Lanterns in Russia#1 .	2.00

---

209 JSon,In Russia #2 . . . . 2.00
210 JSon,In Russia #3 . . . . 2.00
211 JSon,John Stewart proposes
    to Katma Tui 1.75
212 JSon,W:J.Stewart&KatmaTui . 1.75
213 Json,For Want of a Male 1.75
214 IG,5700 A.D. Story 1.75
215 IG,Salaak and Chip quit 1.75
216 IG,V:Carl 1.75
217 JSon,V:Sinestro 1.75
218 BWg,V:Sinestro 1.75
219 BWg,V:Sinestro 1.75
220 JSon,Millenium,pt.3 . . . . 1.75
221 JSon,Millenium 1.75
222 JSon,V:Sinestro 1.75
223 GK,V:Sinestro 1.75
224 GK,V:Sinestro 2.00
Ann.#1 GK 2.00
Ann.#2 JSa,BWg,S:AnM 2.50
Ann.#3 JBy,JL,JR 2.00
Spec.#1 A:Superman 2.00
Spec.#2 MBr,RT,V:Seeker 2.00
TPB rep.#84-#87,#89,Flash
    #217-#219 . . . . 12.95
TPB rep. reprints of #1-#7 . . . . . 8.95

Green Lantern (2nd Series) #60
© DC Comics, Inc.

GREEN LANTERN
[2nd Regular Series] 1990–97
1 PB,A:Hal Jordan,John Stuart,
    Guy Gardner 5.00
2 PB,A:Tattooed Man 3.00
3 PB,Jordan vs.Gardner 4.00
4 PB,Vanishing Cities 2.00
5 PB Return to OA 2.00
6 PB 3GL'sCaptive 2.00
7 PB R:Guardians 2.00
8 PB R:Guardians 2.00
9 JSon,G.Gardner,pt.1 . . . . 3.00
10 JSon,G.Gardner,pt.2 . . . . 3.00
11 JSon,G.Gardner,pt.3 . . . . 3.00
12 JSon,G.Gardner,pt.4 . . . . 3.00
13 Jordan,Gardner,Stuart(giant) . . 2.50
14 PB,Mosaic,pt.1 . . . . 2.00
15 RT,Mosaic,pt.2 . . . . 2.00
16 MBr,RT,Mosaic,pt.3 . . . . 2.00
17 MBr,RT,Mosaic,pt.4 . . . . 2.00

18 JSon,JRu,G.Gardner,
    A:Goldface 2.00
19 MBr,PB,JSon,A:All Four G.L.'s,
    O:Alan Scott,A:Doiby Dickles
    (D.Size-50th Ann.Iss.) 3.00
20 PB,RT,Hal Jordan G.L. Corp
    story begins, A:Flicker 1.75
21 PB,RT,G.L. Corp.,pt.2,
    V:Flicker 1.75
22 PB,RT,G.L. Corp.,pt.3,
    R:Star Sapphire 1.75
23 PB,RT,V:Star Sapphire,
    A:John Stuart 1.75
24 PB,RT,V:Star Sapphire 1.75
25 MBr,JSon,RT,Hal Vs.Guy,
    A:JLA 2.75
26 MBr,V:Evil Star,Starlings 1.50
27 MBr,V:Evil Star,Starlings 1.50
28 MBr,V:Evil Star,Starlings 1.50
29 MBr,RT,R:Olivia Reynolds . . . 1.50
30 MBr,RT,Gorilla Warfare#1 . . . 1.50
31 MBr,RT,Gorilla Warfare#3 . . . 1.50
32 RT(i),A:Floro,Arisia 1.50
33 MBr,RT,Third Law#1,
    A;New Guardians 1.50
34 MBr,RT,Third Law#2,I:Entropy 1.50
35 MBr,RT,Third Law#3,V:Entropy 1.50
36 V:Dr.Light 1.50
37 MBg,RT,A:Guy Gardner 1.50
38 MBr,RT,A:Adam Strange 1.50
39 MBr,RT,A:Adam Strange 1.50
40 RT(i),A:Darkstar,
    V:Reverse Flash 1.75
41 MBr,RT,V:Predator,
    C:Deathstroke 1.50
42 MBr,RT,V:Predator,
    Deathstroke 1.50
43 RT(i),A:Itty 1.50
44 RT(i),Trinity#2,A:L.E.G.I.O.N . 1.75
45 GeH,Trinity#5,A:L.E.G.I.O.N.,
    Darkstars 1.75
46 MBr,A:All Supermen,
    V:Mongul 8.00
47 A:Green Arrow 6.00
48 KM(c),B:Emerald Twilight,I:Kyle
    Rayner (Last Green Lantern) . . 7.00
49 KM(c),GJ(s),A:Sinestro 6.00
50 KM(c),GJ(s),D:Sinestro,Kiliwog,
    Guardians,I:Last Green
    Lantern (in Costume) 8.00
51 V:Ohm,A:Mongul 4.00
52 V:Mongul 2.00
53 A:Superman,V:Mongul 2.00
54 D:Alex,V:Major Force 2.00
55 Zero Hour,A:Alan Scott,
    V:Major Force 2.25
56 Green Lantern and ring 2.00
57 Psimon 2.00
58 Donna Troy,Felix Faust 2.00
59 V:Dr. Polaris 2.00
60 Capital Punishment,pt.3 . . . . . 2.00
61 V:Kalibak,A:Darkstar 2.00
62 V:Duality,R:Ganthet 2.00
63 Parallax View: The Resurrection
    of Hal Jordan,pt.1 . . . . 2.00
64 Parallax View,pt.2,A:Superman,
    Flash,V:Parallax 2.00
65 Siege of ZiCharan,pt.2 . . . . . . 2.00
66 V:Sonar 2.00
67 A:Flash,V:Sonar 2.00
68 RMz,RT,Underworld
    Unleashed tie-in 2.00
69 RMz,RT,Underworld
    Unleashed tie-in 2.00
70 RMz,RT,A:Supergirl 2.00

71 RMz,RT,Hero Quest,pt.1 . . . . 2.00
72 RMz,RT,Hero Quest,pt.2 . . . . 2.00
73 RMz,RT,Hero Quest,pt.3 . . . . 2.00
74 RMz,RT,A:Adam Strange,
    V:Grayven 2.00
75 A:Adam Strange 2.00
76 Green Arrow x-over 2.00
77 Green Arrow x-over 2.00
78 . . . . 2.00
79 V:Sonar 2.00
80 RMz(s),JWi,MGy,V:Dr. Light,
    Final Night tie-in 2.00
81 RMz(s),DBk,RT,Memorial for
    Hal Jordan 4.00
81a deluxe edition + extra stories,
    foil cover on cardstock 6.00
82 RMz(s),TGb,RT,F:Kyle Rayner,
    Alan Scott, Guy Gardner &
    John Stewart 1.75
83 . . . . 1.75
84 "Retribution," pt.1 . . . . 1.75
85 "Retribution," pt.2 . . . . 1.75
86 RMz,JJ,RT,A:Jade, V:Obsidian 1.75
87 RMz,TGb,RT,A:Martian
    Manhunter, vs. alien invasion . 1.75
88 RMz(s),DBk,TA,A:Donna Troy,
    visit Kyle's mom 1.75
89 RM(s),TA,V:Machine Messiah . 1.75
90 RM(s),Why did Kyle Rayner
    become Green Lantern 1.75
91 RMz(s),DBk,TA,V:Desaad . . . 2.00
92 RMz(s),DBk,TA,A:Green Arrow,
    x-over 2.00
93 RMz(s),DBk,TA,F:Deadman . . 2.00
94 RMz(s),PaP,TA,F:Superboy . . 2.00
95 RMz(s),JSn,TA, deep space . . 2.00
96 RMz(s) 2.00
97 RMz(s),MMK,TA,V:Grayven . . 2.00
98 RMz,DBk,TA,Future Shock,pt.1 2.00
99 RMz,DBk,TA,Future Shock,pt.2 2.00
100 RMz,DBk,AT,Kyle Rayner and
    Hal Jordan,V:Sinestro, 48pg . . 3.00
100a deluxe edition 3.00
101 RMz(s),JJ,BWi,Emerald
    Knights,pt.1, bi-weekly 2.00
102 RMz(s),PaP,TA,Emerald
    Knights,pt.2, bi-weekly 2.00
103 RMz(s),JJ,BWi,Emerald
    Knights,pt.3, bi-weekly 2.00
104 RMz(s),JJ,BWi,Greener Pastures
    x-over, concl., Emerald
    Knights,pt.4, bi-weekly 2.00
105 RMz(s),JJ,SEa,BWi,Emerald
    Knights,pt.5, bi-weekly 2.00
106 RMz(s),PaP,TA,Emerald
    Knights,concl. 2.00
Ann.#1 Eclipso,V:Star Sapphire . . 2.75
Ann.#2 Bloodlines#7,I:Nightblade . 2.50
Ann.#3 Elseworlds Story 2.95
Ann.#4 Year One story 3.00
Ann.#5 Legends o/t Dead Earth . . 2.95
Ann.#6 RMz(s),JJ,Low,Pulp
    Heroes, 64pg. 4.00
Ann.#7 SV,RLm,Clv,BWr,Ghosts . 3.00
TPB A New Dawn 10.00
GN Ganthet's Tale, JBy 6.00
Ann.#1 80pg, rep. 5.00
Archives, Vol.1, 2nd print 50.00
Secret Files #1 . . . . 5.00
TPB Emerald Twilight 6.25

GREEN LANTERN & SENTINEL: HEART OF DARKNESS
Feb. 1998
1 (of 3) RMz(s),PaP,DDv 2.00
2 RMz(s),PaP,DDv 2.00
3 RMz(s),PaP,DDv 2.00

GREEN LANTERN CORPS QUARTERLY
1992–94
1 DAb,JSon,FH,PG,MBr,F:Alan
Scott G'nort 3.00
2 DAb,JSon,PG,AG,Alan Scott . . 2.75
3 DAb,RT,F:Alan Scott,G'Nort . . 2.75
4 TA,AG(i),F:H.Jordan,G'Nort . . 2.75
5 F:Alan Scott,I:Adam 2.75
6 JBa,TC,F:Alan Scott 3.25
7 Halloween Issue 3.25
8 GeH,SHa,final issue 3.25

Green Lantern: Mosaic #5
© DC Comics, Inc.

GREEN LANTERN: EMERALD DAWN
[1st Limited Series] 1989–90
1 MBr,RT,I:Mod.Age.Gr.Lantern . 5.00
2 MBr,RT,I:Legion (not group) . . 4.00
3 MBr,RT,V:Legion 3.00
4 MBr,RT,A:Green Lantern Corps 3.00
5 MBr,RT,V:Legion 3.00
6 MBr,RT,V:Legion 3.00
TPB rep#1–#6 . . . . 5.50
[2nd Limited Series] 1991
1 MBr,RT,I:Sinestro,Guy Gardner . . 2.00
2 MBr,RT,V:Alien Aliance 1.75
3 MBr,RT,Sinestro's Home Planet 1.75
4 MBr,RT,Korugar Revolt 1.75
5 MBr,RT,A:G.Gardner 1.75
6 MBr,RT,Trial of Sinestro 1.75

GREEN LANTERN GALLERY
1 one-shot life in pictures 3.50

GREEN LANTERN: GANTHET'S TALE
1 JBy,O:Guardians 7.00

GREEN LANTERN/ GREEN ARROW
1983–84
1 NA rep. 5.00
2 NA,DG rep. 4.00
3 NA,DG rep. 4.00
4 NA,DG rep. 4.00
5 NA,DG rep. 4.00
6 NA,DG rep. 4.00
7 NA,DG rep. 4.00
TPB Roadback 8.95
TPB Traveling Heroes, Vol.1 . . 12.95
TPB Traveling Heroes, Vol.2 . . 12.95

GREEN LANTERN: MOSAIC
1992–93
1 F:John Stewart 2.00
2 D:Ch'p 1.75
3 V:Sinestro 1.50
4 F:The Children on Oa 1.50
5 V:Hal Jordan 1.50
6 A:Kilowog 1.50
7 V:Alien Faction 1.50
8 V:Ethereal Creatures 1.50
9 Christmas issue 1.50
10 V:Guardians 1.50
11 R:Ch'p 1.50
12 V:KKK 1.50
13 V:KKK,Racism 1.50
14 A:Salaak,Ch'p 1.50
15 A:Katma Tui,Ch'p 1.50
16 LMc,A:JLA,Green Lantern . . . 1.50
17 A:JLA 1.50
18 final issue 1.50

GREEN LANTERN PLUS
1 one-shot RMz(s), F:The Ray,
V:Dr. Polaris 2.95

GREEN LANTERN/ SILVER SURFER
1-shot DC/Marvel RMz,TA
A:Thanos vs. Parallax 4.95

GREGORY III
Bookshelf Ed. 4.95
Platinum Ed. 12.00

GRIFFIN
1991–92
1 I:Matt Williams as Griffin 5.50
2 V:Carson 5.25
3 A:Mary Wayne 5.25
4 A:Mary Wayne 5.25
5 Face to Face with Himself 5.25
6 Final Issue 5.25

GROSS POINT
July 1997
1 MWa&BAu(s) parody 2.50
2 Independence Day picnic 2.50
3 Ed Gein High School 2.50
4 paranoid driving instructor 2.50
5 Halloween 2.50
6 trip to Chicago 2.50
7 stuck in Gross Point 2.50

8 Dru Hardly & Nancy Boys 2.50
9 . . . . 2.50
10 Businessman of the Year 2.50
11 Mystery Meat 2.50
12 Cold Hands, Still Heart 2.50
13 terminal illness 2.50
14 The Aisle of Doctor Morose . . 2.50

GUARDIANS OF METROPOLIS
Nov. 1994
1 Kirby characters 1.50
2 Donovan's creations 1.50
3 . . . . 1.50
4 Female Furies 1.50

GUNFIRE
1994–95
1 B:LWn(s),StE,I:Ricochet 2.00
2 StE,V:Ricochet 2.00
3 StE,I:Purge 2.00
4 StE,V:Maraud 3 . . . . 2.00
5 StE,I:Exomorphic Man 2.00
6 New costume 2.00
7 Ragnarok 2.00
8 V:Tattoo 2.00
9 V:Ragnarock 2.00
10 V:Yakuza 2.00
11 V:Yakuza 2.00
12 I:New Weapon 2.00
13 A:JLA,V:Ragnarok, final issue . 2.25

GUNS OF THE DRAGON
Aug., 1998
1 (of 4) TT, set in 1920s 2.50

Guy Gardner #12 © DC Comics, Inc.

GUY GARDNER
1992–94
1 JSon,A:JLA,JLE 2.00
2 JSon,A:Kilowog 1.50
3 JSon,V:Big,Ugly Alien 1.50
4 JSon,G.Gardner vs Ice 1.50
5 JSon,A:Hal Jordan,V:Goldface . 1.50
6 JSon,A:Hal Jordan,V:Goldface . 1.50
7 JSon,V:Goldface 1.50
8 JSon,V:Lobo 1.50

9 JSon,Boodikka 1.50
10 JSon,V:Boodikka 1.50
11 JSon,B:Year One 1.50
12 JSon,V:Batman,Flash,Green
   Lantern 1.50
13 JSon,Year One#3 . . . . 1.50
14 JSon,E:Year One 1.50
15 V:Bad Guy Gardner 1.50
16 B:CDi(s),MaT,V:Guy's Brother . 1.75
Becomes:

GUY GARDNER: WARRIOR
1994–96
17 V:Militia 2.00
18 B:Emerald Fallout,N:Guy Gardner,
   V:Militia 4.00
19 A:G.A.Green Lantern,V:Militia . 4.00
20 A:JLA,Darkstars 2.00
21 E:Emerald Fallout,V:H.Jordan . 2.00
22 I:Dementor 1.75
23 A:Buck Wargo 1.75
24 Zero Hour 1.50
25 A:Buck Wargo 2.50
26 Zero Hour 1.50
27 Capital Punishment 1.50
28 Capital Punishment,pt.2 . . . . . 1.50
29 I:Warriors Bar 1.50
29a Collector's Edition 2.95
30 V:Superman,Supergirl 1.50
31 A:Sentinel,Supergirl,
   V:Dementor 1.75
32 Way of the Warrior,pt.1,A:JLA . 1.75
33 Way of the Warrior,pt.4 . . . . . 1.75
34 . . . . 1.75
35 Return of an Old Foe 1.75
36 Underworld Unleashed tie-in . . 1.75
37 Underworld Unleashed tie-in . . 1.75
38 A new woman 1.75
39 guest stars galore 1.75
40 . . . . 1.75
41 V:Dungeon 1.75
42 Martika revealed as Seductress 1.75
43 V:5 foes 1.75
Ann.#1 Year One Annual, Leechun
   vs. Vuldarians 3.50

GUY GARDNER: REBORN
1992
1 JSon,JRu,V:Goldface,C:Lobo . . 6.00
2 JSon,JRu,A:Lobo,V:Weaponers
   of Qward 5.50
3 JSon,JRu,A:Lobo,N:G.Gardner
   V:Qwardians 5.50

HACKER FILES
1992–93
1 TS,Soft Wars#1,I:Jack Marshall 2.25
2 TS,Soft Wars#2 . . . . 2.00
3 TS,Soft Wars#3 . . . . 2.00
4 TS,Soft Wars#4 . . . . 2.00
5 TS,A:Oracle(Batgirl) 2.00
6 TS,A:Oracle,Green Lantern . . . 2.00
7 TS,V:Digitronix 2.00
8 TS,V:Digitronix 2.00
9 TS,V:Digitronix 1.75
10 V:Digitronix 2.00
11 TS,A:JLE 2.00
12 TS,V:Digitronix,final issue . . . 2.00

HAMMER LOCKE
1992–93
1 I:Hammerlocke 2.50
2 V:Tharn the Iron Spider 1.75

3 V:Tharn the Iron Spider 1.75
4 O:Hammerlocke 1.75
5 V:Sahara Skyhawk 1.75
6 V:Tharn the Iron Spider 1.75
7 V:Tharn 1.75
8 CSp,V:Iron Spider 1.75

HARDCORE STATION
May, 1998
1 (of 6) JSn,JRu,F:Maximillian . 2.50
2 JSn,JRu,V:Synnar 2.50
3 JSn,JRu,F:Kyle Rayner 2.50
4 JSn,JRu,V:Synnar 2.50

Hammer Locke #5 © DC Comics, Inc.

HARDWARE
(Milestone) 1993–96
1 DCw,I:Hardware,Edwin Alva,Reprise,
   Dir.Mark.Ed.,w/A puzzle piece,
   Skybox Card,Poster 4.00
1a NewsstandEd. 2.00
1b Platinum Ed. 6.00
2 DCw,V:Repirise,I:Barraki Young 2.00
3 DCw,O:EDwin Alva,
   I:S.Y.S.T.E.M. 2.00
4 DCw,V:S.Y.S.T.E.M. 2.00
5 DCw,I:Deathwish 2.00
6 DCw,V:Deathwish 1.75
7 DCw,O:Deathwish 1.75
8 DCw(c),O:Hardware 1.75
9 DCw(c),I:Technique 1.75
10 DCw(c),I:Harm,Transit 1.75
11 WS(c),DCw,Shadow War,
   I:Iron Butterfly,Dharma 1.75
12 RB,V:Harm 1.75
13 DCw,A:Reprise 1.75
14 DCw 1.75
15 DCw(c),HuR,V:Alva 1.75
16 Die-Cut(c),JBy(c),DCw,
   N:Hardware 4.25
16a Newsstand ED. 2.25
17 Worlds Collide,pt.2,A:Steel . . 1.75
18 Worlds Collide,pt.9,V:Rift . . . 2.00
19 I:Evan,Tetras 1.75
20 . . . . 1.75
21 Arcana,Helga 1.75
22 Curt & Assistant 1.75
23 . . . . 1.75

24 . . . . 1.75
25 V:Death Row, Sanction 2.95
26 Hunt For Deathwish,pt.1 . . . . 1.75
27 Hunt For Deathwish,pt.2 . . . . 1.75
28 Hunt For Deathwish,pt.3 . . . . 1.75
29 Long Hot Summer, A:The Blood
   Syndicate, spec.low price . . . 1.00
30 Long Hot Summer 2.50
31 . . . . 2.50
32 Control of Alva 2.50
33 HC(c), Cyborg 2.50
34 V:Huaca Aires 2.50
35 A:Sanction 2.50
36 A:Sanction 2.50
37 . . . . 2.50
38 V:Malleus, without armor 2.50
39 F:Sabrina Alva 2.50
40 V:Top Dog 2.50
41 . . . . 2.50
42 . . . . 2.50
43 . . . . 2.50
44 A:Heroes 2.50
45 DGC(s),Hardware & Hard
   Company go back to basics . . 2.50
46 DGC(s),discovery of Edwin
   Alva's artificial intelligence . . 2.50
47 DGC(s),the truth behind a
   brutal murder 2.50
48 . . . . 2.50
49 DGC(s),Moe(c),V:Tyrant 2.50
50 DGC(s), 48pg. anniversary issue 3.95
51 DMc(s) final issue 2.50

HAWK & DOVE
[1st Regular Series] 1968–69
1 SD 50.00
2 SD 40.00
3 GK 35.00
4 GK 35.00
5 GK,C:Teen Titans 40.00
6 GK 35.00

[Limited Series] 1988–89
1 RLd,I:New Dove 5.00
2 RLd,V:Kestrel 4.50
3 RLd,V:Kestrel 4.50
4 RLd,V:Kestrel 4.50
5 RLd,V:Kestrel,O:New Dove . . 4.50
TPB rep. #1–#5 . . . . 9.95

[2nd Regular Series] 1989–91
1 A:Superman,Green Lantern
   Hawkman 2.00
2 V:Aztec Goddess 1.75
3 V:Aztec Goddess 1.75
4 I:The Untouchables 1.50
5 I:Sudden Death, A:1st Dove's
   Ghost 1.50
6 A:Barter,Secrets o/Hawk&Dove 1.50
7 A:Barter,V:Count St.Germain . 1.50
8 V:Count St.Germain 1.50
9 A:Copperhead 1.50
10 V:Gauntlet & Andromeda . . . 1.50
11 A:New Titans,V.M.A.C.,
   Andromeda Gauntlet 1.50
12 A:New Titans,V:Scarab 1.50
13 1960's,I:Shellshock 1.50
14 Prelude to O:Hawk & Dove,
   V:Kestrel 1.50
15 O:Hawk & Dove begins 1.50
16 HawkV:Dove,V:Lord of Chaos 1.50
17 V:Lords-Order & Chaos 1.50
18 The Creeper #1 . . . . 1.50
19 The Creeper #2 . . . . 1.50
20 KM,DG,Christmas Story 1.50
21 Dove 1.50

22 V:Sudden Death 1.50
23 A:Velv.Tiger,SuddenDeath . . . 1.50
24 A:Velv.Tiger,SuddenDeath . . . 1.50
25 Recap 1st 2 yrs.(48 pg) 2.00
26 Dove's past 1.50
27 The Hunt for Hawk 1.50
28 War of the Gods,A:Wildebeest
A:Uncle Sam,final issue,
double size 2.00
Ann.#1 In Hell 2.00
Ann.#2 CS,KGa,ArmageddonPt.5 . 2.00
TPB RLd 9.95

HAWK & DOVE
Sept., 1997
1 (of 5) MBn,DZ,DG,Sasha Martens
& Wiley Wolverman 2.50
2 MBn,DZ,DG,Vixen & Vigilante . 2.50
3 MBn,DZ,DG,grave desecrations 2.50
4 MBn,DZ,DG,V:Suicide Squad . 2.50

Hawkman (1st Series) #2
© DC Comics, Inc.

HAWKMAN
[1st Regular Series]1964–68
1 MA,V:Chac 550.00
2 MA,V:Tralls 200.00
3 MA,V:Sky Raiders 135.00
4 MA,I&O:Zatanna 150.00
5 MA 135.00
6 MA 125.00
7 MA,V:I.Q. 125.00
8 MA 125.00
9 MA,V:Matter Master 125.00
10 MA,V:Caw 125.00
11 MA 75.00
12 MA 75.00
13 MA 75.00
14 GaF,MA,V:Caw 75.00
15 GaF,MA,V:Makkar 75.00
16 GaF,MA,V:Ruthvol 75.00
17 GaF,MA,V:Raven 75.00
18 GaF,MA,A:Adam Strange . . . 50.00
19 GaF,MA,A:Adam Strange . . . 50.00
20 GaF,MA,V:Lionmane 45.00
21 GaF,MA,V:Lionmane 45.00
22 V:Falcon 45.00
23 V:Dr.Malevolo 45.00

24 Robot Raiders from
Planet Midnight 45.00
25 DD,V:Medusa,G.A.Hawkman . 45.00
26 RdM,CCu,DD 45.00
27 DD,JKu(c),V:Yeti 45.00
[2nd Regular Series] 1986–87
1 DH,A:Shadow Thief 3.00
2 DH,V:Shadow Thief 2.00
3 DH,V:Shadow Thief 1.50
4 DH A:Zatanna 1.50
5 DH,V:Lionmane 1.50
6 DH,V:Gentleman Ghost,
Lionmane 1.50
7 DH,Honor Wings 1.50
8 DH,Shadow War contd. 1.50
9 DH,Shadow War contd. 1.50
10 JBy(c),D:Hyatis Corp 1.50
11 End of Shadow War 1.50
12 Hawks on Thanagar 1.50
13 DH,Murder Case 1.50
14 DH,Mystery o/Haunted Masks . 1.50
15 DH,Murderer Revealed 1.50
16 DH,Hawkwoman lost 1.50
17 EH,DH,final issue 1.50
TPB rep.Brave & Bold apps. . . . 19.95
[3rd Regular Series] 1993–96
1 B:JOs(s),JD,R:Hawkman,
V:Deadline 4.00
2 JD,A:Gr.Lantern,V:Meta-Tech . 2.50
3 JD,I:Airstryke 2.25
4 JD,RM 2.00
5 JD(c),V:Count Viper 2.00
6 JD(c),A:Eradicator 2.00
7 JD(c),PuK(s),LMc,B:King of the
Netherworld 2.00
8 LMc,E:King of the Netherworld . 2.00
9 BML(s) 2.00
10 I:Badblood 2.00
11 V:Badblood 2.00
12 V:Hawkgod 2.25
13 V:Hawkgod 2.25
14 New abilities,pt.1 . . . . 2.00
15 New abilities,pt.2 . . . . 2.00
16 Eyes of the Hawk,pt.3 . . . . . 2.00
17 Eyes of the Hawk,pt.4 . . . . . 2.00
18 Seagle,Ellis, Pepoy 2.00
19 F:Hawkman 2.00
21 RLm,V:Shadow Thief,
Gentleman Ghost 2.25
22 Way of the Warrior,pt.3
A:Warrior,JLA 2.25
23 Way of the Warrior,pt.6 . . . . . 2.25
24 . . . . 2.25
25 V:Lionmane,painted(c) 2.25
26 WML,Underworld
Unleashed tie-in 2.25
27 WML,Underworld
Unleashed tie-in 2.25
28 WML,V:Doctor Polaris 2.25
29 HC(c),V:Vandal Savage 2.25
30 . . . . 2.25
31 serial killer has Tangarian
technology 2.25
32 MC,Search for serial killer 2.25
Ann.#1 JD,I:Mongrel 3.75
Ann.#2 Year One Annual 3.95

HAWKWORLD
1989
1 TT,Hawkman, Origin retold . . . 5.00
2 TT,Katar tried for treason 4.00
3 TT,Hawkgirl's debut 4.00
[1st Regular Series] 1990–93
1 GN,Byth on Earth,R:Kanjar Ro . 3.00

2 GN,Katar & Shayera in Chicago 2.50
3 GN,V:Chicago Crime 2.00
4 GN,Byth's Control Tightens . . . 2.00
5 GN,Return of Shadow Thief . . . 2.00
6 GN,Stolen Thanagarian Ship . . 2.00
7 GN,V:Byth 2.00
8 GN,Hawkman vs. Hawkwoman 2.00
9 GN,Hawkwoman in Prison 2.00
10 Shayera returns to Thanagar . 2.00
11 GN,Blackhawk,Express 2.00
12 GN,Princess Treska 2.00
13 TMd,A:Firehawk,V:Marauder . 2.00
14 GN,Shayera's Father 2.00
15 GN,War of the Gods X-over . . 2.00
16 GN War of the Gods X-over . . 2.00
17 GN,Train Terrorists 2.00
18 GN,V:Atilla 2.00
19 GN,V:Atilla 2.00
20 V:Smir'Beau 2.00
21 GN,Thanagar Pt.1,
A:J.S.A. Hawkman 2.00
22 GN,Thanagar Pt.2 . . . . 2.00
23 GN,Thanagar Pt.3 . . . . 2.00
24 GN,Thanagar Pt.4 . . . . 2.00
25 GN,Thanagar Pt.5 . . . . 2.00
26 GN,V:Attila battle armor 2.00
27 JD,B:Flight's End 2.00
28 JD,Flight's End #2 . . . . 2.00
29 TT(c),JDu,Flight's End #3 . . . 2.00
30 TT,Flight's End #4 . . . . 2.00
31 TT,Flight's End #5 . . . . 2.00
32 TT,V:Count Viper,final issue . . 2.50
Ann.#1 A:Flash 4.50
Ann.#2 Armageddon,pt.6 . . . . . . 4.00
Ann.#2a reprint (Silver) 3.50
Ann.#3 Eclipso tie-in 3.25

HAYWIRE
1988–89
1 . . . . 1.50
2 . . . . 1.25
3 thru 13 . . . . 1.00

HEARTLAND
DC/Vertigo Jan. 1997
1 GEn(s),SDi,Kit faces childhood
memories 4.95

HEART OF THE BEAST
GNv SeP 19.95

HECKLER, THE
1992–93
1 KG,MJ,I:The Heckler 1.25
2 KG,MJ,V:The Generic Man . . . 1.25
3 KG,MJ,V:Cosmic Clown 1.25
4 KG,V:Bushwacker 1.25
5 KG,Theater Date 1.25
6 KG,I:Lex Concord 1.25
7 KG,V:Cuttin'Edge 1.25

HELLBLAZER
Jan., 1988
1 B:JaD(s),JRy,F:John
Constantine 25.00
2 JRy,I:Papa Midnight 10.00
3 JRy,I:Blathoxi 8.00
4 JRy,I:Resurrection Crusade,
Gemma 8.00
5 JRy,F:Pyramid of Fear 8.00
6 JRy,V:Resurrection Crusade,
I:Nergal 6.00
7 JRy,V:Resurrection Crusade,

I:Richie Simpson 6.00
8 JRy,AA,Constantine receives
  demon blood,V:Nergal 6.00
9 JRy,A:Swamp Thing 6.00
10 JRy,V:Nergal 6.00
11 MBu,Newcastle Incident,pt.1 .. 5.00
12 JRy,D:Nergal 5.00
13 JRy,John has a Nightmare ... 4.00
14 JRy,B:The Fear Machine,
  I:Mercury,Marj,Eddie 4.00
15 JRy,Shepard's Warning. 4.00
16 JRy,Rough Justice 4.00
17 MkH,I:Mr. Wester 4.00
18 JRy,R:Zed 4.00
19 JRy,I:Simon Hughes 7.00
20 JRy,F:Mr.Webster 5.00
21 JRy,I:Jallakuntilliokan 5.00
22 JRy,E:The Fear Machine. ... 5.00
23 I&D:Jerry O'Flynn 4.00
24 E:JaD(s),I:Sammy Morris ... 4.00
25 GMo(s),DvL,Early Warning ... 4.00
26 GMo(s) 4.00
27 NGa(s),DMc,Hold Me 11.00
28 B:JaD(s),RnT,KeW,F:S.Morris . 4.00

Hellblazer #2 © DC Comics, Inc.

29 RnT,KeW,V:Sammy Morris ... 4.00
30 RnT,KeW,D:Sammy Morris ... 4.00
31 E:JaD(s),SeP,Constantine's
  Father's Funeral 4.00
32 DiF(s),StP,I&D:Drummond ... 3.50
33 B:JaD(s),MPn,I:Pat McDonell . 3.50
34 SeP,R:Mercury,Marj 3.50
35 SeP,Constantine's Past 3.50
36 Future Death,(preview of
  World Without End) 3.50
37 Journey to England's Secret
  Mystics 3.50
38 Constantine's Journey contd. . 3.50
39 Journey to Discovery 3.50
40 DMc,I:2nd Kid Eternity 4.00
41 B:GEn(s),WSm,MPn,Dangerous
  Habits 6.00
42 Dangerous Habits 4.00
43 I:Chantinelle 4.00
44 Dangerous Habits 4.00
45 Dangerous Habits 4.00
46 Dangerous Habits epilogue,
  I:Kit(John's girlfriend) 4.00
47 SnW(i),Pub Where I Was Born 3.50

48 Love Kills 3.50
49 X-mas issue,Lord o/t Dance .. 3.50
50 WSm,Remarkable Lives,A:Lord
  of Vampires (48pgs) 4.00
51 JnS,SeP,Laundromat-
  Possession 3.00
52 GF(c),WSm, Royal Blood 3.00
53 GF(c),WSm, Royal Blood 3.00
54 GF(c),WSm, Royal Blood 3.00
55 GF(c),WSm, Royal Blood 3.00
56 GF(c),B:GEn(s),DvL,
  V:Danny Drake 3.00
57 GF(c),SDi,Mortal Clay#1,
  V:Dr. Amis 3.00
58 GF(c),SDi,Mortal Clay#2,
  V:Dr. Amis 3.00
59 GF(c),WSm,MkB(i),KDM,B:Guys
  & Dolls 3.00
60 GF(c),WSm,MkB(i),F:Tali,
  Chantinelle 4.00
61 GF(c),WSm,MkB(i),E:Guys &
  Dolls, V:First of the Fallen 4.00
62 GF(c),SDi,End of the Line,I:Gemma,
  AIDS storyline insert w/Death . 3.25

Vertigo

63 GF(c),SDi,C:Swamp Thing,Zatanna
  Phantom Stranger 2.50
64 GF(c),SDi,B:Fear & Loathing,
  A:Gabriel (Racism) 2.75
65 GF(c),SDi,D:Dez 2.50
66 GF(c),SDi,E:Fear and Loathing 2.50
67 GF(c),SDi,Kit leaves John ... 2.50
68 GF(c),SDi,F:Lord of Vampires,
  Darius,Mary 2.50
69 GF(c),SDi,D:Lord of Vampires . 2.25
70 GF(c),SDi,Kit in Ireland 2.25
71 GF(c),SDi,A:WWII Fighter Pilot 2.25
72 GF(c),SDi,B:Damnation's
  Flame,A:Papa Midnight 2.25
73 GF(c),SDi,Nightmare NY,
  A:JFK 2.25
74 GF(c),SDi,I:Cedella,A:JFK 2.25
75 GF(c),SDi,E:Damnation'sFlame 2.25
76 GF(c),SDi,R:Brendan 2.25
77 Returns to England 2.25
78 GF(c),SDi,B:Rake at the
  Gates of Hell 2.25
79 GF(c),SDi,In Hell 2.25
80 GF(c),SDi,In London 2.25
81 GF(c),SDi 2.25
82 Kit 2.25
83 Rake,Gates of Hell 2.25
84 John's past 2.25
85 Warped Notions,pt.1 .... 2.25
86 Warped Notions,pt.2 .... 2.25
87 Warped Notions,pt.3 .... 2.25
88 Warped Notions,pt.4 .... 2.25
89 Dreamtime 2.25
90 Dreamtime,pt.2 .... 2.25
91 Visits Battlefield 2.25
92 Critical Mass,pt.1 .... 2.25
93 Critical Mass,pt.2 .... 2.25
94 Critical Mass,pt.3 .... 2.25
95 SeP,Critical Mass,pt.4 ...... 2.25
96 SeP,Critical Mass,pt.5 ...... 2.25
97 SeP,Critical Mass epilogue ... 2.25
98 SeP, helps neighbor 2.25
99 SeP 2.25
100 SeP, In a coma 3.50
101 SeP,deal with a demon 2.25
102 SeP,Difficult Beginnings,
  pt.1 (of 3) 2.25
103 SeP,"Difficult Beginnings, pt.2" 2.25
104 SeP,"Difficult Beginnings, pt.3" 2.25
105 .... 2.25

106 PJe(s),SEp,"In the Line of
  Fire," pt.1 (of 2) 2.25
107 PJe(s),SEp,"In the Line of
  Fire," pt. 2 .... 2.25
108 PJe(s),SeP,a Bacchic
  celebration 2.25
109 PJe(s),SeP,cattle mutilations
  in Northern England 2.25
110 PJe(s),SeP,"Last Man
  Standing," pt.1 .... 2.25
111 PJe(s),SeP,"Last Man
  Standing," pt.2 .... 2.25
112 PJe(s),SeP,"Last Man
  Standing," pt.3 .... 2.25
113 PJe(s),SeP,"Last Man
  Standing," pt.4 .... 2.25
114 PJe(s),SeP,"Last Man
  Standing," pt.5 .... 2.25
115 PJe(s),SeP(s),Dani's ex-
  boyfriend 2.25
116 SeP, "Widdershins" pt.1 (of 2) 2.25
117 SeP, "Widdershins" pt.2 .... 2.25
118 PJe(s),SeP,John's a Godfather 2.50
119 PJe(s),SeP,disasters 2.50
120 PJe(s),SeP,10th anniv. 48pg . 3.50
121 PJe(s),SeP, Up the Down
  Staircase pt.1 .... 2.50
122 PJe(s),SeP, Up the Down
  Staircase pt.2 .... 2.50
123 PJe(s),SeP, Up the Down
  Staircase pt.3 .... 2.50
124 PJe(s),SeP, Up the Down
  Staircase pt.4 .... 2.50
125 PJe(s),SeP, How to Play
  with Fire, pt.1 .... 2.25
126 PJe(s),SeP,Play/Fire,pt.2 ... 2.50
127 PJe(s),SeP,Play/Fire,pt.3 ... 2.50
128 PJe(s),SeP,Play/Fire,pt.4 ... 2.50
129 .... 2.50
130 GEn,JHi,GF,Son of Man,pt.2 . 2.50
Ann.#1 JaD(s),BT,Raven Scar . 7.00
Spec.#1 GF(c),GEn(s),SDi,John
  Constantine's teenage years .. 4.50
TPB Original Sins,rep.#1–#9 ... 19.95
TPB Dangerous Habits,
  rep.#41-#46 .... 14.95
TPB Fear and Loathing 14.95

HELLBLAZER/
THE BOOKS OF MAGIC
Oct., 1997

1 (of 2) PJe,JNR 2.50
2 PJe,JNR 2.50

HERCULES UNBOUND
Oct.–Nov., 1975

1 thru 11 .... @1.25
12 Aug.–Sept. 1977 .... 1.25

HEROES
Milestone 1996

1 Six heroes join 2.50
2 battle royale 2.50
3 .... 2.50
4 .... 2.50
5 .... 2.50
6 final issue 2.50

HEROES AGAINST
HUNGER

1 NA,DG,JBy,CS,AA,BWr,BS,
  Superman,Batman 3.50

HERO HOTLINE
1 thru 6, Mini-series . . . . @1.75

HEX
Sept., 1985
1 MT,I:Hex 2.50
2 MT 2.00
3 MT,V:Conglomerate 2.00
4 MT,V:Conglomerate 2.00
5 MT,A:Chainsaw Killer 2.00
6 MT,V:Conglomerate 2.00
7 MT,Tries to Return to own era . . 2.00
8 MT,The Future 2.50
9 MT,Future Killer Cyborgs 1.50
10 MT,V:Death Cult 1.50
11 MT,V:The Batman 3.00
12 MT,A:Batman,V:Terminators . . 3.00
13 MT,I:New Supergroup 2.50
14 MT,A:The Dogs of War 1.50
15 KG,V:Chainsaw Killer 1.50
16 KG,V:Dogs of War 1.50
17 KG,Hex/Dogs of War T.U.
    V:XXGG 1.50
18 KGr,Confronting the Past,final
    Issue 1.50

HISTORY OF DC UNIVERSE
Sept., 1986
1 GP, From start to WWII 5.00
2 GP, From WWII to present 5.00

A HISTORY OF VIOLENCE
DC/Paradox Press March 1997
GN B&W 9.95

HITCHHIKER'S GUIDE TO THE GALAXY
1 Based on the book 7.00
2 Based on the book 6.50
3 Based on the book 6.50
GN from Douglas Adams book . 14.95

HITMAN
1996–97
1 GEn, F:Tommy Monaghan . . . 11.00
2 GEn, Attempt to kill Joker 8.00
3 GEn(s),JMC, Mawzin & The
    Arkanonne 4.50
4 GEn(s),JMC, ... 3.00
5 GEn(s),JMC, ... 3.00
6 GEn(s),JMC,A:Johnny Navarone,
    Natt the Hatt 3.00
7 GEn(s),JMC, Pat's dead, Hitman
    wants revenge 3.00
8 GEn(s),JMC,barricaded in
    Noonan's Bar, Final Night tie-in 3.00
9 GEn(s),JMC,A:Six-Pack 3.00
10 GEn(s),JMC,A:Green Lantern . 3.00
11 . . . . 2.25
12 GEn(s),JMC,"Local Heroes,
    "A:Green Lantern 2.25
13 . . . . 2.25
14 GEn(s),JMC, "Zombie Night at
    the Aquarium," concl. 2.25
15 GEn(s),JMC, "Ace of
    Killers," pt.1, V:Mawzir 2.25
16 GEn(s),JMC, "Ace of
    Killers," pt.2 . . . . 2.25
17 GEn(s),JMC, "Ace of Killers,"
    pt.3,A:Catwoman, Demon
    Etrigan 2.25
18 GEn(s),JMC, "Ace of Killers,"

pt.4,A:Demon Etrigan, Baytor . 2.25
19 GEn(s),JMC,Ace/Killers,pt.5, . . 2.25
20 GEn(s),JMC,Ace/Killers,concl. . 2.50
21 GEn(s),JMC,Romeo & Juliet . . 2.50
22 GEn(s),JMC,holiday special . . 2.25
23 GEn(s),JMc,"Who Dares Wins,"
    pt.1 . . . . 2.50
24 GEn(s),JMc,Dares/Wins,pt.2 . . 2.50
25 GEn(s),JMc,Dares/Wins,pt.3 . . 2.50
26 GEn(s),JMc,Dares/Wins,pt.4 . . 2.50
27 GEn(s),JMc,Dares/Wins,pt.5 . . 2.50
28 GEn(s),JMC,aftermath 2.50
29 GEn(s),JMC,Tommy's
    Heroes, pt.1 . . . . 2.50
30 GEn(s),JMC,Heroes, pt.2 . . . . 2.50
31 GEn(s),JMC,Heroes, pt.3 . . . . 2.50
Ann.#1 Pulp Heroes (Western) . . 3.95
TPB rep. Demon Annual #2, Batman
    Chronicles #4, Hitman #1–#3 10.00
TPB Ten Thousand Bullets,
    rep. #4–#8 . . . . 10.00

HOPALONG CASSIDY
Feb., 1954
86 GC,Ph(c):William Boyd & Topper,
    'The Secret of the Tattooed
    Burro' 250.00
87 GC,Ph(c),'The Tenderfoot
    Outlaw' 135.00
88 Ph(c),GC,'15 Robbers of Rimfire
    Ridge' 100.00
89 GC,Ph(c),'One-Day
    Boom Town' 100.00
90 GC,Ph(c),'Cowboy Clown
    Robberies' 75.00
91 GC,Ph(c),'The Riddle of
    the Roaring R Ranch' 85.00
92 GC,Ph(c),'The Sky-Riding
    Outlaws' 85.00
93 GC,Ph(c),'The Silver Badge
    of Courage' 85.00
94 GC,Ph(c),'Mystery of the
    Masquerading Lion' 85.00
95 GC,Ph(c),'Showdown at the
    Post-Hole Bank' 85.00
96 GC,Ph(c),'Knights of
    the Range' 85.00
97 GC,Ph(c),'The Mystery of
    the Three-Eyed Cowboy' 85.00
98 GC,Ph(c),'Hopalong's
    Unlucky Day' 85.00
99 GC,Ph(c),'Partners in Peril' . . 85.00
100 GC,Ph(c),'The Secrets
    of a Sheriff' 100.00
101 GC,Ph(c),'Way Out West
    Where The East Begins' 60.00
102 GC,Ph(c),'Secret of the
    Buffalo Hat' 60.00
103 GC,Ph(c),'The Train-Rustlers
    of Avalance Valley' 60.00
104 GC,Ph(c),'Secret of the
    Surrendering Outlaws' 60.00
105 GC,Ph(c),'Three Signs
    to Danger' 60.00
106 GC,Ph(c),'The Secret of
    the Stolen Signature' 60.00
107 GC,Ph(c),'The Mystery Trail
    to Stagecoach Town' 60.00
108 GC,Ph(c),'The Mystery
    Stage From Burro Bend' 60.00
109 GC,'The Big Gun on Saddletop
    Mountain' 60.00
110 GC,'The Dangerous Stunts
    of Hopalong Cassidy' 50.00
111 GC,'Sheriff Cassidy's

    Mystery Clue' 50.00
112 GC,'Treasure Trail to
    Thunderbolt Ridge' 50.00
113 GC,'The Shadow of the
    Toy Soldier' 50.00
114 GC,'Ambush at
    Natural Bridge' 50.00
115 GC,'The Empty-Handed
    Robberies' 50.00
116 GC,'Mystery of the
    Vanishing Cabin' 50.00
117 GC,'School for Sheriffs' 50.00
118 GC,'The Hero of
    Comanche Ridge' 50.00
119 GC,'The Dream Sheriff of
    Twin Rivers' 50.00
120 GC,'Salute to a Star-Wearer' 50.00
121 GC,'The Secret of the
    Golden Caravan' 50.00
122 GC,'The Rocking
    Horse Bandits' 50.00
123 GK,'Mystery of the
    One-Dollar Bank Robbery' . . 50.00
124 GK,'Mystery of the
    Double-X Brand' 50.00
125 GK,'Hopalong Cassidy's
    Secret Brother' 50.00
126 GK,'Trail of the
    Telltale Clues' 50.00
127 GK,'Hopalong Cassidy's
    Golden Riddle' 50.00
128 GK,'The House That
    Hated Outlaws' 50.00
129 GK,'Hopalong Cassidy's
    Indian Sign' 50.00
130 GK,'The Return of the
    Canine Sheriff' 50.00
131 GK&GK(c),'The Amazing
    Sheriff of Double Creek' 50.00
132 GK,'Track of the
    Invisible Indians' 50.00
133 GK,'The Golden Trail
    to Danger' 50.00
134 GK,'Case of the
    Three Crack-Shots' 50.00
135 GK,May-June, 1959 . . . . . . 50.00

HORRORIST
(Vertigo) 1995
1 I:Horrorist 5.95
2 conclusion 5.95

HOT WHEELS
March-April, 1970
1 ATh 25.00
2 thru 5 ATh . . . . @20.00
6 NA 30.00

HOUSE OF MYSTERY
Dec.–Jan., 1952
1 I Fell In LoveWithA Monster 1,700.00
2 The Mark of X 750.00
3 . . . . 600.00
4 The Man With the Evil Eye . . 450.00
5 The Man With the Strangler
    Hands! 450.00
6 The Monster in Clay! 350.00
7 Nine Lives of Alger Denham! 350.00
8 . . . . 350.00
9 . . . . 350.00
10 The Wishes of Doom 350.00
11 Deadly Game of G-H-O-S-T 275.00
12 The Devil's Chessboard . . . 275.00
13 The Theater Of A

Thousand Thrills!	275.00
14	275.00
15 The Man Who Could Change the World	275.00
16 Dead Men Tell No Tales!	225.00
17	200.00
18	200.00
19	200.00
20 The Beast Of Bristol	200.00
21 Man Who Could See Death	200.00
22 The Phantom's Return	200.00
23	200.00
24 Kill The Black Cat	200.00
25 The Man With Three Eyes!	200.00
26	150.00
27 Fate Held Four Aces!	150.00
28 The Wings Of Mr. Milo!	150.00
29	150.00
30	150.00
31 The Incredible Illusions!	150.00
32 Pied Piper of the Sea	150.00
33 Mr. Misfortune!	150.00
34 The Hundred Year Duel	150.00
35	150.00
36 The Treasure of Montezuma!	125.00
37 MD,The Statue That Came to Life	125.00
38 The Voyage Of No Return	125.00
39	125.00
40 The Coins That Came To Life	125.00
41 The Impossible Tricks!	125.00
42 The Stranger From Out There	125.00
43	125.00
44 The Secret Of Hill 14	125.00
45	125.00
46 The Bird of Fate	125.00
47 The Robot Named Think	125.00
48 The Man Marooned On Earth	125.00
49 The Mysterious Mr. Omen	125.00
50	130.00
51 Man Who Stole Teardrops	100.00
52 The Man With The Golden Shoes	100.00
53 The Man Who Hated Mirrors	100.00
54 The Woman Who Lived Twice	100.00
55 I Turned Back Time	100.00
56 The Thing In The Black Box	100.00
57 The Untamed	100.00
58	100.00
59 The Tomb Of Ramfis	100.00
60 The Prisoner On Canvas	100.00
61 JK,Superstition Day	100.00
62 The Haunting Scarecrow	90.00
63 JK,The Lady & The Creature	100.00
64 The Golden Doom	90.00
65 JK,The Magic Lantern	100.00
66 JK,Sinister Shadow	100.00
67 The Wizard of Water	90.00
68 The Book That Bewitched	90.00
69 The Miniature Disasters	90.00
70 JK,The Man With Nine Lives	100.00
71 Menace of the Mole Man	100.00
72 JK,Dark Journey	100.00
73 Museum That Came to Life	80.00
74 Museum That Came To Life	80.00
75 Assignment Unknown!	80.00
76 JK,Prisoners Of The Tiny Universe	90.00
77 The Eyes That Went Berserk	75.00
78 JK(c),The 13th Hour	90.00
79 JK(c),The Fantastic Sky Puzzle	90.00
80 Man With Countless Faces!	75.00
81 The Man Who Made Utopia	75.00
82 The Riddle of the Earth's	

Second Moon	75.00
83 The Mystery of the Martian Eye	75.00
84 JK,BK,The 100-Century Doom	90.00
85 JK(c),Earth's Strangest Salesman	80.00
86 The Baffling Bargains	75.00
87 The Human Diamond	75.00
88 Return of the Animal Man	75.00
89 The Cosmic Plant!	75.00
90 The Invasion Of the Energy Creatures!	75.00
91 DD&SMo(c),The Riddle of the Alien Satellite	75.00
92 DD(c),Menace of the Golden Globule	75.00
93 NC(c),I Fought The Molten Monster	75.00
94 DD&SMo(c),The Creature In Echo Lake	75.00
95 The Wizard's Gift	75.00
96 The Amazing 70-Ton Man	75.00
97 The Alien Who Change History	75.00

House of Mystery #27
© DC Comics, Inc.

98 DD&SMo(c),The Midnight Creature	75.00
99 The Secret of the Leopard God	75.00
100 The Beast Beneath Earth	90.00
101 The Magnificent Monster	70.00
102 Cellmate to a Monster	70.00
103 Hail the Conquering Aliens	70.00
104 I was the Seeing-Eye Man	70.00
105 Case of the Creature X-14	70.00
106 Invaders from the Doomed Dimension	70.00
107 Captives o/t Alien Fisherman	70.00
108 RMo,Four Faces of Frank Forbes	70.00
109 ATh,JKu,Secret of the Hybrid Creatures	70.00
110 Beast Who Stalked Through Time	70.00
111 Operation Beast Slayer	70.00
112 Menace of Craven's Creatures	70.00

113 RMo,Prisoners of Beast Asteroid	70.00
114 The Movies from Nowhere	70.00
115 Prisoner o/t Golden Mask	70.00
116 RMo,Return of the Barsfo Beast	70.00
117 Menace of the Fire Furies	65.00
118 RMo,Secret o/SuperGorillas	65.00
119 Deadly Gift from the Stars	65.00
120 ATh,Catman of KarynPeale	65.00
121 RMo,Beam that Transformed Men	65.00
122 Menace fo the Alien Hero	65.00
123 RMo,Lure o/t Decoy Creature	65.00
124 Secret of Mr. Doom	65.00
125 Fantastic Camera Creature	65.00
126 The Human Totem Poles	65.00
127 RMo,Cosmic Game o/Doom	65.00
128 NC,The Sorcerer's Snares	65.00
129 Man in the Nuclear Trap	65.00
130 The Alien Creature Hunt	65.00
131 Vengeance o/t GeyserGod	60.00
132 MMe,Beware My Invisible Master	60.00
133 MMe,Captive Queen of Beast Island	60.00
134 MMe,Secret Prisoner of Darkmore Dungeon	60.00
135 MMe,Alien Body Thief	60.00
136 MMe,Secret o/t StolenFace	60.00
137 MMe,Tunnel to Disaster	60.00
138 MMe,Creature Must Die	60.00
139 MMe,Creatures of Vengeful Eye	60.00
140 I&Only app.:Astro	60.00
141 MMe,The Alien Gladiator	60.00
142 MMe,The Wax Demons	60.00
143 J'onn J'onzz begins	250.00
144 J'onn J'onzz on Weird World of Gilgana	150.00
145 J'onn J'onzz app	100.00
146 BP,J'onn J'onzz	100.00
147 J'onn J'onzz	100.00
148 J'onn J'onzz	100.00
149 ATh,J'onn J'onzz	100.00
150 MMe,J'onn J'onzz	100.00
151 J'onn J'onzz	100.00
152 MMe,J'onn J'onzz	100.00
153 J'onn J'onzz	100.00
154 J'onn J'onzz	100.00
155 J'onn J'onzz	100.00
156 JM,I:Dial H for Hero (Giantboy Cometeer,Mole)J.J'onzz sty	125.00
157 JM,Dial H for Hero (Human Bullet,Super Charge,Radar Sonar Man) J'onn J'onnzz sty	100.00
158 JM,Dial H for Hero (Quake MasterSquid)J'onn J'onzz sty	90.00
159 JM,Dial H for Hero (Human Starfish,Hypno Man,Mighty Moppet) J'onn J'onzz sty	90.00
160 JM,Dial H for Hero (King Kandy A:Plastic Man,I:Marco Xavier (J'onn J'onzz new secret I.D.)	150.00
161 JM,Dial H for Hero (Magneto, Hornet Man,Shadow Man)	75.00
162 JM,Dial H for Hero (Mr.Echo, Future Man) J'onnJ'onzz sty	75.00
163 JM,Dial H for Hero(Castor&Pollux, King Coil) J'onn J'onzz sty	75.00
164 JM,Dial H for Hero (Super Nova Zip Tide) J'onnJ'onzz sty	75.00
165 JM,Dial H for Hero (Whoozis, Whatsis,Howzis) J'onn J'onzz	

story 75.00
166 JM,Dial H for Hero (Yankee
    Doodle Kid,Chief Mighty Arrow)
    J'onn J'onzz sty 75.00
167 JM,Dial H for Hero (Balloon Boy,
    Muscle Man,Radar Sonar Man)
    J'onn J'onzz sty 75.00
168 JM,Dial H for Hero (Thunderbolt,
    Mole,Cometeer,Hoopster)
    J'onn J'onzz sty 75.00
169 JM,I:Gem Girl in Dial H for
    Hero,J'onnJ'onzz sty 75.00
170 JM,Dial H for Hero (Baron
    BuzzSaw,Don Juan,Sphinx
    Man) J'onn J'onzz sty 75.00
171 JM,Dial H for Hero (King Viking
    Whirl-I-Gig) J'onnJ'onzz sty . . 65.00
172 JM,Dial H for Hero 65.00
173 E:Dial H for Hero,F:J'onn
    Jonzz 65.00
174 New direction,SA pg.13 . . . 25.00
175 I:Cain 25.00
176 SA,Cain's Game Room 25.00
177 Curse of the Car 25.00
178 NA,The Game 30.00
179 BWr,NA,JO,Widow'sWalk . . 65.00
180 GK,WW,BWr,SA,Room 13 . 20.00
181 BWr,The Siren of Satan . . . 20.00
182 ATh,The Devil's Doorway . . 18.00
183 BWr,WW(i),DeadCanKill . . . 22.00
184 ATh,GK,WW,Eye o/Basilisk . 18.00
185 AW,The Beautiful Beast . . . 22.00
186 BWr,NA,Nightmare 25.00
187 ATh,Mask of the Red Fox . . 9.00
188 TD,BWr,House of Madness . 15.00
189 WW(i),Eyes of the Cat 8.00
190 ATh,Fright 11.00
191 BWr,TD,Christmas Story,. . . 11.00
192 JAp,GM,DH,Garnener
    of Eden 8.00
193 BWr 13.00
194 ATh,NR,RH(rep),JK(rep)
    Born Loser 9.00
195 NR,BWr,ThingsOld..Things
    Forgotten 25.00
196 GM,GK,ATh(rep)A Girl &
    Her Dog 8.00
197 DD,NR,House of Horrors . . 8.00
198 MSy,NC,Day of the Demon . . 8.00
199 WW,RB,Sno'Fun 9.00
200 MK,TD,The Beast's Revenge 8.00
201 JAp,The Demon Within 8.00
202 MSy,GC(rep),SA,The Poster
    Plague,John Prentice? 8.00
203 NR,Tower of Prey 8.00
204 BWr,AN,All in the Family . . . 12.00
205 The Coffin Creature 8.00
206 MSy,TP,The Burning 8.00
207 JSn,The Spell 10.00
208 Creator of Evil 8.00
209 AA,JAp,Tomorrow I Hang . . 10.00
210 The Immortal 8.00
211 NR,Deliver Us From Evil . . 10.00
212 MA,AN,Ever After 8.00
213 AN,Back from the Realm of
    the Damned 10.00
214 NR,The Shaggy Dog 10.00
215 The Man Who Wanted Power
    over Women 8.00
216 TD,Look into My Eyes & Kill . 8.00
217 NR,AA,Swamp God 10.00
218 FT,An Ice Place to Visit 8.00
219 AA,NR,Pledge to Satan . . . 8.00
220 AA,AN,They Hunt Butterflies
    Don't They? 8.00

House of Mystery #321
© DC Comics, Inc.

221 FT,BWr,MK,He Who Laughs
    Last 10.00
222 AA,Night of the Teddy Bear . 8.00
223 Demon From the Deep 8.00
224 FR,AA,SheerFear,B:100pg . 11.00
225 AA,FT,AN,See No Evil 9.00
226 AA,FR,NR,SA,Monster in House
    Tour of House of Mystery . . 10.00
227 NR,AA,The Carriage Man . . 9.00
228 FR,NA(i),The Rebel 9.00
229 NR,Nightmare Castle,
    last 100 page 9.00
230 Experiment In Fear 8.00
231 Cold,Cold Heart 9.00
232 Last Tango in Hell 8.00
233 FR,Cake! 8.00
234 AM,Lafferty's Luck 8.00
235 NR,Wings of Black Death . . 8.00
236 SD,NA(i)Death Played a
    Sideshow 10.00
237 FT,Night of the Chameleon . . 8.00
238 . . . . 8.00
239 Day of the Witch 8.00
240 The Murderer 8.00
241 FR,NR,DeathPulls theStrings 8.00
242 FR,The Balloon Vendor 8.00
243 Brother Bear 8.00
244 FT,Kronos..Zagros-Eborak . . 8.00
245 AN,Check the J.C.Demon
    Catalogue Under...Death . . . 8.00
246 DeathVault of Eskimo Kings . 8.00
247 SD,Death Rides the Waves . . 8.00
248 NightJamieGaveUp theGhost 8.00
249 Hit Parade of Death 8.00
250 AN,Voyage to Hell 8.00
251 WW,AA,theCollector,68 pgs 10.00
252 DP,RT,AA,FR,AN,ManKillers 10.00
253 TD,AN,GK,KJ,Beware the
    Demon Child 7.00
254 SD,AN,MR,TheDevil's Place . 8.00
255 RE,GM,SometimesLeopards 10.00
256 DAy,AN,Museum of Murders 10.00
257 RE,MGo,TD(i),MBr,Xmas iss. 8.00
258 SD,RB,BMc,DG(i),The Demon
    and His Boy 8.00
259 RE,RT,MGo,DN,BL,'Hair Today,
    Gone Tomorrow,last giant 9.00

260 Go to Hades 8.00
261 The Husker 8.00
262 FreedFrom Infernos of Hell . 8.00
263 JCr,Is There Vengeance
    After Death? 8.00
264 Halloween Issue 8.00
265 The Perfect Host 8.00
266 The Demon Blade 8.00
267 A Strange Way to Die 8.00
269 Blood on the Grooves 8.00
270 JSh,JRu,JBi,Black Moss . . 8.00
271 TS,HellHound of
    Brackenmoor 8.00
272 DN,DA,theSorcerer's Castle . 8.00
273 The Rites of Inheritance . . . 8.00
274 MR,JBi,Hell Park 8.00
275 JCr,'Final Installment' 8.00
276 SD,MN,'Epode' 8.00
277 HC,AMi,'LimitedEngagement' 8.00
278 'TV or Not TV' 8.00
279 AS,Trial by Fury 8.00
280 VMK,DAy,Hungry Jaws
    of Death 8.00
281 Now Dying in this Corner . . . 8.00
282 JSw,DG,Superman/Radio
    Shack ins 8.00
283 RT,AN'Kill Me Gently' 8.00
284 KG,King and the Dragon . . . 8.00
285 Cold Storage 8.00
286 Long Arm of the Law 8.00
287 NR,AS,BL,Legend o/t Lost . 8.00
288 DSp,Piper at Gates of Hell . . 8.00
289 Brother Bobby's Home for
    Wayward Girls & Boys 8.00
290 TS,I:I..Vampire 8.00
291 TS,DAy,I..Vampire #2 . . . . 8.00
292 TS,MS,TD,RE,DSp,Wendigo . 8.00
293 GT,TS,A:I..Vampire #3 . . . . 8.00
294 CI,TY,GT,TD,The Darkness . 8.00
295 TS,TVE,JCr,I..Vampire #4 . . 8.00
296 CI,BH,Night Women 8.00
297 TS,DCw,TD,I..Vampire #5 . . . 8.00
298 TS,'Stalker on a Starless
    Night' 8.00
299 TS,DSp,I..Vampire #6 . . . . 8.00
300 GK,DA,JSon,JCr,DSp,Anniv. 8.00
301 JDu,TVE,KG,TY '...Virginia' . 8.00
302 TS,NR,DSp,I..Vampire #7 . . 8.00
303 TS,DSp,I..Vampire #8 . . . . 8.00
304 EC,RE,I..Vampire #9 . . . . . 8.00
305 TVE,EC,I..Vampire #10 . . . . 8.00
306 TS,TD,I..Vampire #11,
    A:Jack the Ripper 8.00
307 TS,I..Vampire #12 . . . . 8.00
308 TS,MT,NR,I..Vampire #13 . . . 8.00
309 TS,I..Vampire #14 . . . . 8.00
310 TS(i),I..Vampire #15 . . . . . 8.00
311 I..Vampire #16 . . . . 8.00
312 TS(i),I..Vampire #17 . . . . . 8.00
313 TS(i),CI,I..Vampire #18 . . . . 8.00
314 TS,I..Vampire #19 . . . . 8.00
315 TS(i),TY,I..Vampire #20 . . . 8.00
316 TS(i),GT,TVE,I..Vampire #21 . 8.00
317 TS(i),I..Vampire #22 . . . . . 8.00
318 TS(i),I..Vampire #23 . . . . . 8.00
319 TS,JOy,I..Vampire conc. 8.00
320 GM,Project: Inferior 8.00
321 final issue 8.00
Welcome Back to the House of Mystery
    GN BWr(c) horror stories rep. . 6.00

HOUSE OF SECRETS
Nov.–Dec., 1956
1 MD,JM,The Hand of Doom 1,200.00
2 JPr,RMo,NC,Mask of Fear . . 500.00

3 JM,JK,MMe,The Three	
Prophecies	375.00
4 JM,JK,MMe,Master of	
Unknown	300.00
5 MMe,The Man Who	
Hated Fear	200.00
6 NC,MMe,Experiment 1000	200.00
7 RMo,Island o/t Enchantress	200.00
8 JK,RMo,The Electrified Man	225.00
9 JM,JSt,The Jigsaw Creatures	175.00
10 JSt,NC,I was a Prisoner	
of the Sea	175.00
11 KJ(c),NC,The Man who	
couldn't stop growing	175.00
12 JK,The Hole in the Sky	200.00
13 The Face in the Mist	150.00
14 MMe,The Man who Stole Air	150.00
15 The Creature in the Camera	150.00
16 NC,We matched wits with a	
Gorilla genius	125.00
17 DW,Lady in the Moon	125.00
18 MMe,The Fantastic	
Typewriter	125.00
19 MMe,NC,Lair of the	
Dragonfly	125.00
20 Incredible FireballCreatures	125.00
21 Girl from 50,000 Fathoms	125.00
22 MMe,Thing from Beyond	125.00
23 MMe,I&O:Mark Merlin	135.00
24 NC,Mark Merlin story	125.00
25 MMe,Mark Merlin story	100.00
26 NC,MMe, Mark Merlin story	100.00
27 MMe,Mark Merlin	100.00
28 MME,Mark Merlin	100.00
29 NC,MMe,Mark Merlin	100.00
30 JKu,MMe,Mark Merlin	100.00
31 DD,MMe,RH,Mark Merlin	80.00
32 MMe,Mark Merlin	80.00
33 MMe,Mark Merlin	80.00
34 MMe,Mark Merlin	80.00
35 MMe,Mark Merlin	80.00
36 MMe,Mark Merlin	80.00
37 MMe,Mark Merlin	80.00
38 MMe,Mark Merlin	80.00
39 JKu,MMe,Mark Merlin	80.00
40 NC,MMe,Mark Merlin	80.00
41 MMe,Mark Merlin	80.00
42 MMe,Mark Merlin	80.00
43 RMo,MMe,CI,Mark Merlin	80.00
44 MMe,Mark Merlin	80.00
45 MMe,Mark Merlin	80.00
46 MMe,Mark Merlin	80.00
47 MMe,Mark Merlin	80.00
48 ATh,MMe,Mark Merlin	80.00
49 MMe,Mark Merlin	80.00
50 MMe,Mark Merlin	80.00
51 MMe,Mark Merlin	75.00
52 MMe,Mark Merlin	75.00
53 CI,Mark Merlin	75.00
54 RMo,MMe,Mark Merlin	75.00
55 MMe,Mark Merlin	75.00
56 MMe,Mark Merlin	75.00
57 MMe,Mark Merlin	75.00
58 MMe,O:Mark Merlin	75.00
59 MMe,Mark Merlin	75.00
60 MMe,Mark Merlin	75.00
61 I:Eclipso,A:Mark Merlin	175.00
62 MMe,Eclipso,Mark Merlin	100.00
63 GC,ATh,Eclipso,Mark Merlin	75.00
64 MMe,ATh,M Merlin,Eclipso	75.00
65 MMe,ATh,M Merlin,Eclipso	75.00
66 MMe,ATh,M Merlin,Eclipso	110.00
67 MMe,ATh,M Merlin,Eclipso	75.00
68 MMe,Mark Merlin,Eclipso	70.00
69 MMe,Mark Merlin,Eclipso	70.00

70 MMe,Mark Merlin,Eclipso	70.00
71 MMe,Mark Merlin,Eclipso	70.00
72 MMe,Mark Merlin,Eclipso	70.00
73 MMe,D:Mark Merlin,I:Prince	
Ra-Man; Eclipso	70.00
74 MMe,Prince Ra-Man,Eclipso	70.00
75 MMe,Prince Ra-Man,Eclipso	70.00
76 MMe,Prince Ra-Man,Eclipso	70.00
77 MMe,Prince Ra-Man,Eclipso	70.00
78 MMe,Prince Ra-Man,Eclipso	70.00
79 MMe,Prince Ra-Man,Eclipso	70.00
80 MMe,Prince Ra-Man,Eclipso	70.00
81 I:Abel, new mystery format	
Don't Move It	30.00
82 DD,NA,One & only, fully guaran	
teed super-permanent 100%	30.00
83 ATh,The Stuff that Dreams	
are Made of	20.00
84 DD,If I had but world enough	
and time	20.00
85 DH,GK,NA,Second Chance	30.00
86 GT,GM,Strain	20.00
87 DD,DG,RA,MK,The Coming	
of Ghaglan	30.00

House of Secrets #43
© DC Comics, Inc.

88 DD,The Morning Ghost	30.00
89 GM,DH,Where Dead MenWalk	30.00
90 GT,RB,NA,GM,The Symbionts	35.00
91 WW,MA,The Eagle's Talon	35.00
92 BWr,TD(i),I:Swamp Thing	
(Alex Olson)	475.00
93 JAp,TD,ATh(rep.)Lonely in	
Death	20.00
94 TD,ATh(rep.)Hyde.and	
go Seek	20.00
95 DH,NR,The Bride of Death	18.00
96 DD,JAb,WW, the Monster	22.00
97 JAp,Divide and Murder	20.00
98 MK,ATh(rep),Born Losers	20.00
99 NR,TD(i),Beyond His	
Imagination	20.00
100 TP,TD,AA,Rest in Peace	20.00
101 AN,Small Invasion	20.00
102 NR,A Lonely Monstrosity	20.00
103 AN,Village on Edge o/Forever	15.00
104 NR,AA,GT,Ghosts Don't	
Bother Me...But...	12.00

105 JAp,AA,An Axe to Grind	12.00
106 AN,AA,This Will Kill You	15.00
107 AA,The Night of the Nebbish	15.00
108 A New Kid on the Block	12.00
109 AA,AN...And in Death, there	
is no Escape	12.00
110 Safes Have Secrets, Too	10.00
111 TD,Hair-I-Kari	10.00
112 Case of the Demon Spawn	10.00
113 MSy,NC,NR,Spawns	
of Satan	10.00
114 FBe,Night Game	10.00
115 AA,AN,Nobody Hurts My	
Brother	10.00
116 NR,Like Father,Like Son	10.00
117 AA,AN,Revenge for the Deadly	
Dummy	10.00
118 GE,Very Last Picture Show	10.00
119 A Carnival of Dwarves	10.00
120 TD,AA,The Lion's Share	10.00
121 Ms.Vampire Killer	10.00
122 AA,Requiem for Igor	7.00
123 ATh,A Connecticut Ice Cream	
Man in King Arthur's Court	8.00
124 Last of the Frankensteins	7.00
125 AA,FR,Instant Re-Kill	7.00
126 AN,On Borrowed Time	7.00
127 MSy,A Test of Innocence	7.00
128 AN,Freak Out!	7.00
129 Almost Human	7.00
130 All Dolled Up!	7.00
131 AN,Point of No Return	7.00
132 Killer Instinct	7.00
133 Portraits of Death	7.00
134 NR,Inheritance of Blood	7.00
135 The Vegitable Garden	7.00
136 Last Voyage of Lady Luck	7.00
137 The Harder They Fall	7.00
138 Where Dreams are Born	4.00
139 SD,NR,A Real Crazy Kid	7.00
140 NR,O:Patchwork Man	20.00
141 You Can't Beat the Devil	5.00
142 Playmate	5.00
143 The Evil Side	5.00
144 The Vampire of Broadway	5.00
145 Operation wasSuccessful,But	5.00
146 Snake's Alive	5.00
147 AN,The See-Through Thief	5.00
148 SD,Sorcerer's Apprentice	5.00
149 The Evil One	5.00
150 A:PhantomStranger & Dr.13	5.00
151 MGo,Nightmare	5.00
152 Sister Witch	5.00
153 VM,AN,Don't Look Now	5.00
154 JL,Last issue	5.00

HOUSE OF SECRETS
DC/Vertigo Aug. 1996

1 SSe(s),TKr, judgments on your	
darkest secrets	3.50
2 SSe(s),TKr, F:Rain	2.50
3 SSe(s),TKr,Seattle's citizens	
secrets	2.50
4 SSe(s),TKr,Eric's secrets	
exposed	2.50
5	2.50
6 SSe(s),DFg,Other rooms:	
"Meeting"	2.50
7 SSe(s),TKr,"Blueprint:	
Elevation A"	2.50
8 SSe(s),TKr,"The Road to	
You," pt.1	2.50
9 SSe(s),TKr,"The Road to	
You," pt.2	2.50
10 SSe(s),TKr,"The Road to	

You," pt.3, concl 2.50
11 "The Book of Law" pt.1 (of 5) . 2.50
12 "The Book of Law" pt.2 . . . . . . 2.50
13 SSe,The Book of Law, pt.3 . . . 2.50
14 SSe,The Book of Law, pt.4 . . . 2.50
15 SSe,The Book of Law, pt.5 . . . 2.50
16 SSe,Book of Law, epilogue . . . 2.50
17 SSe,The Road to You, pt.1 . . . 2.50
18 SSe,The Road to You, pt.2 . . . 2.50
19 SSe,The Road to You, pt.3 . . . 2.50
20 SSe,Other Rooms story 2.50
21 SSe,Basement, pt.1 . . . . 2.50
22 SSe,Basement, pt.2 . . . . 2.50
23 SSe,Basement, pt.3 . . . . 2.50
24 SSe,TKr,"Attic" 2.50
TPB Foundation, rep.#1–#5 . . . . 14.95

HUMAN TARGET SPECIAL
1 DG(i),Prequel to T.V. Series . . 2.00

HUNTER'S HEART
1995
1 Cops vs. Serial Killer 4.95
2 . . . . 4.95
3 F:Lieutenant Slidell 4.95

The Huntress #6 © DC Comics, Inc.

HUNTRESS, THE
1989–90
1 JSon/DG 2.00
2 JSon,Search for Family's
   Murderer 2.00
3 JSon,A:La Bruja 1.50
4 JSon,Little Italy/Chinatown
   Gangs 1.50
5 JSon,V:Doctor Mandragora . . . 1.50
6 JSon,Huntress'secrets revealed 1.50
7 JSon,V:Serial Killer 1.50
8 JSon,V:Serial Killer 1.50
9 JSon,V:Serial Killer 1.50
10 JSon,Nuclear Terrorists in NY . 1.50
11 JSon,V:Wyvern,Nuclear
   Terrorists contd. 1.50
12 JSon,V:Nuclear Terrorists cont 1.50
13 JSon,Violence in NY 1.50
14 JSon,Violence contd.,New
   Mob boss 1.50

15 JSon,I:Waterfront Warrior 1.50
16 JSon,Secret of Waterfront
   Warrior revealed 1.50
17 JSon,Batman+Huntress#1 . . . 1.25
18 JSon,Batman+Huntress#2 . . . 1.25
19 JSon,Batman+Huntress#3,final
   issue 1.25

HUNTRESS
[Limited Series] 1994
1 CDi(s),MN,V:Redzone 1.75
2 MN,V:Redzone 1.50
3 MN,V:Redzone 1.75
4 MN,V:Spano,Redzone 1.50

ICON
Milestone 1993–96
1 Direct Market Ed.,MBr,MG,I:Icon,
   Rocket,S.H.R.E.D.,w/poster,
   card,C puzzle piece 3.25
1a Newsstand Ed. 2.00
2 MBr,MG,I:Payback 1.75
3 MBr,MG,V:Payback 1.75
4 MBr,MG,Teen Pregnancy Issue 1.75
5 MBr,MG,V:Blood Syndicate . . . 1.75
6 MBr,MG,V:Blood Syndicate . . . 1.75
7 MBr,MG 1.75
8 MBr,MG,O:Icon 1.75
9 WS(c),MBr,MG,Shadow War,
   I:Donner,Blitzen 1.75
10 MBr,MG,V:Holocaust 1.75
11 MBr,Hero Worship 1.75
12 Sanctimony 1.75
13 MBr,Rocket & Static T.U. 1.75
14 JBy(c) 1.75
15 Worlds Collide,pt.4,A:Superboy 1.75
16 Worlds Collide,pt.11,
   V:Superman,Rift 1.75
17 Mothership Connection 1.75
18 Mothership Connection,pt.2 . . . 1.75
19 Mothership Connection,pt.3 . . . 1.75
20 Rocket 1.75
21 . . . . 1.75
22 . . . . 1.75
23 New Rocket 1.75
24 F:Buck Wild 1.75
25 V:Oblivion 3.00
26 V:Oblivion 1.75
27 Move to Paris Island projects . 2.50
28 Long Hot Summer 2.50
29 Long Hot Summer 2.50
30 Icon Leaves Earth 2.50
31 HC(c) Readers Choice comic . 1.00
32 Rocket, Galactic Corporate . . . 2.50
33 V:Rocket 2.50
34 V:Cooperative 2.50
35 . . . . 2.50
36 Rocket returns to Earth 2.50
37 MBr,RT,F:Rocket 2.50
38 DMD(s),RT 2.50
39 DMD(s),RT,V:Holocaust & Blood
   Syndicate 2.50
40 DMD(s),RT, V:Holocaust 2.50
41 DMD(s),RT, V:Blood Syndicate 2.50
42 DMD(s),RT 2.50
43 DMD(s),RT,"Blood Reign" concl. 2.50
44 DMD(s),RT,V:Smurphs 2.50
45 DMD(s),RT, final issue 2.50
TPB A Hero's Welcome 12.95

IMMORTAL DR. FATE
1995
1 WS,KG,rep. 1.75
2 and 3 KG,rep. . . . . @1.25

IMPACT WINTER SPECIAL
Impact 1991
1 CI/MR/TL,A:All Impact Heros,
   President Kidnapped 2.50

IMPULSE
1995–98
1 Young Flash Adventures 7.00
2 V:Terrorists 3.50
3 In School 3.00
4 V:White Lightning 3.00
5 V:White Lightning 1.75
6 . . . . 1.75
7 V:Gridlock 1.75
8 MWa,Underworld
   Unleashed tie-in 1.75
9 MWa,F:XS, ... 1.75
10 MWa,Dead Heat,pt.3 . . . . 1.75
11 MWa,Dead Heat,pt.5 . . . . 1.75
12 . . . . 1.75
13 MWa,new daredevil in town . . 1.75
14 AWi,A:White Lightning 1.75
15 . . . . 1.75
16 . . . . 1.75
17 . . . . 1.75
18 MPk(s),AWi,Virtual reality
   nightmare 1.75
19 MWa(s),HuR, Bart's dreams . . 1.75
20 MWa(s),HuR, baseball 1.75
21 MWa(s),F:Legion of Super-
   Heroes 1.75
22 MWa(s) 1.75
23 MWa(s),HuR,Mercury at a
   crossroads 1.75
24 MWa(s),HuR,Impulse's mother
   comes from the future 1.75
25 MWa(s),HuR,Impulse & his mom
   in 30th century 1.75
26 MWa(s),Bart Allen back in the
   20th century 1.75
27 MWa(s) 1.75
28 . . . . 1.75
29 BML,Bart searches for Max
   Mercury 1.75
30 BML, pt.2, Genesis tie-in 2.00
31 BML, pt.3,V:Dr. Morlo 2.00
32 BML,Max is home 2.00
33 BML,White Lightning 2.00
34 BML,Devonian Age, pt.1 . . . . 2.00
35 BML 2.00
36 BML,Court Dates 2.00
37 BML,Dr. Morlo 2.00
38 BML,freak snow storm 2.00
39 BML,V:Trickster 2.00
40 BML,WF, kid picnic 2.00
41 Return of Arrowette 2.00
42 BML(s),virtual monsters 2.25
Ann.#2 Pulp Heros (Western) . . 3.95
TPB Reckless Youth MWa(s) rep.
   Flash #92–#94 . . . . 14.95

IMPULSE/ATOM DOUBLE-SHOT
Dec., 1997
1 DJu, x-over concl. 3.00

IMPULSE PLUS
July 1997
1 48pg. with Grossout, ... 2.95

All comics prices listed are for *Near Mint* condition.

INDUSTRIAL GOTHIC
Vertigo 1995
1 Jail Break Plans	2.50
2 thru 5 Jail Break Plans	@2.50

INFERIOR FIVE
March–April, 1967
1 MSy	40.00
2 MSy,A:Plastic Man	20.00
3	15.00
4	15.00
5	15.00
6	15.00
7	15.00
8	15.00
9	15.00
10 A:Superman	15.00
11 JO(c&a)	15.00
12 JO(c&a)	15.00

INFERNO
Aug., 1997
1 (of 4) SI, from Legion	2.50
2 SI,mall grrls	2.50
3 SI,Legion Month tie-in	2.50
4 SI, concl.	2.50

INFINITY, INC.
March, 1984
1 JOy,O:Infinity Inc.	3.00
2 JOy,End of Origin	2.50
3 JOy,O:Jade	2.25
4 JOy,V:JSA	2.25
5 JOy,V:JSA	2.25
6 JOy,V:JSA	2.25
7 JOy,V:JSA	2.25
8 JOy,V:Ultra Humanite	2.25
9 JOy,V:Ultra Humanite	2.25
10 JOy,V:Ultra Humanite	2.00
11 DN,GT,O:Infinity Inc.	2.00
12 Infinity Unmasks,I:Yolanda Montez (New Wildcat)	2.00
13 DN,V:Rose & Thorn	2.00
14 1st TM DC art,V:Chroma	7.00
15 TM,V:Chroma	3.00
16 TM,I:Helix (Mr. Bones)	3.00
17 TM,V:Helix	3.00
18 TM,Crisis	3.00
19 TM,JSA,JLA x-over, I:Mekanique	3.00
20 TM,Crisis	3.00
21 TM,Crisis,I:HourmanII, Dr.Midnight	3.00
22 TM,Crisis	3.00
23 TM,Crisis	3.00
24 TM,Crisis	3.00
25 TM,Crisis,JSA	3.00
26 TM,V:Carcharo	3.00
27 TM,V:Carcharo	3.00
28 TM,V:Carcharo	3.00
29 TM,V:Helix	3.00
30 TM,Mourning of JSA	3.00
31 TM,V:Psycho Pirate	3.00
32 TM,V:Psycho Pirate	3.00
33 TM,O:Obsidian	3.00
34 TM,A: Global Guardians	3.00
35 TM,V:Infinitors	3.00
36 TM,V:Injustice Unl.	3.00
37 TM,TD,O:Northwind	3.00
38 Helix on Trial	1.75
39 O:Solomon Grundy	1.75
40 V:Thunderbolt	1.75
41 Jonni Thunder	1.75
42 TD,V:Hastor,L:Fury	1.75

43 TD,V:Hastor,Silver Scarab	1.75
44 TD,D:Silver Scarab	1.75
45 MGu,A:New Teen Titans, V:Ultra-Humanite	1.75
46 TD,Millenium,V:Floronic Man	1.75
47 TD,Millenium,V:Harlequin	1.75
48 TD,O:Nuklon	1.75
49 Silver Scarab becomes Sandman	2.00
50 TD,V:The Wizard,O:Sandman	2.50
51 W:Fury & Sandman,D:Skyman	1.75
52 V:Helix	1.75
53 V:Justice Unlimited,last issue	1.75
Ann.#1 TM,V:Thorn	4.00
Ann.#2 V:Degaton,x-over Young All-Stars Annual #1	2.00
Spec.#1 TD,A:Outsiders,V:Psycho Pirate	1.75

INVASION!
1988–89
1 TM,I:Vril Dox,Dominators (20th century)	4.00
2 TM,KG,DG,I:L.E.G.I.O.N.	3.00
3 BS,DG,I:Blasters	3.00
Daily Planet-Invasion! 16p	2.00

INVISIBLES
Vertigo 1994–96
1 GMo(s)	3.50
2 GMo(s),Down & Out,pt.1	2.50
3 GMo(s),Down & Out,pt.2	2.50
4 GMo(s),Down & Out,pt.3	2.50
5 Arcadia,pt.1	2.25
6 Arcadia,pt.2	2.25
7 Arcadia,pt.3	2.25
8 Arcadia,pt.4	2.25
9 SeP(c),L:Dane	2.50
10 SeP(c),CWn,Jim Crow v. Zombies	2.50
11 V:New Breed of Hunter	2.50
12	2.50
13 GMO,Sheman,pt.1	2.50
14 GMo,SeP,Sheman,pt.2	2.50
15 GMo,Sheman,pt.3	2.50
16 GMo,An offer from Sir Miles	2.50
17 GMo,Entropy in the U.K.,pt.1	2.50
18 GMo,Entropy in the U.K.,pt.2	2.50
19 GMo,Entropy in the U.K.,pt.3	2.50
20 GMo,F:RaggedRobin,Dane,Boy	2.50
21 GMo,PuJ,F:Dane	2.50
22 GMo(s),MBu,MPn	2.50
23 GMo(s),MBu,MPn	2.50
24 GMo(s),MBu,MPn	2.50
25 GMo(s),MBu,MPn,final issue Aug. 1996	2.50

[Volume 2]
DC/Vertigo 1996
1 GMo(s),PJ,"Black Science," pt.1	2.50
2 GMo(s),PJ,"Black Science," pt.2	2.50
3 GMo(s),PJ,"Black Science," pt.3	2.50
4 GMo(s),PJ,"Black Science," pt.4	2.50
5 GMo(s),PJ,In SanFrancisco,pt.1	2.50
6 GMo(s),PJ,In SanFrancisco,pt.2	2.50
7 GMo(s),PJ,BB(c) "Time Machine Go" concl.	2.50
8 GMo(s),PJ,BB(c) "Sensitive Criminals," pt.1.	2.50
9 GMo(s),PJ,BB(c) "Sensitive Criminals," pt.2	2.50
10 GMo(s),PJ,Sensitive Criminals pt.3, concl.	2.50
11 GMo(s),PJ,BB(c),Hand of Glory pt.1	2.50

12 GMo(s),PJ,BB(c),Glory, pt.2	2.50
13 GMo(s),PJ,BB(c),Glory concl.	2.50
14 GMo(s),BB(c),Archons aftermath	2.50
15 GMo(s),BB(c), The Philadelphia Experiment, pt.1	2.50
16 GMo(s),BB(c),Experiment,pt.2	2.50
17 GMo,CWn,BB,Black Science II pt.1	2.50
18 GMo,CWn,BB,Science,pt.2	2.50
19 GMo,CWn,BB,Science,pt.3	2.50

IRONWOLF
1986
1 HC,rep.	2.00

IRONWOLF: FIRES OF THE REVOLUTION
1992
Hardcov.GN MMi,CR,R:Ironwolf	29.95

Isis #1 © DC Comics, Inc.

ISIS
Oct.–Nov., 1976
1 RE/WW	5.00
2 MN	1.25
3	1.25
4	1.25
5	1.25
6	1.25
7 O:Isis	1.25
8 Dec.–Jan., 1977–78	1.25

IT'S GAMETIME
Sept.–Oct., 1955
1	550.00
2	400.00
3	400.00
4 March-April, 1956	400.00

JACKIE GLEASON AND THE HONEYMOONERS
June-July, 1956
1 Based on TV show	650.00
2	450.00
3	350.00
4	350.00
5	350.00

6	350.00
7	350.00
8	350.00
9	350.00
10	350.00
11	350.00
12 April-May, 1958	400.00

JACK KIRBY'S FOURTH WORLD
Jan. 1997

1 JBy,Worlds of New Genesis & Apokolips become one 2.00
2 JBy,F:Big Barda vs. Thor 2.00
3 JBy,at Wall of the Source ... 2.00
4 JBy,Can Highfather save his son2.00
5 JBy,conflict between the gods . 2.00
6 JBy,Cause of Orion's transformation 2.00
7 JBy,Orion taught lesson 2.00
8 JBy,WS,Genesis tie-in 2.00
9 JBy,WS(c),Genesis aftermath . 2.00
10 JBy,WS, ... 2.00
11 JBy,WS,F:Orion 2.00
12 JBy,WS,F:Mister Miracle 2.00
13 JBy,WS 2.00
14 JBy,WS,Promethean Giant ... 2.00
15 JBy,WS,Armaghetto 2.00
16 JBy,WS,Kalibak vs. Darkseid . 2.00
17 JBy,WS,Darkseid 2.00
18 JBy,WS,Darkseid freed 2.00
19 JBy,WS,two stories 2.00
20 JBy,WS,A:Superman,final issue 2.25

JAGUAR
Impact

1 I&O:Jaguar I: Timon De Guzman, Maxx 13,Prof.Ruiz, Luiza Timmerman 1.25
2 Development of Powers 1.25
3 A:Maxx-13 .... 1.25
4 A:Black Hood 1.25
5 V:Void,The Living Black Hole . 1.25
6 'The Doomster',A:Maxx-13 ... 1.25
7 Jaguar Secret Discovered, V:Void 1.25
8 V:Aryan League 1.25
9 I:Moonlighter(w/trading cards) . 1.25
10 V:Invisible Terror 1.25
11 Defending Comedienne 1.25
12 V:The Bodyguard 1.25
13 V:Purge 1.25
14 'Frightmare in Rio',last iss. ... 1.25
Ann.#1 Earthquest,w/trading card . 2.50

JEMM, SON OF SATURN
Sept., 1984

1 GC/KJ mini-series 1.50
2 GC 1.25
3 GC,Origin 1.25
4 A:Superman 1.25
5 Kin 1.25
6 thru 12 GC, Aug. 1985 .... @1.25

JIMMY WAKELY
Sept.–Oct., 1949

1 Ph(c),ATh,The Cowboy Swordsman 750.00
2 Ph(c),ATh,The Prize Pony .. 350.00
3 Ph(c),ATh,The Return of Tulsa Tom 350.00
4 Ph(c),ATh,FF,HK,Where's

There'sSmokeThere'sGunfire 375.00
5 ATh,The Return of the Conquistadores 275.00
6 ATh,Two Lives of Jimmy Wakely 275.00
7 The Secret of Hairpin Canyon 275.00
8 ATh,The Lost City of Blue Valley 275.00
9 ATh,The Return of the Western Firebrands 250.00
10 ATh,Secret of Lantikin'sLight 250.00
11 ATh,Trail o/a Thousand Hoofs250.00
12 ATh,JKU,The King of Sierra Valley 250.00
13 ATh,The Raiders of Treasure Mountain 250.00
14 ATh(c),JKu,The Badmen of Roaring Flame Valley ... 250.00
15 GK(c),Tommyguns on the Range 250.00
16 GK(c),The Bad Luck Boots . 225.00
17 GK(c),Terror atThunderBasin 225.00
18 July-Aug., 1952 .... 250.00

JLA
Nov. 1996

1 GMo(s),HPo,JhD,V:Hyperclan 20.00
2 .... 15.00
3 GMo(s),HPo,JhD,"War of the Worlds" 10.00
4 GMo(s),HPo,JhD,battle of the super-heroes, conc. 10.00
5 GMo(s),HPo,JhD "Woman of Tomorrow" 6.00
6 GMo(s),HPo,JhD,"Fire in theSky"5.00
7 GMo(s),HPo,JhD,"Heaven on Earth" 5.00
8 GMo(s),HPo,JhD,"Imaginary Stories" F:Green Arrow 5.00
9 GMo(s),V:The Key 5.00
10 GMo(s),HPo,JhD,R:Injustice Gang, pt.1 (of 6) 3.00
11 GMo(s),HPo,JhD,Rock of Ages, pt.2 .... 3.00
12 GMo(s),HPo,JhD,Rock of Ages, pt.3, A:Hourman 3.00
13 GMo(s),HPo,JhD,Rock of Ages, pt.4 .... 3.00
14 GMo(s),HPo,JhD,Rock of Ages, pt.5 .... 3.00
15 GMo(s),HPo,JhD,Rock of Ages pt.6, concl, 48 pg. 3.00
16 GMo(s),HPo,JhD, new member 2.00
17 GMo(s),HPo,JhD, V:Prometheus2.00
18 MWa,Engine of Chance, pt.1 . 2.00
19 MWa,Engine of Chance, pt.2 . 2.00
20 MWa,F:Adam Strange,pt.1 .. 2.00
21 MWa,F:Adam Strange,pt.2 .. 2.00
22 GMo(s),The Star Conqueror .. 2.00
23 GMo,V:Star Conqueror, A:Sandman 2.00
Ann.#1 Pulp Heroes (Hard Boiled) 3.95
Ann. #2 TTn,BWr,Ghosts 3.00
GN New World Order GMo(s),HPo, JhD, rep. #1–#4 .... 5.95
GN American Dreams rep.#5–#9 . 8.00
GN Secret Files 4.00
GN Secret Files deluxe 4.00
GN Secret Files #2 .... 4.00
TPB Rock of Ages 10.00
Giant #1, 7 new stories, 80 pg. . 5.00

JLA: PARADISE LOST
Nov., 1997

1 (of 3) MMr,AOI,F:Zauriel 2.00

2 MMr,AOI,F:Zauriel,Martian Manhunter 2.00

JLA: TOMORROW WOMAN
May, 1998

1-shot TPe,Girlfrenzy 2.00

JLA/WILDC.A.T.S
GMo(s),VS,x-over 5.95

JLA: WORLD WITHOUT GROWN-UPS
June 1998

1 (of 2) I:Young Justice 48pg ... 5.00
2 Young Justice, concl. 5.00

JLA: YEAR ONE
Nov., 1997

1 (of 12) MWa,BAu,BKi,48pg.... 3.00
2 MWa,BAu,BKi,V:Vandal Savage 2.00
3 MWa,BAu,BKi 2.00
4 MWa,BAu,BKi,V:Locus 2.00
5 MWa,BAu,BKi,F:Doom Patrol . 2.00
6 MWa,BAu,BKi,V:Doom Patrol . 2.00
7 MWa,BAu,BKi,V:Weapon Master 2.00
8 MWa,BAu,BKi,MIB,V:Locus .. 2.00
9 MWa,BAu,BKi,MIB,V:Locus .. 2.00
10 MWa,BAu,BKi,MIB,V:Locus .. 2.00

JOHNNY THUNDER
Feb.–March, 1973

1 ATh 5.00
2 GK,MD 4.00
3 ATh,GK,MD,July-Aug., 1973 .. 4.00

The Joker #1 © DC Comics, Inc.

JOKER, THE
1975–76

1 IN,DG,A:TwoFace 22.00
2 IN,JL WillieTheWeeper 13.00
3 JL,A:Creeper 12.00
4 JL,A:GreenArrow 10.00
5 .... 10.00
6 V:Sherlock Holmes 10.00
7 IN,A:Luthor 10.00

8	10.00
9 A:Catwoman	12.00

Greatest Joker Stories Ever Told:

1 HC	45.00
1a SC	16.00
The Devil's Advocate HC GN	24.95
GN	12.95

JONAH HEX
1977–85

1 'Vengeance For A Fallen Gladiator'	42.00
2 'The Lair of the Parrot'	20.00
3 'The Fugitive'	14.00
4 'The Day of Chameleon'	14.00
5 'Welcome to Paradise'	14.00
6 'The Lawman'	10.00
7 'Son of the Apache'	10.00
8 O:Jonah Hex	9.00
9 BWr(c)	9.00
10 GM(c),'Violence at Vera Cruz'	9.00
11 'The Holdout'	7.00
12 JS(c)	7.00
13 'The Railroad Blaster'	7.00
14 'The Sin Killer'	7.00
15 'Saw Dust and Slow Death'	7.00
16 'The Wyandott Verdict!'	5.00
17	5.00
18	5.00
19 'The Duke of Zarkania!'	5.00
20 'Phantom Stage to William Bend'	5.00
21 'The Buryin'!'	5.00
22 'Requiem For A Pack Rat'	5.00
23 'The Massacre of the Celestials!'	5.00
24 'Minister of the Lord'	5.00
25 'The Widow Maker'	5.00
26 'Death Race to Cholera Bend!'	4.00
27 'The Wooden Six Gun!'	4.00
28 'Night of the Savage'	4.00
29 'The Innocent'	4.00
30 O:Jonah Hex	4.50
31 A:Arbee Stoneham	4.00
32 A:Arbee Stoneham	4.00
33 'The Crusador'	4.00
34 'Christmas in an Outlaw Town'	4.00
35 'The Fort Charlotte Brigade'	4.00
36 'Return to Fort Charlotte'	4.00
37 DAy,A:Stonewall Jackson	4.00
38	4.00
39 'The Vow of a Samurai!'	4.00
40 DAy	4.00
41 DAy,'Two for the Hangman!'	4.00
42 'Wanted for Murder'	4.00
43 JKu(c)	4.00
44 JKu(c),DAy	4.00
45 DAy,Jonah gets married	4.00
46 JKu(c),DAy	4.00
47 DAy,'Doom Rides the Sundown Town'	4.00
48 DAy,A:El Diablo	4.00
49 DAy	4.00
50 DAy,'The Hunter'	4.00
51 DAy,'The Comforter'	3.50
52 DAy,'Rescue!'	3.50
53 DAy	3.50
54	3.50
55 'Trail of Blood'	3.50
56 DAy,'The Asylum'	3.50
57 B:El Diablo backup story	3.50
58 DAy,'The Treasure of Catfish Pond'	3.50
59 DAy,'Night of the White Lotus'	3.50
60 DAy,'Domain of the Warlord'	3.50

61 DAy,'In the Lair of the Manchus!'	3.50
62 DAy,'The Belly of the Malay Tiger!'	3.50
63 DAy	3.50
64 DAy,'The Pearl!'	3.50
65 DAy,'The Vendetta!'	3.50
66 DAy'Requiem for a Coward'	3.50
67 DAy,'Deadman's Hand!'	3.50
68 DAy,'Gunfight at Gravesboro!'	3.50
69 DAy,'The Gauntlet!'	3.50
70 DAy	3.50
71 DAy,'The Masquerades'	3.50
72 DAy,'Tarantula'	3.50
73 DAy,Jonah in a wheel chair	3.50
74 DAy,A:Railroad Bill	3.50
75 DAy,JAp,A:Railroad Bill	3.50
76 DAy,Jonah goes to Jail	3.00
77 DAy,'Over the Wall'	3.00
78 DAy,Me Ling returns	3.00
79 DAy,'Duel in the Sand'	3.00
80 A:Turnbull	3.00
81 thru 89 DAy	@3.00
90 thru 92	@3.00

JONAH HEX AND OTHER WESTERN TALES
Sept.–Oct., 1979

1	2.00
2 NA,ATh,SA,GK	3.00
3 Jan.–Feb., 1980	1.75

JONAH HEX: RIDERS OF THE WORM AND SUCH
Vertigo 1995
[Mini-Series]

1 R:Ronah Hex	2.95
2 At Wildes West Ranch	2.95
3 History Lesson	2.95
4 I:Autumn Brothers	2.95
5 V:Big worm, final issue	2.95

JONAH HEX: TWO-GUN MOJO
Vertigo 1993

1 B:JLd(s),TT,SG(i),R:Jonah Hex, I:Slow Go Smith	8.00
1a Platinum Ed.	20.00
2 TT,SG(i),D:Slow Go Smith,I:Doc Williams,Wild Bill Hickok	6.00
3 TT,SG(i),Jonah captured	5.00
4 TT,SG(i),O:Doc Williams	5.00
5 TT,SG(i),V::Doc Williams	5.00

JONNY DOUBLE
DC/Vertigo (July, 1998)

1	3.00
2 MCo(c) detective	3.00

JONNI THUNDER
Feb., 1985

1 DG,origin issue	1.25
2 DG	1.25
3 DG	1.25

JUDGE DREDD
1994–96

1 R:Judge Dredd	2.50
2 Silicon Dreams	2.25
3 Terrorists	2.50
4 Mega-City One crisis	2.25
5 Solitary Dredd	2.25
6 V:Richard Magg	2.25

7	2.25
8 V:Ministry of Fear	2.25
9 V:Mister Synn	2.25
10 D:Judge Dredd	2.25
11 Mega-City One Chaos	2.25
12 V:Wally Squad	2.25
13 Block Wars,pt.1	2.25
14 Block Wars,pt.2	2.25
15 Block Wars,pt.3	2.25
16 R:Judge with a Grudge	2.25
17 F:Judge Cadet Lewis, Nova Scotia	2.25
18 final issue	2.25
Movie Adaptation	5.95

JUDGE DREDD: LEGENDS OF THE LAW
1994–95

1 Organ Donor,pt.1	2.50
2 Organ Donor,pt.2	2.25
3 Organ Donor,pt.3	2.25
4 Organ Donor,pt.4	2.25
5 Trial By Gunfire,pt.1	2.25
6 Trial By Gunfire,pt.2	2.25
7 JHi(c),Trial By Gunfire,pt.3	2.25
8 JBy(s),Fall From Grace,pt.1	2.25
9 Fall From Grace,pt.2	2.25
10 Fall From Grace,pt.3	2.25
11 Dredd of Night,pt.1	2.25
12 Dredd of Night,pt.2	2.25
13 Dredd of Night,pt.3,final issue	2.25

JUNK CULTURE
DC/Vertigo May 1997

1 (of 2) TMK	2.50
2 (of 2) TMK "Deuces Wild"	2.50

JUSTICE, INC.
May-June, 1975

1 AMc,JKu(c),O:Avenger	3.00
2 JK	1.25
3 JK	1.25
4 JK,JKu(c),Nov.–Dec., 1975	1.25

[Mini-Series] 1989

1 PerfectBound 'Trust & Betrayal'	3.95
2 PerfectBound	3.95

JUSTICE LEAGUE AMERICA
(see JUSTICE LEAGUE INTERNATIONAL)

JUSTICE LEAGUE EUROPE
1989–93

1 BS,A:Wonder Woman	4.00
2 BS,Search for Nazi-Killer	3.00
3 BS,A:Jack O'Lantern, Queen Bee	2.50
4 BS,V:Queen Bee	2.50
5 JRu,BS,Metamorpho's Baby, A:Sapphire Starr	2.50
6 BS,V:Injustice League	2.00
7 BS,Teasdale Imperative#2, A:JLA	2.00
8 BS,Teasdale Imperative#4, A:JLA	2.00
9 BS,ANi,A:Superman	2.00
10 BS,V:Crimson Fox	2.00
11 BS,C:DocMagnus&Metal Men	2.00
12 BS,A:Metal Men	2.00

Justice League Europe #42
© DC Comics, Inc.

50 Red Winter#6,Double-sized,
  V:Sonar,J:Metamorpho 3.25
Ann.#1 A:Global Guardians 2.00
Ann.#2 MR,CS,ArmageddonPt.7 . 3.00
Ann.#3 RT(i),Eclipso tie-in 2.75
Justice League Spectacular JLE(c)
  New Direction 1.50
Becomes: **Justice League
International**
[2nd Series]

JUSTICE LEAGUE
[INTERNATIONAL]
[1st Series] 1987
1 KM,TA,New Team,I:Max. Lord . 6.00
2 KM,AG,A:BlueJay & Silver
  Sorceress 4.00
3 KM,AG,J:Booster Gold, V:Rocket
  Lords 3.00
3a Superman Logo 60.00
4 KM,AG,V:Royal Flush 3.00
5 KM,AG,A:The Creeper 3.00
6 KM,AG,A:The Creeper 3.00
Becomes:

JUSTICE LEAGUE
INTERNATIONAL
1988–89
7 KM,AG,L:Dr.Fate,Capt.Marvel,
  J:Rocket Red,Capt.Atom
  (Double size) 3.00
8 KM,AG,KG,Move to Paris Embassy,
  I:C.Cobert,B.U.Glob.Guardians. 2.50
9 KM,AG,KG,Millenium,Rocket
  Red-Traitor 2.50
10 KG,KM,AG,A:G.L.Corps,
  Superman,I:G'Nort 2.50
11 KM,AG,V:Construct,C:Metron . 2.50
12 KG,KM,AG,O:Max Lord 2.50
13 KG,AG,A:Suicide Squad 2.50
14 SL,AG,J:Fire&Ice,L:Ron,
  I:Manga Kahn 2.50
15 SL,AG,V:Magna Kahn 2.00
16 KM,AG,I:Queen Bee 2.00
17 KM,AG,V:Queen Bee 2.00
18 KM,AG,MPn,A:Lobo,Guy Gardner
  (bonus book) 3.00
19 KM,JRu,A:Lobo vs.Guy Gardner,
  J:Hawkman & Hawkwoman . . . 3.00
20 KM,JRu(i),A:Lobo,G.Gardner . . 2.00
21 KM,JRu(i),A:Lobo vs.Guy
  Gardner 2.00
22 KM,JRu,Imskian Soldiers 2.00
23 KM,JRu,I:Injustice League . . . 2.00
24 KM,JRu,DoubleSize + Bonus
  Bk#13,I:JusticeLeagueEurope . 4.00
25 KM(c),JRu(i),Vampire story . . . 2.00
Ann.#1 BWg,DG,CR 2.00
Ann.#2 BWg,JRu,A:Joker 3.00
Ann.#3 KM(c),JRu,JLI Embassies 2.50
Spec.#1 Mr.Miracle 2.00
Spec.#2,The Huntress 2.95
TPB new beginning,rep.#1-#7 . . 12.95
TPB The Secret Gospel of Maxwell
  Lord Rep. #8-#12, Ann.#1 . . . 12.95
Becomes:

JUSTICE LEAGUE
AMERICA
1989–96
26 KM(c),JRu(i),Possessed Blue
  Beetle 2.50
27 KM(c),JRu,DG(i),'Exorcist',
  (c)tribute 2.00

Justice League America #77
© DC Comics, Inc.

28 KM(c),JRu(i), A:Black Hand . . 2.00
29 KM(c),JRu(i),V:Mega-Death . . 2.00
30 KM(c),BWg,JRu,J:Huntress,
  D:Mega-Death 2.00
31 ANi,AH,JRu,Teasdale Imperative
  #1,N:Fire,Ice,A:JLE 3.00
32 ANi,AH,Teasdale Imperative
  #3, A:JLE 3.00
33 ANi,AH,GuyGardner vs.Kilowog 2.50
34 ANi,AH,'Club JLI,'A:Aquaman . 2.50
35 ANi,JRu,AH,A:Aquaman 2.50
36 Gnort vs. Scarlet Skier 2.00
37 ANi,AH,L:Booster Gold 2.00
38 JRu,AH,R:Desparo,D:Steel . . . 2.00
39 JRu,AH,V:Desparo,D:Mr.Miracle,
  Robot 2.00
40 AH,Mr.Miracle Funeral 2.00
41 MMc,MaxForce 2.00
42 MMc,J:L-Ron 2.00
43 AH,KG,The Man Who Knew Too
  Much #1 . . . . 2.00
44 AH,Man Knew Too Much #2 . . 2.00
45 AH,MJ,JRu,Guy & Ice's 2nd
  date 2.00
46 Glory Bound #1,I:Gen.Glory . . 2.00
47 Glory Bound #2,J:Gen.Glory . . 2.00
48 Glory Bound #3,V:DosUberbot 2.00
49 Glory Bound #4 . . . . 2.00
50 Glory Bound #5 (double size) . 2.50
51 JRu,AH,V:BlackHand,
  R:Booster Gold 2.00
52 TVE,Blue Beetle Vs. Guy Gardner
  A:Batman 2.00
53 Breakdowns #1, A:JLE 2.00
54 Breakdowns #3, A:JLE 2.00
55 Breakdowns #5,V:Global
  Guardians 2.00
56 Breakdowns #7, U.N. revokes
  JLA charter 2.00
57 Breakdowns #9,A:Lobo,
  V:Despero 2.00
58 BS,Breakdowns #11,Lobo
  Vs.Despero 2.00
59 BS,Breakdowns #13,
  V:Extremists 2.00
60 KM,TA,Breakdowns #15,
  End of J.L.A.. . . . . 2.00

13 BS,V:One-Eyed Cat, contd
  from JLA #37 . . . . 2.00
14 I:VCR 2.00
15 BS,B:Extremists Vector saga,
  V:One-Eyed Cat,A:BlueJay . . . 2.00
16 BS,A:Rocket Reds, Blue Jay . . 2.25
17 BS,JLI in Another Dimension . . 2.25
18 BS,Extremists Homeworld 2.25
19 BS,E:Extremist Vector Saga . . 2.25
20 MR,I:Beefeater,V:Kilowog 1.75
21 MR,JRu,New JLE embassy in
  London,A:Kilowog 1.50
22 MR,JLE's Cat stolen 1.50
23 BS,O:Crimson Fox 1.50
24 BS,Worms in London 1.50
25 BS,V:Worms 1.50
26 BS,V:Starro 1.50
27 BS,JLE V:JLE,A:JLA,V:Starro . 1.50
28 BS, JLE V:JLE,A:J'onnJ'onzz,
  V:Starro 1.50
29 BS,Breakdowns #2,V:Global
  Guardians 1.75
30 Breakdowns#4,V:J.O'Lantern . 1.50
31 Breakdowns #6,War of the
  Gods tie-in 1.50
32 Breakdowns #8,A:Chief(Doom
  Patrol) 1.50
33 Breakdowns #10,Lobo vs.
  Despero 1.50
34 Breakdowns #12,Lobo
  vs.Despero 1.50
35 Breakdowns #14,V:Extremists,
  D:Silver Sorceress 1.50
36 Breakdowns #16,All Quit 1.50
37 B:New JLE,I:Deconstructo . . . 1.75
38 V:Deconstructo,A:Batman 1.50
39 V:Deconstructo,A:Batman 1.50
40 J:Hal Jordan,A:Metamorpho . . 1.50
41 A:Metamorpho,Wond.Woman . 1.50
42 A:Wonder Woman,V:Echidna . 1.50
43 V:Amos Fortune 1.50
44 V:Amos Fortune 1.50
45 Red Winter#1,V:Rocket Reds . 1.50
46 Red Winter#2 . . . . 1.50
47 Red Winter#3,V:Sonar 1.50
48 Red Winter#4,V:Sonar 1.50
49 Red Winter #5,V:Sonar 1.50

61 DJu,I:Weapons Master,B:New
JLA Line-up,I:Bloodwynd 3.00
62 DJu,V:Weapons Master 2.00
63 DJu,V:Starbreaker 2.00
64 DJu,V:Starbreaker 2.00
65 DJu,V:Starbreaker 2.00
66 DJu,Superman V:Guy Gardner 2.00
67 DJu,Bloodwynd mystery 2.00
68 DJu,V:Alien Land Baron 2.00
69 DJu, Doomsday Pt.1-A ... 10.00
69a 2nd printing 2.00
70 DJu,Funeral for a Friend#1 ... 6.00
70a 2nd printing 2.00
71 DJu,J:Agent Liberty,Black Condor,
The Ray,Wonder Woman ... 5.00
71a Newsstand ed. 2.00
71b 2nd Printing 1.50
72 DJu,A:Green Arrow,Black
Canary,Atom,B:Destiny's Hand 4.00
73 DJu,Destiny's Hand #2 ...... 3.00
74 DJu,Destiny's Hand #3 ...... 2.00
75 DJu,E:Destiny's Hand #4,Martian
Manhunter as Bloodwynd 2.00
76 DJu,Blood Secrets#1,
V:Weaponmaster 1.50
77 DJu,Blood Secrets#2,
V:Weaponmaster 1.50
78 MC,V:The Extremists 1.50
79 MC,V:The Extremists 1.50
80 KWe,N:Booster Gold 1.50
81 KWe,A:Captain Atom 1.50
82 KWe,A:Captain Atom 1.50
83 KWe,V:Guy Gardner 1.50
84 KWe,A:Ice 1.75
85 KWe,V:Frost Giants 1.75
86 B:Cults of the Machine 1.75
87 N:Booster Gold 1.75
88 E:Cults of the Machine 1.75
89 Judgement Day#1,
V:Overmaster 1.75
90 Judgement Day#4 .... 1.50
91 Aftershocks #1 .... 1.75
92 Zero Hour,I:Triumph 1.75
93 Power Girl and child 1.50
94 Scarabus 1.50
95 .... 1.50
96 Funeral 1.50
97 I:Judgment 1.50
98 J:Blue Devil, Ice Maiden 1.50
99 V:New Metahumes 1.50
100 GJ,Woj,V:Lord Havok,dbl.size 3.00
100a Collector's Edition 4.00
101 GJ,Woj,Way of the
Warrior,pt.2 .... 1.75
102 Way of the Warrior,pt.5 ..... 1.75
103 .... 1.75
104 F:Metamorpho 1.75
105 GJ,Woj,Underworld
Unleashed tie-in 1.75
106 GJ,Woj,Underworld
Unleashed tie-in 1.75
107 GJ,Woj,secret of Power
Girl's son 1.75
108 GJ,Woj,The Arcana revealed . 1.75
109 .... 1.75
110 GJ,Woj,V:El Diablo 1.75
111 GJ,Woj,The Purge,pt.1 (of 3) . 1.75
112 GJ,Woj,The Purge,pt.2 (of 3) . 1.75
113 GJ,Woj,The Purge,pt.3 (of 3) . 1.75
Ann.#4 KM(c),I:JL Antartica 3.00
Ann.#5 MR,KM,DJu,Armageddon 3.00
Ann.#5a 2nd Printing,silver 2.00
Ann.#6 DC,Eclipso 2.75
Ann.#7 I:Terrorsmith 2.75
Ann.#8 Elseworlds Story 3.25

Ann.#9 Year One Annual 3.50
Ann.#10 CPr(s),SCi,NNa,"Legends
of the Dead Earth" 2.95
Justice League Spectacular DJu,
JLA(c) New Direction 2.00
Archives Vol. 4 .... 50.00

JUSTICE LEAGUE OF AMERICA: THE NAIL
June 1998
Elseworlds
1 world without a Superman 5.00
2 AID,MFm,Robin & Batgirl dead 5.00
3 AID,MFm,concl. 5.00

JUSTICE LEAGUE INTERNATIONAL
[2nd Regular Series] 1993–94
Prev: Justice League Europe
51 Aztec Cult 1.50
52 V:Aztec Cult 1.50
53 R:Fox's Husband 1.50
54 RoR,I:Creator 1.50
55 RoR,A:Creator 1.50
56 RoR,V:Terrorists 1.50
57 RoR,V:Terrorists 1.50
58 RoR,V:Aliens 1.50
59 RoR,A:Guy Gardner 1.50
60 GJ(s),RoR 1.75
61 GJ(s),V:Godfrey 1.75
62 GJ(s),N:Metamorpho,V:Godfrey 1.75
63 GJ(s),In Africa 1.75
64 GJ(s),V:Cadre 1.75
65 JudgmentDay#3,V:Overmaster 1.75
66 JudgmentDay#6,V:Overmaster 1.75
67 Aftershock #3 .... 1.75
68 Zero Hour, Final Issue 1.50
Ann.#4 Bloodlines#9,I:Lionheart . 2.75
Ann.#5 .... 3.25
Ann.#6 Elseworlds Story 2.95

JUSTICE LEAGUE [INTERNATIONAL] QUARTERLY
1990–94
1 I:Conglomerate 4.00
2 MJ(i),R:Mr.Nebula 3.50
3 V:Extremists,C:Original JLA ... 3.50
4 KM(c),MR,CR,A:Injustice
League. 3.00
5 KM(c),Superhero Attacks 3.00
6 EB,Elongated Man,B.U.Global
Guardians,Powergirl,B.Beetle . 3.00
7 EB,DH,MR.Global Guardians .. 3.00
8 .... 3.00
9 DC,F:Power Girl,Booster Gold . 3.50
10 F:Flash,Fire & Ice 3.50
11 F:JL Women 3.50
12 F:Conglomerate 3.50
13 V:Ultraa 7.00
14 MMi(c),PuK(s),F:Captain Atom,Blue
Beetle,Nightshade,Thunderbolt 3.75
15 F:Praxis 3.50
16 F:Gen Glory 3.50
17 Final Issue 3.50

JUSTICE LEAGUE: A MIDSUMMER'S NIGHTMARE
1996
1 (of 3) MWa(s),FaN,JJ,DaR, ... 5.00
2 MWa(s),FaN,JJ,DaR,Batman &

Superman attempt to free
other heroes 4.00
3 MWa&FaN(s), Know-Man's plot
revealed, finale .... @4.00
TPB Rep. 3 issues 8.95

Justice League of America #15
© DC Comics, Inc.

JUSTICE LEAGUE OF AMERICA
Oct.–Nov., 1960
1 MSy,I&O:Despero 3,000.00
2 MSy,A:Merlin 750.00
3 MSy,I&O:Kanjar Ro 650.00
4 MSy,J:Green Arrow 450.00
5 MSy,I&O:Dr.Destiny 400.00
6 MSy,Prof. Fortune 350.00
7 MSy,Cosmic Fun-House ... 350.00
8 MSy,For Sale-Justice League 350.00
9 MSy,O:JLA 450.00
10 MSy,I:Felix Faust 300.00
11 MSy,A:Felix Faust 225.00
12 MSy,I&O:Dr Light 225.00
13 MSy,A:Speedy 225.00
14 MSy,J:Atom 225.00
15 MSy,V:Untouchable Aliens . 200.00
16 MSy,I:Maestro 175.00
17 MSy,A:Tornado Tyrant ... 175.00
18 MSy,V:Terrane,Ocana 175.00
19 MSy,A:Dr.Destiny 175.00
20 MSy,V:Metal Being 175.00
21 MSy,R:JSA,1st S.A Hourman,
Dr.Fate 350.00
22 MSy,R:JSA 325.00
23 MSy,I:Queen Bee 100.00
24 MSy,A:Adam Strange 100.00
25 MSy,I:Draad,the Conqueror . 100.00
26 MSy,A:Despero 100.00
27 MSy,V:I,A:Amazo 100.00
28 MSy,I:Headmaster Mind,
A:Robin 100.00
29 MSy,I:Crime Syndicate,A:JSA,
1st S.A. Starman 150.00
30 MSy,V:Crime Syndicate,
A:JSA 125.00
31 MSy,J:Hawkman 100.00
32 MSy,I&O:Brain Storm 75.00
33 MSy,I:Endless One 60.00

Justice League of America #35
© DC Comics, Inc.

34 MSy,A:Dr.Destiny,Joker	65.00
35 MSy,A:Three Demons	60.00
36 MSy,A:Brain Storm, Handicap story	60.00
37 MSy,A:JSA,x-over, 1st S.A.Mr.Terrific	100.00
38 MSy,A:JSA,Mr.Terrific	100.00
39 Giant	110.00
40 MSy,A:Shark,Penguin	60.00
41 MSy,I:Key	60.00
42 MSy,A:Metamorpho	50.00
43 MSy,I:Royal Flush Gang	50.00
44 MSy,A:Unimaginable	50.00
45 MSy,I:Shaggy Man	50.00
46 MSy,A:JSA,Blockbuster,Solomon Grundy,1st S.A.Sandman	110.00
47 MSy,A:JSA,Blockbuster, Solomon Grundy	50.00
48 Giant	60.00
49 MSy,A:Felix Faust	40.00
50 MSy,A:Robin	40.00
51 MSy,A:Zatanna,Elong.Man	40.00
52 MSy,A:Robin,Lord of Time	40.00
53 MSy,A:Hawkgirl	40.00
54 MSy,A:Royal Flush Gang	40.00
55 MSy,A:JSA,E-2 Robin	60.00
56 MSy,A:JSA,E-2 Robin	45.00
57 MSy,Brotherhood	40.00
58 Reprint(giant size)	45.00
59 MSy,V:Impossibles	40.00
60 MSy,A:Queen Bee,Batgirl	40.00
61 MSy,A:Lex Luthor,Penguin	40.00
62 MSy,V:Bulleters	28.00
63 MSy,A:Key	28.00
64 DD,I:Red Tornado,A:JSA	32.00
65 DD,A:JSA	32.00
66 DD,A:Demmy Gog	28.00
67 MSy,Giant reprints	45.00
68 DD,V:Choas Maker	30.00
69 DD,L:Wonder Woman	28.00
70 DD,A:Creeper	25.00
71 DD,L:J'onn J'onnz	25.00
72 DD,A:Hawkgirl	25.00
73 DD,A:JSA	25.00
74 DD,D:Larry Lance,A:JSA	25.00
75 DD,J:Black Canary	25.00
76 Giant,MA,two page pin-up	22.00

77 DD,A:Joker,L:Snapper Carr	20.00
78 DD,R:Vigilante	20.00
79 DD,A:Vigilante	20.00
80 DD,A:Tomar-Re,Guardians	20.00
81 DD,V:Jest-Master	20.00
82 DD,A:JSA	15.00
83 DD,A:JSA,Spectre	15.00
84 DD,Devil in Paradise	15.00
85 Giant reprint	25.00
86 DD,V:Zapper	15.00
87 DD,A:Zatanna,I:Silver Sorceress,Blue Jay	17.00
88 DD,A:Mera	17.00
89 DD,A:Harlequin Ellis, (i.e. Harlan Ellison)	17.00
90 CI(c),MA(ci),DD,V:Pale People	17.00
91 DD,A:JSA,V:Solomon Grundy	17.00
92 DD,A:JSA,V:Solomon Grundy	20.00
93 DD:A:JSA,(giant size)	25.00
94 DD,NA,O:Sandman,rep. Adventure #40	70.00
95 DD,rep.More Fun Comics #67, All American Comics #25	30.00
96 DD,I:Starbreaker	20.00
97 DD,MS,O:JLA	15.00
98 DD,A:Sargon,Gold.Age reps	15.00
99 DD,G.A. reps.	15.00
100 DD,A:JSA,Metamorpho, R:7 Soldiers of Victory	20.00
101 DD,A:JSA,7 Soldiers	17.00
102 DD,DG,A:JSA,7 Soldiers D:Red Tornado	17.00
103 DD,DG,Halloween issue, A:Phantom Stranger	10.00
104 DD,DG,A:Shaggy Man, Hector Hammond	10.00
105 DD,DG,J:ElongatedMan	10.00
106 DD,DG,J:RedTornado	10.00
107 DD,DG,I:Freedom Fighters, A:JSA	15.00
108 DD,DG,A:JSA, Freedom Fighters	11.00
109 DD,DG,L:Hawkman	10.00
110 DD,DG,A:John Stewart, Phantom Stranger	20.00
111 DD,DG,I:Injustice Gang	5.00
112 DD,DG,A:Amazo	20.00
113 DD,DG,A:JSA	20.00
114 DD,DG,A:SnapperCarr	20.00
115 DD,FMc,A:J'onnJ'onnz	20.00
116 DD,FMc,I:Golden Eagle	20.00
117 DD,FMc,R:Hawkman	6.00
118 DD,FMc	6.00
119 DD,FMc,A:Hawkgirl	6.00
120 DD,FMc,A:Adam Strange	6.00
121 DD,FMc,W:Adam Strange	6.00
122 DD,FMc,JLA casebook story V:Dr.Light	6.00
123 DD,FMc,A:JSA	7.00
124 DD,FMc,A: JSA	7.00
125 DD,FMc,A:Two-Face	6.00
126 DD,FMc,A:Two-Face	6.00
127 DD,FMc,V:Anarchist	6.00
128 DD,FMc,J:W.Woman	6.00
129 DD,FMC,D:RedTornado	5.00
130 DD,FMc,O:JLASatellite	5.00
131 DD,FMc,V:Queen Bee,Sonar	5.00
132 DD,FMc,A:Supergirl	5.00
133 DD,FMc,A:Supergirl	5.00
134 DD,FMc,A:Supergirl	5.00
135 DD,FMc,A:Squad.of Justice	5.00
136 DD,FMc,A:E-2Joker	9.00
137 DD,FMc,Superman vs. Capt. Marvel	9.00
138 NA(c),DD,FMc,A:Adam	

Justice League of America #207
© DC Comics, Inc.

Strange	5.00
139 NA(c),DD,FMc,A:AdamStrange, Phantom Stranger,doub.size	7.00
140 DD,FMc,Manhunters	7.00
141 DD,FMc,Manhunters	7.00
142 DD,FMc,F:Aquaman,Atom, Elongated Man	7.00
143 DD,FMc,V:Injustice Gang	7.00
144 DD,FMc,O:JLA	7.00
145 DD,FMc,A:Phant.Stranger	7.00
146 J:Red Tornado,Hawkgirl	7.00
147 DD,FMc,A:Legion	7.00
148 DD,FMc,A:Legion	7.00
149 DD,FMc,A:Dr.Light	7.00
150 DD,FMc,A:Dr.Light	7.00
151 DD,FMc,A:Amos Fortune	6.00
152 DD,FMc	6.00
153 GT,FMc,I:Ultraa	6.00
154 MK(c),DD,FMc	6.00
155 DD,FMc	6.00
156 DD,FMc	6.00
157 DD,FMc,W:Atom	6.00
158 DD,FMc,A:Ultraa	6.00
159 DD,FMc,A:JSA,Jonah Hex, Enemy Ace	5.00
160 DD,FMc,A:JSA,Jonah Hex, Enemy Ace	5.00
161 DD,FMc,J:Zatanna	5.00
162 DD,FMc	5.00
163 DD,FMc,V:Mad Maestro	5.00
164 DD,FMc,V:Mad Maestro	5.00
165 DD,FMc	5.00
166 DD,FMc,V:Secret Society	5.00
167 DD,FMc,V:Secret Society	5.00
168 DD,FMc,V:Secret Society	5.00
169 DD,FMc,A:Ultraa	5.00
170 DD,FMc,A:Ultraa	5.00
171 DD,FMc,A:JSA,D:Mr.Terrific	5.00
172 DD,FMc,A:JSA,D:Mr.Terrific	5.00
173 DD,FMc,A:Black Lightning	5.00
174 DD,FMc,A:Black Lightning	5.00
175 DD,FMc,V:Dr.Destiny	5.00
176 DD,FMc,V:Dr.Destiny	4.00
177 DD,FMc,V:Desparo	4.00
178 JSn(c),DD,FMc,V:Desparo	4.00
179 JSn(c),DD,FMc,J:Firestorm	4.00
180 JSn(c),DD,FMc,V:Satin Satan	4.00

181 DD,FMc,L:Gr.Arrow,V:Star . .	5.00
182 DD,FMc,A:Green Arrow,	
V:Felix Faust	5.00
183 JSn(c),DD,FMc,A:JSA,	
NewGods	5.00
184 GP,FMc,A:JSA,NewGods . . .	5.00
185 JSn(c),GP,FMc,A:JSA,	
New Gods	5.00
186 FMc,GP,V:Shaggy Man	4.00
187 DH,FMc,N:Zatanna	4.00
188 DH,FMc,V:Proteus	4.00
189 BB(c),RB,FMc,V:Starro	4.00
190 BB(c),RB,LMa,V:Starro	4.00
191 RB,V:Amazo	4.00
192 GP,O:Red Tornado	4.00
193 GP,RB,JOy,I:AllStarSquad . .	4.00
194 GP,V:Amos Fortune	3.00
195 GP,A:JSA,V:Secret Society . .	3.00
196 GP,RT,A:JSA,V:Secret Soc. .	3.00
197 GP,RT,KP,A:JSA,V:Secret	
Society	3.00
198 DH,BBr,A:J.Hex,BatLash	3.00
199 GP(c),DH,BBr,A:Jonah Hex,	
BatLash	3.00
200 GP,DG,BB (1st Batman),PB,TA,	
BBr,GK,CI,JAp,JKu,Anniv.,A:Adam	
Strange,Phantom Stranger,	
J:Green Arrow	5.00
201 GP(c),DH,A:Ultraa	2.00
202 GP(c),DH,BBr,JLA in Space .	2.00
203 GP(c),DH,RT,V:Royal	
Flush Gang	2.00
204 GP(c),DH,RT,V:R.FlushGang	2.00
205 GP(c),DH,RT,V:R.FlushGang	2.00
206 DH,RT,A:Demons 3	2.00
207 GP(c),DH,RT,A:All Star	
Squadron,JSA	2.50
208 GP(c),DH,RT,A:All Star	
Squadron,JSA	2.50
209 GP(c),DH,RT,A:All Star	
Squadron,JSA	2.50
210 RB,RT,JLA casebook #1	2.00
211 RB,RT,JLA casebook #2	2.00
212 GP(c),RB,PCu,RT,c.book #3 .	2.00
213 GP(c),DH,RT	2.00
214 GP(c),DH,RT,I:Siren Sist.h'd .	2.00
215 GP(c),DH,RT	2.00
216 DH	2.00
217 GP(c),RT(i)	2.00
218 RT(i),A:Prof.Ivo	2.00
219 GP(c),RT(i),A:JSA	2.25
220 GP(c),RT,O:Bl.Canary,A:JSA	2.25
221 Beasts #1	2.00
222 RT(i),Beasts #2	2.00
223 RT(i),Beasts #3	2.00
224 DG(i),V:Paragon	2.00
225 V:Hellrazor	2.00
226 FMc(i),V:Hellrazor	2.00
227 V:Hellrazor,I:Lord Claw	2.00
228 GT,AN,R:J'onnJonzz,War of	
the Worlds,pt.1	2.00
229 War of the Worlds,pt.2	2.00
230 War of the Worlds conc.	2.00
231 RB(i),A:JSA,Supergirl	2.25
232 A:JSA Supergirl	2.25
233 New JLA takes over book,	
B:Rebirth,F:Vibe	2.00
234 F:Vixen	2.00
235 F:Steel	2.00
236 E:Rebirth,F:Gypsy	2.00
237 A:Superman,Flash,WWoman .	2.00
238 A:Superman,Flash,WWoman .	2.00
239 V:Ox	2.00
240 MSy,TMd	2.00
241 GT,V:Amazo	2.00

242 GT,V:Amazo,Mask(Toy tie-in)	
insert	2.00
243 GT,L:Aquaman,V:Amazo	2.00
244 JSon,Crisis,A:InfinityInc,JSA .	2.00
245 LMc,Crisis,N:Steel	2.00
246 LMc,JLA leaves Detroit	2.00
247 LMc,JLA returns to old HQ . .	2.00
248 LMc,F:J'onn J'onzz	2.00
249 LMc,Lead-in to Anniv.	2.00
250 LMc,Anniv.,A:Superman,	
Green Lantern,Green Arrow,	
Black Canary,R:Batman	2.75
251 LMc,V:Despero	1.75
252 LMc,V:Despero,N:Elongated	
Man	1.75
253 LMc,V:Despero	1.75
254 LMc,V:Despero	1.75
255 LMc,O:Gypsy	1.75
256 LMc,Gypsy	1.75
257 LMc,A:Adam,L:Zatanna	1.75
258 LMc,Legends x-over,D:Vibe .	1.75
259 LMc,Legends x-over	1.75
260 LMc,Legends x-over,D:Steel .	1.75
261 LMc,Legends,final issue	4.00
Ann.#1 DG(i),A:Sandman	3.00
Ann.#2 I:NewJLA	2.00
Ann.#3 MG(i),Crisis	2.00

Justice League Task Force #5
© DC Comics, Inc.

JUSTICE LEAGUE TASK FORCE
1993–96

1 F:Mart.Manhunter,Nightwing,	
Aquaman,Flash,Gr.Lantern . . .	2.00
2 V:Count Glass,Blitz	1.75
3 V:Blitz,Count Glass	1.75
4 DG,F:Gypsy,A:Lady Shiva	1.75
5 JAI,Knightquest:Crusade,F:Bronze	
Tiger,Green Arrow,Gypsy	2.00
6 JAI,Knightquest:Search,F:Bronze	
Tiger,Green Arrow,Gypsy	1.75
7 PDd(s),F:Maxima,Wonder Woman,	
Dolphin,Gypsy,Vixen,V:Luta . .	1.75
8 PDd(s),SaV,V:Amazons	1.75
9 GrL,V:Wildman	1.75
10 Purification Plague#1	1.75
11 Purification Plague#2	1.75

12 Purification Plague#3	1.75
13 Jugdement Day#2,	
V:Overmaster	1.75
14 Jugdement Day#5,	
V:Overmaster	1.75
15 Aftershocks #2	1.75
16 Zero Hour,A:Triumph	1.75
17 Savage	1.50
18 Savage	1.50
19 Martian Manhunter	1.50
20 Savage Legacy,pt.4	1.50
21 F:Martian Manhunter	1.50
22 F:Triumph	1.50
23 V:Vampire	1.50
24 F:Von Mauler, Gypsy	1.50
25 A:Impulse & Damage, V:Mystek	1.75
26 Cut Day	1.75
27 F:L-Ron	1.75
28 Triumph vs. Manhunter	1.75
29 A:Glenn Gammeron	1.75
30 Underworld Unleashed tie-in . .	1.75
31 Despero on trial	1.75
32 Despero vs. terrorists	1.75
33	1.75
34 On Earth, or Skartaris?	1.75
35 A:Warlord Travis Morgan	1.75

JUSTICE SOCIETY OF AMERICA
[Limited Series]
April–Nov., 1991

1 B:Veng.From Stars,A:Flash . . .	2.00
2 A:BlackCanary,V:Solomon Grundy,	
C:G.A.Green Lantern	1.75
3 A:G.A.Green Lantern,Black Canary,	
V:Sol.Grundy	1.75
4 A:G.A.Hawkman,C:G.A.Flash . .	1.75
5 A:G.A.Hawkman,Flash	1.75
6 FMc(i),A:Bl.Canary,G.A.Gr.Lantern,	
V:Sol.Grundy,V.Savage	1.75
7 JSA united,V:Vandal Savage . .	1.75
8 E:Veng.FromStar,V:V.Savage,	
Solomon Grundy	1.75
Spec.#1 DR,MG,End of JSA	2.00

[Regular Series] 1992–93

1 V:The New Order	1.75
2 V:Ultra Gen	1.50
3 R:Ultra-Humanite	1.50
4 V:Ultra-Humanite	1.50
5 V:Ultra-Humanite	1.50
6 F:Johnny Thunderbolt	1.50
7 ..Or give me Liberty	1.50
8 Pyramid Scheme	1.50
9 V:Kulak	1.50
10 V:Kulak,final issue	1.50

KAMANDI, THE LAST BOY ON EARTH
Oct.–Nov., 1972

1 JK,O:Kamandi	27.00
2 JK	20.00
3 JK	8.00
4 JK,I:Prince Tuftan	8.00
5 JK	8.00
6 JK	8.00
7 JK	7.00
8 JK	7.00
9 JK	7.00
10 JK	7.00
11 JK	7.00
12 JK	7.00
13 thru 24 JK	@6.00
25 thru 28 JK	@3.00
29 A:Superman	3.00

Kamandi #50 © DC Comics, Inc.

30 JK	3.00
31	3.00
32 Double size	4.00
33 thru 57	@3.00
58 A:Karate Kid	3.00
59 JSn,A:Omac, Sept.–Oct,1978	5.00

KAMANDI: AT EARTH'S END
[Mini-Series] 1993

1 R:Kamandi	2.00
2 V:Kingpin,Big Q	2.00
3 A:Sleeper Zom,Saphira	2.00
4 A:Superman	2.00
5 A:Superman,V:Ben Boxer	2.00
6 final issue	2.00

KARATE KID
March-April, 1976

1 I:Iris Jacobs,A:Legion	4.00
2 A:Major Disaster	3.00
3 thru 10	@3.00
11 A:Superboy/Legion	3.00
12 A:Superboy/Legion	3.00
13 A:Superboy/Legion	3.00
14 A:Robin	3.00
15 July-Aug., 1978	3.00

KENTS, THE
1997

1 (of 12) JOs(s),TT,MiB	2.50
2 JOs(s),TT,MiB, tragedy strikes	2.50
3 JOs,TT,MiB,Jed & Nate Kent	2.50
4 JOs,TT,MiB,Bleeding Kansas, concl.	2.50
5 JOs,TT,Brother vs.Brother pt.1	2.50
6 JOs,TT,Brother vs.Brother pt.2	2.50
7 JOs,TT,MiB,Quantrill, Wild Bill Hickock	2.50
8 JOs,	2.50
9 JOs,TMd,To the Speedy by Hard Ways,pt.1	2.50
10 JOs,TMd,To the Stars,pt.2	2.50
11 JOs,TMd,To the Stars,pt.3	2.50
12 JOs,TMd,To the Stars,pt.4	2.50

KID ETERNITY
1991

1 GMo(s),DFg,O:Kid Eternity	5.50
2 GMo(s),DFg,A:Mr.Keeper	5.50
3 GMo(s),DFg,True Origin revealed, final issue.	5.50

KID ETERNITY
Vertigo 1993–94

1 B:ANo(s),SeP,R:Kid Eternity, A:Mdm.Blavatsky,Hemlock	2.75
2 SeP,A:Sigmund Freud,Carl Jung, A:Malocchio	2.50
3 SeP,A:Malocchio,I:Dr.Pathos	2.25
4 SeP,A:Neal Cassady	2.25
5 SeP,In Cyberspace	2.25
6 SeP,A:Dr.Pathos,Marilyn Monroe	2.25
7 SeP,I:Infinity	2.25
8 SeP,In Insane Asylum	2.25
9 SeP,Asylum,A:Dr.Pathos	2.25
10 SeP,Small Wages	2.25
11 ANi(s),I:Slap	2.25
12 SeP,A:Slap	2.25
13 SeP,Date in Hell,pt.1	2.25
14 SeP,Date in Hell,pt.2	2.25
15 SeP,Date in Hell,pt.3	2.25
16 SeP,The Zone	2.25

KILL YOUR BOYFRIEND
Vertigo 1995

GNv PBd(c)	4.95

KINGDOM COME
Elseworlds 1996

1 MWa,AxR	9.00
2 MWa,AxR,R:JLA	8.00
3 MWa,AxR,A:Capt. Marvel	8.00
4 MWa,AxR, final issue	8.00
HC Elseworlds rep.	29.95
TPB MWa,AxR, rep.	15.00

KISSYFUR
1989

1	2.00

Kobalt #10 © DC Comics, Inc.

KOBALT
Milestone 1994–95

1 JBy(c),I:Kobalt,Richard Page	2.25
2	2.00
3 I:Slick,Volt,Red Light	2.00
4 I:Slick,Volt,Red Light	2.00
5 Richard Page	1.75
6 Volt	1.75
7 Static	1.75
8 A:Hardward	1.75
9	1.75
10 A:Harvest	1.75
11 V:St.Cloud	1.75
12 V:Rabid	1.75
13 V:Harvester	1.75
14 Long Hot Summer, V:Harvester	2.50
15 Long Hot Summer	2.50

KOBRA
1976–77

1 JK,I:Kobra & Jason Burr	4.00
2 I:Solaris	2.50
3 KG/DG,TA,V:Solaris	2.50
4 V:Servitor	2.50
5 RB/FMc,A:Jonny Double	2.50
6 MN/JRu,A:Jonny Double	2.50
7 MN/JRu,A:Jonny Double last iss	2.50

KONG THE UNTAMED
June-July, 1975

1 thru 4	@1.25
5 Feb.–March, 1976	1.25

KORAK, SON OF TARZAN
1975
(Previously published by Gold Key)

46 B:Carson of Venus, 1972	4.00
47	3.50
48 thru 59, 1975	3.00

Becomes: TARZAN FAMILY

KRYPTON CHRONICLES
1981

1 CS,A:Superman	1.50
2 CS,A:Black Flame	1.25
3 CS,O:Name of Kal-El	1.25

LAST DAYS OF THE JUSTICE SOCIETY
1986

1	3.00

LAST ONE
Vertigo 1993

1 B:JMD(s),DSw,I:Myrwann,Patrick Maguire's Story	3.25
2 DSw,Pat's Addiction to Drugs	3.00
3 DSw,Pat goes into Coma	3.00
4 DSw,In Victorian age	3.00
5 DSw,Myrwann Memories	3.00
6 E:JMD(s),DSw,final Issue	3.00

LEADING COMICS
Winter, 1941–42

1 O:Seven Soldiers of Victory, B:Crimson Avenger,Green Arrow & Speedy,Shining Knight, A:The Dummy	3,300.00
2 MMe,V:Black Star	1,100.00
3 V:Dr. Doome	950.00
4 'Seven Steps to Conquest', V:The Sixth Sense	700.00

5 'The Miracles that Money
   Couldn't Buy' 700.00
6 'The Treasure that Time
   Forgot' 600.00
7 The Wizard of Wisstark 600.00
8 Seven Soldiers Go back
   through the Centuries 600.00
9 V:Mr. X,'Chameleon of Crime' 600.00
10 King of the Hundred Isles .. 600.00
11 'The Hard Luck Hat!' 400.00
12 'The Million Dollar
   Challenge!' 400.00
13 'The Trophies of Crime' ... 400.00
14 Bandits from the Book' 400.00
15 (fa) 175.00
16 thru 22 (fa) .... @75.00
23 (fa),I:Peter Porkchops 150.00
24 thru 30 (fa) .... @60.00
31 (fa) 50.00
32 (fa) 50.00
33 (fa) 60.00
34 thru 40 (fa) .... @50.00
41 (fa),Feb.–March, 1950 ..... 50.00

LEAGUE OF JUSTICE
1996
1 (of 2) Elseworlds 5.95
2 (of 2) Elseworlds 5.95

LEAVE IT TO BINKY
Feb.–March, 1948
1 .... 175.00
2 .... 70.00
3 .... 60.00
4 .... 60.00
5 thru 14 .... @30.00
15 SM,Scribbly 40.00
16 thru 60 .... @15.00
61 thru 71 .... @7.50

LEGEND OF
THE SHIELD
Impact 1991–92
1 I:Shield,V:Mann-X,I:Big Daddy,
  Lt.Devon Hall,Arvell Hauser,Mary
  Masterson-Higgins 1.50
2 Shield in Middle East 1.25
3 Shield Goes A.W.O.L. 1.25
4 Hunt for Shield 1.25
5 A:Shield's Partner Dusty 1.25
6 O:Shield, V:The Jewels 1.25
7 Shield/Fly team-up 1.25
8 V:Weapon 1.25
9 Father Vs. Son 1.25
10 Arvell Hauser 1.25
11 inc,Trading cards 1.25
12 .... 1.25
13 Shield court martialed 1.25
14 Mike Barnes becomes Shield . 1.25
15 Shield becomes a Crusader .. 1.25
16 V:Soviets,final issue 1.25
Ann.#1 Earthquest,w/trading card . 2.25

LEGEND OF
WONDER WOMAN
1986
1 Return of Atomia 1.25
2 A:Queens Solalia & Leila 1.25
3 Escape from Atomia 1.25
4 conclusion 1.25

Legends #6 © DC Comics, Inc.

LEGENDS
1986–87
1 JBy,V:Darkseid 3.00
2 JBy,A:Superman 2.00
3 JBy,I:Suicide Squad 2.00
4 JBy,V:Darkseid 2.00
5 JBy,A:Dr. Fate 2.00
6 JBy,I:Justice League 5.00
TPB rep.#1–#6 JBy(c) 9.95

LEGENDS OF
DANIEL BOONE, THE
Oct., 1955–Jan., 1957
1 .... 500.00
2 .... 350.00
3 thru 8 .... 300.00

LEGENDS OF
THE DARK KNIGHT
(see BATMAN)

LEGENDS OF
THE DC UNIVERSE
Dec., 1997
1 JeR,VS,PNe,A:Superman, pt.1 . 2.00
2 JeR,VS,PNe,A:Superman, pt.2 . 2.00
3 JeR,VS,PNe,A:Superman, pt.3 . 2.00
4 BML,MD2,VRu,Moments, pt.1 . 2.00
5 BML,MD2,VRu,Moments, pt.2 . 2.00
6 DTy,KN,Robin meets Superman 2.00
7 DON,DG,Peacemakers, pt.1 .. 2.00
8 DON,DG,Peacemakers, pt.2 .. 2.00
9 DON,DG,Peacemakers, pt.3 .. 2.00
Giant #1 JKu(c), 80 pg. 5.00

LEGENDS OF
THE LEGION
Dec., 1997
1 (of 4) BKi,TPe,TNu,O:Ultra Boy 2.25
2 .... 2.25
3 BKi,TPe,O:Umbra 2.25
4 BKi,TPe,O:Star Boy 2.25

LEGENDS OF THE
WORLD FINEST
1994
1 WS(s),DIB,V:Silver Banshee,Blaze,
  Tullus,Foil(c) 5.25
2 WS(s),DIB,V:Silver Banshee,Blaze,
  Tullus,Foil(c) 5.25
3 WS(s),DIB,V:Silver Banshee,Blaze,
  Tullus,Foil(c) 5.25
TPB 14.95

L.E.G.I.O.N. '89-94
1989–94
1 BKi,V:Computer Tyrants 3.50
2 BKi,V:Computer Tyrants 3.00
3 BKi,V:Computer Tyrants,
  A:Lobo 3.00
4 BKi,V: Lobo 3.00
5 BKi,J:Lobo(in the rest of the
  series),V:Konis-Biz 3.00
6 BKi,V:Konis-Biz 3.00
7 BKi,Stealth vs. Dox 3.00
8 BKi,R:Dox 3.00
9 BKi,J:Phase (Phantom Girl) .. 2.50
10 BKi,Stealth vs Lobo 2.50
11 BKi,V:Mr.Stoorr 2.50
12 BKi,V:Emerald Eye 2.50
13 BKi,V:Emerald Eye 2.50
14 BKi,V:Pirates 2.50
15 BKi,V:Emerald Eye 2.50
16 BKi,J:LarGand 2.50
17 BKi,V:Dragon-Ro 2.50
18 BKi,V:Dragon-Ro 2.50
19 V:Lydea,L:Stealth 2.50
20 Aftermath 2.50
21 D:Lyrissa Mallor,V:Mr.Starr .. 2.50
22 V:Mr.Starr 2.50
23 O:R.J.Brande(double sized) . 3.50
24 BKi,V:Khunds 2.50
25 BKi,V:Khunds 2.50
26 BKi,V:Khunds 2.50
27 BKi,J:Lydea Mallor 2.50
28 KG,Birth of Stealth's Babies .. 2.50
29 BKi,J:Capt.Comet,Marij'n Bek . 2.50
30 BKi,R:Stealth 2.50
31 Lobo vs.Capt.Marvel 3.50
32 V:Space Biker Gang 2.00
33 A:Ice-Man 2.00
34 MPn,V:Ice Man 2.00
35 Legion Disbanded 2.00
36 Dox proposes to Ignea 2.00
37 V:Intergalactic Ninjas 2.00
38 BKi,Lobo V:Ice Man 2.00
39 BKi,D:G'odd,V:G'oddSquad ... 2.00
40 BKi,V:Kyaltic Space Station .. 2.00
41 BKi,A:Stealth'sBaby 2.00
42 BKi,V:Yeltsin-Beta 2.00
43 BKi,V:Yeltsin-Beta 2.00
44 V:Yeltsin-Beta,C:Gr.Lantern .. 2.00
45 .... 2.00
46 BKi,A:Hal Jordan 2.00
47 BKi,Lobo vs Hal Jordan 2.00
48 BKi,R:Ig'nea 2.00
49 BKi,V:Ig'nea 2.00
50 BKi,V:Ig'nea,A:Legion'67 ..... 3.75
51 F:Lobo,Telepath 2.00
52 BKi,V:Cyborg Skull of Darius .. 2.00
53 BKi,V:Shadow Creature 2.00
54 BKi,V:Shadow Creature 2.00
55 BKi,V:Shadow Beast 2.00
56 BKi,A:Masked Avenger 2.00
57 BKi,Trinity,V:Green Lantern ... 2.00
58 BKi,Trinity#6,A:Green Lantern,
  Darkstar 2.00

59 F:Phase 2.00	
60 V:Phantom Riders 2.00	
61 Little Party 2.00	
62 A:R.E.C.R.U.I.T.S. 2.00	
63 A:Superman 2.00	
64 BKi(c),V:Mr.B 2.00	
65 BKi(c),V:Brain Bandit 2.00	
66 Stealth and Dox name child . . 2.00	
67 F:Telepath 2.00	
68 . . . . 1.75	
69 . . . . 2.00	
70 Zero Hour, last issue 2.50	
Ann.#1 A:Superman,V:Brainiac . 5.50	
Ann.#2 Armageddon 2001 . . . . . 3.50	
Ann.#3 Eclipso tie-in 3.25	
Ann.#4 SHa(i),I:Pax 3.75	
Ann.#5 Elseworlds story 3.50	

LEGION OF SUBSTITUTE HEROES
1985
Spec.#1 KG 1.50

LEGION OF SUPER-HEROES
[Reprint Series] 1973
1 rep. Tommy Tomorrow 11.00
2 rep. Tommy Tomorrow 7.00
3 rep. Tommy Tomorrow 7.00
4 rep. Tommy Tomorrow 7.00
[1st Regular Series] 1980–84
Prev: SUPERBOY (& LEGION)
259 JSon,L:Superboy 5.00
260 RE,I:Circus of Death 3.50
261 RE,V:Circus of Death 3.50
262 JSh,V:Engineer 3.50
263 V:Dagon the Avenger 3.50
264 V:Dagon the Avenger 3.50
265 JSn,DG,Superman/Radio Shack
    insert 3.50
266 R:Bouncing Boy,Duo Damsel   3.00
267 SD,V:Kantuu 3.00
268 SD,BWi,V:Dr.Mayavale 3.00
269 V:Fatal Five 3.00
270 V:Fatal Five 3.00

271 V:Tharok (Dark Man) 2.50	
272 CI,SD,O:J:Blok, I:New	
Dial 'H' for Hero 2.50	
273 V:Stargrave 2.50	
274 SD,V:Captain Frake 2.50	
275 V:Captain Frake 2.50	
276 SD,V:Mordru 2.50	
277 A:Reflecto(Superboy) 2.50	
278 A:Reflecto(Superboy) 2.50	
279 A:Reflecto(Superboy) 2.50	
280 R:Superboy 2.50	
281 SD,V:Time Trapper 2.50	
282 V:Time Trapper 2.50	
283 O:Wildfire 2.50	
284 PB,V:Organleggor 2.50	
285 PB,KG(1st Legion)V:Khunds . 3.00	
286 PB,KG,V:Khunds 3.00	
287 KG,V:Kharlak 4.00	
288 KG,V:Kharlak 3.00	
289 KG,Stranded 3.00	
290 KG,B:Great Darkness Saga,	
J:Invisible Kid II 3.00	
291 KG,V:Darkseid's Minions . . . 2.00	
292 KG,V:Darkseid's Minions . . . 2.00	
293 KG,Daxam destroyed 2.00	
294 KG,E:Great Darkness Saga,	
V:Darkseid,A:Auron,Superboy . 2.00	
295 KG,A:Green Lantern Corps . . 1.75	
296 KG,D:Cosmic Boys family . . 1.75	
297 KG,O:Legion,A:Cosmic Boy . 1.75	
298 KG,EC,I:Amethyst 1.75	
299 KG,R:Invisible Kid I 1.75	
300 KG,CS,JSon,DC,KS,DG 2.00	
301 KG,R:Chameleon Boy 1.75	
302 KG,A:Chameleon Boy 1.75	
303 KG,V:Fatal Five 1.75	
304 KG,V:Fatal Five 1.75	
305 KG,V:Micro Lad 1.75	
306 KG,CS,RT,O:Star Boy 1.75	
307 KG,GT,Omen 1.75	
308 KG,V:Omen 1.75	
309 KG,V:Omen 1.75	
310 KG,V:Omen 1.75	
311 KG,GC,New Headquarters . . 1.75	
312 KG,V:Khunds 1.75	
313 KG,V:Khunds 1.75	
Ann.#1 IT,KG,I:Invisible Kid 3.50	
Ann.#2 DGb,W:Karate Kid and	
Princess Projectra 2.00	
Ann.#3 CS,RT,A:Darkseid 2.00	
Ann.#4 reprint 2.00	
Ann.#5 reprint 1.75	
Legion Archives Vol 1 HC 39.95	
Legion Archives Vol 2 HC 39.95	
Legion Archives Vol 3 HC 39.95	
Legion Archives Vol 4 HC 39.95	

Becomes:
TALES OF LEGION OF SUPER HEROES

LEGION OF SUPER-HEROES
[3rd Regular Series] 1984–89
1 KG,V:Legion of Super-Villians . 3.00
2 KG,V:Legion of Super-Villians . 2.50
3 KG,V:Legion of Super-Villians . 2.50
4 KG,D:Karate Kid 2.50
5 KG,D:Nemesis Kid 2.50
6 JO,F:Lightning Lass 2.25
7 SLi,A:Controller 2.25
8 SLi,V:Controller 2.25
9 Sli,V:Sklarians 2.25
10 V:Khunds 2.25
11 EC,KG,L:Orig 3 members . . . 2.00

12 SLi,EC,A:Superboy 2.00	
13 SLi,V:Lythyls,F:TimberWolf . . 2.00	
14 SLi,J:Sensor Girl (Princess	
Projectra),Quislet,Tellus,Polar	
Boy,Magnetic Kid 2.00	
15 GLa,V:Dr. Regulus 2.00	
16 SLi,Crisis tie-in,F:Braniac5 . . 2.00	
17 GLa,O:Legion 2.00	
18 GLa,Crisis tie-in,V:InfiniteMan . 2.00	
19 GLa,V:Controller 2.00	
20 GLa,V:Tyr 2.00	
21 GLa,V:Emerald Empress 1.75	
22 GLa,V:Restorer,A:Universo . . 1.75	
23 SLi,GLa,A:Superboy,	
Jonah Hex 1.75	
24 GLa,NBi,A:Fatal Five 1.75	
25 GLa,V:FatalFive 1.75	
26 GLa,V:FatalFive,O:SensorGirl . 1.75	
27 GLa,GC,A:Mordru 1.75	
28 GLa,L:StarBoy 1.75	
29 GLa,V:Starfinger 1.75	
30 GLa,A:Universo 1.75	
31 GLa,A:Ferro Lad,Karate Kid . 1.75	
32 GLa,V:Universo,I:Atmos 1.75	

Legion of Super-Heroes (3rd
Series) #27 © DC Comics, Inc.

33 GLa,V:Universo 1.75
34 GLa,V:Universo 1.75
35 GLa,V:Universo,R:Saturn Girl . 1.75
36 GLa,R:Cosmic Boy 1.75
37 GLa,V:Universo,I:Superboy
    (Earth Prime) 5.00
38 GLa,V:TimeTrapper,
    D:Superboy 9.00
39 CS,RT,O:Colossal Boy 1.75
40 GLa,I:New Starfinger 1.75
41 GLa,V:Starfinger 1.75
42 GLa,Millenium,V:Laurel Kent . . 1.75
43 GLa,Millenium,V:Laurel Kent . . 1.75
44 GLa,O:Quislet 1.75
45 GLa,CS,MGr,DC,30th Ann. . . . 3.00
46 GLa,Conspiracy 1.75
47 GLa,PB,V:Starfinger 1.75
48 GLa,Conspiracy,A:Starfinger . . 1.75
49 PB,Conspiracy,A:Starfinger . . 1.75
50 KG,V:Time Trapper,A:Infinite
    Man,E:Conspiracy 3.00
51 KG,V:Gorak,L:Brainiac5 . . . . . 1.75
52 KG,V:Gil'Dishpan 1.75

Legion of Super-Heroes (3rd Series) Annual #1 © DC Comics, Inc.

53 KG,V:Gil'Dishpan 1.75
54 KG,V:Gorak 1.75
55 KG,EC,JL,EL,N:Legion 1.75
56 EB,V:Inquisitor 1.75
57 KG,V:Emerald Empress 1.75
58 KG,V:Emerald Empress 1.75
59 KG,MBr,F:Invisible Kid 1.75
60 KG,B:Magic Wars 1.75
61 KG,Magic Wars 1.75
62 KG,D:Magnetic Lad 1.75
63 KG,E:Magic Wars #4,final iss. . 1.75
Ann.#1 KG,Murder Mystery 2.50
Ann.#2 KG,CS,O:Validus,
  A:Darkseid 3.00
Ann.#3 GLa,I:2nd Karate Kid 2.50
Ann.#4 BKi,V:Starfinger 2.50
Ann #5 I:2nd Legion Sub.Heroes . 2.50

[4th Regular Series] 1989–97
1 KG,R:Cosmic Boy, Chameleon 3.00
2 KG,R:Ultra Boy,I:Kono 2.50
3 KG,D:Block,V:Roxxas 2.50
4 KG,V:Time Trapper 2.50
5 KG,V:Mordru,A:Glorith 2.50
6 KG,I:Laurel Gand 2.50
7 KG,V:Mordru 2.25
8 KG,O:Legion 2.25
9 KG,O:Laurel Gand 2.25
10 KG,V:Roxxas 2.25
11 KG,V:Roxxas 2.00
12 KG,I:Kent Shakespeare 2.00
13 KG,V:Dominators,posters . . . 2.00
14 KG,J:Tenzil Kem 2.00
15 KG,Khund Invasion 2.00
16 KG,V:Khunds 2.00
17 KG,V:Khunds 2.00
18 KG,V:Khunds 2.00
19 KG,cont.from Adv.of Superman
  #478,A:Original Dr. Fate 2.25
20 KG,V:Dominators 2.00
21 KG,B:Quiet Darkness,
  A:Lobo,Darkseid 3.00
22 KG,A:Lobo,Darkseid 2.50
23 KG,A:Lobo,Darkseid 2.50
24 KG,E:Quiet Darkness,A:Lobo,
  Darkseid,C:Legionairres 2.75

25 DAb,I:Legionairres 3.00
26 JPn,B:Terra Mosaic,V:B.I.O.N . 2.00
27 JPn,V:B.I.O.N. 2.00
28 JPn,O:Sun Boy 2.00
29 JPn,I:Monica Sade 2.00
30 JPn,V:Dominators 2.00
31 CS,AG,F:Shvaughn as man . . 2.00
32 JPn,D:Karate Kid,Prin.Projectra,
  Chameleon Boy(Legionaires) . 2.00
33 R:Kid Quantum 2.00
34 R:Sun Boy 2.00
35 JPN,V:Dominators 2.00
36 JPn,E:Terra Mosaic 2.00
37 JBr,R:Star Boy,Dream Girl . . . 2.00
38 JPn,Earth is destroyed 5.00
39 SI,A:Legionaires 2.00
40 SI,Legion meets Legionnaires . 2.00
41 SI,F:The Legionnaires 2.25
42 SI,V:Glorith 2.00
43 SI,B:Mordru Arises 2.00
44 SI,R:Karate Kid 2.00
45 SI,R:Roxxas 2.00
46 SI, ... 2.00
47 SI, ... 2.00
48 SI,E:Mordru Arises 2.00
49 F:Matter Eater Lad 2.00
50 W:Tenzil & Saturn Queen,
  R:Wlidfire,V.B.I.O.N. 3.75
51 R:Kent,Celeste,Ivy,V:Grimbor . 2.00
52 F:Timber Wolf 2.00
53 SI,V:Glorith 2.25
54 SI,Foil,Die-Cut(c),
  N:L.E.G.I.O.N 3.25
55 SI,On Rimbor 2.50
56 SI,R:Espionage Squad 2.00
57 SI,R:Khund Legionnaires 2.00
58 SI,D:Laurel Gand 2.00
59 SI,R:Valor,Dawnstar 2.25
60 SI,End of an Era#3 . . . . 2.25
61 SI,End of an Era#6 . . . . 2.25
62 I:New Team 2.00
63 Alien Attack 2.00
64 . . . . 2.00
65 . . . . 2.00
66 I:New Team Members 2.00
67 F:Leviathan 2.00
68 F:Leviathan 2.00
69 V:Durlan 2.25
70 A:Andromeda, Brainiac 5 . . . . 2.25
71 Planet Trom 2.25
72 . . . . 2.25
73 Sibling Rivalry,pt.1 . . . . 2.25
74 Future Tense,pt2 . . . . 2.25
75 Two Timer,pt.1 (of 2) 2.25
76 F:Valor & Triad 2.25
77 F:Brainiac 5 . . . . 2.25
78 . . . . 2.25
79 Fatal Five attacks 2.25
80 V:Fatal Five 2.25
81 R:Dirk Morgna 2.25
82 . . . . 2.25
83 . . . . 2.25
84 . . . . 2.25
85 TPe&TMw(s),LMd,A:Superman,
  back in 20th century 2.25
86 TPe&TMw(s),LMd,Final Night
  tie-in 2.25
87 TPe&TMw(s),LMd,F:Deadman 2.25
88 TPe&TMw(s),LMd,A:Impulse . . 2.25
89 TPe&TMw(s),LMd, ... 2.25
90 TPe&TMw(s),LMd,V:Dr. Psycho 2.25
91 TPe&TMw(s),LMd,Legion back
  together, but trapped in
  timestream 2.25
92 TPe&TMs(s),LMd,"Displaced

in Time" 2.25
93 TPe&TMw(s),MC, All-tragedy
  issue 2.25
94 TPe&TMw(s),LMd,"22 short
  pages about the Legion of
  Super-Heroes" 2.25
95 MFm,F:Brainiac 5 . . . . 2.25
96 MFm,wedding 2.25
97 TPe,LMd,Genesis tie-in 2.50
98 TPe&TMC,LMd,C.O.M.P.U.T.O.
  the Conqueror, pt.1 . . . . 2.50
99 TPe&TMw,LMd,Computo, pt.2 . 2.50
100 TPe&TMw,LMd,Computo, pt.3 6.00
101 TPe&TMw(s),AD&MFm(c),
  F:Sparks 2.50
102 . . . . 2.50
103 TPe&TMw,AD&MFm(c),Star
  Boy 2.50
104 TPe&TMw,AD&MFm(c),
  changes 2.50
105 TPe&TMw,AD&MFm(c),
  Adventures in Action x-over . 2.50
106 TPe&TMw,AD&MFm(c),Dark
  Circle Rising, x-over pt.2 . . . 2.50
107 TPe&TMw,AD&MFm(c),Dark
  Circle Rising, x-over pt.4 . . . . 2.50
108 TPe&TMw,AD&MFm(c),Dark
  Circle Rising, x-over pt.6 . . . . 2.50
109 DDv,AD,MFm,F:Violet 2.50
Ann.#1 O:Ultra Boy,V:Glorith . . . 3.50
Ann.#2 O:Valor 3.50
Ann.#3 N:Timberwolf 4.00
Ann.#4 I:Jamm 3.50
Ann.#5 SI(c),CDo,MFm,TMc,
  Elseworlds Story 3.75
Ann.#6 Year One Annual + pin-ups 3.95
Ann.#7 TPe(s),MC,MFm,"Legends
  of the Dead Earth" 3.50
TPB Great Darkness Saga 17.95
TPB Legion Archives, rep.#1-#3 . 39.95
TPB Legion Archives, rep.#4 . . . 49.95
HC Archives, Vol. 6 rep.Adventure
  #350–358 . . . . 49.95
HC Archives, Vol. 7 . . . . 50.00
GN Secret Files, inc.O:Legion . . 5.00

LEGIONNAIRES
1992–97
1 CSp,V:Mano and the Hand,Bagged
  w/SkyBox promo card 3.50
1a w/out card 2.50
2 CSp,V:Mano 2.00
3 CSp,I:2nd Emerald Empress . . 2.00
4 CSp,R:Fatal Five 2.00
5 CSp,V:Fatal Five 2.00
6 CSp,V:Fatal Five 1.75
7 AH,V:Devil Fish 1.75
8 CDo,F:Brainiac 5 . . . . 1.75
9 CSp,A:Kid Quantum 1.75
10 CSp,A:Kono,I:2nd Kid Pyscho . 1.75
11 CSp,J:2nd Kid Pyscho 1.75
12 CSp,A:2nd Kid Pyscho 1.75
13 FFo,V:Grimbor 1.75
14 V:Grimbor 1.75
15 V:Grimbor 1.75
16 In Time 1.75
17 End of An Era #1 . . . . 1.75
18 Zero Hour, LSH 1.75
19 Problems 1.50
20 Moon Battle 1.50
21 and 22 . . . . @1.50
23 Saturday Night 1.50
24 F:Triad 1.50
25 F:Chameleon 1.50
26 F:Apparition, Ultra Boy 1.75

Circle Rising x-over, pt.1 . . . . . 2.50
63 RSt&TMw(s),JMy,Dark Circle
   Rising, x-over, pt.3 . . . . 2.50
64 RSt&TMw(s),JMy, Dark Circle
   Rising, x-over pt.5 . . . . 2.50
65 RSt&TMw(s),JMy,aftermath . . . 2.50
Ann.#1 Elseworlds Story 2.95
Ann.#2 Year One Story 3.00
Ann.#3 RSt&TMw(s) Legends of the
   Dead Earth 3.50

LEGIONAIRRES THREE
1986
1 EC,Saturn Girl,Cosmic Boy . . . 4.00
2 EC,V:Time Trapper,pt.1 . . . . . . 3.00
3 EC,V:Time Trapper,pt.2 . . . . . . 3.00
4 EC,V:Time Trapper,pt.3 . . . . . . 2.75

LEGION: SCIENCE POLICE
June 1998
1 (of 4) DvM,PR,JRu,set in
   30th century 2.50
2 DvM,PR,JRu,Jarik Shadder . . . 2.50
3 DvM,PR,JRu, ... 2.50

Legionnaires #7 © DC Comics, Inc.

27 V:The Daxamites 2.25
28 V:Daxamites 2.25
29 . . . . 2.25
30 Silbing Rivalry,pt.2 . . . . 2.25
31 Future Tense,pt.3 . . . . 2.25
32 Two Timer, pt.2 . . . . 2.25
33 deadly new villain 2.25
34 Shrinking Violet killed? 2.25
35 . . . . 2.25
36 RSt,V:Fatal Five 2.25
37 RSt,A:Kinetix,The Empress . . . 2.25
38 . . . . 2.25
39 . . . . 2.25
40 . . . . 2.25
41 RSt&TMw(s),JMy,Legion of
   Super-Heroes #84 aftermath . . 2.25
42 RSt&TMw(s),JMy,Mysa vs.
   Kinetix 2.25
43 RSt&TMw(s),JMy,Legionnaire
   try-outs 2.25
44 RSt&TMw(s),JMy,revenge by
   rejected applicants 2.25
45 . . . . 2.25
46 RSt&TMw(s),JMy,M'Onel's life
   hangs by a thread 2.25
47 TPe&TMw(s),JMy,Brainiac 5 has
   plan to return Legionnaires to
   the future 2.25
48 RSt&TMw(s),JMy,"Dawn of the
   Dark Lord," pt.1 . . . . 2.25
49 RSt&TMw(s),JMy,"Dawn of the
   Dark Lord," pt.2 . . . . 2.25
50 RSt&TMw(s),JMy,"The Bride of
   Mordru" 48pg, with poster 3.95
51 "Picking Up the Pieces" 2.25
52 RSt&TMw(s),JMy,"LeVlathan" . 2.25
53 RSt&TMw(s),JMy,F:Monstress 2.25
54 TPe&TMw(s),JMy,F:G.A. Legion 2.25
55 RSt&TMw(s),JMy,V:Composite
   Man 2.25
56 RSt&TMw(s),JMy,F:M'Onel . . . 2.25
57 RSt&TMw(s),JMy,V:Khunds . . 2.25
58 . . . . 2.25
59 RSt&TMw(s),JMy,date night . . 2.50
60 RSt&TMw(s),JMy,2 join, 2 leave 2.50
61 RSt&TMw(s),JMy,Adventures
   in Action x-over 2.50
62 RSt&TMw(s),JMy,Dark

LIFE, THE UNIVERSE AND EVERYTHING
1996
1 thru 3 Doug Adams adapt. . . . @6.95

LIMITED COLLECTORS EDITION
Summer, 1973
21 Shazam 20.00
22 Tarzan 15.00
23 House of Mystery 25.00
24 Rudolph, the Red-nosed
   Reindeer 30.00
25 NA,NA(c),Batman 35.00
27 Shazam 15.00
29 Tarzan 12.00
31 NA,O:Superman 20.00
32 Ghosts 22.00
33 Rudolph 20.00
34 X-Mas with Superheroes 15.00
35 Shazam 20.00
36 The Bible 10.00
37 Batman 20.00
38 Superman 15.00
39 Secret Origins 15.00
40 Dick Tracy 12.00
41 ATh,Super Friends 15.00
42 Rudolph 15.00
43 X-mas with Super-Heroes . . . 15.00
44 NA,Batman 15.00
45 Secret Origins-Super Villians . 12.00
46 ATh,JLA 15.00
47 Superman 12.00
48 Superman-Flash Race 12.00
49 Superboy & Legion of
   Super-Heroes 10.00
50 Rudolph 10.00
51 NA,NA(c),Batman 15.00
52 NA,NA(c),The Best of DC . . . 15.00
57 Welcome Back Kotter 10.00
59 NA,BWr,Batman,1978 . . . . . . 20.00

LITTLE SHOP OF HORRORS
1 GC 2.50

Lobo #4 © DC Comics, Inc.

LOBO
[1st Limited Series] 1990–91
1 SBs,Last Czarnian #1 . . . . . . 4.00
1a 2nd Printing 2.00
2 SBs,Last Czarnian #2 . . . . 3.00
3 SBs,Last Czarnian #3 . . . . 3.00
4 SBs,Last Czarnian #4 . . . . 3.00
Ann.#1 Bloodlines#1,I:Layla 3.75
Lobo Paramilitary X-Mas SBs . . . 5.50
Lobo:Blazing Chain of Love,DCw . 1.50
TPB Last Czarnian,rep.#1-#4 . . . 9.95
TPB Lobo's Greatest Hits 12.95
[Regular Series] 1993–97
1 VS,Foil(c),V:Dead Boys 3.25
2 VS 3.00
3 VS 2.75
4 VS,Quigly Affair 2.75
5 V:Bludhound 2.00
6 I:Bim Simms 2.00
7 A:Losers 2.00
8 A:Losers 2.25
9 V:Lobo 2.25
10 Preacher 2.00
11 Goldstar vs. Rev.Bo 2.00
12 . . . . 2.00
13 . . . . 2.00
14 Lobo, P.I. 2.00
15 Lobo, P.I.,pt.2 . . . . 2.00
16 Lobo, P.I.,pt.3 . . . . 2.00
17 Lobo, P.I.,pt.4 . . . . 2.25
18 Lobo, P.I.,pt.5 . . . . 2.25
19 . . . . 2.25
20 Toilot Fight 2.25
21 AIG,KON,R:Space Cabby 2.25
22 AIG,UnderworldUnleashed tie-in 2.25
23 AIG,Stargaze Rally,pt.1 . . . . . 2.25
24 AIG,Stargaze Rally,pt.2 . . . . . 2.25
25 AIG 2.25
26 AIG,V:Erik the Khund 2.25
27 AIG,V:Billy Krono 2.25
28 AIG,A:Great Big Fat Bastiches 2.25
29 . . . . 2.25
30 . . . . 2.25
31 . . . . 2.25
32 AIG(s),Lobo attends a seance,
   frags himself 2.25

33 AIG(s),Lobo returns from spirit
   world 2.25
34 AIG(s),vs. Japan, whaling, . . . 2.25
35 AIG(s) "Deathtrek" 2.25
36 . . . . 2.25
37 AIG(s),BKi,Lobo's Guide to Girls 2.25
38 AIG(s),Bomandi The Last Boy
   on Earth 2.25
39 AIG(s),"In the Belly of the
   Behemoth,"pt. 1 . . . . 2.25
40 AIG(s),"In the Belly of the
   Behemoth,"pt. 2 . . . . 2.25
41 AIG(s),roommates 2.25
42 AIG(s),A:Perfidia 2.25
43 AIG(s),A:Jonas 2.25
44 AIG(s),Genesis tie-in 2.25
45 AIG(s),battle royale 2.25
46 AIG(s),Jackie Chin 2.25
47 AIG(s),V:Kiljoy Riggs 2.25
48 AIG(s),F:the penguins 2.25
49 AIG(s) 2.25
50 AIG(s),war on DC universe . . 2.25
51 AIG(s),Slater and Candy 2.25
52 AIG(s),Goldstar funeral 2.25
53 AIG(s),disrupted ceremony . . 2.50
54 AIG(s),Good Vibes machine . . 2.50
55 AIG(s),Sheepworld 2.50
56 AIG(s),MPn,GLz,the wedding . 2.50
Ann.#1 Bloodlines 4.00
Ann.#2 Elseworlds Story 3.50
Ann.#3 AIG Year One 4.95
GN Fragtastic Voyage AGr,
   miniaturized 6.00
Spec.#1 Lobo's Big Babe Spring Break,
   Miss Voluptuous Contest 2.00
Spec.#1 Blazing Chains of Love . 2.00
Spec.#1 Bounty Hunting for Fun
   and Profit, F:Fanboy 4.95
one-shot Lobo: Chained AIG(s),
   Lobo in prison 2.00
Convention Special, comic con . . 2.00

LOBO: A CONTRACT ON GAWD
1994
1 AIG(s),KD 2.00
2 AIG(s),KD,A:Dave 2.00
3 AIG(s),KD 1.75
4 AIG(s),KD,Final Issue 1.75

LOBO'S BACK
1992
1 SBs,w/3(c) inside,V:Loo 3.50
1a 2nd printing 1.50
2 SBs,Lobo becomes a woman . 3.00
3 SBs,V:Heaven 2.50
4 SBs,V:Heaven 2.50
TPB GF(c),rep.#1-#4 . . . . 9.95

LOBO: DEATH & TAXES
Aug. 1996
[Mini-series]
1 (of 4) KG&AIG(s) 2.25
2 KG&AIG(s),Interstellar Revenue
   learns Lobo doesn't pay taxes . 2.25
3 KG&AIG(s),Lobo walks into
   IRS trap 2.25
4 KG&AIG(s),Lobo destroys IRS . 2.25

LOBO/DEMON: HELLOWE'EN
1 AIG(s),VGi,perils of helping
   a dragon destroy earth 2.25

LOBO: INFANTICIDE
1992–93
1 KG,V:Su,Lobo Bastards 2.00
2 Lobo at Boot Camp 1.75
3 KG,Lobo Vs.his offspring 1.75
4 KG,V:Lobo Bastards 1.75

LOBO IN THE CHAIR
1 AIG(s) 2.25

LOBO/MASK
1 AIG&JAr(s),DoM,Kwi, humorous
   x-over 5.95
2 AIG&JAr(s),DoM,Kwi, concl. . . . 5.95

LOBO: I QUIT
1 AIG,nicotine withdrawal 2.25

LOBO/JUDGE DREDD: PSYCHO BIKERS VS. MUTANTS FROM HELL
1-shot 4.95

LOBO: PORTRAIT OF A VICTIM
1 VS,I:John Doe 2.00

LOBO: UNAMERICAN GLADIATORS
1993
1 CK,V:Satan's Brothers 2.00
2 CK,V:Jonny Caesar 2.00
3 CK,MMi(c),V:Satan Brothers . . 2.00
4 CK,MMi(c),V:Jonny Caeser . . . 2.00

LOBOCOP
1 StG(s) 2.25

LOIS AND CLARK: THE NEW ADVENTURES OF SUPERMAN
TPB 9.95
TPB stories that became episodes 10.00

LOIS LANE
Aug., 1986
1 and 2 GM . . . . @1.50

LONG HOT SUMMER, THE
Milestone 1995
[Mini-Series]
1 Blood Syndicate v. G.R.I.N.D. . 2.95
2 A:Icon,Xombi,Hardware 2.50

LOONEY TUNES MAG.
1 thru 6 . . . . @2.00

LOONEY TUNES
1994
1 thru 6 Warner Bros. cartoons @1.75
7 thru 11 Warner Bros. . . . . . . @1.75
12 The Cotton Tail Club 1.50
13 F:Tasmanian Devil 1.50
14 Football Season 1.50
15 Jewel Thief 1.50
16 F:Yosemite Sam,Speedy
   Gonzales 1.50
17 F:Sylvester 1.50
18 . . . . 1.50

Looney Tunes #17 © DC Comics, Inc.

19 Ben Hur Spoof 1.50
20 F:Sylvester 1.50
21 thru 23 . . . . @1.50
24 thru 32 . . . . @1.75
33 F:Tasmanian Devil 2.00
34 F:Daffy 2.00
35 F:Daffy DangerDuck 2.00
36 F:Tweety 2.00
37 F:Crusher, Bugs 2.00
38 . . . . 2.00
39 F:Miss Prissy, Foghorn 2.00
40 F:Sylvester and Tweety 2.00
41 F:Porky, Sylvester 2.00
42 F:Sylvester,Pepe 2.00
43 F:Bugs, Sylvester 2.00
44 Frankentweety 2.00
45 Bad Hare Day 2.00

LOOSE CANNON
[Mini-Series] 1995
1 AdP,V:Bounty Hunters 1.75
2 V:Bounty Hunters & The
   Eradicator 1.75
3 A:Eradicator 1.75

LORDS OF THE ULTRAREALM
1986
1 PB 3.50
2 PB 2.00
3 thru 6 PB . . . . @1.50
Spec.#1 PB,DG,Oneshot 2.25

LOSERS SPECIAL
1985
1 Crisis,D:Losers 1.25

MADAME XANADU
1981
1 MR/BB 2.00

MAJOR BUMMER
June 1997
1 JAr(s),DoM,I:Major Bummer . . . 2.50
2 JAr(s),DoM,Major Bummer gets
   new costume 2.50

3 JAr(s),DoM,bad guys arrive . . . 2.50
4 JAr(s),DoM,alien germs 2.50
5 JAr(s),DoM,dinosaurs, Nazis . . 2.50
6 JAr(s),DoM,Mutant bully 2.50
7 JAr(s),DoM 2.50
8 . . . . 2.50
9 JAr(s),DoM,epic fight 2.50
10 JAr(s),DoM,Nunzio dead? 2.50
11 JAr(s),DoM,everyone dies? . . . 2.50
12 JAr(s),DoM,Lou Martin dead . . 2.50
13 JAr(s),DoM,Lauren 2.50
14 JAr(s),DoM,tells the future off . 2.50
15 JAr(s),DoM, final issue 2.50

MAN-BAT
1975–76
1 SD,AM,A:Batman 20.00
2 V:The Ten-Eyed Man 15.00
Reprint NA(c) 10.00

MAN-BAT
1996
1 CDi,terrorizes city 2.25
2 . . . . 2.25
3 CDi,V:Steeljacket, finale 2.25

MAN-BAT vs. BATMAN
1 NA,DG,reprint 4.00

A MAN CALLED A•X
Aug. 1997
1 MWn(s),SwM, part rep. 2.50
2 MWn(s),SwM 2.50
3 MWn(s),SwM, vs. DC universe 2.50
4 MWn(s),SwM,killer cyborg 2.50
5 MWn(s),SwM,R-Mor 2.50
6 MWn(s),SwM, ... 2.50
7 MWn(s),SwM,battle in Bedlam . 2.50
8 MWn(s),SwM,final issue 2.50

MANHUNTER
1988–90
1 from Millenium-Suicide Squad . 1.50
2 in Tokyo,A:Dumas 1.25
3 The Yakuza,V:Dumas 1.25
4 Secrets Revealed-Manhunter,
   Dumas & Olivia 1.25
5 A:Silvia Kandery 1.25
6 A:Argent,contd.Suicide Squad
   Annual #1 . . . . 1.25
7 Vlatavia, V:Count Vertigo 1.25
8 FS,A:Flash,Invasion x-over . . . 1.25
9 FS,Invasion Aftermath extra
   (contd from Flash #22) 1.25
10 Salvage,pt.1 . . . . 1.25
11 Salvage,pt.2 . . . . 1.25
12 . . . . 1.25
13 V:Catman 1.25
14 Janus Directive #5 . . . . 1.25
15 I:Mirage 1.25
16 V:Outlaw 1.25
17 In Gotham,A:Batman 1.50
18 Saints & Sinners,pt.1,R:Dumas 1.25
19 Saints & Sinners,pt.2,V:Dumas 1.25
20 Saints & Sinners,pt.3,V:Dumas 1.25
21 Saints & Sinners,pt.4,
   A:Manhunter Grandmaster . . 1.25
22 Saints & Sinners,pt.5,
   A:Manhunter Grandmaster . . . 1.25
23 Saints & Sinners,pt.6,V:Dumas 1.25
24 DG,Showdown, final issue . . . 1.25
[2nd Series] 1994–95
0 . . . . 2.00

---

1 . . . . 2.00
2 N:Wild Huntsman 2.00
3 V:Malig 2.00
4 Necrodyne 2.00
5 V:Skin Walker 2.00
6 V:Barbarian,Incarnate 2.00
7 V:Incarnate,A:White Lotus
   & Capt. Atom 2.25
8 V:Butcher Boys 2.25
9 V:Butcher Boys 2.25
10 V:Necrodyne 2.25
11 Return of Old Enemy 2.25
12 Underworld Unleashed, finale . 2.25

Man of Steel #6 © DC Comics, Inc.

MAN OF STEEL
1986
1 JBy,DG,I:Modern Superman . . 5.00
1a 2nd edition 3.00
2 JBy,DG,R:Lois Lane 3.50
3 JBy,DG,A:Batman 3.00
4 JBy,DG,V:Lex Luther 3.00
5 JBy,DG,I:Modern Bizarro 3.00
6 JBy,DG,A:Lana Lang 3.00
TPB rep. Man of Steel #1–#6 . . 12.95
TPBa 2nd printing 7.95

MANY LOVES OF
DOBIE GILLIS
May-June, 1960
1 . . . . 150.00
2 . . . . 75.00
3 . . . . 65.00
4 . . . . 65.00
5 thru 9 . . . . @40.00
10 thru 25 . . . . @28.00
26 Oct., 1964 . . . . 28.00

MARTIAN MANHUNTER
1988
1 A:JLI 1.75
2 A:JLI,V:Death God 1.50
3 V:Death God,A:Dr.Erdel 1.50
4 A:JLI,final issue 1.50
[Mini-Series]
1 EB,American Secrets #1 . . . . . 5.25
2 EB,American Secrets #2 . . . . . 4.95
3 EB,American Secrets #3 . . . . . 4.95

MARTIAN MANHUNTER
Aug. 1998
0 JOs,TMd,A:Batman,Superman . 2.00
Ann. #1 TT,AOl,BWr,Ghosts x-over 3.00

MASK
Dec., 1985
1 HC(c),TV tie-in,I:Mask Team . . 2.00
2 HC(c),In Egypt,V:Venom 1.75
3 HC(c),'Anarchy in the U.K.' . . . 1.75
4 HC(c),V:Venom, final issue,
   March, 1986 . . . . 1.00
[2nd Series] Feb., 1987
1 CS/KS,reg.series 1.25
2 CS/KS,V:Venom 1.00
3 CS/KS,V:Venom 1.00
4 CS/KS,V:Venom 1.00
5 CS/KS,Mask operatives hostage 1.00
6 CS/KS,I:Jacana 1.00
7 CS/KS,Mask gone bad? 1.00
8 CS/KS,Matt Trakker,V:Venom . 1.00
9 CS/KS,V:Venom, last issue,
   Oct., 1987 . . . . 1.00

MASTERS OF
THE UNIVERSE
May, 1986
1 GT,AA,O:He-Man 1.50
2 GT,AA,V:Skeletor 1.25
3 GT,V:Skeletor 1.25

MASTERWORKS SERIES
OF GREAT
COMIC BOOK ARTISTS
May, 1983
1 . . . . 2.50
2 . . . . 2.50
3 Dec., 1983 . . . . 2.50

'MAZING MAN
Jan., 1986
1 I:Maze 1.00
2 . . . . 1.00
3 . . . . 1.00
4 . . . . 1.00
5 . . . . 1.00
6 Shea Stadium 1.00
7 Shea Stadium 1.00
8 Cat-Sitting 1.00
9 Bank Hold-up 1.00
10 . . . . 1.00
11 Jones Beach 1.00
12 FM(c),last issue, Dec., 1986 . 1.00
Spec.#1 . . . . 2.25
Spec.#2 . . . . 2.25
Spec.#3 KB/TM 2.25

MEN OF WAR
Aug., 1977
1 I:Gravedigger,Code Name:
   Gravedigger,I:Enemy Ace . . . 1.50
2 JKu(c),The Five-Walled War . . 1.25
3 JKu(c),The Suicide Strategem . 1.25
4 JKu(c),Trail by Fire 1.25
5 JKu(c),Valley of the Shadow . . 1.25
6 JKu(c),A Choice of Deaths . . . 1.25
7 JKu(c),Milkrun 1.25
8 JKu(c),Death-Stroke 1.25
9 JKu(c),Gravedigger-R.I.P. 1.25
10 JKu(c),Crossroads 1.25
11 JKu(c),Berkstaten 1.25
12 JKu(c),Where Is Gravedigger? 1.25

---

13 JKu(c),Project Gravedigger -
   Plus One 1.25
14 JKu(c),The Swirling
   Sands of Death 1.25
15 JKu(c),The Man With the
   Opened Eye 1.25
16 JKu(c),Hide and Seek The Spy 1.25
17 JKu(c),The River of Death . . . 1.25
18 JKu(c),The Amiens Assault . . . 1.25
19 JKu(c),An Angel Named Marie 1.25
20 JKu(c),Cry:Jerico 1.25
21 JKu(c),Home-Is Where
   The Hell Is 1.25
22 JKu(c),Blackout On
   The Boardwalk 1.25
23 JKu(c),Mission: Six Feet Under 1.25
24 JKu&DG(c),The Presidential
   Peril 1.25
25 GE(c),Save the President 1.25
26 March, 1980 . . . . 1.25

MENZ INSANA
DC/Vertigo
GN 7.95

MERCY
Vertigo
Graphic Novel I:Mercy 8.00

METAL MEN
1965–78
[1st Regular Series]
1 RA,I:Missile Men 450.00
2 RA,Robot of Terror 185.00
3 RA,Moon's Invisible Army . . 100.00
4 RA,Bracelet of Doomed Hero 100.00
5 RA,Menace of the Mammoth
   Robots 100.00
6 RA,I:Gas Gang 85.00
7 RA,V:Solar Brain 55.00
8 RA,Playground of Terror 55.00
9 RA,A:Billy 55.00
10 RA,A:Gas Gang 55.00
11 RA,The Floating Furies 50.00
12 RA,A:Missle Men 40.00
13 RA,I:Nameless 40.00
14 RA,A:Chemo 40.00
15 RA,V:B.O.L.T.S. 40.00
16 RA,Robots for Sale 40.00
17 RA(c),RA,V:Bl.Widow Robot 40.00
18 JKu(c),RA 40.00
19 RA,V:Man-Horse of Hades . . 40.00
20 RA,V:Dr.Yes 40.00
21 RA,C:Batman & Robin,Flash
   Wonder Woman 25.00
22 RA,A:Chemo 25.00
23 RA,A:Sizzler 25.00
24 RA,V:Balloonman 25.00
25 RA,V:Chemo 25.00
26 RA,V:Metal Mods 25.00
27 RA,O:Metal Men,rtd 50.00
28 RA 25.00
29 RA,V:Robot Eater 25.00
30 RA,GK,in the Forbidden Zone 25.00
31 RA,GK 23.00
32 RA,Robot Amazon Blues . . . 18.00
33 MS,The Hunted Metal Men . . 18.00
34 MS 18.00
35 MS 18.00
36 MS,The Cruel Clowns 18.00
37 MS,To walk among Men 18.00
38 MS 18.00
39 MS,Beauty of the Beast 18.00
40 MS 18.00

Metal Men #42 © DC Comics, Inc.

41 MS 18.00
42 RA,reprint 10.00
43 RA,reprint 10.00
44 RA,reprint,V:Missile Men 10.00
45 WS 10.00
46 WS,V:Chemo 10.00
47 WS,V:Plutonium Man 10.00
48 WS,A:Eclipso 15.00
49 WS,A:Eclipso 15.00
50 WS,JSa 10.00
51 JSn,V:Vox 10.00
52 JSn,V:Brain Children 10.00
53 JA(c),V:Brain Children 10.00
54 JSn,A:Green Lantern 10.00
55 JSn,A:Green Lantern 10.00
56 JSn,V:Inheritor 10.00

[Limited Series] 1993–94
1 DJu,BBr,Foil(c) 5.00
2 DJu,BBr,O:Metal Men 3.00
3 DJu,BBr,V:Missile Men 3.00
4 DJu,BBr,final issue 3.00

METAMORPHO
July-Aug., 1965
[Regular Series]
1 A:Kurt Vornok 100.00
2 Terror from the Telstar 60.00
3 Who stole the USA 60.00
4 V:Cha-Cha Chaves 40.00
5 V:Bulark 40.00
6 . . . . 40.00
7 thru 9 . . . . @35.00
10 I:Element Girl 45.00
11 thru 17 March-April, 1968 . @20.00
[Limited Series]
1 GN,V:The Orb of Ra 1.75
2 GN,A:Metamorpho's Son 1.75
3 GN,V:Elemental Man 1.75
4 GN,final Issue 1.75

METROPOLIS S.C.U.
Nov. 1994
1 Special Police unit 1.50
2 Eco-terror in Metropolis 1.50
3 Superman 1.50
4 final issue 1.50

MICHAEL MOORCOCK'S MULTIVERSE
DC/Helix (Sept., 1997)
1 WS,three stories, inc. Eternal
   Champion adapt. 2.50
2 WS,Eternal Champion 2.50
3 WS,Moonbeams & Roses . . . 2.50
4 WS,Moonbeams & Roses . . . 2.50
5 . . . . 2.50
6 Duke Elric 2.50
7 Metatemporal Detective 2.50
8 Castle Silverskin 2.50
9 Duke Elric 2.50
10 Eternal Champion 2.50
11 WS, Silverskin 2.50
12 WS, concl. 2.50

MILLENIUM
Jan., 1988
1 JSa,SEt, The Plan 1.75
2 JSa,SEt, The Chosen 1.75
3 JSa,SEt, Reagen/Manhunters . 1.75
4 JSa,SEt, Mark Shaw/Batman . . 1.75
5 JSa,SEt, The CHosen 1.75
6 JSa,SEt, Superman 1.75
7 JSa,SEt, Boster Gold 1.75
8 JSa,SEt,I:New Guardians 1.75

MILLENNIUM FEVER
1995–96
1 Young Love 2.50
2 Nightmares Worsen 2.50
3 Worst Nightmare 2.50
4 . . . . 2.50

MINX, THE
DC/Vertigo (Aug., 1998)
1 PrM,SeP,The Chosen, pt.1 . . . 2.50

MISTER E
1991
1 (From Books of Magic) 1.75
2 A:The Shadower 1.75
3 A:The Shadower 1.75
4 A:Tim Hunter, Dr. Fate, Phantom
   Stranger, final issue 1.75

MISTER MIRACLE
1971–78
1 JK,I:Mr.Miracle 30.00
2 JK,I:Granny Goodness 15.00
3 JK,'Paraniod Pill' 11.00
4 JK,I:Barda 10.00
5 JK,I:Vermin Vundabar 10.00
6 JK,I:Female Furies 10.00
7 JK,V:Kanto 10.00
8 JK,V:Lump 10.00
9 JK,O:Mr.Miracle,C:Darkseid . . . 8.00
10 JK,A:Female Furies 8.00
11 JK,V:Doctor Bedlum 6.00
12 JK 6.00
13 JK 6.00
14 JK 6.00
15 JK,O:Shilo Norman 6.00
16 JK 6.00
17 JK 6.00
18 JK,W:Mr.Miracle & Barda . . . 6.00
19 MR,NA,DG,TA,JRu,AM 6.00
20 MR 4.00
21 MR 4.00
22 MR 4.00
23 MG 4.00
24 MG,RH 4.00

Mister Miracle #18
© *DC Comics, Inc.*

25 MG,RH 4.00
Spec.#1 SR 2.50

[2nd Series] 1989–91

1 IG 2.00
2 IG 1.50
3 IG,A:Highfather,Forever People 1.50
4 IG,A:The Dark,Forever People . 1.50
5 IG,V:TheDark,A:ForeverPeople 1.50
6 A:G.L. Gnort 1.25
7 A:Blue Beetle,Booster Gold . . 1.25
8 RM,A:Blue Beetle,Booster Gold 1.25
9 I:Maxi-Man 1.25
10 V:Maxi-Man 1.25
11 . . . . 1.25
12 . . . . 1.25
13 Manga Khan Saga begins,
   A:L-Ron,A:Lobo 2.50
14 A:Lobo 2.00
15 Manga Khan contd 1.25
16 MangaKhan cont.,JLA#39tie-in 1.25
17 On Apokolips,A:Darkseid 1.25
18 On Apokolips 1.25
19 Return to Earth, contd
   from JLA#42 . . . . 1.25
20 IG,Oberon 1.25
21 Return of Shilo 1.25
22 New Mr.Miracle revealed 1.25
23 Secrets of the 2 Mr. Miracles
   revealed, A:Mother Box 1.25
24 . . . . 1.25
25 . . . . 1.25
26 Monster Party,pt.1 . . . . 1.25
27 Monster Party,pt.2,
   A:Justice League 1.25
28 final issue 1.25

MISTER MIRACLE
1996

1 JK, new mythology 2.00
2 V:Justice League 2.00
2 How can Scott Free save
   Big Barda 2.00
3 accepts his powers 2.00
4 corruption throughout
   the cosmos 2.00
5 SCr 2.00

6 SCr 2.00
7 final issue 2.00

MR. DISTRICT ATTORNEY
Jan.–Feb., 1948

1 The Innocent Forger 800.00
2 The Richest Man In Prison . 350.00
3 The Honest Convicts 250.00
4 The Merchant of Death 250.00
5 The Booby-Trap Killer 250.00
6 The D.A. Meets Scotland Yard 200.00
7 The People vs. Killer Kane . 200.00
8 The Rise and Fall of 'Lucky'
   Lynn 200.00
9 The Case of the Living
   Counterfeit 200.00
10 The D.A. Takes a Vacation . 150.00
11 The Game That Has
   No Winners 150.00
12 Fake Accident Racket 150.00
13 The Execution of Caesar
   Larsen 150.00
14 The Innocent Man In
   Murderers' Row 150.00
15 Prison Train 150.00
16 The Wire Tap Crimes 150.00
17 The Bachelor of Crime 150.00
18 The Case of the Twelve
   O'Clock Killer 150.00
19 The Four King's Of Crime . . 150.00
20 You Catch a Killer 150.00
21 I Was A Killer's Bodyguard . 100.00
22 The Marksman of Crime . . . 100.00
23 Diary of a Criminal 100.00
24 The Killer In The Iron Mask . 100.00
25 I Hired My Killer 100.00
26 The Case of the Wanted
   Criminals 100.00
27 The Case of the Secret Six . 100.00
28 Beware the Bogus Beggars . 100.00
29 The Crimes of Mr. Jumbo . . 100.00
30 Man of a Thousand Faces . . 100.00
31 The Hot Money Gang 100.00
32 The Case o/t Bad Luck Clues 100.00
33 A Crime Is Born 100.00
34 The Amazing Crimes of Mr. X 100.00
35 This Crime For Hire 100.00
36 The Chameleon of Crime . . 100.00
37 Miss Miller's Big Case 100.00
38 The Puzzle Shop For Crime 100.00
39 Man Who Killed Daredevils . 100.00
40 The Human Vultures 100.00
41 The Great Token Take 100.00
42 Super-Market Sleuth 100.00
43 Hotel Detective 100.00
44 S.S. Justice,B:Comics Code . 75.00
45 Miss Miller, Widow 75.00
46 Mr. District Attorney,
   Public Defender 75.00
47 The Missing Persons Racket . 75.00
48 Manhunt With the Mounties . 75.00
49 The TV Dragnet 75.00
50 The Case of Frank Bragan,
   Little Shot 75.00
51 The Big Heist 75.00
52 Crooked Wheels of Fortune . 75.00
53 The Courtroom Patrol 75.00
54 The Underworld Spy Squad . 75.00
55 The Flying Saucer Mystery . . 75.00
56 The Underworld Oracle 75.00
57 The Underworld Employment
   Agency 75.00
58 The Great Bomb Scare 75.00
59 Great Underworld Spy Plot . . 75.00

60 The D.A.'s TV Rival 75.00
61 SMo(c),Architect of Crime . . . 75.00
62 A-Bombs For Sale 75.00
63 The Flying Prison 75.00
64 SMo(c),The Underworld
   Treasure Hunt 75.00
65 SMo(c),World Wide Dragnet . 75.00
66 SMo(c),The Secret of the
   D.A.'s Diary 75.00
67 Jan.–Feb., 1959 . . . . 75.00

MR. PUNCH
HC DMc,NGa,Nightmarish
   tale, 1994 . . . . 24.95

MOBFIRE
1994–95

1 WaP,Gangsters in London 2.50
2 WaP, ... 2.50
3 WaP,The Bocor 2.50
4 WaP,V:Bocor 2.50
5 WaP,Voice in My Head 2.50
6 WaP,Genetic Babies, final issue 2.50

MODESTY BLAISE
1 DG,V:Gabriel 4.95
2 DG,V:Gabriel 4.95
GN Spy Thriller 19.95

MOONSHADOW
Vertigo 1994–95

1 JMD(s),JMu,rep. 2.25
2 thru 4 JMD . . . . @2.25
5 fully painted 2.25
6 . . . . 2.25
7 F:Shady Lady 2.25
8 Rep. Search for Ira 2.25
9 JMD,JMu,A:Tittletat Twins . . . 2.25
10 JMD,JMu,Interplanetary
   Prostitutes 2.25
11 JMu,Ira's life story 2.25
12 Rep. w/6pg new material . . . 2.95

MORE FUN COMICS
(See: NEW FUN COMICS)

MOVIE COMICS
April, 1939

1 'Gunga Din' 2,700.00
2 Stagecoach 1,800.00
3 East Side of Heaven 1,400.00
4 Captain Fury,B:Oregon Trail 1,100.00
5 Man in the Iron Mask 1,100.00
6 Sept., 1939 . . . . 1,400.00

MS. TREE QUARTERLY
1 MGr,A:Batman 3.50
2 A:Butcher 2.95
3 A:Butcher 2.95
4 'Paper Midnight' 3.95
5 Murder/Rape Investigation . . . 3.95
6 Gothic House 3.95
7 . . . . 3.95
8 CI,FMc,Ms Tree Pregnant(c),
   B.U. King Faraday 3.95
9 Child Kidnapped 3.95
10 V:International Mob 3.50

MUKTUK WOLFSBREATH: HARD-BOILED SHAMAN
DC/Vertigo (June 1998)

1 (of 3) TLa,SvP,lady shaman . . 2.50

2 . . . . 2.50
3 TLa,SvP, concl. 2.50

MUTT AND JEFF
1939
1 . . . . 1,200.00
2 . . . . 650.00
3 . . . . 500.00
4 and 5 . . . . @450.00
6 thru 10 . . . . @200.00
11 thru 20 . . . . @125.00
21 thru 30 . . . . @85.00
31 thru 50 . . . . @60.00
51 thru 70 . . . . @40.00
71 thru 80 . . . . @35.00
81 thru 99 . . . . @30.00
100 . . . . 35.00
101 thru 103 . . . . @30.00
104 thru 148 . . . . @20.00

MY GREATEST ADVENTURE
Jan.–Feb., 1955
1 LSt,I Was King Of
　Danger Island 1,300.00
2 My Million Dollar Dive 600.00
3 I Found Captain
　Kidd's Treasure 375.00
4 I Had A Date With Doom . . . 375.00
5 I Escaped From Castle Morte 350.00
6 I Had To Spend A Million . . 350.00
7 I Was A Prisoner On Island X 325.00
8 The Day They Stole My Face 325.00
9 I Walked Through The Doors
　of Destiny 325.00
10 We Found A World Of
　Tiny Cavemen 325.00
11 LSt(c),My Friend, Madcap
　Manning 250.00
12 MMe(c),I Hunted Big Game
　in Outer Space 250.00
13 LSt(c),I Hunted Goliath
　The Robot 250.00
14 LSt,I Had the Midas
　Touch of Gold 250.00
15 JK, I Hunted the Worlds
　Wildest Animals 250.00
16 JK,I Died a Thousand Times 250.00
17 JK,I Doomed the World . . . 250.00
18 JK(c),We Discovered The
　Edge of the World 250.00
19 I Caught Earth's
　Strangest Criminal 250.00
20 JK,I Was Big-Game
　on Neptune 250.00
21 JK,We Were Doomed By
　The Metal-Eating Monster . . 250.00
22 I Was Trapped In The
　Magic Mountains 200.00
23 I Was A Captive In
　Space Prison 200.00
24 NC(c),I Was The Robinson
　Crusoe of Space 200.00
25 I Led Earth's Strangest
　Safari! 200.00
26 NC(c),We Battled The
　Sand Creature 200.00
27 I Was the Earth's First Exile 200.00
28 I Stalked the Camouflage
　Creatures 250.00
29 I Tracked the
　Forbidden Powers 150.00
30 We Cruised Into the
　Supernatural! 150.00

31 I Was A Modern Hercules . . 100.00
32 We Were Trapped In A Freak
　Valley! 100.00
33 I Was Pursued by
　the Elements 100.00
34 DD,We Unleashed The Cloud
　Creatures 100.00
35 I Solved the Mystery of
　Volcano Valley 100.00
36 I Was Bewitched
　By Lady Doom 100.00
37 DD&SMo(c),I Hunted the
　Legendary Creatures! 100.00
38 DD&SMo(c),I Was the Slave
　of the Dream-Master 100.00
39 DD&SMo(c),We were Trapped
　in the Valley of no Return . . 100.00
40 WeBattled the StormCreature 100.00
41 DD&SMo(c),I Was Tried
　by a Robot Court 75.00
42 DD&SMo(c),My Brother
　Was a Robot 75.00
43 DD&SMo(c),I Fought the
　Sonar Creatures 75.00

My Greatest Adventure #3
© DC Comics, Inc.

44 DD&SMo(c),We Fought the
　Beasts of Petrified Island . . . 75.00
45 DD&SMo(c),We Battled the
　Black Narwahl 75.00
46 DD&SMo(c),We Were Prisoners
　of the Sundial of Doom 75.00
47 We Became Partners of the
　Beast Brigade 75.00
48 DD&SMo(c),I Was Marooned
　On Earth 75.00
49 DD&SMo(c),I Was An Ally
　Of A Criminal Creature 75.00
50 DD&SMo(c),I Fought the
　Idol King 75.00
51 DD&SMo(c),We Unleashed
　the Demon of the Dungeon . . 70.00
52 DD&SMo(c),I Was A
　Stand-In For an Alien 70.00
53 DD&SMo(c),I, Creature Slayer 70.00
54 I Was Cursed With
　an Alien Pal 70.00
55 DD&SMo(c),I Beacame The
　Wonder-Man of Space 70.00

56 DD&SMo(c),My Brother-The
　Alien 70.00
57 DD&SMo(c),Don't Touch Me
　Or You'll Die 70.00
58 DD&SMo(c),ATh,I was Trapped
　in the Land of L'Oz 75.00
59 DD&SMo(c),Listen Earth-I
　Am Still Alive 75.00
60 DD&SMo(c),ATh,I Lived in
　Two Worlds 75.00
61 DD&SMo(c),ATh,I Battled For
　the Doom-Stone 75.00
62 DD&SMo(c),I Fought For
　An Alien Enemy 50.00
63 DD&SMo(c),We Braved the
　Trail of the Ancient Warrior . . 50.00
64 DD&SMo(c),They Crowned My
　Fiance Their King! 50.00
65 DD&SMo(c),I Lost the Life
　or Death Secret 50.00
66 DD&SMo(c),I Dueled with
　the Super Spirits 50.00
67 I Protected the Idols
　of Idoro! 50.00
68 DD&SMo(c),My Deadly Island
　of Space 50.00
69 DD&SMo(c),I Was A Courier
　From the Past 50.00
70 DD&SMo(c),We Tracked the
　Fabled Fish-Man! 50.00
71 We Dared to open the Door
　of Danger Dungeon 50.00
72 The Haunted Beach 50.00
73 I Defeiller Mountain 50.00
74 GC(c),We Were Challenged
　By The River Spirit 50.00
75 GC(c),Castaway Cave-Men
　of 1950 . . . . 50.00
76 MMe(c),We Battled the
　Micro-Monster 50.00
77 ATh,We Found the Super-
　Tribes of Tomorrow 55.00
78 Destination-'Dead Man's Alley' 50.00
79 Countdown in Dinosaur Valley 50.00
80 BP,I:Doom Patrol 400.00
81 BP,ATh,I:Dr. Janus 160.00
82 BP,F:Doom Patrol 150.00
83 BP,F:Doom Patrol 150.00
84 BP,V:General Immortus . . . 150.00
85 BP,ATh,F:Doom Patrol 150.00

Becomes:

DOOM PATROL
March, 1964
86 BP,I:Brogherhood of Evil . . . 100.00
87 BP,O:Negative Man 80.00
88 BP,O:Chief 75.00
89 BP,I:Animal-Veg.-MineralMan 75.00
90 BP,A:Brotherhood of Evil . . . 75.00
91 BP,I:Manto, Gargvax 75.00
92 BP,I:Dr.Tyme, A:Mento 75.00
93 BP,A:Brotherhood of Evil . . . 75.00
94 BP,I:Dr.Radich, The Claw . . . 75.00
95 BP,A:Animal-Vegetable
　-Mineral Man 75.00
96 BP,A:General Immortus,
　Brotherhood of Evil 70.00
97 BP,A:General Immortus,
　Brotherhood of Evil 70.00
98 BP,I:Mr.103 . . . . 70.00
99 I:Beast Boy 80.00
100 BP,O:Beast Boy,Robotman 100.00
101 BP,A:Beast Boy 50.00
102 BP,A:Beast Boy,Challengers
　of the Unknown 45.00
103 BP,A:Beast Boy 45.00

DC COMICS

104 BP,W:Elasti-Girl,Mento,
 C:JLA,Teen Titans 45.00
105 BP,A:Beast Boy 45.00
106 BP,O:Negative Man 45.00
107 BP,A:Beast Boy, I:Dr.Death . 45.00
108 BP,A:Brotherhood of Evil .. 45.00
109 BP,I:Mandred 45.00
110 BP,A:Garguax,Mandred,
 Brotherhood of Evil 40.00
111 BP,I:Zarox-13,A:Brotherhood
 of Evil 40.00
112 BP,O:Beast Boy,Madame
 Rouge 40.00
113 BP,A:Beast Boy,Mento 40.00
114 BP,A:Beast Boy 40.00
115 BP,A:Beast Boy 40.00
116 BP,A:Madame Rouge 40.00
117 BP,I:Black Vulture 40.00
118 BP,A:Beast Boy 40.00
119 BP,A:Madam Rouge 40.00
120 I:Wrecker 40.00
121 JO,D:Doom Patrol 100.00
122 rep.Doom Patrol #89 ..... 5.00
123 rep.Doom Patrol #95 ..... 5.00
124 rep.Doom Patrol #90 ..... 5.00
 [2nd Series]
See: DOOM PATROL

MY NAME IS CHAOS
1992
1 JRy,Song Laid Waste to Earth . 4.95
2 JRy,Colonization of Mars ... 4.95
3 JRy,Search for Eternal Beings . 4.95
4 JRy,final issue 4.95

MY NAME IS HOLOCAUST
Milestone 1995
[Mini-Series]
1 F:Holocaust (Blood Syndicate) . 1.75
2 V:Cantano 1.75
3 A:Blood Syndicate 1.75

MYSTERY IN SPACE
April-May, 1951
1 CI&FrG(c),FF,B:Knights of the
 Galaxy,Nine Worlds to
 Conquer 2,800.00
2 CI(c),MA,A:Knights of the
 Galaxy, Jesse James-
 Highwayman of Space ... 1,100.00
3 CI(c),A:Knights of the
 Galaxy, Duel of the Planets . 850.00
4 CI(c),S&K,MA,A:Knights of the
 Galaxy, Master of Doom ... 750.00
5 CI(c),A:Knights of the Galaxy,
 Outcast of the Lost World .. 750.00
6 CI(c),A:Knights of the Galaxy,
 The Day the World Melted . 550.00
7 GK(c),ATh,A:Knights of the Galaxy,
 Challenge o/t Robot Knight . 550.00
8 MA,It's a Women's World .. 550.00
9 MA(c),The Seven Wonders
 of Space 550.00
10 MA(c),The Last Time I
 Saw Earth 550.00
11 GK(c),Unknown Spaceman . 400.00
12 MA,The Sword in the Sky .. 400.00
13 MA(c),MD,Signboard
 in Space 400.00
14 MA,GK(c),Hollywood
 in Space 400.00
15 MA(c),Doom from Station X 400.00
16 MA(c),Honeymoon in Space 400.00
17 MA(c),The Last Mile of Space 400.00

18 MA(c),GK,Chain Gang
 of Space 400.00
19 MA(c),The Great
 Space-Train Robbery 375.00
20 MA(c),The Man in the
 Martian Mask 350.00
21 MA(c),Interplanetary
 Merry- Go-Round 350.00
22 MA(c),The Square Earth ... 350.00
23 MA(c),Monkey-Rocket
 to Mars 350.00
24 MA(c),A:Space Cabby,
 Hitchhiker of Space 350.00
25 MA(c),Station Mars on the Air 325.00
26 GK(c),Earth is the Target .. 325.00
27 The Human Fishbowl 325.00
28 The Radio Planet 325.00
29 GK(c),Space-Enemy
 Number One 325.00
30 GK(c),The Impossible
 World Named Earth 325.00
31 GK(c),The Day the Earth
 Split in Two 300.00
32 GK(c),Riddle of the
 Vanishing Earthmen 300.00

Mystery in Space #9
© DC Comics, Inc.

33 The Wooden World War ... 300.00
34 GK(c),The Man Who
 Moved the World 300.00
35 The Counterfeit Earth 300.00
36 GK(c),Secret of the
 Moon Sphinx 300.00
37 GK(c),Secret of the
 Masked Martians 300.00
38 GK(c),The Canals of Earth . 300.00
39 GK(c),Sorcerers of Space .. 300.00
40 GK(c),Riddle of the
 Runaway Earth 300.00
41 GK(c),The Miser of Space . 250.00
42 GK(c),The Secret of the
 Skyscraper Spaceship 250.00
43 GK(c),Invaders From the
 Space Satellites 250.00
44 GK(c),Amazing Space Flight
 of North America 250.00
45 GK(c),MA,Flying Saucers
 Over Mars 250.00
46 GK(c),MA,Mystery of the

 Moon Sniper 250.00
47 GK(c),MA,Interplanetary Tug
 of War 250.00
48 GK(c),MA,Secret of the
 Scarecrow World 250.00
49 GK(c),The Sky-High Man .. 250.00
50 GK(c),The Runaway
 Space-Train 250.00
51 GK(c),MA,Battle of the
 Moon Monsters 250.00
52 GK(c),MSy,Mirror Menace
 of Mars 250.00
53 GK(c),B:Adam Strange stories,
 Menace o/t Robot Raiders 1,700.00
54 GK(c),Invaders of the
 Underground World 400.00
55 GK(c),The Beast From
 the Runaway World 300.00
56 GK(c),The Menace of
 the Super-Atom 200.00
57 GK(c),Mystery of the
 Giant Footsteps 200.00
58 GK(c),Chariot in the Sky . 200.00
59 GK(c),The Duel of the
 Two Adam Stranges 200.00
60 GK(c),The Attack of the
 Tentacle World 200.00
61 CI&MA(c),Threat of the
 Tornado Tyrant 150.00
62 CI&MA(c),The Beast with
 the Sizzling Blue Eyes 150.00
63 The Weapon that
 Swallowed Men 150.00
64 The Radioactive Menace .. 150.00
65 Mechanical Masters of Rann 150.00
66 Space-Island of Peril 150.00
67 Challenge of the
 Giant Fireflies 150.00
68 CI&MA(c),Fadeaway Doom . 150.00
69 CI&MA(c),Menace of the
 Aqua-Ray Weapon 150.00
70 CI&MA(c),Vengeance of
 the Dust Devil 150.00
71 CI&MA(c),The Challenge of
 the Crystal Conquerors 150.00
72 The Multiple Menace Weapon 100.00
73 CI&MA(c),The Invisible
 Invaders of Rann 100.00
74 CI&MA(c),The Spaceman
 Who Fought Himself 100.00
75 CI&MA(c),The Planet That
 Came to a Standstill 225.00
76 CI&MA(c),Challenge of
 the Rival Starman 100.00
77 CI&MA(c),Ray-Gun in the Sky 100.00
78 CI&MA(c),Shadow People
 of the Eclipse 100.00
79 CI&MA(c),The Metal
 Conqueror of Rann 100.00
80 CI&MA(c),The Deadly
 Shadows of Adam Strange . 100.00
81 CI&MA(c),The Cloud-Creature
 That Menaced Two Worlds .. 75.00
82 CI&MA(c),World War on
 Earth and Rann 75.00
83 CI&MA(c),The Emotion-Master
 of Space 75.00
84 CI&MA(c),The Powerless
 Weapons of Adam Strange .. 75.00
85 CI&MA(c),Riddle of the
 Runaway Rockets 75.00
86 CI&MA(c),Attack of the
 Underworld Giants 75.00
87 MA(c),The Super-Brain of
 Adam Strange,B:Hawkman . 200.00

All comics prices listed are for *Near Mint* condition.   **CVA Page 87**

DC COMICS

Mystery in Space #51
© DC Comics, Inc.

88 CI&MA(c),The Robot Wraith
of Rann 175.00
89 MA(c),Siren o/t Space Ark . 175.00
90 CI&MA(c),Planets and
Peril, E:Hawkman 175.00
91 CI&MA(c),Puzzle of
the Perilous Prisons 35.00
92 DD&SMo(c),The Alien Invasion
From Earth,B:Space Ranger . 40.00
93 DD&SMo(c),The Convict
Twins of Space 40.00
94 DD&SMo(c),The Adam
Strange Story 40.00
95 The Hydra-Head From
Outer Space 40.00
96 The Coins That Doomed
Two Planets 40.00
97 The Day Adam Strange
Vanished 40.00
98 The Wizard of the Cosmos . . 40.00
99 DD&SMo(c),The World-
Destroyer From Space 40.00
100 DD&SMo(c),GK,The Death
of Alanna 40.00
101 GK(c),The Valley of
1,000 Dooms 40.00
102 GK,The Robot World of Rann 40.00
103 The Billion-Dollar Time-
Capsule(Space Ranger),I:Ultra
the Multi-Agent 40.00
104 thru 109 . . . . @15.00
110 Sept. 1966 . . . . 15.00
111 JAp,SD,MR,DSp,Sept. 1980 15.00
112 JAp,TS,JKu(c) 15.00
113 JKu(c),MGo 15.00
114 JKu(c),JCr,SD,DSp 15.00
115 JKu(c),SD,GT,BB 15.00
116 JSn(c),JCr,SD 15.00
117 DN,GT,March, 1981 . . . . . . 15.00

MYSTERY PLAY
Vertigo
HC GMo(s),JMu 19.95

MYTHOS:
THE FINAL TOUR
DC/Vertigo Oct. 1996
1 JNR(s),GyA,PrG,F:Rock Star
Adam Case 5.95
2 JNR(s),PSj,F:Rock Star Adam
Case 5.95
3 JNR(s), finale 5.95

NATHANIEL DUSK
Feb., 1984
1 GC(p) 1.50
2 GC(p) 1.25
3 GC(p) 1.25
4 GC(p), May 1984 . . . . 1.25

NATHANIEL DUSK II
Oct., 1985
1 thru 4 GC,Jan., 1986 . . . . . . @2.00

NAZZ, THE
1990–91
1 Michael'sBook 5.50
2 Johnny'sBook 5.00
3 Search for Michael Nazareth . . 5.00
4 V:Retaliators,final issue 5.00

NEVADA
DC/Vertigo (March, 1998)
1 (of 6) SvG,SL,show girl 2.50
2 SvG,SL,dismembered corpse . . 2.50
3 SvG,SL,stabbed an inhuman . . 2.50
4 SvG,SL,another dimension . . . 2.50
5 SvG,SL 2.50
6 SvG,SL,Big Bang, concl. 2.50

NEW ADVENTURES
OF SUPERBOY
(See: SUPERBOY)

NEW BOOK OF COMICS
1937
1 Dr.Occult 12,000.00
2 Dr.Occult 7,000.00

NEW COMICS
1935
1 . . . . 15,000.00
2 . . . . 6,000.00
3 thru 6 . . . . @4,000.00
7 thru 11 . . . . @3,000.00
Becomes:

NEW ADVENTURE
COMICS
Jan., 1937
12 S&S 3,000.00
13 thru 20 . . . . @2,600.00
21 . . . . 2,600.00
22 thru 31 . . . . @2,200.00
Becomes:

ADVENTURE COMICS

NEW FUN COMICS
Feb., 1935
1 B:Oswald the Rabbit,
Jack Woods 40,000.00
2 . . . . 17,000.00
3 . . . . 8,000.00
4 . . . . 8,000.00

5 . . . . 8,000.00
6 S&S,B:Dr.Occult,
Henri Duval 20,000.00
Becomes:
MORE FUN COMICS
7 S&S,WK 5,200.00
8 S&S,WK 5,000.00
9 S&S,E:Henri Duval 6,000.00
10 S&S 3,500.00
11 S&S,B:Calling all Girls . . . 3,200.00
12 S&S 2,800.00
13 S&S 2,800.00
14 S&S,Color,Dr.Occult 13,000.00
15 S&S 4,800.00
16 S&S,Christmas(c) 4,800.00
17 S&S 4,500.00
18 S&S 2,000.00
19 S&S 2,000.00
20 HcK,S&S 2,000.00
21 S&S 1,900.00
22 S&S 1,900.00
23 S&S 1,900.00
24 S&S 1,900.00
25 S&S 1,700.00
26 S&S 1,700.00
27 S&S 1,700.00
28 S&S 1,700.00
29 S&S 1,700.00
30 S&S 1,700.00
31 S&S 1,700.00
32 S&S,E:Dr. Occult 1,700.00
33 . . . . 1,700.00
34 . . . . 1,700.00
35 . . . . 1,700.00
36 B:Masked Ranger 1,700.00
37 thru 40 . . . . @1,700.00
41 E:Masked Ranger 1,200.00
42 thru 50 . . . . @1,200.00
51 I:The Spectre 4,500.00
52 O:The Spectre,pt.1,
E:Wing Brady 50,000.00
53 O:The Spectre,pt.2,
B:Capt.Desmo 35,000.00
54 E:King Carter,Spectre(c) . . 9,000.00
55 I:Dr.Fate,E:Bulldog Martin,
Spectre(c) 12,000.00
56 B:Congo Bill,Dr.Fate(c) . . . 4,500.00
57 Spectre(c) 2,800.00
58 Spectre(c) 2,800.00
59 A:Spectre 2,500.00
60 Spectre(c) 2,800.00
61 Spectre(c) 2,500.00
62 Spectre(c) 2,200.00
63 Spectre(c),E:St.Bob Neal . 2,200.00
64 Spectre(c),B:Lance Larkin . 2,200.00
65 Spectre(c) 2,200.00
66 Spectre(c) 2,200.00
67 Spectre(c),O:Dr. Fate,
E:Congo Bill,Biff Bronson . 6,500.00
68 Dr.Fate(c),B:Clip Carson . . 2,000.00
69 Dr.Fate(c) 2,000.00
70 Dr.Fate(c),E:Lance Larkin . 2,000.00
71 Dr.Fate(c),I:Johnny Quick . 5,000.00
72 Dr. Fate has Smaller Helmet,
E:Sgt. Carey,Sgt.O'Malley . 1,600.00
73 Dr.Fate(c),I:Aquaman,Green
Arrow,Speedy 12,000.00
74 Dr.Fate(c),A:Aquaman . . . 2,000.00
75 Dr.Fate(c) 1,800.00
76 Dr.Fate(c),MMe,E:Clip Carson,
B:Johnny Quick 1,800.00
77 MMe,Green Arrow(c) 1,800.00
78 MMe,Green Arrow(c) 1,800.00
79 MMe,Green Arrow(c) 1,800.00
80 MMe,Green Arrow(c) 1,800.00

More Fun Comics #41
© DC Comics, Inc.

81	MMe,Green Arrow(c)	1,000.00
82	MMe,Green Arrow(c)	1,000.00
83	MMe,Green Arrow(c)	1,000.00
84	MMe,Green Arrow(c)	1,000.00
85	MMe,Green Arrow(c)	1,000.00
86	MMe	1,000.00
87	MMe,E:Radio Squad	1,000.00
88	MMe,Green Arrow(c)	1,000.00
89	MMe,O:Gr.Arrow&Speedy	1,200.00
90	MMe,Green Arrow(c)	800.00
91	MMe,Green Arrow(c)	750.00
92	MMe,Green Arrow(c)	750.00
93	MMe,B:Dover & Clover	750.00
94	MMe,Green Arrow(c)	750.00
95	MMe,Green Arrow(c)	750.00
96	MMe,Green Arrow(c)	750.00
97	MMe,JKu,E:Johnny Quick	750.00
98	E:Dr. Fate	750.00
99	Green Arrow(c)	750.00
100	Anniversary Issue	1,000.00
101	O&I:Superboy, E:The Spectre	7,500.00
102	A:Superboy	1,000.00
103	A:Superboy	800.00
104	Superboy(c)	650.00
105	Superboy(c)	650.00
106		650.00
107	E:Superboy	650.00
108	A:Genius Jones,'Genius Meets Genius'	150.00
109	A:Genius Jones, The Disappearing Deposits	150.00
110	A:Genius Jones, Birds, Brains and Burglary	150.00
111	A:Genius Jones, Jeepers Creepers	150.00
112	A:Genius Jones, The Tell-Tale Tornado	150.00
113	A:Genius Jones, Clocks and Shocks	150.00
114	A:Genius Jones, The Milky Way	150.00
115	A:Genius Jones,Foolish Questions	150.00
116	A:Genius Jones,Palette For Plunder	150.00
117	A:Genius Jones,Battle of	
	the Pretzel Benders	150.00
118	A:Genius Jones,The Sinister Siren	150.00
119	A:Genius Jones,A Perpetual Jackpot	150.00
120	A:Genius Jones,The Man in the Moon	150.00
121	A:Genius Jones,The Mayor Goes Haywire	125.00
122	A:Genius Jones,When Thug-Hood Was In Floor	125.00
123	A:Genius Jones,Hi Diddle Diddle, the Cat and the Fiddle	125.00
124	A:Genius Jones, The Zany Zoo	125.00
125	Genius Jones, Impossible But True	575.00
126	A:Genius Jones,The Case of the Gravy Spots	125.00
127	Nov.–Dec., 1947	225.00

NEW GODS, THE
Feb.–March, 1971

1	JK,I:Orion	35.00
2	JK	17.00
3	JK	14.00
4	JK,O:Manhunter, rep.	14.00
5	JK,I:Fastbak & Black Racer	14.00
6	JK	14.00
7	JK,O:Orion	14.00
8	JK	14.00
9	JK,I:Forager	14.00
10	JK	14.00
11	JK	14.00
12	DN,DA,R:New Gods	5.00
13	DN,DA	5.00
14	DN,DA	5.00
15	RB,BMc	5.00
16	DN,DA	5.00
17	DN,DA	5.00
18	DN,DA	5.00
19	DN,DA	4.00

NEW GODS
(Reprints) 1984

1	JK reprint	2.25
2	JK reprint	2.00
3	JK reprint	2.00
4	JK reprint	2.00
5	JK reprint	2.00
6	JK rep.+NewMaterial	2.00

NEW GODS
[2nd Series] 1989

1	From Cosmic Odyssey	2.00
2	A:Orion of New Genesis	1.50
3	A:Orion	1.50
4	Renegade Apokolyptian Insect Colony	1.50
5	Orion vs. Forager	1.50
6	A:Eve Donner, Darkseid	1.50
7	Bloodline #1	1.50
8	Bloodline #2	1.50
9	Bloodline #3	1.50
10	Bloodline #4	1.50
11	Bloodline #5	1.50
12	Bloodlines #6	1.50
13	Back on Earth	1.50
14	I:Reflektor	1.50
15	V:Serial Killer	1.50
16	A:Fastbak & Metron	1.50
17	A:Darkseid, Metron	1.50
18	A:YugaKhan,Darkseid, Moniters	1.50

New Gods #3 © DC Comics, Inc.

19	V:Yuga Khan	1.50
20	Darkseid Dethroned, V:Yuga Khan	1.50
21	A:Orion	1.50
22	A:Metron	1.50
23	A:Forever People	1.50
24	A:Forever People	1.50
25	The Pact #1,R:Infinity Man	1.50
26	The Pact #2	1.50
27	Asault on Apokolips,Pact#3	1.50
28	Pact #4, final issue	1.50

[3rd Series] 1995–97

1	F:Orion vs. Darkseid	2.00
2	RaP,Underworld Unleashed tie-in	2.00
3	RaP,Darkseid destroyed	2.00
4	RaP,F:Lightray	2.00
5	RaP,F:Orion	2.00
6		2.00
7	RaP,R:Darkseid	2.00
8	RaP,DZ,F:Highfather,Darkseid	2.00
9 thru 11		@2.00
12	JBy,BWi,F:Metron	1.00
13	JBy,BWi,Orion reappears on Earth	2.00
14	JBy,BWi,A:Forever People, Lightray	2.00
TPB rep. #1–#11,b&w		12.00
Secret Files #1 KK,JBy		5.00

NEW GUARDIANS
1988–89

1	JSon,from Millenium series	2.50
2	JSon,Colombian Drug Cartel	1.75
3	JSon,in South Africa, V:Janwillem's Army	1.25
4	JSon,V:Neo-Nazi Skinheads in California	1.25
5	JSon,Tegra Kidnapped	1.25
6	JSon, In China, Invasion x-over	1.25
7	JSon, Guardians Return Home	1.25
8	JSon, V:Janwillem	1.25
9	JSon, A:Tome Kalmaku, V:Janwillem	1.25
10	JSon, A:Tome Kalmaku	1.25
11	PB,Janwillem's secret	1.25
12	PB,New Guardians Future revealed, final issue	1.25

All comics prices listed are for _Near Mint_ condition.

New Teen Titans #24
© DC Comics, Inc.

NEW TEEN TITANS
Nov., 1980

1 GP,RT,V:Gordanians (see DC
  Comics Presents #26 ...... 12.00
2 GP,RT,I:Deathstroke the
  Terminator, I&D:Ravager ... 12.00
3 GP,I:Fearsome Five 4.00
4 GP,RT,A:JLA,O:Starfire 5.00
5 CS,RT,O:Raven,I:Trigon 5.00
6 GP,V:Trigon,O:Raven 4.00
7 GP,RT,O:Cyborg 4.00
8 GP,RT,A Day in the Life 3.00
9 GP,RT,A:Terminator,
  V:Puppeteer 4.00
10 GP,RT,A:Terminator 5.00
11 GP,RT,V:Hyperion 3.00
12 GP,RT,V:Titans of Myth 3.00
13 GP,RT,R:Robotman 3.00
14 GP,RT,I:New Brotherhood of
  Evil,V:Zahl and Rouge 3.00
15 GP,RT,D:Madame Rouge 3.00
16 GP,RT,I:Captain Carrot 3.00
17 GP,RT,I:Frances Kane 3.00
18 GP,RT,A:Orig.Starfire 3.00
19 GP,RT,A:Hawkman 3.00
20 GP,RT,V:Disruptor 3.00
21 GP,RT,GC,I:Brother Blood,
  Night Force 3.00
22 GP,RT,V:Brother Blood 2.50
23 GP,RT,I:Blackfire 2.50
24 GP,RT,A:Omega Men,I:X-hal . 2.50
25 GP,RT,A:Omega Men 2.50
26 GP,RT,I:Terra,Runaway #1 .. 2.50
27 GP,RT,A:Speedy,Runaway #2 2.50
28 GP,RT,V:Terra 3.00
29 GP,RT,V:Broth.of Evil 2.00
30 GP,RT,V:Broth.of Evil,J:Terra 3.00
31 GP,RT,V:Broth.of Evil 1.50
32 GP,RT,I:Thunder & Lightning . 1.50
33 GP,I:Trident 1.50
34 GP,V:The Terminator 3.00
35 KP,RT,V:Mark Wright 1.50
36 KP,RT,A:Thunder & Lightning . 1.50
37 GP,RT,A:Batman/Outsiders(x-over
  BATO#5),V:Fearsome Five ... 2.00
38 GP,O:Wonder Girl 1.50

39 GP,Grayson quits as Robin ... 5.00
40 GP,A:Brother Blood 1.50
Ann.#1 GP,RT,Blackfire 3.50
Ann.#2 GP,I:Vigilante 3.00
Ann.#3 GP,DG,D:Terra,A:Deathstroke
  V:The H.I.V.E. 3.50
Ann.#4 rep.Direct Ann.#1 ...... 1.25
TPB Judas Contract rep.#39-#44,
  Ann.#3,new GP(c) 14.95

[Special Issues]
Keebler:GP,DG,Drugs 2.50
Beverage:Drugs,RA 2.50
IBM:Drugs 3.00

Becomes:

TALES OF THE
TEEN TITANS
1984–88

41 GP,A:Brother Blood 2.00
42 GP,DG,V:Deathstroke 5.00
43 GP,DG,V:Deathstroke 5.00
44 GP,DG,I:Nightwing,O:Deathstroke
  Joe Wilson becomes Jericho .. 6.00
45 GP,A:Aqualad,V:The H.I.V.E. . 2.00
46 GP,A:Aqualad,V:The H.I.V.E. . 2.00
47 GP,A:Aqualad,V:The H.I.V.E. . 2.00
48 SR,V:The Recombatants 2.00
49 GP,CI,V:Dr.Light,A:Flash ... 2.00
50 GP/DG W:Wonder Girl &
  Terry Long,C:Batman,
  Wonder Woman 2.50
51 RB,A:Cheshire 2.00
52 RB,A:Cheshire 2.00
53 RB,I:Ariel,A:Terminator 2.50
54 RB,A:Terminator 2.50
55 A:Terminator 2.50
56 A:Fearsome Five 1.75
57 A:Fearsome Five 1.75
58 E:MWn(s),A:Fearsome Five .. 1.75
59 rep. DC presents #26 ...... 1.50
60 thru 91 rep. .... @1.50

[Limited Series]

1 GP,O:Cyborg 2.00
2 GP,O:Raven 2.00
3 GD,O:Changling 2.00
4 GP/EC,O:Starfire 2.00

NEW TEEN TITANS
[Direct sales series]
Aug., 1984

1 B:MWn(s),GP,L:Raven 4.00
2 GP,D:Azareth,A:Trigon 3.00
3 GP,V:Raven 3.00
4 GP,V:Trigon,Raven 3.00
5 GP,D:Trigon,Raven disappears 3.00
6 GP,A:Superman,Batman 2.50
7 JL,V:Titans of Myth 2.50
8 JL,V:Titans of Myth 2.50
9 JL,V:Titans of Myth,I:Kole .. 2.50
10 JL,O:Kole 2.50
11 JL,O:Kole 2.50
12 JL,Ghost story 2.50
13 EB,Crisis 2.25
14 EB,Crisis 2.25
15 EB,A:Raven 2.25
16 EB,A:OmegaMen 2.25
17 EB,V:Blackfire 2.25
18 E:MWn(s),EB,V:Blackfire ... 2.25
19 EB,V:Mento 2.25
20 GP(c),EB,V:Cheshire,J.Todd . 2.25
21 GP(c),EB,V:Cheshire,J.Todd . 2.25
22 GP(c),EB,V:Blackfire,Mento,
  Brother Blood 2.25
23 GP(c),V:Blackfire 2.25

24 CB,V:Hybrid 2.25
25 EB,RT,V:Hybrid,Mento,A:Flash 2.25
26 KGa,V:Mento 2.25
27 KGa,Church of Br.Blood 2.00
28 EB,RT,V:BrotherBlood,A:Flash 2.00
29 EB,RT,V:Brother Blood,
  A:Flash,Robin 2.00
30 EB,Batman,Superman 2.25
31 EB,RT,V:Brother Blood,A:Flash
  Batman,Robin,Gr.Lantern Corps
  Superman 2.00
32 EB,RT,Murder Weekend 2.00
33 EB,V:Terrorists 2.00
34 EB,RT,V:Mento,Hybrid 2.00
35 PB,RT,V:Arthur & Eve 2.00
36 EB,RT,I:Wildebeest 2.50
37 EB,RT,V:Wildebeest 2.00
38 EB,RT,A:Infinity 2.00
39 EB,RT,F:Raven 2.00
40 EB,RT,V:Gentleman Ghost ... 2.00
41 EB,V:Wildebeest,A:Puppeteer,
  Trident,Wildebeest 2.00
42 EB,RT,V:Puppeteer,Gizmo,
  Trident,Wildebeest 2.00
43 CS,RT,V:Phobia 2.00
44 RT,V:Godiva 2.00
45 EB,RT,A:Dial H for Hero 2.00
46 EB,RT,A:Dial H for Hero 2.00
47 O:Titans,C:Wildebeest 2.00
48 EB,RT,A:Red Star 2.00
49 EB,RT,A:Red Star 2.00
Ann.#1 A:Superman,V:Brainiac . 2.50
Ann.#2 JBy,JL,O:Brother Blood .. 3.00
Ann.#3 I:Danny Chase 2.50
Ann.#4 V:Godiva 2.50

Becomes:

NEW TITANS
1988–96

50 B:MWn(s),GP,BMc,B:Who is
  Wonder Girl? 4.00
51 GP,BMc 3.00
52 GP,BMc 3.00
53 GP,RT 3.00
54 GP,RT,E:Who is Wonder Girl? 3.00
55 GP,RT,I:Troia 3.00
56 MBr,RT,Tale of Middle Titans . 2.50
57 GP,BMc,V:Wildebeest 2.50
58 GP,TG,BMc,V:Wildebeast 2.50
59 GP,TG,BMc,V:Wildebeast 2.50
60 GP,TG,BMc,3rd A:Tim Drake
  (Face Revealed),Batman 5.00
61 GP,TG,BMc,A:Tim Drake,
  Batman 5.00
62 TG,AV,A:Deathstroke 3.00
63 TG,AV,A:Deathstroke 3.00
64 TG,AV,A:Deathstroke 3.00
65 TG,AV,A:Deathstroke,Tim Drake,
  Batman 3.00
66 TG,AV,V:Eric Forrester 2.50
67 TG,AV,V:Eric Forrester 2.50
68 SE,V:Royal Flush Gang 2.50
69 SE,V:Royal Flush Gang 2.50
70 SE,A:Deathstroke 3.00
71 TG,AV,B:Deathstroke,
  B:Titans Hunt 5.00
72 TG,AV,D:Golden Eagle 4.00
73 TG,AV,I:Phantasm 4.00
74 TG,AV,I:Pantha 3.00
75 TG,AV,IR:Jericho/Wildebeast . 3.00
76 TG,AV,V:Wildebeests 3.00
77 TG,AV,A:Red Star,N:Cyborg . 2.50
78 TG,AV,V:Cyborg 2.50
79 TG,AV,I:Team Titans 3.00
80 KGa,PC,A:Team Titans 2.50
81 CS,AV,War of the Gods 2.50

82 TG,AV,V:Wildebeests	2.50
83 TG,AV,D:Jericho	3.00
84 TG,AV,E:Titans Hunt	2.50
85 TG,AV,I:Baby Wildebeest	2.50
86 CS,AV,E:Deathstroke	2.50
87 TG,AV,A:Team Titans	2.50
88 TG,AV,CS,V:Team Titans	2.50
89 JBr,I:Lord Chaos	2.50
90 TG,AV,Total Chaos#2,A:Team Titans,D'stroke,V:Lord Chaos	2.00
91 TG,AV,Total Chaos#5,A:Team Titans,D'stroke,V:Lord Chaos	2.00
92 E:MWn(s),TG,AV,Total Chaos#8, A:Team Titans,V:Lord Chaos	2.00
93 TG,AV,Titans Sell-Out#3	2.00
94 PJ,F:Red Star & Cyborg	2.00
95 PJ,Red Star gains new powers	2.00
96 PJ,I:Solar Flare, V:Konstantine	2.00
97 TG,AV,B:The Darkening,R:Speedy V:Brotherhood of Evil	2.00
98 TG,AV,V:Brotherhood of Evil	2.00
99 TG,AV,I:Arsenal (Speedy)	2.00

New Titans #86 © DC Comics, Inc.

100 TG,AV,W:Nightwing&Starfire, V:Deathwing,Raven,A:Flash,Team Titans,Hologram(c)	4.00
101 AV(i),L:Nightwing	2.00
102 AV(i),A:Prester John	2.00
103 AV(i),V:Bro. of Evil	2.00
104 Terminus #1	2.00
105 Terminus #2	2.00
106 Terminus #3	2.00
107 Terminus #4	2.00
108 A:Supergirl,Flash	2.00
109 F:Starfire	2.00
110 A:Flash,Serg.Steele	2.00
111 A:Checkmate	2.00
112 A:Checkmate	2.00
113 F:Nightwing	2.25
114 L:Starfire, Nightwing,Panthra, Wildebeest	2.00
115 A:Trigon	2.00
116 Changeling	2.00
117 V:Psimon	2.00
118 V:Raven + Brotherhood	2.00
119 Suffer the Children,pt.1	2.00
120 Forever Evil,pt.2	2.00
121 Forever Evil,pt.3	2.00

122 Crimelord/Syndicate War,pt.2 J:Supergirl	2.25
123 MWn(s),RRa,O:Minion	2.25
124 The Siege of Zi Charan	2.25
125 The Siege of Zi Charan	3.00
126 Meltdown,pt.1	2.25
127 MWn,Meltdown, cont.	2.25
128 MWn,Meltdown, cont.	2.25
129 MWn,Meltdown, cont.	2.25
130 MWn,Meltdown,final issue	2.25
Ann.#5 V:Children of the Sun	3.00
Ann.#6 CS,F:Starfire	3.00
Ann.#7 Armageddon 2001,I:Future Teen Titans	4.00
Ann.#8 PJ,Eclipso,V:Deathstroke	3.75
Ann.#9 Bloodlines#5,I:Anima	3.75
Ann.#10 Elseworlds story	3.75
Ann.#11 Year One Annual	3.95
#0 Spec. Zero Hour,new team	2.00

NEW TITANS SELL-OUT SPECIAL

1 SE,AV,AH,I:Teeny Titans, w/Nightwing poster	3.75

NEW YEAR'S EVIL:
Dec., 1997

Body Doubles #1 DAn,ALa,JoP, JPn(c)	2.00
Dark Nemesis #1 DJu,Ccs,JPn(c)	2.00
Darkseid #1 JBy,SB,JPn(c)	2.00
Gog #1 MWa,JOy,DJa,JPn(c)	2.00
Mr. Mxyzptlk #1 AIG,TMo,JPn(c)	2.00
Prometheus #1 GMo,JPn(c)	2.00
Scarecrow #1 PrM,DFg,JPn(c)	2.00
The Rogues #1 BAu,RoW,JPn(c)	2.00

NEW YORK WORLD'S FAIR

1 1939	25,000.00
2 1940	14,000.00

NIGHT FORCE
Aug., 1982

1 GC,1:Night Force	1.25
2 thru 13 GC	@1.25
14 GC,Sept.,1983	1.25

NIGHT FORCE
Oct. 1996

1 MWn(s),BA,Baron Winters leads	2.25
2 MWn(s)	2.25
3 MWn(s)	2.25
4 MWn(s),EB,"Hell Seems a Heaven"	2.25
5 MWn(s),Low,SMa,"Dreamers of Dreams" pt.1	2.25
6 MWn(s),Low,SMa,"Dreamers of Dreams" pt.2	2.25
7 MWn(s),Low,SMa,"Dreamers of Dreams" pt.3	2.25
8 MWn(s),"Convergence," x-over	2.25
9 MWn(s),Low,Sma,"The Eleventh Man" pt.1 (of 3)	2.25
10 MWn(s),"Eleventh Man" pt.2	2.50
11 MWn(s),"Eleventh Man" pt.3	2.50
12 MWn(s),Lady of the Leopard final issue,Sept. 1997	2.50

NIGHTWING
1995

1 R:Nightwing	3.50
2 N:Nightwing	3.00

3 visit to Kravia (of 4)	3.00
4 conclusion	3.00

NIGHTWING
Aug. 1996

1 CDi(s),SMc,KIS,Nightwing goes to Blühaven	4.00
2 CDi(s),SMc,KIS,V:smugglers	2.50
3 CDi(s),SMc,KIS,run-down bank "held up"	2.25
4 CDi(s),SMc,KIS,V:Lady Vick	2.25
5 CDi(s),SMc,KIS,	2.25
6 CDi(s),SMc,KIS,A:Tim Drake	2.25
7 CDi(s),SMc,KIS,"Rough Justice"	2.25
8 CDi(s),SMc,KIS,V: the kingpin of Blühaven	2.00
9 CDi(s),SMc,KIS,kidnapping, pt.1	2.00
10 CDi(s),SMc,KIS,nightmare or dream?	2.00
11 CDi(s),SMc,V:Soames, Blockbuster	2.00
12 CDi(s),SMc,Mutt	2.00
13 CDi(s),SMc,KIS,A:Batman	2.00
14 CDi(s),SMc,KIS,A:Batman,pt.2	2.00
15 CDi(s),SMc,KIS,A:Batman,pt.3	2.00
16 CDi(s),SMc,KIS,Nightwingmobile	2.00
17 CDi(s),SMc,KIS,V:Man-Bat	2.00
18 CDi(s),SMc,KIS	2.00
19 CDi(s),SMc,KIS,Cataclysm x-over, pt.2	2.00
20 CDi(s),SMc,KIS,Cataclysm	2.00
21 CDi(s),SMc,KIS,post Cataclysm	2.00
22 CDi(s),SMc,KIS,V:Lady Vic	2.00
23 Brotherhood of the Fist x-over, pt.4	2.00
24 CDi(s),SMc,KIS,cop story	2.00
25 CDi(s),SMc,KIS,A:Robin	2.00
Ann.#1 Pulp Heroes (Romance)	3.95
TPB A Knight in Bludhaven,CDi, SMc,KIS, rep. #1–#8	15.00
TPB Ties That Bind, DON,AIG, DG,KIS,rep.	13.00

NIGHTWING: ALFRED'S RETURN

1	3.50

NIGHTWING AND HUNTRESS
March, 1998

1 (of 4) BSz,conflict	2.00
2 BSz,good cop, bad cop	2.00
3 BSz,Malfatti	2.00
4 BSz,concl.	2.00

NUTSY SQUIRREL
Sept.–Oct., 1954

61 SM	40.00
62 thru 71	@25.00
72 Nov., 1957	25.00

OMAC
Sept.–Oct., 1974

1 JK,I&O:Omac	10.00
2 JK,I:Mr.Big	6.00
3 JK,100,000 foes	6.00
4 JK,V:Kafka	6.00
5 JK,New Bodies for Old	6.00
6 JK,The Body Bank	6.00
7 JK,The Ocean Stealers	6.00
8 JK,Last issue	6.00

[2nd Series] 1991

1 JBy,B&W prestige	5.00

2 JBy,The Great Depression era . 4.50
3 JBy,'To Kill Adolf Hitler' 4.50
4 JBy,D:Mr.Big 4.50

OMEGA MEN
Dec., 1982
1 KG,V:Citadel 2.50
2 KG,O:Broot 2.00
3 KG,I:Lobo 4.00
4 KG,D:Demonia,I:Felicity 1.50
5 KG,V:Lobo 3.00
6 KG,V:Citadel,D:Gepsen 2.00
7 O:Citadel,L:Auron 2.00
8 R:Nimbus,I:H.Hokum 2.00
9 V:HarryHokum,A:Lobo 2.00
10 A:Lobo (First Full Story) 3.00
11 V:Blackfire 1.50
12 R:Broots Wife 1.50
13 A:Broots Wife 1.50
14 Karna 1.50
15 Primus Goes Mad 1.50
16 Spotlight Issue 1.50
17 V:Psions 1.50
18 V:Psions 1.50

Omega Men #4 © DC Comics, Inc.

19 V:Psions,C:Lobo 1.75
20 V:Psions,A:Lobo 2.00
21 Spotlight Issue 1.50
22 Nimbus 1.50
23 Nimbus 1.50
24 Okaara 1.50
25 Kalista 1.50
26 V:Spiderguild 1.50
27 V:Psions 1.50
28 V:Psions 1.50
29 V:Psions 1.50
30 R:Primus,I:Artin 1.50
31 Crisis tie-in 1.50
32 Felicity 1.50
33 Regufe World 1.50
34 A:New Teen Titans 1.50
35 A:New Teen Titans 1.50
36 Last Days of Broot 1.50
37 V:Spiderguild,A:Lobo 2.00
38 A:Tweener Network 1.25
Ann.#1 KG,R:Harpis 2.25
Ann.#2 KG,O:Primus 2.25

100% TRUE?
DC/Paradox Press B&W 1996
1 rep. from Paradox Press books 3.50

OUR ARMY AT WAR
Aug., 1952
1 CI(c),Dig Your FoxholeDeep 1,200.00
2 CI(c),Champ 600.00
3 GK(c),No Exit 400.00
4 IN(c),Last Man 400.00
5 IN(c),T.N.T. Bouquet 350.00
6 IN(c),Battle Flag 350.00
7 IN(c),Dive Bomber 350.00
8 IN(c),One Man Army 350.00
9 GC(c),Undersea Raider 350.00
10 IN(c),Soldiers on the
   High Wire 350.00
11 IN(c),Scratch One Meatball . 350.00
12 IN(c),The Big Drop 250.00
13 BK(c),Ghost Ace 250.00
14 Drummer of Waterloo 250.00
15 IN(c),Thunder in the Skies . 250.00
16 IN(c),A Million To One Shot 250.00
17 IN(c),The White Death 250.00
18 IN(c),Frontier Fighter 250.00
19 IN(c),The Big Ditch 250.00
20 IN(c),Abandon Ship 250.00
21 IN(c),Dairy of a Flattop 175.00
22 JGr(c),Ranger Raid 175.00
23 IN(c),Jungle Navy 175.00
24 IN(c),Suprise Landing 175.00
25 JGr(c),Take 'Er Down 175.00
26 IN(c),Sky Duel 175.00
27 IN(c),Diary of a Frogman . . 175.00
28 JGr(c),Detour-War 175.00
29 IN(c),Grounded Fighter 175.00
30 JGr(c),Torpedo Raft 175.00
31 IN(c),Howitzer Hill 175.00
32 JGr(c),Battle Mirror 150.00
33 JGr(c),Fighting Gunner 150.00
34 JGr(c),Point-Blank War 150.00
35 JGr(c),Frontline Tackle 150.00
36 JGr(c),Foxhole Mascot 150.00
37 JGr(c),Walking Battle Pin . . 150.00
38 JGr(c),Floating Pillbox 150.00
39 JGr(c),Trench Trap 150.00
40 RH(c),Tank Hunter 150.00
41 JGr(c),Jungle Target 150.00
42 IN(c),Shadow Targets 150.00
43 JGr(c),A Bridge For Billy . . . 125.00
44 JGr(c),Thunder In The Desert 125.00
45 JGr(c),Diary of a Fighter Pilot 125.00
46 JGr(c),Prize Package 125.00
47 JGr(c),Flying Jeep 125.00
48 JGr(c),Front Seat 125.00
49 JKu(c),Landing Postponed . 125.00
50 JGr(c),Mop-Up Squad 125.00
51 JGr(c),Battle Tag 110.00
52 JGr(c),Pony Express Pilot . . 110.00
53 JGr(c),One Ringside-For War 110.00
54 JKu(c),No-Man Secret 110.00
55 JGr(c),No Rest For A Raider 110.00
56 JKu(c),You're Next 110.00
57 JGr(c),Ten-Minute Break . . . 110.00
58 JKu(c),The Fighting SnowBird 110.00
59 JGr(c),The Mustang Had
   My Number 110.00
60 JGr(c),Ranger Raid 110.00
61 JGr(c),A Pigeon For Easy Co. 100.00
62 JKu(c),Trigger Man 100.00
63 JGr(c),The Big Toss 100.00
64 JKu(c),Tank Rider 100.00
65 JGr(c),Scramble-War Upstairs 100.00
66 RH(c),Gunner Wanted 100.00

67 JKu(c),Boiling Point 100.00
68 JKu(c),End of the Line 100.00
69 JGr(c),Combat Cage 100.00
70 JGr(c),Torpedo Tank 100.00
71 JGr(c),Flying Mosquitoes . . 100.00
72 JGr(c),No. 1 Pigeon 100.00
73 JKu(c),Shooting Gallery . . . 100.00
74 JGr(c),Ace Without Guns . . 100.00
75 JGr(c),Blind Night Fighter . . 100.00
76 JKu(c),Clipped Hellcat 100.00
77 JGr(c),Jets Don't Dream . . . 100.00
78 IN(c),Battle Nurse 100.00
79 JGr(c),What's the Price
   of a B-17? 100.00
80 JGr(c),The Sparrow And
   The...Hawk 100.00
81 JGr(c),Sgt. Rock in The
   Rock of Easy Co. 2,200.00
82 JGr(c),Gun Jockey 500.00
83 JGr(c),B:Sgt.Rock Stories,
   The Rock and the Wall 800.00
84 JGr(c),Laughter On
   Snakehead Hill 175.00
85 JGr(c),Ice Cream Soldier . . 250.00
86 RH(c),Tank 711 . . . . 175.00
87 RH(c),Calling Easy Co. 175.00
88 JKu(c),The Hard Way 175.00
89 RH(c),No Shoot From Easy 175.00
90 JKu(c),3 Stripes Hill 175.00
91 JGr(c),No Answer from Sarge 175.00
92 JGr(c),Luck of Easy 125.00
93 JGr(c),Deliver One Airfield . 125.00
94 JKu(c),Target-Easy Company 125.00
95 JGr(c),Battle Of The Stripes 125.00
96 JGr(c),Last Stand For Easy . 125.00
97 JGr(c),What Makes A
   Sergeant Run? 125.00
98 JKu(c),Soldiers Never Die . . 125.00
99 JKu(c),Easy's Hardest Battle 125.00
100 JKu(c),No Exit For Easy . . 125.00
101 JKu(c),End Of Easy 75.00
102 JKu(c),The Big Star 75.00
103 RH(c),Easy's Had It 75.00
104 JKu(c),A New Kind Of War . 75.00
105 JKu(c),T.N.T. Birthday 75.00
106 JKu(c),Meet Lt. Rock 75.00
107 JKu(c),Doom Over Easy . . . 75.00
108 JGr(c),Unknown Sergeant . . 75.00
109 JKu(c),Roll Call For Heroes . 75.00
110 JKu(c),That's An Order 75.00
111 JKu(c),What's The Price
   Of A Dog Tag 75.00
112 JKu(c),Battle Shadow 75.00
113 JKu(c),Eyes Of A
   Blind Gunner 75.00
114 JKu(c),Killer Sergeant 75.00
115 JKu(c),Rock's Battle Family . 75.00
116 JKu(c),S.O.S. Sgt. Rock . . . 75.00
117 JKu(c),Snafu Squad 60.00
118 RH(c),The Tank Vs. The
   Tin Soldier 60.00
119 JKu(c),A Bazooka For
   Babyface 60.00
120 JGr(c),Battle Tags
   For Easy Co. 50.00
121 JKu(c),New Boy In Easy . . . 50.00
122 JKu(c),Battle of the
   Pajama Commandos 50.00
123 JKu(c),Battle Brass Ring . . . 50.00
124 JKu(c),Target-Sgt. Rock . . . 50.00
125 JKu(c),Hold-At All Costs . . . 50.00
126 RH(c),The End Of
   Easy Company 50.00
127 JKu(c),4 Faces of Sgt. Rock 50.00
128 JKu(c),O:Sgt. Rock 225.00

129 JKu(c),Heroes Need Cowards 50.00	
130 JKu(c),No Hill For Easy ... 50.00	
131 JKu(c),One Pair of	
Dogtags For Sale 50.00	
132 JKu(c),Young Soldiers	
Never Cry 50.00	
133 JKu(c),Yesterday's Hero ... 50.00	
134 JKu(c),The T.N.T. Book ... 50.00	
135 JKu(c),Battlefield Double ... 50.00	
136 JKu(c),Make Me A Hero ... 50.00	
137 JKu(c),Too Many Sergeants 50.00	
138 JKu(c),Easy's Lost Sparrow 50.00	
139 JKu(c),A Firing Squad	
For Easy 50.00	
140 JKu(c),Brass Sergeant 50.00	
141 JKu(c),Dead Man's Trigger . 50.00	
142 JKu(c),Easy's New Topkick . 50.00	
143 JKu(c),Easy's T.N.T. Crop .. 50.00	
144 JKu(c),The Sparrow And	
The Tiger 50.00	
145 JKu(c),A Feather For	
Little Sure Shot 50.00	
146 JKu(c),The Fighting Guns	
For Easy 50.00	
147 JKu(c),Book One:Generals	
Don't Die 50.00	
148 JKu(c),Book Two:Generals	
Don't Die:Generals Are	
Sergeants With Stars 50.00	
149 JKu(c),Surrender Ticket ... 50.00	
150 JKu(c),Flytrap Hill 50.00	
151 JKu(c),War Party,	
I:Enemy Ace 300.00	
152 Jku(c),Last Man-Last Shot 100.00	
153 JKu(c),Easy's Last Stand . 100.00	
154 JKu(c),Boobytrap Mascot .. 50.00	
155 JKu(c),No Stripes For Me .. 65.00	
156 JKu(c),The Human Tank Trap 50.00	
157 JKu(c),Nothin's Ever	
Lost In War 50.00	
158 JKu(c),Iron Major-Rock	
Sergeant 50.00	
159 JKu(c),The Blind Gun 50.00	
160 JKu(c),What's The Color	
Of Your Blood 50.00	
161 JKu(c),Dead End	
For A Dogface 50.00	
162 JKu(c),The Price and	
The Sergeant 50.00	
163 JKu(c),Kill Me-Kill Me 50.00	
164 JKu(c),No Exit For Easy,	
reprint from #100 ...... 60.00	
165 JKu(c),The Return of the	
Iron Major 40.00	
166 JKu(c),Half A Sergeant 40.00	
167 JKu(c),Kill One-Save One .. 40.00	
168 JKu(c),I Knew The	
Unknown Soldier 40.00	
169 JKu(c),Nazi On My Back .. 40.00	
170 JKu(c),Buzzard Bait Hill .. 40.00	
171 JKu(c),The Sergeant MustDie 30.00	
172 JKu(c),A Slug for a Sergeant 30.00	
173 JKu(c),Easy's Hardest Battle,	
reprint from #99 .... 30.00	
174 JKu(c),One Hill Too Many .. 30.00	
175 JKu(c),T.N.T. Letter 30.00	
176 JKu(c),Give Me Your Stripes 30.00	
177 JKu(c),Target-Easy Company,	
reprint from #94 .... 30.00	
178 JKu(c),Only One Medal	
For Easy 30.00	
179 JKu(c),A Penny Jackie	
Johnson 30.00	
180 JKu(c),You Can't	
Kill A General 30.00	

Our Army at War #7 © DC Comics, Inc.

181 RH(c),Monday's Coward-	
Tuesday's Hero 30.00	
182 NA,RH(c),The Desert Rats	
of Easy 35.00	
183 NA,JKu(c),Sergeants Don't	
Stay Dead 35.00	
184 JKu(c),Candidate For A	
Firing Squad 25.00	
185 JKu(c),Battle Flag For A G.I. 25.00	
186 NA,JKu(c),3 Stripes Hill	
reprint from #90 .... 35.00	
187 JKu(c),Shadow of a Sergeant 25.00	
188 JKu(c),Death Comes for Easy 25.00	
189 JKu(c),The Mission Was	
Murder 25.00	
190 JKu(c),What Make's A	
Sergeant Run?, reprint	
from #97 .... 25.00	
191 JKu(c),Death Flies High,	
A:Johnny Cloud 25.00	
192 JKu(c),A Firing Squad	
For A Sergeant 25.00	
193 JKu(c),Blood In the Desert . 25.00	
194 JKu(c),Time For Vengeance 25.00	
195 JKu(c),Dead Town 25.00	
196 JKu(c),Stop The War-I Want	
To Get Off 25.00	
197 JKu(c),Last Exit For Easy .. 25.00	
198 JKu(c),Plugged Nickel 25.00	
199 JKu(c),Nazi Ghost Wolf 25.00	
200 JKu(c),The Troubadour 30.00	
201 JKu(c),The Graffiti Writer .. 25.00	
202 JKu(c),The Sarge Is Dead .. 10.00	
203 JKu(c),Easy's Had It,	
reprint from # 103 .... 25.00	
204 JKu(c) 10.00	
205 JKu(c) 10.00	
206 JKu(c),There's A War On .. 10.00	
207 JKu(c),A Sparrow's Prayer . 10.00	
208 JKu(c),A Piece of Rag...And	
A Hank of Hair 10.00	
209 JKu(c),I'm Still Alive 10.00	
210 JKu(c),I'm Kilroy 10.00	
211 JKu(c),The Treasure of	
St. Daniel 10.00	
212 JKu(c),The Quiet War 10.00	
213 JKu(c),A Letter For Bulldozer 10.00	
214 JKu(c),Where Are You? ... 10.00	

215 JKu(c),Pied Piper of Peril .. 10.00	
216 JKu(c),Doom Over Easy,	
reprint from # 107 .... 25.00	
217 JKu(c),Surprise Party 8.00	
218 JKu(c),Medic! 8.00	
219 JKu(c),Yesterday's Hero 8.00	
220 JKu(c),Stone-Age War 8.00	
221 JKu(c),Hang-Up 8.00	
222 JKu(c),Dig In, Easy 8.00	
223 JKu(c),On Time 8.00	
224 JKu(c),One For The Money .. 8.00	
225 JKu(c),Face Front 8.00	
226 JKu(c),Death Stop 8.00	
227 JKu(c),Traitor's Blood 8.00	
228 JKu(c),It's A Dirty War 8.00	
229 JKu(c),The Battle of the	
Sergeants, reprint from #128. 15.00	
230 JKu(c),Home Is The Hunter .. 8.00	
231 JKu(c),My Brother's Keeper . 8.00	
232 JKu(c),3 Men In A Tub 8.00	
233 JKu(c),Head Count 8.00	
234 JKu(c),Summer In Salerno ... 8.00	
235 JKu(c),Pressure Point 8.00	
236 JKu(c),Face The Devil 8.00	
237 JKu(c),Nobody Cares 8.00	
238 JKu(c),I Kid You Not 8.00	
239 JKu(c),The Soldier 8.00	
240 JKu(c),NA 10.00	
241 JKu(c),War Story 8.00	
242 JKu(c),Infantry 8.00	
243 JKu(c),24 Hour Pass 10.00	
244 JKu(c),Easy's First Tiger ... 12.00	
245 JKu(c),The Prisoner 12.00	
246 JKu(c),Naked Combat 12.00	
247 JKu(c),The Vision 12.00	
248 JKu(c),The Firing Squad ... 12.00	
249 JKu(c),The Luck of Easy,WW 15.00	
250 JKu(c),90 Day Wonder 10.00	
251 JKu(c),The Iron Major 10.00	
252 JKu(c),The Iron Hand 10.00	
253 JKu(c),Rock and Iron 10.00	
254 JKu(c),The Town 10.00	
255 JKu(c),What's It Like 10.00	
256 JKu(c),School For Sergeants 10.00	
257 JKu(c),The Castaway 10.00	
258 JKu(c),The Survivors 10.00	
259 JKu(c),Lost Paradise 10.00	
260 JKu(c),Hell's Island 10.00	
261 JKu(c),The Medal That	
Nobody Wanted 10.00	
262 JKu(c),The Return 10.00	
263 JKu(c),The Cage 10.00	
264 JKu(c),The Hunt 10.00	
265 JKu(c),The Brother 10.00	
266 JKu(c),The Evacuees 10.00	
267 JKu(c),A Bakers Dozen 10.00	
268 JKu(c),The Elite 10.00	
269 JKu(c) 10.00	
270 JKu(c),Spawn of the Devil .. 10.00	
271 JKu(c),Brittle Harvest 10.00	
272 JKu(c),The Bloody Flag ... 10.00	
273 JKu(c),The Arena 10.00	
274 JKu(c),Home Is The Hero .. 10.00	
275 JKu(c),Graveyard Battlefield 10.00	
276 JKu(c),A Bullet For Rock .. 10.00	
277 JKu(c),Gashouse Gang 10.00	
278 JKu(c),Rearguard Action ... 10.00	
279 JKu(c),Mined City 10.00	
280 JKu(c),Mercy Mission 10.00	
281 JKu(c),Dead Man's Eyes ... 10.00	
282 JKu(c),Pieces of Time 10.00	
283 JKu(c),Dropouts 10.00	
284 JKu(c),Linkup 10.00	
285 JKu(c),Bring Him Back 10.00	
286 JKu(c),Firebird 10.00	

DC COMICS

287 JKu(c),The Fifth Dimension . 10.00
288 JKu(c),Defend-Or Destroy .. 10.00
289 JKu(c),The Line 10.00
290 JKu(c),Super-Soldiers 10.00
291 JKu(c),Death Squad 10.00
292 JKu(c),A Lesson In Blood .. 10.00
293 JKu(c),It Figures 10.00
294 JKu(c),Coffin For Easy 10.00
295 JKu(c),The Devil in Paradise 10.00
296 JKu(c),Combat Soldier 10.00
297 JKu(c),Percentages 10.00
298 JKu(c),Return to Chartres .. 10.00
299 JKu(c),Three Soldiers 10.00
300 JKu(c),300th Hill 10.00
301 JKu(c),The Farm 10.00
Becomes:

SGT. ROCK
1977–88
302 JKu(c),Anzio-The Bloodbath,
    part I 8.00
303 JKu(c),Anzio, part II 6.00
304 JKu(c),Anzio, part III 6.00
305 JKu(c),Dead Man's Trigger,
    reprint from #141 ...... 6.00
306 JKu(c),The Last Soldier 6.00
307 JKu(c),I'm Easy 6.00
308 JKu(c),One Short Step 6.00
309 JKu(c),Battle Clowns 6.00
310 JKu(c),Hitler's Wolf Children . 6.00
311 JKu(c),The Sergeant and
    the Lady 6.00
312 JKu(c),No Name Hill 6.00
313 JKu(c),A Jeep For Joey 6.00
314 JKu(c),Gimme Sky 6.00
315 JKu(c),Combat Antenna 6.00
316 JKu(c),Another Hill....... 6.00
317 JKu(c),Hell's Oven 6.00
318 JKu(c),Stone-Age War 6.00
319 JKu(c),To Kill a Sergeant ... 6.00
320 JKu(c),Never Salute a
    Sergeant 6.00
321 JKu(c),It's Murder Out Here . 5.00
322 JKu(c),The Killer 5.00
323 JKu(c),Monday's Hero 5.00
324 JKu(c),Ghost of a Tank 5.00
325 JKu(c),Future Kill, part I 5.00
326 JKu(c),Future Kill, part II ... 5.00
327 JKu(c),Death Express 5.00
328 JKu(c),Waiting For Rock 5.00
329 JKu(c),Dead Heat 5.00
330 JKu(c),G.I. Trophy 5.00
331 JKu(c),The Sons of War 5.00
332 JKu(c),Pyramid of Death 5.00
333 JKu(c),Ask The Dead 5.00
334 JKu(c),What's Holding Up
    The War 5.00
335 JKu(c),Killer Compass 5.00
336 JKu(c),The Red Maple Leaf . 5.00
337 JKu(c),A Bridge Called Charlie 5.00
338 JKu(c),No Escape From
    the Front 5.00
339 JKu(c),I Was Here Before ... 5.00
340 JKu(c),How To Win A War .. 5.00
341 JKu(c),High-Flyer 5.00
342 JKu(c),The 6 sides of
    Sgt. Rock 5.00
343 thru 350 .... @5.00
351 thru 422 .... @2.00

OUR FIGHTING FORCES
Oct.–Nov., 1954
1 IN,JGr(c),Human Booby Trap 700.00
2 RH,IN,IN(c),Mile-Long Step . 350.00
3 RA,JKu(c),Winter Ambush .. 300.00

Our Fighting Fources #8
© *DC Comics, Inc.*

4 RA,JGr(c),The Hot Seat ... 250.00
5 IN,RA,JGr(c),The Iron Punch 250.00
6 IN,RA,JGr(c),The Sitting Tank 200.00
7 RA,JKu,JGr(c),Battle Fist ... 200.00
8 IN,RA,JGr(c),No War
   For A Gunner 200.00
9 JKu,RH,JGr(c),Crash-
   Landing At Dawn 200.00
10 WW,RA,JGr(c),Grenade
   Pitcher 225.00
11 JKu,JGr(c),Diary of a Sub .. 150.00
12 IN,JKu,JGr(c),Jump Seat .. 150.00
13 RA,JGr(c),Beach Party 150.00
14 JA,RA,IN,JGr(c),Unseen War 150.00
15 RH,JKu,JGr(c),Target For
   A Lame Duck 150.00
16 RH,JGr(c),Night Fighter ... 150.00
17 RA,JGr(c),Anchored Frogman 150.00
18 RH,JKu,JGr(c),Cockpit Seat . 150.00
19 RA,JKu(c),Straighten ThatLine 150.00
20 RA,MD,JGr(c),The
   Floating Pilot 150.00
21 RA,JKu(c),The Bouncing
   Baby of Company B 100.00
22 JKu,RA,JGr(c),3 Doorways
   To War 100.00
23 RA,IN,JA,JGr(c),Tin Fish Pilot 100.00
24 RA,RH,JGr(c),Frogman Duel 100.00
25 RA,JKu(c),Dead End 100.00
26 IN,RH,JKu(c),Tag Day 100.00
27 MD,RA,JKu(c),TNT Escort . 100.00
28 RH,MD,JKu(c),AllQuiet atC.P 100.00
29 JKu,JKu(c),Listen To A Jet . 100.00
30 IN,RA,JKu(c),Fort
   For A Gunner 100.00
31 MD,RA,JKu(c),Silent Sub .. 90.00
32 RH,MD,RH(c),PaperWorkWar 90.00
33 RH,JKu,JKu(c),Frogman
   In A Net 90.00
34 JA,JGr,JKu(c),Calling U-217 . 90.00
35 JA,JGr,JKu(c),Mask of
   a Frogman 90.00
36 MD,JA,JKu(c),Steel Soldier .. 90.00
37 JA,JGr,JKu(c),Frogman
   In A Bottle 90.00
38 RH,RA,JGr(c),Sub Sinker .. 90.00
39 JA,RH,RH(c),Last Torpedo .. 90.00

40 JGr,JA,JKu,JKu(c),The
   Silent Ones 90.00
41 JGr,RH,JA,JKu(c),Battle
   Mustang 125.00
42 RH,MD,JGr(c),Sorry-
   Wrong Hill 75.00
43 MD,JKu,JGr(c),Inside Battle . 75.00
44 MD,RH,RA,JGr(c),Big Job
   For Baker 75.00
45 RH,RA,JGr(c),B:Gunner and
   Sarge, Mop-Up Squad . 275.00
46 RH,RA,JGr(c),Gunner'sSquad 125.00
47 RH,JKu(c),TNT Birthday 75.00
48 JA,RH,JGr(c),A Statue
   For Sarge 60.00
49 MD,RH,JGr(c),Blind Gunner . 80.00
50 JA,RH,JGr(c),I:Pooch,My
   Pal, The Pooch 60.00
51 RA,JA,RH(c),Underwater
   Gunner 50.00
52 MD,JKu,JKu(c),The Gunner
   and the Nurse 50.00
53 JA,RA,JGr(c),An Egg
   For Sarge 50.00
54 .... 50.00
55 MD,RH,JGr(c),The Last Patrol 50.00
56 RH,RA,JGr(c),Bridge of Bullets 50.00
57 JA,IN,JGr(c),A Tank For Sarge 50.00
58 JA,JGr(c),Return of the Pooch 50.00
59 RH,JA,JGr(c),Pooch-Patrol
   Leader 50.00
60 RH,JA,JGr(c),Tank Target ... 50.00
61 JA,JGr(c),Pass to Peril 50.00
62 JA,JGr(c),The Flying Pooch . 50.00
63 JA,RH,JGr(c),Pooch-Tank
   Hunter 50.00
64 JK,RH,JGr(c),A Lifeline
   For Sarge 50.00
65 IN,JA,JGr(c),Dogtag Patrol . 50.00
66 JKu,JA,JGr(c),Trail of the
   Ghost Bomber 50.00
67 IN,JA,JGr(c),Purple Heart
   For Pooch 50.00
68 JA,JGr(c),Col. Hakawa's
   Birthday Party 50.00
69 JA,JKu,JGr(c),
   Destination Doom 50.00
70 JA,JKu(c),The Last Holdout . 50.00
71 JA,JGr(c),End of the Marines 22.00
72 JA,JGr(c),Four-Footed Spy .. 18.00
73 IN,JGr(c),The Hero Maker ... 18.00
74 IN,JGr(c),Three On A T.N.T.
   Bull's-Eye 18.00
75 JKu(c),Purple Heart Patrol . 18.00
76 JKu(c),The T.N.T. Seat 18.00
77 JKu(c),No Foxhole-No Home 18.00
78 JGr(c),The Last Medal 18.00
79 JA,JKu(c),Backs to the Sea . 18.00
80 JA,JGr(c),Don't Come Back . 18.00
81 JA,JGr(c),Battle of
   the Mud Marines 18.00
82 JA,JGr(c),Battle of the
   Empty Helmets 18.00
83 RA,JKu(c),Any Marine
   Can Do It 18.00
84 JA,JKu(c),The Gun of Shame 18.00
85 Ja,JKu(c),The TNT Pin-Points 18.00
86 JKu(c),3 Faces of Combat .. 18.00
87 JKu(c),Battle o/t Boobytraps . 18.00
88 GC,JKu(c),Devil Dog Patrol .. 18.00
89 JKu(c),TNT Toothache 18.00
90 JKu(c),Stop the War 18.00
91 JKu(c),The Human Shooting
   Gallery 15.00
92 JA,JKu(c),The Bomb That

Stopped The War 15.00
93 IN,JKu(c),The Human Sharks   15.00
94 RH(c),E:Gunner,Sarge & Pooch,
   The Human Blockbusters . . . 15.00
95 GC,RH(c),B:The Fighting Devil
   Dog, Lt. Rock, The
   Fighting Devil Dog 15.00
96 JA,RH(c),Battle of Fire 15.00
97 IN(c),Invitation To A
   Firing Squad 15.00
98 IN(c),E:The Fighting Devil
   Dog, Death Wore A Grin 15.00
99 JA,JKu(c),B:Capt. Hunter,
   No Mercy in Vietnam 20.00
100 GC,IN(c),Death Also
    Stalks the Hunter 10.00
101 JA,RH(c),Killer of Vietnam . . 10.00
102 RH,JKu(c),Cold Steel
    For A Hot War 10.00
103 JKu(c),The Tunnels of Death 10.00
104 JKu(c),Night Raid In Vietnam 10.00
105 JKu(c),Blood Loyality 10.00
106 IN(c),Trail By Fury 10.00
107 IN(c),Raid Of The Hellcats . 10.00
108 IN(c),Kill The Wolf Pack . . . 10.00
109 IN(c),Burn, Raiders, Burn . . 10.00
110 IN(c),Mountains Full of Death 10.00
111 IN(c),Train of Terror 10.00
112 IN(c),What's In It For
    The Hellcats? 10.00
113 IN(c),Operation-Survival . . . 10.00
114 JKu(c),No Loot For The
    Hellcats 10.00
115 JKu(c),Death In The Desert . 10.00
116 JKu(c),Peril From the Casbah 10.00
117 JKu(c),Colder Than Death . . 10.00
118 JKu(c),Hell Underwater 10.00
119 JKu(c),Bedlam In Berlin . . . 10.00
120 JKu(c),Devil In The Dark . . . 10.00
121 JKu(c),Take My Place 10.00
122 JKu(c),24 Hours To Die . . . 10.00
123 JKu(c),B:Born Losers,No
    Medals No Graves 25.00
124 JKu(c),Losers Take All 10.00
125 Daughters of Death 10.00
126 JKu(c),Lost Town 10.00
127 JKu(c),Angels Over Hell's
    Corner 10.00
128 JKu(c),7 11 War 10.00
129 JKu(c),Ride The Nightmare . 10.00
130 JKu(c),Nameless Target . . . 10.00
131 JKu(c),Half A Man 10.00
132 JKu(c),Pooch, The Winner . 10.00
133 JKu(c),Heads or Tails 10.00
134 JKu(c),The Real Losers . . . 10.00
135 JKu(c),Death Picks A Loser 10.00
136 JKu(c),Decoy For Death . . . 10.00
137 JKu(c),God Of The Losers . 10.00
138 JKu(c),The Targets 10.00
139 JKu(c),The Pirate 10.00
140 JKu(c),Lost...One Loser . . . 10.00
141 JKu(c),Bad Penny, The 10.00
142 JKu(c), 1/2 A Man 10.00
143 JKu(c),Diamonds Are
    For Never 10.00
144 JKu(c),The Lost Mission . . . 10.00
145 JKu(c),A Flag For Losers . . 10.00
146 JKu(c),The Forever Walk . . 10.00
147 NA(c),The Glory Road 10.00
148 JKu(c),The Last Charge . . . 10.00
149 FT(c),A Bullet For
    A Traitor 10.00
150 JKu(c),Mark Our Graves . . . 10.00
151 JKu(c),Kill Me With Wagner 10.00
152 JK(c),A Small Place In Hell . 10.00

153 JK(c),Big Max 10.00
154 JK(c),Bushido,Live By The
    Code, Die By The Code 10.00
155 JK(c),The Partisans 10.00
156 JK(c),Good-Bye Broadway . 10.00
157 JK(c),Panama Fattie 10.00
158 JK(c),Bombing Out On
    The Panama Canal 10.00
159 JK(c),Mile-A-Minute Jones . 10.00
160 JKu(c),Ivan 10.00
161 JKu(c),The Major's Dream . 10.00
162 Gung-Ho 10.00
163 JKu(c),The Unmarked Graves 10.00
164 JKu(c),A Town Full Of Losers 10.00
165 LD(c),The Rowboat Fleet . . 10.00
166 LD(c),Sword of Flame 10.00
167 LD(c),A Front Seat In Hell . . 10.00
168 LD(c),A Cold Day To Die . . 10.00
169 JKu(c),Welcome Home-And
    Die 10.00
170 JKu(c),A Bullet For
    The General 10.00
171 JKu(c),A Long Day...
    A Long War 10.00
172 JKu(c),The Two-Headed Spy 10.00
173 JKu(c),An Appointment
    With A Direct Hit 10.00
174 JKu(c),Winner Takes-Death 10.00
175 JKu(c),Death Warrant 10.00
176 JKu(c),The Loser Is A
    Teen-Ager 10.00
177 JKu(c),This Loser Must Die . 10.00
178 JKu(c),Last Drop For Losers 10.00
179 JKu(c),The Last Loser 10.00
180 JKu(c),Hot Seat In A
    Cold War 10.00
181 JKu(c),Sept.–Oct., 1978 . . . 10.00

OUTCASTS
Oct., 1987

1 . . . . 2.00
2 thru 11 . . . . @1.75

OUTLAWS
1991

1 LMc,I:Hood 2.00
2 LMc,O:Hood 2.00
3 LMc,V:Evil King 2.00
4 LMc,V:Lord Conductor 2.00
5 LMc,Archery contest 2.00
6 LMc,Raid on King's Castle . . . 2.00
7 LMc,Refuge, V:Lord Conductor 2.00

OUTSIDERS, THE
Nov., 1985
[1st Regular Series]

1 JAp,I:Looker 3.00
2 JAp,V:Nuclear Family 2.50
3 JAp,V:Force of July 2.00
4 JAp,V:Force of July 2.00
5 JAp,Christmas Issue 2.00
6 JAp,V:Duke of Oil 2.00
7 JAp,V:Duke of Oil 2.00
8 JAp,Japan 2.00
9 JAp/SD/JOp,Bik Lightning . . . 2.00
10 JAp,I:Peoples Heroes 2.00
11 JAp,Imprisoned in death camp 1.75
12 JAp,Imprisoned in death camp 1.75
13 JAp,desert island 1.75
14 JAp,Looker/murder story 1.75
15 DJu,V:Bio-hazard 1.75
16 Halo vs.Firefly 1.75
17 JAp,J:Batman 1.75
18 JAp,BB,V:Eclipso 2.00

The Outsiders #1 © DC Comics, Inc.

19 JAp,V:Windfall 1.75
20 JAp,Masters of Disaster 1.75
21 JAp,V:Kobra,I:Clayface IV . . . 1.75
22 JAp,V:Strike Force Kobra 1.75
23 Return of People's Heroes . . . 1.75
24 TVE,JAp,V:Skull,A:Duke of Oil 1.75
25 JAp,V:Skull 1.75
26 JAp,in Markovia 1.75
27 EL,Millenium 1.75
28 EL,Millenium,final issue 1.75
Ann.#1,KN,V:Skull,A:Batman . . 2.50
Spec.#1,A:Infinity,Inc 1.75

[2nd Regular Series] 1993–95

1 Alpha,TC(c),B:MiB(s),PaP,
   I:Technocrat,Faust,Wylde 3.00
1a Omega,TC(c),PaP,V:Vampires 3.00
2 PaP,V:Sanction 2.00
3 PaP,V:Eradicator 2.00
4 PaP,A:Eradicator 2.00
5 PaP,V:Atomic Knight,A:Jihad . . 2.00
6 PaP,V:Jihad 2.00
7 PaP,C:Batman 2.00
8 PaP,V:Batman,I:Halo 2.00
9 PaP,V:Batman 2.00
10 PaP,B:Final Blood, R:Looker . 2.25
11 PaP,Zero Hour,E:Final Blood . 2.00
12 PaP 2.00
13 New base 2.00
14 Martial Arts Spectacular 2.00
15 V:New Year's Evil 2.00
16 R:Windfall 2.00
17 A:Green Lantern 2.00
18 Sins of the Father 2.00
19 Sins of the Father, pt.2 . . . . . . 2.25
20 DvA,V:Metamorpho 2.25
21 A:Apokolips 2.25
22 Alien Assassin 2.25
23 V:Defilers 2.25
24 finale 2.25

PARALLAX:
EMERALD NIGHT

1 RMz(s),MMK,MkK, pivotal tie-in
   to Final Night 4.50

All comics prices listed are for *Near Mint* condition.

Peacemaker #2 © DC Comics, Inc.

PEACEMAKER
Jan., 1988
1 A:Dr.Tzin-Tzin 1.25
2 The Wages of Tzin 1.25
3 and 4 . . . . @1.25

PENGUIN TRIUMPHANT
1 JSon,A:Batman,Wall Street . . . 6.00

Peter Porkchops #10
© DC Comics, Inc.

PETER CANNON: THUNDERBOLT
1992–93
1 thru 6 MC . . . . @1.50
7 MC,'Battleground' 1.50
8 MC,Cairo Kidnapped 1.50
9 MC 1.50
10 MC,A:JLA 1.50
11 MC,V:Havoc,A:Checkmate . . . 1.50

---

12 MC,final Issue 1.25

PETER PANDA
Aug.–Sept., 1953
1 . . . . 165.00
2 . . . . 95.00
3 thru 9 . . . . @60.00
10 Aug.–Sept., 1958 . . . . 60.00

PETER PORKCHOPS
Nov.–Dec., 1949
1 . . . . 250.00
2 . . . . 125.00
3 thru 10 . . . . @100.00
11 thru 30 . . . . @75.00
31 thru 61 . . . . @50.00
62 Oct.–Dec., 1960 . . . . 50.00

PHANTOM, THE
Oct., 1987
1 JO,A:Modern Phantom,13th
Phantom 2.00
2 JO,Murder Trial in Manhattan . 1.50
3 JO,A:Chessman 1.50
4 JO,V:Chessman,final issue . . . 1.50

PHANTOM, THE
1989–90
1 LMc,V:Gun Runners 2.50
2 LMc,V:Gun Runners 2.00
3 LMc,V:Drug Smugglers 1.75
4 LMc,In America,A:Diana Palner 1.75
5 LMc,Racial Riots 1.50
6 LMc,in Africa,Toxic Waste
Problem 1.50
7 LMc,'Gold Rush' 1.50
8 LMc,'Train Surfing' 1.50
9 LMc,'The Slave Trade' 1.50
10 LMc,Famine in Khagana 1.50
11 LMc,Phantom/Diana Wedding
proposal 1.50
12 LMc,Phantom framed for
murder 1.50
13 W:Phantom & Diana Palner
C:Mandrake last issue 1.50

PHANTOM STRANGER
Aug.–Sept., 1952
1 . . . . 1,500.00
2 . . . . 900.00
3 . . . . 750.00
4 . . . . 750.00
5 . . . . 750.00
6, June-July, 1953 . . . . 750.00

PHANTOM STRANGER
May-June, 1969
1 Cl rep.&new material 75.00
2 Cl rep.&new material 30.00
3 Cl rep.&new material 25.00
4 NA,I:Tala,1st All-new issue . . 30.00
5 MSy,MA,A:Dr.13 . . . . 25.00
6 MSy,A:Dr.13 . . . . 25.00
7 JAp,V:Tala 25.00
8 JAp,A:Dr.13 . . . . 25.00
9 JAp,A:Dr.13 . . . . 25.00
10 JAp,I:Tannarak 25.00
11 JAp,V:Tannarak 15.00
12 JAp,TD,Dr.13 solo story 15.00
13 JAp,TD,Dr.13 solo 15.00
14 JAp,TD,Dr.13 solo 15.00
15 JAp,ATh(rep),TD,Iron Messiah 10.00
16 JAp,TD,MMes(rep)Dr.13 solo 10.00

Phantom Stranger #33
© DC Comics, Inc.

17 JAp,I:Cassandra Craft 10.00
18 TD,Dr.13 solo 10.00
19 JAp,TD,Dr.13 solo 10.00
20 JAp,'And A Child
Shall Lead Them' 10.00
21 JAp,TD,Dr.13 solo 6.00
22 JAp,TD,I:Dark Circle 6.00
23 JAp,MK,I:Spawn-Frankenstein . 6.00
24 JAp,MA,Spawn Frankenstein . 6.50
25 JAp,MA,Spawn Frankenstein . 6.00
26 JAp,A:Frankenstein 6.00
27 V:Dr. Zorn 6.00
28 BU:Spawn of Frankenstein . . . 6.00
29 V:Dr.Zorn,BU:Frankenstein . . 6.00
30 E:Spawn of Frankenstein 6.00
31 B:BU:Black Orchid 7.00
32 NR,BU:Black Orchid 7.00
33 MGr,A:Deadman 6.50
34 BU:Black Orchid 7.00
35 BU:Black Orchid 7.00
36 BU:Black Orchid 7.00
37 "Crimson Gold,"BU:BlackOrchid 7.00
38 "Images of the Dead" 7.00
39 A:Deadman 6.00
40 A:Deadman 6.00
41 A:Deadman 6.00

PHANTOM STRANGER
Oct., 1987–Jan. 1988
1 MMi,CR,V:Eclipso 3.00
2 and 4 MMi,CR,V:Eclipso . . . @2.25

PHANTOM ZONE, THE
Jan., 1982
1 GD/TD,A:Jax-Ur 1.25
2 GC/TD,A:JLA 1.25
3 GC/TD,A:Mon-El 1.25
4 GC/TD 1.25

PICTURE STORIES FROM THE BIBLE
Autumn, 1942–43
1 thru 4 Old Testament . . . @150.00
1 thru 3 New Testament . . . @175.00

All comics prices listed are for *Near Mint* condition.

PINKY AND THE BRAIN
Warner Bros./DC
1 thru 4	@1.75
5 Oklahoma crud	1.75
6 "Plan Brain From Outer Space"	1.75
7 Yuletide tale	1.75
8	1.75
9 SML(s) back to school	1.75
10 V:Melmouse	1.75
11 "Narftasia"	1.75
12 "Beach Blanket Brain"	1.75
13 "Ali Brain and the Forty Thieves"	1.75
14 "Brainlet"	1.75
15 "Biker Mamas from Heck"	1.75
16 "Verminator II:Judgment Night"	2.00
17 Halloween	2.00
18 "Braintech", Manga-style issue	2.00
19 "Anti-Claus"	2.00
20 "The Mice in Pink"	2.00
21	2.00
22 "The Mouse in the Iron Mask"	2.00
23 King of the Sea Monkeys	2.00
24 Love with Cupcake	2.00
25 Dark Pinky	2.00
26 G.I. Brain	2.00

PLASTIC MAN
[1st Series]
Nov.–Dec., 1966
1 GK,I:Dr.Drome (1966 series begins)	60.00
2 V:The Spider	20.00
3 V:Whed	20.00
4 V:Dr.Dome	20.00
5 1,001 Plassassins	20.00
6 V:Dr.Dome	20.00
7 O:Plastic Man Jr.,A:Original Plastic Man,Woozy Winks	20.00
8 V:The Weasel	12.00
9 V:Joe the Killer Pro	12.00
10 V:Doll Maker(series ends)	12.00
11 (1976 series begins)	6.00
12 I:Carrot-Man	6.00
13 A:Robby Reed	6.00
14 V:Meat By-Product & Sludge	6.00
15 I:Snuffer,V:Carrot-Man	6.00
16 V:Kolonel Kool	6.00
17 O:Plastic Man	6.00
18 V:Professor Klean	6.00
19 I&Only App.Marty Meeker	6.00
20 V:Snooping Sneetches Oct.–Nov., 1977	6.00

PLASTIC MAN
1988–89
1 Mini-series,Origin retold	1.25
2 V:The Ooze Brothers	1.25
3 In Los Angeles	1.25
4 End-series,A:Superman	1.25

PLOP!
Sept.–Oct., 1973
1 SA-AA,GE,ShM	5.00
2 AA,SA	4.00
3 AA,SA	4.00
4 BW,SA	4.00
5 MA,MSy,SA	4.00
6 MSy,SA	4.00
7 SA	3.50
8 SA	3.50
9 SA	3.50
10 SA	3.50
11 ATh,SA	4.00
12 SA	3.50

13 WW(c),SA	5.00
14 WW,SA	5.00
15 WW(c),SA	5.00
16 SD,WW,SA	5.00
17 SA	3.50
18 SD,WW,SA	5.00
19 WW,SA	5.00
20 SA,WW	5.00
21 JO,WW	5.00
22 JO,WW,BW	5.00
23 BW,WW	3.00
24 SA,WW,Nov.–Dec., 1976	2.00

POWER GIRL
[Mini-Series] 1988
1	1.00
2 A:The Weaver, mongo Krebs	1.00
3 V:The Weaver	1.00
4 V:Weaver, final issue	1.00

POWER OF SHAZAM!
1995–97
1 R:Captain Marvel	2.00
2 V:Arson Fiend	1.50
3 V:Ibac	1.50
4 JOy,R:Mary Marvel,Tawky, Tawny	1.75
5 JOy(c&a),F:Mary Marvel, V:Black Adam	1.75
6 R:Captain Marvel	1.75
7 V:Captain Nazi	1.75
8 R:Captain Marvel,Jr.	1.75
9 JOy,MM,V:Black Adam	1.75
10 JOy,MM,V:Seven Deadly Enemies of Man	1.75
11 JOy,MM,R:Ibis as Captain Marvel	1.75
12 JOy,MM,How Billy Batson's father met Shazam	1.75
13 JOy,MM	1.75
14 JOy,GK,MM,F:CaptainMarvelJr	1.75
15 JOy,MM,V:Mr.Mind	1.75
16 thru 18	@1.75
19 JOy(s),GK,MM,Captain Marvel Jr. V:Captain Nazi	1.75
20 JOy(s),PKr,MM,A:Superman	1.75
21 JOy(s),PKr,MM,V:Liquidator	1.75
22 JOy(s),PKr,MM,A:Batman	1.75
23 JOy(s),PKr,MM	1.75
24 JOy(s),PKr,MM,V:Baron Blitz-krieg, prelude to new family	1.75
25 JOy(s),PKr,MM,The Marvel Family '97	1.75
26 JOy(s),PKr,MM,new Capt. Marvel framed for murder	1.75
27 JOy(s),PKr,MM,D:Captain Marvel	1.75
28 JOy(s),DG, V:Patty Patty Bang Bang	1.75
29 JOy(s),DG,F:Hoppy	1.75
30 JOy(c),PKr,DG,V:Mr. Finish	1.75
31 JOy,PKr,DG,Genesis x-over	2.00
32 JOy,PKr,DG,Genesis aftermath	2.00
33 JOy,PKr,DG,Madam M, Sin	2.00
34 JOy,PKr,DG,F:Gangbuster	2.00
35 JOy,PKr,DG,Lightning & Stars, pt.2 x-over	2.00
36 JOy	2.00
37 JOy,MM,DG,F:Capt.Marvel Jr.	2.00
38 JOy,PKr,DG,Monster Society of Evil, pt.1	2.00
39 JOy,PKr,DG,Monster, pt.2	2.00
40 JOy,PKr,DG,Monster, pt.3	2.00
41 JOy,PKr,DG,Monster, pt.4	2.00
42 JOy,DG,new logo & design	2.00

43 JOy,DG,I:Bulletgirl	2.50
Ann.#1 JOy(s),MM,"Legends of the Dead Earth"	2.95
HC JOy(a&s),O:Captain Marvel	22.00
GNv JOy(a&s),O:Captain Marvel	9.95
TPB JOy, reoffer	7.50

Power of the Atom #2
© DC Comics, Inc.

POWER OF THE ATOM
1988–89
1 1st Issue, Origin retold	1.25
2 Return of Powers	1.25
3 I:Strobe	1.25
4 A:Hawkman+bonus book #8	1.25
5 DT,A:Elongated Man	1.25
6 JBy,V:Chronos	1.25
7 GN,Invasion,V:Khunds,Chronos	1.25
8 GN,Invasion,V:Chronos	1.25
9 GN,A:Justice League	1.25
10 GN,I:Humbug	1.25
11 GN,V:Paul Hoben	1.25
12 GN,V:Edg the Destroyer	1.25
13 GN,Blood Stream Journey	1.25
14 GN,V:Humbug	1.25
15 GN,V:Humbug	1.25
16 GN,V:The CIA	1.25
17 GN,V:The Sting	1.25
18 GN,V:The CIA, last issue	1.25

PREACHER
Vertigo 1995–97
1 I:Jesse Custer, Genesis	50.00
2 Saint of Killers	45.00
3 GF(c),I:Angels	40.00
4 GF(c),V:Saint of Killers	30.00
5 Naked City,pt.1	25.00
6 Naked City,pt.2	20.00
7 Naked City,pt.3	15.00
8 GEn,SDi,All in the Family,pt.1	9.00
9 GEn,SDi,All in the Family,pt.2	9.00
10 GEn,SDi,All in the Family,pt.3	8.00
11 GEn,SDi,All in the Family,pt.4	8.00
12 GEn,SDi,All in the Family,pt.5	10.00
13 GEn,SDi,Hunters,pt.1	5.00
14 GEn,SDi,Hunters,pt.2 (of 4)	4.00
15 and 16	@4.00
17 Star captures Cassidy	3.00

All comics prices listed are for *Near Mint* condition.

18 GEn(s),SDi,secret of Jesse
   Custer's cigarette lighter 3.00
19 GEn(s),SDi,"Crusaders," pt.1 . . 3.00
20 GEn(s),SDi,"Crusaders," pt.2 . . 3.00
21 GEn(s),SDi,"Crusaders," pt.3 . . 3.00
22 GEn(s),SDi,"Crusaders," pt.4 . . 3.00
23 GEn(s),SDi,"Crusaders," pt.5 . . 3.00
24 GEn(s),SDi,"Crusaders" concl. 3.00
25 GEn(s),SDi,"Cry Blood, Cry
   Erin" 3.00
26 GEn(s),SDi,"To the Streets of
   Manhattan I Wandered Away" . 2.50
27 GEn(s),SDi, Jessie & Tulip in
   New York, pt.1 . . . . 2.50
28 GEn(s),SDi, Jessie & Tulip in
   New York, pt.2 . . . . 2.50
29 GEn(s),SDi, south to New
   Orleans 2.50
30 GEn,SDi,in New Orleans . . . 2.50
31 GEn,SDi,in New Orleans . . . 2.50
32 GEn,SDi,in New Orleans . . . 2.50
33 GEn,SDi,in New Orleans,concl. 2.50
34 GEn,SDi,War in the Sun,pt.1 . 2.50
35 GEn,SDi,War in the Sun,pt.2 . 2.50
36 GEn,SDi,War in the Sun,pt.3 . 2.50
37 GEn,SDi,War in the Sun,pt.4 . 2.50
38 GEn,SDi,GF,Utah radioactive . 2.50
39 GEn,SDi,GF,out of the desert . 2.50
40 GEn,SDi,GF,Arsefaced World . 2.50
41 . . . . 2.50
42 GEn(s),SDi,GF,V:Meatman . . 2.50
TPB Gone to Texas, rep.#1–#7 . 15.00
TPB Proud Americans GEn(s) . . 15.00
TPB Until the End of the World . 15.00
TPB Ancient History 15.oo

**PREACHER SPECIAL:
CASSIDY:
BLOOD AND WHISKY**
DC/Vertigo (Dec. 1997)
GN GEn(s) 6.00

**PREACHER SPECIAL:
SAINT OF KILLERS**
DC/Vertigo 1996
1 GEn(s),StP 6.00
2 GEn(s),StP 4.50
3 GEn(s),StP 3.50
4 GEn(s),StP 3.00

**PREACHER SPECIAL:
THE GOOD OLD BOYS**
DC/Vertigo
Spec. pardoy 5.50

**PREACHER SPECIAL:
THE STORY OF
YOU-KNOW-WHO**
DC/Vertigo Oct. 1996
1 one-shot, GEn(s),RCa,
   O:Arseface 5.00

PREZ
Aug.–Sept., 1973
1 I:Prez (from Sandman #54) . . 12.00
2 thru 4 F:Prez 8.00

PRIDE & JOY
DC/Vertigo May 1997
[Mini-series]
1 (of 4) GEn(s),JHi, ... 2.50

2 GEn(s),JHi 2.50
3 GEn(s),JHi 2.50
4 GEn(s),JHi,concl. 2.50

PRIMAL FORCE
1994–95
O New Team 2.00
1 Claw 2.00
2 Cataclysm 2.00
3 . . . . 2.00
4 Claw 2.00
5 V:Demons 2.00
6 V:The Four Beasts 2.00
7 Trip to the Past 2.00
8 N.Choles(p),I:New Team 2.25
9 Maltis worsens, Tornado speaks 2.25
10 V:August 2.25
11 . . . . 2.25
12 Black Condor vs. August . . . 2.25
13 Underworld Unleashed tie-in . 2.25
14 final issue 2.25

PRINCE
Piranha Press
1 DCw,KW,based on rock star . 10.00
1a Second printing 2.50
1b 3rd printing 2.00

PRISONER, THE
1988–89
1 Based on TV series 5.00
2 'By Hook or by Crook' 5.00
3 'Confrontation' 5.00
4 'Departure' final issue 5.00

PSYBA-RATS, THE
[Mini-Series] 1995
1 CDi,A:Robin 2.50
2 CDi,A:Robin 1.50
3 CDi,F:Razorsharp,final issue . . 1.50

PSYCHO
1 I:Psycho 12.00
2 Sonya Rescue 10.00
3 'Psycho against the World' . . . 7.00

QUEST FOR CAMELOT
June 1998
1-shot movie adaptation 5.00

QUESTION, THE
Feb., 1987
1 DCw,R:Question,I:Myra,A:Shiva 3.00
2 DCw,A:Batman,Shiva 2.00
3 DCw,I:Mayor Firman 2.00
4 DCw,V:Hatch 2.00
5 DCw,Hub City fall Apart 2.00
6 DCw,Abuse story 2.00
7 DCw,V:Mr.Volk 2.00
8 DCw,I:Mikado 2.00
9 DCw,O:Rodor 2.00
10 DCw,O:Rodor cont. 2.00
11 DCw,Transformation 2.00
12 DCw,Poisoned Ground 2.00
13 DCw,V:The Spartans 2.00
14 DCw,V:The Spartans 2.00
15 DCw,The Klan in Hub City . . 2.00
16 DCw,'Butch Cassidy &
   Sundance Kid' 2.00
17 DCw,A:Green Arrow 2.50
18 DCw,A:Green Arrow 2.50
19 DCw,V:Terrorists 2.00
20 DCw,Travelling Circus 2.00

21 DCw,V:Junior Musto 2.00
22 DCw,Election Night 2.00
23 DCw,Election Night contd . . . 2.00
24 DCw,Election Night contd . . . 2.00
25 DCw,Myra Critically Ill 2.00
26 A:Riddler 2.00
27 DCw 2.00
28 DCw,A:Lady Shiva 2.00
29 DCw,V:Lady Shiva 2.00
30 DCw,A:Lady Shiva 2.00
31 DCw,Hub City Chaos contd . 2.00
32 DCw,Identity Crisis 2.00
33 DCw,Identity Crisis contd . . . 2.00
34 DCw,Identity Crisis contd . . . 2.00
35 DCw,Fate of Hub City 2.00
36 DCw,final issue (contd.G.A.Ann#3
   Question Quarterly #1) 2.00
Ann.#1 DCw,A:Batman,G.A. . . . 3.00
Ann.#2 A:Green Arrow 4.00

QUESTION QUARTERLY
1 DCw 4.50
2 DCw 3.95
3 DCw(c) Film 2.95
4 DCw,MM,'Waiting for Phil' . . . 2.95
5 DCw,MMi,MM,last issue 2.95

RAGMAN
[1st Limited Series] 1976–77
1 I&O:Ragman 5.00
2 I:Opal 3.50
3 V:Mr. Big 3.00
4 JKu(1st interior on character) . 3.00
5 JKu,O:Ragman,final issue . . . 3.00
[2nd Limited Series] 1991–92
1 PB,O:Ragman 3.00
2 PB,O:Ragman Powers 3.00
3 PB,Original Ragman 2.75
4 PB,Gang War 2.75
5 PB,V:Golem 2.75
6 PB,V:Golem,A:Batman 2.75
7 PB,V:Golem,A:Batman 2.75
8 PB,V:Golem,A:Batman 2.75

**RAGMAN: CRY OF THE
DEAD**
1993–94
1 JKu(c),R:Ragman 2.00
2 JKu(c),A:Marinette 2.00
3 JKu(c),V:Marinette 2.00
4 JKu(c),Exorcism 2.00
5 JKu(c),V:Marinette 2.00
6 JKu(c),final issue 2.00

THE RAY
[Limited Series] 1992
1 JQ,ANi,I&O:Ray(Ray Torril) . . . 7.00
2 JQ,ANi,I:G.A. Ray 5.00
3 JQ,ANi,A:G.A. Ray 4.00
4 JQ,ANi,V:Dr.Polaris 6.00
5 JQ,ANi,V:Dr.Polaris 3.00
6 JQ,ANi,C:Lobo,final issue 3.00
TPB In A Blaze of Power 9.95
[Regular Series] 1994–96
1 JQ(c),RPr,V:Brinestone,
   A:Superboy 3.00
1a Newsstand Ed. 1.75
2 RPr,V:Brinestone,A:Superboy . 1.75
3 RPr,I:Death Masque 2.00
4 JQ(c),RPr,I:Death Masque,
   Dr. Polarus 2.00
5 JQ(c),RPr,V:G.A.Ray 2.00
6 JQ(c),RPr,V:Black Canary . . . 2.00

The Ray #1 © DC Comics, Inc.

7 JQ(c),RPr,V:Canary/Ray	2.00
8 V:Lobo,Black Canary	2.00
9 Ray Undoes the past	2.00
10 F:Happy Terrill	2.00
11 30 years in future	2.00
12 V:Mystech	2.00
13 V:Death Masque	2.25
14 The Ray needs help, V:Death Masque	2.25
15 F:Vandal Savage	2.25
16 D:Happy Terrill	2.25
17 I:Josh Terrill,V:Atomic Skull	2.25
18 Underworld Unleashed tie-in	2.25
19 Underworld Unleashed tie-in	2.25
20 F:Black Condor	2.25
21 Black Condor captured	2.25
22	2.25
23 V:Death Masque	2.25
24	2.25
25 double size	3.50
26	2.25
27	2.25
28 CPr,final issue	2.25
Ann.#1 Year One Annual	3.95

REAL FACT COMICS
March-April, 1946

1 S&K,Harry Houdini story	500.00
2 S&K, Rin-Tin-Tin story	350.00
3 H.G. Wells story	300.00
4 Jimmy Stewart story,B:Just Imagine	350.00
5 Batman & Robin(c)	1,500.00
6 O:Tommy Tomorrow	1,000.00
7 'The Flying White House'	150.00
8 VF,A:Tommy Tomorrow	500.00
9 S&K,Glen Miller story	250.00
10 'The Vigilante' by MMe	250.00
11 EK,'How the G-Men Capture Public Enemies!'	150.00
12 'How G-Men are Trained'	150.00
13 Dale Evans story	450.00
14 Will Rogers story,'Diary of Death'	125.00
15 A:The Master Magician-Thurston	125.00
16 A:Four Reno Brothers,	

T.Tommorrow	400.00
17'I Guard an Armored Car'	125.00
18 'The Mystery Man of Tombstone'	125.00
19 'The Weapon that Won the West'	125.00
20 JKu	150.00
21 JKu,July-Aug., 1949	125.00

REAL SCREEN COMICS
Spring, 1945

1 B:Fox & the Crow,Flippity & Flop	850.00
2 (fa)	400.00
3 (fa)	200.00
4 thru 7 (fa)	@150.00
8 thru 11 (fa)	@125.00
12 thru 20 (fa)	@90.00
21 thru 30 (fa)	@75.00
31 thru 40 (fa)	@50.00
41 thru 128 (fa)	@35.00

Becomes:

TV SCREEN CARTOONS

129 thru 137	@40.00
138 Jan.–Feb., 1961	40.00

R.E.B.E.L.S '94

0 New team	2.00
1 L.E.G.I.O.N.,Green Lantern	2.00
2 Dissent	2.00
3	2.00
4 Ship goes Insane	2.00

R.E.B.E.L.S '95

5 F:Dox	2.00
6 Dox Defeated	2.00
7 John Sin	2.00
8 V:Galactic Bank	2.25
9 F:Dox,Ignea,Garv,Strata	2.25
10 V:World Bank	2.25
11	2.25
12 F:Iceman Assassin	2.25
13 Underworld Unleashed tie-in	2.25
14 F:Lyrl Dox	2.25

R.E.B.E.L.S. '96

15 V:Lyrl Dox	2.25
16 V:Lyrl Dox's satellite	2.25

RED TORNADO
1985

1 CI/FMc	1.25
2 CI/FMc,A:Superman	1.25
3 CI/FMc	1.25
4 CI/FMc	1.25

RESTAURANT AT THE END OF THE UNIVERSE
1994

1 Adapt. 2nd book in Hitchhikers' Guide to the Galaxy, I:The Restaurant	7.00
2 V:The Meal	7.00
3 Final issue	7.00

RESURRECTION MAN
March 1997

1 DAn(s),JG,lenticular death's head cover	7.00
2 DAn(s),JG,V:Amazo	5.00
3 DAn(s),JG,"Scorpion Memories" pt.1 (of 3)	2.50
4 DAn(s),JG,"Scorpion Memories" pt.2	2.50

5 DAn(s),JG,"Scorpion Memories" pt.3 concl.	2.50
6 DAn&ALa(s),JoP,Genesis tie-in	2.50
7 DAn&ALa(s),TGb,BG,A:Batman	2.50
8 DAn&ALa(s),BG,Big Howler	2.50
9 DAn&ALa(s),F:Hitman, pt.1	2.50
10 DAn&ALa(s),F:Hitman, pt.2	2.50
11 DAn&ALa(s), Origin of the Species, pt.1	2.50
12 DAn&ALa(s), Origin of the Species, pt.2	2.50
13 DAn&ALa(s),Candy Man	2.50
14 DAn&ALa(s),really dead?	2.50
15 DAn&ALa(s),JG,V:Rider	2.50
16 DAn&ALa(s),BG,Avenging Angels x-over pt.1	2.50
17 DAn&ALa(s),BG,Avenging Angels x-over pt.3	2.50
18 DAn&ALa(s),A:Phantom Stranger, Deadman	2.50

Rima, The Jungle Girl #1 © DC Comics, Inc.

RICHARD DRAGON, KUNG FU FIGHTER
April-May, 1975

1 O:Richard Dragon	1.50
2 JSn/AM	1.50
3 JK	1.25
4 RE/WW	1.25
5 RE/WW	1.25
6 RE/WW	1.25
7 RE/WW	1.25
8 RE/WW	1.25
9 RE	1.25
10 RE	1.25
11 RE	1.25
12 RE	1.25
13 thru 17 RE	@1.25
18 Nov.–Dec., 1977	1.25

RIMA, THE JUNGLE GIRL
April-May, 1974

1 NR,I:Rima,O:Pt. 1	2.00
2 NR,O:Pt.2	1.50
3 NR,O:Pt.3	1.25

DC COMICS

4 NR,O:Pt.4 . . . . 1.25	
5 NR 1.25	
6 NR 1.25	
7 April-May, 1975 . . . . 1.25	

RING, THE
1 GK,Opera Adaption 12.00
2 GK,Sigfried's Father's Sword . . 7.00
3 GK,to save Brunhilde 6.00
4 GK, final issue 6.00
TPB rep.#1 thru #4 . . . . 19.95

RIP HUNTER, TIME MASTER
March-April, 1961
1 . . . . 500.00
2 . . . . 250.00
3 thru 5 . . . . @150.00
6 and 7 4th . . . . @125.00
8 thru 15 . . . . @75.00
16 thru 20 . . . . @75.00
21 thru 28 . . . . @75.00
29 Nov.–Dec., 1965 . . . . 75.00

ROAD TO PERDITION
DC/Paradox/Pocket (April, 1998)
TPB 6"x8" 304pg., b&w 14.00

ROBIN
[1st Limited Series] 1991
1 TL,BB(c),Trial,pt.1(&Poster) . . . 5.00
1a 2nd printing 2.50
1b 3rd printing 1.50
2 TL,BB(c) Trial,pt.2 . . . . 2.50
2a 2nd printing 1.50
3 TL,BB(c) Trial,pt.3 . . . . 2.00
4 TL,Trial,pt.4 . . . . 2.00
5 TL,Final issue,A:Batman 2.00
TPB BB(c),rep.#1–#5,Batman
#455–#457 . . . . 7.95
[2nd Limited Series] 1991
[ROBIN II: THE JOKER'S WILD]
1 Direct,Hologram(c)Joker face . . 2.00
1a (c)Joker straightjacket 2.00
1b (c)Joker standing 2.00
1c (c)Batman 2.00
1d Newsstand(no hologram) 1.00
1e collectors set,extra holo. 5.00
2 Direct,Hologram(c) Robin/Joker
Knife 1.50
2a (c)Joker/Robin-Dartboard 1.50
2b (c)Robin/Joker-Hammer 1.50
2c Newsstand(no hologram) 1.00
2d collectors set,extra holo. 5.00
3 Direct,Holo(c)Robin standing . . 1.50
3a (c)Robin swinging 1.50
3b Newsstand(no hologram) 1.50
3c collectors set,extra holo. 3.00
4 Direct,Hologram 1.50
4a Newsstand (no hologram) 1.25
4b collectors set,extra holo. 1.50
Collectors set (#1 thru #4) 30.00
[3rd Limited Series] 1992–93
[ROBIN III: CRY OF THE HUNTRESS]
1 TL,A:Huntress,Collector's Ed.
movable(c),poster 3.00
1a MZ(c),Newsstand Ed. 1.50
2 TL,V:KGBeast,A:Huntress 2.75
2a MZ(c),Newsstand Ed 1.50
3 TL,V:KGBeast,A:Huntress 2.75
3a MZ(c),newsstand Ed. 1.50
4 TL,V:KGBeast,A:Huntress 2.75
4a MZ(c),newsstand Ed. 1.50

5 TL,V:KGBeast,A:Huntress 2.75
5a MZ(c),newsstand Ed. 1.50
6 TL,V:KGBeast,King Snake,
A:Huntress. 2.75
6a MZ(c),Newsstand Ed. 1.50
[Regular Series] 1993–97
1 B:CDi(s),TG,SHa,V:Speedboyz 4.00
1a Newstand Ed. 2.00
2 TG,V:Speedboyz 2.00
3 TG,V:Cluemaster,
Electrocutioner 1.75
4 TG,V:Cluemaster,Czonk,
Electrocutioner 1.75
5 TG,V:Cluemaster,Czonk,
Electrocutioner 1.75
6 TG,A:Huntress 1.75
7 TG,R:Robin's Father 2.00
8 TG,KnightsEnd#5,A:Shiva . . . 3.00
9 TG,Knights End:Aftermath 2.25
10 TG,Zero Hour,V:Weasel 1.50
11 New Batman 1.50
12 Robin vs. thugs 1.50
13 V:Steeljacket 1.50
14 CDi(s),TG,Return of Bruce
Wayne,Troika,pt.4 . . . . 1.50
14a Collector's edition 2.50
15 Cluemaster Mystery 1.50
16 F:Spoiler 1.50
17 I:Silver Monkey,V:King Snake,Lynx
[New Miraweb format begins] . 2.00
18 Gotham City sabotaged 2.00
19 V:The General 2.00
20 F:Robin 2.00

Robin (1st Limited Series) #1
© DC Comics, Inc.

21 Ninja Camp,pt.1 . . . . 2.00
22 CDi,TG,Ninja Camp,pt.2 . . . . . 2.00
23 CDi,Underworld Unleashed tie-in2.00
24 CDi,V:Charaxes 2.00
25 CDi,F:Green Arrow 2.00
26 . . . . 2.00
27 . . . . 2.00
28 CDi,Contagion: conclusion . . . 2.00
29 CDi,FFo,SnW,A:Maxie Zeus . . 2.00
30 CDi,FFo,SnW,A:Maxie Zeus . . 2.00
31 CDi(s),A:Wildcat 2.00
32 CDi(s),Legacy, pt. 3 x-over . . . 2.00
33 CDi(s),Legacy, pt. 7 x-over . . . 2.00

34 CDi(s),JhD,action at a
Shakespear play 2.00
35 CDi(s),Robin & Spoiler, Final
Night tie-in 2.00
36 CDi(s),V:Toyman, The General 2.00
37 CDi(s),V:The General, Toyman 2.00
38 CDi(s), ... 2.00
39 CDi(s), pt.2 . . . . 2.00
40 CDi(s), ... 2.00
41 CDi(s),F:Tim and Ariana 2.00
42 CDi(s),F:Crocky the Crocodile . 2.00
43 CDi(s),A:Spoiler 2.00
44 CDi(s) Pt.2 (of 2) 2.00
45 CDi(s) Tim Drake grounded . . 2.00
46 CDi(s) Genesis tie-in 2.00
47 CDi,V:General, pt.1 . . . . 2.00
48 CDi,V:General, pt.2 . . . . 2.00
49 CDi,to Paris 2.00
50 CDi(s),F:Lady Shiva & King
Snake, 48pg 3.00
51 CDi(s) 2.00
52 CDi(s) Cataclysm x-over,pt.7 . 2.00
53 CDi(s),SnW,Cataclysm concl. . 2.00
54 CDi(s),SnW,Aftershock 2.00
55 CDi(s),SnW, Brotherhood of
the Fist x-over, pt.3 . . . . 2.00
56 CDi(s),SnW,tearful turning point 2.00
57 CDi(s),SnW,A:Spoiler 2.00
58 CDi(s),SnW,A:Spoiler 2.00
Ann.#1 TL,Eclipso tie-in,V:Anarky 3.00
Ann.#2 KD,JL,Bloodlines#10,
I:Razorsharp 2.75
Ann.#3 Elseworlds Story 3.25
Ann.#4 Year One Annual 2.95
Ann.#5 CDi,Legends of the Dead
Earth 2.95
Ann.#5 Legends o/t Dead Earth . . 2.95
Ann.#6 Pulp Heroes (Western),
CDi(s) 3.95
TPB A Hero Reborn,JAp,TL 4.95
TPB Tragedy and Triumph,
TL,NBy 9.95

ROBIN/ARGENT DOUBLE-SHOT
Dec., 1997
1-shot DJu,CDi,V:Spoiler x-over . . 2.00

ROBIN PLUS
1 MWa&BAu(s), F:Bart Allen, skiing
rips, V:Mystral 2.95
2 LKa,CDi,AWi,ALa,F:Fang 3.00

ROBIN 3000
1 CR,Elseworlds,V:Skulpt 5.25
2 CR,Elseworlds,V:Skulpt 5.25

ROBIN HOOD TALES
Jan.–Feb., 1957–Mar.–Apr., 1958
7 . . . . 200.00
8 thru 14 . . . . @175.00

ROBOTECH DEFENDERS
1 MA,mini-series 3.50
2 MA 3.00

ROGAN GOSH
Vertigo 1994
1 PF PrM(s) (From Revolver) . . . 7.25

RONIN
July, 1983
1 FM,1:Billy 6.00
2 FM,I:Casey 5.00
3 FM,V:Agat 5.00
4 FM,V:Agat 5.00
5 FM,V:Agat 6.00
6 FM,D:Billy 8.00
Paperback, FM inc. Gatefold . . . 12.00

ROOTS OF THE SWAMP THING
July, 1986
1 BWr,rep.SwampThing#1&#2 . . 3.00
2 BWr,rep.SwampThing#3&#4 . . 3.00
3 BWr,rep.SwampThing#5&#6 . . 3.00
4 BWr,rep.SwampThing#7&#8 . . 3.00
5 BWr,rep.SwampThing#9&#10,
H.O.S. #92, final issue 3.00

Rudolph The Red-Nosed Reindeer 1955–56 © DC Comics, Inc.

RUDOLPH THE RED -NOSED REINDEER
Dec., 1950
1950 . . . . 60.00
1951 thru 1954 . . . . @50.00
1955 thru 1962 Winter . . . . . @30.00

SAGA OF RĀS AL GHŪL
1988
1 NA,DG,reprints 5.00
2 rep. 4.00
3 rep.Batman #242&#243 . . . . . . 4.00
4 rep.Batman #244&#245,
Detective #410 . . . . 4.00
TPB reps. 17.95

SAGA OF THE SWAMP THING
1982–85
1 JmP(s),TY,DSp,O:Swamp Thing,
BU:PhantomStranger 4.00
2 Ph(c),TY,DSp,I:Grasp 2.00
3 TY,DSp,V:Vampires 2.00

4 TY,TD,V:Demon 2.00
5 TY 2.00
6 TY,I:General Sunderland 2.00
7 TY 2.00
8 TY 2.00
9 TY 2.00
10 TY 2.00
11 TY,I:Golem 2.00
12 LWn(s),TY 2.00
13 TY,D:Grasp 2.00
14 A:Phantom Stranger 2.00
15 . . . . 2.00
16 SBi,JTo 2.00
17 I:Matthew Cable 4.00
18 JmP(s),LWn(s),SBi,JTo,BWr,
R:Arcane 2.00
19 JmP(s),SBi,JTo,V:Arcane . . . 2.00
20 B:AMo(s),Day,JTo(i),D:Arcane
(Original incarnation) 17.00
21 SBi,JTo,O:Swamp Thing,I:Floronic
Man,D:General Sunderland . . 15.00
22 SBi,JTo,O:Floronic Man 10.00
23 SBi,JTo,V:Floronic Man 10.00
24 SBi,JTo,V:Floronic Man,A:JLA,
In Arkham 10.00
25 SBi,A:Jason Blood,I:Kamara . . 8.00
26 SBi,A:Demon,
D:Matthew Cable 8.00
27 SBi,D:Kamara,A:Demon 8.00
28 SwM,Burial of Alec Holland . . . 7.00
29 SBi,JTo,R:Arcane 7.00
30 SBi,AA,D:Abby,C:Joker,
V:Arcane 9.00
31 RV,JTo,D:Arcane 6.00
32 SwM,Tribute to WK Pogo strip . 6.00
33 rep.H.O.S.#92,A:Cain & Abel . 6.00
34 SBi,JTo,Swamp Thing & Abby
Fall in Love 8.00
35 SBi,JTo,Nukeface,pt.1 . . . . . . 5.00
36 SBi,JTo,Nukeface,pt.2 . . . . . . 5.00
37 RV,JTo,I:John Constantine,
American Gothic,pt.1 . . . . . . 18.00
38 SnW,JTo,V:Water-Vampires
(Pt.1) A:J.Constantine 7.00
39 SBi,JTo,V:Water-Vampires
(Pt.2) A:J.Constantine 6.00
40 SBi,JTo,C:J.Constantine,
The Curse 5.00
41 SBi,AA,Voodoo Zombies #1 . . 3.00
42 SBi,JTo,RoR,
Voodoo Zombies #2 . . . . 3.00
43 SnW,RoR,Windfall,
I:Chester Williams 3.00
44 SBi,JTo,RoR,V:Serial Killer,
C:Batman,Constantine,Mento . 5.00
45 SnW,AA,Ghost Dance 3.00
Ann.#1 MT,TD,Movie Adaption . . 2.00
Ann.#2 AMo(s),E:Arcane,A:Deadman,
Phantom Stranger,Spectre,
Demon,Resurrection of Abby . 7.00
Ann.#3 AMo(s),Ape issue 4.00
TPB rep.#21-#27 . . . . 12.95
TPB rep.#28-#34,Ann.#2 . . . . . 14.95
Becomes:
SWAMP THING

SANDMAN
[1st Regular Series] 1974–75
1 JK,I&O:Sandman,I:General
Electric 12.00
2 V:Dr.Spider 5.00
3 Brain that Blanked
out the Bronx 5.00
4 JK,Panic in the Dream Stream . 5.00

5 JK,Invasion of the Frog Men . . 5.00
6 JK,WW,V:Dr.Spider 6.00
[2nd Regular Series] 1989–93
1 B:NGa(s),SK,I:2nd Sandman . 70.00
2 SK,A:Cain,Abel 30.00
3 SK,A:John Constantine 25.00
4 SK,A:Demon 20.00
5 SK,A:Mr.Miracle,J'onnJ'onzz . 20.00
6 V:Doctor Destiny 18.00
7 V:Doctor Destiny 15.00
8 Sound of her wings,F:Death . 50.00
8a Guest Ed.Pin-Up Cover . . . 125.00
9 Tales in the Sand,Doll's House
prologue 9.00
10 B:Doll's House,A:Desire
& Despair,I:Brut & Glob 8.00
11 MovingIn,A:2ndS-man 8.00
12 Play House,D;2ndS'man 8.00
13 Men of Good Fortune,A:Death,
Lady Constantine 8.00
14 Collectors,D:Corinthian 9.00
15 Into' Night,DreamVortex 6.00
16 E:Doll's House,Lost Hearts . . . 6.00
17 Calliope 6.00
18 Dream of a 1000 Cats 6.00
18a error pg.1 . . . . 30.00
19 Midsummer Nights Dream . . . 5.00
19a error copy 35.00
20 Strange Death Element Girl,
A:Death 5.00
21 Family Reunion,B:Season
of Mists 6.00
22 Season of Mists,I:Daniel Hall 15.00
23 Season of Mists 6.00
24 Season of Mists 6.00
25 Season of Mists 5.00
26 Season of Mists 5.00
27 E:Season of Mists 5.00
28 Ownership of Hell 5.00
29 A:Lady J.Constantine 4.00
30 Ancient Rome;A:Death,Desire . 4.00
31 Ancient Rome,pt.2 . . . . 4.00
32 B:The Game of You 4.00
33 The Game of You 4.00
34 The Game of You 3.00
35 The Game of You 4.00
36 The Game of You,48pgs 4.00
37 The Game of You,Epilogue . . . 3.00
38 Convergence 2.50
39 Convergence,A:Marco Polo . . . 2.50
40 Convergence,A:Cain,Abel,Eve,
Matthew the Raven 2.50
41 JIT,VcL,(i),B:Brief Lives,
F:Endless 3.00
42 JIT,VcL,(i),F:Delirium,Dream . . 2.50
43 JIT,VcL,(i),A:Death,Etain 2.50
44 JIT,VcL,(i),R:Corinthian,
Destruction 2.50
45 JIT,VcL,(i),F:Tiffany,
Ishtar(Belli) 2.50
46 JIT,VcL,(i),F:Morpheus/Bast,A:AIDS
insert story,F:Death 3.00
Vertigo 1994–96
47 JIT,VcL,(i),A:Endless 3.50
48 JIT,VcL,(i),L:Destruction 3.50
49 JIT,VcL,(i),E:Brief Lives,
F:Orpheus 3.50
50 DMc(c),CR,Tales of Baghdad,
pin-upsby TM,DMc,MK 4.00
50a Gold Ed. 20.00
51 BT,MBu(i),B:Inn at the end of
the World,Gaheris' tale 3.00
52 BT,MBu(i),JWk,Cluracan's
Story 3.00
53 BT,DG,MBu(i),MZi,Hob's

DC COMICS

Leviathan 3.00	
54 BT,MiA,MBu(i),R:Prez 3.00	
55 SAp,VcL,BT,MBu(i),F:Klaproth	
Cerements's Story 3.00	
56 BT,MBu(i),DG(i),SLi(i),GyA,TyH(i),	
E:Inn at the end of the World,	
C:Endless 3.00	
57 MaH,B:Kindly Ones,Inc.American	
Freak Preview 4.00	
58 MaH,Kindly Ones,pt.2,	
A:Lucifer 2.50	
59 MaH,Kindly Ones,pt.3,R:Fury . 2.00	
60 MaH,Kindly Ones,pt.4 . . . . . . 2.00	
61 MaH,Kindly Ones,pt.5 . . . . . . 2.00	
62 Kindly Ones,pt.6,Murder 2.00	
63 MaH,Kindly Ones,pt.7,	
A:Rose Walker 2.00	
64 Kindly Ones,pt.8 . . . . 2.00	
65 MaH,Kindly Ones,pt.9,Dream	
Kingdom 2.00	
66 MaH,Kindly Ones,pt.10 . . . . . 2.00	
67 MaH,Kindly Ones,pt.11 . . . . . 2.00	
68 MaH,Kindly Ones,pt.12 . . . . . 2.00	
69 MaH,Kindly Ones finale 4.00	
70 The Wake,pt.1 . . . . 2.00	
71 The Wake,pt.2 . . . . 2.00	
72 NGa,DMc,The Wake,pt.3 . . 2.00	
73 NGa,Sunday Mourning 2.00	
74 NGa,V:Lord of Dreams 2.00	
TPB Preludes & Nocturnes,	
rep. #1–#8 . . . . 20.00	
TPB Doll's House, rep #8–#16 . . 18.00	
HC The Doll's House 29.95	
TPB Dream Country,Rep.#17–#20 15.00	
Fables and Reflections,HC,rep. . 29.95	
Season of Mists,HC,rep.#21–#28 40.00	
Season of Mists,SC 19.95	
TPB A Game of You,rep.#32–#37 20.00	
HC A Game of You,rep.#32–#37 32.00	
HC Brief Lives 29.95	
TPB Brief Lives 19.95	
TPB The Wake #70–#75 . . . . . 20.00	
TPB Fables & Reflections 19.95	
TPB World's End DMc(c) 19.95	
Sandman Covers, 1989–96 . . . 40.00	
Spec.BT,Glow in the Dark(c),The	
Legend of Orpheus,	
(inc. Portrait Gallery) 6.00	

SANDMAN MYSTERY THEATRE
Vertigo 1993–97

1 B:MWg(s),GyD,R:G.A.Sandman,	
B:Tarantula,I:Mr.Belmont,	
Dian Belmont 5.00	
2 GyD,V:Tarantula 3.00	
3 GyD,V:Tarantula 3.00	
4 GyD,E:Tarantula 3.00	
5 JWk,B:The Face 3.00	
6 JWk,The Face #2 . . . . 3.00	
7 JWk,The Face #3 . . . . 3.00	
8 JWk,E:The Face 3.00	
9 RGT,B:The Brute,I:Rocket	
Ramsey 3.00	
10 RGT,The Brute#2 . . . . 3.00	
11 RGT,The Brute#3 . . . . 3.00	
12 RGT,E:The Brute 3.00	
13 GyD,B:The Vamp 3.00	
14 GyD,The Vamp#2 . . . . 3.00	
15 GyD,The Vamp#3 . . . . 3.00	
16 GyD,E:The Vamp 3.00	
17 GyD,B:The Scorpion 3.00	
18 GyD,The Scorpion,pt.2 . . . . . . 3.00	
19 GyD,The Scorpion,pt.3 . . . . . . 3.00	

20 GyD,The Scorpion,pt.4 . . . . . . 3.00	
21 Dr. Death 3.00	
22 Dr. Death,pt.2 . . . . 3.00	
23 Dr. Death,pt.3 . . . . 3.00	
24 Dr. Death,pt.4 . . . . 3.00	
25 The Butcher,pt.1 . . . . 3.00	
26 The Butcher,pt.2 . . . . 3.00	
27 The Butcher,pt.3 . . . . 3.00	
28 The Butcher,pt.4 . . . . 3.00	
29 The Hourman,pt.1 . . . . 3.00	
30 The Hourman,pt.2 . . . . 3.00	
31 The Hourman,pt.3 . . . . 3.00	
32 The Hourman,pt.4 . . . . 3.00	
33 The Python,pt.1 . . . . 3.00	
34 The Python,pt.2 . . . . 3.00	
35 The Python,pt.3 . . . . 3.00	
36 The Python,pt.4 . . . . 3.00	
37 The Mist,pt.1 . . . . 3.00	
38 The Mist,pt.2 . . . . 3.00	
39 The Mist,pt.3 . . . . 3.00	
40 The Mist,pt.4 . . . . 3.00	
41 MWg&SSe(s),GyD, Phantom of	
the Fair pt. 1 . . . . 2.50	
42 MWg&SSe(s),GyD, Phantom of	
the Fair pt. 2 . . . . 2.50	
43 MWg&SSe(s),GyD, Phantom of	
the Fair pt. 3 . . . . 2.50	
44 MWg&SSe(s),GyD, Phantom of	
the Fair pt. 4 . . . . 2.50	
45 MWg&SSe(s),"The Blackhawk,"	
pt.1 . . . . 2.50	
46 MWg&SSe(s),"The Blackhawk,"	
pt.2 . . . . 2.50	
47 MWg&SSe(s),"The Blackhawk,"	
pt.3 . . . . 2.50	
48 MWg&SSe(s),RCa,"The	
Blackhawk" concl. 2.50	
49 MWg&SSe(s),"The Scarlet	
Ghost," pt.1 . . . . 2.50	
50 MWg&SSe(s),"The Scarlet	
Ghost," pt.2, 48pg 3.50	
51 MWg&SSe(s),"The Scarlet	
Ghost," pt.3 . . . . 2.50	
52 MWg&SSe(s),"The Scarlet	
Ghost," pt.4 . . . . 2.50	
53 MWg&SSe(s),The Crone,pt.1 . 2.50	
53 MWg&SSe(s),The Crone,pt.2 . 2.50	
54 SSe&MWg(s),The Crone,pt.3 . 2.50	
55 SSe&MWg(s),The Crone,pt.4 . 2.50	
56 SSe&MWg(s),The Crone, concl. 2.50	
57 SSe&MWg(s),The Cannon,pt.1 2.50	
58 SSe&MWg(s),The Cannon,pt.2 2.50	
59 SSe&MWg(s),The Cannon,pt.3 2.50	
60 SSe&MWg(s),The Cannon,pt.4 2.50	
61 SSe(s),GyD,The City, pt.1 . . . . 2.50	
62 SSe(s),GyD,The City, pt.2 . . . . 2.50	
63 SSe(s),GyD,The City, pt.3 . . . . 2.50	
64 SSe(s),GyD,The City, pt.4 . . . . 2.50	
65 SSe,GyD,The Goblin, pt.1 . . . . 2.50	
66 SSe,GyD,The Goblin, pt.2 . . . . 2.50	
Ann.#1 . . . . 3.95	
TPB The Tarantula 14.95	

SANDMAN: THE WAKE
DC/Vertigo
HC Rep. Sandman #70–#75 . . . 29.95

SCARAB
Vertigo 1993–94

1 GF(c),B:JnS(s),SEa,MkB(i),	
R&O:Scarab,V:Halaku-umid . . 2.25	
2 GF(c),SEa,MkB(i),A:Phantom	
Stranger 2.25	
3 GF(c),SEa,MkB(i),in North	

Carolina 2.25	
4 GF(c),SEa,MkB(i),V:Rathoroch . 2.25	
5 GF(c),SEa,MkB(i) 2.25	
6 GF(c),SEa,MkB(i),V:Gloryboys . 2.25	
7 GF(c),SEa,MkB(i),V:Scientists . 2.25	
8 GF(c),SEa,MkB(i),Final Issue . . 2.25	

SCARE TACTICS
Oct. 1996

1 LKa(s),AWi,ALa,monsters of	
the MTV age 2.25	
2 LKa(s),AWi,ALa,I:Scaremobile . 2.25	
3 LKa(s),AWi,ALa, ... 2.25	
4 LKa(s),AWi,ALa, "Big For His	
Age," O:Grossout 2.25	
5 LKa(s),AWi,ALa, Valentine's Day	
issue 2.25	
6 LKa(s),AWi,Ala, F:Fang 2.25	
7 LKa(s),AWi,ALa, F:The Children	
of the Beast 2.25	
8 LKa(s),AWi,ALa, Convergence,	
x-over, concl. 2.25	
9 LKa(s),AWi,ALa,"Snake Oil"	
concl. 2.25	
10 LKa(s),AWi,ALa,in Gotham . . 2.25	
11 LKa(s),AWi,ALa,A:Batman . . 2.25	

Scarlett #3 © DC Comics, Inc.

SCARLETT
1993–94

1 I:Scarlett,Blood of the Innocent 3.50	
2 Blood of the Innocent cont. . . . 1.75	
3 Blood of the Innocent cont. . . . 1.75	
4 V:The Nomads 1.75	
5 GM,O:Nomads 1.75	
6 thru 8 GM,Blood of the Damned 1.75	
9 GM,V:Undead 1.75	
10 B:Blood of the City 1.75	
11 I:Afterburn 1.75	
12 V:Sligoth 1.75	
13 V:Gearsman 1.75	
14 final issue 1.75	

SCRIBBLY
Aug.–Sept., 1948

1 SM 700.00	
2 . . . . 500.00	
3 . . . . 400.00	

4 . . . . 400.00	
5 . . . . 400.00	
6 thru 10 . . . . @275.00	
11 thru 15, Dec-Jan.1951–52 @250.00	

SCOOBY-DOO
Warner Bros./DC June 1997

1 . . . . 1.75
2 . . . . 1.75
3 A wedding 1.75
4 Mad Hounds of the Hunt 2.00
5 Freddy's Grampa Ted 2.00
6 Ghost Riders in Disguise 2.00
7 Mystery of the Missing Cargo . 2.00
8 . . . . 2.00
9 Mardi Gras 2.00
10 mystery convention 2.00
11 evil genie 2.00
12 comic book con. 2.00
13 real monster 2.00
14 beneath New York city 2.00
15 . . . . 2.00

SEA DEVILS
Sept.–Oct., 1961

1 RH 500.00
2 RH 250.00
3 RH 175.00
4 RH 150.00
5 RH 150.00
6 thru 10 RH . . . . @85.00
11 . . . . 65.00
12 . . . . 65.00
13 JKu,GC,RA 65.00
14 thru 20 . . . . @65.00
21 I:Capt X,Man Fish 40.00
22 thru 35, May-June, 1967 . . @40.00

SEBASTIAN O
Vertigo 1993

1 GMo(s),SY,I:Sebastian O,A:Lord
  Lavender,Roaring Boys 2.50
2 GMo(s),SY,V:Roaring Boys,
  Assassins,A:Abbe 2.50
3 GMo(s),SY,D:Lord Lavender . 2.50

SECRET HEARTS
Sept.–Oct., 1949

1 'Make Believe Sweetheart' . . 400.00
2 ATh,'Love Is Not A Dream' . 175.00
3 'Sing Me A Love Song' 150.00
4 ATh 150.00
5 ATh 150.00
6 . . . . 150.00
7 . . . . 200.00
8 . . . . 125.00
9 . . . . 125.00
10 thru 20 . . . . @125.00
21 thru 26 . . . . @75.00
27 B:Comics Code 50.00
28 thru 30 . . . . @50.00
31 thru 70 . . . . @45.00
71 thru 110 . . . . @25.00
111 thru 120 . . . . @20.00
121 thru 150 . . . . @10.00
151 thru 153, July 1971 . . . . . . @5.00

SECRET ORIGINS
Feb.–March, 1973

1 O:Superman,Batman,Ghost,
  Flash 8.00
2 O:Green Lantern,Atom,
  Supergirl 5.00

---

3 O:Wonder Woman,Wildcat 4.00
4 O:Vigilante by MMe 4.00
5 O:The Spectre 3.00
6 O:Blackhawk,Legion of Super
  Heroes 3.00
7 O:Robin, Aquaman,Oct.–
  Nov., 1974 . . . . 3.00

SECRET ORIGINS
April, 1986

1 JOy,WB,F:Superman 4.00
2 GK,F:Blue Beetle 3.50
3 JBi,F:Captain Marvel 3.00
4 GT,F:Firestorm 2.75
5 GC,F:Crimson Aventer 3.00
6 DG,MR,F:Batman 5.00
7 F:Sandman,Guy Gardner 3.50
8 MA,F:Shadow Lass,Dollman . 2.50
9 GT,F:Skyman,Flash 2.50
10 JL,JO,JA,F:Phantom Stranger . 2.25
11 LMc,TD,F:Hawkman,Powergirl 2.00
12 F:Challengers of the Unknown
  I:G.A. Fury 2.00
13 EL,F:Nightwing 3.00
14 F:Suicide Squad 2.25
15 KMo,DG,F:Deadman,Spectre . 2.25
16 AKu,F:Hourman,Warlord 2.00
17 KGi,F:Green Lantern 2.25
18 . . . . 2.00
19 JM(c),MA 2.00
20 RL,DG,F:Batgirl 3.00
21 GM,MA,F:Jonah Hex 2.00
22 F:Manhunter,Millenium tie-in . 2.00
23 F:Manhunter,Millenium tie-in . 2.00
24 F:Dr.Fate,Blue Devil 2.00

Secret Origin #6
© DC Comics, Inc.

25 F:The Legion 2.00
26 F:Black Lightning 2.00
27 F:Zatanna,Zatara 1.75
28 RLd,GK,F:Nightshade,Midnight 1.75
29 F:Atom,Red Tornado 1.75
30 F:Elongated Man 1.75
31 F:Justice Society of America. . 1.75
32 F:Justice League America. . . . 3.00
33 F:Justice League Inter.. . . . . . 2.00
34 F:Justice League Inter. 2.00
35 KSu,F:Justice League Inter. . . 2.00

---

36 F:Green Lantern 3.00
37 F:Legion of Subst. Heroes . . . 2.00
38 F:Green Arrow,Speedy 2.00
39 F:Batman,Animal Man 3.50
40 F:Gorilla City 2.00
41 F:Flash Villains 2.50
42 DC,F:Phantom Girl 2.00
43 TVE,TT,F:Hawk & Dove 2.00
44 F:Batman,Clayface tie-in 3.00
45 F:Blackhawk,El Diablo 2.00
46 CS,F:All Headquarters 2.00
47 CS,F:The Legion 2.00
48 KG,F:Ambush Bug 2.00
49 F: The Cadmus Project 2.50
50 GP,CI,DG,F:Batman,Robin,
  Flash,Black Canary 4.00
Ann.#1 JBy,F:Doom Patrol 3.00
Ann.#2 CI,MA,F:Flash 2.00
Ann.#3 F:The Teen Titans 3.00
Spec.#1 SK,PB,DG,F:Batman's worst
  Villians,A:Penguin 4.00
TPB DG,New Origin Batman 4.50
GN rep of 1961 Annual 5.00

SECRET SOCIETY OF SUPER-VILLAINS
May-June, 1976

1 A:Capt.Boomerang, Grodd,
  Sinestro 2.50
2 R:Capt.Comet,A:Green Lantern 2.50
3 A:Mantis, Darkseid 2.00
4 A:Kalibak,Darkseid,Gr.Lantern . 2.00
5 RB,D:Manhunter,A:JLA 2.00
6 RB/BL,A:Black Canary 1.50
7 RB/BL,A:Hawkgirl,Lex Luthor . . 1.50
8 RB/BL,A:Kid Flash 1.50
9 RB/BMc,A:Kid Flash, Creeper . 1.50
10 DAy/JAb,A:Creeper 1.25
11 JO,N:Wizard 1.25
12 BMc,A:Blockbuster 1.25
13 A:Crime Syndicate of America . 1.00
14 A:Crime Syndicate of America . 1.00
15 A:G.A.Atom, Dr. Mid Nite 1.25

SECRETS OF HAUNTED HOUSE
April-May, 1975

1 LD(c),Dead Heat 15.00
2 ECh(c),A Dead Man 7.00
3 ECh(c),Pathway To Purgatory . 7.00
4 LD(c),The Face of Death 5.00
5 BWr(c),Gunslinger! 12.00
6 JAp(c),Deadly Allegiance 5.00
7 JAp(c),It'll Grow On You 5.00
8 MK(c),Raising The Devil 5.00
9 LD(c),The Man Who Didn't
  Believe in Ghosts 5.00
10 MK(c),Ask Me No Questions . . 5.00
11 MK(c),Picasso Fever! 5.00
12 JO,F:Yorick's Skull 5.00
13 JO&DG(c),The Cry of the
  Warewolf 5.00
14 MK(c),Selina 5.00
15 LD(c),Over Your Own Dead
  Body 4.00
16 MK(c),Water, Water Every Fear 4.00
17 LD(c),Papa Don 4.00
18 LD(c),No Sleep For The Dying 4.00
19 LD(c),The Manner of Execution 4.00
20 JO(c),The Talisman of the
  Serpent 4.00
21 LD(c),The Death's Head
  Scorpion 4.00
22 LD(c),See How They Die 4.00

---

23 LD(c),The Creeping Red Death 4.00
24 LD(c),Second Chance To Die . 4.00
25 LD(c),The Man Who Cheated
Destiny 4.00
26 MR(c),Elevator to Eternity 4.00
27 DH(c),Souls For the Master . . 4.00
28 DH(c),Demon Rum 4.00
29 MK(c),Duel of Darkness 4.00
30 JO(c),For the Love of Arlo . . . 4.00
31 I:Mister E 6.00
32 The Legend of the Tiger's Paw 3.00
33 In The Attic Dwells Dark Seth . 3.00
34 Double Your Pleasure 3.00
35 Deathwing, Lord of Darkness . 3.00
36 RB&DG(c),Sister Sinister 3.00
37 RB&DG(c),The Third Wish Is
Death 3.00
38 RB&DG(c),Slaves of Satan . . . 3.00
39 RB&DG(c),The Witch-Hounds
of Salem 3.00
40 RB&DG(c),The Were-Witch
of Boston 3.00
41 JKu(c),House at Devil's Tail . . 3.00
42 JKu(c),Mystic Murder 3.00
43 JO(c),Mother of Invention . . . 3.00
44 BWr(c),Halloween God 3.00
45 EC&JO(c),Star-Trakker 3.00
46 March, 1982 . . . . 3.00

SINISTER HOUSE OF SECRET LOVE
Oct.–Nov., 1971
1 . . . . 35.00
2 JJ(c) 15.00
3 ATh 14.00
4 April-May, 1972 . . . . 12.00
Becomes:

SECRETS OF SINISTER HOUSE
June-July, 1972
5 . . . . 18.00
6 . . . . 10.00
7 NR 10.00
8 . . . . 10.00
9 . . . . 10.00
10 NA(i) 20.00
11 . . . . 7.00
12 . . . . 7.00
13 . . . . 7.00
14 . . . . 7.00
15 . . . . 7.00
16 . . . . 7.00
17 DBa 7.00
18 June-July, 1974 . . . . 7.00

SECRETS OF THE LEGION OF SUPER-HEROES
Jan., 1981
1 O:Legion 1.50
2 O:Brainiac 5 . . . . 1.00
3 March, 1981,O:Karate Kid 1.00

SEEKERS
Vertigo
1 & 2 . . . . @2.50

SEEKERS INTO THE MYSTERY
1 . . . . 2.50
2 . . . . 2.50
3 . . . . 2.50

4 JMD,Lucas Hart spirit
resurrected 2.50
5 JMD,JMu, ... 2.50
6 . . . . 2.50
7 . . . . 2.50
8 . . . . 2.50
9 JMD(s),MZi,"Falling Down from
Heaven," pt.4 concl. 2.50
10 JMD(s),JMu,F:Charlie Limbo . . 2.50
11 JMD(s),JIT,"God's Shadow" pt.1 2.50
12 JMD(s),JIT,"God's Shadow" pt.2 2.50
13 JMD(s),JIT,"God's Shadow" pt.3 2.50
14 JMD(s),JIT,"In God's Shadow,"
concl. 2.50
15 JMD(s),JMu,Hart meets
Magician, final issue 2.95

SENSATION COMICS
1942–52
1 I:Wonder Woman,Wildcat 22,000.00
2 I:Etta Candy & the Holiday
Girls, Dr. Poison 3,500.00
3 Diana Price joins Military
Intelligence 2,000.00
4 I:Baroness PaulaVonGunther1,500.00
5 V:Axis Spies 1,200.00
6 Wonder Woman receives magic
lasso,V:Baroness Gunther . 1,200.00
7 V:Baroness Gunther 750.00
8 Meets Gloria Bullfinch 750.00
9 A:The Real Diana Prince . . . 750.00
10 V:Ishti 750.00
11 I:Queen Desira 750.00
12 V:Baroness Gunther 650.00
13 V:Olga,Hitler(c) 900.00
14 . . . . 700.00
15 V:Simon Slikery 700.00
16 V:Karl Schultz 700.00
17 V:Princess Yasmini 700.00
18 V:Quito 700.00
19 Wonder Woman goes
berserk 700.00
20 V:Stoffer 700.00
21 V:American Adolf 600.00
22 V:Cheetah 600.00
23 'War Laugh Mania' 600.00
24 I:Wonder Woman's
mental radio 600.00
25 . . . . 600.00
26 A:Queen Hippolyte 600.00
27 V:Ely Close 600.00
28 V:Mayor Prude 600.00
29 V:Mimi Mendez 600.00
30 V:Anton Unreal 600.00
31 'Grow Down Land' 400.00
32 V:Crime Chief 400.00
33 Meets Percy Pringle 400.00
34 I:Sargon 450.00
35 V:Sontag Henya in Atlantis . 350.00
36 V:Bedwin Footh 350.00
37 A:Mala((1st app. All-Star #8) 350.00
38 V:The Gyp 350.00
39 V:Nero 350.00
40 I:Countess Draska Nishki . . . 350.00
41 V:Creeper Jackson 300.00
42 V:Countess Nishki 300.00
43 Meets Joel Heyday 300.00
44 V:Lt. Sturm 300.00
45 V:Jose Perez 300.00
46 V:Lawbreakers Protective
League 300.00
47 V:Unknown 300.00
48 V:Topso and Teena 300.00
49 V:Zavia 300.00
50 V:'Ears' Fellock 300.00

51 V:Boss Brekel 250.00
52 Meets Prof. Toxino 250.00
53 V:Wanta Wynn 250.00
54 V:Dr. Fiendo 250.00
55 V:Bughumans 250.00
56 V:Dr. Novel 250.00
57 V:Syonide 250.00
58 Meets Olive Norton 250.00
59 V:Snow Man 250.00
60 V:Bifton Jones 250.00
61 V:Bluff Robust 250.00
62 V:Black Robert of Dogwood 250.00
63 V:Prof. Vibrate 250.00
64 V:Cloudmen 250.00
65 V:Lim Slait 250.00
66 V:Slick Skeener 250.00
67 V:Daredevil Dix 250.00
68 'Secret of the Menacing
Octopus' 275.00
69 V:Darcy Wells 250.00
70 Unconquerable Woman of
Cocha Bamba 250.00
71 V:Queen Flaming 250.00

Sensation Comics #103
© DC Comics, Inc.

72 V:Blue Seal Gang 250.00
73 Wonder Woman time
travel story. 250.00
74 V:Spug Spangle 250.00
75 V:Shark 250.00
76 V:King Diamond 250.00
77 V:Boss Brekel 250.00
78 V:Furiosa 250.00
79 Meets Leila and Solala 250.00
80 V:Don Enrago 250.00
81 V:Dr. Frenzi 275.00
82 V:King Lunar 200.00
83 V:Prowd 200.00
84 V:Duke Daxo 200.00
85 Meets Leslie M. Gresham . . 200.00
86 'Secret of the Amazing
Bracelets' 200.00
87 In Twin Peaks(in Old West) 200.00
88 Wonder Woman in Holywood 200.00
89 V:Abacus Rackeett gang . . 200.00
90 'The Secret of the Modern
Sphinx' 200.00
91 . . . . 200.00
92 V:Duke of Deceptions 200.00

93 V:Talbot	200.00
94 Girl Isue	300.00
95	275.00
96	275.00
97	275.00
98 'Strange Mission'	275.00
99 I:Astra	275.00
100	400.00
101 'Battle for the Atom World'	275.00
102 'Queen of the South Seas'	275.00
103 V:Robot Archers	275.00
104 'The End of Paradise Island'	275.00
105 'Secret of the Giant Forest'	275.00
106 E:Wonder Woman	275.00
107 ATh,Mystery issue	450.00
108 ATh,I:Johnny Peril	400.00
109 Ath,A:Johnny Peril	450.00

Becomes:

SENSATION MYSTERY
1952–53

110 B:Johnny Peril	275.00
111 'Spectre in the Flame'	250.00
112 'Death has 5 Guesses'	250.00
113	250.00
114 GC,'The Haunted Diamond'	250.00
115 'The Phantom Castle'	250.00
116 'The Toy Assassins', July–Aug., 1953	250.00

SERGEANT BILKO
May–June, 1957

1 Based on TV show	500.00
2	275.00
3	250.00
4	200.00
5	200.00
6 thru 17	@175.00
18 March–April, 1960	175.00

SERGEANT BILKO'S PVT. DOBERMAN
June–July, 1958

1	300.00
2	175.00
3	125.00
4	125.00
5	125.00
6 thru 10	@100.00
11 Feb.–March, 1960	100.00

SGT. ROCK
(See: OUR ARMY AT WAR)

SGT. ROCK SPECIAL
Oct., 1988

#1 rep.Our Army at War#162-#63	2.00
#2 rep.Brave & Bold #52	2.00
#3 rep.Showcase #45	2.00
#4 rep.Our Army at War#147-#48	2.00
#5 rep.Our Army at War#81&#103	2.00
#6 rep.Our Army at War #160	2.00
#7 rep.Our Army at War #85	2.00
#8 rep.	2.00
#9 thru #20 reprints.	@2.00
Spec. #1 TT,MGo,JKu,CR,(new stories)	2.95

SGT. ROCK'S PRIZE BATTLE TALES
Winter, 1964

1	225.00

SHADE
June–July, 1977
[1st Regular Series]

1 SD,I&O: Shade	4.00
2 SD,V:Form	3.25
3 SD,V:The Cloak	2.75
4 SD,Return to Meta-Zone	2.75
5 SD,V:Supreme Decider	2.75
6 SD,V:Khaos	2.75
7 SD,V:Dr.Z.Z.	2.75
8 SD,last issue	2.75

SHADE, THE
Feb. 1997

1 (of 4) JeR(s),GeH,A:Ludlows	2.25
2 JeR(s),JWi,MGy,poisoned by love of his life	2.25
3 JeR(s),BBl,Golden Age Flash Jay Garrick retiring	2.25
4 JeR(s),MZi,V:last of the Ludlows	2.25

Shade, The Changing Man #3
© DC Comics, Inc.

SHADE, THE CHANGING MAN
July, 1990

1 B:PrM(s),CBa,MPn,I:Kathy George, I&D:Troy Grezer	5.00
2 CBa,MPn,Who Shot JFK#1	4.00
3 CBa,MPn,Who Shot JFK#2	3.00
4 CBa,MPn,V:American Scream	3.00
5 CBa,MPn,V:Hollywood Monsters	3.00
6 CBa,MPn,V:Ed Loot	3.00
7 CBa,MPn,I:Arnold Major	3.00
8 CBa,Mpn,I:Lenny	3.00
9 CBa,MPn,V:Arnold Major	3.00
10 CBa,MPn,Paranioa	2.75
11 CBa,MPn,R:Troy Grezer	2.50
12 CBa,MPn,V:Troy Grezer	2.50
13 CBa,MPn,I:Fish Priest	2.50
14 CBa,MPn,V:Godfather of Guilt	2.50
15 CBa,MPn,I:Spirit	2.50
16 CBa,MPn,V:American Scream	2.50
17 RkB(i),V:Rohug	2.50
18 MPn,E:American Scream	2.50
19 MPn,V:Dave Messiah Seeker	2.50

20 JD,CBa,MPn,RkB,R:Roger	2.50
21 MPn,The Road,A:Stringer	2.25
22 The Road,Childhood	2.25
23 The Road	2.25
24 The Road	2.25
25 The Road	2.25
26 MPn(i),F:Lenny	2.25
27 MPn(i),Shade becomes female	2.25
28 MPn(i),Changing Woman#2	2.25
29 MPn(i),Changing Woman#3	2.25
30 Another Life	2.25
31 Ernest & Jim#1	2.25
32 Ernest & Jim#2	2.25

Vertigo

33 CBa,B:Birth Pains	2.25
34 CBa,RkB(i),GID(i),A:Brian Juno, Garden of Pain	2.25
35 CBa,RkB(i),E:Birth Pains, V:Juno	2.25
36 CBa,PrG(i),RkB(i),B:Passion child, I:Miles Laimling	2.25
37 CBa,RkB(i),Shade/Kathy	2.25
38 CBa,RkB(i),Great American Novel	2.25
39 CBa,SEa,RkB(i),Pond Life	2.25
40 PBd,at Hotel Shade	2.25
41 GID,Pandora's Story,Kathy is pregnant	2.25
42 CBa,RkB(i),SY,B:History Lesson, A:John Constantine	2.50
43 CBa,RkB(i),PBd,Trial of William Matthieson,A:J.Constantine	2.50
44 CBa,RkB(i),E:History Lesson, D:William Matthieson,A:John Constantine	2.50
45 CBa,B:A Season in Hell	2.25
46 CBa(c),GID,Season in Hell#2	2.25
47 CBa(c),GID,A:Lenny	2.25
48 CBa(c),GID	2.25
49 CBa(c),GID,Kathy's Past	2.25
50 GID,BBl,MiA,pin-up gallery	3.25
51 GID,BBl,MiA,Masks,pt.1	2.00
52 GID,BBl,MiA,Masks,pt.2	2.00
53 GID,BBl,MiA,Masks,pt.3	2.00
54 Meeting	2.00
55	2.00
56	2.00
57 MBu,PrM,F:George	2.00
58 PrM,Michael Lark	2.00
59 MBu,PrM,Nasty Infections,pt.1	2.25
60 MBu,PrM,Nasty Infections,pt.2	2.25
61 MBu,PrM,Nasty Infections,pt.3	2.25
62 Nasty Infections,pt.4	2.25
63 Nasty Infections,finale	2.25
64 The Madness	2.25
65 The Roots of Madness,pt.1	2.25
66 The Roots of Madness,pt.2	2.25
67 The Roots of Madness,pt.3	2.25
68 After Kathy,pt.1	2.25
69 After Kathy,pt.2	2.25
70 After Kathy,pt.3, final issue	2.25

SHADO, SONG OF THE DRAGON
1992

1 GM(i),From G.A. Longbow Hunters	5.50
2 GM(i),V:Yakuza	5.00
3 GM(i),V:Yakuza	5.00
4 GM(i),V:Yakuza	5.00

SHADOW, THE
[1st Regular Series] 1973–75

1 MK,The Doom Puzzle	30.00

2 MK,V:Freak Show Killer	22.00
3 MK,BWr	24.00
4 MK,Ninja Story	22.00
5 FR	12.00
6 MK	22.00
7 FR	11.00
8 FR	11.00
9 FR	11.00
10	11.00
11 A:Avenger	11.00
12	11.00

[Limited Series] 1986

1 HC,R:Shadow	6.00
2 HC,O:Shadow	4.00
3 HC,V:Preston Mayrock	3.00
4 HC,V:Preston Mayrock	3.00
TPB rep. #1 thru #4	12.95

[2nd Regular Series] 1987–89

1 BSz,Shadows & Light,pt.1	3.50
2 BSz,Shadows & Light,pt.2	3.50
3 BSz,Shadows & Light,pt.3	3.50
4 BSz,Shadows & Light,pt.4	3.50
5 BSz,Shadows & Light,pt.5	3.50
6 BSz,Shadows & Light,pt.6	3.50
7 MR,KB,Harold Goes to Washington	2.00
8 KB,Seven Deadly Finns,pt.1	2.00
9 KB,Seven Deadly Finns,pt.2	2.00
10 KB,Seven Deadly Finns,pt.3	2.00
11 KB,Seven Deadly Finns,pt.4	2.00
12 KB,Seven Deadly Finns,pt.5	2.00
13 KB,Seven Deadly Finns,pt.6	2.00
14 KB,Body And Soul,pt.1	2.00
15 KB,Body And Soul,pt.2	2.00
16 KB,Body And Soul,pt.3	2.00
17 KB,Body And Soul,pt.4	2.00
18 KB,Body And Soul,pt.5	2.00
19 KB,Body And Soul,pt.6	2.00
Ann.#1 JO,AA,Shadows & Light prologue	3.00
Ann.#2 KB,Agents	2.50

SHADOW CABINET
Milestone 1994–95

0 WS(c),3RL,Shadow War,Foil(c),A:All Milestone characters	3.00
1 JBy(c),3RW,I&D:Corpsickle	2.00
2 3RW,V:Arcadian League	1.75
3 3RW,F:Sideshow	2.00
4 3RW,F:Sideshow	2.00
5	1.75
6	1.75
7	1.75
8 New Cabinet	1.75
9 R:Old Cabinet	1.75
10 V:Red Dog	1.75
11 Death Issue	1.75
12 SYSTEM	1.75
13 A:Hardware,Starlight	1.75
14 Long Hot Summer, Iron Butterfly Starlight	2.50
15 Long Hot Summer	2.50
16 Changing of the Guard	2.50
17 V:Dharma,final issue	2.50

SHADOWDRAGON ANNUAL
1995

Ann.#1 Year One Annual	3.50

SHADOW OF BATMAN

1 reprints of Detective Comics	10.00
2 thru 4	@7.50

SHADOW OF THE BATMAN
1985–86

1 WS,AM,MR,rep.	7.00
2 MR,TA,rep.A:Hugo Strange	5.00
3 MR,TA,rep.A:Penguin	5.00
4 MR,TA,rep.A:Joker	6.00
5 MR,DG,rep.	5.00

SHADOW'S FALL
1994–95

1 JVF,Voyage of self-discovery	2.95
2 JVF,More of tale	2.95
3 JVF,Shen confronts shadow	2.95
4 JVF,Gale wounded	2.95
5 JVF,Shadow goes Berserk	2.95
6 JVF,F:Warren Gale,final issue	2.95

SHADOW STRIKES!, THE
1989–92

1 EB,Death's Head	3.00
2 EB,EB,PoliticalKiller,V:Rasputin	2.50
3 EB,V:Mad Monk,V:Rasputin	2.50
4 EB,D:Mad Monk,V:Rasputin	2.50
5 EB,Shadow & Doc Savage#1	2.50
6 Shadow & Doc Savage #3	2.50
7 RM,A:Wunderkind,O:Shadow's Radio Show	2.50
8 EB,A:Shiwan Khan	2.50
9 Fireworks#2	2.50
10 EB,Fireworks#3	2.50
11 EB,O:Margo Lane	2.50
12 EB,V:Chicago Mob	2.50
13 EB,V:Chicago Mob	2.50
14 EB,V:Chicago Mob	2.50
15 EB,V:Chicago Mob	2.50
16 Assassins,pt.1	2.50
17 Assassins,pt.2	2.50
18 Shrevvie	2.50
19 NY,NJ Tunnel	2.50
20 Shadow+Margo Vs.Nazis	2.50
21 V:Shiwan Khan	2.50
22 V:Shiwan Khan	2.50
23 V:Shiwan Khan	2.50
24 Search for Margo Lane	2.50
25 In China	2.50
26 V:Shiwan Khan	2.50
27 V:Shiwan Khan,Margo Rescued	2.50
28 SL,In Hawaii	2.50
29 DSp,'Valhalla',V:Nazis	2.50
30 The Shadow Year One,pt.1	2.50
31 The Shadow Year One,pt.2	2.50
Ann.#1 DSp 'Crimson Dreams'	4.00

SHADOW WAR OF HAWKMAN
May, 1985

1 AA,V:Thangarians	1.50
2 AA,V:Thangarians	1.25
3 AA,V:Thangarians,A:Aquaman, Elong.Man	1.25
4 AA,V:Thangarians	1.25
Spec.#1 V:Thangarians	1.25

SHAZAM!
1973–78
[1st Regular Series]

1 B:DON(s),CCB,O:Capt.Marvel	5.00
2 CCB,A:Mr.Mind	4.00
3 CCB,V:Shagg Naste	3.00
4 E:DON(s),CCB,V:Ibac	3.00
5 B:ESM(s),CCB,A:Leprechaun	3.00

6 B:DON(s),CCB,Dr,Sivana	3.00
7 CCB,A:Capt Marvel Jr.	3.00
8 CCB,O:Marvel Family	3.50
9 E:DON(S)DC,CCB,A:Mr.Mind, Captain Marvel Jr.	3.00
10 ESM(s)CCB,BO	3.00
11 ViCKS,BO,rep.	3.00
12 BO,DG	3.50
13 BO,KS,A:Luthor	3.50
14 KS,A:Monster Society	3.50
15 KS,BO,Luthor	3.50
16 KS,BO	3.50
17 KS,BO	3.00
18 KS,BO	3.00
19 KS,BO,Mary Marvel	3.00
20 KS,A:Marvel Family	3.00
21 reprint	3.00
22 reprint	3.00
23 reprint	3.00

Shazam! #4 © DC Comics, Inc.

24 reprint	3.00
25 KS,DG,I&O:Isis	3.00
26 KS	3.00
27 KS,A:Kid ternity	3.50
28 KS	3.00
29 KS	3.00
30 KS	3.00
31 KS,A:MinuteMan	3.00
32 KS	3.00
33 KS	3.00
34 O:Capt.Marvel Jr.	3.00
35 DN,KS,A:Marvel Family	3.00

SHAZAM ARCHIVES

1 Rep.Whiz Comics#2-#15	49.95

SHAZAM, THE NEW BEGINNING
April, 1987

1 O:Shazam & Capt.Marvel	1.50
2 V:Black Adam	1.25
3 V:Black Adam	1.25
4 V:Black Adam	1.25

SHERLOCK HOLMES
Sept.–Oct., 1975

1	1.00

SHEVA'S WAR
DC/Helix (Aug., 1998)
1 (of 5) CsM,Iron Empires 3.00

SHOWCASE
1956–70, 1977–78
1 F:Fire Fighters 3,000.00
2 JKu,F:Kings of Wild 800.00
3 F:Frogmen 775.00
4 CI,JKu,I&O:S.A. Flash
(Barry Allen) 26,000.00
5 F:Manhunters 1,000.00
6 JK,I&O:Challengers of the
Unknown 3,500.00
7 JK,F:Challengers 1,700.00
8 CI,F:Flash,I:Capt.Cold ... 10,000.00
9 F:Lois Lane 6,000.00
10 F:Lois Lane 2,500.00
11 JK(c),F:Challengers 1,500.00
12 JK(c),F:Challengers 1,500.00
13 CI,F:Flash,Mr.Element ... 3,800.00
14 CI,F:Flash,Mr.Element ... 5,000.00

DC Showcase #31 © DC Comics, Inc.

15 I:Space Ranger 1,200.00
16 F:Space Ranger 1,000.00
17 GK(c),I:Adam Strange ... 2,200.00
18 GK(c),F:Adam Strange ... 1,100.00
19 GK(c),F:Adam Strange ... 1,200.00
20 I:Rip Hunter 900.00
21 F:Rip Hunter 500.00
22 GK,I&O:S.A. Green Lantern
(Hal Jordan) 4,800.00
23 GK,F:Green Lantern 1,600.00
24 GK,F:Green Lantern 1,600.00
25 JKu,F:Rip Hunter 300.00
26 JKu,F:Rip Hunter 300.00
27 RH,I:Sea Devils 800.00
28 RH,F:Sea Devils 400.00
29 RH,F:Sea Devils 400.00
30 O:Aquaman 750.00
31 GK(c),F:Aquaman 400.00
32 F:Aquaman 400.00
33 F:Aquaman 450.00
34 GK,MA,I&O:S.A. Atom ... 1,400.00
35 GK,MA,F:Atom 800.00
36 GK,MA,F:Atom 600.00
37 RA,I:Metal Man 550.00
38 RA,F:Metal Man 450.00

39 RA,F:Metal Man 350.00
40 RA,F:Metal Man 325.00
41 F:Tommy Tomorrow 175.00
42 F:Tommy Tomorrow 175.00
43 F:Dr.No(James Bond 007) . 400.00
44 F:Tommy Tomorrow 125.00
45 JKu,O:Sgt.Rock 225.00
46 F:Tommy Tomorrow 100.00
47 F:Tommy Tomorrow 100.00
48 F:Cave Carson 75.00
49 F:Cave Carson 75.00
50 MA,CI,F:I Spy 75.00
51 MA,CI,F:I Spy 75.00
52 F:Cave Carson 75.00
53 JKu(c),RH,F:G.I.Joe 75.00
54 JKu(c),RH,F:G.I.Joe 75.00
55 MA,F:Dr.Fate,Spectre,1st S.A.
Green Lantern,Solomon
Grundy 260.00
56 MA,F:Dr.Fate 75.00
57 JKu,F:Enemy Ace 150.00
58 JKu,F:Enemy Ace 125.00
59 F:Teen Titans 100.00
60 MA,F:Spectre 250.00
61 MA,F:Spectre 150.00
62 JO,I:Inferior 5 .... 75.00
63 JO,F:Inferior 5 .... 50.00
64 MA,F:Spectre 150.00
65 F:Inferior 5 .... 50.00
66 I:B'wana Beast 30.00
67 F:B'wana Beast 30.00
68 I:Maniaks 30.00
69 F:Maniaks 30.00
70 I:Binky 30.00
71 F:Maniaks 30.00
72 JKu,ATh,F:Top Gun 30.00
73 SD,I&O:Creeper 125.00
74 I:Anthro 75.00
75 SD,I:Hawk & Dove 100.00
76 NC,I:Bat Lash 50.00
77 BO,I:Angel & Ape 50.00
78 I:Jonny Double 30.00
79 I:Dolphin 50.00
80 NA(c),F:Phantom Stranger . 25.00
81 I:Windy & Willy 25.00
82 I:Nightmaster 60.00
83 BWr,MK,F:Nightmaster 50.00
84 BWr,MK,F:Nightmaster 50.00
85 JKu,F:Firehair 18.00
86 JKu,F:Firehair 18.00
87 JKu,F:Firehair 18.00
88 F:Jason's Quest 7.00
89 F:Jason's Quest 7.00
90 F:Manhunter 6.00
91 F:Manhunter 6.00
92 F:Manhunter 6.00
93 F:Manhunter 6.00
94 JA,JSon,I&O:2nd
Doom Patrol 10.00
95 JA,JSon,F:2nd Doom Patrol .. 9.00
96 JA,JSon,F:2nd Doom Patrol .. 9.00
97 JO,JSon:O:Power Girl 5.00
98 JSon,DG,Power Girl 5.00
99 JSon,DG,Power Girl 5.00
100 JSon,all star issue 6.00
101 JKu(c),AM,MA,Hawkman ... 5.00
102 JKu(c),AM,MA,Hawkman ... 5.00
103 JKu(c),AM,MA,Hawkman ... 5.00
104 RE,OSS Spies 5.00
TPB Rep.1956–59 .... 19.95

SHOWCASE '93
1 AAd(c),EH,AV,F:Catwoman,
Blue Devil,Cyborg 4.00
2 KM(c),EH,AV,F:Catwoman,

DC Showcase #78 © DC Comics, Inc.

Blue Devil,Cyborg 3.50
3 KM(c),EH,TC,F:Catwoman,
Blue Devil,Flash 3.00
4 F:Catwoman,Blue Devil,
Geo-Force 2.50
5 F:KD,DG,BHi,F:Robin,Blue
Devil,Geo-Force 2.50
6 MZ(c),KD,DG,F:Robin,Blue
Devil,Deathstroke 2.50
7 BSz(c),KJ,Knightfall#13,F:Two-
Face,Jade&Obsidian 5.00
8 KJ,Knightfall#14,F:Two-Face,
Peacemaker,Fire and Ice 4.00
9 F:Huntress,Peacemaker,Shining
Knight 2.50
10 BWg,SI,F:Huntress,Batman,
Dr.Light,Peacemaker,Deathstroke,
Katana,M.Manhunter 2.50
11 GP(c),F:Robin,Nightwing,
Peacemaker,Deathstroke,Deadshot,
Katana,Dr.Light,Won.Woman . 2.50
12 AD(c),BMc,F:Robin,Nightwing,
Green Lantern,Creeper 2.50

SHOWCASE '94
1 KN,F:Joker,Gunfire,Orion,Metro 2.25
2 KON(c),E:Joker,B:Blue Beetle . 2.25
3 MMi(c),B:Razorsharpe 2.25
4 AlG(s),DG,F:Arkham Asylum inmates
E:Razorsharpe,Blue Bettle ... 2.25
5 WS(s),CDi(s),PJ,B:Robin & Huntress,
F:Bloodwynd,Loose Cannon .. 2.25
6 PJ,KK(s),F:Robin & Huntress .. 2.25
7 JaL(c),PDd(s),F:Comm. Gordon 2.25
8 AlG(s),O:Scarface,Ventriloquist,
F:Monarch,1st Wildcat 3.00
9 AlG(s),DJ,O:Scarface,Ventriloquist,
F:Monarch,Waverider 2.75
10 JQ(c),AlG(s),F:Azrael,Zero Hour,
B:Black Condor 3.00
11 Black Condor, Man-Bat 2.25
12 Barbara Gordon 2.00

SHOWCASE '95
1 Supergirl 2.50
2 .... 2.50
3 F:Eradicator,Claw 2.25

All comics prices listed are for *Near Mint* condition.

4 A:Catwoman,Hawke 3.00
5 F:Thorne,Firehawk 3.00
6 DRo(c&a),F:Lobo,Bibbo 3.00
7 F:Mongul 3.00
8 .... 3.00
9 F:Lois Lane 3.00
10 F:Gangbuster 3.00
11 F:Agent Liberty 3.00
12 F:Supergirl,Maitresse 3.00

SHOWCASE '96
1 F:Steel & Warrior 3.00
2 F:Steel and Warrior 3.00
3 .... 3.00
4 F:Firebrand 3.00
5 F:Green Arrow & Thorn 3.00
6 F:Superboy, Animated Series . 3.00
7 F:Mary Marvel 3.00
8 F:Superman, Superboy &
  Supergirl 4.00
9 F:Lady Shiva & Shadowdragon,
  Martian Manhunter 3.00
10 F:Ultra Boy, Captain Comet ... 3.00
11 Legion of Super-Heroes 3.00
12 "10,000 Brainiacs" 3.00

SILVER AGE DC CLASSICS
Action #252(rep) 1.50
Adventure #247(rep) 1.50
Brave and Bold #28 (rep) 1.50
Detective #225 (rep) 1.50
Detective #327 (rep) 1.50
Green Lantern #76 (rep) 1.50
House of Secrets #92 (rep) 2.00
Showcase #4 (rep) 1.75
Showcase #22 (rep) 1.50
Sugar & Spike #99(1st printing) .. 1.50

SILVER BLADE
Sept., 1987
1 KJ,GC,maxi-series 1.50
2 thru 12 GC .... @1.50

SKIN GRAFT
Vertigo 1993
1 B:JeP(s),WaP,I:John Oakes,
  A:Tattooed Man(Tarrant) 3.25
2 WaP,V:Assassins 3.00
3 WaP,In Kyoto,I:Mizoguchi Kenji 3.00
4 E:JeP(s),WaP,V:Tarrant,Kenji . 3.00

SKREEMER
May, 1989
1 .... 1.50
2 thru 6 .... @2.00

SKULL AND BONES
1992
1 EH,I&O:Skull & Bones 4.95
2 EH,V:KGB 4.95
3 EH,V:KGB 4.95

SLASH MARAUD
Nov., 1987
1 PG 2.25
2 PG 2.25
3 thru 10 PG .... @2.00

SONIC DISRUPTORS
1987–88
1 thru 10 .... @1.75

SON OF AMBUSH BUG
July, 1986
1 .... 1.00
2 thru 6 KG .... @1.00

*Sovereign Seven #19
© DC Comics, Inc.*

SOVEREIGN SEVEN
1995–98
1 CCI(s),DT,I:Sovereign Seven,
  V:Female Furies,A:Darkseid .. 2.00
2 I:Nike,Kratos,Zelus,Bia 2.00
3 V:Nike,Kratos,Zelus,Bia 2.00
4 I:Skin Dance 2.00
5 CCI,DT,V:Skin Dance 2.00
6 CCI,DT,V:Force Majeure 2.00
7 CCI,DT,Wild Hunt,pt.2 ...... 2.00
8 CCI,DT,Clv,Wild Hunt,pt.3 ... 2.00
9 CCI,DT,Clv 2.00
10 CCI,DT,Clv,Road Trip,pt.1 .. 2.00
11 CCI,DT,Clv,Road Trip,pt.2 (of 3) 2.00
12 CCI(s) 2.00
13 CCI(s) 2.00
14 CCI(s) 2.00
15 CCI,DT,Clv,Sovereign team
  betrayed 2.00
16 CCI,DT,Clv,Network betrays
  Sovereigns, Final Night tie-in . 2.00
17 CCI(s),RLm,Clv,V:Network ... 2.00
18 CCI(s),RLm,Clv,V:Network and
  Kim 2.00
19 CCI(s) 2.00
20 CCI(s),VGi,Finale trapped in
  Forest Fire 2.00
21 CCI(s),RLm,DC,Clv,Danae's
  secret 2.00
22 CCI(s),RLm,DC,Clv,Indigo &
  Rampart fall 2.00
23 CCI(s),RLm,DC,Clv,Finale
  hallucinates 2.00
24 CCI(s),RLm,Clv,A:Superman .. 2.00
25 CCI(s),RLm,Clv,V:Power Girl . 2.00
26 CCI(s),RLm,Clv,A:Hitman 2.00
27 CCI(s),RLm,Clv,Genesis tie-in . 2.25
28 CCI(s),RLm,Clv,A:Impulse ... 2.00
29 CCI(s),RLm,Clv,Sovereign dies 2.00
30 CCI(s),RLm,Clv,revenge 2.00
31 CCI(s),RLm,Clv,F:Power Girl .. 2.25

32 CCI(s),RLm,Clv,F:Power Girl .. 2.25
33 CCI(s),RLm,Clv,F:Power Girl .. 2.25
34 CCI(s),RLm,Clv,in Kuristan ... 2.25
35 CCI(s),RLm,Clv,The Rapture .. 2.25
36 CCI(s),RLm,Clv,final issue ... 2.25
Ann.#1 CCI, Year One Annual ... 3.95
Ann.#2 CCI(s),RL,KJ,Legends of
  the Dead Earth 2.95
TPB CCI(s),DT, rep.#1–#5 ..... 12.95

SOVEREIGN SEVEN PLUS
1 one-shot 2.95

SPACE JAM
Warner Bros./DC Oct. 1996
one-shot comic adaptation of movie 5.95

SPANNER'S GALAXY
Dec., 1984
1 mini-series 1.50
2 thru 6 .... @1.00

*Spectre (1st Series) #1
© DC Comics, Inc.*

SPECTRE, THE
1967–69
1 MA,V:Captain Skull 125.00
2 NA,V:Dirk Rawley 85.00
3 NA,A:Wildcat 75.00
4 NA 75.00
5 NA 75.00
6 MA 45.00
7 MA,BU:Hourman 45.00
8 MA,Parchment of Power
  Perilous 45.00
9 BWr(2nd BWr Art) 50.00
10 MA 45.00
[2nd Regular Series] 1987–89
1 GC,O:Spectre 3.00
2 GC,Cult of BRM 2.50
3 GC,Fashion Model Murders .. 2.00
4 GC 2.00
5 GC,Spectre's Murderer 2.00
6 GC,Spectre/Corrigan separated 2.00
7 A:Zatanna,Wotan 2.00
8 A:Zatanna,Wotan 2.00
9 GM,Spectre's Revenge 2.00

10 GM,A:Batman,Millenium 2.25
11 GM,Millenium 2.00
12 GM,The Talisman,pt.1 . . . . . . 2.00
13 GM,The Talisman,pt.2 . . . . . . 2.00
14 GM,The Talisman,pt.3 . . . . . . 2.00
15 GM,The Talisman,pt.4 . . . . . . 2.00
16 Jim Corrigan Accused 2.00
17 New Direction,'Final Destiny' . . 2.00
18 Search for Host Body 2.00
19 'Dead Again' 2.00
20 Corrigan Detective Agency . . . 2.00
21 A:Zoran 1.75
22 BS,Sea of Darkness,A:Zoran . 1.75
23 A:Lords of Order,
    Invasion x-over 1.75
24 BWg,Ghosts i/t Machine#1 . . . 1.75
25 Ghosts in the Machine #2 . . . . 1.75
26 Ghosts in the Machine #3 . . . . 1.75
27 Ghosts in the Machine #4 . . . . 1.75
28 Ghosts in the Machine #5 . . . . 1.75
29 Ghosts in the Machine #6 . . . . 1.75
30 Possession 1.75
31 Spectre possessed, final issue 1.75
Ann.#1, A:Deadman 2.75
[3rd Regular Series] 1992–97
1 B:JOs(s),TMd,R:Spectre,
    Glow in the dark(c) 9.00
2 TMd,Murder Mystery 7.00
3 TMd,O:Spectre 5.00
4 TMd,O:Spectre 4.00
5 TMd,BB(c),V:Kidnappers 3.50
6 TMd,Spectre prevents evil 3.50
7 TMd 3.50
8 TMd,Glow in the dark(c) 5.00
9 TMd,MWg(c),V:The Reaver . . . 3.00
10 TMd,V:Michael 3.00
11 TMd,V:Azmodeus 3.00
12 V:Reaver 3.00
13 TMd,V:Count Vertigo,
    Glow in the Dark(c) 3.00
14 JoP,A:Phantom Stranger 2.00
15 TMd,A:Phantom Stranger,Demon,
    Doctor Fate,John Constantine . 2.00
16 JAp,V:I.R.A. 2.00
17 TT(c),TMd,V:Eclipso 2.00
18 TMd,D:Eclipso 2.00
19 TMd,V:Hate 2.00
20 A:Lucien 2.00
21 V:Naiad,C:Superman 3.00
22 A:Superman 2.25
23 Book of Judgment, pt.1 . . . . . 2.00
24 Book of Judgment, pt.2 . . . . . 2.00
25 Book of Judgment, pt.3 . . . . . 2.00
26 . . . . 2.00
27 R:Azmodus 2.00
28 V:Azmodus 2.00
29 V:Azmodus 2.00
30 V:Azmodus 2.00
31 Descent into Pandemonium . . 2.25
32 V:Killo 2.25
33 . . . . 2.25
34 Power of the Undead 2.25
35 JOs,TMd,Underworld
    Unleashed tie-in 2.25
36 JOs,TMd,Underworld
    Unleashed tie-in 2.25
37 JOs,TMd,The Haunting of
    America,pt.1 . . . . 2.25
38 JOs,TMd,The Haunting of
    America,pt.2 . . . . 2.25
39 JOs,TMd,The Haunting of
    America,pt.3 . . . . 2.25
40 JOs,TMd,The Haunting of
    America,pt.4 . . . . 2.25
41 JOs,TMd,The Haunting of

America,pt.5 . . . . 2.25
42 JOs,TMd,The Haunting of
    America,pt.6 . . . . 2.25
43 Witchcraft 2.25
44 Madame Xanadu 2.25
45 . . . . 2.25
46 JOs(s),TMd,discovery of the
    Spear of Destiny 2.25
47 JOs(s),TMd,"The Haunting of
    America" Final Night tie-in 2.25
48 JOs(s),TMd,"The Haunting of
    America" 2.25
49 JOs(s),TMd,"The Haunting of
    America" 2.25
50 JOs(s),TMd, ... 2.25
51 JOs(s),TMd,A:Batman,Joker . . 2.25
52 JOs(s),TMd,Nate Kane discovers
    murder evidence 2.25
53 JOs(s),TMd,"Haunting of Jim
    Corrigan" cont. 2.25
54 JOs(s),TMd,hunt for murderer of
    Mister Terrific 2.25
55 JOs(s),TMd,Corrigan implicated
    in murder 2.25
56 JOs(s),TMd,JTo "Haunting if Jim
    Corrigan" 2.50
57 JOs(s),TMd,Spectre & Jim
    Corrigan in Heaven 2.50
58 JOs,TMd,Genesis tie-in 2.50
59 JOs,TMd,BWr(c), alien pod . . 2.50
60 JOs,TMd,Quest for God, cont. . 2.50
61 JOs,TMd,Quest for God, concl. 2.50
62 JOs,TMd,final issue 2.50
Ann.#1 JOs,TMd,Year One 3.95
TPB Punishment and Crimes 9.95
TPB Crimes & Punishments,
    JOs,TMd 10.00

SPEED FORCE
Sept., 1997
1 MWa,BAu,JBy,BML,JAp,BSn,
    Flash stories, 64pg. 4.00

SPELLJAMMER
Sept., 1990
1 RogueShip#1 . . . . 3.00
2 RogueShip#2 . . . . 2.50
3 RogueShip#3 . . . . 2.00

Spelljammer #2 © DC Comics, Inc.

4 RogueShip#4 . . . . 2.00
5 New Planet 1.75
6 Tember, Planet contd 1.75
7 Planet contd 1.75
8 conclusion 1.75
9 Meredith Possessed 1.75
10 Tie-in w/Dragonlance #33&34 . 1.75
11 Dwarf Citidel 1.75
12 Kirstig Vs. Meredith 1.75
13 Tember to the Rescue 1.75
14 Meredith's Son #1 . . . . 1.75
15 Meredith's Son #2 . . . . 1.75

STALKER
1975–1976
1 O&I:Stalker 5.00
2 thru 4 . . . . @2.50

STANLEY & HIS MONSTER
(see FOX AND THE CROW)

STANLEY & HIS MONSTER
1 R:Stanley 1.25
2 I:Demon Hunter 1.25
3 A:Ambrose Bierce 1.25
4 final issue 1.25

S.T.A.R. CORPS
1 A:Superman 2.00
2 I:Fusion,A:Rampage 1.75
3 I:Brainstorm 1.75
4 I:Ndoki 1.75
5 I:Trauma 1.75
6 I:Mindgame 1.75

STAR CROSSED
DC/Helix April 1997
1 (of 3) MHo,Dyltah's romance
    with Saa 2.50
2 MHo,"Love During Wartime" . . 2.50
3 (of 3) 2.50

[NEIL GAIMAN & CHARLES VESS'] STARDUST
DC/Vertigo (Oct., 1997)
1 (of 4) NGa(s),CV 6.00
2 NGa(s),CV adult faerie tale . . . 6.00
3 NGa(s),CV 6.00
4 NGa(s),CV 6.00

STARFIRE
1976–77
1 . . . . 1.50
2 thru 8 . . . . @1.00

STAR HUNTERS
Oct.–Nov., 1977
1 DN&BL 1.00
2 LH&BL 1.00
3 MN&BL,D:Donovan Flint 1.00
4 thru 7 . . . . @1.00

STARMAN
1988–92
1 TL,I&O:New Starman 4.00
2 TL,V:Serial Killer,C:Bolt 3.00
3 TL,V:Bolt 3.00
4 TL,V:Power Elite 2.50

5 TL,Invasion,A:PowerGirl, Firestorm	2.50
6 TL,Invasion,A:G.L.,Atom	2.00
7 TL,Soul Searching Issue	2.00
8 TL,V:LadyQuark	2.00
9 TL,A:Batman,V:Blockbuster	2.00
10 TL,A:Batman,V:Blockbuster	2.00
11 TL,V:Power Elite	2.00
12 TL,V:Power Elite,A:Superman	2.00
13 TL,V:Rampage	2.00
14 TL,A:A:Superman,V:Parasite	2.00
15 TL,V:Deadline	2.00
16 TL,O:Starman	2.00
17 TL,V:Dr.Polaris,A:PowerGirl	2.00
18 TL,V:Dr.Polaris,A:PowerGirl	2.00
19 TL,V:Artillery	2.00
20 TL,FireFighting	2.00
21 TL,Starman Quits	2.00
22 TL,V:Khunds	2.00
23 TL,A:Deadline	2.00
24 TL,A:Deadline	2.00
25 TL,V:Deadline	2.00
26 V:The Mist	2.00
27 V:The Mist	2.00

Starman #1 © DC Comics, Inc.

28 A:Superman	7.00
29 V:Plasmax	2.00
30 Seduction of Starman #1	2.00
31 Seduction of Starman #2	2.00
32 Seduction of Starman #3	2.00
33 Seduction of Starman #4	2.00
34 A:Batman	2.00
35 A:Valor,Mr.Nebula,ScarletSkier	2.00
36 A:Les Mille Yeux	2.00
37 A:Les Mille Yeux	2.00
38 War of the Gods X-over	2.00
39 V:Plasmax	2.00
40 V:Las Vegas	2.00
41 V:Maaldor	2.00
42 Star Shadows,pt.1,A:Eclipso	3.00
43 Star Shadows,pt.2,A:Lobo, Eclipso	2.50
44 Star Shadows,pt.3,A:Eclipso V:Lobo	2.50
45 Star Shadows,pt.4, V:Eclipso	2.50

2nd Series 1994–97

0 New Starman	8.00
1 Threat of the Mist	8.00
2	4.00

3 V:Son of the Mist	4.00
4	4.00
5 V:Starman	4.00
6 Times Past Features	4.00
7 Sinister Circus	3.00
8 TyH(c),Sinister Circus	3.00
9 TyH(c),Mist's daughter breaks out of prison	3.00
10 Sins of the Chile,prelude	3.00
11	3.00
12 JeR,TyH,Sins of the Child,pt.1	3.00
13 JeR,TyH,Sins of the Child,pt.2	3.00
14 JeR,TyH,Sins of the Child,pt.3	3.00
15 JeR,TyH,Sins of the Child,pt.4	3.00
16 JeR,TyH,Sins of the Child,pt.5	3.00
17 JeR,TyH	3.00
18 JeR,TyH,Orig.Starman vs.The Mist	3.00
19 JeR,TyH,Talking with David 2	3.00
20 JeR(s),TyH,GyD,"Sand and Stars," pt.1	3.00
21 JeR(s),TyH,GyD,"Sand and Stars," pt.2	2.50
22 JeR(s),TyH,GyD,"Sand and Stars," pt.3	2.50
23 JeR(s),TyH,GyD,"Sand and Stars," pt.4 concl	2.50
24 JeR(s),TyH,"Hell & Back," pt.1	2.50
25 JeR(s),TyH,"Hell & Back," pt.2	2.50
26 JeR(s),TyH,"Hell & Back," pt.3	2.50
27	2.50
28 JeR(s)Superfreaks and Backstabbers	2.50
29 JeR(s),TyH,GyD,V:The Shade, Starman history	2.50
30 JeR(s),TyH,"Infernal Devices" pt.1 (of 6)	2.50
31 JeR(s),TyH,"Infernal Devices" pt.2	2.50
32 JeR(s),TyH,"Infernal Devices" pt.3	2.50
33 JeR(s),TyH,"Infernal Devices" pt.4,A:Batman, Sentinel	2.50
34 JeR(s),TyH,A:Batman, Sentinel, Floronic Man	2.25
35 JeR(s),TyH,A:Batman, Floronic Man, Sentinel	2.25
36 JeR(s),TyH,F:Will Payton	2.25
37 JeR(s),TyH,F:GoldenAgeHeroes	2.25
38 JeR(s),TyH,new JLE	2.25
39 JeR(s),TyH,Lightning & Stars, pt.1 x-over	2.25
40 JeR(s),TyH	2.25
41 JeR(s),GEr,TyH	2.25
42 JeR(s),MS,Nazis,Demon	2.25
43 JeR(s),TyH,help from JLA	2.25
44 JeR(s),times past story	2.50
45 JeR(s),search for Will Payton	2.50
46 JeR(s),TyH,Bobo	2.50
47 JeR,SY,TyH,	2.50
Ann.#1 Legends o/t Dead Earth	3.50
Ann.#2 Pulp Heroes (Romance)	3.95
Secret Files #1,O:Starmen	5.00
TPB Sins of the Father,rep.#0–#5	12.95
TPB Night and Day, rep. stories from #7–#16	14.95
TPB A Wicked Inclination, rep.	18.00

STARMAN: THE MIST
May, 1998

1-shot F:Mary Marvel,Girlfrenzy	2.00

STAR SPANGLED COMICS
Oct., 1941

1 O:Tarantula,B:Captain X of the R.A.F.,Star Spangled Kid, Armstrong of the Army	3,500.00
2 V:Dr. Weerd	1,400.00
3	750.00
4 V:The Needle	750.00
5 V:Dr. Weerd	750.00
6 E:Armstrong	500.00
7 S&K,O&1st app:The Guardian, B:Robotman,The Newsboy Legion, TNT	6,200.00
8 O:TNT & Dan the Dyna-Mite	1,700.00
9	1,400.00
10	1,400.00
11	1,100.00
12 Newsboy Legion stories, 'Prevue of Peril!'	1,100.00
13 'Kill Dat Story!'	1,100.00
14 'Meanest Man on Earth'	1,100.00
15 'Playmates of Peril'	1,100.00
16 'Playboy of Suicide Slum!'	1,100.00
17 V:Rafferty Mob	1,100.00
18 O:Star Spangled Kid	1,300.00
19 E:Tarantula	1,000.00
20 B:Liberty Belle	1,000.00
21	800.00
22 'Brains for Sale'	800.00
23 'Art for Scrapper's Sake'	800.00
24	800.00
25 'Victuals for Victory'	800.00
26 'Louie the Lug goes Literary'	800.00
27 'Turn on the Heat!'	800.00
28 'Poor Man's Rich Man'	800.00
29 'Cabbages and Comics'	800.00
30	400.00
31 'Questions Please!'	400.00
32	400.00
33	400.00
34 'From Rags to Run!'	400.00
35 'The Proud Poppas'	400.00
36 'Cowboy of Suicide Slum'	400.00
37	400.00
38	400.00
39 'Two Guardians are a Crowd'	400.00
40	400.00
41 Back the 6th War Loan(c)	375.00
42	375.00
43 American Red Cross(c)	375.00
44	375.00
45 7th War Loan (c)	375.00
46	375.00
47	375.00
48	375.00
49	375.00
50	375.00
51 A:Robot Robber	375.00
52 'Rehearsal for Crime'	375.00
53 'The Poet of Suicide Slum'	375.00
54 'Dead-Shot Dade's Revenge'	375.00
55 'Gabby Strikes a Gusher'	375.00
56 'The Treasurer of Araby'	375.00
57 'Recruit for the Legion'	375.00
58 'Matadors of Suicide Slum'	375.00
59	375.00
60	375.00
61	375.00
62 'Prevue of Tomorrow'	375.00
63	375.00
64 'Criminal Cruise'	375.00
65 B:Robin,(c) & stories	1,200.00
66 V:No Face	700.00
67 'The Castle of Doom	550.00

68	550.00
69 'The Stolen Atom Bomb' . .	850.00
70 V:The Clock	550.00
71 'Perils of the Stone Age' . . .	550.00
72 'Robin Crusoe'	550.00
73 V:The Black Magician	550.00
74 V:The Clock	550.00
75 The State vs. Robin	550.00
76 V:The Fence	550.00
77 'The Boy who Wanted Robin	
for Christmas'	550.00
78 ''Rajah Robin'	550.00
79 'V:The Clock,'The Tick-Tock	
Crimes'	550.00
80 'The Boy Disc Jockey'	550.00
81 'The Seeing-Eye Dog Crimes'	450.00
82 'The Boy who Hated Robin'	450.00
83 'Who is Mr. Mystery',B:Captain	
Compass backup story	450.00
84 How can we Fight Juvenile	
Delinquency?	650.00
85 'Peril at the Pole'	450.00
86	475.00
87 V:Sinister Knight	650.00
88 Robin Declares War on	
Batman, B:Batman app. . . .	525.00
89 'Batman's Utility Belt?'	525.00
90 'Rancho Fear!'	525.00
91 'Cops 'n' Robbers?'	525.00
92 'Movie Hero No. 1?'	525.00
93	525.00
94 'Underworld Playhouse' . . .	525.00
95 'The Man with the Midas Touch',	
E:Robin(c),Batman story . . .	525.00
96 B:Tomahawk(c) & stories . .	350.00
97 'The 4 Bold Warriors'	300.00
98	300.00
99 'The Second Pocahontas' . .	300.00
100 'The Frontier Phantom' . . .	300.00
101 Peril on the High Seas . . .	250.00
102	250.00
103 'Tomahawk's Death Duel!' .	250.00
104 'Race with Death!'	250.00
105 'The Unhappy Hunting	
Grounds'	250.00
106 'Traitor in the War Paint' . .	250.00
107 'The Brave who Hunted	
Tomahawk'	250.00
108 'The Ghost called Moccasin	
Foot!'	250.00
109 'The Land Pirates of	
Jolly Roger Hill!'	250.00
110 'Sally Raines Frontier Girl'	275.00
111 'The Death Map of Thunder	
Hill'	275.00
112	300.00
113 FF,V:'The Black Cougar' . .	325.00
114 'Return of the Black Cougar'	350.00
115 'Journey of a Thousand	
Deaths'	300.00
116 'The Battle of Junction Fort'	300.00
117 'Siege?'	300.00
118 V:Outlaw Indians	250.00
119 'The Doomed Stockade?' .	225.00
120 'Revenge of Raven Heart!'	225.00
121 'Adventure in New York!' . .	225.00
122 'I:Ghost Breaker,(c)& stories	250.00
123 'The Dolls of Doom'	200.00
124 'Suicide Tower'	200.00
125 The Hermit's Ghost Dog!' .	200.00
126 'The Phantom of Paris!' . .	200.00
127 'The Supernatural Alibi!' . .	200.00
128 C:Batman,'The Girl who	
lived 5,000 Years!'	200.00
129 'The Human Orchids'	250.00

Star Spangled Comics #63
© DC Comics, Inc.

130 'The Haunted Town',	
July, 1952	275.00

Becomes:

STAR SPANGLED
WAR STORIES
Aug., 1952

131 CS&StK(c),I Was A Jap	
Prisoner of War	800.00
132 CS&StK(c),The G.I. With	
The Million-Dollar Arm	600.00
133 CS&StK(c),Mission-San	
Marino	500.00
3 CS&StK(c),Hundred-Mission	
Mitchell	275.00
4 CS&StK(c),The Hot Rod Tank	275.00
5 LSt(c),Jet Pilot	275.00
6 CS(c),Operation Davy Jones	275.00
7 CS(c),Rookie Ranger,The . .	200.00
8 CS(c),I Was A	
Holywood Soldier	200.00
9 CS&StK(c),Sad Sack Squad	200.00
10 CS,The G.I. & The Gambler	200.00
11 LSt(c),The Lucky Squad . . .	200.00
12 CS(c),The Four Horseman of	
Barricade Hill	200.00
13 No Escape	200.00
14 LSt(c),Pitchfork Army	200.00
15 The Big Fish	200.00
16 The Yellow Ribbon	200.00
17 IN(c),Prize Target	200.00
18 IN(c),The Gladiator	200.00
19 IN(c),The Big Lift	200.00
20 JGr(c),The Battle of	
the Frogmen	200.00
21 JGr(c),Dead Man's Bridge . .	150.00
22 JGr(c),Death Hurdle	150.00
23 JGr(c),The Silent Frogman .	150.00
24 JGr(c),Death Slide	150.00
25 JGr(c),S.S. Liferaft	150.00
26 JGr(c),Bazooka Man	150.00
27 JGr(c),Taps for a Tail Gunner	150.00
28 JGr(c),Tank Duel	150.00
29 JGr(c),A Gun Called Slugger	150.00
30 JGr(c),The Thunderbolt Tank	150.00
31 IN(c),Tank Block	100.00
32 JGr(c),Bridge to Battle	100.00

33 JGr(c),Pocket War	100.00
34 JGr(c),Fighting...Snowbirds .	100.00
35 JGr(c),Zero Hour	100.00
36 JGr(c),A G.I. Passed Here .	100.00
37 JGr(c),A Handful of T.N.T. .	100.00
38 RH(c),One-Man Army	100.00
39 JGr(c),Flying Cowboy	100.00
40 JGr(c),Desert Duel	100.00
41 IN(c),A Gunner's Hands	85.00
42 JGr(c),Sniper Alley	85.00
43 JGr(c),Top Kick Brother	85.00
44 JGr(c),Tank 711	
Doesn't Answer	85.00
45 JGr(c),Flying Heels	85.00
46 JGr(c),Gunner's Seat	85.00
47 JGr(c),Sidekick	85.00
48 JGr(c),Battle Hills	85.00
49 JGr(c),Payload	85.00
50 JGr(c),Combat Dust	85.00
51 JGr(c),Battle Pigeon	70.00
52 JGr(c),Cannon-Man	70.00
53 JGr(c),Combat Close-Ups . . .	70.00
54 JGr(c),Flying Exit	70.00
55 JKu(c),The Burning Desert . .	70.00
56 JKu(c),The Walking Sub	70.00
57 JGr(c),Call For a Frogman . .	70.00
58 JGr(c),MD,Waist Punch	70.00
59 JGr(c),Kick In The Door . . .	70.00
60 JGr(c),Hotbox	70.00
61 JGr(c),MD,Tow Pilot	70.00
62 JGr(c),The Three GIs	70.00
63 JGr(c),Flying Range Rider . .	70.00
64 JGr(c),MD,Frogman Ambush .	70.00
65 JGr(c),JSe,Frogman Block . .	70.00
66 JGr(c),Flattop Pigeon	70.00
67 RH(c),MD,Ashcan Alley	70.00
68 JGr(c),The Long Step	70.00
69 JKu(c),Floating Tank, The' . .	70.00
70 JKu(c),No Medal For	
Frogman	65.00
71 JKu(c),Shooting Star	65.00
72 JGr(c),Silent Fish	65.00
73 JGr(c),MD,The Mouse &	
the Tiger	65.00
74 JGr(c),MD,Frogman Bait	65.00
75 JGr(c),MD,Paratroop	
Mousketeers	65.00
76 MD,JKu(c),Odd Man	65.00
77 MD,JKu(c),Room to Fight . . .	65.00
78 MD,JGr(c),Fighting Wingman	65.00
79 MD,JKu(c),Zero Box	65.00
80 MD,JGr(c),Top Gunner	65.00
81 MD,RH(c),Khaki Mosquito . .	65.00
82 MD,JKu(c),Ground Flier	65.00
83 MD,JGr(c),Jet On	
My Shoulder	65.00
84 MD,IN(c),O:Mademoiselle	
Marie	150.00
85 IN(c),A Medal For Marie . . .	80.00
86 JGr(c),A Medal For Marie . .	80.00
87 JGr(c),T.N.T. Spotlight	75.00
88 JGr(c),The Steel Trap	75.00
89 IN(c),Trail of the Terror	75.00
90 RA(c),Island of	
Armored Giants	350.00
91 JGr(c),The Train of Terror . .	55.00
92 Last Battle of the	
Dinosaur Age	125.00
93 Goliath of the Western Front .	55.00
94 JKu(c),The Frogman and	
the Dinosaur	125.00
95 Guinea Pig Patrol,Dinosaurs	125.00
96 Mission X,Dinosaur	125.00
97 The Sub-Crusher, Dinosaur	125.00
98 Island of Thunder, Dinosaur	125.00

99 The Circus of Monsters,	
Dinosaur 125.00	
100 The Volcano of Monsters,	
Dinosaur 150.00	
101 The Robot and the Dinosaur 125.00	
102 Punchboard War,Dinosaur 125.00	
103 Doom at Dinosaur Island,	
Dinosaur 125.00	
104 The Tree of Terror,	
Dinosaurs 125.00	
105 The War of Dinosaur Island 125.00	
106 The Nightmare War,	
Dinosaurs 125.00	
107 Battle of the Dinosaur	
Aquarium 125.00	
108 Dinosaur D-Day 125.00	
109 The Last Soldiers 125.00	
110 thru 133 . . . . @125.00	
134 NA 100.00	
135 . . . . 75.00	
136 . . . . 75.00	
137 Dinosaur 75.00	
138 Enemy Ace 100.00	
139 O:Enemy Ace 90.00	
140 . . . . 65.00	
141 . . . . 65.00	
142 . . . . 50.00	
143 . . . . 50.00	
144 NA,JKu 60.00	
145 . . . . 50.00	
146 . . . . 50.00	
147 . . . . 50.00	
148 . . . . 50.00	
149 . . . . 50.00	
150 JKu,Viking Prince 50.00	
151 I:Unknown Soldier 50.00	
152 . . . . 15.00	
153 . . . . 15.00	
154 O:Unknown Soldier 40.00	
155 . . . . 10.00	
156 I:Battle Album 8.00	
157 thru 160 . . . . 6.00	
161 E:Enemy Ace 6.00	
162 thru 170 . . . . @10.00	
171 thru 200 . . . . @8.00	
201 thru 204 . . . . @2.50	
Becomes:	
UNKNOWN SOLDIER	
April-May, 1977	
205 thru 247 . . . . @1.25	
248 and 249 O:Unknown Soldier @1.25	
250 . . . . 1.25	
251 B:Enemy Ace 1.25	
252 thru 268 . . . . @1.25	

STAR TREK
1984–88
[1st Regular Series]

1 TS,The Wormhole Connection 15.00	
2 TS,The Only Good Klingon . . . 8.00	
3 TS,Errand of War 7.00	
4 TS,Deadly Allies 7.00	
5 TS,Mortal Gods 7.00	
6 TS,Who is Enigma? 6.00	
7 EB,O:Saavik 6.00	
8 TS,Blood Fever 6.00	
9 TS,Mirror Universe Saga #1 . . 6.00	
10 TS,Mirror Universe Saga #2 . . 6.00	
11 TS,Mirror Universe Saga #3 . . 6.00	
12 TS,Mirror Universe Saga #4 . . 6.00	
13 TS,Mirror Universe Saga #5 . . 5.00	
14 TS,Mirror Universe Saga #6 . . 5.00	
15 TS,Mirror Universe Saga #7 . . 5.00	
16 TS,Mirror Universe Saga end . 5.00	

17 TS,The D'Artagnan Three 5.00	
18 TS,Rest & Recreation 5.00	
19 DSp,W.Koenig story 5.00	
20 TS,Girl 5.00	
21 TS,Dreamworld 5.00	
22 TS,The Wolf #1 . . . . 5.00	
23 TS,The Wolf #2 . . . . 4.00	
24 TS,Double Blind #1 . . . . 4.00	
25 TS,Double Blind #2. . . . . 4.00	
26 TSV:Romulans 4.00	
27 TS,Day in the Life 4.00	
28 GM,The Last Word 4.00	
29 Trouble with Bearclaw 4.00	
30 CI,F:Uhura 4.00	
31 TS,Maggie's World 4.00	
32 TS,Judgment Day 4.00	
33 TS,20th Anniv. 4.50	
34 V:Romulans 2.50	
35 GM,Excelsior 2.50	
36 GM,StarTrek IV tie-in 2.50	
37 StarTrek IV tie-in 2.50	
38 AKu,The Argon Affair 2.50	
39 TS,A:Harry Mudd 2.50	
40 TS,A:Harry Mudd 2.50	
41 TS,V:Orions 2.50	
42 TS,The Corbomite Effect . . . 2.50	
43 TS,Paradise Lost #1 . . . . . . 2.50	
44 TS,Paradise Lost #2 . . . . . . 2.50	
45 TS,Paradise Lost #3 . . . . . . 2.50	
46 TS,Getaway 2.50	
47 TS,Idol Threats 2.50	
48 TS,The Stars in Secret	
Influence 2.50	
49 TS,Aspiring to be Angels . . . 2.50	
50 TS,Anniv. 3.50	
51 TS,Haunted Honeymoon . . . 2.50	
52 TS,'Hell in a Hand Basket' . . . 2.50	
53 'You're Dead,Jim' 2.50	
54 Old Loyalties 2.50	
55 TS,Finnegan's Wake 2.50	
56 GM,Took place during 5 year	
Mission 2.50	
Ann.#1 All Those Years Ago . . . 4.00	
Ann.#2 DJw,The Final Voyage . . . 3.00	
Ann.#3 CS,F:Scotty 3.00	
Star Trek III Adapt.TS 2.50	
Star Trek IV Adapt. TS 2.50	
StarTrek V Adapt. 2.50	

[2nd Regular Series]
1989–96

1 The Return 10.00	
2 The Sentence 5.00	
3 Death Before Dishonor 4.00	
4 Reprocussions 4.00	
5 Fast Friends 4.00	
6 Cure All 4.00	
7 Not Sweeney! 4.00	
8 Going,Going 3.50	
9 ...Gone 3.50	
10 Trial of James Kirk #1 . . . . . 3.50	
11 Trial of James Kirk #2 . . . . . 3.50	
12 Trial of James Kirk #3 . . . . . 3.50	
13 Return of Worthy #1 . . . . . . 3.50	
14 Return of Worthy #2 . . . . . . 3.50	
15 Return of Worthy #3 . . . . . . 3.50	
16 Worldsinger 3.00	
17 Partners? #1 . . . . 3.00	
18 Partners? #2 . . . . 3.00	
19 Once A Hero 3.00	
20 . . . . 3.00	
21 Kirk Trapped 3.00	
22 A:Harry Mudd 3.00	
23 The Nasgul,A:Harry Mudd . . . 3.00	
24 25th Anniv.,A:Harry Mudd . . . 3.50	
25 Starfleet Officers Reunion . . . 2.50	

Star Trek (2nd Series) #56
© DC Comics, Inc.

26 Pilkor 3 . . . . 2.50	
27 Kirk Betrayed 2.50	
28 V:Romulans 2.50	
29 Mediators 2.50	
30 Veritas #1 . . . . 2.50	
31 Veritas #2 . . . . 2.50	
32 Veritas #3 . . . . 2.50	
33 Veritas #4 . . . . 2.50	
34 JD,F:Kirk,Spock,McCoy 2.50	
35 Tabukan Syndrome#1 . . . . . 2.50	
36 Tabukan Syndrome#2 . . . . . 2.50	
37 Tabukan Syndrome#3 . . . . . 2.50	
38 Tabukan Syndrome#4 . . . . . 2.50	
39 Tabukan Syndrome#5 . . . . . 2.50	
40 Tabukan Syndrome#6 . . . . . 2.50	
41 Runaway 2.50	
42 Helping Hand 2.50	
43 V:Binzalans 2.50	
44 Acceptable Risk 2.50	
45 V:Trelane 2.50	
46 V:Captain Klaa 2.50	
47 F:Spock & Saavik 2.50	
48 The Neutral Zone 2.50	
49 weapon from Genesis 2.50	
50 "The Peacemaker" 4.00	
51 "The Price" 2.00	
52 V:Klingons 2.00	
53 Timecrime #1 . . . . 2.00	
54 Timecrime #2 . . . . 2.00	
55 Timecrime #3 . . . . 2.00	
56 Timecrime #4 . . . . 2.00	
57 Timecrime #5 . . . . 2.00	
58 F:Chekov 2.00	
59 Uprising 2.00	
60 Hostages 2.00	
61 On Talos IV 2.25	
62 Alone,pt.1, V:aliens 2.25	
63 Alone,pt.2 . . . . 2.25	
64 Kirk 2.25	
65 Kirk in Space 2.25	
66 Spock 2.25	
67 Ambassador Stonn 2.25	
68 . . . . 2.25	
69 Wolf in Cheap Clothing,pt.1 . 2.25	
70 Wolf in Cheap Clothing,pt.2 . . 2.25	
71 Wolf in Cheap Clothing,pt.3 . . 2.50	
72 Wolf in Cheap Clothing,pt.4 . . 2.50	

73 Star-crossed,pt.1 . . . . 2.50
74 Star-crossed,pt.2 . . . . 2.25
75 Star-crossed,pt.3 . . . . 4.00
76 Tendar 2.25
77 to the Romulan Neutral Zone . 2.50
78 The Chosen,pt.1 (of 3) 2.50
79 The Chosen,pt.2 . . . . 2.50
80 The Chosen,pt.3 . . . . 2.50
Ann.#1 GM,sty by G.Takei(Sulu) . 4.00
Ann.#2 Kirks 1st Yr At Star
  Fleet Academy 4.00
Ann #3 KD,F:Ambassador Sarek . 3.50
Ann.#4 F:Spock on Pike's ship . 3.50
Ann.#6 Convergence,pt.1 . . . . . 3.95
Spec.#1 PDd(s),BSz 3.75
Spec.#2 The Defiant 3.95
Spec.#3 V:Orion pirates 3.95
Debt of Honor,AH,CCI(s),HC . . . 27.00
Debt of Honor SC 14.95
Spec. 25th Anniv. 6.95
Star Trek VI,movie adapt(direct) . 5.95
Star Trek VI,movie(newsstand) . 2.95
TPB Best of Star Trek reps. 19.95
TPB Who Killed Captain Kirk?,
  rep.Star Trek#49-#55 . . . . . 16.95
TPB The Ashes of Eden, Shatner
  novel adapt. 14.95

STAR TREK:
THE ASHES OF EDEN
1995
TPB adaptation of novel 14.95

STAR TREK: THE
MODALA IMPERATIVE
1991
1 Planet Modula 6.00
2 Modula's Rebels 4.50
3 Spock/McCoy rescue Attempt . 4.00
4 Rebel Victory 4.00
TPB reprints both minis 19.95

STAR TREK: THE
NEXT GENERATION
Feb., 1988
[1st Regular Series]
1 based on TV series,Where No
  Man Has Gone Before 15.00
2 Spirit in the Sky 10.00
3 Factor Q 8.00
4 Q's Day 8.00
5 Q's Effects 8.00
6 Here Today 8.00
[2nd Regular Series] 1989–95
1 Return to Raimon 16.00
2 Murder Most Foul 9.00
3 Derelict 7.50
4 The Hero Factor 7.50
5 Serafin's Survivors 6.00
6 Shadows in the Garden 6.00
7 The Pilot 5.00
8 The Battle Within 5.00
9 The Pay Off 5.00
10 The Noise of Justice 5.00
11 The Imposter 4.00
12 Whoever Fights Monsters . . . 4.00
13 The Hand of the Assassin 4.00
14 Holiday on Ice 4.00
15 Prisoners of the Ferengi 3.50
16 I Have Heard the Mermaids
  Singing 3.50
17 The Weapon 3.50
18 MM,Forbidden Fruit 3.50

19 The Lesson 3.50
20 Lost Shuttle 3.50
21 Lost Shuttle cont. 3.50
22 Lost Shuttle cont. 3.50
23 Lost Shuttle cont. 3.50
24 Lost Shuttle conc. 3.50
25 Okona S.O.S. 3.50
26 Search for Okona 3.50
27 Worf,Data,Troi,Okona trapped
  on world 3.50
28 Worf/K'Ehleyr story 3.50
29 Rift,pt.1 . . . . 3.50
30 Rift,pt.2 . . . . 3.50
31 Rift conclusion 3.50
32 . . . . 3.50
33 R:Mischievous Q 3.50
34 V:Aliens,F:Mischievous Q . . . 3.50
35 Way of the Warrior 3.50
36 Shore Leave in Shanzibar#1 . 3.25
37 Shore Leave in Shanzibar#2 . 3.25
38 Shore Leave in Shanzibar#3 . 3.25
39 Divergence #1 . . . . 3.25
40 Divergence #2 . . . . 3.25
41 V:Strazzan Warships 3.25

Star Trek The Next Generation #9
© DC Comics, Inc.

42 V:Strazzans 3.25
43 V:Strazzans 3.25
44 Disrupted Lives 3.25
45 F:Enterprise Surgical Team . . . 3.25
46 Deadly Labyrinth 3.25
47 Worst of Both World's#1 . . . . . 3.00
48 Worst of Both World's#2 . . . . . 3.00
49 Worst of Both World's#3 . . . . . 3.00
50 Double Sized,V:Borg 4.00
51 V:Energy Beings 3.00
52 in the 1940's 3.00
53 F:Picard 3.00
54 F:Picard 3.00
55 Data on Trial 3.00
56 Abduction 3.00
57 Body Switch 3.00
58 Body Switch 3.00
59 B:Children in Chaos 3.00
60 Children in Chaos#2 . . . . 3.00
61 E:Children in Chaos 3.00
62 V:Stalker 3.00
63 A:Romulans 3.00
64 Geordie 3.00

65 Geordie 3.00
66 . . . . 3.00
67 Friends/Strangers 3.00
68 Friends/Strangers,pt.2 . . . . . . 3.00
69 Friends/Strangers,pt.3 . . . . . . 3.00
70 Friends/Strangers,pt.4 . . . . . . 3.00
71 War of Madness,pt.1 . . . . 2.50
72 War of Madness,pt.2 . . . . 2.50
73 War of Madness,pt.3 . . . . 2.50
74 War of Madness,pt.4 . . . . 2.50
75 War of Madness,pt.5 . . . . 4.00
76 F:Geordi 2.50
77 Gateway, pt.1 . . . . 2.50
78 Gateway, pt.2 . . . . 2.50
79 Crew transformed into androids 2.50
80 Mysterious illness 2.50
Ann.#1 A:Mischievous Q 4.50
Ann.#2 BP,V:Parasitic Creatures . 4.00
Ann.#3 . . . . 2.50
Ann.#4 MiB(s),F:Dr.Crusher 4.00
Ann.#6 Convergence,pt.2 . . . . . 3.95
Series Finale 4.25
Spec.#1 . . . . 3.75
Spec.#2 CCI(s) 4.00
Star Trek N.G.:Sparticus 5.00
TPB Beginnings, BSz(c) rep. 19.95

STAR TREK:
THE NEXT GENERATION
— BEGINNINGS
TPB 160pg. 19.95

STAR TREK:
THE NEXT GENERATION
DEEP SPACE NINE
1994–95
1 Crossover with Malibu 2.50
2 . . . . 2.50

STAR TREK:
THE NEXT GENERATION
ILL WIND
1995–96
1 Solar-sailing race 2.50
2 Explosion Investigated 2.50
3 A bomb aboard ship 2.50
4 finale 2.50

STAR TREK
THE NEXT GENERATION
MODALA IMPERATIVE
1991
1 A:Spock,McCoy 6.00
2 Modula Overrun by Ferengi . . . 5.00
3 Picard,Spock,McCoy & Troi
  trapped 4.00
4 final issue 4.00

STAR TREK
THE NEXT GENERATION
SHADOWHEART
1994–95
1 thru 3 . . . . @2.25
4 Worf Confront Nikolai 2.25

STAR TREK:
REVISITATIONS
TPB rep. #22-#24,F:Gary Seven,
#49-#50,F:Harry Mudd, 176pg 19.95

Static #13 © DC Comics, Inc.

STATIC
Milestone 1993–96

1 JPL,I:Static,Hotstreak,Frieda Goren, w/poster,card,D puzzle piece	4.00
1a Newstand Ed.	2.00
1b Platinum Ed.	8.00
2 JPL,V:Hotstreak,I:Tarmack	2.00
3 JPL,V:Tarmack	2.00
4 JPL,A:Holocaust,I:Don Cornelius	1.75
5 JPL,I:Commando X	1.75
6 JPL,V:Commando X	1.75
7 3RW,V:Commando X	1.75
8 WS(c),3RW,Shadow War,I:Plus	1.75
9 3RW,I:Virus	1.75
10 3RW,I:Puff,Coil	1.75
11 3RW,V:Puff,Coil	1.75
12 3RW,I:Joyride	1.75
13 I:Shape Changer	1.75
14 Worlds collide,V:Rift	2.75
15 V:Paris Bloods	1.75
16 Revelations	1.75
17 Palisade	1.75
18 Princess Nightmare	1.75
19	1.75
20	1.75
21 A:Blood Syndicate	1.75
22 V:Rabis	1.75
23 A:Boogieman	1.75
24 A:Dusk	1.75
25 Long Hot Summer, V:Dusk, 48pgs	3.95
26 Long Hot Summer	2.50
27	2.50
28 Drug Raid	2.50
29 HC(c), Friend Drug Dealer	2.50
30 Deals with Friend's Death	2.50
31 GK	2.50
32 V:Swarm	2.50
33	2.50
34 V:Ruberband Man	2.50
35 new Prometheus	2.50
36 JP,V:Sinister Botanist	2.50
37	2.50
38	2.50
39	2.50
40 JMr	2.50
41 Virgil's relationship with Daisy	2.50

42 V:six enemies	2.50
43 A:Brickhouse, V:Frieda Goren	2.50
44	2.50
45 MBr(s),JMr,Static lays a trap for Laserjet	2.50
46 MBr(s),JMr	2.50
47 DMD(s),JMr, final issue	2.50

STEEL
1994–98

1 JBg(c),B:LSi(s),CsB,N:Steel	3.00
2 JBg(c),CsB,V:Toastmaster	2.00
3 JBg(c),CsB,V:Amertek	2.00
4 JBg(c),CsB	2.00
5 JBg(c),CsB,V:Sister's Attacker	2.00
6 JBg(c),CsB,Worlds Collide,pt.5	2.00
7 Worlds Collide,pt.6	1.75
8 Zero Hour,I:Hazard	1.75
9 F:Steel	1.50
10 F:Steel	1.50
11	1.50
12	1.50
13 A:Maxima	1.50
14 A:Superman	1.50
15 R:White Rabbit	1.50
16 V:White Rabbit [new Miraweb format begins]	2.00
17 Steel controls armor powers	2.00
18 Abduction	2.00
19	2.00
20 Body Rejects Armor	2.00
21 LSi,Underworld Unleashed tie-in	2.00
22 Steel separated from Superboy	2.00
23 Steel attacked	2.00
24 V:Hazard's	2.00
25	2.00
26 Natasha gains superpowers	2.00
27 LSi,V:Hazard	2.00
28	2.00
29	2.00
30	2.00
31 LSi(s),V:Armorbeast	2.00
32 V:Blockbuster	2.00
33 JAp,DG,Natasha's drug abuse	2.00
34 CPr(s),DCw,TP,A:Natasha, in Jersey City	2.00
35 CPr(s),DCw,TP,	2.00
36 CPr(s),DCw,TP,Combing the sewers of Jersey City	2.00
37 CPr(s),DCw,TP,John Irons, Amanda Quick & Skorpio a romantic triangle	2.00
38 CPr(s),DCw,TP,A:The Question	2.00
39 CPr(s),DCw,TP,V:Crash	2.00
40 CPr(s),VGi,Steel tries out new hammer	2.00
41 CPr(s),DCw,TMo, John Irons guilty of murder?	2.00
42 CPr(s),DCw,TP,Irons and Amanda assaulted	2.00
43 CPr(s),DCw,TP,to Metropolis	2.00
44 CPr(s),DCw,TP,Genesis tie-in	2.50
45 CPr(s),DCw,TP,seek policeman	2.50
46 CPr(s),DCw,TP,F:Superboy	2.50
47 CPr(s),DCw,TP,F:Amanda	2.50
48	2.50
49 CPr(s),DCw,TP,V:Deadline	2.50
50 CPr(s),DCw,TP,Millennium Giants	2.50
51 CPr(s),DCw,TP,bounty hunter	2.50
52 CPr(s),final issue	2.50
1-shot, movie adaptation	5.00
Ann.#1 Elseworlds story	2.95
TPB THe Forging of a Hero LSi(s)	19.95

STEEL, THE INDESTRUCTIBLE MAN
March, 1978

1 DH,I:Steel	1.00
2 DH	1.00
3 DH	1.00
4 DH	1.00
5 Oct.–Nov., 1978	1.00

STRANGE ADVENTURES
1950–74

1 The Menace of the Green Nebula	2,400.00
2 S&K,JM(c),Doom From Planet X	1,100.00
3 The Metal World	700.00
4 BP,The Invaders From the Nth Dimension	700.00
5 The World Inside the Atom	650.00
6 The Confessions of a Martian	650.00
7 The World of Giant Ants	650.00
8 MA,ATh,Evolution Plus	650.00
9 MA,B:Captain Comet,The Origin of Captain Comet	1,500.00
10 MA,CI,The Air Bandits From Space	650.00
11 MA,CI,Day the Past Came Back	450.00
12 MA,CI,GK(c),The Girl From the Diamond Planet	450.00
13 MA,CI,GK(c),When the Earth was Kidnapped	450.00
14 MA,CI,GK(c),Destination Doom	450.00
15 MA,CI,GK(c),Captain Comet-Enemy of Earth	425.00
16 MA,CI,GK(c),The Ghost of Captain Comet	425.00
17 MA,CI,GK(c),Beware the Synthetic Men	425.00
18 CI,MA(c),World of Flying Men	425.00
19 CI,MA(c),Secret of the Twelve Eternals	425.00
20 CI,Slaves of the Sea Master	425.00
21 CI,MA(c),Eyes of the Other Worlds	350.00
22 CI,The Guardians of the Clockwork Universe	350.00
23 CI,MA(c),The Brain Pirates of Planet X	350.00
24 CI,MA(c),Doomsday on Earth	350.00
25 CI,GK(c),The Day That Vanished	350.00
26 CI,Captain Vs. Miss Universe	350.00
27 CI,MA(c),The Counterfeit Captain Comet	350.00
28 CI,Devil's Island in Space	350.00
29 CI,The Time Capsule From 1,000,000 B.C.	350.00
30 CI,MA(c),Menace From the World of Make-Believe	325.00
31 CI,Lights Camera Action	325.00
32 CI,MA(c),The Challenge of Man-Ape the Mighty	325.00
33 CI,MA(c),The Human Beehive	325.00
34 CI,MA(c)	325.00
35 CI,MA(c),Cosmic Chessboard	325.00
36 CI,MA(c),The Grab-Bag Planet	325.00
37 CI,MA(c),The Invaders From the Golden Atom	325.00
38 CI,MA(c),Seeing-Eye Humans	325.00
39 CI,MA(c),The Guilty Gorilla	350.00
40 CI,MA(c),The Mind Monster	300.00

41 CI,MA(c),The Beast From Out
of Time 300.00
42 CI,MD,MA(c),The Planet of
Ancient Children 300.00
43 CI,MD,MA(c),The Phantom
Prize Fighter 300.00
44 CI,MA(c),The Planet That
Plotted Murder 300.00
45 CI,MD,MA(c),Gorilla World . 300.00
46 CI,MA(c),E:Captain Comet
Interplanetary War Base . . . 300.00
47 CI,MA(c),The Man Who Sold
the Earth 300.00
48 CI,MA(c),Human Phantom . 300.00
49 CI,MA(c),The Invasion
from Indiana 300.00
50 CI,MA(c),The World Wrecker 250.00
51 CI,MA(c),The Man Who
Stole Air 250.00
52 CI,MA(c),Prisoner of the
Parakeets 250.00
53 CI,MA(c),The Human Icicle . 250.00
54 CI,MA(c),The Electric Man . 175.00
55 CI,MA(c),The Gorilla Who
Challanged the World,pt.I . . 175.00

Strange Adventures #5
© DC Comics, Inc.

56 CI,The Jungle Emperor,pt.II 175.00
57 CI,The Spy from Saturn . . . 175.00
58 CI,I Hunted the Radium Man 175.00
59 CI,The Ark From Planet X . . 175.00
60 CI,Across the Ages 175.00
61 CI,The Mirages From Space 175.00
62 CI,The Fireproof Man 175.00
63 CI,I Was the Man in the Moon175.00
64 CI,GK(c),Gorillas In Space . 175.00
65 CI,GK(c),Prisoner From Pluto 175.00
66 CI,GK(c),The Human Battery 175.00
67 CI,GK(c),Martian Masquerader175.00
68 CI,The Man Who Couldn't
Drown 175.00
69 CI,Gorilla Conquest of Earth 175.00
70 CI,Triple Life of Dr. Pluto . . 175.00
71 CI,MSy,Zero Hour For Earth 150.00
72 CI,The Skyscraper That Came
to Life 150.00
73 CI,Amazing Rain of Gems . 150.00
74 CI,The Invisible Invader
From Dimension X 150.00
75 CI,Secret of the Man-Ape . . 150.00

76 CI,B:Darwin Jones,The Robot
From Atlantis 150.00
77 CI,A:Darwin Jones,The World
That Slipped Out of Space . 150.00
78 CI,The Secret of the Tom
Thumb Spaceman 150.00
79 CI,A:Darwin Jones,Invaders
from the Ice World 150.00
80 CI,Mind Robbers of Venus . 150.00
81 CI,The Secret of the
Shrinking Twins 150.00
82 CI,Giants of the Cosmic Ray 125.00
83 CI,Assignment in Eternity . . 125.00
84 CI,Prisoners of the Atom
Universe 125.00
85 CI,The Amazing Human Race125.00
86 CI,The Dog That Saved the
Earth 125.00
87 CI,New Faces For Old 125.00
88 CI,A:Darwin Jones,The Gorilla
War Against Earth 125.00
89 CI,Earth For Sale 125.00
90 CI,The Day I Became a
Martian 125.00
91 CI,Midget Earthmen of Jupiter125.00
92 CI,GK(c),The Amazing Ray
of Knowledge 125.00
93 CI,GK(c),A:Darwin Jones,
Space-Rescue By Proxy . . . 125.00
94 MA,CI,GK(c),Fisherman of
Space 125.00
95 CI,The World at my Doorstep 125.00
96 CI,MA(c),The Menace of
Saturn's Rings 125.00
97 CI,MA(c),MSy,Secret of the
Space-Giant 125.00
98 CI,GK(c),MSy,Attack on Fort
Satellite 125.00
99 CI,MSy,GK(c),Big Jump Into
Space 125.00
100 CI,MSy,The Amazing Trial
of John (Gorilla) Doe 135.00
101 CI,MSy,GK(c),Giant From
Beyond 80.00
102 MSy,GK(c),The Three Faces
of Barry Morrell 80.00
103 GK(c),The Man Who
Harpooned Worlds 80.00
104 MSy,GK(c),World of Doomed
Spacemen 80.00
105 MSy,GK(c),Fisherman From
the Sea 80.00
106 MSy,CI,GK(c),Genie in the
Flying Saucer 80.00
107 MSy,CI,GK(c),War of the
Jovian Bubble-Men 80.00
108 MSy,CI,GK(c),The Human
Pet of Gorilla Land 80.00
109 MSy,CI,GK(c),The Man Who
Weighted 100 Tons 80.00
110 MSy,CI,GK(c),Hand From
Beyond 80.00
111 MSy,CI,GK(c),Secret of
the Last Earth-Man 80.00
112 MSy,CI,GK(c),Menace of
the Size-Changing Spaceman 80.00
113 MSy,CI,GK(c),Deluge From
Space 80.00
114 MSy,CI,GK(c),Secret of the
Flying Buzz Saw 80.00
115 MSy,CI,GK(c),The Great
Space-Tiger Hunt 80.00
116 MSy,CI,RH,GK(c),Invasion
of the Water Warriors 80.00
117 MSy,CI,GK(c),I:Atomic

Knights 600.00
118 MSy,CI,The Turtle-Men of
Space 125.00
119 MSy,CI,MA(c),Raiders
From the Giant World 100.00
120 MSy,CI,MA,Attack of the Oil
Demons 250.00
121 MSy,CI,MA(c),Invasion of the
Flying Reptiles 65.00
122 MSy,CI,MA(c),David and the
Space-Goliath 65.00
123 MSy,CI,MA(c),Secret of the
Rocket-Destroyer 100.00
124 MSy,CI,MA(c),The Face-Hunter
From Saturn 75.00
125 MSy,CI,The Flying Gorilla
Menace 65.00
126 MSy,CI,MA(c),Return of the
Neanderthal Man 100.00
127 MSy,CI,MA(c),Menace
From the Earth-Globe 65.00
128 MSy,CI,MA(c),The Man
With the Electronic Brain . . . 65.00
129 MSy,CI,MA(c),The Giant
Who Stole Mountains 70.00
130 MSy,CI,MA.War With the
Giant Frogs 65.00
131 MSy,CI,MA(c),Emperor
of the Earth 65.00
132 MSy,CI,MA(c),The Dreams
of Doom 70.00
133 MSy,CI,MA(c),The Invisible
Dinosaur 65.00
134 MSy,CI,MA(c), The Aliens
Who Raided New York 70.00
135 MSy,CI,MA(c),Fishing Hole
in the Sky 65.00
136 MSy,CI,MA(c),The Robot
Who Lost Its Head 50.00
137 MSy,CI,MA(c),Parade of the
Space-Toys 50.00
138 MSy,CI,MA(c),Secret of the
Dinosaur Skeleton 70.00
139 MSy,CI,MA(c),Space-Roots
of Evil 50.00
140 MSy,CI,MA(c),Prisoner of
the Space-Patch 50.00
141 MSy,CI,MA(c),Battle Between
the Two Earths 65.00
142 MSy,CI,MA(c),The Return of
the Faceless Creature 50.00
143 MSy,CI,MA(c),The Face in
the Atom-Bomb Cloud 50.00
144 MSy,CI,MA(c),A:Atomic
Knights, When the Earth
Blacked Out 85.00
145 MSy,CI,MA,The Man Who
Lived Forever 50.00
146 MSy,CI,MA(c),Perilous Pet
of Space 50.00
147 MSy,CI,MA(c),The Dawn-
World Menace 60.00
148 MSy,CI,MA(c),Earth Hero,
Number One 50.00
149 MSy,CI,MA(c),Raid of
the Rogue Star 50.00
150 MSy,CI,MA(c),When Earth
Turned into a Comet 55.00
151 MSy,CI,MA(c),Invasion Via
Radio-Telescope 50.00
152 MSy,MA(c),The Martian
Emperor of Earth 50.00
153 MSy,MA(c),Threat of the
Faceless Creature 50.00
154 CI,MSy,MA,GK(c),Earth's

Friendly Invaders 50.00
155 MSy,MA,GK(c),Prisoner
 of the Undersea World 50.00
156 MSy,CI,MA(c),The Man
 With the Head of Saturn 50.00
157 MSy,CI,MA(c),Plight of
 the Human Cocoons 50.00
158 MSy,CI,MA(c),The Mind
 Masters of Space 50.00
159 MSy,CI,MA(c),The Maze
 of Time 50.00
160 MSy,CI,MA(c),A:Atomic
 Knights, Here Comes the
 Wild Ones 50.00
161 MSy,CI,MA(c),Earth's Frozen
 Heat Wave,E:Space Museum 35.00
162 CI,MA(c),Mystery of the
 12 O'Clock Man 35.00
163 MA(c),The Creature in
 the Black Light 35.00
164 DD&SMo(c),I Became
 a Robot 35.00
165 DD&SMo(c),I Broke the
 Supernatural Barrier 35.00
166 DD&SMo(c),I Lived in
 Two Bodies 35.00
167 JkS(c),The Team That
 Conquered Time 35.00
168 JkS(c),I Hunted Toki
 the Terrible 35.00
169 DD&SMo(c),The Prisoner
 of the Hour Glass 35.00
170 DD&SMo(c),The Creature
 From Strange Adventures . . . 35.00
171 The Diary o/t 9-Planet Man? 35.00
172 DD&SMo(c),I Became
 the Juggernaut Man 35.00
173 The Secret of the
 Fantasy Films 35.00
174 JkS(c),The Ten Ton Man . . 35.00
175 Danger: This Town is
 Shrinking 35.00
176 DD&SMo(c),The Case of
 the Cosmonik Quartet 35.00
177 I Lived a Hundred Lives,
 O:Immortal Man 35.00
178 JkS(c),The Runaway Comet 35.00
179 JkS(c),I Buried Myself Alive . 35.00
180 CI,I:Animal Man,'I Was the
 Man With Animal Powers . . 225.00
181 The Man of Two Worlds . . . 15.00
182 JkS(c),The Case of the
 Blonde Bombshell 15.00
183 JM(c),The Plot to Destroy
 the Earth 15.00
184 GK(c),A:Animal Man,The
 Return of the Man With
 Animal Powers 150.00
185 JkS(c),Ilda-Gangsters Inc. . . 15.00
186 Beware the Gorilla Witch . . 15.00
187 JkS(c),O:The Enchantress . 20.00
188 SD,JkS(c),I Was the
 Four Seasons 15.00
189 SD,JkS(c),The Way-Out
 Worlds of Bertram Tilley . . . 15.00
190 CI,A:Animal Man,A-Man-the
 Hero with Animal Powers . . 150.00
191 JkS(c),Beauty vs. the Beast 15.00
192 Freak Island 15.00
193 The Villian Maker 15.00
194 JkS(c),The Menace of the
 Super- Gloves 15.00
195 JkS(c),Secret of the Three
 Earth Dooms,A:Animal Man 100.00
196 JkS(c),Mystery of the

Strange Adventures #231
© DC Comics, Inc.

Orbit Creatures 15.00
197 The Hostile Hamlet 12.00
198 JkS(c),Danger! Earth
 is Doomed 12.00
199 Robots of the Round Table . 12.00
200 . . . . 12.00
201 JkS,Animal Man 50.00
202 . . . . 12.00
203 . . . . 12.00
204 . . . . 12.00
205 CI,I&O:Deadman 85.00
206 NA,MSy 75.00
207 NA 50.00
208 NA 50.00
209 NA 50.00
210 NA 50.00
211 NA 50.00
212 NA 50.00
213 NA 50.00
214 NA 50.00
215 NA 50.00
216 NA 50.00
217 MA,MSy,A:Adam Strange . . 12.00
218 MA,CI,MSy 11.00
219 CI,JKu 11.00
220 CI,JKu 11.00
221 CI 11.00
222 MA,New Adam Strange . . . 13.00
223 MA,CI 11.00
224 MA,CI 11.00
225 MA,JKu 11.00
226 MA,JKu,New Adam Strange 13.00
227 JKu 11.00
228 NA(c) 25.00
229 . . . . 11.00
230 GM(c) 11.00
231 E:Atomic Knights 11.00
232 JKu 10.00
233 JKu 10.00
234 JKu 10.00
235 NA(c) 20.00
236 . . . . 10.00
237 . . . . 10.00
238 MK(c) 10.00
239 . . . . 10.00
240 MK(c) 10.00
241 . . . . 10.00

242 MA 10.00
243 F:Adam Strange 10.00
244 Oct.–Nov., 1974 . . . . 10.00

STRANGE SPORTS STORIES
Sept.–Oct. 1973
1 CS,DG 25.00
2 thru 6 . . . . @15.00

STREETS
1993
1 Tenderloin 4.95
2 Procurement 4.95
3 . . . . 4.95

SUGAR & SPIKE
April-May, 1956
1 SM 1,000.00
2 SM 500.00
3 SM 400.00
4 SM 350.00
5 SM 350.00
6 thru 10 SM . . . . @250.00
11 thru 20 SM . . . . @200.00
21 thru 29 SM . . . . @100.00
30 SM,A:Scribbly 125.00
31 thru 50 SM . . . . @100.00
51 thru 70 SM . . . . @70.00
71 thru 79 SM . . . . @50.00
80 SM,I:Bernie the Brain 50.00
81 thru 97 SM . . . . @30.00
98 SM,Oct.–Nov., 1971 . . . . . . 30.00

STUCK RUBBER BABY SOFTCOVER
DC/Paradox Press
GN by Howard Cruise 14.00

SUICIDE SQUAD
1987–91
1 LMc,Legends,I:Jihad 2.50
2 LMc,V:The Jihad 2.00
3 LMc,V:Female Furies 1.75
4 LMc,V:William Hell 1.75
5 LM,A:Penguin 2.50
6 LM,A:Penguin 2.50
7 LMc,V:Peoples Hero 1.50
8 LMc,O:SquadMembers 1.50
9 LMc,Millenium 1.50
10 LMc,A:Batman 1.50
11 LMc,A:Vixen,Speedy 1.50
12 LMc,Enchantress,
 V:Nightshade 1.50
13 LMc,X-over,JLI#13 . . . . 2.00
14 Nightshade Odyssey #1 . . . 1.50
15 Nightshade Odyssey #2 . . . 1.50
16 R:Shade 3.00
17 LMc,V:The Jihad 1.25
18 LMc,V:Jihad 1.25
19 LMc,Personal Files 1988 . . . 1.25
20 LMc,V:Mirror Master 1.25
21 LMc,bonus book #10 . . . . . 1.25
22 LMc,D:Senator Cray 1.25
23 LMc,Invasion 1.25
24 LMc,V:Guerillas 1.25
25 L:Nightshade 1.25
26 D:Rick Flag,Jihad 1.25
27 Janus Directive #2 . . . . 1.25
28 Janus Directive #8 . . . . 1.25
29 Janus Directive #8 . . . . 1.25
30 Janus Directive #10 . . . . . . 1.25
31 Personal Files 1989 . . . . . . 1.25

Suicide Squad #54 © DC Comics, Inc.

32 V:Female Furies	1.25
33 GI,V:Female Furies	1.25
34 GI,V:Granny Goodness	1.25
35 LMc,GI,V:Female Furies	1.25
36 GI,D:Original Dr.Light	1.25
37 GI,A:Shade,The Changing Man,V:Loa	1.50
38 LMc,GI,O:Bronze Tiger	1.25
39 GI,D:Loa	1.25
40 Phoenix Gambit #1,A:Batman Int. Poster	1.50
41 Phoenix Gambit #2	1.25
42 Phoenix Gambit,A:Batman	1.25
43 Phoenix Gambit,A:Batman	1.25
44 I:New Atom,O:Captain Boomerang	1.25
45 A:Kobra	1.00
46 A:Kobra	1.00
47 GI,A:Kobra,D:Ravan	1.00
48 GI,New Thinker	1.00
49 GI,New Thinker	1.00
50 GI,50 Years of S.Squad	2.00
51 A:Deadshot	1.00
52 R:Docter Light	1.00
53 GI,The Dragon's Horde #1	1.00
54 GI,The Dragon's Horde #2	1.00
55 GI,The Dragon's Horde #3	1.00
56 GI,The Dragon's Horde #4	1.00
57 GI,The Dragon's Horde conc.	1.00
58 GI,War of the Gods x-over	1.00
59 GI,A:Superman, Batman, Aquaman,A:Jihad, Hayoth	1.25
60 GI,A:Superman,Batman, Aquaman,Jihad,The Hayoth	1.25
61 GI,A:Superman,Batman, Aquaman,V:Jihad	1.25
62 GI,R:Ray Palmer,A:Batman Superman,Aquaman	1.25
63 GI,I:Gvede, Lord of Death	1.25
64 GI,A:Task Force X	1.25
65 GI,Bronze Tiger	1.25
66 GI,Final Iss.E:Suicide Squad	1.25
Ann.#1 GN,V:Argent,A:Manhunter	1.75

SUPERBOY
1949–76

1 Superman (c)	6,800.00
2 'Superboy Day'	1,500.00
3	1,200.00
4 The Oracle of Smallville	800.00
5 Superboy meets Supergirl, Pre-*Adventure* #252	750.00
6 I:Humpty Dumpty,the Hobby Robber	700.00
7 WB,V:Humpty Dumpty	700.00
8 CS,I:Superbaby,V:Humpty Dumpty	650.00
9 V:Humpty Dumpty	650.00
10 CS,I:Lana Lang	650.00
11 CS,2nd Lang,V:Humpty Dumpty	550.00
12 CS,The Heroes Club	550.00
13 CS,Scout of Smallville	550.00
14 CS,I:Marsboy	550.00
15 CS,A:Superman	550.00
16 CS,A:Marsboy	375.00
17 CS,Superboy's Double	375.00
18 CS,Lana Lang-Hollywood Star	375.00
19 CS,The Death of Young Clark Kent	375.00
20 CS,The Ghost that Haunted Smallville	375.00
21 CS,Lana Lang-Magician	275.00
22 CS,The New Clark Kent	275.00
23 CS,The Super Superboy	275.00
24 CS,The Super Fat Boy of Steel	275.00
25 CS,Cinderella of Smallville	275.00
26 CS,A:Superbaby	275.00
27 CS,Clark Kent-Runaway.	275.00
28 CS,The Man Who Defeated Superboy	275.00
29 CS,The Puppet Superboy	275.00
30 CS,I:Tommy Tuttle	200.00
31 CS,The Amazing Elephant Boy From Smallville	200.00
32 CS,His Majesty King Superboy	200.00
33 CS,The Crazy Costumes of the Boy of Steel	200.00
34 CS,Hep Cats o/Smallville	200.00
35 CS,The Five Superboys	200.00
36	200.00
37 CS,I:Thaddeus Lang	200.00
38 CS,Public Chimp #1	200.00
39 CS,Boy w/Superboy Powers	200.00
40 CS,The Magic Necklace	175.00
41 CS,Superboy Meets Superbrave	175.00
42 CS,Gaucho of Smallville	175.00
43 CS,Super-Farmer o/Smallville	175.00
44 The Amazing Adventure of Superboy's Costume	175.00
45 A Trap For Superboy	175.00
46 The Battle of Fort Smallville	175.00
47 CS,A:Superman	175.00
48 CS,Boy Without Super-Suit	175.00
49 I:Metallo (Jor-El's Robot)	200.00
50 The Super-Giant of Smallville	175.00
51 I:Krypto	150.00
52 CS,The Powerboy from Earth	150.00
53 CS,A:Superman	150.00
54 CS,The Silent Superboy	150.00
55 CS,A:Jimmy Olson	150.00
56 CS,A:Krypto	150.00
57 CS,One-Man Baseball Team	150.00
58 CS,The Great Kryptonite Mystery	150.00
59 CS,A:Superbaby	150.00
60 The 100,000 Cowboy	150.00
61 The School For Superboys	125.00

Superboy #89 © DC Comics, Inc.

62 I:Gloria Kent	125.00
63 CS,The Two Boys of Steel	125.00
64 CS,A:Krypto	125.00
65 Superboy's Moonlight Spell	125.00
66 The Family with X-Ray Eyes	125.00
67 I:Klax-Ar	125.00
68 O&I:Bizarro	500.00
69 How Superboy Learned To Fly	100.00
70 O:Superboy's Glasses	100.00
71 A:Superbaby	100.00
72 The Flying Girl of Smallville	100.00
73 CS,A:Superbaby	100.00
74 A:Jor-El & Lara	100.00
75 A:Superbaby	100.00
76 I:Super Monkey	100.00
77 Superboy's Best Friend	100.00
78 O:Mr.Mzyzptlk	150.00
79 A:Jar-El & Lara	85.00
80 Superboy meets Supergirl	125.00
81 The Weakling From Earth	75.00
82 A:Bizarro Krypto	75.00
83 I:Kryptonite Kid	75.00
84 I:William Tell	75.00
85 Secret of Mighty Boy	75.00
86 I:PeteRoss,A:Legion	150.00
87 I:Scarlet Jungle of Krypton	80.00
88 The Invader from Earth	80.00
89 I:Mon-El	250.00
90 A:Pete Ross	75.00
91 CS,Superboy in Civil War	75.00
92 CS,I:Destructo,A:Lex Luthor	75.00
93 A:Legion	65.00
94 I:Superboy Revenge Squad, A:Pete Ross	50.00
95 Imaginary Story,The Super Family From Krypton	50.00
96 A:Pete Ross,Lex Luthor	50.00
97 Krypto Story	40.00
98 Legion,I&O:Ultraboy	55.00
99 O: The Kryptonite Kid	45.00
100 I:Phantom Zone	175.00
101 The Handsome Hound of Steel	35.00
102 O:Scarlet Jungle of Krypton	35.00
103 CS,A:King Arthur, Jesse James Red Kryptonite	35.00
104 O:Phantom Zone	35.00

All comics prices listed are for *Near Mint* condition.

Superboy #143 © DC Comics, Inc.

Superboy #147 © DC Comics, Inc.

Superboy #168 © DC Comics, Inc.

105 CS,'The Simpleton of Steel'	35.00
106 CS,A:Brainiac	35.00
107 CS,I:Superboy Club of Smallville	40.00
108 The Kent's First Super Son	35.00
109 The Super Youth of Bronze	35.00
110 A:Jor-El	35.00
111 Red Kryptonite Story	35.00
112 CS,A:Superbaby	35.00
113 'The Boyhood of Dad Kent'	35.00
114 A:Phantom Zone, Mr.Mxyzptlk	35.00
115 A:Phantom Zone,Lex Luthor	35.00
116 'The Wolfboy of Smallville'	35.00
117 A:Legion	35.00
118 CS,'The War Between Superboy and Krypto'	35.00
119 V:Android Double	30.00
120 A:Mr.Mxyzptlk	30.00
121 CS,A:Jor-El,Lex Luthor	30.00
122 Red Kryptonite Story	30.00
123 CS,The Curse of the Superboy Mummy	30.00
124 I:Insect Queen	30.00
125 O:Kid Psycho	30.00
126 O:Krypto	30.00
127 A:Insect Queen	32.00
128 A:Phantom Zone,Kryptonite Kid,Dev En	32.00
129 rep.A:Mon-El,SuperBaby	35.00
130	20.00
131 A;Lex Luthor,Mr.Mxyzptlk,I: Space Canine Patrol Agents	20.00
132, CS,A:Space Canine Patrol Agents	20.00
133 A:Robin, repr.	20.00
134 'The Scoundrel of Steel'	20.00
135 A:Lex Luthor	20.00
136 A:Space Canine Agents	20.00
137 Mysterious Mighty Mites	20.00
138 giant, Superboy's Most Terrific Battles	35.00
139 'The Samson of Smallville'	15.00
140 V:The Gambler	15.00
141 No Mercy for a Hero	15.00
142 A:Super Monkey	15.00
143 NA(c),'The Big Fall'	15.00
144 'Superboy's Stolen Identity'	15.00

145 NA(c)Kents become young	15.00
146 NA(c),CS,'The Runaway'	15.00
147 giant O:Legion	25.00
148 NA(c),CS,C:PolarBoy	14.00
149 NA(c),A:Bonnie & Clyde	14.00
150 JAb,V:Mr.Cipher	14.00
151 NA(c),A:Kryptonite Kid	14.00
152 NA(c),WW	14.00
153 NA(c),WW,A;Prof Mesmer	12.00
154 WW(i),A:Jor-El & Lara 'Blackout For Superboy'	12.00
155 NA(c),WW,'Revolt of the Teenage Robots'	12.00
156 giant	16.00
157 WW	12.00
158 WW,A:Jor-El & Lara	12.00
159 WW(i),A:Lex Luthor	12.00
160 WW,'I Chose Eternal Exile'	12.00
161 WW,'The Strange Death of Superboy'	12.00
162 A:Phantom Zone	12.00
163 NA(c),'Reform School Rebel'	12.00
164 NA(c),'Your Death Will Destroy Me'	12.00
165 giant	16.00
166 NA(c),A:Lex Luthor	12.00
167 NA(c),MA,A:Superbaby	12.00
168 NA(c),MA,Hitler	12.00
169 MA,A:Lex Luthor	12.00
170 MA,A:Genghis Khan	12.00
171 MA,A:Aquaboy	12.00
172 MA(i),GT,A:Legion, O:Lightning Lad,Yango	13.00
173 NA(c),GT,DG,O:CosmicBoy	12.00
174 giant	16.00
175 NA(c),Rejuvenation of Ma & Pa Kent	12.00
176 NA(c),MA,GT,WW,A:Legion	12.00
177 MA,A:Lex Luthor	8.00
178 NA(c),MA,Legion Reprint	8.00
179 MA,A:Lex Luthor	8.00
180 MA,O:Bouncing Boy	8.00
181 MA	8.00
182 MA,A:Bruce Wayne	8.00
183 MA,GT,CS(rep),A:Legion	8.00
184 MA,WW,O:Dial H rep.	8.00
185 A:Legion	10.00
186 MA	5.00

187 MA	5.00
188 MA,DC,O:Karkan,A:Legn	5.00
189 MA	5.00
190 MA,WW	5.00
191 MA,DC O:SunBoy retold	5.00
192 MA	5.00
193 MA,WW,N:Chameleon Boy, Shrinking Violet	5.00
194 MA	5.00
195 MA,WW,I:Wildfire, N:Phantom Girl	5.00
196 last Superboy solo	8.00
197 DC,Legion begins, New Costumes,I:Tyr	11.00
198 DC N:Element Lad, Princess Projects	6.00
199 DC,A:Tyr, Otto Orion	6.00
200 DC,M:Bouncing Boy & Duo Damsel	11.00
201 DC,Wildfire returns	6.00
202 N:Light Lass	3.00
203 MGr,D:Invisible Kid	18.00
204 MGr,A:Supergirl	5.00
205 MGr,CG,100 pages	6.00
206 MGr,A:Ferro Lad	5.00
207 MGr,O:Lightning Lad	5.00
208 MGr,CS,68pp,Legion of Super Villains	7.00
209 MGr,N:Karate Kid	5.00
210 MGr,O:Karate Kid	7.00
211 MGr	4.00
212 MGr,L:Matter Eater Lad	4.00
213 MGr,V:Benn Pares	4.00
214 MGr,V:Overseer	4.00
215 MGr,A:Emerald Empress	4.00
216 MGr,I:Tyroc	4.00
217 MGr,I:Laurel Kent	4.00
218 J:Tyroc,A:Fatal Five	4.00
219 MGr,A:Fatal Five	4.00
220 MGi,BWi	4.00
221 MGr,BWi,I:Grimbor	3.00
222 MGr,BWi,MN,BL,A:Tyroc	3.00
223 MGr,BWi	3.00
224 MGr,BWi,V:Pulsar Stargrave	3.00
225 MGr(c),BWi,JSh,MN	3.00
226 MGr(c),MN,JSh,JA, I:Dawnstar	3.00
227 MGr(c),JSon,JA,V:Stargrave	3.00
228 MGr(c),JSh,JA,	

D:Chemical King 3.00
229 MGr(c),JSh,JA,V:Deregon . . . 3.00
230 MGr(c),JSh,V:Sden 3.00
Becomes:
SUPERBOY & THE LEGION OF SUPER-HEROES
1976–79
231 MGr(c),JSh,MN,JA,doub.size
begins,V:Fatal Five 5.00
232 MGr(c),JSh,RE,JA,V:
Dr.Regulus 5.00
233 MGr(c),JSh,BWi,MN,BL,
I:Infinite Man 5.00
234 MGr(c),RE,JA,V:Composite
Creature 5.00
235 MGr,GT 5.00
236 MGr(c),BMc,JSh,MN,JRu,
V:Khunds 5.00
237 MGr(c),WS,JA 5.00
238 JSn(c),reprint 5.00
239 MGR(c),JSn,JRu,Ultra Boy
accused 5.00
240 MGr(c),HC,BWi,JSh,BMc,
O:Dawnstar;V:Grimbor 5.00
241 JSh,BMc,A:Ontir 5.00
242 JSh,BMc,E:Double Size . . . 5.00
243 MGr(c),JA,JSon 5.00
244 JSon,V:Dark Circle 5.00
245 MA,JSon,V:Mordru 5.00
246 MGr(c),JSon,DG,MA,
V:Fatal Five 3.00
247 JSon,JA,anniv.issue. 3.00
248 JSon 3.00
249 JSon,JA 3.00
250 JSn,V:Omega 3.00
251 JSn,Brainiac 5 goes insane . . 3.00
252 JSon,V:Starburst bandits . . . 2.00
253 JSon,I:Blok,League of
Super Assassins 2.00
254 JSon,V:League of Super
Assassins 2.00
255 JSon,A:Jor-El 2.00
256 JSon 2.00
257 SD,JSon,DA,V:Psycho
Warrior 2.00
258 JSon,V:Psycho Warrior 2.00
Becomes:
Legion of Super Heroes
[2nd Series]

[NEW ADVENTURES OF] SUPERBOY
Jan., 1980
1 KS 1.50
2 KS 1.25
3 KS 1.25
4 KS 1.25
5 KS 1.25
6 KS 1.25
7 KS,JSa 1.25
8 thru 33 KS . . . . @1.25
34 KS,I:Yellow Peri 1.25
35 thru 44 KS . . . . @1.25
45 KS,I:Sunburst 1.25
46 KS,A:Sunburst 1.25
47 KS,A:Sunburst 1.25
48 KS 1.25
49 KS,A:Zatara 1.25
50 KS,KG,A:Legion 1.50
51 KS,FM(c)In Between Years . . 1.25
52 KS 1.25
53 KS 1.25

New Adventures of Superboy #11
© DC Comics, Inc.

54 KS 1.25

SUPERBOY
1990–91
1 TV Tie-in,JM,photo(c) 1.25
2 JM,T.J.White Abducted 1.25
3 JM,'Fountain of Youth' 1.25
4 JM,'Big Man on Campus' 1.25
5 JM,Legion Homage 1.25
6 JM,Luthor 1.25
7 JM,Super Boy Arrested 1.25
8 JM,AAd(i),Bizarro 1.25
9 JM/CS,PhantomZone#1 . . . . . 1.25
10 JM/CS,PhantomZone#2 . . . . . 1.25
11 CS 1.25
12 CS,X-Mas in Smallville 1.25
Becomes:
ADVENTURES OF SUPERBOY
1991
13 A:Mr.Mxyzptlk 1.75
14 CS,A:Brimstone 1.25
15 CS,Legion Homage 1.25
16 CS,Into the Future 1.25
17 CS,A:Luthor 1.25
18 JM,'At the Movies' 1.25
19 JM,Blood Transfusion 1.25
20 JM,O:Nicknack,(G.Gottfried
script) 1.25
21 V:Frost Monster 1.25
22 . . . . 1.25
Spec.#1 CS,A:Ma Kent 1.75

SUPERBOY
[2nd Series]
1994–97
1 B:KK(s),TG,DHz,V:Sidearm . . . 3.00
2 TG,DHz,I:Knockout 2.50
3 TG,DHz,I:Scavenger 2.00
4 TG,DHz,MeP,I:Lock n' Load . . 2.00
5 TG,DHz,I:Silver Sword 2.00
6 TG,DHz,Worlds Collide,pt.3
C:Rocket 1.75
7 Worlds Collide, pt.8,V:Rift . . . 1.75
8 Zero Hour,A:Superboy 1.50

9 Silican Dragon 1.50
10 Monster 1.50
11 Techno 1.50
12 Copperhead 1.50
13 Watery Grave,pt.1 . . . . 1.50
14 Watery Grave,pt.2 . . . . 1.50
15 Watery Grave,pt.3 . . . . 1.50
16 TG,DHz,KK,V:Loose Cannon
[New Miraweb format begins] . 2.00
17 TG,DHz,KK Looking for
Roxy Leech 2.00
18 V:Valor 2.00
19 . . . . 2.00
20 R:Scavenger 2.00
21 KK,TG,DHz,Future Tense,Pt.1 2.00
22 KK,TG,DHz,Underworld
Unleashed x-over 2.00
23 KK,TG,DHz,V:Technician 2.00
24 KK,TG,DHz,V:Silversword 2.00
25 New Gods 3.00
26 KK,DHz,Losin'it,pt.2 . . . . 2.00
27 KK,DHz,Losin'it,pt.3 . . . . 2.00
28 KK,DHz,Losin'it,pt.4 (of 6) . . . 2.00
29 . . . . 2.00
30 . . . . 2.00
31 . . . . 2.00
32 RMz(s),RBe,DHz,V:King Shark 2.00

Superboy (2nd Series) #9
© DC Comics, Inc.

33 RMz(s),RBe,DHz, survivors flee
to Hawaii, Final Night tie-in . . . 2.00
34 RMz(s),RBe,DHz, V:Dubbilex . 2.00
35 RMz(s),RBe,DHz, Superboy
abducted 2.00
36 RMz(s),RBe,DHz,V:King SHark 2.00
37 RMz(s),SB,V:Sledge 2.00
38 RMz(s),RBe,DHz,"Meltdown,"
pt.1 (of 3) 2.00
39 RMz(s),RBe,DHz,"Meltdown,"
pt.2 . . . . 2.00
40 RMz(s),RBe,DHz,"Meltdown,"
pt.2 x-over 2.00
41 RMz(s),RBe,DHz,"Meltdown,"
pt.3 concl. 2.00
42 SB, ... 2.00
43 SB,Lanie & Ken 2.00
44 SB,island of teenagers 2.00
45 RMz,DHz,TGu,A:Legion 2.00
46 RMz,DHz,TGu,V:Silver Sword . 2.00

47 RMz,DHz,TGu,F:Green Lantern 2.00
48 BKs,DHz,TGu,theme park 2.00
49 DHz 2.00
50 KK,TGu,Last Boy on Earth pt.1 2.00
51 KK,TGu,Last Boy on Earth pt.2 2.00
52 KK,TGu,Last Boy on Earth pt.3 2.00
53 KK,TGu,Last Boy on Earth pt.4 2.00
54 KK,TGu,A:Wild Men 2.00
55 KK,TGu,V:Grokk, Hex 2.00
56 KK,TGu,Project Cadmus 2.00
Ann.#1 Elseworlds Story 3.25
Ann.#2 KK,BKs, Year One 3.95
Ann.#3 Legends o/t Dead Earth . 2.95
Ann.#4 Pulp Heroes (High-
Adventure) 3.95

SUPERBOY & THE RAVERS

1 KK&SMt(s),PaP,DDv, ... 2.00
2 KK&SMt(s),PaP,DDv,InterC.E.P.T.
pursues Superboy and Kaliber 2.00
3 KK&SMT(s),PaP,DDv,teleported
to Rann,V:Half-Life 2.00
4 KK&SMt(s),PaP,DDv,A:Adam
Strange 2.00
5 KK&SMt(s),PaP,DDv,O:Hero .. 2.00
6 KK&SMt(s),PaP,DDv, ... 2.00
7 KK&SMt(s),PaP,DDv, "Road Trip,"
pt.1,A:Impulse 2.00
8 KK&SMt(s),PaP,DDv, "Road Trip,"
pt.2,A:Guy Gardner 2.00
9 KK&SMt(s),PaP,DDv, "Road Trip,"
pt.3,A:Aura 2.00
10 KK&SMt(s),DDv, "Meltdown,"
pt. 4 .... 2.00
11 KK&SMt(s),PaP,DDv, Superboy
presumed dead 2.00
12 KK(s),AaL, ... 2.00
13 KK(s),SMt,F:Hero,Sparx 2.00
14 KK&SMt(s),Genesis tie-in 2.00
15 KK&SMt(s),new Rave 2.00
16 KK&SMt(s),Half-Life 2.00
17 KK&SMt(s),Kaliber 2.00
18 KK&SMt(s),V:Qward 2.00
19 .... 2.00

SUPERBOY PLUS
Nov. 1996
1 RMz(s),ASm,F:Captain
Marvel Jr. 2.95
2 LKa,AWi,ALa,F:Slither 3.00

SUPERBOY/RISK DOUBLE-SHOT
Dec., 1997
1 DJu,JoP,x-over 2.00

SUPER DC GIANT
1970–71, 1976
S-13 Binky 12.00
S-14 Top Guns of the West 5.00
S-15 Western Comics 5.00
S-16 Best of the Brave & the Bold 5.00
S-17 Love 1970 .... 5.00
S-18 Three Mouseketeers 5.00
S-19 Jerry Lewis 5.00
S-20 House of Mystery 7.50
S-21 Love 1971 .... 5.00
S-22 Top Guns of the West 5.00
S-23 The Unexpected 7.50
S-24 Supergirl 6.00
S-25 Challengers of the Unknown 5.00
S-26 Aquaman 5.00

Super DC Giant #S-14
© DC Comics, Inc.

S-27 Strange Flying Saucer
Advengures (1976) 5.00

SUPER FRIENDS
Nov., 1976
1 ECh(c),JO,RE,'Fury of the
Superfoes',A:Penguin 18.00
2 RE,A:Penguin 10.00
3 RF(c),RF,A:JLA 7.00
4 RF,V:Riddler,I:Skyrocket 7.00
5 RF(c),RF,V:Greenback 7.00
6 RF(c),RF,A:Atom 5.00
7 RF(c),RF,I:Zan & Jana,
A:Seraph 5.00
8 RF(c),RF,A:JLA 5.00
9 RF(c),RF,A:JLA,I:Iron Maiden . 5.00
10 RF(c),RF'TheMonkeyMenace' . 5.00
11 RF(c),RF 4.00
12 RF(c),RF,A:TNT 4.00
13 RF(c),RF 4.00
14 RF(c),RF 4.00
15 RF(c),RF, A:The Elementals . 4.00
16 RF(c),RF,V:The Cvags 4.00
17 RF(c),RF,A:Queen Hippolyte . 4.00
18 KS(c),V:Tuantra,Time Trapper . 4.00
19 RF(c),RF,V:Menagerie Man . 4.00
20 KS(c),KS,V:Frownin' Fritz 4.00
21 RF(c),RF,V:Evil Superfriends
Doubles 3.50
22 RF(c),RF,V:Matador Mob 3.50
23 FR(c),RF,V:Mirror Master 3.50
24 RF(c),RF,V:Exorians 3.50
25 RF(c),RF,V:Overlord,
A:Green Lantern, Mera 3.50
26 RF(c),RF,A:Johnny Jones 3.50
27 RF(c),RF,'The Spaceman Who
Stole the Stars 3.50
28 RF(c),RF,A:Felix Faust 3.50
29 RF(c),RF,B.U.KS,'Scholar From
the Stars 3.50
30 RF(c),RF,V:Grodd & Giganta . 3.50
31 RF(c),RF,A:Black Orchid 4.00
32 KS(c),KS,A:Scarecrow 3.00
33 RF(c),RF,V:Menagerie Man .. 3.00
34 RF(c)RF,'The Creature That
Slept a Million Years' 3.00

35 RT,'Circus o/t Super Stars ... 3.00
36 RF(c),RF,A:Plastic Man
& Woozy 3.00
37 RF(c),RF,A:Supergirl;
B.U. A:Jack O'Lantern 3.00
38 RF(c),RF,V:Grax;
B.U. A:Serpah 3.00
39 RF(c),RF,A:Overlord;
B.U. A:Wonder Twins 3.00
40 RF(c),RF,V:The Monacle;
B.U. Jack O'Lantern 3.00
41 RF(c),RF,V:Toyman;
B.U. A:Seraph 3.00
42 RT,A:Flora,V:Flame; B.U.Wonder
Twins' Christmas Special 3.00
43 KS(c),RT,V:Futuro; B.U.JSon
A:Plastic Man 3.00
44 KS(c),RT,'Peril o/t Forgotten
Identities'; B.U.Jack O'Lantern . 3.00
45 KS(c),RT,A:Bushmaster,
Godiva, Rising Sun, Olympian,
Little Mermaid, Wild Huntsman;
B.U. Plastic Man,V: Sinestro .. 3.00
46 RT,V:The Conqueror;
B.U. BO,Seraph 3.00
47 KS(c),RT,A:Green Fury
Aug. 1981 .... 4.00

SUPERGIRL
[1st Regular Series]
Nov., 1972—Sept. 1974
1 'Trail of the Madman';
Superfashions From Fans;
B.B.U. DG,Zatanna 25.00
2 BO(c)A:Prof.Allan,Bottle
City of Kandor 10.00
3 BO(c),'The Garden of Death' . 10.00
4 V:Super Scavanger 10.00
5 BO(c),A:Superman,V:Dax; B.U.
MA:Rep.Hawkman #4 ..... 15.00
6 BO(c),'Love & War' 10.00
7 BO(c),A:Zatanna 10.00
8 BO(c),A:Superman,Green
Lantern, Hawkman 15.00
9 BO(c),V:Sharkman 10.00
10 A:Prey,V:Master Killer 10.00

[DARING NEW ADVENTURES OF] SUPERGIRL
[2nd Regular Series]
Nov. 1982
1 CI,BO,I:Psi; B.B.U:Lois Lane .. 1.50
2 CI,BO,C:Decay 1.50
3 CI,BO,V:Decay,'Decay Day' .. 1.50
4 CI,BO,V:The Gang 1.50
5 CI,BO,V:The Gang 1.50
6 CI,BO,V:The Gang 1.50
7 CI,BO,V:The Gang 1.50
8 CI,BO,A:Doom Patrol 1.50
9 CI,BO,V:Reactron
A:Doom Patrol 1.50
10 CI,BO,'Radiation Fever' 1.50
11 CI,BO,V:Chairman 1.50
12 CI,BO,V:Chairmann 1.50
13 CI,BO,N:Supergirl,A:Superman
V:Blackstarr 1.50
Becomes:

SUPERGIRL
Dec., 1983–Sept. 1984
14 GK(c),CI,BO,V:Blackstarr
A:Rabbi Nathan Zuber 1.50
15 CI,BO,V:Blackstarr,

A:Blackstarr's Mom 1.50
16 KG/BO(c),CI,BO,
A:Ambush Bug 1.50
17 CI/DG(c),CI,BO,V:Matrix
Prime 1.50
18 DG(c),CI,BO, V:Kraken 1.50
19 EB/BO(c),CI,BO,'Who Stole
Supergirl's Life' 1.50
20 CI,BO,C:JLA,Teen Titans:
Teh Parasite 1.50
21 EB/BO(c),EB,Kryptonite Man . . 1.50
22 EB(c),CI,BO,'I Have Seen the
Future & it is Me' 1.50
23 EB(c),CI,BO,'The Future
Begins Today 1.50
Spec.#1 JL/DG(c),GM,Movie Adapt.1.50
Spec.#1 AT,Honda give-away . . . 1.50
[Limited Series] 1994
1 KGa(c),B:RSt(s),JBr,O:Supergirl 5.00
2 KGa(c),JBr 4.00
3 KGa(c),JBr,D:Clones 3.00
4 KGa(c),RSt(s),JBr,final Issue . . 3.00

SUPERGIRL
Sept. 1996

1 PDd(s),GFr,CaS, ... 11.00
2 PDd(s),GFr,CaS,V:Chakat 5.00
3 PDd(s),GFr,CaS,V:Grodd, Final
Night tie-in 4.00
4 PDd(s),GFr,CaS,transformed into
savage 3.00
5 PDd(s),GFr,CaS,Supergirl visits
the Kents,V:Chemo 3.00
6 PDd(s),GFr,CaS, ... 3.00
7 PDd(s),GFr,CaS,Supergirl learns
about Linda Danvers 3.00
8 PDd(s),GFr,CaS,Buzz gets date
with Supergirl 3.00
9 PDd(s),GFr,CaS,V:Tempus . . . 3.00
10 PDd(s),Linda tries to relax . . . 3.00
11 PDd(s),CaS,V:Silver Banshee . 3.00
12 PDd(s),Mattie possessed by
Silver Banshee 3.00
13 CaS, 3 girls dreams invaded by
incubus 2.50
14 PDa,CaS,Genesis tie-in 2.00
15 PDa,CaS,V:Extremists 2.00
16 PDa,CaS,F:Power Girl 2.00
17 PDa,CaS,L-Ron, Despero 2.00
18 PDa,CaS,V:Despero 2.00
19 . . . . 2.00
20 PDa,CaS,Millennium Giants . . 2.00
21 PDa,CaS,Comet 2.00
22 PDa, ... 2.00
23 PDa,A:Steel 2.00
24 PDa,Avenging Angels x-over . . 2.00
25 PDa,truth about Comet 2.00
26 PDd,truth discovered 2.00
Ann.#1 Legends o/t Dead Earth . . 2.95
Ann. #2 TPe,CDi,ACa, Pulp Heroes4.00
TPB rep. Supergirl #1–#9 . . . . . 15.00

SUPERGIRL/LEX
LUTHOR SPECIAL
1993
1 JBr,F:Supergirl,Lex Luthor 4.00

SUPERGIRL/PRISM
DOUBLE-SHOT
Dec., 1997
1 DJu,TGb,Clv, x-over 2.00

SUPER HEROES
BATTLE SUPER GORILLA
Winter, 1976
1 Superman Flash rep. 1.00

Superman #6 © DC Comics, Inc.

SUPERMAN
1939–86

1 JoS,O:Superman,reprints Action
Comics #1-#4 . . . . 130,000.00
2 JoS,I:George Taylor 10,000.00
3 JoS,V:Superintendent
Lyman 6,500.00
4 JoS,V:Lex Luthor 5,000.00
5 JoS,V:Lex Luthor 3,500.00
6 JoS,V:'Brute' Bashby 2,500.00
7 JoS,I:Perry White 2,400.00
8 JoS,V:Jackal 2,100.00
9 JoS,V:Joe Gatson 2,100.00
10 JoS,V:Lex Luthor 2,000.00
11 JoS,V:Rolf Zimba 1,600.00
12 JoS,V:Lex Luthor 1,600.00
13 JoS,I:Jimmy Olsen,V:Lex
Luthor,'The Archer' 1,600.00
14 JoS,I:Lightning Master . . . 2,000.00
15 JoS,V:The Evolution King . 1,500.00
16 JoS,V:Mr. Sinus 1,400.00
17 JoS,V:Lex Luthor,Lois Lane first
suspects Clark is Superman 1,400.00
18 JoS,V:Lex Luthor 1,300.00
19 JoS,V:Funnyface,
1st Imaginary story 1,300.00
20 JoS,V:Puzzler,Leopard . . . 1,300.00
21 JoS,V:Sir Gauntlet 1,000.00
22 JoS,V:Prankster 1,000.00
23 JoS,Propaganda story . . . 1,000.00
24 V:Cobra King 1,200.00
25 Propaganda story 1,000.00
26 I:J.Wilbur Wolfingham,
A:Mercury 1,000.00
27 V:Toyman 1,000.00
28 V:J.Wilbur Wolfingham,
A:Hercules 1,000.00
29 V:Prankster 1,000.00
30 I&O:Mr. Mxyztplk 1,400.00
31 V:Lex Luthor 900.00
32 V:Toyman 900.00
33 V:Mr. Mxyztptlk 900.00

34 V:Lex Luthor 900.00
35 V:J.Wilbur Wolfingham . . . 900.00
36 V:Mr. Mxyztptlk 900.00
37 V:Prankster,A:Sinbad 900.00
38 V:Lex Luthor 900.00
39 V:J.Wilbur Wolfingham . . . 900.00
40 V:Mr. Mxyztptlk,A:Susie
Thompkins 900.00
41 V:Prankster 600.00
42 V:J.Wilbur Wolfingham . . . 600.00
43 V:Lex Luthor 600.00
44 V:Toyman,A:Shakespeare . . 600.00
45 A:Hocus & Pocus,Lois Lane
as Superwoman 600.00
46 V:Mr. Mxyztptlk,Lex Luthor,
Superboy flashback 600.00
47 V:Toyman 600.00
48 V:Lex Luthor 600.00
49 V:Toyman 600.00
50 V:Prankster 600.00
51 V:Mr. Mxyztptlk 500.00
52 V:Prankster 500.00
53 WB,O:Superman 2,000.00
54 V:Wrecker 500.00
55 V:Prankster 500.00
56 V:Prankster 500.00
57 V:Lex Luthor 500.00
58 V:Tiny Trix 500.00
59 V:Mr.Mxyztptlk 500.00
60 V:Toyman 500.00
61 I:Kryptonite,V:Prankster . . 1,000.00
62 V:Mr.Mxyztptlk,A:Orson
Welles 500.00
63 V:Toyman 500.00
64 V:Prankster 500.00
65 V:Mala,Kizo and U-Ban . . . 500.00
66 V:Prankster 500.00
67 A:Perry Como,I:Brane
Taylor 500.00
68 V:Lex Luthor 500.00
69 V:Prankster,A:Inspector
Erskine Hawkins 500.00
70 V:Prankster 500.00
71 V:Lex Luthor 450.00
72 V:Prankster 450.00
72a giveaway 750.00
73 Flashback story 450.00
74 V:Lex Luthor 450.00
75 V:Prankster 450.00

Superman #84 © DC Comics, Inc.

76 A:Batman (Superman & Batman revel each other's identities)	1,300.00
77 A:Pocahontas	425.00
78 V:Kryptonian snagriff, A:Lana Lang	425.00
79 V:Lex Luthor,A:Inspector Erskine Hawkins	425.00
80 A:Halk Kar	425.00
81 V:Lex Luthor	425.00
82 V:Mr. Mxyzptlk	400.00
83 V:'The Brain'	400.00
84 Time-travel story	400.00
85 V:Lex Luthor	400.00
86 V:Mr.Mxyzptlk	400.00
87 WB,V:The Thing from 40,000 AD'	400.00
88 WB,V:Lex Luthor,Toyman, Prankster team	425.00
89 V:Lex Luthor	400.00
90 V:Lex Luthor	425.00
91 'The Superman Stamp'	400.00
92 Goes back to 12th Century England	400.00
93 V:'The Thinker'	400.00
94 'Clark Kent's Hillbilly Bride'	400.00
95 A:Susie Thompkins	400.00
96 V:Mr. Mxyzptlk	350.00
97 'Superboy's Last Day In Smallville'	350.00
98 'Clark Kent, Outlaw!'	350.00
99 V:Midnite gang	350.00
100 F:Superman-Substitute Schoolteacher	1,700.00
101 A:Lex Luthor	275.00
102 I:Superman Stock Company	275.00
103 A:Mr.Mxyzptlk	275.00
104 F:Clark Kent,Jailbird	275.00
105 A:Mr.Mxyzptlk	275.00
106 A:Lex Luthor	300.00
107 F:Superman In 30th century (pre-Legion)	250.00
108 I:Perry White Jr.	250.00
109 I:Abner Hokum	250.00
110 A:Lex Luthor	250.00
111 Becomes Mysto the Great	225.00
112 A:Lex Luthor	225.00
113 A:Jor-El	225.00
114 V:The Great Mento	225.00
115 V:The Organizer	225.00
116 Return to Smallville	225.00
117 A:Lex Luthor	225.00
118 F:Jimmy Olsen	225.00
119 A:Zoll Orr	225.00
120 V:Gadget Grim	225.00
121 I:XL-49 (Futureman)	200.00
122 In the White House	200.00
123 CS,pre-Supergirl tryout A:Jor-El & Lara	225.00
124 F:Lois Lane	200.00
125 F:Superman College Story	200.00
126 F:Lois Lane	200.00
127 WB,I&O:Titano	225.00
128 V:Vard & Boka	200.00
129 WB,I&O:Lori Lemaris	225.00
130 A:Krypto,the Superdog	200.00
131 A:Mr. Mxyzptlk	150.00
132 A:Batman & Robin	150.00
133 F:Superman Joins Army	150.00
134 A:Supergirl & Krypto	150.00
135 A:Lori Lemaris,Mr.Mxyzptlk	150.00
136 O:Discovery Kryptonite	150.00
137 CS,I:Super-Menace	150.00
138 A:Titano,Lori Lemaris	150.00

Superman #235 © DC Comics, Inc.

139 CS,O:Red Kryptonite	150.00
140 WB,I:Bizarro Jr,Bizarro Supergirl,Blue Kryptonite.	165.00
141 I:Lyla Lerrol,A:Jor-EL & Lara	125.00
142 WB,CS,A:Al Capone	125.00
143 WB,F:Bizarro meets Frankenstein	125.00
144 O:Superboy's 1st Public Appearance	125.00
145 F:April Fool's Issue	125.00
146 F:Superman's life story	175.00
147 CS,I:Adult Legion	150.00
148 CS,V:Mxyzptlk	150.00
149 CS:A:Luthor,C:JLA	150.00
150 CS,KS,V:Mxyzptlk	75.00
151 CS	75.00
152 A:Legion	75.00
153 CS	75.00
154 CS,V:Mzyzptlk	75.00
155 WB,CS,V:Cosmic Man	75.00
156 CS,A:Legion,Batman	75.00
157 CS,I:Gold kryptonite	80.00
158 CS,I:Nightwing&Flamebird	75.00
159 CS,Imaginary Tale F:Lois Lane	75.00
160 CS,F:Perry White	75.00
161 D:Ma & Pa Kent	80.00
162 A:Legion	80.00
163 CS	55.00
164 CS,Luthor,I:Lexor	55.00
165 CS,A:Saturn Woman	55.00
166 CS	55.00
167 CS,I:Ardora,Brainiac	100.00
168 CS	55.00
169 Great DC Contest	55.00
170 CS,A:J.F.Kennedy,Luthor	55.00
171 CS,Mxyzptlk	55.00
172 CS,Luthor,Brainiac	55.00
173 CS,A:Batman	55.00
174 Mxyzptlk	55.00
175 CS,Luthor	55.00
176 CS,Green Kryptonite	55.00
177 Fortress of Solitude	55.00
178 CS, Red Kryptonite	55.00
179 CS,Clark Kent in Marines	55.00
180 CS	55.00
181 Superman 2965	55.00

182 CS,Toyman	55.00
183 giant	55.00
184 Secrets of the Fortress	50.00
185 JM,Superman's Achilles Heel	50.00
186 CS,The Two Ghosts of Superman	50.00
187 giant	50.00
188 V:Zunial,The Murder Man	55.00
189 WB,The Mystery of Krypton's Second Doom	50.00
190 WB,I:Amalak	50.00
191 The Prisoner of Demon	50.00
192 CS,Imaginary Story, I:Superman Jr.	50.00
193 giant	50.00
194 CS,Imaginary,A:Supes Jr.	40.00
195 CS,V:Amalak	40.00
196 WB,reprint	40.00
197 giant	50.00
198 CS,F:The Real Clark Kent	40.00
199 CS,F:Superman/Flash race, A:JLA	225.00
200 WB,A:Brainiac	40.00
201 CS,F:Clark Kent Abandons Superman	30.00
202 A:Bizarro,(giant size)	35.00
203 F:When Superman Killed His Friends	30.00
204 NA(c),RA,A:Lori Lemaris	30.00
205 NA(c),I:Black Zero	30.00
206 NA(c),F:The Day Superman Became An Assistant	30.00
207 CS,F:The Case Of the Collared Crimefighter	35.00
208 NA(c),CS	30.00
209 CS,F:The Clark Kent Monster	30.00
210 CS,F:Clark Kent's Last Rites	30.00
211 CS,RA	30.00
212 giant	40.00
213 CS,JA,V:Luthor,C:Brainiac 5	30.00
214 NA(c),CS,JA,F:The Ghosts That Haunted Superman	25.00
215 NA(c),CS,JA,V:Luthor, Imaginary Story	25.00
216 JKu(c),RA,Amalgam in Nam	25.00
217 CS,A:Mr.Mxyzptlk	30.00
218 CS,JA,A:Mr.Mxyzptlk	25.00
219 CS,F:Clark Kent-Hero, Superman Public Enemy	25.00
220 CS,A:Flash	25.00
221 CS,F:The Two Ton Superman	25.00
222 giant	40.00
223 CS,A:Supergirl	25.00
224 CS,Imaginary Story	25.00
225 CS,F:The Secret of the Super Imposter	25.00
226 CS,F:When Superman Became King Kong	25.00
227 Krypton,(giant)	30.00
228 CS,DA	25.00
229 WB,CS	25.00
230 CS,DA,Luthor	25.00
231 CS,DA,Luthor	25.00
232 F:Krypton,(giant)	30.00
233 CS,MA,I:Quarrum	25.00
234 NA(c),CS,MA	25.00
235 CS,MA	25.00
236 CS,MA,DG,A:Green Arrow	25.00
237 NA(c),CS,MA	25.00
238 CS,MA,GM	25.00
239 giant	35.00
240 CS,DG,MK,A:I-Ching	11.00
241 CS,MA,A:Wonder Woman	11.00
242 CS,MA,A:Wonder Woman	12.00

243 CS,MA	11.00
244 CS,MA	11.00
245 100 pg reprints	25.00
246 CS,MA,RB,I:S.T.A.R. Labs	10.00
247 CS,MA,Guardians o/Universe	10.00
248 CS,MA,A:Luthor,I:Galactic Golem	10.00
249 CS,MA,DD,NA,I:Terra-Man	15.00
250 CS,MA,Terraman	10.00
251 CS,MA,RB	10.00
252 NA(c),rep.100pgs	25.00
253 CS,MA	10.00
254 CS,MA,NA	10.00
255 CS,MA,DG	6.00
256 CS,MA	6.00
257 CS,MA,DD,DG,A:Tomar-Re	6.00
258 CS,MA,DC	6.00
259 CS,MA,A:Terra-Man	6.00
260 CS,DC,I:Valdemar	6.00
261 CS,MA,V:Star Sapphire	6.00
262 CS,MA	6.00
263 CS,MA,DD,FMc	6.00
264 DC,CS,I:SteveLombard	6.00
265 CS,MA	6.00
266 CS,MA,DD,V:Snowman	6.00
267 CS,MA,BO	6.00
268 CS,BO,DD,MA,A:Batgirl	6.00
269 CS,MA	6.00
270 CS,MA,V:Valdemar	6.00
271 CS,BO,DG,V:Brainiac	6.00
272 100pg.reprints	22.00
273 CS,DG	6.00
274 CS	6.00
275 CS,DG,FMc	6.00
276 CS,BO,I&O:Captain Thunder	6.00
277 CS	6.00
278 CS,BO,Terraman,100page	20.00
279 CS,Batgirl,Batman	5.00
280 CS,BO	5.00
281 CS,BO,I:Vartox	5.00
282 CS,KS,N:Luthor	5.00
283 CS,BO,Mxyzptlk	5.00
284 CS,BO,100p reprint	20.00
285 CS,BO	5.00
286 CS,BO	5.00
287 CS,BO,R:Krypto	5.00
288 CS,BO	5.00
289 CS,BO,JL	5.00
290 CS,V:Mxyzptlk	5.00
291 CS,BO	5.00
292 CS,BO,AM,O:Luthor	5.00
293 CS,BO	5.00
294 CS,JL,A:Brain Storm	5.00
295 CS,BO	5.00
296 CS,BO,Identity Crisis #1	5.00
297 CS,BO,Identity Crisis #2	5.00
298 CS,BO,Identity Crisis #3	5.00
299 CS,BO,Identity Crisis #4 A:Luthor,Brainiac,Bizarro	5.00
300 CS,BO,2001,anniversary	18.00
301 BO,JL,V:Solomon Grundy	4.00
302 JL,BO,V:Luthor,A:Atom	4.00
303 CS,BO,I:Thunder&Lightning	4.00
304 CS,BO,V:Parasite	4.00
305 CS,BO,V:Toyman	4.00
306 CS,BO,V:Bizarro	4.00
307 NA(c),JL,FS,A:Supergirl	4.00
308 NA(c),JL,FS,A:Supergirl	4.00
309 JL,FS,A:Supergirl	3.50
310 CS,V:Metallo	3.50
311 CS,FS,A:Flash	2.50
312 CS,FS,A:Supergirl	3.50
313 NA(c),CS,DA,A:Supergirl	3.50
314 NA(c),CS,DA,A:Gr.Lantern	3.50
315 CS,DA,V:Blackrock	3.50

316 CS,DA,V:Metallo	3.50
317 NA(c),CS,DA,V:Metallo	3.50
318 CS	3.00
319 CS,V:Solomon Grundy	3.00
320 CS,V:Solomon Grundy	3.00
321 CS,V:Parasite	3.00
322 CS,V:Solomon Grundy	3.00
323 CS,DA,I:Atomic Skull	3.00
324 CS,A:Atomic Skull	3.00
325 CS	3.00
326 CS,V:Blackrock	3.00
327 CS,KS,V:Kobra,C:JLA	3.00
328 CS,KS,V:Kobra	3.00
329 KS,CS	3.00
330 CS,F:glasses explained	3.00
331 CS,I:Master Jailer	3.00
332 CS,V:Master Jailer	3.00
333 CS,V:Bizarro	3.00
334 CS	3.00
335 CS,W:Mxyzptlk	3.00
336 CS,V:Rose And Thorn	3.00
337 CS,A:Brainiac,Bizarro	3.00
338 CS,F:Kandor enlarged	3.00
339 CS,I:N.R.G.X	3.00

Superman #272 © DC Comics, Inc.

340 CS,V:N.R.G.X	3.00
341 CS,F:Major Disaster	3.00
342 CS,V:Chemo	3.00
343 CS	3.00
344 CS,A:Phantom Stranger	3.00
345 CS,'When time ran backward'	3.00
346 CS,'Streak of Bad Luck'	3.00
347 JL	3.00
348 CS	3.00
349 CS,V:Mxyzptlk	3.00
350 CS,'Clark Kent's Vanishing Classmate'	3.00
351 CS,JL,A:Mxyzptlk	3.00
352 CS,RB	3.00
353 CS,origin	3.00
354 CS,JSon,I:Superman 2020	3.00
355 CS,JSon,F:Superman 2020	3.00
356 CS,V:Vartox	3.00
357 CS,DCw,F:Superman 2020	3.00
358 CS,DG,DCw	3.00
359 CS	3.00
360 CS,AS,F:World of Krypton	3.00
361 CS,AS	3.00
362 CS,KS,DA	3.00

363 CS,RB,C:Luthor	3.00
364 GP(c),RB,AS	3.00
365 CS,KS	3.00
366 CS,KS	3.00
367 CS,GK,F:World of Krypton	3.00
368 CS,AS	3.00
369 RB,FMc,V:Parasite	3.00
370 CS,KS,FMc,A:Chemo	3.00
371 CS	3.00
372 CS,GK,F:Superman 2021	3.00
373 CS,V:Vartox	3.00
374 GK(c),CS,DA,KS,V:Vartox	3.00
375 CS,DA,GK,V:Vartox	3.00
376 CS,DA,CI,BO,SupergirlPrev.	2.75
377 GK(c),CS,V:Terra-Man	2.75
378 CS	2.75
379 CS,V:Bizarro	2.75
380 CS	2.75
381 GK(c),CS	2.75
382 GK(c),CS	2.75
383 CS	2.75
384 GK(c),CS	2.75
385 GK(c),CS,V:Luthor	2.75
386 GK(c),CS,V:Luthor	2.75
387 GK(c),CS	2.75
388 GK(c),CS	2.75
389 GK(c),CS	2.75
390 GK(c),CS,V:Vartox	2.75
391 GK(c),CS,V:Vartox	2.75
392 GK(c),CS,V:Vartox	2.75
393 IN,DG,V:Master Jailer	2.75
394 CS,V:Valdemar	2.75
395 CS,V:Valdemar	2.75
396 CS	2.75
397 EB,V:Kryptonite Man	2.75
398 CS,AS,DJ	2.75
399 CS,BO,EB	2.75
400 HC(c),FM,AW,JO,JSo,MR, TA,WP,MK,KJ,giant	6.00
401 CS,BO,V:Luthor	2.75
402 CS,BO,WB	2.75
403 CS,BO,AS	2.75
404 CI,BO,V:Luthor	2.75
405 KS,KK,AS,F:Super-Batman	2.75
406 IN,AS,KK	2.75
407 IN,V:Mxyzptlk	2.75
408 CS,AW,JRu,F:Nuclear Holocaust	2.75
409 CS,AW,KS	2.75
410 CS,AW,V:Luthor	2.75
411 CS,MA,F:End Earth-Prime	2.75
412 CS,AW,V:Luthor	2.75
413 CS,AW,V:Luthor	2.75
414 CS,AW,Crisis tie-in	3.00
415 CS,AW,Crisis,W:Super Girl	3.00
416 CS,AW,Luthor	2.75
417 CS,V:Martians	2.75
418 CS,V:Metallo	2.75
419 CS,V:Iago	2.75
420 CS,F:Nightmares	2.75
421 CS,V:Mxyzptlk	2.75
422 BB(c),CS,TY,LMa,V:Werewolf	2.75
423 AMo(s),CS,GP,F:Last Superman	8.00
Ann.#1 I:Supergirl Rep	900.00
Ann.#2 I&O:Titano	400.00
Ann.#3 I:Legion	300.00
Ann.#4 O:Legion	250.00
Ann.#5 A:Krypton	200.00
Ann.#6 A:Legion	200.00
Ann.#7 O:Superman,Silver Anniv.	150.00
Ann.#8 F:Secret origins	125.00
Ann.#9 GK(c),ATh,TA,CS, A:Batman	6.00
Ann.#10 CS,MA,F:Sword of	

Superman Annual #11
© DC Comics, Inc.

Superman 5.00
Ann.#11 AMo(s),DGb,A:Batman,
Robin,Wonder Woman 6.00
Ann.#12 BB(c),AS,A:Lex Luthor,
Last War Suit 3.00
Game Give-away 10.00
Giveaway CS,AT 2.00
Pizza Hut 1977 . . . . 6.00
Radio Shack 1980 JSw,DG 5.00
Radio Shack 1981 CS 5.00
Radio Shack 1982 CS 5.00
Spec.#1 GK 3.50
Spec.#2 GK,V:Brainiac 3.50
Spec.#3 IN,V:Amazo 3.50
Superman III Movie,CS 1.50
Superman IV Movie,DH,DG,FMc . 1.50
Becomes:
ADVENTURES OF
SUPERMAN
1987
424 JOy,I:Man O'War 2.50
425 JOy,Man O'War 2.25
426 JOy,Legends,V:Apokolips . . . 2.25
427 JOy,V:Qurac 2.25
428 JOy,V:Qurac,I:JerryWhite . . . 2.25
429 JOy,V:Concussion 2.25
430 JOy,V:Fearsome Five 2.25
431 JOy,A:Combattor 2.00
432 JOy,I:Jose Delgado 2.00
433 JOy,V:Lex Luthor 2.00
434 JOy,I:Gang Buster 2.50
435 JOy,A:Charger 2.00
436 JOy,Millenium x-over 2.00
437 JOy,Millenium x-over 2.00
438 JOy,N:Brainiac 2.50
439 JOy,R:Superman Robot 2.00
440 JOy,A:Batman,Wond.Woman 2.00
441 JOy,V:Mr.Mxyzptlk 2.00
442 JOy,V:Dreadnaught,A:JLI . . . 2.00
443 JOy,DHz,I:Husque 2.00
444 JOy,Supergirl SagaPt.2 . . . . 2.00
445 JOy,V:Brainiac 2.00
446 JOy,A:Gangbuster,
A:Luthor's Old Costume 2.00
447 JOy,A:Gangbuster 2.00
448 JOy,I:Dubbilex,A:Gangbuster . 2.00

449 JOy,Invasion X-over 2.00
450 JOy,Invasion X-over 2.00
451 JOy,'Superman in Space' . . . 2.00
452 DJu,V:Wordbringer 2.00
453 JOy,DJu,A:Gangbuster 2.00
454 JOy,DJu,I:New Mongul 2.50
455 DJu,ATb,A:Eradicator 3.50
456 DJu,ATb,V:Turmoil 2.00
457 DJu,V:Intergang 2.00
458 DJu,KJ,R:Elastic Lad
(Jimmy Olsen) 2.00
459 DJu,V:Eradicator 3.00
460 DJu,NKu,V:Eradicator 3.00
461 DJu,GP,V:Eradicator 3.00
462 DJu,ATb,Homeless
Christmas Story 2.00
463 DJu,ATb,Superman Races
Flash 3.00
464 DJu,ATb,Day of Krypton
Man #2,A:Lobo 3.50
465 DJu,ATb,Day of Krypton
Man #5,V:Draaga 3.00
466 DJu,DG,V:Team Excalibur
Astronauts,I:Hank Henshaw
(becomes Cyborg Superman) . 4.50
467 DJu,ATb,A:Batman 2.50
468 DJu,ATb,Man Of Steel's
Journal,V:Hank Henshaw 3.00
469 DJu,ATb,V:Dreadnaught 2.00
470 DJu,ATb,Soul Search #3,
D:Jerry White 2.00
471 CS,Sinbad Contract #2 . . . . . 2.00
472 DJu,ATb,Krisis of Krimson
Kryptonite #2 . . . . 3.00
473 DJu,ATb,A:Green Lantern,
Guy Gardner 2.00
474 DJu,ATb,Drunk Driving issue . 2.00
475 DJu,ATb,V:Kilgrave,Sleez . . . 2.00
476 DJu,BBr,Time & Time Again,pt.1,
A:Booster Gold,Legion 2.00
477 DJu,BBr,T & T Again,pt.4,
A:Legion 2.00
478 DJu,BBr,T & T Again,pt.7,
A:Legion,Linear Man 2.00
479 EH,Red Glass Trilogy#2 . . . . 2.00
480 JOy,DJu,BMc,TG,BBr,CS,
Revenge of the Krypton
Man,pt.3 . . . . 3.00
481 1st TG Supes,DHz,V:Parasite 2.00
482 TG,DHz,V:Parasite 2.00
483 TG,DHz,V:Blindspot 2.00
484 TG,Blackout #1,V:Mr.Z 2.00
485 TG,DHz,Blackout #5,A:Mr.Z . 3.00
486 TG,V:Purge 2.00
487 TG,DHz,X-mas,A:Agent
Liberty 2.00
488 TG,Panic in the Sky,pt.3,
V:Brainiac. 3.00
489 TG,Panic in the Sky,Epiloge . 2.50
490 TG,A:Agent Liberty,Husque . 1.75
491 TG,DHz,V:Cerberus,Metallo . 1.75
492 WS(c),V:Sons of Liberty,
A:Agent Liberty 1.75
493 TG,Blaze/Satanus War,pt.1 . 1.75
494 TG,DHz,I:Kismet 1.75
495 TG,DHz,A:Forever People,
Darkseid 1.75
496 V:Mr.Mxyzptlk,C:Doomsday . 2.00
496a 2nd printing 1.50
497 TG,Doomsday Pt.3,A:Maxima,
Bloodwynd 5.00
497a 2nd printing 1.75
498 TG,Funeral for a Friend#1 . . 4.00
498a 2nd Printing 1.25
499 TG,DHz,Funeral for a

The Adventures of Superman #485
© DC Comics, Inc.

Friend#5 . . . . 3.50
500 JOy(c),B:KK(s),TG,DJu,JBg,JG,
BBr,Bagged,Superman in limbo,
I:Four Supermen,Direct Sales . 3.50
500a Newsstand Ed. 3.00
500b Platinum Ed. 15.00
501 TG,Reign of Supermen#2,Direct
Sales,Die-Cut(c),Mini-poster
F:Superboy 3.00
501a Newstand Ed. 2.00
502 TG,A:Supergirl,V:Stinger 2.00
503 TG,Cyborg Superman Vs.
Superboy 2.50
504 TG,DHz,A:All Supermen,
V:Mongul 2.50
505 TG,DHz,Superman returns to
Metropolis,Holografx(c) 2.50
505a Newstand Ed. 2.00
506 TG,DHz,A:Guardian 1.75
507 Spilled Blood#1,V:Bloodsport 1.75
508 BKi,A:Challengers of the
Unknown 1.75
509 BKi,A:Auron 1.75
510 BKi,Bizarro's World#2,
V:Bizarro 1.75
511 BKi,A:Guardian 1.75
512 BKi,V:Parasite 1.75
513 BKi,Battle for Metropolis #4 . . 1.75
514 BKi,Fall of Metropolis #4 . . . 1.75
515 BKi,Massacre in Metropolis . . 1.75
516 BKi,Zero Hour,I:Alpha
Centurion 1.50
517 BKi,deathtrap 1.50
518 BKi 1.50
519 KK,BKi,Secret of Superman's
Tomb 1.50
520 SI,KK,JMz,100 crimes at
midnight 1.50
521 SI,KK,R:Thorn 1.50
522 SI,KKIdentity known 1.50
523 SI,KK,Death of C.Kent,pt.2 . . 1.50
524 SI,KK,Death of C.Kent,pt.6
[New Miraweb format begins] . 2.00
525 SI,KK 2.00
526 Bloodsport vs. Bloodsport . . . 2.00
527 . . . . 2.00
528 Trial of Superman,prelude . . . 2.00

529 Trial of Superman 2.00
530 KK,SI,JMz,Trial of Superman 2.00
531 KK,SI,JMz,Trial of Superman,
  concl. 2.00
532 KK,SI,JMz, return of Lori
  Lemaris 2.00
533 KK,SI,JMz 2.00
534 KK,SI,JMz,V:Lord Satannus . 2.00
535 KK,SI,JMz,Lois & LoriLemaris 2.00
536 . . . . 2.00
537 . . . . 2.00
538 . . . . 2.00
539 F:Guardian and the Newsboy
  Legion 2.00
540 KK(s),TyD,KIS,A:Ferro, Final
  Night tie-in 2.00
541 KK(s),SI,JMz,on Honeymoon,
  A:Superboy,Tana Moon,Kekona 2.00
542 KK&JOy(s),PR,JMz,V:Misa . . 2.00
543 . . . . 2.00
544 KK(s),SI,JMz,"Who Killed Clark
  Kent in braod daylight? 2.00
545 KK(s),SEa,JMz,Return of the
  Atomic Skull,new blue costume 2.00

Adventures of Superman #499
© DC Comics, Inc.

546 KK(s),SI,JMz,V:Metallo, uses
  new powers 2.00
547 KK(s),SI,JMz,Superman goes
  to Kandor,A:The Atom 2.00
548 KK(s),SI,JMz,V:Lex Luthor . . 2.00
549 KK(s),SI,JMz,F:Jimmy Olsen . 2.00
550 KK(s),SI,TGu,JMz,DRo, 48pg 3.50
551 DJu,TGu,DRo,Genesis,
  V:Cyborg 2.00
552 KK,TGu,DRo,V:Parasite 2.00
553 KK,TGu,DRo,disappearances 2.00
554 KK,TGu,DRo,disappearances 2.00
555 KK,TRu,DRo,Red/Blue x-over 2.00
556 KK,TRu,DRo,Red & Blue . . . 2.00
557 KK,VS,DRo,Millennium Giants
  x-over 2.00
558 KK,JOy,DRo,silver age?,pt.1 . 2.00
559 KK,JOy,DRo,silver age?,pt.2 . 2.00
560 KK,JOy,DRo,silver age?,pt.3 . 2.00
561 KK,JOy,TGu,DRo,Waverider . 2.00
562 KK(s),JOy,TGu,DRo,Lexcom . 2.00
Ann.#1 JSn(c),DJu,I:Word Bringer 3.00
Ann.#2 CS/JBy,KGa/DG,BMc,

A:L.E.G.I.O.N.'90 (Lobo) 4.00
Ann.#3 BHi,JRu,DG,
  Armageddon 2001. . . . . 3.00
Ann.#4 BMc,A:Lobo,Guy Gardner,
  Eclipso tie-in 3.00
Ann.#5 TG,I:Sparx 2.75
Ann.#6 MMi(c),Elseworlds Story . 3.00
Ann.#7 Year One Story 4.00
Ann.#8 Legends o/t Dead Earth . 2.95
Ann.#9 Pulp Heroes (Western) . . 3.95

SUPERMAN'S BUDDY
1954
1 w/costume 1,000.00
1 w/out costume 400.00

SUPERMAN'S CHRISTMAS ADVENTURE
1 (1940) 4,000.00
2 (1944) 900.00

SUPERMAN AND THE GREAT CLEVELAND FIRE
1948
1 for Hospital Fund 500.00

SUPERMAN (miniature)
1942
1 Py-Co-Pay Tooth Powder
  Give- Away 650.00
2 CS,Superman Time Capsule 450.00
3 CS,Duel in Space 400.00
4 CS,Super Show in Metropolis 400.00

SUPERMAN RECORD COMIC
1966
1 w/record 125.00
1 w/out record 75.00

SUPERMAN SPECTACULAR
1982
1 A:Luthor & Terra-Man 2.50

SUPERMAN-TIM STORE PAMPHLETS
1942
Superman-Tim store Monthly
  Membership Pamphlet, 16
  pages of stories, games,
  puzzles (1942), each 700.00
Superman-Tim store Monthly
  Membership Pamphlet, 16
  pages of stories, games,
  puzzles (1943), each 300.00
Superman-Tim store Monthly
  Membership Pamphlet, 16
  pages of stories, games,
  puzzles (1944), each 225.00
Superman-Tim store Monthly
  Membership Pamphlet, 16
  pages of stories, games,
  puzzles (1945), each 175.00
Superman-Tim store Monthly
  Membership Pamphlet, 14-16
  pages of stories, games,
  puzzles, 5"x8" color(c),
  (1946), each 300.00
Superman-Tim stamp
  album, 1946 . . . . 250.00

Superman-Tim store Monthly
  Membership Pamphlet, 14-16
  pages of stories, games,
  puzzles, 5"x8" color(c),
  (1947), each 200.00
Superman-Tim stamp album,
  Superman story, 1947 . . . . 275.00
Superman-Tim store Monthly
  Membership Pamphlet, 14-16
  pages of stories, games,
  puzzles, 5"x8" color(c),(1948),
  each 150.00
Superman-Tim stamp
  album, 1948 . . . . 175.00
Superman-Tim store Monthly
  Membership Pamphlet, 14-16
  pages of stories, games,
  puzzles, 5"x8" color(c),
  (1949), each 150.00
Superman-Tim store Monthly
  Membership Pamphlet, 14-16
  pages of stories, games,
  puzzles, 5"x8" color(c)
  (1950), each 200.00

SUPERMAN WORKBOOK
1945
1 rep. Superman #14 . . . . . . 1,000.00

SUPERMAN
[2nd Regular Series] 1987–98
1 JBy,TA,I:Metallo 5.00
2 JBy,TA,V:Luthor 3.00
3 JBy,TA,Legends tie-in 2.50
4 JBy,KK,V:Bloodsport 2.25
5 JBy,KK,V:Host 2.00
6 JBy,KK,V:Host 2.00
7 JBy,KK,V:Rampage 2.00
8 JBy,KK,A:Superboy,Legion . . . 2.00
9 JBy,KK,V:Joker 4.00
10 JBy,KK,V:Rampage 2.00
11 JBy,KK,V:Mr.Mxyzptlk 2.00
12 JBy,KK,A:Lori Lemerias 2.00
13 JBy,KK,Millenium 2.00
14 JBy,KK,A:Green Lantern 2.00
15 JBy,KK,I:New Prankster 2.00
16 JBy,KK,A:Prankster 2.00
17 JBy,KK,O:Silver Banshee 2.00
18 MMi,KK,A:Hawkman 2.00
19 JBy,V:Skyhook 2.00
20 JBy,KK,A:Doom Patrol 2.50
21 JBy,A:Supergirl 2.00
22 JBy,A:Supergirl 2.00
23 MMi,CR,O:Silver Banshee . . . 2.00
24 KGa,V:Rampage 2.00
25 KGa,V:Brainiac 2.00
26 KGa,BBr,V:Baron Sunday . . . 2.00
27 KGa,BBr,V:Guardian 2.00
28 KGa,BBr,Supes Leaves Earth . 2.00
29 DJu,BBr,V:Word Bringer 2.00
30 KGa,DJu,A:Lex Luthor 2.00
31 DJu,PCu,V:Mxyzptlk 2.00
32 KGa,V:Mongul 2.00
33 KGa,A:Cleric 2.00
34 KGa,V:Skyhook 2.00
35 CS,KGa,A:Brainiac 2.00
36 JOy,V:Prankster 2.00
37 JOy,A:Guardian 2.00
38 JOy,Jimmy Olsen Vanished . . 2.00
39 JOy,KGa,V:Husque 2.00
40 JOy,V:Four Armed Terror 2.00
41 JOy,Day of Krypton Man #1,
  A:Lobo 3.50
42 JOy,Day of Krypton Man #4,

V:Draaga 3.50
43 JOy,V:Krypton Man 2.00
44 JOy,A:Batman 2.00
45 JOy,F:Jimmy Olsen's Dairy . . 2.00
46 DJu,JOy,A:Jade,Obsidian,
   I:New Terra-Man 2.00
47 JOy,Soul Search #2,V:Blaze . . 2.00
48 CS,Sinbad Contract #1 . . . . . 2.00
49 JOy,Krisis of K.Kryptonite#1 . . 3.00
50 JBy,KGa,DJu,JOy,BBr,CS,Krisis
   of Krimson Kryptonite #4,
   Clark Proposes To Lois 6.00
50a 2nd printing 1.50
51 JOy,I:Mr.Z 1.75
52 KGa,V:Terra-Man 1.75
53 JOy,Superman reveals i.d.. . . . 3.50
53a 2nd Printing 1.25
54 JOy,KK,Time & Time Again#3 . 1.75
55 JOy,KK,Time & Time Again#6 . 1.75
56 EH,KK,Red Glass Trilogy#1 . . 1.75
57 JOy,DJu,BBr,ATi,JBg,BMc,TG,
   Revenge o/t Krypton Man #2 . . 3.50
58 DJu,BBr,I:Bloodhounds 1.75
59 DJu,BBr,A:Linear Men 1.75
60 DJu,EB,I:Agent Liberty,
   V:Intergang 2.00
61 DJu,BBr,A:Waverider,
   V:Linear Men 1.75
62 DJu,BBr,Blackout #4,A:Mr.Z . . 1.75
63 DJu,A:Aquaman 1.75
64 JG,Christmas issue 1.75
65 DJu,Panic in the Sky#2,
   I:New Justice League 3.50
66 DJu,Panic in the Sky#6,
   V:Brainiac 8.00
67 DJu,Aftermath 1.75
68 DJu,V:Deathstroke 1.75
69 WS(c),DJu,A:Agent Liberty . . . 1.75
70 DJu,BBr,A:Robin,V:Vampires . 1.75
71 DJu,Blaze/Satanus War 1.75
72 DJu,Crisis at Hand#2 . . . . 1.75
73 DJu,A:Waverider,V:Linear
   Men,C:Doomsday 4.00
73a 2nd printing 1.50
74 DJu,V:Doomsday,A:JLA 7.00
74a 2nd printing 1.75
75 DJu,V:Doomsday,D:Superman,
   Collectors Ed. 15.00
75a newstand Ed. 9.00
75b 2nd printing 4.00
75c 3rd printing 1.50
75d 4th Printing 1.50
75e Platinum Ed. 60.00
76 DJu,BBr,Funeral for Friend#4 . 3.00
77 DJu,BBr,Funeral for Friend#8 . 3.00
78 DJu,BBr,Reign of Supermen#3,
   Die-Cut(c),Mini poster,F:Cyborg
   Supes,A:Doomsday 2.50
78a Newsstand Ed. 2.00
79 DJu,BBr,Memorial Service for
   Clark 2.00
80 DJu,Doomsday,Coast City Blows up,
   V:Mongul 4.00
81 DJu,O:Cyborg Superman 3.50
82 DJu,Chromium(c),A:All Supermen,
   V:Cyborg Superman 5.00
82a Newstand Ed. 2.25
83 DJu,A:Batman 1.75
84 DJu,V:Toyman 1.75
85 DJu,V:Toyman 1.75
86 DJu,A:Sun Devils 1.75
87 DJu(c&s),SI,JRu,Bizzaro's
   World#1, R:Bizarro 1.75
88 DJu(c&s),SI,JRu,Bizzaro's
   World#5, D:Bizarro 1.75

Superman (2nd Regular Series) #39
© DC Comics, Inc.

89 DJu(c&s),V:Cadmus Project . . 1.75
90 DJu(c&s),Battle for
   Metropolis#3 . . . . 1.75
91 DJu(c&s),Fall of Metropolis#3 . 1.75
92 Massacre in Metropolis 1.75
93 Zero Hour,A:Batman 1.75
94 Conduit 1.75
95 Brainiac 1.75
96 Virtual Reality 1.75
97 Shadow Dragon 1.75
98 R:Shadow Strike 1.75
99 R:Agent Liberty 1.75
100 BBr,DJu,Death of C.Kent,pt.1 . 2.95
100a Collectors Edition 3.95
101 Death of Clark Kent,pt.5
   [New Miraweb format begins] . . 2.00
102 DJu,A:Captain Marvel 2.00
103 O:Arclight 2.00
104 . . . . 2.00
105 A:Green Lantern 2.00
106 DJu,RF,The Trial of Superman 2.00
107 DJu,RF,The Trial of Superman 2.00
108 DJu,RF,The Trial of Superman 2.00
109 DJu,RF,V:Kill Fee 2.00
110 . . . . 2.00
111 DJu,RF,Cat Grant in charge . . 2.00
112 DJu,RF,Lois & Clark 2.00
113 DJu(s),RF,JRu, ... 2.00
114 DJu(s),RF,JRu,A:Brainiac . . . 2.00
115 DJu(s),RF,JRu,Lois leaves
   Metropolis 2.00
116 DJu(s),RF,JRu,battle city siga
   concl., V:Daxamite,B.U. Teen
   Titans preview 2.00
117 DJu(s),RF,JRu,V: his own
   robots, Final Night tie-in 2.00
118 DJu(s),RF,JRu,F:time-lost
   Legion of Super Heroes 2.00
119 DJu(s),RF,JRu,A:Legion of
   Super Heroes 2.00
120 DJu(s),RF,JRu, ... 2.00
121 DJu(s),RF,JRu,"They Call it
   Suicide Slum" 2.00
122 DJu(s),RF,JRu,Lois visits
   Fortress of Solitude 2.00
123 DJu(s),RF,Jru,Superman gets
   New Costume 2.00

123a collector's edition, glow-in-
   the-dark cover, ... 2.00
124 DJu(s),RF,JRu,A:Scorn, prince
   of Kandor 2.00
125 DJu(s),RF,JRu,Kandor and
   Metropolis,A:Atom 2.00
126 DJu(s),RF,JRu,A:Batman . . . 2.00
127 DJu(s),RF,JRu,F:Jimmy Olsen 2.00
128 DJu(s),RF,JRu, Genesis tie-in 2.00
129 DJu(s),PR,JRu,A:Scorn 2.00
130 DJu(s),RF,JRu,dragon's tooth 2.00
131 DJu(s),RF,JRu,Luthor &
   Contessa's kid 2.00
132 DJu,RF,JRu,Red/Blue x-over . 2.00
133 . . . . 2.00
134 DJu,RF,JRu,Millennium Giants 2.00
135 DJu,RF,JRu,aftermath 2.00
136 DJu,PR,JRu,The Superman
   of 2999 A.D., pt.1 . . . . 2.00
137 DJu,PR,JRu,2999 AD,pt.2 . . . 2.00
138 DJu,PR,JRu,2999 AD,pt.3 . . . 2.00
139 DJu(s),JSn,JRu,V:Dominus . . 2.00
Ann.#1 RF,BBr,A:Titano 2.00
Ann.#2 RF,BBr,R:Newsboy Legion
   & Guardian 3.00
Ann.#3 DAb(1st Work),TA,DG,
   Armageddon 2001. . . . . 9.00
Ann.#3a 2nd printing(silver) 2.00
Ann.#4 Eclipso 2.75
Ann.#5 Bloodlines#6,DL,I:Myriad . 2.75
Ann.#6 Elseworlds Story 2.95
Ann.#7 WS(c),Year One Annual
   A:Dr. Occult 3.95
Ann.#8 Legends o/t Dead Earth . . 2.95
Ann.#9 Pulp Heroes (High-
   Adventure) DJu 3.95
Ann.#10 DJu(s),PR,Clv,BWr,
   Ghosts 3.00
Giant Ann.#1 Replica edition 5.00
Spec.#0 PeerPressure,pt.3 (1994) 2.00
Spec. Superman: Lois Lane,
   Girlfrenzy (1998) 2.00
Spec.#1 WS,V:L.Luthor,'Sandman' 6.00
Spec. Superman Plus One (1997) 3.00
Spec.#1 Superman: The Earth
   Stealers, JBy,CS,JOy (1988) . . 3.50
   2nd printing 3.00
Spec. Superman Forever, KK,DJu,LSi,
   JBy,SI,DG, Luthor's kidnapped
   daughter (1998) 5.00
   Deluxe ed.,AxR(c), lenticular . . 6.00
Spec.#1 Superman: The Legacy of
   Superman,WS,JG,F:Guardian,
   Waverider,Sinbad (1993) 4.00
Spec. Superman/Toyman (1996) . 2.00
Spec. Whatever Happened to the
   Man of Tomorrow 6.00
Newstime-The Life and Death of
   the Man of Steel-Magazine,
   DJu,BBr,JOy,JG,JBg 3.25
Spec.#1 Superman Gallery (1993) 2.95
GN The Death of Superman rep. Man
   of Steel #17–#19, Superman
   #73–#75, Adventures of Superman
   #496–#497, Action Comics
   #683–#684 & Justice League
   #69 (1993) 6.00
   Later printings 5.95
   Platinum Edition 15.00
GN Superman At Earth's End
   (Elseworlds 1995) 4.95
GN Superman: Distant Fires, HC,GK,
   nuclear winter (1997) 6.00
GN Superman: Earth Day 1991, KGa
   Metropolis 'Clean-Up' 5.50

GN Superman For Earth (1991) . . 4.95
GN Superman: Kal, Medieval
   Superman (Elseworlds 1995) . 5.95
GN Superman's Metropolis, RLo &
   RTs(s),TMK, in Fritz Lang's
   Metropolis (Elseworlds 1996) . 5.95
GN Superman Red/Superman Blue,
   V:Toyman, Cyborg, Superman
   split into two entities (1997) . . 4.00
   Deluxe, 3-D cover 5.00
GN Superman Secret Files, DJu,JOy,
   etc.,inc. O:Superman (1997) . . 5.00
GN Superman Secret Files: Villains
   (1997) 5.00
GN Superman: Silver Banshee, 48pg,
   prestige format (1998) 5.00
GN Superman: Speeding Bullets,
   EB (Elseworlds 1993) 6.00
GN Superman, Under a Yellow Sun
   by Clark Kent,KGa (1994) . . 5.95
GN Superman: The Wedding Album,
   collector's edition, 96 pg.,
   cardstock cover 4.95
TPB The Wedding and Beyond rep 5.00
TPB Superman: The Death of Clark
   Kent, rep.Superman:Man of Steel
   #43–#46, Superman #99–#102,
   Action Comics #709–#711, Adv.
   of Superman #523–#525, Superman:
   Man of Tomorrow #1 (1997) . 20.00
TPB Eradication 13.00
TPB Exile 15.00
TPB Krisis of the Krimson Kryptonite
   rep. Superman #49–#50, Adven-
   tures of Superman #472–#473,
   Action Comics #659–#660 and
   Starman #28 . . . . 12.95
TPB Panic in the Sky rep. 9.95
TPB Return of Superman rep. Reign
   of Superman 14.95
TPB Time and Time Again (1994) 7.50
TPB World Without Superman . . . 7.50
Archives, Vol. 1 S&S rep. 50.00
Archives, Vol. 2 S&S rep. 50.00
Archives, Vol. 3 S&S rep. 50.00
Archives, Vol. 4 S&S rep. 50.00
Superman Archives HC rep 39.95
Greatest Superman Stories Ever Told:
   HC 75.00
   TPB 15.95

SUPERMAN ADVENTURES
Sept. 1996
1 PDi(s),RBr,TA, from animated
   TV show 1.75
2 SMI,RBr,TA,V:Metallo 1.75
3 SMI(s),RBr,TA,V:Brainiac 1.75
4 SMI(s), ... 1.75
5 SMI(s),BBI,TA,V:Livewire 1.75
6 SMI(s),RBr,TA,Metropolis
   in ruins 1.75
7 SMI(s),RBr,TA,V:Jax-Ur, Mala . 1.75
8 SMI(s),RBr,TA,V:Jax-Ur 1.75
9 SMI(s),MM,TA,"Return of
   the Hero" 1.75
10 SMI(s),RBr,TA,V:Toyman 1.75
11 SMI(s),RBr,TA,struck down
   by strange malady 1.75
12 SMI(s),RBr,TA,BB, Kryptonian
   virus, concl. 1.75
13 SMI(s),RBr,TA,BB, alien races 2.00
14 TA,Angela Chen 2.00
15 RBr,TA,Superman's pal Bibbo . 2.00
16 MMr(s),TA, meets Man of Steel 2.00
17 . . . . 2.00

18 TA,should Clark quit? 2.00
19 TA,V:Multi-Face 2.00
20 RBr,TA,V:MasterTrax 2.00
21 Supergirl Adventures, 64pg. . . 4.00
22 MMr,TA,RBr,War Games, pt.1 . 2.00
23 MMr,TA,RBr,War Games, pt.2 . 2.00
24 MMr,TA,RBr,V:Parasite 2.00
Ann.#1 JoS,DDv,V:Akamin 4.00
TPB rep.#1–#6 . . . . 8.00
Spec. #1 Superman vs. Lobo –
   Misery in Space, DvM,MM,
   A:Man of Tomorrow 3.00

SUPERMAN:
THE DARK SIDE
Elseworlds, Aug., 1998
1 JFM,KD,First Son of Apokolips 5.00

Superman/Doomsday #3
© DC Comics, Inc.

SUPERMAN/DOOMSDAY:
HUNTER/PREY
1994
1 DJu(a&s),BBr,R:Doomsday,R:Cyborg
   Superman,A:Darkseid 5.50
2 DJu(a&s),BBr,V:Doomsday,Cyborg
   Superman,A:Darkseid 5.25
3 DJu(a&s),BBr,V:Doomsday . . . 5.25
TPB Rep. #1-#3 . . . . 14.95

SUPERMAN FAMILY
Prev: Superman's Pal,
Jimmy Olsen
1974–82
164 KS,NC(c),Jimmy Olsen:'Death
   Bites with Fangs of Stone' . . 25.00
165 KS,NC(c),Supergirl:'Princess
   of the Golden Sun' 15.00
166 KS,NC(c),Lois Lane:'The
   Murdering Arm of Metropolis' 15.00
167 KS,NC(c),Jimmy Olsen:'A
   Deep Death for Mr. Action' . . 15.00
168 NC(c),Supergirl:'The Girl
   with the See-Through Mind' . 15.00
169 NC(c),Lois Lane:'Target of
   the Tarantula' 15.00
170 KS(c),Jimmy Olsen:'The Kid

Who Adopted Jimmy Olsen' . 12.00
171 ECh(c),Supergirl:'Cleopatra-
   Queen of America' 12.00
172 KS(c),Lois Lane:'The Cheat
   the Whole World Cheered' . . 12.00
173 KS(c),Jimmy Olsen:'Menace
   of the Micro-Monster' 12.00
174 KS(c),Supergirl:'Eyes of
   the Serpent' 12.00
175 KS(c),Lois Lane:'Fadeout
   For Lois' 12.00
176 KS(c),Jimmy
   Olsen:'Nashville, Super-Star' . 12.00
177 KS(c),Supergirl:'Bride
   of the Stars' 7.00
178 KS(c),Lois Lane:'The Girl
   With the Heart of Steel' 7.00
179 KS(c),Jimmy Olsen:'I Scared
   Superman to Death' 7.00
180 KS,Supergirl:'The Secret of
   the Spell-Bound Supergirl' 7.00
181 ECh(c),Lois Lane:'The Secret
   Lois Lane Could Never Tell' . . 7.00
182 CS&NA(c),Jimmy Olsen:
   'Death on Ice' 8.00
183 NA(c),Supergirl:'Shadows
   of Phantoms' 6.00
184 NA(c),Supergirl:'The
   Visitors From The Void' 6.00
185 NA(c),Jimmy Olsen: The
   Fantastic Fists and Fury
   Feet of Jimmy Olsen' 6.00
186 JL&DG(c),Jimmy Olsen:
   'The Bug Lady' 6.00
187 JL(c),Jimmy Olsen:'The
   Dealers of Death' 6.00
188 JL&DG(c),Jimmy Olsen:
   'Crisis in Kandor' 6.00
189 JL(c),Jimmy Olsen:'The
   Night of the Looter' 6.00
190 Jimmy Olsen:'Somebody
   Stole My Town' 6.00
191 Superboy:'The Incredible
   Shrinking Town' 6.00
192 RA&DG(c),Superboy:'This
   Town For Plunder' 6.00
193 RA&DG(c),Superboy:'Menace
   of the Mechanical Monster' . . . 6.00
194 MR,Superboy:'When
   the Sorcerer Strikes' 7.00
195 RA&DG(c),Superboy:'The Curse
   of the Un-Secret Identity' 5.00
196 JL&DG(c),Superboy:'The
   Shadow of Jor-El' 5.00
197 JL(c),Superboy:'Superboy's
   Split Personality' 5.00
198 JL(c),Superboy:'Challenge
   of the Green K-Tastrophe' 5.00
199 RA&DG(c),Superboy:'The
   Case of Cape Caper' 5.00
200 RA&DG(c),Lois Lane:
   'Unhappy Anniversary' 7.00
201 RA&DG(c),Supergirl:'The
   Face on Cloud 9' 3.00
202 RA&DG(c),Supergirl:'The
   Dynamic Duel' 3.00
203 RA&DG(c),Supergirl:'The
   Supergirl From Planet Earth' . . 3.00
204 RA&DG(c),Supergirl:'The
   Earth-quake Enchantment' . . . 3.00
205 RA&DG(c),Supergirl:'Magic
   Over Miami' 3.00
206 RA&DG(c),Supergirl:'Strangers
   at the Heart's Core' 3.00
207 RA&DG(c),Supergirl:'Look

Homeward, Argonian' 3.00
208 RA&DG(c),Supergirl:'The
  Super-Switch to New York' . . . 3.00
209 Supergirl:'Strike Three-
  You're Out' 3.00
210 Supergirl:'The Spoil Sport
  of New York' 3.00
211 RA&DG(c):Supergirl:'The Man
  With the Explosive Mind' 3.00
212 RA&DG(c):Supergirl:'Payment
  on Demand' 3.00
213 . . . . 3.00
214 . . . . 3.00
215 . . . . 3.00
216 thru 222 . . . . @3.00

SUPERMAN FOR ALL SEASONS
June, 1998
1 (of 4) JLb,TSe, from farmboy
  to superhero 5.00
2 JLb,TSe,V:Lex Luthor 5.00

Superman: The Man of Steel #12
© DC Comics, Inc.

SUPERMAN: THE MAN OF STEEL
1991–97
1 B:LSi(s),DJu,BMc,JOy,BBr,TG,
  Revenge o/t Krypton Man#1 . . 5.00
2 JBg,V:Cerberus 3.00
3 JBg,War of the Gods X-over . . 2.50
4 JBg,V:Angstrom 2.50
5 JBg,CS,V:Atomic Skull 2.50
6 JBg,Blackout#3,A:Mr.Z 2.50
7 JBg,V:Cerberus 2.50
8 KD,V:Jolt,Blockhouse 2.50
9 JBg,Panic in the Sky#1,
  V:Brainiac. 3.00
10 JBg,Panic in the Sky#5,
  D:Draaga 2.50
11 JBg,V:Flashpoint 2.00
12 JBg,V:Warwolves 2.00
13 JBg,V:Cerberus 2.00
14 JBg,A:Robin,V:Vampires 2.00
15 KG,KGa,Blaze/Satanus War . . 2.00
16 JBg,Crisis at Hand#1 . . . . . . 2.00

17 JBg,V:Underworld,
  C:Doomsday 6.00
17a 2nd printing 1.50
18 JBg,I:Doomsday,V:Underworld 8.00
18a 2nd printing 4.00
18b 3rd printing 2.00
19 JBg,Doomsday,pt.5 . . . . 5.00
19a 2nd printing 2.00
20 JBg,Funeral for a Friend#3 . . 3.00
21 JBg,Funeral for a Friend#7 . . . 3.00
22 JBg,Reign of Supermen#4,Direct
  Sales,Die-Cut(c),mini-poster,
  F:Man of Steel 2.50
22a Newsstand Ed. 1.75
23 JBg,V:Superboy 2.00
24 JBg,V:White Rabbit,A:Mongul . 2.00
25 JBg,A:Real Superman 3.00
26 JBg,A:All Supermen,V:Mongul,
  Cyborg Superman 2.50
27 JBg,A:Superboy,Lex Luthor . . 2.00
28 JBg(c),A:Steel 1.75
29 LSi(s),JBg,Spilled Blood#3,
  V:Hi-Tech,Blood Thirst 1.75
30 LSi(s),JBg,V:Lobo,Vinyl(c) . . . 2.50
30a Newstand Ed. 1.75
31 MBr,A:Guardian 1.75
32 MBr,Bizarro's World#4,
  V:Bizarro 1.75
33 MBr,V:Parasite 1.75
34 JBg,A:Lex Men,Dubbile Men . . 1.75
35 JBg,Worlds Collide#1,
  I:Fred Bentson 1.75
36 JBf,Worlds Collide,pt.10,V:Rift
  A:Icon 1.75
37 JBg,Zero Hour,A:Batman 1.75
38 Mystery 1.50
39 JBg,Luthor 1.50
40 . . . . 1.50
41 Locke 1.50
42 F:Locke 1.50
43 V:Deathtrap 1.50
44 Prologue to Death 1.50
45 JGb,DJa,Death of Clark Kent,
  [New Miraweb format begins] . 2.00
46 JBg,DJa,A:Shadowdragon . . . 2.00
47 O:Bloodsport 2.00
48 . . . . 2.00
49 Skyhook 2.00
50 JBg,DJa,The Trial of
  Superman, 48pg 2.95
51 JBg,DJa,The Trial of Superman 2.00
52 JBg,The Trial of Superman . . 2.00
53 JBg,DRo,A:Lex Luthor,Contessa 2.00
54 JBg 2.00
55 JBg,DJa, Clark dates Lori
  Lemaris 2.00
56 JBg,DJa, manipulator revealed 2.00
57 RSt,JBg,DJa, more twisters . . 2.00
58 LSi(s),JBg,DJa,A:Supergirl . . . 2.00
59 LSi(s),JBg,DJa,Parasite, Steel . 2.00
60 LSi(s),JBg,DJa,R:Bottled City
  of Kandor 2.00
61 LSi(s),JBg,DJa,V:Riot 2.00
62 LSi(s),JBg,DJa, Superman
  looses powers, Final Night tie-in 2.00
63 LSi(s),JBg,DJa,Clark is
  kidnapped & revealed identity . 2.00
64 LSi(s),JBg,DJa,Superman tries to
  restore his powers 2.00
65 LSi(s),SB,DJa,V:Superman
  Revenge Squad 2.00
66 LSi(s),JBg,DJa,V:Rajiv 2.00
67 LSi(s),JBg,DJa,New powers
  prequel 2.00
68 LSi(s),JBg,DJa,V:Metallo 2.00

69 KK&LSi(s),SEa,DJa,A:Atom,
  in Kandor 2.00
70 LSi(s),SEa,DJa,V:Saviour 2.00
71 LSi(s),SEa,DJa,V:Mainframe,
  Superman Revenge Squad . . . 2.00
72 LSi(s),SEa,JP,DJa,JBg,Genesis
  V:Mainframe 2.00
73 LSi&MWa(s),SEa,DJa,V:Revenge
  Squad 2.00
74 LSi(s),SEa,DJa,dragon's tooth . 2.00
75 LSi(s),DJa,JBg,Mr.Mxyzptlk dies
  parody of Superman #75 . . . . 2.00
76 LSi(s),JBb,DJa,V:Mokkari 2.00
77 . . . . 2.00
78 JBg, Millennium Giants, pt.1
  x-over 2.00
79 JBg, Millennium Giants 2.00
80 LSi,JBg,DJa,golden age?,pt.1 . 2.00
81 LSi,JBg,DJa,golden age?,pt.2 . 2.00
82 LSi,JBg,DJa,golden age?,pt.3 . 2.00
83 LSi,SEa,DJa,Dominus 2.00
Ann.#1 Eclipso tie-in,A:Starman . 2.75
Ann.#2 Bloodlines#2,I:Edge 2.75
Ann.#3 MBr,Elseworlds Story . . . 2.95
Ann.#4 Year One Annual 2.95
Ann.#5 Legends o/t Dead Earth . 2.95
Ann.#6 Pulp Heroes (Hard Boiled)
  LSi(s),DJa 3.95
Gallery 1 . . . . 3.50
TPB 7.50

Superman: The Man of Tomorrow #7
© DC Comics, Inc.

SUPERMAN: THE MAN OF TOMORROW
1995–96
1 TGu,BBr,RSt(s),V:Lex Luthor . . 2.00
2 v:Parasite 2.00
3 TG,BBr, The Trial of Superman 2.00
4 RSt(s),PR,BBr,A:Shazam 2.00
5 RSt(s),PR,BBr,Wedding of Lex
  Luthor 2.00
6 RSt(s),PR,BBr,Superman V:
  Jackal again 2.00
7 RSt(s),PR,BBr, ... 2.00
8 RSt(s),PR,BBr,V:Carbide 2.00
9 RSt(s),PR,BBr,Ma and Pa Kent
  open their album 2.00

10 . . . .
11 LSi(s),PR,DJa,BBr 2.00

SUPERMAN'S GIRL FRIEND, LOIS LANE
1958–74

1 CS,KS	2,700.00
2 CS,KS	750.00
3 CS,KS,spanking panel shown	500.00
4 CS,KS	400.00
5 CS,KS	375.00
6 CS,KS	300.00
7 CS,KS	300.00
8 CS,KS	250.00
9 CS,KS, A:Pat Boone	250.00
10 CS,KS	250.00
11 CS,KS	200.00
12 CS,KS	200.00
13 CS,KS	175.00
14 KS,'Three Nights in the Fortress of Solitude'	150.00
15 KS,I:Van-Zee	150.00
16 KS, Lois' Signal-Watch	150.00
17 KS,CS,A:Brainiac	150.00
18 KS,A:Astounding Man	150.00
19 KS,'Superman of the Past' .	125.00
20 KS,A:Superman	125.00
21 KS,A:Van-Zee	125.00
22 KS,A:Robin Hood	125.00
23 KS,A:Elastic Lass, Supergirl	125.00
24 KS,A:Van-Zee, Bizarro	125.00
25 KS,'Lois Lane's Darkest Secret'	110.00
26 KS,A:Jor-El	110.00
27 KS,CS,A:Bizarro	110.00
28 KS,A:Luthor	110.00
29 CS,A:Aquaman,Batman,Green Arrow	110.00
30 KS,A:Krypto,Aquaman	65.00
31 KS,A:Lori Lemaris	60.00
32 KS,CS,A:Bizarro	60.00
33 KS,CS,A:Phantom Zone,Lori Lemaris, Mon-El	65.00
34 KS,A:Luthor,Supergirl	60.00
35 KS,CS,A:Supergirl	60.00
36 KS,CS,Red Kryptonite Story .	60.00
37 KS,CS,'The Forbidden Box' .	60.00
38 KS,CS,A:Prof.Potter, Supergirl	60.00
39 KS,CS,A:Supergirl,Jor-El, Krypto, Lori Lemaris	60.00
40 KS,'Lois Lane, Hag!'	60.00
41 KS,CS,'The Devil and Lois Lane'	60.00
42 KS,A:Lori Lemaris	60.00
43 KS,A:Luthor	60.00
44 KS,A:Lori Lemaris,Braniac, Prof. Potter	60.00
45 KS,CS,'The Superman-Lois Hit Record'	60.00
46 KS,A:Luthor	60.00
47 KS,'The Incredible Delusion' .	60.00
48 KS,A:Mr. Mxyzptlk	60.00
49 KS,The Unknown Superman .	60.00
50 KS,A:Legion	50.00
51 KS,A:Van-Zee & Lori Lemaris	40.00
52 KS,'Truce Between Lois Lane and Lana Lang'	40.00
53 KS,A:Lydia Lawrence	40.00
54 KS,CS,'The Monster That Loved Lois Lane'	40.00
55 KS,A:Superigrl	40.00
56 KS,'Lois Lane's Super-Gamble!'	42.00
57 KS,'The Camera From	

Outer Space'	40.00
58 KS,'The Captive Princess' . . .	40.00
59 KS,CS,A:Jor-El & Batman . . .	40.00
60 KS,'Get Lost,Superman!'	40.00
61 KS,A:Mxyzptlk	40.00
62 KS,A:Mxyzptlk	40.00
63 KS,'The Satanic Schemes of S.K.U.L.'	40.00
64 KS,A:Luthor	40.00
65 KS,A:Luthor	40.00
66 KS,'They Call Me the Cat!' . .	40.00
67 KS,'The Bombshell of the Boulevards'	40.00
68 giant size	45.00
69 KS,Lois Lane's Last Chance .	40.00
70 KS,I:Silver Age Catwoman, A:Batman,Robin,Penguin . .	225.00
71 KS,A:Catwoman,Batman, Robin,Penguin	130.00
72 KS,CS,A:Ina Lemaris	25.00
73 KS,'The Dummy and the Damsell'	25.00
74 KS,A:Justice League & Bizarro World,I:Bizarro Flash	35.00

Superman's Girl Friend, Lois Lane #111
© DC Comics, Inc.

75 KS,'The Lady Dictator'	25.00
76 KS,A:Hap-El	25.00
77 giant size	25.00
78 KS,Courtship,Kryptonian Style	25.00
79 KS,B:NA(c)	15.00
80 KS,'Get Out of My Life, Superman'	15.00
81 KS,'No Witnessesin Outerspace'	15.00
82 GT,A:Brainiac&Justice League	15.00
83 GT,'Witch on Wheels'	15.00
84 GT,KS,'Who is Lois Lane?' . .	15.00
85 GT,KS,A:Kandorians	15.00
86 giant size	25.00
87 GT,KS,A:Cor-Lar	15.00
88 GT,KS,'Through a Murderer's Eyes'	15.00
89 CS,A:Batman & Batman Jr. . .	25.00
90 GT,A:Dahr-nel	15.00
91 GT,A:Superlass	15.00
92 GT,A:Superhorse	15.00
93 GT,A:Wonder Woman	15.00
94 GT,KS,A:Jor	15.00

95 giant size	25.00
96 GT,A:Jor	12.00
97 GT,KS,A:Lori Lemaris, Luma Lynai,Lyla Lerrol	12.00
98 GT,A:Phantom Zone	12.00
99 GT,KS,A:Batman	12.00
100 GT,A:Batman	12.00
101 GT,KS,'The Super-Reckless Lois Lane'	12.00
102 GT,KS,When You're Dead, You're Dead	12.00
103 GT,KS,A:Supergirl	12.00
104 giant size	25.00
105 RA,I&O:Rose & Thorn	30.00
106 WR,'I am Curious Black!' . .	12.00
107 WR,The Snow-Woman Wept	12.00
108 WR,The Spectre Suitor	12.00
109 WR,'I'll Never Fall in Love Again'	12.00
110 WR,'Indian Death Charge!' .	12.00
111 WR,A:Justice League	12.00
112 WR,KS,A:Lori Lemaris	10.00
113 giant size	25.00
114 WR,KS,A:Rose & Thorn . . .	10.00
115 WR,A:The Black Racer	10.00
116 WR,A:Darkseid & Desaad .	10.00
117 WR,'S.O.S From Tomorrow!'	10.00
118 WR,A:Darkseid & Desaad .	10.00
119 WR,A:Darkseid & Lucy Lane	10.00
120 WR,'Who Killed Lucy Lane?'	10.00
121 WR,A:The Thorn	10.00
122 WR,A:The Thorn	10.00
123 JRo,'Ten Deadly Division of the 100'	10.00
124 JRo,'The Hunters'	8.00
125 JRo,'Death Rides Wheels!' .	8.00
126 JRo,'The Brain Busters' . . .	8.00
127 JRo,'Curse of the Flame' . .	8.00
128 JRo,A:Batman & Aquaman .	8.00
129 JRo,'Serpent in Paradise' . .	8.00
130 JRo,'The Mental Murster' . .	8.00
131 JRo,Superman–Marry Me!' .	8.00
132 JRo,Zatanna B.U.	8.00
133 JRo,'The Lady is a Bomb' . .	8.00
134 JRo,A:Kandor	8.00
135 JRo,'Amazing After-Life of Lois Lane'	8.00
136 JRo,A:Wonder Woman	8.00
137 JRo,'The Stolen Subway' . .	10.00
Ann.#1	175.00
Ann.#2	125.00

SUPERMAN'S PAL, JIMMY OLSEN
1954–74

1 CS,'The Boy of 100 Faces!'	4,200.00
2 CS,The Flying Jimmy Olsen	1,200.00
3 CS,'The Man Who Collected Excitement	650.00
4 CS,'King For A Day!'	450.00
5 CS,'The Story of Superman's Souvenirs	425.00
6 CS,Kryptonite story	350.00
7 CS,'The King of Marbles' . . .	350.00
8 CS,'Jimmy Olsen, Crooner' .	325.00
9 CS,'The Missile of Steel' . . .	325.00
10 CS,'Jungle Jimmy Olsen' . . .	325.00
11 CS,'TNT.Olsen,The Champ'	250.00
12 CS,'Invisible Jimmy Olsen' .	250.00
13 CS,'Jimmy Olsen's Super Issue'	225.00
14 CS,'The Boy Superman' . . .	225.00
15 CS,'Jimmy Olsen,Speed Demon'	225.00
16 CS,'The Boy Superman' . . .	225.00

All comics prices listed are for *Near Mint* condition.

DC COMICS

17 CS,J.Olsen as cartoonist . . 225.00
18 CS,A:Superboy 225.00
19 CS,'Supermam's Kid Brother 200.00
20 CS,'Merman of Metropolis' . 200.00
21 CS,'The Wedding of Jimmy
   Olsen' 175.00
22 CS,'The Super Brain of
   Jimmy Olsen' 175.00
23 CS,'The Adventure of
   Private Olsen' 175.00
24 CS,'The Gorilla Reporter' . . 175.00
25 CS,'The Day There Was
   No Jimmy Olsen 175.00
26 CS,'Bird Boy of Metropolis' . 150.00
27 CS,'The Outlaw Jimmy Olsen' 150.00
28 CS,'The Boy Who Killed
   Superman' 150.00
29 CS,A:Krypto 150.00
30 CS,'The Son of Superman' . 150.00
31 CS,I:Elastic Lad 125.00
32 CS,A:Prof.Potter 125.00
33 CS,'Human Flame Thrower' 125.00
34 CS,'Superman's Pal of Steel' 125.00
35 CS,'Superman's Enemy' . . . 125.00
36 CS,I:Lois Lane,O:Jimmy Olsen
   as Superman's Pal 125.00
37 CS,O:Jimmy Olsen's SignalWatch,
   A:Elastic Lad(Jimmy Olsen) 125.00
38 CS,'Olsen's Super-Supper' . 125.00
39 CS,'The Super-Lad of Space' 125.00
40 CS,A:Supergirl,Hank White
   (Perry White's son) 125.00
41 CS,'The Human Octopus' . . 90.00
42 CS,'Jimmy The Genie' 90.00
43 WB,CS,'Jimmy Olsen's Private
   Monster' 90.00
44 CS,'Miss Jimmy Olsen' 90.00
45 CS,A:Kandor 90.00
46 CS,A:Supergirl,Elastic Lad . 90.00
47 CS,'Monsters From Earth!' . . 90.00
48 CS,I:Superman Emergency
   Squad 90.00
49 CS,A:Congorilla & Congo Bill 90.00
50 CS,A:Supergirl,Krypto,Bizarro 90.00
51 CS,A:Supergirl 75.00
52 CS,A:Mr. Mxyzptlk,
   Miss Gzptlsnz 75.00
53 CS,A:Kandor,Lori Lemaris,
   Mr.Mxyzptlk 75.00
54 CS,A:Elastic Lad 75.00
55 CS,A:Aquaman,Thor 75.00
56 KS,Imaginary story 75.00
57 KS,A:Supergirl,Imaginary story 40.00
58 CS,C:Batman 40.00
59 CS,A:Titano 40.00
60 CS,'The Fantastic Army of
   General Olsen' 40.00
61 CS,Prof. Potter 40.00
62 CS,A:Elastic Lad,Phantom
   Zone 40.00
63 CS,A:Supergirl,Kandor 45.00
64 CS,'Jimmy Olsen's
   Super-Romance 35.00
65 CS,A:Miss Gzptlsnz 35.00
66 CS,KS,A:Mr. Mxyzptlk 35.00
67 CS,'The Dummy That Haunted
   Jimmy Olsen' 35.00
68 CS,'The Helmet of Hate' . . . 35.00
69 CS,A:Nightwing,Flamebird . . 35.00
70 A:Supergirl,Lori Lemaris,
   Element Lad 35.00
71 CS,A:Mr. Mxyzptlk 30.00
72 CS,A:Legion of Super-Heroes,
   Jimmy Olsen becomes honorary
   member 35.00

Superman's Pal, Jimmy Olsen #149
© DC Comics, Inc.

73 A:Kandor 35.00
74 CS,A:Mr. Mxyzptlk,Lex Luthor 30.00
75 CS,A:Supergirl 30.00
76 CS,A:Legion of Super-Heroes 30.00
77 CS,Jimmy Olsen becomes
   Colossal Boy, A:Titano 30.00
78 CS,A:Aqualad 30.00
79 CS,'The Red-Headed Beetle
   of 1,000 B.C.' 30.00
80 CS,A:Bizarro 30.00
81 CS,KS,A:Lori Lemaris,I&O
   only A:Mighty Eagle 30.00
82 CS,'The Unbeatable Jimmy
   Olsen' 30.00
83 CS,A:Kandor 30.00
84 CS,A:Titano 30.00
85 CS,C:Legion of Super-Heroes 35.00
86 CS,A:Congorilla,Braniac . . . 30.00
87 A:Lex Luthor,Brainiac,Legion
   of Super-Villians 35.00
88 C:Legion of Super-Heroes . . 30.00
89 I:Agent Double-Five,C:John F.
   Kennedy 30.00
90 CS,A:Mr. Mxyzptlk 30.00
91 CS,C:Batman & Robin 30.00
92 JM,A:Batman,Robin,Supergirl 30.00
93 CS,'The Batman-Superman of
   Earth-X!' 30.00
94 O:Insect Queen retold 30.00
95 Giant 35.00
96 I:Tempus 25.00
97 A:Fortress of Solitude 25.00
98 'The Bride of Jungle Jimmy' . 25.00
99 A:Legion of Super-Heroes . . . 25.00
100 A:Legion of Super-Heroes . . 35.00
101 A:Jor-El and Lara 15.00
102 'Superman's Greatest Double
   Cross!' 15.00
103 'The Murder of Clark Kent!' . 12.00
104 Giant 30.00
105 V:Tempus 12.00
106 CS,A:Legion of Super-Heroes 12.00
107 A:Krypto 12.00
108 CS,'The Midas of Metropolis' 12.00
109 A:Lex Luthor 12.00
110 CS,'Jimmy Olsen's Blackest
   Deeds!' 12.00

111 . . . . 12.00
112 . . . . 12.00
113 V:Magnaman 35.00
114 'The Wrong Superman!' . . . 12.00
115 A:Aquaman 12.00
116 A:Brainiac 12.00
117 'Planet of the Capes' 12.00
118 A:Lex Luthor 12.00
119 'Nine Lives Like a Cat!' . . . 12.00
120 V:Climate King 12.00
121 thru 125 . . . . @12.00
126 CS,Riddle of Kryptonite Plus 12.00
127 CS,Jimmy in Revolutionary
   War 12.00
128 I:Mark Olsen(Jimmy's Father) 12.00
129 MA,A:Mark Olsen 12.00
130 MA,A:Robin,Brainiac 12.00
131 . . . . 30.00
132 MA,When Olsen Sold out
   Superman 12.00
133 JK,B:New Newsboy Legion,
   I:Morgan Edge 45.00
134 JK,I:Darkseid 60.00
135 JK,I:New Guardian 22.00
136 JK,O:New Guardian,
   I:Dubbilex 15.00
137 JK,I:Four Armed Terror 15.00
138 JK,V:Four Armed Terror . . . 15.00
139 JK,A:Don Rickles,I:Ugly
   Mannheim 15.00
140 . . . . 14.00
141 JK,A:Don Rickles,Lightray
   B:Newsboy Legion rep 14.00
142 JK,I:Count Dragorian 14.00
143 JK,V:Count Dragorian 14.00
144 JK,A Big Thing in a Deep
   Scottish Lake 14.00
145 JK,Brigadoon 14.00
146 JK,Homo Disastrous 14.00
147 JK,Superman on New
   Genesis,A:High Father,
   I:Victor Volcanium 14.00
148 JK,V:Victor Volcanium,
   E:Newsboy Legion rep 14.00
149 BO(i),The Unseen Enemy,
   B:Plastic Man rep 10.00
150 BO(i) A Bad Act to Follow . . 10.00
151 BO(i),A:Green Lantern 10.00
152 MSy,BO,I:Real Morgan Edge 10.00
153 MSy,Murder in Metropolis . . 10.00
154 KS,The Girl Who Was Made
   of Money 10.00
155 KS,Downfall of Judas Olsen 10.00
156 KS,Last Jump for
   a Skyjacker 10.00
157 KS,Jimmy as Marco Polo . . 10.00
158 KS,A:Lena Lawrence
   (Lucy Lane) 10.00
159 KS,Jimmy as Spartacus . . . 10.00
160 KS,A:Lena Lawrence
   (Lucy Lane) 10.00
161 KS,V:Lucy Lane 10.00
162 KS,A:Lex Luthor 10.00
163 KS,Jimmy as Marco Polo . . 10.00

SUPERMAN:
SAVE THE PLANET
Aug., 1998

1 LSi,SEa,DRo,JP,KN, last
   front page 3.00
1 collector's edition 4.00

SUPERMAN, THE SECRET YEARS
Feb., 1985
1 CS,KS,FM(c) 1.50
2 CS,KS,FM(c) 1.25
3 CS,KS,FM(c) 1.25
4 CS,KS,FM(c), May 1985 . . . . . 1.25

SUPERMAN VS. AMAZING SPIDER-MAN
April, 1976
1 RA/DG,oversized 75.00
1a 2nd printing, signed 125.00

SUPERMAN/ WONDER WOMAN: WHOM GODS DESTROY
Elseworlds Oct. 1996
Mini-series
1 CCl(s),DAb, Lois becomes the
   immortal Wonder Woman . . . 4.95
2 CCl(s),DAb, search for Lana
   Lang 4.95
3 . . . . 4.95
4 CCl(s),DAb, romance of the
   century, concl. 4.95

SUPER POWERS
1984
[Kenner Action Figures]
1 A:Batman & Joker 3.50
2 A:Batman & Joker 3.50
3 A:Batman & Joker 3.50
4 A:Batman & Joker 3.50
5 JK(c),JK,A:Batman & Joker . . . 3.50
[2nd Series] 1985–86
1 JK,'Seeds of Doom' 2.00
2 JK,'When Past & Present Meet' 2.00
3 JK,'Time Upon Time' 2.00
4 JK,'There's No Place Like Rome 2.00
5 JK,'Once Upon a Tomorrow' . . 2.00
6 JK,'Darkkseid o/t Moon' 2.00
[3rd Series] 1986
1 Cl,'Threshold' 1.50
2 Cl,'Escape' 1.50

Super Powers #2 © DC Comics, Inc.

3 Cl,'Machinations' 1.50
4 Cl,'A World Divided' 1.50

SUPER-TEAM FAMILY
1975–78
1 rep. 10.00
2 Creeper/Wildcat 6.00
3 RE/WW,Flash & Hawkman . . . 6.00
4 . . . . 5.00
5 . . . . 5.00
6 . . . . 5.00
7 . . . . 5.00
8 JSh,Challengers 7.00
9 JSh,Challengers 7.00
10 JSh,Challengers 7.00
11 Supergirl,Flash,Atom 7.00
12 Green Lantern,Hawkman 7.00
13 Aquaman, Capt. Comet 7.00
14 Wonder Woman,Atom 7.00
15 Flash & New Gods 9.00

SWAMP THING
[1st Regular Series]
Oct.–Nov., 1972
1 B:LWn(s),BWr,O:Swamp Thing 80.00
2 BWr,I:Arcane 40.00
3 BWr,I:Patchwork Man 30.00
4 BWr 25.00
5 BWr 25.00
6 BWr 25.00
7 BWr,A:Batman 30.00
8 BWr,Lurker in Tunnel 13 . . . . 20.00
9 BWr 20.00
10 E:BWr,A;Arcane 20.00
11 thru 22 NR . . . . @6.00
23 NR,reverts to Dr.Holland . . . 6.00
24 NR 6.00
TPB rep.#1-#10,House of Secrets
#92, Dark Genesis Saga 19.95

SWAMP THING
1986–96
Previously:
SAGA OF THE SWAMP THING
46 B:AMo(s) cont'd,SBi,JTo,Crisis,
   A:John Constantine,Phantom
   Stranger 4.00
47 SBi,Parliment of Trees,Full
   origin,A:Constantine 3.00
48 SBi,JTo,V:Brujeria,
   A:Constantine. 3.00
49 SBi,AA,A:Constantine,Demon,Ph.
   Stranger,Spectre,Deadman . . 3.00
50 SBi,RV,JTo,concl.American
   Gothic,D:Zatara&Sargon,
   Double Size 6.00
51 RV,AA,L:Constantine 3.00
52 RV,AA,Arkham Asylum,A:Flor.
   Man,Lex Luthor,C:Joker,
   2-Face,Batman 4.00
53 JTo,V:Batman,Swamp Thing
   Banished to Space 4.00
54 JTo script,RV,AA,C:Batman . . 3.00
55 RV,AA,JTo,A:Batman,. 3.00
56 RV,AA,My Blue Heaven 3.00
57 RV,AA,A:Adam Strange 3.00
58 RV,AA,A:Adam Strange,GC,
   Spectre preview 3.00
59 JTo,RV,AA,D:Patchwork Man . 3.00
Direct Sales Only
60 JTo,Loving the Alien 3.00
61 RV,AA,All Flesh is Grass
   G.L.Corps X-over 3.00
62 RV(&script),AA,Wavelength,

Swamp Thing #74 © DC Comics, Inc.

A:Metron,Darkseid 3.00
63 RV,AA,Loose Ends(reprise) . . 3.00
64 E:AMo(s),SBi,TY,RV,AA,
   Return of the Good Gumbo . . . 3.00
65 RV,JTo,A:Constantine 3.50
66 RV,Elemental Energy 2.50
67 RV,V:Solomon Grundy,
   Hellblazer preview 4.00
68 RV,O:Swamp Thing 2.50
69 RV,O:Swamp Thing 2.50
70 RV,AA,Quest for SwampThing 2.50
71 RV,AA,Fear of Flying 2.50
72 RV,AA,Creation 2.50
73 RV,AA,A:John Constantine . . 3.00
74 RV,AA,Abbys Secret 2.50
75 RV,AA,Plant Elementals 2.50
76 RV,AA,A:John Constantine . . 3.00
77 TMd,AA,A:John Constantine . . 3.00
78 TMd,AA,Phantom Pregnancy . 2.50
79 RV,AA,A:Superman,Luthor . . 2.50
80 RV,AA,V:Aliends 2.50
81 RV,AA,Invasion x-over 2.50
82 RV,AA,A:Sgt.Rock & Easy Co. 2.50
83 RV,AA,A:Enemy Ace 2.50
84 RV,AA,A:Sandman 10.00
85 RV,TY,Time Travel contd. . . . 2.50
86 RV,TY,A:Tomahawk 2.50
87 RV,TY,A:Demon,A:Demon . . . 2.50
88 RV,TY,A:Demon,Golden
   Gladiator 2.50
89 MM,AA,The Dinosaur Age . . . 2.50
90 BP,AA,Birth of Abbys Child
   (Tefe) 2.75
91 PB,AA,Abbys Child (New
   Elemental) 2.50
92 PB,AA,Ghosts of the Bayou . . 2.50
93 PB,AA,New Power 2.50
94 PB,AA,Ax-Murderer 2.50
95 PB,AA,Toxic Waste Dumpers . 2.50
96 PB,AA,Tefes Powers 2.50
97 PB,AA,Tefe,V:Nergal,
   A:Arcane 2.50
98 PB,AA,Tefe,in Hell 2.50
99 PB,AA,Tefe,A:Mantago,
   John Constantine 3.00
100 PB,AA,V:Angels of Eden,
   (48 pages) 3.50
101 AA,A:Tefe 2.50

Swamp Thing #76 © DC Comics, Inc.

102 V:Mantagos Zombies,inc. prev.
   of Worlds Without End 2.50
103 Green vs. Grey 2.50
104 Quest for Elementals,pt.1 . . . 2.50
105 Quest for Elementals,pt.2 . . . 2.50
106 Quest for Elementals,pt.3 . . . 2.50
107 Quest for Elementals,pt.4 . . . 2.50
108 Quest for Elementals,pt.5 . . . 2.50
109 Quest for Elementals,pt.6 . . . 2.50
110 TMd,A:Father Tocsin 2.50
111 V:Ghostly Zydeco Musician . . 2.50
112 TMd,B:Swamp Thing
   for Governor 2.50
113 E:Swamp Thing for Governor   2.50
114 TMd,Hellblazer 2.75
115 TMd,A:Hellblazer,V:Dark
   Conrad 2.75
116 From Body of Swamp Thing . 2.25
117 JD,The Lord of Misrule,
   Mardi Gras 2.25
118 A Childs Garden,A:Matthew
   the Raven 2.25
119 A:Les Perdu 2.25
120 F:Lady Jane 2.25
121 V:Sunderland Corporation . . 2.25
122 I:The Needleman 2.25
123 V:The Needleman 2.25
124 In Central America 2.25
125 V:Anton Arcane,20th Anniv. . 3.75
126 Mescalito 2.25
127 Project Proteus #1 . . . . 2.25
128 Project proteus #2 . . . . 2.25
Vertigo
129 CV(c),B:NyC(s),SEa,KDM(i),
   Sw.Thing's Deterioration 2.25
130 CV(c),SEa,KDM(i),A:John
   Constantine,V:Doctor Polygon . 2.25
131 CV(c),SEa,KDM(i),I:Swamp
   Thing's,Doppleganger,
   F:The Folk 3.00
132 CV(c),SEa,KDM(i),
   V:Doppleganger 3.00
133 CV(c),SEa,KDM(i),R:General
   Sunderland,V:Thunder Petal . . 3.00
134 CV(c),SEa,KDM(i),Abby Leaves,
   C:John Constantine 3.00
135 CV(c),SEa,KDM(i),A:J.Constantine,
   Swamp Thing Lady Jane meld   3.00

136 CV(c),RsB,KDM(i),A:Lady Jane,
   Dr.Polygon,John Constantine . 3.00
137 CV(c),E:NyC(s),RsB,KDM(i),
   IR:Sunderland is Anton Arcane,
   A:J.Constantine 3.00
138 CV(c),DiF(s),RGu,KDM,B:Mind
   Fields 3.00
139 CV(c),DiF(s),RGu,KDM,A:Black
   Orchid,In Swamp Thing's mind,
   cont'd fr.Black Orchid #5 . . . . 3.00
140 B:Bad Gumbo 3.00
140a Platinum Ed. 10.00
141 A:Abigail Arcane 3.00
142 Bad Gumbo#3 . . . . 3.00
143 E:Bad Gumbo 3.00
144 In New York City 3.00
145 In Amsterdam 3.00
146 V:Nelson Strong 3.00
147 Hunter 3.00
148 Sargon 3.00
149 Sargon 3.00
150 V:Sargon 3.50
151 . . . . 2.25
152 River Run,pt.1 . . . . 2.25
153 River Run 2.25
154 River Run 2.25
155 River Run 2.25
156 PJ,River Run 2.25
157 . . . . 2.25
158 . . . . 2.25
159 Swamp Dog 2.25
160 PhH,KDM,Atmospheres 2.25
161 Atmospheres 2.25
162 Atmospheres 2.25
163 Atmospheres 2.25
164 . . . . 2.25
165 CS,KDM,F:Chester Williams . 2.25
166 PhH,KDM,Trial by Fire,pt.1 . 2.25
167 PhH,KDM,Trial by Fire,pt.2 . 2.25
168 MMr(s),PhH,KDM,Trial by Fire,
   pt.3 . . . . 2.25
169 MMr(s),PhH,KDM,Trial by Fire,
   pt.4 . . . . 2.25
170 MMr(s),PhH,KDM,Trial by Fire,
   pt.5 . . . . 2.25
171 MMr(s),PhH,KDM,"Trial by Fire,"
   pt.6 last issue 2.25
Ann.#4 PB/AA,A:Batman 2.75
Ann.#5 A:BrotherPower Geek . . . 3.25
Ann.#6 Houma 3.50
Ann.#7 CV(c),NyC(s),MBu(i),Childrens
   Crusade,F:Tefe,A:Maxine,BU:
   Beautyand the Beast 4.25

SWORD OF SORCERY
Feb.–March, 1973
1 MK(c),HC 25.00
2 BWv,NA,Hc 30.00
3 BWv,HC,MK,WS 25.00
4 HC,WS 10.00
5 Nov.–Dec., 1973 . . . . 10.50

SWORD OF THE ATOM
Sept., 1983
1 GK 1.50
2 thru 4 GK . . . . @1.25
Spec.#1 GK 1.25
Spec.#2 GK 1.25
Spec.#3 PB 1.50

SYSTEM, THE
DC/Vertigo 1996
TPB by Peter Kuper 12.95

TAILGUNNER JO
Sept., 1988
1 . . . . 1.25
2 . . . . 1.25
3 . . . . 1.25
4 . . . . 1.25
5 . . . . 1.25
6 . . . . 1.25

TAKION
1996
1 PuK,AaL,Josh Sanders
   becomes Takion 1.75
2 thru 4 . . . . @1.75
5 PuK,AaL,Adventures of Source
   Elemental" cont. 1.75
6 PuK,AaL,Final Night tie-in 1.75
7 PuK,AaL,Arzaz trains Takion,
   final issue 1.75

TALES OF THE GREEN LANTERN CORPS
May, 1981
1 JSon,FMc,O:Green Lantern . . . 1.50
2 JSon,FMc 1.25
3 JSon,FMc 1.25

Tales of the Legion of Super
Heroes #352 © DC Comics, Inc.

TALES OF THE LEGION OF SUPER HEROES
Aug., 1984
(Previously:
   Legion of Super Heroes)
314 KG,V:Ontiir 1.50
315 KG(i),V:Dark Circle 1.50
316 KG(i),O:White Witch 1.50
317 KG(i),V:Dream Demon 1.50
318 KG(i),V:Persuader 1.50
319 KG(i),V:Persuader,
   A:Superboy 1.50
320 DJu,V:Magpie 1.50
321 DJu,Exile,V:Kol 1.50
322 DJu,Exile,V:Kol 1.50
323 DJu,Exile,V:Kol 1.50
324 DJu,EC,V:Dev-Em 1.50

325 DJu,V:Dark Circle 1.50
326 reprint of Baxter #1 . . . . 1.00
327 reprint of Baxter #2 . . . . 1.00
328 reprint of Baxter #3 . . . . 1.00
329 reprint of Baxter #4 . . . . 1.00
330 reprint of Baxter #5 . . . . 1.00
331 reprint of Baxter #6 . . . . 1.00
332 reprint of Baxter #7 . . . . 1.00
333 reprint of Baxter #8 . . . . 1.00
334 reprint of Baxter #9 . . . . 1.00
335 reprint of Baxter #10 . . . . 1.00
336 reprint of Baxter #11 . . . . 1.00
337 reprint of Baxter #12 . . . . 1.00
338 reprint of Baxter #13 . . . . 1.00
339 reprint of Baxter #14 . . . . 1.00
340 reprint of Baxter #15 . . . . 1.00
341 reprint of Baxter #16 . . . . 1.00
342 reprint of Baxter #17 . . . . 1.00
343 reprint of Baxter #19 . . . . 1.00
344 reprint of Baxter #19 . . . . 1.00
345 reprint of Baxter #20 . . . . 1.00
346 reprint of Baxter #21 . . . . 1.00
347 reprint of Baxter #22 . . . . 1.00
348 reprint of Baxter #23 . . . . 1.00
349 reprint of Baxter #24 . . . . 1.00
350 reprint of Baxter #25 . . . . 1.00
351 reprint of Baxter #26 . . . . 1.00
352 reprint of Baxter #27 . . . . 1.00
353 reprint of Baxter #28 . . . . 1.00
354 reprint of Baxter #29 . . . . 1.00
Ann.#4 rep. Baxter Ann.#1 . . . . . . 1.00
Ann.#5 rep. Baxter Ann.#2 . . . . . . 1.00

TALES OF THE
NEW TEEN TITANS
June, 1982

1 GP, O:Cyborg 2.00
2 GP, O:Raven 2.00
3 GD, O:Changling 2.00
4 GP/EC,O:Starfire 2.00

TALES OF THE
TEEN TITANS
(see NEW TEEN TITANS)

TALES OF THE
UNEXPECTED
1956–68

1 The Out-Of-The-World Club 1,000.00
2 . . . . 500.00
3 . . . . 375.00
4 Seven Steps to the Unknown 375.00
5 . . . . 375.00
6 'The Girl in the Bottle' 275.00
7 NC(c),Pen That Never Lied . 275.00
8 . . . . 275.00
9 LSt(c),The Amazing Cube . . 275.00
10 MMe(c),The Strangest Show
On Earth 275.00
11 LSt(c),Who Am I? 175.00
12 JK,Four Threads of Doom . . 200.00
13 JK(c),Weapons of Destiny . . 200.00
14 SMo(c),The Forbidden Game 175.00
15 JK,MMe,Three Wishes
to Doom 200.00
16 JK,The Magic Hammer 200.00
17 JK,Who Is Mr. Ashtar? 200.00
18 JK(c),MMe,A Man Without A
World 200.00
19 NC,Man From Two Worlds . 150.00
20 NC(c),The Earth Gladiator . 150.00
21 JK,The Living Phantoms . . . 200.00
22 JK(c),The Man From Robot

Island 200.00
23 JK,The Invitation From Mars! 200.00
24 LC,The Secret Of Planetoid
Zero! 175.00
25 The Sorcerer's Asteroid! . . . 175.00
26 MMe,The Frozem City 175.00
27 MMe,The Prison In Space . 175.00
28 The Melting Planet 175.00
29 The Phantom Raider 175.00
30 The Jinxed Planet 175.00
31 RH,Keep Off Our Planet . . . 125.00
32 Great Space Cruise Mystery 125.00
33 The Man Of 1,000 Planets . 125.00
34 Ambush In Outer Space . . . 125.00
35 MMe,I was a Space Refugee 125.00
36 The Curse Of The
Galactic Goodess 125.00
37 The Secret Prisoners
Of Planet 13 . . . . 125.00
38 The Stunt Man Of Space . . 125.00
39 The Creatures From The
Space Globe 125.00
40 B:Space Ranger,The Last
Days Of Planet Mars! 900.00
41 SMo(c),The Destroyers From
The Stars! 300.00
42 The Secret Of The
Martian Helmet 300.00
43 The Riddle Of The Burning
Treasures,I:Space Ranger . 700.00
44 DD&SMo(c),The Menace Of
The Indian Aliens 225.00
45 DD&SMo(c),The Sheriff
From Jupiter 225.00
46 DD&SMo(c),The
Duplicate Doom! 225.00
47 DD(c),The Man Who Stole
The Solar System 150.00
48 Bring 'Em Back Alive-
From Space 150.00
49 RH,The Fantastic Lunar-Land 150.00
50 MA,King Barney The Ape . . 150.00
51 Planet Earth For Sale 125.00
52 Prisoner On Pluto 125.00
53 InterplanetaryTroubleShooter 125.00
54 The Ugly Sleeper Of Klanth,
Dinosaur 150.00
55 The Interplanetary
Creature Trainer 125.00
56 B:Spaceman At Work,Invaders
From Earth 125.00
57 The Jungle Beasts Of Jupiter 125.00
58 The Boss Of The
Saturnian Legion 125.00
59 The Man Who Won A World 125.00
60 School For Space Sleuths . 125.00
61 The Mystery Of The
Mythical Monsters 100.00
62 The Menace Of The Red
Snow Crystals 100.00
63 Death To Planet Earth 100.00
64 Boy Usurper Of Planet Zonn 100.00
65 The Creature That
Couldn't Exist 100.00
66 MMe,Trap Of The Space
Convict 100.00
67 The Giant That
Devoured A Village 100.00
68 Braggart From Planet Brax . 75.00
69 Doom On Holiday Asteroid . . 75.00
70 The Hermit Of Planetoid X . 75.00
71 Manhunt In Galaxy G-2! . . . 75.00
72 The Creature Of 1,000 Dooms 75.00
73 The Convict Defenders
Of Space! 75.00

74 Prison Camp On Asteroid X-3! 75.00
75 The Hobo Jungle Of Space . . 75.00
76 The Warrior Of Two Worlds! . 75.00
77 Dateline-Outer Space 75.00
78 The Siren Of Space 75.00
79 Big Show On Planet Earth! . . 75.00
80 The Creature Tamer! 75.00
81 His Alien Master! 75.00
82 Give Us Back Our Earth!,
E:Space Ranger 75.00
83 DD&SMo(c),The Anti-Hex
Merchant! 45.00
84 DD&SMo(c),The Menace Of
The 50-Fathom Men 45.00
85 JkS(c),The Man Who Stole My
Powers,B:Green Glob 45.00
86 DD&SMo(c),They'll Never
Take Me Alive! 40.00
87 JkS(c),The Manhunt Through
Two Worlds 40.00
88 DD&SMo(c),GK,The Fear
Master 40.00
89 DD,SMo(c),Nightmare on Mars 40.00
90 JkS(c),The Hero Of 5,000 BC 40.00
91 JkS(c),The Prophetic Mirages,
I:Automan 40.00
92 The Man Who Dared To Die! 40.00
93 JkS(c),Prisoners Of Hate
Island 40.00
94 The Monster Mayor - USA . . 40.00
95 The Secret Of Chameleo-Man 40.00
96 Wanted For Murder...1966...
6966 . . . . 40.00
97 One Month To Die 40.00
98 Half-Man/Half Machine 40.00
99 JkS(c),Nuclear Super-Hero! . 40.00
100 Judy Blonde, Secret Agent! . 40.00
101 The Man In The Liquid Mask! 35.00
102 Bang!Bang! You're Dead . . 35.00
103 JA,ABC To Disaster 35.00
104 NA(c),Master Of The
Voodoo Machine 35.00

Becomes:

UNEXPECTED, THE
1968–82

105 The Night I Watched
Myself Die 40.00

Tales of the Unexpected #6
© DC Comics, Inc.

---

106 B:Johnny Peril,The Doorway
Into Time 25.00
107 MD,JkS(c),The Whip Of Fear! 28.00
108 JkS(c),Journey To
A Nightmare 25.00
109 JkS(c),Baptism By Starfire! . 25.00
110 NA(c),Death Town, U.S.A.! . 30.00
111 NC(c),Mission Into Eternity . 25.00
112 NA(c),The Brain Robbers! . . 30.00
113 NA(c),The Shriek Of
Vengeance 30.00
114 NA(c),My Self-My Enemy! . . 30.00
115 BWr,NA(c),Diary Of
A Madman 30.00
116 NC(c),Express Train
To Nowhere! 15.00
117 NC(c),Midnight Summons
The Executioner! 15.00
118 NA(c),A:Judge Gallows,Play
A Tune For Treachery 18.00
119 BWr,NC(c),Mirror,Mirror
On The Wall 15.00
120 NC(c),Rambeau's Revenge . 15.00
121 BWr,NA(c),Daddy's
Gone-A-Hunting 25.00
122 WW,DG(c),The Phantom
Of The Woodstock Festival . . 15.00
123 NC(c),Death Watch! 15.00
124 NA(c),These Walls Shall
Be Your Grave 18.00
125 NC(c),Screech Of Guilt! . . . 15.00
126 ATh,NC(c),You Are Cordially
Invited To Die! 15.00
127 GT,JK,ATh,NC(c),Follow The
Piper To Your Grave 15.00
128 DW,BWr,NC(c),Where Only
The Dead Are Free! 25.00
129 NC(c),Farewell To A
Fading Love 15.00
130 NC(c),One False Step 15.00
131 NC(c),Run For Your Death! . 15.00
132 MD,GT,NC(c),The Edge Of
Madness 15.00
133 WW,JkS(c),A:Judge Gallows,
Agnes Doesn't Haunt Here
Anymore! 18.00
134 GT,NC(c),The Restless Dead 15.00
135 NC(c),Death, Come
Walk With Me! 10.00
136 SMo,GT,NC(c),An Incident
of Violence 12.00
137 WW,NC(c),Dark Vengeance! 15.00
138 NC(c),Strange Secret of
the Huan Shan Idol 15.00
139 GT,NC(c),The 2 Brains of
Beast Bracken! 12.00
140 JkS(c),The Anatomy of Hate 10.00
141 NC(c),Just What Did Eric
See? 10.00
142 NC(c),Let The Dead Sleep! . 10.00
143 NC(c),Fear is a Nameless
Voice 10.00
144 NC(c),The Dark Pit of
Dr. Hanley 10.00
145 NC(c),Grave of Glass 10.00
146 NC(c),The Monstrosity! 10.00
147 NC(c),The Daughter of
Dr. Jekyll 10.00
148 NC(c),Baby Wants Me Dead! 10.00
149 NC(c),To Wake the Dead . . 10.00
150 NC(c),No One Escapes From
Gallows Island 10.00
151 NC(c),Sorry, I'm Not Ready
To Die! 10.00
152 GT,NC(c),Death Wears Many

Faces 10.00
153 NC(c),Who's That Sleeping
In My Grave? 10.00
154 NC(c),Murder By Madness . 10.00
155 NC(c),Non-Stop Journey
Into Fear 10.00
156 NC(c),A Lunatic Is Loose
Among Us! 10.00
157 NC(c),The House of
the Executioner 10.00
158 NC(c),Reserved for Madmen
Only 10.00
159 NC(c),A Cry in the Night . . . 10.00
160 NC(c),Death of an Exorcist . 10.00
161 BWr,NC(c),Has Anyone
Seen My Killer 20.00
162 JK,NC(c),I'll Bug You
To Your Grave 12.00
163 DD,LD(c),Room For Dying . . 5.00
164 House of the Sinister Sands . 5.00
165 LD(c),Slayride in July 5.00
166 LD(c),The Evil Eyes of Night . 5.00
167 LD(c),Scared Stiff 5.00
168 LD(c),Freak Accident 5.00
169 LD(c),What Can Be Worse
Than Dying? 5.00
170 LD(c),Flee To Your Grave . . 5.00
171 LD(c),I.O.U. One Corpse . . . 5.00
172 LD(c),Strangler in Paradise . 5.00
173 LD(c),What Scared Sally? . . 5.00
174 LD(c),Gauntlet of Fear 5.00
175 LD(c),The Haunted Mountain 5.00
176 JkS(c),Having A
Wonderful Crime 5.00
177 ECh(c),Reward for the Wicked 5.00
178 LD(c),Fit To Kill! 5.00
179 LD(c),My Son, The Mortician . 5.00
180 GT,LD(c),The Loathsome
Lodger of Nightmare Inn 7.00
181 LD(c),Hum of the Haunted . . 5.00
182 LD(c),Sorry, This Coffin
is Occupied 5.00
183 LD(c),The Dead Don't
Always Die 5.00
184 LD(c),Wheel of Misfortune! . . 5.00
185 LD(c),Monsters from a
Thousand Fathoms 5.00
186 LD(c),To Catch a Corpse . . . 5.00
187 LD(c),Mangled in Madness . 5.00
188 LD(c),Verdict From The Grave 5.00
189 SD,LD(c),Escape From the
Grave 6.00
190 LD(c),The Jigsaw Corpse . . 4.00
191 MR,JO(c),Night of the Voodoo
Curse 6.00
192 LD(c),A Killer Cold & Clammy 4.00
193 DW,LD(c),Don't Monkey the
Murder 4.00
194 LD(c),Have I Got a Ghoul
For You 4.00
195 JCr,LD(c),Whose Face is at
My Window 6.00
196 LD(c),The Fear of Number 13 4.00
197 LD(c),Last Laugh of a Corpse 4.00
198 JSn(c),Rage of the
Phantom Brain 4.00
199 LD(c),Dracula's Daughter . . . 4.00
200 GT,RA&DG(c),A:Johnny Peril,
House on the Edge of Eternity 6.00
201 Do Unto Others 4.00
202 JO,LD(c),Death Trap 4.00
203 MK(c),Hang Down Your
Head, Joe Mundy 4.00
204 DN,JKu(c),Twinkle, Twinkle
Little Star 4.00

205 JkS,A:Johnny Peril,The Second
Possession of Angela Lake . . . 4.00
206 JkS,A:Johnny Peril,The
Ultimate Assassin 4.00
207 JkS,A:Johnny Peril,Secret of
the Second Star 4.00
208 JkS,A:Johnny Peril,Factory
of Fear 4.00
209 JkS,Game for the Ghastly . . . 4.00
210 Vampire of the Apes,Time
Warp 4.00
211 A:Johnny Peril,The Temple
of the 7 Stars 4.00
212 JkS,MK(c),A:Johnny Peril,The
Adventure of the Angel's Smile 4.00
213 A:Johnny Peril,The Woman
Who Died Forever 4.00
214 JKu(c),Slaughterhouse Arena 4.00
215 JKu(c),Is Someone
Stalking Sandra 4.00
216 GP,JKu(c),Samurai Nightmare 4.00
217 ShM,DSp,EC(c),Dear Senator 4.00
218 KG,ECh&DG(c),I'll Remember
You Yesterday 4.00
219 JKu(c),A Wild Tale 4.00
220 ShM,JKu(c),The Strange
Guide 4.00
221 SD,ShM,JKu(c),Em the
Energy Monster 4.00
222 KG,SD(c) 4.00

TALES OF THE WILDERNESS
1 GK,special 2.00

TALOS OF THE WILDERNESS SEA
Aug. 1987
1-shot GK 2.00

TANGENT COMICS
(All Oct. 1997)
The Atom #1 DJu,PR,V:Fatal Five 3.00
The Flash #1, TDz,GFr,CaS 3.00
Doom Patrol #1 DJu,SCh, ... 3.00
Green Lantern #1 JeR,JWi,MGy . 3.00
The Joker #1 KK,MHy, ... 3.00
Metal Men #1 MRz,MkK 3.00
Nightwing #1 JOs,JD 3.00
Sea Devils #1 KBk,VGi,TP 3.00
The Secret Six #1 CDi,TG, ... 3.00

TANGENT '98
(All June 1998)
The Batman #1 DJu,KJ 2.00
JLA #1 DJu,DBk,V:UltraHumanites 2.00
Joker's Wild #1 KK 2.00
Nightwing: Night Force #1 JOs . . 2.00
Powergirl #1 RMz 2.00
The Superman #1 Harvey Dent . . 2.00
Tales of the Green Lantern #1 . . . 2.00
The Trials of the Flash #1,
V:Plastic Man 2.00
Wonder Woman #1 PDa, ... 2.00

TANK GIRL
1995
1 Movie Adaptation 5.95

DC COMICS

DC COMICS

TANK GIRL: APOCALYPSE
1995–96
1 AlG,BBo(c) 2.25
2 AlG,BBo(c)Tank Girl Pregnant . 2.25
3 AlG,BBo(c) 2.25
4 AlG, finale 2.25

TANK GIRL: THE ODYSSEY
Vertigo 1995
1 New Limited Series 2.25
2 BBo(c),Land of Milk & Honey . 2.25
3 I:The Sirens 2.25

Tarzan #213 © DC Comics, Inc.

TARZAN
April, 1972
(Previously published by Gold Key)
207 JKu,O:Tarzan,pt.1 . . . . 5.00
208 thru 210 JKu,O:Tarzan,pt.2–4 3.00
211 thru 258 Feb., 1977 . . . . . @2.00

TARZAN FAMILY
Nov.–Dec., 1975
(Previously: Korak, Son of Tarzan)
60 B:Korak 1.25
61 thru 66 Nov.–Dec.,1976 . . . @1.25

TEAM TITANS
1992–94
1 KM,Total Chaos#3,A:New Titans,
  Deathstroke,V:Lord Chaos,
  BU:KGa,Killowat 2.50
1a BU:AV(i),Mirage 2.50
1b BU:MN,GP,Nightrider 2.50
1c BU:AH,Redwing 2.50
1d BU:GP(i),Terra 2.50
2 KM,Total Chaos#6,A:New
  Titans, V:Chaos,C:Battalion . . 2.00
3 KM,Total Chaos#9,V:Lord
  Chaos, A:New Titans 2.00
4 KM,Titans Sell-Out#4,
  J:Battalion, Troia 2.00
5 KM,A:Battalion 2.00
6 ANi,A:Battalion 2.00

7 PJ,I:Nightwing of 2001 . . . . . . 2.00
8 PJ,A:Raven 2.00
9 PJ,V:Bloodwing 2.00
10 PJ,V:Vampiric Creatures 2.00
11 PJ,F:Battalion 2.00
12 PJ,F:Battalion 2.00
13 PJ,New Direction 2.00
14 PJ,V:Clock King,Chronos,Calander
  Man,Time Commander 2.00
15 PJ 2.00
16 PJ,F:Nightrider 2.00
17 PJ,A:Deathwing 2.00
18 IR:Leader 2.00
19 V:Leader 2.00
20 PJ,V:Lazarium 2.00
21 PJ,V:US Government 2.00
22 PJ,A:Chimera 2.25
23 PJ,I:Warhawk(Redwing) 2.25
24 PJ,Zero Hour,R.Kole,last issue 2.25
Ann.#1 I:Chimera 3.50
Ann.#2 PJ,Elseworlds Story 3.75

TEEN BEAT
Nov.–Dec., 1967
1 Monkees photo 17.00
Becomes:
TEEN BEAM
2 Monkees 14.00

TEEN TITANS
[1st Series]
Jan., 1966
1 NC,Titans join Peace Corps . 200.00
2 NC,I:Garn Akaru 100.00
3 NC,I:Ding Dong Daddy . . 60.00
4 NC,A:Speedy 60.00
5 NC,I:Ant 60.00
6 NC,A:Beast Boy 45.00
7 NC,I:Mad Mod 35.00
8 IN/JAb,I:Titans Copter 35.00
9 NC,A:Teen Titan Sweatshirts . 35.00
10 NC,I:Bat-Bike 35.00
11 IN/NC A:Speedy 30.00
12 NC,in Spaceville 35.00
13 NC,Christmas story 25.00
14 NC,I:Gargoyle 25.00
15 NC,I:Capt. Rumble 25.00
16 NC,I:Dimension X 25.00
17 NC,A:Mad Mod 25.00
18 NC,1:Starfire (Russian) 30.00
19 GK,WW,J:Speedy 21.00
20 NA,NC J:Joshua 23.00
21 NA,NC,A:Hawk,Dove 23.00
22 NA,NC,O:Wondergirl 23.00
23 GK,NC,N:Wondergirl 12.00
24 GK,NC 12.00
25 NC,I:Lilith,A:J.L.A 12.00
26 NC,I:Mal 14.00
27 NC 12.00
28 NC,A:Ocean Master 12.00
29 NC,A:Ocean Master 12.00
30 NC,A:Aquagirl 12.00
31 NC,GT,A:Hawk,Dove 12.00
32 NC,I:Gnarrk 9.00
33 GT,NS,A:Gnarrk 9.00
34 GT,NC 9.00
35 GT,NC,O:Mal 9.00
36 GT,NC,JAp,V:Hunchback . . . 9.00
37 GT,NC 9.00
38 GT,NC 9.00
39 GT,NC,Rep.Hawk & Dove . . . 9.00
40 NC,A:Aqualad 9.00
41 NC,DC,Lilith Mystery 9.00
42 NC 9.00

Teen Titans (1st Series) #28
© DC Comics, Inc.

43 NC,Inherit the Howling Night . . 9.00
44 C:Flash 9.00
45 IN,V:Fiddler 9.00
46 IN,A:Fiddler 12.00
47 C:Two-Face 6.00
48 I:Bumblebee,Harlequin,
  A:Two-Face 11.00
49 R:Mal As Guardian 6.00
50 DH,I:Teen Titans West 10.00
51 DH,A:Teen Titans West 6.00
52 DH,A:Teen Titans West 6.00
53 O:Teen Titans, A:JLA 8.00

TEEN TITANS, THE
Aug. 1996
1 DJu(s),GP,"Titan's Children,"
  pt.1 (of 3) 4.00
2 DJu(s),GP,"Titan's Children,"
  pt.2,V:Prysm 3.00
3 DJu(s),GP,"Titan's Children,"
  pt.3 . . . . 2.50
4 DJu(s),GP,"Coming Out," pt.1,
  A:Robin 2.00
5 DJu(s),GP,"Coming Out," pt.2 . 2.00
6 DJu(s),DJu,GP,F:Risk 2.00
7 DJu(s),DJu,GP,The Atom quits
  team 2.00
8 DJu(s),DJu,GP,J:Atom,V:Dark
  Nemesis 2.00
9 DJu(s),DJu,GP,"Lost World of
  Skartaris," pt.1 . . . . 2.00
10 DJu(s),DJu,GP,"Lost World of
  Skartaris," pt.2 . . . . 2.00
11 DJu(s),DJu,GP,"Lost World of
  Skartaris" concl.,A:Warlord, . 2.00
12 DJu(s),DJu,GP,Original Titans,
  pt.1 (of 4) 48pg 2.95
13 DJu,GP,Original Titans, pt.2
  Genesis tie-in 2.00
14 DJu,GP,Original Titans, pt.3 . . 2.00
15 DJu,GP,Original Titans, pt.4 . . 2.00
16 DJu,GP,aftermath 2.00
17 DJu,PJ,team reunites 2.00
18 DJu,PR 2.00
19 DJu,PJ,Millennium Giants,
  A:Superman Red 2.00

20 DJu, night with the Titans	2.00
21 DJu,Titans Hunt,pt.1	2.00
22 DJu,Titans Hunt,pt.2	2.00
23 DJu,Titans Hunt,pt.3	2.00
24 DJu,Titans Hunt,pt.4, final issue	2.00
Ann.#1 Pulp Heroes (High-Adventure)	3.95

TEEN TITANS SPOTLIGHT
Aug., 1986

1 DCw,DG,Starfire "Apartheid"	1.50
2 DCw,DG,Starfire Apartheid#2	1.00
3 RA,Jericho	1.00
4 RA,Jericho	1.00
5 RA,Jericho	1.00
6 RA,Jericho	1.00
7 JG,Hawk	1.50
8 JG,Hawk	1.00
9 Changeling	1.00
10 EL,Aqualad And Mento	1.50
11 JO,Brotherhood of Evil	1.00
12 EC,Wondergirl	1.00
13 Cyborg	1.00
14 1stNightwing/Batman Team-up	2.50
15 EL,Omega Men	1.50
16 Thunder And Lightning	1.00
17 DH,Magennta	1.00
18 ATi,Aqualad,A:Aquaman	1.50
19 Starfire,A:Harbinger,Millenium X-over	1.00
20 RT(i),Cyborg	1.00
21 DSp,Flashback sty w/orig.Teen Titans	1.25

TEMPEST
Sept. 1996
Mini-series

1 (of 4) from Aquaman	1.75
2 new costume	1.75
3 O:Tempest	1.75
4 finale	1.75

TEMPUS FUGITIVE
1990

1 KSy,Time Travel,I:Ray 27	4.95
2 KSy,Viet Nam	4.95
3 KSy,World War I	4.95
4 KSy,final issue	4.95

TERMINAL CITY
DC/Vertigo 1996–97

1 thru 3 DMt(s),MLr,	@2.50
4 DMt(s),MLr,I:Kid Gloves	2.50
5 DMt(s),MLr,Missing link on the loose	2.50
6 DMt(s),MLr,	2.50
7 DMt(s),MLr,A:Lady in Red	2.50
8 DMt(s),MLr,	2.50
9 (of 9) DMt(s),MLr,finale	2.50
TPB rep. mini-series	20.00

TERMINAL CITY: AERIAL GRAFFITI
DC/Vertigo (Sept., 1997)

1 (of 5) DMt,MLr,MCo(c)	2.50
2 DMt,MLr,MCo(c),F:Cosmo Quinn	2.50
3 DMt,MLr,MCo(c),	2.50
4 DMt,MLr,MCo(c)	2.50

3-D BATMAN
1953, 1966

1 rep.Batman #42 & #48	900.00
1a A:Tommy Tomorrow (1966)	250.00

THRILLER
Nov., 1983

1 TVE	1.75
2 TVE,O:Thriller	1.50
3 TVE	1.50
4 TVE	1.50
5 TVE,DG,Elvis satire	1.50
6 TVE,Elvis satire	1.50
7 TVE	1.50
8 TVE	1.50
9 TVE	1.50
10 TVE	1.50
11 AN	1.50
12 AN	1.50

THRILLKILLER
Elseworlds

1 HC(s),DIB,F:Robin and Batgirl	3.50
2 HC(s),DIB,	3.00
3 HC(s),DIB,conl.	3.00

THRILLKILLERS '62
Feb., 1998

GN HC,DIB	5.00

TIMBER WOLF
1992–93

1 AG(i),V:Thrust	2.00
2 V:Captain Flag	1.50
3 AG(i),V:Creeper	1.50
4 AG(i),V:Captain Flag	1.50
5 AG(i),V:Dominators,Capt.Flag	1.50

TIME BREAKERS
DC/Helix

1 (of 5) RaP(s),CWn,time paradoxes created	2.50
2 RaP(s),CWn,	2.50
3 RaP(s),CWn,expedition to 20th century England	2.50
4 RaP(s),CWn,Angela travels back in time	2.50
5 RaP(s),CWn,final issue	2.50

TIME MASTERS
Feb., 1990

1 ATi,O:Rip Hunter,A:JLA	2.50
2 ATi,A:Superman	2.00
3 ATi,A:Jonah Hex, Cave Carson	2.00
4 ATi,Animal Man #22 x-over	2.00
5 ATi,A:Viking Prince	2.00
6 ATi,A:Dr.Fate	2.00
7 ATi,A:GrLantern,Arion	2.00
8 ATi,V:Vandal Savage	2.00

TITANS: SCISSORS, PAPER, STONE
Elseworlds March 1997

1 Manga style	4.95

TITANS SELL-OUT SPECIAL

1 SE,AV,I:Teeny Titans, w/Nightwing poster	3.75

Time Warp #5 © DC Comics, Inc.

TIME WARP
Oct.–Nov., 1979

1 JAp,RB,SD,MK(c),DN,TS	15.00
2 DN,JO,TS,HC,SD,MK(c),GK	10.00
3 DN,SD,MK(c),TS	10.00
4 MN,SD,MK(c),DN	10.00
5 DN,MK(c),July 1980	1.00

TOMAHAWK
1950–72

1 Prisoner Called Tomahawk	1,200.00
2 FF(4pgs),Four Boys Against the Frontier	500.00
3 Warpath	325.00
4 Tomahawk Wanted: Dead or Alive	325.00
5 The Girl Who Was Chief	325.00
6 Tomahawk-King of the Aztecs	250.00
7 Punishment of Tomahawk	250.00
8 The King's Messenger	250.00
9 The Five Doomed Men	250.00
10 Frontied Sabotage	250.00
11 Girl Who Hated Tomahawk	200.00
12 Man From Magic Mountain	200.00
13 Dan Hunter's Rival	200.00
14 The Frontier Tinker	200.00
15 The Wild Men of Wigwam Mountain	200.00
16 Treasure of the Angelique	200.00
17 Short-Cut to Danger	200.00
18 Bring In M'Sieur Pierre	200.00
19 The Lafayette Volunteers	200.00
20 NC(c),The Retreat of Tomahawk	200.00
21 NC(c),The Terror of the Wrathful Spirit	125.00
22 CS(c),Admiral Tomahawk	125.00
23 CS(c),The Indian Chief From Oxford	125.00
24 NC(c),Adventure In the Everglades	125.00
25 NC(c),The Star-Gazer of Freemont	125.00
26 NC(c),Ten Wagons For Tomahawk	125.00
27 NC(c),Frontier Outcast	125.00

28 I:Lord Shilling	150.00
29 The Conspiracy of Wounded Bear	175.00
30 The King of the Thieves	125.00
31 NC(c),The Buffalo Brave From Misty Mountain	100.00
32 NC(c),The Clocks That Went to War	100.00
33 The Paleface Tribe	100.00
34 The Capture of General Washington	100.00
35 Frontier Feud	100.00
36 NC(c),A Cannon for Fort Reckless	100.00
37 NC(c),Feathered Warriors	100.00
38 The Frontier Zoo	100.00
39 The Redcoat Trickster	100.00
40 Fearless Fettle-Daredevil	100.00
41 The Captured Chieftain	100.00
42 The Prisoner Tribe	100.00
43 Tomahawk's Little Brother	100.00
44 The Brave Named Tomahawk	100.00
45 The Last Days of Chief Tory	100.00
46 The Chief With 1,000 Faces	75.00
47 The Frontier Rain-Maker	75.00
48 Indian Twin Trouble	75.00
49 The Unknown Warrior	75.00
50 The Brave Who Was Jinxed	75.00
51 General Tomahawk	75.00
52 Tom Thumb of the Frontier	75.00
53 The Four-Footed Renegade	75.00
54 Mystery of the 13th Arrows	75.00
55 Prisoners of the Choctaw	75.00
56 The Riddle of the Five Little Indians	75.00
57 The Strange Fight at Fort Bravo	100.00
58 Track of the Mask	50.00
59 The Mystery Prisoner of Lost Island	50.00
60 The Amazing Walking Fort	50.00
61 Tomahawk's Secret Weapons	50.00
62 Strongest Man in the World	50.00
63 The Frontier Super Men	50.00
64 The Outcast Brave	50.00
65 Boy Who Wouldn't Be Chief	50.00
66 DD&SMo(c),A Trap For Tomahawk	50.00
67 DD&SMo(c),Frontier Sorcerer	50.00
68 DD&SMo(c),Tomahawk's Strange Ally	50.00
69 DD&SMo(c),Tracker-King of the Wolves	50.00
70 DD&SMo(c),Three Tasks for Tomahawk	50.00
71 DD&SMo(c),The Boy Who Betrayed His Country	50.00
72 DD&SMo(c),The Frontier Pupil	50.00
73 DD&SMo(c),The Secret of the Indian Sorceress	50.00
74 DD&SMo(c),The Great Paleface Masquerade	50.00
75 DD&SMo(c),The Ghost of Lord Shilling	50.00
76 DD&SMo(c),The Totem-Pole Trail	50.00
77 DD&SMo(c),The Raids of the One-Man Tribe	50.00
78 DD&SMo(c),The Menace of the Mask	50.00
79 DD&SMo(c),Eagle Eye's Debt of Honor	50.00
80 DD&SMo(c),The Adventures of Tracker	35.00
81 The Strange Omens of the Indian Seer	35.00
82 The Son of the Tracker	35.00
83 B:Tomahawk Rangers, Against the Tribe	35.00
84 There's a Coward Among the Rangers	35.00
85 The Wispering War	35.00
86 Rangers vs. King Colossus	20.00
87 The Secrets of Sgt. Witch Doctor	20.00
88 The Rangers Who Held Back the Earth	20.00
89 The Terrible Tree-Man	20.00
90 The Prisoner In The Pit	20.00
91 The Tribe Below the Earth	20.00
92 The Petrified Sentry of Peaceful Valley	20.00
93 The Return of King Colosso	20.00
94 Rip Van Ranger	20.00
95 The Tribe Beneath the Sea	20.00
96 The Ranger Killers	20.00
97 The Prisoner Behind the Bull's-Eye	20.00
98 The Pied Piper Rangers	20.00
99 The Rangers vs.ChiefCobweb	20.00
100 The Weird Water-Tomahawk	20.00
101 Tomahawk, Enemy Spy	15.00
102 The Dragon Killers	15.00
103 The Frontier Frankenstein	15.00
104 The Fearful Freak of Dunham's Dungeon	15.00
105 The Attack of the Gator God	15.00
106 The Ghost of Tomahawk	15.00
107 Double-Cross of the Gorilla Ranger	15.00
108 New Boss For the Rangers	15.00
109 The Caveman Ranger	15.00
110 Tomahawk Must Die	15.00
111 Vengeance of the Devil-Dogs	15.00
112 The Rangers vs. Tomahawk	15.00
113 The Mad Miser of Carlisle Castle	15.00
114 The Terrible Power of Chief Iron Hands	15.00
115 The Deadly Flaming Ranger	15.00
116 NA(c),The Last Mile of Massacre Trail	15.00
117 NA(c),Rangers'Last Stand	15.00
118 NA(c),Tomahawk, Guilty of Murder	15.00
119 NA(c),Bait For a Buzzard	15.00
120 NC(c),The Coward Who Lived Forever	15.00
121 NA(c),To Kill a Ranger	15.00
122 IN(c),Must the Brave Die	15.00
123 NA(c),The Stallions of Death	15.00
124 NA(c),The Valley of No Return	15.00
125 NA(c),A Chief's Feather For Little Bear	15.00
126 NA(c),The Baron of Gallows Hill	15.00
127 NA(c),The Devil is Waiting	15.00
128 NA(c),Rangers-Your 9 Lives For Mine	15.00
129 NA(c),Treachery at Thunder Ridge	15.00
130 NA(c),Deathwatch at Desolation Valley	15.00
131 JKu(c),B:Son of Tomahawk, Hang Him High	15.00
132 JKu(c),Small Eagle...Brother Hawk	10.00
133 JKu(c),Scalp Hunter	10.00
134 JKu(c),The Rusty Ranger	10.00
135 JKu(c),Death on Ghost Mountain	10.00
136 JKu(c),A Piece of Sky	15.00
137 JKu(c),Night of the Knife	15.00
138 JKu(c),A Different Kind of Christmas	15.00
139 JKu(c),Death Council	20.00
140 Jku(c),The Rescue	15.00

TOR
May-June, 1975

1 JKu,O:Tor	1.25
2 thru 6, Tor reprints	@1.25

TOTAL JUSTICE
Sept. 1996

1 thru 3 CPr(s),RBe,DG, toy line tie-in	@2.25

TOTAL RECALL
1990

1 Movie Adaption	3.00

TOXIC GUMBO
DC/Vertigo (March, 1998)

1-shot GN	6.00

TRANSMETROPOLITAN
DC/Helix July 1997

1 WEI,DaR,JeM, gonzo journalism in 21st century	2.50
2 WEI,DaR,Angels 8 district	2.50
3 WEI,DaR, riot in Angels 8	2.50
4 WEI,DaR, Vs President of US	2.50
5 WEI,DaR, Watches TV	2.50
6 WEI,DaR,evangelicals	2.50
7 WEI,DaR	2.50
8 WEI,DaR,AnotherColdMorning	2.50
9 WEI,DaR,Wild in the Country	2.50
10 WEI,DaR,Freeze Me with Your Kiss, pt.1	2.50
11 WEI,DaR,Freeze Me, pt.2	2.50
12 WEI,DaR,Freeze Me, pt.3	2.50
13 WEI,DaR,JaL(c),Year of the Bastard, pt.1	2.50
14 WEI,DaR,JaL(c),Bastard,pt.2	2.50
TPB Back on the Street	8.00

TRIUMPH
[Mini-Series] 1995

1 From Zero Hour	1.75
2 Teamates Peril	1.75
3 V:Mind Readers	1.75

TRUE FAITH
DC/Vertigo (Aug., 1997)

TPB GEn,WaP, series rep.	13.00

TSR WORLDS
TSR 1990

1 I:SpellJammer	4.50

TV SCREEN CARTOONS
(see REAL SCREEN COMICS)

2020 VISIONS
DC/Vertigo April 1997

1 (of 12) the Disunited States of America	2.25
2 JaD(s),	2.25
3 JaD(s),	2.25

DC COMICS

4 JaD(s),WaP, "La Tormenta"
pt.1 (of 3) 2.25
5 JaD(s),WaP, "La Tormenta" pt.2 2.25
6 JaD(s),WaP,"La Tormenta,pt.3 . 2.25
7 JaD(s),"Renegade," pt.1 ..... 2.25
8 JaD(s),"Renegade," pt.2 ..... 2.25
9 JaD(s),"Renegade," pt.3 ..... 2.25
10 JaD(s),Repro-Man,pt.1 ..... 2.25
11 JaD(s),Repro-Man,pt.2 ..... 2.25
12 JaD(s),Repro-Man,pt.3 ..... 2.25

TWILIGHT
1990–91
1 JL,Last Frontier 5.50
2 JL,K.SorensenVs.T.Tomorrow . 4.95
3 JL,K.SorensenVs.T.Tomorrow . 4.95

UNAUTHORIZED BIO OF LEX LUTHOR
1 EB 3.95

UNCLE SAM
DC/Vertigo (Nov, 1997)
GN 1 (of 2) AxR 5.00
GN 2 AxR 5.00

UNDERWORLD
Dec., 1987
1 EC,New Yorks Finest 1.25
2 EC,A:Black Racer 1.25
3 EC,V:Black Racer 1.25
4 EC,final issue 1.25

UNDERWORLD UNLEASHED
1995–96
1 PWa,F:Neron 5.00
2 PWa,Neron Vs.Green Lantern . 4.00
3 PWa,conclusion 4.00
Abyss—Hell's Sentinel 1-shot ... 3.00
Apokolips-Dark Uprising 1-shot . 3.00
Batman—Devil's Asylum 1-shot
AIG,BSz 3.00
Patterns of Fear 1-shot 3.00

UNEXPECTED, THE
(see TALES OF THE UNEXPECTED)

UNKNOWN SOLDIER
(see STAR SPANGLED)

UNKNOWN SOLDIER
April, 1977
1 True Origin revealed,Viet
Nam 1970 .... 1.50
2 Origin contd.,Iran 1977 ..... 1.50
3 Origin contd.Afghanistan1982 . 1.50
4 Nicaragua 1.50
5 Nicaragua contd. 1.50
6 .... 1.50
7 Libia 1.50
8 Siberia, U.S.S.R. 1.75
9 North Korea 1952 .... 1.75
10 C.I.A. 1.75
11 C.I.A., Army Intelligence 1.75
12 final issue,Oct.1982 ...... 1.75

UNKNOWN SOLDIER
DC/Vertigo Feb. 1997
1 (of 4) GEn(s),KPI,F:maverick

CIA agent 2.50
2 GEn(s),KPI,search for Unknown
Soldier continues 2.50
3 GEn(s),KPI,search for Unknown
Soldier continues 2.50
4 GEn(s),KPI,intrigue, finale 2.50
TPB series rep. 13.00

UNTOLD LEGEND OF BATMAN
July, 1980
1 JA,JBy,(1st DC work)O:Batman 6.00
2 JA,O:Joker&Robin 4.50
3 JA,O:Batgirl 4.50

V
(TV Adaptation)
Feb., 1985
1 Cl/TD 1.35
2 Cl/TD 1.25
3 Cl/TD 1.25
4 Cl/TD 1.25
5 Cl/TD 1.25
6 Cl/TD 1.25
7 Cl/TD 1.25
8 Cl/TD 1.25
9 Cl/TD 1.25
10 Cl/TD 1.25
11 Cl/TD 1.25
12 Cl/TD 1.25
13 Cl/TD 1.25
14 Cl/TD 1.25
15 Cl/TD 1.25
16 Cl/TD 1.25
17 DG 1.25
18 DG 1.25

Valor #20 © DC Comics, Inc.

VALOR
1992–94
1 N:Valor,A:Lex Luthor Jr 2.00
2 MBr,AG,V:Supergirl 1.50
3 MBr,AG,V:Lobo 1.50
4 MBr,AG,V:Lobo 1.50
5 MBr,A:Blasters 1.50
6 A:Blasters,V:Kanjar Ru 1.50
7 A:Blasters 1.50

8 AH(c),V:The Unimaginable ... 1.50
9 AH(c),PCu,A:Darkstar 1.50
10 AH(c),V:Unimaginable 1.50
11 A:Legionnaires 1.50
12 AH(c),B:D.O.A. 3.00
13 AH(c),D:Valor's Mom 3.00
14 AH(c),A:JLA,Legionnaires .. 2.50
15 SI(c),D.O.A #4. .... 2.00
16 CDo,D.O.A #5. .... 2.00
17 CDo,LMc,D:Valor 1.75
18 A:Legionnaires 1.75
19 CDo,A:Legionnaires,V:Glorith . 1.75
20 CDo,A:Wave Rider 1.75
21 .... 1.75
22 End of an Era,pt.2 .... 1.75
23 Zero Hour 2.50

VAMPS
Vertigo 1994–95
1 BB(c) 3.00
2 BB(c) 2.50
3 thru 5 BB(c) .... @2.25
6 BB(c),last issue 2.25
TPB 9.95

VAMPS: HOLLYWOOD & VEIN
Vertigo 1996
1 F:Mink 2.25
2 .... 2.25
3 I:Maggot 2.25
4 F:Mink,Screech 2.25
5 off to rescue Hugh Evans (of 6) 2.25
6 .... 2.25

VERMILLION
DC/Helix Aug. 1996
1 ADv,MKu(c) Lucius Shepard
story 2.50
2 ADv,MKu(c) Jonathan Cave's
cover blown 2.50
3 ADv,riot aboard space ship,
Ildiko's tale 2.50
4 ADv,Starship's engines run wild 2.50
5 ADv 2.50
6 ADv,Creation of Vermillion 2.50
7 ADv,Jonathan Cave discovers
hiding place of enemy 2.50
8 ADv,"Joyland" 2.50
9 GEr, the library in Kaia Mortai . 2.50
10 GEr, "Lord Iron and Lady
Manganese, pt.2 .... 2.50
11 GEr,"Lord Iron and Lady
Manganese" concl. 2.50
12 final issue 2.50

V FOR VENDETTA
Sept., 1988
1 Reps.Warrior Mag(U.K.),I:V,
A:M.Storm (Moore scripts) ... 5.00
2 Murder Spree 3.50
3 Govt. Investigators close in .. 3.00
4 T.V. Broadcast take-over 3.00
5 Govt.Corruption Expose 3.00
6 Evey in Prison 3.00
7 Evey released 2.50
8 Search for V,A:Finch 2.50
9 V:Finch 2.50
10 D:V 2.50
TPB 1990 .... 14.95

VERTIGO GALLERY: DREAMS AND NIGHTMARES
1995
1 Various artists 3.50

VERTIGO JAM
1993
1 GF(c),NGa(s),ANo(s),PrM(s),GEn(s),
JaD(s),KN,SDi,SEa,NyC(s),EiS,PhH,
KDM(i),SeP,MiA,RaP(s),MPn(i),
Vertigo Short Stories 4.50

VERTIGO PREVIEW
1992
Preview of new Vertigo titles,
new Sandman story 1.75

VERTIGO VERITE: HELL ETERNAL
Feb, 1998
1-shot JaD,SeP 7.00

VERTIGO VERITE: THE SYSTEM
1 thru 3 . . . . @2.95
GN Seven Miles a Second 7.95

VERTIGO VERITE: THE UNSEEN HAND
DC/Vertigo 1996
1 thru 3 TLa . . . . @2.50
4 TLa, final issue 2.50

VERTIGO VISIONS: DR. OCCULT
1 F:Dr. Occult 3.95

VERTIGO VISIONS: DR. THIRTEEN
DC/Vertigo (July 1998)
GN evil artificial intelligence 6.00

VERTIGO VISIONS: THE GEEK
1993
1 RaP(s),MiA,V:Dr.Abuse 4.25

VERTIGO VISIONS: PHANTOM STRANGER
1993
1 AaK(s),GyD,The Infernal House 3.75

VERTIGO VISIONS: THE EATERS
1995
1 I:The Quills 4.95

VERTIGO VISIONS: TOMAHAWK
DC/Vertigo (May, 1998)
GN RaP,TY 5.00

VERTIGO: WINTER'S EDGE
DC/Vertigo (, 1998)
TPB BB(c) rep. 8.00

Vigilante #33 © DC Comics, Inc.

VIGILANTE
Oct., 1983
1 KP,DG,F:Adrian Chase 3.50
2 KP 3.00
3 KP,Cyborg 2.50
4 DN,V:Exterminator 2.50
5 KP 2.50
6 O:Vigilante 3.00
7 O:Vigilante 3.00
8 RA,V:Electrocutioner 2.50
9 RA,V:Electrocutioner 2.50
10 RA,DG,avenges J.J. 2.50
11 RA,V:Controller 2.00
12 GK,"Journal" 2.00
13 GK,"Locke Room Murder" 2.00
14 RA,V:Hammer 2.00
15 RA,V:Electrocutioner 2.00
16 RA 2.00
17 Moore 3.00
18 Moore 3.00
19 RA 2.00
20 A:Nightwing 2.50
21 A:Nightwing 2.50
22 . . . . 2.00
23 V:Electrocutioner 2.00
24 "Mother's Day" 2.00
25 RM,V:Police Torturers 2.00
26 V:Electrocutioner 2.00
27 V:Electrocutioner 2.00
28 New Vigilante 2.00
29 RM,New Vigilante 2.00
30 RM,D:Glitz Jefferson 2.00
31 RM,New York Violence 2.00
32 RM,New York Violence 2.00
33 RM,V:Rapist 2.00
34 . . . . 2.00
35 JBy(c),O:MadBomber 2.00
36 MGr(c),V:Peacemaker 2.25
37 MGr,RM,V:Peacemaker 2.25
38 MGr,PeaceMaker 2.25
39 White Slavery 2.00
40 HC(c),White Slavery 2.00
41 . . . . 2.00
42 A:Peacemaker,V:Terrorists . . . 2.00
43 V:PeaceMaker 2.00
44 DC,V:Qurac 2.00
45 I:Black Thorn 2.00

46 Viigilante in Jail 2.00
47 A:Batman 2.50
48 I:Homeless Avenger 2.00
49 . . . . 2.00
50 KSy(c)D:Vigilante 2.50
Ann.#1 . . . . 3.00
Ann.#2 V:Cannon 2.50

VIGILANTE: CITY LIGHTS, PRAIRIE JUSTICE
1995–96
1 JeR,MCo,(of 4) 2.50
2 JeR,V:Bugsy Siegel 2.50
3 JeR 2.50
4 finale 2.50

VIPER
1994
1 Based on the TV Show 2.25
2 . . . . 2.00
3 . . . . 2.00
4 final issue 2.00

WANDERERS
June, 1988
1 I:New Team 1.25
2 V:The Performer 1.25
3 A:Legion of Superheroes 1.25
4 V:Controller Hunters 1.25
5 O:Wanderers 1.25
6 V:Terrorists 1.25
7 V:Medtorians 1.25
8 O:Psyche 1.25
9 O:Psyche 1.25
10 F:Quantum Queen 1.25
11 F:Quantum Queen 1.25
12 V:Aliens 1.25
13 V:Dinosaurs 1.25

WANTED: THE WORLD'S MOST DANGEROUS VILLIANS
July-Aug., 1972
1 rep. Batman,Green Lantern . . . 4.00
2 Batman/Joker/Penguin 5.00
3 . . . . 3.00
4 . . . . 3.00
5 . . . . 3.00
6 . . . . 3.00
7 . . . . 3.00
8 . . . . 3.00
9 . . . . 3.00

WARLORD
Jan., 1976
1 MGr,O:Warlord 14.00
2 MGr,I:Machiste 8.00
3 MGr,'War Gods of Skartaris' . . . 6.00
4 MGr,'Duel of the Titans' 6.00
5 MGr,'The Secret of Skartaris' . . 6.00
6 MGr,I:Mariah,Stryker 5.00
7 MGr,O:Machiste 5.00
8 MGr,A:Skyra 5.00
9 MGr,N:Warlord 5.00
10 MGr,I:Ashiya 5.00
11 MGr,rep.1st Issue special #8 . 4.00
12 MGr,I:Aton 4.00
13 MGr,D:Stryker 4.00
14 MGr,V:Death 4.00
15 MGr,I:Joshua 4.00
16 MGr,I:Saaba 4.00

DC COMICS

17 MGr,'Citadel of Death' 4.00	81 DJu,DA,RR,'Thief's Magic' . . . 2.00
18 MGr,I:Shadow 4.00	82 DJu,DA,RR,'Revolution' 2.00
19 MGr,'Wolves of the Steppes' . . 4.00	83 DJu,RR,'All the President's
20 MGr,I:Joshua clone 5.00	Men' 2.00
21 MGr,D:Joshua clone,Shadow . 3.00	84 DJu,DA,RR,'Hail to the Chief' . 2.00
22 MGr'Beast in the Tower' 3.00	85 DJu,RR,'The Price of Change' 2.00
23 MGr,'Children of Ba'al' 3.00	86 DJ,DA,No Barren Earth 2.00
24 MGr,I:ligia 3.00	87 DJu,RB,RR,I:Hawk 2.00
25 MGr,I:Ahir 3.00	88 DJu,RB,RR,I:Patch,E:Barren
26 MGr,'The Challenge' 3.00	Earth 2.00
27 MGr,'Atlantis Dying' 3.00	89 RB,I:Sabertooth 2.00
28 MGr,I:'Wizard World' 3.00	90 RB,'Demon's of the Past' . . . 2.00
29 MGr,I:Mongo Ironhand' 3.00	91 DJu,DA,I:Maddox,O:Warlord
30 MGr,C:Joshua 3.00	O:Jennifer 1.75
31 MGr,'Wing over Shamballah' . . 3.00	92 NKu,'Evil in Ebony' 2.00
32 MGr,I:Shakira 3.00	93 RR,A:Sabertooth 1.75
33 MGr,Birds of Prey,A:Shakira . . 3.00	94 'Assassin's Prey' 1.75
34 MGr,Sword of the Sorceror,	95 AKu,'Dragon's Doom' 2.00
I:Hellfire 3.00	96 'Nightmare Prelude' 1.75
35 MGr,C:Mike Grell 3.00	97 RB,A:Saaba,D:Scarhart 1.75
36 MGr,'Interlude' 3.00	98 NKu,Crisis tie-in 2.00
37 MGr,JSn,I:Firewing,B:Omac . . 6.00	99 NKu'Fire and Sword' 2.00
38 MGr,I:Jennifer,A:Omac 3.00	100 AKu,D:Greamore,Sabertooth . 2.00
39 MGr,JSn,'Feast of Agravar' . . . 4.00	101 MGr,'Temple of Demi-god' . 1.75
40 MGr,N:Warlord 3.00	
41 MGr,A:Askir 2.50	
42 MGr,JSn,A:Tara,Omac 3.50	
43 MGr,JSn,'Berserk'A:Omac . . . 3.50	
44 MGr,'The Gamble' 3.00	
45 MGr,'Nightmare in Vista	
Vision',A:Omac 3.00	
46 MGr,D:Shakira 3.00	
47 MGr,I:Mikola,E:Omac 3.00	
48 MGr,EC,TY,I:Arak,Claw(B) . . . 3.00	
49 MGr,TY,A:Shakira,E:Claw . . . 2.50	
50 MGr,'By Fire and Ice' 2.50	
51 MGr,TY,rep.#1,	
I(B):Dragonsword 2.00	
52 MGr,TY,'Back in the U.S.S.R. . 2.50	
53 MT,TY,'Sorcerer's Apprentice' . 2.00	
54 MT,'Sorceress Supreme',	
E:Dragonsword 2.00	
55 MT,'Have a Nice Day' 2.00	
56 MT,JD,I:Gregmore,(B):Arion . . 2.00	
57 MT,'The Two Faces of	
Travis Morgan' 2.00	
58 MT,O:Greamore 2.00	
59 MGr,A:Joshua 2.00	
60 JD,'Death Dual' 2.00	
61 JD,A:Greamore 2.00	
62 JD,TMd,A:Mikola,E:Arion . . . 2.00	
63 JD,RR,I(B):Barren Earth 2.00	
64 DJu,RR'Elsewhere' 2.00	
65 DJu,RR,A:Wizard World,	
No Barren Earth 2.00	
66 DJu'Wizard World',	
No Barren Earth 2.00	
67 DJu,RR,'The Mark' 2.00	
68 DJu,RR 2.00	
69 DJu,RR 2.00	
70 DJu,'Outback' 2.00	
71 DJu/DA,'The Journey Back'	
No Barren Earth 2.00	
72 DJu,DA,I:Scarhart,No Barren	
Earth 2.00	
73 DJ,DA,'Cry Plague' 2.00	
74 DJu,No Barren Earth 2.00	
75 DJu,'All Dreams Must Pass'	
No Barren Earth 2.00	
76 DJu,DA,RR,A:Sarga 2.00	
77 DJu,DA,RR,Let My People Go 2.00	
78 DJu,RR,'Doom's Mouth' 2.00	
79 PB,RM,'Paradox',No Barren	
Earth 2.00	
80 DJu,DA,RR,'Future Trek' 2.00	

Warlord Annual #6 © DC Comics, Inc.

102 I:Zuppara,Error-Machiste	
with two hands 1.75	
103 JBi,'Moon Beast' 1.75	
104 RR,'Dragon Skinner' 1.75	
105 RR,'Stailers of Skinner' 1.75	
106 RR,I:Daimon 1.75	
107 RR,'Bride of Yano' 1.75	
108 RR,I:Mortella 1.75	
109 RR,A:Mortella 1.75	
110 RR,A:Skyra III 1.75	
111 RR,'Tearing o/t Island Sea' . . 1.75	
112 RR,'Obsession' 1.75	
113 RR,'Through Fiends	
Destroy Me' 1.75	
114 RR,'Phenalegeno Dies' 1.75	
115 RR,'Citadel of Fear' 1.75	
116 RR,'Revenge of the Warlord' . 1.75	
117 RR,A:Power Girl 1.75	
118 RR,A:Power Girl 1.75	
119 RR,A:Power Girl 1.75	
120 ATb,A:Power Girl 1.75	
121 ATb,A:Power Girl 1.75	
122 ATb,A:Power Girl 1.75	
123 JD,TMd,N:Warlord 1.75	

124 JD,TMd,I:Scavenger 1.75	
125 JD,TMd,D:Tara 1.75	
126 JD,TMd,A:Machiste 1.75	
127 JD,'The Last Dragon' 1.75	
128 JD,I:Agife 1.75	
129 JD,Vision of Quest 1.75	
130 JD,A:Maddox 1.75	
131 JD,RLd,'Vengeful Legacies . . 3.00	
132 'A New Beginning' 1.75	
133 JD,final issue (44pg) 2.00	
Ann.#1 MGr,A:Shakira 3.00	
Ann.#2 I:Krystovar 1.75	
Ann.#3 DJu,'Full Circle' 1.75	
Ann.#4 A:New Gods,	
Legends tie-in 1.75	
Ann.#5 AKu,Hellfire 1.75	
Ann.#6 F:New Gods 1.50	
TPB Warlord:Savage Empire,	
Rep.#1-#10,#12,Special #8 . . 19.95	
[Limited Series]	
1 Travis Morgan retrospective . . . 1.75	
2 Fate of T. Morgan revealed . . . 1.75	
3 Return of Deimos 1.75	
4 V:Deimos 1.75	
5 MGr(c),Skartaros at War 1.75	
6 finale 1.75	

WAR OF THE GODS

1 GP,A:Lobo,Misc.Heroes,Circe	
(direct) 1.75	
2 GP,A:Misc.Heroes,V:Circe,	
w/poster 1.75	
2a (Newsstand) 1.75	
3 GP,A:Misc.Heroes,V:Circe,	
w/poster 1.75	
3a Newsstand 1.75	
4 GP,A:Misc.Heroes,V:Circe,	
w/poster 1.75	
4a Newsstand 1.75	

WASTELAND
Dec., 1987

1 Selection of Horror stories 1.75	
2 . . . . 1.75	
3 . . . . 1.75	
4 . . . . 1.75	
5 'The big crossover story' 1.75	
6 . . . . 1.75	
7 'Great St.Louis Electrical	
Giraffe Caper' 1.75	
8 'Dead Detective' 1.75	
9 . . . . 1.75	
10 TT,African Folk Tale 1.75	
11 'Revenge o/t Swamp Creature' 1.75	
12 JO,'After the Dead Detective' . 1.75	
13 TT(c),JO 2.00	
14 JO,RM,'Whistling Past the	
Graveyard' 2.00	
15 JO,RM 2.00	
16 JO 2.00	
17 JO 2.00	
18 JO,RM,final issue 2.00	

WATCHMEN
Sept., 1986

1 B:AMo,DGb,D:Comedian 7.50	
2 DGb,Funeral for Comedian . . . 5.00	
3 DGb,F:Dr.Manhattan 5.00	
4 DGb,O:Dr.Manhattan 5.00	
5 DGb,F:Rorschach 5.00	
6 DGb,O:Rorschach 5.00	
7 DGb,F:Nite Owl 5.00	
8 DGb,F:Silk Spectre 5.00	
9 DGb,O:Silk Spectre 5.00	

10 DGb,A:Rorschach 5.00
11 DGb,O:Ozymandius 5.00
12 DGb,D:Rorsharch 5.00
TPB rep.#1-#12 . . . . 14.95
TPB 20.00

WEB, THE
Impact 1991–92
1 I:Gunny, Bill Grady, Templar . . 1.25
2 O:The Web, I:Brew, Jump,
   Sunshine Kid 1.00
3 Minions of Meridian, I:St.James 1.00
4 Agent Jump vs. UFO 1.00
5 Agent Buster/Fly team-up
   V:Meridian 1.00
6 I:Posse,A:Templar 1.00
7 V:Meridian's Forces 1.00
8 R: Studs 1.00
9 Earthquest,pt.1 . . . . 2.50
10 V:Templar 1.25
11 V:Templar 1.25
12 "The Gauntlet",A:Shield 1.25
13 Frenzy#1 . . . . 1.25
14 Frenzy#2 . . . . 1.25
Ann.#1 Earthquest,w/trading card . 2.50

The Weird #2 © DC Comics, Inc.

WEIRD, THE
April, 1988
1 BWr,A:JLI 4.00
2 BWr,A:JLI 3.00
3 BWr,V:Jason 3.00
4 final issue 2.50

WEIRD
DC/Paradox Press 1997
1 B&W magazine 3.00
2 . . . . 3.00
3 . . . . 3.00

WEIRD WAR TALES
Sept.–Oct., 1971
1 JKu(c),JKu,RH,Fort which
   Did Not Return 175.00
2 JKu,MD,Military Madness . . . 60.00
3 JKu(c),RA,The Pool 55.00
4 JKu(c),Ghost of Two Wars . . . 50.00

5 JKu(c),RH,Slave 50.00
6 JKu(c),Pawns, The Sounds
   of War 25.00
7 JKu(c),JKu,RH,Flying Blind . . 25.00
8 NA(c),The Avenging Grave . . 40.00
9 NC(c),The Promise 25.00
10 NC(c),Who is Haunting
   the Haunted Chateau 25.00
11 NC(c),ShM,Oct. 30, 1918:
   The German Trenches, WWI . 15.00
12 MK(c),God of Vengeance . . . 15.00
13 LD(c),The Die-Hards 15.00
14 LD(c),ShM,The Ghost of
   McBride's Woman 15.00
15 LD(c),Ace King Just Flew
   In From Hell 15.00
16 LD(c),More Dead Than Alive . 15.00
17 GE(c),Dead Man's Hands . . . 15.00
18 GE(c),Captain Dracula 15.00
19 LD(c),The Platoon That
   Wouldn't Die 15.00
20 LD(c),Operation Voodoo . . . 15.00
21 LD(c),One Hour To Kill 10.00
22 LD(c),Wings of Death 10.00
23 LD(c),The Bird of Death 10.00
24 LD(c),The Invisible Enemy . . 10.00
25 LD(c),Black Magic...White
   Death 10.00
26 LD(c),Jump Into Hell 10.00
27 LD(c),Survival of the
   Fittest 10.00
28 LD(c),Isle of Forgotten
   Warriors 10.00
29 LD(c),Breaking Point 10.00
30 LD(c),The Elements of Death 10.00
31 LD(c),Death Waits Twice . . . 10.00
32 LD(c),The Enemy, The Stars . 10.00
33 LD(c),Pride of the Master
   Race 10.00
34 LD(c),The Common Enemy . . 10.00
35 LD(c),The Invaders 10.00
36 JKu(c),Escape 15.00
37 LD(c),The Three Wars of
   Don Q 10.00
38 JKu(c),Born To Die 7.00
39 JKu(c),The Spoils of War 7.00
40 ECh(c),Back From The Dead . 7.00
41 JL(c), The Dead Draftees of
   Regiment Six 7.00
42 JKu(c),Old Soldiers Never
   Die 7.00
43 ECh(c),Bulletproof 7.00
44 JKu(c),ShM,The Emperor
   Weehawken 7.00
45 JKu(c),The Battle of Bloody
   Valley 7.00
46 Kill Or Be Killed 7.00
47 JKu(c),Bloodbath of the Toy
   Soldiers 7.00
48 JL(c),Ultimate Destiny 7.00
49 The Face Of The Enemy 7.00
50 ECh(c),-An Appointment With
   Destiny 7.00
51 JKu(c),Secret Weapon 7.00
52 JKu(c),The Devil Is A
   Souvenir Hunter 7.00
53 JAp(c),Deadly Dominoes 7.00
54 GM(c),Soldier of Satan 7.00
55 JKu(c),A Rebel Shall Rise
   From The Grave 7.00
56 AM(c),The Headless Courier . . 7.00
57 RT(c),Trial By Combat 7.00
58 JKu(c),Death Has A Hundred
   Eyes 7.00
59 The Old One 7.00

60 JKu(c),Night Flight 7.00
61 HC(c),Mind War 4.00
62 JKu(c),The Grubbers 4.00
63 JKu(c),Battleground 4.00
64 JKu(c),Deliver Me For D-Day . 4.00
65 JKu(c),The Last Cavalry
   Charge 4.00
66 JKu(c),The Iron Star 4.00
67 JKu(c),The Attack of the
   Undead 4.00
68 FM,JKu(c),The Life and Death of
   Charlie Golem 4.00
69 JKu(c),The Day After Doomsday4.00
70 LD(c),The Blood Boat 4.00
71 LD(c),False Prophet 4.00
72 JKu(c),Death Camp 4.00
73 GE(c),The Curse of Zopyrus . . 4.00
74 GE(c),March of the Mammoth . 4.00
75 JKu(c),The Forgery 4.00
76 JKu(c),The Fire Bug 4.00
77 JKu(c),Triad 4.00
78 JKu(c),Indian War In Space . . 4.00
79 JKu(c),The Gods Themselves . 4.00
80 JKu(c),An Old Man's Profession 4.00
81 JKu(c),It Takes Brains To
   Be A Killer 4.00
82 GE(c),Funeral Fire 4.00
83 GE(c),Prison of the Mind 4.00
84 JKu(c),Devil's Due 4.00
85 thru 124 June 1983 . . . . . . @4.00

WEIRD WAR TALES
DC/Vertigo April 1997
1 (of 4) anthology 2.50
2 MK(c) 2.50
3 . . . . 2.50
4 . . . . 2.50

All Star Western #3 © DC Comics, Inc.

ALL-STAR WESTERN
Aug.–Sept. 1970
1 NA(c),CI 25.00
2 NA(c),GM,B:Outlaw 15.00
3 NA(c),GK,O:El Diablo 12.00
4 NA(c),GK,JKu,GM 12.00
5 NA(c),JAp,E:Outlaw 12.00
6 GK,B:Billy the Kid 12.00
7 . . . . 15.00

8 E:Billy the Kid	15.00
9 FF	15.00
10 GM,I:Jonah Hex	200.00
11 GM,A:Jonah Hex	100.00

Becomes:

WEIRD WESTERN TALES
June–July, 1972

12 NA,BWr,JKu	60.00
13	50.00
14 ATh	25.00
15 NA(c),GK	25.00
16 thru 28	@15.00
29 O:Jonah Hex	25.00
30	10.00
31 thru 38	@10.00
39 I&O:Scalphunter	10.00
40 thru 70	@6.00

WEIRD WORLDS
Aug.–Sept., 1971

1 JO,MA,John Carter	30.00
2 NA,JO(c),MA,BWr	25.00
3 MA,NA	15.00
4 MK(c),MK	10.00
5 MK(c),MK	10.00
6 MK(c),MK	10.00
7 John Carter ends	10.00
8 HC,I:Iron Wolf	10.00
9 and 10 HC	@10.00

Western Comics #35 © DC Comics, Inc.

WESTERN COMICS
Jan.–Feb., 1948

1 MMe,B:Vigilante,Podeo Rick, WyomingKid,CowboyMarshal	600.00
2 MMe,Vigilante vs. Dirk Bigger	300.00
3 MMe,Vigilante vs. Pecos Kid	225.00
4 MMe,Vigilante as Pecos Kid	225.00
5 I:Nighthawk	200.00
6 Wyoming Kid vs. 'The Murder Mustang'	175.00
7 Wyoming Kid in 'The Town That Was Never Robbed	175.00
8 O:Wyoming Kid	200.00
9 Wyoming Kid vs. Jack Slaughter	150.00
10 Nighthawk in 'Tunnel ofTerror'	150.00
11 Wyoming Kid vs. Mayor Brock	125.00

12 Wyoming Kid vs. Baldy Ryan	125.00
13 I:Running Eagle	125.00
14 Wyoming Kid in 'The Siege of Praire City	125.00
15 Nighthawk in 'Silver, Salt and Pepper	125.00
16 Wyoming Kid vs. Smilin' Jim	125.00
17 BP,Wyoming Kid vs. Prof. Penny	125.00
18 LSt on Nighthawk,WyomingKid in 'Challenge of the Chiefs'	125.00
19 LSt,Nighthawk in 'The Invisible Rustlers	125.00
20 LSt,Nighthawk in 'The Mystery Mail From Defender Dip'	100.00
21 LSt,Nighthawk in 'Rattlesnake Hollow'	100.00
22 LSt,I:Jim Pegton	100.00
23 LSt,Nighthawk reveals ID to Jim	100.00
24 The $100,000 Impersonation	100.00
25 V:Souix Invaders	100.00
26 The Storming of the Sante Fe Trail	100.00
27 The Looters of Lost Valley	100.00
28 The Thunder Creek Rebellion	100.00
29 Six Guns of the Wyoming Kid	100.00
30 V:Green Haired Killer	100.00
31 The Sky Riding Lawman	100.00
32 Death Rides the Stage Coach	100.00
33	100.00
34 Prescription For Killers	100.00
35 The River of Rogues	100.00
36 Nighthawk(c),Duel in the Dark	75.00
37 The Death Dancer	75.00
38 Warpath in the Sky	75.00
39 Death to Fort Danger	75.00
40 Blind Man's Bluff	75.00
41 thru 60	@75.00
61 thru 85	@50.00

WHERE IN THE WORLD IS CARMEN SANDIEGO?
DC/Helix 1996

1 thru 3	@1.75
4	1.75

WHO'S WHO
1985–87

1	2.00
2 thru 9	@1.50
10 inc.	1.25
11 inc. Infinity Inc.	1.25
12 inc. Kamandi	1.25
13 inc. Legion of Super Heroes/ Villains	1.25
14 inc.	1.25
15 inc. Metal Men	1.25
16 inc. New Gods	1.25
17 inc. Outsiders	1.25
18 inc. Power Girl	1.25
19 inc. Robin	1.25
20 inc.	1.25
21 inc. The Spectre	1.25
22 inc. Superman	1.25
23 inc. Teen Titans	1.25
24 inc. Unknown Soldier	1.25
25 inc.	1.25
26 inc.	1.25

WHO'S WHO
(PACKET)

1 inc. Superman	6.00
1a 2nd printing	5.50

2 inc. Flash	5.50
2a 2nd printing	5.00
3 inc. Green Lantern	5.50
4 inc. Wonder Woman	5.50
5 inc. Batman	5.50
6 inc. Hawkman	5.50
7 inc. Shade	5.50
8 inc. Lobo	6.00
9 inc. Legion of Super-Heroes	5.50
10 inc. Robin	5.50
11 inc. L.E.G.I.O.N. '91	5.50
12 inc. Aquaman	5.50
13 Villains issue, inc. Joker	6.00
14 inc. New Titans	5.50
15 inc. Doom Patrol	5.50
16 inc. Catwoman,final issue	5.00

WHO'S WHO IN IMPACT

1 Shield	4.95
2 Black Hood	4.95

WHO'S WHO IN THE LEGION
1987–88

1 History/Bio of Legionnaires	1.25
2 inc. Dream Girl	1.25
3 inc. Karate Kid	1.25
4 inc. Lightning Lad	1.25
5 inc. Phantom Girl	1.25
6 inc. Timber Wolf	1.25
7 wraparound(c)	1.25

WHO'S WHO IN STAR TREK
1987

1 HC(c)	6.00
2 HC(c)	6.00

WHO'S WHO UPDATE '87

1 inc. Blue Beetle	1.50
2 inc. Catwoman	1.25
3 inc. Justice League	1.25
4	1.25
5 inc. Superboy	1.25

WHO'S WHO UPDATE '88

1 inc. Brainiac	1.25
2 inc. JusticeLeagueInternational	1.25
3 inc. Shado	1.25
4 inc. Zatanna	1.25

WHO'S WHO UPDATE '93

1 F:Eclipso,Azrael	5.25

WILD DOG
Sept., 1987

1 mini series DG(i),I:Wild Dog	1.00
2 DG(i),V:Terrorists	1.00
3 DG(i)	1.00
4 DG(i),O:Wild Dog, final issue	1.00
Spec.#1	2.50

WINDY & WILLY
May-June, 1969

1 thru 4	@20.00

WISE SON:
THE WHITE WOLF
DC/Milestone Sept. 1996
1 by Ho Che Anderson 2.50
2 thru 4 . . . . @2.50

WITCHCRAFT
Vertigo 1994
1 CV(c),Three Witches from
Sandman 4.00
2 F:Mildred 3.50
3 Final issue 3.25
TPB rep. mini-series 14.95

WITCHCRAFT:
LA TERREUR
Feb., 1998
1 (of 3) JeR, sequel 2.50
2 JeR 2.50
3 JeR 2.50

WONDER WOMAN
1942–86
1 O:Wonder Woman,A:Paula
Von Gunther 17,000.00
2 I:Earl of Greed,Duke of
Deception and Lord Conquest,
A:Mars 2,500.00
3 Paula Von Gunther reforms 1,500.00
4 A:Paula Von Gunther 1,200.00
5 I:Dr. Psycho,A:Mars 1,200.00
6 I:Cheetah 1,000.00
7 . . . . 1,000.00
8 I:Queen Clea 1,000.00
9 I:Giganto 1,000.00
10 I:Duke Mephisto Saturno . 1,000.00
11 I:Hypnoto 750.00
12 I:Queen Desira 750.00
13 V:King Rigor & the Seal Men 750.00
14 I:Gentleman Killer 750.00
15 I:Solo 750.00
16 I:King Pluto 750.00
17 Wonder Woman goes to
Ancient Rome 750.00
18 V:Dr. Psycho 750.00
19 V:Blitz 750.00

20 V:Nifty and the Air Pirates . . 750.00
21 I:Queen Atomia 650.00
22 V:Saturno 650.00
23 V:Odin and the Valkyries . . 650.00
24 I:Mask 650.00
25 V:Purple Priestess 650.00
26 I:Queen Celerita 650.00
27 V:Pik Socket 650.00
28 V:Cheetah,Clea,Dr. Poison,
Giganta,Hypnata,Snowman,
Zara (Villainy,Inc.) 550.00
29 V:Paddy Gypso 550.00
30 'The Secret of the
Limestone Caves' 550.00
31 V:Solo 450.00
32 V:Uvo 450.00
33 V:Inventa 450.00
34 V:Duke of Deception 450.00
35 'Jaxo,Master of Thoughts' . . 450.00
36 V:Lord Cruello 450.00
37 A:Circe 450.00
38 V:Brutex 450.00
39 'The Unmasking of Wonder
Woman' 450.00
40 'Hollywood Goes To Paradise
Island' 450.00
41 'Wonder Woman,Romance
Editor' 350.00
42 V:General Vertigo 350.00
43 'The Amazing Spy Ring
Mystery' 350.00
44 V:Master Destroyer 350.00
45 'The Amazon and the
Leprachaun' 600.00
46 V:Prof. Turgo 275.00
47 V:Duke of Deception 275.00
48 V:Robot Woman 275.00
49 V:Boss 275.00
50 V:Gen. Voro 275.00
51 V:Garo 200.00
52 V:Stroggo 200.00
53 V:Crime Master of Time . . . 200.00
54 A:Merlin 200.00
55 'The Chessmen of Doom' . . 200.00
56 V:Plotter Gang 200.00
57 V:Mole Men 200.00
58 V:Brain 200.00
59 V:Duke Dozan 200.00
60 A:Paula Von Gunther 200.00
61 'Earth's Last Hour' 175.00
62 V:Angles Andrews 175.00
63 V:Duke of Deception 175.00
64 V:Thought Master 175.00
65 V:Duke of Deception 175.00
66 V:Duke of Deception 175.00
67 'Confessions of a Spy' 175.00
68 'Landing of the Flying
Saucers' 175.00
69 A:Johann Gutenberg,Chris.
Columbus, Paul Revere
and the Wright Brothers . . . 175.00
70 I:Angle Man 175.00
71 'One-Woman Circus' 165.00
72 V:Mole Goldings 150.00
73 V:Prairie Pirates 150.00
74 'The Carnival of Peril' 150.00
75 V:Angler 150.00
76 . . . . 150.00
77 V:Smokescreen gang 150.00
78 V:Angle Man 150.00
79 V:Spider 150.00
80 V:Machino 150.00
81 V:Duke of Deception,
Angle Man 150.00
82 A:Robin Hood 150.00

83 'The Boy From Nowhere' . . 150.00
84 V:Duke of Deception,
Angle Man 150.00
85 V:Capt. Virago 150.00
86 V:Snatcher 150.00
87 'The Day the Clocks Stopped' 150.00
88 V:Duke of Deception 150.00
89 'The Triple Heroine' 150.00
90 Wonder Woman on Jupiter . 150.00
91 'The Interplanetary Olympics' 125.00
92 V:Angle Man 125.00
93 V:Duke of Deception 125.00
94 V:Duke of Deception,
A:Robin Hood 125.00
95 O:Wonder Woman's tiara . . 135.00
96 V:Angle Man 125.00
97 'The Runaway Time Express' 125.00
98 . . . . 125.00
99 V:Silicons 125.00
100 Anniversary Issue 150.00
101 V:Time Master 100.00
102 F:Steve Trevor 100.00
103 V:Gadget-Maker 100.00
104 A:Duke of Deception 100.00
105 O,I:Wonder Woman 500.00
106 W.Woman space adventure 100.00
107 Battles space cowboys . . . 100.00
108 Honored by U.S. Post Off. 100.00
109 V:Slicker 100.00
110 I:Princess 1003 . . . . 100.00
111 I:Prof. Menace 100.00
112 V:Chest of Monsters 75.00
113 A:Queen Mikra 75.00
114 V:Flying Saucers 75.00
115 A:Angle Man 75.00
116 A:Professor Andro 75.00
117 A:Etta Candy 75.00
118 A:Merman 75.00
119 A:Mer Boy 75.00
120 A:Hot & Cold Alien 75.00
121 A:Wonder Woman Family . . 60.00
122 I:Wonder Tot 60.00
123 A:Wonder Girl,Wonder Tot . 60.00
124 A:Wonder Girl,Wonder Tot . 60.00
125 WW-Battle Prize 60.00
126 I:Mr.Genie 60.00
127 Suprise Honeymoon 50.00
128 O:InvisiblePlane 45.00

Wonder Woman #12
© DC Comics, Inc.

Wonder Woman #48
© DC Comics, Inc.

129 A:WonderGirl,WonderTot	45.00
130 A:Angle Man	45.00
131	45.00
132 V:Flying Saucer	45.00
133 A:Miss X	45.00
134 V:Image-Maker	45.00
135 V:Multiple Man	45.00
136 V:Machine Men	45.00
137 V:Robot Wonder Woman	45.00
138 V:Multiple Man	45.00
139 Amnesia revels Identity	45.00
140 A:Morpheus,Mr.Genie	45.00
141 A:Angle Man	45.00
142 A:Mirage Giants	45.00
143 A:Queen Hippolyte	45.00
144 I:Bird Boy	45.00
145 V:Phantom Sea Beast	45.00
146 $1,000 Dollar Stories	45.00
147 Wonder Girl becomes Bird Girl and Fish Girl	45.00
148 A:Duke of Deception	45.00
149 Last Day of the Amazons	45.00
150 V:Phantome Fish Bird	45.00
151 F:1st Full Wonder Girl story	30.00

Wonder Woman #176
© DC Comics, Inc.

152 F:Wonder Girl	30.00
153 V:Duke of Deception	30.00
154 V:Boiling Man	30.00
155 I married a monster	30.00
156 V:Brain Pirate	30.00
157 A:Egg Fu,the First	30.00
158 A:Egg Fu,the First	30.00
159 Origin	35.00
160 A:Cheetah,Dr. Psycho	30.00
161 A:Angle Man	30.00
162 O:Diana Prince	30.00
163 A:Giganta	30.00
164 A:Angle Man	30.00
165 A:Paper Man,Dr.Psycho	30.00
166 A:Egg Fu,The Fifth	30.00
167 A:Crimson Centipede	30.00
168 RA,ME,V:Giganta	30.00
169 RA,ME,Crimson Centipede	30.00
170 RA,ME,V:Dr.Pyscho	30.00
171 A:Mouse Man	20.00
172 IN,A:Android Wonder Woman	20.00
173 A:Tonia	20.00
174 A:Angle Man	20.00

175 V:Evil Twin	20.00
176 A:Star Brothers	20.00
177 A:Super Girl	20.00
178 MSy,DG,I:New Wonder Woman	25.00
179 D:Steve Trevor,I:Ching	20.00
180 MSy,DG,wears no costume I:Tim Trench	15.00
181 MSy,DG,A:Dr.Cyber	15.00
182 MSy,DG	15.00
183 MSy,DG,V:War	15.00
184 MSy,DG,A:Queen Hippolyte	15.00
185 MSy,DG,V:Them	15.00
186 MSy,DG,I:Morgana	15.00
187 MSy,DG,A:Dr.Cyber	15.00
188 MSy,DG,A:Dr.Cyber	15.00
189 MSy,DG	15.00
190 MSy,DG	15.00
191 MSy,DG	15.00
192 MSy,DG	15.00
193 MSy,DG	15.00
194 MSy,DG	15.00
195 MSy,WW	16.00
196 MSy,DG,giant,Origin rep.	18.00
197 MSy,DG	15.00
198 MSy,DG	15.00
199 JJ(c),DG	25.00
200 JJ(c),DG	15.00
201 DG,A:Catwoman	10.00
202 DG,A:Catwoman,I:Fafhrd & the Gray Mouser	10.00
203 DG,Womens lib	10.00
204 DH,BO,rewears costume	15.00
205 DH,BO	10.00
206 DH,O:Wonder Woman	10.00
207 RE	10.00
208 RE	10.00
209 RE	10.00
210 RE	10.00
211 RE,giant	10.00
212 CS,A:Superman,tries to rejoin JLA	10.00
213 IN,A:Flash	5.00
214 CS,giant,A:Green Lantern	8.00
215 A:Aquaman	5.00
216 A:Black Canary	5.00
217 DD,A:Green Arrow	5.00
218 KS,Red Tornado	5.00
219 CS,A:Elongated Man	5.00
220 DG,NA,A:Atom	5.00
221 CS,A:Hawkman	5.00
222 A:Batman	5.00
223 R:Steve Trevor	5.00
224	5.00
225	5.00
226	5.00
227	5.00
228 B:War stories	5.00
229	5.00
230 V:Cheetah	5.00
231	5.00
232 MN,A:JSA	5.00
233 GM	5.00
234	5.00
235	5.00
236	5.00
237 RB(c),O:Wonder Woman	6.00
238 RB(c)	4.00
239 RB(c)	4.00
240	4.00
241 JSon,DG,A:Spectre	4.00
242	3.00
243	3.00
244	3.00
245	3.00

246	3.00
247	3.00
248 D:Steve Trevor	3.00
249 A:Hawkgirl	3.00
250 I:Orana	3.00
251 O:Orana	3.00
252	3.00
253	3.00
254	3.00
255 V:Bushmaster	3.00
256 V:Royal Flush Gang	3.00
257	3.00
258	3.00
259	3.00
260	3.00
261	3.00
262 RE,A:Bushmaster	3.00
263	3.00
264	3.00
265	3.00
266	3.00
267 R:Animal Man	12.00
268 A:Animal Man	10.00
269 WW(i),Rebirth of Wonder Woman,pt.1	2.50

Wonder Woman #236
© DC Comics, Inc.

270 Rebirth,pt.2	2.50
271 JSon,B:Huntress,Rebirth,pt.3	2.50
272 JSon	2.50
273 JSon,A:Angle Man	2.50
274 JSon,I:Cheetah II	2.50
275 JSon,V:Cheetah II	2.50
276 JSon,V:Kobra	2.50
277 JSon,V:Kobra	2.50
278 JSon,V:Kobra	2.50
279 JSon,A:Demon,Catwoman	3.00
280 JSon,A:Demon,Catwoman	3.00
281 JSon,Earth 2 Joker	3.50
282 JSon,Earth 2 Joker	3.50
283 Earth 2 Joker	3.50
284	2.00
285 JSon,V:Red Dragon	2.00
286	2.00
287 DH,RT,JSon,Teen Titans	2.25
288 GC,RT,New Wonder Woman	2.00
289 GC,RT,JSon,New W.Woman	2.00
290 GC,RT,JSon,New W.Woman	2.00
291 GC,FMc,A:Zatanna	2.00

292 GC,FMc,RT,Supergirl 2.00	25 CMa,Invasion,A:JLA 1.25	69 PCu, Exodus In Space#4 . . . . 1.50
293 GC,FMc,Starfire,Raven 2.00	26 CMa,Invasion,V:Capt.Atom . . . 1.25	70 PCu,Exodus In Space#5 . . . . 1.50
294 GC,FMc,JSon,V:Blockbuster . 2.00	27 CMa,V:Khunds,A:Cheetah . . . 1.25	71 BB(c),DC,RT,Return fr.space . 1.50
295 GC,FMc,JSon,Huntress 2.00	28 CMa,V:Cheetah 1.25	72 BB(c),O:retold 1.75
296 GC,Fmc,JSon 2.00	29 CMa,V:Cheetah 1.25	73 BB(c),Diana gets a job 1.50
297 MK(c),GC,FMc,JSon 2.00	30 CMa,V:Cheetah 1.25	74 BB(c),V:White Magician 1.50
298 GC,FMc,JSon 2.00	31 CMa,V:Cheetah 1.25	75 BB(c),A:The White Magician . . 1.50
299 GC,FMc,JSon 2.00	32 TG,V:Amazons,A:Hermes 1.25	76 BB(c),A:Doctor Fate 1.50
300 GC,FMc,RA,DG,KP,RB,KG	33 CMa,V:Amazons,Cheetah . . . 1.25	77 BB(c) 1.50
C:New Teen Titans 3.25	34 CMa,I:Shim'Tar 1.25	78 BB(c),A:Flash 1.50
301 GC,FMc 2.00	35 CMa,V:Shim'Tar 1.25	79 BB(c),V:Mayfly,A:Flash 1.50
302 GC,FMc,V:Artemis 2.00	36 CMa,A:Hermes 1.25	80 BB(c),V:Ares Buchanan 1.50
303 GC,FMc,Huntress 2.00	37 CMa,V:Discord,A:Superman . 1.25	81 BB(c),V:Ares Buchanan 1.50
304 GC,FMc,Huntress 2.00	38 CMa,V:Eris 1.25	82 BB(c),V:Ares Buchanan 1.50
305 GC,Huntress,I:Circe 5.00	39 CMa,V:Eris,A:Lois Lane 1.25	83 BB(c),V:Ares Buchanan 1.50
306 DH,Huntress 2.00	40 CMa,V:Eris,A:Lois Lane 1.25	84 BB(c),V:Ares Buchanan 1.75
307 DH,Huntress,Black Canary . 2.00	41 CMa,RT,F:Julia,Ties that Bind . 1.25	85 BB(c) 15.00
308 DH,Huntress,Black Canary . . 2.00	42 CMa,RT,V:Silver Swan 1.25	86 BB(c),Turning Point 2.50
309 DH,Huntress 2.00	43 CMA,RT,V:Silver Swan 1.25	87 BB(c),No Quarter,NoSanctuary 2.50
310 DH,Huntress 2.00	44 CMa,RT,V:SilverSwan 1.25	88 BB(c),A:Superman 8.00
311 DH,Huntress 2.00	45 CM,RT,Pandora's Box 1.25	89 BB(c),A:Circle 7.00
312 DH,DSp,A:Gremlins 2.00	46 RT,Suicide Issue,D:Lucy 1.50	90 New Direction 8.00
313 DH,V:Circe 2.00	47 RT,A:Troia 1.25	91 Choosing Wonder Woman . . . 5.00
314 DH,Huntress 2.00		92 New Wonder Woman 5.00
315 DH,Huntress 2.00		93 New Wonder Woman 4.00
316 DH,Huntress 2.00		94 . . . . 6.00
317 DH,V:Cereberus 2.00		95 V:Cheetah 6.00
318 DH,V:Space Aliens 2.00		96 V:The Joker 6.00
319 DH,V:Dr.Cyber 2.00		97 V:The Joker 6.00
320 DH 2.00		98 BB(c),F:Artemis 3.00
321 DH,Huntress 2.00		99 BB(c),A:White Magician 3.00
322 IN 2.00		100 BB(c) White Magician defeats
323 DH,A:Cheetah, Angle Man . 2.00		Artemis 6.00
324 DH 2.00		100a Collector's ed., holo(c) . . . 3.95
325 DH 2.00		101 V:White Magician 3.00
326 DH 2.00		102 V:Metron,Darkseid 2.25
327 DH,Crisis 2.00		103 JBy,A:Darkseid 2.00
328 DH,Crisis 2.00		104 JBy,Diana takes crown? . . . 2.00
329 DH,Crisis, giant 2.00		105 JBy,Grecian artifact comes
		to life 2.00
## WONDER WOMAN		106 JBy,A:The Demon,Phantom
[2nd Regular Series] 1987–97		Stranger 2.00
1 GP,O:Amazons,Wonder Woman 4.00		107 . . . . 2.00
2 GP,I:Steve Trevor 3.00		108 JBy,F:The Demon,Arion,The
3 GP,I:Julia Vanessa 2.50		Phantom Stranger 2.00
4 GP,V:Decay 2.00		109 JBy,V:The Flash,I:Champion . 2.00
5 GP,V:Deimos,Phobos 2.00		110 JBy,V:Sinestro 2.00
6 GP,V:Ares 1.50		111 JBy,I:New Wonder Girl,
7 GP,I:Myndi Mayer 1.50		V:Doomsday 2.00
8 GP,O:Legends,A:JLA,Flash . . 1.50		112 JBy,V:Doomsday,A:Superman 2.50
9 GP,I:New Cheetah 1.50		113 JBy,Wonder Girl vs. Decay . . 2.00
10 GP,V:Seven Headed Hydra,		114 JBy,V:Doctor Psycho 2.00
Challenge of the Gods,pt.1,	48 RTP,A:Troia 1.25	115 JBy,beneath the Arctic ice . . 2.00
gatefold(c) 1.50	49 recap of 1st four years 1.25	116 JBy,beneath the Arctic ice . . 2.00
10a regular(c) 1.50	50 RT,SA,BB,AH,CM,KN,PCR,MW	117 JBy,V:Earth Moovers 2.00
11 GP,V:Echidna,Challenge	A:JLA,Superman 2.00	118 JBy 2.00
of the Gods,pt.3 . . . . 1.50	51 RT,V:Mercury 1.25	119 JBy,fight to regain Cheetah's
12 GP,Millenium,V:Pan, Challenge	52 CM,KN,Shards,V:Dr.Psycho . . 1.25	humanity, cont. 2.00
of the Gods,pt.3,	53 RT,A:Pariah 1.25	120 JBy,48pg., pin-ups 3.00
Millenium x-over 1.50	54 RT,V:Dr.Psycho 1.25	121 JBy,Wonder Woman reverting
13 GP,Millenium,A:Ares,Challenge	55 RT,V:Dr.Psycho 1.25	to clay 2.00
of the Gods,pt.4 . . . . 1.50	56 RT,A:Comm.Gordon 1.25	122 JBy,Gods of Olympus are back 2.00
14 GP,A:Hercules 1.50	57 RT,A:Clark Kent,Bruce Wayne 1.25	123 JBy,R:Artemis 2.00
15 GP,I:New Silver Swan 1.50	58 RT,War of the Gods,V:Atlas . . 2.00	124 JBy,A:Demon 2.00
16 GP,V:Silver Swan 1.50	59 RT,War of the Gods,	125 JBy,A:Donna Troy & JLA . . . 2.00
17 GP,DG,V:Circe 1.50	A:Batman Robin 2.00	126 JBy,JL,Genesis tie-in 2.00
18 GP,DG,V:Circe,+Bonus bk#4 . 1.50	60 RT,War of the Gods,	127 JBy,JL(c),new era 2.00
19 GP,FMc,V:Circe 1.50	A:Batman, Lobo 2.00	128 JBy,JL,V:Egg Fu 2.00
20 GP,BMc,D:Myndi Mayer 1.50	61 RT,War of the Gods,V:Circe . . 2.00	129 JBy,JL,Hippolyta debuts as
21 GP,BMc,L:Greek Gods,	62 War o/t Gods,Epilogue. 1.50	replacement Wonder Woman . 2.00
Destruction of Olympus 1.50	63 BB(c)A:Deathstroke,Cheetah . 1.75	130 JBy,JL,pt.1,A:Golden-age
22 GP,BMc,F:Julia, Vanessa . . . 1.50	64 BB(c),Kidnapped Child 1.50	Flash 2.00
23 GP,R:Hermes,V:Phobos,	65 BB(c),PCu,V:Dr.Psycho 1.50	131 JBy,pt.2 . . . . 2.00
Prelude to New Titans #50 . . . 1.50	66 BB(c),PCu,Exodus In Space#1 1.50	132 JBy,pt.3,A:Justice Society . . . 2.00
24 GP,V:Ixion, Phobos 1.50	67 BB(c),PCu,Exodus In Space#2 1.50	133 . . . . 2.00
	68 BB(c),PCu,Exodus In Space#3 1.50	

Wonder Woman (2nd Regular Series) #67 © DC Comics, Inc.

134 JBy,Who is Donna Troy? ... 2.00
135 JBy,secret revealed 2.00
136 JBy,back to Earth 2.00
137 CPr,V:Circe, pt.1 .... 2.00
138 MBr,F:Hippolyta,V:Circe,pt.2 . 2.00
Ann.#1,GP,AAd,RA,BB,JBo,JL,CS
  Tales of Paradise Island 2.00
Ann.#2 CM,F:Mayer Agency 2.50
Ann.#3 Eclipso tie-in 2.50
Ann.#4 Year One Annual 3.50
Ann.#5 JBy,DC,NBy,Legends of the
  Dead Earth 2.95
Ann.#6 Pulp Heroes (Macabre) . 3.95
Ann.#7 Ghosts 3.00
Spec #1 A:Deathstroke,Cheetah . 2.25
Spec.#0 History of Amazons ... 7.00
TPB The Contest, rep. #90,#0
  #91-#93 .... 9.95
TPB The Challenge of Artemas . . 9.95
TPB Second Genesis JBy, rep.
  #101–#105 .... 9.95
GN Amazonia, BML 8.00
GN The Once and Future Story . . 5.00
GN Amazonia 8.00
Archives, Vol. 1 .... 50.00

WONDER WOMAN: DONNA TROY
May, 1998
1-shot Girlfrenzy 2.00

WONDER WOMAN PLUS
Nov. 1996
1 CPr(s),MC,TP,Jesse Quick and
  Wonderwoman 2.95

WORLD OF KRYPTON
July, 1979
1 HC/MA.O:Jor-El 1.50
2 HC/MA,A:Superman 1.00
3 HC 1.00

[2nd Series] 1987–88
1 MMi,John Byrne script 1.00
2 MMi,John Byrne script 1.00
3 MMi,John Byrne script 1.00
4 MMi,A:Superman 1.00

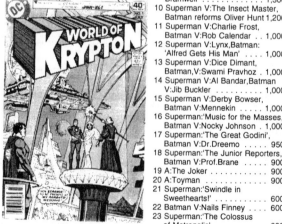

World of Krypton #1
© DC Comics, Inc.

WORLD OF METROPOLIS
1988
1 DG(i),O:Perry White 1.00
2 DG(i),O:Lois Lane 1.00
3 DG(i),Clark Kent 1.00
4 DG(i),O:Jimmy Olsen 1.00

WORLD OF SMALLVILLE
1988
1 KS/AA,Secrets of Ma&Pa Kent 1.25
2 KS/AA,'Stolen Moments' 1.25
3 KS/AA,Lana Lang/Manhunter . . 1.25
4 KS/AA,final issue 1.25

WORLDS COLLIDE
1994
1 MBr(c),3RW,CsB,Ccs,DCw,
  TG,A:Blood Syndicate,Icon,
  Hardware,Static,Superboy,
  Superman,Steel,Vinyl Cling(c) . 4.25
1a Newsstand Ed. 2.75

WORLD'S BEST COMICS
Spring, 1941
1 Superman vs. the Rainmaker,
  Batman vs. Wright 14,000.00
Becomes:
WORLD'S FINEST COMICS
1941–86
2 Superman V:'The Unknown X',
  Batman V:Ambrose Taylor . 3,700.00
3 I&O:Scarecrow 2,900.00
4 Superman V:Dan Brandon,
  Batman V:Ghost Gang ... 2,000.00
5 Superman V:Lemuel P.Potts,
  Batman V:Brains Kelly ... 2,000.00
6 Superman V:Metalo,Batman
  meets Scoop Scanlon 1,400.00
7 Superman V:Jenkins,Batman
  V:Snow Man Bandits 1,400.00
8 Superman:'Talent Unlimited'
  Batman V:Little Nap Boyd,
  B:Boy Commandos 1,300.00
9 Superman:'One Second to
  Live',Batman V:Bramwell B.
  Bramwell 1,300.00
10 Superman V:The Insect Master,
  Batman reforms Oliver Hunt 1,200.00
11 Superman V:Charlie Frost,
  Batman V:Rob Calendar . . 1,000.00
12 Superman V:Lynx,Batman:
  'Alfred Gets His Man' 1,000.00
13 Superman V:Dice Dimant,
  Batman,V:Swami Pravhoz . 1,000.00
14 Superman V:Al Bandar,Batman
  V:Jib Buckler 1,000.00
15 Superman V:Derby Bowser,
  Batman V:Mennekin 1,000.00
16 Superman:'Music for the Masses,
  Batman V:Nocky Johnson . 1,000.00
17 Superman:'The Great Godini',
  Batman V:Dr.Dreemo 1,000.00
18 Superman:'The Junior Reporters,
  Batman V:Prof.Brane 900.00
19 A:The Joker 900.00
20 A:Toyman 900.00
21 Superman:'Swindle in
  Sweethearts!' 600.00
22 Batman V:Nails Finney 600.00
23 Superman:'The Colossus
  of Metropolis' 600.00
24 .... 600.00

25 Superman V:Ed Rook,Batman:
  'The Famous First Crimes' . 600.00
26 'Confessions of Superman' . 600.00
27 'The Man Who Out-Supered
  Superman 600.00
28 A:Lex Luther,Batman V:Glass
  Man 600.00
29 Superman:'The Books that
  couldn't be Bound' 600.00
30 Superman:'Sheriff Clark Kent',
  Batman V:Joe Coyne 600.00
31 'Superman's Super-Rival',Batman:
  'Man with the X-Ray Eyes' . 550.00
32 Superman visits
  Ancient Egypt 550.00
33 'Superman Press, Inc.',
  Batman V:James Harmon . . 550.00
34 'The Un-Super Superman' . 550.00
35 Daddy Superman,A:Penguin 550.00
36 Lois Lane,Sleeping Beauty . 550.00
37 'The Superman Story',Batman
  V:T-Gun Jones 550.00
38 If There were No Superman 550.00
39 Superman V:Big Jim Martin,
  Batman V:J.J.Jason 550.00
40 Superman V:Check,Batman:'4
  Killers Against Fate!' 550.00
41 I:Supermanium,
  E:Boy Commandos 425.00
42 Superman goes to Uranus,
  A:Marco Polo & Kubla Khan 425.00
43 A:J.Wilbur Wolfingham 425.00
44 Superman:'The Revolt of the
  Thought Machine' 425.00
45 Superman:'Lois Lane and Clark
  Kent,Private Detectives 425.00
46 Superman V:Mr. 7 ...... 425.00
47 Superman:'The Girl Who
  Hated Reporters 425.00
48 A:Joker 425.00
49 Superman meets the
  Metropolis Shutterbug
  Society, A:Penguin 425.00
50 'Superman Super Wrecker' . 425.00
51 Superman:'The Amazing
  Talents of Lois Lane' 425.00
52 A:J.Wilbur Wolfingham 425.00
53 Superman V:Elias Toomey . 425.00

World's Finest Comics #47
© DC Comics, Inc.

54 'The Superman Who Avoided
    Danger!' 425.00
55 A:Penguin 425.00
56 Superman V:Dr.Vallin,Batman
    V:Big Dan Hooker 425.00
57 'The Artificial Superman' . . . 425.00
58 Superman V:Mr.Fenton 425.00
59 A:Lex Luthor,Joker 425.00
60 A:J.Wilbur Wolfingham 425.00
61 A:Joker,'Superman's
    Blackout' 250.00
62 A:Lex Luthor 250.00
63 Superman:'Clark Kent,
    Gangster' 250.00
64 Superman:'The Death of Lois
    Lane,Batman:'Bruce Wayne...
    Amateur Detective' 250.00
65 'The Confessions of Superman',
    Batman V:The Blaster 600.00
66 'Superman,Ex-Crimebuster;
    Batman V:Brass Haley 425.00
67 Superman:'Metropolis-Crime
    Center!' 425.00
68 Batman V:The Crimesmith . 425.00
69 A:Jor-El,Batman
    V:Tom Becket 425.00
70 'The Two Faces of Superman',
    Batman:'Crime Consultant' . 425.00
71 B:Superman/Batman
    team-ups 850.00
72 V:Heavy Weapon gang 600.00
73 V:Fang 600.00
74 'The Contest of Heroes' . . . 500.00
75 V:The Purple Mask Mob . . . 425.00
76 'When Gotham City
    Challenged Metropolis 325.00
77 V:Prof.Pender 325.00
78 V:Varrel mob 325.00
79 A:Aladdin 325.00
80 V:Mole 325.00
81 Meet Ka Thar from future . . 275.00
82 A:Three Musketeers 275.00
83 'The Case of the Mother
    Goose Mystery' 275.00
84 V:Thad Linnis gang 275.00
85 Meet Princess Varina 275.00
86 V:Henry Bartle 275.00
87 V:Elton Craig 275.00
88 1st team-up Luthor & Joker . 300.00
89 I:Club of Heroes 275.00
90 A:Batwoman 275.00
91 V:Rohtul,descendent of Lex
    Luthor 200.00
92 Ist & only A:Skyboy 175.00
93 V:Victor Danning 200.00
94 O:Superman/Batman team,
    A:Lex Luthor 550.00
95 'Battle o/t Super Heroes' . . . 175.00
96 'Super-Foes from Planet X' . 175.00
97 V:Condor Gang 175.00
98 I:Moonman 175.00
99 JK,V:Carl Verril 175.00
100 A:Kandor, Lex Luthor 325.00
101 A:Master 150.00
102 V:Jo-Jo Groff gang,
    B:Tommy Tomorrow 150.00
103 'The Secrets of the
    Sorcerer's Treasure 150.00
104 A:Lex Luthor 150.00
105 V:Khalex 150.00
106 V:Duplicate Man 150.00
107 'The Secret of the Time
    Creature' 150.00
108 'The Star Creatures' 150.00
109 V:Fangan 150.00

World's Finest Comics #106
© DC Comics, Inc.

110 'The Alien Who Doomed
    Robin!' 150.00
111 V:Floyd Frisby 150.00
112 . . . . 150.00
113 1st Bat-Mite/Mr.Mxyzptlk
    team-up 150.00
114 'Captives o/t Space Globes' 150.00
115 The Curse That Doomed
    Superman 125.00
116 V:Vance Collins 125.00
117 A:Batwoman,Lex Luthor . 125.00
118 V:Vath-Gar 125.00
119 V:General Grambly 125.00
120 V:Faceless Creature 125.00
121 I:Miss Arrowette 125.00
122 V:Klor 60.00
123 A:Bat-Mite & Mr. Mxyzptlk . 60.00
124 V:Hroguth,E:Tommy
    Tomorrow 60.00
125 V:Jundy,B:Aquaman 60.00
126 A:Lex Luthor 60.00
127 V:Zerno 60.00
128 V:Moose Morans 60.00
129 Joker/Luthor T.U. 75.00
130 . . . . 60.00
131 V:Octopus 60.00
132 V:Denny Kale,Shorty Biggs . 60.00
133 . . . . 60.00
134 V:Band of Super-Villians . . . 60.00
135 V:The Future Man 60.00
136 The Batman Nobody
    Remembered 60.00
137 A:Lex Luthor 60.00
138 V:General Grote 60.00
139 V:Sphinx Gang,E:Aquaman . 60.00
140 CS,V:Clayface 60.00
141 CS,A:Jimmy Olsen 60.00
142 CS,O:Composite Man 60.00
143 CS,A:Kandor,I:Mailbag 50.00
144 CS,A:Clayface,Brainiac 50.00
145 CS,Prison for Heroes 50.00
146 CS,Batman,Son of Krypton . 50.00
147 CS,A:Jimmy Olsen 50.00
148 CS,A:Lex Luthor,Clayface . . 50.00
149 CS,The Game of the
    Secret Identities 50.00
150 CS,V:Rokk and Sorban 35.00

151 CS,A:Krypto,BU:Congorilla . 35.00
152 CS,A:The Colossal Kids,Bat-
    mite,V:Mr.Mxyzptlk 35.00
153 CS,V:Lex Luthor 35.00
154 CS,The Sons of Batman &
    Superman(Imaginary) 35.00
155 CS,The 1000th Exploit of
    Batman & Superman 35.00
156 CS,I:BizarroBatman,V:Joker 100.00
157 CS,The Abominable Brats
    (Imaginary story) 35.00
158 CS,V:Brainiac 35.00
159 CS,A:Many Major villians,I:Jim
    Gordon as Anti-Batman & Perry
    White as Anti-Superman 35.00
160 V:Dr Zodiac 35.00
161 CS,80 page giant 40.00
162 V:The Jousting Master 25.00
163 CS,The Court of No Hope . . 25.00
164 CS,I:Genia,V:Brainiac 25.00
165 CS,The Crown of Crime . . . 25.00
166 CS,V:Muto & Joker 28.00
167 CS,The New Superman &
    Batman(Imaginary) V:Luthor . 25.00
168 CS,R:Composite Superman . 25.00
169 The Supergirl/Batgirl Plot;
    V:Batmite,Mr.Mxyzptlk 25.00
170 80 page giant,reprint 25.00
171 CS,V:The Executioners 25.00
172 CS,Superman & Batman
    Brothers (Imaginary) 25.00
173 CS,The Jekyll-Hyde Heroes 25.00
174 CS,Secrets of the Double
    Death Wish 25.00
175 NA(1st Batman),C:Flash . . . 20.00
176 NA,A:Supergirl & Batgirl . . 20.00
177 V:Joker & Luthor 22.00
178 CS,The Has-Been Superman 15.00
179 CS,giant 22.00
180 RA,ME,Supermans Perfect
    Crime 15.00
181 RA,ME 15.00
182 RA,ME,The Mad Manhunter 15.00
183 RA,ME,Supermans Crimes
    of the Ages 15.00
184 RA,ME,A:JLA,Robin 15.00
185 CS,The Galactic Gamblers . 15.00
186 RA,ME,The Bat Witch 15.00
187 RA,ME,Demon Superman . . 15.00
188 giant,reprint 22.00
189 RA,ME,V:Lex Luthor 15.00
190 RA,V:Lex Luthor 10.00
191 RA,A:Jor-El,Lara 10.00
192 RA,The Prison of No Escape 10.00
193 The Breaking of Batman
    and Superman 10.00
194 RA,ME,Inside the Mafia . . . 10.00
195 RA,ME,Dig Now-Die Later . . 10.00
196 CS,The Kryptonite Express,
    E:Batman 10.00
197 giant 30.00
198 DD,B:Superman T.U.,
    A:Flash 90.00
199 DD,Superman & Flash race . 90.00
200 NA(c),DD,Prisoners of the
    Immortal World; A:Robin 8.00
201 NA(c),DD,A Prize of Peril,
    A:Green Lantern,Dr. Fate 7.00
202 NA(c),DD,Vengeance of the
    Tomb Thing,A:Batman 7.00
203 NA(c),DD,Who's Minding the
    Earth,A:Quamar 7.00
204 NA(c),DD,Journey to the
    End of Hope,A:Wonder Woman 7.00
205 NA(c),DD,The Computer that

All comics prices listed are for *Near Mint* condition.

Captured a Town,Frazetta Ad,
  A:Teen Titans 15.00
206 DD,giant reprint 25.00
207 DD,Superman,A:Batman,
  V:Dr.Light 12.00
208 NA(c),DD,A:Dr Fate 12.00
209 NA(c),DD,A:Green Arrow,
  Hawkman,I&V:The Temper . 12.00
210 NA(c),DD,A:Batman 12.00
211 NA(c),DD,A:Batman 12.00
212 CS(c),And So My World
  Begins,A:Martian Manhunter . 12.00
213 DD,Peril in a Very Small
  Place,A:The Atom 12.00
214 DD,A:Vigilante 12.00
215 DD,Saga of the Super Sons
  (Imaginary story) 12.00
216 DD,R:Super Sons,Little Town
  with a Big Secret 12.00
217 DD,MA,Heroes with
  Dirty Hands 12.00
218 DD,DC,A:Batman,
  BU:Metamorpho 12.00
219 DD,Prisoner of Rogues Rock;
  A:Batman 12.00
220 DD,MA,Let No Man Write My
  Epitaph,BU:Metamorpho 12.00
221 DD,Cry Not For My Forsaken
  Son; R:Super Sons 12.00
222 DD,Evil In Paradise 12.00
223 DD,giant,A:Deadman,Aquaman
  Robotman 15.00
224 DD,giant,A:Super Sons,
  Metamorpho,Johnny Quick . . 15.00
225 giant,A:Rip Hunter,Vigilante,
  Black Canary,Robin 12.00
226 A:Sandman,Metamorpho,
  Deadman,Martian Manhunter . 15.00
227 MGr,BWi,A:The Demonic Duo,
  Vigilante,Rip Hunter,Deadman,
  I:Stargrave 15.00
228 ATh,A:Super Sons,Aquaman,
  Robin,Vigilante 15.00
229 I:Powerman,A:Metamorpho . 12.00
230 A:Super-Sons,Deadman,
  Aquaman 12.00
231 A:Green Arrow,Flash 12.00
232 DD,The Dream Bomb 12.00
233 A:Super-Sons 12.00
234 CS,Family That Fled Earth . 12.00
235 DD,V:Sagitaurus 12.00
236 DD,A:The Atom 12.00
237 Intruder from a Dead World . 12.00
238 DD,V:Luthor,A:Super-Sons. . 12.00
239 CS,A:Gold(from Metal Men) 12.00
240 DD,A:Kandor 10.00
241 Make Way For a New World 10.00
242 EC,A:Super-Sons 10.00
243 CS,AM,A:Robin 10.00
244 NA(c),JL,MA,MN,TA,giant
  B:Green Arrow 10.00
245 NA(C),CS,MA,MN,TA,
  GM,JSh,BWi,giant 10.00
246 NA(c),KS,MA,MN,TA,GM,
  DH,A:JLA 10.00
247 KS,GM,giant 10.00
248 KS,GM,DG,TVE,A:Sgt.Rock 10.00
249 KS,SD,TVE,A:Phantom
  Stranger,B:Creeper 10.00
250 GT,SD,Superman,Batman,
  Wonder Woman,Green Arrow,
  Black Canary,team-up 8.00
251 GT,SD,JBi,BL,TVE,RE,
  JA,A:Poison Ivy,Speedy,
  I:CountVertigo 8.00

World's Finest Comics #238
© *DC Comics, Inc.*

252 GT,TVE,SD,JA,giant 8.00
253 KS,DN,TVE,SD,B:Shazam . . 5.00
254 GT,DN,TVE,SD,giant 5.00
255 JL,DA,TVE,SD,DN,KS,
  E:Creeper 5.00
256 MA,DN,KS,DD,Hawkman,Black
  Lightning,giant 5.00
257 DD,FMc,DN,KS,GT,RB,
  RT,giant 5.00
258 NA(c),RB,JL,DG,DN,KS,RT,
  giant 5.00
259 RB,DG,MR,MN,DN,KS 5.00
260 RB,DG,MN,DN 5.00
261 RB,DG,AS,RT,EB,DN,
  A:Penguin, Terra Man 6.00
262 DG,DN,DA,JSon,RT,
  Aquaman 5.00
263 RB,DG,DN,TVE,JSh,Aquaman,
  Adam Strange 5.00
264 RB,DG,TVE,DN,Aquaman . . . 5.00
265 RB,DN,RE,TVE 5.00
266 RB,TVE,DN 5.00
267 RB,DG,TVE,AS,DN,
  A:Challengers of the Unknown 5.00
268 DN,TVE,BBr,RT,AS 5.00
269 RB,FMc,TVE,BBr,AS,DN,DA . 5.00
270 NA(c),RB,RT,TVE,AS,
  DN,LMa 5.00
271 GP(c),RB,FMc,O:Superman/
  Batman T.U. 6.00
272 RB,DN,TVE,BBr,AS 4.00
273 TVE,LMa,JSon,AS,DN,DA,
  A:Plastic Man 4.00
274 TVE,LMa,BBr,GC,AS,DN,
  Green Arrow 4.00
275 RB,FMc,TVE,LMa,DSp,AS,
  DN,DA,A:Mr.Freeze 4.00
276 GP(c),RB,TVE,LMa,DSp,CI,
  DN,DA 4.00
277 GP(c),RT,TVE,DSp,AS,DN,
  DH,V:Dr.Double X 4.00
278 GP(c),RB,TVE,LMa,DSp,DN . 4.00
279 KP,TVE,LMa,AS,DN,
  B:Kid Eternity 4.00
280 RB,TVE,LMa,AS,DN 4.00
281 GK(c),IN,TVE,LMa,AS,DN . . . 4.00
282 IN,FMc,GK,CI,last giant

E:Kid Eternity 4.00
283 GT,FMc,GK 4.00
284 GT,DSp,A:Legion,E:G.Arrow . 4.00
285 FM(c),RB,A:Zatanna 4.00
286 RB,A:Flash 4.00
287 TVE,A:Flash 4.00
288 A:JLA 4.00
289 GK(c),Kryll way of Dying 4.00
290 TD(i),I:Stalagron 4.00
291 WS(c),TD(i),V:Stalagron 4.00
292 . . . . 4.00
293 . . . . 4.00
294 . . . . 4.00
295 FMc(i) 4.00
296 RA 4.00
297 GC,V:Pantheon 4.00
298 V:Pantheon 4.00
299 GC,V:Pantheon 4.00
300 RA,GP,KJ,MT,FMc,A:JLA . . . 5.00
301 Rampage 2.25
302 DM,NA(rep) 2.25
303 Plague 2.25
304 SLi,O:Null&Void 2.25
305 TVE,V:Null&Void 2.25
306 SLi,I:Swordfish & Barracuda . 2.25
307 TVE,V:Null&Void 2.25
308 GT,Night and Day 2.25
309 MT,AA,V:Quantum 2.25
310 I:Sonik 2.25
311 A:Monitor 2.25
312 AA,I:Network 2.25
313 AA(i),V:Network 2.25
314 AA(i),V:Executrix 2.25
315 V:Cathode 2.25
316 LSn,I:Cheapjack 2.25
317 LSn,V:Cheapjack 2.25
318 AA(i),A:Sonik 2.25
319 AA(i),I:REM 2.25
320 AA(i),V:REM 2.25
321 AA,V:Chronos 2.25
322 KG,The Search 2.25
323 AA(i),final issue 2.25

WORLD'S FINEST
[Limited Series] 1990
1 SR,KK,Worlds Apart 8.00

World's Finest (Ltd. Series) #1
© *DC Comics, Inc.*

2 SR,KK,Worlds Collide 6.00
3 SR,KK,Worlds At War 6.00
TPB rep.#1-#3 . . . . 19.95

WORLD'S FINEST: SUPERBOY/ROBIN
Oct. 1996
1 (of 2) CDi&KK(s),TG,SHa,
   V:Poison Ivy, Metallo 4.95
2 CDi&KK(s),TG,SHa, V:Poison
   Ivy, Metallo 4.95

WORLD'S GREATEST SUPER-HEROES
1977
1 A:Batman,Robin 2.50

WORLD WITHOUT END
1990
1 The Host, I:Brother Bones 5.00
2 A:Brother Bones 3.50
3 . . . . 3.50
4 House of Fams 2.50
5 Female Fury 2.50
6 conclusion 2.50

WRATH OF THE SPECTRE
May, 1988
1 JAp,rep.Adventure #431-#433 . 2.50
2 JAp,rep.Adventure #434-#436 . 2.50
3 JAp,rep.Adventure #437-#440 . 2.50
4 JAp,reps.,final issue 2.50

XENOBROOD
1994–95
0 New team 1.50
1 Battles 1.50
2 Bestiary 1.50
3 A:Superman 1.50
4 V:Bestiary 1.50
5 V:Vimian 1.50
6 final issue 1.50

XERØ
March 1997
1 Cpr(s),Ccs,Trane Walker/Xero   1.75
2 CPr(s),Ccs,"The Rookie" 1.75
3 Cpr(s),Ccs,"The Beast" 1.75
4 CPr(s) 1.75
6 CPr, Genesis tie-in 1.75
7 CPr(s),O:ZerØ, pt.1 . . . . 1.75
8 CPr,O:Zero 2.00
9 CPr(s), ... 2.00
10 CPr,a matter of ethics 2.00
11 . . . . 2.00
12 CPr, final issue, Xero dead . . . 2.00

XOMBI
Milestone 1994–96
0 WS(c),DCw,Shadow War,Foil(c),
   I:Xombi,Twilight 2.50
1 JBy(c),B:Silent Cathedrals 2.00
1a Platinum ed. 15.00
2 I:Rabbi Simmowitz,Golms,Liam
   Knight of the Spoken Fire 1.75
3 A:Liam 2.00
4 Silent Cathedrals 2.00
5 Silent Cathedrals 1.75
6 Silent Cathedrals 1.75
7 School of Anguish 1.75
8 School of Anguish,pt.2 . . . . . . 1.75

Xombi #5 © DC Comics, Inc.

9 School of Anguish,pt.3 . . . . . . 1.75
10 School of Anguish,pt.4 . . . . . . 1.75
11 School of Anguish,pt.5 . . . . . . 1.75
12 Truth and Surprises 1.75
13 V:Kinderessen 1.75
14 Long Hot Summer, A:Cheryl
   Saltz 2.50
15 Long Hot Summer 2.50
16 Long Hot Summer 2.50
17 Reader's Choice 2.50
18 Serpent's Tail 2.50
19 Mister Missy, Bellhop 2.50
20 . . . . 2.50
21 final issue 3.50

YOUNG ALL STARS
June, 1987
1 I:IronMunro&FlyingFox,D:TNT . 4.50
2 V:Axis Amerika 2.50
3 V:Axis Amerika 2.00
4 I:The Tigress 2.00
5 I:Dyna-mite,O:Iron Munro 2.00
6 . . . . 2.00
7 Baseball Game,A:Tigress 2.00
8 Millenium 2.00
9 Millenium 2.00
10 Hugo Danner 2.00
11 'Birth of Iron Munro' 2.00
12 'Secret of Hugo Danner' 2.00
13 'V:Deathbolt,Ultra-Humanite . . 2.00
14 Fury+Ultra Humanite 2.00
15 IronMunro At high school 2.00
16 Ozyan Inheritance 2.00
17 Ozyan Inheritance 2.00
18 Ozyan Inheritance 2.00
19 Ozyan 2.00
20 O:Flying Fox 2.00
21 Atom & Evil#1 . . . . 2.00
22 Atom & Evil#2 . . . . 2.00
23 Atom & Evil#3 . . . . 2.00
24 Atom & Evil#4 . . . . 2.00
25 . . . . 2.00
26 End of the All Stars? 2.00
27 'Sons of Dawn' begins 2.00
28 Search for Hugo Danner 2.00
29 A:Hugo Danner 2.00
30 V:Sons of Dawn 2.00

31 V:Sons of Dawn,last issue . . . 2.00
Ann.#1 MG,V:Mekanique 2.50

YOUNG HEROES IN LOVE
April 1997
1 DeM,F:Hard Drive 1.75
2 DeM,sex, lies and superheroics 1.75
3 A:Superman 1.75
4 F:Hard Drive 1.75
5 Genesis tie-in 2.00
6 The Rat Pack 2.00
7 Secret Identity Issu 2.00
8 V:Scarecrow 2.00
9 F:Frostbite & Bonfire 2.00
10 V:Grundo'mu 2.00
11 V:Grundo'mu 2.00
12 Hard Drive dead? 2.00
13 New leader picked 2.00
14 Man of Inches vs. Man
   of Candles 2.00
15 Junior vs. Birthday Boy 2.00
16 DeM,Zip-Kid 2.00
17 DeM,Monstergirl's Uncle 2.50

YOUNG JUSTICE
July 1998
1 PDd,TNu,Robin,Superboy,
   Impulse 2.50
2 PDd,TNu,V:Super-Cycle 2.50

YOUNG JUSTICE: THE SECRET
May, 1998
1-shot Impulse, Superboy, Robin . 2.00

YOUNG LOVE
Sept.–Oct., 1963
39 . . . . 30.00
40 thru 50 . . . . @20.00
51 thru 70 . . . . @15.00
71 thru 80 . . . . @12.00
81 thru 126 . . . . @10.00

ZATANNA
1987
1 R:Zatanna 2.25
2 N:Zatanna 2.25
3 Come Together 2.25
4 V:Xaos 2.25

ZERO HOUR: CRISIS IN TIME
1994
4 DJu(a&s),JOy,A:All DC Heroes,
   D;2nd Flash 1.50
3 DJu(a&S),JOy,D:G.A.Sandman,
   G:A.Atom,Dr.Fate,1st Wildcat
   IR:Time Trapper is Rokk Krinn,
   Hawkmen merged 1.50
2 DJu(a&s),Joy 1.50
1 DJu(a&s),JOy,b:Power Gir's
   Child 1.50
0 DJu(A&S),JOy,Gatefold(c),Extant
   vs. Spectre 1.50

DC COMICS

Bruce Wayne, Agent of S.H.I.E.L.D. #1
© DC/Marvel

Generation Hex #1
© DC/Marvel

Magneto & The Magnetic Men #1
© DC/Marvel

AMAZON
DC 1996–97
1 JBy,TA 3.00
1 one-shot JBy,Princess Ororo
   is Wonder Woman 2.00

ASSASSINS
DC 1996–97
1 DGC,SMc 3.00
1 one-shot DGC(s),SMc,F:Dare
   and Catsai 2.00

BAT-THING
DC 1997
1 one-shot LHa(s),RDm,BSz,
   V:motorcycle gang 2.00

BRUCE WAYNE:
AGENT OF S.H.I.E.L.D.
Marvel Comics 1996
1 CDi, ... 3.00

BULLETS & BRACELETS
Marvel Comics 1996
1 JOs,GFr,CaS 3.00

CHALLENGERS OF
THE FANTASTIC
Marvel 1997
1 KK,TGu,AV 2.00

DARK CLAW
ADVENTURES, THE
DC 1997
1 one-shot TTy,RBr,V:Ladia Talia 2.00

DC VERSUS MARVEL
MARVEL VERSUS DC
1 (DC)DJu 6.00
1a 2nd printing 4.00
2 (Marvel)PDd,DJu 5.00
2a 2nd printing 4.00

3 (Marvel)DJu 4.00
4 (DC)PDd,DJu 4.00
TPB rep. mini series #1–#4 . . . . 12.95

DOCTOR STRANGEFATE
DC Comics 1996–97
1 RMz,KN . . . .
1 one-shot RMz(s),JL,KN,Supreme
   Lord of Order 2.00

EXCITING X-PATROL
Marvel 1997
1 BKs,BHi 2.00

GENERATION HEX
DC 1997
1 one-shot,PrM(s),AdP,F:Jono Hex,
   Madam Banshee 2.00

IRON LANTERN
Marvel 1997
1 KB,PSm,AW 2.00

JLX
DC Comics 1996–97
1 MWa,GJ, ... 3.00
1 one-shot,MWa(s),GJ,HPo,JhD . 2.00

JLX UNLEASHED
DC 1997
1 one-shot, CPr,"The Inextinguish-
   able Flame" 2.00

LEGENDS OF
THE DARK CLAW
DC Comics 1996–97
1 LHa,JBa, ... 3.00
1 one-shot LHa(s),JBa, ... 2.00
1 2nd printing 2.00

LOBO THE DUCK
DC 1997
1 one-shot, AlG,VS, ... 2.00

MAGNETO &
THE MAGNETIC MEN
Marvel Comics 1996
1 MWa,GJ,JMs,ATi 3.00

MAGNETIC MEN
FEATURING MAGNETO
Marvel 1997
1 TPe,BKi,DPs 2.00

SPEED DEMON
Marvel Comics 1996
1 HMe,SvL,AM 3.00

SPIDER-BOY
Marvel Comics 1996
1 KK,MeW 3.00

SPIDER-BOY TEAM-UP
Marvel Comics 1997
1 KK,RSt 2.00

SUPER-SOLDIER
DC Comics 1996–97
1 MWa,DGb 3.00
1-shot MWa(s),DGb,V:Ultra-
   Metallo, Green Skull, Hydra . . 2.00

SUPER SOLDIER:
MAN OF WAR
DC 1997
1 one-shot MWa(s),DGb,JP,
   V:Nazis 2.00

THORION OF
THE NEW ASGODS
Marvel 1997
1 KG,JR2 . . . . 2.00

X-PATROL
Marvel Comics 1996
1 KK,BKs, ... 3.00

MARVEL

ABOMINATIONS
1996
1 (of 3) IV,AMe, Future Imperfect
  spin-off 1.50
2 IV,AMe, ... 1.50
3 IV,AMe, ... 1.50

ABRAHAM STONE
1995
1 JKu, Early 20th century 6.95
2 Wandering Man in the 20s 6.95

ACTION FORCE
March, 1987
1 U.K. G.I. Joe Series 1.50
2 thru 39 . . . . @1.00
40 1988 . . . . 1.00

ACTUAL CONFESSIONS
See: LOVE ADVENTURES

ACTUAL ROMANCES
Oct., 1949
1 . . . . 45.00
2 Photo Cover 25.00

ADVENTURE INTO FEAR
See: FEAR

ADVENTURE INTO MYSTERY
Atlas 1956–57
1 BEv(c),Future Tense 250.00
2 Man on the 13th Floor 150.00
3 Next Stop Eternity 125.00
4 AW, The Hex 150.00
5 BEv,The People Who Weren't 100.00
6 The Wax Man 100.00
7 . . . . 100.00

ADVENTURES INTO TERROR
See: JOKER COMICS

ADVENTURES INTO WEIRD WORLDS
Jan., 1952–June 1954
1 RH,GT,The Walking Death . 375.00
2 The Thing in the Bottle . . . 250.00
3 The Thing That Waited 150.00
4 BEv,RH,TheVillageGraveyard 150.00
5 BEv,I Crawl Thru Graves . . . 150.00
6 The Ghost Still Walks 150.00
7 Monsters In Disguise 150.00
8 Nightmares 150.00
9 Do Not Feed 150.00
10 BEv,Down In The Cellar . . . 150.00
11 Phantom 125.00
12 Lost In the Graveyard 125.00
13 Where Dead Men Walk 125.00
14 A Shriek In the Night 125.00
15 Terror In Our Town 125.00
16 The Kiss of Death 125.00
17 RH,He Walks With A Ghost . 125.00
18 Ivan & Petroff 125.00
19 It Happened One Night 125.00
20 The Doubting Thomas 125.00
21 What Happened In the Cave 135.00
22 RH,The Vampire's Partner . 125.00
23 The Kiss of Death 100.00
24 Halfway Home 100.00
25 BEv,JSt,The Mad Mamba . . 100.00
26 Good-Bye Earth 125.00
27 The Dwarf of Horror Moor . . 250.00
28 DW,Monsters From the Grave 150.00
29 Bone Dry 100.00
30 JSt,The Impatient Ghost . . . 100.00

ADVENTURES OF CAPTAIN AMERICA
Sept., 1991
1 KM,JRu,O:Capt. America 5.75
2 KM,KWe,TA,O:Capt.America . . 5.50
3 KM,KWe,JRu,D:Lt.Col.Fletcher 5.50
4 KWe,JRu,V:Red Skull 5.50

ADVENTURES OF CYCLOPS & PHOENIX
1994
1 SLo(s),GeH,AV,O:Cable 4.00
2 SLo(s),GeH,AV,O:Cable 3.50
3 SLo(s),GeH,AV,O:Cable 3.50
4 SLo(s),GeH,AV,O:Cable 3.50
TPB Rep. #1-#4 . . . . 14.95

ADVENTURES OF HOMER GHOST
Atlas June–Aug., 1957
1 . . . . 30.00
2 . . . . 25.00

ADVENTURES OF PINKY LEE
Atlas July, 1955
1 . . . . 150.00
2 . . . . 65.00
3 thru 5 . . . . @54.00

ADVENTURES OF SNAKE PLISSKIN
1997
1-shot LKa, *Escape From L.A.*
  movie adapt. 3.00

ADVENTURES OF SPIDER-MAN
1996
1 from animated TV show 1.00
2 V:Hammerhead 1.00
3 thru 8 . . . . 1.00
8 AS,V:Kingpin 1.00
9 MHi,A:Dr. Strange, ... 1.00
10 AS,V:The Beetle 1.00
11 AS,V:Doctor Octopus, Venom . 1.00
12 AS,V:Doctor Octopus, Venom . 1.00

ADVENTURES OF THE UNCANNY X-MEN
1995
1 Rep. 1.00

ADVENTURES OF THE X-MEN
1996–97
1 from animated TV show 1.00
2 X-Factor vs. X-Men 1.00
3 thru 7 . . . . 1.00
8 RMc,BHr,GyM,Gambit back in
  New Orleans 1.00
9 RMc,GyM,F:Storm 1.00
10 RMc,A:Vanisher 1.00
11 RMc,V:Man-Thing 1.00
12 RMc,Age of Apocalypse 1.00

Adventures on the Planet of the
Apes #1 © Marvel Entertainment Group

ADVENTURES ON THE PLANET OF THE APES
Oct., 1975
1 GT,Planet of the Apes Movie
  Adaptation 2.50
2 GT,Humans Captured 2.50
3 GT,Man Hunt 2.50
4 GT,Trial By Fear 2.50
5 GT, Fury in the
  Forbidden Zone 2.50
6 GT,The Forbidden Zone,Cont'd 2.50
7 AA,Man Hunt Cont'd 2.50
8 AA,Brent & Nova Enslaved . . . 2.50
9 AA,Mankind's Demise 2.50
10 AA,When Falls the Lawgiver . . 2.50
11 AA,The Final Chapter;
  Dec., 1976 . . . . 2.50

ADVENTURES OF THE THING
April–July 1992
1 rep. Marvel 2 in 1 #50 . . . . . . 2.50
2 rep. Marvel 2 in 1 #80
  B.U. Ghost Rider 1.50
3 rep. Marvel 2 in 1 #51 . . . . . . 1.50
4 rep. Marvel 2 in 1 #77 . . . . . . 1.50

All comics prices listed are for *Near Mint* condition.

AGE OF INNOCENCE
1995
1-shot Timeslid aftermath 2.50

AIRTIGHT GARAGE
Epic July–Oct. 1993
1 thru 4 rep.Moebius GNv .... @2.50

AKIRA
Epic Sept., 1988
1 The Highway,I:Kaneda,Tetsuo,
   Koy,Ryu,Colonel,Takaski ... 15.00
1a 2nd printing 3.00
2 Pursuit,I:Number27,(Masaru) .. 7.00
2a 2nd printing 3.50
3 Number 41,V:Clown Gang ... 6.00
4 King of Clowns,V:Colonel 7.00
5 Cycle Wars,V:Clown Gang ... 6.00
6 D:Yamagota 5.00
7 Prisoners and Players,I:Miyo .. 5.00
8 Weapon of Vengeance 5.00
9 Stalkers 5.00
10 The Awakening 5.00
11 Akira Rising 4.50
12 Enter Sakaki 4.50
13 Desperation 4.50
14 Caught in the Middle 4.50
15 Psychic Duel 4.50
16 Akira Unleashed 4.50
17 Emperor of Chaos 4.50
18 Amid the Ruins 4.00
19 To Save the Children 4.00
20 Revelations 4.00
21 .... 4.00
22 .... 4.00
23 .... 4.00
24 Clown Gang 4.00
25 Search For Kay 4.00
26 Juvenile A Project 4.00
27 Kay and Kaneda 4.00
28 Tetsuo 4.00
29 Tetsuo 4.00
30 Tetsuo,Kay,Kaneda 4.00
31 D:Kaori,Kaneda,Vs.Tetsuo .. 4.00
32 Tetsuo'sForces vs.U.S.Forces . 4.00
33 Tetsuo V:Kaneda 4.00
34 64pt. R:Otomo 7.00
35 Leads toward final battle 7.00
36 Lady Miyako 7.00
37 ghost of Tetsuo 7.00
38 conclusion 7.00
TPB Akira:Reprints#1-#3 ..... 13.95
TPB Akira:Reprints#4-#6 ..... 13.95
TPB Akira:Reprints#7-#9 ..... 13.95
TPB Akira:Reprints#10-#12 .... 14.95
TPB Akira:Reprints#13-#15 .... 14.95
TPB Akira:Reprints#16-#18 .... 14.95
TPB Akira:Reprints#19-#21 .... 16.95
TPB Akira:Reprints#22-#24 .... 16.95
TPB Akira:Reprints#25-#27 .... 16.95
TPB Akira:Reprints#28-#30 .... 17.95

ALADDIN
1 .... 1.50
2 .... 1.50
3 .... 1.50
4 .... 1.50
5 A:Queen Tatiana 1.50
6 A:Zena 1.50
7 Genie Convention 1.50
8 Body Switch 1.50
9 Archery Contest 1.50
10 Genie winds back his powers . 1.50
11 Magic Carpet Grand Prix 1.50

12 F:Iago 1.50

Alf #5 © Marvel Entertainment Group

ALF
Star March, 1988
1 Photo Cover 1.50
1a 2nd printing 1.00
2 Alf Causes trouble 1.50
3 More adventures 1.50
4 Willie on Melmac 1.50
5 I:Alf's evil twin 1.50
6 Photo Cover 1.50
7 Pygm-Alien 1.50
8 Ochmoneks' Garage 1.25
9 Alf's Independence Day 1.25
10 Alf goes to College 1.25
11 Halloween special 1.00
12 Alf loses memory 1.00
13 Racetrack of my Tears 1.00
14 Night of the Living Bread .. 1.25
15 Alf on the Road 1.00
16 More Adventures 1.00
17 Future vision 1.00
18 More Adventures 1.00
19 The Alf-strologer 1.00
20 Alf the Baby Sitter,pt.1 .... 1.00
21 Alf the Baby Sitter,pt.2 .... 1.00
22 X-Men parody 1.00
23 Alf visits Australia 1.00
24 Rhonda visits Earth 1.00
25 More Adventures 1.00
26 Alf gets a job 1.00
27 Alf lost 1.00
28 Alf's Amnesia 1.00
29 Alf/Brian reporters 1.00
30 Shakespeare Baby 1.00
31 Alf's Summer Camp 1.00
32 Arnold Schwarzemeimac 1.00
33 Dungeons & Dragons Spoof . 1.00
34 Alf-Red & Alf-Blue(2 Alfs) ... 1.00
35 Gone with the Wind 1.00
36 More Adventures 1.00
37 Melmacian Gothic 1.00
38 Boundtree Hunters 1.00
39 Pizarro Alf 1.00
40 A:Zoreo 1.00
41 TV 1.00
42 V:Alf 1.00
43 House Break-in 1.00
44 A:Fantastic Fur 1.00

45 Melmenopaus 1.00
46 Goes to Center of Earth 1.00
47 Meteor Bye-Products,pt.1 .... 1.00
48 Meteor Bye-Products,pt.2 .... 1.00
49 1st Rhonda solo story 1.00
50 Final Issue, giant size 1.75
Ann.#1 Evol.War 3.00
Ann.#2 .... 1.75
Spring Spec.#1 .... 1.75
Holiday Spec.#2 .... 2.00

ALIEN LEGION
Epic April, 1984
1 FC,TA,I:Sarigar,Montroc 4.00
2 FC,TA,CP,V:Harkilons 3.50
3 FC,TA,CW,V:Kroyzo 3.00
4 FC,TA,CW,F:Skob 3.00
5 FC,CW,D:Skob 3.00
6 FC,CW,WPo,V:Harkilons 3.00
7 CW,WPo,I:Lora 2.50
8 CW,WPo,V:Harkilons 2.50
9 CW,V:Harkilons 2.50
10 CW,LSn,V:Harkilons 2.50
11 CW,LSn,V:Harkilons 2.50
12 LSn,A:Aob-Sin 2.50
13 LSn,F:Montroc 2.50
14 LSn,V:Cordar 2.50
15 LSn,V:Alphor,Betro,&Gamoid . 2.50
16 LSn,J:Tomaro 2.50
17 LSn,Durge on Drugs 2.50
18 LSn,V:Dun 2.50
19 LSn,A:GalarcyScientist 2.50
20 LSn,L:Skilene 2.50
[2nd Series] Aug. 1987
1 LSn,I:Guy Montroc 3.00
2 LSn,V:Quallians 2.50
3 LSn,Hellscope 2.50
4 LSn,V:Harkilons 2.50
5 LSn,F:JuggerGrimrod 2.50
6 LSn,F:JuggerGrimrod 2.50
7 LSn,A:Guy Montroc 2.50
8 LSn,I:Nakhira 2.50
9 LSn,V:Harkilons 2.50
10 LSn,V:Harkilons 2.50
11 LSn,V:Harkilons 2.50
12 LSn,Tamara Pregnant 2.50
13 LSn,V:MomojianKndrel ... 2.50
14 LSn,J:Saravil 2.50
15 LSn,J:Spellik 2.50
16 LSn,D:Jugger's Father 2.50
17 LSn,O:JuggerGrimrod 2.50
18 LSn,O:JuggerGrimrod 2.50
GN Grimrod 5.95

ALIEN LEGION: BINARY DEEP
Epic 1993
1-shot with trading card 3.50

ALIEN LEGION: JUGGER GRIMROD
Epic Aug. 1992
Book One 5.95

ALIEN LEGION: ONE PLANET AT A TIME
Epic Heavy Hitters May 1993
1 HNg,CDi,One Planet at a Time 4.95
2 HNg,CDi 4.95
3 HNg,CDi 4.95

All comics prices listed are for *Near Mint* condition.

ALIEN LEGION: ON THE EDGE
Epic Nov. 1990

1 LSn,V:B'Be No N'ngth	4.95
2 LSn,V:B'Be No N'ngth	4.95
3 LSn,V:B'Be No N'ngth	4.95
4 LSn,V:B'Be No N'ngth	4.95

ALIEN LEGION: TENANTS OF HELL
Epic 1991

1 LSn,Nomad Squad On Combine IV	4.50
2 LSn,L:Torie Montroc,I:Stagg	4.50
TPB Alien Legion:Slaughterworld	9.95

All-Select Comics #5
© Marvel Entertainment Group

ALL-SELECT COMICS
Fall, 1943
Timely (Daring Comics)

1 B:Capt.America,Sub-Mariner, Human Torch;WWII	7,500.00
2 A:Red Skull,V:Axis Powers	2,500.00
3 B:Whizzer,V:Axis	1,500.00
4 V: Axis	1,300.00
5 E:Sub-Mariner,V:Axis	1,200.00
6 A:The Destroyer,V:Axis	900.00
7 E:Whizzer,V:Axis	900.00
8 V:Axis Powers	900.00
9 V:Axis Powers	900.00
10 E:Capt.America,Human Torch; A:The Destroyer	900.00
11 I:Blonde Phantom,A:Miss America	1,500.00

Becomes:
BLONDE PHANTOM

12 B:Miss America;The Devil's Playground	1,000.00
13 B:Sub-Mariner;Horror In Hollywood	650.00
14 E:Miss America;Horror At Haunetd Castle	600.00
15 The Man Who Deserved To Die	600.00
16 A:Capt.America,Bucky; Modeled For Murder	800.00

17 Torture & Rescue	550.00
18 Jealously,Hate & Cruelty	550.00
19 Killer In the Hospital	550.00
20 Blonde Phantom's Big Fall	550.00
21 Murder At the Carnival	550.00
22 V: Crime Bosses	550.00

Becomes:
LOVERS

23 Love Stories	80.00
24 My Dearly Beloved	40.00
25 The Man I Love	50.00
26 thru 29	@30.00
30	40.00
31 thru 36	@30.00
37	50.00
38	50.00
39	30.00
40	30.00
41	30.00
42 thru 65	@30.00
66	25.00
67 ATh	40.00
68 thru 86 Aug. 1957	@25.00

ALL SURPRISE
Timely Fall, 1943

1 (fa),F:Super Rabbit,Gandy, Sourpuss	200.00
2	100.00
3	75.00
4 thru 10	@75.00
11 HK	100.00
12 Winter, 1946	75.00

ALL-TRUE CRIME
See: OFFICIAL TRUE CRIME CASES

ALL WINNERS COMICS
Summer, 1941

1 S&K,BEv,B:Capt.America & Bucky, Human Torch & Toro,Sub-Mariner A:The Angel,Black Marvel	15,000.00
2 S&K,B:Destroyer,Whizzer	4,000.00
3 BEv,Bucky & Toro Captured	2,400.00
4 BEv,Battle For Victory For America	2,500.00
5 V:Nazi Invasion Fleet	1,500.00
6 V:Axis Powers,A: Black Avenger	1,600.00
7 V:Axis Powers	1,200.00
8 V:Axis Powers	1,100.00
9 V:Nazi Submarine Fleet	1,100.00
10 V:Nazi Submarine Fleet	1,200.00
11 V: Nazis	1,000.00
12 A:Red Skull,E:Destroyer; Jap P.O.W. Camp	1,200.00
13 V:Japanese Fleet	1,000.00
14 V:Japanese Fleet	1,000.00
15 Japanese Supply Train	1,000.00
16 In Alaska V:Gangsters	1,000.00
17 V:Gansters;Atomic Research Department	1,000.00
18 V:Robbers;Internal Revenue Department	1,100.00
19 I:All Winners Squad, Fall, 1946	3,000.00
21 A:All-Winners Squad;Riddle of the Demented Dwarf	2,500.00

Becomes:
ALL TEEN COMICS

20 F:Georgie,Willie, Mitzi,Patsy Walker	50.00

Becomes:
TEEN COMICS

21 A:George,Willie,Mitzi, Patsy Walker	75.00
22 A:George,Willie,Margie, Patsy Walker	50.00
23 A:Patsy Walker,Cindy,George	50.00
24	75.00
25	50.00
26	60.00
27	50.00
28	75.00
29	50.00
30	75.00
31 thru 34	@50.00
35 May, 1950	50.00

Becomes:
JOURNEY INTO UNKNOWN WORLDS
Atlas Sept. 1950

36(1) RH,End of the Earth	1,600.00
37(2) BEv,GC,When Worlds Collide	800.00
38(3) GT,Land of Missing Men	600.00
4 MS,RH,Train to Nowhere	375.00
5 MS,Trapped in Space	375.00
6 GC,RH,World Below the Atlantic	375.00
7 BW,RH,House That Wasn't	650.00
8 RH,The Stone Thing	375.00
9 MS,JSt,The People Who Couldn't Exist	450.00
10 THe Undertaker	375.00
11 BEv,Frankie Was Afraid	275.00
12 The Last Voice You Hear	275.00
13 The Witch Woman	200.00
14 BW,BEv,CondemnedBuilding	500.00
15 They Crawl By Night	500.00
16 Scared to Death	225.00
17 BEv,GC,RH,The Ice Monster Cometh	225.00
18 The Broth Needs Somebody	250.00
19 GC,The Long Wait	250.00
20 GC,RH,The Race That Vanished	200.00
21 thru 25	@175.00
26 thru 35	@150.00
36 thru 44	@125.00
45 AW,SD	135.00
46	100.00
47	100.00
48 GW	100.00
49	100.00
50 JDa,RC	125.00
51 WW,SD,JSe	135.00
52	100.00
53 RC,BP	125.00
54 AT,BP	125.00
55 AW,RC,BEv	125.00
56 BEv	125.00
57 JO	100.00
58 MO	100.00
59 AW,August, 1957	125.00

ALL WINNERS COMICS
[2nd Series] August, 1948

1 F:Blonde Phantom,A:Capt.America Sub-Mariner,Human Torch	1,800.00

Becomes:
ALL WESTERN WINNERS

2 B,I&O:Black Rider,B:Two-Gun Kid, Kid-Colt	550.00

3 Black Rider V: Satan 300.00
4 Black Rider Unmasked 275.00
Becomes:

WESTERN WINNERS
5 I Challenge the Army 225.00
6 The Mountain Mystery 175.00
7 Ph(c) Randolph Scott 175.00
Becomes:

BLACK RIDER
8 Ph(c),B:Black Rider;Valley
of Giants 350.00
9 Wrath of the Redskin 150.00
10 O:Black Rider 175.00
11 Redmen on the Warpath . . . 125.00
12 GT,The Town That Vanished 125.00
13 The Terrified Tribe 125.00
14 The Tyrant of Texas 125.00
15 Revolt of the Redskins 100.00
16 . . . . 100.00
17 . . . . 100.00
18 . . . . 100.00
19 SSh,GT,A:Two-Gun Kid . . . 100.00
20 GT 110.00
21 SSh,GT,A:Two-Gun Kid . . . 100.00
22 SSh,A:Two-Gun Kid 100.00
23 SSh,A:Two-Gun Kid 100.00
24 SSh,JSt 100.00
25 SSh,JSt,A:Arrowhead 100.00
26 SSh,A:Kid-Colt 100.00
27 SSh,A:Kid-Colt 110.00
Becomes:

WESTERN TALES OF BLACK RIDER
28 JSe,D:Spider 125.00
29 . . . . 90.00
30 . . . . 90.00
31 . . . . 90.00
Becomes:

GUNSMOKE WESTERN
32 F:Kid Colt,Billy Buckskin . . 125.00
33 . . . . 100.00
34 . . . . 75.00
35 . . . . 100.00
36 . . . . 100.00
37 . . . . 75.00
38 . . . . 50.00
39 . . . . 50.00
40 . . . . 75.00
41 . . . . 35.00
42 . . . . 35.00
43 . . . . 35.00
44 . . . . 40.00
45 . . . . 40.00
46 thru 55 . . . . @35.00
56 . . . . 40.00
57 thru 76 . . . . @35.00
77 July, 1963 . . . . 30.00

ALPHA FLIGHT
August, 1983
1 JBy,I:Puck,Marrina,Tundra . . 3.00
2 JBy,I:Master,Vindicator Becomes
Guardian,B:O:Marrina 2.00
3 JBy,O:Master,A:Namor,Invisible
Girl, ... 2.00
4 JBy,A:Namor,Invisible Girl,
E:O:Marrina,A:Master 2.00
5 JBy,B:O:Shaman,F:Puck . . . 2.00
6 JBy,E:O:Shaman,I:Kolomag . . 2.00
7 JBy,B:O:Snowbird,I:Delphine
Courtney & Deadly Ernest . . . 2.00
8 JBy,E:O:Snowbird,O:Deadly
Ernest,I:Nemesis 2.00

9 JBy,O:Aurora,A:Wolverine,
Super Skrull 2.00
10 JBy,O:Northstar,V:SuperSkrull . 2.00
11 JBy,I:Omega Flight,Wild Child
O:Sasqatch 2.00
12 JBy,D:Guardian,V:Omega
Flight 2.00
13 JBy,C:Wolverine,Nightmare . . . 3.00
14 JBy,V:Genocide 2.00
15 JBy,R:Master 2.00
16 JBy,BWi,V:Master,C:Wolverine
I:Madison Jeffries 2.25
17 JBy,BWi,A:Wolverine,X-Men . . 3.00
18 JBy,BWi,J:Heather,I:Ranaq . . . 2.00
19 JBy,I:Talisman,V:Ranaq 2.00
20 JBy,I:Gilded Lily,N:Aurora . . . 2.00
21 JBy,BWi,O:Gilded Lily,Diablo . . 2.00
22 JBy,BWi,I:Pink Pearl 2.00
23 JBy,BWi,D:Sasquatch,
I:Tanaraq 2.00
24 JBy,BWi,V:Great Beasts,J:Box 2.00
25 JBy,BWi,V:Omega Flight
I:Dark Guardian 2.00

Alpha Flight #22
© Marvel Entertainment Group

26 JBy,BWi,A:Omega Flight,Dark
Guardian 2.00
27 JBy,V:Omega Flight 2.00
28 JBy,Secret Wars II,V:Omega
Flight,D:Dark Guardian 2.00
29 MMi,V:Hulk,A:Box 2.00
30 MMi,I&O:Scramble,R:Deadly
Ernest 2.00
31 MMi,D:Deadly Ernest,
O:Nemesis 2.00
32 MMi(c),JBg,O:Puck,I:2nd
Vindicator 2.00
33 MMi(c),SB,X-Men,I:Deathstrike 3.00
34 MMi(c),SB,Wolverine,V:
Deathstrike 3.00
35 DR,R:Shaman 2.00
36 MMi(c),DR,A:Dr.Strange 2.00
37 DR,O:Pestilence,N:Aurora . . . 2.00
38 DR,A:Namor,V:Pestilence . . . 2.00
39 MMi(c),DR,WPo,A:Avengers . . 2.25
40 DR,WPo,W:Namor & Marrina . 2.25
41 DR,WPo,I:Purple Girl,
J:Madison Jeffries 2.25
42 DR,WPo,I:Auctioneer,J:Purple Girl,
A: Beta Flight 2.25

43 DR,WPo,V:Mesmero,Sentinels 2.25
44 DR,WPo,D:Snowbird,
A:Pestilence 2.25
45 JBr,WPo,R:Sasquatch,
L:Shaman 2.25
46 JBr,WPo,I:2nd Box 2.25
47 MMi,WPo,TA,Vindicator solo . 2.25
48 SL(i),I:Omega 2.25
49 JBr,WPo,I:Manikin,D:Omega . . 2.25
50 WS(c),JBr,WPo,L:Northstar,Puck,
Aurora,A:Loki,Double size . . . 2.50
51 JLe(1st Marv),WPo(i),V:Cody . 4.00
52 JBr,WPo(i),I:Bedlam,
A:Wolverine 3.00
53 JLe,WPo(i),I:Derangers,Goblyn
D&V:Bedlam,A:Wolverine . . . 3.00
54 WPo(i),O&J:Goblyn 2.00
55 JLe,TD,V:Tundra 2.50
56 JLe,TD,V:Bedlamites 2.50
57 JLe,TD,V:Crystals,
C:Dreamqueen 2.50
58 JLe,AM,V:Dreamqueen 2.50
59 JLe,AM,I:Jade Dragon,R:Puck . 2.50
60 JLe,AM,V:J.Dragon,D.Queen . 2.50
61 JLe,AM,on Trial
(1st JLe X-Men) 2.50
62 JLe,AM,V:Purple Man 2.50
63 MG,V:U.S.Air Force 2.00
64 JLe,AM,V:Great Beasts 2.50
65 JLe(c),AM(i),Dream Issue . . . 2.00
66 JLe(c),I:China Force 2.00
67 JLe(c),O:Dream Queen 2.00
68 JLe(c),V:Dream Queen 2.00
69 JLe(c),V:Dream Queen 2.00
70 MM(i),V:Dream Queen 2.00
71 MM(i),I:Sorcerer 2.00
72 V:Sorcerer 2.00
73 MM(i),V:Sorcerer 2.00
74 MM(i),Alternate Earth 2.00
75 JLe(c),MMi(i),Double Size . . . 3.00
76 MM(i),V:Sorcerer 2.00
77 MM(i),V:Kingpin 2.00
78 MM(i),A:Dr.Strange,Master . . 2.00
79 MM(i),AofV,V:Scorpion,Nekra . 2.00
80 MM(i),AofV,V:Scorpion,Nekra . 2.00
81 JBy(c),MM(i),B:R:Northstar . . 2.00
82 JBy(c),MM(i),E:R:Northstar . . . 2.00
83 JSh 2.00
84 MM(i),Northstar 2.00
85 MM(i) 2.00
86 MBa,MM,V:Sorcerer 2.00
87 JLe(c),MM(i),A:Wolverine . . . 3.00
88 JLe(c),MM(i),A:Wolverine . . . 3.00
89 JLe(c),MM(i),R:Guardian,A:
Wolverine 3.00
90 JLe(c),MM(i),A:Wolverine . . . 3.00
91 MM(i),A:Dr.Doom 2.00
92 Guardian vs.Vindicator 2.00
93 MM(i),A:Fant.Four,I:Headlok . 2.00
94 MM(i),V:Fant.Four,Headlok . . 2.00
95 MM(i),Lifelines 2.00
96 MM(i),A:Master 2.00
97 B:Final Option,A:Her 2.00
98 A:Avengers 2.00
99 A:Avengers 2.00
100 JBr,TMo,DR,LMa,E:Final Option
A:Galactus,Avengers,D:
Guardian,G-Size 2.50
101 TMo,Final Option Epilogue,
A:Dr.Strange,Avengers 2.00
102 TMo,I:Weapon Omega, ... 2.00
103 TMo,V:Diablo,U.S.Agent . . . 2.00
104 TMo,N:Alpha Flight,Weapon
Omega is Wild Child 2.00
105 TMo,V:Pink Pearl 2.00

106 MPa,Aids issue,Northstar
　acknowledges homosexuality . 2.50
106a 2nd printing 2.50
107 A:X-Factor,V:Autopsy 2.00
108 A:Soviet Super Soldiers 2.00
109 V:Peoples Protectorate 2.00
110 PB,Infinity War,I:2nd Omega
　Flight,A:Wolverine 2.00
111 PB,Infinity War,V:Omega
　Flight,A:Wolverine 2.00
112 PB,Infinity War,V:Master 2.00
113 V:Mauler 2.00
114 A:Weapon X 2.00
115 PB,I:Wyre,A:Weapon X 2.00
116 PB,I:Rok,V:Wyre 2.00
117 PB,V:Wyre 2.00
118 PB,V:Thunderball 2.00
119 PB,V:Wrecking Crew 2.00
120 PB,10th Anniv.,V:Hardliners,
　w/poster 2.50

Alpha Flight #48
© Marvel Entertainment Group

121 PCu,V:Brass Bishop,A:Spider-
　Man,Wolverine,C:X-Men 2.00
122 PB,BKi,Inf.Crusade 2.00
123 PB,BKi,Infinity Crusade 2.00
124 PB,BKi,Infinity Crusade 2.00
125 PB,V:Carcass 2.00
126 V:Carcass 2.00
127 SFu(s),Infinity Crusade 2.00
128 B:No Future 2.00
129 C:Omega Flight 2.00
130 E:No Future,last issue,
　Double Sized 2.50
Ann.#1 LSn,V:Diablo,Gilded Lily . . 3.00
Ann.#2 JBr,BMc 2.00
Spec.#1 PB,A:Wolverine,
　O:First Team,V:Egghead 3.75
Spec.#1–#3 Newsstand versions
　of #97–#99 . . . . @1.50
Spec.#4 Newsstand ver.of #100 . . 2.00

ALPHA FLIGHT
1997
1 SSe,ScC, former team kidnapped,
　I:Murmur, Radius,Flex,Guardian 2.00
2 SSe,ScC 2.00

2 variant cover 2.00
3 SSe,ScC 2.00
4 SSe,ScC,V:Mesmero 2.00
5 SSe,ScC,A:Mesmero 2.00
6 SSe,What's up with Sasquatch? 2.00
7 SSe,Evils explode 2.00
8 SSe,ScC,North & South prelude 2.00
9 SSe,ScC,North & South pt.1,
　X-men x-over 2.00
10 SSe,Flung into Prometheus Pit 2.00
11 SSe,race to save 2 worlds . . . 2.00
12 SSe,Alphan dies,48pg. double
　size 3.00
13 SSe,F:Basil Killbrew 2.00
14 SSe,I:Brass Bishop 2.00
15 SSe 2.00
Spec. #1 SSe,"In the Beginning,"
　Flashback, A:Wolverine 2.00

ALPHA FLIGHT SPECIAL
1991
1 thru 4 reprints . . . . @1.50

AMAZING ADVENTURES
June, 1961
1 JK,SD,O&B:Dr.Droom;Torr 1,200.00
2 JK,SD,This is Manoo 500.00
3 JK,SD,Trapped in the
　Twilight World 450.00
4 JK,SD, I Am X 425.00
5 JK, SD, Monsteroso 425.00
6 JK,SD,E:Dr.Droom; Sserpo . 450.00
Becomes:

AMAZING ADULT FANTASY
Dec., 1961
7 SD,Last Man on Earth 600.00
8 SD,The Coming of the Krills 500.00
9 SD,The Terror of Tim Boo Ba 450.00
10 SD,Those Who Change . . . 450.00
11 SD,In Human Form 450.00
12 SD,Living Statues 450.00
13 SD,At the Stroke of Midnight 450.00
14 SD,Beware of the Giants . . 475.00
Becomes:

AMAZING FANTASY
August, 1962
15 JK(c),SD,I&O:Spider-Man,I:Aunt
　May, Flash Thompson, Burglar,
　I&D:Uncle Ben 28,000.00
Marvel Milestone rep.#15 (1992) . 2.95
[Second Series] 1995
15a gold Rep. (1995) 25.00
16 KBk, O:Spider-Man,painted . . 4.00
17 KBk, More early adventures . . 4.00
18 KBk,conclusion 4.00

AMAZING ADVENTURES
August, 1970
[1st Regular Series]
1 JK,JB,B:Inhumans,Bl.Widow . 25.00
2 JK,JB,A:Fantastic Four 11.00
3 JK,GC,BEv,V:Mandarin 10.00
4 JK,GC,BEv,V:Mandarin 10.00
5 NA,TP,DH,BEv,V:Astrologer . 12.00
6 NA,DH,SB,V:Maximus 10.00
7 NA,DH,BEv 10.00
8 NA,DH,BEv,E:Black Widow,
　A:Thor,(see Avengers #95) . . 10.00
9 MSy,BEv,V:Magneto 12.00
10 GK(c),MSy,V:Magneto,
　E:Inhumans 12.00
11 GK(c),TS,B:O:New Beast,

Amazing Adventures #21
© Marvel Entertainment Group

A:X-Men 17.00
12 GK(c),TS,MP,A:Iron Man . . . 10.00
13 JR(c),TS,V:New Br'hood
　Evil Mutants,I:Buzz Baxter
　(Mad Dog) 10.00
14 GK(c),TS,JM,V:Quasimodo . . 10.00
15 JSn(c),TS,A:X-Men,V:Griffin . . 10.00
16 JSn(c),FMc(i),V:Juggernaut . . 10.00
17 JSn,A:X-Men,E:Beast 10.00
18 HC,NA,B:Killraven 10.00
19 HC,Sirens on 7th Avenues . . . 6.00
20 Coming of the Warlords 6.00
21 Cry Killraven 6.00
22 Killraven 6.00
23 Killraven 6.00
24 New Year Nightmare-2019AD . 6.00
25 RB,V:Skar 6.00
26 GC,V:Ptson-Rage Vigilante . . 6.00
27 CR,JSn,V:Death Breeders . . . 6.00
28 JSn,CR,V:Death Breeders . . . 6.00
29 CR,Killraven 6.00
30 CR,Killraven 6.00
31 CR,Killraven 6.00
32 CR,Killraven 6.00
33 CR,Killraven 6.00
34 CR,D:Hawk 6.00
35 KG,Killraven Continued 6.00
36 CR,Killraven Continued 6.00
37 CR,O:Old Skull 6.00
38 CR,Killraven Continued. 6.00
39 CR,E:Killraven 6.00
[2nd Regular Series]
1 rep.X-Men#1,38,Professor X . . 7.00
2 rep.X-Men#1,39,O:Cyclops . . . 6.00
3 rep.X-Men#2,40,O:Cyclops . . . 6.00
4 rep.X-Men#2,41,O:Cyclops . . . 6.00
5 rep.X-Men#3,42,O:Cyclops . . . 6.00
6 JBy(c),rep.X-Men#3,43,Cyclops 6.00
7 rep.X-Men#4,44,O:Iceman 6.00
8 rep.X-Men#4,45,O:Iceman 6.00
9 JBy(c),X-Men#5,46,O:Iceman . 6.00
10 rep.X-Men#5,47,O:Iceman . . . 6.00
11 rep.X-Men#6,48,Beast 6.00
12 rep.X-Men#6,Str.Tales#168 . . 6.00
13 rep.X-Men #7 . . . . 6.00
14 rep.X-Men #8 . . . . 6.00

MARVEL

AMAZING COMICS
Timely Comics Fall, 1944
1 F:Young Allies,Destroyer,
Whizzer, Sergeant Dix . . . 1,500.00
Becomes:

COMPLETE COMICS
2 F:Young Allies,Destroyer,Whizzer
Sergeant Dix; Winter'44-5 . 1,000.00

AMAZING DETECTIVE CASES
Atlas Nov., 1950
3 Detective/Horror Stories . . . 150.00
4 Death of a Big Shot 100.00
5 . . . . 100.00
6 Danger in the City 100.00
7 . . . . 75.00
8 . . . . 75.00
9 GC, The Man Who Wasn't . . 75.00
10 GT 75.00
11 The Black Shadow 100.00
12 MS,BK, Harrigan's Wake . . 100.00
13 BEv,JSt, ... 150.00
14 Hands Off; Sept., 1952 . . . . 100.00

AMAZING HIGH ADVENTURE
August, 1984
1 BSz,JSo,JS 3.00
2 PS,AW,BSz,TA,MMi,BBl,CP,CW 2.50
3 MMi,VM,JS 2.50
4 JBo,JS,SBi 2.50
5 JBo; Oct., 1986 . . . . 2.50

AMAZING SCARLET SPIDER
1 MBa,LMa,VirtualMortality,pt.2 . . 1.95
2 TDF,MBa,CyberWar,pt.2 . . . . . 1.95

AMAZING SPIDER-MAN
March, 1963
1 JK(c),SED,I:Chameleon,J.Jonah &
John Jameson,A:F.Four . 20,000.00
2 SD,I:Vulture,Tinkerer
C:Mysterio(disguised) 3,000.00
3 SD,I&O:Dr.Octopus 2,000.00
4 SD,I&O:Sandman,I:Betty
Brant,Liz Allen 1,700.00
5 SD,V:Dr.Doom,C:Fant.Four 1,500.00
6 SD,I&O:Lizard,The Connors 1,200.00
7 SD,V:Vulture 850.00
8 SD,JK,I:Big Brain,V:Human
Torch,A:Fantastic Four 800.00
9 SD,I&O:Electro 900.00
10 SD,I:Enforcers,Big Man . . 800.00
11 SD,V:Dr.Octopus,
D:Bennett Brant 500.00
12 SD,V:Dr.Octopus 450.00
13 SD,I:Mysterio 650.00
14 SD,I:Green Goblin,
V:Enforcers, Hulk 1,600.00
15 SD,I:Kraven,A:Chameleon . 600.00
16 SD,A:Daredevil,
V:Ringmaster 400.00
17 SD,2nd A:Green Goblin,
A:Human Torch 600.00
18 SD,V:Sandman,Enforcers,
C:Avengers,F.F.,Daredevil . 400.00
19 SD,V:Sandman,I:Ned Leeds
A:Human Torch 300.00
20 SD,I&O:Scorpion 400.00
21 SD,A:Beetle,Human Torch . 250.00

22 SD,V:The Clown,Masters of
Menace 225.00
23 SD,V:GreenGoblin(3rd App.) 350.00
24 SD,V:Mysterio 185.00
25 SD,I:Spider Slayer,Spencer
Smythe,C:Mary Jane 250.00
26 SD,I:CrimeMaster,V:Green
Goblin 275.00
27 SD,V:CrimeMaster,
Green Goblin 250.00
28 SD,I:Molten Man,Peter Parker
Graduates High School,rare
in near-mint condition 350.00
29 SD,V:Scorpion 150.00
30 SD,I:Cat Burglar 150.00
31 SD,I:Gwen Stacy,Harry Osborn

Amazing Spider-Man #4
© Marvel Entertainment Group

Prof.Warren,V:Dr.Octopus . . 175.00
32 SD,V:Dr.Octopus 150.00
33 SD,V:Dr.Octopus 150.00
34 SD,V:Kraven 150.00
35 SD,V:Molten Man 150.00
36 SD,I:The Looter 150.00
37 SD,V:Professor Stromm,
I:Norman Osborn 160.00
38 SD,V:Joe Smith(Boxer) 150.00
39 JR,IR:Green Goblin is Norman
Osborn 225.00
40 JR,O:Green Goblin 325.00
41 JR,I:Rhino,C:Mary Jane . . 160.00
42 JR,V:John Jameson,I:Mary
Jane (Face Revealed) 150.00
43 JR,O:Rhino 100.00
44 JR,V:Lizard(2nd App.) 100.00
45 JR,V:Lizard 100.00
46 JR,I&O:Shocker 110.00
47 JR,V:Kraven 100.00
48 JR,I:Fake Vulture,A:Vulture . 100.00
49 JR,V:Fake Vulture,Kraven . . 100.00
50 JR,I:Kingpin,Spidey Quits,
C:Johnny Carson 400.00
51 JR,V:Kingpin 150.00
52 JR,V:Kingpin,I:Robbie
Robertson,D:Fred Foswell . . 85.00
53 JR,V:Dr.Octopus 75.00
54 JR,V:Dr.Octopus 70.00

55 JR,V:Dr.Octopus 70.00
56 JR,V:Dr.Octopus,I:Capt.Stacy 75.00
57 JR,DH,A:Kazar 70.00
58 JR,DH,V:Spencer Smythe,
Spider Slayer 70.00
59 JR,DH,V:Kingpin 75.00
60 JR,DH,V:Kingpin 75.00
61 JR,DH,V:Kingpin 75.00
62 JR,DH,V:Medusa 55.00
63 JR,DH,V:1st & 2nd
Vulture 55.00
64 JR,DH,V:Vulture 55.00
65 JR,JM,V:Prisoners 55.00
66 JR,DH,V:Mysterio 55.00
67 JR,JM,V:Mysterio,I:Randy
Robertson 55.00
68 JR,JM,V:Kingpin 60.00
69 JR,JM,V:Kingpin 60.00
70 JR,JM,V:Kingpin 60.00
71 JR,JM,V:Quicksilver,C:Scarlet
Witch,Toad,A:Kingpin 50.00
72 JR,JB,JM,V:Shocker 50.00
73 JR,JB,JM,I:Man Mountain Marko,
Silvermane 50.00
74 JR,JM,V:Silvermane 45.00
75 JR,JM,V:Silvermane,A:Lizard 45.00
76 JR,JM,V:Lizard,A:H.Torch . . 45.00
77 JR,JM,V:Lizard,A:H.Torch . . 45.00
78 JR,JM,I&O:Prowler 50.00
79 JR,JM,V:Prowler 45.00
80 JR,JB,JM,V:Chameleon 45.00
81 JR,JB,JM,I:Kangaroo 45.00
82 JR,JM,V:Electro 45.00
83 JR,I:Richard Fisk(as Schemer),
Vanessa(Kingpin's wife)
V:Kingpin 50.00
84 JR,JB,JM,V:Schemer,Kingpin 45.00
85 JR,JB,JM,V:Schemer,Kingpin 45.00
86 JR,JM,V:Black Widow, C:Iron
Man, Hawkeye 45.00
87 JR,JM,Reveals ID to his
friends,changes mind 45.00
88 JR,JM,V:Dr.Octopus 45.00
89 GK,JR,V:Dr.Octopus 45.00
90 GK,JR,V:Dr.Octopus
D:Capt.Stacy 60.00
91 GK,JR,I:Bullit 45.00
92 GK,JR,V:Bullit,A:Iceman . . . 45.00
93 JR,V:Prowler 45.00
94 JR,SB,V:Beetle,O:Spider-Man 70.00
95 JR,SB,London,V:Terrorists . . 45.00
96 GK,JR,A:Green Goblin,Drug
Mention,No Comic Code 90.00
97 GK,V:Green Goblin,Drugs . . . 75.00
98 GK,V:Green Goblin,Drugs . . . 75.00
99 GK,Prison Riot,A:Carson . . . 50.00
100 JR(c),GK,Spidey gets four
arms from serum 180.00
101 JR(c),GK,I:Morbius,the
Living Vampire,A:Lizard . . . 135.00
101a Reprint,Metallic ink 2.50
102 JR(c),GK,O:Morbius,
V:Lizard 100.00
103 GK,V:Kraven,A:Kazar 30.00
104 GK,V:Kraven,A:Kazar 30.00
105 GK,V:Spenser Smythe,
Spider Slayer 30.00
106 JR,V:Spenser Smythe,
Spider Slayer 27.00
107 JR,V:Spenser Smythe,
Spider Slayer 27.00
108 JR,R:Flash Thompson,
I:Sha-Shan,V:Vietnamese . . . 27.00
109 JR,A:Dr.Strange,
V:Vietnamese 27.00

110 JR,I:The Gibbon 27.00	146 RA,JR,V:Scorpion 25.00	210 JR2,JSt,I:Madame Web 8.00
111 JR,V:The Gibbon,Kraven . . 27.00	147 JR(c),RA,V:Tarantula 25.00	211 JR2,JM,A:Sub-mariner 6.00
112 JR,Spidey gets an Ulcer . . . 27.00	148 GK(c),RA,V:Tarantula,IR:Jackal	212 JR2,JM,I:Hydro-Man 6.00
113 JSn,JR,I:Hammerhead	is Prof.Warren 30.00	213 JR2,JM,V:Wizard 6.00
V:Dr.Octopus 30.00	149 K&R(c),RA,D:Jackal 45.00	214 JR2,JM,V:Frightful Four,
114 JSn,JR,V:Hammerhead,Dr.	150 GK(c),RA,V:Spenser Smythe 20.00	A: Namor,Llyra 6.00
Octopus,I:Jonas Harrow 30.00	151 RA,JR,V:Shocker 17.00	215 JR2,JM,V:Frightful Four,
115 JR,V:Hammerhead,	152 K&R(c),RA,V:Shocker 17.00	A: Namor,Llyra 6.00
Dr.Octopus 30.00	153 K&R(c),RA,V:Paine 17.00	216 JR2,JM,A:Madame Web 6.00
116 JR,JM,V:The Smasher 27.00	154 JR(c),SB,V:Sandman 17.00	217 JR2,JM,V:Sandman,
117 JR,JM,V:Smasher,Disruptor 27.00	155 JR(c),SB,V:Computer 16.00	Hydro-Man 6.00
118 JR,JM,V:Smasher,Disruptor 27.00	156 JR(c),RA,I:Mirage,W:Ned	218 FM(c),JR2,JM,AM,V:Sandman
119 JR,A:Hulk 45.00	Leeds & Betty Brant 16.00	Hydro-Man 6.00
120 GK,JR,V:Hulk 45.00	157 JR(c),RA,V:Dr.Octopus . . . 16.00	219 FM(c),LMc,JM,V:Grey
121 GK,JR,V:Green Goblin	158 JR(c),RA,V:Dr.Octopus . . . 16.00	Gargoyle,A:Matt Murdock 6.00
D:Gwen Stacy,Drugs 125.00	159 JR(c),RA,V:Dr.Octopus . . . 16.00	220 BMc,A:Moon Knight 6.00
122 GK,JR,D:Green Goblin . . . 135.00	160 K&R(c),RA,V:Tinkerer 16.00	
	161 K&R(c),RA,A:Nightcrawler,	

Amazing Spider-Man #34
© Marvel Entertainment Group

Amazing Spider-Man #100
© Marvel Entertainment Group

	C:Punisher 16.00	
	162 JR(c),RA,Nightcrawler,	
	Punisher,I:Jigsaw 16.00	
	163 JR(c),RA,Kingpin 10.00	
	164 JR(c),RA,Kingpin 10.00	
	165 JR(c),RA,Lizard 10.00	
	166 JR(c),RA,Lizard 10.00	
	167 JR(c),RA,V:Spiderslayer,	
	I:Will-o-the Wisp 10.00	
	168 JR(c),KP,V:Will-o-the Wisp . 12.00	
	169 RA,V:Dr.Faustas 10.00	
	170 RA,V:Dr.Faustas 10.00	
	171 RA,A:Nova 11.00	
	172 RA,V:Molten Man 10.00	
	173 JR(c),RA,JM,V:Molten Man . 10.00	
	174 RA,TD,JM,A:Punisher 15.00	
	175 RA,JM,A:Punisher,D:Hitman 15.00	
	176 RA,TD,V:Green Goblin 12.00	
	177 RA,V:Green Goblin 12.00	
	178 RA,JM,V:Green Goblin 12.00	
	179 RA,V:Green Goblin 12.00	
	180 RA,IR&V:Green Goblin is Bart	
	Hamilton) 12.00	221 JM(i),A:Ramrod 5.00
	181 GK(c),SB,O:Spider-Man.. . . 8.00	222 WS(c),BH,JM,I:SpeedDemon 5.00
	182 RA,A:Rocket Racer 7.00	223 JR2,AM,A:Red Ghost 5.00
	183 RA,BMc,V:Rocket Racer . . . 7.00	224 JR2,V:Vulture 5.00
123 GK,JR,A:Powerman 25.00	184 RA,V:White Tiger 7.00	225 JR2,BWi,V:Foolkiller 5.00
124 GK,JR,I:Man-Wolf 26.00	185 RA,V:White Tiger 7.00	226 JR2,JM,A:Black Cat 5.00
125 RA,JR,O:Man-Wolf 25.00	186 KP,A:Chameleon,Spidey	227 JR2,JM,A:Black Cat 5.00
126 JM(c),RA,JM,V:Kangaroo,	cleared by police of charges . . 7.00	228 RL,Murder Mystery 5.00
A: Human Torch 25.00	187 JSn,BMc,A:Captain	229 JR2,JM,V:Juggernaut 7.00
127 JR(c),RA,V:3rd Vulture,	America,V:Electro 8.00	230 JR2,JM,V:Juggernaut 7.00
A:Human Torch 25.00	188 KP,A:Jigsaw 7.00	231 JR2,AM,V:Cobra 5.00
128 JR(c),RA,V:3rd Vulture 25.00	189 JBy,JM,A:Man-Wolf 8.00	232 JR2,JM,V:Mr.Hyde 5.00
129 K&R(c),RA,I:Punisher,	190 JBy,JM,A:Man-Wolf 8.00	233 JR2,JM,V:Tarantula 5.00
Jackal 135.00	191 KP,V:Spiderslayer 6.00	234 JR2,DGr,V:Tarantula 5.00
130 JR(c),RA,V:Hammerhead,	192 KP,JM,V:The Fly 6.00	235 JR2,V:Tarantula,C:Deathlok
Dr.Octopus,I:Spider-Mobile . . 22.00	193 KP,JM,V:The Fly 6.00	O:Will-o-the Wisp 5.00
131 JR(c),RA,V:Hammerhead,	194 KP,I:Black Cat 16.00	236 JR2,D:Tarantula 5.00
Dr.Octopus 22.00	195 KP,AM,JM,O:Black Cat 7.00	237 BH,A:Stilt Man 5.00
132 GK(c),JR,V:Molten Man . . . 20.00	196 AM,JM,D:Aunt May,A:Kingpin 6.00	238 JR2,JR,I:Hobgoblin (inc.
133 JR(c),RA,V:Molten Man . . . 20.00	197 KP,JM,V:Kingpin 6.00	Tattoo transfer) 75.00
134 JR(c),RA,I:Tarantula,C:	198 SB,JM,V:Mysterio 6.00	238a w/out Tattoo 12.00
Punisher(2nd App.) 27.00	199 SB,JM,V:Mysterio 6.00	239 JR2,V:Hobgoblin 35.00
135 JR(c),RA,V:Tarantula,	200 JR(c),KP,JM,D:Burglar,Aunt May	240 JR2,BL,Vulture 5.00
A:Punisher 55.00	alive,O:Spider-Man 25.00	241 JR2,O:Vulture 5.00
136 JR(c),RA,I:2nd GreenGoblin 40.00	201 KP,JM,A:Punisher 10.00	242 JR2,Mad Thinker 5.00
137 GK(c),RA,V:Green Goblin . . 35.00	202 KP,JM,A:Punisher 10.00	243 JR2,Peter Quits School 5.00
138 K&R(c),RA,I:Mindworm 25.00	203 FM(c),KP,A:Dazzler 7.00	244 JR2,KJ,V:Hobgoblin 9.00
139 K&R(c),RA,I:Grizzly,V:Jackal 25.00	204 JR2(c),KP,V:Black Cat 6.00	245 JR2,V:Hobgoblin 12.00
140 GK(c),RA,I:Gloria Grant,	205 KP,JM,V:Black Cat 6.00	246 JR2,DGr,Daydreams issue . . 5.00
V:Grizzly,Jackal 25.00	206 JBy,GD,V:Jonas Harrow . . . 8.00	247 JR2,JR,V:Thunderball 5.00
141 JR(c),RA,V:Mysterio 25.00	207 JM,V:Mesmero 6.00	248 JR2,BBr,RF,TA,V:Thunderball,
142 JR(c),RA,V:Mysterio 25.00	208 JR2,AM,BBr,V:Fusion(1stJR2	Kid who Collects Spider-Man . 5.00
143 K&R(c),RA,I:Cyclone 25.00	SpM art),I:Lance Bannon . . . 7.00	
144 K&R(c),RA,V:Cyclone 25.00	209 KJ,BMc,JRu,BWi,AM,	
145 K&R(c),RA,V:Scorpion 25.00	I:Calypso, V:Kraven 8.00	

249 JR2,DGr,V:Hobgoblin,
  A:Kingpin 10.00
250 JR2,KJ,V:Hobgoblin 10.00
251 RF,KJ,V:Hobgoblin,Spidey
  Leaves for Secret Wars . . 10.00
252 RF,BBr,returns from Secret
  Wars,N:Spider-Man 25.00
253 RL,I:Rose 8.00
254 RL,JRu,V:Jack O'Lantern . . . 5.00
255 RF,JRu,Red Ghost 5.00
256 RF,JRu,I:Puma,A:Black Cat . . 6.00
257 RF,JRu,V:Puma,
  A:Hobgoblin 8.00
258 RF,JRu,A:Black Cat,Fant.Four,
  Hobgoblin,V:Black Costume . 11.00
259 RF,JRu,A:Hobgoblin,O:

Amazing Spider-Man #201
© Marvel Entertainment Group

  Mary Jane 12.00
260 RF,JRu,BBr,V:Hobgoblin 8.00
261 CV(c),RF,JRu,V:Hobgoblin . . 8.00
262 Ph(c),BL,Spidey Unmasked . . 7.00
263 RF,BBr,I:Spider-Kid 4.00
264 Paty,V:Red Nine 4.00
265 RF,JRu,V:Black Fox,
  I:Silver Sable 10.00
265a 2nd printing 1.50
266 RF,JRu,I:Misfits,Toad 4.00
267 BMc,PDd(s),A:Human Torch . 4.00
268 JBy(c),RF,JRu,Secret WarsII . 4.00
269 RF,JRu,V:Firelord 4.00
270 RF,BMc,V:Firelord,
  A:Avengers,I:Kate Cushing . . . 4.00
271 RF,JRu,A:Crusher Hogan,
  V:Manslaughter 4.00
272 SB,KB,I&O:Slyde 4.00
273 RF,JRu,Secret Wars II,
  A:Puma 4.00
274 TMo,JR,Secret Wars II,
  Beyonder V:Mephisto,A:1st
  Ghost Rider 6.00
275 RF,JRu,V:Hobgoblin,O:Spidey
  (From Amaz.Fantasy#15) 7.00
276 RF,BBr,V:Hobgoblin 6.00
277 RF,BL,CV,A:Daredevil,
  Kingpin 5.00
278 A:Hobgoblin,V:Scourge,

  D:Wraith 4.00
279 RL,A:Jack O'Lantern,
  2nd A:Silver Sable 4.00
280 RF,BBr,V:Sinister Syndicate,
  A:Silver Sable,Hobgoblin,
  Jack O'Lantern 4.00
281 RF,BBr,V:Sinister Syndicate,
  A:Silver Sable,Hobgoblin,
  Jack O'Lantern 10.00
282 RL,BL,A:X-Factor 4.00
283 RF,BL,V:Titania,Absorbing
  Man,C:Mongoose 4.00
284 RF,BBr,JRu,B:Gang War,
  A: Punisher,Hobgoblin 7.00
285 MZ(c),A:Punisher,Hobgoblin . 9.00
286 ANi(i),V:Hobgoblin,A:Rose . . 8.00
287 EL,ANi,A:Daredevil,Hobgoblin 6.00
288 E:Gang War,A:Punisher,
  Falcon,Hobgoblin,Daredevil,
  Black Cat, Kingpin 7.00
289 TMo,IR:Hobgoblin is Ned Leeds,
  I:2nd Hobgoblin (Jack O'
  Lantern) 20.00
290 JR2,Peter Proposes 4.00
291 JR2,V:Spiderslayer 4.00
292 AS,V:Spiderslayer,Mary
  Jane Accepts proposal 4.00
293 MZ,BMc,V:Kraven 10.00
294 MZ,BMc,D:Kraven 10.00
295 BSz(c),KB(i),Mad Dog,pt.#2 . 4.00
296 JBy(c),AS,V:Dr.Octopus 4.00
297 AS,V:Dr.Octopus 4.00
298 TM,BMc,V:Chance,C:Venom
  (not in costume) 35.00
299 TM,BMc,V:Chance,I:Venom . 20.00
300 TM,O:Venom 65.00
301 TM,A:Silver Sable 15.00
302 TM,V:Nero,A:Silver Sable . . 15.00
303 TM,A:Silver Sable,Sandman 15.00
304 TM,JRu,V:Black Fox,Prowler
  I:Jonathan Caesar 12.00
305 TM,JRu,V:BlackFox,Prowler 12.00
306 TM,V:Humbug,Chameleon . 11.00
307 TM,O:Chameleon 11.00
308 TM,V:Taskmaster,J.Caesar . 11.00
309 TM,I:Styx & Stone 11.00
310 TM,V:Killershrike 11.00
311 TM,Inferno,V:Mysterio 11.00
312 TM,Inferno,Hobgoblin V:
  Green Goblin 15.00
313 TM,Inferno,V:Lizard 10.00
314 TM,X-mas issue,V:J.Caesar 10.00
315 TM,V:Venom,Hydro-Man . . 20.00
316 TM,V:Venom 20.00
317 TM,V:Venom,A:Thing 20.00
318 TM,V:Scorpion 8.00
319 TM,V:Scorpion,Rhino 8.00
320 TM,B:Assassin Nation Plot
  A:Paladin,Silver Sable 8.00
321 TM,A:Paladin,Silver Sable . . 6.00
322 TM,A:Silver Sable,Paladin . . 6.00
323 TM,A:Silver Sable,Paladin,
  Captain America 6.00
324 TM(c),EL,AG,V:Sabretooth,A:
  Capt.America,Silver Sable . . 10.00
325 TM,E:Assassin Nation Plot,
  V:Red Skull,Captain America,
  Silver Sable 6.00
326 V:Graviton,A of V. 4.00
327 EL,AG,V:Magneto,A of V. . . . 5.00
328 TM,V:Hulk,A of V. 8.00
329 EL,V:Tri-Sentinel 6.00
330 EL,A:Punisher,Black Cat . . . 6.00
331 EL,A:Punisher,C:Venom 6.00
332 EL,V:Venom,Styx & Stone . . 8.00

333 EL,V:Venom,Styx & Stone . . 8.00
334 EL,B:Sinister Six,A:Iron Man . 4.00
335 EL,TA,A:Captain America . . . 4.00
336 EL,D:Nathan Lubensky,
  A:Dr.Strange,Chance 3.50
337 WS(c),EL,TA,A:Nova 3.50
338 EL,A:Jonathan Caesar 3.50
339 EL,JR,E:Sinister Six,A:Thor
  D:Jonathan Caesar 3.50
340 EL,V:Femme Fatales 3.00
341 EL,V:Tarantula,Powers Lost . 3.00
342 EL,A:Blackcat,V:Scorpion . . . 3.00
343 EL,Powers Restored,
  C:Cardiac,V:Chameleon 3.00
344 EL,V:Rhino,I:Cardiac,Cletus
  Kassady(Carnage),A:Venom . 10.00

Amazing Spider-Man #266
© Marvel Entertainment Group

345 MBa,V:Boomerang,C:Venom,
  A:Cletus Kassady(infected w/
  Venom-Spawn) 12.00
346 EL,V:Venom 8.00
347 EL,V:Venom 8.00
348 EL,A:Avengers 3.00
349 EL,A:Black Fox 3.00
350 EL,V:Doctor Doom,Black Fox 4.00
351 MBa,A:Nova,V:Tri-Sentinal . . 4.00
352 MBa,A:Nova,V:Tri-Sentinal . . 3.00
353 MBa,B:Round Robin:The Side
  Kick's Revenge,A:Punisher,
  Nova,Moon Knight,Darkhawk . 3.00
354 MBa,A:Nova,Punisher,
  Darkhawk,Moon Knight 3.00
355 MBa,A:Nova,Punisher,
  Darkhawk,Moon Knight 3.00
356 MBa,A:Moon Knight,
  Punisher,Nova 3.00
357 MBa,A:Moon Knight,
  Punisher,Darkhawk,Nova 3.00
358 MBa,E:Round Robin:The Side
  Kick's Revenge,A:Darkhawk,
  Moon Knight,Punisher,Nova,
  Gatefold(c) 3.00
359 CMa,A:Cardiac,C:Cletus
  Kasady (Carnage) 6.00
360 CMa,V:Cardiac,C:Carnage . . 7.00
361 MBa,I:Carnage 12.00

361a 2nd printing 1.50
362 MBa,V:Carnage,Venom 7.00
362a 2nd printing 1.50
363 MBa,V:Carnage,Venom, . . . 5.00
364 MBa,V:Shocker 2.50
365 MBa,JR,V:Lizard,30th Anniv.,
    Hologram(c),w/poster,Prev.of
    Spider-Man 2099 by RL 7.00
366 JBi,A:Red Skull,Taskmaster . 2.50
367 JBi,A:Red Skull,Taskmaster . 2.50
368 MBa,B:Invasion of the Spider
    Slayers #1,BU:Jonah Jameson 2.00
369 MBa,V:Electro,BU:Green
    Goblin 2.00
370 MBa,V:Scorpion,BU:A.May . . 2.00
371 MBa,V:Spider-Slayer.
    BU:Black Cat 2.00
372 MBa,V:Spider-Slayer 2.00
373 MBa,V:Sp.-Slayer,BU:Venom 3.00
374 MBa,V:Venom 4.00
375 MBa,V:Venom,30th Anniv.,Holo
    graphx(c) 6.00
376 V:Styx&Stone,A:Cardiac . . . 2.00
377 V:Cardiac,O:Styx&Stone 2.00
378 MBa,Total Carnage#3,V:Shriek,
    Carnage,A:Venom,Cloak 2.00
379 MBa,Total Carnage#7,
    V:Carnage,A:Venom 2.00
380 MBa,Maximum Carnage#11 . 2.00
381 MBa,V:Dr.Samson,A:Hulk . . . 1.75
382 MBa,V:Hulk,A:Dr.Samson . . . 1.75
383 MBa,V:Jury 1.75
384 MBa,AM,V:Jury 1.75
385 B:DvM(s),MBa,RyE,V:Jury . . 1.50
386 MBa,RyE,B:Lifetheft,V:Vulture 3.00
387 MBa,RyE,V:Vulture 3.00
388 Blue Foil(c),MBa,RyE,RLm,TP,
    E:Lifetheft,D:Peter's Synthetic
    Parents,BU:Venom,Cardiac,
    Chance, ... 4.00
388a Newsstand Ed. 3.00
389 MBa,RyE,E:Pursuit,
    V:Chameleon, ... 1.75
390 MBa,RyE,B:Shrieking,
    A:Shriek,w/cel 3.25
390a Newsstand Ed. 1.75
391 MBa,RyE,V:Shriek,Carrion . . 2.00
392 MBa,RyE,V:Shriek,Carrion . . 2.00
393 MBa,RyE,E:Shrieking,
    V:Shriek,Carrion 2.00
394 MBa,RyE,Power & Responsibility,
    pt.2,V:Judas Traveller, ... 4.00
394a w/flip book,2 covers 2.00
395 MBa,RyE,R:Puma 1.75
396 MBa,RyE,A:Daredevil,
    V:Vulture, Owl 1.75
397 MBa,Web of Death,pt.1,
    V:Stunner,Doc Ock 2.50
398 MBa,Web of Death,pt.3 . . . . . 1.75
399 MBa,Smoke and Mirrors,pt.2 . 1.75
400 MBa,Death of a Parker 9.00
400a die-cut cover 4.00
401 MBa,The Mark of Kaine,pt.2 . 1.75
402 MBa,R:Judas Travellor 1.75
403 MBa,JMD,LMa The Trial of
    Peter Parker, pt.2 . . . . 1.75
404 Maximum Clonage 1.75
405 JMD,DaR,LMa,Exiled,pt.2, . . 1.75
406 I:New Doc Ock 1.75
407 TDF,MBa,LMa,Return of
    Spider-Man,pt.2 . . . . 1.75
408 TDF,MBa,LMa,Media
    Blizzard,pt.2 . . . . 1.75
409 . . . . 1.75
410 . . . . 1.75

411 TDF,MBa,LMa,Blood
    Brothers,pt.2 . . . . 1.75
412 . . . . 1.75
413 . . . . 1.75
414 A:The Rose 1.75
415 Onslaught saga,V:Sentinels . 2.50
416 Onslaught epilogue 3.00
417 TDF,RG,secrets of Scrier &
    Judas Traveler 2.00
418 Revelations,pt.3, R:Norman
    Osborn 2.50
419 TDF,SSr,V:Black Tarantula . . 1.75
420 TDF,SSr,X-Man x-over,pt.1 . . 1.75
421 TDF,SSr,I:Dragonfly; Electro
    Kidnapped 2.50
422 TDF,SSr,V:Electro,Tarantula . 2.50
423 TDF,V:Electro 1.75
424 TDF,JoB,V:Black Tarantula, The
    Hand, Dragonfly, Delilah,
    The Rose, Elektra 1.75
425 TDF,SSr, V:Electro,double size 3.50
426 TDF,SSr,V:Doctor Octopus . . 1.50
427 TDF,SSr,JR gatefold cover,
    V:Doctor Octopus 2.50
428 TDF,SSr,V:Doctor Octopus . . 2.00
429 TDF,A:Daredevil, X-Man,
    Absorbing Man, Titania 2.00
430 TDF,SSr,V:Carnage,A:Silver
    Surfer 2.00
431 TDF,SSr,V:Carnage (with Silver
    Surfer's powers) 2.00
432 SSr,JR2,Spider-Hunt,pt.2
    x-over 2.00
432a variant cover 3.50
433 TDF,TL,Identity Crisis prelude,
    good-bye to Joe Robertson . . . 2.00
434 TDF,JoB,Identity Crisis, as
    Ricochet vs. Black Tarantula . . 2.00
435 TDF,MD2,Ricochet,A:Delilah . 2.00
436 TDF,JoB,V:Black Tarantula . . 2.00
437 TDF,JoB,V:Plant Man 2.00
Bi-weekly
438 TDF,V:Daredevil 2.00
439 TDF,future history chronicle . 2.00
440 JBy,The Gathering of the Five,
    Pt.2 (of 5) x-over 2.00

Amazing Spider-Man #406
© Marvel Entertainment Group

Minus 1 Spec., TDF,JBe, flashback,
    early Kingpin 2.00
Ann.#1 SD,I:Sinister Six 600.00
Ann.#2 SD,A:Dr.Strange 250.00
Ann.#3 JR,DH,A:Avengers 100.00
Ann.#4 A:H.Torch,V:Mysterio,
    Wizard 90.00
Ann.#5 JR(c),A:Red Skull,I:Peter
    Parker's Parents 100.00
Ann.#6 JR(c),Rep.Ann.#1,Fant.
    Four Ann.#1,SpM #8 . . . . . . 35.00
Ann.#7 JR(c),Rep.#1,#2,#38 . . . 28.00
Ann.#8 Rep.#46,#50 . . . . 28.00
Ann.#9 JR(c),Rep.Spec.SpM #2 . 20.00
Ann.#10 JR(c),GK,V:Human Fly . 12.00
Ann.#11 GK(c),DP,JM,JR2,AM, . 12.00
Ann.#12 JBy(c),KP,Rep.#119,
    #120 . . . . 12.00
Ann.#13 JBy,TA,V:Dr.Octopus . . 10.00
Ann.#14 FM,TP,A:Dr.Strange,
    V:Dr.Doom,Dormammu 12.00
Ann.#15 FM,KJ,BL,Punisher . . . 15.00
Ann.#16 JR2,JR,I:New Captain
    Marvel,A:Thing 7.00
Ann.#17 EH,JM,V:Kingpin 5.00
Ann.#18 RF,BL,JG,V:Scorpion . . . 5.00
Ann.#19 JR(c),MW,V:Spiderslayer 5.00
Ann.#20 BWi(i),V:Iron Man 2020 . 5.00
Ann.#21 JR(c),PR,W:SpM,direct 16.00
Ann.#21a W:SpM,news stand . . 12.00
Ann.#22 JR(c),MBa(1stSpM),SD,
    JG,RLm,TD,Evolutionary War,
    I:Speedball,New Men 7.00
Ann.#23 JBy(c),RLd,MBa,RF,
    AtlantisAttacks#4,A:She-Hulk . 7.00
Ann.#24 GK,SD,MZ,DGr,
    A:Ant Man 4.00
Ann.#25 EL(c),SB,PCu,SD,
    Vibranium Vendetta#1,Venom . 6.00
Ann.#26 Hero Killers#1,A:New
    Warriors,BU:Venom,Solo 5.00
Ann.#27 TL,I:Annex,w/card 3.50
Ann.#28 SBt(s),V:Carnage,BU:Cloak &
    Dagger,Rhino 3.25
Ann. '96 two new stories, 48pg, . 3.00
Ann. '97 RSt,TL,RJn, 48pg, ... 3.00
Ann. '98 TL,TDF,F:Spider-Man & Devil
    Dinosaur, 48pg 3.00
G-Size Superheroes #1 GK,
    A:Morbius,Man-Wolf 30.00
G-Size #1 JR(c),RA,DH,
    A:Dracula 12.00
G-Size #2 K&R(c),RA,AM,
    A:Master of Kung Fu 10.00
G-Size #3 GK(c),RA,DocSavage 10.00
G-Size #4 GK(c),RA,Punisher . . 35.00
G-Size #5 GK(c),RA,V:Magnum . 8.00
G-Size #6 Rep.Ann.#4 . . . . 7.00
G-Size Spec.#1 O:Symbiotes . . . 4.50
Marvel Milestone rep. #1 (1993) . . 2.95
Marvel Milestone rep. #3 (1995) . . 2.95
Marvel Milestone rep. #129 (1992) 2.95
Marvel Milestone rep. #149 (1994) 2.95
GNv Fear Itself RA,A:S.Sable . 12.95
GNv Spirits of the Earth CV,Scotland,
    V:Hellfire Club 25.00
TPB Assassination Plot,
    rep.#320-325 . . . . 14.95
TPB Carnage,rep.#361-363 . . . . . 6.95
TPB Cosmic Adventures rep.
    Amaz.SpM #327-329,Web #59
    61,Spec.SpM #158-160 . . . . 19.95
TPB Kraven's Last Hunt, Reps. AS
    #293,294,Web.#31,32,P.Parker
    #131,132,SC 15.95

MARVEL

HC 19.95
TPB Origin of the Hobgoblin rep.#238,
239,244,245,249-251 . . . . . 14.95
TPB Saga of the Alien Costume,reps.
#252-259 . . . . 9.95
TPB Spider-Man Vs. Venom,reps.
A.SpM#298-300,315-317 . . . 10.00
TPB Venom Returns rep.Amaz.SpM.
#331-333,344-347 . . . . 12.95
TPB The Wedding,Reps.A.S.
#290-292,Ann#21 . . . . 12.95
Nothing Can Stop the Juggernaut,
reps.#229,230 . . . . 3.95
Sensational Spider-Man,reps.
Ann.#14,15; 4.95
Skating on Thin Ice(Canadian) . 15.00
Skating on Thin Ice(US) 1.50
Soul of the Hunter MZ,BMc,
R:Kraven 7.00
Unicef:Trial of Venom,
A:Daredevil,V:Venom 50.00
See Also:
PETER PARKER;
SPECTACULAR SPIDER-MAN;
WEB OF SPIDER-MAN

AMAZING SPIDER-MAN INDEX
SEE: OFFICIAL MARVEL INDEX TO THE AMAZING SPIDER-MAN

AMAZING SPIDER-MAN COLLECTION
1 Mark Bagley card set 2.95
2 and 3 MBa, from card set . . @2.95

AMAZING X-MEN, THE
March–June 1995
1 X-Men after Xavier 6.00
2 Exodus,Dazzler,V:Abyss 3.50
3 F:Bishop 3.00
4 V:Apocalypse 2.50
TPB Rep. #1-#4 . . . . 8.95

AMERICAN TAIL II
Dec., 1991
1 movie adaption 1.00
2 movie adaption 1.00

A-NEXT
Aug. 1998
1 TDF,RF,BBr,Next Generation of
Avengers 2.00

ANIMAX
Star Comics Dec., 1986–June 1987
1 Based on Toy Line 1.00
2 thru 4 . . . . @1.00

ANNEX
Aug.–Nov. 1994
1 WMc,I:Brace, Crucible of Power 2.00
2 WMc,V:Brace, Crucible, pt.2 . . 1.75
3 Crucible of Power, pt.3 . . . . . . 1.75
4 Crucible of Power, pt.4 . . . . . . 1.95

ANNIE
(Treasury Edition)
Oct., 1982
1 Movie Adaptation 1.25

---

2 Nov., 1982 . . . . 1.25

ANNIE OAKLEY
Atlas Spring, 1948
1 A:Hedy Devine 275.00
2 CCB,I:Lana,A:Hedy Devine . 175.00
3 . . . . 150.00
4 . . . . 150.00
5 . . . . 100.00
6 . . . . 75.00
7 . . . . 75.00
8 . . . . 75.00
9 AW, ... 80.00
10 . . . . 60.00
11 June, 1956 . . . . 65.00

A-1
1993
1 The Edge 5.95
2 Cheeky,Wee Budgie Boy 5.95
3 King Leon 5.95
4 King Leon 5.95

APOCALYPSE STRIKEFILES
1 After Xavier special 2.50

ARCHANGEL
1996
1-shot B&W 2.50

ARIZONA KID
Atlas March, 1951
1 RH,Coming of the Arizons Kid 125.00
2 RH,Code of the Gunman . . . 50.00
3 RH(c) 42.00
4 . . . . 42.00
5 . . . . 40.00
6 Jan., 1952 . . . . 40.00

ARRGH!
Dec., 1974
Satire
1 Vampire Rats 15.00
2 . . . . 10.00
3 Beauty And the Big Foot . . . 10.00
4 The Night Gawker 10.00
5 Sept., 1975 . . . . 10.00

ARROWHEAD
April, 1954
1 Indian Warrior Stories 100.00
2 . . . . 50.00
3 . . . . 50.00
4 Nov., 1954 . . . . 50.00

ASTONISHING
See: MARVEL BOY

ASTONISHING TALES
August, 1970
1 BEv(c),JK,WW,KaZar,Dr.Doom 35.00
2 JK,WW,Ka-Zar,Dr.Doom 20.00
3 BWS,WW,Ka-Zar,Dr.Doom . . 25.00
4 BWS,WW,Ka-Zar,Dr.Doom . . 25.00
5 BWS,GT,Ka-Zar,Dr.Doom . . . 25.00
6 BWS,BEv,GT,I:Bobbi Morse . 25.00
7 HT,GC,Ka-Zar,Dr.Doom 15.00
8 HT,TS,GT,GC,TP,Ka-Zar 15.00
9 GK(c),JB,Ka-Zar,Dr.Doom . . 12.00
10 GK(c),BWS,SB,Ka-Zar 15.00
11 GK,O:Kazar 12.00

Astonishing Tales #2
© Marvel Entertainment Group

12 JB,DA,NA,V:Man Thing 12.00
13 JB,RB,DA,V:Man Thing 6.00
14 GK(c),rep. Kazar 6.00
15 GK,TS,Kazar 6.00
16 RB,AM,A:Kazar 6.00
17 DA,V:Gemini 6.00
18 JR(c),DA,A:Kazar 6.00
19 JR(c),DA,JSn,JA,I:Victorious . 6.00
20 JR(c),A:Kazar 6.00
21 RTs(s),DAy,B:It 6.00
22 RTs(s),DAy,V:Granitor 6.00
23 RTs(s),DAy,A:Fin Fang Foom . 6.00
24 RTs(s),DAy,E:It 6.00
25 RB(a&s),B:I&O:Deathlok,
GP(1st art) 30.00
26 RB(a&s),I:Warwolf 7.00
27 RB(a&s),V:Warwolf 7.00
28 RB(a&s),V:Warwolf 7.00
29 rep.Marv.Super Heroes #18 . . 8.00
30 RB(a&s),KP, ... 7.00
31 RB(a&s),BW,KP,V:Ryker 7.00
32 RB(a&s),KP,V:Ryker 6.00
33 RB(a&s),KJ,I:Hellinger 6.00
34 RB(a&s),KJ,V:Ryker 6.00
35 RB(a&s),KJ,I:Doomsday-Mech 6.00
36 RB(a&s),KP,E:Deathlok,
I:Godwulf 20.00

ASTONISHING X-MEN, THE
March–June 1995
1 Uncanny X-Men 5.00
2 V:Holocaust 3.50
3 V:Abyss 3.00
4 V:Beast,Infinities 2.50
TPB Rep. #1-#4 . . . . 8.95

A-TEAM
March, 1984
1 . . . . 1.00
2 . . . . 1.00
3 May, 1984 . . . . 1.00

ATOMIC AGE
Epic Nov., 1990
1 AW 4.50
2 AW 4.50
3 AW,Feb., 1991 . . . . 4.50

AVENGERS
Sept., 1963

1 JK,O:Avengers,V:Loki 2,500.00
2 JK,V:Space Phantom 625.00
3 JK,V:Hulk,Sub-Mariner 400.00
4 JK,R&J:Captain America . 1,500.00
5 JK,L:Hulk,V:Lava Men 250.00
6 JK,I:Masters of Evil 180.00
7 JK,V:Baron Zemo,
  Enchantress 180.00
8 JK,I:Kang 190.00
9 JK(c),DH,I&D:Wonder Man . 215.00
10 JK(c),DH,I:Immortus 175.00
11 JK(c),DH,A:Spider-Man,
  V:Kang 200.00
12 JK(c),DH,V:Moleman,
  Red Ghost 125.00
13 JK(c),DH,I:Count Nefaria .. 125.00
14 JK,DH,V:Count Nefaria 125.00
15 JK,DH,D:Baron Zemo 100.00
16 JK,J:Hawkeye,Scarlet Witch,
  Quicksilver 135.00
17 JK(c),DH,V:Mole Man,A:Hulk 100.00
18 JK(c),DH,V:The Commisar . 100.00
19 JK(c),DH,I&O:Swordsman,
  O:Hawkeye 90.00
20 JK(c),DH,WW,V:Swordsman,
  Mandarin 60.00
21 JK(c),DH,WW,V:Power Man
  (not L.Cage),Enchantress ... 60.00
22 JK(c),DH,WW,V:Power Man . 60.00
23 JK(c),DH,JR,V:Kang 40.00
24 JK(c),DH,JR,V:Kang 40.00
25 JK(c),DH,V:Dr.Doom 50.00
26 DH,V:Attuma 40.00
27 DH,V:Attuma,Beetle 40.00
28 JK(c),DH,I:1st Goliath,
  I:Collector 42.00
29 DH,V:Power Man,Swordsman 40.00
30 JK(c),DH,V:Swordsman 40.00
31 DH,V:Keeper of the Flame .. 40.00
32 DH,I:Bill Foster 30.00
33 DH,O:Sons of the Serpent
  A:Bill Foster 30.00
34 DH,V:Living Laser 30.00
35 DH,V:Mandarin 30.00
36 DH,V:The Ultroids 30.00
37 GK(c),DH,V:Ultroids 30.00
38 GK(c),DH,V:Enchantress,
  Ares,J:Hercules 30.00
39 DH,V:Mad Thinker 30.00
40 DH,V:Sub-Mariner 30.00
41 JB,V:Dragon Man,Diablo 25.00
42 JB,V:Dragon Man,Diablo 25.00
43 JB,V:Red Guardian 25.00
44 JB,V:Red Guardian,
  O:Black.Widow 25.00
45 JB,V:Super Adoptoid 25.00
46 JB,V:Whirlwind 25.00
47 JB,GT,V:Magneto 28.00
48 GT,I&O:New Black Knight ... 28.00
49 JB,V:Magneto 28.00
50 JB,V:Typhon 25.00
51 JB,GT,R:Iron Man,Thor
  V:Collector 25.00
52 JB,J:Black Panther,
  I:Grim Reaper 30.00
53 JB,GT,A:X-Men; x-over
  X-Men #45 .... 40.00
54 JB,GT,V:Masters of Evil
  I:Crimson Cowl(Ultron) 25.00
55 JB,I:Ultron,V:Masters of Evil . 20.00
56 JB,D:Bucky retold,
  V:Baron Zemo 20.00
57 JB,I:Vision,V:Ultron 70.00

Avengers #10
© Marvel Entertainment Group

58 JB,O&J:Vision 45.00
59 JB,I:Yellowjacket 20.00
60 JB,W:Yellowjacket & Wasp .. 18.00
61 JB,A:Dr.Strange,x-over
  Dr. Strange #178 .... 17.00
62 JB,I:Man-Ape,A:Dr.Strange .. 17.00
63 GC,I&O:2nd Goliath(Hawkeye)
  V:Egghead 16.00
64 GC,V:Egghead,O:Hawkeye .. 16.00
65 GC,V:Swordsman,Egghead .. 16.00
66 BWS,I:Ultron 6,Adamantium . 17.00
67 BWS,V:Ultron 6 .... 17.00
68 SB,V:Ultron 13.00
69 SB,I:Nighthawk,Grandmaster,
  Squadron Supreme, V:Kang . 15.00
70 SB,O:Squadron Supreme
  V:Kang 13.00
71 SB,I:Invaders,V:Kang 25.00
72 SB,A:Captain Marvel,
  I:Zodiac 12.00
73 HT(i),V:Sons of Serpent 12.00
74 JB,TP,V:Sons of Serpent,
  IR:Black Panther on TV 12.00
75 JB,TP,I:Arkon 13.00
76 JB,TP,V:Arkon 12.00
77 JB,TP,V:Split-Second Squad . 12.00
78 SB,TP,V:Lethal Legion 12.00
79 JB,TP,V:Lethal Legion 12.00
80 JB,TP,I&O:Red Wolf 13.00
81 JB,TP,A:Red Wolf 12.00
82 JB,TP,V:Ares,A:Daredevil ... 12.00
83 JB,TP,I:Valkyrie,
  V:Masters of Evil 20.00
84 JB,TP,V:Enchantress,Arkon . 12.00
85 JB,V:Squadron Supreme ... 12.00
86 JB,JM,A:Squad Supreme ... 12.00
87 SB(i),O:Black Panther,
  V: A.I.M. 30.00
88 SB,JM,V:Psyklop,A:Hulk,
  Professor.X 12.00
89 SB,B:Kree/Skrull War 12.00
90 SB,V:Sentry #459,Ronan,
  Skrulls 12.00
91 SB,V:Sentry #459,Ronan,
  Skrulls 12.00
92 SB,V:Super Skrull,Ronan, ... 12.00
93 NA,TP,V:Super-Skrull,G-Size 55.00
94 NA,JB,TP,V:Super-Skrull,

95 NA,TP,V:Maximus,Skrulls,
  A:Inhumans,O:Black Bolt ... 35.00
96 NA,TP,V:Skrulls,Ronan 35.00
97 GK&BEv(c),JB,TP,E:Kree-Skrull
  War,V:Annihilus,Ronan,Skrulls,
  A:Golden Age Heroes 18.00
98 BWS,SB,V:Ares,R:Hercules,
  R&N:Hawkeye 25.00
99 BWS,TS,V:Ares 25.00
100 BWS,JSr,V:Ares & Kratos .. 75.00
101 RB,DA,A:Watcher 9.00
102 RB,JSt,V:Grim Reaper,
  Sentinels 9.00
103 RB,JSt,V:Sentinels 9.00
104 RB,JSt,V:Sentinels 9.00
105 JB,JM,V:Savage Land
  Mutates; A:Black Panther 9.00
106 GT,DC,JB,TP,V:Space Phantom 9.00
107 GT,DC,JSn,V:Space
  Phantom, Grim Reaper 11.00
108 DH,DC,JSt,V:Space
  Phantom,Grim Reaper 9.00
109 DH,FMc,V:Champion,
  L:Hawkeye 9.00
110 DH,V:Magneto,A:X-Men ... 22.00
111 DH,J:Bl.Widow,A:Daredevil,
  X-Men,V:Magneto 22.00
112 DH,I:Mantis,V:Lion-God,
  L:Black Widow 15.00
113 FBe(i),V:The Living Bombs .. 8.00
114 JR(c),V:Lion-God,J:Mantis,
  Swordsman 8.00
115 JR(c),A:Defenders,V:Loki,
  Dormammu 9.00
116 JR(c),A:Defenders,S.Surfer
  V:Loki,Dormammu 9.00
117 JR(c),FMc(i),A:Defenders,Silv.
  Surfer,V:Loki,Dormammu 9.00
118 JR(c),A:Defenders,S.Surfer
  V:Loki,Dormammu 9.00
119 JR(c),DH(i),V:Collector 7.00
120 JSn(c),DH(i),V:Zodiac 7.00
121 JR&JSn(c),JB,DH,V:Zodiac .. 7.00
122 K&R(c),V:Zodiac 7.00
123 JR(c),DH(i),O:Mantis 7.00
124 JR(c),JB,DC,V:Kree,O:Mantis 7.00
125 JR(c),JB,DC,V:Thanos 16.00
126 DC(i),V:Klaw,Solarr 8.00
127 GK(c),SB,JSon,A:Inhumans,
  V:Ultron,Maximus 8.00
128 K&R(c),SB,JSon,V:Kang 7.00
129 SB,JSon,V:Kang 7.00
130 GK(c),SB,JSon,V:Slasher,
  Titanic Three 7.00
131 GK(c),SB,JSon,V:Kang,
  Legion of the Unliving 7.00
132 SB,JSon,Kang,Legion
  of the Unliving 6.00
133 GK(c),SB,JSon,O:Vision 7.00
134 K&R(c),SB,JSon,O:Vision .. 7.00
135 JSn&JR(c),GT,O:Mantis,
  Vision,C:Thanos 8.00
136 K&R(c),rep Amazing Adv#12 . 7.00
137 JR(c),GT,J:Beast,
  Moondragon 7.00
138 GK(c),GT,V:Toad 6.00
139 K&R(c),GT,V:Whirlwind 6.00
140 K&R(c),GT,V:Whirlwind 6.00
141 GK(c),GP,V:Squad.Sinister . 5.00
142 K&R(c),GP,V:Squadron
  Sinister,Kang 5.00
143 GK(c),GP,V:Squadron
  Sinister,Kang 5.00
144 GP,GK(c),V:Squad.Sinister,

Avengers #103
© Marvel Entertainment Group

O&J:Hellcat,O:Buzz Baxter . . 5.00
145 GK(c),DH,V:Assassin 5.00
146 GK(c),DH,KP,V:Assassin . . 15.00
147 GP,V:Squadron Supreme . . 5.00
148 JK(c),GP,V:Squad.Supreme . 5.00
149 GP,V:Orka 5.00
150 GP,JK,rep.Avengers #16 . . . 5.00
151 GP,new line-up,
    R:Wonder Man 4.50
152 JB,JSt,I:New Black Talon . . 5.00
153 JB,JSt,V:L.Laser,Whizzer . . 4.50
154 GP,V:Attuma 4.50
155 SB,V:Dr.Doom,Attuma 4.50
156 SB,I:Tyrak,V:Attuma 4.50
157 DH,V:Stone Black Knight . . 4.50
158 JK(c),SB,I&O:Graviton, ... 4.50
159 JK(c),SB,V:Graviton, ... 4.50
160 GP,V:Grim Reaper 4.50
161 GP,V:Ultron,A:Ant-Man 4.50
162 GP,V:Ultron,I:Jocasta 4.50
163 GT,A:Champions,V:Typhon . 4.50
164 JBy,V:Lethal Legion 6.00
165 JBy,V:Count Nefario 6.00
166 JBy,V:Count Nefario 6.00
167 GP,A:Guardians,A:Nighthawk,
    Korvac,V:Porcupine 4.00
168 GP,A:Guardians,V:Korvac,
    I:Gyrich 4.00
169 SB,I:Eternity Man 4.00
170 GP,R:Jocasta,C:Ultron,
    A:Guardians 4.00
171 GP,V:Ultron,A:Guardians,
    Ms Marvel 4.00
172 SB,KJ,V:Tyrak 4.00
173 SB,V:Collector 4.00
174 GP(c),V:Collector 4.00
175 V&O:Korvac,A:Guardians . . 4.00
176 V:Korvac,A:Guardians 4.00
177 DC(c),D:Korvac,A:Guardians . 4.00
178 CI,V:Manipulator 4.00
179 JM,AG,V:Stinger,Bloodhawk . 4.00
180 JM,V:Monolith,Stinger,
    D:Bloodhawk 4.00
181 JBy,GD,I:Scott Lang 5.00
182 JBy,KJ,V:Maximoff 4.00

183 JBy,KJ,J:Ms.Marvel 4.00
184 JBy,KJ,J:Falcon,
    V:Absorbing Man 4.00
185 JBy,DGr,O:Quicksilver & Scarlet
    Witch,I:Bova,V:Modred 4.00
186 JBy,DGr,V:Modred,Chthon . . 4.00
187 JBy,DGr,V:Chthon,Modred . . 4.00
188 JBy,DGr,V:The Elements . . . 4.00
189 JBy,DGr,V:Deathbird 4.00
190 JBy,DGr,V:Grey Gargoyle,
    A:Daredevil 4.00
191 JBy,DGr,V:Grey Gargoyle,
    A:Daredevil 4.00
192 I:Inferno 3.00
193 FM(c),SB,DGr,O:Inferno . . . 3.00
194 GP,JRu,J:Wonder Man 3.00
195 GP,JRu,A:Antman,
    I&C:Taskmaster 5.00
196 GP,JA,A:Antman,
    V:Taskmaster, ... 3.00
197 CI,JAb,V:Red Ronin 3.00
198 GP,DGr,V:Red Ronan 3.00
199 GP,DGr,V:Red Ronan 3.00
200 GP,DGr,V:Marcus,
    L:Ms.Marvel 5.00
201 GP,DGr,F:Jarvis 3.00
202 GP,V:Ultron 3.00
203 CI,V:Crawlers,F:Wonderman . 3.00
204 DN,DGr,V:Yellow Claw 3.00
205 DGr,V:Yellow Claw 3.00
206 GC,DGr,V:Pyron 3.00
207 GC,DGr,V:Shadowlord 3.00
208 GC,DGr,V:Berserker 3.00
209 DGr,A:Mr.Fantastic,V:Skrull . 3.00
210 GC,DGr,V:Weathermen . . . 3.00
211 GC,DGr,Moon Knight,J:Tigra . 3.00
212 DGr,V:Elfqueen 3.00
213 BH,DGr,L:Yellowjacket 3.00
214 BH,DGr,V:Gh.Rider,A:Angel . 5.00
215 DGr,A:Silver Surfer,
    V:Molecule Man 2.50
216 DGr,A:Silver Surfer,
    V:Molecule Man 2.50
217 BH,DGr,V:Egghead,
    R:Yellowjacket,Wasp3 . . . . . 2.50
218 DP,V:M.Hardy 2.50
219 BH,A:Moondragon,Drax . . . 2.50
220 BH,DGr,D:Drax,V:MnDragon . 2.50
221 J:She Hulk 2.50
222 V:Masters of Evil 2.50
223 A:Antman 2.50
224 AM,A:Antman 2.50
225 A:Black Knight 2.50
226 A:Black Knight 2.50
227 J:2nd Captain Marvel,
    O:Avengers 2.50
228 V:Masters of Evil 2.50
229 JSt,V:Masters of Evil 2.50
230 A:Cap.Marvel,L:Yellowjacke . 2.50
231 AM,JSi,J:2nd Captain Marvel,
    Starfox 2.50
232 AM,JSi 2.50
233 JBy,V:Annihilus 2.50
234 AM,JSi,O:ScarletWitch 2.50
235 AM,JSi,V:Wizard 2.50
236 AM,JSi,A:SpM,V:Lava Men . 2.50
237 AM,JSi,A:SpM,V:Lava Men . 2.50
238 AM,JSi,V:Moonstone,
    O:Blackout 3.00
239 AM,JSi,A:David Letterman . 3.50
240 AM,JSi,A:Dr.Strange 2.50
241 AM,JSi,V:Morgan LeFey . . . 2.50
242 AM,JSi,Secret Wars 2.50
243 AM,JSi,Secret Wars 2.50
244 AM,JSi,V:Dire Wraiths 2.50

Avengers #130
© Marvel Entertainment Group

245 AM,JSi,V:Dire Wraiths 2.50
246 AM,JSi,V:Eternals 2.50
247 AM,JSi,A:Eternals,V:Deviants . 2.50
248 AM,JSi,A:Eternals,V:Deviants . 2.50
249 AM,JSi,A:Maelstrom 2.50
250 AM,JSi,A:W.CA.
    V:Maelstrom 3.50
251 BH,JSi,A:Paladin 2.50
252 BH,JSi,J:Hercules
    V:Blood Brothers 2.50
253 BH,JSi,J:Black Knight 2.50
254 BH,JSi,A:W.C.A. 2.50
255 TP,p(c),JB,Legacy of
    Thanos/Santuary II 2.50
256 JB,TP,A:Kazar 2.50
257 JB,TP,D:Savage Land,
    I:Nebula 3.00
258 JB,TP,A:SpM,Firelord,Nebula . 2.50
259 JB,TP,V:Nebula 2.50
260 JB,TP,SecretWarsII,
    IR:Nebula is Thanos' Grand
    daughter 2.50
261 JB,TP,Secret War II 2.50
262 JB,TP,J:Submariner 2.50
263 JB,TP,X-Factor tie-in,
    Rebirth,Marvel Girl,pt.1 . . . . . 6.00
264 JB,TP,I:2nd Yellow Jacket . . . 2.50
265 JB,TP,Secret War II 2.50
266 JB,TP,Secret Wars II,A:
    Silver Surfer 2.50
267 JB,TP,V:Kang 2.50
268 JB,TP,V:Kang 2.50
269 JB,TP,V:Kang,A:Immortus . . 2.50
270 JB,TP,V:Moonstone 2.50
271 JB,TP,V:Masters of Evil . . . 2.50
272 JB,TP,A:Alpha Flight 2.50
273 JB,TP,V:Masters of Evil . . . 2.50
274 JB,TP,V:Masters of Evil . . . 2.50
275 JB,TP,V:Masters of Evil . . . 2.50
276 JB,TP,V:Masters of Evil . . . 2.50
277 JB,TP,V:Masters of Evil . . . 2.50
278 JB,TP,V:Tyrok,J:Dr.Druid . . 2.50
279 JB,TP,new leader 2.50
280 BH,KB,O:Jarvis 2.50
281 JB,TP,V:Olympian Gods . . . 2.50

282 JB,TP,V:Cerberus 2.50	344 SEp,TP,I:Proctor 2.00
283 JB,TP,V:Olympian Gods 2.50	345 SEp,TP,Oper. Galactic Storm
284 JB,TP,V:Olympian Gods 2.50	Pt.5,V:Kree,Shiar 1.75
285 JB,TP,V:Zeus 2.50	346 SEp,TP,Oper. Galactic Storm
286 JB,TP,V:Fixer 2.50	Pt.12,I:Star Force 1.75
287 JB,TP,V:Fixer 2.50	347 SEp,TP,Oper. Galactic Storm
288 JB,TP,V:Sentry 459 . . . . 2.50	Pt.19,D:Kree Race,Conclusion 2.00
289 JB,TP,J:Marrina 2.50	348 SEp,TP,F:Vision 1.75
290 JB,TP,V:Adaptoid 2.50	349 SEp,TP,V:Ares 1.75
291 JB,TP,V:Marrina 2.50	350 SEp,TP,rep.Avengers#53,A:Prof.
292 JB,TP,V:Leviathon 2.50	X,Cyclops,V:StarJammers 3.00
293 JB,TP,V:Leviathon 2.50	351 KWe,V:Star Jammers 1.75
294 JB,TP,V:Nebula 2.50	352 V:Grim Reaper 1.75
295 JB,TP,V:Nebula 2.50	353 V:Grim Reaper 1.75
296 JB,TP,V:Nebula 2.50	354 V:Grim Reaper 1.75
297 JB,TP,V:Nebula 2.50	355 BHs(s),SEp,I:Gatherers,
298 JB,TP,Inferno,Edwin Jarvis . 2.50	Coal Tiger 2.00
299 JB,TP,Inferno,V:Orphan	356 B:BHs(s),SEp,TP,A:Bl.Panther
Maker,R:Gilgemesh 2.50	D:Coal Tiger 1.75
300 JB,TP,WS,Inferno,V:Kang,	357 SEp,TP,A:Watcher 1.75
O:Avengers,J:Gilgemesh,	358 SEp,TP,V:Arkon 1.75
Mr.Fantastic,Invis.Woman 4.00	359 SEp,TP,A:Arkon 1.75
301 BH,DH,A:SuperNova 2.00	360 SEp,TP,V:Proctor,double-size,
302 RB,TP,V:SuperNova,	bronze foil(c) 4.00
A:Quasar 2.00	361 SEp,I:Alternate Vision 1.50
303 RB,TP,V:SuperNova,A:FF . . . 2.00	362 SEp,TP,V:Proctor 1.50
304 RB,TP,V:U-Foes,Puma 2.00	363 SEp,TP,V:Proctor,D:Alternate
305 PR,TP,V:Lava Men 2.00	Vision,C:Deathcry,Silver Foil(c),
306 PR,TP,O:Lava Men 2.00	30th Anniv., ... 3.00
307 PR,TP,V:Lava Men 2.00	364 SEp,TP,I:Deathcry,V:Kree . . . 1.50
308 PR,TP,A:Eternals,J:Sersi . . . 2.00	365 SEp,TP,V:Kree 1.50
309 PR,TP,V:Blastaar 2.00	366 SEp,TP,V:Kree,N:Dr.Pym,Gold
310 PR,TP,V:Blastaar 2.00	Foil(c) 4.50
311 PR,TP,Acts of Veng.,V:Loki . 2.00	367 F:Vision 2.00
312 PR,TP,Acts of Vengeance,	368 SEp,TP,Bloodties#1,
V:Freedom Force 2.00	A:X-Men 3.00
313 PR,TP,Acts of Vengeance,	369 SEp,TP,E:BHs(s),Bloodties#5,
V:Mandarin,Wizard 2.00	D:Cortez,V:Exodus,Platinum
314 PR,TP,J:Sersi,A:Spider-Man,	Foil(c) 3.00
V:Nebula 2.00	370 SEp(c),TP(c),GI,V:Deviants,
315 PR,TP,A:SpM,V:Nebula 2.00	A:Kro,I:Delta Force 1.50
316 PR,TP,J:Spider-Man 2.00	371 GM,TP,V:Deviants,A:Kro 1.50
317 PR,TP,A:SpM,V:Nebula 2.00	372 B:BHs(s),SEp,TP,I:2nd
318 PR,TP,A:SpM,V:Nebula 2.00	Gatherers,A:Proctor 1.50
319 PR,B:Crossing Line 2.00	373 SEp,TP,I:Alternate Jocasta,
320 PR,TP,A:Alpha Flight 2.00	V:Sersi 1.50
321 PR,Crossing Line#3 . . . . 2.00	374 SEp,TP,O&IR:Proctor is Alternate
322 PR,TP,Crossing Line#4 . . . . 2.00	Black Knight 1.50
323 PR,TP,Crossing Line#5 . . . . 2.00	375 SEp,TP,Double Sized,D:Proctor,
324 PR,TP,E:Crossing Line 2.00	L:Sersi,Black Knight 3.25
325 V:MotherSuperior,	376 F:Crystal,I:Terrigen 1.75
Machinesmith 2.00	377 F:Quicksilver 1.50
326 TP,I:Rage 5.00	378 TP,I:Butcher 1.50
327 TP,V:Monsters 2.00	379 TP,Hercules,V:Hera 1.50
328 TP,O:Rage 4.00	379a Avengers Double Feature #1
329 TP,J:Sandman,Rage 2.00	flip-book with Giant-Man #1 . . . 2.50
330 TP,V:Tetrarch of Entropy . . . 2.00	380 Hera 6.00
331 TP,J:Rage,Sandman 2.00	380a Avengers Double Feature #2
332 TP,V:Dr.Doom 2.00	flip-book with Giant Man #2 . . . 5.00
333 HT,V:Dr.Doom 2.00	381 Quicksilvr, Scarlet Witch 4.00
334 NKu,TP,B:Collector,	381a Avengers Double Feature #3
A:Inhumans 2.00	flip-book with Giant Man #3 . . . 2.50
335 RLm(c),SEp,TP,V:Thane	382 Wundagore 1.50
Ector,A:Collector 1.75	382a Avengers Double Feature #4
336 RLm(c),SEp,TP 1.75	flip-book with Giant Man #4 . . . 2.50
337 RLm(c),SEp,TP,V:ThaneEctor 1.75	383 A:Fantastic Force,V:Arides . . . 1.50
338 RLm(c),SEp,TP,A:Beast, . . . 1.75	384 Hercules Vs. Stepmom 4.00
339 RLm(c),SEp,TP,E:Collector . 1.75	385 V:Red Skull 3.00
340 RLm(c),F:Capt.Amer.,Wasp . 1.75	386 F:Black Widow 3.00
341 SEp,TP,A:New Warriors,V:Sons	387 Taking A.I.M.,pt.1 . . . . 3.00
of Serpents 1.75	388 Taking A.I.M.,pt.4 . . . . 3.00
342 SEP,TP,A:New Warriors,	389 B:Mike Deodato 3.00
V:Hatemonger 1.75	390 BHs,TP,The Crossing, prelude 3.00
343 SEp,TP,J:Crystal,C&I:2nd	391 BHs,Cont. From Avg. Crossing 3.00
Swordsman,Magdalene 2.00	392 BHs,TP,The Crossing 2.25

Avengers Giant Size Special #1
© Marvel Entertainment Group

393 BHs,TP,The Crossing 2.25	
394 BHs,TP,The Crossing 2.25	
395 BHs,TP,Timeslide concludes . 2.00	
396 . . . . 2.00	
397 TP,Incred.Hulk #440 x-over . . 2.00	
398 TP,V:Unknown foe 2.00	
399 . . . . 2.00	
400 MeW,MWa,double size 4.50	
401 MeW,MWa,Onslaught saga . . 2.50	
402 MWa,MD2,Onslaught, finale . 2.50	
Ann.#1 DH,V:Mandarin,	
Masters of Evil 60.00	
Ann.#2 DH,JB,V:Scar.Centurion . 35.00	
Ann.#3 rep.#4,T.ofSusp.#66-68 . 25.00	
Ann.#4 rep.#5,#6 . . . . 12.00	
Ann.#5 JK(c),rep.#8,#11 . . . . . 12.00	
Ann.#6 GP,HT,V:Laser,Nuklo,	
Whirlwind 10.00	
Ann.#7 JSn,JRu,V:Thanos,A:Captain	
Marvel,D:Warlock(2nd) 15.00	
Ann.#8 GP,V:Dr.Spectrum 6.00	
Ann.#9 DN,V:Arsenal 5.00	
Ann.#10 MGo,A:X-Men,Spid.Woman,	
I:Rogue,V:Bro/Evil Mutants . . 30.00	
Ann.#11 DP,V:Defenders 5.00	
Ann.#12 JG,V:Inhumans,Maximus 4.00	
Ann.#13 JBy,V:Armin Zola 4.00	
Ann.#14 JBy,KB,V:Skrulls 4.00	
Ann.#15 SD,KJ,V:Freedom Force 4.00	
Ann.#16 RF,BH,TP,JR2,BSz,KP,AW,	
MR,BL,BWi,JG,KN,A:Silver	
Surfer,Rebirth Grandmaster . . 4.50	
Ann.#17 MBr,MG,Evol.Wars,J:2nd	
Yellow Jacket 4.00	
Ann.#18 MBa,MG,Atlan.Attack#8,	
J:Quasar 3.00	
Ann.#19 HT,Terminus Factor . . . 2.50	
Ann.#20 Subterran.Odyssey#1 . . 2.50	
Ann.#21 Citizen Kang#4 . . . . . . 2.50	
Ann.#22 I:Bloodwraith,w/card . . . 3.25	
Ann.#23 JB 3.25	
G-Size#1 JR(c),RB,DA,I:Nuklo . . 10.00	
G-Size#2 JR(c),DC,O:Kang,	
D:Swordsman,O:Rama-Tut . . . 7.00	
G-Size#3 GK(c),DC,V:Kang,Legion	
of the Unliving 5.00	
G-Size#4 K&R(c),DH,W:Scarlet Witch	
&Vision,O:Mantis,Moondragon . 7.00	

G-Size#5 rep,Annual #1. . . . . . . 3.00
GNv Death Trap:The Vault RLm,
A:Venom 20.00
Marvel Milestone rep. #1 (1993) . . 2.95
Marvel Milestone rep. #4 (1995) . . 2.95
Marvel Milestone rep. #16 (1993) . 2.95
TPB Greatest Battles of the
Avengers 15.95
TPB Korvac Saga,rep.#167-177 . 12.95
TPB Yesterday Quest,Rep.#181,182
185-187 . . . . 6.95

AVENGERS
Nov. 1996
1 RLd,JV,CYp,JSb,Heroes Reborn,
F:Thor, Captain America,
V:Loki 6.00
1A Variant cover 7.50
1 gold signature edition, bagged 20.00
2 RLd,JV,CYp,JSb,V:Kang 2.50
3 RLd,JV,CYp,JSb,V:Kang,A:Nick
Fury 2.50
4 RLd,JLb,CYp,JSb, ... 2.50
4A variant cover 2.50
5 RLd,CYp,JSb,V:Hulk,concl. . . . 2.00
6 RLd,JLb,CYp,JSb,"Industrial
Revolution," pt.1 x-over 2.00
7 RLd,JLb,IaC,JSb, ... 2.00
8 RLd,JLb,IaC,JSb,F:Simon
Williams (Wonder Man),V:Ultron,
Lethal Legion 2.00
9 JLb,RLd,IaC,F:Vision, Wonder
Man 1.95
10 WS, ... 1.95
11 . . . . 2.00
12 WS,Galactus Saga, x-over . . . 2.00
13 JeR, Wildstorm x-over 2.00
Minus 1 Spec., JLb,RLd,IaC,JSb,
flashback 1.95

AVENGERS
Dec. 1997
1 GP,KBk,AV,F:Everyone,48 pg. . 3.00
2 KBk,GP,AV,A:Scarlet Witch . . . 2.00
3 KBk,GP,AV,trapped in midieval
present 2.00
4 KBk,GP,AV,who makes the team?2.00
5 KBk,GP,AV,Squadron Supreme 2.00
6 KBk,GP,AV:SquadronSupreme2.00
7 KBk,GP,AV,Live Kree or Die, pt.4,
concl 2.00
8 KBk,GP,AV,I:Triathlon 2.00
9 KBk,GP,AV,V:Moses Magnum . 2.00
Ann. '98 Avengers/Squadron Supreme
KBk,CPa,GP, 48pg 2.50
Rough Cut Edition KBk,GP, 48pg,
original pencils of #1, b&w . . . 3.00

AVENGERS INDEX
SEE: OFFICIAL MARVEL
INDEX TO THE AVENGERS

AVENGERS LOG
1994
1 GP(c),History of the Avengers . 2.25

AVENGERS SPOTLIGHT
August, 1989
Formerly: Solo Avengers
21 AM,DH,TMo,JRu,Hawkeye,
Starfox 1.25
22 AM,DH,Hawkeye,O:Swordsman 1.25
23 AM,DH,KD,Hawkeye,Vision . . 1.25

24 AM,DH,Hawkeye,O:Espirita . . . 1.25
25 AM,TMo,Hawkeye,Rick Jones . 1.25
26 A of V,Hawkeye,Iron Man 1.25
27 A of V,AM,DH,DT,Hawkeye,
Avengers 1.25
28 A of V,AM,DH,DT,Hawkeye,
Wonder Man,Wasp 1.25
29 A of V,DT,Hawkeye,Iron Man . 1.25
30 AM,DH,Hawkeye,New Costume 1.25
31 AM,DH,KW,Hawkeye,US.Agent 1.25
32 AM,KW,Hawkeye,U.S.Agent. . 1.25
33 AM,DH,KW,Hawkeye,US.Agent 1.25
34 AM,DH,KW,SLi(c),Hawkeye
U.S.Agent 1.25
35 JV,Gilgamesh 1.25
36 AM,DH,Hawkeye 1.25
37 BH,Dr.Druid 1.25
38 JBr,Tigra 1.25
39 GCo,Black Knight 1.25
40 Vision,Last Issue 1.25

AVENGERS STRIKEFILE
1994
1 BHa(s),Avengers Pin-ups 2.00

AVENGERS:
THE CROSSING
1995
1 BHs,Death of an Avenger,
chromium cover,48pg. 6.00

AVENGERS: THE
TERMINATRIX OBJECTIVE
1993
1 B:MGu(s),MG,Holografx(c),
V:Terminatrix 2.75
2 MG,V:Terminatrix,A:Kangs 2.00
3 MG,V:Terminatrix,A:Kangs 2.00
4 MG,Last issue 2.00

AVENGERS: TIMESLIDE
1996
1 BHs,TKa,End of the Crossing
Megallic chrome cover 4.95

Avengers Unplugged #5
© Marvel Entertainment Group

AVENGERS/ULTRAFORCE
1995
1 V:Malibu's Ultraforce 3.95

AVENGERS UNLEASHED
1 V:Count Nefarious 1.00
Becomes:
AVENGERS UNPLUGGED
1996
2 Crushed by Graviton 1.00
3 x-over with FF Unplugged 1.00
4 . . . . 1.00
5 . . . . 1.00

AVENGERS WEST COAST
Sept., 1989
Prev: West Coast Avengers
47 JBy,V:J.Random 2.00
48 JBy,V:J.Random 2.00
49 JBy,V:J.Random,W.Man 2.00
50 JBy,R:G.A.Human Torch 2.00
51 JBy,R:Iron Man 2.00
52 JBy,V:MasterPandmonum . . . 2.00
53 JBy,Acts ofVeng.,V:U-Foes . . 2.00
54 JBy,Acts ofVeng,V:MoleMan . 2.00
55 JBy,Acts ofVeng.finale,V:Loki
Magneto kidnaps Sc.Witch . . . 2.50
56 JBy,V:Magneto 2.50
57 JBy,V:Magneto 2.50
58 V:Vibro, ... 2.00
59 TMo,V:Hydro-Man,A:Immortus 2.00
60 PR,V:Immortus 2.00
61 PR,V:Immortus 2.00
62 V:Immortus 2.00
63 PR,I:Living Lightning 2.00
64 F:G.A.Human Torch 2.00
65 PR,V:Ultron,Grim Reaper 2.00
66 PR,V:Ultron,Grim Reaper 2.00
67 PR,V:Ultron,Grim Reaper 2.00
68 PR,V:Ultron 2.00
69 PR,USAgent vs Hawkeye,
I:Pacific Overlords 2.50
70 DR,V:Pacific Overlords 1.75
71 DR,V:Pacific Overlords 1.75
72 DR,V:Pacific Overlords 1.75
73 DR,V:Pacific Overlords 1.75
74 DR,J:Living Lightning,Spider
Woman,V:Pacific Overlords. . . 1.75
75 HT,A:F.F,V:Arkon,double 2.00
76 DR,Night Shift,I:Man-Demon . . 1.50
77 DR,A:Satannish & Nightshift . . 1.50
78 DR,V:Satannish & Nightshift . . 1.50
79 DR,A:Dr.Strange,V:Satannish . 1.50
80 DR,Galactic Storm,pt.2 . . . . . . 1.50
81 DR,Galactic Storm,pt.9 . . . . . . 1.50
82 DR,Galactic Storm,pt.16
A:Lilandra 1.50
83 V:Hyena 1.50
84 DR,I:Deathweb,A:SpM,
O:Spider-Woman 1.75
85 DR,A:SpM,V:Death Web 1.50
86 DR,A:SpM,V:Death Web 1.50
87 DR,A:Wolverine,V:Bogatyri . . . 1.75
88 DR,A:Wolverine,V:Bogatyri . . . 1.75
89 DR,V:Ultron 1.50
90 DR,A:Vision,V:Ultron 1.50
91 DR,V:Ultron,I:War Toy 1.50
92 DR,V:Goliath(Power Man) 1.50
93 DR,V:Doctor Demonicus 1.50
94 DR,J:War Machine 1.75
95 DR,A:Darkhawk,V:Doctor
Demonicus 1.50
96 DR,Inf.Crusade x-over 1.50
97 ACe,Inf.Crusade,V:Power

Platoon 1.50
98 DR,I:4th Lethal Legion 1.50
99 DR,V:4th Lethal Legion 1.50
100 DR,D:Mockingbird,V:4th Lethal
  Legion,Red Foil(c) 3.50
101 DR,Bloodties#3,V:Exodus . . . 4.00
102 DR,L:Iron Man,Spider-Woman,
  US Agent,Scarlet Witch,War
  Machine,last issue 4.00
Ann.#4 JBy,TA,MBa,Atlan.Attacks
  #12,V:Seven Brides of Set . . . 4.00
Ann.#5 Terminus Factor 3.50
Ann.#6 Subterranean Odyssey#5 . 2.50
Ann.#7 Assault on Armor City#4 . 2.25
Ann.#8 DR,I:Raptor w/card 3.25

BALDER THE BRAVE
Nov., 1985
1 WS,SB,V:Frost Giants 1.50
2 WS,SB,V:Frost Giants 1.25
3 WS,SB,V:Frost Giants 1.25
4 WS,SB,V:Frost Giants;Feb,1986 1.25

Barbie #52
© Marvel Entertainment Group

BARBIE
Jan., 1991
1 polybagged with Credit Card . . 6.00
2 . . . . 2.50
3 . . . . 2.50
4 Ice Skating 2.50
5 Sea Cruise 2.50
6 Sun Runner Story 2.50
7 Travel issue 2.50
8 TV Commercial 2.50
9 Music Tour Van 2.50
10 Barbie in Italy 2.50
11 Haunted Castles 2.50
12 Monkey Bandit 2.50
13 MW,A:Skipper,Ken 2.50
14 Country Fair 2.50
15 Barbie in Egypt,pt.1 . . . . 2.50
16 Barbie in Egypt,pt.2 . . . . 2.50
17 Weightwatchers/Art issue 2.50
18 V:heavy Metal Band 2.50
19 A:Surfer Pal 2.50
20 Skipper at Special Olympics . . 2.50
21 I:Whitney,female fire fighter . . . 2.50
22 Barbie in Greece 2.50

23 thru 27 . . . . @2.50
28 Valentine's Day Issue 2.50
29 Skipper babysits 2.50
30 Cowgirls on the Range 2.50
31 Rest and Relaxation 2.50
32 A:Dandy the Gorilla 2.50
33 thru 41 . . . . @2.50
42 thru 49 . . . . @2.50
50 Anniv. issue, Disney World(c) . 3.00
51 Vet's assistant 2.00
52 Valentines Day Special 2.00
53 Marooned 2.00
54 Female Inventors 2.00
55 in Nashville 2.00
56 Sherlock Barbie 2.00
57 Nashville 2.00
58 Barbie Teaches Skating 2.00
59 Famous Females 2.00
60 Halloween Hero 2.00
61 Alaska Gold Rush 2.00
62 Christmas/Nutcracker 2.00
63 . . . . 2.00
64 . . . . 2.00
65 Under Antarctica 2.00
66 . . . . 2.00

BARBIE FASHION
Jan., 1991
1 polybagged with dorknob hanger 5.00
2 thru 63 . . . . @2.50

BATTLE
Atlas March, 1951
1 They called Him a Coward . 175.00
2 The War Department Secrets . 75.00
3 The Beast of the Bataan . . 60.00
4 I:Buck Private O'Toole 60.00
5 Death Trap Of Gen. Wu. . . . 60.00
6 RH 60.00
7 Enemy Sniper 60.00
8 A Time to Die 60.00
9 RH 50.00
10 . . . . 50.00
11 thru 20 . . . . @40.00
21 . . . . 45.00
22 . . . . 40.00
23 . . . . 45.00
24 . . . . 40.00
25 . . . . 35.00
26 JR 35.00
27 . . . . 35.00
28 JSe 35.00
29 . . . . 35.00
30 . . . . 35.00
31 RH 35.00
32 JSe,GT 35.00
33 GC,JSe,JSt 35.00
34 JSe 35.00
35 . . . . 35.00
36 BEv 35.00
37 RA,JSt 40.00
38 . . . . 30.00
39 . . . . 30.00
40 . . . . 30.00
41 . . . . 30.00
42 thru 46 . . . . @30.00
47 JO 30.00
48 . . . . 30.00
49 JDa 40.00
50 BEv 30.00
51 . . . . 30.00
52 GWb 30.00
53 BP 30.00
54 . . . . 30.00

55 GC,AS,BP 40.00
56 . . . . 30.00
57 . . . . 30.00
58 . . . . 30.00
59 . . . . 30.00
60 A:Combat Kelly 30.00
61 A:Combat Kelly 30.00
62 A:Combat Kelly 30.00
63 SD 55.00
64 JK 75.00
65 JK 75.00
66 JSe,JK,JDa 75.00
67 JSe,JK,AS,JDa 75.00
68 JSe,JK,AW,SD 75.00
69 RH,JSe,JK,SW 60.00
70 BEv,SD; June, 1960 . . . . . . 60.00

BATTLE ACTION
Atlas Feb., 1952
1 . . . . 150.00
2 . . . . 75.00
3 . . . . 40.00
4 . . . . 40.00
5 . . . . 40.00
6 . . . . 40.00
7 . . . . 40.00
8 . . . . 40.00
9 . . . . 40.00
10 . . . . 40.00
11 thru 15 . . . . @35.00
16 thru 26 . . . . @32.00
27 . . . . 35.00
28 . . . . 30.00
29 . . . . 30.00
30 August, 1957 . . . . 35.00

BATTLE BRADY
See: MEN IN ACTION

BATTLEFIELD
Atlas April, 1952
1 RH, Slaughter on Suicide
  Ridge 125.00
2 . . . . 50.00
3 Ambush Patrol 50.00
4 . . . . 50.00
5 Into the Jaws of Death 50.00
6 thru 10 . . . . @35.00
11 GC,May, 1953 . . . . 35.00

BATTLEFRONT
Atlas June, 1952
1 RH(c),Operation Killer 175.00
2 . . . . 55.00
3 Spearhead 55.00
4 Death Trap of General Chun . 50.00
5 Terror of the Tank Men 40.00
6 A:Combat Kelly 40.00
7 A:Combat Kelly 40.00
8 A:Combat Kelly 40.00
9 A:Combat Kelly 40.00
10 A:Combat Kelly 40.00
11 thru 20 . . . . @35.00
21 thru 39 . . . . @30.00
40 AW 50.00
41 . . . . 20.00
42 AW 50.00
43 thru 48 August,1957 . . . . . @35.00

BATTLEGROUND
Atlas Sept., 1954
1 . . . . 125.00
2 JKz 50.00

3 thru 8	@40.00
9	40.00
10	35.00
11 AW	60.00
12	30.00
13 AW	60.00
14 JD	35.00
15	30.00
16	30.00
17	30.00
18 AS	60.00
19	30.00
20 August, 1957	30.00

Battlestar Galactica #9
© Marvel Entertainment Group

BATTLESTAR GALACTICA
March, 1979

1 EC,B:TV Adaptation; Annihalation	3.00
2 EC,Exodus	2.50
3 EC,Deathtrap	2.50
4 WS,Dogfight	2.50
5 WS,E:TV Adaptation;Ambush	2.50
6 Nightmare	2.00
7 Commander Adama Trapped	2.00
8 Last Stand	2.00
9 Space Mimic	2.00
10 This Planet Hungers	2.00
11 WS,Starbuck's Dilemma	2.00
12 WS,Memory Ends	2.00
13 WS,All Out Attack	2.00
14 Radiation Threat	2.00
15 Ship of Crawling Death	2.00
16	2.00
17 Animal on the Loose	2.00
18 Battle For the Forbidden Fruit	2.00
19 Starbuck's Back	2.00
20 Duel to the Death	2.00
21 To Slay a Monster..To Deatroy a World	2.00
22 WS,A Love Story?	2.00
23 Dec., 1981	2.00

BATTLETIDE
1990

1 thru 4 F: Death's Head II and Killpower	@1.75

BATTLETIDE II
1993

1 Foil embossed cover	2.95
2 thru 8 F: Death's Head II and Killpower	@1.75

BEAST
March 1997

1 (of 3) KG,CNn,F:Karma, Cannonball, V:Viper & Spiral	2.50
2 KG,CNn,V:Spiral	2.50
3 KG,CNn, concl.	2.50

BEAUTY AND THE BEAST
Jan., 1985

1 DP,Beast & Dazzler,direct	3.00
1a DP,Beast & Dazzler,UPC	2.00
2 DP,Beast & Dazzler	2.00
3 DP,Beast & Dazzler	2.00
4 DP,Beast & Dazzler	2.00

BEAUTY AND THE BEAST
1992

1	1.50
2 Wardrobe's birthday party	1.50
3	1.50
4	1.50
5	1.50
6 Lumiere takes Cogsworth's job	1.50
7 Belle & Chip caught in snow	1.50
8	1.50
9 Can Beast prove his love?	1.50
10 Chip & Belle have a snow ball	1.50
11 History of Beast's Castle	1.50
12	1.50
13 The Dessert Disaster	1.50

BEAVIS & BUTT-HEAD
March 1994

1 Based on the MTV Show	5.00
1a 2nd Printing	2.50
2 Dead from the Neck up	3.50
3 Break out at Burger World	3.00
4 Tattoo Parlor	2.25
5 Field Day	2.25
6 Revulsion	2.25
7 Oldies bot	2.25
8 Be a clown	2.25
9 Makin' movies	2.25
10 Halloween	2.25
11	2.00
12	2.00
13	2.00
14 Join Biker Gang	2.00
15 Spring Break	2.00
16 Capture The Flag	2.00
17 with video camera	2.00
18 Woodsuck	2.00
19 break-up?	2.00
20 Solar Eclipse	2.00
21 Male Cheerleaders	2.00
22 Antics at theme park	2.00
23 Witless	2.00
24 Holiday suck-tacular	2.00
25	1.95
26	1.95
27 Easter spirit	1.95
28	1.95
TPB Greatest Hits, rep.#1–#4	12.95
TPB Holidazed and Confused	12.95

BEST OF MARVEL '96
TPB 224pg.	19.95

BEST WESTERN
June, 1949

58 A:KidColt,BlackRider,Two-Gun Kid;Million DollarTrainRobbery	125.00
59 A:BlackRider,KidColt,Two-Gun Kid;The Black Rider Strikes	100.00

Becomes:

WESTERN OUTLAWS & SHERIFFS

60 PH(c),Hawk Gaither	100.00
61 Ph(c),Pepper Lawson	75.00
62 Murder at Roaring House Bridge	75.00
63 thru 65	@75.00
66	50.00
67	70.00
68 thru 72	@50.00
73 June, 1952	40.00

BEWARE
March, 1973

1 Reprints	4.50
2 thru 8	@2.50

Becomes:

TOMB OF DARKNESS

9 Reprints	2.00
10 thru 22	@1.00
23 November, 1976	2.00

BIKER MICE FROM MARS
1993

1 I:Biker Mice	1.50
2 thru 3	1.50

BILL & TED'S BOGUS JOURNEY
Nov., 1991

1 Movie Adaption	3.25

BILL & TED'S EXCELLENT COMICS
Dec., 1991

1 From Movie; Wedding Reception	1.25
2 Death Takes a Vacation	1.25
3 'Daze in the Lives'	1.25
4 Station Plague	1.25
5 Bill & Ted on Trial	1.25
6 Time Trial	1.25
7 Time Trial, Concl	1.25
8 History Final	1.25
9 I:Morty(new Death)	1.25
10 'Hyperworld'	1.25
11 Lincoln assassination	1.25
12 Last issue	1.25

BILLY BUCKSKIN WESTERN
Atlas Nov., 1955

1 MD,Tales of the Wild Frontier	100.00
2 MD,Ambush	75.00
3 MD,AW, Thieves in the Night	75.00

Becomes:

2-GUN KID

4 SD,A: Apache Kid	75.00

Becomes:

TWO-GUN WESTERN

5 B:Apache Kid,Doc Holiday, Kid Colt Outlaw	75.00
6	40.00
7	40.00

8 RC	50.00
9 AW	60.00
10	35.00
11 AW	60.00
12 Sept., 1957,RC	45.00

BISHOP
1994

1 Mountjoy, foil cover	4.50
2 foil stamped cover	4.00
3 JOs	3.50
4 V:Mountjoy	3.50

BISHOP: XAVIER'S SECURITY ENFORCER
Nov., 1997

1 (of 3) JOs,SEp	2.50
2 JOs,SEp,hunted by X.S.E.	2.50
3 JOs,SEp,Bishop v. Rook, concl.	2.50

BIZARRE ADVENTURES
See: MARVEL PREVIEW

BLACK AXE

1 JR2(c),A:Death's Head II	2.00
2 JR2(2),A:Sunfire,V:The Hand	2.00
3 A:Death's Head II,V:Mesphisto	2.00
4 in ancient Egypt	2.00
5 KJ(c),In Wakanda	2.00
6 KJ(c),A:Black Panther	2.00
7 KJ(c),A:Black Panther	1.75
8 thru 13	@1.75

BLACK CAT
Limited Series]

1 Wld,A:Spider-Man,V:Cardiac, I:Faze	1.75
2 Wld,V:Faze	1.50
3 Wld,Cardiac	1.50
4 Wld,V:Scar	1.50

Black Dragon #3
© Marvel Entertainment Group

BLACK DRAGON
Epic May 1985

1 JBo	4.00
2 thru 6 JBo	@3.00

BLACK GOLIATH
Feb., 1976—Nov., 1976

1 GT,O:Black Goliath,Cont's From Powerman #24	5.00
2 GT,V:Warhawk	4.00
3 GT,D:Atom-Smasher	4.00
4 KP,V:Stilt-Man	4.00
5 D:Mortag	4.00

BLACK KNIGHT, THE
Atlas May, 1955—April, 1956

1 O: Crusader;The Black Knight Rides	650.00
2 Siege on Camelot	500.00
3 Blacknight Unmasked	400.00
4 Betrayed	400.00
5 SSh,The Invincible Tartar	400.00

BLACK KNIGHT
June, 1990—Sept., 1990

1 TD,R:Original Black Knight	2.00
2 TD,A:Dreadknight	1.75
3 RB,A:Dr.Strange	1.75
4 RB,TD,A:Dr Strange, Valkyrie	1.75

BLACK KNIGHT: EXODUS
1996

1-shot R:Black Knight,A:Sersi, O:Exodus	2.50

BLACK PANTHER
[1st Series]
Jan., 1977—May, 1979

1 JK,V:Collectors	9.00
2 JK,V:Six Million Year Man	5.00
3 JK,V:Ogar	3.50
4 JK,V:Collectors	3.50
5 JK,V:Yeti	3.50
6 JK,V:Ronin	3.50
7 JK,V:Mister Little	3.50
8 JK,D:Black Panther	3.50
9 JK,V:Jakarra	3.50
10 JK,V:Jakarra	3.50
11 JK,V:Kilber the Cruel	3.50
12 JK,V:Kilber the Cruel	3.50
13 JK,V:Kilber the Cruel	3.50
14 JK,A:Avengers,V:Klaw	3.50
15 JK,A:Avengers,V:Klaw	3.50

BLACK PANTHER
July 1988—Oct. 1988
[1st Mini-Series]

1 I:Panther Spirit	2.50
2 V:Supremacists	2.50
3 A:Malaika	2.50
4 V:Panther Spirit	2.50

[2nd Mini-Series]
PANTHER'S PREY
May, 1991

1 DT,A:W'Kabi,V:Solomon Prey	4.95
2 thru 4 DT,V:Solomon Prey	@4.95

BLACK RIDER
See: ALL WINNERS COMICS

BLACK RIDER RIDES AGAIN
Atlas Sept., 1957

1 JK,Treachery at Hangman's Ridge	150.00

BLACKSTONE, THE MAGICIAN
May, 1948—Sept., 1948

2 B:Blonde Phantom	450.00
3	300.00
4 Bondage(c)	325.00

BLACKWULF
1994—95

1 AMe,Embossied(c),I:Mammoth, Touchstone,Toxin,D:Pelops, V:Tantalus,	2.75
2 AMe,I:Sparrow,Wildwind	1.75
3 AMe,I:Scratch	1.50
4 AMe,I:Giant-man	1.50
5 AMe	1.50
6 AMe,Tantalus	1.50
7 AMe,V:Tantalus	1.50
8 AMe	1.50
9 Seven Worlds of Tantalus,pt.1 A:Daredevil	1.50
10 Seven Worlds of Tantalus,pt.2, last issue	1.50

BLADE, THE VAMPIRE HUNTER
1994—95

1 Foil(c),Clv(i),R:Dracula	3.00
2 Clv(i),V:Dracula	1.95
3 Clv(i)	1.95
4 Clv(i)	1.95
5 Clv(i)	1.95
6 Clv(i)	1.95
7 Clv(i)	1.95
8 Bible John, Morbius	1.95
9	1.95
10 R:Dracula	1.95
11 Dracula Untombed,pt.2	1.95

BLADE
Feb., 1998

1 DMG, movie tie-in,	3.00

BLADE
Aug. 1998

1-shot movie adaptation, 48pg.	6.00

BLADE: CRESCENT CITY BLUES
Jan., 1998

1-shot MPe,V:Deacon Frost	3.50

BLADE RUNNER
Oct., 1982

1 AW, Movie Adaption	1.50
2 AW,	1.50

BLAZE
[Limited Series] 1993–94

1 HMe(s),RoW,A:Clara Menninger	2.00
2 HMe(s),RoW,I:Initiate	2.00
3 HMe(s),RoW,	2.00
4 HMe(s),RoW,D:Initiate,Last issue	2.00

[Regular Series] Aug. 1994

1 HMz,LHa,foil (c)	3.25
2 HMz,LHa,I:Man-Thing	2.25
3 HMz,LHa,V:Ice Box Bob	1.95
4 HMz,LHa,Apache Autumn,pt.1	1.95
5 HMz,LHa,Apache Autumn,pt.2	1.95
6 Apache Autumn,pt.3	1.95

MARVEL

Blaze #8
© *Marvel Entertainment Group*

7 Carnivale Quintano 1.95
8 A:Arcae 1.95
9 Clara's Eyeballs 1.95
10 Undead M.C. 1.95
11 A:Punisher 1.95
12 reunited with children, final iss. 1.95

BLAZE CARSON
Sept., 1948
1 SSh(c),Fight,Lawman
  or Crawl 175.00
2 Guns Roar on Boot Hill . . . 150.00
3 A:Tex Morgan 150.00
4 A:Two-Gun Kid 150.00
5 A:Tex Taylor 150.00
Becomes:

REX HART
6 CCB,Ph(c),B:Rex Hart,
  A:Black Rider 150.00
7 Ph(c),Mystery at Bar-2 Ranch 125.00
8 Ph(c),The Hombre Who
  Killed His Friends 125.00
Becomes:

WHIP WILSON
9 Ph(c),B:Whip Wilson,O:Bullet;
  Duel to the Death 450.00
10 Ph(c),Wanted for Murder . . 250.00
11 Ph(c) 250.00
Becomes:

GUNHAWK, THE
12 The Redskin's Revenge . . . 100.00
13 GT,The Man Who Murdered
  Gunhawk 75.00
14 . . . . 75.00
15 . . . . 75.00
16 . . . . 75.00
17 . . . . 75.00
18 Dec., 1951 . . . . 75.00

BLAZE, THE WONDER COLLIE
Oct., 1949
2 Ph(c),Blaze-Son of Fury . . . 150.00
3 Ph(c), Lonely Boy;Feb.,1950 125.00

BLONDE PHANTOM
See: ALL-SELECT COMICS

BLOOD
Feb., 1988—April, 1988
1 . . . . 6.00
2 thru 4 . . . . @5.00

BLOOD & GLORY
1993
1 KJ Cap & the Punisher 5.95
2 KJ Cap & the Punisher 5.95
3 KJ Cap & the Punisher 5.95

BLOODLINES
Epic 1992
1 F:Kathy Grant-Peace Corps . . . 5.95

BLOODSEED
1993
1 LSh,I:Bloodseed 2.25
2 LSh,V:Female Bloodseed 2.25

BOOK OF THE DEAD
1993–94
1 thru 4 Horror rep . . . . @2.00
5 and 6 . . . . @1.75

BOZZ CHRONICLES, THE
Epic Dec., 1985
1 thru 5 . . . . @1.75
6 May, 1986 . . . . 1.75

BRATS BIZARRE
Epic *Heavy Hitters* 1994
1 with trading card 3.25
2 thru 4 with trading card . . . . @2.50

BREAK THE CHAIN
1 KB,KRS-One,w/audio tape 7.00

BRUTE FORCE
August, 1990
1 JD/JSt 1.00
2 . . . . 1.00
3 . . . . 1.00
4 November, 1990 . . . . 1.00

BUCK DUCK
Atlas June, 1953
1 (fa)stories 60.00
2 and 3 . . . . @25.00
4 Dec., 1953 . . . . 25.00

BUCKAROO BANZAI
Dec., 1984
1 Movie Adaption 3.00
2 Conclusion, Feb., 1985 . . . . . 2.00

BUG
1997
1-shot 48pg 3.00

BULLWINKLE & ROCKY
Star Nov., 1987
1 EC&AM,Based on 1960's TV
  Series 3.00
2 EC&AM, ... 2.00
3 EC&AM,Rumpled Mudluck
  Thyme Mag 2.00

---

4 EC&AM,Boris and Natasha . . . 2.00
5 EC&AM, ... 2.00
6 EC&AM,Wassamatta Me 2.00
7 EC&AM,Politics,Moose V:Boris 2.00
8 EC&AM,Superhero, March,1989 2.00
9 EC 2.00
TPB, Bullwinkle & Rocky Collection
  AM,early stories 4.95

CABLE
[Limited Series] 1992
1 JR2,DGr,V:Mutant Liberation
  Front,A:Weapon X 4.00
2 JR2,DGr,V:Stryfe,O:Weapon X 3.00
[Regular Series] May 1993
1 B:FaN(s),ATi,O:Cable,V:New
  Canaanites,A:Stryfe,foil(c) . . 5.00
2 ATi,V:Stryfe 2.50
3 ATi,A:Six Pack 2.25
4 ATi,A:Six Pack 2.25
5 DaR,V:Sinsear 2.25
6 DT,A:Tyler,Zero,Askani,
  Mr.Sinister,C:X-Men 2.50
7 V:Tyler,A:Askani,X-Men,Domino 2.50
8 O:Cable,V:Tyler,A:X-Men,Cable is
  Nathan Summers 2.50
9 MCW,B:Killing Field,A:Excalibur,
  V:Omega Red 2.25
10 MCW,A:Acolytes,Omega Red . 2.25
11 MCW,E:Killing Field,D:Katu . . 2.25
12 SLo(s),B:Fear & Loathing,
  V:Senyaka 2.25
13 V:D'Spayre 2.00
14 V:S'yM 2.25
15 A:Thorn 2.25
16 Foil(c),Dbl-size,A:Jean,Scott
  Logan,V:Phalanx 10.00
16a Newsstand ed. 2.50
17 Deluxe ed. 2.25
17a Newsstand ed. 1.50
18 Deluxe ed. 2.25
18a Newsstand ed. 1.50
19 Deluxe ed. 2.25
19a Newsstand ed. 1.50
20 V:Legion, Deluxe ed. w/card . . 4.00
20a Newsstand ed. 1.50
21 Cable makes tough decisions,
  A:Domino 2.25
22 V:Fortress 2.25
23 IaC,A:Domino 2.25
24 F:Blaquesmith 2.00
25 IaC,SHa,F:Cable's Wife,foil(c) . 5.00
26 Tries to return to X-Mansion . 2.00
27 IaC, A:Domino 2.00
28 IaC,SHa,concl. war in Genosha 2.00
29 . . . . 2.00
30 . . . . 2.00
31 IaC, cont.X-Men/Cable war . . . 2.00
32 Onslaught saga 3.00
33 Onslaught saga 3.00
34 Onslaught saga 3.00
35 Onslaught saga 3.00
36 . . . . 2.00
37 JLb,IaC,SHa,V:Askani'son,Kane 2.00
38 JLb,IaC,SHa,V:PSycho-Man,
  A:Kane 2.00
39 JLb,IaC,SHa,V:Psycho-Man . . 2.00
40 TDz,IaC,SHa,A:Renee Majcomb 2.00
41 TDz,SHa,F:Bishop 2.00
42 TDz,RGr,SHa,"The Prophecy
  of the Twelve" 2.00
43 TDz,RGr,Images of Nathan's
  past 2.00
44 TDz,RGr,SHa,A:Madelyne Pryor
  (Cable's mom) 2.00

MARVEL

Cable #20
© *Marvel Entertainment Group*

45 JeR,RGr,Zero Tolerance,
  "No Escape,"pt.2 . . . . 2.00
46 JeR,RGr,SHa,Zero Tolerance,
  "No Escape," pt.2 (of 3) 2.00
47 JeR,RGr,SHa, Operation Zero
  Tolerance, V:Batsion 2.00
48 JeR,SHa,V:Hellfire Club 2.00
49 JeR,SHa,V:Hellfire Club 2.00
50 JeR,SHa,A:Cyclops, Phoenix,
  Union Jack, 48pg 3.00
51 JeR,Hellfire Hunt 2.00
52 JeR,Hellfire Hunt, pt.5 . . . . . . 2.00
53 JoC,Hellfire Hunt, concl. 2.00
54 JoC,A:Black Panther,V:Klaw . . 2.00
55 JoC,A:Irene Merryweather,
  Domino 2.00
56 JoC,V:Stilt-Man & Hydro-Man . 2.00
57 JoC,Cable powers altered by
  EMP wave 2.00
58 JoC,Persecution, pt.1 . . . . 2.00
59 JoC,I:Agent 18,V:Zzaxx 2.00
Ann. '98 AOI(c) F:Cable vs. Machine
  Man, O:Bastion 3.00
Minus 1 Spec., TDz,JeR, flashback 1.95
TPB Cable,rep.New Mutants
  #87-94 . . . . 15.95

CABLE & X-FORCE

Cable & X-Force '95 Spec. 3.95
Cable & X-Force '96 Spec.48pg. . 3.00
Cable & X-Force '97 Spec.#1
  JFM,CJ,V:Malekith,48pg. 3.00

CADILLACS & DINOSAURS
Epic Nov., 1990

1 Rep.Xenozoic Tales 3.00
2 Rep.Xenozoic Tales 2.50
3 Rep.Xenozoic Tales 2.50
4 Rep.Xenozoic Tales 2.50
5 Rep.Xenozoic Tales 2.50
6 Rep.Xenozoic Tales, April,1991 2.50

CAGE
1992–93

1 DT,R:Luke Cage,I:Hardcore, . . 2.50

---

2 DT,V:Hammer 1.50
3 DT,A:Punisher,V:Untouchables 1.50
4 DT,A:Punisher,V:Untouchables 1.50
5 DT,I:New Power Man 1.50
6 DT,V:New Power Man 1.50
7 DT,A:Avengers West Coast . . . 1.50
8 DT,V:Steele,Wonder Man 1.50
9 V:Rhino,A:Hulk 1.50
10 DT,V:Hulk,Rhino 1.50
11 DT,V:Rapidfire 1.50
12 A:Iron Fist,double size 2.00
13 V:The Thinker 1.50
14 PCu,I:Coldfire 1.50
15 DT,For Love Nor Money#2,
  A:Silver Sable,Terror 1.50
16 DT,For Love Nor Money#5,
  A:Silver Sable,Terror 1.50
17 DT,Infinty Crusade 1.50
18 A:Dred,V:Creed 1.50
19 A:Dakota North 1.50
20 Last issue 1.50

CAMP CANDY
May, 1990

1 thru 6, Oct. 1990 . . . . @1.00

CAPTAIN AMERICA COMICS
Timely/Atlas May, 1941

1 S&K,Hitler(c),I&O:Capt.America &
  Bucky,A:Red Skull,B:Hurricane,
  Tuk the Caveboy 55,000.00
2 S&K,RC,AAv,Hitler(c),
  I:Circular Shield;Trapped
  in the Nazi Stronghold . . 10,000.00
3 S&K,RC,AAv,Stan Lee's 1st Text,
  A:Red Skull,Bondage(c) . . 8,500.00
4 S&K,AAv,Horror Hospital . 5,000.00
5 S&K,AAv,Ringmaster's
  Wheel of Death 4,500.00
6 S&K,AAv,O:Father Time,
  E:Tuk 4,000.00
7 S&K,A: Red Skull 4,500.00
8 S&K, The Tomb 4,000.00
9 S&K,RC,V:Black Talon . . . 3,500.00
10 S&K,RC,Chamber
  of Horrors 3,500.00
11 AAv,E:Hurricane;Feuding
  Mountaneers 3,000.00
12 AAv,B:Imp,E:Father Time;
  Pygmie's Terror 2,800.00
13 AAv,O:Secret Stamp;All Out
  For America 3,000.00
14 AAv,V:Japs;Pearl Harbor
  Symbol cover 2,800.00
15 AAv,Den of Doom 2,800.00
16 AAv,A:R.Skull;CapA
  Unmasked 3,400.00
17 AAv,I:Fighting Fool;
  Graveyard 2,500.00
18 AAv,V:Japanese 2,200.00
19 AAv,V:Ghouls,
  B:Human Torch 1,800.00
20 AAv,A:Sub-Mariner,V:Nazis 1,800.00
21 SSh(c),Bucky Captured . . 1,700.00
22 SSh(c),V:Japanese 1,700.00
23 SSh(c),V:Nazis 1,700.00
24 SSh(c),V:Black
  Dragon Society 1,700.00
25 SSh(c),V:Japs;Drug Story . 1,700.00
26 ASh(c),V:Nazi Fleet 1,600.00
27 ASh(c)CapA&Russians
  V:Nazis, E:Secret Stamp . . 1,600.00
28 ASh(c),NaziTortureChamber1,600.00

---

29 ASh(c),V:Nazis;French
  Underground 1,600.00
30 SSh(c),Bucky Captured . . 1,600.00
31 ASh(c),Bondage(c) 1,500.00
32 SSh(c),V: Japanese Airforce1,500.00
33 ASh(c),V:Nazis;BrennerPass1,500.00
34 SSh(c),Bondage(c) 1,500.00
35 SSh(c),CapA in Japan . . 1,500.00
36 SSh(c),V:Nazis;Hitler(c) . . 2,000.00
37 ASh(c),CapA in Berlin,
  A:Red Skull 1,600.00
38 ASh(c),V:Japs;Bondage(c) 1,400.00
39 ASh(c),V:Japs;Boulder Dam 1,400.00
40 SSh(c),V:Japs;Ammo Depot 1,400.00
41 ASh(c),FinalJapaneseWar(c)1,300.00
42 ASh(c),V:Bank Robbers . . 1,300.00
43 ASh(c),V:Gangsters 1,300.00
44 ASh(c),V:Gangsters 1,300.00
45 ASh(c),V:Bank Robbers . . 1,300.00
46 ASh(c),Holocaust(c) 1,300.00
47 ASh(c),Final Nazi War(c) . 1,300.00
48 ASh(c),V:Robbers 1,200.00
49 ASh(c),V:Sabatuers 1,200.00
50 ASh(c),V:Gorilla Gang . . . 1,300.00
51 ASh(c),V:Gangsters 1,200.00
52 ASh(c),V:AtomBombThieves1,200.00
53 ASh(c),V:Burglars 1,200.00
54 ASh(c),TV Studio,
  V:Gangsters 1,200.00
55 V:Counterfeiters 1,200.00
56 SSh(c),V:Art Theives 1,200.00
57 Symbolic CapA(c) 1,200.00
58 ASh(c),V:Bank Robbers . . 1,200.00
59 SSh(c)O:CapA Retold;Private
  Life of Captain America . . 2,500.00
60 V:The Human Fly 1,200.00
61 SSh(c),V:Red Skull;
  Bondage(c) 1,900.00
62 SSh(c),Kingdom of Terror . 1,200.00
63 SSh(c),I&O:Asbestos Lady;
  The Parrot Strikes 1,300.00
64 Diamonds Spell Doom . . . 1,200.00
65 When Friends Turn Foes . 1,200.00
66 O:Golden Girl;Bucky Shot . 1,400.00
67 E:Toro(in Human Torch);
  Golden Girl Team-Up 1,200.00
68 A:Golden Girl;Riddle of
  the Living Dolls 1,200.00
69 Weird Tales of the Wee
  Males, A:Sun Girl 1,200.00
70 A:Golden Girl,Sub-Mariner,
  Namora;Worlds at War . . . 1,200.00
71 A:Golden Girl; Trapped . . . 1,200.00
72 Murder in the Mind 1,200.00
73 The Outcast of Time 1,200.00
74 A:Red Skull;Capt.America's
  Weird Tales 3,800.00
75 Thing in the Chest 1,200.00
76 JR(c),Capt.America,Commie
  Smasher 1,200.00
77 Capt.A,Commie Smasher . . 800.00
78 JR(c),V:Communists;
  Sept.,1954 . . . . 800.00
Marvel Milestone rep. #1 (1995) . . 3.95

CAPTAIN AMERICA
Prev: **Tales of Suspense**
April, 1968

100 JK,A:Avengers 300.00
101 JK,I:4th Sleeper 75.00
102 JK,V:Red Skull,4th Sleeper . 40.00
103 JK,V:Red Skull 40.00
104 JK,DA,JSo,V:Red Skull . . . 40.00
105 JK,DA,A:Batroc 40.00
106 JK,Cap.Goes Wild 40.00

MARVEL

Captain America #132
© Marvel Entertainment Group

107 JK,Red Skull 40.00
108 JK,Trapster 40.00
109 JK,O:Captain America 50.00
110 JSo,JSt,A:Hulk,Rick Jones
    in Bucky Costume 55.00
111 JSo,JSt,I:Man Killer 60.00
112 JK,GT,Album 35.00
113 JSo,TP,Avengers,
    D:Madame Hydra 60.00
114 JR,SB,C:Avengers 20.00
115 JB,SB,A:Red Skull 20.00
116 GC,JSt,A:Avengers 20.00
117 JR(c),GC,JSt,I:Falcon 50.00
118 JR(c),GC,JSt,A:Falcon 20.00
119 GC,JSt,O:Falcon 20.00
120 GC,JSt,A:Falcon 20.00
121 GC,JSt,V:Man Brute 15.00
122 GC,JSt,Scorpion 12.00
123 GC,JSt,A:NickFury,
    V:Suprema 12.00
124 GC,JSt,I:Cyborg 12.00
125 GC,Mandarin 12.00
126 JK&BEv(c),GC,A:Falcon . . 12.00
127 GC,WW,A:Nick Fury 12.00
128 GC,V:Satan's Angels 12.00
129 GC,Red Skull 12.00
130 GC,I:Batroc 15.00
131 GC,V:Hood 11.00
132 GC,A:Bucky Barnes 11.00
133 GC,O:Modok,B:Capt.America/
    Falcon Partnership 11.00
134 GC,V:Stone Face 11.00
135 JR(c),GC,TP,A:Nick Fury . . 11.00
136 GC,BEv,V:Tyrannus 11.00
137 GC,BEv,A:Spider-Man 13.00
138 JR,A:Spider-Man 12.00
139 JR,Falcon solo 9.00
140 JR,O:Grey Gargoyle 9.00
141 JR,JSt,V:Grey Gargoyle 7.00
142 JR,JSt,Nick Fury 7.00
143 JR,Red Skull 10.00
144 GM,JR,N:Falcon,V:Hydra . . 7.00
145 GK,JR,V:Hydra 7.00
146 JR(c),SB,V:Hydra 6.00
147 GK(c),SB,V:Hydra 6.00

148 SB,JR,Red Skull 6.00
149 GK(c),SB,JM,V:Batroc 6.00
150 K&R(c),SB,V:The Stranger . . 6.00
151 SB,V:Mr.Hyde 6.00
152 SB,V:Scorpion,Mr.Hyde 6.00
153 SB,JM,V:50's Cap 6.00
154 SB,V:50's Cap 6.00
155 SB,FMc,O:50's Cap 6.00
156 SB,FMc,V:50's Cap 6.00
157 SB,I:The Viper 6.00
158 SB,V:The Viper 6.00
159 SB,V:PlantMan,Porcupine . . . 6.00
160 SB,FMc,V:Solarr 6.00
161 SB,V:Dr.Faustus 6.00
162 JSn(c),SB,V:Dr.Faustus 6.00
163 SB,I:Serpent Squad 7.00
164 JR(c),I:Nightshade 7.00
165 SB,FMc,V:Yellow Claw 6.00
166 SB,FMc,V:Yellow Claw 6.00
167 SB,V:Yellow Claw 6.00
168 SB,I&O:Phoenix
    (2nd Baron Zemo) 7.00
169 SB,FMc,C:Black Panther 6.00
170 K&R(c),SB,C:Black Panther . 6.00
171 JR(c),SB,A:Black Panther . . . 6.00
172 GK(c),SB,C:X-Men 15.00
173 GK(c),SB,A:X-Men 16.00
174 GK(c),SB,A:X-Men 16.00
175 SB,A:X-Men 16.00
176 JR(c),SB,O:Capt.America . . . 8.00
177 JR(c),SB,A:Lucifer,Beast 6.00
178 SB,A:Lucifer 6.00
179 SB,A:Hawkeye 6.00
180 GK(c),SB,I:1st Nomad(Cap) . 8.00
181 GK(c),SB,I&O:New Cap 7.00
182 FR,Madam Hydra 7.00
183 GK(c),FR,R:Cap,D:New Cap . 8.00
184 K&R(c),HT,A:Red Skull 5.00
185 GK(c),SB,FR,V:Red Skull . . . 5.00
186 GK(c),FR,O:Falcon 6.00
187 K&R(c),FR,V:Druid 5.00
188 GK(c),SB,V:Druid 5.00
189 GK(c),FR,V:Nightshade 5.00
190 GK(c),FR,A:Nightshade 5.00
191 FR,A:Stilt Man,N.Fury 5.00
192 JR(c),FR,A:Dr.Faustus 5.00
193 JR(c),JK,'Mad Bomb' 5.00
194 JK,I:Gen.Heshin 5.00
195 JK,1984 . . . . 5.00
196 JK,Madbomb 5.00
197 JK,Madbomb 5.00
198 JK,Madbomb 5.00
199 JK,Madbomb 5.00
200 JK,Madbomb 7.00
201 JK,Epilogue 4.00
202 JK,Night People 4.00
203 JK,Night People 4.00
204 JK,I:Argon 4.00
205 JK,V:Argon 4.00
206 JK,I:Swine 4.00
207 JK,V:Swine 4.00
208 JK,I:Arnim Zola,D:Swine . . . 4.00
209 JK,O:Arnim Zola,I:Primus . . 4.00
210 JK,A:Red Skull 4.00
211 JK,A:Red Skull 4.00
212 JK,A:Red Skull 4.00
213 JK,I:Night Flyer 4.00
214 JK,D:Night Flyer 4.00
215 GT,Redwing 4.00
216 Reprint,JK 4.00
217 JB, I:Quasar(Marvel Boy)
    I:Vamp 5.00
218 SB,A:Iron Man 4.00
219 SB,JSt,V:TheCorporation . . . 4.00
220 SB,D:L.Dekker 4.00

Captain America #145
© Marvel Entertainment Group

221 SB,Ameridroid 4.00
222 SB,I:Animus(Vamp) 4.00
223 SB,Animus 4.00
224 MZ,V:Animus 4.00
225 SB,A:Nick Fury 4.00
226 SB,A:Nick Fury 4.00
227 SB,A:Nick Fury 4.00
228 SB,Constrictor 4.00
229 SB,R:SuperAgents of Shield . 4.00
230 SB,A:Hulk 4.00
231 SB,DP,A:Grand Director . . . 4.00
232 SB,DP,V:Grand Director . . . 4.00
233 SB,DP,D:Sharon Carter 4.00
234 SB,DP,A:Daredevil 4.00
235 SB,FM,A:Daredevil 4.00
236 SB,V:Dr.Faustus 4.00
237 SB,'From the Ashes' 4.00
238 SB,V:Hawk Riders 4.00
239 JBy,JRu,V:Hawk Riders . . . 4.00
240 SB,V:A Guy Named Joe . . . 4.00
241 A:Punisher 9.00
242 JSt,A:Avengers 3.00
243 GP(c),RB,V:Adonis 3.00
244 TS,'A Monster Berserk' 3.00
245 CI,JRn,Nazi Hunter 3.00
246 GP(c),JBi,V:Joe 3.00
247 JBy,V:BaronStrucker 4.00
248 JBy,JRu,Dragon Man 4.00
249 JBy,O:Machinesmith,
    A:Air-Walker 4.00
250 JBy,Cap for Pres 4.00
251 JBy,V:Mr.Hyde 4.00
252 JBy,V:Batrok 4.00
253 JBy,V:Baron Blood 4.00
254 JBy,D:B.Blood,UnionJack,I:3rd
    Union Jack 4.00
255 JBy,40th Anniv.,O:Cap 4.00
256 GC,V:Demon Druid 2.50
257 A:Hulk 2.50
258 MZ,V:Blockbuster 2.50
259 MZ,V:Dr. Octopus 2.50
260 AM,In Jail 2.50
261 MZ,A:Nomad 3.00
262 MZ,V:Ameridroid 2.50
263 MZ,V:Red Skull 2.50
264 MZ,X-Men 4.00
265 MZ,A:Spider-Man,N.Fury . . . 3.00
266 MZ,A:Spider-Man 3.00

267 MZ,V:Everyman 2.50
268 MZ,A:Defenders(x-over from
   Def.#106) 2.50
269 MZ,A:Team America 2.50
270 MZ,V:Tess-One 2.50
271 MZ,V:Mr.X 2.50
272 MZ,I:Vermin 3.00
273 MZ,A:Nick Fury 2.50
274 MZ,D:SamSawyer 2.50
275 MZ,V:Neo-Nazis 2.50
276 MZ,V:Baron Zemo 2.50
277 MZ,V:Baron Zemo 2.50
278 MZ,V:Baron Zemo 2.50
279 MZ,V:Primus 2.50
280 MZ,V:Scarecrow 2.50
281 MZ,A:Spider Woman,
   R:'50's Bucky 2.50
282 MZ,I:2nd Nomad 6.00
282a (second primting) 2.00
283 MZ,A:Viper 4.00
284 SB,Nomad 3.00
285 MZ,V:Porcupine 3.00
286 MZ,V:Deathlok 5.00
287 MZ,V:Deathlok 5.00
288 MZ,V:Deathlok,D:Hellinger . 5.00
289 MZ,A:Red Skull 2.50
290 JBy(c),RF,A:Falcon 2.50
291 JBy(c),HT,V:Tumbler 2.50
292 I&O:Black Crow 2.50
293 V:Mother Superior 2.50
294 R:Nomad 2.50
295 V:Sisters of Sin 2.50
296 V:Baron Zemo 2.50
297 O:Red Skull 2.50
298 V:Red Skull 2.50
299 V:Red Skull 2.50
300 D:Red Skull 4.00
301 PNe,A:Avengers 2.00
302 PNe,I:Machete,V:Batroc 2.00
303 PNe,V:Batroc 2.00
304 PNe,V:Stane Armor 2.00
305 PNe,A:Capt.Britain,V:Modred 2.00
306 PNe,A:Capt.Britain,V:Modred 2.00
307 PNe,I:Madcap 2.00
308 PNe,I:Armadillo,
   Secret WarsII 2.00
309 PNe,V:Madcap 2.00
310 PNe,V:Serpent Society,I:Cotton
   Mouth,Diamondback 2.50
311 PNe,V:Awesome Android . . 2.00
312 PNe,I:Flag Smasher 2.00
313 PNe,D:Modok 2.00
314 PNe,A:Nighthawk 2.00
315 PNe,V:Serpent Society 2.00
316 PNe,A:Hawkeye 2.00
317 PNe,I:Death-Throws 2.00
318 PNe,V&D:Blue Streak 2.00
319 PNe,V:Scourge,D:Vamp . . . 2.00
320 PNe,V:Scourge 2.00
321 PNe,V:Flagsmasher,
   I:Ultimatum 2.00
322 PNe,V:Flagsmasher 2.00
323 PNe,I:Super Patriot
   (US Agent) 5.00
324 PNe,V:Whirlwind,Trapster . . . 2.00
325 I:Slug,A:Nomad 2.00
326 V:Dr.Faustus 2.00
327 MZ(c)V:SuperPatriot 3.00
328 MZ(c),I:Demolition Man 2.00
329 MZ(c),A:Demolition Man . . . 2.00
330 A:Night Shift,Shroud 2.00
331 A:Night Shift,Shroud 2.00
332 BMc,Rogers resigns 7.00
333 B:John Walker Becomes
   6th Captain America 5.00

334 I:4th Bucky 4.00
335 V:Watchdogs 3.00
336 A:Falcon 2.50
337 TMo,I:The Captain 2.50
338 KD,AM,V:Professor Power . . 2.50
339 KD,TD,Fall of Mutants,
   V:Famine 2.50
340 KD,AM,A:Iron Man, ... 2.00
341 KD,AM,I:Battlestar,A:Viper . . 2.00
342 KD,AM,A:D-Man,Falcon,
   Nomad,Viper 2.00
343 KD,AM,A:D-Man,Falcon,
   Nomad 2.00
344 KD,AM,A:D-Man,Nomad . . . 2.50
345 KD,AM,V:Watchdogs 2.00
346 KD,AM,V:Resistants 2.00
347 KD,AM,V:RWinger&LWinger . 2.00
348 KD,AM,V:Flag Smasher 2.00
349 KD,AM,V:Flag Smasher 2.00
350 KD,AM,doub-size,Rogers Ret.
   as Captain Am,V:Red Skull,
   E:6th Cap 4.00
351 KD,AM,A:Nick Fury 2.00
352 KD,AM,I:Supreme Soviets . . 2.00

Captain America #279
© Marvel Entertainment Group

353 KD,AM,V:Supreme Soviets . . 2.00
354 KD,AM,I:USAgent,
   V:Machinesmith 3.00
355 RB,AM,A:Falcon,Battlestar . . 2.00
356 AM,V:Sisters of Sin 2.00
357 KD,AM,V:Sisters of Sin
   Baron Zemo,Batroc 2.00
358 KD,B:Blood Stone Hunt 2.00
359 KD,V:Zemo,C:Crossbones . . 2.00
360 KD,I:Crossbones 2.00
361 KD,V:Zemo,Batroc 2.00
362 KD,V:Zemo,Crossbones 2.00
363 KD,E:Blood Stone Hunt,
   V:Crossbones,C:Wolverine . . 2.00
364 KD,V:Crossbones 2.00
365 KD,Acts of Vengeance,
   V:SubMariner,Red Skull 2.00
366 1st RLm Capt.Amer.,Acts of
   Vengeance,V:Controller 2.00
367 KD,Acts of Vengeance,
   Magneto Vs. Red Skull 2.50
368 RLm,V:Machinesmith 2.00
369 RLm,I:Skeleton Crew 2.00
370 RLm,V:Skeleton Crew 2.00

371 RLm,V:Trump,Poundcakes . . 2.00
372 RLm,B:Streets of Poison,
   Cap on Drugs,C:Bullseye 2.50
373 RLm,V:Bullseye,A:Bl.Widow . 2.00
374 RLm,V:Bullseye,A:Daredevil . 2.00
375 RLm,V:Daredevil 2.00
376 RLm,A:Daredevil 2.00
377 RLm,V:Crossbones,Bullseye . 2.00
378 RLm,E:Streets of Poison,Red
   Skull vs Kingpin,V:Crossbones 2.00
379 RLm(c),V:Serpent Society . . . 2.00
380 RLm,V:Serpent Society 2.00
381 RLm,V:Serpent Society 2.00
382 RLm,V:Serpent Society 2.00
383 RLm(c),RLm,50th Anniv.
   64Pages 4.00
384 RLm,A:Jack Frost 2.00
385 RLm,A:USAgent 2.00
386 RLm,Cap./USAgent T.U. 2.00
387 B:Superia Strategem 2.00
388 A:Paladin 2.00
389 Superia Strategem #3 . . . . . . 2.00
390 Superia Strategem #4 . . . . . . 2.00
391 Superia Strategem #5 . . . . . . 2.00
392 E:Superia Strategem 2.00
393 V:Captain Germany 2.00
394 A:Red Skull,Diamondback . . . 2.00
395 A:Red Skull,Crossbones 2.00
396 I:2nd Jack O'Lantern 2.00
397 V:Red Skull,X-Bones,Viper . . 2.00
398 Operation:Galactic Storm
   Pt.1,V:Warstar 2.00
399 Operation Galactic Storm
   Pt.8,V:Kree Empire 2.00
400 Operation Galactic Storm
   Pt.15,BU:rep.Avengers #4 . . . . 4.00
401 R:D-Man,A:Avengers 2.00
402 RLe,B:Man & Wolf,
   A:Wolverine 2.00
403 RLe,A:Wolverine 2.00
404 RLe,A:Wolverine 2.00
405 RLe,A:Wolverine 2.00
406 RLe,A:Wolverine 2.00
407 RLe,A:Wolverine,Cable 2.00
408 RLe,E:Man & Wolf 1.50
409 RLe,V:Skeleton Crew 1.50
410 RLe,V:Crossbones,Skel.Crew 1.50
411 RLe,V:Snapdragon 1.50
412 RLe,V:Batroc,A:Shang-Chi . . 1.50
413 A:Shang-Chi,V:Superia 1.50
414 RLe,A:Kazar,Black Panther . . 1.50
415 Rle,A:Black Panther,Kazar . . 1.50
416 RLe,Savage Land Mutates,
   A:Black.Panther,Kazar 1.50
417 RLe,A:Black Panther,Kazar,
   V:AIM 1.50
418 RLe,V:Night People 1.50
419 RLe,V:Viper 1.50
420 RLe,I:2nd Blazing Skull,
   A:Nightshift 3.00
421 RLe,V:Nomad 1.50
422 RLe,I:Blistik 1.50
423 RTs(s),MCW,V:Namor 1.50
424 MGv(s),A:Sidewinder 1.50
425 B:MGu(s),DHv,Embossed(c),I:2nd
   Super Patriot,Dead Ringer . . . 3.50
426 DHv,A:Super Patriot,Dead Ringer,
   V:Resistants 1.50
427 DHv,V:Super Patriot,Dead
   Ringer 1.75
428 DHv,I:Americop 1.75
429 DHv,V:Kono 1.50
430 Daemon Dran, Americop 1.75
431 DHv,I:Free Spirit 1.50
432 DHv,Fighting Chance 1.50

All comics prices listed are for _Near Mint_ condition.

433 DHv,Baron Zemo 1.50
434 DHv,A:Fighting Spirit,
  V:King Cobra 1.50
435 DHv,Fighting Chance 1.50
436 V:King Cobra, Mister Hyde,
  Fighting Chance conclusion . . 1.50
437 Cap in a Coma 1.50
438 I:New Body Armor 1.50
439 Dawn's Early Light,pt.2 . . . . . 1.50
440 Taking A.I.M.,pt.1 . . . . 1.50
441 Taking A.I.M.,pt.3 . . . . 1.50
442 Batroc, Cap,V:Zeitgeist 1.50
443 MGu,24 hours to live 1.50
444 MWa,RG,President Kidnapped 6.00
445 MWa,RG,R:Captain America . 4.00
446 MWa,RG,Operation
  Rebirth,pt.2 . . . . 3.50
447 MWa,RG,Op.Rebirth,pt.3 . . . 3.50
448 MWa,RG,Operation
  Rebirth,pt.4,double size 6.00
449 MWa,RG,A:Thor 2.50
450 MWa,RG,Man Without a
  Country, pt,1 . . . . 2.50
450a alternate cover 4.00
451 MWa,RG,DRo,Man Without
  A Country,pt.2,new costume . . 2.00
452 MWa,RG,Man Without a
  Country, pt.3 . . . . 2.00
453 MWa,RG Man Without a
  Country, concl.,old costume . . 2.00
454 MWa,RG,A:Avengers 2.00
Ann.#1 rep. 22.00
Ann.#2 rep. 11.00
Ann.#3 JK, ... 5.00
Ann.#4 JK,V:Magneto,I:Mutant
  Force 10.00
Ann.#5 'Deathwatcher' 4.00
Ann.#6 A:Contemplator 4.00
Ann.#7 O:Shaper of Worlds 4.00
Ann.#8 MZ,A:Wolverine 35.00
Ann.#9 MBa,SD,Terminus Factor
  #1,N:Nomad 4.50
Ann.#10 MM,Baron Strucker,pt.3
  (see Punisher Ann.#4) 2.50
Ann.#11 Citizen Kang#1 . . . . 2.50
Ann.#12 I:Bantam,w/card 3.25
Ann.#13 RTs(s),MCW, ... 3.25
Drug Wars PDd(s),SaV,A:New
  Warriors 2.00
G-Size#1 GK(c),rep.O:Cap.Amer. . 7.00
HC vol.Slipcase Rep.#1
  thru #10 (From 1940's) 75.00
Medusa Effect RTs(s),MCW,RB,
  V:Master Man 2.95
Movie Adapt 2.00
Spec.#1 Rep.Cap.A #110,#111 . . 2.00
Spec.#2 Rep.Cap.A #113
  & Strange Tales #169 . . . . . . 2.00
TPB Bloodstone Hunt,rep.
  #357-364 . . . . 15.95
TPB Captain America: Man Without
  a Country, MWa,RG,SK, rep.
  (1998) 15.00
TPB Streets of Poison,
  rep. #372–#377
TPB War and Remembrance,
  rep. #247–#255 . . . . 12.95
Collector's Preview 1.95
Ashcan .75

[2nd Series] Nov. 1996
1 RLd,CDi,JSb, Heroes Reborn,
  I:Nick Fury,48pg. 5.00
1A Stars and stripes background
  variant cover 7.50
1b gold signature edition,

cardstock cover 18.00
1c San Diego Con edition 25.00
2 RLd,JLb,JSb,Falcon & Red Skull 3.00
3 RLd,JLb,JSb,A:Hulk,V:Red Skull
  & Master Man 2.50
4 RLd,JLb,JSb,F:Prince Namor, . 2.50
5 RLd,JLb,JSb,V:Crossbones . . . 2.50
6 RLd,JLb,JSb,"Industrial
  Revolution," epilogue,A:Cable . 2.50
7 RLd,JLb,DaF, ... 2.00
8 RLd,JLb,SPa,A:Nick Fury,
  WWII story 2.00
9 JLb,RLd,SPa,WWII story. 2.00
10 JLb,RLd,SPa,WWII story, concl. 2.00
11 JeR,JoB,Odyssey across
  America, pt.4, concl. 2.00
12 JeR,JoB,Heroes Reborn, Galactus
  concl. 3.00
13 JeR,RLm,Wildstorm x-over . . 2.50
Ashcan, ComicCon 5.00

[3rd Series] Nov. 1997
1 MWa,RG,BWi,A:Lady Deathstrike,
  Red Skull, Sharon Carter, 48pg 3.00
2 MWa,RG,BWi,A devastating loss 2.00
3 MWa,RG,BWi,V:Hydra 2.00
4 MWa,RG,BWi,F:Batroc 2.00
5 MWa,RG,BWi,V:Hordes of Hydra 2.00
6 MWa,RG,V:Skrulls 2.00
7 MWa,NKu,Power and Glory concl. 2.00
8 MWa,Nku,Live Kree or Die, pt.2
  x-over 2.00
9 MWa,NKu,American Nightmare,
  pt.1 . . . . 2.00
10 MWa,NKu,American Nightmare,
  pt.2 . . . . 2.00

CAPTAIN AMERICA:
SENTINEL OF LIBERTY
July 1998
1 MWa,RG,new foe, in future . . 2.00
1 signed by MWa & RG 25.00
2A MWa,RG(c&a) F:Invaders,
  V:Nazis 2.00
2B variant JSm(c) 2.00

CAPTAIN BRITAIN
CLASSICS
1 AD rep. 2.50

CAPTAIN CONFEDERACY
Epic Nov., 1991
1 I:Capt.Confederacy,Kid Dixie . . 2.25
2 Meeting of Superhero Reps . . 2.25
3 Framed for Murder 2.25
4 Superhero conference,final iss. 2.25

CAPTAIN JUSTICE
March, 1988
1 Based on TV Series 1.00
2 April, 1988 . . . . 1.00

CAPTAIN MARVEL
May, 1968
1 GC,O:retold,V:Sentry#459 . . 75.00
2 GC,V:Super Skrull 25.00
3 GC,V:Super Skrull 25.00
4 GC,Sub-Mariner 20.00
5 DH,I:Metazoid 20.00
6 DH,I:Solam 12.00
7 JR(c),DH,V:Quasimodo 12.00
8 DH,I:Cuberex 12.00
9 DH,D:Cuberex 12.00
10 DH,V:Number 1 . . . . 12.00

Captain Marvel #62
© Marvel Entertainment Group

11 BWS(c),I:Z0 . . . . 12.00
12 K&R(c),I:Man-Slayer 9.00
13 FS,V:Man-Slayer 9.00
14 FS,Iron Man 9.00
15 TS,DA,Z0 . . . . 8.00
16 DH,Ronan 8.00
17 GK,DA,O:R.Jones ret,N:Capt.
  Marvel 9.00
18 GK,JB,DA,I:Mandroid 8.00
19 GK,DA,Master.of.MM 8.00
20 GK,DA,I:Rat Pack 8.00
21 GK,DA,Hulk 8.00
22 GK(c),WB,V:Megaton 8.00
23 GK(c),WB,FMc,V:Megaton . . 8.00
24 GK(c),WB,ECh,I:L.Mynde . . . 8.00
25 1st JSn,Cap.Marvel,Cosmic
  Cube Saga Begins 15.00
26 JSn,DC,Thanos(2ndApp.)
  A:Thing 20.00
27 JSn,V:Thanos,A:Mentor,
  Starfox, I:Death 12.00
28 JSn,DGr,Thanos Vs.Drax,
  A:Avengers 12.00
29 JSn,AM,O:Zeus,C:Thanos
  I:Eon,O:Mentor 9.00
30 JSn,AM,Controller,C:Thanos . . 9.00
31 JSn,AM,Avengers,
  Thanos,Drax,Mentor 9.00
32 JSn,AM,DGr,O:Drax,
  Moondragon,A:Thanos 9.00
33 JSn,KJ,E:Cosmic Cube Saga
  1st D:Thanos 12.00
34 JSn,JA,V:Nitro(leads to
  his Death) 7.00
35 GK(c),AA,Ant Man 5.00
36 AM,Watcher,Rep.CM#1 . . . . 5.00
37 AM,KJ,Nimrod 5.00
38 AM,KJ,Watcher 5.00
39 AM,KJ,Watcher 5.00
40 AM,AMc,Watcher 5.00
41 AM,BWr,CR,BMc,TA,Kree . . 4.00
42 AM,V:Stranger,C:Drax 4.00
43 AM,V:Drax 4.00
44 GK(c),AM,V:Drax 4.00
45 AM,I:Rambu 4.00
46 AM,TA,D:Fawn 4.00
47 AM,TA,A:Human Torch 4.00
48 AM,TA,I:Chetah 4.00

49 AM,V:Ronan,A:Cheetah 4.00
50 AM,TA,Avengers,
   V:Super Adaptiod 3.00
51 AM,TA,V:Mercurio,4-D Man . . 3.00
52 AM,TA,V:Phae-dor 3.00
53 AM,TA,A:Inhumans 3.00
54 PB,V:Nitro 3.00
55 PB,V:Death-grip 3.00
56 PB,V:Death-grip 3.00
57 PB,V:Thor,A;Thanos 5.00
58 PB,Drax/Titan 3.00
59 PB,Drax/Titan,I:Stellarax 3.00
60 PB,Drax/Titan 3.00
61 PB,V:Chaos 3.00
62 PB,V:Stellarax 3.00
G-Size #1 reprints 8.00

CAPTAIN MARVEL
1989
1 MBr,I:Powerkeg,V:Moonstone . 3.00
1 DyM(s),MBr,V:Skinhead(1993) . 2.00
PF Death of Captain Marvel 7.95
TPB Life of Captain Marvel,JSn . 14.95

CAPTAIN MARVEL
1995
1 FaN,R:Captain Marvel(son of) . 1.95
2 FaN,V:X-Treme,Erik the Red . . 1.95
3 FaN,V:X-treme 1.95
4 thru 6 FaN . . . . @1.95

CAPTAIN PLANET
Oct., 1991
1 I&O:Captain Planet 1.00
2 V:Dr.Blights' Smog Monster . . . 1.00
3 V:Looten Plunder 1.00
4 'Pollutionland' 1.25
5 V:Duke Nukem 1.25
6 A:Capt.Pollution,Eco-Villains . . 1.25
7 thru 9 . . . . @1.25
10 V:Litterbug 1.25
11 BHi,V:Greedly 1.25
12 V:Looten Plunder,last issue . . . 1.25

CAPT. SAVAGE & HIS
LEATHERNECK RAIDERS
Jan., 1968
1 SSh(c),C:Sgt Fury;The Last
   Bansai 35.00
2 SSh(c),O:Hydra;Return of Baron
   Strucker 20.00
3 SSh,Two Against Hydra 20.00
4 SSh,V:Hydra;The Fateful Finale20.00
5 SSh,The Invincible Enemy . . 20.00
6 Mission;Save a Howler 20.00
7 SSh,Objective:Ben Grimm . . 22.00
8 Mission:Foul Ball 20.00
Becomes:

CAPT. SAVAGE & HIS
BATTLEFIELD RAIDERS
9 . . . . 6.00
10 To the Last Man 5.00
11 V:Sergeant Fury 5.00
12 V:The Japanese 3.75
13 The Junk Heap Juggernauts . . 5.00
14 Savage's First Mission 5.00
15 Within the Temple Waits Death 5.00
16 V:The Axis Powers 5.00
17 V:The Axis Powers 5.00
18 V:The Axis Powers 5.00
19 March, 1970 . . . . 5.00

CARE BEARS
Star Nov., 1985
1 . . . . 1.50
2 thru 14 . . . . @1.00
Marvel
15 thru 20 . . . . @1.00

CARNAGE
1-shot Carnage: Its a Wonderful
   Life (1996) 2.00
1-shot Carnage: Mindbomb
   foil cover (1996) 2.95

CARTOON KIDS
Atlas 1957
1 A:Dexter the Demon,Little
   Zelda,Willie,Wise Guy 50.00

CAR WARRIORS
Epic 1990
1 Based on Roll Playing Game . . 2.25
2 Big Race Preparations 2.25
3 Ft.Delorean-Lansing Race begin 2.25
4 Race End, Final issue 2.25

CASEY–CRIME
PHOTOGRAPHER
August, 1949
1 Ph(c),Girl on the Docks . . . 150.00
2 Ph(c),Staats Cotsworth 75.00
3 Ph(c),He Walked With Danger 75.00
4 Ph(c),Lend Me Your Life . . . 75.00
Becomes:

TWO GUN WESTERN
[1st Series]
5 JB,B,I&O:Apache Kid 150.00
6 The Outcast 100.00
7 Human Sacrifice 100.00
8 JR,DW,A:Kid Colt,Texas Kid,
   Doc Holiday 100.00
9 A:Kid Colt,Marshall"Frosty"
   Bennet Texas Kid 100.00
10 . . . . 100.00
11 thru 14 June, 1952 . . . . . . @75.00

CASPER
1996
1 From Animated TV show 1.50
2 visit to Harvey Castle 1.50
3 and 4 . . . . 1.00

CAT, THE
Nov., 1972—June 1973
1 JM,I&O:The Cat 15.00
2 JM,V:The Owl 10.00
3 BEv,V:Kraken 10.00
4 JSn,V:Man-Bull 10.00

CENTURY:
DISTANT SONS
1996
1-shot DAn,48pg. 2.95

CHAMBER OF CHILLS
Nov., 1972
1 SSh,A Dragon Stalks By
   Night,(H.Ellison Adapt.) 25.00
2 FB,BEv,SD,Monster From the
   Mound,(RE Howard Adapt.) . 15.00
3 FB,BEv,SD, Thing on the Roof 15.00
4 FB,BEv,SD, Opener of the

Crypt,(J.Jakes,E.A.Poe Adapt) 15.00
5 FB,BEv,SD, Devils Dowry . . . 15.00
6 FB,BEv,SD, Mud Monster . . . 15.00
7 thru 24 FB,BEv,SD . . . . . @15.00
25 FB,BEv,SD November, 1976 . 15.00

Chamber of Darkness #5
© Marvel Entertainment Group

CHAMBER OF DARKNESS
Oct., 1969
1 JB, Tales of Maddening Magic 50.00
2 NA(script),Enter the Red Death 25.00
3 JK,BWS,JB, Something Lurks
   on Shadow Mountain 30.00
4 JK Monster Man Came Walking,
   BU:BWS 60.00
5 JK,SD, And Fear Shall Follow
   plus Lovecraft adapt. 20.00
6 SD 20.00
7 SD,JK,BWr, Night of the
   Gargoyle 35.00
8 DA,BEv, Beast that Walks Like
   a Man Special, 5 Tales of
   Maddening Magic,Jan. 1972 . 20.00
Becomes:

MONSTERS ON
THE PROWL
9 SAD,BWS,Monster Stories
   Inc,Gorgilla 25.00
10 JK,Roc 15.00
11 JK,A Titan Walks the Land . . 15.00
12 HT,JK,Gomdulla The Living
   Pharoah 15.00
13 HT,JK,Tragg 15.00
14 JK,SD,Return of the Titan . . . 15.00
15 FrG,JK,The Thing Called It . . 15.00
16 JSe,SD,JK, Serpent God of
   Lost Swamp,A:King Kull 15.00
17 JK,SD,Coming of Colossus . . 15.00
18 JK,SD,Bruttu 15.00
19 JK,SD,Creature From the
   Black Bog 15.00
20 JK,SD,Oog Lives Again 15.00
21 JK,SD,A Martian Stalks
   the City 15.00
22 JK,SD,Monster Runs Amok . . 12.00
23 JK,The Return of Grogg 12.00
24 JK,SD, Magnetor 12.00
25 JK,Colossus Lives Again . . . 12.00

MARVEL

26 JK,SD,The Two Headed Thing 12.00
27 JK,Sserpo 12.00
28 JK,The Coming of Monsteroso 12.00
29 JK,SD Monster at my Window 12.00
30 JK,Diablo Demon from the 5th
 Dimension, Oct., 1974 . . . . . 12.00

CHAMPIONS
June, 1986
1 GK(c),DH,I&O:Champions . . . 20.00
2 DH,O:Champions 14.00
3 GT,Assault on Olympus 13.00
4 GT,'Murder at Malibu' 12.00
5 DH,I:Rampage 12.00
6 JK(c),GT,V:Rampage 12.00
7 GT,O:Black Widow,I:Darkstar . 12.00
8 BH,O:Black Widow 12.00
9 BH,BL,V:Crimson Dynamo . . . 12.00
10 BH,BL,V:Crimson Dynamo . . . 12.00
11 JBy,A:Black Goliath,Hawkeye 13.00
12 JBy,BL,V:Stranger 13.00
13 JBy,BL,V:Kamo Tharn 13.00
14 JBy,I:Swarm 13.00
15 JBy,V:Swarm 13.00
16 BH,A:Magneto,Dr.Doom,
 Beast 12.00
17 GT,JBy,V:Sentinels,last issue 13.00

CHILDREN OF THE VOYAGE
Frontier 1993
1 F:Sam Wantling 3.25
2 Counterfeit Man 2.25
3 V:Voyager 2.25
4 Last Issue 2.25

Chili #8
© Marvel Entertainment Group

CHILI
May, 1969
1 . . . . 50.00
2 . . . . 25.00
3 . . . . 15.00
4 . . . . 15.00
5 . . . . 15.00
6 thru 15 . . . . @12.00
16 thru 20 . . . . @10.00
21 thru 25 . . . . @8.00

26 Dec., 1973 . . . . 8.00
Spec.#1, 1971 . . . . 15.00

CHUCK NORRIS
Star Jan.–Sept., 1987
1 SD 1.00
2 thru 5 . . . . @1.00

CINDY COMICS
See: KRAZY COMICS

CLANDESTINE
Oct. 1994–Sept. 1995
Preview issue, Intro (1994) 1.50
1 MFm,AD,foil(c) 3.25
2 Wraparound (c),A:Silver Surfer 2.50
3 I:Argent,Kimera,A:SilverSurfer . 2.50
4 R:Adam 2.50
5 MFm,AD,O:Adam Destine . . . 2.50
6 A:Spider-Man 2.50
7 A:Spider-Man 2.50
8 A:Dr.Strange 2.50
9 Training Time 2.50
10 A:Britanic 2.50
11 V:Modan 2.50
12 Aftermath 2.50
13 Who Will Lead 2.50
14 Vincent Vs. Adam 2.50
TPB AD,MFm (1997) 12.00

CLASSIC CONAN
See: CONAN SAGA

CLASSIC X-MEN
See: X-MEN

CLIVE BARKER'S BOOK OF THE DAMNED
Epic Nov., 1991
1 JBo,Hellraiser companion 4.95
2 MPa,Hellraiser Companion . . . 4.95

CLIVE BARKER'S HELLRAISER
Epic 1989–93
1 BWr,DSp 7.00
2 . . . . 6.00
3 . . . . 6.50
4 . . . . 4.50
5 . . . . 4.50
6 . . . . 4.50
7 The Devil's Brigade #1 . . . . . 4.50
8 The Devil's Brigade #2&3 . . . 4.50
9 The Devil's Brigade #4&5 . . . 4.50
10 The Devil's Brigade #6&7
 foil Cover 5.00
11 The Devil's Brigade #8&9 . . . 4.50
12 The Devil's Brigade #10-12 . . 4.50
13 MMi,RH,Devil's Brigade #13 . . 4.50
14 The Devil's Brigade #14 . . . . . 4.95
15 The Devil's Brigade #15 . . . . . 4.95
16 E:Devil's Brigade 4.95
17 BHa,DR,The Harrowing 4.95
18 O:Harrowers 4.95
19 A:Harrowers 4.95
20 NGa(s),DMc,Last Laugh 4.95
Dark Holiday Spec.#1 (1992) . . . 4.95
Spring Slaughter Spec.#1 (1994) . 6.95
Summer Spec.#1 (1992) 5.95

CLOAK & DAGGER
(Limited Series) Oct., 1983
1 RL,TA,I:Det.O'Reilly,
 Father Delgado 2.50
2 RL,TA,V:Duane Hellman 2.00
3 RL,TA,V:Street Gang 2.00
4 RL,TA,O:Cloak & Dagger, . . . 2.00

CLOAK & DAGGER
[1st Regular Series] July 1985
1 RL,Pornography 2.00
2 RL,Dagger's mother 1.50
3 RL,A:Spider-Man 2.00
4 RL,Secret Wars II 1.50
5 RL,I:Mayhem 1.50
6 RL,A:Mayhem 1.50
7 RL,A:Mayhem 1.50
8 TA, Drugs 1.50
9 AAd,TA,A:Mayhem 2.50
10 BBI,TA,V:Dr. Doom 1.50
11 BBI,TA,Last Issue 1.50

[Mutant Misadventures of] CLOAK & DAGGER
[2nd Regular Series] Oct., 1988
1 CR(i),A:X-Factor 3.00
2 CR(i),C:X-Factor,V:Gromitz . . 2.50
3 SW(i),JLe(c),A:Gromitz 2.00
4 TA(i),Inferno,R:Mayhem 2.00
5 TA(i),R:Mayhem 2.00
6 TA(i),A:Mayhem 1.75
7 A:Crimson Daffodil,V:Ecstacy . 1.75
8 Acts of Vengeance prelude . . . 1.75
9 Acts of Vengeance 2.00
10 Acts of Vengeance,"X-Force"
 name used,Dr.Doom 2.00
11 . . . . 1.50
12 A:Dr.Doom 1.50
13 A:Dr.Doom 1.50
14 & 15 RL . . . . @1.50
16 RL,A:Spider-Man 2.00
17 A:Spider-Man, ... 2.00
18 Inf.Gauntlet X-over,
 A:Spider-Man, Ghost Rider . . 2.50
19 O:Cloak & Dagger,final issue . 2.50
GNv Predator and Prey 14.95

A CLUELESS VALENTINE
1 characters from movie, 48pg . 2.50

CODENAME: GENETIX
1993
1 PGa,A:Wolverine 2.00
2 PGa,V:Prime EvilA:Wolverine . 2.00
3 . . . . 2.00
4 A:Wolverine,Kazar 2.00

CODE OF HONOR
1996
1 (of 4) CDi,TnS,I:Jeff Piper,
 fully painted 5.95
2 thru 4 CDi, ... @5.95

CODE NAME: SPITFIRE
See: SPITFIRE AND THE TROUBLESHOOTERS

COLOSSUS
Aug., 1997
1-shot BRa,Colossus & Meggan
 V:Arcade, 48pg 3.00

COLOSSUS: GOD'S COUNTRY
PF V:Cold Warriors 6.95

COMBAT
Atlas June, 1952
1 War Stories, Bare Bayonets . 125.00
2 Break Thru,(Dedicated to US
  Infantry) 65.00
3 . . . . 35.00
4 . . . . 50.00
5 thru 10 . . . . @35.00
11 April, 1953 . . . . 35.00

COMBAT CASEY
See: WAR COMBAT

COMBAT KELLY AND THE DEADLY DOZEN
Atlas Nov., 1951
1 RH,Korean war stories 150.00
2 Big Push 75.00
3 The Volunteer 50.00
4 V:Communists 50.00
5 OW,V:Communists 50.00
6 V:Communists 50.00
7 V: Communists 50.00
8 Death to the Reds 50.00
9 . . . . 50.00
10 . . . . 50.00
11 . . . . 45.00
12 thru 16 . . . . @50.00
17 A:Combat Casey 75.00
18 A:Battle Brady 35.00
19 V:Communists 35.00
20 V:Communists 35.00
21 Transvestite Cover 40.00
22 thru 40 . . . . @30.00
41 thru 44 August, 1957 . . . . @30.00

COMBAT KELLY
June, 1972
1 JM, Stop the Luftwaffe 20.00
2 The Big Breakout 10.00
3 O:Combat Kelly 10.00
4 Mutiny,A:Sgt.Fury and the
  Howling Commandoes 10.00
5 Escape or Die 10.00
6 The Fortress of Doom 10.00
7 Nun Hostage,V:Nazis 10.00
8 V:Nazis 10.00
9 Oct., 1973 . . . . 10.00

COMET MAN
Feb., 1987
1 BSz(c),I:Comet Man 1.50
2 BSz(c),A:Mr.Fantastic 1.00
3 BSz(c),A:Hulk 1.00
4 BSz(c),A:Fantistic Four 1.00
5 BSz(c),A:Fantastic Four 1.00
6 BSz(c),Last issue, July,1987 . 1.00

COMIX BOOK
(black & white magazine) 1974
1 . . . . 25.00
2 . . . . 20.00
3 . . . . 25.00
4 . . . . 12.00
5 1976 . . . . 12.00

COMIX ZONE
1 video game tie-in 2.50

2 video game tie-in 2.50

COMMANDO ADVENTURES
Atlas June, 1957
1 Seek, Find and Destroy 45.00
2 MD, Hit 'em and Hit 'em
  Hard, August,1957 . . . . . . 40.00

COMPLETE COMICS
See: AMAZING COMICS

COMPLETE MYSTERY
August, 1948
1 Seven Dead Men 325.00
2 Jigsaw of Doom 300.00
3 Fear in the Night 300.00
4 A Squealer Dies Fast 300.00
Becomes:

TRUE COMPLETE MYSTERY
5 Rice Mancini,
  The Deadly Dude 150.00
6 Ph(c),Frame-up that Failed . 100.00
7 Ph(c),Caught 100.00
8 Ph(c),The Downfall of Mr.
  Anderson, Oct., 1949 . . . . 100.00

CONAN
1995–96
1 Pit Fighter 2.95
2 LHa,Hyborean tortue factory . . 2.95
3 V:Cannibals 2.95
4 LHa,JP,Rune Conan Prelude . . 2.95
5 LHa,V:yeti 2.95
6 LHa, the plague 2.95
7 LHa,BBl,V:The Iron Man 2.95
8 . . . . 2.95
9 . . . . 2.95
10 Conan kidnapped by Amazons 2.95
11 . . . . 2.95

CONAN THE ADVENTURER
1994–95
1 RT(s),RK,Red Foil(c) 3.00
2 RT(s),RK 1.75
3 RT(s),RK 1.50
4 . . . . 1.50
5 . . . . 1.50
6 . . . . 1.50
7 . . . . 1.50
8 . . . . 1.50
9 . . . . 1.50
10 . . . . 1.50
11 Torture Chamber 1.50
12 Abominations of Yondo 1.50
13 Seven Warriors 1.50
14 RTs,Young Conan,last issue . . 1.50

CONAN THE BARBARIAN
Oct., 1979
1 BWS/DA,O:Conan,A:Kull . . . 225.00
2 BWS/SB,Lair o/t Beast-Men . . 80.00
3 BWS,SB,Grey God Passes . . 135.00
4 BWS,SB,Tower o/t Elephant . 60.00
5 BWS,Zukala's Daughter 60.00
6 BWS,SB,Devil Wings Over
  Shadizar 35.00
7 BWS,SB,DA,C:Thoth-Amon,
  I:Set 35.00
8 BWS,TS,TP,Keepers o/t Crypt 35.00

9 BWS,SB,Garden of Fear 35.00
10 BWS,SB,JSe,Beware Wrath of
   Anu;BU:Kull 50.00
11 BWS,SB,Talons of Thak 50.00
12 BWS,GK,Dweller in the Dark,
   Blood of the Dragon B.U. . . . 25.00
13 BWS,SB,Web o/t Spider-God 25.00
14 BWS,SB,Green Empress of
   Melnibone 40.00
15 BWS,SB 40.00
16 BWS,Frost Giant's Daughter . 25.00
17 GK,Gods of Bal-Sagoth,
   A:Fafnir 11.00
18 GK,DA,Thing in the Temple,
   A:Fafnir 11.00
19 BWS,DA,Hawks from
   the Sea 22.00
20 BWS,DA,Black Hound of
   Vengeance,A:Fafnir 22.00
21 BWS,CR,VM,DA,SB, Monster
   of the Monoliths 20.00
22 BWS,DA,rep.Conan #1 . . . . 22.00
23 BWS,DA,Shadow of the
   Vulture,I:Red Sonja 30.00

Conan the Barbarian #3
© Marvel Entertainment Group

24 BWS,Song of Red Sonja . . . 38.00
25 JB,SB,JSe,Mirrors of Kharam
   Akkad,A:Kull 8.00
26 JB,Hour of the Griffin 6.00
27 JB,Blood of Bel-Hissar 5.00
28 JB,Moon of Zembabwei 5.00
29 JB,Two Against Turan 5.00
30 JB,The Hand of Nergal 5.00
31 JB,Shadow in the Tomb 4.00
32 JB,Flame Winds of Lost Khitai 4.00
33 JB,Death & 7 Wizards 4.00
34 JB,Temptress in the Tower
   of Flame 4.00
35 JB,Hell-Spawn of Kara-Shehr . 4.00
36 JB,Beware of Hyrkanians
   bearing Gifts 4.00
37 NA,Curse of the Golden Skull 12.00
38 JB,Warrior & Were-Woman . . 3.50
39 JB,Dragon from the
   Inland Sea 3.50
40 RB,Fiend from Forgotten City . 3.50
41 JB,Garden of Death & Life . . . 5.00
42 JB,Night of the Gargoyle 5.00

Conan the Barbarian #14
© Marvel Entertainment Group

43 JB,Tower o/Blood,A:RedSonja 5.00
44 JB,Flame&Fiend,A:RedSonja . 6.00
45 JB,Last Ballad of Laza-Lanti . . 6.00
46 JB,JSt,Curse of the Conjurer . . 4.00
47 JB,DA,Goblins in the
   Moonlight 4.00
48 JB,DG,DA,Rats Dance at Raven
   gard,BU:Red Sonja 4.00
49 JB,DG,Wolf-Woman 4.00
50 JB,DG,Dweller in the Pool . . . 4.00
51 JB,DG,Man Born of Demon . . 4.00
52 JB,TP,Altar and the Scorpion . 4.00
53 JB,FS,Brothers of the Blade . . 4.00
54 JB,TP,Oracle of Ophir 4.00
55 JB,TP,Shadow on the Land . . . 4.00
56 JB,High Tower in the Mist 4.00
57 MP,Incident in Argos 4.00
58 JB,Queen o/tBlackCoast,
   2nd A:Belit 6.00
59 JB,Ballad of Belit,O:Belit 3.50
60 JB,Riders o/t River Dragons . . 3.50
61 JB,She-Pirate,I:Amra 3.50
62 JB,Lord of the Lions,O:Amra . . 3.50
63 JB,Death Among Ruins,
   V&D:Amra 3.50
64 JSon,AM,rep.Savage Tales#5 . 3.50
65 JB,Fiend o/tFeatheredSerpent . 3.50
66 JB,Daggers & Death Gods,
   C:Red Sonja 3.50
67 JB,Talons of the Man-Tiger,
   A:Red Sonja 3.50
68 JB,Of Once & Future Kings,
   V:KingKull,A:Belit,Red Sonja . . 3.50
69 VM,Demon Out of the Deep . . 3.50
70 JB,City in the Storm 3.50
71 JB,Secret of Ashtoreth 3.50
72 JB,Vengeance in Asgalun 3.50
73 JB,..In the Well of Skelos 3.50
74 JB,Battle at the Black Walls
   C:Thoth-Amon 3.50
75 JB,Hawk-Riders of Harakht . . . 3.50
76 JB,Swordless in Stygia 3.50
77 JB,When Giants Walk
   the Earth 3.50
78 JB,rep.Savage Sword #1,

A:Red Sonja 3.50
79 HC,Lost Valley of Iskander . . . 3.50
80 HC,Trial By Combat 3.50
81 HC,The Eye of the Serpent . . 3.00
82 HC,The Sorceress o/t Swamp . 3.00
83 HC,The Dance of the Skull . . . 3.00
84 JB,Two Against the Hawk-City,
   I:Zula 3.00
85 JB,Of Swordsmen & Sorcerers,
   O:Zulu 3.00
86 JB,Devourer of the Dead 3.00
87 TD, rep. Savage Sword #3. . . . 3.00
88 JB,Queen and the Corsairs . . . 3.00
89 JB,Sword & the Serpent,
   A:Thoth-Amon 3.00
90 JB,Diadem of the Giant-Kings . 3.00
91 JB,Savage Doings in Shem . . 3.00
92 JB,The Thing in the Crypt 3.00
93 JB,Of Rage & Revenge 3.00
94 JB,BeastKing ofAbombi,L:Zulu 3.00
95 JB,The Return of Amra 3.00
96 JB,Long Night of Fang
   & Talon,pt.1 . . . . 3.00
97 JB,Long Night of Fang
   & Talon,pt.2 . . . . 3.00
98 JB,Sea-Woman 3.00
99 JB,Devil Crabs o/t Dark Cliffs . 3.00
100 JB,Death on the Black Coast,
   D:Belit (double size) 3.50
101 JB,The Devil has many Legs . 1.75
102 JB,The Men Who
   Drink Blood 1.75
103 JB,Bride of the Vampire 1.75
104 JB,The Vale of Lost Women . 1.75
105 JB,Whispering Shadows 1.75
106 JB,Chaos in Kush 1.75
107 JB,Demon of the Night 1.75
108 JB,Moon-Eaters of Darfar . . . 1.75
109 JB,Sons o/t Bear God 1.75
110 JB,Beward t/Bear o/Heaven . 1.75
111 JB,Cimmerian Against a City . 1.75
112 JB,Buryat Besieged 1.75
113 JB,A Devil in the Family 1.75
114 JB,The Shadow of the Beast . 1.75
115 JB,A War of Wizards, A:Red
   Sonja Double size 10th Anniv.
   (L:Roy Thomas script) 2.50
116 JB,NA,Crawler in the Mist . . . 1.75
117 JB,Corridor of Mullah-Kajar . . 1.75
118 JB,Valley of Forever Night . . 1.75
119 JB,Voice of One Long Gone . 1.75
120 JB,The Hand of Erlik 1.75
121 JB,BMc,Price of Perfection . . 1.75
122 JB,BMc,The City Where Time
   Stood Still 1.75
123 JB,BMc,Horror Beneath the
   Hills 1.75
124 JB,BMc,the Eternity War 1.75
125 JB,BMc,the Witches ofNexxx . 1.75
126 JB,BMc,Blood Red Eye
   of Truth 1.75
127 GK,Snow Haired Woman
   of the Wastes 1.75
128 GK,And Life Sprang Forth
   From These 1.75
129 GK,The Creation Quest 1.75
130 GK,The Quest Ends 1.75
131 GK,The Ring of Rhax 1.75
132 GK,Games of Gharn 1.75
133 GK,The Witch of Widnsor . . . 1.75
134 GK,A Hitch in Time 1.75
135 MS,JRu,The Forest o/t Night . 1.75
136 JB,The River of Death 1.75
137 AA,Titans Gambit 1.75
138 VM,Isle of the Dead 1.75

Conan the Barbarian #84
© Marvel Entertainment Group

139 VM,In the Lair of
   the Damned 1.75
140 JB,Spider Isle 1.75
141 JB,The Web Tightens 1.75
142 JB,The Maze,the Man,
   the Monster 1.75
143 JB,Life Among the Dead 1.75
144 JB,The Blade & the Beast . . . 1.75
145 Son of Cimmeria 1.75
146 JB,Night o/t Three Sisters . . . 1.75
147 JB,Tower of Mitra 1.75
148 JB,The Plague of Forlek 1.75
149 JB,Deathmark 1.75
150 JB,Tower of Flame 1.75
151 JB,Vale of Death 1.50
152 JB,Dark Blade of
   Jergal Zadh 1.50
153 JB,Bird Men of Akah Ma'at . . 1.50
154 JB,the Man-Bats of
   Ur-Xanarrh 1.50
155 JB,SL,The Anger of Conan . . 1.50
156 JB,The Curse 1.50
157 JB,The Wizard 1.50
158 JB,Night of the Wolf 1.50
159 JB,Cauldron of the Doomed . 1.50
160 Veil of Darkness 1.50
161 JB,House of Skulls,A:Fafnir . . 1.50
162 JB,Destroyer in the Flame,
   A:Fafnir 1.50
163 JB,Cavern of the Vines of
   Doom,A:Fafnir 1.50
164 The Jeweled Sword of Tem . 1.50
165 JB,V:Nadine 1.50
166 JB,GI,Blood o/t Titan,A:Fafnir 1.50
167 JB,Creature From Time's
   Dawn,A:Fafnir 1.50
168 JB,Bird Woman & the Beast . 1.50
169 JB,Tomb of the Scarlet Mage 1.50
170 JB,Dominion of the Dead,
   A&D:Fafnir 1.50
171 JB,Barbarian Death Song . . . 1.50
172 JB,Reavers in Borderland . . . 1.50
173 JB,Honor Among Thieves . . . 1.50
174 JB,V:Tetra 1.50
175 JB,V:Spectre ofDeath 1.50
176 JB,Argos Rain 1.50
177 JB,V:Nostume 1.50
178 JB,A:Tetra,Well of Souls 1.50

179 JB,End of all there is,A:Kiev . 1.50	252 ECh 1.50	Ann.#5 JB,W:Conan/Zenobia 2.00
180 JBV:AnitRenrut 1.50	253 ECh,V:Kulan-Goth(X-Men	Ann.#6 GK,King of the
181 JB,V:KingMaddoc II 1.50	Villain) 1.50	Forgotten People 2.00
182 JB,V:King of Shem 1.50	254 ECh,V:Shuma-Gorath (Dr.	Ann.#7 JB,Red Shadows
183 JB,V:Imhotep 1.50	Strange Villain) 1.50	& Black Kraken 1.50
184 JB,V:Madoc 1.50	255 ECh,V:Shuma-Gorath 1.50	Ann.#8 VM,Dark Night of the
185 JB,R:Tetra 1.50	256 ECh,D:Nemedia's King 1.50	White Queen 1.50
186 JB,The Crimson Brotherhood 1.50	257 ECh,V:Queen Vammator 1.50	Ann.#9 . . . . 1.50
187 JB,V:Council of Seven 1.50	258 AA(i),A:Kulan Gath 1.50	Ann.#10 Scorched Earth
188 JB,V:Devourer-Souls 1.50	259 V:Shuma-Gorath 1.50	(Conan #176 x-over) 1.50
189 JB,V:Devourer-Souls 1.50	260 AA(i),V:Queen Vammatar . . . 1.50	Ann.#11 . . . . 1.50
190 JB,Devourer-Souls 1.50	261 V:Cult of the Death Goddess . 1.50	Conan-Barbarian Movie Spec.#1 . 1.25
191 Deliverance 1.50	262 V:The Panther 1.50	Conan-Barbarian Movie Spec.#2 . 1.25
192 JB,V:TheKeeper 1.50	263 V:Malaq 1.50	Conan-Destroyer Movie Spec.#1 . 1.25
193 Devourer-Souls 1.50	264 V:Kralic 1.50	Red Nails Special Ed.BWS 4.00
194 V:Devourer-Souls 1.50	265 V:Karlik 1.50	TPB Conan & Ravagers Out
195 Blood of Ages 1.50	266 Conan the Renegade(adapt) . 1.50	of Time 9.95
196 V:Beast 1.50	267 adaption of Tor 1.50	TPB Conan the Reaver 9.95
197 A:Red Sonja 1.50	268 adaption of Tor 1.50	TPB Conan the Rogue,JB,V:Romm 9.95
198 A:Red Sonja 1.50	269 V:Agohoth,Prince Borin 1.50	TPB Horn of Azroth 9.95
199 O:Kaleb 1.50	270 Devourer of the Dead 1.50	TPB Skull of Set 9.95
200 JB,D.sizeV:Dev-Souls 2.00	271 V:Devourer of Souls 1.50	
201 NKu,GI,Thulsa Doom 1.50	272 V:Devourer 1.50	**CLASSIC CONAN**
202 . . . . 1.50	273 V:Purple Lotus 1.50	**June, 1987**
203 V:Thulsa Doom 1.50		1 BWS,rep. 2.00
204 VS,GI,A:Red Sonja,I:Strakkus 1.50		2 BWS,rep. 2.00
205 A:Red Sonja 1.50		3 BWS,rep. 2.00
206 VS,GI,Heku trilogy,pt.1 . . . . . 1.50		**Becomes:**
207 VS,GI,Heku,pt.2,O:Kote 1.50		**CONAN SAGA**
208 VS,GI,Heku,pt.3 . . . . 1.50		4 rep. 3.00
209 VS,GI,Heku epilogue 1.50		5 rep. 3.00
210 VS,GI,V:Sevante 1.50		6 rep. 3.00
211 VS,GI,V:Sevante 1.50		7 rep. 3.00
212 EC,GI 1.50		8 rep. 3.00
213 V:Ghamud Assassins 1.50		9 rep. 3.00
214 AA 1.50		10 rep. 3.00
215 VS,AA,Conan Enslaved 1.50		11 rep. 2.50
216 V:Blade of Zed 1.50		12 rep. 2.50
217 JLe(c),V:Blade of Zed 1.50		13 rep. 2.50
218 JLe(c),V:Picts 1.50		14 rep.Savage Sword #5 . . . . . . 2.50
219 JLe(c),V:Forgotten Beasts . . 1.50		15 rep.Savage Sword #7 . . . . . . 2.50
220 Conan the Pirate 1.50		16 rep.Savage Sword #12 . . . . . 2.50
221 Conan the Pirate 1.50		17 rep.Savage Sword 2.50
222 AA,DP,Revenge 1.50		18 rep.Savage Sword 2.50
223 AA,Religious Cult 1.50		19 rep.Savage Sword #28 . . . . . 2.50
224 AA,Cannibalism 1.50		20 rep.Savage Sword #25 . . . . . 2.50
225 AA,Conan Blinded 1.50		21 rep.Savage Sword 2.50
226 AA,Quest for Mystic Jewel . . 1.50		22 rep.Giant Size Conan #1&2 . . 2.50
227 AA,Mystic Jewel,pt.2 . . . . . . 1.50		23 rep.Hour of the Dragon 2.50
228 AA,Cannibalism,pt.1 . . . . 1.50		24 rep.Hour of the Dragon 2.50
229 AA,Cannibalism,pt.2 . . . . 1.50		25 rep.Savage Sword 2.50
230 FS,SDr,Citadel,pt.1 . . . . 1.50		26 rep.Savage Sword #11 . . . . . 2.50
231 FS,DP,Citadel,pt.2 . . . . 1.50		27 rep.Savage Sword #15 . . . . . 2.50
232 RLm,Birth of Conan 3.00		28 rep.Savage Sword #16 . . . . . 2.25
233 RLm,DA,B:Conan as youth . 2.00		29 rep.Savage Sword #17 . . . . . 2.25
234 RLm,DA 2.00	274 V:She-Bat 1.50	30 rep.Savage Sword #18 . . . . . 2.25
235 RLm,DA 2.00	275 RTs(s),Last Issue cont. in	31 rep.Savage Sword #19 . . . . . 2.25
236 RLm,DA 2.00	Savage Sword of Conan 5.00	32 rep.Savage Sword #5 . . . . . . 2.25
237 DA,V:Jormma 1.50	G-Size#1 GK,TS,Hour of the	33 rep.Savage Sword #5 . . . . . . 2.25
238 DA,D:Conan 1.50	Dragon, inc.rep.Conan#3,	34 rep.Savage Sword # 2.25
239 Conan Possessed 1.50	I:Belit 8.00	35 rep.Savage Sword #32 . . . . . 2.25
240 Conan Possessed 1.50	G-Size#2 GK,TS,Conan Bound,	36 rep.Savage Sword #12 . . . . . 2.25
241 TM(c),R:RoyThomasScript . 3.50	inc. rep Conan #5 . . . . 5.00	37 rep.Savage Sword #34 . . . . . 2.25
242 JLe(c),A:Red Sonja 2.50	G-Size#3 GK,TS,To Tarantia	38 rep.Conan #94&#95 . . . . 2.25
243 WPo(c),V:Zukala 2.00	& the Tower,inc.rep.Conan#6 . 5.00	39 rep.Conan #96&#97 . . . . 2.25
244 A:Red Sonja,Zula 1.50	G-Size#4,GK,FS,Swords of the	40 rep.Savage Sword #26 . . . . . 2.25
245 A:Red Sonja,V:King	South,inc.rep.Conan #7 . . . . . 5.00	41 rep.Savage Sword #27 . . . . . 2.25
of Vampires 1.50	G-Size#5 rep.Conan #14,#15	42 rep.Savage Sword #40 . . . . . 2.25
246 A:Red Sonja,V:MistMonster . 1.50	& Back-up story #12 . . . . 5.00	43 rep.Savage Sword #41 . . . . . 2.25
247 A:Red Sonja,Zula 1.50	KingSz.#1 rep.Conan #2,#4 . . . 13.00	44 rep.Savage Sword #42 . . . . . 2.25
248 V:Zulu 1.50	Ann.#2 BWS,Phoenix on the Sword	45 rep.Savage Sword #43 . . . . . 2.25
249 A:Red Sonja,Zula 1.50	A:Thoth-Amon 4.00	46 rep.Savage Sword #15 . . . . . 2.25
250 A:RedSonja,Zula,V:Zug	Ann.#3 JB,HC,Mountain of	47 rep.Savage Sword #22 . . . . . 2.25
double size. 2.00	the Moon God, B.U.Kull story . 2.00	48 rep.Savage Sword #23 . . . . . 2.25
251 Cimmeria,V:Shumu Gorath . 1.50	Ann.#4 JB,Return of the	
	Conqueror,A:Zenobia 2.00	

Conan The Barbarian Movie Special #2
© Marvel Entertainment Group

49 rep.Sav.Sword Super Spec#2 . 2.25
50 rep.Conan #58 . . . . 2.25
51 rep.Conan #59&#60 . . . . 2.25
52 rep.Conan #61 . . . . 2.25
53 thru 63 rep.Savage Sword . @2.25
64 thru 94 rep. . . . . @2.25
95 D:Belit 2.25
96 . . . . 2.25
97 Red Sonja rep. 2.25
98 rep. #106–#108 . . . . 2.25

Conan Classics #5
© Marvel Entertainment Group

CONAN CLASSICS
1994–95
1 rep. Conan #1 . . . . 2.00
2 rep. Conan #2 . . . . 2.00
3 rep. Conan #3 . . . . 1.75
4 thru 8 rep. Conan #4–#8 . . . . 1.50
9 Garden of Fear 1.50
10 V:Anu 1.50
11 New Sword Manuever 1.50

CONAN/RUNE
1995
1 BWS,Conan Vs. Rune 3.50

CONAN
1 CCt, ... 2.00
2 CCt,V:Sorcerer 2.00
3 (of 3) CCt. 2.00

CONAN:
RIVER OF BLOOD
April 1998
1 (of 3) Valeria, vs. giant crocs . . 2.50
2 Caught in the middle of a war . . 2.50
3 Lord of the Crocodiles, concl. . 2.50

CONAN THE BARBARIAN
VS. THE LORD OF
THE SPIDERS
Jan., 1998
1 (of 3) RTs,V:Harpagus 2.50
2 RTs, ... 2.50
3 RTs,V:Harpagus 2.50

CONAN:
THE RETURN OF STYRM
July 1998
1 (of 3) V:Mecora 2.50
2 (of 3) V:Mecora 3.00

CONAN: THE USURPER
Oct., 1997
1 (of 3) CDi,KJ,Conan attacks
Cimmeria? 2.50
2 CDi,KJ, ... 2.50
3 CDi,KJ, concl. 2.50

KING CONAN
March, 1980
1 JB/ECh,I:Conn,V:Thoth-Amon . 3.00
2 JB,Black Sphinx of Nebthu . . . 2.50
3 JB,Dragon Wings Over
Zembabwei 2.50
4 JB,V:Thoth-Amon 2.50
5 JB,The Sorcerer in the Realm
of Madness 2.50
6 JB,The Lady's Name Is..Trouble 2.50
7 PS,JB 2.75
8 A:Queen Reclaimed 2.75
9 JB,V:Medusa Monster 2.25
10 V:Sea Monster 2.25
11 V:Giant Totem Monster 1.75
12 V:Monster 1.75
13 V:Monster 1.75
14 V:Demon 1.75
15 V:Sea Monster 1.75
16 Conan Into Battle 1.75
17 A:Conn 1.75
18 King of the Freaks? 1.75
19 MK(c),Skull & X-Bones cover . 1.75
Becomes:
CONAN THE KING
20 MS,The Prince is Dead 2.00
21 MS,Shadows 2.00
22 GI/MS,The Black Dragons,Prince
Conan II back-up story begins . 2.00
23 MS/GI,Ordeal 2.00
24 GI/MS,Fragments:AWitch'sTale 2.00
25 MS/GI,Daggers 2.00
26 MS/GI,PrinceConanII B.U.ends 2.00
27 MS/GI,A Death in Stygia 2.00
28 MS/GI,Call of the Wild,
A:Red Sonja 2.00
29 MS,The Sleeping Lion 2.00
30 GI,Revenge on the Black River 2.00
31 GI,Force of Arms 2.00
32 GI,Juggernaut 2.00
33 . . . . 2.00
34 . . . . 2.00
35 . . . . 2.00
36 . . . . 2.00
37 AW,Sack of Belverus 2.00
38 MM,A:Taurus,Leora 2.00
39 The Tower 2.00
40 . . . . 2.00
41 V:Leora 2.00
42 Thee Armada,A:Conn 2.00
43 . . . . 2.00
44 . . . . 2.00
45 V:Caliastros 2.00
46 V:Caliastros 2.00
47 TD,V:Caliastros 2.00
48 . . . . 2.00
49 . . . . 2.00
50 GI,50th Anniversary issue . . . 2.00
51 GI,Death of Prince Conn 2.00
52 GI,Prince Conn story contd . . 2.00

53 GI,A:Thoth-Amon 2.00
54 GI,V:Thoth-Amon 2.00
55 GI,Sorcerers Ring,final issue . . 2.00

CONAN THE SAVAGE
1995–96
(Black & White Magazine)
1 New Series 2.95
2 CDi,Conan a gladiator 2.95
3 V:Monster 2.95
4 CDi,Conan vs. Rune 2.95
5 MBn,VMk,Ice age tale 2.95
6 Bros.Hildebrandt(c),V:FallenIdol 2.95
7 CDi,F:Iron Maidens 2.95
8 & 9 . . . . @2.95
10 JB story, 48pg. 2.95

CONEHEADS
1994
1 Based Saturday Night Live . . . 2.00
2 There Goes the Neighborhood . 2.00
3 In Paris 1.75

CONSPIRACY
Dec., 1997
1 (of 2) DAn,Were the origins of
Marvel's superheroes really a
conspiracy, not an accident? . . 3.00
2 DAn,concl. 3.00

CONTEST OF CHAMPIONS
June, 1982
1 JR2,Grandmaster vs. Mistress
Death, A:Alpha Flight 7.00
2 JR2,Grandmaster vs. Mistress
Death, A:X-Men 5.00
3 JR2,D:Grandmaster, Rebirth
Collector, A:X-Men 5.00

COPS: THE JOB
1992
1 MGo(c),V:Serial killer 1.50
2 MGo(c) 1.25
3 MGo(c),V:Eviscerator 1.25
4 MGo(c),D:Eviscerator,Nick . . . 1.25

COSMIC POWERS
1994
1 RMz(s),RLm,JP,F:Thanos . . . 2.75
2 RMz(s),JMr,F:Terrax 2.75
3 RMz(s),F:Jack of Hearts 2.75
4 RMz(s),RLm,F:Legacy 2.75
5 RMz(s),F&O:Morg 2.75
6 RMz(s),F&O:Tyrant 2.75

COSMIC POWERS
UNLIMITED
1995–96
1 Surfer vs. Thanos 3.95
2 Jack of Hearts vs. Jakar 3.95
3 GWt,JB,F:Lunatik,64pg. 3.95
4 GWt,SEa,cont.StarMasters#3 . 3.95
5 GWt,SEa,R:Captain Universe . 3.95

COUNT DUCKULA
Star Nov., 1988
1 O:CountDuckula,B:DangerMouse 1.25
2 A:Danger Mouse 1.00
3 thru 15 . . . . @1.00

COWBOY ACTION
See: WESTERN THRILLERS

COWBOY ROMANCES
Oct., 1949
1 Ph(c),Outlaw and the Lady . 150.00
2 Ph(c),William Holden/Mona
  Freeman,Streets of Laredo . 100.00
3 Phc,Romance in
  Roaring Valley 75.00
Becomes:
YOUNG MEN
4 A Kid Names Shorty 125.00
5 Jaws of Death 75.00
6 Man-Size 75.00
7 The Last Laugh 75.00
8 Adventure stories continued . . 75.00
9 Draft Dodging story 75.00
10 US Draft Story 75.00
11 Adventure stories continued . 50.00
12 B:On the Battlefield,
  inc.Spearhead 50.00
13 RH,Break-through 50.00
14 RH,Fox Hole 50.00
15 Battlefield stories cont, ... 50.00
16 Sniper Patrol 50.00
17 Battlefield stories cont, ... 50.00
18 BEv,Warlord 50.00
19 BEv 50.00
20 BEv,E:On the Battlefield . . . 50.00
21 B:Flash Foster and his High
  Gear Hot Shots 50.00
22 Screaming Tires 50.00
23 E:Flash Foster and his High
  Gear Hot Shots 50.00
24 BEv,B:Capt. America,Human
  Torch,Sub-Mariner,O:Capt.
  America,Red Skull 1,200.00
25 BEv,JR, Human Torch,Capt.
  America,Sub-Mariner 750.00
26 BEv,Human Torch, Capt.
  America,Sub Mariner 750.00
27 Bev, Human Torch/Toro
  V:Hypnotist 750.00
28 E:Human Torch, Capt.America,
  Sub Mariner,June, 1954 . . . 750.00

COWGIRL ROMANCES
See: DARING MYSTERY

COYOTE
Epic June, 1983
1 SL, ... 1.50
2 SL 1.50
3 BG 1.50
4 SL 1.50
5 SL 1.50
6 SL 1.50
7 SL,SD 1.50
8 SL 1.50
9 SL,SD 1.50
10 SL 1.50
11 FS,1st TM art,O:Slash 4.00
12 TM 2.00
13 TM 2.00
14 FS,TM,A:Badger 2.00
15 SL 1.50
16 SL,A:Reagan,Gorbachev . . . 1.50

CRASH RYAN
Epic Oct., 1984
1 War Story 1.75
2 Doomsday 1.50
3 Fortress Japan 1.50
4 Jan., 1985 . . . . 1.50

CRAZY
Atlas Dec., 1953
1 BEv,satire, Frank N.Steins
  Castle 175.00
2 BEv,Beast from 1000 Fathoms150.00
3 Bev,Madame Knockwurst's
  Whacks Museum 125.00
4 BEv,I Love Lucy satire 125.00
5 BEv,Censorship satire 125.00
6 BEv,satire 125.00
7 BEv,satire,July, 1954 . . . . . 125.00

CRAZY
Feb., 1973–June 1973
1 Not Brand Echh reps,
  Forbushman 20.00
2 Big,Batty Love & Hisses issue 15.00
3 Stupor-Man,A:FantasticalFour 15.00

CREATURES ON THE LOOSE
See: TOWER OF SHADOWS

CRIME CAN'T WIN
See: KRAZY COMICS

CRIME FIGHTERS
April, 1948—Nov., 1949
1 Police Stories 175.00
2 Jewelry robbery 75.00
3 The Nine who were Doomed . 75.00
4 Human Beast at Bay 50.00
5 V:Gangsters 50.00
6 Pickpockets 50.00
7 True Cases, Crime Can't Win 50.00
8 True Cases, Crime Can't Win 50.00
9 Ph(c),It Happened at Night . . 50.00
10 Ph(c),Killer at Large 50.00
Atlas Sept., 1954–Jan., 1955
11 V:Gangsters 75.00
12 V:Gangsters 75.00
13 Clay Pidgeon 75.00

CRITICAL MASS
Epic Jan.–July, 1990
1 KS,GM,BSzF:ShadowlineSaga . 4.95
2 . . . . 4.95
3 GM,SDr,JRy 4.95
4 . . . . 4.95
5 JZ 4.95
6 . . . . 4.95
7 July, 1990 . . . . 4.95

CROSSOVER CLASSICS
TPB Marvel and D.C. GP(c),reprints
both Spider-Man/Superman,the
Batman/Hulk and the X-Men/New
Teen Titans Battles 18.00

CRYPT OF SHADOWS
Jan., 1973
1 BW,RH,Midnight on Black
  Mountain 20.00
2 Monster at the Door 15.00
3 Dead Man's Hand 15.00
4 CI,Secret in the Vault 15.00
5 JM,The Graveyard Ghoul . . . 15.00
6 BEv,Don't Bury Me Deep . . . 15.00
7 JSt,The Haunting of Bluebeard 15.00
8 How Deep my Grave 15.00
9 Beyond Death 15.00
10 A Scream in the Dark 15.00

11 The Ghouls in my Grave 10.00
12 Behind the Locked Door 10.00
13 SD,Back From the Dead 10.00
14 The Thing that Creeps 10.00
15 My Coffin is Crowded 10.00
16 . . . . 10.00
17 In the Hands of Shandu 10.00
18 SD,Face of Fear 10.00
19 SD,Colossus that Challenged
  the World 10.00
20 A Monster walks Among Us . 10.00
21 SD,Death Will Be Mine,
  Nov. 1975 . . . . 10.00

CUPID
Dec., 1949
1 Ph(c),Cora Dod's Amazing
  Decision 100.00
2 Ph(c),Betty Page, Mar. 1950 200.00

CURSE OF THE WEIRD
1993–94
1 thru 4 SD,rep. 50's Sci-Fi . . . 1.50

CUTTING EDGE
1995
1 WML,F:Hulk,Ghosts of the
  Future tie-in 2.95

CYBERSPACE 3000
1 A:Dark Angel,Galactus,V:Badoon,
  Glow in the dark(c) 3.00
2 SeT,A:Galactus,Dark Angel . 2.00
3 SeT,A:Galactus,Keeper 2.00
4 SeT,A:Keeper 2.00
5 SeT,A:Keeper 2.00
6 SeT,A:Warlock 2.00
7 SeT,I:Gamble 2.00
8 SeT,A:Warlock 2.00
9 SeT 1.75
10 SeT 1.75
11 SeT 1.75

DAILY BUGLE
B&W 1996
1 (of 3) KIK,GA 2.50

Dakota North #3
© Marvel Entertainment Group

2 KIK,GA	2.50
3 KIK,GA	2.50

DAKOTA NORTH
1986
1 (Now in Cage)	1.50
2	1.25
3	1.25
4	1.25
5 Feb., 1987	1.25

DAMAGE CONTROL
May, 1989
1 EC/BWi;A:Spider-Man	2.50
2 EC/BWi;A:Fant.Four	2.00
3 EC/BWi;A:Iron Man	2.00
4 EC/BWi;A:X-Men	2.00

[2nd Series] 1989–90
1 EC,A:Capt.America&Thor	3.00
2 EC,A:Punisher	2.50
3 EC	2.00
4 EC,Punisher	2.00

[3rd Series]1991
1 Clean-up Crew Returns	1.50
2 A:Hulk,New Warriors	1.50
3 A:Avengers W.C.,Wonder Man, Silver Surfer	1.50
4 A:SilverSurfer & others	1.50

DANCES WITH DEMONS
Frontier 1993
1 CAd	2.95
2 CAd,V:Manitou	1.95
3 CAd,V:Manitou	1.95
4 CAd,last issue	1.95
5 Okay, there's more!	1.95
6	1.95

DAREDEVIL
April, 1964
1 B:StL(s),JK(c),BEv,I&O:Daredevil, I:Karen Page,Foggy Nelson	2,000.00
2 JK(c),JO,V:Electro	550.00
3 JK(c),JO,I&O:The Owl	375.00
4 JK(c),JO,I&O:Killgrave	325.00
5 JK(c),WW,V:Masked Matador	225.00
6 WW,I&O Original Mr. Fear	150.00
7 WW,I:Red Costume,V:Namor	275.00
8 WW,I&O:Stiltman	150.00
9 WW(i),Killers Castle	150.00
10 WW(i),V:Catman	150.00
11 WW(i),R:Cat	125.00
12 JK,JR,2nd A:Kazar	125.00
13 JK,JR,O:Ka-Zar	75.00
14 JR,If This Be Justice	75.00
15 JR,A:Ox	75.00
16 JR,A:Spider-Man, I:Masked Marauder	125.00
17 JR,A:Spider-Man	100.00
18 DON(s),JR,I:Gladiator	60.00
19 JR,V:Gladiator	60.00
20 JR(c),GC,V:Owl	50.00
21 GC,BEv,V:Owl	40.00
22 GC,V:Tri-man	40.00
23 GC,V:Tri-man	40.00
24 GC,A:Ka-Zar	40.00
25 GC,V:Leapfrog	40.00
26 GC,V:Stiltman	40.00
27 GC,Spider-Man	40.00
28 GC,V:Aliens	40.00
29 GC,V:The Boss	40.00
30 BEv(c),GC,A:Thor	40.00
31 GC,V:Cobra	30.00

32 GC,V:Cobra	30.00
33 GC,V:Beetle	30.00
34 BEv(c),GC,O:Beetle	30.00
35 BEv(c),GC,A:Susan Richards	30.00
36 GC,A:FF	30.00
37 GC,V:Dr.Doom	30.00
38 GC,A:FF	30.00
39 GC,GT,V:Unholy Three	30.00
40 GC,V:Unholy Three	30.00
41 GC,D:Mike Murdock	25.00
42 GC,DA,I:Jester	25.00
43 JK(c),GC,A:Capt.America	24.00
44 JSo(c),GC,V:Jester	20.00
45 GC,V:Jester	20.00
46 GC,V:Jester	20.00
47 GC,'Brother Take My Hand'	20.00
48 GC,V:Stiltman	20.00
49 GC,V:Robot,I:Starr Saxon	20.00
50 JR(c),BWS,JCr,V:Robot	25.00
51 B:RTs(s),BWS,V:Robot	25.00
52 BWS,JCr,A:Black Panther	25.00
53 GC,O:Daredevil	27.00
54 GC,V:Mr.Fear,A:Spidey	15.00
55 GC,V:Mr.Fear	12.00

Daredevil #24
© Marvel Entertainment Group

56 GC,V:Death Head	12.00
57 GC,V:Death Head	12.00
58 GC,V:Stunt Master	11.00
59 GC,V:Torpedo	11.00
60 GC,V:Crime Wave	11.00
61 GC,V:Cobra	11.00
62 GC,O:Night Hawk	11.00
63 GC,V:Gladiator	11.00
64 GC,A:Stuntmaster	11.00
65 GC,V:BrotherBrimstone	11.00
66 GC,V:BrotherBrimstone	11.00
67 BEv(c),GC,Stiltman	11.00
68 AC,V:Kragg Blackmailer, a:Bl.Panther,DD'sID Rev	11.00
69 E:RTs(s),GC,V:Thunderbolts, A:Bl.Panther(DD's ID Rev)	11.00
70 GC,V:Terrorists	11.00
71 RTs(s),GC,V:Terrorists	16.00
72 GyC(s),GC,Tagak,V:Quother	10.00
73 GC,V:Zodiac	10.00
74 B:GyC(s),GC,I:Smasher	10.00
75 GC,V:El Condor	10.00
76 GC,TP,V:El Condor	10.00

77 GC,TP,V:Manbull	10.00
78 GC,TP,V:Manbull	10.00
79 GC,TP,V:Manbull	10.00
80 GK(c),GC,TP,V:Owl	10.00
81 GK(c),GC,JA,A:Black Widow	22.00
82 GK(c),GC,JA,V:Scorpion	10.00
83 JR(c),BWS,BEv,V:Mr.Hyde	12.00
84 GK(c),GC,Assassin	10.00
85 GK(c),GC,A:Black Widow	10.00
86 GC,TP,V:Ox	10.00
87 GC,TP,V:Electro	10.00
88 GK(c),GC,TP,O:Black Widow	10.00
89 GC,TP,A:Black Widow	10.00
90 E:StL(s),GK(c),GC,TP,V:Ox	10.00
91 GK(c),GC,TP,I:Mr. Fear III	10.00
92 GK(c),GC,TP,A:BlackPanther	11.00
93 GK(c),GC,TP,A:Black Widow	10.00
94 GK(c),GC,TP,V:Damon Dran	10.00
95 GK(c),GC,TP,V:Manbull	10.00
96 GK(c),GC,ECh,V:Manbull	10.00
97 GK(c),V:Dark Messiah	10.00
98 E:GyC(s),GC,ECh,V:Dark Messiah	10.00
99 B:SvG(s),JR(c),V:Hawkeye	10.00
100 GC,V:Angar the Screamer	25.00
101 RB,A:Angar the Screamer	8.00
102 A:Black Widow	7.00
103 JR(c),DH,A:Spider-Man	7.00
104 GK(c),DH,V:Kraven	7.00
105 DH,JSn,DP,C:Thanos	15.00
106 JR(c),DH,A:Black Widow	7.00
107 JSn(c),JB(i),A:Capt.Marvel	7.00
108 K&R(c),PG(i),V:Beetle	7.00
109 GK(c),DH(i),V:Beetle	7.00
110 JR(c),GC,A:Thing,O:Nekra	7.00
111 JM(i),I:Silver Samurai	8.50
112 GK(c),GC,V:Mandrill	7.00
113 JR(c),V:Gladiator	7.00
114 GK(c),I:Death Stalker	7.00
115 V:Death Stalker	6.00
116 GK(c),GC,V:Owl	6.00
117 E:SvG(s),K&R(c),V:Owl	6.00
118 JR(c),DH,I:Blackwing	6.00
119 GK(c),DH(i),V:Crusher	6.00
120 GK(c),V:Hydra,I:El Jaguar	6.00
121 GK(c),A:Shield	5.00
122 GK(c),V:Blackwing	5.00
123 V:Silvermane,I:Jackhammer	5.00
124 B:MWn(s),GK(c),GC,KJ, I:Copperhead	5.00
125 GK(c),KJ(i),V:Copperhead	5.00
126 GK(c),KJ(i),D: 2nd Torpedo	5.00
127 GK(c),KJ(i),V:3rd Torpedo	5.00
128 GK(c),KJ(i),V:Death Stalker	5.00
129 KJ(i),V:Man Bull	5.00
130 KJ(i),V:Brother Zed	5.00
131 KJ(i),I&O:2nd Bullseye	20.00
132 KJ(i),V:Bullseye	5.00
133 JM(i),GK(c),V:Jester	4.00
134 JM(i),V:Chamelon	4.00
135 JM(i),V:Jester	4.00
136 JB,JM,V:Jester	4.00
137 JB,V:Jester	4.00
138 JBy,A:Ghost Rider	7.00
139 SB,V:A Bomber	4.00
140 SB,V:Gladiator	4.00
141 GC,Bullseye	4.00
142 GC,V:Bullseye	4.00
143 E:MWn(s),GC,V:Cobra	4.00
144 GT,V:Manbull	4.00
145 GT,V:Owl	4.00
146 GC,V:Bullseye	5.00
147 GC,V:Killgrave	3.00
148 GC,V:Deathstalker	3.00
149 KI,V:Smasher	3.00

All comics prices listed are for *Near Mint* condition.

150 GC,KJ,I:Paladin 4.00	224 DM,V:Sunturion 2.50	267 JR2,AW,V:Bullet 2.50
151 GC,Daredevil Unmasked 3.00	225 DM,V:Vulture 2.50	268 JR2,AW,V:TheMob 2.50
152 KJ,V:Paladin 3.00	226 FM(plot),V:Gladiator 3.00	269 JR2,AW,V:Pyro&Blob 2.50
153 GC,V:Cobra 3.00	227 FM,Kingpin,Kar.Page 6.00	270 JR2,AW,A:Spider-Man,
154 GC,V:Mr. Hyde 3.00	228 FM,DM,V:Kingpin 4.00	I:Blackheart 3.00
155 V:Avengers 3.00	229 FM,Kingpin,Turk 4.00	271 JR2,AW,I:Number9 . . . . 2.50
156 GC,V:Death Stalker 3.00	230 R:Matt's Mother 4.00	272 JR2,AW,I:Shotgun 3.00
157 GC,V:Death Stalker 3.00	231 FM,DM,V:Kingpin 4.00	273 JR2,AW,V:Shotgun 2.50
158 FM,V:Death Stalker 40.00	232 FM,V:Kingpin,Nuke 4.00	274 JR2,AW,V:Inhumans 2.50
159 FM,V:Bullseye 22.00	233 FM,Kingpin,Nuke,Capt.Am. . . 4.00	275 JR2,AW,ActsOfVen.,V:Ultron . 2.50
160 FM,Bullseye 10.00	234 SD,KJ,V:Madcap 2.00	276 JR2,AW,ActsOfVen.,V:Ultorn . 2.50
161 FM,V:Bullseye 10.00	235 SD,KJ,V:Mr. Hyde 2.00	277 RL,AW,Vivian's Story 2.00
162 SD,JRu,'Requiem' 3.50	236 BWS,A:Black Widow 4.00	278 JR2,AW,V:Blackheart,
163 FM,V:Hulk,I:Ben Urich 10.00	237 AW(i),V:Klaw 2.00	A:Inhumans 2.50
164 FM,KJ,A:Avengers 10.00	238 SB,SL,AAd(c)V:Sabretooth . . 6.00	279 JR2,AW,V:Mephisto,
165 FM,KJ,V:Dr.Octopus 10.00	239 AAd(c),AW,GI(i),V:Rotgut . . . 2.00	A:Inhumans 2.50
166 FM,KJ,V:Gladiator 10.00	240 AW,V:Rotgut 2.00	280 JR2,AW,V:Mephisto,
167 FM,KJ,V:Mauler 10.00	241 MZ(c),TM,V:Trixter 3.00	A:Inhumans 2.50
168 FM,KJ,I&O:Elektra 45.00	242 KP,V:Caviar Killer 2.00	281 JR2,AW,V:Mephisto,
169 FM,KJ,V:Bullseye 12.00	243 AW,V:Nameless One 2.00	A:Inhumans 2.50
170 FM,KJ,V:Bullseye 12.00	244 TD(i),V:Nameless One 2.00	282 JR2,AW,V:Mephisto,
171 FM,KJ,V:Kingpin 7.00	245 TD(i),A:Black Panther 2.00	A:Silver Surfer, Inhumans 2.50
172 FM,KJ,V:Bullseye 7.00	246 TD(i),V:Chance 2.00	283 MBa,AW,A:Captain America . . 2.00
173 FM,KJ,V:Gliadator 7.00	247 KG,A:Black Widow 2.00	284 LW,AW,R:Bullseye 2.00
174 FM,KJ,A:Gladiator 7.00		285 LW,AW,B:Bullseye
175 FM,KJ,A:Elektra,V:Hand . . . 8.00		become DD#1 . . . . 2.00
176 FM,KJ,A:Elektra 7.00		286 LW,AW,GCa,Fake
177 FM,KJ,A:Stick 8.00		Daredevil #2 . . . . 2.00
178 FM,KJ,A:PowerMan&I.Fist . . . 7.00		287 LW,AW,Fake Daredevil #3 . . 2.00
179 FM,KJ,V:Elektra 7.00		288 LW,AW,A:Kingpin 2.00
180 FM,KJ,V:Kingpin 7.00		289 LW,AW,A:Kingpin 2.00
181 FM,KJ,V:Bullseye,D:Elektra,		290 LW,AW,E:Fake Daredevil . . . 2.00
A:Punisher 12.00		291 LW,AW,V:Bullet 2.00
182 FM,KJ,A:Punisher 7.00		292 LW,A:Punisher,V:Tombstone . 2.00
183 FM,KJ,V:PunisherDrug 7.00		293 LW,A:Punisher,V:Tombstone . 2.00
184 FM,KJ,V:PunisherDrug 7.00		294 LW,V:The Hand 1.75
185 FM,KJ,V:King Pin 5.00		295 LW,V:The Hand,
186 FM,KJ,V:Stiltman 5.00		A:GhostRider. 1.75
187 FM,KJ,A:Stick 5.00		296 LW,AW,V:The Hand 1.75
188 FM,KJ,A:Black Widow 5.00		297 B:DGC(s),LW,AW,B:Last Rites,
189 FM,KJ,A:Stick,A:BlackWidow . 5.00		V:Typhoid Mary,A:Kingpin 3.50
190 FM,KJ,R:Elektra 6.00		298 LW,AW,A:Nick Fury,Kingpin . 2.50
191 FM,TA,A:Bullseye 5.00		299 LW,AW,A:Nick Fury,Kingpin . 2.50
192 KJ,V:Kingpin 3.00		300 LW,AW,E:Last Rites, ... 4.00
193 KJ,Betsy 3.00		301 V:The Owl 1.75
194 KJ,V:Kingpin 3.00		302 V:The Owl 1.75
195 KJ,Tarkington Brown 3.00		303 V:The Owl 1.75
196 KJ,A:Wolverine 9.00		304 AW,Non-action issue 1.75
197 V:Bullseye 2.50		305 AW,A:Spider-Man 1.75
198 V:Dark Wind 2.50		306 AW,A:Spider-Man 1.75
199 V:Dark Wind 2.50		307 1st SMc DD,Dead Man's Hand #1,
200 JBy(c),V:Bullseye 3.00	*Daredevil #100*	A:Nomad 3.00
201 JBy(c),A:Black Widow 2.50	© *Marvel Entertainment Group*	308 SMc,Dead Man's Hand #5,
202 I:Micah Synn 2.50		A:Punisher,V:Silvermane 2.00
203 JBy(c),I:Trump 2.50	248 RL,AW,A:Wolverine,	309 SMc,Dead Man's Hand#7,
204 BSz(c),V:Micah Synn 2.50	V:Bushwhacker 6.00	A:Nomad,Punisher 2.00
205 I:Gael 2.50	249 RL,AW,V:Wolverine,	310 SMc,Inf.War,V:Calipso 2.00
206 V:Micah Synn 2.50	Bushwhacker 6.00	311 SMc,V:Calypso 2.00
207 BSz(c),A:Black Widow 2.50	250 JR2,AW,I:Bullet 3.50	312 Firefighting issue 1.75
208 Harlan Ellison 3.00	251 JR2,AW,V:Bullet 3.00	313 SMc,V:Pyromaniac 2.00
209 Harlan Ellison 3.00	252 JR2,AW,Fall o/Mutants 4.50	314 SMc,V:Mr.Fear,I:Shock 2.00
210 DM,V:Micah Synn 2.50	253 JR2,AW,V:Kingpin 3.00	315 SMc,V:Mr.Fear 2.00
211 DM,V:Micah Synn 2.50	254 JR2,AW,I:Typhoid Mary . . . 10.00	316 Goes Underground 1.75
212 DM,V:Micah Synn 2.50	255 JR2,AW,A:Kingpin,TMary . . . 5.00	317 SMc,Comedy Issue 2.00
213 DM,V:Micah Synn 2.50	256 JR2,AW,V:Kingpin,TMary . . . 5.00	318 SMc,V:Taskmaster 2.00
214 DM,V:Micah Synn 2.50	257 JR2,AW,A:Punisher 5.00	319 SMc,Fall from Grace Prologue,
215 DM,A:Two-Gun Kid 2.50	258 RLm,V:Bengal 3.50	A:Silver Sable,Garrett,Hand . . 5.00
216 DM,V:Gael 2.50	259 JR2,AW,V:TyphoidMary 4.00	319a 2nd Printing 2.00
217 BS(c),V:Gael 2.50	260 JR2,AW,V:T.Mary,K.pin 4.00	320 SMc,B:Fall from Grace,
218 KP,V:Jester 2.50	261 JR2,AW,HumanTorch 2.50	V:Crippler,S.Sable,A:Stone . . 5.00
219 FM,JB 3.00	262 JR2,AW,Inferno 2.50	321 SMc,N:Daredevil,A:Venom,
220 DM,D:Heather Glenn 2.50	263 JR2,AW,Inferno 2.50	Garret, V:Hellspawn,Glow
221 DM,Venice 2.50	264 SD,AW,MM,V:The Owl 2.50	in the Dark(c) 3.00
222 DM,A:Black Widow 2.50	265 JR2,AW,Inferno 2.50	321a Newsstand Ed. 3.00
223 DM,Secret Wars II 2.50	266 JR2,AW,V:Mephisto 2.50	322 SMc,A:Venom,Garret,Siege . . 3.00

MARVEL

323 SMc,V:Venom,A:Siege,Garret,
   I:Erynys 2.50
324 SMc,A:Garret,R:Elektra,
   A:Stone, Morbius 2.50
325 SMc,E:Fall from Grace, A:Garret,
   Siege,Elektra,Morbius,V:Hand,
   D:Hellspawn,Double size 3.00
326 SMc,B:Tree of Knowledge,
   I:Killobyte,A:Capt.America 2.00
327 E:DGC(s),SMc,A:Capt.Amer. . 2.00
328 GtW(s),V:Wirehead,A:Captain
   America,S.Sable,Wild Pack . . 1.75
329 B:DGC(s),SMc,A:Captain
   America, S.Sable,Iron Fist 1.75
330 SMc,A:Gambit 1.75
331 SMc,A:Captain America,
   VLHydra 1.75
332 A:Captain America,Gambit . . 1.75
333 TGb,GWt 1.75
334 TGb,GWt 1.75
335 . . . . 1.75
336 . . . . 1.50
337 V:Kingpin,A:Blackwulf 1.50
338 Wages of Sin,pt.1 . . . . 1.50

Daredevil #181
© Marvel Entertainment Group

339 Wages of Sin,pt.2 . . . . 1.50
340 R:Kingpin 1.50
341 Kingpin 1.50
342 DGc,KP,V:Kingpin 1.50
343 Without Costume 1.50
344 Identity Crisis,pt.1 . . . . 1.95
345 Identity Crisis,pt.2 . . . . 1.95
346 V:Sir 1.95
347 V:mystery man 1.95
348 In NY City 1.95
349 Retreats to the Chaste 1.95
350 Double size 2.95
351 . . . . 1.95
352 Return of Matt Murdock 1.95
353 KK,CNr,A:Mr. Hyde 1.95
354 KK,CNr,A:Spider-Man 1.50
355 KK,CNr,A:Pyro 1.50
356 KK,CNr, ... 1.50
357 KK,CNr, ... 1.50
358 KK,CNr,MRy,A:Mysterio 1.50
359 KK,CNr,A:Absorbing Man . . 1.50
360 KK,CNr,MRy,V:Onslaught . . . 1.50
361 KK,CNr,MRy,A:Black Widow . 1.50
362 KK,CNr,Romance 2.00

363 KK,GC,CaS,V:Insomnia 2.00
364 KK,CNr,MRy,V:Insomnia 2.00
365 CNr,MRy,V:Mr. Fear,
   A:Molten Man 2.00
366 GC,V:Gladiator 2.00
367 GC,V:Gladiator, concl. 2.00
368 GC,A:Black Widow and Omega
   Red 2.00
369 AOI,V:Soviet Super Soldiers . 2.00
370 GC,Black Widow, concl. 2.00
371 AOI,Matt Murdock & Karen
   Page's relationship 2.00
372 AOI,Killers after Karen Page . 2.00
373 AOI,V:The 3 . . . . 2.00
374 AOI,V:Mr. Fear 2.00
375 AOI,RL,V:Mr. Fear,double size 3.00
376 SLo,CHm,Daredevil deep
   undercover 2.00
377 SLo,TMo,SHa,Flying Blind,pt.2 2.00
378 SLo,TMo,SHa,Flying Blind,pt.3 2.00
379 SLo,CHm,Flying Blind,concl. . 2.00
380 DGC,LW,RbC, V:Bullseye,Bush-
   wacker,Kingpin, double size . 3.00
Minus 1 Spec., GC, flashback . . . 1.95
Ann.#1 GC 30.00
Ann.#2 reprints 8.00
Ann.#3 reprints 8.00
Ann.#4 (1976)GT,A:Black
   Panther,Namor 6.00
Ann.#5 (1989)MBa,JLe,JR2,KJ,
   WPo,AM,Atlantis Attacks,
   A:Spider-Man 5.00
Ann.#6 TS,Lifeform#2,A:Typhoid
   Mary 2.75
Ann.#7 JG,JBr,Von Strucker
   Gambit,pt.1,A:Nick Fury 2.50
Ann.#8 Sys.Bytes#2,A:Deathlok . 2.75
Ann.#9 MPa,I:Devourer,w/card,tie-in
   to "Fall From Grace" 5.00
Ann.#10 I:Ghostmaker,A:Shang
   Chi, Elektra 3.25
G-Size #1 GK(c),reprints 12.00
TPB Born Again,rep.#227-#233 . 10.95
TPB Fall of the Kingpin,
   rep.#297-300 . . . . 15.95
TPB Gangwar,Reprints
   #169-#172,#180 . . . . 12.95
TPB Marked for Death,reps#159-
   161,163,164 . . . . 9.95
Daredevil/Punisher:Child's Play
   reprints#182-#184 . . . . 7.00

DAREDEVIL/BATMAN
1997
Spec. DGC,SMc, 48pg 6.00

DAREDEVIL/
DEADPOOL '97
Spec, BCh, JHo, Two annuals in
   one, 48pg 5.00

DAREDEVIL/SHI
SHI/DAREDEVIL
Marvel/Crusade 1996
1 (Daredevil/Shi) TSg,AW,
   x-over,pt.1 . . . . 2.95
1 (Shi/Daredevil)x-over, pt.2 . . . . 2.95

DAREDEVIL: THE MAN
WITHOUT FEAR
1993–94
1 B:FM(s),JR2,AW,O:Daredevil,
   A:Stick,D:Daredevil's Father . . 7.00

2 JR2,AW,A:Stick,Stone,Elektra . 6.00
3 JR2,AW,A:Elektra,Kingpin 5.00
4 JR2,AW,A:Kingpin,I:Mickey . . . 5.00
5 JR2,AW,A:Mickey,Last Issue . . 5.00
TPB rep.#1#5 . . . . 15.95

DARING MYSTERY
COMICS
Timely Jan., 1940
1 ASh(c),JSm,O:Fiery Mask,
   A:Monako John Steele,Doc Doyle,
   Flash FosterBarney Mullen,
   Sea Rover, Bondage (c) . 17,500.00
2 ASh(c),JSm,O:Phantom Bullet
   A:Zephyr Jones & K4,Laughing
   Mask Mr.E,B:Trojak 6,500.00
3 ASh(c),JSm,A:Phantom
   Reporter,Marvex,Breeze
   Barton, B:Purple Mask . . . 4,000.00
4 ASh(c),A:G-Man Ace,K4,
   Monako,Marvex,E:Purple
   Mask,B:Whirlwind Carter . 2,400.00
5 JSm,B:Falcon,A:Fiery Mask,K4,
   Little Hercules,Bondage(c) 2,400.00
6 S&K,O:Marvel Boy,A:Fiery
   Mask, Flying Fame,Dynaman,
   Stuporman,E:Trojak 3,000.00
7 S&K,O:Blue Diamond,A:The Fin,
   Challenger,Captain Daring,
   Silver Scorpion,Thunderer . 2,500.00
8 S&K,O:Citizen V,A:Thunderer,
   Fin Silver Scorpion,Captain
   Daring Blue Diamond 2,000.00
Becomes:

DARING COMICS
9 ASh(c),B:Human Torch,Toro,
   Sub Mariner 900.00
10 ASh(c),A;The Angel 750.00
11 ASh(c),A:The Destroyer . . . 750.00
12 E:Human Torch,Toro,Sub-
   Mariner, Fall, 1945 . . . . 750.00
Becomes:

JEANIE COMICS
13 B:Jeanie,Queen of the
   Teens Mitzi,Willie 100.00
14 Baseball(c) 75.00
15 Schoolbus(c) 75.00
16 Swimsuit(c) 100.00
17 HK,Fancy dress party(c),
   Hey Look 75.00
18 HK,Jeanie'sDate(c),Hey Look 75.00
19 Ice-Boat(c),Hey Look 75.00
20 Jukebox(c) 50.00
21 . . . . 50.00
22 HK,Hey Look 75.00
23 . . . . 50.00
24 . . . . 50.00
25 . . . . 50.00
26 . . . . 50.00
27 E:Jeanie,Queen of Teens . . . 50.00
Becomes:

COWGIRL ROMANCES
28 Ph(c),Mona Freeman/MacDonald
   Carey,Copper Canyon 150.00

DARK ANGEL
See: HELL'S ANGEL

DARK CRYSTAL
April, 1983
1 movie adaption 1.00
2 movie adaption,May 1983 . . . . 1.00

DARK GUARD
1993–94
1 A:All UK Heroes 2.95
2 A:All UK Heroes 1.75
3 V:Leader,MyS-Tech 1.75
4 V:MyS-Tech 1.75
5 . . . . 1.75
6 and 7 . . . . @1.75

DARKHAWK
March, 1991
1 MM,I&O:Darkhawk,
 A:Hobgoblin 4.00
2 MM,A:Spider-Man,V:Hobgoblin 2.50
3 MM,A:Spider-Man,V:Hobgoblin 2.50
4 MM,I:Savage Steel 2.50
5 MM,I:Portal 2.50
6 MM,A:Cap.Am,D.D.,Portal,
 V:U-Foes 2.50
7 MM,I:Lodestone 2.00
8 MM,V:Lodestone 2.00
9 MM,A:Punisher,V:Savage Steel 2.00
10 MM,A&N:Tombstone 2.00
11 MM,V:Tombstone 2.00
12 MM,V:Tombstone,R:Dark
 Hawks'Father 2.00
13 MM,V:Venom 3.00
14 MM,V:Venom,D:Dark
 Hawks Father 3.00
15 MM,Heart of the Hawk,concl . . 2.00
16 MM,V:Terrorists 2.00
17 MM,I:Peristrike Force 2.00
18 MM,V:Mindwolf 2.00
19 MM,R:Portal,A:Spider-Man,V:The
 Brotherhood of Evil Mutants . . 2.00
20 MM,A:Spider-Man,Sleepwalker,
 V:Brotherhood of Evil Mutants . 2.00
21 MM,B:Return to Forever 1.75
22 MM,A:Ghost Rider 1.75
23 MM,I:Evilhawk 1.75
24 V:Evilhawk 1.50
25 MM,O:Darkhawk,V:Evilhawk,
 Holo-graphx(c) 2.50
26 A:New Warriors 1.50
27 A:New Warriors,V:Zarrko 1.50
28 A:New Warriors,Zarrko 1.50
29 A:New Warriors 1.50
30 I:Purity 1.50
31 Infinity Crusade 1.50
32 R:Savage Steel 1.50
33 I:Cuda 1.50
34 V:Cuda 1.50
35 DFr(s),V:Venom 1.50
36 DFr(s),V:Scokers,A:Venom . . . 1.50
37 DFr(s),V:Venom 1.50
38 DFr(s),N:Darkhawk 1.50
39 DFr(s) 1.50
40 DFr(s) 1.75
41 DFr(s) 1.75
42 DFr(s), V:Portal,I:Shaper 1.75
43 DFr(s) 1.75
44 DFr(s) 1.75
45 DFr(s),A:Portal 1.75
46 DFr(s) 1.75
47 . . . . 1.50
48 R:Darkhawk,V:Mahari 1.50
49 V:Overhawk 1.50
50 V:Overhawk 2.50
Ann.#1 MM,Assault on ArmorCity . 3.00
Ann.#2 GC,AW,I:Dreamkiller,
 w/Trading card 3.00
Ann.#3 I:Damek 3.00

DARKHOLD
1992–94
1 RCa,I:Redeemers,Polybagged
 w/poster,A:Gh.Rider,Blaze . . 3.00
2 RCa,R:Modred 2.50
3 A:Modred,Scarlet Witch 2.00
4 V:Sabretooth,N'Garai 2.00
5 A:Punisher, Ghost Rider 2.00
6 RCa,V:Dr.Strange 2.00
7 A:Dr.Strange,V:Japanese Army 2.00
8 Betrayal #1 . . . . 2.00
9 Diabolique 2.00
10 V:Darkholders 2.00
11 Midnight Massacre#3,D:Modred,
 Vicki 2.50
12 V:Chthon 2.00
13 V:Missing Link 2.00
14 Vicki's Secret revealed 2.00
15 Siege of Darkness,pt.#4 . . . . . 2.00
16 Siege of Darkness,pt.#12 . . . . 2.00

DARK MAN
MOVIE ADAPTION
Sept., 1990
1 BH/MT/TD 2.00
2 BH/TD 1.50
3 BH/TD,final issue 1.50

DARKMAN
Sept., 1990
1 JS,R:Darkman 3.50
2 JS,V:Witchfinder 2.95
3 JS,Witchfinder 2.95
4 JS,V:Dr.West 2.95
5 JS,Durant 2.95
6 JS,V:Durant 2.95

DATE WITH MILLIE
Atlas Oct., 1956
[1st Series]
1 . . . . 125.00
2 . . . . 75.00
3 thru 7 . . . . @50.00
[2nd Series] Oct., 1959
1 . . . . 60.00
2 thru 7 . . . . @40.00
Becomes:

LIFE WITH MILLIE
8 . . . . 40.00
9 & 10 . . . . @30.00
11 thru 20 . . . . @25.00
Becomes:

MODELING WITH MILLIE
21 . . . . 35.00
22 thru 54 June, 1967 . . . . . . @25.00

DATE WITH PATSY
Sept., 1957
1 A:Patsy Walker 50.00

DAYDREAMERS
Aug., 1997
1 (of 3) JMD,MEg,HSm 2.50
2 JMD,MEg,HSm, ... 2.50
3 JMD,TDz,MEg,HSm,concl. . . . 2.50

DAZZLER
March, 1981
1 AA,JR2,A:X-Men,Spm,
 O:Dazzler 2.50
2 WS,JR2,AA,X-Men,A:SpM . . . 2.00

Dazzler #20
© *Marvel Entertainment Group*

3 JR2,Dr.Doom 1.50
4 FS,Dr.Doom 1.50
5 FS,I:Blue Shield 1.50
6 FS,Hulk 1.50
7 FS,Hulk 1.50
8 FS,Quasar 1.50
9 FS,D:Klaw 1.50
10 FS,Galactus 1.50
11 FS,Galactus 1.50
12 FS,The Light That Failed . . . 1.50
13 FS,V:Grapplers 1.50
14 FS,She Hulk 1.50
15 FS,BSz,Spider Women 1.50
16 FS,BSz,Enchantress 1.50
17 FS,Angel,V:Doc Octopus 1.50
18 FS,BSz,A:Fantastic Four,Angel,
 V:Absorbing Man 1.50
19 FS,Blue Bolt,V:Absorbing Man 1.50
20 FS,V:Jazz and Horn 1.50
21 FS,A:Avengers,F.F.,C:X-Men,
 (double size) 1.50
22 FS,V:Rogue,Mystique 2.00
23 FS,V:Rogue,A:Powerman,
 Iron Fist 2.00
24 FS,V:Rogue,A:Powerman,
 Iron Fist 1.75
25 FS,'The Jagged Edge' 1.50
26 FS,Lois London 1.50
27 FS,Fugitive 2.00
28 FS,V:Rogue 1.50
29 FS,Roman Nekoboh 1.50
30 FS,Moves to California 1.50
31 FS,The Last Wave 1.50
32 FS,A:Inhumans 1.50
33 Chiller 1.50
34 FS,Disappearance 1.50
35 FS,V:Racine Ramjets 1.50
36 JBy(c),FS,V:Tatterdemalion . . . 1.50
37 JBy(c),FS 1.50
38 PC,JG,X-Men 5.00
39 PC,JG,Caught in the grip of
 death 1.50
40 PC,JG,Secret Wars II 1.75
41 PC,JG,A:Beast 1.50
42 PC,JG,A:Beast,last issue 2.00

MARVEL

DEADLIEST HEROES OF KUNG FU
Summer, 1975
1 Magazine size 3.50

DEADLY FOES OF SPIDER-MAN
May, 1991
1 AM,KGa,V:Sinister Syndicate . . 4.00
2 AM,Boomerang on Trial 3.00
3 AM,Deadly Foes Split 3.00
4 AM,Conclusion 3.00
TPB rep. #1–#4 . . . . 12.95

DEADLY HANDS OF KUNG FU
April, 1974
1 NA(c),JSa,JSon,O:Sons of
  the Tiger, B:Shang-Chi,
  Bruce Lee Pin-up 30.00
2 NA(c),JSa 25.00
3 NA(c),JSon,A:Sons of the Tiger 20.00
4 NA(Bruce Lee)(c),JSon,Bruce
  Lee biography 20.00
5 BWS,PG 15.00
6 GP,JSon,A:Sons of the Tiger 15.00
7 GP,JSon,A:Sons of the Tiger 20.00
8 GP,JSon,A:Sons of the Tiger . 12.00
9 GP,JSon,A:Sons of the Tiger 12.00
10 GP,JSon,A:Sons of the Tiger 20.00
11 NA(c),GP,JSon,A:Sons
  of the Tiger 12.00
12 NA(c),GP,JSon,A:Sons
  of the Tiger 10.00
13 GP,JSon,A:Sons of the Tiger 10.00
14 NA(c),GP,HC,JSon,A:Sons
  of the Tiger 35.00
15 JS,PG,JSn,,Annual #1 . . . . . 15.00
16 JSn,A:Sons of the Tiger 10.00
17 NA(c),JSn,KG,A:Sons
  of the Tiger 10.00
18 JSn,A:Sons of the Tiger 10.00
19 JSn,I:White Tiger 15.00
20 GP,O:White Tiger 10.00
21 . . . . 8.00
22 KG,C:Jack of Hearts 10.00
23 GK,Jack of Hearts 15.00
24 KG,Ironfist 15.00
25 I:Shimaru 15.00
26 . . . . 15.00
27 . . . . 9.00
28 Bruce Lee Special 40.00
29 Ironfist vs. Shang Chi 15.00
30 Swordquest 10.00
31 JSon, Jack of Hearts 10.00
32 MR,JSon,Daughters of the
  Dragon 10.00
33 MR,Feb., 1977 . . . . 12.00
Spec. Album Ed.,NA, Sum.1974 15.00

DEAD OF NIGHT
Dec., 1973
1 JSt,Horror reprints,A Haunted
  House is not a Home 15.00
2 BEv(c),House that Fear Built 10.00
3 They Lurk Below 10.00
4 Warewolf Beware 10.00
5 Deep Down 10.00
6 Jack the Ripper 10.00
7 SD,The Thirteenth Floor 10.00
8 Midnight Brings Dark Madness 10.00
9 Deathride 10.00
10 SD,I Dream of Doom 10.00

11 GK/BWr(c),I:Scarecrow, Fires
  of Rebirth,Fires of Death
  August, 1975 . . . . 10.00

DEADPOOL
1993
1 B:FaN(s),JMd,MFm(i),
  V:Slayback,Nyko 4.00
2 JMd,MFm(i),V:Black Tom
  Cassidy,Juggernaut 3.00
3 JMd,MFm(i),I:Comcast,
  Makeshift,Rive,A:Slayback . . 2.50
4 E:FaN(s),JMd,MFm(i),
  A:Slayback,Kane 2.50
[2nd Limited Series] 1994
1 A:Banshee,Syrin,Juggernaut
  Black Tom 2.00
2 A:Banshee,Syrin,V:Juggernaut . 2.00
3 A:Syrin,Juggernaut 2.00
4 Final issue 2.00

Deadpool #3
© Marvel Entertainment Group

DEADPOOL
1996
1 NMa,V:Sasquatch,48pg, ... 2.95
2 NMa,A:Copycat 1.95
3 NMa,A:Siryn 1.95
4 NMa,Will Hulk cure him? 1.95
5 NMa,A:Siryn,T-Ray 1.95
6 NMa,I: 1.95
7 AaL,A:Typhoid Mary 1.95
8 NMa, cont. from Daredevil/
  Deadpool '97,A:Gerry 1.95
9 NMa, new villain 2.00
10 NMa,A:Great Lake Avengers . . 2.00
11 NMa,Fall through time, A:Alfred 4.00
12 NMa,Typhoid Mary, Zoe Cullodon &
  Siryn return 2.00
13 NMa,V:T-Ray 2.00
14 WMc,Deal of a Lifetime 2.00
15 WMc,A:Landau, Luckman & Lake2.00
16 WMc, in middle east 2.00
17 WMc, Landau, Luckman & Lake's
  plan 2.00
18 WMc,V:Ajax 2.00
19 WMc,more secrets of blind Al . 2.00
20 Cosmic Messiah 2.00
Ann. '98 BCh(c) F:Deadpool & Death,

  48pg 3.00
Minus 1 Spec., ALo, flashback,
  O:Deadpool 1.95
TPB MWa,IaC,Sins of the Past,
  rep. limited series 6.00
TPB Circle Chase,FaN,JMd,MFm, 12.95

DEATH³
1993
1 I:Death Metal,Death Wreck . . . 2.95
2 V:Ghost Rider 1.75
3 A:Hulk,Cable,Storm,Thing . . . 1.75
4 Last issue 1.75

DEATHLOK
[Limited Series] July, 1990
1 JC,SW,I:Michael Colins
  (2nd Deathlok) 3.00
2 JC,SW,V:Wajler 2.00
3 DCw,SW,V:Cyberants 2.00
4 DCw,SW,V:Sunfire,final issue . 2.00
[Regular Series] 1991–94
1 DCw,MM,V:Warwolf 2.50
2 DCw,MM,A:Dr.Doom,Machine Man,
  Forge 2.50
3 DCw,MM,V:Dr.Doom,
  A:Mr.Fantastic 2.50
4 DCw,MM,A:X-Men,F.F.,Vision,
  O:Mechadoom 2.50
5 DCw,MM,V:Mechadoom,
  A:X-Men,Fantastic Four 2.50
6 DCw,MM,A:Punisher,
  V:Silvermane 2.50
7 DCw,MM,A:Punisher,
  V:Silvermane 2.50
8 A:Main Frame,Ben Jacobs 2.00
9 DCw,MM,A:Ghost Rider,
  V:Nightmare 2.50
10 DCw,MM,A:GhR,V:Nightmare . 2.50
11 DCw,MM,V:Moses Magnum . . 2.00
12 DCw,MM,Biohazard Agenda . . 2.00
13 DCw,MM,Biohazard Agenda . . 2.00
14 DCw,MM,Biohazard Agenda . . 2.00
15 DCw,MM,Biohazard Agenda . . 2.00
16 DCw,MM,Inf.War,V:Evilok 2.00
17 WMc,MM,B:Cyberwar 2.00
18 WMc,A:Silver Sable 2.00
18a Newstand Ed. 1.75
19 SMc,Cyberwar#3 . . . . 2.00
20 SMc,Cyberwar#4 . . . . 2.00
21 E:Cyberwar,A:Cold Blood
  Nick Fury 2.00
22 V:MosesMagnum,A:Bl.Panther 2.00
23 A:Bl.Panther,V:Phreak,Stroke 2.00
24 V:MosesMagnum,A:Bl.Panther 2.00
25 V:MosesMagnum,A:Black
  Panther,holo-grafx(c) 2.50
26 V:Hobogoblin 2.00
27 R:Siege 2.00
28 Infinty Crusade 2.00
29 Inner Fears 2.00
30 KHd,V:Hydra 2.00
31 GWt(s),KoK,B:Cyberstrike,
  R:1st Deathlok 2.00
32 GWt(s),KoK,A:Siege 2.00
33 GWt(s),KoK,V:Justice Peace . . 2.00
34 GWt(s),KoK,E:Cyberstrike,V:Justice
  Peace,final issue 2.00
Ann.#1 JG,I:Timestream 2.75
Ann.#2 I:Tracer,w/card 2.95

DEATHLOK SPECIAL
1991
1 Rep.Mini Series 2.50

2 Rep.Mini Series	2.50
3 Rep.Mini Series	2.50
4 Rep.Mini Series, final issue	2.50

DEATH METAL
Marvel UK 1994

1 JRe,I:Argon,C:Alpha Flight	1.95
2 JRe,V:Alpha Flight	1.95
3 JRe,I:Soulslug	1.95
4 Re,Last Issue	1.95

DEATH METAL VS. GENETIX
Marvel UK 1993–94

1 PaD,w/card	2.95
2 PaD,w/card	2.95

DEATH'S HEAD
Marvel UK Dec., 1988

1 V:Backbreaker	5.00
2 A:Dragons Claws	4.00
3	4.00
4 V:Plague Dog	3.00
5 V:Big Shot	3.00
6 V:Big Shot	3.00
7 & 8	@3.00
9 A:Fantastic Four	3.50
10 A:Iron Man	3.50
TPB Reprints#1-#10	12.95

DEATH'S HEAD
[Limited Series]

1 A:'Old' Death's Head	1.95

DEATH'S HEAD II
Marvel UK March, 1992
[Limited Series]

1 LSh,I:2nd Death's Head, D:1st Death's Head	5.00
1a 2nd printing,Silver	3.00
2 LSh,A:Fantastic Four	3.00
2a 2nd printing,Silver	3.00
3 LSh,I:Tuck	3.50
4 LSh,A:Wolverine,Spider-Man, Punisher	3.50

[Regular Series] 1992

1 LSh,A:X-Men,I:Wraithchilde	3.00
2 LSh,A:X-Men	2.25
3 LSh,A:X-Men,V:Raptors	2.25
4 LSh,A:X-Men,V:Wraithchilde	2.25
5 V:UnDeath's Head II, A:Warheads	2.25
6 R:Tuck,V:Major Oak	2.25
7 V:Major Oak	2.25
8 V:Wizard Methinx	2.25
9 BHi,V:Cybernetic Centaurs	2.25
10 DBw,A:Necker	2.25
11 SCy,R:Charnel	2.25
12 DAn(s),SvL,V:Charnel	2.25
13 SvL,A:Liger	2.25
14 SvL,Brain Dead Cold,Blue Foil(c)	3.25
15 SvL,V:Duplicates	2.25
16 SvL,DAn	2.25
17 SvL,DAn	1.95
18 SvL,DAn	1.95
Spec. Gold Ed. LSh(a&s)	3.95

DEATH'S HEAD II/DIE CUT
Marvel UK 1993

1 I:Die Cut	3.25
2 O:Die Cut	1.75

DEATH'S HEAD II/ KILLPOWER: BATTLETIDE
[1st Limited Series]

1 GSr,A:Wolverine	2.50
2 thru 4 GSr,A:Wolverine	@2.00

[2nd Limited Series]

1 A:Hulk	3.25
2 V:Hulk	1.75
3 A:Hulk	1.75
4 last issue	1.75

DEATH-WRECK
Marvel UK 1994

1 A:Death's Head II	1.95
2 V:Gangsters	1.95
3 A:Dr.Necker	1.95
4 last issue	1.95

DEEP, THE
Nov., 1977

1 CI,Movie Adaption	2.00

Defenders #35
© Marvel Entertainment Group

DEFENDERS
August, 1972

1 SB,I&D:Necrodames	65.00
2 SB,V:Calizuma	30.00
3 GK(c),SB,JM,V:UndyingOne	25.00
4 SB,FMc,Bl.Knight,V:Valkyrie	25.00
5 SB,FMc,D:Omegatron	25.00
6 SB,FMc,V:Cyrus Black	20.00
7 SB,FBe,A:Hawkeye	20.00
8 SB,FBe,Avengers,SilverSurfer	20.00
9 SB,FMc,Avengers	20.00
10 SB,FBe,Thor vs. Hulk	22.00
11 SB,FBe,A:Avengers	10.00
12 SB,JA,Xemnu	8.00
13 GK(c),SB,KJ,J:Night Hawk	8.00
14 SB,DGr,O:Hyperion	8.00
15 SB,KJ,A:Professor X,V:Magneto, Savage Land Mutates	12.00
16 GK(c),SB,Professor X,V:Magneto, Savage Land Mutates	12.00
17 SB,DGr,Power Man	7.00
18 GK(c),SB,DGr,A:Power Man	7.00
19 GK(c),SB,KJ,A:Power Man	7.00
20 K&R(c),SB,A:Thing	7.00

21 GK(c),SB,O:Valkyrie	5.00
22 GK(c),SB,V:Sons o/t Serpent	5.00
23 GK(c),SB,A:Yellow Jacket	5.00
24 GK(c),SB,BMc,A:Daredevil	5.00
25 GK(c),SB,JA,A:Daredevil	5.00
26 K&R(c),SB,A:Guardians	8.00
27 K&R(c),SB,A:Guardians C:Starhawk	8.00
28 K&R(c),SB,A:Guardians I:Starhawk	7.00
29 K&R(c),SB,A:Guardians	7.00
30 JA(i),A:Wong	4.00
31 GK(c),SB,JM,Nighthawk	4.00
32 GK(c),SB,JM,O:Nighthawk	4.00
33 GK(c),SB,JM,V:Headmen	4.00
34 SB,JM,V:Nebulon	4.00
35 GK(c),SB,KJ,I:Red Guardian	4.00
36 GK(c),SB,KJ,A:Red Guardian	10.00
37 GK(c),SB,KJ,J:Luke Cage	4.00
38 SB,KJ,V:Nebulon	10.00
39 SB,KJ,V:Felicia	4.00
40 SB,KJ,V:Assassin	4.00
41 KG,KJ,Nighthawk	4.00
42 KG,KJ,V:Rhino	4.00
43 KG,KJ,Cobalt Man,Egghead	4.00
44 KG,KJ,J:Hellcat,V:Red Rajah	4.00
45 KG,KJ,Valkyrie V:Hulk	4.00
46 KG,KJ,L:DrStrange,LukeCage	4.00
47 KG,KJ,Moon Knight	4.00
48 KG,A:Wonder Man	4.00
49 KG,O:Scorpio	4.00
50 KG,Zodiac,D:Scorpio	4.00
51 KG,Moon Knight	4.00
52 KG,Hulk,V:Sub Mariner	4.00
53 KG,DC,MG,TA,C&I:Lunatik	3.00
54 MG,Nigh Fury	3.00
55 CI,O:Red Guardian	3.00
56 CI,KJ,Hellcat,V:Lunatik	3.00
57 DC,Ms.Marvel	3.00
58 Return of Dr.Strange	3.00
59 I:Belathauzer	3.00
60 V:Vera Gemini	3.00
61 Spider-Man,A:Lunatik	2.50
62 Hercules,C:Polaris	2.50
63 Mutli Heroes	2.50
64 Mutli Heroes	2.50
65 Red Guardian	2.50
66 JB,Valkyrie I	2.50
67 Valkryie II	2.50
68 HT,When Falls the Mountain	2.50
69 HT,A:The Anything Man	2.50
70 HT,A:Lunatik	2.50
71 HT,O:Lunatik	2.50
72 HT,V:Lunatik	2.50
73 HT,Foolkiller,V:WizardKing	3.00
74 HT,Foolkiller,L:Nighthawk	5.00
75 HT,Foolkiller	4.00
76 HT,O:Omega	2.00
77 HT,Moon Dragon	2.00
78 HT,Yellow Jacket	2.00
79 HT,Tunnel World	2.00
80 HT,DGr,Nighthawk	2.00
81 HT,Tunnel World	2.00
82 DP,JSt,Tunnel World	2.00
83 DP,JSt,Tunnel World	2.00
84 DP,JSt,Black Panther	2.00
85 DP,JSt,Black Panther	2.00
86 DP,JSt,Black Panther	2.00
87 DP,JSt,V:Mutant Force	2.00
88 DP,JSt,Matt Mardock	2.00
89 DP,JSt,D:Hellcat's Mother,O:Mad-Dog	2.00
90 DP,JSt,Daredevil	2.00
91 DP,JSt,Daredevil	2.00
92 DP,JSt,A:Eternity,	

Son of Satan 3.00
93 DP,JSt,Son of Satan 3.00
94 DP,JSt,I:Gargoyle 2.00
95 DP,JSt,V:Dracula,O:Gargoyle . 2.00
96 DP,JSt,Ghost Rider 3.00
97 DP,JSt,False Messiah 2.00
98 DP,JSt,A:Man Thing 2.00
99 DP,JSt,Conflict 2.00
100 DP,JSt,DoubleSize,V:Satan . . 3.00
101 DP,JSt,Silver Surfer 2.00
102 DP,JSt,Nighthawk 2.00
103 DP,JSt,I:Null 2.00
104 DP,JSt,Devilslayer,J:Beast . . 2.00
105 DP,JSt,V:Satan 2.00
106 DP,Daredevil,D:Nighthawk . . 2.00
107 DP,JSt,Enchantress,A:D.D. . . 2.00
108 DP,A:Enchantress 2.00
109 DP,A:Spider-Man 2.50
110 DP,A:Devilslayer 2.00
111 DP,A:Hellcat 2.00
112 DP,A:SquadronSupreme . . . 2.00
113 DP,A:SquadronSupreme . . . 2.00
114 DP,A:SquadronSupreme . . . 2.00
115 DP,A:Submariner 2.00

Defenders #108
© Marvel Entertainment Group

116 DP,Gargoyle 2.00
117 DP,Valkyrie 2.00
118 DP,V:Miracleman 2.00
119 DP,V:Miracleman 2.00
120 DP,V:Miracleman 2.00
121 DP,V:Miracleman 2.00
122 DP,A:Iceman 2.00
123 DP,I:Cloud,V:Secret Empire . 2.00
124 DP,V:Elf 2.00
125 DP,New Line-up:Gargoyle,Moon
dragon,Valkyrie,Iceman,Beast,
Angel,W:Son of Satan & Hellcat
I:Mad Dog 3.00
126 DP,A:Nick Fury 2.00
127 DP,V:Professor Power 2.00
128 DP,V:Professor Power 2.00
129 DP,V:Professor Power,New
Mutants X-over 2.00
130 DP,V:Professor Power 2.00
131 DP,V:Walrus,A:Frogman 2.00
132 DP,V:Spore Monster 2.00
133 DP,V:Spore Monster 2.00
134 DP,I:Manslaughter 2.00
135 DP,V:Blowtorch Brand 2.00

136 DP,V:Gargoyle 2.00
137 DP,V:Gargoyle 2.00
138 DP,O:Moondragon 2.00
139 DP,A:Red Wolf,V:Trolls 2.00
140 DP,V:Asgardian Trolls 2.00
141 DP,All Flesh is Grass 2.00
142 DP,V:M.O.N.S.T.E.R. 2.00
143 DP,I:Andromeda,Runner 2.00
144 DP,V:Moondragon 2.00
145 DP,V:Moondragon 2.00
146 DP,Cloud 2.00
147 DP,A:Andromeda,I:Interloper . 2.00
148 DP,A:Nick Fury 2.00
149 DP,V:Manslaughter,O:Cloud . 2.00
150 DP,O:Cloud,double-size 3.00
151 DP,A:Interloper 2.00
152 DP,Secret Wars II,D:Moon-
dragon,Valkyrie,Gargoyle 3.00
G-Size#1 GK(c),JSn,AM,O:Hulk . 12.00
G-Size#2 GK,KJ,Son of Satan . . 8.00
G-Size#3 JSn,DA,JM,DN,A:D.D.. . 6.00
G-Size#4 GK(c),DH,A:YellowJack . 6.00
G-Size#5 K&R(c),DH,A:Guardians . 6.00
Ann.#1 SB,KJ 6.00

DEFENDERS OF
DYNATRON CITY
1992
1 FC,I:Defenders of Dynatron City
(from video game & TV ser.) . . 1.25
2 FC,O:Defender of D.City 1.25
3 FC,A:Dr Mayhem 1.25
4 FC 1.25
5 FC,V:Intelligent Fleas 1.25
6 FC,V:Dr.Mayhem 1.25

DEFENDERS OF
THE EARTH
Jan., 1987—Sept., 1984
1 AS,Flash Gordon & Mandrake . 2.00
2 AS,Flash Gordon & Mandrake . 2.00
3 AS,O:Phantom 2.00
4 AS,O:Mandrake 2.00

DELLA VISION
Atlas April, 1955
1 The Television Queen 80.00
2 . . . . 55.00
3 . . . . 55.00
Becomes:
PATTY POWERS
4 . . . . 35.00
5 . . . . 22.00
6 . . . . 22.00
7 Oct., 1956 . . . . 22.00

DENNIS THE MENACE
Nov., 1981–Nov., 1982
1 . . . . 1.25
2 thru 13 . . . . @1.00

DESTROYER, THE
Nov., 1989
1 Black & White Mag. 3.50
2 thru 9 . . . . @2.25
10 June 1990 . . . . 2.25
TPB rep. B/w mag(color) 9.95

THE DESTROYER:
TERROR
Dec., 1991
1 V:Nuihc 1.95

2 V:Nuihc 1.95
3 GM,V:Nuihc 1.95
4 DC,'The Last Dinosaur' 1.95

DEVIL DINOSAUR
April, 1978—Dec., 1978
1 JK,I:Devil Dinosaur,Moon Boy . 4.00
2 JK,War With the Spider God . . 3.00
3 JK,Giant 3.00
4 JK,Objects From the Sky . . . 3.00
5 JK,The Kingdom of the Ants . . 3.00
6 JK,The Fall 3.00
7 JK,Prisoner of the Demon Tree 3.00
8 JK,V:Dino Riders 3.00
9 JK,Lizards That Stand 3.00

DEVIL DINOSAUR
SPRING FLING
1997
Spec. F:Devil Dinosaur,
Moon-Boy, 48pg 2.99

DEVIL-DOG DUGAN
Atlas July, 1956
1 War Stories 75.00
2 . . . . 50.00
3 . . . . 35.00
Becomes:
TALE OF THE MARINES
4 BP,War Stories 40.00
Becomes:
MARINES AT WAR
5 War Stories 30.00
6 . . . . 30.00
7 The Big Push,August, 1957 . 30.00

DEXTER THE DEMON
See: MELVIN THE MONSTER

DIE-CUT
Marvel UK 1993–94
1 A:Beast 2.50
2 V:X-Beast 1.75
3 A:Beast,Prof.X 1.75
4 V:Red Skull 1.75

DIE-CUT VS. G-FORCE
Marvel UK 1993
1 SFr(s),LSh(c),I:G-Force 2.75
2 SFr(s),LSh(c),Last issue 2.75

DIGITEK
Marvel UK 1992–93
1 DPw,I:Digitek,C:Deathlok 2.25
2 DPw,A:Deathlok,V:Bacillicons . 2.25
3 DPw,A:Deathlok,V:Bacillicons . 2.25
4 DPw,V:Bacillicons 2.25

DINO RIDERS
Feb., 1989
1 Based on Toys 1.00
2 . . . . 1.00
3 May, 1989 . . . . 1.00

DINOSAURS: A
CELEBRATION
Epic 1992
Horns and Heavy Armor 4.95
Bone-Heads and Duck-Bills 4.95
Terrible Claws and Tyrants 4.95

MARVEL

Egg Stealers and Earth Shakers . 4.95
TPB 192pg 12.95

DISNEY AFTERNOON
1994–95
1 DarkwingDuck vs.FearsomeFive 1.50
2 . . . . 1.50
3 . . . . 1.50
4 DarkwingDuck:Gum w/t Wind . . 1.50
5 F:Baloo, Mrs. Cunningham . . . 1.50
6 . . . . 1.50
7 F:Darkwing Duck 1.50
8 . . . . 1.50
9 DarkwingDuck:Borsht to Death 1.50
10 F:Scrooge & Mrs. Beakley . . . 1.50

Disney Comic Hits #6
© Marvel Entertainment Group

DISNEY COMIC HITS
1995
1 . . . . 1.50
2 F:Lion King 1.50
3 F:Pocahontas 1.50
4 F:Toy Story 1.50
5 Holiday 1.50
6 Aladdin 1.50
7 . . . . 1.50
8 Lion King story 1.50
9 thru 13 . . . . @1.50
14 F:Toy Story characters 1.50
15 101 Dalmations 1.50
16 101 Dalmatians 1.50
17 final issue 1.50

DISNEY PRESENTS
1 F:Aladdin 1.50
2 F:Timon & Pummba 1.50
3 . . . . 1.50

DOC SAMSON
1996
1 From The Incredible Hulk 1.95
2 A:She-Hulk 1.95
3 . . . . 1.95
4 . . . . 1.95

DOC SAVAGE
Oct., 1972
1 JM,Pulp Adapts,Death Eighty
  Stories High 15.00
2 JSo(c),The Feathered Serpent
  Strikes 10.00
3 JSo(c),Silver Death's Head . . 10.00
4 JSo(c),The Hell Diver 9.00
5 GK(c),Night of the Monsters . . 9.00
6 JSo(c),Where Giants Walk 9.00
7 JSo(c),Brand of the Werewolfs . 9.00
8 In the Lair of the Werewolf
  Jan., 1974 . . . . 9.00
G-Size#1 thru #2 Reprints 8.00

DOC SAVAGE
August, 1975
(black & white magazine)
1 JB,Ph(c),Ron Ely 8.00
2 JB 6.00
3 JB 6.00
4 . . . . 6.00
5 thru 7 . . . . @6.00
8 Spring 1977 . . . . 6.00

DR. STRANGE
[1st Series]
Prev: Strange Tales
June, 1968
169 DA,O:Dr.Strange 125.00
170 DA,A:Ancient One 40.00
171 TP,DA,V:Dormammu 35.00
172 GC,TP,V:Dormammu 35.00
173 GC,TP,V:Dormammu 35.00
174 GC,TP,I:Satannish 35.00
175 GC,TP,I:Asmodeus 35.00
176 GC,TP,V:Asmodeus 35.00
177 GC,TP,D:Asmodeus,
  N:Dr.Strange 35.00
178 GC,TP,A:Black Knight 35.00
179 BWS(c),rep.Amazing Spider-
  Man Ann.#2 . . . . 35.00
180 GC,TP,V:Nightmare 35.00
181 FB(c),GC,TP,I:Demons of
  Despair 35.00
182 GC,TP,V:Juggernaut 40.00
183 BEv(c),GC,TP,
  I:Undying Ones 40.00
[2nd Regular Series] 1974–87
1 FB,DG,I:Silver Dagger 35.00
2 FB,DG,I:Soul Eater 15.00
3 FB,A:Dormammu 7.00
4 FB,DG,V:Death 6.00
5 FB,DG,A:Silver Dagger 6.00
6 FB(c),GC,KJ,A:Umar,I:Gaea . . 5.00
7 GC,JR,A:Dormammu 5.00
8 GK(c),GC,TP,O:Clea 5.00
9 GK(c),GC,A:Dormammu,O:Clea 5.00
10 B:MWn(s),GK(c),GC,A:Eternity 5.00
11 JR(c),GC,TP,A:Eternity 4.50
12 GC,TP,A:Eternity 4.50
13 GC,TP,A:Eternity 4.50
14 GC,TP,A:Dracula 4.50
15 GC,TP,A:Devil 4.50
16 GC,TP,A:Devil 4.50
17 GC,TP,A:Styggro 4.50
18 GC,A:Styggro 4.50
19 GC,AA,I:Xander 4.50
20 A:Xander 4.50
21 DA,O:Dr.Strange 4.00
22 I:Apalla 4.00
23 E:MWn(s),JSn,A:Wormworld . 4.00
24 JSn,A:Apalla,I:Visamajoris . . 4.00
25 AM,V:Dr.Strange Yet 4.00

26 JSn,A:The Ancient One 4.00
27 TS,A:Stygyro,Sphinx 4.00
28 TS,A:Ghost Rider,
  V:In-Betweener 5.00
29 TS,A:Nighthawk 4.00
30 I:Dweller 3.50
31 TS,A:Sub Mariner 3.50
32 A:Sub Mariner 3.50
33 TS,A:The Dreamweaver 3.50
34 TS,A:Nightmare,D:CyrusBlack . 3.50
35 TS,V:Dweller,I:Ludi 3.50
36 Thunder of the Soul 3.50
37 Fear,the Final Victor 3.50
38 GC,DG,A:Baron Mordo 3.50
39 GC,DG,A:Baron Mordo 3.50
40 GC,A:Asrael 3.50
41 GC,A:Man Thing 3.00
42 GC,A:Black Mirror 3.00
43 V:Shadow Queen 3.00
44 GC,A:Princess Shialmar 3.00
45 GC,A:Demon in the Dark . . . 3.00
46 FM,A:Sibylis 3.00
47 MR,TA,I:Ikonn 3.00
48 MR,TA,Brother Voodoo 3.00

Doctor Strange (2nd Series) #34
© Marvel Entertainment Group

49 MR,TA,A:Baron Mordo 3.00
50 MR,TA,A:Baron Mordo 3.00
51 MR,TA,A:Sgt. Fury,
  V:Baron Mordo 3.00
52 MR,TA,A:Nightmare 2.50
53 MR,TA,A:Nightmare,Fantastic
  Four,V:Rama-Tut 2.50
54 PS,V:Tiboro 2.50
55 MGo,TA,V:Madness 2.50
56 PS,TA,O:Dr.Strange 4.00
57 KN,TA,A:Dr.Doom 2.50
58 DGr,TA,V:Dracula 2.50
59 DGr,TA,V:Dracula 2.50
60 DGr,TA,Scarlet Witch 2.50
61 DGr,TA,V:Dracula 2.50
62 SL,V:Dracula 2.50
63 CP,V:Topaz 2.50
64 TSa,'Art Rage' 2.50
65 PS,Charlatan 2.50
66 PS,'The Cosen One' 2.50
67 SL,A:Jessica Drew,Shroud . . 2.50
68 PS,A:Black Knight 2.25
69 PS,A:Black Knight 2.25
70 BBI,V:Umar 2.25

MARVEL

71 DGr,O:Dormammu 2.25
72 PS,V:Umar 2.25
73 PS,V:Umar 2.25
74 MBg,Secret Wars II 2.25
75 A:Fantastic Four 2.25
76 A:Fantastic Four 2.25
77 A:Topaz 2.25
78 A:Cloak,I:Ecstacy 3.00
79 A:Morganna 2.00
80 A:Morganna,C:Rintah 2.00
81 V:Urthona,I:Rintah 2.00
Ann.#1 CR,'Doomworld' 4.50
G-Size#1 K&R(c),reps Strange
    Tales#164–#168 . . . . 6.00
GN Dr.Strange: What is it that
    Distrubs you, Stephen?, CR,
    revised from Dr.Strange Ann.#1,
    48pg bookshelf (Aug. 1997) . . 6.00
[3rd Regular Series] 1988–96
1 V:Dorammu 4.00
2 V:Dorammu 3.00
3 I:Dragon Force 3.00
4 EL(c),A:Dragon Force 3.00
5 JG,V:Baron Mordo 3.50
6 JG,I:Mephista 3.00
7 JG,V:Agamotto,Mephisto 3.00
8 JG,V:Mephisto & Satanish 3.00
9 JG,O:Dr.Strange 3.00
10 JG,V:Morbius 3.50
11 JG,A of V,V:Hobgoblin,
    C:Morbius 4.00
12 JG,A of V,V:Enchantress 2.75
13 JG,A of V,V:Arkon 2.75
14 JG,B:Vampiric Verses,
    A:Morbius 3.50
15 JG,A:Morbius,Amy Grant(C) . . 3.50
16 JG,A:Morbius,Brother Voodoo . 3.50
17 JV,TD,A:Morbius,Br.Voodoo . . 3.50
18 JG,E:Vampiric Verses,A:Morbius,
    Brother Voodoo,R:Varnae 3.50
19 GC,A:Azrael 2.50
20 JG,TD,A:Morbius,V:Zom 3.50
21 JG,TD,B:Dark Wars,
    R:Dormammu 2.50
22 JG,TD,LW,V:Dormammu 2.50
23 JG,LW,V:Dormammu 2.50
24 JG,E:Dark Wars,V:Dormammu 2.50
25 RLm,A:Red Wolf, Black Crow . 2.50
26 GI,V:Werewolf By Night 2.50
27 GI,V:Werewolf By Night 2.50
28 X-over Ghost Rider #12,
    V:Zodiac 3.00
29 A:Baron Blood 2.50
30 Topaz' Fate 2.50
31 TD,Inf.Gauntlet,A:Silver Surfer 3.00
32 Inf.Gauntlet,A:Warlock,Silver
    Surfer,V:Silver Dagger 2.50
33 Inf.Gauntlet,V:Thanos,
    Zota,A:Pip 2.50
34 Inf.Gauntlet,V:Dr.Doom,
    A:Pip,Scarlet Witch 2.50
35 Inf.Gauntlet,A:Thor,Pip,
    Scarlet Witch 2.50
36 Inf.Gauntlet,A:Warlock(leads
    into Warlock&Inf.Watch#1) . . 3.00
37 GI,V:Frankensurfer 2.00
38 GI,Great Fear #1 . . . . 2.00
39 GI,Great Fear #2 . . . . 2.00
40 GI,Great Fear #3,A:Daredevil . 2.00
41 GI,A:Wolverine 3.00
42 GI,Infinity War,V:Galactus,A:
    Silver Surfer 2.25
43 GI,Infinity War,Galactus Vs.
    Agamotto,A:Silver Surfer 2.00
44 GI,Infinity War,V:Juggernaut . . 2.00

45 GI,Inf.War,O:Doctor Strange . . 2.00
46 GI,Inf.War,R:old costume 2.00
47 GI,Inf.War,V:doppleganger . . . 2.00
48 GI,V:The Vishanti 2.00
49 GI,R:Dormammu 2.00
50 GI,A:Hulk,Ghost Rider,Silver
    Surfer,V:Dormammu(leads into
    Secret Defenders)holo-grafx(c) 3.50
51 GI,V:Religious Cult 2.00
52 GI,A:Morbius 2.00
53 GI,Closes Mansion,L:Wong . . . 2.00
54 GI,Infinity Crusade 2.00
55 GI,Inf.Crusade 2.00
56 GI,Inf.Crusade 2.00
57 A:Kyllian,Urthona 2.00
58 V:Urthona 2.00
59 GI,V:Iskelior 2.00
60 B:DQ(s),Siege of
    Darkness,pt.#7 . . . . 4.00
61 Siege of Darkness,pt.#15 . . . . 3.25
62 V:Dr.Doom 2.25
63 JJ(c),V:Morbius 2.00
64 MvR,V:Namor 2.00
65 MvR,V:Namor,Vengeance 2.25

Doctor Strange (3rd Series) #50
© Marvel Entertainment Group

66 A:Wong 2.25
67 R:Clea 2.25
68 MvR 1.95
69 MvR 1.95
70 A:Hulk 1.95
71 V:Hulk 1.95
72 Metallic(c),Last Rites,pt.1 . . . 1.95
73 Last Rites,pt.2 . . . . 1.95
74 SY,DQ,Last Rites,pt.3 . . . . . . 1.95
75 Prismatic cover 3.50
76 I:New Costume 1.95
77 Mob Clean-up 1.95
78 R:Chton 1.95
79 Doc's new Asylum 1.95
80 Missing for months? 1.95
81 A:Nick Fury 1.95
82 A:Hellstorm 1.95
83 V:Tempo Mob,Dormammu . . . 1.95
84 The Homecoming,pt.1 . . . . . . 1.95
85 The Homecoming,pt.2 . . . . . . 1.95
86 The Homecoming,pt.3 . . . . . . 1.95
87 The Homecoming,pt.4 . . . . . . 1.95
88 The Fall of the Tempo,pt.1 . . . 1.95
89 The Fall of the Tempo,pt.2 . . . 1.95

90 final issue 1.95
Ann #2 Return of Defenders,Pt4 . 5.00
Ann #3 GI,I:Killiam,w/card 3.25
Ann.#4 V:Salome 2.95
Spec. Dr. Strange/Ghost Rider#1
    Newsstand vers. of Dr.
    Strange #28 (1991) 6.00
Spec.#1 Dr. Strange vs. Dracula
    rep. MWn(s),GC (1994) 2.00
GNv Triumph and Torment MBg,
    F:Dr. Strange & Dr.Doom . . . 9.95
    HC 14.95
Ashcan 75

DR. STRANGE CLASSICS
March, 1984
1 SD,Reprints 1.75
2 . . . . 1.75
3 . . . . 1.75
4 June, 1984 . . . . 1.75

DOCTOR WHO
1984–86
1 BBC TV Series,UK reprints,
    Return of the Daleks 4.50
2 Star Beast 3.00
3 Transformation 3.00
4 A:K-9,Daleks 3.00
5 V:Time Witch,Colin Baker
    interview 3.00
6 B:Ancient Claw saga 3.00
7 . . . . 3.00
8 The Collector 3.00
9 The Life Bringer 3.00
10 This is your Life 3.00
11 The Deal 3.00
12 End of the Line 3.00
13 V:The Cybermen 3.00
14 Clash of the Neutron Knight . . 3.00
15 B:Peter Davison-Dr. Who . . . 3.00
16 Into the Realm of Satan, . . . 3.00
17 Peter Davison Interview 3.00
18 A:Four Dr.Who's 3.00
19 A:The Sontarans 3.00
20 The Stockbridge Horror 3.00
21 The Stockbridge Horror 3.00
22 The Stockbridge Horror 3.00
23 The Unearthly Child 3.00

DR. ZERO
Epic April, 1988
1 BSz,DCw,I:Dr.Zero 2.00
2 BSz,DCw 1.50
3 BSz,DCw 1.50
4 thru 6 . . . . @1.50
7 DSp 1.50
8 End series, August, 1989 . . . . 1.50

DOLLY DILL
1945
1 Newsstand 80.00

DOMINO
1996
1 thru 3 . . . . @1.95

DOOM 2099
1993–96
1 PB,I:Doom 2099,V:Tiger Wylde,
    foil(c) 3.00
2 I:Rook Seven 2.00
3 PB,V:Tiger Wylde 2.00
4 PB,V:Tiger Wylde 2.00

MARVEL

5 PB,I:Fever	2.00
6 I:Duke Stratosphear	2.00
7 PB,I:Paloma,V:Duke,Fever Haze	2.00
8 PB,C:Ravage	2.00
9 EC,V:Jack the Ripper	2.00
10 PB,w/Poster	2.00
11 PB,I:Thandaza	1.75
12 PB,V:Thandaza	1.75
13 PB(c),JFm(s),V:Necrotek	1.75
14 RLm(c),PB,Fall o/t Hammer#4	1.75
15 PB,I:Radian	1.75
16 EC(a&s),	1.75
17 PB,V:Radian,w/card	1.75
18 PB,	1.75
19 PB,C:Bloodhawk	1.75
20 PB,A:Bloodhawk	1.75
21 PB,Shadow King	1.75
22 PB,R:Duke Stratosphere	1.50
23 PB,R:Tyger Wylde	1.50
24 PB	1.50
25 PB	2.50
25a foil cover	3.25
26	1.50
27 Revolution	1.50
28 Prologue to D-Day	1.50

Becomes:
DOOM 2099 A.D.

29 Doom Invades America	1.95
29a Chromium Cover	3.50
30 D:Corporate Head	1.95
31 PB,One Nation Under Doom	1.95
32 Ravage Aftermath	1.95
33	1.95
34 I:Anthony Herod	1.95
35 E:One Nation Under Doom	1.95
36	1.95
37	1.95
38	1.95
39	1.95
40 Rage Against Time,pt.1	1.95
41 Rage Against Time,pt.2	1.95

DOPEY DUCK COMICS
Timely Fall, 1945

1 A:Casper Cat,Krazy Krow	100.00
2 A:Casper Cat,Krazy Krow	90.00

Becomes:
WACKY DUCK

3 Paperchase(c)	75.00
4 Wacky Duck(c)	100.00
5 Duck & Devil(c)	65.00
6 Cliffhanger(c)	65.00
1 Baketball(c)	50.00
2 Traffic Light(c)	50.00

Becomes: JUSTICE COMICS

DOUBLE DRAGON
July, 1991

1 I:Billy&Jimmy Lee	1.00
2 Dragon Statue Stolen,V:Stelth	1.00
3 Billy Vs. Jimmy	1.00
4 Dragon Force out of control	1.00
5 V:Stealth	1.00
6 V:Nightfall, final issue	1.00

DOUBLE EDGE
1995

Alpha Punisher vs. Nick Fury	4.95
Omega D:Major Character	4.95

D.P. 7
Nov., 1986

1 O:DP7	1.00

2 V:Headhunter	1.00
3 RT,Headhunters	1.00
4 RT,V:Wompus	1.00
5 RT,Exorcist	1.00
6 RT,I:The Sweat Shop	1.00
7 RT,V:Clinic	1.00
8 RT,V:Clinic	1.00
9 RT,AW,I:New Paranormals	1.00
10 RT,I:Mysterious People	1.00
11 AW(i)V:Regulator	1.00
12 O:Randy	1.00
13 O:Charly	1.00
14 AW	1.00
15	1.00
16 V:BlackPower	1.00
17	1.00
18 Pitt tie-in	1.00
19	1.25
20 Spitfire	1.25
21	1.25
22	1.25
23 A:PsiForce	1.25
24 A:Mastodon	1.25
25 V:Famileech	1.50
26 V:Famileech	1.50
27 The Pitt	1.50
28 V:The Candidate	1.25
29 Deadweight	1.50
30 V:Para-troop	1.25
31 A:Chrome	1.50
32 I:The Cure,last issue, June 1989	1.50
Ann.#1,I:Witness	1.00

DRACULA LIVES
B&W Magazine, 1973—75

1	10.00
2 O:Dracula	7.50
3	6.00
4 MP	5.00
5 thru 13	@4.00

DRAFT, THE
1988

1 Sequel to The Pit	3.75

DRAGON LINES
Epic Heavy Hitters 1993
[1st Limited Series]

1 RLm,V:Terrorist on Moon, Embossed(c)	3.00
2 RLm,V:Kuei Emperor	2.25
3 RLm,V:Spirit Boxer	2.25
4 RLm,K:Kuei Emperor	2.25

[Regular Series]

1 B:PQ(s),RLm,I:Tao	2.50
2 RLm,	2.50

DRAGONSLAYER
Oct.–Nov., 1981

1 Movie adapt.	1.25
2 Movie adapt.	1.25

DRAGON STRIKE

1 Based on TSR Game	1.50

DRAGON'S TEETH/ DRAGON'S CLAWS
July, 1988

1 GSr,I:Mercy Dragon, Scavenger,Digit Steel	1.75
2 GSr,V:Evil Dead	1.50
3 GSr,Go Home	1.50

Dragon's Teeth/Dragon's Claws #2
© Marvel Entertainment Group

4 GSr	1.50
5 GSr,I:Death's Head	18.00
6 thru 10 GSr	@1.75

DREADLANDS
Epic

1 Post-Apocalyptic Mini-series	3.95
2 Trapped in Prehistoric Past	3.95
3 V:Alien Time Travelers	3.95
4 Final Issue	3.95

DREADSTAR
Epic Nov., 1982

1 JSn,I:Lord Papal	4.00
2 JSn,O:Willow	2.50
3 JSn,V:Lord Papal	2.25
4 JSn,I:Z	2.25
5 JSn,V:Teutun	2.25
6 JSn,BWr,Interstellar Toybox	2.25
7 JSn,BWr,V:Dr.Mezlo	2.25
8 JSn,V:Z	2.25
9 JSn,V:Z	2.25
10 JSn,V:Z	2.25
11 JSn,O:Lord Papal	2.00
12 JSn,I:Dr.Delphi	2.00
13 JSn,V:Infra Red & Ultra Violet	2.00
14 JSn,V:Lord Papal	2.00
15 JSn,new powers	2.00
16 JSn,V:Lord Papal	2.00
17 JSn,V:Willows father	2.00
18 JSn,V:Dr.Mezlo	2.00
19 JSn,V:Dr.Mezlo	2.00
20 JSn,D:Oedi	2.00
21 JSn,D:Dr.Delphi	2.00
22 JSn,V:Lord Papal	2.00
23 JSn,V:Lord Papal	2.00
24 JSn,JS,V:Lord Papal	2.00
25 JSn,V:Lord Papal	2.00
26 JSn,R:Oedi	2.00
Ann.#1 JSn,The Price	2.50

See COLOR PUB. section

DREADSTAR & COMPANY
July, 1985
1 JSo,reprint 1.25
2 JSo,rep. 1.00
3 JSo,rep. 1.00
4 JSo,rep. 1.00
5 JSo,rep,Dec., 1985. . . . . 1.00

DROIDS
Star April, 1986
1 JR 3.00
2 AW 3.00
3 JR/AW 3.00
4 AW 3.00
5 AW 3.00
6 EC/AW,A:Luke Skywalker 3.00
7 EC/AW,A:Luke Skywalker 3.00
8 EC/AW,A:Luke Skywalker 3.00

DRUID
1995
1 R:Dr. Druid Surprise!!! 2.50
2 F:Nekra 1.95
3 deranged canibal wisemen . . . 1.95
4 Why Must He Die? 1.95

DUNE
April–June, 1985
1 Movie Adapt,Rep. Marvel
　Super Spec,BSz 1.50
2 Movie Adapt,BSz, ... 1.50
3 Movie Adapt,BSz, ... 1.50

DYNOMUTT
Nov., 1977
1 Based on TV series 10.00
2 thru 5 . . . . @8.00
6 Sept., 1978 . . . . 8.00

EARTHWORM JIM
1995–96
1 I:Earthworm Jim 2.25
2 Cow tipping 2.25
3 V:Lawyers,conclusion 2.25

Ectokid #4
© Marvel Entertainment Group

ECTOKID
Razorline 1993–94
1 I:Dex Mungo,BU:Hokum & Hex 2.75
2 O:Dex 2.00
3 I:Ectosphere 2.00
4 I:Brothers Augustine 2.00
5 A:Saint Sinner 2.00
6 Highway 61 Revisited 2.00
7 . . . . 2.00
8 V:Ice Augustine 1.75
9 Love is like a Bullet 1.95
10 . . . . 1.95
Ectokid Unleashed 2.95

ELECTRIC UNDERTOW
Dec., 1989
1 MBa,Strike Force 3.95
2 MBa, Will Deguchis 3.95
3 MBa, Alien Invaders 3.95
4 MBa,Attack on Beijing 3.95
5 MBa, Morituri defeated,March,
1990 . . . . 3.95

ELEKTRA
Nov. 1996
1 PrM,MD2, ... 2.95
1A variant (c) 4.00
2 PrM,MD2,V:Bullseye, round two 1.95
3 PrM,MD2, ... 1.95
4 PrM,MD2 . . . . 1.95
5 PrM,MD2 . . . . 1.95
6 PrM,MD2 . . . . 1.95
7 PrM,MD2,A:Konrad,The Architect1.95
8 PrM,MD2,V:The Architect . . . 1.95
9 PrM,MD2,V:The Four Winds . . 1.95
10 PrM,MD2,V:Daredevil,"American
　Samurai," pt.1 . . . . 1.95
11 PrM,MD2,F:Daredevil 2.00
12 PrM,MD2,F:Daredevil,V:American
　Samuri 2.00
13 PrM,MD2,F:Daredevil, concl. . 2.00
14 LHa,MD2,A:Wolverine 2.00
15 LHa,MD2,A:Silver Samurai . . 2.00
16 LHa,MD2,A Hole in the Soul . 2.00
17 LHa,MD2,V:The Hand 2.00
18 LHa,MD2,A:Shang-Chi&Kingpin 2.00
19 LHa,MD2,last issue 2.00
Minus 1 Spec.,PMg,MD2,flashback 1.95

ELEKTRA: ASSASSIN
August, 1986
1 FM,BSz,V:Shield 6.00
2 FM,BSz,I:Garrett 5.00
3 FM,BSz,V:Shield,A:Garrett . . 5.00
4 FM,BSz,V:Shield,A:Garrett . . . 5.00
5 FM,BSz,I:Chastity,A:Garrett . . 5.00
6 FM,BSz,A:Nick Fury,Garrett . . 5.00
7 FM,BSz,V:Ken Wind,A:Garrett . 5.00
8 FM,BSz,V:Ken Wind,A:Garrett . 5.00
TPB Rep #1-8 . . . . 12.95

ELEKTRA LIVES AGAIN
Graphic Novel FM,R:Elektra,A:Matt
　Murdock,V:The Hand 30.00
TPB FM, rep. of HC, 80pg. 6.95

ELEKTRA: ROOT OF EVIL
1 V:Snakeroot 2.95
2 V:Snakeroot 2.95
3 Elektra's Brother 2.95
4 V:The Hand 2.95

ELEKTRA: SAGA
Feb., 1984
1 FM,rep.Daredevil 7.00
2 FM,rep.Daredevil 7.00
3 FM,rep.Daredevil 7.00
4 FM,rep.Daredevil 7.00
TPB Reprints#1-#4 . . . . 16.95
GN Book One FM,KJ, rep. from
　Daredevil, 96pg 3.95
GN Book Two FM,KJ, rep. from
　Daredevil, 96pg 3.95

ELEKTRA/WITCHBLADE
1-shot "Devil's Reign,"
pt.6, x-over 2.95

ELFQUEST
August, 1985
1 WP,reprints 4.00
2 WP 2.50
3 WP 2.50
4 WP 2.50
5 WP 2.50
6 WP,Young Cutter V:Mad Coil . 2.50
7 WP,Young Cutter V:Mad Coil . . 2.25
8 WP 2.25
9 WP 2.25
10 WP,A:Cutter, Skywise 2.25
11 WP,I:Two Edge 2.25
12 WP,The Mysterious Forest . . 2.25
13 WP,The Forest, A:Leetah . . . 2.25
14 WP,A:The Bone Woman 2.25
15 WP,The Forest, continued . . . 2.25
16 WP,Forbidden Grove 2.00
17 WP,Blue Mountain 2.00
18 WP,Secrets 2.00
19 WP,Twisted Gifts 2.00
20 WP,Twisted Gifts 2.00
21 WP 2.00
22 WP,A:Winnowill 2.00
23 WP,Blue Mountain,A:Winnowill 2.00
24 WP,The Quest Usurped 2.00
25 WP,Northern Wastelands . . . 2.00
26 WP,Rayeks Story 2.00
27 WP,Battle Preparations 2.00
28 WP,Elves vs. Trolls 2.00
29 WP,Battle Beneath Blue
　Mountain 2.00
30 and 31 WP . . . . @2.00
32 WP,Conclusion, March 1988 . 2.00

ELSEWHERE PRINCE
Epic May–Oct., 1990
1 thru 6 . . . . @2.00

ELVIRA
Oct., 1988
Spec.B&W, Movie Adapt. 2.00

EPIC
1992
1 Wildcards,Hellraiser 4.95
2 Nightbreed,Wildcards 4.95
3 DBw,MFm,Alien Legion 4.95
4 Stalkers,Metropol,Wildcards . . 4.95

EPIC GRAPHIC NOVEL
Moebius 1: Upon a Star 10.00
Moebius 2: Arzach 10.00
Moebius 3: Airtight Garage . . . 10.00
Moebius 4: Long Tomorrow . . . 10.00
Moebius 5: 10.00
Moebius 6: Pharadonesia 10.00

Last of Dragons	7.00
The Incal 1 Moebius	11.00
The Incal 2 Moebius	11.00
The Incal 3 Moebius	11.00
JBo,Someplace Strange	7.00
MZ,Punisher	16.95

EPIC ILLUSTRATED
Spring, 1980

1 Black and White/Color Mag.	6.00
2 thru 10	@4.50
11 thru 15	@3.50
16	4.00
17 thru 20	@3.00
21 thru 25	@3.00
26 thru 34, March, 1986	@5.50

EPIC LITE
Epic Nov., 1991

One-shot short stories	3.95

ESSENTIAL SPIDER-MAN
1997

Vol. 1 StL,SD, rep. Amaz. Fant. #15, Amaz Sp.-M #1–#20, Ann. #1	13.00
Vol. 2 StL,SD, rep. Amaz. Sp.-M #21–#43, Ann.#2&#3	13.00
Vol. 3 StL,JR,Lizard,Vulture, Kraven	13.00

ESSENTIAL WOLVERINE
May 1998

Vol 3 TPB	13.00

ESSENTIAL X-MEN

Vol. 2 rep. Uncanny X-Men #120-#145	14.95
Vol. 3 rep. Uncanny X-Men #145-#161, Annuals #3-#5	14.95

ETERNALS
[1st Series] July, 1976

1 JK,I:Ikaris,25 cent edition	6.00
2 JK,I:Ajak,25 cent edition	5.00
3 JK,I:Sersi	5.00
4 JK,Night of the Demons	4.00
5 JK,I:Makarri,Zuras Thena,Domo	4.00
6 JK,Gods & Men at City College	4.00
7 JK,V:Celestials	4.00
8 JK,I:Karkas, Reject	4.00
9 JK,I:Sprite,Reject vs. Karkas	4.00
10 JK,V:Celestials	4.00
11 JK,I:Kingo Sunen	4.00
12 JK,I:Uni-Mind	4.00
13 JK,I:FOrgottenOne(Gilgamesh)	4.00
14 JK,V:Hulk	4.00
15 JK,V:Hulk	4.00
16 JK,I:Dromedan	4.00
17 JK,I:Sigmar	4.00
18 JK,I:Nerve Beast	4.00
19 JK,Secret o/t Pyramid	4.00
Ann.#1 JK,V:Timekillers	3.00

[2nd Series] Oct., 1985

1 SB,I:Cybele	1.50
2 SB,V:Deviants	1.50
3 SB,V:Deviants	1.50
4 SB,V:Deviants	1.50
5 SB,V:Deviants	1.50
6 SB,V:Deviants	1.50
7 SB,V:Deviants	1.50
8 WS,SB,V:Deviants	1.50
9 WS,SB,V:Deviants	1.50
10 WS,SB,V:Deviants	1.50
11 WS,KP,V:Deviants	1.50
12 WS,KP,V:Deviants	1.50

ETERNALS: HEROD FACTOR
Nov., 1991

1 MT/BMc,A:Sersi (giant size)	2.50

EVERYMAN
Epic 1991

1-Shot.Supernatural Story (Animated Cel Artwork)	4.50

EWOKS
Star June, 1985—Sept., 1987

1 Based on TV Series	3.00
2	2.50
3	2.50
4 A:Foonars	2.50
5 Wicket vs. Ice Demon.	2.50
6 Mount Sorrow, A:Teebo	2.50
7 A:Logray,V:Morag	2.50
8	2.50
9 Lost in Time	2.50
10 Lost in Time	1.50
11 Kneesaa Shrunk,A:Fleebogs	1.50
12	1.50
13	1.50
14 Teebo- King for a Day	1.50
15	1.50

EXCALIBUR
April, 1988

1 AD,Special,O:Excalibur, V:Technet	5.00
1a 2nd Printing	2.50
1b 3rd Printing	2.00
2 AAd,Mojo Mayhem,A:X-Babies	2.50
3 Air Apparent Spec.RLm,KJ,JG,TP, RL,EL,JRu,A:Coldblood	3.00

[Regular Series]

1 B:CCl(s),AD,V:Warwolves, I:Widget	5.00
2 AD,V:Warwolves,I:Kylun	4.00
3 AD,V:Juggernaut	3.50
4 AD,V:Arcade,Crazy Gang	3.00
5 AD,V:Arcade	3.00
6 AD,Inferno,I:Alistaire Stuart	3.00
7 AD,Inferno	3.00
8 RLm,JRu,A:New Mutants	3.00
9 AD,I:Nazi-Excalibur	3.00
10 MR,V:Nazi-Excalibur	3.00
11 MR,V:Nazi-Excalibur	3.00
12 AD,Fairy Tale Dimension	3.00
13 AD,The Prince,N:Capt.Britian	3.00
14 AD,Too Many Heroes	2.50
15 AD,I:US James Braddock	2.50
16 AD,V:Anjulie	2.50
17 AD,C:Prof.X,Starjammers	2.50
18 DJ,DA,V:Jamie Braddock	2.50
19 RL,TA,AM,V:Jamie Braddock	2.50
20 RLm,JRu,V:Demon Druid	2.50
21 I:Crusader X	2.50
22 V:Crusader X	2.50
23 AD,V:Magik	2.50
24 AD,Return Home,C:Galactus	2.50
25 E:CCl(s),AM,A:Galactus,Death, Watcher	2.50
26 RLm,JRu,V:Mastermind	2.50
27 BWS,BSz,A:Nth Man	3.00
28 BBl,Night at Bar	2.50
29 JRu,V:Nightmare,A:PowerPack	2.50
30 DR,AM,A:Doctor Strange	2.50

Excalibur #99
© Marvel Entertainment Group

31 DR,AM,V:Son of Krakoa	2.50
32 V:Mesmero	2.50
33 V:Mesmero	2.50
34 V:Mesmero	2.50
35 AM,Missing Child	2.50
36 AM,V:Silv.Sable,Sandman	2.50
37 A:Avengers W.C.,Dr.Doom	2.50
38 A:Avengers W.C.,Dr.Doom	2.50
39 A:Avengers W.C.,Dr.Doom	2.50
40 O:Excalibur,Trial-Lockheed	2.50
41 V:Warwolves,C:Cable	3.00
42 AD,Team Broken Up	3.50
43 AD,Nightcrawler,V:Capt.Brit	3.00
44 AD,Capt.Britain On Trial	3.00
45 AD,I:N-Men,	3.00
46 AD,Return of Kylun,C:Cerise	3.00
47 AD,I:Cerise	3.00
48 AD,A:Anti-Phoenix	3.00
49 AD,MFm,V:Necrom,R:Merlyn	3.00
50 AD,Phoenix,V:Necrom,Merlyn	4.00
51 V:Giant Dinosaurs	2.00
52 O:Phoenix,A:Prof X,MarvGirl	2.00
53 A:Spider-Man,V:The Litter	2.00
54 AD,MFm,V:Crazy Gang	2.50
55 AD,MFm,A:Psylocke	2.50
56 AD,MFm, V:Saturyne,Jamie Braddock	2.50
57 A:X-Men,Alchemy,V:Trolls	2.75
58 A:X-Men,Alchemy,V:Trolls	2.75
59 A:Avengers	2.25
60 A:Avengers	2.25
61 AD,MFm,Phoenix Vs.Galactus	2.25
62 AD,MFm,A:Galactus	2.25
63 AD,MFm,V:Warpies	2.25
64 AD,MFm,V:RCX,R:Rachel	2.25
65 AD,MFm,R:Dark Phoenix	2.25
66 AD,MFm,V:Ahab,Sentinels, O:Widget	2.25
67 AD,MFm,V:Ahab,Sentinels	2.25
68 V:Starjammers	2.00
69 A:Starjammers	2.00
70 A:Starjammers	2.00
71 DaR,Hologram(c),N:Excalibur	4.00
72 KeL,V:Siena Blaze	2.00
73 TSr,V:Siena Blaze	2.00

74 InC,A:Mr.Sinster,Siena Blaze . 2.00
75 SLo(s),KeL,I:Daytripper(Amanda
   Sefton),Britannic(Capt.Britain),
   BU:Nightcrawler 3.50
75a Newstand Ed. 2.25
76 KeL,V:D'spayre 2.00
77 KeL,R:Doug Ramsey 2.00
78 A:Zero,Doug Ramsey 2.25
79 A:Zero,Doug Ramsey 2.25
80 A:Zero,Doug Ramsey 2.25
81 Doug Ramsey 2.25
82 . . . . 2.50
82a foil(c) 3.50
83 regular ed. 1.50
83a Deluxe ed. Kitty,Nightcrawler . 2.25
84 regular ed. 1.50
84a Deluxe ed. 2.25
85 regular ed. 1.50
85a Deluxe ed. 2.25
86 regular ed. 1.50
86a Deluxe ed. 2.25
87 KeL,Secrets of the Genoshan
   Mutate Technology 1.95
88 Dream Nails,pt.1 . . . . 1.95
89 Dream Nails,pt.2 . . . . 1.95
90 Between Uncreated,Phalanx . . 2.95
91 F:Colossus 1.95
92 F:Colossus 1.95
93 F:Wolfsbane 1.95
94 A:Karma & Psylocke 1.95
95 . . . . 1.95
96 . . . . 1.95
97 BWi,B.Braddock's secrets told . 1.95
98 . . . . 1.95
99 European Hellfire Club,
   Onslaught 1.95
100 Onslaught saga, double size . 2.95
101 . . . . 1.95
102 . . . . 1.95
103 WEI,F:Colossus,Kitty &
   Nichtcrawler 1.95
104 JAr,BHi,PNe,Douglock's
   dark side 1.95
105 JAr,BHi,PNe,V:Moonstar, . 1.95
106 . . . . 1.95
107 SvL,New direction 1.95
108 Dragons of the Crimson Dawn 1.95
109 V:Spiral,A:Captain Britain . . . 1.95
110 V:The Dragons of the
   Crimson Dawn 1.95
111 F:Shadowcat,R:Rory Cambell
   (Ahab?) 1.95
112 Quicksilver tie-in 1.95
113 BRa,Colossus & Meggan . . . 2.00
114 BRa,Vanisher 2.00
115 BRa,Quarantine,F:GenerationX 2.00
116 BRa,Legacy Virus, cont. 2.00
117 BRa,F:Kitty Pryde, Colossus &
   Nightcrawler 2.00
118 BRa,V:Creatures from the
   Shadows 2.00
119 BRa,V:Nightmare 2.00
120 BRa,F:Kitty Pryde & Pete
   Wisdom 2.00
121 BRa,to Egypt 2.00
122 BRa,V:Original X-Men? 2.00
123 BRa,V:Mimic 2.00
124 BBr,Captain Britain's bachelor
   party 2.00
125 TvS,SHa, W:Captain Britain &
   Meggan, final issue 3.00
Minus 1 Spec., flashback,
   F:Nightcrawler 1.95
Ann.#1 I:Khaos,w/card 3.25
Spec #1 The Possession 4.00

Spec #2 RLm,DT,JG,RL,
   A:Original X-Men 2.75
PF Cold Blood 4.95
GN Weird War III 9.95
TPB Wild, Wild Life 5.95

FACTOR X
1995
1 After Xavier 4.00
2 Scott vs. Alex Summers 3.00
3 Cyclops vs. Havok 2.50
4 Jean & Scott 2.50
TPB Rep. #1–#4 . . . . 8.95

FAFHRD AND THE GRAY MOUSER
Epic Oct., 1990
1 MMi,Fritz Leiber adapt. 5.00
2 & 3 MMi . . . . @5.00
4 MMi, Feb. 1991 . . . . 5.00

FAITHFUL
Nov., 1949
1 Ph(c),I Take This Man 75.00
2 Ph(c),Love Thief,Feb.,1950 . . 60.00

FALCON
Nov., 1983
1 PS,V:Nemesis 2.00
2 V:Sentinels 1.50
3 V:Electro 1.50
4 A:Capt.America, Feb., 1984 . . 1.50

FALLEN ANGELS
April, 1987
1 KGa,TP,A:Sunspot,Warlock . . 3.00
2 KGa,TP,I:Gomi,Fallen Angels . 2.50
3 KGa,TP,A:X-Factor 2.50
4 KGa,TP,A:Moon Boy, Devil
   Dinosaur 2.50
5 JSon,D:Angel,Don 2.50
6 JSon,Coconut Grove 2.50
7 KGa,Captured in CoconutGrove 2.50
8 KGa,L:Sunspot,Warlock 2.50

FANTASTIC FORCE
1994–96
1 Foil stamped cover 2.50
2 Moses 2.25
3 . . . . 2.25
4 A:Captain America 2.25
5 I:Dreadface 2.25
6 F:Vibraxis 1.75
7 V:Doom 1.75
8 V:Crimson Cadre 1.75
9 Atlantis Rising 1.75
10 A:Human Torch 1.75
11 A:Black Panther 1.75
12 V:Vanguard 1.75
13 J:She-Hulk 1.75
14 V:Wakanda 1.75
15 End of the Fantastic Force? . . 1.75
16 End of the Fantastic Force? . . 1.75
17 . . . . 1.75
18 . . . . 1.75

FANTASTIC FOUR
Nov., 1961
1 JK,I&O:Mr.Fantastic,Thing
   Invisible Girl,Human Torch
   Mole Man 19,000.00
2 JK,I:Skrulls 3,500.00
3 JK,I:Miracleman 2,500.00

4 JK,R:Submariner 2,900.00
5 JK,JSt,I&O:Doctor Doom . . 3,000.00
6 JK,V:Doctor Doom 1,600.00
7 JK,I:Kurrgo 850.00
8 JK,I:Alicia Masters,I&O:
   Puppet Master 850.00
9 JK,V:Submariner 800.00
10 JK,V:Doctor Doom,I:Ovoids . 800.00
11 JK,I:Impossible Man 700.00
12 JK,V:Hulk 1,100.00
13 JK,SD,I&O:Red Ghost,
   I:Watcher 500.00
14 JK,SD,V:Submariner 300.00
15 JK,I:Mad Thinker 300.00
16 JK,V:Doctor Doom 300.00
17 JK,V:Doctor Doom 300.00
18 JK,I:Super Skrull 300.00
19 JK,I&O:Rama Tut 300.00
20 JK,I:Molecule Man 325.00
21 JK,I:Hate Monger 250.00
22 JK,V:Mole Man 250.00
23 JK,V:Doctor Doom 250.00
24 JK,I:Infant Terrible 250.00
25 JK,Thing vs.Hulk 400.00

Fantastic Four #27
© Marvel Entertainment Group

26 JK,V:Hulk,A:Avengers 375.00
27 JK,A:Doctor Strange 175.00
28 JK,1st X-Men x-over 250.00
29 JK,V:Red Ghost 125.00
30 JK,I&O:Diablo 125.00
31 JK,V:Mole Man 100.00
32 JK,V:Superskrull 100.00
33 JK,I:Attuma 100.00
34 JK,I:Gideon 100.00
35 JK,I:Dragon Man,A:Diablo . . 100.00
36 JK,I:Medusa,Frightful Four . 100.00
37 JK,V:Skrulls 90.00
38 JK,V:Frightful Four,I:Trapster . 90.00
39 JK,WW,A:Daredevil 90.00
40 JK,A:Daredevil,Dr.Doom 90.00
41 JK,V:Fright.Four,A:Medusa . 75.00
42 JK,V:Frightful Four 75.00
43 JK,V:Frightful Four 75.00
44 JK,JSt,I:Gorgon,
   V:Dragon Man 80.00
45 JK,JSt,I:Inhumans(Black Bolt,
   Triton,Lockjaw,Crystal,
   Karnak) 90.00
46 JK,JSt,V:Seeker 75.00

47 JK,JSt,I:Maximus,Attilan,	
Alpha Primitives 75.00	
48 JK,JSt,I:Silver Surfer,	
C:Galactus 850.00	
49 JK,JSt,A:Silver Surfer,	
V:Galactus 250.00	
50 JK,JSt,V:Galactus,Silver	
Surfer,I:Wyatt Wingfoot . . . 275.00	
51 JK,JSt,I:Negative Zone . . . 65.00	
52 JK,JSt,I:Black Panther 100.00	
53 JK,JSt,I:Klaw,Vibranium . . . 100.00	
54 JK,JSt,I:Prester John 60.00	
55 JK,JSt,A:Silver Surfer 90.00	
56 JK,JSt,O:Klaw,A:Inhumans,	
C:Silver Surfer 65.00	
57 JK,JSt,V:Doc Doom,	
A:Silver Surfer. 65.00	
58 JK,JSt,V:Doc Doom,	
A:Silver Surfer. 65.00	
59 JK,JSt,V:Doc Doom,	
A:Silver Surfer. 65.00	
60 JK,JSt,V:Doc Doom,	
A:Silver Surfer. 65.00	
61 JK,JSt,V:Sandman,	
A:Silver Surfer 65.00	
62 JK,JSt,I:Blastaar 45.00	
63 JK,JSt,V:Blastaar 50.00	
64 JK,JSt,I:The Kree,Sentry . . . 50.00	
65 JK,JSt,I:Ronan,Supreme	
Intelligence 50.00	
66 JK,JSt,O:Him,A:Crystal . 100.00	
67 JK,JSt,I:Him 125.00	
68 JK,JSt,V:Mad Thinker 60.00	
69 JK,JSt,V:Mad Thinker 50.00	
70 JK,JSt,V:Mad Thinker 50.00	
71 JK,JSt,V:Mad Thinker 50.00	
72 JK,JSt,A:Watcher,S.Surfer . 50.00	
73 JK,JSt,A:SpM,DD,Thor 35.00	
74 JK,JSt,A:Silver Surfer 45.00	
75 JK,JSt,A:Silver Surfer 45.00	
76 JK,JSt,V:Psycho Man,S.Surf . 40.00	
77 JK,JSt,V:Galactus,S.Surfer . . 40.00	
78 JK,JSt,V:Wizard 35.00	
79 JK,JSt,A:Crystall,V:Mad	
Thinker 35.00	
80 JK,JSt,A:Crystal 35.00	
81 JK,JSt,J:Crystal,V:Wizard . . 35.00	
82 JK,JSt,V:Maximus 35.00	
83 JK,JSt,V:Maximus 35.00	
84 JK,JSt,V:Doctor Doom 25.00	
85 JK,JSt,V:Doctor Doom 25.00	
86 JK,JSt,V:Doctor Doom 25.00	
87 JK,JSt,V:Doctor Doom 25.00	
88 JK,JSt,V:Mole Man 25.00	
89 JK,JSt,V:Mole Man 25.00	
90 JK,JSt,V:Skrulls 22.00	
91 JK,JSt,V:Skrulls,I:Torgo . . . 22.00	
92 JK,JSt,V:Torgo,Skrulls 22.00	
93 JK,V:Torgo,Skrulls 22.00	
94 JK,JSt,I:Agatha Harkness . . 22.00	
95 JK,JSt,I:Monocle 22.00	
96 JK,JSt,V:Mad Thinker 20.00	
97 JK,JSt,V:Monster from	
Lost Lagoon 20.00	
98 JK,JSt,V:Kree Sentry 20.00	
99 JK,JSt,A:Inhumans 20.00	
100 JK,JSt,V:Puppetmaster 75.00	
101 JK,JSt,V:Maggia 20.00	
102 JK,JSt,V:Magneto 22.00	
103 JR,V:Magneto 22.00	
104 JR,V:Magneto 22.00	
105 JR,L:Crystal 20.00	
106 JR,JSt,'Monster's Secret' . . 20.00	
107 JB,JSt,V:Annihilus 20.00	
108 JK,JB,JR,JSt, V:Annihilus . . 20.00	

109 JB,JSt,V:Annihilus 20.00	
110 JB,JSt,V:Annihilus 20.00	
111 JB,JSt,A:Hulk 20.00	
112 JB,JSt,Thing vs. Hulk 50.00	
113 JB,JSt,I:Overmind 15.00	
114 JR(c),JB,V:Overmind 15.00	
115 JR(c),JB,JSt,I:Eternals 15.00	
116 JB,JSt,O:Stranger 15.00	
117 JB,JSt,V:Diablo 11.00	
118 JR(c),JB,JM,V:Diablo 11.00	
119 JB,JSt,V:Klaw 11.00	
120 JB,JSt,I:Gabriel(Airwalker)	
(Robot) 11.00	
121 JB,JSt,V:Silver Surfer,D:	
Gabriel Destroyer 15.00	
122 JR(c),JB,JSt,V:Galactus,	
A:Silver Surfer 15.00	
123 JB,JSt,V:Galactus,	
A:Silver Surfer 14.00	
124 JB,JSt,V:Monster 8.00	
125 E:StL(s),JB,JSt,V:Monster . . 8.00	
126 B:RTs(s),JB,JSt,	
O:FF,MoleMan 8.00	
127 JB,JSt,V:Mole Man 8.00	

Fantastic Four #88
© Marvel Entertainment Group

128 JB,JSt,V:Mole Man 10.00	
129 JB,JSt,I:Thundra,	
V:Frightful Four 8.00	
130 JSo(c),JB,JSt,V:Frightful Four 7.00	
131 JSo(c),JB,JSt,V:QuickSilver . . 7.00	
132 JB,JSt,J:Medusa 7.00	
133 JSt(i),V:Thundra 7.00	
134 JB,JSt,V:Dragon Man 7.00	
135 JB,JSt,V:Gideon 7.00	
136 JB,JSt,A:Shaper 7.00	
137 JB,JSt,A:Shaper 7.00	
138 JB,JSt,O:Miracle Man 7.00	
139 JB,V:Miracle Man 7.00	
140 JB,JSt,O:Annihilus 7.00	
141 JR(c),JB,JSt,V:Annihilus . . . 7.00	
142 RB,JSt,A:Doc Doom 7.00	
143 GK(c),RB,V:Doc Doom 7.00	
144 RB,JSt,V:Doc Doom 7.00	
145 JSt&GK(c),RA,I:Ternak 7.00	
146 RA,JSt,V:Ternak 7.00	
147 RB,JSt,V:Subby 7.00	
148 RB,JSt,V:Frightful Four 7.00	
149 RB,JSt,V:Sub-Mariner. 7.00	

150 GK(c),RB,JSt,W:Crystal &	
Quicksilver,V:Ultron 9.00	
151 RB,JSt,O:Thundra 5.00	
152 JR(c),RB,JM,A:Thundra 5.00	
153 GK(c),RB,JSt,A:Thundra . . . 5.00	
154 GK(c),rep.Str.Tales #127 . . . 5.00	
155 RB,JSt,A:Surfer 8.00	
156 RB,JSt,A:Surfer,V:Doom . . . 8.00	
157 RB,JSt,A:Surfer 8.00	
158 RB,JSt,V:Xemu 5.00	
159 RB,JSt,V:Xemu 5.00	
160 K&R(c),JB,V:Arkon 4.50	
161 RB,JSt,V:Arkon 4.50	
162 RB,DA,JSt,V:Arkon 4.50	
163 RB,JSt,V:Arkon 4.50	
164 JK(c),GP,JSt,V:Crusader,R:	
Marvel Boy,I:Frankie Raye . . . 4.50	
165 GP,JSt,O:Crusader,	
O&D:Marvel Boy 4.50	
166 GP,V:Hulk 6.00	
167 JK(c),GP,JSt,V:Hulk 6.00	
168 RB,JSt,J:Luke Cage 5.00	
169 RB,JSt,V:Puppetmaster 5.00	
170 GP,JSt,L:Luke Cage 5.00	
171 JK(c),RB,GP,JSt,I:Gor 4.00	
172 JK(c),GP,JSt,V:Destroyer . . . 5.00	
173 JB,JSt,V:Galactus,O:Heralds . 5.00	
174 JB,V:Galactus 5.00	
175 JB,A:High Evolutionary 4.00	
176 GP,JSt,V:Impossible Man . . . 4.00	
177 JP,JS,A:Frightful Four	
I:Texas Twister,Capt.Ultra . . . 3.50	
178 GP,V:Frightful Four,Brute . . . 3.50	
179 JSt,V:Annihilus 3.50	
180 reprint #101 . . . . 3.50	
181 E:RTs(s),JSt,V:Brute,	
Annihilus 3.50	
182 SB,JSt,V:Brute,Annihilus . . . 3.50	
183 SB,JSt,V:Brute,Annihilus . . . 3.50	
184 GP,JSt,V:Eliminator 3.50	
185 GP,JSt,V:Nich.Scratch 3.50	
186 GP,JSi,I:Salem's Seven 3.50	
187 GP,JSt,V:Klaw,Molecule Man 3.50	
188 GP,JSt,V:Molecule Man 3.50	
189 reprint FF Annual #4 . . . . . . 3.50	
190 SB,O:Fantastic Four 4.00	
191 GP,JSt,V:Plunderer,	
Team Breaks Up 3.50	
192 GP,JSt,V:Texas Twister 3.50	
193 KP,JSt,V:Darkoth,Diablo . . . 3.50	
194 KP,V:Darkoth,Diablo 3.50	
195 KP,A:Sub-Mariner 3.50	
196 KP,V:Invincible Man (Reed),	
A:Dr.Doom,Team Reunited . . . 3.50	
197 KP,JSt,Red Ghost 3.50	
198 KP,JSt,V:Doc Doom 3.50	
199 KP,JSt,V:Doc Doom 3.50	
200 KP,JSt,V:Doc Doom 5.00	
201 KP,JSt,FF's Machinery 3.00	
202 KP,JSt,V:Quasimodo 3.00	
203 KP,JSt,V:Mutant 3.00	
204 KP,JSt,V:Skrulls 3.00	
205 KP,JSt,V:Skrulls 3.00	
206 KP,JSt,V:Skrulls,A:Nova 3.00	
207 SB,JSt,V:Monocle,A:SpM . . . 3.00	
208 SB,V:Sphinx,A:Nova 2.50	
209 JBy,JSt,I:Herbie,A:Nova 4.00	
210 JBy,JS,A:Galactus 3.00	
211 JBy,JS,I:Terrax,A:Galactus . . 4.00	
212 JBy,JSt,V:Galactus,Sphinx . . 3.00	
213 JBy,JSt,V:Terrax,Galactus	
Sphinx 3.00	
214 JBy,JSt,V:Skrull 3.00	
215 JBy,JSt,V:Blastaar 3.00	
216 JBy,V:Blastaar 3.00	

217 JBy,JSt,A:Dazzler 3.00
218 JBy,JSt,V:FrightfulFour,
   A:Spider-Man 4.00
219 BSz,JSt,A:Sub-Mariner 3.00
220 JBy,JSt,A:Vindicator 3.50
221 JBy,JSt,V:Vindicator 3.50
222 BSz,JSt,V:Nicholas Scratch . . 3.00
223 BSz,JSt,V:Salem's Seven . . . 3.00
224 BSz,A:Thor 3.00
225 BSz,A:Thor 3.00
226 BSz,A:Shogun 3.00
227 BSz,JSt,V:Ego-Spawn 3.00
228 BSz,JSt,V:Ego-Spawn 3.00
229 BSz,JSt,I:Firefrost,Ebon
   Seeker 3.00
230 BSz,JSt,A:Avengers,
   O:Firefrost & Ebon Seeker . . . 3.00
231 BSz,JSt,V:Stygorr 3.00
232 JBy,New Direction,V:Diablo . . 5.00
233 JBy,V:Hammerhead 3.50
234 JBy,V:Ego 3.50
235 JBy,O:Ego 3.50
236 JBy,V:Dr.Doom,A:Puppet
   Master, 20th Anniv. 4.50

Fantastic Four #148
© Marvel Entertainment Group

237 JBy,V:Solons 3.50
238 JBy,O:Frankie Raye,
   new Torch 3.50
239 JBy,I:Aunt Petunia,
   Uncle Jake 4.50
240 JBy,A:Inhumans,b:Luna 3.50
241 JBy,A:Black Panther 3.50
242 JBy,A:Daredevil,Thor,Iron Man
   Spider-Man,V:Terrax 3.50
243 JBy,A:Daredevil,Dr.Strange,
   Spider-Man,Avengers,V:Galactus,
   Terrax 4.00
244 JBy,A:Avengers,Dr.Strange,
   Galactus, Frankie Raye
   Becomes Nova 4.00
245 JBy,V:Franklin Richards 3.00
246 JBy,V:Dr.Doom,
   A:Puppet Master 3.00
247 JBy,A:Dr.Doom,I:Kristoff,
   D:Zorba 3.00
248 JBy,A:Inhumans 3.00

249 JBy,V:Gladiator 3.00
250 JBy,A:Capt.America,SpM
   V:Gladiator 3.00
251 JBy,A:Annihilus 2.50
252 JBy,1st sideways issue,V:
   Ootah,A:Annihilus,w/tattoo . . 3.00
252a w/o tattoo 2.00
253 JBy,V:Kestorans,A:Annihilus . 3.00
254 JBy,V:Mantracora,
   A:She-Hulk,Wasp 3.00
255 JBy,A:Daredevil,Annihilus,
   V:Mantracora 3.00
256 JBy,A:Avengers,Galactus,
   V:Annihilus,New Costumes . . 3.00
257 JBy,A:Galactus,Death,Nova,
   Scarlet Witch 3.50
258 JBy,A:Dr.Doom,D:Hauptmann 3.00
259 JBy,V:Terrax,Dr.Doom,
   C:Silver Silver 3.00
260 JBy,V:Terrax, Dr.Doom,
   A:Silver Surfer,Sub-Mariner . . . 4.00
261 JBy,A:Sub-Mariner,Marrina,
   Silver Surfer,Sc.Witch,Lilandra . 4.00
262 JBy,O:Galactus,A:Odin,
   (J.Byrne in story) 3.00
263 JBy,V:Messiah,A:Mole Man . . 3.00
264 JBy,V:Messiah,A:Mole Man . . 3.00
265 JBy,A:Trapster,Avengers,
   J:She-Hulk,Secret Wars 3.00
266 KGa,JBy,A:Hulk,Sasquatch,
   V:Karisma 3.00
267 JBy,A:Hulk,Sasquatch,Morbius,
   V:Dr.Octopus,Sue miscarries . . 3.00
268 JBy,V:Doom's Mask 3.00
269 JBy,R:Wyatt Wingfoot,
   I:Terminus 3.00
270 JBy,V:Terminus 3.00
271 JBy,V:Gormuu 3.00
272 JBy,I:Warlord (Nathaniel
   Richards) 3.00
273 JBy,V:Warlord 3.00
274 JBy,AG,cont.from Thing#19,
   A:Spider-Man's Black Costume 3.00
275 JBy,AG,V:T.J.Vance 3.00
276 JBy,JOy,V:Mephisto,
   A:Dr.Strange 3.00
277 JBy,JOy,V:Mephisto,
   A:Dr.Strange,R:Thing 3.00
278 JBy,JOy,O:Dr.Doom,A:Kristoff
   (as Doom) 3.00
279 JBy,JOy,V:Dr.Doom(Kristoff),
   I:New Hate-Monger 3.00
280 JBy,JOy,I:Malice,
   V:Hate-Monger 3.00
281 JBy,JOy,A:Daredevil,V:Hate
   Monger,Malice 3.00
282 JBy,JOy,A:Power Pack,Psycho
   Man,Secret Wars II 3.00
283 JBy,JOy,V:Psycho-Man 3.00
284 JBy,JOy,V:Psycho-Man 3.00
285 JBy,JOy,Secret Wars II
   A:Beyonder 3.00
286 JBy,TA,R:Jean Grey,
   A:Hercules Capt.America 3.50
287 JBy,JSt,A:Wasp,V:Dr.Doom . 3.00
288 JBy,JSt,V:Dr.Doom,Secret
   Wars II 3.50
289 JBy,AG,D:Basilisk,V:Blastaar,
   R:Annihilus 3.00
290 JBy,AG,V:Annihilus 3.00
291 JBy,CR,A:Nick Fury 3.00
292 JBy,AG,A:Nick Fury,V:Hitler . 3.00
293 JBy,AG,A:Avengers.W.C. . . . 3.00
294 JOy,AG,V:FutureCentralCity . 2.50
295 JOy,AG,V:Fut.Central City . . . 2.50

296 BWS,KGa,RF,BWi,AM,KJ,JB,
   SL,MS,JRu,JOy,JSt,25th
   Anniv.,V:MoleMan 3.00
297 JB,SB,V:Umbra-Sprite 2.50
298 JB,SB,V:Umbra-Sprite 2.50
299 JB,SB,She-Hulk,V:Thing,
   A:Spider-Man,L:She-Hulk 2.50
300 JB,SB,W:Torch & Fake Alicia
   (Lyja),A:Puppet-Master,Wizard,
   Mad Thinker,Dr.Doom 3.00
301 JB,SB,V:Wizard,MadThinker . 2.25
302 JB,SB,V:Project Survival 2.25
303 JB,RT,A:Thundra,V:Machus . 2.25
304 JB,JSt,V:Quicksilver,
   A:Kristoff 2.25
305 JB,JSt,V:Quicksilver,
   J:Crystal,A:Dr.Doom 2.25
306 JB,JSt,A:Capt.America,
   J:Ms.Marvel,V:Diablo 2.25
307 JB,JSt,L:Reed&Sue,V:Diablo . 2.25
308 JB,JSt,I:Fasaud 2.25
309 JB,JSt,V:Fasaud 2.25
310 KP,JSt,V:Fasaud,N:Thing
   & Ms.Marvel 2.25

Fantastic Four #285
© Marvel Entertainment Group

311 KP,JSt,A:Black Panther,
   Dr.Doom,V:THRob 2.25
312 KP,JSt,A:Black Panther,
   Dr.Doom,X-Factor 2.25
313 SB,JSt,V:Lava Men,
   A:Moleman 2.00
314 KP,JSt,V:Belasco 2.00
315 KP,JSt,V:Mast.Pandem. 2.00
316 KP,JSt,A:CometMan 2.00
317 KP,JSt,L:Crystal 2.00
318 KP,JSt,V:Dr.Doom 2.00
319 KP,JSt,G-Size,O:Beyonder . . 2.25
320 KP,JSt,Hulk vs Thing 2.50
321 RLm,RT,A:She-Hulk 2.00
322 KP,JSt,Inferno,V:Graviton . . 2.00
323 KP,JSt,RT,Inferno A:Mantis . . 2.00
324 KP,JSt,RT,A:Mantis 2.00
325 RB,RT,A:Silver Surfer,
   D:Mantis 2.50
326 KP,RT,I:New Frightful Four . . 2.00
327 KP,RT,V:Frightful Four 2.00

328 KP,RT,V:Frightful Four 2.00	379 PR,V:Ms.Marvel 2.00	410 . . . . 1.50
329 RB,RT,V:Mole Man 2.00	380 PR,A:Dr.Doom,V:Hunger 2.00	411 . . . . 1.50
330 RB,RT,V:Dr.Doom 2.00	381 PR,D:Dr.Doom,Mr.Fantastic,	412 TDF,PR,DBi,Mr.Fantastic
331 RB,RT,V:Ultron 2.00	V:Hunger 5.00	vs. Sub-Mariner 1.50
332 RB,RT,V:Aron 2.00	382 PR,V:Paibok,Devos,Huntara . 3.00	413 . . . . 1.50
333 RB,RT,V:Aron,Frightful Four . 2.00	383 PR,V:Paibok,Devos,Huntara . 2.00	414 Galactus vs. Hyperstorm . . . 1.50
334 RB,Acts of Vengeance 2.00	384 PR,A:Ant-Man,V:Franklin	415 Onslaught saga, A:X-Men . . . 2.50
335 RB,RT,Acts of Vengeance . . 2.00	Richards 2.00	416 Onslaught saga, A:Dr. Doom,
336 RLm,Acts of Vengeance, . . . 2.00	385 PR,A:Triton,Tiger Shark,	double size, finale 2.50
337 WS,A:Thor,Iron Man,	Starblast#7 . . . . 2.00	Ann.#1 JK,SD,I:Atlantis,Dorma,
B:Timestream saga 4.00	386 PR,Starblast#11,A:Namor,Triton,	Krang,V:Namor,O:FF 550.00
338 WS,V:Deathshead,A:Thor,	b:Johnny & Lyja child 1.75	Ann.#2 JK,JSt,O:Dr.Doom . . . 350.00
Iron Man 2.50	387 Die-Cut & Foil (c),PR,N:Invisible	Ann.#3 JK,W:Reed and Sue . . 145.00
339 WS,V:Gladiator 2.50	Woman,J:Ant-Man,A:Namor . 3.25	Ann.#4 JK,JSt,I:Quasimodo . . . 75.00
340 WS,V:Black Celestial 2.50	387a Newsstand Ed. 1.75	Ann.#5 JK,JSt,A:Inhumans,Silver
341 WS,A:Thor,Iron Man 2.50	388 PR,I:Dark Raider,V:FF,	Surfer,Black Panther,
342 A:Rusty,C:Spider-Man 2.50	Avengers,w/cards 2.00	I:Psycho Man 120.00
343 WS,V:Stalin 2.50	389 PR,I:Raphael Suarez,A:Watcher,	Ann.#6 JK,JSt,I:Annihilus,
344 WS,V:Stalin 2.50	V:Collector 2.00	Franklin Richards 50.00
345 WS,V:Dinosaurs 2.50	390 PR,V:Galactus 2.00	Ann.#7 JK(c),reprints 25.00
346 WS,V:Dinosaurs 2.50	391 PR,I:Vibraxas 1.75	Ann.#8 JR(c),reprints 15.00
347 AAd,ATi(i)A:Spider-Man,	392 Dark Raider 1.75	Ann.#9 JK(c),reprints. 15.00
GhostRider,Wolverine,Hulk . . . 4.00	393 . . . . 1.75	Ann.#10 reprints Ann.#3 . . . . . . 15.00
347a 2nd printing 2.00		Ann.#11 JK(c),JB,A:The Invaders . 7.00
348 AAd,ATi(i)A:Spider-Man,		Ann.#12 A:The Invaders 7.00
GhostRider,Wolverine,Hulk . . . 4.00		Ann.#13 V:The Mole Man 7.00
348a 2nd printing 2.00		Ann.#14 GP,V:Salem's Seven . . . 7.00
349 AAd,ATi(i),AM(i)A:Spider-Man,		Ann.#15 GP,V:Dr.Doom,Skrulls . 5.00
Wolverine,GhostRider,Hulk,		Ann.#16 V:Dragonlord 5.00
C:Punisher 3.50		Ann.#17 JBy,V:Skrulls 5.00
350 WS,Am(i),R:Ben Grimm as		Ann.#18 KGa,V:Skrulls,W:Black
Thing,(48p) 3.00		Bolt and Medusa,A:Inhumans . 5.00
351 MBa,Kubic 2.50		Ann.#19 JBy,V:Skrulls 5.00
352 WS,Reed Vs.Dr.Doom 2.50		Ann.#20 TD(i),V:Dr.Doom 4.00
353 WS,E:Timestream Saga,		Ann.#21 JG,JSt,Evol.Wars 4.00
A:Avengers, ... 2.50		Ann.#22 RB,Atlantis Attacks,
354 WS,Secrets of the Time		A:Avengers 4.00
Variance Authority 2.50		Ann.#23 JG,GCa,Days of Future
355 AM,V:Wrecking Crew 2.00		Present #1 . . . . 5.00
356 B:TDF(s),PR,A:New Warriors,		Ann.#24 JG,AM,Korvac Quest #1,
V:Puppet Master 2.00		A:Guardians of the Galaxy . . . 3.00
357 PR,V:Mad Thinker,		Ann.#25 Citizen Kang #3 . . . . 2.50
Puppetmaster, ... 2.00		Ann.#26 HT,I:Wildstreak,
358 PR,AAd,30th Anniv.,1st Marv. Die		V:Dreadface,w/card 3.25
Cut(c),D:Lyja,V:Paibok,BU:		Ann.#27 MGu,V:Justice Peace . . 3.25
Dr.Doom 3.00		G-Size#1 RB,Thing/Hulk 15.00
359 PR,I:Devos the Devastator . . 2.00		G-Size#2 K&R(c),JB,Time to Kill . 9.00
360 PR,V:Dreadface 2.00		G-Size#3 RB,JSt,Four Horseman . 9.00
361 PR,V:Dr.Doom,X-masIssue . . 2.00		G-Size#4 JB,JSt,I:Madrox 10.00
362 PR,A:Spider-Man,		G-Size#5 JK(c),V:Psycho Man,
I:WildBlood 2.00	*Fantastic Four #394*	Molecule Man 7.00
363 PR,I:Occulus,A:Devos 2.00	*© Marvel Entertainment Group*	G-Size#6 V:Annihilus 7.00
364 PR,V:Occulus 2.00		Spec.#1 Rep.Ann.#1 JBy(c) 2.00
365 PR,V:Occulus 2.00	394 Neon(c) w/insert print 2.95	TPB Rep.#347-349 . . . . 5.95
366 PR,Infinity War,R:Lyja 2.00	394a Newsstand ed.,no bag/inserts 1.75	TPB Nobody Gets Out Alive, rep.
367 PR,Inf.War,A:Wolverine 2.00	395 Thing V:Wolverine 1.75	Fant.Four #387–#392 + new. 15.95
368 PR,V:Infinity War X-Men . . . 2.00	396 . . . . 1.75	TPB Trial of Galactus,reprints
369 PR,Inf.War,R:Malice,	397 Resurrection,pt.1 . . . . 1.75	#242-244,#257-262 . . . . 9.95
A:Thanos 2.00	398 regular edition 1.50	Marvel Milestone rep. #1 (1991) . 2.95
370 PR,Inf.War,V:Mr.Fantastic	398a Enhanced cover 2.75	Marvel Milestone rep. #5 (1992) . 2.95
Doppleganger 2.00	399 Watcher's Lie 1.75	Ashcan .75
371 PR,V:Lyja,foil(c) 4.00	399a Foil stamped cover 2.50	Spec. The Origin of Galactus . . . 2.50
371a 2nd Printing 3.00	400 Watcher's Lie,pt.3 . . . . 3.95	**[2nd Series]** Nov. 1996
372 PR,A:Spider-Man,Silver	401 V:Tantalus 1.50	1 JLe,BCi,SW, 48pg 5.00
Sable 2.00	402 Atlantis Rising,Namor	1A Mole Man cover 10.00
373 PR,V:Aron,Silver sable 2.00	vs. Black Bolt 1.50	1B Gold signature, bagged,
374 PR,V:Secret Defenders 2.00	403 TDF,PR,DBi,F:Thing,Medusa 1.50	limited 20.00
375 V:Dr.Doom,A:Inhumans,Lyja,	404 R:Namor,I:New Villian 1.50	2 JLe,BCi,V:Namor 4.00
Holo-Grafix(c) 3.00	405 J:Namor 1.50	3 JLe,BCi,SW,A:Avengers 3.00
376 PR,A:Nathan Richards,V:Paibok,	406 TDF,PR,DBI,R:Dr. Doom,	4 JLe,BCi,SW,I:Black Panther . . . 3.00
Devos,w/Dirt Magazine 2.75	I:Hyperstorm 1.50	4A x-mas cover 3.00
376a w/out Dirt Magazine 2.00	407 TDF,PR,DBi,Return of	5 JLe,BCi,SW,V:Dr. Doom 3.00
377 PR,V:Paibok,Devos,Klaw,	Reed Richards 1.50	6 JLe,BCi,SW,Industrial Revolution
I:Huntara 2.00	408 TDF,PR,DBi,Original FF unite 1.50	prologue 2.50
378 PR,A:Sandman,SpM,DD 2.00	409 TDF,PR,DBi,All new line-up . 1.50	7 JLe,BCi,BBh,V:Blastaar 2.00

MARVEL

8 JLe,BCi,BBh,V:Inhumans 2.00
9 JLe,BCi,BBh,V:Inhumans 2.00
10 JLe,BCi,BBh,A:Silver Surfer,
Tyrax 2.00
11 JLe,BCi,BBh,A:Silver Surfer,
Firelord, Terrax 2.00
12 JLe,BCi,BBh,GalactusSaga,pt.1,
reunited 2.00
13 JeR,Wildstorm x-over 2.00
Ashcan, signed, numbered 10.00
[3rd Series] Nov. 1997
1 SLo,AD,MFm, The Ruined, 48pg
debut 3.00
2 SLo,AD,MFm,A:Iconoclast 2.00
3 SLo,AD,MFm,V:Red Ghost . . . 2.00
4 SLo,SvL,ATi,A:Silver Surfer,
double size 3.00
4 signed by SLo, (500 copies) . 20.00
5 SLo,SvL,ATi,V:The Crucible . . . 2.00
6 CCi,SvL, new villains 2.00
7 CCi,SvL,ATi,V:Technet 2.00
8 CCi,SvL,V:Captain Britain corp. 2.00
9 CCi,SvL,A:Spider-Man 2.00
10 CCi,SvL,ATi 2.00

FANTASTIC FOUR: ATLANTIS RISING
1995
1 B:Atlantis Rising 3.95
2 TDF,MCW,finale, acetate(c) . . . 3.95

FANTASTIC FOUR INDEX
SEE: OFFICIAL MARVEL INDEX TO THE FANTASTIC FOUR

FANTASTIC FOUR ROAST
1 FH/MG/FM/JB/MA/TA,May,1982 5.00

FANTASTIC FOUR 2099
1996
1 Cont. from 2099 Genesis 3.95
2 V:Stark/Fujikawa elite guard . . 1.95
3 . . . . 1.95
4 . . . . 1.95
5 A:Spider-Man 2099 . . . . 1.95

FANTASTIC FOUR UNLIMITED
1993–96
1 HT,A:Bl.Panther,V:Klaw 4.50
2 HT,JQ(c),A:Inhumans 4.25
3 HT,V:Blastaar,Annihilus 4.25
4 RTs(s),HT,V:Mole Man,A:Hulk . 4.25
5 RTs(s),HT,V:Frightful Four 4.25
6 RTs(s),HT,V:Namor 3.95
7 HT,V:Monsters 3.95
8 . . . . 3.95
9 A:Antman 3.95
10 RTs,HT,V:Maelstrom,A:Eternals 3.95
11 RTs,HT,Atlantis Rising fallout . 3.95
12 RTs,TDF,V:Hyperstorm 3.95
13 . . . . 3.95

FANTASTIC FOUR UNPLUGGED
1995–96
1 comic for a buck 1.00
2 Reed Richard's Will 1.00
3 F:Mr. Fantastic 1.00
4 . . . . 1.00
5 Back in NY,V:Blastaar 1.00

FANTASTIC FOUR VS. X-MEN
Feb., 1987
1 JBg,TA,V:Dr.Doom 5.00
2 JBg,TA,V:Dr.Doom 3.00
3 JBg,TA,V:Dr.Doom 3.00
4 JBg,TA,V:Dr.Doom, June 1987 3.00
TPB Reprints Mini-series 12.95

FANTASTIC WORLD OF HANNA-BARBERA
Dec., 1977
1 . . . . 1.00
2 . . . . 1.00
3 June, 1978 . . . . 1.00

Fantasy Masterpieces #9
© Marvel Entertainment Group

FANTASY MASTERPIECES
Feb., 1966
1 JK/DH/SD,reprints 75.00
2 JK,SD,DH,Fin Fang Foom . . . 35.00
3 GC,DH,JK,SD,Capt.A rep. 25.00
4 JK,Capt.America rep. 25.00
5 JK,Capt.America rep. 25.00
6 JK,Capt.America rep. 25.00
7 SD,Sub Mariner rep. 25.00
8 H.Torch & Sub M.rep. 30.00
9 SD,MF,O:Human Torch Rep . 30.00
10 rep.All Winners #19 . . . . 25.00
11 JK,(rep),O:Toro 25.00
Becomes:
MARVEL SUPER-HEROES

FANTASY MASTERPIECES
[Volume 2]
Dec., 1979
1 JB,JSt,Silver Surfer rep. 5.00
2 JB,JSt,Silver Surfer rep. 5.00
3 JB,JSt,Silver Surfer rep. 5.00
4 JB,JSt,Silver Surfer rep. 5.00
5 JB,JSt,Silver Surfer rep. 5.00
6 JB,JSt,Silver Surfer rep. 5.00
7 JB,JSt,Silver Surfer rep. 5.00
8 JB/JSn,Warlock rep.Strange
Tales #178 . . . . 4.00

9 JB,JSn,rep.StrangeTales#179 . 4.00
10 JB,JSn,rep.StrangeTales#180 . 4.00
11 JB,JSn,rep.StrangeTales#181 . 4.00
12 JB,JSn,rep.Warlock #9 . . . . . . 4.00
13 JB,JSn,rep.Warlock #10 . . . . . 4.00
14 JB,JSn,rep.Warlock #11 . . . . . 4.00

FAREWELL TO WEAPONS
1 DirtBag,W/Nirvana Tape 3.50

FEAR
Nov., 1970
1 1950's Monster rep. B:I Found
Monstrum,The Dweller
in the Black Swamp 30.00
2 X The Thing That Lived 20.00
3 Zzutak, The Thing That
Shouldn't Exist 20.00
4 I Turned Into a Martian 20.00
5 I Am the Gorilla Man 20.00
6 The Midnight Monster 20.00
7 I Dream of Doom 12.00
8 It Crawls By Night! 12.00
9 Dead Man's Escape 12.00
Becomes:

ADVENTURE INTO FEAR
1972
10 GM,B:Man-Thing 25.00
11 RB,I:Jennifer Kale,Thog 10.00
12 JSn,RB 10.00
13 VM,Where World's Collide . . . 8.00
14 VM,Plague o/t Demon Cult . . . 8.00
15 VM,Lord o/t Dark Domain . . . 8.00
16 VM,ManThing in Everglades . . 8.00
17 VM,I:Wundarr(Aquarian) 8.00
18 VM 8.00
19 VM,FMc,I:Howard the Duck,
E:Man-Thing 25.00
20 PG,B:Morbius 28.00
21 GK,V:Uncanny Caretaker 8.00
22 RB,V:Cat-Demond 8.00
23 1st CR art,A World He
Never Made 8.00
24 CR,V:Blade, The Vampire
Slayer 20.00
25 You Always Kill the One
You Love 7.00
26 V:Uncanny Caretaker 7.00
27 V:Simon Stroud 7.00
28 Doorway Down into Hell 7.00
29 Death has a Thousand Eyes . . 7.00
30 Bloody Sacrifice 7.00
31 last issue,Dec. 1975 . . . . 7.00

FEUD
Epic 1993
1 I:Skids,Stokes,Kite 2.50
2 V:Grunts,Skide,Stockers 2.25
3 . . . . 2.25
4 . . . . 2.25

FIGHT MAN
1993
1 I:Fight Man 2.00

FIRESTAR
March, 1986
1 MW,SL,O:Firestar,A:X-Men,
New Mutants 4.00
2 MW,BWI,A:New Mutants 5.00
3 AAd&BSz(c),MW,SL,
A:White Queen 3.00
4 MW,SL,V:White Queen 3.00

FISH POLICE
1992–93
1 V:S.Q.U.I.D,Hook	1.25
2 V:Hook	1.25
3 V:Hook	1.25
4 V:Hook	1.25
5 V:Goldie Prawn	1.25
6 Shark Bait #1	1.25

FLASH GORDON
1995
1 R:Flash Gordon	2.00
2 AW,V:Ming, final issue	2.95

FLINTSTONE KIDS
Star Comics August, 1987
1 thru 10	@1.00
11 April, 1989	1.00

FLINTSTONES
Oct., 1977–Feb. 1979
1 From TV Series	1.50
2	1.25
3	1.25
4 A:Jetsons	1.25
5 thru 7	@1.25

FLYING HERO BARBIE
1 Super Hero Barbie	1.50

Foolkiller #4
© Marvel Entertainment Group

FOOLKILLER
Oct., 1990
1 I:Kurt Gerhardt (Foolkiller III)	3.50
2 O:Foolkiller I & II	3.00
3 Old Costume	3.00
4 N:Foolkiller	2.50
5 Body Count	2.50
6 Fools Paradise	2.00
7 Who the Fools Are	2.00
8 Sane Must Inherit Earth,A:SpM	2.00
9 D:Darren Waite	2.00
10 New Identity, July 1991	2.00

FOORFUR
Star Comics August, 1987
1 thru 6	@1.00

FORCE WORKS
1994–96
1 TmT,Pop-up(c),I:Century,V:Kree, N:US Agent	4.75
2 TmT,V:Scatter	1.75
3 TmT,V:Scatter	1.50
4 Civil War	1.50
5 regular cover	1.50
5a Neon(c),bagged w/print	2.95
6 Hands of the Mandarin,pt.1	1.50
7 Hands of the Mandarin,pt.2	1.50
8 DAn,ALa,Christmas Party	1.50
9 I:Dream Guard	1.50
10 V:Dream Guard	1.50
11 F:War Machine	1.50
12 V:Recorder	2.50
13 DAn,ALa,A:Avengers	1.50
14	1.50
15 DAn,ALa,O:Century	1.50
16	1.50
17 DAn,ALa,The Crossing	1.50
18 DAn,ALa,The Crossing	1.50
19 DAn,ALa,The Crossing	1.50
20 DAn,cont.Avengers:Timeslide	1.50

FOR YOUR EYES ONLY
1 HC,James Bond rep.	2.00
2 HC,James Bond rep.	2.00

FRAGGLE ROCK
1985
1 thru 8	@1.00

[Volume 2] April, 1988
1 thru 5 rep.	@1.00
6 Sept., 1988	1.00

FRANCIS, BROTHER OF THE UNIVERSE
1980
1-shot SB	2.50

FRANKENSTEIN
See: MONSTER OF FRANKENSTEIN

FRED HEMBECK
1-shot Destroys the Marvel Universe, parody (1989)	2.00
1-shot Sells the Marvel Universe parody (1990)	1.50

FRIGHT
June, 1975
1 Son of Dracula	10.00

FRONTIER WESTERN
Feb., 1956
1 RH,	125.00
2 AW,GT	75.00
3 MD	75.00
4 MD	50.00
5 RC	60.00
6 AW,	75.00
7 JR	50.00
8 RC	50.00
9	50.00
10 August, 1957	50.00

FUNNY FROLICS
Summer, 1945
1 (fa)	125.00
2	75.00
3	50.00
4	50.00
5 HK	60.00

FURTHER ADVENTURES OF CYCLOPS AND PHOENIX
1996
1 thru 4	1.95
TPB PrM,JPL, O:Mr. Sinister,	12.00

FURY
1994
1 MCW,O:Fury,A:S.A. Heroes	3.25

FURY/AGENT 13
March 1998
1 (of 2) TKa,is Nick Fury alive?	3.00
2 TKa,MZ(c),Sharon Carter's searches for Nick	3.00

FURY OF S.H.I.E.L.D.
1995
1 Foil etched cover	2.50
2 A:Iron Man	1.95
3 J:Hydra	1.95
4 w/decoder card	2.50

GALACTIC GUARDIANS
1994
1 KWe,C:Woden	1.75
2 KWe,I:Hazmat,Savant,Ganglia	1.50
3 KWe	1.50
4 KWe,final issue	1.50

GAMBIT
1997
1 HMe(c),LW,KJ,V:Assassin'sGuild, D:Henri LeBeau,Embossed(c)	5.00
1a Gold Ed.	15.00
2 LW,KJ,C:Gideon,A:Rogue	3.00
3 LW,KJ,A:Candra,Rogue, D:Gambit's Father	3.00
4 LW,KJ,A:Candra,Rogue,D:Tithe Collector	3.00
TPB Rep.#1-#4	8.95

GAMBIT
1997
1 (of 4) HMe,KJ,In Miami	2.50
2 HMe,KJ,	2.50
3 HMe,KJ,In the Vatican	2.50
4 HMe V:Stoker, concl.	2.50

GAMBIT AND THE X-TERNALS
1995
1 X-Force after Xavier	3.50
2 V:Deathbird,Starjammers	2.50
3 V:Imperial Guard	2.25
4 Charles Kidnapped	2.25

GARGOYLE
June, 1985
1 BWr(c),from 'Defenders'	2.00
2 thru 4	@1.50

GARGOYLES
1995–96
1 TV Series		2.50
2 TV Series		1.50
3 F:Broadway		1.50
4 V:Statues		1.50
5 Humanoid Gargoyles		1.50
6 Medusa Project concl.		1.50
7 Demona & Triad		1.50
8 I:The Pack		1.50
9 V:Demonia,Triad		1.50
10 Demonia gains magical powers		1.50
11 Elisa turns to Xanatos		1.50
12 Sorceress traps Gargoyles		1.50
13 Behind Enemy Lines		1.50
14		1.50
15		1.50
16 Hammer of Fear		1.50

GENE DOGS
Marvel UK 1993–94
1 I:Gene DOGS,w/cards		2.75
2 V:Genetix		2.00
3 V:Hurricane		2.00
4 last issue		1.75

GENERATION NEXT
1995
1 Generation X AX		3.50
2 Genetic Slave Pens		2.50
3 V:Sugar Man		2.25
4 V:Sugar Man		2.25

GENERATION X
Oct. 1994
1 CBa,Banshee & White Queen		4.00
2 CBa,SLo		2.00
2a Deluxe edition		4.00
3 CBa		2.00
3a Deluxe edition		3.50
4 CBa,V:Nanny,Orphanmaker		2.00
4a Deluxe edition		3.00
5 SLo,CBa,MBu,two new young mutants at the Academy		2.25
6 A:Wolverine		2.25
7 SLo,F:Banshee,A:White Queen		2.25
8 F:Banshee		2.00
9 SLo,TG,Chamber in a kilt		2.00
10 SLo,TG,MBu,Banshee vs. OmegaRed		2.00
11 SLo,TG,V:Omega Red		2.00
12 SLo,TG,V:Emplate		2.00
13		2.00
14		2.00
15 SLo,MBu,Synch goes psycho		2.00
16		2.00
17 SLo,CBa,Onslaught saga, X-Cutioner vs. Skin		2.00
18 SLo,CBa,Onslaught saga		2.00
19 SLo,CBa,		2.00
20 SLo,CBa,		2.00
21 SLo,CBa,MBu,F:Skin & Chamber, A:Beverly Switzer, Howard the Duck		1.95
22 SLo,CBa,		1.95
23 SLo,CBa,V:Black Tom Cassidy		1.95
24 SLo,MBy,F:Monet,Emplate		1.95
25 SLo,CBa,double size		2.95
26 SLo,CBa,Shot down over the Atlantic		1.95
27 SLo,CBa,on nuclear sub.		1.95
28 SLo,CBa,No Exit prelude		1.95
29 JeR,CBa, V:Sentinels		1.95
30 JeR,CBa, V:Zero Tolerance		1.95

31 JeR,CBa,		2.00
32 TDF,MBu,F:Banshee, Moira McTaggert		2.00
33 LHa,MBu,new direction		2.00
34 LHa,Truth behind M		2.00
35 LHa,Jubilee,V:Emplate		2.00
36 LHa,Final Fate of M		2.00
37 LHa,Final Fate of M		2.00
38 LHa,TyD,kids save universe		2.00
39 LHa,TyD, multi-dimensional trip		2.00
40 LHa,TyD,Penance mystery revealed		2.00
41 LHa,TyD,Jubilee,V:Bastion, Omega Red, Sabretooth		2.00
42 LHa,TyD,results of EMP wave		2.00
43 LHa,TyD,V:Bianca LaNiege		2.00
Minus 1 Spec., JeR,CBa, flashback, F:Banshee		1.95
Ann. '95 SLo,J:Mondo, V:Hellfire Club		3.95
Ann. '96 GN MGo,JJ,DPs,V:Fenris		2.95
Ann. '97, Haunted by Ghosts of Hellions		2.00

GENERATION X/GEN 13
Dec., 1997
1-shot JeR,SvL,V:Mr. Pretorious		4.00
1a variant cover CBa (1:4)		4.00

GENERATION X: UNDERGROUND
March 1998
1-shot by Jim Mahfood, b&w		2.50

GENERIC COMIC
1		1.50

Genetix #1
© Marvel Entertainment Group

GENETIX
Marvel UK 1993–94
1 B:ALa(s),w/cards		2.75
2 I:Tektos		2.00
3 V:Tektos		1.75
4 PGa,V:MyS-Tech		1.75
5 PGa,V:MyS-Tech		1.75
6 V:Tektos		1.95

GEORGIE COMICS
Spring, 1945
1 Georgie stories begin		120.00
2 Pet Shop (c)		55.00
3 Georgie/Judy(c)		40.00
4 Wedding Dress(c)		40.00
5 Monty/Policeman(c)		40.00
6 Classroom(c)		40.00
7 Fishing(c)		45.00
8 Soda Jerk(c)		35.00
9 Georgie/Judy(c),HK,Hey Look		45.00
10 Georgie/Girls(c),HK,Hey Look		45.00
11 Table Tennis(c),A:Margie,Millie		30.00
12 Camping(c)		30.00
13 Life Guard(c),HK,Hey Look		40.00
14 Classroom(c),HK,Hey Look		45.00
15 Winter Sports(c)		25.00
16		25.00
17 HK,Hey Look		25.00
18		25.00
19 Baseball(c)		25.00
20 Title change to Georgie & Judy Comics		25.00
21 Title change to Georgie & Judy Comics		20.00
22 Georgie comics		20.00
23		20.00
24		20.00
25		40.00
26		20.00
27		20.00
28		20.00
29		35.00
30 thru 38		@20.00
39 Oct., 1952		20.00

GETALONG GANG
May, 1985—March, 1986
1 thru 6		@1.00

GHOST RIDER
[1st Regular Series] Sept., 1973
1 GK,JSt,C:Son of Satan		45.00
2 GK,I:Son of Satan,A:Witch Woman		15.00
3 JR,D:Big Daddy Dawson, new Cycle		12.00
4 GK,A:Dude Jensen		12.00
5 GK,JR,I:Roulette		12.00
6 JR,O:Ghost Rider		11.00
7 JR,A:Stunt Master		11.00
8 GK,A:Satan,I:Inferno		10.00
9 GK,TP,O:Johnny Blaze		11.00
10 JSt,A:Hulk		11.00
11 GK,KJ,SB,A:Hulk		10.00
12 GK,KJ,FR,A:Phantom Eagle		8.00
13 GK,JS,GT,A:Trapster		8.00
14 GT,A:The Orb		8.00
15 SB,O:The Orb		8.00
16 DC,GT,Blood in the Water		8.00
17 RB,FR,I:Challenger		8.00
18 RB,FR,A:Challenger, Spider-Man		9.00
19 GK,FR,A:Challenger		8.00
20 GK,KJ,JBy,A:Daredevil		10.00
21 A:Gladiator,D:Eel		5.00
22 AM,DH,KP,JR,A:Enforcer		5.00
23 JK,DH,DN,I:Water Wiz.		5.00
24 GK,DC,DH,A:Enforcer		5.00
25 GK,DH,A:Stunt Master		5.00
26 GK,DP,A:Dr. Druid		5.00
27 SB,DP,A:Hawkeye		5.00
28 DP,A:The Orb		5.00
29 RB,DP,A:Dormammu		5.00

30 DP,A:Dr.Strange	5.00
31 FR,DP,BL,A:Bounty Hunt.	5.00
32 KP,BL,DP,A:Bounty Hunt.	5.00
33 DP,I:Dark Riders	5.00
34 DP,C:Cyclops	5.00
35 JSn,AM,A:Death	6.00
36 DP,Drug Mention	5.00
37 DP,I:Dick Varden	5.00
38 DP,A:Death Cult	5.00
39 DP,A:Death Cult	5.00
40 DP,I:Nuclear Man	5.00
41 DP,A:Jackal Gang	5.00
42 DP,A:Jackal Gang	5.00
43 CI:Crimson Mage	5.00
44 JAb,CI,A:Crimson Mage	5.00
45 DP,I:Flagg Fargo	5.00
46 DP,A:Flagg Fargo	5.00
47 AM,DP	5.00
48 BMc,DP	5.00
49 DP,I:The Manitou	5.00
50 DP,A:Night Rider	6.00
51 AM,PD,A:Cycle Gang	4.00
52 AM,DP	4.00
53 DP,I:Lord Asmodeus	4.00

Ghost Rider #68
© *Marvel Entertainment Group*

54 DP,A:The Orb	4.00
55 DP,A:Werewolf By Night	4.00
56 DP,A:Moondark,I:Night Rider	4.00
57 AM,DP,I:The Apparition	4.00
58 DP,FM,A:Water Wizard	4.00
59 V:Water Wizard,Moon Dark	4.00
60 DP,HT,A:Black Juju	4.00
61 A:Arabian Knight	4.00
62 KJ,A:Arabian Knight	4.00
63 LMc,A:The Orb	4.00
64 BA,V:Azmodeus	4.00
65 A:Fowler	4.00
66 BL,A:Clothilde	4.00
67 DP,A:Sally Stantop	4.00
68 O:Ghost Rider	4.00
69	4.00
70 I:Jeremy	4.00
71 DP,I:Adam Henderson	4.00
72 A:Circus of Crime	4.00
73 A:Circus of Crime	4.00
74 A:Centurions	4.00

75 I:Steel Wind	4.00
76 DP,A:Mephisto,I:Saturnine	4.00
77 O:Ghost Rider's Dream	4.00
78 A:Nightmare	4.00
79 A:Man Cycles	4.00
80 A:Centurions	4.00
81 D:Ghost Rider	9.00

[2nd Regular Series] 1990–98

1 JS,MT,I:2nd Ghost Rider, Deathwatch	6.00
1a 2nd printing	2.00
2 JS,MT,I:Blackout	3.50
3 JS,MT,A:Kingpin,V:Blackout, Deathwatch	3.00
4 JS,MT,V:Mr.Hyde	3.00
5 JLe(c),JS,MT,A:Punisher	3.00
5a rep.Gold	2.50
6 JS,MT,A:Punisher	3.00
7 MT,V:Scarecrow	3.00
8 JS,MT,V:H.E.A.R.T	3.00
9 JS,MT,A:Morlocks,X-Factor	2.50
10 JS,MT,V:Zodiac	2.50
11 LSn,MT,V:Nightmare, A:Dr.Strange	2.50
12 JS,MT,A:Dr.Strange	2.50
13 MT,V:Snow Blind,R:J.Blaze	2.50
14 MT,Blaze Vs.Ghost Rider	2.50
15 MT,A:Blaze,V:Blackout Glow in Dark(c)	3.00
15a 2nd printing (gold)	2.50
16 MT,A:Blaze,Spider-Man, V:Hobgoblin	2.50
17 MT,A:Spider-Man,Blaze, V:Hobgoblin	2.50
18 MT,V:Reverend Styge	2.25
19 MT,A:Mephisto	2.25
20 MT(i),O:Zodiac	2.25
21 MT(i),V:Snowblind, A:Deathwatch	2.25
22 MT,A:Deathwatch,Ninjas	2.25
23 MT,I:Hag & Troll,A:Deathwatch	2.25
24 MT,V:Deathwatch,D:Snowblind, C:Johnny Blaze	2.25
25 V:Blackout (w/Center spread pop-up)	2.50
26 A:X-Men,V:The Brood	2.50
27 A:X-Men,V:The Brood	2.50
28 NKu,JKu,Rise of the Midnight Sons#1,V:Lilith,w/poster	2.50
29 NKu,JKu,A:Wolverine,Beast	2.50
30 NKu,JKu,V:Nightmare	2.25
31 NKu,JKu,Rise o/t Midnight Sons#6, A:Dr.Strange,Morbius, Nightstalkers,Redeemers, V:Lilith,w/poster	2.25
32 BBi,A:Dr.Strange	2.00
33 BBi,AW,V:Madcap (inc.Superman tribute on letters page)	2.00
34 BBi,V:Deathwatchs' ninja	2.00
35 BBi,AW,A:Heart Attack	2.00
36 BBi,V:Mr.Hyde,A:Daredevil	2.00
37 BBi,A:Archangel,V:HeartAttack	2.00
38 MM,V:Scarecrow	2.00
39 V:Vengeance	2.00
40 Midnight Massacre#2, D:Demogblin	2.50
41 Road to Vengeance#1	2.00
42 Road to Vengeance#2	2.00
43 Road to Vengeance#3	2.00
44 Siege of Darkness,pt.#2	2.00
45 Siege of Darkness,pt.#10	2.00
46 HMe(s),New Beginning	2.00
47 HMe(s),RG	2.00
48 HMe(s),RG,A:Spider-Man	2.00
49 HMe(s),RG,A:Hulk,w/card	2.25

50 Red Foil(c),AKu,SMc,A:Blaze, R:2nd Ghost Rider	3.25
50a Newsstand Ed.	2.75
51 SvL	2.25
52 SvL	1.95
53 SvL,V:Blackout	1.95
54 SvL,V:Blackout	1.95
55 V:Mr.Hyde	1.95
56 The Next Wave	1.95
57 A:Wolverine	1.95
58 HMe,SvL,Betrayal,pt.1	1.95
59 Betrayal,pt.2	1.95
60 Betrayal,pt.3	1.95
61 Betrayal,pt.4	1.95
62 EventInChains,pt.1,A:Fury	1.95
63 EventInChains,pt.2	1.95
64 EventInChains,pt.3	1.95
65 EventInChains,pt.4,R:Blackout	1.95
66 V:Blackout	1.95
67 A:Gambit,V:Brood	1.95
68 A:Gambit,Wolverine,V:Brood	1.95
69 Domestic Violence	1.95
70 New Home in Bronx	1.95
71	1.95
72	1.95
73 John Blaze is back	1.95
74 A:Blaze, Vengeance	1.95
75	1.50
76 V:Vengeance	1.50
77 A:Dr. Strange	1.50
78 new costume, A:Dr. Strange	1.50
79 IV,New costume, A:Valkyrie,	1.50
80 IV,V:Furies,Valkyrie, A:Black Rose	1.50
81 IV,A:Howard the Duck, Devil Dinosaur	1.50
82 IV,A:Devil Dinosaur,	1.50
83 IV,A:Scarecrow,Lilith	1.50
84 IV,A:Scarecrow, Lilith	1.95
85 IV,V:Lilith, Scarecrow	1.95
86 IV,rampage through the Bronx	1.95
87 IV,KIK,AM,	1.95
88 IV, V:Pao Fu,Blackheart	1.95
89 IV,JS,	2.00
90 IV,JS,Last Temptation, pt.1	2.00
91 IV,JS,A:Blackheart	2.00
92 IV,JS,Journey into the past	2.00
93 IV,JS,MT,Last Temptation concl., double sized	3.00
94 IV,JS,MT,Becomes Lord of the Underworld, last issue	2.00
Ann.#1 I:Night Terror,w/card	3.25
Ann.#2 F:Scarecrow	2.95
GN Ghost Rider/Captain America: Fear, AW, V:Scarecrow (1992)	6.25
TPB Midnight Sons,rep.GhR#28,31, Morbius#1,Darkhold#1,Spirirts of Vengeance#1,Nightstalkers#1	19.95
TPB Resurrected rep.#1-#7	12.95
TPB Ghost Rider/Wolverine/Punisher: Dark Design (1994)	5.95
TPB Ghost Rider/Wolverine/Punisher: Hearts of Darkness, JR2/KJ,V: Blackheart, double gatefold cover (1991)	5.50
Poster Book	4.95
Spec. Crossroads	3.95
Minus 1 Spec., IV,JS, flashback	1.95

GHOST RIDER/BALLISTIC
Marvel/Top Cow 1996

1-shot WEI,BTn,"Devil's Reign," pt.3, x-over	2.95

MARVEL

GHOST RIDER/BLAZE SPIRITS OF VENGEANCE
1992–94
1 AKu,polybagged w/poster,V:Lilith, Rise of the Midnight Sons#2 . . 3.50
2 AKu,V:Steel Wind 2.50
3 AKu,CW,V:The Lilin 2.00
4 AKu,V:Hag & Troll,C:Venom . . 3.00
5 AKu,BR,Spirits of Venom#2, A:Venom,Spidey,Hobgoblin . . . 5.00
6 AKu,Spirits of Venom#4,A:Venom, Spider-Man,Hobgoblin 3.50
7 AKu,V:Steel Vengeance 2.00
8 V:Mephisto 2.00
9 I:Brimstone 2.00
10 AKu,V:Vengeance 2.00
11 V:Human Spider Creature 2.00
12 AKu,BR,Vengeance,glow in the dark(c) 3.25
13 AKu,Midnight Massacre#5 . . . 2.50
14 Missing Link#2 . . . . 2.00
15 Missing Link#3 . . . . 2.00
16 V:Zarathos,Lilith 2.00
17 HMe(s),Siege/Darkness,pt.8 . . 2.00
18 HMe(s),Siege/Darkness,pt.13 . . 2.00
19 HMe(s),HMz,V;Vampire 2.00
20 HMe(s),A:Steel Wind 2.00
21 HMe(s),HMz,V:Werewolves . . . 2.00
22 HMe(s),HMz,V:Cardiac 2.25
23 HMe(s),HMz,A:Steel Wind . . . 2.25

GHOST RIDER/CYBLADE
Marvel/Top Cow 1996
1-shot IV,ACh,"Devil's Reign," pt.2, x-over 2.95

GHOST RIDER 2099
1994–96
1 Holografx(c),LKa,CBa,MBu,I:Ghost Rider 2099,w/card 2.75
1a Newsstand Ed. 1.75
2 LKa,CBa,MBu 1.75
3 LKa,CBa,MBu,I:Warewolf 1.75
4 LKa,CBa,MBu,V:Warewolf 1.75
5 LKa,CBa,MBu 1.75
6 LKa,CBa,MBu 1.75
7 LKa,CBa,MBu 1.75
8 LKa,CBa,MBu 1.75
9 . . . . 1.50
10 . . . . 1.50
11 V:Bloodsport Society 1.50
12 I:Coda 1.50
Becomes:
GHOST RIDER 2099 A.D.
13 F:Doom 2.00
14 Deputized by Doom 2.00
15 One Nation Under Doom 2.00
16 V:Max Synergy 2.00
17 . . . . 2.00
18 V:L-Cipher 2.00
19 V:L-Cipher 2.00
20 . . . . 2.00
21 V:Vengeance 2099 . . . . 2.00
22 V:Vengeance 2099 . . . . 2.00
23 . . . . 2.00
24 . . . . 2.00
25 Double size final issue 3.00

GIANT-SIZE CHILLERS
1975
1 AA, ... 15.00
2 . . . . 10.00
3 BWr,Night of the Gargoyle . . . 15.00

Giant-Size Chillers #1
#2 © Marvel Entertainment Group

GIANT-SIZE CHILLERS
1974
1 I&O:Lilith,F:Curse of Dracula . 20.00
Becomes:
GIANT-SIZE DRACULA
2 Vengeance of the Elder Gods . 15.00
3 rep. Uncanny Tales #6 . . . . . 12.00
4 SD,Demon of Devil's Lake . . . 12.00
5 JBy, 1st Marvel art 20.00

G.I. JOE: A REAL AMERICAN HERO
June, 1982
1 HT,BMc,Baxter paper 3.00
2 DP,JAb,North Pole 2.50
3 HT,JAb,Trojan Robot 2.00
4 HT,JAb,Wingfield 2.00
5 DP,Central Park 2.00
6 HT,V:Cobra 2.00
7 HT,Walls of Death 2.00
8 HT,Sea Strike 2.00
9 The Diplomat 2.00
10 Springfield 2.00
11 Alaska Pipeline 2.00
12 V:Snake Eyes 2.50
13 Rio Lindo 2.00
14 V:Destro 2.00
15 A:Red Eye 2.00
16 V:Cobra 2.00
17 Loose Ends 2.00
18 V:Destro 2.00
19 D:General Kwinn 2.00
20 JBy(c),GI,Clutch 2.00
21 SL(i),Silent Interlude 2.00
22 V:Destro 2.00
23 I:Duke 1.75
24 RH,I:Storm Shadow 2.00
25 FS,I:Zartan 2.00
26 SL(i),O:Snake Eyes 2.50
27 FS,O:Snake Eyes 2.00
28 Swampfire 2.00
29 FS,V:Destro 2.00
30 JBy(c),FS,V:Dreddnoks 2.00
31 V:Destro 1.75
32 FS,V:Dreddnoks 2.00
33 FS,Celebration 1.75
34 Shakedown 1.75

35 JBy(c),MBr,V:Dreddnoks 1.75
36 MBr,Shipwar 1.75
2a to 36a 2nd printings . . . . @1.00
37 FS,Twin Brothers,I:Flint 2.00
38 V:Destro 2.00
39 Jungle 2.00
40 Hydrofoil 2.00
41 . . . . 2.00
42 A:Stormshadow 2.00
43 Death Issue,New Joe 2.00
44 V:Cobra 2.00
45 V:Cobra 2.00
46 V:Cobra 2.00
47 V:Cobra,D:Stormshadow 2.00
48 V:Cobra 2.00
49 V:Cobra,I:Serpentor 2.00
50 I:G.I.Joe Missions,R:S'shadow 2.25
51 V:Cobra Emperor 1.50
52 V:Stormshadow 1.50
53 Hawk V:Cobra 1.50
54 V:Destro 1.50
55 The Pit 1.50
56 V:Serpentor 1.50
57 V:Destro 1.50
58 V:Cobra 1.50
59 Armor 1.50
60 TM,I:Zanzibar 2.50
61 MR,D:Cobra Commander 1.25
62 Trial 1.25
63 A:GI Joe Snow Job 1.25
64 V:Baroness 1.25
65 V:Cobra 1.25
66 Stalker Rescued 1.25
67 . . . . 1.25
68 I:Battleforce 2000 . . . . 1.25
69 TSa 1.25
70 V:Destro 1.25
71 . . . . 1.25
72 . . . . 1.25
73 . . . . 1.25
74 . . . . 1.25
75 MR 1.25
76 D:Serpentor 1.25
77 MR,V:Cobra 1.25
78 V:Cobra 1.25
79 MR,V:Dreadnoks 1.25
80 V:Cobra 1.25
81 MR,V:Dreadnoks 1.00
82 MR,V:Cobra 1.00
83 I:RoadPig 1.00
84 MR,O:Zartan 1.00
85 Storm Shadow,Vs.Zartan 1.00
86 MR,25th Anniv. 1.00
87 TSa,V:Cobra 1.00
88 TSa,V:Python Patrol 1.00
89 MBr,V:Road Pig 1.00
90 MBr,R:Red Ninjas 1.00
91 TSa,V:Red Ninjas,D:Blind Masters 1.00
92 MBr,V:Cobra Condor 1.00
93 MBr,V:Baroness 1.00
94 MBr,A:Snake Eyes 1.00
95 MBr,A:Snake Eyes 1.00
96 MBr,A:Snake Eyes 1.00
97 . . . . 1.00
98 MBr,R:Cobra Commander . . . 1.00
99 HT 1.00
100 MBr 1.50
101 MBr 1.00
102 MBr 1.00
103 MBr,A:Snake Eyes 1.00
104 MBr,A:Snake Eyes 1.00
105 MBr,A:Snake Eyes 1.00
106 MBr,StormShadowStalker . . . 1.00
107 . . . . 1.00

G.I. Joe #16
© Marvel Entertainment Group

108 I:G.I.Joe Dossiers	1.00
109 Death Issue	1.00
110 Mid-East Crisis	1.00
111 A:Team Ninjas	1.00
112 A:Team Ninjas	1.00
113 V:Cobra	1.00
114 V:Cobra	1.00
115 Story Concl.Dusty Dossier	1.00
116 Destro:Search&Destroy #1	1.00
117 Destro:Search&Destroy #2	1.00
118 Destro:Search&Destroy #3	1.00
119 HT,Android Dopplegangers	1.00
120 V:Red Ninjas,Slice & Dice	1.00
121 V:Slice & Dice	1.25
122 V:Slice & Dice	1.25
123 I:Eco-Warriors,A:Big Man	1.25
124 V:Headman	1.25
125 V:Headhunters	1.25
126 R:Firefly	1.25
127 R:Original G.I.Joe	1.25
128 V:Firefly	1.25
129 V:Cobra Commander	1.25
130 V:Cobra Commander	1.25
131 V:Cobra Commander	1.25
132 V:Cobra	1.25
133 V:Cobra	1.25
134 V:Red Ninjas, Firefly, Hostilities	1.25
135 V:Cobra Ninja w/card	1.75
136 w/Trading Card	1.75
137 V:Night Creepers,w/card	1.75
138 V:Night Creepers,w/card	1.75
139 R:Transformers,V:Cobra	1.25
140 A:Transformers	1.25
141 A:Transformers	1.25
142 A:Transformers	1.25
143 F:Scarlet	1.25
144 O:Snake Eyes	1.25
145 V:Cobra	1.25
146 F:Star Brigade	1.25
147 F:Star Brigade	1.25
148 F:Star Brigade	1.25
149	1.25
150 Cobra Commander vs. Snake Eyes	2.00

151 V:Cobra	1.50
152 First G.I. Joe	1.50
153 V:Cobra	1.50
154	1.50
155 final issue	1.50
SC GI Joe and the Transformers	4.95
Spec. TM rep.#61	1.50
Ann.#1	3.00
Ann.#2	2.00
Ann.#3	2.00
Ann.#4	2.00
Ann.#5	2.00
Yearbook #1 (1985)	2.50
Yearbook #2 (1986)	2.50
Yearbook #3 (1987)	2.50
Yearbook #4 (1988)	2.50

G.I. JOE
EUROPEAN MISSIONS
June, 1988

1 British rep.	1.25
2	1.50
3	1.50
4	1.50
5 thru 15	@1.75

G.I. JOE
SPECIAL MISSIONS
Oct., 1986

1 HT,New G.I. Joe	1.75
2 HT	1.50
3 HT	1.50
4 HT	1.50
5 HT	1.50
6 HT,Iron Curtain	1.50
7 HT	1.50
8 HT	1.50
9 HT	1.50
10 thru 21 HT	@1.00
22	1.00
23 HT	1.00
24	1.00
25 HT	1.00
26 HT	1.00
27	1.00
28 HT,final	1.00

G.I. Joe and the Transformers #1
© Marvel Entertainment Group

G.I. JOE AND
THE TRANSFORMERS
1987

1 HT,mini-series	1.75
2 HT,Cobra	1.50
3 HT,Cobra,Deceptions	1.00
4 HT,Cobra,Deceptions	1.00

G.I. JOE UNIVERSE

1 Biographies rep.#1	2.50
2	2.00
3 MZ(c)	2.00
4	1.25

G.I. TALES
See: SERGEANT BARNEY BARKER

GIRL COMICS
Atlas Nov., 1949

1 Ph(c),True love stories,I Could Escape From Love	125.00
2 Ph(c),JKu,Blind Date	75.00
3 BEv,Ph(c),Liz Taylor	100.00
4 PH(c),Borrowed Love	45.00
5 Love stories	45.00
6 same	45.00
7 same	45.00
8 same	45.00
9 same	45.00
10 The Deadly Double-Cross	45.00
11 Love stories	45.00
12 BK,The Dark Hallway	50.00

Becomes:

GIRL CONFESSIONS

13	50.00
14	30.00
15	30.00
16 BEv	35.00
17 BEv	35.00
18 BEv	35.00
19	25.00
20	25.00
21 thru 34	@17.00
35 August, 1954	17.00

GIRLS' LIFE
Atlas Jan., 1954

1	50.00
2	25.00
3	20.00
4	20.00
5	20.00
6 November, 1954	20.00

GLADIATOR/SUPREME
1997

1 KG,ASm,x-over	5.00

GODZILLA
August, 1977

1 HT,JM,Based on Movie Series	8.00
2 HT,FrG,GT,Seattle Under Seige	6.00
3 HT,TD,A;Champions	4.00
4 TS,TD,V;Batragon	4.00
5 TS,KJ,Isle of the Living Demons	6.00
6 HT,A Monster Enslaved	6.00
7 V:Red Ronin	6.00
8 V:Red Ronin	6.00
9 Las Gamble in Las Vegas	6.00
10 V:Yetrigar	6.00

MARVEL

11 V;Red Ronin,Yetrigar	4.00
12 Star Sinister	4.00
13 V:Mega-Monster	4.00
14 V:Super-Beasts	4.00
15 Stampede	4.00
16 Jaws of Fear	4.00
17 Godzilla Shrunk	4.00
18 Battle Beneath Eighth Avenue	4.00
19 Panic on the Pier	4.00
20 A;Fantastic Four	4.50
21 V:Devil Dinosaur	4.00
22 V:Devil Dinosaur	4.00
23 A;Avengers	4.50
24 July, 1979	4.00

GOLDEN AGE OF MARVEL
TPB RyI 10.00

GREATEST SPIDER-MAN & DAREDEVIL TEAM-UPS
TPB 175pg 10.00

GREEN GOBLIN
1995–96

1 I:New Green Goblin	2.95
2 TDF,SMc,V:Rhino	1.95
3 TDF,SMc,CyberWar tie-in	1.95
4 TDF,SMc,V:Hobgoblin	1.95
5 TDF,V:Hobgoblin	1.95
6	1.95
7	1.95
8 TDF,SMc,I:Angelface	1.95
9	1.95
10	1.95
11	1.95
12 Onslaught saga	1.95
13 Onslaught saga	1.95

GROO CHRONICLES
Epic 1989

1 SA	5.00
2 SA	4.00
3 SA	4.00
4 SA	4.00
5 SA	4.00
6 SA	3.50

[SERGIO ARAGONE'S] GROO, THE WANDERER
(see Pacific, Eclipse)
Epic 1985–95

1 SA,I:Minstrel	9.00
2 SA,A:Minstrel	6.00
3 SA,Medallions	5.00
4 SA,Airship	4.00
5 SA,Slavers	4.00
6 SA,The Eye of the Kabala	4.00
7 SA,A:Sage	4.00
8 SA,A:Taranto	4.00
9 SA,A:Sage	4.00
10 SA,I:Arcadio	4.00
11 SA,A:Arcadio	4.00
12 SA,Groo Meets the Thespians	4.00
13 SA,A:Sage	4.00
14 SA	4.00
15 SA,Monks	4.00
16 SA,A:Taranto	4.00
17 SA,Pirannas	4.00
18 SA,I:Groo Ella	4.00
19 SA,A:Groo Ella	3.00
20 SA,A:Groo Ella	3.00
21 SA,I:Arba,Dakarba	3.00

Groo The Wanderer #18
© Marvel Entertainment Group

22 SA,Ambassador	3.00
23 SA,I:Pal,Drumm	3.00
24 SA,Arcadio's	3.00
25 SA,Taranto	3.00
26 SA,A:Arba,Taranto	3.00
27 SA,A:Minstrel,Sage	3.00
28 SA	3.00
29 SA,I:Ruferto	4.00
30 SA,A:Ruferto	3.00
31 SA,A:Pal,Drumm	2.00
32 SA,C:Sage	2.00
33 SA,Pirates	2.00
34 SA,Wizard's amulet	2.00
35 SA,A:Everybody	2.00
36 SA,A:Everybody	2.00
37 SA,A:Ruferto	2.00
38 SA,Dognappers	2.00
39 SA,A:Pal,Drumm	2.00
40 SA	2.00
41 SA,I:Granny Groo	2.00
42 SA,A:Granny Groo	2.00
43 SA,A:Granny Groo	2.00
44 SA,A:Ruferto	2.00
45 SA	2.00
46 SA,New Clothes	2.00
47 SA,A:Everybody	2.00
48 SA,A:Ruferto	2.00
49 SA,C:Chakaal	2.00
50 SA,double size	3.00
51 SA,A:Chakaal	2.00
52 SA,A:Chakaal	2.00
53 SA,A:Chakaal	2.00
54 SA,A:Ahak	2.00
55 SA,A:Ruferto	2.00
56 SA,A:Minstrael	2.00
57 SA,A:Ruferto	2.00
58 SA,A:Idol	2.00
59 SA	2.00
60 SA,A:Ruferto	2.00
61 SA,A:Horse	2.00
62 SA,A:Horse	1.75
63 SA,A:Drumm	1.75
64 SA,A:Artist	1.75
65 SA	1.75
66 SA	1.75
67 SA	1.75
68 SA	1.75
69 SA	1.75

70 SA	1.50
71 SA	1.50
72 SA	1.50
73 SA,Amnesia,pt1	1.50
74 SA,Amnesia,pt2	1.50
75 SA,Memory Returns	1.50
76 SA	1.50
77 SA	1.50
78 SA,R:Weaver,Scribe	1.50
79 SA,Groo the Assassin	1.50
80 SA,I:Thaiis,pt.1	1.50
81 SA,Thaiis,pt.2	1.50
82 SA,Thaiis,pt.3	1.50
83 SA,Thaiis,pt.4	1.50
84 SA,Thaiis Conclusion	1.50
85 SA,Groo turns invisible	1.50
86 SA,Invisible Groo	1.50
87 SA,Groo's Army	1.50
88 SA,V:Cattlemen,B.U. Sage	2.50
89 SA,New Deluxe Format	2.25
90 SA,Worlds 1st Lawyers	2.25
91 SA,Bonus Pages	2.25
92 SA,Groo Becomes Kid Groo	2.25
93 SA,Groo destroys glacier	2.25
94 SA	2.25
95 SA,Endangered Species	2.25
96 SA,Wager of the Gods#1	2.25
97 SA,Wager of the Gods#2	2.25
98 SA,Wager of the Gods#3	2.25
99 SA,E:Wager of the Gods	2.25
100 SA,Groo gets extra IQ points	2.75
101 SA,Groo loses intelligence	2.25
102 SA,F:Newly literate Groo	2.25
103 SA,General Monk	2.25
104 SA,F:Oso,Ruferto	2.25
105 SA,V:Minotaurs	2.25
106 SA,B:Man of the People	2.25
107 SA,Man of the People#2	2.25
108 SA,Man of the People#3	2.25
109 SA,E:Man of the People	2.25
110 SA,Mummies	2.25
111 SA,The Man who Killed Groo	2.25
112 SA,Rufferto Avenged	2.25
113 SA	2.25
114 SA,V:Vultures	2.25
115 SA	2.25
116 SA,Early unto Morning	2.25
117 SA	2.25
118 SA	2.25
119 SA	2.25
120 Groo hangs up swords	2.25
GNv Death of Groo	8.00
GNv 2nd print	8.00
TPB Groo Adventures	8.95
TPB Groo Carnival	8.95
TPB Groo Expose	8.95
TPB GRoo Festival	8.95
TPB Groo Garden	10.95

GROOVY
March, 1968—July, 1968

1 Monkeys,Ringo Starr,Photos	50.00
2 Cartoons,Gags,Jokes	40.00
3	40.00

GUARDIANS OF THE GALAXY
June, 1990

1 B:JV(a&s),I:Taserface,R:Aleta	4.00
2 MZ(c),JV,V:Stark,C:Firelord	3.00
3 JV,V:Stark,I:Force,C:Firelord	3.00
4 JV,V:Stark,A:Force,Firelord	3.00
5 JV,TM(c),V:Force,I:Mainframe (Vision)	3.00

6 JV,V:Force,Vance Possesses
   Capt.America Shield 3.00
7 GP(c),JV,I:Malevolence,
   O:Starhawk 3.50
8 SLi(c),JV,V:Yondu,C:Rancor .. 3.50
9 RLd(c),JV,I:Replica,Rancor ... 3.50
10 JLe(c),JV,V:Rancor,The Nine
   I&C:Overkill(Taserface) 3.50
11 BWi(c),JV,V:Rancor,I:Phoenix . 3.50
12 ATb(c),JV,V:Overkill
   A:Firelord 2.50
13 JV,A:Ghost Rider,Force,
   Malevolence 3.00
14 JS(c),JV,A:Ghost Rider,Force,
   Malevolence 3.00
15 JSn(c),JV,I:Protege,V:Force .. 2.50
16 JV,V:Force,A:Protege,
   Malevolence,L:Vance Astro ... 2.50
17 JV,V:Punishers(Street Army),
   L:Martinex,N:Charlie-27, ... 2.50
18 JV,V:Punishers,I&C:Talon,A:
   Crazy Nate 3.00
19 JV,V:Punishers,A:Talon 2.50
20 JV,I:Major Victory (Vance Astro)
   J:Talon & Krugarr 2.50

Guardians of the Galaxy #20
© Marvel Entertainment Group

21 JV,V:Rancor 2.50
22 JV,V:Rancor 2.50
23 MT,V:Rancor,C:Silver Surfer .. 2.50
24 JV,A:Silver Surfer 3.00
25 JV, Prismatic Foil(c)
   V:Galactus,A:SilverSurfer 3.50
25a 2nd printing,Silver 2.50
26 JV,O:Guardians(retold) 2.00
27 JV,Infinity War,O:Talon,
   A:Inhumans 2.00
28 JV,Inf.War,V:Various Villians .. 2.00
29 HT,Inf.War,V:Various Villians . 2.00
30 KWe,A:Captain America 2.00
31 KWe,V:Badoon,A:Capt.A. 1.75
32 KWe,V:Badoon Gladiator 1.75
33 KWe,A:Dr.Strange,R:Aleta ... 1.50
34 KWe,J:Yellowjacket II 1.50
35 KWe,A:Galatic Guardians,
   V:Bubonicus 1.50
36 KWe,A:Galatic Guardians,
   V:Dormammu 1.50
37 KWe,V:Dormammu,A:Galatic
   Guardians 1.50

38 KWe,N:Y.jacket,A:Beyonder .. 1.50
39 KWe,Rancor Vs. Dr.Doom,Holo-
   grafx(c) 3.25
40 KWe,V:Loki,Composite 1.50
41 KWe,V:Loki,A:Thor 1.50
42 KWe,I:Woden 1.50
43 KWe,A:Woden,V:Loki 1.50
44 KWe,R:Yondu 1.50
45 KWe,O:Starhawk 1.50
46 KWe,N:Major Victory 1.50
47 KWe,A:Beyonder,Protoge,
   Overkill 1.50
48 KWe,V:Overkill 1.75
49 KWe,A:Celestial 1.75
50 Foil(c),R:Yondu,Starhawk separated,BU:O:Guardians 3.25
51 KWe,A:Irish Wolfhound 1.50
52 KWe,A:Drax 1.50
53 KWe,V:Drax 1.50
54 KWe,V:Sentinels 1.50
55 KWe,Ripjack 1.50
56 Ripjack 1.50
57 R:Keeper 1.50
58 .... 1.50
59 A:Keeper 1.50
60 F:Starhawk 1.50
61 F:Starhawk 1.50
62 Guardians Stop War of the Worlds
   last issue 1.50
Ann.#1 Korvac Quest #4,I:Krugarr 3.00
Ann.#2 HT,I:Galactic Guardians,
   System Bytes #4 .... 3.00
Ann.#3 CDo,I:Irish Wolfhound,
   w/Trading card 3.25
Ann.#4 V:Nine 3.25
TPB rep #1 thru #6 .... 12.95

GUNHAWK, THE
See: BLAZE CARSON

GUNHAWKS
Oct., 1972
1 SSh,B:Reno Jones & Kid
   Cassidy Two Rode Together . 10.00
2 Ride out for Revenge 8.00
3 Indian Massacre 8.00
4 Trial by Ordeal 8.00
5 The Reverend Mr. Graves 8.00
6 E:Reno Jones & Kid Cassidy
   D:Kid Cassidy 8.00
7 A Gunhawks Last Stand
   A;Reno Jones, Oct., 1973 ... 8.00

GUNRUNNER
Marvel UK 1993–94
1 I:Gunrunner,w/trading cards ... 2.95
2 A:Ghost Rider 2.00
3 V:Cynodd 2.00
4 .... 2.00
5 A:Enhanced 2.00
6 final issue 1.75

GUNSLINGER
See: TEX DAWSON, GUNSLINGER

GUNSMOKE WESTERN
See: ALL WINNERS COMICS

HARROWERS
1993–94
1 MSt(s),GC,F:Pinhead 3.25
2 GC,AW(i), ... 2.75

3 GC,AW(i), ... 2.75
4 GC,AW(i), ... 2.75
5 GC,AW(i),Devil's Pawn#1 .... 2.75
6 GC,AW(i),Devil's Pawn#2 .... 2.75

HARVEY
Oct., 1970–Dec., 1972
1 .... 40.00
2 thru 6 .... @25.00

HARVEY PRESENTS: CASPER
1 .... 1.50

HAVOK & WOLVERINE
Epic March, 1988
1 JMu,KW,V:KGB,Dr.Neutron .. 5.00
2 JMu,KW,V:KGB,Dr.Neutron .. 4.00
3 JMu,KW,V:Meltdown 4.00
4 JMu,KW,V:Meltdown,Oct.1989 . 4.00
TPB rep.#1-4 .... 16.95

HAWKEYE
[1st Limited Series] Sept., 1983
1 A:Mockingbird 3.00
2 I:Silencer 2.50
3 I:Bombshell,Oddball 2.00
4 V:Crossfire,W:Hawkeye &
   Mockingbird, (Dec. 1983) 2.00
[2nd Limited Series] 1994
1 B:CDi(s),ScK,V:Trickshot,
   I:Javelynn,Rover 2.00
2 ScK,V:Viper 2.00
3 ScK,A:War Machine,N:Hawkeye,
   V:Secret Empire 2.00
4 E:CDi(s),ScK,V:Trickshot,Viper,
   Javelynn 2.00

HAWKEYE: EARTH'S MIGHTIEST MARKSMAN
Aug. 1998
1-shot TDF,MBa,JJ,DR,AM 48pg . 3.00

HEADMASTERS
STAR July, 1987
1 FS,Transformers 1.25
2 and 3 .... @1.00
4 Jan., 1988 .... .75

HEATHCLIFF
Star April, 1985
1 thru 16 .... @1.00
17 Masked Moocher 1.00
18 thru 49 .... @1.00
50 Double-size 1.00
51 thru 55 .... @1.00

HEATHCLIFF'S FUNHOUSE
Star May, 1987
1 thru 9 .... @1.00
10 1988 .... 1.00

HEAVY HITTERS
Ann.#1 (1993) 4.00

HEDY DEVINE COMICS
Aug., 1947—Sept., 1952
22 I:Hedy Devine 80.00
23 BW,Beauty and the Beach,

HK,Hey Look 90.00
24 High Jinx in Hollywood,
  HK, Hey Look 90.00
25 Hedy/Bull(c),HK,Hey Look . . . 80.00
26 Skating(c),HK,Giggles&Grins . 60.00
27 Hedy at Show(c),HK,Hey Look 70.00
28 Hedy/Charlie(c),HK,Hey Look 70.00
29 Tennis(c),HK,Hey Look 70.00
30 . . . . 70.00
31 thru 50 . . . . @40.00

HEDY WOLFE
Atlas August, 1957
1 Patsy Walker's Rival 50.00

HELLHOUND
1993–94
1 Hellhound on my Trial 2.50
2 Love in Vain 2.50
3 Last Fair Deal Gone Down . . . 2.25

HELLRAISER
**See: CLIVE BARKER'S
HELLRAISER**

HELLRAISER III
HELL ON EARTH
1 Movie Adaptation,(prestige) . . . 4.95
1a Movie Adapt.(magazine) 2.95

HELLSTORM,
PRINCE OF LIES
1993
1 R:Daimon Hellstrom,
  Parchment(c) 3.50
2 A:Dr.Strange,Gargoyle 3.00
3 O:Hellstorm. 2.75
4 V:Ghost Rider 2.75
5 MB, ... 2.50
6 MB,V:Dead Daughter 2.50
7 A:Armaziel 2.50
8 Hell is where the heart is 2.25
9 LKa(s),Highway to Heaven . . . 2.25
10 LKa(s),Heaven's Gate 2.25
11 LKa(s),PrG,Life in Hell 2.25
12 Red Miracles 2.25
13 Red Miracles Sidewalking . . . 2.25
14 Red Miracles Murder is Easy . 2.25
15 Cigarette Dawn 2.75
16 Down Here 2.25
17 The Saint of the Pit 2.00
18 . . . . 2.00
19 . . . . 2.00
20 . . . . 2.00
21 final issue 2.00

HELL'S ANGEL
1992
1 GSr,A:X-Men,O:Hell's Angel . 3.00
2 GSr,A:X-Men,V:Psycho Warriors 2.50
3 GSr,A:X-Men,V:MyS-Tech . . . 2.00
4 GSr,A:X-Men,V:MyS-Tech . . . 2.00
5 GSr,A:X-Men,V:MyS-Tech . . . 2.00
6 Gfr,A:X-Men,V:MyS-Tech . . . 2.00
Becomes:
DARK ANGEL
7 DMn,A:Psylocke,V:MyS-Tech . 2.00
8 DMn,A:Psylocke 2.00
9 A:Punisher 2.00
10 MyS-Tech Wars tie-in 2.00
11 A:X-Men,MyS-Tech wars tie-in 2.00
12 A:X-Men 2.00

13 A:X-Men,Death's Head II 2.00
14 Afthermath#2 . . . . 1.75
15 Afthermath#3 . . . . 1.75
16 SvL,E:Afthermath,last issue . . 1.75

HERCULES AND THE
HEART OF CHAOS
Limited Series Aug., 1997
1 (of 3) TDF,RF,PO, ... 2.50
2 TDF,RF,PO, ... 2.50
3 TDF,RF,PO,V:Ares, concl. . . . 2.50

HERCULES PRINCE
OF POWER
Sept., 1982
1 BL,I:Recorder 3.00
2 BL,I:Layana Sweetwater 2.00
3 BL,V:The Brothers,C:Galactus . 2.00
4 BL,A:Galactus 2.00
[2nd Series] March, 1984
1 BL,I:Skyypi 2.50
2 BL,A:Red Wolf 1.50
3 BL,A:Starfox 1.50
4 BL,D:Zeus, June, 1984 . . . . . 1.50
TPB BL rep. Vol.1 #1–#4 and
  Vol.2 #1–#4 . . . . 6.00

HERO
May, 1990
1 . . . . 2.50
2 . . . . 2.00
3 . . . . 1.50
4 RH 1.50
5 RH 1.50
6 Oct., 1990 . . . . 1.50

HERO FOR HIRE
June, 1972
1 GT,JR,I&O:Power Man 35.00
2 GT,A:Diamond Back 12.00
3 GT,I:Mace 10.00
4 V:Phantom of 42nd St. 10.00
5 GT,A:Black Mariah 10.00
6 V:Assassin 7.00
7 GT,Nuclear Bomb issue 7.00
8 GT,A:Dr.Doom 7.00
9 GT,A:Dr.Doom,Fant.Four 7.00
10 GT,A:Dr.Death,Fant.Four . . . 7.00
11 GT,A:Dr.Death 6.00
12 GT,C:Spider-Man 6.00
13 A:Lion Fang 6.00
14 V:Big Ben 6.00
15 Cage Goes Wild 6.00
16 O:Stilletto,D:Rackham 6.00
Becomes: POWER MAN

HEROES FOR HIRE
July, 1997
1 JOs,PFe,F:Iron Fist 1.99
2 JOs,PFe,V:Nitro 1.99
2A Variant PFe cover 1.99
3 JOs,PFe,V:Nitro 1.99
4 JOs,Power Man vs. Iron Fist . . 2.00
5 JOs,V:Sersi, Diabolical Deviants 2.00
6 JOs,PFe, Deviants 2.00
7 JOs V:Thunderbolts 2.00
8 JOs,Iron Fist's agenda revealed 2.00
9 JOs,Search for Punisher 2.00
10 JOs,Deadpool hired 2.00
11 JOs,PFe,A:Deadpool, V:Silver
  Sable and Wild Pack 2.00
12 JOs,PFe,Traitor revealed, 48pg 3.00
13 JOs,PFe,V:Master 2.00

14 JOs,F:Black Knight 2.00
15 JOs,PFe,Siege of Wundagore,
  pt.1 (of 5) 2.00
16 JOs,PFe,Siege of Wundagore,
  pt.3 . . . . 2.00
Ann.'98 JOs,BWi,PFe,Heroes For
  Hire/Quicksilver, The Siege of
  Wundagore, pt.5 (of 5) 48pg . . 3.00

Heroes For Hope #1
© Marvel Entertainment Group

HEROES FOR HOPE
1 TA/JBy/HC/RCo/BWr,A:XMen . 7.00

HEROES REBORN:
THE RETURN
Oct., 1997
½ Heroes Reborn prequel, (Marvel/
  Wizard 1996) 7.50
1 (of 4) PDd,ATi,SvL,F:Franklin
  Richards 2.50
2 PDd,ATi,SvL, F:Spider-Man,
  Thunderbolts & Doctor Strange 2.50
3 PDd,SvL,ATi,A UniverseMayDie 2.50
4 PDd,SvL,ATi, crossover to Marvel
  Universe? 2.50

HOKUM & HEX
Razorline 1993–94
1 BU:Saint Sinner 2.75
2 I:Analyzer 2.00
3 I:Wrath 2.00
4 I:Z-Man 2.00
5 V:Hyperkind 2.00
6 B:Bloodshed 2.00
7 V:Bloodshed 2.00
8 V:Bloodshed 2.00
9 E:Bloodshed,final issue 2.25

HOLIDAY COMICS
Jan., 1951
1 LbC(c),Christmas(c) 175.00
2 LbC(c),Easter Parade(c) . . . 200.00
3 LbC(c),4th of July(c) 125.00
4 LbC(c),Summer Vacation . . . 75.00
5 LbC(c),Christmas(c) 80.00

6 LbC(c),Birthday(c) 90.00
7 LbC(c),Rodeo (c) 75.00
8 LbC(c),Christmas(c)
Oct., 1952 . . . . 75.00

HOLLYWOOD SUPERSTARS
Epic Nov., 1990
1 DSp 2.00
2 thru 5 DSp, March, 1991 . . @2.25

HOMER, THE HAPPY GHOST
March, 1955
1 . . . . 75.00
2 . . . . 35.00
3 . . . . 20.00
4 thru 15 . . . . @20.00
16 thru 22 . . . . @18.00
[2nd Series] Nov., 1969
1 . . . . 15.00
2 thru 5 . . . . @10.00

HOOK
1992
1 JRy,GM,movie adaption 1.00
2 JRy,Return to Never Land 1.00
3 Peter Pans Magic 1.00
4 conclusion 1.00
Hook Super Spec.#1 . . . . 2.95

HORRORS, THE
Jan., 1953—April, 1954
11 LbC(c),The Spirit of War . . 175.00
12 LbC(c),Under Fire 150.00
13 LbC(c),Terror Castle 150.00
14 LbC(c),Underworld Terror . . 150.00
15 LbC(c),The Mad Bandit 150.00

HOT SHOTS
AVENGERS
1 Painted Pin-ups (1995) 2.95
SPIDER-MAN
1 Painted pin-ups 2.95
X-MEN
1 Painted pin-ups 2.95

HOUSE II
1 1987, Movie Adapt. 2.00

HOWARD THE DUCK
Jan., 1976
1 FB,SL,A:Spider-Man,I:Beverly . 7.00
2 FB,V:TurnipMan&Kidney Lady . 2.00
3 JB,Learns Quack Fu 1.50
4 GC,V:Winky Man 1.50
5 GC,Becomes Wrestler 1.50
6 GC,V:Gingerbread Man 1.50
7 GC,V:Gingerbread Man 1.50
8 GC,A:Dr.Strange,ran for Pres. . 1.50
9 GC,V:Le Beaver 1.25
10 GC,A:Spider-Man 2.00
11 GC,V:Kidney Lady 1.25
12 GC,I:Kiss 4.00
13 GC,A:Kiss 4.00
14 GC,Howard as Son of Satan . . 2.00
15 GC,A:Dr.Strange,A:Dr.Bong . . 1.25
16 GC,DC,JB,DG,TA,
V:Incredible Creator 1.25
17 GC,D:Dr.Bong 1.25
18 GC,Howard the Human #1 . . . 1.25
19 GC,Howard the Human #2 . . . 1.25

20 GC,V:Sudd 1.25
21 GC,V:Soofi 1.25
22 A:ManThing,StarWars Parody . 1.25
23 A:ManThing,StarWars Parody . 1.25
24 GC,NightAfter..SavedUniverse . 1.25
25 GC,V:Circus of Crime 1.25
26 GC,V:Circus of Crime 1.25
27 GC,V:Circus of Crime 1.25
28 GC,Cooking With Gas 1.25
29 Duck-Itis Poster Child 1978 . . 1.25
30 Iron Duck,V:Dr. Bong 1.25
31 Iron Duck,V:Dr. Bong 1.25
32 V:Gopher 1.25
33 BB(c),The Material Duck 1.25
Ann.#1, V:Caliph of Bagmom . . . 1.25
Holiday Spec. LHa,ATi,PFe (1996) 3.00

HOWARD THE DUCK MAGAZINE
(B&W) Oct., 1979–March 1981
1 . . . . 2.50
2 & 3 . . . . @1.50
4 Beatles,Elvis,Kiss 5.00
5 thru 9 . . . . @1.50

HUGGA BUNCH
Star Oct., 1986—Aug., 1987
1 . . . . 1.25
2 thru 6 . . . . @1.00

HULK 2099
1994–95
1 GJ,Foil(c),V:Draco 2.50
2 GJ,V:Draco 1.50
3 I:Golden Boy 1.50
4 . . . . 1.50
5 Ultra Hulk 1.50
Becomes:
HULK 2099 A.D.
6 Gamma Ray Scientist 1.50
7 A:Doom,Dr.Apollo 1.95
8 One Nation Under Doom 1.95
9 California Quake 1.95

HUMAN FLY
July, 1987
1 I&O:Human Fly,A:Spider-Man . 5.00
2 A:Ghost Rider 7.50
3 DC,JSt(c),DP,'Fortress of Fear' 1.75
4 JB/TA(c),'David Drier' 1.75
5 V:Makik 1.75
6 Fear in Funland 1.75
7 ME,Fury in the Wind 1.75
8 V:White Tiger 1.75
9 JB/TA(c),ME,V:Copperhead,A:
White Tiger,Daredevil 1.75
10 ME,Dark as a Dungeon 1.75
11 ME,A:Daredevil 1.75
12 ME,Suicide Sky-Dive 1.75
13 BLb/BMc(c),FS,V:Carl Braden . 1.75
14 BLb/BMc(c),SL,Fear Over
Fifth Avenue 1.75
15 BLb/BMc(c),War in the
Washington Monument 1.75
16 BLb/BMc(c),V:Blaze Kendall . 1.75
17 BLb,DP,Murder on the Midway 1.75
18 V:Harmony Whyte 1.75
19 BL(c),V:Jacopo Belbo
March, 1979 . . . . 1.75

RED RAVEN COMICS
Timely Comics August, 1940
1 JK,O:Red Raven,I:Magar,A:Comet

Pierce & Mercury,Human Top,
Eternal Brain 11,000.00
Becomes:
HUMAN TORCH
Fall, 1940–Aug. 1954
2 (#1)ASh(c),BEv,B:Sub-Mariner
A:Fiery Mask,Falcon,Mantor,
Microman 20,000.00
3 (#2)Ash(c),BEv,V:Sub-
Mariner,Bondage(c) 4,500.00
4 (#3)Ash(c),BEv,O:Patriot . . 3,500.00
5 (#4)V:Nazis,A:Patriot,Angel
crossover 2,500.00
5a(#5)ASh(c),V:Sub-Mariner . 4,000.00
6 ASh(c),Doom Dungeon . . . 1,500.00
7 ASh(c),V:Japanese 1,600.00
8 ASh(c),BW,V:Sub-Mariner . 2,500.00
9 ASh(c),V:General Rommel . 1,500.00
10 ASh(c),BW,V:Sub-Mariner . 2,000.00
11 ASh(c),Nazi Oil Refinery . . 1,300.00
12 ASh(c),V:Japanese,
Bondage(c) 1,600.00
13 ASh(c),V:Japanese,
Bondage(c) 1,300.00
14 ASh(c),V:Nazis 1,300.00
15 ASh(c),Toro Trapped 1,300.00
16 ASh(c),V:Japanese 900.00
17 ASh(c),V:Japanese 900.00
18 ASh(c),V:Japanese,
MacArthurs HQ 900.00
19 ASh(c),Bondage(c) 900.00
20 ASh(c),Last War Issue 900.00
21 ASh(c),V:Organized Crime . 900.00
22 ASh(c),V:Smugglers 900.00
23 ASh(c),V:Giant Robot 900.00
24 V:Mobsters 900.00
25 The Masked Monster 900.00
26 Her Diary of Terror 900.00
27 SSh(c),BEv,V:The Asbestos
Lady 900.00
28 BEv,The Twins Who Weren't 900.00
29 You'll Die Laughing 900.00
30 BEv,The Stranger,A:Namora 800.00
31 A:Namora 700.00
32 A:Sungirl,Namora 700.00
33 Capt.America crossover . . . 750.00
34 The Flat of the Land 700.00
35 A;Captain America,Sungirl . 750.00

Human Torch #3
© *Marvel Entertainment Group*

36 A:Submariner 700.00
37 BEv,A:Submariner 700.00
38 BEv,A:Submariner 700.00

HUMAN TORCH
Sept., 1974
1 JK,rep.StrangeTales #101 . . . 12.00
2 rep.Strange Tales #102 . . . . . . 8.00
3 rep.Strange Tales #103 . . . . . . 8.00
4 rep.Strange Tales #104 . . . . . . 8.00
5 rep.Strange Tales #105 . . . . . . 8.00
6 rep.Strange Tales #106 . . . . . . 8.00
7 rep.Strange Tales #107 . . . . . . 8.00
8 rep.Strange Tales #108 . . . . . . 8.00

HYPERKIND
Razorline
1 I:Hyperkind,BU:EctoKid 2.75
2 I:Bliss 2.00
3 V:Living Void 2.00
4 FBk(s),I:Paragon John 2.00
5 V:Paragon John 2.00
6 Vetus Unleashed 2.00
7 Ambertrance 2.00
8 I:Tempest 2.00
9 I:Lazurex,w/card 2.25

HYPERKIND UNLEASHED
1994
1 BU,V:Thermakk 2.95

ICEMAN
Dec., 1984
1 DP,mini-series 2.00
2 DP,V:Kali 1.50
3 DP,A:Original X-Men,Defenders
   Champions 1.50
4 DP,Oblivion,June, 1985 . . . . . 1.50

IDEAL
Timely July, 1948
1 Antony and Cleopatra . . . 225.00
2 The Corpses of Dr.Sacotti . 200.00
3 Joan of Arc 175.00
4 Richard the Lionhearted
   A:The Witness 300.00
5 Phc,Love and Romance . . . 125.00
Becomes:

LOVE ROMANCES
6 Ph(c),I Loved a Scoundrel . . 75.00
7 Ph(c) 50.00
8 Ph(c) 55.00
9 thru 12 Ph(c) . . . . @35.00
13 thru 20 . . . . @35.00
21 BK 50.00
22 . . . . 30.00
23 . . . . 30.00
24 BK 45.00
25 . . . . 45.00
26 thru 35 . . . . @30.00
36 BK 45.00
37 . . . . 30.00
38 BK 45.00
39 thru 44 . . . . @30.00
45 MB 40.00
46 . . . . 30.00
47 . . . . 30.00
48 . . . . 25.00
49 ATh 45.00
50 . . . . 25.00
51 . . . . 25.00
52 . . . . 25.00
53 ATh 45.00

54 . . . . 25.00
55 . . . . 25.00
56 . . . . 25.00
57 MB 40.00
58 thru 74 . . . . @25.00
75 MB 35.00
76 . . . . 25.00
77 MB 35.00
78 . . . . 25.00
79 . . . . 25.00
80 RH(c) 30.00
81 . . . . 25.00
82 MB,JK(c) 30.00
83 JSe,JK(c) 40.00
84 JK 30.00
85 JK 30.00
86 thru 95 . . . . @20.00
96 JK 45.00
97 . . . . 25.00
98 JK 45.00
99 JK 45.00
100 thru 104 . . . . @25.00
105 JK 40.00
106 JK,July, 1963 . . . . 40.00

IDEAL COMICS
Timely Fall, 1944
1 B:Super Rabbit,Giant Super
   Rabbit V:Axis(c) 125.00
2 Super Rabbit at Fair(c) 75.00
3 Beach Party(c) 65.00
4 How to Catch Robbers 65.00
Becomes:

WILLIE COMICS
5 B:Willie,George,Margie,Nellie
   Football(c) 80.00
6 Record Player(c) 50.00
7 Soda Fountain(c),HK,Hey Look 55.00
8 Fancy Dress(c) 50.00
9 . . . . 50.00
10 HK,Hey Look 50.00
11 HK,Hey Look 50.00
12 . . . . 40.00
13 . . . . 50.00
14 thru 18 . . . . @35.00
19 . . . . 50.00
20 Li'L Willie Comics 35.00

Illuminator #3
© Marvel Entertainment Group

21 Li'L Willie Comics 35.00
22 . . . . 35.00
23 May, 1950 . . . . 35.00

IDOL
Epic 1992
1 I:Idol 2.95
2 Phantom o/t Set 2.95
3 Conclusion 2.95

ILLUMINATOR
1993
1 . . . . 5.00
2 . . . . 5.00
3 . . . . 3.00
4 . . . . 3.00

IMMORTALIS
1 A:Dr.Strange 1.95
2 A:Dr.Strange 1.95
3 A:Dr.Strange,V:Vampires . . . 1.95
4 Mephisto, final issue 1.75

IMPERIAL GUARD
[Limited Series] 1997
1 (of 3) BAu,Woj, ... 2.00
2 and 3 BAu,Woj . . . . @2.00

IMPOSSIBLE MAN SUMMER VACATION
1990–91
1 GCa,DP 2.50
2 . . . . 2.00
Summer Fun Spec. TPe, Vacation
   on Earth 2.50

INCAL, THE
Epic Nov., 1988
1 Moebius,Adult 2.50
2 Moebius,Adult 2.00
3 Moebius,Adult, Jan., 1989 . . . 2.00

INCOMPLETE DEATH'S HEAD
1993
1 thru 10 rep.Death's Head #1
   thru #10 . . . . @2.00
11 rep.Death's Head #11 . . . . . . 1.75

INCREDIBLE HULK
May, 1962
1 JK,I:Hulk(Grey Skin),Rick Jones,
   Thunderbolt Ross,Betty Ross,
   Gremlin,Gamma Base . . 11,000.00
2 JK,SD,O:Hulk,(Green skin) 2,500.00
3 JK,O:rtd.,I:Ring Master,
   Circus of Crime 1,600.00
4 JK,V:Mongu 1,400.00
5 JK,I:General Fang 1,400.00
6 SD,I:Metal Master 2,000.00
See: Tales to Astonish #59-#101
April, 1968
102 MSe,GT,O:Retold 135.00
103 MSe,I:Space Parasite 75.00
104 MSe,O&N:Rhino 60.00
105 MSe,GT,I:Missing Link . . . 50.00
106 MSe,HT,GT 45.00
107 HT,V:Mandarin 45.00
108 HT,JMe,A:Nick Fury 45.00
109 HT,JMe,A:Ka-Zar 45.00
110 HT,JMe,A:Ka-Zar 45.00

111 HT,DA,I:Galaxy Master 30.00	155 HT,JSe,I:Shaper of Worlds .. 7.00	223 SB,V:Leader 3.50
112 HT,DA,O:Galaxy Master ... 30.00	156 HT,V:Hulk 7.00	224 SB,V:The Leader 3.50
113 HT,DA,V:Sandman 30.00	157 HT,I:Omnivac,Rhino 7.00	225 SB,V:Leader,A:Doc Samson . 3.50
114 HT,DA 30.00	158 HT,C:Warlock,V:Rhino 7.00	226 SB,JSt,A:Doc Samson 3.50
115 HT,DA,A:Leader 30.00	159 HT,V:Abomination,Rhino 7.00	227 SB,JK,A:Doc Samson 3.50
116 HT,DA,V:Super Humanoid . 30.00	160 HT,V:Tiger Shark 6.00	228 SB,BMc,I:Moonstone,V:Doc
117 HT,DA,A:Leader 30.00	161 HT,V:Beast 8.00	Samson 3.50
118 HT,V:Sub-Mariner 30.00	162 HT,I:Wendigo I 9.50	229 SB,O:Moonstone,V:Doc
119 HT,V:Maximus 18.00	163 HT,I:Gremlin 6.00	Samson 3.50
120 HT,V:Maximus 16.00	164 HT,I:Capt.Omen 6.00	230 JM,BL,A:Bug Thing 3.50
121 HT,I:The Glob 18.00	165 HT,I:Aquon 6.00	231 SB,I:Fred Sloan 3.50
122 HT,V:Thing 35.00	166 HT,I:Zzzax 6.00	232 SB,A:Capt.America 3.50
123 HT,V:Leader 18.00	167 HT,JAb,V:Modok 6.00	233 SB,A:Marvel Man 3.50
124 HT,SB,V:Rhino,Leader ... 18.00	168 HT,JAb,I:Harpy 6.00	234 SB,Marvel Man Changes name
125 HT,V:Absorbing Man 18.00	169 HT,JAb,I:Bi-Beast 6.00	to Quasar 3.50
126 HT,A:Dr.Strange 18.00	170 HT,JAb,V:Volcano 6.00	235 SB,A:Machine Man 3.50
127 HT,Moleman vs.Tyrannus	171 HT,JAb,A:Abomination,Rhino 6.00	236 SB,A:Machine Man 3.50
I:Mogol 12.00	172 HT,JAb,X:X-Men 10.00	237 SB,A:Machine Man 3.50
128 HT,A:Avengers 12.00	173 HT,V:Cobolt Man 6.00	238 SB,JAb,Jimmy Carter 3.50
129 HT,V:Glob 12.00	174 HT,V:Cobolt Man 6.00	239 SB,I:Gold Bug 3.50
130 HT,Banner Vs Hulk 12.00	175 JAb,V:Inhumans 6.00	240 SB,Eldorado 3.50
131 HT,A:Iron Man 10.00	176 HT,JAb,A:Man-Beast,C:Warlock	241 SB,A:Tyrannus 3.00
132 HT,JSe,V:Hydra 10.00	Crisis on Counter-Earth ... 14.00	242 SB,Eldorado 3.00
133 HT,JSe,I:Draxon 10.00	177 HT,JAb,D:Warlock 15.00	243 SB,A:Gammernon 3.00
	178 HT,JAb,Warlock Lives 15.00	244 SB,A:It 3.00
	179 HT,JAb, ... 6.00	245 SB,A:Super Mandroid 3.00
	180 HT,JAb,I:Wolverine	246 SB,V:Capt.Marvel 3.00
	V:Wendigo I 100.00	247 SB,A:Bat Dragon 3.00
	181 HT,JAb,A:Wolverine (1st	248 SB,V:Gardener 3.00
	Full Story),V:Wendigo II .. 425.00	249 SD,R:Jack Frost 3.00
	182 HT,JAb,I&D:Crackajack	250 SB,A:Silver Surfer 10.00
	Jackson,C:Wolverine 65.00	251 MG,A:3-D Man 3.00
	183 HT,V:Zzzaz 5.00	252 SB,A:Woodgod 3.00
	184 HT,V:Living Shadow 5.00	253 SB,A:Woodgod 3.00
	185 HT,V:General Ross 5.00	254 SB,I:U-Foes 3.00
	186 HT,I:Devastator 5.00	255 SB,V:Thor 3.00
	187 HT,JSt,V:Gremlin 5.00	256 SB,I&O:Sabra 3.00
	188 HT,JSt,I:Droog 5.00	257 SB,I&O:Arabian Knight 3.00
	189 HT,JSt,I:Datrine 5.00	258 I:Soviet Super Soldiers 3.00
	190 HT,MSe,Toadman 5.00	259 SB,A:Soviet Super-Soldiers
	191 HT,JSt,Toadman,I:Glorian ... 5.00	O:Darkstar 3.00
	192 HT,V:The Lurker 5.00	260 SB,Sugata 3.00
	193 HT,JSt,Doc.Samson regains	261 SB,V:Absorbing Man 3.00
	Powers 5.00	262 SB,I:Glazer 3.00
	194 SB,JSt,V:Locust 5.00	263 SB,Avalanche 3.00
	195 SB,JSt,V:Abomination 5.00	264 SB,A:Corruptor 3.00
	196 SB,JSt,V:Army 5.00	265 SB,I:Rangers 3.50
	197 BWr(c),SB,JSt,A:Man-Thing . 5.00	266 SB,V:High Evolutionary ... 2.50
	198 SB,JSt,A:Man-Thing 5.00	267 SB,V:Rainbow,O:Glorian .. 2.50
	199 SB,JSt,V:Shield,Doc Samson 5.00	268 SB,I:Pariah 2.50
	200 SB,JSt,Multi,Hulk in Glenn	269 SB,I:Bereet 2.50
	Talbots Brain 30.00	270 SB,A:Abomination 2.50

Incredible Hulk #129
© Marvel Entertainment Group

134 HT,SB,I:Golem 10.00	201 SB,JSt,V:Fake Conan 4.00	271 SB,I:Rocket Raccoon,
135 HT,SB,V:Kang 10.00	202 SB,JSt,A:Jarella 4.00	20th Anniv. 2.50
136 HT,SB,I:Xeron 10.00	203 SB,JSt,A:Jarella 4.00	272 SB,C:X-Men,I:Wendigo III .. 5.00
137 HT,V:Abomination 10.00	204 SB,JSt,I:Kronus 4.00	273 SB,A:Alpha Flight 4.00
138 HT,V:Sandman 10.00	205 SB,JSt,D:Jarella 4.00	274 SB,Beroct 2.50
139 HT,V:Leader 10.00	206 SB,JSt,C:Dr.Strange 4.00	275 SB,JSt,I:Megalith 2.50
140 HT,V:Psyklop 10.00	207 SB,JSt,A:Dr.Strange 4.00	276 SB,JSt,V:U-Foes 2.50
141 HT,JSe,I&O:Doc Samson .. 11.00	208 SB,JSt,V:Absorbing Man ... 4.00	277 SB,JSt,U-Foes 2.50
142 HT,JSe,V:Valkyrie,A:Doc	209 SB,JSt,V:Absorbing Man ... 4.00	278 SB,JSt,C:X-Men,
Samson 7.00	210 SB,A:Dr.Druid,O:Merlin II ... 4.00	Avengers,Fantastic Four 2.50
143 DA,JSe,V:Dr.Doom 7.00	211 SB,A:Dr.Druid 4.00	279 SB,JSt,C:X-Men,
144 DA,JSe,V:Dr.Doom 7.00	212 SB,I:Constrictor 4.50	Avengers,Fantastic Four 2.50
145 HT,JSe,O:Retold 9.00	213 SB,TP,I:Quintronic Man ... 4.00	280 SB,JSt,Jack Daw 2.50
146 HT,JSe,Leader 7.00	214 SB,Jack of Hearts 4.00	281 SB,JSt,Trapped in Space ... 2.50
147 HT,JSe,Doc Samson loses	215 SB,V:Bi-Beast 3.50	282 SB,JSt,A:She Hulk 2.50
Powers 7.00	216 SB,Gen.Ross 3.50	283 SB,JSt,A:Avengers 2.50
148 HT,JSe,I:Fialan 7.00	217 SB,I:Stilts,A:Ringmaster ... 3.50	284 SB,JSt,A:Avengers 2.50
149 HT,JSe,I:Inheritor 7.00	218 SB,KP,Doc Samson versus	285 SB,JSt,Northwind,V:Zzzax ... 2.50
150 HT,JSe,I:Viking,A:Havoc ... 10.00	Rhino 3.50	286 SB,JSt,V:Soldier 2.50
151 HT,JSe,C:Ant Man 7.00	219 SB,V:Capt.Barravuda 3.50	287 SB,JSt,V:Soldier 2.50
152 HT,DA,Many Cameos 7.00	220 SB,Robinson Crusoe 3.50	288 SB,JSt,V:Abomination 2.50
153 HT,JSe,C:Capt.America ... 7.00	221 SB,AA,A:Sting Ray 3.50	289 SB,JSt,V:Modok 2.50
154 HT,JSe,A:Ant Man,	222 JSn,AA,Cavern of Bones ... 3.50	290 SB,JSt,V:Modok 2.50
V:Chameleon 7.00		

291 SB,JSt,V:Thunderbolt Ross . . 2.50	
292 SB,JSt,V:Dragon Man 2.50	
293 SB,V:Nightmare 2.50	
294 SB,V:Boomerang 2.50	
295 SB,V:Boomerang 2.50	
296 SB,A:Rom 2.50	
297 SB,V:Nightmare 2.50	
298 KN(c),SB,V:Nightmare 2.50	
299 SB,A:Shield 2.50	
300 SB,A:Spider-Man,Avengers	
Doctor Strange 6.00	
301 SB,Crossroads 2.50	
302 SB,Crossroads 2.50	
303 SB,V:The Knights 2.50	
304 SB,V:U-Foes 2.50	
305 SB,V:U-Foes 2.50	
306 SB,V:Klaatu 2.50	
307 SB,V:Klaatu 2.50	
308 SB,V:Puffball Collective 2.50	
309 SB,V:Goblin & Glow 2.50	
310 Crossroads 2.50	
311 Crossroads 2.50	
312 Secret Wars II,O:Bruce 3.50	
313 A:Alpha Flight 2.50	
314 JBy,V:Doc Samson 5.00	
315 JBy,A:Doc Samson,Banner	
& Hulk Separated 3.00	
316 JBy,A:Avengers,N:Doc	
Samson 3.00	
317 JBy,I:Hulkbusters,A:Doc	
Samson 3.00	
318 JBy,A:Doc Samson 3.00	
319 JBy,W:Bruce & Betty 5.00	
320 AM,A:Doc Samson 2.50	
321 AM,A:Avengers 2.50	
322 AM,A:Avengers 2.50	
323 AM,A:Avengers 2.50	
324 AM,R:Grey Hulk(1st since #1),	
A:Doc Samson 10.00	
325 AM,Rick Jones as Hulk 3.50	
326 A:Rick Jones,New Hulk 6.00	
327 AM,F:General Ross 2.50	
328 AM,1st PDd(s),Outcasts 7.00	
329 AM,V:Enigma 5.00	
330 1st TM Hulk,D:T-bolt Ross . 15.00	
331 TM,V:Leader 11.00	
332 TM,V:Leader 7.00	
333 TM,V:Leader 7.00	
334 TM,I:Half-life 7.00	
335 HorrorIssue 4.00	
336 TM,A:X-Factor 5.00	
337 TM,A:X-Factor,	
A:Doc Samson 5.00	
338 TM,I:Mercy,V:Shield 5.00	
339 TM,A:RickJones 5.00	
340 TM,Hulk vs Wolverine 28.00	
341 TM,V:Man Bull 4.00	
342 TM,V:Leader 4.00	
343 TM,V:Leader 4.00	
344 TM,V:Leader 4.00	
345 TM,V:Leader,Double-Size . . 7.00	
346 TM,EL,L:Rick Jones 6.00	
347 In Las Vegas,I:Marlo Chandler,	
V:Absorbing Man 4.00	
348 V:Absorbing Man 3.00	
349 A:Spider-Man 3.50	
350 Hulk vs Thing,A:Beast	
V:Dr.Doom 4.00	
351 R:Jarella's World 3.00	
352 V:Inquisitor 3.00	
353 R:Bruce Banner 3.00	
354 V:Maggia 3.00	
355 V:Glorian 3.00	
356 V:Glorian,Cloot 3.00	
357 V:Glorian,Cloot 3.00	

Incredible Hulk #278
© Marvel Entertainment Group

358 V:Glorian,Cloot 3.00	
359 JBy(c),C:Wolverine(illusion) . . 4.00	
360 V:Nightmare & Dyspare 3.00	
361 A:Iron Man,V:Maggia 3.00	
362 V:Werewolf By Night 3.00	
363 Acts of Vengeance 3.00	
364 A:Abomination,B:Countdown . 3.00	
365 A:Fantastic Four 3.00	
366 A:Leader,I:Riot Squad 3.00	
367 1st DK Hulk,I:Madman(Leader's	
brother),E:Countdown 8.00	
368 SK,V:Mr.Hyde 4.00	
369 DK,V:Freedom Force 3.00	
370 DK,R:Original Defenders . . . 3.00	
371 DK,BMc,A:Orig.Defenders . . 3.00	
372 DK,R:Green Hulk 9.00	
373 DK,Green Hulk & Grey Hulk . 4.00	
374 DK,BMc,Skrulls,	
R:Rick Jones 4.00	
375 DK,BMc,V:Super Skrull 4.00	
376 DK,BMc,Green Hulk,Grey	
Hulk & Banner fight 5.00	
377 DK,BMc,New Green Hulk,	
combination of green,grey, and	
Bruce Banner,A:Ringmaster . 11.00	
377a 2nd printing (gold) 5.00	
378 V:Rhino,Christmas Issue . . . 3.00	
379 DK,MFm,I:Pantheon 4.00	
380 A:Nick Fury,D:Crazy-8 . . . . . 3.00	
381 DK,MFm,Hulk J:Pantheon . . 4.00	
382 DK,MFm,A:Pantheon 4.00	
383 DK,MFm,Infinity Gauntlet . . . 4.00	
384 DK,MFm,Infinity Gauntlet . . . 4.00	
385 DK,MFm,Infinity Gauntlet . . . 4.00	
386 DK,MFm,V:Sabra,A:Achilles . 4.00	
387 DK,MFm,V:Sabra,A:Achilles . 4.00	
388 DK,MFm,I:Speed Freak,Jim	
Wilson,revealed to have AIDS . 5.00	
389 1st Comic art By Gary Barker	
(Garfield),A:Man-Thing,Glob . 4.00	
390 DK,MFm,B:War & Pieces,	
C:X-Factor 4.00	
391 DK,MFm,V:X-Factor 4.00	
392 DK,MFm,E:War & Pieces,	
A:X:Factor 4.00	

393 DK,MFm,R:Igor,A:Soviet Super Sol-	
diers,30th Anniv.,Green foil(c) . 5.00	
393a 2nd printing,Silver 2.50	
394 MFm(i),F:Atalanta,I:Trauma . . 3.00	
395 DK,MFm,A:Punisher,	
I:Mr.Frost 3.00	
396 DK,MFm,A:Punisher,	
V:Mr.Frost 3.00	
397 DK,MFm,B:Ghost of the	
Past,V:U-Foes,A:Leader 3.00	
398 DK,MFm,D:Marlo,V:Leader . . 3.00	
399 JD,A:FF,Dr.Strange 3.00	
400 JD,MFm,E:Ghost of the Past,	
V:Leader,1st Holo-grafx(c),1st	
GFr Hulk(pin-up) 3.50	
400a 2nd Printing 2.50	
401 JDu,O:Agememnon 2.00	
402 JDu,V:Juggernaut 2.00	
403 GFr,V:Red Skull,A:Avengers . 3.00	
404 GFr,V:Red Skull,Juggernaut,	
A:Avengers 3.50	
405 GFr,Ajax Vs. Achilles 2.75	
406 GFr,V:Captain America 2.00	
407 GFr,I:Piecemeal,A:Madman,	
B:O:Ulysses 2.00	
408 GFr,V:Madman,Piecemeal,	
D:Perseus,A:Motormouth,	
Killpower 1.75	
409 GFr,A:Motormouth,Killpower,	
V:Madman 1.75	
410 GFr,A:Nick Fury,S.H.I.E.L.D.,	
Margo agrees to marry Rick . 1.75	
411 GFr,V:Nick Fury,S.H.I.E.L.D. . 1.75	
412 PaP,V:Bi-Beast,A:She-Hulk . 1.75	
413 GFr,CaS,B:Troyjan War,	
I:Cassiopea,Armageddon,	
V:Trauma 1.75	
414 GFr,CaS,V:Trauma,C:S.Surfer 1.75	
415 GFr,CaS,V:Trauma,A:Silver	
Surfer,Starjammers 1.75	
416 GFr,CaS,E:Troyjan War,D:Trauma,	
A:S.Surfer,Starjammers 1.75	
417 GFr,CaS,Rick's/Marlo's Bachelor/	
Bachelorette Party 1.75	
418 GFr,CaS,W:Rick & Marlo,	
A:Various Marvel persons,	
Die Cut(c) 2.75	
418a Newsstand Ed. 1.75	
419 CaS,V:Talos 1.75	
420 GFr,CaS,AIDS Story,	
D: Jim Wilson 1.75	
421 CaS,B:Myth Conceptions . . . 1.75	
422 GFr,Myth Conceptions,pt.2 . . 1.75	
423 GFr,CaS,MythConcept.,pt.3 . . 1.50	
424 B:Fall of the Hammer 1.50	
425 Regular Edition 1.50	
425a Enhanced cover 3.50	
426 PDa,LSh,R:Mercy 1.50	
426a Deluxe edition 1.95	
427 A:Man-Thing 1.50	
427a Deluxe edition 1.95	
428 Suffer The Children 1.95	
429 Abortion Issue 1.95	
430 A:Speed Freak 1.95	
431 PDa,LSh R:Abomination 1.95	
432 V:Abomination 1.95	
433 PDd,V:Abomination 1.95	
434 Funeral of the Year 1.95	
435 Hulk Vs. Rhino baseball . . . 2.50	
436 AMe,Ghosts of the	
Future,pt.1 . . . . 1.95	
437 PDd,AMe,Ghosts of the	
Future,pt.2 . . . . 1.95	
438 PDd,AMe,Ghosts of the	
Future,pt.3 . . . . 1.95	

439 PDd,AMe,Ghosts of the
  Future,pt.4 . . . . 1.95
440 PDd,AMe, ... 1.95
441 PDd,AMe,A:She-Hulk . . . 1.95
442 A:Molecule Man, She-Hulk . . 1.95
443 Janis 1.50
444 Onslaught saga, V:Cable . . 1.50
445 Onslaught saga 1.50
446 blamed for loss of Fantastic Four
  and Avengers 1.50
447 PDd,MD2,F:The Unleashed
  Hulk 1.50
447a Variant Tank Smashing cover 5.00
448 PDd,MD2,V:The Pantheon . . 1.50
449 PDd,MD2,I:Thunderbolts . . . 1.50
450 PDd,MD2,F:Doctor Strange,
  56pg. 2.95
451 PDd,MD2, ... 1.50
452 PDd,MD2, ... 1.50
453 PDd,MD2,V:Future Hulk 1.50
454 PDd,AKu,MFm,A God,
  in Savage Land 1.50
455 PDd,AKu,MFm,in X-Mansion . 2.00
456 PDd,AKu,MFm,A:Apocalypse 2.00

Incredible Hulk #313
© Marvel Entertainment Group

457 PDd,Hulk vs. Juggernaut . . 2.00
458 PDd,AKu,MFm,V:Mercy 2.00
459 PDd,AKu,MFm,V:Abomination 2.00
460 PDa,AKu,MFm, Return of Bruce
  Banner 2.00
461 PDa,V:Thunderbolt Ross 2.00
462 PDa,AKu,MFm,V:Thunderbolt
  Ross 2.00
463 PDa,AKu,MFm,V:Thunderbolt
  Ross 2.00
464 PDa,AKu,MFm,V:Troygens & Silver
  Surfer 2.00
465 PDa,MFm,Poker game 2.00
466 PDa,AKu,MFm,tragic loss . . 2.00
467 PDa,AKu,MFm,Hulk attempts
  suicide 2.00
468 JoC,new direction, ... 2.00
469 JoC,LMa,F:Super-Adaptoid . . 2.00
Spec.#1,A:Inhumans (1968) 75.00
Spec.#2 rep.O:Hulk,A:Leader
  (1969) 50.00
Spec.#3 rep.A:Leader (1971) . . . 18.00
Spec.#4 IR:Hulk/Banner (1972) . 15.00

Ann.#5 V:Xemnu,Diablo (1976) . 10.00
Ann.#6 HT,A:Dr.Strange,I:Paragon
  (Her) (1977) 6.00
Ann.#7 JBy,BL,A:Angel,Iceman
  A:Doc Samson (1978) 7.00
Ann.#8 Alpha Flight (1979) 6.00
Ann.#9 Checkmate (1980) 3.00
Ann.#10,A:CaptainUniverse(1981) 3.00
Ann.#11 RB,JSt,A:Spider-Man,
  Avengers,V:Unis (1982) 4.00
Ann.#12 (1983) 3.00
Ann.#13 (1984) 3.00
Ann.#14 JBy,SB (1985) 3.00
Ann.#15 V:Abomitation (1986) . . . 3.00
Ann.#16 HT,Life Form #3,
  A:Mercy (1987) 3.00
Ann.#17 Subterran.Odyssey #2
  (1991) 3.00
Ann #18 KM,TA,TC(1st Work),Return
  of the Defenders,Pt.1 (1992) . . 7.00
Ann.#19 I:Lazarus,w/card (1993) . 3.25
Ann.#20 SvL,SI (1994) 1.75
Ann.'98 F:Hulk&Sub-Mariner, 48pg 3.00
Marvel Milestone rep. #1 (1991) . 2.95
G-Size#1 rep.Greatest Foes . . 10.00
Minus 1 Spec., PDd,AKu,MFm,
  flashback 1.95
Spec. '97 Onslaught aftermath . . 3.00
TPB Ground Zero rep.#340-345 . 12.95
TPB Future Imperfect, PDd,GP,
  96pg 12.00
TPB Ghosts of the Past,
  Rep. #396–#400 . . . . 12.00
TPB Transformations, 176pg. . . 12.00
TPB Beauty and the Beast, . . . 17.00

INCREDIBLE HULK: FUTURE IMPERFECT
1 GP,V:Maestro 10.00
2 GP,V:Maestro 8.00
TPB Rep. 12.95

INCREDIBLE HULK MEGAZINE
TPB six stories, 96pg 3.95

INCREDIBLE HULK/PITT
1997
Spec. PDd,DK,x-over 6.00

INCREDIBLE HULK VS. WOLVERINE
Oct., 1986
1 HT,rep #181 B:,V:Wolverine. . 12.00

INDEPENDENCE DAY
1996
0 . . . . 1.50
1 . . . . 1.50
2 . . . . 1.50
TPB rep. #0–#2, 96pg 6.95

[Further Adventures of] INDIANA JONES
Jan., 1983
1 JBy/TA 2.00
2 JBy/TA 1.50
3 . . . . 1.50
4 KGa 1.50
5 KGa 1.50
6 HC/TA 1.50
7 thru 24 KGa . . . . @1.50

25 SD,What Lurks Within the Tomb 1.50
26 SD 1.50
27 SD 1.50
28 SD 1.50
29 SD 1.50
30 SD 1.50
31 SD,The Summit Meeting 1.50
32 SD,Fly the Friendly Skies . . . 1.50
33 SD 1.50
34 SD, March, 1986 . . . . 1.50

INDIANA JONES AND THE LAST CRUSADE
1 B&W,Mag.,movie adapt, 1989. . 2.95
[Mini-Series] 1989
1 Rep,Movie adapt, 1989. . . . . 1.25
2 Rep,Movie adapt. 1.25
3 Rep,Movie adapt 1.25
4 Rep,Movie adapt. 1.25

INDIANA JONES AND THE TEMPLE OF DOOM
1984
1 Movie adapt 1.25
2 Movie adapt. 1.25
3 Movie adapt. 1.25

INFINITY CRUSADE
1993
1 RLm,AM,I:Goddess,A:Marvel
  Heroes,foil(c) 4.00
2 RLm,AM,V:Goddess 3.00
3 RLm,AM,V:Goddess,Mephisto . 3.00
4 RLm,AM,V:Goddess,A:Magnus . 3.00
5 RLm,AM,V:Goddess 3.00
6 RLm,AM,V:Goddess 3.00

INFINITY GAUNTLET
July, 1991
1 GP,O:Infinity Gauntlet 5.00
2 GP,JRu,2ndRebirth:Warlock . . 4.00
3 GP,JRu,I:Terraxia 4.00
4 GP,JRu,RLm,V:Thanos 4.00
5 JRu,RLm,V:Thanos,D:Terraxia . 4.00
6 RLm,JRu,V:Nebula 4.00
TPB rep. #1 thru 6 . . . . 24.95

INFINITY WAR
1992
1 RLm,AM,R:Magus,Thanos 5.00
2 RLm,AM,V:Magus,A:Everyone . 3.00
3 RLm,AM,V:Magus,A:Everyone . 2.50
4 RLm,AM,Magus gets Gauntlet . 2.50
5 RLm,AM,V:Magus 2.50
6 RLm,AM,V:Magus 2.50

INHUMANOIDS
Star Jan.–July, 1987
1 Hasbro Toy 1.25
2 O:Inhumanoids 1.25
3 V:D'Compose 1.25
4 A:Sandra Shore 1.25

INHUMANS
Oct., 1975
1 GP,V:Blastaar 10.00
2 GP,V:Blastaar 5.00
3 GP,I:Kree S 4.00
4 GK,Maximus 4.00
5 GK,V:Maximus 4.00
6 GK,Maximus 4.00
7 GK,DP,I:Skornn 4.00

8 GP,DP,Skornn 4.00	23 FR,FS,GK(c),I:Scarlet Scarab . 3.00	14 JCr,V:Night Phantom 28.00
9 reprint,V:Mor-Tog 4.00	24 FR,FS,GK(c),rep.Marvel	15 JCr,GT,A:Red Ghost 28.00
10 KP,D:Warkon 4.00	Mystery #17 . . . . 4.00	16 JCr,GT,V:Unicorn 20.00
11 KP,JM,I:Pursuer 4.00	25 FR,FS,GK(c),V:Scarlet Scarab 3.00	17 JCr,GT,I:Madam Masque,
12 KP,Hulk 4.00	26 FR,FS,GK(c),V:Axis Agent . . 3.00	Midas 22.00
Spec.#1(The Untold Saga),	27 FR,FS,GK(c),V:Axis Agent . . . 3.00	18 JCr,GT,V:Madame Masque . . 20.00
O:Inhumans 4.00	28 FR,FS,I:2nd Human Top,	19 JCr,GT,V:Madame Masque . . 20.00
Spec. Atlantis Rising story 2.95	Golden Girl,Kid Commandos . . 3.00	20 JCr,I:Charlie Gray 20.00
	29 FR,FS,I:Teutonic Knight 3.00	21 JCr,I:Eddie 15.00
INTERFACE	30 FR,FS,V:Teutonic Knight 3.00	22 JCr,D:Janice Cord 15.00
Epic Dec., 1989	31 FR,FS,V:Frankenstein 3.00	23 JCr,I:Mercenary 17.00
1 ESP 2.50	32 FR,FS,JK(c),A:Thor 4.50	24 JCr,GT,V:Madame Masque . . 15.00
2 thru 7 . . . . @2.00	33 FR,FS,JK(c),A:Thor 4.50	25 JCr,A:Sub-Mariner 17.00
8 . . . . 2.25	34 FR,FS,V:Master Man 3.00	26 JCr,DH,J:Val-Larr 12.00
	35 FR,FS,I:Iron Cross 3.00	27 JCr,DH,I:Firebrand 12.00
	36 FR,FS,O:Iron Cross 3.00	28 E:AGw(s),JCr,DH,
	37 FR,FS,V:Iron Cross 3.00	V:Controller 12.00
	38 FR,FS,V:Lady Lotus 3.00	29 B:StL,AyB(s),DH,V:Myrmidon 13.00
	39 FR,FS,O:Lady Lotus 3.00	30 DH,I:Monster Master 13.00
	40 FR,FS,V:Baron Blood 3.00	31 DH,I:Mastermind 12.00
	41 E:RTs(s)FR,FS,V:Super Axis,	32 GT,I:Mechanoid 12.00
	double-size 5.00	33 DH,I:Spy Master 12.00
	Ann.#1 A:Avengers,R:Shark 5.00	34 DH,A:Spy Master 12.00
	G-Size#1 FR,rep.Submariner#1 . . 5.00	35 DH,A:Daredevil,Spymaster . 12.00
	[Limited Series] 1993	36 E:AyB(s),DH,I:RamRod 12.00
	1 R:Invaders 2.00	37 DH,A:Ramrod 12.00
	2 V:Battle Axis 2.00	38 GT,Jonah 12.00
	3 R:Original Vison (1950's) 2.00	39 HT,I:White Dragon 10.00
	4 V:The Axis 2.00	40 GT,V:White Dragon 10.00
		41 GT,JM,I:Slasher 10.00
	IRON FIST	42 GT,I:Mikas 10.00
	Nov., 1975	43 GT,JM,A:Mikas,I:Guardsmen 10.00
	1 JBy,A:Iron Man 45.00	44 GT,A:Capt.America 10.00
	2 JBy,V:H'rythl 17.00	45 GT,A:Guardsman 10.00
	3 JBy,KP,KJ,V:Ravager 12.00	46 GT,D:Guardsman 10.00
	4 JBy,V:Radion 14.00	47 BS,JM,O:Iron Man 15.00
	5 JBy,V:Scimitar 12.00	48 GT,V:Firebrand 10.00
	6 JBy,O:Misty Knight 10.00	49 GT,V:Adaptoid 10.00
	7 JBy,V:Khimbala Bey 10.00	50 B:RTs(s),GT,V:Prin.Python . . 10.00
	8 JBy,V:Chaka 10.00	51 GT,C:Capt.America 10.00
	9 JBy,V:Chaka 10.00	52 GT,I:Raga 10.00
	10 JBy,DGr,A:Chaka 10.00	53 GT,JSn,I:BlackLama 10.00
	11 JBy,V:Wrecking Crew 10.00	54 GT,BEv,Sub-Mariner,I:Madame
	12 JBy,DGr,V:Captain America . 10.00	MacEvil (Moondragon) 17.00
	13 JBy,A:Boomerang 10.00	55 JSn,I:Destroyer,Thanos,Mentor
	14 JBy,I:Sabretooth 150.00	Starfox(Eros),Blood Bros. . . . 50.00
	15 JBy,A&N:Wolverine,A:X-Men	56 JSn,I:Fangor 15.00
	Sept. 1977 . . . . 35.00	57 GT,R:Mandarin 10.00
	Marvel Milestone rep. #14 (1992) . 4.00	58 GT,V:Mandarin 10.00
		59 GT,A:Firebrand 10.00
	IRON FIST	60 GT,C:Daredevil 10.00
	May 1998	61 GT,Marauder 10.00
	1 (of 3) DJu,JG, from Heroes For	62 whiplash 10.00
	Hire 2.50	63 GT,A:Dr.Spectrum 10.00
	2 DJu,JG,search for Scorpio Key,	64 GT,I:Rokk 10.00
	V:S.H.I.E.L.D. 2.50	65 GT,O:Dr.Spectrum 10.00
	3 DJu,JG,concl. 2.50	66 GT,V:Thor 10.00
		67 GT,V:Freak 10.00
	IRON MAN	68 GT,O:Iron Man 12.00
	May, 1968	69 GT,V:Mandarin 9.00
	1 B:StL,AGw(s),JCr,GC,	70 GT,A:Sunfire 9.00
	I:Mordius 350.00	71 GT,V:Yellow Claw 7.50
	2 JCr,I:Demolisher 110.00	72 E:RTs(s),GT,V:Black Lama . . 7.50
	3 JCr,V:The Freak 75.00	73 B:LWn(s),KP,JM,V:Titanic
	4 JCr,A:Unicorn 65.00	Three 7.50
	5 JCr,GT,I:Cerebos 50.00	74 KP,V:Modok 7.50
	6 JCr,GT,V:Crusher 60.00	75 V:Black Lama 7.50
	7 JCr,GT,V:Gladiator 35.00	76 Rep,A:Hulk 7.50
	8 JCr,GT,O:Whitney Frost 32.00	77 V:Thinker 7.50
	9 JCr,GT,A:Mandarin 30.00	78 GT,V:Viet Cong 7.50
	10 JCr,GT,V:Mandarin 30.00	79 GT,I:Quasar(not Current one) . 7.50
	11 JCr,GT,V:Mandarin 28.00	80 JK(c),O:Black Lama 7.50
	12 JCr,GT,I:Controller 28.00	81 A:Black Lama 6.00
	13 JCr,GT,A:Nick Fury 28.00	82 MSe,A:Red Ghost 6.00
		83 E:LWn(s),HT,MSe,Red Ghost . 6.00

Invaders #17
© Marvel Entertainment Group

INVADERS
August, 1975

1 FR,JR(c),A:Invaders,
A:Mastermind 20.00
2 FR,JR(c)I:Brain Drain 7.00
3 FR,JR(c),I:U-Man 6.00
4 FR,O&V:U-Man 5.00
5 RB,JM,V:Red Skull 5.00
6 FR,V:Liberty Legion 5.00
7 FR,I:Baron Blood,
1st Union Jack 5.00
8 FR,FS,J:Union Jack 5.00
9 FR,FS,O:Baron Blood 5.00
10 FR,FS,rep.Captain
America Comics#22 . . . . 5.00
11 FR,FS,I:Blue Bullet 4.00
12 FR,FS,I:Spitfire 4.00
13 FR,FS,GK(c),I:Golem,
Half Face 4.00
14 FR,FS,JK(c),I:Crusaders 4.00
15 FR,FS,JK(c),V:Crusaders . . . 4.00
16 FR,JK(c),V:Master Man 4.00
17 FR,FS,GK(c),I:Warrior Woman 4.00
18 FR,FS,GK(c),R:1st Destroyer . 4.00
19 FR,FS,V:Adolph Hitler 4.00
20 FR,FS,GK(c),I&J:2nd Union Jack
BU:rep.Marvel Comics #1 . . . 7.50
21 FR,FS,GK(c),BU:rep.Marvel
Mystery #10 . . . . 5.50
22 FR,FS,GK(c),O:Toro 3.00

Iron Man #11
© Marvel Entertainment Group

84 HT,A:Dr.Ritter 6.00
85 HT,MSe,A:Freak 6.00
86 B:MWn(s),GT,I:Blizzard 7.00
87 GT,V:Blizzard 6.00
88 E:MWn(s),GT,
　V:Blood Brothers 6.00
89 GT,A:D.D.,Blood Bros. 6.00
90 JK(c),GT,Controller,A:Thanos . 7.50
91 GT,BL,A:Controller 6.00
92 JK(c),GT,V:Melter 6.00
93 JK(c),HT,V:Kraken 6.00
94 JK(c),HT,V:Kraken 6.00
95 JK(c),GT,PP,V:Ultimo 6.00
96 GT,DP,V:Ultimo 6.00
97 GT,DP,I:Guardsman II 6.00
98 GT,DP,A:Sunfire 6.00
99 GT,V:Mandarin 6.00
100 JSn(c),GT,V:Mandarin 16.00
101 GT,I:Dread Knight 5.00
102 GT,O:Dread Knight 5.00
103 GT,V:Jack of Hearts 5.00
104 GT,V:Midas 5.00
105 GT,V:Midas 5.00
106 GT,V:Midas 5.00
107 KP,V:Midas 5.00
108 CI,A:Growing Man 5.00
109 JBy(c),CI,V:Van Guard 5.00
110 KP,I:C.Arcturus 5.00
111 KP,O:Rigellians 5.00
112 AA,KP,V:Punisher from
　Beyond 5.00
113 KP,HT,V:Unicorn,Spymaster . 5.50
114 KG,I:Arsenal 5.00
115 JR2,O:Unicorn,V:Ani-men . . 5.00
116 JR2,BL,V:MadameMasque . . 5.00
117 BL,JR2,1st Romita Jr 6.00
118 JBy,BL,A:Nick Fury 8.00
119 BL,JR2,Alcholic Plot 6.00
120 JR2,BL,A:Sub-Mariner,
　I:Rhodey(becomes War Machine),
　Justin Hammer 6.00
121 BL,JR2,A:Submariner 5.00
122 DC,CI,BL,O:Iron Man 5.00
123 BL,JR2,V:Blizzard 5.00
124 BL,JR2,A:Capt.America 4.00
125 BL,JR2,A:Ant-Man 4.00
126 BL,JR2,V:Hammer 4.00
127 BL,JR2,Battlefield 4.00

128 BL,JR2,Alcohol 6.00
129 SB,A:Dread Night 3.50
130 BL,V:Digital Devil 3.50
131 BL,V:Hulk 3.50
132 BL,V:Hulk 3.50
133 BL,A:Hulk,Ant-Man 3.50
134 BL,V:Titanium Man 3.50
135 BL,V:Titanium Man 3.50
136 V:Endotherm 3.50
137 BL,Fights oil rig fire 3.50
138 BL,Dreadnought,Spymaster . . 3.50
139 BL,Dreadnought,Spymaster . . 3.50
140 BL,V:Force 3.50
141 BL,JR2,V:Force 3.50
142 BL,JR2,Space Armor 3.50
143 BL,JR2,V:Sunturion 3.50
144 BL,JR2,Sunturion,O:Rhodey . 3.50
145 BL,JR2,A:Raiders 3.50
146 BL,JR2,I:Black Lash 3.50
147 BL,JR2,V:Black Lash 3.00
148 BL,JR2,V:Terrorists 3.00
149 BL,JR2,V:Dr.Doom 3.00
150 BL,JR2,V:Dr.Doom,Dble . . . 5.00
151 TA,BL,A:Antman 3.00
152 BL,JR2,New Armor 3.00
153 BL,JR2,V:Living Laser 3.00
154 BL,JR2,V:Unicorn 3.00
155 JR2,V:Back-Getters 3.00
156 JR2,I:Mauler 3.25
157 V:Spores 3.00
158 CI,AM,Iron Man Drowning . . . 3.00
159 PS,V:Diablo 3.00
160 SD,V:Serpent'sSquad 3.00
161 A:Moon Knight 3.00
162 V:Space Ships 3.00
163 V:Chessmen 3.00
164 LMc,A:Bishop 3.00
165 LMc,Meltdown 3.00
166 LMc,V:Melter 2.50
167 LMc,Alcholic Issue 2.50
168 LMc,A:Machine Man 2.50
169 LMc,B:Rhodey as 2nd
　Ironman 13.00
170 LMc,2nd Ironman 12.00
171 LMc,2nd Ironman 3.00
172 LMc,V:Firebrand 3.00
173 LMc,Stane International 3.00
174 LMc,Alcoholism 3.50
175 LMc,Alcoholism 3.50
176 LMc,Alcoholism 3.50
177 LMc,Alcoholism 3.00
178 LMc,V:Wizard 3.00
179 LMc,V:Mandarin 3.00
180 LMc,V:Mandarin 3.00
181 LMc,V:Mandarin 3.00
182 LMc,Secret Wars 3.00
183 LMc,Turning Point 3.00
184 LMc,Moves to California 3.00
185 LMc,V:Zodiac Field 3.00
186 LMc,I:Vibro 3.00
187 LMc,V:Vibro 3.00
188 LMc,I:New Brother's Grimm . 3.00
189 LMc,I:Termite 3.00
190 LMc,O:Terminatir,A:Scar.Witch . 3.00
191 LMc,New Grey Armor 5.00
192 LMc,V:Iron Man(Tony Stark) . 5.00
193 LMc,V:Dr.Demonicus 3.00
194 LMc,I:Scourge,A:West Coast
　Avengers 3.00
195 LMc,A:Shaman 3.00
196 LMc,V:Dr.Demonicus 3.00
197 LMc,Secret Wars II 3.00
198 SB,V:Circuit Breaker 3.00
199 LMc,E:Rhodey as 2nd Ironman,
　V:Obadiah Stone 3.00

Iron Man #126
© Marvel Entertainment Group

200 LMc,D:Obadiah Stone 6.00
201 MBr,V:Madam Masque 2.00
202 A:Kazar 2.00
203 MBr,A:Hank Pym 2.00
204 MBr,V:Madame Masque 2.00
205 MBr,V:A.I.M. 2.00
206 MBr,V:Goliath 2.00
207 MBr,When t/Sky Rains Fire . . 2.00
208 MBr,V:A.I.M. 2.00
209 V:Living Laser 2.00
210 MBr,V:Morgan Le Fey 2.00
211 AS,V:Living Laser 2.00
212 DT,V:Iron Monger 2.00
213 A:Dominic Fortune 2.00
214 A:Spider-Woman 2.00
215 BL,AIM 2.00
216 BL,MBr,D:Clymenstra 2.00
217 BL,MRr,V:Hammer 2.00
218 BL,MBr,Titanic 2.00
219 BL,V:The Ghost 2.00
220 BL,MBr,V:The Ghost,
　D:Spymaster 2.00
221 BL,MBr,V:The Ghost 2.00
222 BL,MBr,R:Abrogast 2.00
223 BL,MBr,V:Blizzard,Beetle . . . 2.00
224 BL,V:Justin Hammer,Force . . 2.00
225 BL,MBr,B:Armor Wars 5.00
226 BL,MBr,V:Stingray 4.50
227 BL,MBr,V:Mandroids, ... 4.00
228 BL,MBr,V:Guardsmen 4.00
229 BL,D:Titanium Man 4.00
230 V:Firepower, ... 4.00
231 V:Firepower,N:Iron Man 4.00
232 BWS,Nightmares,E:Armor
　Wars 4.50
233 JG,BL,A:AntMan 2.00
234 JG,BL,A:Spider-Man 3.00
235 JG,BL,V:Grey Gargoyle 2.00
236 JG,BL,V:Grey Gargoyle 2.00
237 JG,BL,V:SDI Monster 2.00
238 JG,BL,V:Rhino,D:M.Masque . 2.00
239 JG,BL,R:Ghost 2.00
240 JG,BL,V:Ghost 2.00
241 BL,V:Mandarin 2.00
242 BL,BWS,V:Mandarin 3.00
243 BL,BWS,Stark Paralyzed . . . 3.00
244 BL,V:Fixer,A:Force(D.Size) . . 5.00
245 BL(c),V:Dreadnaughts 2.00

MARVEL

246 BL,HT,V:A.I.M.,Maggia 2.00
247 BL,A:Hulk 2.25
248 BL,Tony Stark Cured 2.25
249 BL,V:Dr.Doom 2.00
250 BL,V:Dr.Doom,A of V 2.00
251 HT,AM,V:Wrecker,A of V 2.00
252 HT,AM,V:Chemistro,A of V . . 2.00
253 BL,V:Slagmire 2.00
254 BL,V:Spymaster 2.00
255 HT,V:Devestator
      I:2nd Spymaster 2.00
256 JR2,V:Space Station 2.00
257 V:Samurai Steel 2.00
258 JR2,BWi,B:Armor Wars II,V:
      Titanium Man 2.25
259 JR2,BWi,V:Titanium Man . . . 2.00
260 JR2,BWi,V:Living Laser 2.00
261 JR2,BWi,A:Mandarin 1.75
262 JR2,BWi,A:Mandarin 1.75
263 JR2,BWi,A:Wonderman,
      V:Living Laser 1.75
264 JR2,BWi,A:Mandarin 1.75
265 JR2,BWi,V:Dewitt 1.50
266 JR2,BWi,E:Armor Wars II . . . 1.50
267 PR,BWi,B:New O:Iron Man,
      Mandarin,V:Vibro 1.75
268 PR,BWi,E:New O:Iron Man. . 1.75
269 PR,BWi,A:Black Widow 1.75
270 PR,BWi,V:Fin Fang Foom . . . 1.75
271 PR,BWi,V:Fin Fang Foom . . . 1.75
272 PR,BWi,O:Mandarin 1.75
273 PR,BWi,V:Mandarin 1.75
274 MBr,BWi,V:Mandarin 1.75
275 PR,BWi,A:Mandarin,Fin Fang
      Foom (Double size) 2.00
276 PR,BWi,A:Black Widow 1.75
277 PR,BWi,A:Black Widow 1.75
278 BWi,Galactic Storm,pt.6
      A:Capt.America,V:Shatterax . . 1.75
279 BWi,Galactic Storm,pt.13,
      V:Ronan,A:Avengers 1.75
280 KHd,V:The Stark 1.75
281 KHd,I&V:Masters of Silence,
      C:War Machine Armor 3.50
282 KHd,I:War Machine Armor,
      V:Masters of Silence 3.50
283 KHd,V:Masters of Silence . . . 2.50
284 KHd,Stark put under Cryogenic
      Freeze,B:Rhodey as Iron Man . 3.00
285 KHd,BWi(i),Tony's Funeral . . 2.00
286 KHd,V:Avengers West Coast . 1.75
287 KHd,I:New Atom Smasher . . . 1.75
288 KHd,30th Anniv.,V:Atom
      Smasher,foil(c) 4.50
289 KHd,V:Living Laser,
      R:Tony Stark 1.50
290 KHd,30th Anniv.,N:Iron Man,
      Gold foil(c) 4.50
291 KHd,E:Rhodey as Iron Man,
      Becomes War Machine 2.00
292 KHd,Tony reveals he is alive . 1.50
293 KHd,V:Controller 1.50
294 KHd,Infinity Crusade 1.50
295 KHd,Infinity Crusade 1.50
296 KHd,V:Modam,V:Omega Red . 1.50
297 KHd,V:Modam,Omega Red . . 1.50
298 KHd(c),I:Earth Mover 1.50
299 KHd(c),R:Ultimo 1.50
300 KHd,TMo,N:Iron Man,I:Iron
      Legion,A:War Machine,V:Ultimo
      Foil(c) 5.00
300a Newstand Ed. 2.75
301 KHd,B:Crash and Burn,
      A:Deathlok,C:Venom 2.00
302 KHd,V:Venom 2.00

303 KHd,V:New Warriors,
      C:Thundrstrike 2.00
304 KHd,C:Hulk,V:New Warriors,
      Thundrstrike,N:Iron Man 2.00
305 KHd,V:Hulk, ... 2.00
306 KHd,E:Stark Enterprise 2.00
307 TMo,I:Vor/Tex,R:Mandarin . . 2.00
308 TMo,Vor/Tex 2.00
309 TMo,Vor/Tex 2.00
310 regular 2.00
310a Neon(c),with insert print . . . 3.50
311 V:Mandarin 2.00
312 double size 3.00
313 LKa,TMo,AA Meeting 2.00
314 LKa,TMo,new villain 2.00
315 A:Black Widow 2.00
316 I:Slag,A:Crimson Dynamo . . 2.00
317 In Dynamos Armor 3.00
318 LKa,TMo,V:Slag 2.00
319 LKa,TMo,New Space Armor . 2.00
320 F:Hawkeye 2.00
321 Cont. From Avg. Crossing . . . 2.00
322 TKa,TheCrossing,V:JackFrost 2.00
323 TKa,V:Avengers 2.00

80¢ 163
MARVEL COMICS GROUP
THE INVINCIBLE
IRON MAN
THE CHALLENGE OF...
...THE CHESSMEN!

Iron Man #163
© Marvel Entertainment Group

324 TKa,The Crossing 2.00
325 TKa,Avengers:Timeslide after 3.50
326 . . . . 2.00
327 . . . . 2.00
328 TKa,Tony Stark at ColumbiaU 2.00
329 thru 332 final issue 2.00
Ann.#1 rep.Iron Man #25 . . . . . . 25.00
Ann.#2 rep.Iron Man #6 . . . . 10.00
Ann.#3 SB,Manthing 6.00
Ann.#4 DP,GT,V:Modok,
      A:Champions 4.00
Ann.#5 JBr,A:Black Panther 2.50
Ann.#6 A:Eternals,V:Brother
      Tode 2.50
Ann.#7 LMc,A:West Coast
      Avengers, I:New Goliath 2.50
Ann.#8 A:X-Factor 3.00
Ann.#9 V:Stratosfire,A:Sunturion . 2.50
Ann.#10 PS,BL,Atlantis Attacks #2
      A:Sub-Mariner 3.00
Ann.#11 SD,Terminus Factor #2 . 2.00
Ann.#12 Subterran.Odyssey #4 . . 2.00
Ann.#13 GC,AW,Assault on Armor

City,A:Darkhawk 2.50
Ann.#14 TMo,I:Face Theif,w/card,
      BU:War Machine 3.25
Ann.#15 GC,V:Controller 3.25
Spec.#1 rep.Sub-Mariner x-over . 20.00
Spec.#2 rep.(1971) 8.00
Marvel Milestone rep. #55 (1992) . 2.95
G-Size#1 Reprints 8.00
1-shot Iron Man/Force Works Collec-
      tors' Preview, Neon wrap-around
      cover, double size, X-over 1.95
1-shot Iron Manual, BSz(c),Guide
      to Iron Man's technology 1.75
GN Iron Man 2020 . . . . 5.95
TPB Armor Wars rep.#225-#232 . 12.95
TPB Many Armors of Iron Man . 15.95
TPB Power of Iron Man 9.95
TPB JR2,BL,Iron Man vs. Dr. Doom
      rep. #149-#150,#249-#250 . . 12.95
Iron Manual BSz(c),guide to Iron
      Man's technology 2.00

[2nd Series] Nov. 1996
1 JLe,SLo,WPo,SW,A:Bruce
      Banner, New O:Hulk,48pg., . . 4.00
1A variant Hulk showing cover . . 5.00
1 gold signature edition, bagged 35.00
2 JLe,SLo,WPo,SW 3.00
3 JLe,SLo,WPo,SW,Heroes brawl 2.50
4 JLe,SLo,WPo,SW,V:Laser 2.25
4A X-mas cover 4.00
5 JLe,SLo,WPo,SW, Whirlwind . . 2.00
6 JLe,SLo,WPo,SW,"Industrial
      Revolution," pt.2 x-over 2.00
7 JLe,SLo,WPo,SW,A:Pepper
      Potts,Villain revealed 2.00
8 JLe,SLo,RBn,fate of Rebel . . . 2.00
9 JLe,SLo,RBn,V:Mandarin 2.00
10 JLe,SLo,RBn,F:The Hulk 2.00
11 JLb,RBn,V:Dr. Doom,A:Hydra 2.00
12 WPo,JLe,JLb,F:Dr. Doom,
      Galactus 2.00
13 JeR,LSn,Wildstorm x-over 2.00

[3rd Series] 1997
1 SCh,KBk,V:Mastermind,48 pg. . 3.00
2 KBk,SCh,in Switzerland 2.00
3 KBk,SCh,V:Hydra Dreadnought
      Robot 2.00
4 KBk,SCh,R:Firebrand 2.00
5 KBk,SCh,V:Firebrand 2.00
6 KBk,F:Black Widow 2.00
7 KBk,SCh,Live Kree or Die, pt.1
      x-over 2.00
8 KBk,SCh,secret identity out . . . 2.00
9 KBk,SCh,A:Black Widow 2.00

IRON MAN:
AGE OF INNOCENCE
1-shot Avengers:Timeslide 2.50

IRON MAN &
SUBMARINER
April 1968
1 GC, 2 stories 225.00

IRON MAN:
THE IRON AGE
June 1998
1 (of 2) KBk,48pg bookshelf 6.00
2 KBk,48pg bookshelf, concl. . . . 6.00

ISLAND OF DR. MOREAU
Oct., 1977
1 GK(c),movie adapt. 2.00

IT'S A DUCK'S LIFE
Feb., 1950
1 F;Buck Duck,Super Rabbit . . 75.00
2 . . . . 35.00
3 thru 10 . . . . @25.00
11 Feb., 1952 . . . . 25.00

JACK OF HEARTS
Jan., 1984
1 Mini series 1.50
2 O:Jack of Hearts 1.00
3 . . . . 1.00
4 Final issue,April 1984 . . . . 1.00

JAMES BOND JR.
1992
1 I&O:JamesBondJr.(TVseries) . 3.00
2 Adventures Contd. 1.50
3 V:Goldfinger,Odd Job 1.50
4 thru 6 . . . . @1.50
V:Scumlord 1.50
8 V:Goldfinger,Walter D.Plank . . 1.50
9 V:Dr.No in Switzerland 1.50
10 V:Robot,Dr.DeRange 1.50
11 V:S.C.U.M. 1.50
12 V:Goldfinger,Jaws 1.50

JANN OF THE JUNGLE
See: JUNGLE TALES

JEANIE COMICS
See: DARING MYSTERY

JIHAD
Epic
1 Cenobites vs. Nightbreed 4.50
2 E:Cenobites vs. Nightbreed . . 4.50

JOHN CARTER, WARLORD OF MARS
June, 1977
1 GK,DC,O:John Carter,Created by Edgar Rice Burroughs 5.00
2 GK/DC(c),GK,RN, White Apes of Mars 3.00
3 GK,RN,Requiem for a Warlord . 3.00
4 GK,RN, Raiding Party 3.00
5 GK,RN,Giant Battle Issue 3.00
6 GK/DC(c),GK,Alone Against a World 3.00
7 GK,TS,Showdown 3.00
8 GK,RN,Beast With Touch of Stone 3.00
9 GK,RN,Giant Battle Issue 3.00
10 GK,The Death of Barsoom? . . 3.00
11 RN,O:Dejah Thoris 2.00
12 RN,City of the Dead 2.00
13 RN,March of the Dead 2.00
14 RN,The Day Helium Died 2.00
15 RN,GK,Prince of Helium Returns 2.00
16 RN,John Carters Dilemma . . . 2.00
17 BL,What Price Victory 5.00
18 FM,Tars Tarkas Battles Alone . 1.50
19 RN(c),War With the Wing Men 1.50
20 RN(c),Battle at the Bottom of the World 1.50
21 RN(c),The Claws of the Banth 1.50
22 RN(c),The Canyon of Death . . 1.50
23 Murder on Mars 1.50
24 GP/TA(c),Betrayal 1.50
25 Inferno 1.50

26 Death Cries the Guild of Assassins 1.50
27 Death Marathon 1.50
28 Guardians of the Lost City Oct., 1979 . . . . 2.50
Ann.#1 RN(c),GK,Battle story . . 2.00
Ann.#2 RN(c),GK,Outnumbered . 2.00
Ann.#3 RN(c),GK,Battle story . . 2.00

JOKER COMICS
Timely April, 1942
1 BW,I&B:Powerhouse Pepper, A:Stuporman 1,600.00
2 BW,I:Tessie the Typist 650.00
3 BW,A:Tessie the Typist, Squat Car Squad 450.00
4 BW,Squat Car (c) 450.00
5 BW,same 450.00
6 BW, ... 250.00
7 BW 250.00
8 BW 250.00
9 BW 250.00
10 BW,Shooting Gallery (c) . . . 250.00
11 BW 200.00
12 BW 200.00
13 BW 200.00
14 BW 200.00
15 BW 200.00
16 BW 200.00
17 BW 200.00
18 BW 200.00
19 BW 200.00
20 BW 200.00
21 BW 175.00
22 BW 175.00
23 BW,HK,'Hey Look' 175.00
24 BW,HK,'Laff Favorites' 175.00
25 BW,HK,same 175.00
26 BW,HK,same 175.00
27 BW 175.00
28 . . . . 50.00
29 BW 175.00
30 BW 175.00
31 BW 125.00
32 B:Millie,Hedy 50.00
33 HK 50.00
34 . . . . 35.00
35 HK 50.00
36 HK 50.00
37 . . . . 35.00
38 . . . . 35.00
39 . . . . 35.00
40 . . . . 35.00
41 A:Nellie the Nurse 35.00
42 I:Patty Pin-up 50.00
Becomes:

ADVENTURES INTO TERROR
43(1)AH,B:Horror Stories 450.00
44(2)AH,'Won't You Step Into My Palor' 325.00
3 GC,'I Stalk By Night' 175.00
4 DR,'The Torture Room' . . . 175.00
5 GC,DR,'The Hitchhiker' . . . 200.00
6 RH,'The Dark Room' 175.00
7 GT(c),BW,'Where Monsters Dwell' 375.00
8 JSt,'Enter... the Lizard' . . . 150.00
9 RH(c),JSt,'The Dark Dungeon' 165.00
10 'When the Vampire Calls' . . 165.00
11 JSt,'Dead Man's Escape' . . 100.00
12 BK,'The Man Who Cried Ghost' 150.00

Journey Into Mystery #104
© Marvel Entertainment Group

13 BEv(c),'The Hands of Death' 125.00
14 GC,'The Hands' 100.00
15 'Trapped by the Tarantula' . 100.00
16 RH(c),'Her Name Is Death' . 100.00
17 'I Die Too Often',Bondage(c) 100.00
18 'He's Trying To Kill Me' 100.00
19 'The Girl Who Couldn't Die' . 125.00
20 . . . . 125.00
21 . . . . 100.00
22 . . . . 100.00
23 . . . . 100.00
24 MF,GC 125.00
25 thru 30 . . . . @100.00
31 May, 1954 . . . . 100.00

JOURNEY INTO MYSTERY
June, 1952
1 RH(c),B:Mystery/Horror stories 2,500.00
2 'Don't Look' 800.00
3 'I Didn't See Anything' 600.00
4 RH,BEv(c),'I'm Drowning,' severed hand (c) 600.00
5 RH,BEv(c),'Fright' 400.00
6 BEv(c),'Till Death Do Us Part' 400.00
7 BEv(c),'Ghost Guard' 400.00
8 'He Who Hesitates' 400.00
9 BEv(c),'I Made A Monster' . 400.00
10 'The Assassin of Paris' 400.00
11 RH,GT,'Meet the Dead' . . . 375.00
12 'A Night At Dragmoor Castle' 325.00
13 'The Living and the Dead' . . 325.00
14 DAy,RH,'The Man Who Owned A World' 325.00
15 RH(c),'Till Death Do Us Part' 325.00
16 DW,'Vampire Tale' 325.00
17 SC,'Midnight On Black Mountain' 325.00
18 'He Wouldn't Stay Dead' . . . 325.00
19 JF,'The Little Things' 325.00
20 BEv,BP,'After Man, What' . . 325.00
21 JKu,'The Man With No Past' . 325.00
22 'Haunted House' 325.00

23 GC,'Gone, But Not Forgotten' 200.00
24 'The Locked Drawer' 200.00
25 'The Man Who Lost Himself' 200.00
26 'The Man From Out There' . 200.00
27 'BP,JSe,'Masterpiece' 200.00
28 'The Survivor' 200.00
29 'Three Frightened People' . . 200.00
30 JO,'The Lady Who Vanished' 200.00
31 'The Man Who Had No Fear' 200.00
32 'Elevator In The Sky' 200.00
33 SD,AW,'There'll Be Some
  Changes Made' 225.00
34 BP,BK,'The Of The
  Mystic Ring' 200.00
35 LC,JF,'Turn Back The Clock' 200.00
36 'I, The Pharaoh' 200.00
37 BEv(c),'The Volcano' 200.00
38 SD,'Those Who Vanish' . . . 200.00
39 BEv(c),DAy,WW,'The
  Forbidden Room' 200.00
40 BEv(c),JF,'The Strange
  Secret Of Henry Hill' 200.00
41 BEv(c),GM,RC,'I Switched
  Bodies' 175.00
42 BEv(c),GM,'What Was
  Farley's Other Face 175.00
43 AW,'Ghost Ship' 175.00
44 thru 50 SD,JK . . . . @175.00
51 thru 55 SD,JK . . . . @175.00
56 thru 61 SD,JK . . . . @175.00
62 SD,JK,I:Xemnu 225.00
63 thru 68 SD,JK . . . . @175.00
69 thru 82 . . . . @225.00
83 JK,SD,I&O:Thor 4,500.00
84 JK,SD,DH,I:Executioner . . 1,000.00
85 JK,SD,I:Loki,Heimdall,Balder,
  Tyr,Odin,Asgard 600.00
86 JK,SD,DH,V:Tomorrow Man 375.00
87 JK,SD,V:Communists 300.00
88 JK,SD,V:Loki 300.00
89 JK,SD,O:Thor(rep) 300.00
90 SD,I:Carbon Copy 150.00
91 JSt,SD,I:Sandu 175.00
92 JSt,SD,V:Loki,I:Frigga 175.00
93 DAy,JK,SD,I:Radioactive
  Man 175.00
94 JSt,SD,V:Loki 135.00
95 JSt,SD,I:Duplicator 135.00
96 JSt,SD,I:Merlin II 125.00
97 JK,I:Lava Man,O:Odin 150.00
98 DH,JK,I&O:Cobra 125.00
99 DH,JK,I:Mr.Hyde,Surtur . . . 125.00
100 DH,JK,V:Mr.Hyde 125.00
101 JK,V:Tomorrow Man 100.00
102 JK,I:Sif,Hela 100.00
103 JK,I:Enchantress,
  Executioner 100.00
104 JK,Giants 100.00
105 JK,V:Hyde,Cobra 100.00
106 JK,O:Balder 100.00
107 JK,I:Grey Gargoyle,Karnilla 100.00
108 JK,A:Dr.Strange 100.00
109 JK,V:Magneto 135.00
110 JK,V:Hyde,Cobra,Loki 75.00
111 JK,V:Hyde,Cobra,Loki 75.00
112 JK,V:Hulk,O:Loki 200.00
113 JK,V:Grey Gargoyle 75.00
114 JK,I&O:Absorbing Man 75.00
115 JK,O:Loki,V:Absorbing Man 100.00
116 JK,V:Loki,C:Daredevil 75.00
117 JK,V:Loki 75.00
118 JK,I:Destroyer 75.00
119 JK,V:Destroyer,I:Hogun,
  Fandrall,Volstagg 75.00
120 JK,A:Avengers,Absorbing

Man 75.00
121 JK,V:Absorbing Man 75.00
122 JK,V:Absorbing Man 75.00
123 JK,V:Absorbing Man 75.00
124 JK,A:Hercules 75.00
125 JK,A:Hercules 75.00
Annual #1, JK,I:Hercules 160.00
Becomes: THOR

JOURNEY INTO MYSTERY
[2nd series] Oct., 1972
1 GK,TP,MP,'Dig Me No Grave' 15.00
2 GK,'Jack the Ripper' 8.00
3 JSn,TP,'Shambler From
  the Stars' 8.00
4 GC,DA,'Haunter of the Dark',
  H.P. Lovecraft adaptation 8.00
5 RB,FrG,'Shadow From the
  Steeple',R. Bloch adaptation . 8.00
6 Mystery Stories 7.00
7 thru 19 . . . . @7.00

JOURNEY INTO UNKNOWN WORLDS
See: ALL WINNERS COMICS

J-2
Aug. 1998
1 TDF,RLm,AM,F:J2 with the powers
  of Juggernaut 2.00

JUGGERNAUT
1997
1-shot 48pg. 2.99

JUNGLE ACTION
Atlas Oct., 1954
1 JMn,JMn(c),B:Leopard Girl . 225.00
2 JMn,JMn(c) 275.00
3 JMn,JMn(c) 150.00
4 JMn,JMn(c) 150.00
5 JMn,JMn(c) 150.00
6 JMn,JMn(c),August, 1955 . . 150.00

JUNGLE ACTION
Oct., 1972—Nov., 1976
1 JB(c),Lorna,Tharn,Jann
  reprints 15.00
2 GK(c),same 10.00
3 JSn(c),same 10.00
4 GK(c),same 10.00
5 JR(c),JB,B:Black Panther,
  V:Man-Ape 15.00
6 RB/FrG(c),RB,V:Kill-Monger . 10.00
7 RB/KJ(c),RB,V:Venomn 10.00
8 RB/KJ(c),RB,GK,
  O:Black Panther 10.00
9 GK/KJ(c),RB,V:Baron Macabre 10.00
10 GK/FrG(c),V:King Cadaver . . 10.00
11 GK(c),V:Baron Macabre,Lord
  Karnaj 10.00
12 RB/KJ(c),V:Kill Monger 8.00
13 GK/JK(c),V:White Gorilla,
  Sombre 8.00
14 GK(c),V:Prehistoric
  Monsters 8.00
15 GK(c),V:Prehistoric
  Monsters 8.00
16 GK(c),V:Venomm 8.00
17 GK(c),V:Kill Monger 8.00
18 JKu(c),V:Madame Slay 8.00

LORNA THARN JANN

Jungle Action #1
© Marvel Entertainment Group

19 GK(c),V:KKK,'Sacrifice
  of Blood' 8.00
20 V:KKK,'Slaughter In The
  Streets' 8.00
21 V:KKK,'Cross Of Fire, Cross
  Of Death' 7.00
22 JB(c),V:KKK,Soul Stranger . . 7.00
23 JBy(c),V:KKK 7.00
24 GK(c),I:Wind Eagle 7.00

JUNGLE TALES
Atlas Sept., 1954
1 B:Jann of the Jungle,Cliff
  Mason,Waku 225.00
2 GT,Jann Stories cont. 175.00
3 Cliff Mason,White Hunter,
  Waku Unknown Jungle . . . 150.00
4 Cliff Mason,Waku,Unknown
  Jungle 150.00
5 RH(c),SSh,Cliff Mason,Waku,
  Unknown Jungle 150.00
6 DH,SSh,Cliff Mason,Waku,
  Unknown Jungle 150.00
7 DH,SSh,Cliff Mason,Waku,
  Unknown Jungle 150.00
Becomes:

JANN OF THE JUNGLE
8 SH,SSh,'The Jungle Outlaw' 175.00
9 'With Fang and Talons' . . . 100.00
10 AW,'The Jackal's Lair' 110.00
11 'Bottonless Pit' 80.00
12 'The Lost Safari' 80.00
13 'When the Trap Closed' 80.00
14 V:Hunters 80.00
15 BEv(c),DH,V:Hunters 80.00
16 BEv(c),AW,'Jungle Vengeance'25.00
17 BEv(c),DH,AW,June, 1957 . 125.00

JUSTICE
Nov., 1986
1 I:Justice 1.25
2 . . . . 1.00
3 Yakuza Assassin 1.00
4 thru 8 . . . . @1.00
9 KG 1.00

10 thru 18	@1.00
19 thru 31	@1.25
32 Last issue,A:Joker	1.50

JUSTICE COMICS
Atlas Fall, 1947

7(1) B:FBI in Action,'Mystery of White Death'	175.00
8(2),HK,'Crime is For Suckers'	125.00
9(3),FBI Raid	100.00
4 Bank Robbery	100.00
5 Subway(c)	85.00
6 E:FBI In Action	85.00
7 Symbolic(c)	85.00
8 Funeral(c)	85.00
9 B:'True Cases Proving Crime Can't Win'	85.00
10 Ph(c),Bank Hold Up	85.00
11 Ph(c),Behind Bars	85.00
12 Ph(c),The Crime of Martin Blaine	60.00
13 Ph(c),The Cautiouc Crook	75.00
14 Ph(c)	75.00
15 Ph(c)	60.00
16 F:"Ears"Karpik-Mobster	50.00
17 'The Ragged Stranger'	50.00
18 'Criss-Cross'	50.00
19 'Death Of A Spy'	50.00
20 'Miami Mob'	50.00
21 'Trap'	50.00
22 'The Big Break'	50.00
23 thru 51	@45.00
52 'Flare Up'	50.00

Becomes:
TALES OF JUSTICE
May, 1955—Aug., 1957

53 BEv,'Keeper Of The Keys'	125.00
54 thru 57	@85.00
58 BK	100.00
59 BK	100.00
60 thru 63	@50.00
64 RC,DW,JSe	75.00
65 RC	75.00
66 JO,AT	75.00
67 DW	75.00

JUSTICE: FOUR BALANCE

1 A:Thing, Yancy Street Gang	1.75
2 V:Hate Monger	1.75
3 the story continues...	1.75
4 ...to its conclusion	1.75

KATHY
Atlas Oct., 1959—Feb., 1964

1 'Teenage Tornado'	45.00
2	25.00
3 thru 15	@20.00
16 thru 27	@15.00

KA-ZAR
[Reprint Series] Aug., 1970

1 X-Men ID	17.00
2 Daredevil 12, 13	12.00
3 DDH,Spider-Man,March, 1971	12.00

[1st Series] Jan., 1974

1 O:Savage Land	3.00
2 DH,JA,A:Shanna The She-Devil	2.50
3 DH,V:Man-God,A:El Tigre	2.50
4 DH,V:Man-God	2.50
5 DH,D:El-Tigre	2.50
6 JB/AA,V:Bahemoth	2.00
7 JB/BMc'Revenge of the	

Ka-Zar (1st Series) #1
© Marvel Entertainment Group

River-Gods'	2.00
8 JB/AA,'Volcano of Molten Death'	2.00
9 JB,'Man Who Hunted Dinosaur'	2.00
10 JB,'Dark City of Death'	2.00
11 DH/FS,'Devil-God of Sylitha'	1.50
12 RH,'Wizard of Forgotten Death'	1.50
13 V:Lizard Men	1.50
14 JAb,V:Klaw	1.50
15 VM,V:Klaw,'Hellbird'	1.50
16 VM,V:Klaw	1.50
17 VM,V:Klaw	1.50
18 VM,V:Klaw,Makrum	1.50
19 VM,V:Klaw,Raknor the Slayer	1.50
20 VM,V:Klaw,'Fortress of Fear'	1.50

[2nd Series] Apr. 1981

1 BA,O:Ka-Zar	2.00
2 thru 7 BA	@1.50
8 BA,Kazar Father	1.50
9 BA	1.50
10 BA,Direct D	1.50
11 BA/GK,Zabu	1.50
12 BA,Panel Missing	1.50
12a Scarce Reprint	2.00
13 BA	1.50
14 BA/GK,Zabu	1.50
15 BA	1.50
16	1.50
17 Detective	1.50
18	1.50
19	1.50
20 A:Spider-Man	2.00
21	2.00
22 A:Spider-Man	2.00
23 A:Spider-Man	2.00
24 A:Spider-Man	2.00
25 A:Spider-Man	2.00
26 A:Spider-Man	2.00
27 A:Buth	1.50
28 Pangea	1.50
29 W:Kazar & Shanna, Doub.Size	1.50
30 V:Pterons	1.50
31 PangeaWarII	1.50
32 V:Plunderer	1.50
33 V:Plunderer	1.50
34 Last Issue Doub.Size	2.00

[3rd Series] 1997

1 MWa,NKu,Ka-Zar, Shanna, Zabu, V:Gregor, 40pg	5.00
1a 2nd printing	2.50
2 MWa,NKu,V:Gregor	4.00
2A NKu variant cover	3.00
3 MWa,NKu,Ka-Zar's son dead?	3.00
4 MWa,NKu,in New York City	3.00
5 MWa,NKu,	2.50
6 MWa,V:Rampaging Rhino	2.00
7 MWa,NKu,F:Shanna the She-Devil	2.00
8 MWa,NKu, Urban Jungle, pt.1	2.00
9 MWa,NKu, Urban Jungle, pt.2	2.00
10 MWa,NKu, Urban Jungle, pt.3	2.00
11 MWa,NKu, Urban Jungle, pt.4, concl.	2.00
12 MWa,A:High Evolutionary	2.00
13 MWa,A:High Evolutionary	2.00
14 MWa,NKu,end old & begin new storyline, double size	3.00
15 A:Punisher	3.00
16 A:Punisher	2.00
17 Ka-Zar clears his name, A:Jameka	2.00
18 People of the Savage Land revolt	2.00
Ann. '97 V:Garrok, the Petrified Man	2.50
Ann. '98 Kazar/Daredevil heroes unite	3.00

KA-ZAR OF THE SAVAGE LAND
1996

1-shot CDi,V:Sauron, 48pg. prelude to series	3.00

KA-ZAR: SIBLING RIVALRY
1997

1 MWa,TDz, Flashback	1.95

KELLYS, THE
See: KID KOMICS

KENT BLAKE OF THE SECRET SERVICE
May, 1951—July, 1953

1 U.S. Govt. Secret Agent stories,Bondage cover	125.00
2 JSt,Drug issue,'Man with out A Face	75.00
3 'Trapped By The Chinese Reds'	50.00
4 Secret Service Stories	50.00
5 RH(c),'Condemned To Death'	50.00
6 Cases from Kent Blake files	50.00
7 RH(c),Behind Enemy Lines	50.00
8 V:Communists	50.00
9 thru 14	@50.00

KICKERS INC.
Nov., 1986

1 SB,O:Kickers	1.25
2 SB	1.00
3 RF,Witches	1.00
4 RF,FIST	1.00
5 RF,A:D.P.7	1.00
6 thru 8 RF	@1.00
9	1.00
10 TD	1.00

11	1.00
12 Oct., 1987	1.00

KID & PLAY

1 Based on Rap Group	1.25
2 Drug Issue	1.25
3 At your Friends Expense	1.25
4	1.25
5	1.25
6 Record Contract	1.25
7 Fraternity Pledging	1.25
8 Kid and Cindy become an item	1.25
9 C:Marvel Heroes	1.25

KID COLT OUTLAW
Atlas Aug., 1948

1 B:Kid Colt,A:Two-Gun Kid	600.00
2 'Gun-Fighter and the Girl'	300.00
3 'Colt-Quick Killers For Hire'	250.00
4 'Wanted',A:Tex Taylor	250.00
5 'Mystery of the Misssing Mine',A:Blaze Carson	250.00
6 A:Tex Taylor,'Valley of the Warewolf'	150.00
7 B:Nimo the Lion	150.00
8	150.00
9	135.00
10 'The Whip Strikes',E:Nimo the Lion'	160.00
11 O:Kid Colt	150.00
12	125.00
13 DRi	125.00
14	125.00
15 'Gun Whipped in Shotgun City'	125.00
16	125.00
17	125.00
18 DRi	125.00
19	100.00
20 'The Outlaw'	100.00
21 thru 30	@100.00
31	75.00
32	75.00
33 thru 45 A:Black Rider	@60.00
46 RH(c)	50.00
47 DW	50.00
48 RH(c),JKu	50.00
49	50.00
50	50.00
51 thru 56	@45.00
57 AW	50.00
58 AW	50.00
59 AW	50.00
60 AW	50.00
61	25.00
62	25.00
63	25.00
64	30.00
65	30.00
66 thru 78	@25.00
79 Origin Retold	30.00
80 thru 86	@25.00
87 JDa(reprint)	30.00
88 AW	35.00
89 AW,Matt Slade	35.00
90 thru 99	@15.00
100	25.00
101	20.00
102	15.00
103 'The Great Train Robbery'	15.00
104 JKu(c),DH,'Trail of Kid Colt'	15.00
105 DH,V:Dakota Dixon	15.00

106 JKu(c),'The Circus of Crime'	15.00
107	15.00
108 BEv	15.00
109 DAy,V:The Barracuda	15.00
110 GC,V:Iron Mask	15.00
111 JKu(c),V:Sam Hawk, The Man Hunter	15.00
112 JKu(c),V:Mr. Brown	15.00
113 JKu(c),GC,V:Bull Barton	15.00
114 JKu(c),Return of Iron Mask	15.00
115 JKu(c),V:The Scorpion	15.00
116 JKu(c),GC,V:Dr. Danger & Invisible Gunman	15.00
117 JKu(c),GC,V:The Fatman & His Boomerang	15.00
118 V:Scorpion,Bull Barton, Dr. Danger	15.00
119 DAy(c),JK,V:Bassett The Badman	15.00
120 'Cragsons Ride Again'	15.00
121 A:Rawhide Kid,Iron Mask	10.00
122 V:Rattler Ruxton	10.00
123 V:Ringo Barker	10.00
124 A:Phantom Raider	10.00
125 A:Two-Gun Kid	10.00
126 V:Wes Hardin	9.00
127 thru 129	@9.00
130 O:Kid Colt	9.00
131 thru 150	@9.00
151 thru 200 reprints	@7.00
201 thru 228 reprints	@5.00
229 April, 1979	5.00

KID FROM DODGE CITY
Atlas July, 1957—Sept., 1957

1	50.00
2	25.00

KID FROM TEXAS
Atlas June, 1957—Aug., 1957

1	50.00
2	25.00

KID KOMICS
Timely Feb., 1943

1 SSh(c),BW,O:Captain Wonder & Tim Mulrooney I:Whitewash, Knuckles,Trixie Trouble, Pinto Pete Subbie	3,000.00
2 AsH(c),F:Captain Wonder Subbie, B:Young Allies, B:Red Hawk,Tommy Tyme	1,400.00
3 ASh(c),A:The Vision & Daredevils	1,000.00
4 ASh(c),B:Destroyer,A:Sub-Mariner, E:Red Hawk,Tommy Tyme	900.00
5 ASh(c),V:Nazis	650.00
6 ASh(c),V:Japanese	650.00
7 ASh(c),B;Whizzer	600.00
8 ASh(c),V:Train Robbers	600.00
9 ASh(c),V:Elves	600.00
10 ASh(c),E:Young Allies, The Destoyer,The Whizzer	600.00

Becomes:
KID MOVIE KOMICS

11 F:Silly Seal,Ziggy Pig HK,Hey Look	175.00

Becomes:
RUSTY COMICS

12 F:Rusty,A:Mitzi	100.00
13 Do not Disturb(c)	50.00
14 Beach(c),BW,HK,Hey Look	75.00

15 Picnic(c),HK,Hey Look	60.00
16 Juniors Grades,HK,HeyLook	60.00
17 John in Trouble,HK,HeyLook	60.00
18 John Fired	40.00
19 Fridge raid(c),HK	40.00
20 And Her Family,HK	65.00
21 And Her Family,HK	100.00
22	100.00

Becomes:
KELLYS, THE

23 F:The Kelly Family(Pop, Mom,Mike,Pat & Goliath)	75.00
24 Mike's Date,A;Margie	50.00
25 Wrestling(c)	50.00

Becomes:
SPY CASES

26(#1) Spy stories	150.00
27(#2) BEv,Bondage(c)	100.00
28(#3) Sabotage,A:Douglas Grant Secret Agent	100.00
4 The Secret Invasion	90.00
5 The Vengeance of Comrade de Casto	90.00
6 A:Secret Agent Doug Grant	90.00
7 GT,A:Doug Grant	90.00
8 Atom Bomb(c),Frozen Horror	75.00
9 Undeclared War	70.00
10 Battlefield Adventures	60.00
11 Battlefield Adventures	55.00
12 Battlefield Adventures	55.00
13 Battlefield Adventures	55.00
14 Battlefield Adventures	55.00
15 Doug Grant	55.00
16 Doug Grant	55.00
17 Doug Grant	55.00
18 Contact in Ankara	55.00
19 Final Issue,Oct., 1953	55.00

KID SLADE GUNFIGHTER
See: MATT SLADE

KILLFRENZY

1	1.95
2 Castle Madspike	1.95

KILLPOWER:
THE EARLY YEARS
1993

1 B:MiB,Goes on Rampage	3.25
2 thru 3 O:Killpower	2.00
4 E:MiB,last issue	2.00

KING ARTHUR & THE
KNIGHTS OF JUSTICE
1993–94

1 Based on Cartoon	1.25
2 Based on Cartoon	1.25
3 Based on Cartoon	1.25

KING CONAN:
See: CONAN THE KING

KINGPIN
Nov., 1997

1-shot StL,JR, bookshelf 48pg	6.00

KISSNATION
1997

1 Rock & Roll, A:X-Men	10.00

KITTY PRYDE: AGENT OF S.H.I.E.L.D.
Oct., 1997
1 (of 3) LHa,V:Ogun 2.50
2 LHa,V:Ogun 2.50
3 LHa,Ogun's Slave? 2.50

KITTY PRIDE & WOLVERINE
Nov., 1984
1 AM,V:Ogun 6.00
2 AM,V:Ogun 4.00
3 thru 5 AM,V:Ogun . . . . @4.00
6 AM,D:Ogun, April, 1985 . . . . . . 3.00

Knights of Pendragon #11
© Marvel Entertainment Group

KNIGHTS OF PENDRAGON
[1st Regular Series] July, 1990
1 GEr 2.75
2 thru 7 . . . . @2.25
8 inc.SBi Poster 2.25
9 V:Bane Fisherman 2.25
10 Cap.Britain/Union Jack 2.25
11 A:Iron Man 2.25
12 A:Iron Man,Union Jack 2.25
13 O:Pendragon 2.25
14 A:Mr.Fantastic,Invisible Woman
    Black Panther 2.25
15 BlackPanther/Union Jack T.U. . 2.25
16 A:Black Panther 2.25
17 D:Albion, Union Jack,
    A:Black Panther 2.25
18 A:Iron Man,Black Panther 2.25
[2nd Regular Series]
1 GEr,A:Iron Man,R:Knights of
    Pendragon,V:MyS-TECH . . . 2.25
2 A:Iron Man,Black Knight 2.00
3 PGa,A:Iron Man,Black Knight . . 2.00
4 Gawain Vs. Bane 2.00
5 JRe,V:Magpie 2.00
6 A:Spider-Man 2.00
7 A:Spider-Man,V:Warheads 2.00
8 JRe,A:Spider-Man 2.00
9 A:Spider-Man,Warheads 2.00
10 V:Baron Blood 2.00
11 . . . . 2.00

12 MyS-TECH Wars,V:Skire 2.00
13 A:Death's Head II 2.00
14 A:Death's Head II 2.00
15 D:Adam,A:Death's Head II . . . 2.00

KRAZY KOMICS
Timely July, 1942
1 B:Ziggy Pig,Silly Seal 350.00
2 Toughy Tomcat(c) 150.00
3 Toughy Tomcat/Bunny(c) . . . 100.00
4 Toughy Tomcat/Ziggy(c) 100.00
5 Ziggy/Buzz Saw(c) 100.00
6 Toughy/Cannon(c) 100.00
7 Cigar Store Indian(c) 100.00
8 Toughy/Hammock(c) 100.00
9 Hitler(c) 100.00
10 Newspaper(c) 125.00
11 Canoe(c) 75.00
12 Circus(c) 100.00
13 Pirate Treasure(c) 75.00
14 Fishing(c) 75.00
15 Ski-Jump(c) 75.00
16 Airplane(c) 60.00
17 Street corner(c) 60.00
18 Mallet/Bell(c) 60.00
19 Bicycle(c) 60.00
20 Ziggy(c) 60.00
21 Toughy's date(c) 60.00
22 Crystal Ball(c) 60.00
23 Sharks in bathtub(c) 60.00
24 Baseball(c) 60.00
25 HK,Krazy Krow(c) 75.00
26 Super Rabbit(c) 60.00
Becomes:

CINDY COMICS
27 HK,B:Margie,Oscar 100.00
28 HK,Snow sled(c) 75.00
29 . . . . 75.00
30 . . . . 75.00
31 HK 75.00
32 . . . . 40.00
33 A;Georgie 40.00
34 thru 40 . . . . @40.00
Becomes:

CRIME CAN'T WIN
41 Crime stories 175.00
42 . . . . 100.00
43 GT,Horror story 120.00
4 thru 11 . . . . @75.00
12 Sept., 1953 . . . . 75.00

KRAZY KOMICS
Timely
[2nd Series] Aug., 1948
1 BW,HK,B:Eustice Hayseed . 300.00
2 BW,O:Powerhouse Pepper
    November, 1948 . . . . 225.00

KRAZY KROW
Summer, 1945
1 B:Krazy Krow 100.00
2 . . . . 65.00
3 Winter, 1945-46 . . . . 65.00

KREE-SKRULL WAR
Sept.–Oct., 1983
1 & 2 JB,NA,reprints . . . . @5.00

KRULL
Nov.–Dec., 1983
1 Ph(c),BBI,movie adapt 1.00
2 BBI,rep.,Marvel Super Spec. . . . 1.00

Kull The Conqueror #5
© Marvel Entertainment Group

KULL THE CONQUEROR
[1st Series] June, 1971
1 MSe,RA,WW,A King Comes
    Riding,O:Kull 15.00
2 MSe,JSe,Shadow Kingdom . . . 7.00
3 MSe,JSe,Death Dance of
    Thulsa Doom 7.00
4 MSe,JSe,Night o/t Red Slayers 4.00
5 MSe,JSe,Kingdom By the Sea . 4.00
6 MSe,JSe,Lurker Beneath
    the Sea 3.00
7 MSe,JSe,Delcardes'Cat,
    A:Thulsa Doom 3.00
8 MSe,JSe,Wolfshead 3.00
9 MSe,JSe,The Scorpion God . . 3.00
10 MSe,Swords o/t White Queen . 3.00
11 MP,King Kull Must Die, O:Kull
    cont.,A:Thulsa Doom 3.00
12 MP,SB,Moon of Blood,V:Thulsa
    Doom,B:SD,B.U.stories 3.00
13 MP,AM,Torches From Hell,
    V:Thulsa Doom 3.00
14 MP,JA,The Black Belfry,
    A:Thulsa Doom 3.00
15 MP,Wings o/t Night-Beast,
    E:SD,B.U.stories 3.00
16 EH,Tiger in the Moon,
    A:Thulsa Doom 3.00
17 AA,EH,Thing from Emerald
    Darkness 3.00
18 EH,AA,Keeper of Flame
    & Frost 3.00
19 EH,AA,The Crystal Menace . . 3.00
20 EH,AA,Hell Beneath Atlantis . . 3.00
21 City of the Crawling Dead . . . 2.00
22 Talons of the Devil-Birds 2.00
23 Demon Shade 2.00
24 Screams in the Dark 2.00
25 A Lizard's Throne 2.00
26 Into Death's Dimension 2.00
27 The World Within 2.00
28 Creature and the Crown,
    A:Thulsa Doom 2.00
29 To Sit the Topaz Throne,
    V:Thulsa Doom, final issue . . . 2.00
[2nd Series] 1982
1 JB,Brule 2.50

2 Misareenia 2.00
[3rd Series] 1983–85
1 JB,BWi,DG,Iraina 1.50
2 JB,Battle to the Death 1.25
3 JB 1.00
4 JB 1.00
5 JB 1.00
6 JB 1.00
7 JB,Masquerade Death 1.00
8 JB 1.00
9 JB 1.00
10 JB 1.00

KULL AND THE BARBARIANS
May, 1975
1 NA,GK,reprint Kull #1 . . . . 5.00
2 BBI,reprint,Dec., 1983 . . . . . . 2.00
3 NA,HC,O:Red Sonja 3.00

LABRYNTH
1986–87
1 Movie adapt 2.00
2 and 3 . . . . @1.50

LAFF-A-LYMPICS
1978–79
1 F;Hanna Barbera 12.00
2 thru 5 . . . . @10.00
6 thru 13 . . . . @10.00

LANA
August, 1948
1 F:Lana Lane The Show Girl,
A:Rusty,B:Millie 100.00
2 HK,Hey Look,A:Rusty 60.00
3 Show(c),B:Nellie 40.00
4 Ship(c) 40.00
5 Audition(c) 40.00
6 Stop sign(c) 40.00
7 Beach(c) 40.00
Becomes:

LITTLE LANA
8 Little Lana(c) 26.00
9 Final Issue,March, 1950 . . . . 26.00

LANCE BARNES: POST NUKE DICK
Epic 1993
1 I:Lance Barnes 2.50
2 Cigarettes 2.50
3 Warring Mall Tribe 2.50
4 V:Ex-bankers,last issue 2.50

LAST AMERICAN
Epic 1990–91
1 . . . . 3.50
2 . . . . 3.00
3 . . . . 2.50
4 Final issue. 2.25

THE LAST AVENGERS STORY
1 PDd, Alterverse,Future world . 5.95
2 PDd, Final fate,fully painted . . 5.95
TPB PDd,AOI, rep. Alterniverse
story, 96pg. 12.95

LAST STARFIGHTER, THE
Oct.–Dec., 1984
1 JG(c),BBI,Movie adapt. 1.00

2 Movie adapt 1.00
3 BBI 1.00

LAWBREAKERS ALWAYS LOSE!
Spring, 1948–Oct. 1949
1 Partial Ph(c),Adam and Eve,
HK,Giggles and Grins . . . 200.00
2 FBI V:Fur Theives 100.00
3 . . . . 75.00
4 Asylum(c) 75.00
5 . . . . 75.00
6 Pawnbroker(c) 75.00
7 Crime at Midnight 125.00
8 Prison Break 65.00
9 Ph(c),He Prowled at Night . . 65.00
10 Phc(c),I Met My Murderer . . 65.00

LAWDOG
1 B:CDi(s),FH,I:Lawdog 2.50
2 FH,V:Vocal-yokel Cultist 2.25
3 FH,Manical Nazis 2.25
4 FH,V:Zombies 2.25
5 FH 2.25
6 FH 2.25
7 FH,V:Zombies 2.25
8 FH,w/card 2.25
9 FH,w/card 2.25
10 last issue, w/card 2.25

LAWDOG & GRIMROD: TERROR AT THE CROSSROADS
1993
1 . . . . 3.50

LEGION OF MONSTERS
Sept., 1975
(black & white magazine)
1 NA(c),GM,I&O:Legion of
Monsters,O:Manphibian . . 30.00

LEGION OF NIGHT
Oct., 1991
1 WPo/SW,A:Fin Fang Foom . . . 5.50
2 WPo,V:Fin Fang Foom 5.50

LETHAL FOES OF SPIDER-MAN
1993
1 B:DFr(s),SMc,R:Stegron 2.00
2 SMc,A:Stegron 2.00
3 SMc,V:Spider-Man 2.00
4 E:DFr(s),SMc,Last Issue 2.00

LIFE OF CAPTAIN MARVEL
August, 1985
1 rep.Iron Man #55,
Capt.Marvel #25,26 . . . . 9.00
2 rep.Capt.Marvel#26-28 . . . . . 6.50
3 rep.Capt.Marvel#28-30
Marvel Feature #12 . . . . 6.00
4 rep.Marvel Feature #12,Capt.
Marvel #31,32,Daredevil#105 . 6.00
5 rep.Capt.Marvel #32-#34 . . . . 6.00

LIFE OF CHRIST
1993
1 Birth of Christ 3.00
2 MW,The Easter Story 3.00

LIFE OF POPE JOHN-PAUL II
1983
1 JSt, Jan., 1983 . . . . 5.00
1a Special reprint 3.00

LIFE WITH MILLIE
See: DATE WITH MILLIE

LIGHT AND DARKNESS WAR
Epic Oct., 1988
1 . . . . 4.00
2 . . . . 3.00
3 thru 6 Dec., 1989 . . . . . . @2.50

LINDA CARTER, STUDENT NURSE
Atlas Sept., 1961
1 . . . . 40.00
2 thru 9, Jan., 1963 . . . . . @30.00

LION KING
1 based on Movie 2.75

Li'l Kids #1
© Marvel Entertainment Group

LI'L KIDS
Aug., 1970–June 1973
1 . . . . 30.00
2 thru 12 . . . . @15.00

LI'L PALS
Sept., 1972
1 . . . . 20.00
2 thru 5, May, 1973 . . . . . . @18.00

LITTLE ASPRIN
July, 1949
1 HK,A;Oscar 100.00
2 HK 50.00
3 Dec., 1949 . . . . 35.00

LITTLE LANA
See: LANA

LITTLE LENNY
June, 1949
1 .... 50.00
2 .... 35.00
3 November, 1949 .... 35.00

LITTLE LIZZIE
June, 1949
1 Roller Skating(c) 60.00
2 Soda(c) 40.00
3 Movies(c) 40.00
4 Lizzie(c) 40.00
5 Lizzie/Swing(c) April,1950 ... 40.00
[2nd Series] Sept., 1953
1 .... 40.00
2 .... 30.00
3 Jan., 1954 .... 30.00

LITTLE MERMAID, THE
1993
1 .... 1.50
2 Reception for Pacifica royalty .. 1.50
3 TrR,Ariel joins fish club 1.50
4 .... 1.50
5 .... 1.50
6 TrR,Ariel decorates coral"tree" . 1.50
7 TrR,Flogglefish banished 1.50
8 .... 1.50
9 Annual Sea Horse Tournament 1.50
10 TrR,AnnualBlowfishTournament 1.50
11 TrR,Sharkeena,King Triton ... 1.50
12 .... 1.50
13 Lobster Monster 1.50

LOGAN
1-shot HMe,48pg 5.95
1-shot Logan: Path of the
  Warrior (1996) 5.00
1-shot Logan: Shadow Society,
  HMe,TCk Early life of
  Wolverine (1996) 5.00

LOGAN'S RUN
Jan., 1977
1 GP,From Movie 6.00
2 GP,Cathedral Kill 5.00
3 GP,Lair of Laser Death 5.00
4 GP,Dread Sanctuary 5.00
5 GP,End Run 5.00
6 MZ,B.U.Thanos/Drax 10.00
7 TS,Cathedral Prime 5.00

LONGSHOT
Sept., 1985
1 AAd,WPo(i),BA,I:Longshot 8.00
2 AAd,WPo(i),I:RicoshetRita ... 6.00
3 AAd,WPo(i),I:Mojo,Spiral 6.00
4 AAd,WPo(i),A:Spider-Man 6.00
5 AAd,WPo(i),A:Dr. Strange 6.00
6 AAd,WPo(i),A:Dr. Strange 6.00
TPB Reprints #1-#6 .... 16.95
1-shot, JMD,MZi,AW, 48pg
  (Dec. 1997) 4.00

LOOSE CANNONS
1 and 2 DAn .... @2.50
3 DAn 2.75

LORNA, THE JUNGLE GIRL
Atlas 1953–57
1 Terrors of the Jungle,O:Lorna 250.00

2 Headhunter's Strike
  I:Greg Knight 125.00
3 .... 100.00
4 .... 100.00
5 .... 100.00
6 RH(c),GT 90.00
7 RH(c) 90.00
8 Jungle Queen Strikes Again . 90.00
9 .... 90.00
10 White Fang 90.00
11 Death From the Skies 90.00
12 Day of Doom 75.00
13 thru 17 .... @75.00
18 AW(c) 85.00
19 thru 26 .... @60.00

LOVE ADVENTURES
Atlas Oct., 1949
1 Ph(c) 100.00
2 Ph(c),Tyrone Power/Gene
  Tierney 100.00
3 thru 12 .... @50.00
Becomes:
ACTUAL CONFESSIONS
13 .... 16.00
14 Dec., 1952 .... 16.00

LOVE DRAMAS
Oct., 1949
1 Ph(c),JKa 100.00
2 Jan., 1950 .... 75.00

LOVE ROMANCES
See: IDEAL

LOVERS
See: ALL-SELECT COMICS

LOVE SECRETS
Oct., 1949
1 .... 70.00
2 Jan., 1950 .... 40.00

LUNATIK
1995
1 KG 1.95
2 V:The Avengers 1.95
3 conclusion 1.95

MACHINE MAN
April, 1978
1 JK,From 2001 .... 3.00
2 JK 2.50
3 JK,V:Ten-For,The Mean
  Machine 2.50
4 JK,V;Ten-For,Battle on A
  Busy Street 2.50
5 JK,V;Ten-For,Day of the
  Non-Hero 2.50
6 JK,V;Ten-For 2.50
7 JK,With A Nation Against Him . 2.50
8 JK,Escape:Impossible 2.50
9 JK,In Final Battle 2.50
10 SD,Birth of A Super-Hero 2.50
11 SD,V:Binary Bug 2.50
12 SD,"Where walk the Gods" ... 2.50
13 SD,Xanadu 2.50
14 SD,V:Machine Man 2.50
15 SD,A:Thing,Human Torch 2.50
16 SD,I:Baron Brimstone And the
  Satan Squad 2.50
17 SD,Madam Menace 2.50

Machine Man #15
© Marvel Entertainment Group

18 A:Alpha Flight 3.50
19 I:Jack o'Lantern 15.00

MACHINE MAN
[Limited-Series]
Oct., 1984
1 HT,BWS,V:Baintronics 2.50
2 HT,BWS,C:Iron Man of 2020 .. 2.50
3 HT,BWS,I:Iron Man of 2020 .. 3.00
4 HT,BWS,V:Iron Man of 2020 .. 2.50
TPB rep.#1-4 .... 5.95

MACHINE MAN 2020
1994
1 rep. limited series #1–#2 .... 2.00
2 rep. limited series #3–#4 .... 2.00

MAD ABOUT MILLIE
April, 1969
1 .... 35.00
2 thru 16 .... @15.00
17 Dec., 1970 .... 15.00
Ann.#1 .... 12.00

MADBALLS
Star Sept., 1986
1 Based on Toys 1.25
2 thru 9 .... @1.00
10 June, 1988 .... 1.00

MAD DOG
1 from Bob TV Show 1.50
2 V:Trans World Trust Corp. 1.25
3 V:Cigarette Criminals 1.25
4 V:Dogs of War 1.25
5 thru 6 .... @1.95

MADE MEN
May 1998
1-shot HMe gangster epic 6.00

MAGIK
Dec., 1983
1 JB,TP,F:Storm and Illyana 3.50

2 JB,TP,A:Belasco,Sym 3.00
3 TP,A:New Mutants,Belasco . . . 3.00
4 TP,V:Belasco,A:Sym 3.00

MAGNETO
1993
0 JD,JBo,rep. origin stories. 6.00
0a Gold ed. 10.00
0b Platinum ed. 15.00

MAGNETO
1996
1 (of 4) PrM,KJo,JhB, Joseph . . . 2.00
2 PrM,KJo,JhB, Joseph's search
   for his past life 2.00
3 PrM,KJo,JhB 2.00
4 PrM,KJo,JhB, concl. 2.00

MAN COMICS
Atlas 1949–53
1 GT, Revenge 140.00
2 GT, Fury in his Fists 75.00
3 Mantrap 60.00
4 The Fallen Hero 60.00
5 Laugh,Fool,Laugh 60.00
6 Black Hate 50.00
7 The Killer 50.00
8 BEv,An Eye For an Eye 55.00
9 B:War Issues,Here Comes
   Sergeant Smith 35.00
10 Korean Communism 35.00
11 RH,Cannon Fodder 35.00
12 The Black Hate 35.00
13 GC,RH,Beach Head 35.00
14 GT,No Prisoners 45.00
15 . . . . 35.00
16 . . . . 30.00
17 RH 30.00
18 thru 20 . . . . @30.00
21 GC 30.00
22 BEv,BK,JSt 60.00
23 thru 26 . . . . @30.00
27 E:War Issues 30.00
28 Where Mummies Prowl 30.00

MANDRAKE
1995
1 fully painted series 2.95
2 V:Octon 2.95
3 final issue 2.95

MAN FROM ATLANTIS
Feb., 1978–Aug., 1978
1 TS,From TV Series,O:Mark
   Harris 5.00
2 FR,FS,The Bermuda Triangle
   Trap 3.00
3 FR,FS,Undersea Shadow 3.00
4 FR,FS,Beware the Killer
   Spores 3.00
5 FR,FS,The Ray of the
   Red Death 3.00
6 FR,FS,Bait for the Behemoth . 3.00
7 FR,FS,Behold the Land
   Forgotten 3.00

MAN-THING
[1st Series] Jan., 1974
1 FB,JM,A:Howard the Duck . . . 14.00
2 VM,ST,Hell Hath No Fury 7.00
3 VM,JA,I:Original Foolkiller 6.00
4 VM,JA,O&D:Foolkiller 4.00
5 MP,Night o/t Laughing Dead . . 4.00

MARVEL COMICS GROUP.
THE MOST STARTLING SWAMP CREATURE OF ALL!
THE **MAN-THING**
DEATH-WINDS OF THE EVERGLADES!

Man Thing #3
© *Marvel Entertainment Group*

6 MP,V:Soul-Slayers,Drug Issue . 4.00
7 MP,A Monster Stalks Swamp . . 4.00
8 MP,Man Into Monster 4.00
9 MP,Deathwatch 4.00
10 MP,Nobody Dies Forever 4.00
11 MP,Dance to the Murder 4.00
12 KJ,Death-Cry of a Dead Man . 4.00
13 TS,V:Captain Fate 4.00
14 AA,V:Captain Fate 4.00
15 A Candle for Saint Cloud 4.00
16 JB,TP,Death of a Legend . . . 4.00
17 JM,Book Burns in Citrusville . . 4.00
18 JM,Chaos on the Campus . . . 4.00
19 JM,FS,I:Scavenger 4.00
20 JM,A:Spider-Man,Daredevil,
   Shang-Chi,Thing 4.50
21 JM,O:Scavenger,Man Thing . 4.00
22 JM,C:Howard the Duck 4.00
G-Size #1 MP,SD,JK,rep.TheGlob 5.00
G-Size #2 JB,KJ,The
   Monster Runs Wild 4.00
G-Size #3 AA,A World He
   Never Made 4.00
G-Size #4 FS,EH,inc.Howard the
   Duck vs.Gorko 4.00
G-Size #5 DA,EH,inc.Howard the
   Duck vs.Vampire 6.00
[2nd Series] 1979–1981
1 JM,BWi 2.00
2 BWi,JM,Himalayan Nightmare . 1.50
3 BWi,JM,V:Snowman 1.50
4 BWi,DP,V:Mordo,A:Dr Strange . 1.50
5 DP,BWi,This Girl is Terrified . . 1.50
6 DP,BWi,Fraternity Rites 1.25
7 BWi,DP Return of Captain Fate 1.25
8 BWi,DP,V:Captain Fate 1.25
9 BWi(c),Save the Life of My
   Own Child 1.25
10 BWi,DP,Swampfire 1.25
11 Final issue 1.25
[3rd Series] Oct., 1997
1 JMD,LSh, non-code 3.00
2 JMD,LSh, reunion with ex-wife,
   A:Dr. Strange 3.00
3 JMD,LSh, visit to Devil Slayer . 3.00
4 JMD,LSh, V:Devil-Slayer 3.00

5 JMD,LSh, new abilities revealed 3.00
6 JMD,LSh, V:Cult of Entropy . . . 3.00
7 JMD,LSh, Muck Monster, Namor 3.00
8 JMD,LSh, Muck Monster turned back
   into Ted Sallis 3.00
Storyline continues in Strange Tales

MARINES AT WAR
See: DEVIL-DOG DUGAN

MARINES IN ACTION
Atlas June, 1955
1 B:Rock Murdock,Boot Camp
   Brady 50.00
2 thru 13 . . . . @30.00
14 Sept., 1957 . . . . 30.00

MARINES IN BATTLE
Atlas Aug., 1954
1 RH,B:Iron Mike McGraw . . . 125.00
2 . . . . 60.00
3 thru 6 . . . . @45.00
7 . . . . 50.00
8 . . . . 45.00
9 . . . . 45.00
10 . . . . 45.00
11 thru 16 . . . . @40.00
17 . . . . 60.00
18 thru 22 . . . . @40.00
23 . . . . 60.00
24 . . . . 40.00
25 Sept., 1958 . . . . 50.00

MARK HAZZARD: MERC
Nov., 1986–Oct. 1987
1 GM,O:Mark Hazard 1.50
2 GM 1.00
3 M,Arab Terrorists 1.00
4 GM 1.00
5 GM 1.00
6 GM 1.00
7 GM 1.00
8 GM 1.00
9 NKu/AKu 1.00
10 thru 12 . . . . @1.00
Ann.#1 D:Merc 1.25

MARSHALL LAW
Epic 1987–89
1 . . . . 4.50
2 . . . . 3.00
3 thru 6 . . . . @2.50

MARVEL ACTION HOUR: FANTASTIC FOUR
1994–95
1 regular 1.50
1a bagged with insert print from
   animated series 3.00
2 V:Puppet Master 1.50
3 . . . . 1.50
4 V:Sub-Mariner 1.50
5 . . . . 1.50
6 R:Skrulls 1.50
7 V:Doctor Doom 1.50
8 Wanted by the Law 1.50

MARVEL ACTION HOUR: IRON MAN
1994–95
1 regular 1.50
1a bagged with insert print from

MARVEL

Marvel Action Hour: Iron Man #5
© Marvel Entertainment Group

animated series	3.25
2 V:War Machine	1.50
3 V:Ultimo	1.50
4 A:Force Works, Hawkeye, War Machine	1.50
5 O:Iron Man	1.50
6 V:Fing Fang Foom	1.50
7 V:Mandarin	1.50
8 V:Robots	1.50

MARVEL ACTION UNIVERSE
TV Tie-in, Jan., 1989
1 Rep.Spider-Man & Friends . . . 2.50

MARVEL ADVENTURES
STARRING DAREDEVIL
Dec., 1975–Oct. 1976
1 Rep,Daredevil #22 . . . . 5.00
2 thru 5, Rep,Daredevil #23-26 @3.00
6 DD #27 . . . . 3.00

MARVEL ADVENTURES
Feb. 1997
1 RMc,F:The Hulk 1.50
2 RMc,F:Spider-Man 1.50
3 RMc,F:Quicksilver & Scarlet Witch 1.50
4 RMc,BHr,F:Hulk,V:Brotherhood of Evil Mutants 1.50
5 RMc,BHr,F:Spider-Man, The X-Men 1.50
6 RMc,BHr,A:Spider-Man,Invisible Woman, Human Torch 1.50
7 RMc,F:Hulk,V:Tyrannus 1.50
8 RMc,V:Molto 1.50
9 RMc,F:Fantastic Four, Subterranean War, concl. 1.50
10 RMc,Sky-Rider vs. Gladiator . . 1.50
11 RMc,F:Spider-Man,Sandman . . 1.50
12 RMc,F:Fantastic Four,V:Frightful Four 1.50
13 AM,F:Spider-Man, Silver Surfer 1.50
14 RMc,F:The Hulk,A:Dr. Strange, Juggernaut 1.50

15 RMc,F:X-Men,V:Beast's army . 1.50
16 RMc,F:Silver Surfer 1.50
17 RMc,F:Spider-Man, Iron Man . 1.50
18 RMc,F:Sentinel of Liberty 1.50
19 RMc,F:The Avengers 1.50

MARVEL & DC PRESENTS
Nov., 1982
1 WS,TA,X-Men & Titans,A:Darkseid, Deathstroke(3rd App.), ... 18.00

MARVEL BOY
Dec., 1950
1 RH,O:Marvel Boy,Lost World 700.00
2 BEv,The Zero Hour 600.00
Becomes:

ASTONISHING
3 BEv,Marvel Boy,V:Mr Death 700.00
4 BEv,Stan Lee,The Screaming Tomb 500.00
5 BEv,Horro in the Caves of Doom 500.00
6 BEv,My Coffin is Waiting E:Marvel Boy 500.00
7 JR,Nightmare 200.00
8 RH,Behind the Wall 200.00
9 RH(c),The Little Black Box . 200.00
10 BEv,Walking Dead 200.00
11 BF,JSt.Mr Mordeau 175.00
12 GC,BEv,Horror Show 175.00
13 BK,MSy,Ghouls Gold 175.00
14 BK,The Long Jump Down . . 175.00
15 BEv(c),Grounds for Death . . 160.00
16 BEv(c),DAy,SSh,Don't Make a Ghoul of Yourself 175.00
17 Who Was the Wilmach Werewolf? 160.00
18 BEv(c),JR,Vampire at my Window 200.00
19 BK,Back From the Grave . . 175.00
20 GC,Mystery at Midnight . . . 150.00
21 Manhunter 125.00
22 RH(c),Man Against Werewolf 125.00
23 The Woman in Black 150.00
24 JR,The Stone Face 125.00
25 RC,I Married a Zombie 150.00
26 RH(c),I Died Too Often 125.00
27 . . . . 125.00
28 No Evidence 125.00
29 BEv(c),GC,Decapitation(c) . 125.00
30 Tentacled eyeball story . . . 175.00
31 . . . . 125.00
32 A Vampire Takes a Wife . . . 125.00
33 SMo 125.00
34 Transformation 125.00
35 . . . . 125.00
36 Pithecanthrope Giant 125.00
37 BEv,Poor Pierre 125.00
38 The Man Who Didn't Belong 100.00
39 . . . . 100.00
40 . . . . 100.00
41 . . . . 100.00
42 . . . . 100.00
43 . . . . 100.00
44 RC 110.00
45 BK 110.00
46 . . . . 100.00
47 BK 110.00
48 . . . . 100.00
49 . . . . 100.00
50 . . . . 100.00
51 . . . . 100.00
52 . . . . 100.00

53 . . . . 110.00
54 . . . . 110.00
55 . . . . 125.00
56 . . . . 100.00
57 . . . . 150.00
58 . . . . 90.00
59 . . . . 90.00
60 . . . . 95.00
61 . . . . 90.00
62 . . . . 95.00
63 August, 1957 . . . . 95.00

MARVEL CHILLERS
Oct., 1975
1 GK(c),I:Mordred the Mystic . . . 6.00
2 E:Mordred 4.00
3 HC/BWr(c),B:Tigra,The Were Woman 4.00
4 V:Kraven The Hunter 4.00
5 V:Rat Pack,A:Red Wolf 4.00
6 RB(c),JBy,V:Red Wolf 4.00
7 JK(c),GT,V:Super Skrull E:Tigra,Oct., 1976 . . . . 4.00
GN MGu(s),LSh,F:The Hulk 5.00
GN LHa(s) F:Wolverine 5.00

MARVEL CHRISTMAS SPECIAL
1 DC/AAd/KJ/SB/RLm,A:Ghost Rider X-Men,Spider-Man 2.25

MARVEL CLASSICS COMICS
1976–78
1 GK/DA(c),B:Reprints from Pendulum Illustrated Comics Dr.Jekyll & Mr. Hyde 15.00
2 GK(c),AN,Time Machine 10.00
3 GK/KJ(c) The Hunchback of Notre Dame 10.00
4 GK/DA(c),20,000 Leagues– Beneath the Sea by Verne . . 10.00
5 GK(c),RN,Black Beauty 10.00
6 GK(c),Gullivers Travels 10.00
7 GK(c),Tom Sawyer 10.00
8 GK(c),AN,Moby Dick 10.00
9 GK(c),NR,Dracula 10.00
10 GK(c),Red Badge of Courage 10.00
11 GK(c),Mysterious Island 10.00
12 GK/DA(c),AN,3 Musketeers . . 10.00
13 GK(c),Last of the Mohicans . . 10.00
14 GK(c),War of the Worlds 10.00
15 GK(c),Treasure Island 10.00
16 GK(c),Ivanhoe 9.00
17 JB/ECh(c),The Count of Monte Cristo 9.00
18 ECh(c),The Odsyssey 9.00
19 JB(c),Robinson Crusoe 9.00
20 Frankenstein 9.00
21 GK(c),Master of the World . . . 9.00
22 GK(c),Food of the Gods 9.00
23 Moonstone by Wilkie Collins . . 9.00
24 GK/RN(c),She 9.00
25 The Invisible Man by H.G.Wells 9.00
26 JB(c),The Illiad by Homer . . . 9.00
27 Kidnapped 9.00
28 MGo(1st art) The Pit and the Pendulum 12.00
29 The Prisoner of Zenda 9.00
30 The Arabian Nights 9.00
31 The First Men in the Moon . . . 9.00
32 GK(c),White Fang 9.00
33 The Prince and the Pauper . . . 9.00
34 AA,Robin Hood 9.00

MARVEL

Marvel Classics Comics #19
© Marvel Entertainment Group

35 FBe,Alice in Wonderland 9.00
36 A Christmas Carol 9.00

MARVEL COLLECTORS ITEM CLASSICS
Feb., 1965

1 SD,JK,reprint FF #2 . . . . 75.00
2 SD,JK,reprint FF #3 . . . . 35.00
3 SD,JK,reprint FF #4 . . . . 35.00
4 SD,JK,reprint FF #7 . . . . 35.00
5 SD,JK,reprint FF #8 . . . . 25.00
6 SD,JK,reprint FF #9 . . . . 25.00
7 SD,JK,reprint FF #13 . . . . . . 25.00
8 SD,JK,reprint FF #10 . . . . . . 25.00
9 SD,JK,reprint FF #14 . . . . . . 25.00
10 SD,JK,reprint FF #15 . . . . . . 25.00
11 SD,JK,reprint FF #16 . . . . . . 20.00
12 SD,JK,reprint FF #17 . . . . . . 20.00
13 SD,JK,reprint FF #18 . . . . . . 20.00
14 SD,JK,reprint FF #20 . . . . . . 20.00
15 SD,JK,reprint FF #21 . . . . . . 20.00
16 SD,JK,reprint FF #22 . . . . . . 20.00
17 SD,JK,reprint FF #23 . . . . . . 20.00
18 SD,JK,reprint FF #24 . . . . . . 20.00
19 SD,JK,reprint FF #27 . . . . . . 20.00
20 SD,JK,reprint FF #28 . . . . . . 20.00
21 SD,JK,reprint FF #29 . . . . . . 20.00
22 SD,JK,reprint FF #30 . . . . . . 20.00
Becomes:

MARVEL'S GREATEST COMICS

23 SD,JK,reprint FF#31 . . . . 4.00
24 SD,JK,reprint FF#32 . . . . 4.00
25 SD,JK,reprint FF#33 . . . . 4.00
26 SD,JK,reprint FF#34 . . . . 4.00
27 SD,JK,reprint FF#35 . . . . 4.00
28 SD,JK,reprint FF#36 . . . . 4.00
29 JK,reprint FF#37 . . . . 4.00
30 JK,reprint FF#38 . . . . 4.00
31 JK,reprint FF#40 . . . . 4.00
32 JK,reprint FF#42 . . . . 4.00
33 JK,reprint FF#44 . . . . 4.00
34 JK,reprint FF#47 . . . . 4.00
35 JK,reprint FF#48 . . . . 8.50
36 JK,reprint FF#49 . . . . 7.00
37 JK,reprint FF#50 . . . . 7.00

38 JK,reprint FF#51 . . . . 3.00
39 JK,reprint FF#52 . . . . 3.00
40 JK,reprint FF#53 . . . . 3.00
41 JK,reprint FF#54 . . . . 3.00
42 JK,reprint FF#55 . . . . 3.00
43 JK,reprint FF#56 . . . . 3.00
44 JK,reprint FF#61 . . . . 3.00
45 JK,reprint FF#62 . . . . 3.00
46 JK,reprint FF#63 . . . . 3.00
47 JK,reprint FF#64 . . . . 3.00
48 JK,reprint FF#65 . . . . 3.00
49 JK,reprint FF#66 . . . . 6.00
50 JK,reprint FF#67 . . . . 6.00
51 thru 75 JK,reprint FF . . . . . @1.75
76 thru 82 JK,reprint FF . . . . . @1.25
83 thru 95 Reprint FF . . . . . . @1.25
96 Reprint FF#, Jan., 1981 . . . . . 1.25

MARVEL COMICS
Oct.-Nov., 1939

1 FP(c),BEv,CBu,O:Sub-Mariner
I&B:The Angel,A:Human Torch,
Kazar,Jungle Terror,
B:The Masked Raider . 110,000.00
Becomes:

MARVEL MYSTERY COMICS

2 CSM(c),BEv,CBu,PGn,
B:American, Ace,Human
Torch,Sub-Mariner,Kazar 21,000.00
3 ASh(c),BEv,CBu,PGn,
E:American Ace 9,000.00
4 ASh(c),BEv,CBu,PGn,
I&B:Electro,The Ferret,
Mystery Detective 7,200.00
5 ASh(c),BEv,CBu,PGn,
Human Torch(c) 16,000.00
6 ASh(c),BEv,CBu,PGn,
Angel(c) 5,000.00
7 ASh(c),BEv,CBu,PGn,
Bondage(c) 5,000.00
8 ASh(c),BEv,CBu,PGn,Human
TorchV:Sub-Mariner 7,200.00
9 ASh(c),BEv,CBu,PGn,Human
Torch V:Sub-Mariner(c) . 18,000.00
10 ASh(c),BEv,CBu,PGn,B:Terry
Vance Boy Detective 5,000.00
11 ASh(c),BEv,CBu,PGn,
Human Torch V:Nazis(c) . . 2,800.00
12 ASh(c),BEv,CBu,
PGn,Angel(c) 3,000.00
13 ASh(c),BEv,CBu,PGn,S&K,
I&B:The Vision 3,500.00
14 ASh(c),BEv,CBu,PGn,S&K,
Sub-Mariner V:Nazis 1,800.00
15 ASh(c),BEv,CBu,PGn,S&K,
Sub-Mariner(c) 1,900.00
16 ASh(c),BEv,CBu,PGn,S&K,
HumanTorch/NaziAirbase . 1,800.00
17 ASh(c),BEv,CBu,PGn,S&K
Human Torch/Sub-Mariner 2,000.00
18 ASh(c),BEv,CBu,PGn,S&K,
Human Torch & Toro(c) . . 1,600.00
19 ASh(c),BEv,CBu,PGn,S&K,
O:Toro,E:Electro 1,800.00
20 ASh(c),BEv,CBu,PGn,S&K,
O:The Angel 1,800.00
21 ASh(c),BEv,CBu,PGn,S&K,
I&B:The Patriot 1,600.00
22 ASh(c),BEv,CBu,PGn,S&K,
Toro/Bomb(c) 1,400.00
23 ASh(c),BEv,CBu,PGn,S&K,
O:Vision,E:The Angel 1,400.00
24 ASh(c),BEv,CBu,S&K,

Human Torch(c) 1,400.00
25 BEv,CBu,S&K,ASh Nazi(c) 1,400.00
26 ASh(c),BEv,CBu,S&K,
Sub-Mariner(c) 1,300.00
27 ASh(c),BEv,CBu,
S&K,E:Kazar 1,300.00
28 ASh(c),BEv,CBu,S&K,Bondage
(c),B:Jimmy Jupiter 1,300.00
29 ASh(c),BEv,CBu,Bondage(c)1,300.00
30 BEv,CBu,Pearl Harbor(c) . 1,300.00
31 BEv,CBu,HUman Torch(c) 1,100.00
32 CBu,I:The Boboes 1,100.00
33 ASHc(c),CBu,Japanese(c) 1,100.00
34 ASh(c),CBu,V:Hitler 1,300.00
35 ASh(c),Beach Assault(c) . . 1,100.00
36 ASh(c),Nazi Invasion of
New York(c) 1,100.00
37 SSh(c),Nazi(c) 1,100.00
38 SSh(c),Battlefield(c) 1,100.00
39 ASh(c),Nazis/U.S(c) 1,100.00
40 ASh(c),Zeppelin(c) 1,100.00
41 ASh(c),Jap. Command(c) . 1,000.00
42 ASh(c),Japanese Sub(c) . . 1,000.00
43 ASh(c),Destroyed Bridge(c) 1,000.00
44 ASh(c),Nazi Super Plane(c) 1,000.00
45 ASh(c),Nazi(c) 1,000.00
46 ASh(c),Hitler Bondage(c) . 1,000.00
47 ASh(c),Ruhr Valley Dam(c) 1,000.00
48 ASh(c),E:Jimmy Jupiter,
Vision,Allied Invasion(c) . . 1,000.00
49 SSh(c),O:Miss America,
Bondage(c) 1,300.00
50 ASh(c),Bondage(c),Miss
Patriot 1,100.00
51 ASh(c),Nazi Torture(c) 900.00
52 ASh(c),Bondage(c) 900.00
53 ASh(c),Bondage(c) 900.00
54 ASh(c),Bondage(c) 900.00
55 ASh(c),Bondage(c) 900.00
56 ASh(c),Bondage(c) 900.00
57 ASh(c),Torture/Bondage(c) . 900.00
58 ASh(c),Torture(c) 900.00
59 ASh(c),Testing Room(c) . . . 900.00
60 ASh(c),Japanese Gun(c) . . 900.00
61 Torturer Chamber(c) 900.00
62 ASh(c),Violent(c) 900.00
63 ASh(c),NaziHighCommand(c) 900.00
64 ASh(c),Last Nazi(c) 900.00
65 ASh(c),Bondage(c) 900.00
66 ASh(c),Last Japanese(c) . . 900.00
67 ASh(c),Treasury raid(c) . . . 800.00
68 ASh(c),Torture Chamber(c) . 800.00
69 ASh(c),Torture Chamber(c) . 800.00
70 Cops & Robbers(c) 800.00
71 ASh(c),Egyptian(c) 800.00
72 Police(c) 800.00
73 Werewolf Headlines(c) 800.00
74 ASh(c),Robbery(c),E:The
Patriot 800.00
75 Tavern(c),B:Young Allies . . 800.00
76 ASh(c),Shoot-out(c),B:Miss
America 800.00
77 Human Torch/Sub-Mariner(c) 800.00
78 Safe Robbery(c) 800.00
79 Super Villians(c),E:The
Angel 800.00
80 I:Capt.America(in Marvel) 1,000.00
81 Mystery o/t Crimson Terror . 850.00
82 I:Sub-Mariner/Namora Team-up
O:Namora,A:Capt.America 1,800.00
83 The Photo Phantom,E:Young
Allies 750.00
84 BEv,B:The Blonde Phantom 1,000.00
85 BEv,A:Blonde Phantom,
E;Miss America 750.00

86 BEv,Blonde Phantom ID
Revealed,E:Bucky 850.00
87 BEv,I:Capt.America/Golden
Girl Team-up 900.00
88 BEv,E:Toro 800.00
89 BEv,I:Human Torch/Sun Girl
Team-up 850.00
90 BEv,Giant of the Mountains 850.00
91 BEv,I:Venus,E:Blonde
Phantom,Sub-Mariner 850.00
92 BEv,How the Human Torch was
Born,D:Professor Horton,I:The
Witness,A:Capt.America .. 2,000.00
92a Marvel #33(c)rare,reprints 10,000.00

Becomes:

MARVEL TALES
August, 1949

93 The Ghoul Strikes 1,000.00
94 BEv,The Haunted Love 700.00
95 The Living Death 500.00
96 MSy,The Monster Returns . 500.00
97 DRi,MSy,The Wooden Horror 600.00
98 BEv,BK,MSy,The Curse of
the Black Cat 500.00
99 DRi,The Secret of the Wax
Museum 500.00
100 The Eyes of Doom 500.00
101 The Man Who Died Twice . 500.00
102 BW,A Witch Among Us ... 650.00
103 RA,A Touch of Death 550.00
104 RH(c),BW,BEv,The Thing
in the Mirror 700.00
105 RH(c),GC,JSt,The Spider . 500.00
106 RH(c),BK,BEv,In The Dead of
the Night 400.00
107 GC,OW,BK,The Thing in the
Sewer 400.00
108 RH(c),BEv,JR,Horror in the
Moonlight 250.00
109 BEv(c),Sight for Sore Eyes 250.00
110 RH,SSh,A Coffin for Carlos 250.00
111 BEv,Horror Under the Earth 250.00
112 The House That Death Built 250.00
113 RH,Terror Tale 250.00
114 BEv(c),GT,JM,2 for Zombie 250.00
115 The Man With No Face ... 250.00
116 JSt 250.00
117 BEv(c),GK,Terror in the
North 250.00
118 RH,DBr,GC,A World
Goes Mad 250.00
119 RH,They Gave Him A Grave 250.00
120 GC,Graveyard(c) 250.00
121 GC,Graveyard(c) 250.00
122 JKu,Missing One Body ... 250.00
123 No Way Out 250.00
124 He Waits at the Tombstone 250.00
125 JF,Horror House 250.00
126 DW,It Came From Nowhere 200.00
127 BEv(c),GC,MD,Gone is the
Gargoyle 200.00
128 Emily,Flying Saucer(c) ... 200.00
129 You Can't Touch Bottom . 200.00
130 RH(c),JF,The Giant Killer . 200.00
131 GC,BEv,Five Fingers 200.00
132 .... 150.00
133 .... 150.00
134 BK,JKu,Flying Saucer(c) .. 150.00
135 thru 141 .... @125.00
142 .... 125.00
143 .... 125.00
144 .... 135.00
145 .... 125.00
146 .... 100.00
147 .... 125.00

148 .... 100.00
149 .... 100.00
150 .... 100.00
151 .... 100.00
152 .... 125.00
153 .... 135.00
154 .... 100.00
155 .... 100.00
156 .... 100.00
157 .... 125.00
158 .... 100.00
159 August, 1957 .... 125.00

Marvel Comics Presents #100
© *Marvel Entertainment Group*

MARVEL COMICS PRESENTS
Sept., 1988

1 WS(c),B:Wolverine(JB,KJ),Master
of Kung Fu(TS),Man-Thing(TGr,DC)
F:Silver Surfer(AM) 10.00
2 F:The Captain(AM) 5.00
3 JR2(c),F:The Thing(AM) 4.00
4 F:Thor(AM) 4.00
5 F:Daredevil(DT,MG) 4.00
6 F:Hulk 4.00
7 F:Submariner(SD) 4.00
8 CV(c),E:Master of Kung Fu,F:
Iron Man(JS) 4.00
9 F:Cloak,El Aquila 4.00
10 E:Wolverine,B:Colossus(RL,CR),
F:Machine Man(SD,DC) 4.00
11 F:Ant-Man(BL),Slag(RWi) .. 3.00
12 E:Man-Thing,F:Hercules(DH),
Namorita(FS) 3.00
13 B:Black Panther(GC,TP),F:
Shanna,Mr.Fantastic &
Invisible Woman 3.00
14 F:Nomad(CP),Speedball(SD) . 3.00
15 F:Marvel Girl(DT,MG),Red
Wolf(JS) 3.00
16 F:Kazar(JM),Longshot(AA) .. 3.00
17 E:Colossus,B:Cyclops(RLm),
F:Watcher(TS) 4.00
18 F:She-Hulk(JBy,BWi),Willie
Lumpkin(JSt) 3.00
19 RLd(c)B:Dr.Strange(MBg),
I:Damage Control(EC,AW) .. 3.00
20 E:Dr.Strange,F:Clea(RLm) .. 3.00

21 F:Thing,Paladin(RWi,DA) 3.00
22 F:Starfox(DC),Wolfsbane &
Mirage 3.00
23 F:Falcon(DC),Wheels(RWi) .. 3.00
24 E:Cyclops,Havok(RB,JRu),
F:Shamrock(DJ,DA) 3.00
25 F:Ursa Major,I:Nth Man ... 4.00
26 B&I:Coldblood(PG),F:Hulk . 2.50
27 F:American Eagle(RWi) 2.50
28 F:Triton(JS) 2.50
29 F:Quasar(PR) 2.50
30 F:Leir(TMo) 2.50
31 EL,E:Havok,B:Excalibur
(EL,TA) 4.00
32 TM(c),F:Sunfire(DH,DC) 3.00
33 F:Namor(JLe) 4.00
34 F:Captain America(JsP) 3.00
35 E:Coldblood,F:Her(EL,AG) ... 4.00
36 BSz(c),F:Hellcat(JBr) 4.00
37 E:Bl.Panther,F:Devil-Slayer ... 3.00
38 E:Excalibur,B:Wonderman(JS),
Wolverine(JB),F:Hulk(MR,DA) . 4.00
39 F:Hercules(BL),Spider-Man . 3.50
40 F:Hercules(BL),Overmind(DH) . 3.50
41 F:Daughters of the Dragon(DA),
Union Jack(KD) 3.50
42 F:Iron Man(MBa),Siryn(LSn) . 3.50
43 F:Iron Man(MBa),Siryn(LSn) . 3.50
44 F:Puma(BWi),Dr.Strange 3.50
45 E:Wonderman,F:Hulk(HT),
Shooting Star 3.50
46 RLd(c),B:Devil-Slayer,F:Namor,
Aquarian 3.50
47 JBy(c),E:Wolverine,F:Captain
America,Arabian Knight(DP) . 3.50
48 B:Wolverine&Spider-Man(EL),
F:Wasp,Storm&Dr.Doom 5.00
49 E:Devil-Slayer,F:Daredevil(RWi),
Gladiator(DH) 4.50
50 E:Wolverine&Spider-Man,B:Comet
Man(KJo),F:Captain Ultra(DJ),
Silver Surfer(JkS) 4.50
51 B:Wolverine(RLd),F:Iron Man
(MBr,DH),Le Peregrine 4.00
52 F:Rick Jones,Hulk(RWi,TMo) . 4.00
53 E:Wolverine,Comet Man,F:
Silver Sable&Black Widow
(RLd,BWi),B:Stingray 4.00
54 B:Wolverine&Hulk(DR),
Werewolf,F:Shroud(SD,BWi) .. 6.00
55 F:Collective Man(GLa) 6.00
56 E:Stingray,F:Speedball(SD) .. 6.00
57 DK(c),B:Submariner(MC,MFm),
Black Cat(JRu) 6.00
58 F:Iron Man(SD) 6.00
59 E:Submariner,Werewolf,
F:Punisher 6.00
60 B:Poison,Scarlet Witch,
F:Captain America(TL) 6.00
61 E:Wolverine&Hulk,
F:Dr.Strange 6.00
62 F:Wolverine(PR),Deathlok(JG) 6.00
63 F:Wolverine(PR),E:Scarlet
Witch,Thor(DH) 4.00
64 B:Wolverine&Ghost Rider(MT),
Fantastic Four(TMo),F:Blade .. 4.00
65 F:Starfox(ECh) 3.50
66 F:Volstagg 3.50
67 E:Poison,F:Spider-Man(MG) .. 3.50
68 B:Shanna(PG),E:Fantastic Four
F:Lockjaw(JA,AM) 3.50
69 B:Daredevil(DT),F:Silver Surfer 3.50
70 F:BlackWidow&Darkstar(DH) . 3.50
71 E:Wolverine&Ghost Rider,F:
Warlock(New Mutants)(SMc) .. 3.50

MARVEL

72 B:Weapon X(BWS),E:Daredevil,
  F:Red Wolf(JS) 7.00
73 F:Black Knight(DC),
  Namor(JM) 5.00
74 F:Constrictor(SMc),Iceman &
  Human Torch(JSon,DA) 5.00
75 F:Meggan & Shadowcat,
  Dr.Doom(DC) 5.00
76 F:Death's Head(BHi,MFm),
  A:Woodgod(DC) 5.00
77 E:Shanna,B:Sgt.Fury&Dracula
  (TL,JRu),F:Namor 4.50
78 F:Iron Man(KSy),Hulk&Selene . 4.50
79 E:Sgt.Fury&Dracula,F:Dr.Strange,
  Sunspot(JBy) 4.50
80 F:Daughters of the Dragon,Mister
  Fantastic(DJ),Captain America
  (SD,TA) 4.50
81 F:Captain America(SD,TA),
  Daredevil(MR,AW),Ant-Man . . 4.00
82 B:Firestar(DT),F:Iron Man(SL),
  Power Man 4.00
83 F:Hawkeye,Hum.Torch(SD,EL) 4.00
84 F:Weapon X 4.00
85 B:Wolverine(SK),Beast(RLd,JaL-
  1st Work),F:Speedball(RWi),
  I:Cyber 7.00
86 F:PaladinE:RLd on Beast 5.00
87 F:Firestar,F:Shroud(RWi) 5.00
88 F:Solo,Volcana(BWi) 5.00
89 F:Spitfire(JSn),Mojo(JMa) . . . 5.00
90 B:Ghost Rider & Cable,F:
  Nightmare 4.50
91 F:Impossible Man 3.50
92 E:Wolverine,Beast,
  F:Northstar(JMa) 3.50
93 SK(c),B:Wolverine,Nova,
  F:Daredevil 3.00
94 F:Gabriel 3.00
95 SK(c),E:Wolverine,F:Hulk . . . 3.00
96 B:Wolverine(TT),E:Nova,
  F:Speedball 3.00
97 F:Chameleon,Two-Gun Kid,
  E:Ghost Rider/Cable 3.00
98 E:Wolverine,F:Ghost Rider,
  Werewolf by Night 2.50
99 F:Wolverine,Ghost Rider,
  Mary Jane,Captain America. . . 2.50
100 SK,F:Ghost Rider,Wolverine,
  Dr.Doom,Nightmare 3.00
101 SK(c),B:Ghost Rider&Doctor
  Strange,Young Gods,Wolverine
  &Nightcrawler,F:Bar With
  No Name 2.00
102 RL,GC,AW,F:Speedball 2.00
103 RL,GC,AW,F:Puck 2.00
104 RL,GC,AW,F:Lockheed 2.00
105 RL,GC,AW,F:Nightmare 2.00
106 RL,GC,AW,F:Gabriel,E:Ghost
  Rider&Dr.Strange 2.00
107 GC,AW,TS,B:Ghost Rider&
  Werewolf 2.00
108 GC,AW,TS,SMc,E:Wolverine&
  Nightcrawler,B:Thanos 2.00
109 SLi,TS,SMc,B:Wolverine&
  Typhoid Mary,E:Young Gods . 2.00
110 SLi,SMc,F:Nightcrawler 2.00
111 SK(c),SLi,RWi,F:Dr.Strange,
  E:Thanos 2.00
112 SK(c),SLi,F:Pip,Wonder Man,
  E:Ghost Rider&Werewolf 2.00
113 SK(c),SLi,B:Giant Man,
  Ghost Rider&Iron Fist 1.75
114 SK(c),SLi,F:Arabian Knight . . 1.75
115 SK(c),SLi,F:Cloak&Dagger . . 1.75

116 SK(c),SLi,E:Wolverine &
  Typhoid Mary 1.75
117 SK,PR,B:Wolverine&Venom,
  I:Ravage 2099 . . . . 4.00
118 SK,PB,RWi,E:Giant Man,
  I:Doom 2099 . . . . 3.00
119 SK,GC,B:Constrictor,E:Ghost
  Rider&Iron Fist,F:Wonder Man 3.00
120 SK,GC,E:Constrictor,B:Ghost
  Rider/Cloak & Dagger,
  F:Spider-Man 2.50
121 SK,GC,F:Mirage,Andromeda . 2.50
122 SK(c),GK,E:Wolverine&Venom,
  Ghost Rider&Cloak&Dagger,F:
  Speedball&Rage,Two-Gun Kid 2.50
123 SK(c),DJ,SLi,B:Wolverine&Lynx,
  Ghost Rider&Typhoid Mary,
  She-Hulk,F:Master Man 1.75
124 SK(c),DJ,MBa,SLi,F:Solo . . . 1.75
125 SLi,SMc,DJ,B:Iron Fist 1.75
126 SLi,DJ,E:She-Hulk 1.75
127 SLi,DJ,DP,F:Speedball 1.75
128 SLi,DJ,RWi,F:American Eagle 1.75
129 SLi,DJ,F:Ant Man 1.75

Marvel Comics Presents #163
© Marvel Entertainment Group

130 DJ.SLi,RWi,E:Wolverine&Lynx,
  Ghost Rider&Typhoid Mary,Iron
  Fist,F:American Eagle 1.75
131 MFm,B:Wolverine,Ghost Rider&
  Cage,Iron Fist&Sabretooth,
  F:Shadowcat 1.75
132 KM(c),F:Iron Man 1.75
133 F:Cloak & Dagger 1.75
134 SLi,F:Vance Astro 1.75
135 SLi,F:Daredevil 1.75
136 B:Gh.Rider&Masters of Silence,
  F:Iron Fist,Daredevil 1.75
137 F:Ant Man 1.75
138 B:Wolverine,Spellbound 1.75
139 F:Foreigner 1.75
140 F:Captain Universe 1.75
141 BCe(s),F:Iron Fist 1.75
142 E:Gh.Rider&Masters of Silence,
  F:Mr.Fantastic 1.75
143 Siege of Darkness,pt.#3,
  B:Werewolf,Scarlet Witch,
  E:Spellbound 2.00
144 Siege of Darkness,pt.#6,
  B:Morbius 2.00

145 Siege of Darkness,pt.#11 . . . 2.00
146 Siege of Darkness,pt.#14 . . . 1.75
147 B:Vengeance,F:Falcon,Masters of
  Silence,American Eagle 1.75
148 E:Vengeance,F:Capt.Universe,
  Black Panther 1.75
149 F:Daughter o/t Dragon,Namor,
  Vengeance,Starjammers 1.75
150 ANo(s),SLi,F:Typhoid Mary,DD,
  Vengeance,Wolverine 1.75
151 ANo(s),F:Typhoid Mary,DD,
  Vengeance 1.75
152 CDi(s),PR,B:Vengeance,Wolverine,
  War Machine,Moon Knight . . . 1.75
153 CDi(s),A:Vengeance,Wolverine,
  War Machine,Moon Knight . . . 1.75
154 CDi(s),E:Vengeance,Wolverine,
  War Machine,Moon Knight . . . 1.75
155 CDi(s),B:Vengeance,Wolverine,
  War Machine,Kymaera 1.75
156 B:Shang Chi,F:Destroyer . . . 1.50
157 F:Nick Fury 1.50
158 AD,I:Clan Destine,E:Kymaera,
  Shang Chi,Vengeance 1.75
159 B:Hawkeye, New Warriors,
  F:Fun,E:Vengeance 1.75
160 B:Vengeance,Mace 2.00
161 E:Hawkeye 1.75
162 B:Tigra,E:Mace 1.75
163 E:New Warriors 1.75
164 Tigra, Vengeance 1.75
165 Tigra, Vengeance 1.75
166 Turbo, Vengeance 1.75
167 Turbo, Vengeance 1.75
168 Thing, Vengeance 1.75
169 Mandarin, Vengeance 1.75
170 Force, Vengeance 1.75
171 Nick Fury 1.75
172 Lunatik 1.75
173 . . . . 1.75
174 . . . . 1.75
175 . . . . 1.75
TPB Ghost Rider & Cable,rep
  #90-97 . . . . 3.95
TPB Save the Tyger,rep.Wolverine
  story from #1-10 . . . . 3.95

MARVEL COMICS
SUPER SPECIAL
[Magazine, 1977]

1 JB,WS,Kiss,Features &Photos 65.00
2 JB,Conan(1978) 6.00
3 WS,Close Encounters 5.00
4 GP,KJ,Beatles story 25.00
Becomes:

MARVEL SUPER SPECIAL

5 Kiss 1978 . . . . 35.00
6 GC,Jaws II 3.00
7 Does Not Exist
8 Battlestar Galactica(Tabloid) . . 3.00
9 Conan 4.00
10 GC,Starlord 3.00
11 JB,RN,Weirdworld, ... 3.00
12 JB,Weirdworld, ... 3.00
13 JB,Weirdworld, ... 3.00
14 GC,Meteor,adapt 3.00
15 Star Trek 6.00
15a Star Trek 9.00
16 AW,B:Movie Adapts,Empire
  Strikes Back 7.00
17 Xanadu 2.00
18 HC(c),JB,Raiders of the Lost
  Ark 2.00
19 HC,For Your Eyes Only 5.00

20 Dragonslayer	2.50
21 JB,Conan	1.00
22 JSo(c),AW,Bladerunner	2.00
23 Annie	2.00
24 Dark Crystal	2.00
25 Rock and Rule	2.00
26 Octopussy	2.50
27 AW,Return of the Jedi	6.00
28 PH(c),Krull	2.00
29 DSp,Tarzan of the Apes	2.00
30 Indiana Jones and the Temple of Doom	2.50
31 The Last Star Fighter	2.00
32 Muppets Take Manhattan	2.00
33 Buckaroo Banzai	2.00
34 GM,Sheena	2.00
35 JB,Conan The Destroyer	2.00
36 Dune	2.00
37 2010	2.00
38 Red Sonja	2.00
39 Santa Claus	2.00
40 JB,Labrynth	2.00
41 Howard the Duck,Nov.,1986	2.00

MARVEL DOUBLE FEATURE
Dec., 1973

1 JK,GC,B:Tales of Suspense Reprints,Capt.America, Iron-Man	4.00
2 JK,GC ,A:Nick Fury	2.50
3 JK,GC	2.50
4 JK,GC,Cosmic Cube	2.50
5 JK,GC,V:Red Skull	2.50
6 JK,GC,V:Adaptoid	2.50
7 JK,GC,V:Tumbler	2.50
8 JK,GC,V:Super Adaptoid	2.50
9 GC,V:Batroc	2.50
10 GC	2.50
11 GC,Capt.America Wanted	2.50
12 GC,V:Powerman,Swordsman	2.50
13 GC,A:Bucky	2.50
14 GC,V:Red Skull	2.50
15 GK,GC,V:Red Skull	2.50
16 GC,V:Assassin	2.50
17 JK,GC,V:Aim,Iron Man & Sub-Mariner #1	4.00
18 JK,GC,V:Modok,Iron Man #1	5.00
19 JK,GC,E:Capt.America	5.00
20 JK(c)	2.50
21 Capt.America,Black Panther March, 1977	2.50

MARVEL FANFARE
March, 1972

1 MG,TA,PS,F:Spider-Man, Daredevil,Angel	7.00
2 MG,SM,FF,TVe,F:SpM,Ka-Zar	5.00
3 DC,F:X-Men	5.00
4 PS,TA,MG,F:X-Men,Deathlok	5.00
5 MR,F:Dr.Strange	4.00
6 F:Spider-Man,Scarlet Witch	4.50
7 F:Hulk/Daredevil	3.00
8 CI,TA,GK,F:Dr.Strange	3.00
9 GM,F:Man Thing	3.00
10 GP,B:Black Widow	3.50
11 GP,D:M.Corcoran	3.50
12 GP,V:Snapdragon	3.50
13 GP,E:B.Widow,V:Snapdragon	3.50
14 F:Fantastic Four,Vision	2.75
15 BWS,F:Thing,Human Torch	3.00
16 DC,JSt,F:Skywolf	2.50
17 DC,JSt,F:Skywolf	2.50
18 FM,JRu,F:Captain America	3.00

Marvel Fanfare #33
© Marvel Entertainment Group

19 RL,F:Cloak and Dagger	2.50
20 JSn,F:Thing&Dr.Strange	3.00
21 JSn,F:Thing And Hulk	3.00
22 KSy,F:Iron Man	2.50
23 KSy,F:Iron Man	2.50
24 F:Weird World	3.00
25 F:Weird World	2.50
26 F:Weird World	2.50
27 F:Daredevil	2.50
28 KSy,F:Alpha Flight	2.50
29 JBy,F:Hulk	3.00
30 BA,AW,F:Moon Knight	2.50
31 KGa,F:Capt.America, Yellow Claw	2.50
32 KGa,PS,F:Capt.America, Yellow Claw	2.50
33 JBr,F:X-Men	5.00
34 CV,F:Warriors Three	2.50
35 CV,F:Warriors Three	2.50
36 CV,F:Warriors Three	2.50
37 CV,F:Warriors Three	2.50
38 F:Captain America	2.50
39 JSon,F:Hawkeye,Moon Knight	2.50
40 DM,F:Angel,Storm,Mystique	3.00
41 DGb,F:Dr.Strange	2.50
42 F:Spider-Man	3.00
43 F:Sub-Mariner,Human Torch	2.50
44 KSy,F:Iron Man vs.Dr.Doom	2.50
45 All Pin-up Issue,WS,AAd,MZ, JOy,BSz,KJ,HC,PS,JBy	3.00
46 F:Fantastic Four	2.50
47 MG,F:Spider-Man,Hulk	3.00
48 KGa,F:She-Hulk	2.50
49 F:Dr.Strange	2.50
50 JSon,JRu,F:Angel	3.00
51 JB,JA,GC,AW,F:Silver Surfer	4.00
52 F:Fantastic Four	2.50
53 GC,AW,F:Bl.Knight,Dr.Strange	2.50
54 F:Black Knight,Wolverine	3.50
55 F:Powerpack,Wolverine	3.50
56 CI,DH,F:Shanna t/She-Devil	2.50
57 BBl,AM,F:Shanna,Cap.Marvel	2.50
58 BBl,F:Shanna,Vision/Sc.Witch	2.50
59 BBl,F:Shanna,Hellcat	2.50
60 PS,F:Daredevil,Capt.Marvel	2.50

MARVEL FANFARE
Second Series 1996

1 Captain America, Falcon	1.00
2 New Fantastic Four	1.00
3 BbB,F:Spider-Man, Ghost Rider,	1.00
4 F:Longshot	1.00
5 F:Longshot	1.00
6 F:Power Man & Iron Fist V. Sabretooth	1.00

MARVEL FEATURE
[1st Regular Series]
Dec., 1971

1 RA,BE,NA,I&O:Defenders & Omegatron	85.00
2 BEv,F:The Defenders	50.00
3 BEv,F:The Defenders	45.00
4 F:Ant-Man	15.00
5 F:Ant-Man	11.00
6 F:Ant-Man	10.00
7 CR,F:Ant-Man	10.00
8 JSc,CR,F:Ant-Man,O:Wasp	10.00
9 CR,F:Ant-Man	10.00
10 CR,F:Ant-Man	10.00
11 JSn,JSt,F:Thing & Hulk	15.00
12 JSn,JSt,F:Thing,Iron Man, Thanos,Blood Brothers	12.00

Marvel Feature #7
© Marvel Entertainment Group

[2nd Regular Series]
(All issues feature Red Sonja)

1 DG,The Temple of Abomination	5.00
2 FT,Blood of the Hunter	2.00
3 FT,Balek Lives	2.00
4 FT,Eyes of the Gorgon	2.00
5 FT,The Bear God Walks	2.00
6 FT,C:Conan,Belit	2.00
7 FT,V:Conan,A:Belit,Conan#68	2.00

MARVEL FRONTIER COMICS SPECIAL

1 All Frontier Characters	3.25
1994	2.95

MARVEL FUMETTI BOOK
April, 1984

1 NA(c),Stan Lee, All photos	1.25

MARVEL GRAPHIC NOVEL
1982
1 JSn,D:Captain Marvel,A:Most
Marvel Characters 30.00
1a 2nd printing 10.00
1b 3rd-5th printing 7.00
2 F:Elric,Dreaming City 12.00
2a 2nd printing 7.00
3 JSn,F:Dreadstar 12.00
3a 2nd-3rd printing 7.00
4 BMc,I:New Mutants,Cannonball
Sunspot,Psyche,Wolfsbane .. 22.00
4a 2nd printing 10.00
4b 3rd-4th printing 8.00
5 BA,F:X-Men 17.00
5a 2nd printing 9.00
5b 3rd-5th printing 7.00
6 WS,F:Starslammers 10.00
6a 2nd printing 7.00
7 CR,F:Killraven 7.00
8 RWi,AG,F:Super Boxers 8.00
8a 2nd printing 7.00
9 DC,F:Futurians 12.00
9a 2nd printing 7.00
10 RV,F:Heartburst 8.00
10a 2nd printing 6.00
11 VM,F:Void Indigo 12.00
12 F:Dazzler the Movie 10.00
12a 2nd printing 6.00
13 MK,F:Starstruck 7.00
14 JG,F:SwordsofSwashbucklers . 6.00
15 CV,F:Raven Banner 6.00
16 GLa,F:Alladin Effect 6.00
17 MS,F:Living Monolith 7.00
18 JBy,F:She-Hulk 9.00
18 later printings 8.00
19 F:Conan 6.00
20 F:Greenberg the Vampire ... 6.00
21 JBo,F:Marada the She-wolf .. 6.00
22 BWr,Hooky,F:Spider-Man .. 12.00
23 DGr,F:Dr.Strange 6.00
24 FM,BSz,F:Daredevil 10.00
25 F:Dracula 8.00
26 FC,TA,F:Alien Legion 6.00
27 BH,F:Avengers 6.00
28 JSe,F:Conan the Reaver 6.50
29 BWr,F:Thing & Hulk 8.00
30 F:A Sailor's Story 6.00
31 F:Wolf Pack 6.00
32 SA,F:Death of Groo 15.00
33 F:Thor 6.00
34 AW,F:Cloak & Dagger 6.00
35 MK/RH,F:The Shadow 12.00
36 F:Willow movie adaption 7.00
37 BL,F:Hercules 6.00
38 JB,F:Silver Surfer 15.00
39 F:Iron Man,Crash 14.50
40 JZ,F:The Punisher 12.00
41 F:Roger Rabbit 7.00
42 F:Conan of the Isles 9.00
43 EC,F:Ax 6.00
44 BJ,F:Arena 6.00
45 JRy,F:Dr.Who 9.00
46 TD,F:Kull 7.00
47 GM,F:Dreamwalker 7.00
48 F:Sailor's Storm II 7.00
49 MBd,F:Dr.Strange&Dr.Doom . 16.00
50 F:Spider-Man,Parallel Lives .. 9.00
51 F:Punisher,Intruder 10.00
52 DSp,F:Roger Rabbit 9.00
53 PG,F:Conan 6.95
54 HC,F:Wolverine & Nick Fury . 17.00

MARVEL HEROES
1 StL,FaN,Mega-Jam,48pg 2.95

MARVEL: HEROES AND LEGENDS 1997
Aug., 1997
one-shot, Stan Lee, JR(c) 6.00

MARVEL HOLIDAY SPECIAL
1 StG(s),PDd(s),SLo(s),RLm,PB, 3.25
1-shot MWa,KK 2.95

MARVEL KNIGHTS TOUR BOOK
Aug. 1998
One-shot, cardstock cover 3.00

MARVEL MASTERPIECES COLLECTION
1993
1 Joe Jusko Masterpiece Cards . 3.25
2 F:Wolverine,Thanos,Apocalypse 3.00
3 F:Gambit,Venom,Hulk 3.00
4 F:Wolverine Vs. Sabretooth ... 3.00

MARVEL MASTERPIECES II COLLECTION
1994
1 thru 3 w/cards .... @3.00

MARVEL MILESTONE EDITIONS 1991–95
SEE: ORIGINAL TITLES

MARVEL MINI-BOOKS
1966
(black & white)
1 F:Capt.America,Spider-Man,Hulk
Thor,Sgt.Fury 12.00
2 F:Capt.America,Spider-Man,Hulk
Thor,Sgt.Fury 12.00
3 F:Capt.America,Spider-Man,Hulk
Thor,Sgt.Fury 12.00
4 thru 6 F:Capt.America,Spider-Man,
Hulk,Thor,Sgt.Fury ...... @12.00

MARVEL MOVIE PREMIERE
B&W Magazine, 1975
1 Land That Time Forgot,
Burroughs adapt 5.00

MARVEL MOVIE SHOWCASE FEATURING STAR WARS
Nov., 1982
1 Rep,Stars Wars #1-6 .... 4.00
2 Dec., 1982 .... 4.00

MARVEL MOVIE SPOTLIGHT FEATURING RAIDERS OF THE LOST ARK
Nov., 1982
1 Rep,Raiders of Lost Ark#1-3 .. 3.00

MARVEL MYSTERY COMICS
See: MARVEL COMICS

MARVEL NO-PRIZE BOOK
Jan., 1983
1 MGo(c),Stan Lee as
Dr Doom(c) 3.00

MARVEL: PORTRAITS OF A UNIVERSE
1 Fully painted moments 3.00
2 Fully painted moments 3.00
3 F:Death of Elektra 3.00
4 final issue 3.00

Marvel Premiere #61
© Marvel Entertainment Group

MARVEL PREMIERE
April, 1972
1 GK,O:Warlock,Receives Soul Gem,
Creation of Counter Earth ... 40.00
2 GK,JK,F:Warlock 25.00
3 BWS,F:Dr.Strange 28.00
4 FB,BWS,F:Dr.Strange 14.00
5 MP,CR,F:Dr.Strange,I:Sligguth 10.00
6 MP,FB,F:Dr.Strange 10.00
7 MP,CR,F:Dr.Strange,I:Dagoth 10.00
8 JSn,F:Dr.Strange 10.00
9 NA,F:Dr.Strange 10.00
10 FB,F:Dr.Strange,
D:Ancient One 10.00
11 NA,FB,F:Dr.Strange,I:Shuma 10.00
12 NA,FB,F:Dr.Strange 10.00
13 NA,FB,F:Dr.Strange 10.00
14 NA,FB,F:Dr.Strange 10.00
15 GK,DG,I&O:Iron Fist,pt.1 .. 50.00
16 DG,O:Iron Fist,pt.2,V:Scythe . 25.00
17 DG,'Citadel on the
Edge of Vengeance' 15.00
18 DG,V:Triple Irons 15.00
19 DG,A:Ninja 13.00
20 I:Misty Knight 13.00
21 V:Living Goddess 13.00
22 V:Ninja 13.00
23 PB,V:Warhawk 13.00
24 PB,V:Monstroid 13.00
25 1st JBy,AMc,E:Iron Fist 18.00
26 JK,GT,F:Hercules 7.00
27 F:Satana 7.00
28 F:Legion Of Monsters:A:Ghost
Rider,Morbius,Werewolf. 15.00
29 JK,I:Liberty Legion,

O:Red Raven 5.00
30 JK,F:Liberty Legion 5.00
31 JK,I:Woodgod 5.00
32 HC,F:Monark 5.00
33 HC,F:Solomon Kane 5.00
34 HC,F:Solomon Kane 5.00
35 I&O:Silver Age 3-D Man 5.00
36 F:3-D Man 5.00
37 F:3-D Man 5.00
38 AN,MP,I:Weird World 5.00
39 AM,I:Torpedo(1st solo) 5.00
40 AM,F:Torpedo 5.00
41 TS,F:Seeker 3000 . . . . 5.00
42 F:Tigra 5.00
43 F:Paladin 5.00
44 KG,F:Jack of Hearts(1stSolo) . 5.00
45 GP,F:Manwolf 5.00
46 GP,F:Manwolf 5.00
47 JBy,I:2nd Antman(Scott Lang) . 5.00
48 JBy,F:2nd Antman 4.00
49 F:The Falcon 4.00
50 TS,TA,F:Alice Cooper 7.00
51 JBi,F:Black Panther,V:Klan . . . 3.00
52 JBi,F:B.Panther,V:Klan 3.00
53 JBi,F:B.Panther,V:Klan 3.00
54 GD,TD,I:Hammer 3.00
55 JSt,F:Wonderman(1st solo) . . . 4.00
56 HC,TA,F:Dominic Fortune 2.50
57 WS(c),I:Dr.Who 3.50
58 TA(c),FM,F:Dr.Who 3.00
59 F:Dr.Who 3.00
60 WS(c),DGb,F:Dr.Who 3.00
61 TS,F:Starlord 3.00

MARVEL PRESENTS
Oct., 1975

1 BMc,F:Bloodstone 10.00
2 BMc,O:Bloodstone 9.00
3 AM,B:Guardians/Galaxy 16.00
4 AM,I:Nikki 12.00
5 AM,'Planet o/t Absurd' 12.00
6 AM,V:Karanada 12.00
7 AM,'Embrace the Void' 12.00
8 AM,JB,JSt,reprint.S.Surfer#2 . 15.00
9 AM,O:Starhawk 12.00

10 AM,O:Starhawk 12.00
11 AM,D:Starhawk's Children . . 12.00
12 AM,E:Guardians o/t Galaxy . 12.00

MARVEL PREVIEW
Feb., 1975
(black & white magazine)

1 NA,AN,Man Gods From
  Beyond the Stars 5.00
2 GM(c),O:Punisher 80.00
3 GM(c),Blade the Vampire Slayer 8.00
4 GM(c),I&O:Starlord 9.00
5 Sherlock Holmes 9.00
6 Sherlock Holmes 9.00
7 KG,Satana,A:Sword in the Star 9.00
8 GM,MP,Legion of Monsters . 11.00
9 Man-God,O:Starhawk 6.00
10 JSn,Thor the Mighty 6.00
11 JBy,I:Starlord 6.00
12 MK,Haunt of Horror 3.50
13 JSn(c),Starhawk 5.00
14 JSn(c),Starhawk 5.00
15 MK(c),Starhawk 3.50
16 GC,Detectives 3.00
17 GK,Black Mask 3.00
18 GC,Starlord 3.00
19 Kull 3.00
20 HC,NA,GP,Bizarre Adventures 4.00
21 SD,Moonlight 4.00
22 JB,King Arthur 3.00
23 JB,GC,FM,Bizarre Adventures . 5.00
24 Debut Paradox 3.00

Becomes:

BIZARRE ADVENTURES

25 MG,TA,MR,Lethal Ladies 3.00
26 JB(c),King Kull 3.00
27 JB,AA,GP,Phoenix,A:Ice-Man . 6.00
28 MG,TA,FM,NA,The Unlikely
  Heroes,Elektra 4.00
29 JB,WS,Horror 3.50
30 JB,Tomorrow 3.00
31 JBy,After the Violence Stops . . 3.50
32 Gods 3.00
33 Ph(c),Horror 3.00
34 PS,Christmas Spec,Son of Santa
  Howard the Duck,Feb.,1983 . . 3.50

MARVEL PREVIEW
1993
Preview of 1993 . . . . 3.95

MARVEL SAGA
Dec., 1985

1 JBy,Fantastic Four,Wolv. 2.50
2 Hulk 1.50
3 Spider-Man 2.50
4 X-Men 2.50
5 Thor 1.50
6 Fantastic Four 1.50
7 Avengers 1.50
8 X-Men 2.00
9 Angel 1.50
10 X-Men 2.00
11 X-Men 2.00
12 O:Capt. America 1.50
13 O:Daredevil,Elektra 1.50
14 O:Green Goblin 2.00
15 Avengers 1.50
16 Daredevil,X-Men 2.00
17 Kazar,X-Men 2.00
18 Hawkeye-Quicksilver 1.50
19 SpM,Thor,Daredevil 2.00
20 Daredevil,Giant Man 1.50

21 FF,V:Frightful Four 1.50
22 Wedding 1.50
23 . . . . 1.50
24 . . . . 1.50
25 O:Silver Surfer,Dec.,1987 . . . . 2.25

MARVEL SPECTACULAR
August, 1973

1 JK,rep Thor #128 . . . . 8.00
2 JK,rep Thor #129 . . . . 5.00
3 JK,rep Thor #130 . . . . 5.00
4 JK,rep Thor #133 . . . . 5.00
5 JK,rep Thor #134 . . . . 5.00
6 JK,rep Thor #135 . . . . 5.00
7 JK,rep Thor #136 . . . . 5.00
8 JK,rep Thor #137 . . . . 5.00
9 JK,rep Thor #138 . . . . 5.00
10 JK,rep Thor #139 . . . . 5.00
11 JK,rep Thor #140 . . . . 4.00
12 JK,rep Thor #141 . . . . 4.00
13 JK,rep Thor #142 . . . . 4.00
14 JK,rep Thor #143 . . . . 4.00
15 JK,rep Thor #144 . . . . 4.00
16 JK,rep Thor #145 . . . . 4.00
17 JK,rep Thor #146 . . . . 4.00
18 JK,rep Thor #147 . . . . 4.00
19 JK,rep Thor#148,Nov.,1975 . . 4.00

MARVEL SPOTLIGHT
[1st Regular Series] Nov., 1971

1 NA(c)WW,F:Red Wolf 25.00
2 MP,BEv,NA,I&O:Werewolf . . . 75.00
3 MP,F:Werewolf 30.00
4 SD,MP,F:Werewolf 30.00
5 SD,MP,I&O:Ghost Rider 75.00
6 MP,TS,F:Ghost Rider 35.00
7 MP,TS,F:Ghost Rider 35.00
8 JM,MB,F:Ghost Rider 35.00
9 TA,F:Ghost Rider 25.00
10 SD,JM,F:Ghost Rider 25.00
11 SD,F:Ghost Rider 25.00
12 SD,2nd A:Son of Satan 25.00
13 F:Son of Satan 10.00
14 JM,F:Son of Satan,I:Ikthalon . 10.00
15 JM, F:Son of Satan,

I:Baphomet 7.00	18 JB(c),reprint,Avengers #57 . . . 4.00
16 JM,F:Son of Satan 7.00	19 JB(c),reprint,Avengers #58 . . . 4.00
17 JM,F:Son of Satan 7.00	20 JB(c),reprint,Avengers #59 . . . 4.00
18 F:Son of Satan, I:Allatou 7.00	21 Reprint,Avengers #60 . . . . 3.00
19 F:Son of Satan 7.00	22 JB(c),reprint,Avengers #61 . . . 3.00
20 F:Son of Satan 7.00	23 Reprint,Avengers #63 . . . . 3.00
21 F:Son of Satan 7.00	24 Reprint,Avengers #64 . . . . 3.00
22 F:Son of Satan, Ghost Rider . . 8.00	25 Reprint,Avengers #65 . . . . 3.00
23 F:Son of Satan 7.00	26 Reprint,Avengers #66 . . . . 3.00
24 JM,F:Son of Satan 7.00	27 BWS,Reprint,Avengers #67 . . . 3.00
25 GT,F:Sinbad 4.00	28 BWS,Reprint,Avengers #68 . . . 3.00
26 F:The Scarecrow 4.00	29 Reprint,Avengers #69 . . . . 3.00
27 F:The Sub-Mariner 4.00	30 Reprint,Avengers #70 . . . . 3.00
28 F:Moon Knight (1st full solo) . 11.00	31 Reprint,Avengers #71 . . . . 3.00
29 F:Moon Knight 10.00	32 Reprint,Avengers #72 . . . . 3.00
30 JSt,JB,F:Warriors Three 6.00	33 Reprint,Avengers #73 . . . . 3.00
31 HC,JSn,F:Nick Fury 6.00	34 Reprint,Avengers #74 . . . . 3.00
32 I:Spiderwoman, Jessica Drew . 9.00	35 JB(c),Reprint,Avengers #75 . . . 3.00
33 F:Deathlok, I:Devilslayer 6.00	36 JB(c),Reprint,Avengers #75 . . . 3.00
	37 JB(c),Reprint,Avengers #76 . . . 3.00

MARVEL SPOTLIGHT
[2nd Regualar Series] July, 1979

1 PB,F:Captain Marvel 2.50	
1a No'1' on Cover 4.00	
2 FM(c),F:Captain Marvel,A:Eon . 2.00	
3 PB,F:Captain Marvel 2.00	
4 PB,F:Captain Marvel 2.00	
5 FM(c),SD,F:Dragon Lord 2.00	
6 F:Star Lord 2.00	
7 FM(c),F:StarLord 2.00	
8 FM,F:Captain Marvel 2.50	
9 FM(c),SD,F:Captain Universe . 2.00	
10 SD,F:Captain Universe 2.00	
11 SD,F:Captain Universe 2.00	

MARVEL SPOTLIGHT ON CAPTAIN AMERICA
1 thru 4, Captain America rep. @2.95

MARVEL SPOTLIGHT ON DR. STRANGE
1 thru 4, Dr. Strange, rep. . . @2.95

MARVEL SPOTLIGHT ON SILVER SURFER
1 thru 4, Silver Surfer, rep. . . . @2.95

MARVEL SUPER ACTION
Jan., 1976

1-shot TD,GE,FS,MP,HC,F:Punisher,
Weirdworld,Dominic Fortune,
I:Huntress(Mockingbird) 65.00

MARVEL SUPER ACTION
May, 1977–Nov. 1981

1 JK,reprint,Capt.America #100 . . 8.00	
2 JK,reprint,Capt.America #101 . . 6.00	
3 JK,reprint,Capt.America #102 . . 6.00	
4 BEv,RH,reprint,Marvel Boy #1 . 6.00	
5 JK,reprint,Capt.America #103 . . 6.00	
6 JK,reprint,Capt.America #104 . . 5.00	
7 JK,reprint,Capt.America #105 . . 5.00	
8 JK,reprint,Capt.America #106 . . 5.00	
9 JK,reprint,Capt.America #107 . . 5.00	
10 JK,reprint,Capt.America #108 . . 5.00	
11 JK,reprint,Capt.America #109 . . 5.00	
12 JSo,reprint,Capt.America #110 . 5.00	
13 JSo,reprint,Capt.America #111 . 5.00	
14 JB,reprint,Avengers #55 . . . . . 5.00	
15 JB,reprint,Avengers #56 . . . . . 5.00	
16 Reprint,Avengers,annual #2 . . 4.00	
17 Reprint,Avengers # 4.00	

MARVEL SUPERHEROES
Oct., 1966

1-shot Rep. D.D. #1, Avengers #2,
Marvel Mystery #8 . . . . 75.00

MARVEL SUPER-HEROES
[1st Regular Series] 1967–71
(Prev.: Fantasy Masterpieces)

12 GC,I&O:Captain Marvel . . . 125.00	
13 GC,2nd A:Captain Marvel . . . 65.00	
14 F:Spider-Man 110.00	
15 GC,F:Medusa 30.00	
16 I:Phantom Eagle 30.00	
17 O:Black Knight 30.00	
18 GC,I:Guardians o/t Galaxy . . . 50.00	
19 F:Kazar 15.00	
20 F:Dr.Doom,Diablo 15.00	
21 thru 31 reprints . . . . @12.00	
32 thru 55 rep. Hulk/Submariner	
from Tales to Astonish . . . @5.00	
56 reprints Hulk #102 . . . . 3.50	
57 thru 105 reps.Hulk issues . @3.00	

MARVEL SUPERHEROES
[2nd Regular Series] May, 1990

1 RLm,F:Hercules,Moon Knight,	
Magik,Bl.Panther,Speedball . . . 4.00	
2 . . . . 3.50	
3 F:Captain America,Hulk,Wasp . 4.00	
4 AD,F:SpM,N.Fury,D.D.,Speedball	
Wond.Man,Spitfire,Bl.Knight . 3.50	
5 F:Thor,Thing,Speedball,	
Dr.Strange 3.50	
6 RB,SD,F:X-Men,Power Pack,	
Speedball,Sabra 3.00	
7 RB,F:X-Men,Cloak & Dagger . . 2.75	
8 F:X-Men,Iron Man,Namor 2.50	
9 F:Avengers W.C,Thor,Iron Man 3.00	
10 DH,F:Namor,Fantastic Four,	
Ms.Marvel#24 . . . . 3.50	
11 F:Namor,Ms.Marvel#25 . . . . . 3.00	
12 F:Dr.Strange,Falcon,Iron Man . 3.00	
13 F:Iron Man 2.75	
14 BMc,RWi,F:Iron Man,	
Speedball, Dr.Strange 2.75	
15 KP,DH,F:Thor,Iron Man,Hulk . 2.75	
Holiday Spec.#1 AAd,DC,JRu,F:FF,	
X-Men,Spider-Man,Punisher . . 3.25	
Holiday Spec.#2 AAd(c),SK,MGo,	
RLm,SLi,F:Hulk,Wolverine,	
Thanos,Spider-Man 3.25	
Fall Spec.RB,A:X-Men,Shroud,	
Marvel Boy,Cloak & Dagger . . 2.25	

MARVEL SUPERHEROES MEGAZINE
1 thru 6 rep. . . . . @2.95

MARVEL SUPER SPECIAL
See: MARVEL COMICS

MARVEL SWIMSUIT
1992
1 Schwing Break 4.95

MARVEL TAILS
Nov., 1983
1 ST,Peter Porker 2.00

MARVEL TALES
1964

1 All reprints,O:Spider-Man . . . 250.00	
2 rep.Avengers #1,X-Men #1,	
Hulk #3 . . . . 100.00	
3 rep.Amaz.SpM.#6 . . . . 40.00	
4 rep.Amaz.SpM.#7 . . . . 25.00	
5 rep.Amaz.SpM.#8 . . . . 25.00	
6 rep.Amaz.SpM.#9 . . . . 25.00	
7 rep.Amaz.SpM.#10 . . . . 25.00	
8 rep.Amaz.SpM.#13 . . . . 20.00	
9 rep.Amaz.SpM.#14 . . . . 24.00	
10 rep.Amaz.SpM.#15 . . . . 24.00	
11 rep.Amaz.SpM.#16 . . . . 24.00	
12 rep.Amaz.SpM.#17 . . . . 24.00	
13 rep.Amaz.SpM.#18	
rep.1950's Marvel Boy 20.00	
14 rep.Amaz.SpM.#19,	
reps.Marvel Boy 15.00	
15 rep.Amaz.SpM.#20,	
reps.Marvel Boy 15.00	
16 rep.Amaz.SpM.#21,	
reps.Marvel Boy 15.00	
17 thru 22 rep.Amaz.SpM.	
#22-#27 . . . . @12.00	
23 thru 27 rep.Amaz.SpM.	
#30-#34 . . . . @12.00	
28 rep.Amaz.SpM.#35&36 . . . . . 12.00	
29 rep.Amaz.SpM.#39&40 . . . . . 12.00	
30 rep.Amaz.SpM.#58&41 . . . . . 12.00	

31 rep.Amaz.SpM.#42 . . . . 12.00
32 rep.Amaz.SpM.#43&44 . . . . . 12.00
33 rep.Amaz.SpM.#45&47 . . . . . 12.00
34 rep.Amaz.SpM.#48 . . . . 6.00
35 rep.Amaz.SpM.#49 . . . . 6.00
36 thru 41 rep.
   Amaz.SpM.#51-#56 . . . . @6.00
42 thru 53 rep.
   Amaz.SpM.#59-#70 . . . . @6.00
54 thru 80 rep.
   Amaz.SpM#73-#99 . . . . @6.00
81 rep.Amaz.SpM.#103 . . . . 6.00
82 rep.Amaz.SpM.#103-4 . . . . . 6.00
83 thru 97 rep.
   Amaz.SpM#104-#118 . . . . . @6.00
98 rep.Amaz.SpM.#121 . . . . 6.00
99 rep.Amaz.SpM.#122 . . . . 6.00
100 rep.Amaz.SpM.#123,BU:Two
   Gun Kid,Giant-Size 3.50
101 thru 105 rep.Amaz.
   SpM.#124-#128 . . . . @3.00
106 rep.Amaz.SpM.#129,
   (I:Punisher) 4.00
107 thur 110 rep.Amaz.
   SpM.#130-133 . . . . @2.00
111 Amaz.SpM#134,A:Punisher . . 4.00
112 Amaz.SpM#135,A:Punisher . . 3.00
113 thru 125 rep.Amaz.Spider
   Man #136-#148 . . . . @2.00
126 rep.Amaz.Spider-Man#149 . . 4.00
127 rep.Amaz.Spider-Man#150 . . 3.00
128 rep.Amaz.Spider-Man#151 . . 4.00
129 thru 136 rep.Amaz.Spider
   Man #152-#159 . . . . @2.50
137 rep.Amaz.Fantasy#15 . . . . . 7.00
138 rep.Amaz.SpM.#1 . . . . 7.00
139 thru 149 rep.
   AmazSpM#2-#12 . . . . @2.50
150 rep.AmazSpM Ann#1 . . . . . 2.50
151 rep.AmazSpM#13 . . . . 4.00
152 rep.AmazSpM#14 . . . . 4.00
153 thru 190
   rep.AmazSpM#15-52 . . . . . @2.00
191 rep. #96-98 . . . . 2.25
192 rep. #121-122 . . . . 2.25
193 thru 198 rep.Marv.Team
   Up#59-64 . . . . @2.00
199 . . . . 2.00
200 rep. SpM Annual 14 . . . . . . 2.00
201 thru 206 rep.Marv.
   Team Up#65-70 . . . . @2.00
207 . . . . 2.00
208 . . . . 2.00
209 MZ(c),rep.SpM#129,Punisher 3.00
210 MZ(c),rep.SpM#134 . . . . . . 4.00
211 MZ(c),rep.SpM#135 . . . . . . 4.00
212 MZ(c),rep.Giant-Size#4 . . . . 4.00
213 MZ(c),rep.Giant-Size#4 . . . . 4.00
214 MZ(c),rep.SpM#161 . . . . . . 4.00
215 MZ(c),rep.SpM#162 . . . . . . 3.00
216 MZ(c),rep.SpM#174 . . . . . . 3.00
217 MZ(c),rep.SpM#175 . . . . . . 3.00
218 MZ(c),rep.SpM#201 . . . . . . 3.00
219 MZ(c),rep.SpM#202 . . . . . . 3.00
220 MZ(c),rep.Spec.SpM #81 . . . 3.00
221 MZ(c),rep.Spec.SpM #82 . . . 3.00
222 MZ(c),rep.Spec.SpM #83 . . . 2.00
223 thru 227 TM(c),rep.
   SpM #88-92 . . . . @2.25
228 TM(c),rep.Spec.SpM.#17 . . . 2.00
229 TM(c),rep.Spec.SpM.#18 . . . 2.00
230 TM(c),rep.SpM #203 . . . . . . 2.00
231 TM(c),rep.Team-Up#108 . . . 2.00
232 TM(c),rep. 2.00
233 TM(c),rep. X-Men 2.00

Marvel Tales #134
© *Marvel Entertainment Group*

234 TM(c),rep. X-Men 2.00
235 TM(c),rep. X-Men 2.00
236 TM(c),rep. X-Men 2.00
237 TM(c),rep. 2.00
238 TM(c),rep. 2.00
239 TM(c),rep.SpM,Beast 2.00
240 rep.SpM,Beast,MTU#90 . . . 1.50
241 rep.MTU#124 . . . . 1.50
242 rep.MTU#89,Nightcrawler . . . 1.50
243 rep.MTU#117,SpM,Wolverine 1.50
244 MR(c),rep. 1.50
245 MR(c),rep. 1.50
246 MR(c),rep. 1.50
247 MR(c),rep.MTU Annual #6 . . 1.50
248 MR(c),rep. 1.50
249 MR(c),rep.MTU #14 . . . . . . 1.50
250 MR(c),rep.MTU #100 . . . . . 1.50
251 rep.Amaz.SpM.#100 . . . . . . 1.50
252 rep.Amaz.SpM.#101 . . . . . . 3.50
253 rep.Amaz.SpM.#102 . . . . . . 3.00
254 rep.MTU #15,inc.2 Ghost
   Rider pin-ups by JaL 3.00
255 SK(c),rep.MTU #58,
   BU:Ghost Rider 1.75
256 rep. MTU 1.50
257 rep.Amaz.SpM.#238 . . . . . . 1.50
258 rep.Amaz.SpM.#239 . . . . . . 1.50
259 thru 261 rep.Amaz.SpM.#249
   thru 251 . . . . 1.50
262 rep Marvel Team-Up #53 . . . 1.25
263 rep Marvel Team-Up #54 . . . 1.25
264 rep.B:Amaz.SpM.Ann.#5 . . . 1.25
265 rep.E:Amaz.SpM.Ann.#5 . . . 1.25
266 thru 274 rep.Amaz.SpM#252
   thru #260 . . . . @1.25
275 rep.Amaz.SpM#261 . . . . . . 1.25
276 rep.Amaz.SpM#263 . . . . . . 1.25
277 rep.Amaz.SpM#265 . . . . . . 1.25
278 thru 282 rep.Amaz.SpM#268
   thru 272 . . . . 1.25
283 rep.Amaz.SpM#273 . . . . . . 1.25
284 rep.Amaz.SpM#275 . . . . . . 1.25
285 rep.Amaz.SpM#276 . . . . . . 1.25
286 rep.Amaz.SpM#277 . . . . . . 1.25
287 rep.Amaz.SpM#278 . . . . . . 1.25
288 rep.Amaz.SpM#280 . . . . . . 1.50
289 rep.Amaz.SpM#281 . . . . . . 1.25
290 & 291 rep.Amaz.SpM 1.50

MARVEL TALES
See: MARVEL COMICS

MARVEL TEAM-UP
March, 1972
(Spider-Man in all,unless *)
1 RA,F:Hum.Torch,V:Sandman . 90.00
2 RA,F:Hum.Torch,V:Sandman . 35.00
3 F:Human Torch,V:Morbius . . . 50.00
4 GK,F:X-Men,A:Morbius 50.00
5 GK,F:Vision 20.00
6 GK,F:Thing,O:Puppet Master,
   V:Mad Thinker 20.00
7 RA,F:Thor 20.00
8 JM,F:The Cat 20.00
9 RA,F:Iron Man 20.00
10 JM,F:Human Torch 20.00
11 JM,F:The Inhumans 18.00
12 RA,F:Werewolf 20.00
13 GK,F:Captain America 25.00
14 GK,F:Sub-Mariner 15.00
15 RA,F:Ghostrider 15.00
16 GK,JM,F:Captain Marvel . . . 14.00
17 GK,F:Mr.Fantastic,
   A:Capt.Marvel 14.00
18 *F:Hulk,Human Torch 14.00
19 SB,F:Ka-Zar 14.00
20 SB,F:Black Panther 17.00
21 SB,F:Dr.Strange 7.00
22 SB,F:Hawkeye 7.00
23 *F:Human Torch,Iceman,
   C:Spider-Man,X-Men 8.00
24 JM,F:Brother Voodoo 7.00
25 JM,F:Daredevil 7.00
26 *F:H.Torch,Thor,V:Lavamen . . 7.00
27 JM,F:The Hulk 7.00
28 JM,F:Hercules 7.00
29 *F:Human Torch,Iron Man . . . 7.00
30 JM,F:The Falcon 7.00
31 JM,F:Iron Fist 7.00
32 *F:Hum.Torch,Son of Satan . . 7.00
33 SB,F:Nighthawk 7.00
34 SB,F:Valkyrie 7.00
35 SB,*F:H.Torch,Dr.Strange . . . 7.00
36 SB,F:Frankenstein 6.00
37 SB,F:Man-Wolf 6.00
38 SB,F:Beast 5.00
39 SB,F:H.Torch,I:Jean Dewolff . . 5.00
40 SB,F:Sons of the Tiger 5.00
41 SB,F:Scarlet Witch 5.00
42 SB,F:Scarlet Witch,Vision . . . 5.00
43 SB,F:Dr.Doom 5.00
44 SB,F:Moon Dragon 5.00
45 SB,F:Killraven 5.00
46 SB,F:Deathlok 6.00
47 F:The Thing 5.00
48 SB,F:Iron Man,I:Wraith 5.00
49 SB,F:Iron Man 5.00
50 SB,F:Dr.Strange 5.00
51 SB,F:Iron Man 4.00
52 SB,F:Captain America 4.00
53 1st JBy New X-Men,F:Hulk . . 25.00
54 JBy,F:Hulk,V:Woodgod 6.00
55 JBy,F:Warlock,I:Gardener . . . 8.00
56 SB,F:Daredevil 5.00
57 SB,F:Black Widow 5.00
58 SB,F:Ghost Rider,V:Trapster . . 5.00
59 JBy,F:Yellowjacket,V:Equinox . 5.00
60 JBy,F:Wasp,V:Equinox 5.00
61 JBy,F:Human Torch 5.00
62 JBy,F:Ms.Marvel 5.00
63 JBy,F:Iron Fist 5.50
64 JBy,F:Daughters o/t Dragon . 5.00
65 JBy,I:Captain Britain(U.S.)

```
         I:Arcade . . . . . . . . . . . . . . . . 7.50
66 JBy,F:Captain Britain . . . . . . . 6.00
67 JBy,F:Tigra,V:Kraven . . . . . . . 5.00
68 JBy,F:Man-Thing,I:D'Spayre . . 5.00
69 JBy,F:Havok . . . . . . . . . . . . . 6.00
70 JBy,F:Thor . . . . . . . . . . . . . . 5.00
71 F:The Falcon,V:Plantman . . . . 4.00
72 F:Iron Man . . . . . . . . . . . . . . 4.00
73 F:Daredevil . . . . . . . . . . . . . 4.00
74 BH,F:Not ready for prime time
   players(Saturday Night Live) . . 5.00
75 JBy,F:Power Man . . . . . . . . . 4.00
76 HC,F:Dr.Strange . . . . . . . . . . 4.00
77 HC,F:Ms.Marvel . . . . . . . . . . 4.00
78 DP,F:Wonderman . . . . . . . . . 4.00
79 JBy,TA,F:Red Sonja . . . . . . . 5.00
80 SpM,F:Dr.Strange,Clea . . . . . 4.00
81 F:Satana . . . . . . . . . . . . . . . 4.00
82 SB,F:Black Widow . . . . . . . . 5.00
83 SB,F:Nick Fury . . . . . . . . . . . 4.00
84 SB,F:Master of Kung Fu . . . . . 5.00
85 SB,F:Bl.Widow,Nick Fury . . . . 5.00
86 BMc,F:Guardians o/t Galaxy . 4.00
87 GC,F:Black Panther . . . . . . . 4.00
88 SB,F:Invisible Girl . . . . . . . . . 4.00
89 RB,F:Nightcrawler . . . . . . . . 4.50
90 BMc,F:The Beast . . . . . . . . . 4.00
91 F:Ghost Rider . . . . . . . . . . . . 4.00
92 Cl,F:Hawkeye,I:Mr.Fear IV . . . 3.50
93 Cl,F:Werewolf
   I:Tatterdemalion (named) . . . . 4.00
94 MZ,F:Shroud . . . . . . . . . . . . 3.50
95 I:Mockingbird(Huntress) . . . . 4.00
96 F:Howard the Duck . . . . . . . . 3.50
97 *F:Hulk,Spiderwoman . . . . . . 3.50
98 F:Black Widow . . . . . . . . . . . 3.50
99 F:Machine Man . . . . . . . . . . 3.50
100 FM,JBy,F:F.F.,I:Karma,
    BU:Storm & Bl.Panther . . . . . 8.00
101 F:Nighthawk . . . . . . . . . . . . 3.00
102 F:Doc Samson,Rhino . . . . . . 3.00
103 F:Antman . . . . . . . . . . . . . . 3.00
104 *F:Hulk,Ka-zar . . . . . . . . . . 3.00
105 *F:Powerman,Iron Fist,Hulk . 3.00
106 HT,F:Captain America . . . . . 3.00
107 HT,F:She-Hulk . . . . . . . . . . 3.00
108 HT,F:Paladin . . . . . . . . . . . 3.00
109 HT,F:Dazzler . . . . . . . . . . . 3.00
110 HT,F:Iron Man . . . . . . . . . . 3.00
111 HT,F:Devil Slayer . . . . . . . . 3.00
112 HT,F:King Kull . . . . . . . . . . 3.00
113 HT,F:Quasar,V:Lightmaster . . 3.00
114 HT,F:Falcon . . . . . . . . . . . . 3.00
115 HT,F:Thor . . . . . . . . . . . . . 3.00
116 HT,F:Valkyrie . . . . . . . . . . . 3.00
117 HT,F:Wolv,V:Prof Power . . . 12.00
118 HT,F:Professor X . . . . . . . . 4.00
119 KGa,F:Gargoyle . . . . . . . . . 3.00
120 KGa,F:Dominic Fortune . . . . 3.00
121 KGa,F:Human Torch,I:Leap
    Frog(Frog Man) . . . . . . . . . . 3.00
122 KGa,F:Man-Thing . . . . . . . . 3.00
123 KGa,F:Daredevil . . . . . . . . . 3.00
124 KGa,F:Beast . . . . . . . . . . . 3.00
125 KGa,F:Tigra . . . . . . . . . . . . 3.00
126 BH,F:Hulk . . . . . . . . . . . . . 3.00
127 KGa,F:Watcher,X-mas issue . 3.00
128 Ph(c)KGa,F:Capt.America. . . 3.00
129 KGa,F:The Vision . . . . . . . . 3.00
130 KGa,F:The Scarlet Witch . . . 3.00
131 KGa,F:Leap Frog . . . . . . . . 3.00
132 KGa,F:Mr.Fantastic . . . . . . . 3.00
133 KGa,F:Fantastic Four . . . . . . 3.00
134 F:Jack of Hearts . . . . . . . . . 3.00
135 F:Kitty Pryde . . . . . . . . . . . 3.00
```

Marvel Team-Up #61
© Marvel Entertainment Group

```
136 F:Wonder Man . . . . . . . . . . 3.00
137 *F:Aunt May & F.Richards . . . 3.00
138 F:Sandman,I:New Enforcers . 3.00
139 F:Sandman,Nick Fury . . . . . 3.00
140 F:Black Widow . . . . . . . . . . 3.00
141 SpM(2nd App Black Costume)
    F:Daredevil . . . . . . . . . . . . . 4.00
142 F:Captain Marvel(2nd one) . . 3.00
143 F:Starfox . . . . . . . . . . . . . . 3.00
144 F:M.Knight,V:WhiteDragon . . 3.00
145 F:Iron Man . . . . . . . . . . . . . 3.00
146 F:Nomad . . . . . . . . . . . . . . 3.50
147 F:Human Torch . . . . . . . . . . 3.00
148 F:Thor . . . . . . . . . . . . . . . . 3.00
149 F:Cannonball . . . . . . . . . . . 3.50
150 F:X-Men,V:Juggernaut . . . . . 5.50
Ann.#1 SB,F:New X-Men . . . . . . 16.00
Ann.#2 F:The Hulk . . . . . . . . . . . 5.00
Ann.#3 F:Hulk,PowerMan . . . . . . 4.00
Ann.#4 F:Daredevil,Moon Knight . 3.00
Ann.#5 F:Thing,Scarlet Witch,
    Quasar,Dr.Strange . . . . . . . . 3.00
Ann.#6 F:New Mutants,Cloak &
    Dagger(cont.New Mutants#22) 4.00
Ann.#7 F:Alpha Flight . . . . . . . . . 3.00
```

MARVEL TEAM-UP INDEX
SEE: OFFICIAL MARVEL INDEX TO MARVEL TEAM-UP

MARVEL TEAM-UP
1997

```
1 TPe,PO,AW, F:Spider-Man,
  Generation X . . . . . . . . . . . . . 1.99
2 TPe,PO,AW, F:Spider-Man &
  Hercules . . . . . . . . . . . . . . . . 2.00
3 TPe,DaR,AW, F:Spider-Man &
  Sandman . . . . . . . . . . . . . . . 2.00
4 TPe,DaR,F:Spider-Man &
  Man-Thing . . . . . . . . . . . . . . 2.00
5 TPe,DaR,F:Spider-Man &
  Mystery guest . . . . . . . . . . . . 2.00
6 TPe,F:Spider-Man & Sub-Mariner 2.00
```

```
7 MWn,TPe,F:Spider-Man & Blade 2.00
8 TPe,F:Sub-Mariner & Doctor
  Strange . . . . . . . . . . . . . . . . . 2.00
9 TPe,F:Sub-Mariner & Captain
  America . . . . . . . . . . . . . . . . . 2.00
10 TPe,AW,F:Sub Mariner & Thing 2.00
11 TPe,AW,PO,F:Sub-Mariner & Iron
  Man, final issue . . . . . . . . . . . 2.00
```

MARVEL
Treasury Edition Sept., 1974

```
1 SD,Spider-Man,I:Contemplator 25.00
2 JK,F:Fant.Four,Silver Surfer . . 12.00
3 F:Thor . . . . . . . . . . . . . . . . . . 10.00
4 BWS,F:Conan . . . . . . . . . . . . . 9.00
5 O:Hulk . . . . . . . . . . . . . . . . . . 8.00
6 GC,FB,SD,F:Dr.Strange . . . . . 8.00
7 JB,JK,F:The Avengers . . . . . . . 9.00
8 F:X-Mas stories . . . . . . . . . . . 10.00
9 F:Super-Hero Team-Up . . . . . . 8.00
10 F:Thor . . . . . . . . . . . . . . . . . 8.00
11 F:Fantastic Four . . . . . . . . . . 8.00
12 F:Howard the Duck . . . . . . . . 8.00
13 F:X-Mas stories . . . . . . . . . . 8.00
14 F:Spider-Man . . . . . . . . . . . . 8.00
15 BWS,F:Conan,Red Sonja . . . 10.00
16 F:Defenders . . . . . . . . . . . . . 8.00
17 F:The Hulk . . . . . . . . . . . . . . 8.00
18 F:Spider Man,X-Men . . . . . . 10.00
19 F:Conan . . . . . . . . . . . . . . . 10.00
20 F:Hulk . . . . . . . . . . . . . . . . . 10.00
21 F:Fantastic Four . . . . . . . . . . 10.00
22 F:Spider-Man . . . . . . . . . . . . 10.00
23 F:Conan . . . . . . . . . . . . . . . 10.00
24 F:The Hulk . . . . . . . . . . . . . . 10.00
25 F:Spider-Man,Hulk . . . . . . . . 10.00
26 GP,F:Hulk,Wolverine,Hercules 12.00
27 HT,F:Hulk,Spider-Man . . . . . 10.00
28 JB,JSt,F:SpM/Superman . . . 18.00
```

MARVEL TREASURY OF OZ
(oversized) 1975

```
1 JB,movie adapt. . . . . . . . . . . . 4.00
```

MARVEL TREASURY SPECIAL

```
Vol. I Spider-Man, 1974 . . . . . . . 4.00
Vol. II Capt. America, 1976 . . . . 3.50
```

MARVEL TRIPLE ACTION
Feb., 1972

```
1 Rep. . . . . . . . . . . . . . . . . . . . 4.00
2 thru 47 rep. . . . . . . . . . . . . . @1.50
G-Size#1 F:Avengers . . . . . . . . 3.00
G-Size#2 F:Avengers . . . . . . . . 3.00
```

MARVEL TWO-IN-ONE
Jan., 1974
(Thing in all, unless *)

```
1 GK,F:Man-Thing . . . . . . . . . . 40.00
2 GK,JSt,F:Namor,Namorita . . . 12.00
3 F:Daredevil . . . . . . . . . . . . . . 12.00
4 F:Capt.America,Namorita . . . . 12.00
5 F:Guardians of the Galaxy . . . 14.00
6 F:Dr.Strange . . . . . . . . . . . . . 14.00
7 F:Valkyrie . . . . . . . . . . . . . . . 6.00
8 F:Ghost Rider . . . . . . . . . . . . 7.00
9 F:Thor . . . . . . . . . . . . . . . . . . 5.00
10 KJ,F:Black Widow . . . . . . . . 5.00
11 F:Golem . . . . . . . . . . . . . . . 4.00
12 F:Iron Man . . . . . . . . . . . . . . 4.00
13 F:Power Man . . . . . . . . . . . . 4.00
```

MARVEL

14 F:Son of Satan 5.00
15 F:Morbius 5.00
16 F:Ka-zar 4.00
17 F:Spider-Man 4.50
18 F:Spider-Man 4.50
19 F:Tigra 4.00
20 F:The Liberty Legion 4.00
21 F:Doc Savage 3.50
22 F:Thor,Human Torch 3.50
23 F:Thor,Human Torch 3.50
24 SB,F:Black Goliath 3.50
25 F:Iron Fist 4.00
26 F:Nick Fury 4.00
27 F:Deathlok 4.00
28 F:Sub-Mariner 3.00
29 F:Master of Kung Fu 3.00
30 JB,F:Spiderwoman 4.00
31 F:Spiderwoman 3.00
32 F:Invisible girl 3.00
33 F:Modred the Mystic 3.00
34 F:Nighthawk,C:Deathlok 3.50
35 F:Skull the Slayer 3.00
36 F:Mr.Fantastic 3.00
37 F:Matt Murdock 3.00
38 F:Daredevil 3.00
39 F:The Vision 3.00
40 F:Black Panther 3.00
41 F:Brother Voodoo 3.00
42 F:Captain America 3.00
43 JBy,F:Man-Thing 5.00
44 GD,F:Hercules 3.00
45 GD,F:Captain Marvel 4.50
46 F:The Hulk 5.00
47 GD,F:Yancy Street Gang,
   I:Machinesmith 3.00
48 F:Jack of Hearts 3.00
49 GD,F:Dr.Strange 3.00
50 JBy,JS,F:Thing & Thing 3.50
51 FM,BMc,F:Wonderman,Nick
   Fury, Ms.Marvel 4.00
52 F:Moon Knight,I:Crossfire . . . 3.00
53 JBy,JS,F:Quasar,C:Deathlok . . 3.50
54 JBy,JS,D:Deathlok,
   I:Grapplers 6.00
55 JBy,JS,I:New Giant Man 3.00
56 GP,GD,F:Thundra 2.50
57 GP,GD,F:Wundarr 2.50
58 GP,GD,I:Aquarian,A:Quasar . 2.50
59 F:Human Torch 2.50
60 GP,GD,F:Impossible Man,
   I:Impossible Woman 2.50
61 GD,F:Starhawk,I&O:Her 3.00
62 GD,F:Moondragon 3.00
63 GD,F:Warlock 3.00
64 DP,GD,F:Stingray,
   I:Serpent Squad 2.50
65 GP,GD,F:Triton 2.50
66 GD,F:Scarlet Witch,
   V:Arcade 2.50
67 F:Hyperion,Thundra 2.50
68 F:Angel,V:Arcade 2.50
69 GD,F:Guardians o/t Galaxy . . . 2.50
70 F:The Inhumans 2.50
71 F:Mr.Fantastic,I:Deathurge,
   Maelstrom 2.50
72 F:Stingray 2.50
73 F:Quasar 2.50
74 F:Puppet Master,Modred 2.50
75 F:The Avengers,O:Blastaar . . 2.50
76 F:Iceman,O:Ringmaster 2.50
77 F:Man-Thing 2.50
78 F:Wonder Man 2.50
79 F:Blue Diamond,I:Star Dancer . 2.50
80 F:Ghost Rider 2.00
81 F:Sub-Mariner 2.00

Marvel Two-In-One #84
© *Marvel Entertainment Group*

82 F:Captain America 2.00
83 F:Sasquatch 3.00
84 F:Alpha Flight 3.00
85 F:Giant-Man 2.00
86 O:Sandman 2.25
87 F:Ant-Man 2.00
88 F:She-Hulk 2.00
89 F:Human Torch 2.00
90 F:Spider-Man 2.25
91 V:Sphinx 2.00
92 F:Jocasta,V:Ultron 2.00
93 F:Machine Man,D:Jocasta 2.25
94 F:Power Man,Iron Fist 2.00
95 F:Living Mummy 2.00
96 F:Sandman,C:Marvel Heroes . 2.00
97 F:Iron Man 2.00
98 F:Franklin Richards 2.00
99 JBy(c),F:Rom 2.50
100 F:Ben Grimm 2.50
Ann.#1 SB,F:Liberty Legion 5.00
Ann.#2 JSn,2nd D:Thanos,A:Spider
   Man,Avengers,Capt.Marvel,
   I:Lord Chaos,Master Order . . 12.00
Ann.#3 F:Nova 4.00
Ann.#4 F:Black Bolt 3.50
Ann.#5 F:Hulk,V:Pluto 3.00
Ann.#6 I:American Eagle 3.00
Ann.#7 I:Champion,A:Hulk,Thor,
   DocSamson,Colossus,Sasquatch,
   WonderMan 3.50

OFFICIAL HANDBOOK OF THE MARVEL UNIVERSE
Jan., 1983
1 Abomination-Avengers'
   Quintet 7.50
2 BaronMordo-Collect.Man 6.00
3 Collector-Dracula 5.00
4 Dragon Man-Gypsy Moth 5.00
5 Hangman-Juggernaut 5.00
6 K-L 4.00
7 Mandarin-Mystique 4.00
8 Na,oria-Pyro 4.00
9 Quasar to She-Hulk 4.00
10 Shiar-Sub-Mariner 4.00
11 Subteraneans-Ursa Major 4.00
12 Valkyrie-Zzzax 4.00

13 Book of the Dead 4.00
14 Book of the Dead 4.00
15 Weaponry 4.00
[2nd Series]
1 Abomination-Batroc 5.00
2 Beast-Clea 4.00
3 Cloak & D.-Dr.Strange 4.00
4 Dr.Strange-Galactus 4.00
5 Gardener-Hulk 4.00
6 Human Torch-Ka-Zar 3.25
7 Kraven-Magneto 3.25
8 Magneto-Moleman 3.25
9 Moleman-Owl 3.25
10 . . . . 3.25
11 . . . . 2.50
12 S-T 2.50
13 . . . . 2.50
14 V-Z 2.50
15 . . . . 2.50
16 Book of the Dead 2.50
17 Handbook of the Dead,inc.
   JLe illus. 2.50
18 . . . . 2.50
19 . . . . 2.50
20 Inc.RLd illus. 2.50
Marvel Universe Update
1 thru 8 . . . . @1.75
Marvel Universe Packet
1 inc. Spider-Man 5.50
2 inc. Captain America 4.50
3 inc. Ghost Rider 5.00
4 inc. Wolverine 4.50
5 inc. Punisher 4.25
6 inc. She-Hulk 3.95
7 inc. Daredevil 3.95
8 inc. Hulk 3.95
9 inc. Moon Knight 3.95
10 inc. Captain Britain 3.95
11 inc. Storm 3.95
12 inc. Silver Surfer 3.95
13 inc. Ice Man 4.50
14 inc. Thor 4.50
15 thru 22 . . . . @4.50
23 inc. Cage 4.50
24 inc. Iron Fist 4.50
25 inc.Deadpool,Night Thrasher . . 4.50
26 inc. Wonderman 4.95
27 inc.Beta Ray Bill,Pip 4.95
28 inc.X-Men 4.95
29 inc.Carnage 4.95
30 thru 36 . . . . @4.95

MARVEL X-MEN COLLECTION
1994
1 thru 3 JL from the 1st series
   X-Men Cards 3.25

MARVEL UNIVERSE
1996
1 Post Onslaught 2.95

MARVEL UNIVERSE
April 1998
1 CPa(c),RSt,SEp,AW,F:Human
   Torch,Capt.Am.,Namor,48pg . . 3.00
2A JBy(c),RSt,SEp,AW,V:Hydra,
   Baron Strucker 2.00
2B DGb(c) 2.00
3 RSt,SEp,AW,V:Hydra 2.00
4 RSt,MM, all-star jam cover,
   F:Monster Hunters 2.00
5 MM,RSt,F:The Monster Hunters 2.00

MARVEL

MARVEL VALENTINE'S SPECIAL
1997
1-shot MWa,TDF, 48pg 2.99

MARVEL: SHADOWS & LIGHT
B&W 1996
1-shot MGo,JPL,KJ,48pg. 2.95

MARVELS
1 B:KBk(s),AxR,I:Phil Sheldon,
  A:G.A.Heroes,Human Torch Vs
  Namor 8.00
2 AxR,A:S.A.Avengers,FF,X-Men 6.00
3 AxR,FF vs Galactus 5.00
4 AxR,Final issue 5.00
HC rep.#1-#4 . . . . 34.95

MARVIN MOUSE
Atlas Sept., 1957
1 BEv,F:Marvin Mouse 30.00

MASTER OF KUNG FU, SPECIAL MARVEL ED.
April, 1974
Prev: SPECIAL MARVEL EDITION
17 JSn,I:Black Jack Tarr 20.00
18 PG,1st Gulacy Art 14.00
19 PG,A:Man-Thing 10.00
20 GK(c),PG,AM,V:Samurai . . . 10.00
21 AM,Season of Vengeance..
  Moment of Death 8.00
22 PG,DA,Death 8.00
23 AM,KJ,River of Death 8.00
24 JSn,WS,AM,ST,Night of the
  Assassin 8.00
25 JSt(c),PG,ST,Fists Fury...
  Rites of Death 8.00
26 KP,ST,A:Daughter of
  Fu Manchu 7.00
27 SB,FS,A:Fu Manchu 7.00
28 EH,ST,Death of a Spirit 7.00
29 PG,V:Razor-Fist 7.00
30 PG,DA,Pit of Lions 7.00
31 GK&DA(c),PG,DA,Snowbuster 7.00
32 GK&ME(c),SB,ME,Assault on an
  Angry Sea 7.00
33 PG,Messenger of Madness,
  I:Leiko Wu 7.00
34 PG,Captive in A Madman's
  Crown 7.00
35 PG,V:Death Hand 7.00
36 The Night of the Ninja's 7.00
37 V:Darkstrider & Warlords of
  the Web 5.00
38 GK(c),PG,A:The Cat 5.00
39 GK(c),PG,A:The Cat 5.00
40 PG,The Murder Agency 5.00
41 . . . . 5.00
42 GK(c),PG,TS,V:Shockwave . . 5.00
43 PG,V:Shockwave 5.00
44 SB(c),PG,V:Fu Manchu 5.00
45 GK(c),PG,Death Seed 5.00
46 PG,V:Sumo 5.00
47 PG,The Cold White
  Mantle of Death 5.00
48 PG,Bridge of a 1,000 Dooms . 5.00
49 PG,V:Shaka Kharn,The
  Demon Warrior 5.00
50 PG,V:Fu Manchu 5.00
51 PG(c),To End...To Begin 5.00

Master of Kung Fu #31
© Marvel Entertainment Group

52 Mayhem in Morocco 4.00
53 . . . . 4.00
54 JSn(c),Death Wears Three
  Faces 4.00
55 PG(c),The Ages of Death . . . 4.00
56 V:The Black Ninja 4.00
57 V:Red Baron 4.00
58 Behold the Final Mask 4.00
59 GK(c),B:Phoenix Gambit,
  Behold the Angel of Doom . . . 4.00
60 A:Dr.Doom,Doom Came 4.00
61 V:Skull Crusher 3.50
62 Coast of Death 3.50
63 GK&TA(c),Doom Wears
  Three Faces 3.50
64 PG(c),To Challenge a Dragon . 3.50
65 V:Pavane 3.50
66 V:Kogar 3.50
67 PG(c),Dark Encounters 3.50
68 Final Combats,V:The Cat . . . 3.50
69 . . . . 3.50
70 A:Black Jack Tarr,Murder
  Mansion 3.50
71 PG(c),Ying & Yang (c) 3.50
72 V:Shockwave 3.50
73 RN(c),V:Behemoths 3.50
74 TA(c),A:Shockwave 3.50
75 Where Monsters Dwell 3.50
76 GD,Battle on the Waterfront . . 3.75
77 GD,I:Zaran 3.75
78 GD,Moving Targets 3.75
79 GD,This Side of Death 3.75
80 GD,V:Leopard Men 3.75
81 GD,V:Leopard Men 3.75
82 GD,Flight into Fear 3.75
83 GD, ... 3.75
84 GD,V:Fu Manchu 3.75
85 GD,V:Fu Manchu 3.75
86 GD,V:Fu Manchu 3.75
87 GD,V:Zaran, ... 3.75
88 GD,V:Fu Manchu 3.75
89 GD,D:Fu Manchu 3.75
90 MZ,Death in Chinatown 3.75
91 GD,Gang War,drugs 4.00
92 GD,Shadows of the Past 3.75

93 GD,Cult of Death 3.75
94 GD,V:Agent Synergon 3.75
95 GD,Raid 3.75
96 GD,I:Rufus Carter 3.75
97 GD,V:Kung Fu's Dark Side . . . 3.75
98 GD,Fight to the Finish 3.75
99 GD,Death Boat 3.75
100 GD,Doublesize 5.00
101 GD,Not Smoke,Nor Beads,
  Nor Blood 3.75
102 GD,Assassins,1st GD(p) 4.00
103 GD,V:Assassins 3.75
104 GD,Fight without Reason,
  C:Cerberus 3.75
105 GD,I:Razor Fist 3.75
106 GD,C:Velcro 3.75
107 GD,A:Sata 3.75
108 GD 3.75
109 GD,Death is a Dark Agent . . 3.75
110 GD,Perilous Reign 3.75
111 GD 3.75
112 GD(c),Commit and Destroy . . 3.75
113 GD(c),V:Panthers 3.75
114 Fantasy o/t Autumn Moon . . . 3.75
115 GD 3.75
116 GD 3.75
117 GD,Devil Deeds Done
  in Darkness 3.75
118 GD,D:Fu Manchu,double 3.75
119 GD 3.75
120 GD,Dweller o/t Dark Stream . 3.75
121 Death in the City of Lights' . . 2.00
122 . . . . 2.00
123 V:Ninjas 2.00
124 . . . . 2.00
125 . . . . 2.00
G-Size#1,CR,PG 3.00
G-Size#2 PG,V:Yellow Claw 2.00
G-Size#3 . . . . 2.00
G-Size#4 JK,V:Yellow Claw 2.00
Spec.#1 Bleeding Black 3.25

MASTER OF KUNG FU: BLEEDING BLACK
1 V:ShadowHand, 1991 . . . . 2.95

MASTERS OF TERROR
July–Sept., 1975
1 GM(c),FB,BWS,JSn,NA 3.00
2 JSn(c),GK,VM, ... 2.00

MASTERS OF THE UNIVERSE
Star May, 1986–March, 1988
1 I:Hordak 1.50
2 thru 12 . . . . @1.00
Movie #1 GT 2.00

MATT SLADE, GUNFIGHTER
Atlas May, 1956
1 AW,AT,F:Matt Slade,Crimson
  Avenger 100.00
2 AW,A:Crimson Avenger 75.00
3 A:Crimson Avenger 60.00
4 A:Crimson Avenger 60.00
Becomes:

KID SLADE GUNFIGHTER
5 F:Kid Slade 60.00
6 . . . . 40.00
7 AW,Duel in the Night 60.00
8 July, 1957 . . . . 40.00

MAVERICK
1997

1 JGz,F:Christopher Nord/David North/Maverick, 48pg	2.99
2 JGz,A:Victor Creed and Logan	2.00
2a variant cover	2.00
3 JGz,V:Puck & Vindicator	2.00
4 JGz,A:Wolverine	2.00
5 JGz,A:The Blob	2.00
6 JGz,V:Sabretooth	2.00
7 JGz,V:Sabretooth	2.00
8 JGz,V:The Confessor	2.00
9 JGz,Maverick's secrets	2.00
10 JGz,V:Ivan the Terrible, Chris Bradley becomes Bolt	2.00
11 JGz,A:Darkstar,Vanguard, Ursa Major	2.00
12 JGz, double sized last issue	3.00
1-shot LHa, V:Sabretooth,48pg	2.95

MELVIN THE MONSTER
Atlas July, 1956

1	60.00
2 thru 6	@40.00

Becomes:

DEXTER THE DEMON
Sept., 1957

7	25.00

MEMORIES
Epic

1 Space Adventures	2.50

MENACE
Atlas May, 1953

1 RH,BEv,GT,One Head Too Many	450.00
2 RH,BEv,GT,JSt,Burton'sBlood	300.00
3 BEv,RH,JR,The Werewolf	225.00
4 BEv,RH,The Four Armed Man	225.00
5 BEv,RH,GC,GT,I&O:Zombie	350.00
6 BEv,RH,JR,The Graymoor Ghost	225.00
7 JSt,RH,Fresh out of Flesh	175.00
8 RH,The Lizard Man	175.00
9 BEv,The Walking Dead	200.00
10 RH(c),Half Man,Half...	175.00
11 JKz,JR,Locked In,May, 1954	175.00

MEN IN ACTION
Atlas April, 1952

1 Sweating it Out	60.00
2 US Infantry stories	35.00
3 RH	25.00
4 War stories	25.00
5 Squad Charge	25.00
6 War stories	25.00
7 RH(c),BK,No Risk Too Great	45.00
8 JRo(c),They Strike By Night	25.00
9 SSh(c),Rangers Strike Back	25.00

Becomes:

BATTLE BRADY

10 SSh(c),F:Battle Brady	100.00
11 SSh(c)	75.00
12 SSh(c),Death to the Reds	50.00
13	50.00
14 Final Issue,June, 1953	50.00

MEN IN BLACK

1 ANi, prequel to movie (1997)	4.00
Spec. Movie Adaptation (1997)	4.00

MEN IN BLACK: RETRIBUTION
Aug., 1997

1 continuation from movie	2.50

MEN'S ADVENTURES
See: TRUE WESTERN

MEPHISTO vs. FOUR HEROES
April–July, 1987

1 JB,BWi,A:Fantastic Four	2.50
2 JB,BWi,A:X-Factor	2.25
3 JB,AM,A:X-Men	2.25
4 JB,BWi,A:Avengers	2.00

METEOR MAN
1993–94

1 R:Meteor Man	1.25
2 V:GhostStrike,Malefactor,Simon	1.25
3 A:Spider-Man	1.25
4 A:Night Thrasher	1.25
5 Exocet	1.25
6 final issue	1.25

[TED McKEEVER'S} METROPOL
Epic 1991–92

1 Ted McKeever	2.95
2	2.95
3	2.95
4	2.95
5	2.95
6	2.95
7	2.95
8 Return of Eddy Current	2.95
9 'Wings of Silence'	2.95
10 'Rotting Metal,Rusted Flesh'	2.95
11 'Diagram of the Heart'	2.95
12	2.95

METROPOL A.D.
Epic 1992

1 R:The Angels	3.50
2 V:Demons	3.50
3 V:Nuclear Arsenal	3.50

MICRONAUTS
[1st Series] Jan., 1979

1 MGo,JRu,O:Micronauts	3.00
2 MGo,JRu,Earth	2.50
3 MGo,JRu	2.00
4 MGo	2.00
5 MGo,V:Prometheus	2.00
6 MGo	2.00
7 MGo,A:Man Thing	2.00
8 MGo,BMc,I:Capt. Univ.	2.50
9 MGo,I:Cilicia	2.00
10 MGo	2.00
11 MGo	2.00
12 MGo	2.00
13 HC,F:Bug	1.50
14 HC,V:Wartstaff	1.50
15 HC,AM,A:Fantastic Four	1.50
16 HC,AM,A:Fantastic Four	1.50
17 HC,AM,A:Fantastic Four	1.50
18 HC,Haunted House Issue	1.50
19 PB,V:Odd John	1.50
20 PB,A:Antman	1.50
21 PB,I:Microverse	1.50
22 PB	1.50
23 PB,V:Molecule Man	1.50

Micronauts #1
© Marvel Entertainment Group

24 MGo,V:Computrex	1.50
25 PB,A:Mentallo	1.50
26 PB,A:Baronkarza	1.25
27 PB,V:Hydra,A:Shield	1.25
28 PB,V:Hydra,A:Shield	1.25
29 PB,Doc Samson	1.25
30 PB,A:Shield	1.25
31 PB,A:Dr.Strange	1.25
32 PB,A:Dr.Strange	1.25
33 PB,A:Devil of Tropica	1.25
34 PB,A:Dr.Strange	1.25
35 O:Microverse	1.50
36 KG,Dr.Strange	1.50
37 KG,Nightcrawler	3.50
38 GK,1st direct	2.50
39 SD	1.75
40 GK,A:FF	1.75
41 GK,Dr.Doom	1.25
42 GK	1.25
43	1.25
44	1.25
45 Arcade	1.25
46	1.25
47	1.25
48 JG	2.00
49 JG,V:BaronKarza	1.50
50 JG,V:BaronKarza	1.50
51 JG	1.50
52 JG	1.50
53 JG,V:Untouchables	1.50
54 JG,V:Tribunal	1.50
55 JG,V:KarzaWorld	1.50
56 JG,Kaliklak	1.50
57 JG,V:BaronKarza	1.50
58 JG,V:BaronKarza	1.50
59 JG,V:TheMakers	1.50
Ann.#1,SD	2.00
#2 SD	1.50

[2nd Series]

1 V:The Makers	1.50
2 AAd(c),V:The Makers	1.50
3 Huntarr'sEgg	1.00
4 V:The Makers	1.00
5 The Spiral Path	1.00
6 L:Bug	1.00
7 Acroyear	1.00
8 V:Scion	1.00
9 R:Devil	1.00

All comics prices listed are for _Near Mint_ condition.

MARVEL

10 V:Enigma Force	1.00
11 V:Scion	1.00
12 V:Scion	1.00
13 V:Dark Armada	1.00
14 V:Keys of the Zodiac	1.00
15 O:Marionette	1.00
16 Secret Wars II	1.50
17 V:Scion	1.00
18 Acroyear	1.00
19 R:Baron Karza	1.00
20 Last Issue	1.25

MICRONAUTS
(Special Edition) Dec., 1983

1 MGo/JRu,rep.	2.00
2 MGo/JRu,rep.	2.00
3 Rep.MG/JRu	2.00
4 Rep.MG/JRu	2.00
5 Rep.MG/JRu,April, 1984	2.00

MIDNIGHT MEN
Epic *Heavy Hitters* 1993

1 HC,I:Midnight Men	2.75
2 HC,J:Barnett	2.25
3 HC,Pasternak is Midnight Man	2.25
4 HC,Last issue	2.25

MIDNIGHT SONS UNLIMITED
1993–95

1 JQ,JBi,MT(c),A:Midnight Sons	4.25
2 BSz(c),F:Midnight Sons	4.25
3 JR2(c),JS,A:Spider-Man	4.25
4 Siege of Darkness #17, D:2nd Ghost Rider	4.25
5 DQ(s),F:Mordred,Vengeance, Morbius,Werewolf,Blaze, I:Wildpride	4.25
6 DQ(s),F:Dr.Strange	3.95
7 DQ(s),F:Man-Thing	3.95
8	3.95
9 J:Mighty Destroyer	3.95

MIGHTY MARVEL WESTERN
Oct., 1968

1 JK,All reprints,B:Rawhide Kid Kid Colt,Two-Gun Kids	25.00
2 JK,DAy,Beware of the Barker Brothers	20.00
3 HT(c),JK,DAy,Walking Death	20.00
4 HT(c),DAy	20.00
5 HT(c),DAy,Ambush	20.00
6 HT(c),DAy Doom in the Desert	20.00
7 DAy,V:Murderous Masquerader	20.00
8 HT(c),DAy,Rustler's on the Range	20.00
9 JSe(c),JK,DAy,V:Dr Danger	20.00
10 OW,DH,Cougar	20.00
11 V:The Enforcers	15.00
12 JK,V:Blackjack Bordon	15.00
13 V:Grizzly	15.00
14 JK.V:The Enforcers	15.00
15 Massacre at Medicine Bend	15.00
16 JK,Mine of Death	15.00
17 Ambush at Blacksnake Mesa	15.00
18 Six-Gun Thunderer	15.00
19 Reprints cont	15.00
20 same	15.00
21 same	10.00
22	10.00
23 same	10.00
24 JDa,E:Kid Colt	10.00

25 B:Matt Slade	10.00
26 thru 31 Reprints	@10.00
32 JK,AW,Ringo Kid #23	7.00
33 thru 36 Reprints	@7.00
37 JK,AW Two-Gun #51	7.00
38 thru 45 Reprints	@7.00
46 same,Sept., 1976	7.00

MIGHTY HEROES
Nov., 1997

1-shot SLo, Diaper Man, Rope Man, Cuckoo Man, Tornado Man, Strong Man, etc.	3.00

SABAN'S MIGHTY MORPHIN POWER RANGERS

1 SLo,FaN,New ongoing series	2.25
2 FaN,RLm,JP,more	1.75
3 FaN,RLm,JP,more adventures	1.75
4 LSn,JP,V:Glob monster	1.75
5	1.75
6	1.75
7 Close Encounter with Alien	1.75
Photo Adaptation	2.95

SABAN'S MIGHTY MORPHIN POWER RANGERS: NINJA RANGERS/ VR TROOPERS

1 FaN,RLm,JP,flip book	1.75
2 JP,flip book	1.75
3 New outfits	1.75
4	1.75
5	1.75
6	1.75

MIGHTY MOUSE
[1st Series] Fall, 1946

1 Terytoons Presents	900.00
2	450.00
3	300.00
4 Summer, 1947	300.00

Mighty Mouse #3
© *Marvel Entertainment Group*

MIGHTY MOUSE
Oct., 1990

1 EC,Dark Mite Returns	3.00
2 EC,V:The Glove	2.00
3 EC/JBr(c)Prince Say More	1.50
4 EC/GP(c)Alt.Universe #1	1.50
5 EC,Alt.Universe #2	1.50
6 'Ferment',A:MacFurline'	1.50
7 EC,V:Viral Worm	1.25
8 EC,BAT-BAT:Year One, O:Bug Wonder	1.25
9 EC,BAT-BAT:Year One, V:Smoker	1.25
10 'Night o/t Rating Lunatics'	1.25

MILLIE THE MODEL
Winter, 1945

1 O:Millie the Model, Bowling(c)	450.00
2 Totem Pole(c)	275.00
3 Anti-Noise(c)	175.00
4 Bathing Suit(c)	175.00
5 Blame it on Fame	175.00
6 Beauty and the Beast	175.00
7 Bathing Suit(c)	175.00
8 Fancy Dress(c),HK,Hey Look	175.00
9 Paris(c),BW	200.00
10 Jewelry(c),HK,Hey Look	175.00
11 HK,Giggles and Grins	125.00
12 A;Rusty,Hedy Devine	100.00
13 A;Hedy Devine,HK,Hey Look	125.00
14 HK,Hey Look	125.00
15 HK,Hey Look	75.00
16	100.00
17 thru 20	@80.00
21 thru 30	@60.00
31 thru 75	@50.00
76 thru 99	@30.00
100	35.00
101 thru 126	@25.00
127 Millie/Clicker	30.00
128 A:Scarlet Mayfair	25.00
129 The Truth about Agnes	25.00
130 thru 153	@25.00
154 B:New Millie	25.00
155 thru 206	@25.00
207 Dec., 1973	25.00
Ann.#1 How Millie Became a Model	150.00
Ann.#2 Millies Guide to the world of Modeling	125.00
Ann.#3 Many Lives of Millie	75.00
Ann.#4 Many Lives of Millie	30.00

MISS AMERICA COMICS
1944

1 Miss America(c),pin-ups	1,200.00

MISS AMERICA MAGAZINE
Nov., 1944—Nov. 1958

2 Ph(c),Miss America costume I;Patsy Walker,Buzz Baxter, Hedy Wolfe	1,000.00
3 Ph(c),A:Patsy Walker,Miss America	400.00
4 Ph(c),Betty Page,A:Patsy Walker,Miss America	400.00
5 Ph(c),A:Patsy Walker,Miss America	400.00
6 Ph(c),A:Patsy Walker	75.00
7 Patsy Walker stories	50.00
8 same	50.00
9 same	50.00

---

10 same 50.00
11 same 50.00
12 same 50.00
13 thru 18 . . . . @50.00
21 . . . . 55.00
22 thru 45 . . . . @35.00
46 thru 93 . . . . @30.00

MISS FURY COMICS
Timely Winter, 1942-43
1 Newspaper strip reprints,
ASh(c) O:Miss Fury 2,700.00
2 V:Nazis(c) 1,200.00
3 Hitler/Nazi Flag(c) 1,000.00
4 ASh(c),Japanese(c) 750.00
5 ASh(c),Gangster(c) 700.00
6 Gangster(c) 650.00
7 Gangster(c) 600.00
8 Atom-Bomb Secrets(c)
Winter, 1946 . . . . 600.00

MISTY
Star Dec., 1985
1 F:Millie the Models Niece 1.50
2 thru 5 . . . . @1.00
6 May, 1986 . . . . 1.00

MITZI COMICS
Timely Spring, 1948
1 HK:Hey Look,Giggles
and Grins 125.00
Becomes:
MITZI'S BOYFRIEND
2 F:Chip,Mitzi/Chip(c) 50.00
3 Chips adventures 35.00
4 thru 7 same . . . . @35.00
Becomes:
MITZI'S ROMANCES
8 Mitzi/Chip(c) 40.00
9 . . . . 35.00
10 Dec., 1949 . . . . 35.00

MODELING WITH MILLIE
See: DATE WITH MILLIE

MOEBIUS
Epic Oct., 1987
1 . . . . 12.00
2 . . . . 12.00
3 . . . . 15.00
4 . . . . 12.00
5 . . . . 12.00
6 1988 . . . . 12.00

MOEBIUS: FUSION
1 128pg Sketchbook 19.95

MOLLY MANTON'S ROMANCES
Sept., 1949
1 Ph(c),Dare Not Marry 85.00
2 Ph(c),Romances of 60.00
Becomes:
ROMANTIC AFFAIRS
3 Ph(c) 35.00

MONSTER MENACE
1 thru 4 SD,rep. . . . . @1.25

MONSTER OF FRANKENSTEIN
Jan., 1973
1 MP,Frankenstein's Monster . . 40.00
2 MP,Bride of the Monster . . . 25.00
3 MP,Revenge 25.00
4 MP,Monster's Death 25.00
5 MP,The Monster Walks
Among Us 25.00
Becomes:
FRANKENSTEIN
1973–75
6 MP,Last of the Frankensteins . 15.00
7 JB,The Fiend and the Fury . . 15.00
8 JB,A:Dracula 25.00
9 JB,A:Dracula 25.00
10 JB,Death Strikes Frankenstein 15.00
11 Carnage at CastleFrankenstein 10.00
12 Frankenstein's Monster today 10.00
13 Undying Fiend 10.00
14 Fury of the Night Creature . . 10.00
15 Trapped in a Nightmare 10.00
16 The Brute and the Berserker . 10.00
17 Phoenix Aflame 10.00
18 Children of the Damned
Sept., 1975 . . . . 10.00

MONSTERS ON THE PROWL
See: CHAMBER OF DARKNESS

MONSTERS UNLEASHED
July, 1973
1 GM(c),GC,DW,B&W Mag . . . 30.00
2 JB,FB,BEv,B:Frankenstein . . 25.00
3 NA(c),GK,GM,GT,B:Man-Thing . 25.00
4 JB,GC,BK,I:Satana 25.00
5 JB 15.00
6 MP 15.00
7 AW 15.00
8 GP,NA 20.00
9 A:Wendigo 20.00
10 O:Tigra 20.00
11 FB(C),April, 1975 . . . . 20.00
Ann.#1 GK 20.00

MOON KNIGHT
[1st Regular Series] Nov., 1980
1 BSz,O:Moon Knight 6.00
2 BSz,V:Slasher 4.00
3 BSz,V:Midnight Man 3.50
4 BSz,V:Committee of 5 . . . . . . 3.50
5 BSz,V:Red Hunter 3.50
6 BSz,V:White Angels 3.50
7 BSz,V:Moon Kings 3.50
8 BSz,V:Moon Kings, Drug 3.00
9 BSz,V:Midnight Man 3.00
10 BSz,V:Midnight Man 3.00
11 BSz,V:Creed (Angel Dust) . . . 3.00
12 BSz,V:Morpheus 3.00
13 BSz,A:Daredevil & Jester 3.00
14 BSz,V:Stained Glass Scarlet . . 3.00
15 FM(c),BSz,1st Direct 4.00
16 V:Blacksmith 3.00
17 BSz,V:Master Sniper 3.00
18 BSz,V:Slayers Elite 3.00
19 BSz,V:Arsenal 3.00
20 BSz,V:Arsenal 3.00
21 A:Bother Voodoo 2.25
22 BSz,V:Morpheus 2.50
23 BSz,V:Morpheus 2.50

Moon Knight (1st Series) #1
© Marvel Entertainment Group

24 BSz,V:Stained Glass Scarlet . . 2.50
25 BSz,Black Specter 2.50
26 KP,V:Cabbie Killer 2.00
27 A:Kingpin 2.00
28 BSz,"Spirits in the Sands" . . . 2.00
29 BSz,V:Werewolf 3.00
30 BSz,V:Werewolf 3.00
31 TA,V:Savage Studs 2.00
32 KN,Druid Walsh 2.00
33 KN,V:Druid Walsh 2.00
34 KN,Marc Spector 2.00
35 KN,X-Men,FF,V:The Fly
DoubleSized 3.00
36 A:Dr.Strange 2.00
37 V:Zohar 2.00
38 V:Zohar 2.00
[2nd Regular Series] 1985
1 O:Moon Knight,DoubleSize . . . 2.50
2 Yucatan 2.00
3 V:Morpheus 2.00
4 A:Countess 2.00
5 V:Lt.Flint 2.00
6 GI,LastIssue 2.00
[3rd Regular Series] 1989–94
1 V:Bushmaster 5.00
2 A:Spider-Man 4.00
3 V:Bushmaster 2.50
4 RH,A:Midnight,Black Cat . . . 2.50
5 V:Midnight,BlackCat 2.50
6 A:BrotherVoodoo 2.50
7 A:BrotherVoodoo 2.50
8 TP,A:Punisher,A of V 4.00
9 TP,A:Punisher,A of V 4.00
10 V:Killer Shrike,A of V 2.00
11 TP,V:Arsenal 2.00
12 TP,V:Bushman,A:Arsenal 2.00
13 TP,V:Bushman 2.00
14 TP,V:Bushman 2.00
15 TP,Trial o/Marc Spector #1,A:
Silv.Sable,Sandman,Paladin . 3.00
16 TP,Trial o/Marc Spector #2,A:
Silv.Sable,Sandman,Paladin . 3.00
17 TP,Trial o/Marc Spector #3 . . 3.00
18 TP,Trial o/Marc Spector #4 . . 3.00
19 RLd(c),TP,SpM,Punisher 3.50
20 TP,A:Spider-Man,Punisher . . . 3.00
21 TP,Spider-Man,Punisher 3.00

All comics prices listed are for *Near Mint* condition.

22 I:Harbinger 2.00
23 Confrontation 2.00
24 A:Midnight 2.00
25 MBa,TP,A:Ghost Rider 3.00
26 BSz(c),TP,B:Scarlet Redemption
  V:Stained Glass Scarlet 2.00
27 TP,V:Stained Glass Scarlet . . . 2.00
28 TP,V:Stained Glass Scarlet . . . 2.00
29 TP,V:Stained Glass Scarlet . . . 2.00
30 TP,V:Stained Glass Scarlet . . . 2.00
31 TP,E:Scarlet Redemption,
  A:Hobgoblin 2.50
32 TP,V:Hobgoblin,SpM(in Black) 3.00
33 TP,V:Hobgoblin,A:Spider-Man . 3.00
34 V:Killer Shrike 2.00
35 TP,Return of Randall Spector
  Pt.1,A:Punisher 2.00
36 TP,A:Punisher,Randall 2.00
37 TP,A:Punisher,Randall 2.00
38 TP,A:Punisher,Randall 2.00
39 TP,N:Moon Knight,A:Dr.Doom . 2.00
40 TP,V:Dr.Doom 2.00
41 TP,Infinity War,I:Moonshade . . 2.00
42 TP,Infinity War,V:Moonshade . 2.00
43 TP(i),Infinity War 2.00
44 Inf.War,A:Dr.Strange.FF 2.00
45 V:Demogoblin 2.00
46 V:Demogoblin 2.00
47 Legacy Quest Scenario 2.00
48 I:Deadzone 2.00
49 V:Deadzone 2.00
50 A:Avengers,I:Hellbent,
  Die-cut(c) 3.50
51 A:Gambit,V:Hellbent 2.00
52 A:Gambit,Werewolf 2.00
53 "Pang" 2.00
54 . . . . 2.00
55 SPa,V:Sunstreak 9.00
56 SPa,V:Seth 10.00
57 SPa,Inf.Crusade 6.00
58 SPa(c),A:Hellbent 3.00
59 SPa(c), ... 3.00
60 E:TKa(s),SPa,D:Moonknight . . 6.00
Spec.#1 ANi,A:Shang-Chi 2.50
1-shot Moon Knight: Divided We Fall
  DCw,V:Bushman (1992) 4.95

MOON KNIGHT
(Special Edition) Nov., 1983
1 BSz,reprints 2.00
2 BSz,reprints 2.00
3 BSz,reprints,Jan., 1984 . . . . . . 2.00

MOON KNIGHT
Nov. 1997–Feb. 1998
1 (of 4) DgM, Moon Knight returns 2.50
1 signed by Tommy Lee Edwards
  (250 copies) 20.00
2 DgM,A:Scarlet 2.50
3 DgM,Resurrection War,V:Black
  Spectre 2.50
4 DgM,Resurrecton War, concl. . 2.50

MOONSHADOW
Epic May, 1985
1 JMu,O:Moonshadow 5.00
2 JMu,Into Space 3.50
3 JMu,The Looney Bin 3.50
4 JMu,Fights Ira 3.50
5 JMu,Prisoner 3.50
6 JMu,Hero of War 3.50
7 JMu,UnkshussFamily 3.50
8 JMu,Social Outcast 3.50
9 JMu,Search For Ira 3.50

10 JMu,Internat.House of T 3.50
11 JMu,UnkshussFamily 3.50
12 JMu,UnkshussFamily,Feb.1987 3.50

Morbius #14
© *Marvel Entertainment Group*

MORBIUS
1992–95
1 V:Lilith,Lilin,A:Blaze,Gh.Rider,
  Rise o/t Midnight Sons #3,
  polybagged w/poster 4.00
2 V:Simon Stroud 2.50
3 A:Spider-Man 2.00
4 I:Dr.Paine,C:Spider-Man 2.00
5 V:Basilisk,(inc Superman tribute
  on letters page) 2.00
6 V:Basilisk 2.00
7 V:Vic Slaughter 2.00
8 V:Nightmare 2.00
9 V:Nightmare 2.00
10 Two Tales 2.00
11 A:Nightstalkers 2.00
12 Midnight Massacre#4 . . . . . . 2.50
13 R:Martine,A:Lilith 2.00
14 RoW,V:Nightmare,A:Werewolf . 2.00
15 A:Ghost Rider,Werewolf 2.00
16 GWt(s),Siege of Darkness#5 . . 2.00
17 GWt(s),Siege of Darkness#17 . 2.00
18 GWt(s),A:Deathlok 2.00
19 GWt(s),A:Deathlok 2.00
20 GWt(s),I:Bloodthirst 2.00
21 B:Dance of the Hunter,A:SpM . 2.25
22 A:Spider-Man 2.25
23 E:Dance of the Hunter,A:SpM . 2.25
24 Return of the Dragon 2.25
25 RoW 2.50
26 . . . . 1.95
27 . . . . 1.95
28 A:Werewolf 1.95
29 . . . . 1.95
30 New Morbius 1.95
31 A:Mortine 1.95
32 Another Kill 1.95

MORBIUS REVISITED
1993
1 WMc,rep.Fear #20 . . . . 1.95
2 WMc,rep.Fear #28 . . . . 1.95
3 WMc,rep.Fear #29 . . . . 1.95

4 WMc,rep.Fear #30 . . . . 1.95
5 WMc,rep.Fear #31 . . . . 1.95

MORT THE DEAD TEENAGER
1993–94
1 LHa(s),I:Mort 1.75
2 thru 4 LHa(s), ... 1.75

MOTHER TERESA
1984
1 Mother Teresa Story 2.00

MOTOR MOUTH & KILLPOWER
Marvel UK 1992–93
1 GFr,A:Nick Fury,I:Motor
  Mouth,Killpower 3.00
2 GFr,A:Nick Fury, ... 2.00
3 GFr,V:Killpower,A:Punisher . . . 2.00
4 GFr,A:Nick Fury,Warheads,
  Hell's Angel,O:Killpower 2.00
5 GFr,A:Excalibur,Archangel 2.00
6 GFr,A:Cable,Punisher 2.00
7 EP,A:Cable,Nick Fury 2.00
8 JFr,A:Cable,Nick Fury 2.00
9 JFr,A:Cable,N.Fury,V:Harpies . 2.00
10 V:Red Sonja 2.00
11 V:Zachary Sorrow 2.00
12 A:Death's Head II 2.00
13 A:Death's Head II 2.00

Ms. Marvel #2
© *Marvel Entertainment Group*

MS. MARVEL
Jan., 1977
1 JB,O:Ms Marvel 7.00
2 JB,JSt,V:Scorpion 5.00
3 JB,JSt,V:Doomsday Man 3.00
4 JM,JSt,V:Destructor 3.00
5 JM,JSt,A:V:Vision 3.00
6 JM,JSt,V:Grotesk 3.00
7 JM,JSt,V:Modok 3.00
8 JM,JSt,V:Grotesk 3.00
9 KP,JSt,I:Deathbird 5.00
10 JB,TP,V:Deathbird,Modok . . . 3.00
11 V:Elementals 3.00
12 V:Hecate 3.00

---

13 Bedlam in Boston 2.00
14 V:Steeplejack 2.00
15 V:Tigershark 2.00
16 V:Tigershark,A:Beast 14.00
17 . . . . 6.00
18 I:Mystique,A;Avengers 17.00
19 A:Captain Marvel 3.00
20 V:Lethal Lizards,N:Ms.Marvel . 2.00
21 V:Lethal Lizards 2.00
22 V:Deathbirds 2.00
23 The Woman who Fell to Earth
    April, 1979 . . . . 2.00

MUPPET BABIES
Star August, 1984
1 thru 10 . . . . @1.00
11 thru 20 . . . . @1.00
21 thru 25 July, 1989 . . . . @1.00

MUPPETS TAKE MANHATTAN
1 movie adapt,November, 1984 . 1.00
2 movie adapt 1.00
3 movie adapt,Jan., 1985 . . . . . . 1.00

MUTANTS: THE AMAZING X-MEN
1 X-Men After Xavier 3.50
2 Exodus, Dazzler,V:Abyss 2.25
3 F:Bishop 1.95
4 V:Apocalypse 1.95

MUTANTS: THE ASTONISHING X-MEN
1 Uncanny X-Men 3.50
2 V:Holocaust 2.25
3 V:Abyss 1.95
4 V:Beast,Infinities 1.95

MUTANTS: GENERATION NEXT
1 Generation X Ax 3.50
2 Genetic Slave Pens 2.25
3 V:Sugar Man 1.95
4 V:Sugar Man 1.95

MUTANT X
Aug. 1998
1 HMe,TR,F:Havok, 48pg 3.00

MUTATIS
Epic
1 I:Mutatis 2.25
2 O:Mutatis 2.25
3 A:Mutatis 2.25

MY DIARY
Dec., 1949–March 1950
1 Ph(c),The Man I Love 75.00
2 Ph(c),I Was Anybody's Girl . . 60.00

MY LOVE
July, 1949
1 Ph(c),One Heart to Give 75.00
2 Ph(c),Hate in My Heart 50.00
3 Ph(c), ... 50.00
4 Ph(c),Betty Page, April,1950 200.00

MY LOVE
Sept., 1969
1 Love story reprints 25.00

2 thru 9 . . . . @4.00
10 . . . . 5.00
11 thru 38 . . . . @3.00
39 March, 1976 . . . . 3.00

MY ROMANCE
Sept., 1948
1 Romance Stories 75.00
2 . . . . 50.00
3 . . . . 50.00
Becomes:
MY OWN ROMANCE
4 Romance Stories Continue . . 75.00
5 thru 10 . . . . @40.00
11 thru 20 . . . . @35.00
21 thru 50 . . . . @30.00
51 thru 54 . . . . @25.00
55 ATh 35.00
56 thru 60 . . . . @25.00
61 thru 70 . . . . @20.00
71 AW 55.00
72 thru 76 . . . . @20.00
Becomes:
TEENAGE ROMANCE
77 Romance Stories Continue . . 20.00
78 thru 85 . . . . @20.00
86 March, 1962 . . . . 20.00

MYS-TECH WARS
Marvel UK 1993
1 BHi,A:FF,X-Men,Avengers 2.00
2 A:FF,X-Men,X-Force 2.00
3 BHi,A:X-Men,X-Force 2.00
4 A:Death's Head II 2.00

MYSTERY TALES
Atlas March, 1952
1 GC,Horror Strikes at Midnight 600.00
2 BK,BEv,OW,The Corpse
    is Mine 325.00
3 RH,GC,JM, The Vampire
    Strikes 250.00
4 Funeral of Horror 250.00
5 Blackout at Midnight 250.00
6 . . . . 250.00
7 JRo,The Ghost Hunter 250.00
8 BEv 250.00
9 BEv(c),the Man in the Morgue 250.00
10 BEV(c),GT,What Happened
    to Harry 250.00
11 BEv(c) 175.00
12 GT,MF 200.00
13 . . . . 175.00
14 BEv(c),GT 175.00
15 RH(c),EK 175.00
16 . . . . 175.00
17 RH(c) 175.00
18 AW,DAy,GC 185.00
19 . . . . 165.00
20 Electric Chair 165.00
21 JF,MF,Decapitation 175.00
22 JF,MF 200.00
23 thru 27 . . . . @150.00
28 . . . . 125.00
29 thru 32 . . . . @135.00
33 BEv 125.00
34 . . . . 125.00
35 BEv 125.00
36 . . . . 135.00
37 DW 125.00
38 . . . . 125.00
39 BK 135.00
40 . . . . 135.00

41 thru 43 . . . . @125.00
44 AW 150.00
45 SD 135.00
46 RC,SD,JP 150.00
47 DAy 150.00
48 . . . . 125.00
49 GM,AT 125.00
50 JO,AW 150.00
51 DAy 150.00
52 . . . . 125.00
53 . . . . 125.00
54 RC,August, 1957 . . . . 150.00

Mystical Tales #1
© Marvel Entertainment Group

MYSTICAL TALES
Atlas June, 1956
1 BEv,BP,JO,Say the Magical
    Words 300.00
2 BEv(c),JO,Black Blob 200.00
3 BEv(c),RC,Four Doors To . . 175.00
4 BEv(c).The Condemned . . . 175.00
5 AW,Meeting at Midnight . . . 175.00
6 BK,AT,He Hides in the Tower 150.00
7 BEv,JF,JO,AT,FBe,The
    Haunted Tower 150.00
8 BK,SC, Stone Walls Can't
    Stop Him,August, 1957 . . . 150.00

MYSTIC COMICS
Timely March, 1940
[1st Series]
1 ASh(c),O;The Blue Blaze,Dynamic
    Man,Flexo,B:Dakor the Magician
    A:Zephyr Jones,3X's,Deep Sea
    Demon,Bondage(c) 12,000.00
2 ASh(c),B:The Invisible Man
    Mastermind, ... 3,500.00
3 ASh(c),O:Hercules 2,500.00
4 ASh(c),O:Thin Man,Black Widow
    E:Hercules,Blue Blazes,Dynamic
    Man,Flexo,Invisible Man . . 2,800.00
5 ASh(c)O:The Black Marvel,
    Blazing Skull,Super Slave
    Terror,Sub-Earth Man . . . 2,500.00
6 ASh(c),O:The Challenger,
    B:The Destroyer 2,800.00
7 S&K(c),B:The Witness,O:Davey
    and the Demon,E;The Black

All comics prices listed are for *Near Mint* condition.

Widow,Hitler(c) 3,000.00
8 Bondage(c) 1,500.00
9 MSy,DRi,Hitler/Bondage(c) . 1,500.00
10 E:Challenger,Terror 1,500.00
[2nd Series] Oct., 1944
1 B:The Angel,Human Torch,
Destroyer,Terry Vance,
Tommy Tyme,Bondage(c)   1,800.00
2 E:Human Torch,Terry
Vance,Bondage(c) 1,000.00
3 E:The Angel,Tommy Tyme
Bondage(c) 900.00
4 ASh(c),A:Young Allies
Winter, 1944-45 . . . . 800.00

MYSTIC
[3rd Series] March, 1951
1 MSy,Strange Tree 650.00
2 MSy,Dark Dungeon 350.00
3 GC,Jaws of Creeping Death   300.00
4 BW,MSy,The Den of the
Devil Bird 600.00
5 MSy,Face 200.00
6 BW,She Wouldn't Stay Dead 550.00
7 GC,Untold Horror waits
in the Tomb 200.00
8 DAy(c),BEv,GK,A Monster
Among Us 200.00
9 BEv 200.00
10 GC 200.00
11 JR,The Black Gloves 175.00
12 GC 175.00
13 In the Dark 175.00
14 The Corpse and I 175.00
15 GT,JR,House of Horror 175.00
16 A Scream in the Dark 175.00
17 BEv,Behold the Vampire . . . 175.00
18 BEv(c),The Russian Devil . . 175.00
19 Swamp Girl 175.00
20 RH(c) 175.00
21 BEv(c),GC 150.00
22 RH(c) 150.00
23 RH(c),RA,Chilling Tales . . . 150.00
24 GK,How Many Times Can
You Die 150.00
25 RH(c),RA,E.C.Swipe 150.00
26 Severed Head(c) 150.00
27 Who Walks with a Zombie . 135.00
28 DW,Not Enough Dead 135.00
29 SMo,The Unseen 135.00
30 RH(c),DW 135.00
31 SC,JKz 135.00
32 The Survivor 135.00
33 thru 36 . . . . @135.00
37 thru 51 . . . . @125.00
52 . . . . 125.00
53 thru 57 . . . . @125.00
58 thru 60 . . . . @110.00
61 . . . . 100.00

'NAM, THE
Dec., 1986
1 MGo,Vietnam War 3.00
1a 2nd printing 1.50
2 MGo,Dust Off 2.50
3 MGo,Three Day Pass 2.00
4 MGo,TV newscrew 2.00
5 MGo,Top Sgt. 2.00
6 MGo,Monsoon 2.00
7 MGo,Cedar Falls 2.00
8 MGo,5th to the 1st 2.00
9 MGo,ActionIssue 2.00
10 MGo,Saigon 2.00
11 MGo,Christmas 1.75

The 'Nam #15
© Marvel Entertainment Group

12 MGo,AgentOrange 1.75
13 MGo 1.75
14 . . . . 1.75
15 ReturningVets 1.75
16 . . . . 1.75
17 Vietcong 1.75
18 . . . . 1.75
19 . . . . 1.75
20 . . . . 1.75
21 . . . . 1.75
22 Thanksgiving 1.75
23 XmasTruce of'67 . . . . 1.75
24 TetOffensive 1.75
25 TetOffensive-KheSanh 1.75
26 Homefront Issue 1.75
27 Candle in the Wind 1.75
28 Borderline 1.75
29 PeaceTalks 1.75
30 TheBunker 1.75
31 Fire and Ice 1.75
32 Nam in America 1.75
33 SpecialistDaniels 1.75
34 OperationPhoenix 1.75
35 Xmas-BobHope 1.75
36 RacialTension 1.75
37 Colorblind 1.75
38 Minefields 1.75
39 . . . . 1.75
40 . . . . 1.75
41 ,A:Thor,Iron Man, Cap.Am . . . 1.75
42 . . . . 1.75
43 . . . . 1.75
44 SDr 1.75
45 . . . . 1.75
46 . . . . 1.75
47 TD 1.75
48 TD 1.75
49 Donut Dolly #1 . . . . 1.75
50 HT,Donut Dolly #2 DoubSz . . 2.00
51 HT,Donut Dolly #3 . . . . 1.75
52 Frank Castle(Punisher)#1 . . . . 3.00
52a 2nd printing 2.00
53 Punisher #2 . . . . 2.00
54 Death of Joe Hallen #1 . . . . . 1.75
55 TD,Death of Joe Hallen #2 . . . 1.50

56 TD,Death of Joe Hallen #3 . . . 1.50
57 TD,Death of Joe Hallen #4 . . . 1.50
58 TD,Death of Joe Hallen #5 . . . 1.50
59 P.O.W. Story #1 . . . . 1.50
60 P.O.W. Story #2 . . . . 1.50
61 P.O.W. Story #3 . . . . 1.50
62 Speed & Ice,pt.1 . . . . 1.50
63 Speed & Ice,pt.2 . . . . 1.50
64 Speed & Ice,pt.3 . . . . 1.50
65 Speed & Ice,pt.4 . . . . 1.75
66 RH,Speed & Ice,pt.5 . . . . 1.75
67 A:Punisher 2.00
68 A:Punisher 2.00
69 A:Punisher 2.00
70 Don Lomax writes 1.75
71 Vietnamese Point of View 1.75
72 The trials of war 1.75
73 War on the Homefront 1.75
74 Seige at An Loc 1.75
75 My Lai Massacre 2.25
76 R:Rob Little 1.75
77 Stateside 1.75
78 . . . . 1.75
79 Beginning of the End#1 . . . . . 1.75
80 MGo(c),'68 Tet Offensive 1.75
81 MGo(c),TET Offensive ends . . 1.75
82 TET Offensive 1.75
83 thru 84 Last issue 1.75

'NAM MAGAZINE, THE
(B&W) Aug., 1988–May 1989
1 Reprints 3.00
2 thru 10 . . . . @2.50

NAMORA
Fall, 1948
1 BEv,DR 1,200.00
2 BEv,A:Sub-Mariner,Blonde
Phantom 1,000.00
3 BEv,A:Sub-Mariner,Dec.,1948 950.00

NAMOR THE
SUB-MARINER
April, 1990
1 JBy,BWi,I:Desmond
& Phoebe Marrs 3.50
2 JBy,BWi,V:Griffin 2.50
3 JBy,BWi,V:Griffin 2.50
4 JBy,A:Reed & Sue Richards,
Tony Stark 2.50
5 JBy,A:FF,IronMan,C:Speedball 2.50
6 JBy,V:Sluj 2.50
7 JBy,V:Sluj 2.50
8 JBy,V:Headhunter,R:D.Rand . . 2.50
9 JBy,V:Headhunter 2.50
10 JBy,V:Master Man,Warrior
Woman 2.00
11 JBy,V:Mast.Man,War.Woman . 2.00
12 JBy,R:Invaders,Spitfire 2.00
13 JBy,Namor on Trial,A:Fantastic
Four,Captain America,Thor . . . 2.00
14 JBy,R:Lady Dorma,A:Kazar
Griffin 2.00
15 JBy,A:Iron Fist 2.00
16 JBy,A:Punisher,V:Iron Fist . . . 2.00
17 JBy,V:Super Skrull(Iron Fist) . . 2.00
18 JBy,V:SuperSkrull,A:Punisher . 2.00
19 JBy,V:Super Skrull,D:D.Marrs . 2.00
20 JBy,Search for Iron Fist,
O:Namorita 2.00
21 JBy,Visit to K'un Lun 2.00
22 JBy,Fate of Iron Fist,
C:Wolverine 2.00
23 JBy,BWi,Iron Fist Contd.,

C:Wolverine	2.00
24 JBy,BWi,V:Wolverine	2.50
25 JBy,BWi,V:Master Khan	2.00
26 JaL,BWi,Search For Namor	5.00
27 JaL,BWi,V:Namorita	4.00
28 JaL,BWi,A:Iron Fist	3.00
29 JaL,BWi,After explosion	2.50
30 JaL,A:Doctor Doom	2.50
31 JaL,V:Doctor Doom	2.50
32 JaL,V:Doctor Doom,	
Namor regains memory	2.50
33 JaL,V:Master Khan	2.00
34 JaL,R:Atlantis	2.00
35 JaL,V:Tiger Shark	2.00
36 JaL,I:Suma-Ket,A:Tiger Shark	2.00
37 JaL,Blue Holo-Grafix,Altantean	
Civil War,N:Namor	2.50
38 JaL,O:Suma-Ket	2.00
39 A:Tigershark,V:Suma-Ket	1.50
40 V:Suma-Ket	1.50
41 V:War Machine	1.50
42 MCW,A:Stingray,V:Dorcas	1.50
43 MCW,V:Orka,Dorcas	1.50

Namor, The Sub-Mariner #57
© Marvel Entertainment Group

44 I:Albatross	1.50
45 GI,A:Sunfire,V:Attuma	1.50
46 GI,	1.50
47 GI,Starblast #2	1.50
48 GI,Starblast #9,A:FF	1.50
49 GI,A:Ms. Marrs	1.50
50 GI,Holo-grafx(c),A:FF	3.00
50a Newsstand Ed.	2.00
51 AaL,	1.75
52 GI,I:Sea Leopard	1.75
53 GI,V:Sea Leopard	1.75
54 GI,I:Llyron	1.50
55 GI,V:Llyron	1.50
56 GI,V:Llyron	1.50
57 A:Capt. America, V:Llyron	1.50
58	1.50
59 GI,V:Abomination	1.50
60 A:Morgan Le Fay	1.50
61 Atlantis Rising	1.50
62 V:Triton	1.50
Ann.#1 Subterran.Odyssey #3	2.00
Ann.#2 Return o/Defenders,pt.3	4.00
Ann.#3 I:Assassin,A:Iron Fist,	
w/Trading card	3.25
Ann.#4 V:Hydra	3.25

NAVY ACTION
August, 1954

1 US Navy War Stories	100.00
2 Navy(c)	50.00
3 thru 17	@35.00
18 August, 1957	35.00

NAVY COMBAT
Atlas June, 1955

1 DH,B;Torpedo Taylor	100.00
2 DH	50.00
3 DH	35.00
4 DH	35.00
5 DH	35.00
6 A:Battleship Burke	35.00
7 thru 10	@35.00
11 MD	30.00
12 RC	55.00
13	25.00
14	30.00
15	25.00
16	25.00
17 AW	65.00
18	25.00
19	25.00
20 Oct., 1958	25.00

NAVY TALES
Atlas Jan., 1957

1 BEv(c),BP,Torpedoes	100.00
2 AW,RC,One Hour to Live	80.00
3 JSe(c)	65.00
4 JSe(c),GC,JSt,RC,July, 1957	65.00

NELLIE THE NURSE
Atlas 1945

1 Beach(c)	225.00
2 Nellie's Date(c)	100.00
3 Swimming Pool(c)	85.00
4 Roller Coaster(c)	85.00
5 Hospital(c),HK,Hey Look	85.00
6 Bedside Manner(c)	75.00
7 Comic book(c)A:Georgie	75.00
8 Hospital(c),A:Georgie	75.00
9 BW,Nellie/Swing(c)A:Millie	100.00
10 Bathing Suit(c),A:Millie	80.00
11 HK,Hey Look	100.00
12 HK,Giggles 'n' Grins	90.00
13 HK	60.00
14 HK	75.00
15 HK	75.00
16 HK	75.00
17 HK.A:Annie Oakley	75.00
18 HK	75.00
19	60.00
20	60.00
21	50.00
22	50.00
23	50.00
24	50.00
25	50.00
26	50.00
27	50.00
28 HK,Rusty Reprint	55.00
29 thru 35	@40.00
36 Oct., 1952	40.00

NEW ADVENTURES OF CHOLLY & FLYTRAP
Epic

1	4.95
2	3.95
3	3.95

NEW MUTANTS, THE
March, 1983

1 BMc,MG,O:New Mutants	8.00
2 BMc,MG,V:Sentinels	5.00
3 BMc,MG,V:Brood Alien	4.00
4 SB,BMc,A:Peter Bristow	4.00
5 SB,BMc,A:Dark Rider	4.00
6 SB,AG,V:Viper	4.00
7 SB,BMc,V:Axe	4.00
8 SB,BMc,I:Amara Aquilla	4.00
9 SB,TMd,I:Selene	4.00
10 SB,BMc,C:Magma	4.00
11 SB,TMd,I:Magma	4.00
12 SB,TMd,J:Magma	4.00
13 SB,TMd,I:Cypher(Doug Ramsey)	
A:Kitty Pryde,Lilandra	5.00
14 SB,TMd,J:Magik,A:X-Men	4.00
15 SB,TMd,Mass.Academy	4.00
16 SB,TMd,V:Hellions,I:Warpath	
I:Jetstream	5.00
17 SB,TMd,V:Hellions,A:Warpath	5.00
18 BSz,V:Demon Bear,I:New	
Warlock,Magus	8.00
19 BSz,V:Demon Bear	4.00
20 BSz,V:Demon Bear	4.00
21 BSz,O&J:Warlock,doub.sz	7.00
22 BSz,A:X-Men	4.50
23 BSz,Sunspot,Cloak & Dagger	4.00
24 BSz,A:Cloak & Dagger	4.00
25 BSz,A:Cloak & Dagger	8.00
26 BSz,I:Legion(Prof.X's son)	11.00
27 BSz,V:Legion	6.00
28 BSz,O:Legion	5.00
29 BSz,V:Gladiators,I:Guido	
(Strong Guy)	3.00
30 BSz,A:Dazzler	3.00
31 BSz,A:Shadowcat	3.00
32 SL,V:Karma	3.00
33 SL,V:Karma	3.00
34 SL,V:Amahl Farouk	3.00
35 BSz,J:Magneto	3.00
36 BSz,A:Beyonder	3.00
37 BSz,D:New Mutants	3.00
38 BSz,A:Hellions	3.00
39 BSz,A:White Queen	3.00
40 JG,KB,V:Avengers	3.00
41 JG,TA,Mirage	3.00
42 JG,KB,A:Dazzler	3.00
43 SP,V:Empath,A:Warpath	3.00
44 JG,V:Legion	5.00
45 JG,A:Larry Bodine	3.00
46 JG,KB,Mutant Massacre	3.50
47 JG,KB,V:Magnus	3.00
48 JG,CR,Future	3.00
49 VM,Future	3.00
50 JG,V:Magus,R:Prof.X	5.00
51 KN,A:Star Jammers	3.00
52 RL,DGr,Limbo	3.00
53 RL,TA,V:Hellions	3.00
54 SB,TA,N:New Mutants	3.00
55 BBl,TA,V:Aliens	3.00
56 JBr,TA,V:Hellions,A:Warpath	3.00
57 BBl,TA,I&J:Bird-Boy	3.00
58 BBl,TA,Bird-Boy	3.00
59 BBl,TA,Fall of Mutants,	
V:Dr.Animus	3.00
60 BBl,TA,F.of M.,D:Cypher	2.50
61 BBl,TA,Fall of Mutants	2.50
62 JMu,TA:Magma,Hellions	2.50
63 BHa,JRu,Magik	2.50
64 BBl,TA,R:Cypher	2.50
65 BBl,TA,V:FreedomForce	2.50
66 BBl,TA,V:Forge	2.50
67 BBl,I:Gosamyr	2.50
68 BBl,V:Gosamyr	2.50

All comics prices listed are for *Near Mint* condition.   CVA Page 239

MARVEL

New Mutants #9
© *Marvel Entertainment Group*

69 BBl,AW,I:Spyder 2.50
70 TSh,AM,V:Spyder 2.50
71 BBl,AW,V:N'Astirh 2.50
72 BBl,A,Inferno 2.50
73 BBl,W,A:Colossus 3.00
74 BBl,W,A:X-Terminators 2.50
75 JBy,Mc,Black King,V:Magneto . 4.50
76 RB,TP,J:X-Terminators 2.50
77 RB,V:Mirage 2.50
78 RL,AW,V:FreedomForce 2.50
79 BBl,AW,V:Hela 2.50
80 BBl,AW,Asgard 2.50
81 LW,TSh,JRu,A:Hercules 2.50
82 BBl,AW,Asgard 2.50
83 BBl,Asgard 2.50
84 TSh,AM,A:QueenUla 2.50
85 RLd&TMc(c),BBl,V:Mirage . . 5.00
86 RLd,BWi,V:Vulture,C:Cable . 10.00
87 RLd,BWi,I:Mutant Liberation
   Front,Cable 25.00
87a 2nd Printing 2.00
88 RLd,2nd Cable,V:Freedom
   Force 12.00
89 RLd,V:Freedom Force 8.00
90 RLd,A:Caliban,V:Sabretooth . . 8.00
91 RLd,A:Caliban,Masque,
   V:Sabretooth 8.00
92 RLd(c),BH,V:Skrulls 4.00
93 RLd,A:Wolverine,Sunfire,
   V:Mutant Liberation Front 8.00
94 RLd,A:Wolverine,Sunfire,
   V:Mutant Liberation Front 7.00
95 RLd,Extinction Agenda,V:Hodge
   A:X-Men,X-Factor,D:Warlock . . 7.00
95a 2nd printing(gold) 5.00
96 RLd,ATb,JRu,Extinction Agenda
   V:Hodge,A:X-Men,X-Factor . . 7.00
97 E:LSi(s),RLd(c),JRu,Extinction
   Agenda,V:Hodge 7.00
98 FaN(s),RLd,I:Deadpool,Domino,
   Gideon,L:Rictor 9.00
99 FaN(s),RLd,I:Feral,Shatterstar,
   L:Sunspot,J:Warpath 7.00
100 FaN(s),RLd,J:Feral,Shatterstar,
   I:X-Force,V:Masque,Imperial

Protectorate,A:MLF 9.00
100a 2nd Printing(Gold) 4.00
100b 3rd Printing(Silver) 3.50
Ann.#1 BMc,TP,L.Cheney 7.00
Ann.#2 AD,V:Mojo,I:Psylocke,Meggan
   (American App.) 7.00
Ann.#3 AD,PN,V:Impossible Man . 3.00
Ann.#4 JBr,BMc,Evol.Wars 6.00
Ann.#5 RLd,JBg,MBa,KWi,Atlantis
   Attacks,A:Namorita,I:Surf . . . 15.00
Ann.#6 RLd(c),Days o/Future Present
   V:FranklinRichards,(Pin-ups) . . 6.00
Ann.#7 JRu,RLd,Kings of Pain,
   I:Piecemeal & Harness,
   Pin-ups X-Force 5.00
Spec #1,AAd,TA,Asgard War . . . 6.00
Summer Spec.#1 BBl,Megapolis . 3.50
TPB New Mutants: Demon Bear,
   CCI/BSz,Rep #18–#21 . . . . . 8.95

NEW MUTANTS
Sept. 1997
1 (of 3) BRa,BCh,F:Cannonball,
   Moonstar, Wolfsbane,Karma &
   Sunspot 2.50
2 BRa,BCh,meeting with mutants
   of the past 2.50
3 BRa,BCh, will Magik return
   for good? 2.50

NEW WARRIORS
July, 1990
1 B:FaN(s),MBa,AW,V:Terrax,
   O:New Warriors 5.00
1a Gold rep. 2.50
2 FaN(s),MBa,AW,I:Midnight's Fire,
   Silhouette 3.50
3 MBa,LMa(i),V:Mad Thinker . . . 3.50
4 MBa,LMa(i),I:Psionex 3.50
5 MBa,LMa(i),V:Star Thief,
   C:White Queen 3.50
6 MBa,LMa(i),V:StarThief,
   A:Inhumans 3.50
7 MBa,LMa(i),V:Bengal,
   C:Punisher 3.50
8 MBa,LMa(i),V:Punisher,
   I:Force of Nature 3.50
9 MBa,LMa(i),V:Punisher,Bengal,
   Force of Nature 3.50
10 MBa,LMa(i),V:Hellions,White
   Queen,I:New Sphinx 3.50
11 MBa,LMa(i),V:Sphinx,
   B:Forever Yesterday 2.50
12 MBa,LMa(i),V:Sphinx 2.50
13 MBa,LMa(i),V:Sphinx,
   E:Forever Yesterday 2.50
14 MBa,LMa(i),A:Namor,
   Darkhawk 2.50
15 MBa,LMa(i),V:Psionex,
   R:Terrax,N:Nova 2.50
16 MBa,LMa(i),A:Psionex,
   V:Terrax 2.50
17 MBa,LMa(i),A:Silver Surfer,Fant.
   Four,V:Terrax,I:Left Hand . . . 2.50
18 MBa,LMa(i),O:Night Thrasher . 2.00
19 MBa,LMa(i),V:Gideon 2.00
20 MBa,LMa(i),V:Clan Yashida,
   Marvel Boy kills his father 2.00
21 MBa,LMa(i),I:Folding Circle . . 2.00
22 MBa,LMa(i),A:Darkhawk,Rage . 2.00
23 MBa,LMa(i),V:Folding Circle . . 2.00
24 LMa(i),V:Folding Circle 2.00
25 MBa,LMa(i),Die-Cut(c),Marvel Boy
   found guilty of murder,D:Tai,
   O:Folding Circle 2.50

26 DaR,LMa(i),V:Guardsmen 2.00
27 DaR,LMa(i),Inf.War,Speedball Vs.
   his doppelganger,N:Rage 2.00
28 DaR,LMa(i),I:Turbo,Cardinal . . 2.00
29 DaR,LMa(i),V:Trans-Sabal . . . 2.00
30 DaR,LMa(i),V:Trans Sabal . . . 2.00
31 DaR,LMa(i)A:Cannonball,Warpath,
   Magma,O&N:Firestar 2.00
32 DaR,LMa(i),B:Forces of Darkness,
   Forces of Light,A:Spider-Man,
   Archangel,Dr.Strange 1.75
33 DaR,LMa(i),A:Cloak & Dagger,
   Turbo,Darkhawk 1.75
34 DaR,LMa(i),A:Avengers,SpM,
   Thing,Torch,Darkhawk,
   C:Darkling 1.75
35 DaR,LMa(i),A:Turbo 1.75
36 DaR,LMa(i),A:Turbo 1.75
37 F:Marvel Boy,V:Wizard 1.75
38 DaR,LMa(i),D:Rage's granny,
   V:Poison Memories 1.75
39 DaR,LMa(i),L:Namorita 1.75
40 DaR,LMa(i),B:Starlost,
   V:Supernova 2.50
40a Newsstand Ed. 1.50
41 DaR,LMa(i),V:Supernova 1.75
42 DaR,LMa(i),E:Starlost,N:Nova,
   V:Supernova 1.75
43 DaR,LMa(i),N&I:Justice
   (Marvel Boy) 1.75
44 Ph(c),DaR,LMa(i),N&I:Kymaera
   (Namorita) 1.75
45 DaR,LMa(i),Child's Play#2,
   N:Silhouette,Speedball,
   V:Upstarts 1.75
46 DaR,LMa(i),Child's Play#4,
   V:Upstarts 1.75
47 DaR,LMa(i),Time&TimeAgain,pt.1,
   A:Sphinx,I:Powerpax 1.75
48 DaR,LMa(i),Time&TimeAgain,pt.4,
   J:Cloak&Dagger,Darkhawk,Turbo,
   Powerpax,Bandit 1.75
49 DaR,LMa(i),Time&TimeAgain,pt.8
   V:Sphinx 1.75
50 reg. (c) 1.75
50a Glow-in-the-dark(c),V:Sphinx . 3.25
51 revamp 1.50
52 R:Psionex 1.50
53 V:Psionex 1.50
54 V:Speedball 1.50
55 V:Soldiers of Misfortune 1.50
56 V:Soldiers 1.50
57 A:Namor 1.50
58 F:Sabra 1.50
59 F:Speedball 1.50
60 Nova Omega,pt.2 . . . . 2.50
61 J:Scarlet Spider,Maximum
   Clonage prologue 1.50
62 F:Scarlet Spider,Maximum
   Clonage tie-in 1.50
63 F:Firestar 1.50
64 I:Psionix 1.50
65 F:Scarlet Spider,V:Kymaera . . 1.50
66 F:Speedball 1.50
67 Nightmare in Scarlet,pt.2 . . . . 1.50
68 Future Shock,pt.1 . . . . 1.50
69 . . . . 1.50
70 . . . . 1.50
71 Future Shock,pt.4 . . . . 1.50
Ann.#1 MBa,A:X-Force,V:Harness,
   Piecemeal,Kings of Pain #2 . . 4.00
Ann.#2 Hero Killers #4,V:Sphinx . 2.75
Ann.#3 LMa(i),E:Forces of Light,
   Forces of Darkness,I:Darkling
   w/card 3.25

Ann.#4 DaR(s),V:Psionex 3.25
TPB New Beginnings rep.Thor #411,
  412,New Warriors #1-#4 . . . . 12.95

NFL SUPERPRO

1 . . . . 7.00
Spec.#1 reprints 2.00
[Regular Series] Oct., 1991
1 A:Spider-Man,I:Sanzionaire . . . 2.50
2 V:Quickkick 1.25
3 I:Instant Replay 1.00
4 V:Sanction 1.00
5 A:Real NFL Player 1.25
6 Racism Iss.,recalled by Marvel . 6.00
7 thru 11 . . . . @1.25
12 V:Nefarious forces of evil 1.25

Nick Fury, Agent of S.H.I.E.L.D. #4
© Marvel Entertainment Group

NICK FURY, AGENT OF S.H.I.E.L.D.

[1st Regular Series] June, 1968
1 JSo/JSt,I:Scorpio 40.00
2 JSo,A:Centaurius 25.00
3 JSo,DA,V:Hell Hounds 18.00
4 FS,O:Nick Fury 17.00
5 JSo,V:Scorpio 20.00
6 FS,"Doom must Fall" 11.00
7 FS,V:S.H.I.E.L.D. 11.00
8 FS,Hate Monger 6.00
9 FS,Hate Monger 6.00
10 FS,JCr,Hate Monger 6.00
11 BS(c),FS,Hate Monger 6.00
12 BS 8.00
13 . . . . 5.00
14 . . . . 4.00
15 I:Bullseye 24.00
16 JK,rep. 4.00
17 JK,rep. 4.00
18 JK,rep. 4.00
[Limited Series] 1983–94
1 JSo,rep. 3.00
2 JSo,rep. 3.00
[2nd Regular Series] 1989–93
1 BH,I:New Shield,V:Death's
  Head(not British hero) 3.00
2 KP,V:Death's Head 2.00
3 KP,V:Death's Head 1.50

4 KP,V:Death's Head 1.50
5 KP,V:Death's Head 1.50
6 KP,V:Death's Head 1.50
7 KP,Chaos Serpent #1 . . . . 1.50
8 KP,Chaos Serpent #2 . . . . 1.50
9 KP,Chaos Serpent #3 . . . . 1.50
10 KP,Chaos Serpent ends,
  A:Capt.America 1.50
11 D:Murdo MacKay 1.50
12 Hydra Affair #1 . . . . 1.50
13 Hydra Affair #2 . . . . 1.50
14 Hydra Affair #3 . . . . 1.50
15 Apogee of Disaster #1 . . . . . . 1.50
16 Apogee of Disaster #2 . . . . . . 1.50
17 Apogee of Disaster #3 . . . . . . 1.50
18 Apogee of Disaster #4 . . . . . . 1.50
19 Apogee of Disaster #5 . . . . . . 1.50
20 JG,A:Red Skull 2.50
21 JG,R:Baron Strucker 2.00
22 JG,A:Baron Strucker,R:Hydra . 2.00
23 JG,V:Hydra 2.00
24 A:Capt.Am,Thing,V:Mandarin . 1.75
25 JG,Shield Vs. Hydra 2.00
26 JG,A:Baron Strucker,
  C:Wolverine 2.50
27 JG,V:Hydra,A:Wolverine 2.50
28 V:Hydra,A:Wolverine 2.50
29 V:Hydra,A:Wolverine 2.50
30 R:Leviathan,A:Deathlok 2.00
31 A:Deathlok,V:Leviathan 2.00
32 V:Leviathan 2.00
33 Super-Powered Agents 2.00
34 A:Bridge(X-Force),V:Balance
  of Terror 2.00
35 A:Cage,V:Constrictor 2.00
36 . . . . 2.00
37 . . . . 2.00
38 Cold War of Nick Fury #1 . . . 2.00
39 Cold War of Nick Fury #2 . . . 2.00
40 Cold War of Nick Fury #3 . . . 2.00
41 Cold War of Nick Fury #4 . . . 2.00
42 I:Strike Force Shield 2.00
43 R:Clay Quatermain 2.00
44 A:Captain America 2.00
45 A:Bridge 2.00
46 V:Gideon,Hydra 2.00
47 V:Baron Strucker,last issue . . . 2.00
TPB Death Duty V:Night Raven . . 5.95
TPB Captain America 5.95
TPB Scorpion Connection 7.95
Ashcan .75

NICK FURY, VERSUS S.H.I.E.L.D.

June, 1988
1 JSo(c),D:Quatermail 6.00
2 BSz(c),Into The Depths 5.00
3 Uneasy Allies 4.00
4 V:Hydra 3.00
5 V:Hydra 3.00
6 V:Hydra, Dec., 1988 . . . . 3.00
TPB Reprints #1-#6 . . . . 15.95

NIGHTBREED

Epic April, 1990
1 . . . . 4.00
2 . . . . 3.00
3 . . . . 2.50
4 . . . . 2.50
5 JG 2.50
6 BBl,Blasphemers,pt.1 . . . . 2.50
7 JG,Blasphemers,pt.2 . . . . 2.50
8 BBl,MM,Blasphemers,pt.3 . . . . 2.50
9 BBl,Blasphemers,pt.4 . . . . 2.50

10 BBl,Blasphemers,pt.5 . . . . 2.50
11 South America,pt.1 . . . . 2.25
12 South America,pt.2 . . . . 2.25
13 Emissaries o/Algernon Kinder . 2.25
14 Rawhead Rex Story 2.25
15 Rawhead Rex 2.25
16 Rawhead Rex 2.25
17 KN(i),V:Werewolves 2.25
18 V:Werewolves 2.25
19 V:Werewolves 2.25
20 Trapped in the Forest 2.25
21 V:Ozymandias 2.50
22 V:Ozymandias 2.50
23 F:Peloquin 2.50
24 Search for New Midian 2.50
25 Search for New Midian 2.50
Nightbreed:Genesis, Rep.#1-#4 . . 9.95

NIGHTCAT

1 DCw,I&O:Night Cat 4.50

NIGHTCRAWLER

Nov., 1985
1 DC,A:Bamfs 4.00
2 DC 3.00
3 DC,A:Other Dimensional X-Men 3.00
4 DC,A:Lockheed,V:Dark Bamf
  Feb., 1986 . . . . 3.00

NIGHTHAWK

July 1998
1 (of 3) RCa,BWi,Nighthawk shake
  off coma 2.50
2 (of 3) RCa,BWi,V:Mephisto . . . 2.50

NIGHTMARE

1994
1 ANo 1.95
2 ANo 1.95
3 ANo 1.95

NIGHTMARE CIRCUS

1 video-game tie-in 2.50
2 video-game tie-in 2.50

NIGHTMARE ON ELM STREET

Oct., 1989
1 RB/TD/AA.,Movie adapt 3.00
2 AA,Movie adapt,Dec., 1989 . . . 2.25

NIGHTMASK

Nov., 1986
1 O:Night Mask 1.25
2 V:Gnome 1.00
3 V:Mistress Twilight 1.00
4 EC,D:Mistress Twilight 1.00
5 EC,Nightmare 1.00
6 EC 1.00
7 EC 1.00
8 EC 1.00
9 . . . . 1.00
10 Lucian 1.00
11 . . . . 1.00
12 Oct. 1987 . . . . 1.00

NIGHT NURSE

Nov., 1972
1 The Making of a Nurse 75.00
2 Moment of Truth 50.00
3 . . . . 50.00
4 Final Issue,May, 1973 . . . . . 50.00

MARVEL

MARVEL

NIGHT RIDER
Oct., 1974
1 Reprint Ghost Rider #1 . . . . . 10.00
2 Reprint Ghost Rider #2 . . . . . . 7.00
3 Reprint Ghost Rider #3 . . . . . . 7.00
4 Reprint Ghost Rider #4 . . . . . . 7.00
5 Reprint Ghost Rider #5 . . . . . . 7.00
6 Reprint Ghost Rider #6
August, 1975 . . . . 7.00

NIGHTSTALKERS
1992–94
1 TP(i),Rise o/t Midnight Sons#5
A:GR,J.Blaze,I:Meatmarket,
polybagged w/poster 3.00
2 TP(i),V:Hydra 2.50
3 TP(i),V:Dead on Arrival 2.00
4 TP(i),V:Hydra 2.00
5 TP(i),A:Punisher 2.00
6 TP(i),A:Punisher 2.00
7 TP(i),A:Ghost Rider 2.00
8 Hannibal King vs Morbius 2.00
9 MPa,A:Morbius 2.00
10 Midnight Massacre#1,D:Johnny
Blaze,Hannibal King 2.50
11 O:Blade 2.00
12 V:Vampires 2.00
13 V:Vampires 2.00
14 Wld,Siege of Darkness#1 . . . . 2.00
15 Wld,Siege of Darkness#9 . . . . 2.00
16 V:Dreadnought 2.00
17 F:Blade 2.00
18 D:Hannibal King,Frank Drake,
last issue 2.00

NIGHT THRASHER
[Limited Series] 1992–93
1 B:FaN(s),DHv,N:Night Thrasher,
V:Bengal 2.50
2 DHv,I:Tantrium 2.25
3 DHv,V:Gideon 2.25
4 E:FaN(s),DHv,A:Silhoutte 2.25
[Regular Series] 1993–95
1 B:FaN(s),MBa,JS,V:Poison
Memories 3.25
2 JS,V:Concrete Dragons 2.00
3 JS(c),I:Aardwolf,A:Folding Circle 2.00
4 JS(c),V:Aardwolf,I:Air Force . . 2.00
5 JS,V:Air Force 2.00
6 Face Value,A:Rage 2.00
7 DdB,V:Bandit 2.00
8 DdB,V:Bandit 2.00
9 DdB,A:Tantrum 2.00
10 DdB,A:Iron Man,w/card 2.25
11 DdB,Time & Time Again,pt.2 . . 2.25
12 DdB,Time & Time Again,pt.5 . . 2.25
13 Lost in the Shadows,pt.1 . . . . 1.95
14 Lost in the Shadows,pt.2 . . . . 1.95
15 Money Don't Buy,pt.1 . . . . 1.95
16 A:Prowler 1.95
17 . . . . 1.95
18 . . . . 1.95
19 V:Tantrum 1.95
20 . . . . 1.95
21 Rage vs. Grind 1.95

NIGHTWATCH
1994–95
1 RLm,I:Salvo,Warforce Holo(c) . 3.00
1a Newsstand ed. 1.75
2 RLm,AM,I:Flashpoint 1.50
3 RLm,AM,V:Flashpoint 1.50
4 RLm,A:Warrent,V:Gauntlet . . . 1.75
5 I:Sunstreak,A:Venom 1.50

6 V:Venom 1.50
7 I:Cardiaxe 1.50
8 V:Cardiaxe 1.50
9 origins 1.50
10 . . . . 1.50
11 . . . . 1.50
12 . . . . 1.50

NOCTURNE
1995
1 DAn, in London 1.50
2 DAn,O:Nocturne 1.50
3 Interview with Amy 1.50
4 V:Dragon 1.50

NO ESCAPE
1994
1 & 2 Movie adaptation . . . . . @1.50

NOMAD
[Limited Series] Nov., 1990
1 B:FaN(s),A:Capt.America 3.00
2 A:Capt.America 2.50
3 A:Capt.America 2.50
4 A:Capt.America, final issue,
Feb. 1989 . . . . 2.50
[Regular Series] 1992–94
1 B:FaN(s),R:Nomad,[Gatetfold(c),
map] 3.00
2 V:Road Kill Club 2.50
3 V:U.S.Agent 2.00
4 DeadMan's Hand#2,V:Deadpool 2.00
5 DeadMan's Hand#4,V:Punisher 2.00
6 DeadMan's Hand#8,A:Punisher,
Daredevil 2.00
7 Infinity War,V:Gambit,
Doppleganger 2.00
8 L.A.Riots 2.00
9 I:Ebbtide 2.00
10 A:Red Wolf 2.00
11 in Albuquerque 2.00
12 In Texas 2.00
13 AIDS issue 2.00
14 Hidden in View 2.00
15 Hidden in View 2.00
16 A:Gambit 2.00
17 Bucky Kidnapped 2.00
18 A:Captain America,Slug 2.00
19 FaN(s),Faustus Affair 2.00
20 A:Six Pack 2.00
21 A:Man-Thing 2.00
22 American Dreamers#1,V:Zaran 2.00
23 American Dreamers#2 . . . . . . 2.00
24 American Dreamers#3 . . . . . . 2.00
25 American Dreamers#4, finale . 2.00

NORTHSTAR
1994
1 SFr,DoC,V:Weapon:P.R.I.M.E. . 2.00
2 SFr,DoC,V:Arcade 2.00
3 SFr,DoC,V:Arcade 2.00
4 SFr,DoC,final issue 2.00
N Presents James O'Barr 2.50

NOT BRAND ECHH
August, 1967
1 JK(c),BEv,Forbush Man(c) . . 35.00
2 MSe,FrG,Spidey-Man,Gnat-Man
& Rotten 20.00
3 MSe(C),JK,FrG,O:Charlie
America 20.00
4 GC,JTg,TS,Scaredevil,
ECHHs-Men 20.00

Not Brand Echh #3
© *Marvel Entertainment Group*

5 JK,TS,GC,I&O:Forbush Man . 20.00
6 MSe(c),GC,TS,W:Human Torch 20.00
7 MSe(c),GC,TS,O:Fantastical
Four,Stupor Man 20.00
8 MSe(c),GC,TS,C:Beatles . . . 22.00
9 Bulk V:Sunk-Mariner 25.00
10 JK,The Worst of... . . . . 25.00
11 King Konk 25.00
12 Frankenstein,A:Revengers . . 25.00
13 Stamp Out Trading Cards(c) . 25.00

NOTHING CAN STOP THE JUGGERNAUT
1989
1 JR2,rep.SpM#229&#230 . . . . . 3.95

NOVA
[1st Regular Series] Sept., 1976
1 B:MWn(s),JB,JSt,I&O:Nova . . . 7.00
2 JB,JSt,I:Condor,Powerhouse . . 4.00
3 JB,JSt,I:Diamondhead 3.00
4 SB,TP,A:Thor,I:Corruptor 3.00
5 SB,V:Earthshaker 3.00
6 SB,V:Condor,Powerhouse,
Diamondhead,I:Sphinx 3.00
7 SB,War in Space,O:Sphinx . . . 3.00
8 V:Megaman 3.00
9 V:Megaman 3.00
10 V:Condor,Powerhouse,
Diamond-head Sphinx 3.00
11 V:Sphinx 2.50
12 A:Spider-Man 3.00
13 I:Crimebuster,A:Sandman . . . 2.50
14 A:Sandman 2.00
15 CI,C:Spider-Man, Hulk 2.00
16 CI,A:Yellow Claw 2.00
17 A:Yellow Claw 2.00
18 A:Yellow Claw, Nick Fury . . . 2.00
19 CI,TP,I:Blackout 2.00
20 What is Project X? 2.00
21 JB,BMc,JRu 2.00
22 CI,I:Comet 2.00
23 CI,V:Dr.Sun 2.00
24 CI,I:New Champions,V:Sphinx . 2.00
25 E:MWn(s),CI,A:Champions,
V:Sphinx 2.00

Nova (2nd Series) #4
© Marvel Entertainment Group

[2nd Regular Series] 1994–95
1 B:FaN(s),ChM,V:Gladiator,Foil
  Embossed(c) 3.00
2 ChM,V:Tail Hook Rape 2.00
3 ChM,A:Spider-Man,Corruptor . 2.00
4 ChM,I:NovaO:O 2.00
5 ChM,R:Condor,w/card 2.25
6 ChM,Time & Time Again,pt.3 . . 2.25
7 ChM,Time & Time Again,pt.6 . . 2.25
8 ChM,I:Shatterforce 2.25
9 ChM,V:Shatterforce 1.95
10 ChM,V:Diamondhead 1.95
11 ChM,V:Diamondhead 1.95
12 ChM,A:Inhumans 1.95
13 ChM,A:Inhumans 1.95
14 A:Condor 1.95
15 V:Brethren of Zorr 1.95
16 Countdown Conclusion 1.95
17 Nova Loses Powers 1.96
18 Nova Omega,pt.1 . . . . 1.95

Nth MAN
August, 1989
1 . . . . 2.00
2 . . . . 1.00
3 . . . . 1.00
4 . . . . 1.00
5 thru 7 . . . . @1.00
8 DK 2.00
9 thru 16, finale, Sept., 1990 . @1.00

OBNOXIO THE CLOWN
April, 1983
1 X-Men 2.00

OFFCASTES
Epic *Heavy Hitters* 1993
1 MV,I:Offcastes 2.50
2 MV,V:Kaoro 1.95
3 MV,Last Issue 1.95

OFFICIAL MARVEL INDEX:
1985–88
TO THE AMAZING SPIDER-MAN
Index 1 . . . . 3.00
Index 2 thru 9 . . . . @2.50
TO THE AVENGERS
Index 1 thru 7 . . . . @2.50
TO THE FANTASTIC FOUR
Index 1 thru 12 . . . . @2.25
TO MARVEL TEAM-UP
Index 1 thru 6 . . . . @1.75
TO THE X-MEN
Index 1 thru 7 . . . . @2.95
[Vol. 2] 1994
Index 1 thru 5 . . . . @1.95

OFFICIAL MARVEL TIMELINE
1-shot, 48pg 5.95

OFFICIAL TRUE CRIME CASES
Fall, 1947
24 (1)SSh(c),The Grinning Killer 150.00
25 (2)She Made Me a Killer,HK 110.00
Becomes:
ALL-TRUE CRIME
26 SSh(c),The True Story of Wilbur
  Underhill 200.00
27 Electric Chair(c),Robert Mais 150.00
28 Cops V:Gangsters(c) 75.00
29 Cops V:Gangsters(c) 75.00
30 He Picked a Murderous Mind 75.00
31 Hitchiking Thugs(c) 75.00
32 Jewel Thieves(c) 75.00
33 The True Story of Dinton
  Phillips 75.00
34 Case of the Killers Revenge . 75.00
35 Ph(c),Date with Danger 75.00
36 Ph(c) 75.00
37 Ph(c),Story of Robert Marone 75.00
38 Murder Weapon,Nick Maxim . 75.00
39 Story of Vince Vanderee 75.00
40 . . . . 75.00
41 Lou "Lucky" Raven 75.00
42 BK,Baby Face Nelson 85.00
43 Doc Channing Paulson 70.00
44 Murder in the Big House 70.00
45 While the City Sleeps 70.00
46 . . . . 70.00
47 Gangster Terry Craig 70.00
48 GT,They Vanish By Night . . . 70.00
49 BK,Squeeze Play 75.00
50 Shoot to Kill 70.00
51 Panic in the Big House 70.00
52 Prison Break, Sept., 1952 . . . 70.00

OLYMPIANS
Epic July, 1991
1 Spoof Series 3.95
2 Conclusion 3.95

OMEGA THE UNKNOWN
March, 1976
1 JM,I:Omega 4.00
2 JM,A:Hulk 2.50
3 JM,A:Electro 2.00
4 JM,V:Yellow Claw 2.00
5 JM,V:The Wrench 2.00

6 JM,V:Blockbuster 2.00
7 JM,V:Blockbuster 2.00
8 JM,C:New Foolkiller,V:Nitro . . . 5.00
9 JM,A:New Foolkiller,
  D:Blockbuster 7.00
10 JM,D:Omega the Unknown . . . 2.00

ONE, THE
Epic July, 1985
1 thru 5 . . . . @1.75
6 Feb., 1986 . . . . 1.75

101 WAYS TO END THE CLONE SAGA
1-shot (1997) 2.50

ONSLAUGHT
1996–97
Marvel Universe: AKu,SLo,MWd,
  Marvel Heroes vs. Onslaught . 7.00
Marvel Universe: Gold edition . . 20.00
X-Men: AKu,SLo,MWd (1996) . . . 6.00
X-Men: Gold editon 20.00
Onslaught: Epilogue (1997) 3.00
TPB Book 1, rep. X-Men #53 & #54,
  Uncanny X-Men 322 & 334
  and Onslaught X-Men 12.95
TPB Book 2, rep. X-Man #18 & #19
  and X-Force #57 & 58 . . . . . . 9.95
TPB Book 3, rep. Uncanny X-Men
  #335, Avengers #401, FF #415,
  X-Men #55 . . . . 9.95
TPB Book 4, rep. Inc.Hulk #444
  & #445, Cable #34 & #35 . . . . 9.95
TPB Book 5, rep. X-Factor #125,
  Punisher #11, Green Goblin #12,
  Amaz. Sp.-M. #415, Sp.-M. #72 9.95
TPB Book 6, rep. Uncanny X-Men
  #336, X-Men #56, Avengers #402,
  FF #416 & Onslaught: Marvel
  Universe 12.95

ONYX OVERLORD
Epic 1992–93
1 JBi,Sequel to Airtight Garage . . 3.00
2 JBi,The Joule 2.75
3 JBi,V:Overlord 2.75
4 V:Starbilliard 2.75

OPEN SPACE
Dec., 1989–Aug. 1990
1 . . . . 6.00
2 thru 4 . . . . @5.25

ORIGINAL GHOST RIDER
1992–94
1 MT(c),rep Marvel Spotlight#5 . . 2.25
2 rep.Marvel Spotlight#6 . . . . . . 2.00
3 rep.Marvel Spotlight#7 . . . . . . 2.00
4 JQ(c),rep.Marvel Spotlight#8 . . 2.00
5 KM(c),rep.Marvel spotlight#9 . . 2.00
6 rep.Marvel Spotlight#10 . . . . . 2.00
7 rep.Marvel Spotlight#11 . . . . . 2.00
8 rep.Ghost Rider#1 . . . . 2.00
9 rep.Ghost Rider#2 . . . . 2.00
10 rep.Marvel Spotlight#12 . . . . 2.00
11 rep.Ghost Rider#3 . . . . 2.00
12 rep.Ghost Rider#4 . . . . 2.00
13 rep.Ghost Rider#38 . . . . 2.00
14 rep.Ghost Rider#6 . . . . 1.75
15 rep.Ghost Rider#7 . . . . 1.75
15 rep.Ghost Rider#8 . . . . 1.75
18 rep.Ghost Rider#9 . . . . 1.75

MARVEL

18 rep.Ghost Rider#10 . . . . 1.75
19 rep.Ghost Rider#11 . . . . 1.75
20 rep.Ghost Rider#12 . . . . 1.75
21 rep.Ghost Rider#13 . . . . 1.75
22 rep.Ghost Rider#14 . . . . 1.75
23 rep.Ghost Rider#15 . . . . 1.95

ORIGINAL GHOST RIDER RIDES AGAIN
July, 1991
1 rep.GR#68+#69(O:JohnnyBlaze) 3.00
2 rep.G.R. #70,#71 . . . . 2.00
3 rep.G.R. #72,#73 . . . . 2.00
4 rep.G.R. #74,#75 . . . . 2.00
5 rep.G.R. #76,#77 . . . . 2.00
6 rep.G.R. #78,#79 . . . . 2.00
7 rep.G.R. #80,#81 . . . . 2.00

ORIGINS OF MARVEL COMICS
TPB StL,JK,SD reprinting, 260pg 25.00

OSBORN JOURNALS, THE
1997
1-shot KHt,F:Norman Osborn . . . 3.00

OUR LOVE
Sept., 1949
1 Ph(c),Guilt of Nancy Crane . 100.00
2 Ph(c),My Kisses Were Cheap 50.00
Becomes:
TRUE SECRETS
3 Love Stories,continued 75.00
4 . . . . 50.00
5 . . . . 50.00
6 BEv 60.00
7 . . . . 50.00
8 . . . . 50.00
9 . . . . 50.00
10 . . . . 50.00
11 thru 21 . . . . @35.00
22 BEv 50.00
23 thru 39 . . . . @30.00
40 Sept., 1956 . . . . 30.00

OUR LOVE STORY
Oct., 1969
1 . . . . 30.00
2 . . . . 15.00
3 . . . . 15.00
4 . . . . 15.00
5 JSo 50.00
6 thru 13 . . . . @15.00
14 Gary Friedrich &Tarpe Mills . 20.00
15 thru 37 . . . . @10.00
38 Feb., 1976 . . . . 10.00

OUTLAW FIGHTERS
Atlas August, 1954
1 GT,Western Tales 85.00
2 GT 50.00
3 . . . . 50.00
4 A;Patch Hawk 50.00
5 RH, Final Issue,April, 1955 . . 50.00

OUTLAW KID
Atlas Sept., 1954
1 SSh,DW,B&O:Outlaw Kid,A;Black
Rider 175.00
2 DW,A:Black Rider 60.00
3 DW,AW,GWb 75.00
4 DW(c),Death Rattle 65.00

5 . . . . 65.00
6 . . . . 65.00
7 . . . . 65.00
8 AW,DW 80.00
9 . . . . 75.00
10 . . . . 75.00
11 thru 17 . . . . @50.00
18 AW 60.00
19 Sept., 1957 . . . . 50.00
[2nd series] August, 1970
1 JSe(c),DW,Jo,Showdown,rep 20.00
2 DW,One Kid Too Many . . . 15.00
3 HT(c),DW,Six Gun Double
Cross 15.00
4 DW 12.00
5 DW 12.00
6 DW 12.00
7 HT(c),DW,Treachery on
the Trail 12.00
8 HT(c),DW,RC,Six Gun Pay Off 12.00
9 JSe(c),DW,GWb,The Kids
Last Stand 10.00
10 GK(c),DAy,NewO:Outlaw Kid 10.00
11 GK(c),Thunder Along the
Big Iron 10.00
12 The Man Called Bounty Hawk 10.00
13 The Last Rebel 10.00
14 The Kid Gunslingers of
Calibre City 10.00
15 GK(c),V:Madman of Monster
Mountain 10.00
16 The End of the Trail 10.00
17 thru 29 . . . . @10.00
30 Oct., 1975 . . . . 10.00

OVER THE EDGE AND UNDER A BUCK
1995–96
1 F:Daredevil vs. Mr. Fear 1.00
2 F:Doctor Strange 1.00
3 F:Hulk 1.00
4 in Cypress Hills 1.00
5 . . . . 1.00
6 F:Daredevil 1.00
7 Doc & Nightmare 1.00

PARAGON
1 I:Paragon,Nightfire 5.00

PATSY & HEDY
Atlas Feb., 1952
1 B:Patsy Walker&Hedy Wolfe 125.00
2 Skating(c) 75.00
3 Boyfriend Trouble 50.00
4 Swimsuit(c) 50.00
5 Patsy's Date(c) 50.00
6 Swimsuit/Picnic(c) 50.00
7 Double-Date(c) 50.00
8 The Dance 50.00
9 . . . . 50.00
10 . . . . 50.00
11 thru 25 . . . . @35.00
26 thru 50 . . . . @25.00
51 thru 60 . . . . @20.00
61 thru 109 . . . . @15.00
110 Feb., 1967 . . . . 15.00

PATSY & HER PALS
May, 1953
1 MWs(c),F:Patsay Walker . . 90.00
2 MWs(c),Swimsuit(c) 60.00
3 MWs(c),Classroom(c) 50.00
4 MWs(c),Golfcourse(c) 50.00

5 MWs(c).Patsy/Buzz(c) 50.00
6 thru 10 . . . . @50.00
11 thru 28 . . . . @35.00
29 August, 1957 . . . . 35.00

PATSY WALKER
1945–Dec. 1965
1 F:Patsy Walker Adventures 350.00
2 Patsy/Car(c) 175.00
3 Skating(c) 125.00
4 Perfume(c) 125.00
5 Archery Lesson(c) 125.00
6 Bus(c) 125.00
7 Charity Drive(c) 125.00
8 Organ Driver Monkey(c) . . . 125.00
9 Date(c) 125.00
10 Skating(c),Wedding Bells . . 125.00
11 Date with a Dream 100.00
12 Love in Bloom,Artist(c) 100.00
13 Swimsuit(c),There Goes My
Heart;HK,Hey Look 100.00
14 An Affair of the Heart,
HK,Hey Look 100.00
15 Dance(c) 75.00
16 Skating(c) 75.00
17 Patsy's Diary(c),HK,Hey Look 100.00
18 Autograph(c) 75.00
19 HK,Hey Look 100.00
20 HK,Hey Look 100.00
21 HK,Hey Look 100.00
22 HK,Hey Look 100.00
23 . . . . 65.00
24 . . . . 65.00
25 HK,Rusty 100.00
26 . . . . 50.00
27 . . . . 50.00
28 . . . . 50.00
29 . . . . 50.00
30 HK,Egghead Double 75.00
31 . . . . 50.00
32 thru 57 . . . . @30.00
58 thru 99 . . . . @25.00
100 . . . . 25.00
101 thru 124 . . . . @15.00
Fashion Parade #1 . . . . 75.00

Peter Parker #82
© Marvel Entertainment Group

PETER PARKER, THE SPECTACULAR SPIDER-MAN
Dec., 1976

1 SB,V:Tarantula	55.00
2 SB,V:Kraven,Tarantula	20.00
3 SB,I:Lightmaster	15.00
4 SB,V:Vulture,Hitman	15.00
5 SB,V:Hitman,Vulture	15.00
6 SB,V:Morbius,rep.M.T.U.#3	18.00
7 SB,V:Morbius,A:Human Torch	25.00
8 SB,V:Morbius	20.00
9 SB,I:White Tiger	10.00
10 SB,A:White Tiger	10.00
11 JM,V:Medusa	8.00
12 SB,V:Brother Power	8.00
13 SB,V:Brother Power	8.00
14 SB,V:Brother Power	8.00
15 SB,V:Brother Power	8.00
16 SB,V:The Beetle	8.00
17 SB,A:Angel & Iceman Champions disbanded	9.00
18 SB,A:Angel & Iceman	9.00
19 SB,V:The Enforcers	8.00
20 SB,V:Lightmaster	8.00
21 JM,V:Scorpion	8.00
22 MZ,A:Moon Knight,V:Cyclone	8.00
23 A:Moon Knight,V:Cyclone	8.00
24 FS,A:Hypno-Hustler	6.00
25 JM,FS,I:Carrion	8.00
26 JM,A:Daredevil,V:Carrion	7.00
27 DC,FM,I:Miller Daredevil, V:Carrion	20.00
28 FM,A:Daredevil,V:Carrion	16.00
29 JM,FS,V:Carrion	7.00
30 JM,FS,V:Carrion	7.00
31 JM,FS,D:Carrion	7.00
32 BL,JM,FS,V:Iguana	5.50
33 JM,FS,O:Iguana	5.50
34 JM,FS,V:Iguana,Lizard	5.50
35 V:Mutant Mindworm	5.50
36 JM,V:Swarm	5.50
37 DC,MN,V:Swarm	5.50
38 SB,V:Morbius	7.00
39 JM,JR2,V:Schizoid Man	5.50
40 FS,V:Schizoid Man	5.50
41 JM,V:Meteor Man,A:GiantMan	5.00
42 JM,A:Fant.Four,V:Frightful 4	5.00
43 JBy(c),MZ,V:The Ringer, V:Belladonna	5.00
44 JM,V:The Vulture	5.00
45 MSe,V:The Vulture	5.00
46 FM(c),MZ,V:Cobra	5.00
47 MSe,A:Prowler II	5.00
48 MSe,A:Prowler II	5.00
49 MSe,I:Smuggler	5.00
50 JR2,JM,V:Mysterio	5.00
51 MSe&FM(c),V:Mysterio	5.00
52 FM(c),D:White Tiger	5.00
53 JM,FS,V:Terrible Tinkerer	5.00
54 FM,WS,MSe,V:Silver Samurai	5.00
55 LMc,JM,V:Nitro	5.00
56 FM,JM,V:Jack-o-lantern	16.00
57 JM,V:Will-o-the Wisp	5.00
58 JBy,V:Ringer,A:Beetle	6.00
59 JM,V:Beetle	5.00
60 JM&FM(c),O:Spider-Man, V:Beetle	5.50
61 JM,V:Moonstone	4.50
62 JM,V:Goldbug	4.50
63 JM,V:Molten Man	4.50
64 JM,I:Cloak&Dagger	9.00
65 BH,JM,V:Kraven,Calypso	4.50
66 JM,V:Electro	4.00

Peter Parker Annual #3
© Marvel Entertainment Group

67 AMb,V:Boomerang	4.00
68 LMc,JM,V:Robot of Mendell Stromm	4.00
69 AM,A:Cloak & Dagger	7.00
70 A:Cloak & Dagger	7.00
71 JM,Gun Control issue	4.00
72 AM,V:Dr.Octopus	4.00
73 AM,JM,V:Dr.Octopus,A:Owl	4.00
74 AM,JM,V:Dr.Octopus,R:Bl.Cat	4.00
75 AM,JM,V:Owl,Dr.Octopus	4.50
76 AM,Black Cat on deathbed	3.50
77 AM,V:Gladiator,Dr.Octopus	3.50
78 AM,V:Dr.Octopus,C:Punisher	3.50
79 AM,V:Dr.Octopus,A:Punisher	4.00
80 AM,F:J.Jonah Jameson	3.50
81 A:Punisher	7.00
82 A:Punisher	7.00
83 A:Punisher	7.00
84 AM,F:Black Cat	3.50
85 AM,O:Hobgoblin powers (Ned Leeds)	20.00
86 FH,V:Fly	3.50
87 AM,Reveals I.D.to Black Cat	3.50
88 AM,V:Cobra,Mr.Hyde	3.50
89 AM,Secret Wars,A:Kingpin	4.00
90 AM,Secret Wars	7.00
91 AM,V:Blob	3.50
92 AM,I:Answer	3.50
93 AM,V:Answer	3.50
94 AM,A:Cloak & Dagger,V: Silver Mane	3.50
95 AM,A:Cloak & Dagger,V: Silvermane	3.50
96 AM,A:Cloak & Dagger,V: Silvermane	3.50
97 HT,JM,A:Black Cat	3.50
98 HT,JM,I:Spot	3.50
99 HT,JM,V:Spot	3.50
100 AM,V:Kingpin,C:Bl.Costume	6.00
101 JBy(c),AM,V:Killer Shrike	3.00
102 JBy(c),AM,V:Backlash	3.00
103 AM,V:Blaze;Not John Blaze	3.00
104 JBy(c),AM,V:Rocket Racer	3.00
105 AM,A:Wasp	3.00
106 AM,A:Wasp	3.00
107 RB,D:Jean DeWolf,I:SinEater	5.00
108 RB,A:Daredevil,V:Sin-Eater	4.00
109 RB,A:Daredevil,V:Sin-Eater	4.00

110 RB,A:Daredevil,V:Sin-Eater	4.00
111 RB,Secret Wars II	3.00
112 RB,A:Santa Claus,Black Cat	3.00
113 RB,Burglars,A:Black Cat	3.00
114 BMc,V:Lock Picker	3.00
115 BMc,A:Black Cat,Dr.Strange, I:Foreigner	3.50
116 A:Dr.Strange, Foreigner, Black Cat, Sabretooth	7.00
117 DT,C:Sabretooth,A:Foreigner, Black Cat,Dr.Strange	5.00
118 MZ,D:Alexander,V:SHIELD	3.00
119 RB,BMc,V:Sabretooth, A:Foreigner,Black Cat	7.00
120 KG	3.00
121 RB,BMc,V:Mauler	3.00
122 V:Mauler	3.00
123 V:Foreigner,Black Cat	3.00
124 V:Dr.Octopus	3.00
125 V:Wr.Crew,A:Spiderwoman	3.00
126 JM,A:Sp.woman,V:Wrecker	3.00
127 AM,V:Lizard	3.00
128 C:DDevil,A:Bl.Cat,Foreigner	3.50
129 A:Black Cat,V:Foreigner	3.00
130 A:Hobgoblin	6.00
131 MZ,BMc,V:Kraven	10.00
132 MZ,BMc,V:Kraven	10.00
133 BSz(c),Mad Dog,pt.3	8.00
Ann.#1 RB,JM,V:Dr.Octopus	5.00
Ann.#2 JM,I&O:Rapier	4.50
Ann.#3 JM,V:Manwolf	4.50
Ann.#4 AM,O:Aunt May,A:Bl.Cat	5.00
Ann.#5 I:Ace,Joy Mercado	4.50
Ann.#6 V:Ace	4.50
Ann.#7 Honeymoon iss,A:Puma	4.50

Becomes:
SPECTACULAR SPIDER-MAN

PETER PORKER
Star May, 1985

1 Parody	2.50
2	1.50
3	1.50
4	1.50
5 V:Senior Simians	1.50
6 A Blitz in Time	1.50
7	1.50
8 Kimono My House	1.25
9 Uncouth my Tooth	1.25
10 Lost Temple of the Golden Retriever	1.25
11 Dog Dame Afternoon	1.25
12 The Gouda,Bad & Ugly	1.25
13 Halloween issue	1.25
14 Heavy Metal Issue	1.25
15	1.25
16 Porker Fried Rice,Final Issue	1.25
17 Sept., 1987	1.25

PETER, THE LITTLE PEST
Nov., 1969

1 F:Peter	35.00
2 Rep,Dexter & Melvin	25.00
3 Rep,Dexter & Melvin	25.00
4 Rep,Dexter & Melvin, May, 1970	25.00

PHANTOM

1 Lee Falk's Phantom	4.00
2 V:General Babalar	4.00
3 final issue	4.00

MARVEL

PHANTOM 2040
1 Based on cartoon 2.50
2 V:Alloy 2.50
3 MPa,V:Crime Syndicate 2.50
4 Vision Quest 2.50

PHOENIX
(UNTOLD STORY)
April, 1984
1 JBy,O:Phoenix (R.Summers) . 12.00

PILGRIM'S PROGRESS
1 adapts John Bunyans novel . . 10.00

PINHEAD
1993–94
1 Red Foil(c),from Hellraiser 2.95
2 DGC(s),V:Cenobites 2.50
3 DGC(s),V:Cenobites 2.50
4 DGC(s),V:Cenobites 2.50
5 DGC(s),Devil in Disguise 2.50
6 DGC(s), ... 2.50

PINHEAD VS.
MARSHALL LAW
1993
1 KON,In Hell 2.95
2 KON 2.95

PINOCHIO & THE
EMPEROR OF THE NIGHT
March, 1988
1 Movie adapt. 1.25

PINT-SIZED X-BABIES:
MURDERAMA
June 1998
1-shot, Mojo, Arcade, 48pg, ... 3.00

PIRATES OF
DARK WATERS
Nov., 1991
1 based on T.V. series 1.00
2 Search for 13 Treasures 1.00
3 V:Albino Warriors,Konk 1.00
4 A:Monkey Birds 1.25
5 Tula Steals 1st Treasuer 1.25
6 thru 9 . . . . @1.25

PITT, THE
March, 1988
1 SB,SDr,A:Spitfire 4.50

PLANET OF THE APES
Aug., 1974–Feb. 1977
(black & white magazine)
1 MP 30.00
2 MP 20.00
3 . . . . 10.00
4 . . . . 10.00
5 . . . . 10.00
6 thru 10 . . . . @10.00
11 thru 20 . . . . @10.00
21 thru 29 . . . . @15.00

PLANET TERRY
Star April, 1985
1 thru 11 . . . . @1.00
12 March, 1986 . . . . 1.00

Plasmer #1
© *Marvel Entertainment Group*

PLASMER
Marvel UK 1993–94
1 A:Captain America 3.50
2 A:Captain Britain,Black Knight . 2.25
3 A:Captain Britain 2.25
4 A:Captain Britain 2.25
5 thru 7 . . . . 1.95

PLASTIC FORKS
Epic 1990
1 . . . . 5.50
2 thru 5 . . . . @5.25

POLICE ACADEMY
Nov., 1989
1 Based on TV Cartoon 1.25
2 . . . . 1.00
3 . . . . 1.00
4 and 5 . . . . @1.00
6 Feb., 1990 . . . . 1.00

POLICE ACTION
Jan., 1954
1 JF,GC,Riot Squad 125.00
2 JF,Over the Wall 75.00
3 . . . . 50.00
4 DAy 50.00
5 DAy 50.00
6 . . . . 50.00
7 BPNov., 1954 . . . . 50.00

POLICE BADGE
See: SPY THRILLERS

POPPLES
Star Dec., 1986
1 Based on Toys 1.00
2 . . . . 1.00
3 . . . . 1.00
4 . . . . 1.00
5 August, 1987 . . . . 1.00

POWDERED TOAST-MAN
Spec. F:Powder Toast-Man 3.25

POWERHOUSE PEPPER
COMICS
1943—Nov., 1948
1 BW,Movie Auditions(c) . . . 1,100.00
2 BW,Dinner(c) 600.00
3 BW,Boxing Ring(c) 500.00
4 BW,Subway(c) 500.00
5 BW,Bankrobbers(c) 700.00

POWER LINE
Epic May, 1988
1 BMc(i) 2.25
2 Aw(i) 2.00
3 A:Dr Zero 2.00
4 . . . . 2.00
5 thru 7 GM . . . . @2.00
8 GM Sept., 1989 . . . . 2.00

POWER MAN
Prev:　　Hero for Hire
Feb., 1974
17 GT,A:Iron Man 10.00
18 GT,V:Steeplejack 7.00
19 GT,V:Cottonmouth 7.00
20 GT,Heroin Story 7.00
21 V:Original Power Man 5.00
22 V:Stiletto & Discus 5.00
23 V:Security City 5.00
24 GT,I:BlackGoliath(BillFoster) . . 5.00
25 A:Circus of Crime 5.00
26 GT,V:Night Shocker 5.00
27 GP,AMc,V:Man Called X 5.00
28 V:Cockroach 5.00
29 V:Mr.Fish 5.00
30 RB,KJ,KP,I:Piranha 5.00
31 SB,NA(i),V:Piranha 5.00
32 JSt,FR,A:Wildfire 3.50
33 FR,A:Spear 3.50
34 FR,A:Spear,Mangler 3.50
35 DA,A:Spear,Mangler 3.50
36 V:Chemistro 3.50
37 V:Chemistro 3.50
38 V:Chemistro 3.50
39 KJ,V:Chemistro,Baron 3.50
40 V:Baron 3.50
41 TP,V:Thunderbolt,Goldbug . . . 3.50
42 V:Thunderbolt,Goldbug 3.50
43 AN,V:Mace 3.50
44 TP,A:Mace 3.50
45 JSn,A:Mace 4.00
46 GT,I:Zzzax(recreated) 3.50
47 BS,A:Zzzax 4.00
48 JBy,A:Iron Fist 4.00
49 JBy,A:Iron Fist 4.00
Becomes:
POWER MAN & IRON FIST
50 JBy,I:Team-up with Iron Fist . . 2.50
51 MZ,Night on the Town 2.50
52 MZ,V:Death Machines 2.50
53 SB,O:Nightshade 2.50
54 TR,O:Iron Fist 2.50
55 Chaos at the Coliseum 2.50
56 Mayhem in the Museum 2.50
57 X-Men,V:Living Monolith 6.00
58 1st El Aguila(Drug) 2.00
59 BL(c),TVE,V:Big Apple
　　Bomber 1.75
60 BL(c),V:Terrorists 1.75
61 BL(c),V:The Maggia 1.75
62 BL(c),KGa,V:Man Mountain
　　D:Thunderbolt 1.75
63 BL(c),Cage Fights Fire 1.75
64 DGr&BL(c),V:Suetre,Muerte . . 1.75

Power Man and Iron Fist #77
© Marvel Entertainment Group

65 BL(c),A:El Aquila, ... 1.75
66 FM(c),Sabretooth(2nd App.) . 30.00
67 V:Bushmaster 1.75
68 FM(c),V:Athur Nagan 2.00
69 V:Soldier 2.00
70 FM(c)V:El Supremo 1.75
71 FM(c),I:Montenegro 1.75
72 FM(c),V:Chako 1.75
73 FM(c),V:Rom 1.75
74 FM(c),V:Ninja 1.75
75 KGa,O:IronFist 2.50
76 KGa,V:Warhawk 2.50
77 KGa,A:Daredevil 2.50
78 KGa,A:El Aguila,Sabretooth
(Slasher)(3rd App.) 20.00
79 V:Dredlox 1.75
80 KJ(c),V:Montenegro 1.75
81 V:Black Tiger 1.75
82 V:Black Tiger 1.75
83 V:Warhawk 1.75
84 V:Constrictor,A:Sabertooth
(4th App.) 18.00
85 KP,V:Mole Man 1.75
86 A:Moon Knight 1.75
87 A:Moon Knight 1.75
88 V:Scimtar 1.75
89 V:Terrorists 1.75
90 V:Unus BS(c) 1.75
91 "Paths and Angles" 1.75
92 V:Hammeread,I:New Eel 1.75
93 A:Chemistro 1.75
94 V:Chemistro 1.75
95 Danny Rand 1.75
96 V,Chemistro 1.75
97 K'unlun,A:Fera 1.75
98 V:Shades & Commanche 1.75
99 R:Daught.of Dragon 1.75
100 O:K'unlun,DoubleSize 1.75
101 A:Karnak 1.75
102 V:Doombringer 1.75
103 O:Doombringer 1.75
104 V:Dr.Octopus,Lizard 1.75
105 F:Crime Buster 1.75
106 Luke Gets Shot 1.75
107 JBy(c),Terror issue 1.75
108 V:Inhuman Monster 1.75
109 V:The Reaper 1.75
110 V:Nightshade,Eel 1.75

111 I:Captain Hero 1.75
112 JBy(c),V:Control7 . . . . 1.75
113 JBy(c),A:Capt.Hero 1.75
114 JBy(c),V:Control7 . . . . 1.75
115 JBy(c),V:Stanley 1.75
116 JBy(c),V:Stanley 1.75
117 R:K'unlun 1.75
118 A:Colleen Wing 1.75
119 A:Daught.of Dragon 1.75
120 V:Chiantang 1.75
121 Secret Wars II 1.75
122 V:Dragonkin 1.75
123 V:Race Killer 1.75
124 V:Yellowclaw 1.75
125 MBr,LastIssue;D:Iron Fist . . . 3.00
G-Size#1 reprints 4.00
Ann.#1 Earth Shock 5.00

POWER PACHYDERMS
Sept., 1989
1 Elephant Superheroes 1.50

POWER PACK
August, 1984
1 JBr,BWi,I&O:Power Pack,
I:Snarks 2.50
2 JBr,BWi,V:Snarks 2.00
3 JBr,BWi,V:Snarks 2.00
4 JBr,BWi,V:Snarks 2.00
5 JBr,BWi,V:Bogeyman 2.00
6 JBr,BWi,A:Spider-Man 2.00
7 JBr,BWi,A:Cloak & Dagger . . . 2.00
8 JBr,BWi,A:Cloak & Dagger . . . 2.00
9 BA,BWi,A:Marrina 1.50
10 BA,BWi,A:Marrina 1.50
11 JBr,BWi,V:Morlocks 2.00
12 JBr,BWi,A:X-Men,V:Morlocks . 3.00
13 BA,BWi,Baseball issue 1.50
14 JBr,BWi,V:Bogeyman 1.50
15 JBr,BWi,A:Beta Ray Bill 1.50
16 JBr,BWi,I&O:Kofi,J:Tattletale
(Franklin Richards) 2.00
17 JBr,BWi,V:Snarks 1.50
18 BA,SW,Secret Wars II,
V:Kurse 2.00
19 BA,SW,Doub.size,Wolverine . . 4.00
20 BMc,A:NewMutants 1.50
21 BA,TA,C:Spider-Man 1.50
22 JBg,BWi,V:Snarks 1.50
23 JBg,BWi,V:Snarks,C:FF 1.50
24 JBg,BWi,V:Snarks,C:Cloak . . . 2.00
25 JBg,BWi,A:FF,V:Snarks 1.25
26 JBg,BWi,A:Cloak & Dagger . . . 1.25
27 JBg,AG,A:Wolverine,X-Factor,
V:Sabretooth 4.00
28 A:Fantastic Four,Hercules 1.25
29 JBg,DGr,A:SpM,V:Hobgoblin . . 2.00
30 VM,Crack 1.25
31 JBg,I:Trash 1.25
32 JBg,V:Trash 1.25
33 JBg,A:Sunspot,Warlock,
C:Spider-Man 1.75
34 TD,V:Madcap 1.25
35 JBg,A:X-Factor,D:Plague 1.75
36 JBg,V:Master Mold 1.25
37 SDr(i),I:Light-Tracker 1.25
38 SDr(i),V:Molecula 1.25
39 V:Bogeyman 1.25
40 A:New Mutants,V:Bogeyman . . 1.75
41 SDr(i),V:The Gunrunners 1.25
42 JBg,SDr,V:Bogeyman . . 2.00
43 JBg,SDr,AW,Inferno,
V:Bogeyman 2.00
44 JBr,Inferno,A:New Mutants . . . 2.25
45 JBr,End battle w/Bogeyman . . 1.50

Power Pack #7
© Marvel Entertainment Group

46 WPo,A:Punisher,Dakota North   2.00
47 JBg,I:Bossko 1.50
48 JBg,Toxic Waste #1 . . . . . . 1.50
49 JBg,JSh,Toxic Waste #2 . . . . 1.50
50 AW(i),V:Snarks 1.50
51 GM,I:Numinus 1.50
52 AW(i),V:Snarks,A:Numinus . . . 1.50
53 EC,A of V,A:Typhoid Mary . . . 1.50
54 JBg,V:Mad Thinker 1.50
55 DSp,V:Mysterio 1.50
56 TMo,A:Fant.Four,Nova 1.50
57 TMo,A:Nova,V:Star Stalker . . . 1.50
58 TMo,A:Galactus,Mr.Fantastic . 1.50
59 TMo,V:Ringmaster 1.50
60 TMo,V:Puppetmaster 1.50
61 TMo,V:Red Ghost & Apes 1.50
62 V:Red Ghost & Apes
(last issue) 1.50
Holiday Spec.JBr,Small Changes . 2.25

PRINCE NAMOR,
THE SUB-MARINER
Sept., 1984
1 I:Dragonrider, Dara 2.50
2 I:Proteus 1.50
3 . . . . 1.25
4 Dec., 1984 . . . . 1.25

PRINCE VALIANT
1994–95
1 JRy,CV,Thule, Camelot
and the Misty Isles 4.00
2 JRy,CV 4.00
3 JRy,CV 4.00
4 JRy,CV, final issue 4.00

PRIVATE EYE
Atlas Jan., 1951
1 . . . . 85.00
2 . . . . 55.00
3 GT 55.00
4 . . . . 40.00
5 . . . . 40.00
6 JSt 40.00
7 . . . . 40.00
8 March, 1952 . . . . 40.00

PROFESSOR XAVIER AND THE X-MEN
1995
1 1st Year Together 1.00
2 V:The Vanisher 1.00
3 FaN,F:The Blob 1.00
4 V:Magneto & Brotherhood 1.00
5 . . . . 1.00
6 . . . . 1.00
7 FdS,Sub-Mariner 1.00
8 thru 12 . . . . 1.00
13 AHo,F:Juggernaut 1.00
14 JGz,V:Juggernaut, ... 1.00
15 JGz,F:Quicksilver & Scarlet
    Witch 1.00
16 . . . . 1.00
17 JGz,V:Sentinels,F:Beast 1.00
18 JGz,X-Men vs. Sentinels,
    final issue 1.00

PROWLER, THE
1994
1 Creatures of the Night, pt.1 . . . 1.75
2 V:Nightcreeper, Creatures, pt.2 1.75
3 Creatures of the Night, pt.3 . . . 1.75
4 V:Vulture, Creatures, pt.4 . . . . 1.75

PSI FORCE
Nov., 1986
1 MT,O:PSI Force 1.25
2 MT 1.00
3 MT,CIA 1.00
4 MT,J:Network 1.00
5 MT 1.00
6 MT(c) 1.00
7 MT(c) 1.00
8 MT 1.00
9 MT(c) 1.00
10 PSI Hawk 1.00
11 . . . . 1.00
12 MT(c) 1.00
13 . . . . 1.00
14 AW 1.00
15 . . . . 1.00
16 RLm 1.25
17 RLm 1.25
18 RLm 1.25
19 RLm 1.25
20 RLm,V:Medusa Web;Rodstvow 1.50
21 RLm 1.50
22 RLm,A:Nightmask 1.50
23 A:D.P.7 . . . . 1.50
24 . . . . 1.50
25 . . . . 1.25
26 . . . . 1.25
27 thru 31 . . . . @1.50
32 June, 1989 . . . . 1.50
Ann.#1 . . . . 1.25

PSYCHONAUTS
Epic 1993–94
1 thru 4 War in the Future 4.95

PSYLOCKE & ANGEL: CRIMSON DAWN
1997
1 SvL,ATi,V:Obsideon 3.00
2 SvL,ATi, ... 3.00
3 BRa,SvL,ATi 3.00
4 (of 4) BRa,SvL,ATi 3.00

Punisher (Limited Series) #1
© Marvel Entertainment Group

PUNISHER
[Limited Series] Jan., 1986
1 MZ,Circle of Blood,double size 10.00
2 MZ,Back to the War 6.00
3 MZ,V:The Right 5.00
4 MZ,V:The Right 4.00
5 V:Jigsaw,end Mini-Series 4.00
[Regular Series] 1987–95
1 KJ,V:Wilfred Sobel,Drugs 5.00
2 KJ,V:General Trahn,Bolivia . . 3.00
3 KJ,V:Colonel Fryer 2.50
4 KJ,I:The Rev,Microchip Jr. . . . 2.50
5 KJ,V:The Rev 2.50
6 DR,KN,V:The Rosettis 2.50
7 DR,V:Ahmad,D:Rose 2.50
8 WPo,SW(1st Punisher),
    V:Sigo & Roky 3.00
9 WPo,SW,D:MicrochipJr,V:Sigo . 2.50
10 WPo,SW,A:Daredevil (x-over
    w/Daredevil #257) 3.00
11 WPo,SW,O:Punisher 2.00
12 WPo,SW,V:Gary Saunders . . . 2.00
13 WPo,SW,V:Lydia Spoto 2.00
14 WPo,SW,I:McDowell,Brooks . . 2.00
15 WPo,SW,V:Kingpin 2.00
16 WPo,SW,V:Kingpin 2.00
17 WPo,SW,V:Kingpin 2.00
18 WPo,SW,V:Kingpin,C:X-Men . . 2.00
19 LSn,In Australia 2.00
20 WPo(c),In Las Vegas 2.00
21 EL,SW,Boxing Issue 2.00
22 EL,SW,I:Saracen 2.00
23 EL,SW,V:Scully 2.00
24 EL,SW,A:Shadowmasters 2.00
25 EL,AW,A:Shadowmasters 2.00
26 RH,Oper.Whistle Blower#1 . . . 2.00
27 RH,Oper.Whistle Blower#2 . . . 2.00
28 BR,A:Dr.Doom,A of Veng. . . . 2.00
29 BR,A:Dr.Doom,A of Veng. . . . 2.00
30 BR,V:Geltrate 2.00
31 BR,V:Bikers #1 . . . . 2.00
32 BR,V:Bikers #2 . . . . 2.00
33 BR,V:The Reavers 2.00
34 BR,V:The Reavers 2.00
35 BR,MF,Jigsaw Puzzle #1 . . . . 2.00
36 MT,MF,Jigsaw Puzzle #2 . . . . 2.00
37 MT,Jigsaw Puzzle #3 . . . . . . 2.00

38 BR,MF,Jigsaw Puzzle #4 . . . . 2.00
39 JSh,Jigsaw Puzzle #5 . . . . . . 2.00
40 BR,JSh,Jigsaw Puzzle #6 . . . . 2.00
41 BR,TD,V:Terrorists 2.00
42 MT,V:Corrupt Mili. School . . . 2.00
43 BR,Border Run 2.00
44 Flag Burner 2.00
45 One Way Fare 2.00
46 HH,Cold Cache 2.00
47 HH,Middle East #1 . . . . 2.00
48 HH,Mid.East #2,V:Saracen . . 2.00
49 HH,Punisher Hunted 2.00
50 HH,MGo(c),I:Yo Yo Ng 2.00
51 Chinese Mafia 2.00
52 Baby Snatchers 2.00
53 HH,in Prison 2.00
54 HH,in Prison 2.00
55 HH,in Prison 2.00
56 HH,in Prison 2.00
57 HH,in Prison 2.00
58 V:Kingpin's Gang,A:Micro . . . 2.50
59 MT(c),V:Kingpin 2.00
60 VM,AW,Black Punisher,
    A:Luke Cage 2.00
61 VM,A:Luke Cage 2.00
62 VM,AW,A:Luke Cage 1.50
63 MT(c),VM,V:Thieves 1.50
64 Eurohit #1 . . . . 1.50
65 thru 70 Eurohit . . . . @1.50
71 AW(i) 1.50
72 AW(i) 1.50
73 AW(i),Police Action #1 . . . . . 1.50
74 AW(i),Police Action #2 . . . . . 1.50
75 AW(i),Police Action #3,foil(c),
    double size 2.50
76 LSn,in Hawaii 1.50
77 VM,Survive#1 . . . . 1.50
78 VM,Survive#2 . . . . 1.50
79 VM,Survive#3 . . . . 1.50
80 Goes to Church 1.50
81 V:Crooked Cops 1.50
82 B:Firefight 1.50
83 Firefight#2 . . . . 1.50
84 E:Firefight 1.50
85 Suicide Run 2.00
86 Suicide Run#3,Foil(c), ... 2.00
87 Suicide Run#6 . . . . 1.50
88 LSh(c),Suicide Run#9 . . . . . . 1.50
89 . . . . 1.75
90 Hammered 1.75
91 Silk Noose 1.75
92 Razor's Edge 1.75
93 Killing Streets 1.75
94 B:No Rules 1.50
95 No Rules 1.50
96 . . . . 1.50
97 CDi 1.50
98 . . . . 1.50
99 . . . . 1.50
100 New Punisher 3.00
100a Enhanced ed. 4.00
101 CC,Raid's Franks Tomb 1.50
102 A:Bullseye 1.50
103 Countdown 4 . . . . 1.50
104 CDi,Countdown 1, V:Kingpin,
    final issue 1.50
Ann.#1 MT,A:Eliminators,
    Evolutionary War. 5.00
Ann.#2 JLe,Atlantis Attacks #5,
    A:Moon Knight 3.50
Ann.#3 LS,MT,Lifeform #1 . . . . . 3.00
Ann.#4 Baron Strucker,pt.2
    (see D.D.Annual #7) 3.00
Ann.#5 System Bytes #1 . . . . . . 2.50
Ann.#6 I:Eradikator,w/card 3.25

GNv	5.00
Summer Spec.#1 VM,MT	3.50
Summer Spec.#2 SBs(c)	2.50
Summer Spec.#3 V:Carjackers	2.50
Summer Spec.#4	3.25
Spec. Punisher/Batman,CDi,JR2, 48pg (1994)	5.00
Spec.#1 Punisher/Daredevil, rep. Daredevil	6.00
Punisher:No Escape A:USAgent, Paladin (1990)	5.50
Punisher Movie Spec.BA (1989)	5.95
GNv Punisher: The Prize (1990)	5.50
Punisher:Bloodlines DC	6.25
Punisher:Blood on the Moors	16.95
Punisher:G-Force	5.25
Punisher:Origin of Mirco Chip #1, O:Mirco Chip	2.00
Punisher:Origin of Mirco Chip #2 V:The Professor	2.00
Classic Punisher rep early B&W magazines	7.00
Punisher:Back To School Spec. #1 JRy,short stories	3.25
#2 BSz	2.95
Punisher:Die Hard in the Big Easy Mardi Gras	5.25
Holiday Spec.#1 V:Young Mob Capo	3.25
Holiday Spec #2	2.95
Punisher:Ghosts of the Innocent#1 TGr, V:Kingpin's Dead Men	5.95
Punisher:Ghosts of the Innocent#2 TGr, V:Kingpin,Snake	5.95
TPB Punisher: Eye For An Eye	9.95

[2nd Regular Series] 1995

1 JOs,TL,CIv,Punisher sent to the Electric Chair, foil(c)	2.95
2 JOs,TL,CIv,Crime family boss	1.95
3 JOs,TL,CIv,V:Hatchetman	1.95
4 JOs,TL,CIv,A:Daredevil,Jigsaw	1.95
5	1.95
6	1.95
7 JOs,TL,CIv,V:Son of Nick Fury	1.95
8	1.50
9	1.50
10	1.50
11 Onslaught saga	1.50
12 A:X-Cutioner	3.00
13 JOs,TL, Working for S.H.I.E.L.D.?, A:X-Cutioner	1.50
14	1.50
15 JOs,TL, X-Cutioner	1.50
16 JOS,TL, concl.?	1.50
17 JOS,TL,A:Daredevil,Doc Samson, Spider-Man	1.50
18 JOS,TL,Frank Castle amnesia?	1.95
19 JOS,TL,V:Taskmaster	1.95
20 JOS,TL, fugitive Punisher	1.95

PUNISHER ARMORY
July, 1990

1 JLe(c)	3.00
2 JLe(c)	2.00
3	2.00
4 thru 6	@2.00
7 thru 10	@2.00

PUNISHER/ CAPTAIN AMERICA: BLOOD AND GLORY

1 thru 3 KJ,V:Drug Dealers	@6.25

CLASSIC PUNISHER

1 TDz	4.95

PUNISHER KILLS THE MARVEL UNIVERSE
1995

1-shot Alterniverse	5.95

PUNISHER MAGAZINE
Oct., 1989

1 MZ,rep.,Punisher #1	2.50
2 MZ,rep	2.25
3 thru 13 KJ,rep.	@2.25
14 rep. PWJ #1&#2	2.25
15 rep. PWJ	2.25
16 rep.,1990	2.25

PUNISHER MEETS ARCHIE
1994

1 JB	4.25
1a newsstand ed.	3.25

PUNISHER MOVIE COMIC
Nov., 1989

1 Movie adapt.	1.50
2 Movie adapt.	1.50
3 Movie adapt,Dec., 1989	1.50

PUNISHER P.O.V.
July, 1991

1 BWr,Punisher/Nick Fury	5.50
2 BWr,A:Nick Fury,Kingpin	5.50
3 BWr,V:Mutant Monster, A:Vampire Slayer	5.50
4 BWr,A:Nick Fury	5.25

PUNISHER 2099
1993–95

1 TMo,Jake Gallows family Killed, foil(c)	2.50
2 TMo,I:Fearmaster,Kron,Multi Factor	2.25
3 TMo,V:Frightening Cult	2.25
4 TMo,V:Cyber Nostra	1.75
5 TMo,V:Cyber Nostra,Fearmaster	1.75
6 TMo,V:Multi-Factor	1.75
7 TMo,Love and Bullets#1	1.75
8 TMo,Love and Bullets#2	1.75
9 TMo,Love and Bullets#3	1.75
10 TMo,I:Jigsaw	1.50
11 TMo,V:Jigsaw	1.50
12 TMo,A:Spider-Man 2099	1.50
13 TMo,Fall of the Hammer#5	1.50
14 WSm	1.50
15 TMo,V:Fearmaster, I:Public Enemy	1.50
16 TMo,V:Fearmaster, Public Enemy	1.75
17 TMo,V:Public Enemy	1.75
18 TMo,I:Goldheart	1.75
19 TMo,I:Vendetta	1.50
20	1.50
21	1.50
22 V:Hotwire	1.50
23 I:Synchron,V:Hotwire	1.50
24 V:Synchron	1.50
25 Enhanced cover	2.95
25a newsstand ed.	2.25
26 V:Techno-Shaman	1.50
27 R:Blue Max	1.50

Becomes:

PUNISHER 2099 A.D.

28 Minister of Punishment	1.95
29 Minister of Punishment	1.95
30 One Nation Under Doom	1.95
31	1.95
32 Out of Ammo	1.95
33 Counddown to final issue	1.95
34 final issue	1.95

Punisher War Journal #1
© Marvel Entertainment Group

PUNISHER WAR JOURNAL
Nov., 1988

1 CP,JLe,O:Punisher	3.00
2 CP,JLe,A:Daredevil	2.50
3 CP,JLe,A:Daredevil	2.50
4 CP,JLeV:The Sniper	2.50
5 CP,JLe,V:The Sniper	2.50
6 CP,JLe,A:Wolverine	2.50
7 CP,JLe,A:Wolverine	2.50
8 JLe,I:Shadowmasters	2.50
9 JLe,A:Black Widow	2.50
10 JLe,V:Sniper	2.50
11 JLe,Shock Treatment	2.00
12 JLe,AM,V:Bushwacker	2.00
13 JLe(c),V:Bushwacker	2.00
14 JLe(c),DR,RH,A:Spider-Man	2.00
15 JLe(c),DR,RH,A:Spider-Man	2.00
16 MT(i),Texas Massacre	2.00
17 JLe,AM,Hawaii	2.00
18 JLe,AM,Kahuna,Hawaii	2.00
19 JLe,AM,Traume in Paradise	2.00
20 AM	2.00
21 TSm,AM	2.00
22 TSm,AM,Ruins #1	2.00
23 TSm,AM,Ruins #2	2.00
24	2.00
25 MT	2.00
26 MT,A:Saracen	2.00
27 MT,A:Saracen	2.00
28 MT	2.00
29 MT,A:Ghostrider	2.00
30 MT,A:Ghostrider	2.00
31 NKu,Kamchatkan Konspiracy#1	2.00
32 Kamchatkan Konspiracy #2	2.00
33 Kamchatkan Konspiracy #3	2.00
34 V:Psycho	2.00

MARVEL

35 Movie Stuntman 2.00
36 Radio Talk Show #1 . . . . 2.00
37 Radio Talk Show #2 . . . . 2.00
38 . . . . 2.00
39 DGr,V:Serial Killer 2.00
40 MWg 1.75
41 Armageddon Express 1.75
42 Mob run-out 1.75
43 JR2(c) 1.75
44 Organ Donor Crimes 1.75
45 Dead Man's Hand #3,V:Viper . 2.00
46 Dead Man's Hand #6,V:Chainsaw
    and the Praetorians 1.75
47 Dead Man's Hand #7,A:Nomad,
    D.D,V:Hydra,Secret Empire . . . 1.75
48 B:Payback 1.75
49 JR2(c),V:Corrupt Cop 1.75
50 MT,V:Highjackers,I:Punisher
    2099 . . . . 2.00
51 E:Payback 1.75
52 A:Ice(from The'Nam) 1.75
53 A:Ice(from the Nam) 1.75
54 Hyper#1 . . . . 1.75
55 Hyper#2 . . . . 1.75
56 Hyper#3 . . . . 1.75
57 A:Ghost Rider,Daredevil 1.75
58 A:Ghost Rider,Daredevil 1.75
59 F:Max the Dog 1.75
60 CDi(s),F:Max the Dog 1.75
61 CDi(s),Suicide Run#1,Foil(c) . . 3.00
62 CDi(s),Suicide Run#4 . . . . . . 2.00
63 CDi(s),Suicide Run#7 . . . . . . 2.00
64 CDi(s),Suicide Run#10 . . . . . . 3.00
64a Newsstand Ed. 2.50
65 B:Pariah 2.00
66 A:Captain America 2.25
67 Pariah#3 . . . . 2.25
68 A:Spider-Man 2.25
69 E:Pariah 1.95
70 . . . . 1.95
71 . . . . 1.95
72 V:Fake Punisher 1.95
73 E:Frank Castle 1.95
74 . . . . 1.95
75 MT(c) 2.50
76 First Entry 1.95
77 R:Stone COld 1.95
78 V:Payback,Heathen 1.95
79 Countdown 3 . . . . 1.95
80 Countdown 0, A:Nick Fury,
    V:Bullseye, final issue 1.95
TPB reprints #6,7 . . . . 4.95

PUNISHER WAR ZONE
1992
1 JR2,KJ,Punisher As Johnny Tower
   Die-Cut Bullet Hole(c) 3.00
2 JR2,KJ,Mafia Career 2.00
3 JR2,KJ,Punisher/Mafia,contd . . 2.00
4 JR2,KJ,Cover gets Blown 2.00
5 JR2,KJ,A:Shotgun 2.00
6 JR2,KJ,A:Shotgun 2.00
7 JR2,V:Rapist in Central Park . . 2.00
8 JR2,V:Rapist in Central Park . . 2.00
9 JR2,V:Magnificent Seven 2.00
10 JR2,V:Magnificent Seven 2.00
11 JR2,MM,V:Magnificent Seven . 2.00
12 Punisher Married 2.00
13 Self-Realization 2.00
14 Psychoville#3 . . . . 2.00
15 Psychoville#4 . . . . 2.00
16 Psychoville#5 . . . . 2.00
17 Industrial Esponiage 2.00
18 Jerico Syndrome#2 . . . . 2.00
19 Jerico Syndrome#3 . . . . 2.00

Punisher War Zone #1
© Marvel Entertainment Group

20 B:2 Mean 2 Die 2.00
21 2 Mean 2 Die#2 . . . . 2.00
22 A:Tyger Tyger 2.00
23 Suicide Run#2,Foil(c) 3.25
24 Suicide Run#5, ... 2.00
25 Suicide Run#8, ... 2.50
26 CDi(s),JB,Pirates 2.00
27 CDi(s),JB, ... 2.25
28 CDi(s),JB,Sweet Revenge 2.25
29 CDi(s),JB,The Swine 2.25
30 CDi(s),JB 1.95
31 CDi(s),JB,River of Blood,pt.1 . . 1.95
32 CDi(s),JB,River of Blood,pt.2 . . 1.95
33 CDi(s),JB,River of Blood,pt.3 . . 1.95
34 CDi(s),JB,River of Blood,pt.4 . . 1.95
35 River of Blood,pt.5 . . . . 1.95
36 River of Blood,pt.6 . . . . 1.95
37 O:Max 1.95
38 Dark Judgment,pt.1 . . . . 1.95
39 Dark Judgment,pt.2 . . . . 1.95
40 In Court 1.95
41 CDi,Countdown 2, final issue . 1.95
Ann.#1 Jb,MGo,(c),I:Phalanx,
   w/Trading card 3.25
Ann.#2 CDi(s),DR 2.95

PUNISHER: YEAR ONE
1994
1 O:Punisher 2.50
2 O:Punisher 2.50
3 O:Punisher 2.50
4 finale 2.50

PUSSYCAT
(B&W Magazine) Oct., 1968
1 BEv,BWa,WW 125.00

QUASAR
Oct., 1989
1 O:Quasar 2.50
2 V:Deathurge,A:Eon 2.00
3 A:Human Torch,V:The Angler . 2.00
4 Acts of Vengeance,A:Aquarian . 2.00
5 A of Veng,V:Absorbing Man . . . 2.00

6 V:Klaw,Living Laser,Venom,
   Red Ghost 3.00
7 MM,A:Cosmic SpM,V:Terminus 2.50
8 MM,A:New Mutants,BlueShield 2.00
9 MM,A:Modam 2.00
10 MM,A:Dr.Minerva 2.00
11 MM,A:Excalibur,A:Modred . . . 2.00
12 MM,A:Makhari,Blood Bros. . . . 1.75
13 JLe(c)MM,J.into Mystery #1 . . 1.75
14 TM(c)MM,J.into Mystery #2 . . . 2.00
15 MM,Journey into Mystery #3 . . 1.75
16 MM,Double sized 2.00
17 MM,Race,A:Makkari,Whizzer,
   Quicksilver,Capt.Marv,Super
   Sabre,Barry Allen Spoof 2.25
18 GCa,N:Quasar 1.75
19 GCa,B:Cosmos in Collision,
   C:Thanos 2.00
20 GCa,A:Fantastic Four 2.00
21 GCa,V:Jack of Hearts 2.00
22 GCa,D:Quasar,A:Ghost Rider . 2.00
23 GCa,A:Ghost Rider 2.00
24 GCa,A:Thanos,Galactus,
   D:Maelstrom 2.00
25 GCa,A:Eternity & Infinity,N:Quasar,
   E:Cosmos Collision 2.00
26 GCa,Inf.Gauntlet,A:Thanos . . . 2.50
27 GCa,Infinity Gauntlet,I:Epoch . 2.00
28 GCa,A:Moondragon,Her,
   X-Men 2.00
29 GCa,A:Moondragon,Her 1.50
30 GCa,What If? tie-in 1.50
31 GCa,R:New Universe 1.50
32 GCa,Op.GalacticStorm,pt.3 . . 1.50
33 GCa,Op.GalacticStorm,pt.10 . . 1.50
34 GCa,Op.GalacticStorm,pt.17 . . 1.50
35 GCa,Binary V:Her 1.50
36 GCa,V:Soul Eater 1.50
37 GCa,V:Soul Eater 1.50
38 GCa,Inf.War,V:Warlock 1.50
39 SLi,Inf.War,V:Deathurge 1.50
40 SLi,Inf.War,V:Deathurge 1.50
41 R:Marvel Boy 1.50
42 V:Blue Marvel 1.50
43 V:Blue Marvel 1.50
44 V:Quagmire 1.50
45 V:Quagmire,Antibody 1.50
46 Neutron,Presence 1.50
47 1st Full Thunderstrike Story . . 1.50
48 A:Thunderstrike 1.50
49 Kalya Vs. Kismet 1.50
50 A:Man-Thing,Prism(c) 3.25
51 V:Angler,A:S.Supreme 1.50
52 V:Geometer 1.50
53 . . . . 1.50
54 MGu(s),Starblast #2 . . . . 1.50
55 MGu(s),A:Stranger 1.50
56 MGu(s),Starblast #10 . . . . 1.50
57 MGu(s),A:Kismet 1.50
58 . . . . 1.50
59 A:Thanos,Starfox 1.50
60 final issue 1.50

QUESTPROBE
August, 1984
1 JR,A:Hulk,I:Chief Examiner . . . 2.00
2 AM,JM,A:Spider-Man 1.75
3 JSt,A:Thing & Torch 1.50

QUICKSILVER
Sept. 1997
1 CJ,TPe, V:Exodus, cont. from
   Excalibur #113 . . . . 3.00
2 TPe,CJ,A:Knights of Wundagore 2.00
3 TPe,CJ,V:Arkon 2.00

4 TPe, Crystal returns	2.00
5 TPe,V:Inhumans	2.00
6 TPe,Inhumands trilogy concl.	2.00
7 JOs,F:The Black Knight	2.00
8 JOs,F:Pietro,V:Pyro	2.00
9 JOs,Savage Land concl.,A:High Evolutionary	2.00
10 JOS,Live Kree or Die, pt.3, x-over	2.00
11 JOs,The Seige of Wundagore, pt.2 (of 5)	2.00
12 JOs,The Seige of Wundagore, pt.4 (of 5) 48pg.	3.00

QUICK-TRIGGER WESTERN
See: WESTERN THRILLERS

RAIDERS OF THE LOST ARK
Sept., 1981

1 JB/KJ,movie adaption	2.00
2 JB/KJ,	1.75
3 JB/KJ,Nov.,1981	1.75

RAMPAGING HULK, THE
May 1998

1 RL,double size, savage Hulk era	3.00
2A RL,DGr,I:Ravage	2.00
2B JQ,JP,variant cover	2.00
3 RL,DGr,V:Ravage, concl.	2.00

Ravage 2099 #20
© Marvel Entertainment Group

RAVAGE 2099
1992–95

1 PR,I:Ravage	2.50
2 PR,V:Deathstryk	2.00
3 PR,V:Mutroids	2.00
4 PR,V:Mutroids	1.50
5 PR,Hellrock	1.50
6 PR,N:Ravage	1.50
7 PR,new Powers	1.50
8 V:Deathstryke	1.50
9 PR,N:Ravage	1.50

10 V:Alchemax	1.50
11 A:Avatarr	1.50
12 Ravage Transforms	1.50
13 V:Fearmaster	1.50
14 V:Punisher 2099	1.50
15 Fall of the Hammer #2	1.50
16 I:Throwback	1.50
17 GtM,V:Throwback,O:X-11	1.50
18 GtM,w/card	1.75
19 GtM,	1.75
20 GtM,V:Hunter	1.50
21 Savage on the Loose	1.50
22 Exodus	1.50
23 Blind Justice	1.50
24 Unleashed	1.50
25 Flame Bearer	2.25
25a Deluxe ed.	2.95
26 V:Megastruck	1.50
27 V:Deathstryke	1.50
28 R:Hela	1.50
29 V:Deathstryke	1.50
30 King Ravage	1.50

Becomes:
RAVAGE 2099 A.D.

31 V:Doom	1.95
32 One Nation Under Doom	1.95
33 Final issue	1.95

RAWHIDE KID
Atlas March, 1955—May, 1979

1 B:Rawhide Kid & Randy, A:Wyatt Earp	650.00
2 Shoot-out(c)	250.00
3 V:Hustler	175.00
4 Rh(c)	175.00
5 GC	175.00
6 Six-Gun Lesson	150.00
7 AW	150.00
8	150.00
9	150.00
10 thru 16	@100.00
17 JK,O:Rawhide Kid	100.00
18 thru 20	@100.00
21	90.00
22	90.00
23 JK,O:Rawhide Kid Retold	150.00
24 thru 30	@75.00
31 JK,DAy,No Law in Mesa	85.00
32 JK,DAy,Beware of the Parker Brothers	85.00
33 JK(c),JDa,V:Jesse James	75.00
34 JDa,JK,V:Mister Lightning	75.00
35 JK(c),GC,JDa,I&D:The Raven	75.00
36 DAy,A Prisoner in Outlaw Town	65.00
37 JK(c),DAy,GC,V:The Rattler	65.00
38 DAy.V:The Red Raven	65.00
39 DAy	65.00
40 JK(c),DAy,A:Two Gun Kid	65.00
41 JK(c),The Tyrant of Tombstone Valley	65.00
42 JK	65.00
43 JK	65.00
44 JK(c),V:The Masked Maverick	65.00
45 JK(c),O:Rawhide Kid Retold	75.00
46 JK(c),ATh	50.00
47 JK(c),The Riverboat Raiders	40.00
48 GC,V:Marko the Manhunter	35.00
49 The Masquerader	35.00
50 A:Kid Colt,V:Masquerader	35.00
51 DAy,Trapped in the Valley of Doom	35.00
52 DAy,Revenge at Rustler's Roost	35.00

53 Guns of the Wild North	35.00
54 DH,BEv,The Last Showdown	35.00
55	35.00
56 DH,JTgV:The Peacemaker	35.00
57 V:The Scorpion	35.00
58 DAy	35.00
59 V:Drako	35.00
60 DAy,HT,Massacre at Medicine Bend	35.00
61 DAy,TS,A:Wild Bill Hickok	30.00
62 Gun Town,V:Drako	30.00
63 Shootout at Mesa City	30.00
64 HT,Duel of the Desparadoes	30.00
65 JTg,HT,BE	30.00
66 JTg,BEv,Death of a Gunfighter	30.00
67 Hostage of Hungry Hills	30.00
68 JB,V:The Cougar	30.00
69 JTg,The Executioner	30.00
70 JTg,The Night of the Betrayers	25.00
71 JTg,The Last Warrior	25.00
72 JTg,The Menace of Mystery Valley	25.00
73 JTg,The Manhunt	25.00
74 JTg,The Apaches Attack	25.00
75 JTg,The Man Who Killed The Kid	25.00
76 JTg,V:The Lynx	25.00
77 JTg,The Reckoning	25.00
78 JTg	25.00
79 JTg,AW,The Legion of the Lost	25.00
80 Fall of a Hero	25.00
81 thru 85	@25.00
86 JK,O:Rawhide Kid retold	25.00
87 thru 99	@12.00
100 O:Rawhide Kid retold	15.00
101 thru 135	@12.00
126 thru 151	@10.00

RAWHIDE KID
August, 1985

1 JSe,mini-series	1.50
2 thru 4	@1.25

RAZORLINE FIRST CUT
1993

1 Intro Razorline	1.00

REAL EXPERIENCES
See: TESSIE THE TYPIST

RED RAVEN
See: HUMAN TORCH

RED SONJA
[1st Series] Jan., 1977

1 FT,O:Red Sonja,'Blood of the Unicorn'	3.50
2 FT,'Demon of the Maze'	2.50
3 FT,'The Games of Gita'	2.00
4 FT,'The Lake of the Unknown'	2.00
5 FT,'Master of the Bells'	2.00
6 FT,'The Singing Tower'	1.25
7 FT,'Throne of Blood'	1.25
8 FT,Vengeance o/t Golden Circle	1.25
9 FT,'Chariot o/t Fire-Stallions'	1.25
10 FT,Red Lace,pt.1	1.25
11 FT,Red Lace,pt.2	1.25
12 JB/JRu,'Ashes & Emblems'	1.25
13 JB/AM,'Shall Skranos Fall'	1.25
14 SB/AM,'Evening on the Border'	1.25
15 JB/TD,'Tomb of 3 Dead Kings' May, 1979	1.25

Red Sonja (2nd Series) #1
© Marvel Entertainment Group

[2nd Series] Feb., 1983
1	TD,GC, The Blood That Binds	1.25
2	GC, March,1983	1.00

[3rd Series] August, 1983
1		1.25
2 thru 13		@1.25
1 movie adaption, 1985		1.25
2 movie adaption, 1985		1.25

RED SONJA
1-shot Bros.Hildebrandt(c),48pg		2.95

RED WARRIOR
Atlas Jan.–Dec., 1951
1	GT,Indian Tales	100.00
2	GT(c),The Trail of the Outcast	65.00
3	The Great Spirit Speaks	50.00
4	O:White Wing	50.00
5		50.00
6	Final Issue	50.00

RED WOLF
May, 1972–Sept. 1973
1	SSh(c),GK,JSe,F:Red Wolf & Lobo	10.00
2	GK(c),SSh,Day of the Dynamite Doom	7.00
3	SSh,War of the Wolf Brothers	7.00
4	SSh,V:Man-Bear	7.00
5	GK(c),SSh	7.00
6	SSh,JA,V;Devil Rider	7.00
7	SSh,JA,Echoes from a Golden Grave	7.00
8	SSh,Hell on Wheels	7.00
9	DAy,To Die Again,O:Lobo	7.00

REN AND STIMPY SHOW
1992–96
1	Polybagged w/Air Fowlers, Ren(c)	5.00
1a	Stimpy(c)	4.00
1b	2nd Printing	3.00
1c	3rd Printing	2.00
2	Frankenstimpy	3.00
2a	2nd Printing	2.00
3	Christmas issue	3.00

3a	2nd Printing	2.00
4	Where's Stimpy?	3.00
5	Teacher Bingo	3.00
6	A:SpM,V:Powdered Toast Man	3.00
7	F:Offical Yak Shaving Day	3.00
8	F:Bun Boy Burger Bunny	3.00
9	Untamed World	3.00
10	Bug Out	3.00
11	Ren's Peaceful Place	3.00
12	Teacher Bingo	3.00
13	Halloween issue	2.50
14	Mars needs Vecro	2.50
15	Christmas Spec.	2.25
16		2.25
17	This Year's Model	2.25
18	U.S. Ohhhhh No!	2.25
19	Minimalist issue	2.25
20	F:Muddy Mudskipper	2.25
21	I'm The Cat	2.25
22	Badtime Stories	1.95
23	Athletics	1.95
24	Halloween	1.95
25	regular (c)	1.95
25a	die-cut(c),A new addition	2.95
26		1.95
27		1.95
28	Filthy the Monkey	1.95
29	Loch Ness Mess	1.95
30	Pinata game	1.95
31	Sausage Castle	1.95
32	Join Circus, UFO Abduction	1.95
33	Bowling	1.95
34	lottery ticket	1.95
35	Pasta Monster	1.95
36	Ren Cabby Driver	1.95
37	Medical experiment	1.95
38	Cat who Knew too Much	1.95
39	Mad Computer	1.95
40		1.95
41		1.95
42	at Cap'n Salty Wet World	1.95
Spec.#1		3.25
Spec.#2		3.25
Spec.#3 Powder Toast Man		2.95
Spec.#4		2.95
Spec.#5 Virtual Stupidity		2.95
Spec.#6 History of Music		2.95
Holiday Special		2.95
Spec. Radio Dazed & Confused		1.95
Spec. Around the World in a Daze		2.95
TPB Running Joke,rep.#1-4,w/new material		13.25
TPB Pick of the Litter		13.25
TPB Tastes Like Chicken		13.25
TPB Your Pals		12.95
TPB Seech Little Monkeys		12.95

RETURN OF THE JEDI
1	AW,movie adapt	3.00
2	AW,movie adapt	3.00
3	AW,movie adapt	3.00
4	AW,movie adapt	3.00

REX HART
See: BLAZE CARSON

RICHIE RICH
1	Movie Adaptation	2.95

RINGO KID
[2nd Series] Jan., 1970
1	AW,Reprints	15.00
2	JSe,Man Trap	8.00
3	JR,the Man From the Panhandle	8.00

4	HT(c),The Golden Spur	8.00
5	JMn,Ambush	8.00
6	Capture or Death	8.00
7	HT(c),JSe,JA,Terrible Treasure of Vista Del Oro	8.00
8	The End of the Trail	8.00
9	JSe,Mystery of the Black Sunset	8.00
10	Bad day at Black Creek	8.00
11	Bullet for a Bandit	8.00
12	A Badge to Die For	15.00
13	DW,Hostage at Fort Cheyenne	6.00
14	Showdown in the Silver Cartwheel	6.00
15	Fang,Claw, and Six-Gun	6.00
16	Battle of Cattleman's Bank	6.00
17	Gundown at the Hacienda	6.00
18		6.00
19	Thunder From the West	6.00
20	AW	6.00
21 thru 29		@6.00
30	Nov., 1973	6.00

RINGO KID WESTERN
Atlas August, 1954
1	JSt,O:Ringo Kid,B:Ringo Kid	185.00
2	I&O:Arab,A:Black Rider	85.00
3		50.00
4		50.00
5		50.00
6		55.00
7		55.00
8	JSe	55.00
9		30.00
10	JSe(c),AW	40.00
11	JSe(c)	30.00
12	JO	30.00
13	AW	40.00
14 thru 20		@30.00
21	Sept., 1957	30.00

ROBOCOP
March, 1990
1	LS,I:Nixcops	9.00
2	LS,V:Nixcops	5.00
3	LS	3.50
4	LS	3.00
5	LS,WarzonePt1	3.00
6	LS,WarzonePt2	3.00
7	LS	2.50
8	LS,V:Gang-5	2.50
9	LS,V:Vigilantes	2.50
10	LS	2.50
11	HT	2.50
12	LS,Robocop Army #1	2.00
13	LS,Robocop Army #2	2.00
14	LS,Robocop Army #3	2.00
15	LS,Robocop Army #4	2.00
16	TV take over	2.00
17	LS,V:The Wraith	2.00
18	LS,Mindbomb #1	2.00
19	LS,Mindbomb #2	2.00
20	In Detroit	2.00
21	LS,Beyond the Law,pt.1	2.00
22	LS,Beyond the Law,pt.2	2.00
23	LS,Beyond the Law,pt.3,final	2.00
Robocop Movie Adapt		4.95
Robocop II Movie Adapt		4.95

ROBOCOP II
August, 1990
1	MBa,rep.Movie Adapt	2.00
2 and 3	MBa,rep.Movie adapt	@1.50

ROBOTIX
Feb., 1986
1 Based on toys 1.00

ROCKET RACCOON
May, 1985—Aug., 1985
1 thru 4 MM .... @1.50

ROCKO'S MODERN LIFE
1994
1 and 2 .... @2.25
3 and 4 .... @1.95

ROGUE
1995
1 Enhanced cover 4.50
2 A:Gambit 4.00
3 Gamtit or Rogue? 2.95
4 final issue 2.95

ROM
Dec., 1979
1 SB,I&O:Rom 3.00
2 FM(c),SB,V:Dire Wraiths 2.50
3 FM(c),SB,I:Firefall 2.50
4 SB,A:Firefall 2.00
5 SB,A:Dr.Strange 2.00
6 SB,V:Black Nebula 1.50
7 SB,V:Dark Nebula 1.50
8 SB,V:Dire Wraiths 1.50
9 SB,V:Serpentyne 1.50
10 SB,V:U.S.Air Force 1.50
11 SB,V:Dire Wraiths 1.50
12 SB,A:Jack O' Hearts 1.75
13 SB,V:Plunderer 1.25
14 SB,V:Mad Thinker 1.25
15 SB,W:Brandy and Dire Wraith . 1.25
16 SB,V:Watchwraith 1.25
17 SB,A:X-Men 3.00
18 SB,A:X-Men 3.00
19 SB,JSt,C:X-Men 1.50
20 SB,JSt,A:Starshine 1.25
21 SB,JSt,A:Torpedo 1.25
22 SB,JSt,A:Torpedo 1.25
23 SB,JSt,A:Powerman,Iron Fist . 1.25
24 SB,JSt,A:Nova 1.25
25 SB,JSt,Double-Sized 1.50
26 SB,JSt,V:Galactus 1.00
27 SB,JSt,V:Galactus 1.00
28 SB,JSt,D:Starshine 1.00
29 SB,Down in the Mines 1.00
30 SB,JSt,A:Torpedo 1.00
31 SB,JSt,V:Evil Mutants,Rogue . 2.00
32 SB,JSt,V:Evil Mutants 2.00
33 SB,V:Sybil 1.00
34 SB,A:Sub-Mariner 1.00
35 SB,A:Sub-Mariner 1.00
36 SB,V:Scarecrow 1.00
37 SB,A:Starshine 1.00
38 SB,A:Master of Kung Fu 1.00
39 SB,A:Master of Kung Fu 1.00
40 SB,A:Torpedo 1.00
41 SB,A:Dr.Strange 1.00
42 SB,A:Dr.Strange 1.00
43 SB,Rom Becomes Human 1.00
44 SB,A:Starshine,O:Gremlin ... 1.00
45 SB,V:Soviet Super Soldiers ... 1.00
46 SB,V:Direwraiths 1.00
47 SB,New Look for Wraiths 1.00
48 SB,V:Dire Wraiths 1.00
49 SB,V:Dire Wraiths 1.00
50 SB,D:Torpedo,V:Skrulls 1.25
51 SB,F:Starshine 1.00
52 BSz(c),SB,V:Dire Wraiths 1.00

Rom #1
© Marvel Entertainment Group

53 SB,BSz,V:Dire Wraiths 1.00
54 V:Dire Wraiths 1.00
55 V:Dire Wraihs 1.00
56 A:Alpha Flight 2.00
57 A:Alpha Flight 2.00
58 JG(c),A:Antman 1.00
59 SD,BL,V:Microbe Menace 1.00
60 SD,TP,V:Dire Wraiths 1.00
61 SD,V:Wraith-Realm 1.00
62 SD,A:Forge 1.25
63 SD,V:Dire Wraiths 1.00
64 SD,V:Dire Wraiths 1.00
65 SD,A:X-Men,Avengers 1.25
66 SD,Rom leaves Earth 1.25
67 SD,V:Scorpion 1.00
68 BSz(c)SD,Man & Machine ... 1.00
69 SD,V:Ego 1.00
70 SD 1.00
71 SD,V:Raak 1.00
72 SD,Secret Wars II 1.25
73 SD,JSt 1.00
74 SD,JBy,Code of Honor 1.00
75 SD,CR,Doublesize,last issue .. 1.50
Ann.#1 PB,A:Stardust 1.50
Ann.#2 I:Knights of Galador 1.25
Ann.#3 A:New Mutants 2.00
Ann.#4 V:Gladiator 1.25

ROMANCE DIARY
Dec., 1949
1 .... 75.00
2 March, 1950 .... 60.00

ROMANCES OF THE WEST
Nov., 1949
1 Ph(c),Calamity Jane,
Sam Bass 150.00
2 March, 1950 .... 100.00

ROMANCE TALES
Oct., 1949
(no #1 thru 6)
7 .... 75.00

8 .... 50.00
9 March, 1950 .... 50.00

ROMANTIC AFFAIRS
See: MOLLY MANTON'S ROMANCES

ROYAL ROY
Star May, 1985
1 thru 5 .... @1.00
6 March, 1986 .... 1.00

RUGGED ACTION
Atlas Dec., 1954
1 Man-Eater 65.00
2 JSe,DAy,Manta-Ray 50.00
3 DAy 50.00
4 .... 50.00
Becomes:

STRANGE STORIES OF SUSPENSE
5 RH,The Little Black Box ... 300.00
6 BEv,The Illusion 150.00
7 JSe(c),BEv,Old John's House 165.00
8 AW,BP,TYhumbs Down 165.00
9 BEv(c),Nightmare 150.00
10 RC,MME,AT 165.00
11 .... 125.00
12 .... 125.00
13 .... 100.00
14 AW 125.00
15 BK 100.00
16 August, 1957 .... 100.00

RUINS
1995
1 Marvel's Alterverse 4.95
2 Fully painted, 32pg 4.95

RUSTY COMICS
See: KID KOMICS

SABRETOOTH
[Limited Series] 1993
1 B:LHa(s),MT,A:Wolverine 5.00
2 MT,A:Mystique,C:Wolverine ... 4.00
3 MT,A:Mystique,V:Wolverine 3.50
4 E:LHa(s),MT,D:Birdy 3.00
TPB rep. #1-#4 .... 12.95

SABRETOOTH CLASSICS
1994–95
1 rep. Power Man/Iron Fist #66 .. 1.75
2 rep. Power Man/Iron Fist #78 .. 1.75
3 rep. Power Man/Iron Fist #84 .. 1.75
4 rep. Spider-Man #116 ...... 1.75
5 rep. Spider-Man #119 ...... 1.50
6 reprints 1.50
7 reprints 1.50
8 reprints 1.50
9 reprints 1.50
10 Morlock Massacre 1.50
11 rep. Daredevil #238 .... 1.50
12 rep. V:Wolverine 1.50
13 rep. 1.50
14 A:Mauraders 1.50
15 Mutant Massacre, rep.
Uncanny X-Men #221 ...... 1.50

SABRETOOTH
Spec.#1 FaN, cont.from X-Men#48 4.95

MARVEL

SABRETOOTH
Oct., 1997
1-shot,F:Wildchild 2.50

SABRETOOTH
& MYSTIQUE
1 JGz,AOI, ... 1.95
2 thru 4 JGz,AOI . . . . @1.95

SACHS & VIOLENS
Epic 1993–94
1 GP,PDd(s) 3.00
2 GP,PDd(s),V:Killer 2.50
3 GP,PDd(s),V:White Slavers . . 2.50
4 GP,PDd(s),D:Moloch 2.25

SAGA OF CRYSTAR
May, 1983
1 O:Crystar 2.25
2 A:Ika 1.50
3 A:Dr.Strange 1.50
4 . . . . 1.50
5 . . . . 1.50
6 A:Nightcrawler 2.00
7 I:Malachon 1.50
8 . . . . 1.50
9 . . . . 1.50
10 Chaos 1.50
11 Alpha Flight,Feb., 1985 . . . . . 2.00

SAGA OF ORIGINAL
HUMAN TORCH
1 RB,O:Original Human Torch . . 3.00
2 RB,A:Toro 2.50
3 RB,V:Adolph Hitler 2.50
4 RB,Torch vs. Toro 2.50

ST. GEORGE
Epic June, 1988
1 KJ,Shadow Line 1.25
2 KJ,I:Shrek 1.25
3 KJ 1.50
4 KJ 1.50
5 . . . . 1.50
6 . . . . 1.50
7 DSp 1.50
8 Oct., 1989 . . . . 1.50

SAINT SINNER
Razorline 1993–94
1 I:Phillip Fetter 2.75
2 F:Phillip Fetter 2.00
3 in Vertesque 2.00
4 . . . . 2.00
5 Arcadia 2.00
6 . . . . 2.00
7 The Child Stealer 2.00
8 . . . . 1.95

SAM & MAX
GO TO THE MOON
1 Dirtbag Special,w/Nirvana Tape 4.00
[Regular Series]
1 MMi,AAd,F:Skull Boy 3.25
2 AAd,MMi 2.95
3 . . . . 2.95

SAMURAI CAT
Epic 1991
1 I:MiaowaraTomokato 2.25
2 I:Con-Ed,V:Thpaghetti-Thoth . . 2.25

3 EmpireStateStrikesBack 2.25

SATANA
Nov., 1997
1 JaL,WEI,AOI,V:Doctor Strange,
non-code series 3.00
2 WEI,AOI,to the gates of Hell . . 3.00

Savage Sword of Conan #10
© *Marvel Entertainment Group*

SAVAGE SWORD
OF CONAN
August, 1974
(black & white magazine)
1 BWS,JB,NA,GK,O:Blackmark,
3rdA:Red Sonja,Boris(c) 75.00
2 NA(c),HC,GK,'Black Colossus,'
B.U.King Kull;B.U.Blackmark . 35.00
3 JB,BWS,GK,'At The Mountain
of the Moon God;B.U.s:
Kull;Blackmark 30.00
4 JB,RCo,GKIron Shadows in the
Moon B.U.Blackmark,Boris(c) 15.00
5 JB,A WitchShall beBorn,Boris(c)15.00
6 AN,'Sleeper 'Neath the Sands' 12.50
7 JB,Citadel at the Center
of Time Boris(c) 12.50
8 inc.GK,'Corsairs against Stygia 12.50
9 Curse of the Cat-Goddess,
Boris(c),B.U.King Kull 12.50
10 JB,'Sacred Serpent of Set'
Boris(c) 10.00
11 JB,'The Abode of the Damned' 10.00
12 JB,Haunters of Castle Crimson
Boris(c) 10.00
13 GK,The Thing in the Temple,
B.U. Solomon Kane 10.00
14 NA,Shadow of Zamboula,
B.U.Solomon Kane 10.00
15 JB,Boris(c),'Devil in Iron' 10.00
16 JB,BWS,People of the Black
Circle,B.U.Bran Mak Morn . . . 10.00
17 JB,'On to Yimsha!,
B.U.Bran Mak Morn 10.00
18 JB,'The Battle of the Towers'
B.U. Solomon Kane 10.00
19 JB,'Vengeance in Vendhya'
B.U. Solomon Kane 10.00
20 JB,'The Slithering Shadow'

B.U. Solomon Kane 10.00
21 JB,'Horror in the Red Tower' . 10.00
22 JB,'Pool o/t Black One'
B.U. Solomon Kane 10.00
23 JB,FT,'Torrent of Doom'
B.U. Solomon Kane 10.00
24 JB,BWS,'Tower of the
Elephant'B.U.Cimmeria 10.00
25 DG,SG,Jewels of Gwahlur,
B.U.Solomon Kane. 10.00
26 JB,TD,Beyond the Black River,
B.U.Solomon Kane 8.00
27 JB/TD,Children of Jhebbal Sag 8.00
28 JB,AA,Blood of the Gods . . . 8.00
29 ECh,FT,Child of Sorcery,
B.U. Red Sonja 8.00
30 FB,The Scarlet Citadel 8.00
31 JB/TD,The Flaming Knife,pt.1 . 8.00
32 JB/TD,Ghouls of Yanaldar,pt.2 8.00
33 GC,Curse of the Monolith,
B.U.Solomon Kane 8.00
34 Cl/AA,MP,Lair o/t Ice Worm;B.U.
Solomon Kane,B.U.King Kull . . 8.00
35 ECh,Black Tears 8.00
36 JB,AA,Hawks over Shem 8.00
37 SB,Sons of the White Wolf
B.U. Solomon Kane 8.00
38 JB,TD,The Road of the Eagles 8.00
39 SB/TD,The Legions of the Dead,
B.U.Solomon Kane concl. 8.00
40 JB/TD,A Dream of Blood 8.00
41 JB/TD,Quest for the Cobra Crown
A:Thoth-Amon,B.U.Sol.Kane . . 8.00
42 JB/TD,Devil-Tree of Gamburu,
A:Thoth-Amon,B.U.Sol.Kane . . 8.00
43 JB/TD,King Thoth-Amon,
B.U.King Kull 8.00
44 SB/TD,The Star of Khorala . . . 8.00
45 JB/TD,The Gem in the Tower,
B.U. Red Sonja 8.00
46 EC/TD,Moon of Blood,
B.U. Hyborian Tale 8.00
47 GK/JB/JRu,Treasure of Tranicos
C:Thoth-Amon 8.00
48 JB/KJ,A Wind Blows from Stygia
C:Thoth-Amon 8.00
49 JB/TD,When Madness Wears the
Crown, B.U.Hyborian Tale 6.00
50 JB/TD,Swords Across the
Alimane 6.00
51 JB/TD,Satyrs' Blood 6.00
52 JB/TD,Conan the Liberator . . . 6.00
53 JB,The Sorcerer and the Soul,
B.U. Solomon Kane 6.00
54 JB,The Stalker Amid the Sands,
B.U. Solomon Kane 6.00
55 JB,Black Lotus & Yellow Death
B.U. King Kull 6.00
56 JB/TD,The Sword of Skelos . . 6.00
57 JB/TD,Zamboula 6.00
58 JB/TD,KGa,For the Throne of
Zamboula,B.U.OlgerdVladislav 6.00
59 AA,ECh,City ofSkulls,B.U.Gault 6.00
60 JB,The Ivory Goddess 6.00
61 JB,Wizard Fiend of Zingara . . . 6.00
62 JB/ECh,Temple of the Tiger,
B.U. Solomon Kane 6.00
63 JB/ECh,TP/BMc,GK,Moat of Blood
I:Chane of the Elder Earth . . . 6.00
64 JB/ECh,GK,Children of Rhan,
B.U. Chane 6.00
65 GK,JB,Fangs of the Serpent,
B.U. Bront 6.00
66 thru 75 . . . . @6.00
76 thru 80 . . . . @5.00

All comics prices listed are for *Near Mint* condition.

81 JB/ECh,Palace of Pleasure,
   B.U. Bront 5.00
82 AA,BWS,Devil in the Dark.Pt.1
   B.U.repConan#24,Swamp Gas 5.00
83 AA,MW,NA,ECh,Devil in the Dark
   Pt.2,B.U. Red Sonja,Sol.Kane . 5.00
84 VM,Darksome Demon of
   Rabba Than 5.00
85 GK,Daughter of the God King . 5.00
86 GK,Revenge of the Sorcerer . . 5.00
87 . . . . 5.00
88 JB,Isle of the Hunter 5.00
89 AA,MW,Gamesman of Asgalun,
   B.U. Rite of Blood 5.00
90 JB,Devourer of Souls 5.00
91 JB,VM,Forest of Friends,
   B.U. The Beast,The Chain . . . 5.00
92 JB,The Jeweled Bird 5.00
93 JB/ECh,WorldBeyond the Mists 5.00
94 thru 101 . . . . @5.00
102 GD,B.U.Bran Mac Morn 4.00
103 GD,White Tiger of Vendhya,
   B.U. Bran Mac Morn 4.00
104 . . . . 4.00
105 . . . . 4.00
106 Feud of Blood 4.00
107 thru 118 . . . . @4.00
119 ECh,A:Conan's Sister 4.00
120 Star of Thama-Zhu 4.00
121 . . . . 4.00
122 . . . . 4.00
123 ECh,Secret of the GreatStone 4.00
124 ECh,Secret of the Stone 4.00
125 Altar of the Goat God 4.00
126 The Mercenary 4.00
127 Reunion in Scarlet,Return
   of Valeria 4.00
128 . . . . 4.00
129 . . . . 4.00
130 Reavers of the Steppes 4.00
131 GI,Autumn of the Witch 4.00
132 ECh,Masters o/t Broadsword . 4.00
133 . . . . 4.00
134 Conan the Pirate 4.00
135 Conan the Pirate 4.00
136 NKu,Stranded on DesertIsland 4.00
137 ECh,The Lost Legion 4.00
138 ECh,Clan o/t Lizard God 4.00
139 ECh,A:Valeria 4.00
140 ECh,The Ghost's Revenge . . 4.00
141 ECh 4.00
142 ECh,V:Warlord 4.00
143 ECh 4.00
144 ECh 4.00
145 ECh 4.00
146 ECh 4.00
147 ECh 4.00
148 BMc 4.00
149 TGr,BMc,Conan Enslaved . . . 4.00
150 ECh 4.00
151 ECh 4.00
152 ECh,Valley Beyond the Stars 4.00
153 Blood on the Sand,Pt.1 . . . . . 4.00
154 Blood on the Sand,Pt.2 . . . . . 4.00
155 ECh,V:Vampires 4.00
156 V:Corinthian Army 4.00
157 V:Hyborians 4.00
158 ECh,The Talisman-Gem 4.00
159 Conan Enslaved 4.00
160 . . . . 4.00
161 V:Magician/Monsters 4.00
162 AW,Horned God,B.U.Sol.Kane 3.00
163 V:Picts 3.00
164 Conan's Revenge 3.00
165 B.U. King Kull 3.00

Savage Sword of Conan #90
© Marvel Entertainment Group

166 ECh,Conan in New World,Pt.1 3.00
167 ECh,Conan in New World,Pt.2 3.00
168 ECh,Conan in New
   World,concl 3.00
169 . . . . 3.00
170 AW,A:Red Sonja,Valeria
   B.U. Solomon Kane 3.00
171 TD,Conan Youth Story 2.50
172 JS,JRu,Haunted Swamp,
   B.U.King Kull,Valeria,
   Red Sonja 2.50
173 ECh,Under Siege 2.50
174 AA,Red Stones of
   Rantha Karn 2.50
175 The Demonslayer Sword 2.50
176 FH,TT,V:Wizard,B.U. Witch
   Queen,Dagon,Ghouls 2.50
177 LMc,TD,ECh,Conan the Prey,
   B.U.King Conan,Red Sonja . . . 2.50
178 AA,The Dinosaur God 2.50
179 ECh,A:Red Sonja,Valeria,
   B.U.Conan 2.50
180 ECh,Sky-God Bardisattva,
   B.U. King Kull 2.50
181 TD,Conan the Pagan God?,
   B.U. Voodoo Tribe 2.50
182 RB/RT,V:Killer Ants 2.50
183 ECh,V:Kah-Tah-Dhen,
   B.U.King Kull 2.50
184 AA,Return of Sennan 2.50
185 The Ring of Molub 2.50
186 AW,A:Thulsa Doom 2.50
187 ECh,A:Conan's Brother? 2.50
188 V:Kharban the Sorcerer 2.50
189 A:Search Zukala for Gem . . . 2.50
190 JB/TD,Skull on the Seas,pt.1 . 2.25
191 JB/ECh,Skull on the Seas,pt.2
   Thulsa Doom Vs.Thoth-Amon . 2.25
192 JB/ECh,Skull on the Seas,pt.3
   B.U. King Kull 2.25
193 JB/ECh,Skull on the Seas concl.
   V:Thulsa Doom & Thoth-Amon 2.25
194 JB/ECh,Wanted for Murder,
   B.U. Li-Zya 2.25
195 JB/ECh,V:Yamatains,
   Giant Tortoise 2.25
196 JB/ECh,Treasure of the Stygian
   Prince-Toth-Mekri,A:Valeria . . . 2.25

197 RTs,JB,EC,Red Hand 2.25
198 RTs,JB,EC,Red Hand 2.25
199 RTs,JB,EC,V:Black Zarona . . 2.25
200 RTs,JB,ECh,JJu(c),The Barbarian
   from Cross Plains 2.25
201 RTs,MCW,return to Tarantia . 2.25
202 RTs,JB,ECh,Conan in the City
   City of Magicians,pt.1 . . . . . . 2.25
203 RTs,JB,ECh,Conan in the City
   City of Magicians,pt.2 . . . . . . 2.25
204 RTs,JB,ECh,Conan in the City
   City of Magicians,pt.3 . . . . . . 2.25
205 RTs,JB,ECh,Conan in the City
   City of Magicians,pt.4 . . . . . . 2.25
206 RTs,JB,ECh,BLr(c),Conan in the
   City of Magicians,concl. 2.25
207 RTs,JB,ECh,MK(c), Conan and
   the Spider God, pt.1 . . . . 2.25
208 RTs,JB,ECh, Conan and the
   Spider God, pt.2 . . . . 2.25
209 RTs,JB,Conan and the
   Spider God,pt.3 . . . . 2.25
210 RTs,Conan and the
   Spider God,pt.4 . . . . 2.25
211 RTs,Conan and the Gods of
   the Mountain,pt.1 . . . . 2.25
212 RTs,Conand and the Gos of
   the Mountain,pt.2 . . . . 2.25
213 RTs,Conan and the Gods of
   the Mountain,pt.3 . . . . 2.25
214 RTs,Conan and the Gods of
   the Mountain,pt.4 . . . . 2.25
215 RTs,JuB(c),Conan and the Gods
   of the Mountain,concl.. . . . . . 2.25
216 RTs,AA,Vengeance of Nitocris 2.25
217 RTs,Conan theMercenary,pt.1 2.25
218 RTs,Conan theMercenary,pt.2 2.25
219 RTs,A:Solomon Kane 2.25
220 RTs,V:Skull Out of Time 2.25
221 RTs,C.L.Moore story adapt. . 2.25
222 RTs,The Haunter of the Towers
   B.U.JB,Conan Barbarian #1 . . 2.25
223 RTs,A:Tuzune Thune 2.25
224 RTs,JWk,The Dwellers Under the
   Tombs,adapt. B.U.V:Dinosaurs 2.25
225 . . . . 2.25
226 RTs,EN(c),The Four Ages
   of Conan, A:Red Sonja 2.25
227 RTs,JBu, besieged in a lost
   city, B.U. Kull,Red Sonja 2.25
228 RTs,AN,Conan in chains! . . . 2.25
229 RTs 2.25
230 RTs, Acheron falls, Ring of
   Tkrubu,pt.2, R:Kull 2.25
231 RTs, V:Tuzoun Thune, B.U.
   EM,Red Sonja 2.25
232 RTs 2.25
233 A:Juma the Black, Kull 2.25
234 RTs,JBu, A:Nefartari;
   A:Red Sonja, Zula 2.25
235 RTs,JBu,The Daughter of
   Raktauanishi, final issue 2.25
Ann.#1 SB,BWS,inc.'Beware the
   Wrath of Anu',B.U. King
   Kull Vs.Thulsa Doom 2.25

SAVAGE TALES
May, 1971
(black & white magazine)
1 GM,BWS,JR,I&O:Man-Thing,
   B:Conan,Femizons,A:Kazar 150.00
2 GM,FB,BWS,AW,BWr,A:King
   Kull rep,Creatures on
   the Loose #10 . . . . 50.00
3 FB,BWS,AW,JSo 35.00

4 NA(c),E:Conan	20.00
5 JSn,JB,B:Brak the Barbarian	20.00
6 NA(c),JB,AW,B:Kazar	8.00
7 GM,NA	6.00
8 JB,A:Shanna,E:Brak	5.00
9 MK,A:Shanna	5.00
10 RH,NA,AW,A:Shanna	5.00
11 RH	5.00
12 Summer, 1975	5.00
Ann.#1 GM,GK,BWS,O:Kazar	6.00

SAVAGE TALES
Nov., 1985
(black & white magazine)

1 MGo,I:The 'Nam	3.00
2 MGo	2.00
3 MGo	2.00
4 MGo	2.00
5 MGo	2.00
6 MGo	2.00
7 MGo	2.00
8 MGo	2.00
9 MGo,March, 1987	2.00

SCARLET SPIDER
1995–96

1 HMe,GK,TP,VirtualMortality,pt.3	1.95
2 HMe,JR2,AW,CyberWar,pt.3	1.95
3 and 4 HMe	@1.95

SCARLET SPIDER UNLIMITED
1995

1 True Origin,64pg	3.95

SCARLET WITCH
1994

1 ALa(s),DAn(s),JH,I:Gargan, C:Master Pandemonium	2.00
2 C:Avengers West Coast	2.00
3 A:Avengers West Coast	2.00
4 V:Lore,last issue	2.00

SCOOBY-DOO
Oct., 1977

1 B:DynoMutt	9.00
2 thru 8	@8.00
9 Feb., 1979	8.00

SECRET DEFENDERS
93–95

1 F:Dr.Strange(in all),Spider Woman,Nomad,Darkhawk, Wolverine,V:Macabre	3.25
2 F:Spider Woman,Nomad,Darkhawk, Wolverine,V:Macabre	2.50
3 F:Spider Woman,Nomad,Darkhawk, Wolverine,V:Macabre	2.00
4 F:Namorita,Punisher, Sleepwalker,V:Roadkill	2.00
5 F:Naromita,Punisher, Sleepwalker, V:Roadkill	2.00
6 F:Spider-Man,Scarlet Witch,Captain America,V:Suicide Pack	2.00
7 F:Captain America,Scarlet Witch, Spider-Man	2.00
8 F:Captain America,Scarlet Witch, Spider-Man	2.00
9 F:War Machine,Thunderstrike, Silver Surfer	2.00
10 F:War Machine,Thunderstrike, Silver Surfer	2.00
11 TGb,F:Hulk,Nova,Northstar	2.00

12 RMz(s),TGb,F:Thanos	2.75
13 RMz(s),TGb,F:Thanos,Super Skrull, Rhino,Nitro,Titanium Man	2.00
14 RMz(s),TGb,F:Thanos,Super Skrull, Rhino,Nitro,Titanium Man, A:Silver Surfer	2.00
15 F:Dr.Druid,Cage,Deadpool	2.25
16 F:Dr.Druid,Cage,Deadpool	2.25
17 F:Dr.Druid,Cage,Deadpool	2.25
18 F:Iron Fist,Giant Man	2.25
19 F:Dr.Druid,Cadaver, Shadowoman	1.95
20 V:Venom	1.95
21 V:Slaymaker	1.95
22 Final Defense,pt.1	1.95
23 Final Defense,pt.2	1.95
24 Final Defense,pt.3	1.95
25 V:Dr.Druid	1.95

SECRET WARS
May, 1984

1 MZ,A:X-Men,Fant.Four,Avengers, Hulk,SpM in All,I:Beyonder	4.00
2 MZ,V:Magneto	3.00
3 MZ,I:Titania & Volcana	3.00
4 BL,V:Molecule Man	3.00
5 BL,F:X-Men	3.00
6 MZ,V:Doctor Doom	3.00
7 MZ,I:New Spiderwoman	3.50
8 MZ,I:Alien Black Costume (for Spider-Man)	12.00
9 MZ,V:Galactus	2.00
10 MZ,V:Dr.Doom	2.00
11 MZ,V:Dr.Doom	2.00
12 MZ,Beyonder Vs. Dr.Doom	2.50
TPB rep #1–#12	19.95

Secret Wars II #1
© Marvel Entertainment Group

SECRET WARS II
July, 1985

1 AM,SL,A:X-Men,New Mutants	2.00
2 AM,SL,A:Fantastic Four	1.50
3 AM,SL,A:Daredevil	1.50
4 AM,I:Kurse	1.50
5 AM,SL,I:Boom Boom	2.50
6 AM,SL,A:Mephisto	1.50
7 AM,SL,A:Thing	1.50
8 AM,SL,A:Hulk	1.50

9 AM,SL,A:Everyone,double-size	2.00

SECTAURS
June, 1985

1 Based on toys	1.50
2	1.00
3	1.00
4	1.00
5 thru 10 1986	@1.00

SEEKER 3000
April 1998

1 (of 4) DAn,IEd,sci-fi adventure, 48pg	3.00
2 DAn,IEd,encounter with aliens	3.00
3 DAn,IEd,V:Hkkkt	2.50
4 DAn,IEd,V:Hkkkt, concl.	2.50

SEMPER FI
Dec., 1988

1 JSe	2.00
2 JSe	1.50
3 JSe	1.50
4 JSe	1.50
5 JSe	1.50
6	1.50
7 and 8	@1.00
9 August, 1989,final issue	1.00

SENSATIONAL SPIDER-MAN

1 KM/TP/KJ,rep. (1989)	5.95

SENSATIONAL SPIDER-MAN
Jan. 1996

0 DJu,KJ,Return of Spider-Man,pt.1 Lenticular cover	5.00
1 DJu,KJ,Media Blizzard,pt.1, V:New Mysterio	1.95
2 DJu,KJ,Return of Kaine,pt.2	1.95
3 DJu,KJ,Web of Carnage,pt.1	1.95
4 DJu,KJ,Blood Brothers,pt.1	1.95
5 DJu	1.95
6 DJu	1.95
7 TDz,A:Onslaught	1.95
8 TDz,The Looter	1.95
9 TDz,Onslaught tie-in	1.95
10 TDz,RCa,V:Swarm	1.95
11 TDz,Revelations, pt.2	1.95
11A bagged with card, etc.	5.00
12 TDz,SwM,V:Trapster	1.95
13 TDz,RCa,A:Ka-zar, Shanna	1.95
14 TDz,RCa,Savage Land saga	1.95
15 TDz,RCa,Savage Land saga	1.95
16 TDz,RCa,R:Black Cat, V:Prowler,Vulture	1.95
17 TDz,RCa,V:Black Cat, Prowler,Vulture	1.95
18 TDz,RCa,V:Vulture	1.95
19 TDz,RCa,R:Living Monolith	2.00
20 TDz,RCa,Living Pharoah, concl.	2.00
21 TDz,RCa,Techomancers	2.00
22 TDz,RCa,A:Doctor Strange	2.00
23 TDz,RCa,A:Doctor Strange	2.00
24 TDz,RCa,A:S.H.I.E.L.D., Looter	2.00
25 TDz,RCa,Spider-Hunt,pt1 x-over	3.00
26 TDz,RCa,JoB,Identity Crisis prelude	2.00
27 TDz,RCa,MeW,Identity Crisis, as Hornet V:Phaeton	2.00
28 TDz,RCa,as Hornet, V:Vulture	2.00
29 TDz,RCa,V:Arcade, Black Cat	2.00

30 TDz,A:Black Cat,V:Arcade ... 2.00	
31 TDz,MeW,RCa,V:Rhino 2.00	
32 TDz,JoB,The Gathering of the	
Five, pt.1 (of 5) 2.00	
Minus 1 Spec.,TDz,RCa, flashback 1.95	
TPB In the Savage Land	
rep.#13-#15 .... 6.00	
Wizard mini-comic 1.00	
TPB Sensational Spider-Man '96	
JMD,SwM, seq. to Kraven's	
Last Hunt, 64pg. 2.95	

SERGEANT BARNEY BARKER
August, 1956

1 JSe,Comedy 100.00	
2 JSe,Army Inspection(c) 75.00	
3 JSe,Tank(c) 75.00	

Becomes:

G.I. TALES

4 JSe,At Grips with the Enemy 45.00	
5 .... 30.00	
6 JO,BP,GWb, July, 1957 .... 35.00	

SGT. FURY & HIS HOWLING COMMANDOS
May, 1963–Dec. 1981

1 Seven Against the Nazis . 1,000.00	
2 JK,Seven Doomed Men .. 300.00	
3 JK,Midnight on Massacre	
Mountain 175.00	
4 JK,V:Lord Ha-Ha,D:Junior	
Juniper 175.00	
5 JK,V:Baron Strucker 175.00	
6 JK,The Fangs of the Fox .. 125.00	
7 JK,Fury Court Martial 125.00	
8 JK,V:Dr Zemo,I:Percival	
Pinkerton 125.00	
9 DAy,V:Hitler 125.00	
10 DAy,On to Okinwawa,I:Capt.	
Savage 125.00	
11 DAy,V:Capt.Flint 75.00	
12 DAy,Howler deserts 75.00	
13 DAy,JK,A:Capt.America ... 275.00	
14 DAy,V:Baron Strucker 75.00	
15 DAy,SD,Too Small to Fight	
Too Young to Die 75.00	
16 DAy,In The Desert a Fortress	
Stands 75.00	
17 DAy,While the Jungle Sleeps 75.00	
18 DAy,Killed in Action 75.00	
19 DAy,An Eye for an Eye 75.00	
20 DAy,V:the Blitz Squad 75.00	
21 DAy,To Free a Hostage 50.00	
22 DAy,V:Bull McGiveney 50.00	
23 DAy,The Man who Failed ... 50.00	
24 DAy,When the Howlers Hit	
the Home Front 50.00	
25 DAy,Every Man my Enemy .. 50.00	
26 DAy,Dum Dum Does it the	
Hard Way 50.00	
27 DAy,O:Fury's Eyepatch 50.00	
28 DAy,Not a Man Shall Remain	
Alive 50.00	
29 DAy,V:Baron Strucker 50.00	
30 DAy,Incident in Italy 50.00	
31 Day,Into the Jaws of Death .. 25.00	
32 DAy,A Traitor in Our Midst .. 25.00	
33 DAy,The Grandeur That was	
Greece 25.00	
34 DAy,O:Howling Commandoes 25.00	
35 DAy,Berlin Breakout,J:Eric	
Koenig 25.00	

36 DAy,My Brother My Enemy .. 25.00	
37 DAy,In the Desert to Die 25.00	
38 This Ones For Dino 25.00	
39 Into the Fortress of Fear 25.00	
40 That France Might be Free . 25.00	
41 V:The Blitzers 25.00	
42 Three Were AWOL 25.00	
43 Scourge of the Sahara,A:Bob	
Hope,Glen Miller 25.00	
44 JSe,The Howlers First Mission 25.00	
45 JSe,I:The War Lover 25.00	
46 JSe,They Also Serve 25.00	
47 Tea and Sabotage 25.00	
48 A:Blitz Squad 25.00	
49 On to Tarawa 25.00	
50 The Invasion Begins 25.00	
51 The Assassin 25.00	
52 Triumph at Treblinka 25.00	
53 To the Bastions of Bavaria . 25.00	
54 Izzy Shoots the Works 25.00	
55 Cry of Battle, Kiss of Death .. 20.00	
56 Gabriel Blow Your Horn 20.00	
57 TS,The Informer 20.00	

Sgt. Fury #64
© Marvel Entertainment Group

58 Second Front 20.00	
59 D-Day for Dum Dum 20.00	
60 Authorised Personnel Only . 20.00	
61 The Big Breakout 20.00	
62 The Basic Training of Fury .. 20.00	
63 V:Nazi Tanks 20.00	
64 The Peacemonger,A:Capt	
Savage 20.00	
65 Eric Koenig,Traitor 20.00	
66 Liberty Rides the Underground 20.00	
67 With a Little Help From My	
Friends 20.00	
68 Welcome Home Soldier 20.00	
69 While the City Sleeps 20.00	
70 The Missouri Marauders ... 20.00	
71 Burn,Bridge,Burn 20.00	
72 Battle in the Sahara 20.00	
73 Rampage on the	
Russian Front 20.00	
74 Each Man Alone 20.00	
75 The Deserter 15.00	
76 He Fought the Red Baron .. 15.00	
77 A Traitor's Trap,A:Eric Koenig 15.00	
78 Escape or Die 15.00	
79 Death in the High Castle 15.00	

80 To Free a Hostage 15.00	
81 The All American 15.00	
82 Howlers Hit The	
Home Front,rep 15.00	
83 Dum DumV:Man-Mountain	
McCoy 15.00	
84 The Devil's Disciple 15.00	
85 Fury V:The Howlers 15.00	
86 Germ Warfare 15.00	
87 Dum Dum does it...rep 15.00	
88 Save General Patton 15.00	
89 O:Fury's eyepatch,rep 15.00	
90 The Chain That Binds 15.00	
91 Not A Man...rep 12.00	
92 Some Die Slowly 12.00	
93 A Traitor...rep 12.00	
94 GK(c),Who'll Stop the Bombs 12.00	
95 7 Doomed Men, rep 12.00	
96 GK(c),Dum-Dum Sees it	
Through 12.00	
97 Till the Last Man Shall Fail .. 12.00	
98 A:Deadly Dozen 12.00	
99 Guerillas in Greece 12.00	
100 When a Howler Falls 12.00	
101 Pearl Harbor 7.00	
102 Death For A Dollar 7.00	
103 Berlin Breakout 7.00	
104 The Tanks Are Coming 7.00	
105 My Brother,My Enemy 7.00	
106 Death on the Rhine 7.00	
107 Death-Duel in the Desert .. 7.00	
108 Slaughter From the Skies ... 7.00	
109 This Ones For Dino,rep ... 7.00	
110 JSe(c),The Reserve ----- 7.00	
111 V:Colonel Klaw 7.00	
112 V:Baron Strucker 7.00	
113 That France Might	
Be Free,rep 7.00	
114 Jungle Bust Out 7.00	
115 V:Baron Strucker 7.00	
116 End of the Road 7.00	
117 Blitz Over Britain 7.00	
118 War Machine 7.00	
118 War Machine 7.00	
119 They Strike by Machine 7.00	
120 Trapped in the Compound of	
Death 7.00	
121 An Eye for an Eye 5.00	
122 A;The Blitz Squad 5.00	
123 To Free a Hostage 5.00	
124 A:Bull McGiveney 5.00	
125 The Man Who Failed 5.00	
126 When the Howlers Hit Home.. 5.00	
127 Everyman My Enemy,rep ... 5.00	
128 Dum Dum does it...rep 5.00	
129 O:Fury's Eyepatch 5.00	
130 A:Baron Strucker 5.00	
131 Armageddon 5.00	
132 Incident in Italy 5.00	
133 thru 140 .... @5.00	
141 thru 150 .... @5.00	
151 thru 160 .... @4.00	
161 thru 167 .... @4.00	
Ann.#1 Korea #4,#5 .... 90.00	
Ann.#2 This was D-Day 50.00	
Ann.#3 Vietnam 30.00	
Ann.#4 Battle of the Bulge 15.00	
Ann.#5 Desert Fox 7.50	
Ann.#6 Blaze of Battle 7.50	
Ann.#7 Armageddon 7.50	

SERGIO ARAGONES MASSACRES MARVEL
1996

1-shot Parody 4.95	

SEVEN BLOCK
Epic 1990
1 . . . . 2.50

SHADOWMASTERS
Oct., 1989–Jan. 1990
1 RH	11.00
2	7.00
3	6.00
4	5.00

SHADOWRIDERS
1993
1 I:Shadowriders,A:Cable, Ghost Rider	2.00
2 A:Ghost Rider	2.00
3 A:Cable	2.00
4 A:Cable	2.00

SHADOWS & LIGHT
Dec. 1997
1 BSf,RMz,LWn,BWr,GeH,SD,B&W anthology series	3.00
2 JSn,LW,LSh,GK	3.00
3 BL,JSn	3.00
4 three new tales	3.00

Shanna, The She-Devil #1
© Marvel Entertainment Group

SHANNA, THE SHE-DEVIL
Dec., 1972–Aug. 1973
1 GT,F:Shanna	7.50
2 RA,The Dungeon of Doom . . .	5.00
3 RA,The Hour of the Bull	3.00
4 RA,Mandrill	3.00
5 JR(c),RA,V:Nekra	3.00

SHEENA
Dec., 1984–Feb. 1985
1 and 2 Movie adapt . . . . @1.00

SHE-HULK
[1st Regular Series]Feb., 1980
1 JB,BWi,I&O:She-Hulk	6.00
2 BWi,D:She-Hulk's best friend . .	3.00
3 BWi,Wanted for Murder	3.00
4 BWi,V:Her Father	3.00

5 BWi,V:Silver Serpent	3.00
6 A:Iron Man	2.50
7 BWi,A:Manthing	2.50
8 BWi,A:Manthing	2.50
9 BWi,Identity Crisis	2.50
10 V:The Word	2.50
11 BWi,V:Dr.Morbius	2.50
12 V:Gemini	2.50
13 V:Man-Wolf	2.00
14 V:Hellcat	2.00
15 V:Lady Kills	2.00
16 She Hulk Goes Berserk	2.00
17 V:Man-Elephant	2.00
18 V:Grappler	2.00
19 V:Her Father	2.00
20 A:Zapper	2.00
21 V:Seeker	2.00
22 V:Radius	2.00
23 V:Radius	2.00
24 V:Zapper	2.00
25 Double-sized,last issue	2.50

[2nd Regular Series] 1989–94
1 JBy,V:Ringmaster	2.50
2 JBy	2.25
3 JBy,A:Spider-Man	2.25
4 JBy,I:Blond Phantom	2.25
5 JBy	2.25
6 JBy,A:U.S.1,Razorback	2.25
7 JBy,A:U.S.1,Razorback	2.25
8 JBy,A:Saint Nicholas	2.25
9 AM(i)	2.00
10 AM(i)	2.00
11	2.00
12	2.00
13 SK(c)	2.00
14 MT(c),A:Howard the Duck . . .	2.00
15 SK(c)	2.00
16 SK(c)	2.00
17 SK(c),V:Dr.Angst	2.00
18 SK(c)	2.00
19 SK(c),V:Nosferata	2.00
20 SK(c),Darkham Asylum	2.00
21 SK(c),V:Blonde Phantom	2.00
22 SK(c),V:Blonde Phantom,A:All Winners Squad	2.00
23 V:Blonde Phantom	2.00
24 V:Deaths'Head	4.00
25 A:Hercules,Thor	2.00
26 A:Excalibur	2.00
27 Cartoons in N.Y.	2.00
28 Game Hunter Stalks She-Hulk	2.00
29 A:Wolv.,Hulk,SpM,Venom . . .	2.50
30 MZ(c),A:Silver Surfer,Thor Human Torch	2.25
31 JBy,V:Spragg the Living Hill . .	2.50
32 JBy,A:Moleman,V:Spragg . . .	2.00
33 JBy,A:Moleman,V:Spragg	2.00
34 JBy,Returns to New York	2.00
35 JBy,V:X-Humed Men	2.00
36 JBy,X-mas issue (#8 tie-in) . . .	2.00
37 JBy,V:Living Eraser	2.00
38 JBy,V:Mahkizmo	2.00
39 JBy,V:Mahkizmo	2.00
40 JBy,V:Spraggs,Xemnu	2.00
41 JBy,V:Xemnu	2.00
42 JBy,V:USArcher	2.00
43 JBy,V:Xemnu	2.00
44 JBy,R:Rocket Raccoon	2.00
45 JBy,A:Razorback	2.00
46 JBy,A:Rocket Raccoon	2.00
47 V:D'Bari	2.00
48 JBy,A:Rocket Raccoon	2.00
49 V:Skrulls,D'Bari	2.00
50 JBy,WS,TA,DGb,AH,HC,	

D:She-Hulk	4.00
51 TMo,V:Savage She-Hulk	2.00
52 D:She-Hulk,A:Thing,Mr.Fantastic, I:Rumbler,V:Titania	2.00
53 AH(c),A:Zapper	2.00
54 MGo(c),A:Wonder Man	2.00
55 V:Rumbler	2.00
56 A:War Zone	2.00
57 A:Hulk	2.00
58 V:Electro	2.00
59 V:Various Villains	2.00
60 last issue	2.00
TPB rep. #1–#8	12.95

SHE HULK: CEREMONY
1989
1 JBr/SDr	4.00
2 JBr/FS	4.00

SHIELD
Feb., 1973
1	9.00
2	5.00
3	5.00
4	5.00
5 Oct., 1973	5.00

Shogun Warriors #10
© Marvel Entertainment Group

SHOGUN WARRIORS
Feb., 1979
1 HT,DGr,F:Raydeen, Combatra, Dangard Ace	4.00
2 HT,DGr,V:Elementals of Evil . .	2.50
3 AM(c),HT,DGr,V:Elementals of Evil	2.50
4 HT,DGr,'Menace of the Mech Monsters'	2.50
5 HT,DGr,'Into The Lair of Demons'	2.50
6 HT,ME	2.00
7 HT,ME	2.00
8 HT,ME	2.00
9 'War Beneath The Waves' . . .	2.00
10 'Five Heads of Doom'	2.00
11 TA(c)	2.00
12 WS(c)	2.00
13 'Demons on the Moon'	2.00
14 V:Dr. Demonicus	2.00

15	2.00
16	2.00
17	2.00
18	2.00
19 A:Fantastic Four	2.50
20 Sept., 1980	2.00

SHROUD
Limited Series 1994
1 B:MiB(s),MCW,A:Spider-Man, V:Scorpion	2.00
2 MCW,A:Spider-Man,V:Scorpion	2.00
3 MCW,I:Kali	2.00
4 MCW,Final Issue	2.00

SILVERHAWKS
August, 1987
1 thru 5	@1.00
6 June, 1988	1.00

SILVER SABLE
1992–95
1 Foil stamped(c),A:Sandman, Spider-Man	3.00
2 I:Gattling	2.00
3 V:Gattling,Foreigner	1.75
4 Infinity War,V:Doctor Doom . . .	1.75
5 Infinity War,V:Doctor Doom . . .	1.50
6 A:Deathlok	1.50
7 A:Deathlok	1.50
8 V:Hydra	1.50
9 O:Silver Sable	1.50
10 A:Punisher,Leviathan	1.50
11 Cyber Warriors,Hydra	1.50
12 V:Cyberwarriorss,R:Sandman .	1.50
13 For Love Nor Money#3, A:Cage,Terror	1.50
14 For Love Nor Money#6, A:Cage,Terror	1.50
15 V:Viper,A:Captain America . . .	1.50
16 SBt,Infnty Crusade	1.50
17 Infinity Crusade	1.50
18 A:Venom	1.50
19 Siege of Darkness x-over	1.50
20 GWt(s),StB,BU:Sandman,Fin .	1.50
21 Gang War	1.50
22	1.50
23 GWt(s),A:Deadpool,Daredevil, BU:Sandman	1.50
24 GWt(s),BU:Crippler,w/card . . .	1.75
25 V:Hydra	2.25
26 F:Sandman	1.75
27 A:Code Blue	1.50
28 F:Chen	1.50
29 A:Wild Pack	1.50
30 problems with law	1.50
31 V:terrorists	1.50
32 A:The Foreigner	1.50
33 V:Hammerhead	1.50
34	1.50
35 Li'l Silvie Tale	1.50

SILVER SURFER
[1st Series] August, 1968
1 B:StL(s),JB,JSr,GC,O:Silver Surfer, O:Watcher,I:Shala Bal	450.00
2 JB,JSr,GC,A:Watcher	200.00
3 JB,JSr,GC,I:Mephisto	150.00
4 JB,A:Thor,low distribution scarce	425.00
5 JB,A:Fant.Four,V:Stranger . . .	85.00
6 JB,FB,A:Watcher	100.00
7 JB,A:Watcher,I:Frankenstein's Monster	85.00

8 JB,DA,A:Mephisto,I:Ghost . . .	60.00
9 JB,DA,A:Mephisto,A:Ghost . .	60.00
10 JB,DA,South America	60.00
11 JB,DA	50.00
12 JB,DA,V:The Abomination . . .	50.00
13 JB,DA,V:Doomsday Man . . .	50.00
14 JB,DA,A:Spider-Man	75.00
15 JB,DA,A:Human Torch	50.00
16 JB,V:Mephisto	50.00
17 JB,V:Mephisto	50.00
18 E:StL(s),JK,V:Inhumans	50.00

[2nd Regular Series] 1982
1 JBy,TP,Direct Only,V:Mephisto	10.00

Silver Surfer (3rd Series) #85
© Marvel Entertainment Group

[3rd Regular Series] July 1987
1 MR,JRu,A:Fantastic Four, Galactus,V:Champion	10.00
2 MR,A:Shalla Bal,V:Skrulls . . .	7.00
3 MR,V:Collector & Runner	6.00
4 MR,JRu,A:Elders,I:Obliterator	6.00
5 MR,JRu,V:Obliterator	6.00
6 MR,JRu,O:Obliterator,A:Kree, Skrulls	6.00
7 MR,JRu,V:Supremor,Elders/ Soul Gems	5.00
8 MR,JRu,V:Supremor	5.00
9 MR,Elders Vs.Galactus	5.00
10 MR,A:Galactus,Eternity	5.00
11 JSon,JRu,V:Reptyl	4.50
12 MR,JRu,V:Reptyl,A:Nova . . .	4.50
13 JSon,DC,V:Ronan	4.50
14 JSon,JRu,V:Skrull Surfer . . .	4.50
15 RLm,JRu,A:Fantastic Four . .	8.00
16 RLm,Inbetweener possesses Soul Gem,A:Fantastic Four . .	5.00
17 RLm,A:Inbetweener,Galactus, Fantastic Four,D:Trader, Possessor,Astronomer	5.00
18 RLm,Galactus V:Inbetweener .	5.00
19 RLm,MR,V:Firelord	4.50
20 RLm,A:Superskrull,Galactus . .	4.50
21 MR,DC,V:Obliterator	4.50
22 RLm,V:Ego	4.50
23 RLm,V:Dragon	4.50
24 RLm,V:G.I.G.O.	4.50
25 RLm,V:Ronan,Kree Skrull War	4.50

26 RLm,V:Nenora	4.50
27 RLm,V:Stranger	4.50
28 RLm,D:Super Skrull,V:Reptyl .	4.50
29 RLm,V:Midnight Sun	4.50
30 RLm,V:Midnight Sun	4.50
31 RLm,O:Living Tribunal & Stranger (double size)	5.50
32 RF,JSt,A:Mephisto	4.50
33 RIm,V:Impossible Man	4.50
34 RLm,(1stJSn),2nd R:Thanos .	7.00
35 RLm,A:Thanos,R:Drax	5.00
36 RLm,V:Impossible Man,A:Warlock Capt.Marvel,C:Thanos	3.00
37 RLm,V:Drax,A:Mentor	3.00
38 RLm,V:Thanos(continued in Thanos Quest)	4.00
39 JSh,V:Algol	3.50
40 RLm,V:Dynamo City	3.00
41 RLm,V:Dynamo City,A:Thanos	3.00
42 RLm,V:Dynamo City,A:Drax . .	3.00
43 RLm,V:DynamoCity	3.00
44 RLm,R:Thanos,Drax, O:Inf.Gems	3.00
45 RLm,Thanos vs. Mephisto . . .	4.00
46 RLm,R:Warlock,A:Thanos . . .	5.00
47 RLm,Warlock V:Drax, A:Thanos	4.00
48 RLm,A:Galactus,Thanos	4.00
49 RLm,V:Thanos Monster	3.00
50 RLm,Silver Stamp(D.size), V:Thanos Monster	8.00
50a 2nd printing	2.50
50b 3rd printing	2.00
51 RLm,Infinity Gauntlet x-over . .	3.00
52 RLm,Infinity Gauntlet x-over . .	3.00
53 RLm,Infinity Gauntlet x-over . .	2.50
54 RLm,I.Gauntlet x-over,V:Rhino	2.50
55 RLm,I.Gauntlet x-over,Universe According to Thanos,pt.1	2.50
56 RLm,I.Gauntlet x-over,Universe According to Thanos,pt.2	2.50
57 RLm,Infinity Gauntlet x-over . .	2.50
58 RLm(c),Infinity Gauntlet x-over, A:Hulk,Namor,Dr.Strange . . .	2.50
59 RLm(c),TR,Infinity Gauntlet, Thanos V:Silver Surfer	2.50
60 RLm,V:Midnight Sun, A:Inhumans	2.00
61 RLm,I:Collection.Agency	2.00
62 RLm,O:Collection Agency . . .	2.00
63 RLm,A:Captain Marvel	2.00
64 RLm,V:Dark Silver Surfer . . .	2.00
65 RLm,R:Reptyl,I:Princess Alaisa	2.00
66 RLm,I:Avatar,Love & Hate . . .	2.00
67 RLm(c),KWe,Inf.War,V:Galactus A:DrStrange	2.00
68 RLm(c),KWe,Inf.War,O:Nova . .	2.00
69 RLm(c),KWe,Infinity War, A:Galactus	2.00
70 RLm(c),Herald War#1,I:Morg .	2.00
71 RLm(c),Herald War#2,V:Morg .	2.00
72 RLm(c),Herald War#3,R:Nova .	2.00
73 RLm,R:Airwalker	2.00
74 RLm,V:Terrax	2.00
75 RLm,E:Herald Ordeal,V:Morg, D:Nova	3.00
76 RLm,A:Jack of Hearts	1.50
77 RLm,A:Jack of Hearts	1.50
78 RLm,R:Morg,V:Nebula	1.50
79 RLm,V:Captain Atlas	1.50
80 RLm,I:Ganymede,Terrax Vs.Morg	1.50
81 RLm,O:Ganymedel:Tyrant . . .	1.50
82 RLm,V:Tyrant,double sized . . .	2.50

MARVEL

83 Infinity Crusade 1.50
84 RLm(c),Infinity Crusade 1.50
85 RLm(c),Infinity Crusade 2.50
86 RLm(c), Blood & Thunder,pt.2
   V:Thor,A:Beta Ray Bill 1.50
87 RLm(c),Blood & Thunder,pt.7 . 1.50
88 RLm(c),Blood & Thunder,pt.10 1.50
89 RLm(c),CDo,C:Legacy 1.50
90 RLm(c),A:Legacy,C:Avatar . . . 1.50
91 RLm 1.50
92 RLm,V:Avatar 1.75
93 V:Human Torch 1.75
94 A:Fantastic Four, Warlock 1.75
95 SEa,A:Fantastic Four 1.50
96 A:Fantastic Four,Hulk 1.50
97 A:Fantastic Four,R:Nova 1.50
98 R:Champion 1.50
99 A:Nova 1.50
100 V:Mephisto 2.25
100a enhanced ed. 4.50
101 RMz,JoP,A:Shalla Bal 1.50
102 V:Galactus 1.50
103 I:Death quad 1.50
104 Surfer Rampage 1.50
105 V:Super Skrull 1.50
106 A:Legacy,Morg 1.50
107 TGb,BAn,A:Galactus,Morg,
   Tyrant 1.50
108 Galactus Vs. Tyrant 1.50
109 Morg has Ultimate Nulifier . . . 1.50
110 JB,F:Nebula 1.50
111 GP,TGb,BAn,to Other Side
   of Galaxy 1.95
112 GP,TGb,BAn, ... 1.95
113 GP,TGb,BAn,V:Blackbody . . . 1.95
114 . . . . 1.95
115 GP,TGb,BAn,Surfer in pieces 1.95
116 GP,TGb,BAn,Pieces cause
   trouble 1.95
117 . . . . 1.95
118 . . . . 1.50
119 . . . . 1.50
120 . . . . 1.50
121 A:Quasar, Beta Ray Bill 1.50
122 GP,SEa, returns to Marvel
   Universe 1.50
123 GP,RG 1.50
124 GP,RG 1.50
125 RG,V:Hulk, double size 2.50
126 JMD,RG,BWi,A:Dr. Strange . . 1.50
127 JMD,RG,BWi,A:Alicia Masters 1.50
128 JMD,RG,BWi,V:Puppet Master 1.50
129 JMD,RG,BWi,back in time,
   late 1940s 1.50
130 JMD,CNr,BWi, trapped in past 1.50
131 JMD,RG,BWi, ... 1.50
132 JMD,PaP,Puppet Master
   missing 2.00
133 JMD,MRy,PaP,V:PuppetMaster2.00
134 JMD,TGm,MRy,Regains his
   memories, pt.1 (of 4) 2.00
135 JMD,TGm,MRy,Alicia summons
   Scrier 2.00
136 JMD,TGm,MRy, ... 2.00
137 JMD,TGm,MRy,Mephisto v.
   Scrier 2.00
138 JMD,RCz,MRy,A:The Thing,
   tie-in 2.00
139 JMD,RCz,MRy,V:Gargoyle . . 2.00
140 JMD,JMu,on Zenn-La untouched
   by Galactus 2.00
141 JMD,JMu,A:Sama-D,Alicia
   Masters 2.00
142 JMD,JMu,Tenebrae,The Union,
   Cipher 2.00

143 JMD,DCw,Tenebrae,V:Psycho
   Man 2.00
Bi-Weekly Issues
144 JMD,JMu,V:Psycho-Man,
   A:Tenebrae 2.00
145 JMD,JMu,A:Psycho-Man,
   Tenebrae,Cypphyrr 2.00
Minus 1 Spec., JMD,RG,BWi,
   flashback, first human contact . 1.95
Spec. Silver Surfer: Dangerous Arti-
   facts,RMz, Galactus,T hanos
   (1996) 3.95
Spec. Silver Surfer: Inner Demons,
   rep. JMD,RGa,BWi (1998) . . . 3.00
Ann.#1 RLm,JSon,Evolution War . 7.00
Ann.#2 RLm,Atlantis Attacks 5.00
Ann.#3 RLm,Lifeform #4 . . . . 4.00
Ann.#4 RLm,Korvac Quest #3,A:
   Guardians of Galaxy 3.00
Ann.#5 RLm,Ret.o/Defenders #3 . 2.50
Ann.#6 RLm(c),I:Legacy,w/card . . 3.75
Ann.'97 1 JMD,VS,KJ,V:Scrier,
   48pg 2.00
Ann.'98 MPe,RBe,TDF,F:Thor,
   48pg 3.00
TPB Silver Surger, The Enslavers,
   KP 16.95
TPB Homecoming,A:Moondragon 12.95
TPB Silver Surfer: Parable, StL,Moe,
   rep. of hc, 64pg (1998) 6.00
TPB Rebirth of Thanos,reprints
   #34-38 . . . . 12.95
TPB StL,JK, new origin 13.00
Ashcan .75

SILVER SURFER
Epic Dec., 1988
1 Moebius,V:Galactus 3.00
2 Moebius,V:Galactus 3.00
Graphic Novel 14.95

SILVER SURFER/ SUPERMAN
Marvel/DC 1996
Spec. GP,RLm,TA, x-over 5.95

SILVER SURFER VS. DRACULA
1994
1 rep,MWn(s),GC,TP 1.75

SILVER SURFER/ WARLOCK: RESURRECTION
1993
1 JSn,V:Mephisto,Death 3.50
2 JSn,TA,V:Death 3.00
3 JSn,TA,V:Mephisto 3.00
4 JSn,TA,V:Mephisto 3.00

SILVER SURFER/ WEAPON ZERO
Marvel/Top Cow 1997
1-shot Devil's Reign, pt.8 . . . . . . 4.00

SISTERHOOD OF STEEL
Epic Dec., 1984
1 I:Sisterhood 2.00
2 . . . . 2.00
3 . . . . 2.00
4 thru 8 . . . . @1.50

Six From Sirius #3
© Marvel Entertainment Group

SIX FROM SIRIUS
Epic July, 1984
1 PG,limited series 3.00
2 PG 2.00
3 PG 2.00
4 PG 2.00

SIX FROM SIRIUS II
Epic Feb., 1986
1 PG 1.75

SIX-GUN WESTERN
Atlas Jan., 1957
1 JSe(c),RC,JR,'Kid Yukon
   Gunslinger' 125.00
2 SSh,AW,DAy,JO,'His Guns
   Hang Low' 100.00
3 AW,BP,DAy 100.00
4 JSe(c),JR,GWb 50.00

SKELETON WARRIORS
1995
1 based on cartoon 1.50
2 Legion of Light 1.50
3 V:Grimstar 1.50
4 Grimskull abandons Legion
   of Light 1.50

SKRULL KILL CREW
1995
1 I:Kill Crew 2.95
2 V:Hydra 2.95
3 V:Captain America 2.95
4 V:Fantastic Four 2.95
5 Conclusion 2.95

SKULL, THE SLAYER
August, 1975
1 GK(c),O:Skull the Slayer 2.50
2 GK(c),'Man Against Gods' . . . 1.50
3 'Trapped in the Tower
   of Time' 1.50
4 'Peril of the Pyramids',
   A:Black Knight 1.50
5 A:Black Knight 1.50

6 'The Savage Sea' 1.50
7 'Dungeon of Blood' 1.50
8 JK(c),Nov., 1976 . . . . 1.50

SLAPSTICK
1992–93
1 TA(i),I:Slapstick 1.50
2 TA(i),A:Spider-Man,V:Overkill . . 1.25
3 V:Dr.Denton 1.25
4 A:GR,DD,FF,Cap.America 1.25

SLEDGE HAMMER
Feb., 1988
1 . . . . 1.25
2 March, 1988 . . . . 1.00

SLEEPWALKER
June, 1991
1 BBI,I:Rick Sheridan,C:8-Ball . . . 3.00
2 BBI,V:8-Ball 2.00
3 BBI,A:Avengers,X-Men,X-Factor,
  FF,I:Cobweb,O:Sleepwalker . . 1.75
4 RL,I:Bookworm 1.75
5 BBI,A:SpM,K.Pin,V:Ringleader . 1.75
6 BBI,A:SpM,Inf.Gauntlet x-over . 1.75
7 BBI,Infinity Gauntlet x-over,
  V:Chain Gang 1.75
8 BBI,A:Deathlok 1.50
9 BBI,I:Lullabye 1.50
10 BBI,MM,I:Dream-Team 1.50
11 BBI,V:Ghost Rider 1.50
12 JQ,A:Nightmare 2.50
13 BBI,MM,I:Spectra 1.50
14 BBI,MM,V:Spectra 1.50
15 BBI,MM,I:Thought Police 1.50
16 BBI,MM,A:Mr.Fantastic,Thing . 1.50
17 BBI,A:Spider-Man,Darkhawk,
  V:Brotherhood o/Evil Mutants . 1.50
18 JQ(c),Inf.War,A:Prof.X 1.50
19 V:Cobweb,w/pop out Halloween
  Mask 2.00
20 V:Chain Gang,Cobweb 1.50
21 V:Hobgoblin 1.50
22 V:Hobgoblin,8-Ball 1.50
23 V:Cobweb,Chain Gang 1.50
24 Mindfield#6 . . . . 1.50
25 O:Sleepwalker,Holo-grafx(c) . . 3.50
26 V:Mindspawn 1.50
27 A:Avengers 1.50
28 I:Psyko 1.50
29 DG,V:Psyko 1.50
30 V:Psyko 1.50
31 DG(ci),A:Spectra 1.50
32 V:Psyko 1.50
33 V:Mindspawn,Last issue 1.50
Holiday Spec.#1 JQ(c) 2.25

SLEEZE BROTHERS
August, 1989
1 Private Eyes 1.75
2 . . . . 1.75
3 . . . . 1.75
4 . . . . 1.75
5 . . . . 1.75
6 . . . . 1.75

SMURFS
Dec., 1982
1 . . . . 3.00
2 . . . . 3.00
3 . . . . 3.00
Treasury Edition 15.00

SOLARMAN
Jan., 1989
1 JM 1.25
2 MZ/NR,A:Dr.Doom, May, 1990 . 1.25

SOLO
[Limited Series] 1994
1 RoR,I:Cygnus 1.75
2 RoR,V:A.R.E.S. 1.75
3 RoR,V:Spidey 1.75
4 final issue 1.75

SOLO AVENGERS
Dec., 1987
1 MBr,JRu,JLe,AW,Hawkeye;
  Mockingbird 4.00
2 MBr,JRu,KD,BMc,Hawkeye;
  Capt.Marvel 1.50
3 MBr,JRu,BH,SDr,Hawkeye;
  Moon Knight 1.50
4 RLm,JRu,PR,BL,Hawkeye;
  Black Knight 2.00
5 MBr,JRu,JRy,Hawkeye;
  Scarlet Witch 1.50
6 MBr,JRu,TGr,Hawkeye;Falcon . 1.25
7 MBr,JG,BL,Hawkeye;Bl.Widow . 1.25
8 MBr,Hawkeye;Dr.Pym 1.25
9 MBr,JBr,SDr,Hawkeye;Hellcat . 1.25
10 MBr,LW,Hawkeye;Dr.Druid . . . 1.25
11 MBr,JG,BL,Hawkeye;Hercules . 1.25
12 RLm,SDr,Hawkeye; New
  Yellow Jacket 2.00
13 RLm,JG,Hawkeye;WonderMan 2.00
14 AM,AD,JRu,Hawkeye;She-Hulk 1.25
15 AM,Hawkeye;Wasp 1.25
16 AM,DP,JA,Hawkeye;
  Moondragon 1.25
17 AM,DH,DC,Hawkeye;
  Sub-Mariner 1.25
18 RW,DH,Hawkeye;Moondragon 1.25
19 RW,DH,Hawkeye,BlackPanther 1.25
20 RW,DH,Hawkeye;Moondragon 1.25
Becomes:
AVENGERS SPOTLIGHT

SOLOMON KANE
Sept., 1985
1 F:Solomon Kane 1.50
2 . . . . 1.00
3 BBI,'Blades of the Brotherhood' 1.00
4 MMi 1.00
5 'Hills of the Dead' 1.00
6 . . . . 1.00

SON OF SATAN
Dec., 1975–Feb. 1977
1 GK(c),JM,F:Daimon Hellstrom 12.00
2 Demon War,O:Possessor . . . 10.00
3 . . . . 7.00
4 The Faces of Fear 7.00
5 V:Mind Star 7.00
6 A World Gone Mad 7.00
7 Mirror of Judgement 7.00
8 RH,To End in Nightmare 7.00

SOVIET SUPER SOLDIERS
1 AMe,JS,I:Redmont 4 . . . . 2.00

SPACEMAN
Atlas Sept., 1953
1 BEv(c),F:Speed Carter and
  the Space Sentinals 450.00

2 JMn,'Trapped in Space' . . . 300.00
3 BEv(c),JMn,V:Ice Monster . . 250.00
4 JMn 250.00
5 GT 250.00
6 JMn,'The Thing From Outer
  Space',Oct., 1954 . . . . 250.00

SPACE SQUADRON
Atlas June, 1951
1 F:Capt. Jet Dixon,Blast,Dawn,
  Revere,Rusty Blake 450.00
2 GT(c), ... 400.00
3 'Planet of Madness',GT 300.00
4 . . . . 300.00
5 . . . . 300.00
Becomes:
SPACE WORLDS
April, 1952
6 'Midnight Horror' 300.00

SPECIAL COLLECTOR'S EDITION
Dec., 1975
1 Kung-Fu,Iron Fist 6.00

SPECIAL MARVEL EDITION
Jan., 1971
1 JK,B:Thor,B:Reprints 15.00
2 JK,V:Absorbing Man 12.00
3 JK,'While a Universe
  Trembles' 12.00
4 JK,'Hammer and the Holocaust',
  E:Thor 12.00
5 JSe(c),JK,DAy,B:Sgt. Fury . . 12.00
6 HT(c),DAy,'Death Ray of
  Dr. Zemo' 7.00
7 DAy,V:Baron Strucker 7.00
8 JSe(c),DAy'On To Okinawa' . . 7.00
9 DAy,'Crackdown of
  Captain Flint 7.00
10 DAy 7.00
11 JK,DAy,A:Captaim
  America & Bucky 7.00
12 DAy,V:Baron Strucker 7.00
13 JK/DAy(c),DAy,SD,'Too Small
  to Fight, Too Young To Die' . . 7.00
14 DAy,E:Reprints,Sgt. Fury . . . 7.00
15 JSn,AM,I:Shang-Chi & Master of
  Kung Fu,I&O:Nayland Smith,
  Dr. Petrie 45.00
16 JSn,AM,I&O:Midnight 20.00
KingSz.Ann.#1 A:Iron Fist 18.00
Becomes:
MASTER OF KUNG FU

SPECTACULAR SCARLET SPIDER
1995
1 SB,BSz,Virtual Morality,pt.4 . . . 1.95
2 SB,BSz,CyberWar,pt.4 . . . . . . 1.95

SPECTACULAR SPIDER-MAN
(Magazine) July, 1968
1 . . . . 65.00
2 V:Green Goblin,Nov.1968 . . 110.00

SPECTACULAR SPIDER-MAN

Dec., 1976
Prev: Peter Parker

134 SB,A:Sin-Eater,V:Electro	4.00
135 SB,A:Sin-Eater,V:Electro	3.00
136 SB,D:Sin-Eater,V:Electro	3.00
137 SB,I:Tarantula II	3.00
138 SB,A:Capt.A.,V:TarantulaII	3.00
139 SB,O:Tombstone	4.00
140 SB,A:Punisher,V:Tombstone	3.00
141 SB,A:Punisher,V:Tombstone	3.00
142 SB,A:Punisher,V:Tombstone	3.00
143 SB,A:Punisher,D:Persuader, I:Lobo Brothers.	3.00
144 SB,V:Boomerang	3.00
145 SB,A:Boomerang	3.00
146 SB,R:Green Goblin	5.00
147 SB,V:Hobgoblin (Demonic Power)	20.00
148 SB,Inferno	3.00
149 SB,V:Carrion II	9.00
150 SB,A:Tombstone,Trial J.Robertson	3.00
151 SB,V:Tombstone	3.00
152 SB,O:Lobo Bros.,A:Punisher, Tombstone	4.00
153 SB,V:Hammerhead,A: Tombstone	3.00
154 SB,V:Lobo Bros.,Puma	3.00
155 SB,V,Tombstone	3.00
156 SB,V:Banjo,A:Tombstone	3.00
157 SB,V:Shocker,Electro, A:Tombstone	3.00
158 SB,Super Spider Spec., I:Cosmic Spider-Man	12.00
159 Cosmic Powers,V:Brothers Grimm	7.00
160 SB,A:Hydro Man,Shocker, Rhino,Dr.Doom	6.00
161 SB,V:Hobgoblin,Hammerhead, Tombstone	3.00
162 SB,V:Hobgoblin,Carrion II	3.00
163 SB,V:Hobgoblin,D:Carrion II	3.00
164 SB,V:Beetle	2.50
165 SB,SDr,D:Arranger,I:Knight & Fogg	2.50
166 SB,O:Knight & Fogg	2.50
167 SB,D:Knight & Fogg	2.50
168 SB,A:Kingpin,Puma, Avengers	2.50
169 SB,I:Outlaws,A:R.Racer, Prowler,Puma,Sandman	2.50
170 SB,A:Avengers,Outlaws	2.50
171 SB,V:Puma	2.50
172 SB,V:Puma	2.50
173 SB,V:Puma	2.50
174 SB,A:Dr.Octopus	2.50
175 SB,A:Dr.Octopus	2.50
176 SB,I:Karona	2.50
177 SB,V:Karona,A:Mr.Fantastic	2.50
178 SB,B:Child Within,V:Green Goblin,A:Vermin	3.50
179 SB,V:Green Goblin,Vermin	3.00
180 SB,V:Green Goblin,Vermin	3.00
181 SB,V:Green Goblin	3.00
182 SB,V:Green Goblin	3.00
183 SB,V:Green Goblin	3.00
184 SB,E:Child Within,V:Green Goblin	3.00
185 SB,A:Frogman,White Rabbit	2.00
186 SB,B:FuneralArrangements V:Vulture	2.00
187 SB,V:Vulture	2.00

Spectacular Spider-Man #198
© *Marvel Entertainment Group*

188 SB,E:Funeral Arrangements V:Vulture	2.00
189 SB,30th Ann.,Hologram(c), V:Green Goblin	8.00
189a Gold 2nd printing	3.25
190 SB,V:Rhino,Harry Osborn	2.00
191 SB,Eye of the Puma	1.75
192 SB,Eye of the Puma	1.75
193 SB,Eye of the Puma	1.75
194 SB,Death of Vermin#1	1.75
195 SB,Death of Vermin#2	1.75
195a Dirtbag Spec,w/Dirt#2 tape	2.50
196 SB,Death of Vermin#3	1.75
197 SB,A:X-Men,V:Prof.Power	1.75
198 SB,A:X-Men,V:Prof.Power	1.75
199 SB,A:X-Men,Green Goblin	2.00
200 SB,V:Green Goblin,D:Harry Osborn,Holografx(c)	5.00
201 SB,Total Carnage,V:Carnage, Shriek,A:Black Cat,Venom	1.75
202 SB,Total Carnage#9,A:Venom, V:Carnage	1.75
203 SB,Maximum Carnage#13	1.75
204 SB,A:Tombstone	1.75
205 StG(s),SB,V:Tombstone, A:Black Cat	1.75
206 SB,V:Tombstone	1.75
207 SB,A:The Shroud	1.50
208 SB,A:The Shroud	1.50
209 StB,SB,I:Dead Aim, BU:Black Cat	1.50
210 StB,SB,V:Dead Aim, BU:Black Cat	1.50
211 Pursuit#2,V:Tracer	1.50
212	1.75
213 ANo(s),V:Typhiod Mary,w/cel	3.25
213a Newsstand Ed.	1.75
214 V:Bloody Mary	1.75
215 V:Scorpion	1.75
216 V:Scorpion	1.75
217 V:Judas Traveller,clone	2.00
217a Foil(c),bonus stuff	5.00
218 V:Puma	1.75
219 Back from the Edge,pt.2	2.00
220 Web of Death,pt.3	2.50
221 Web of Death,finale	3.00
222 The Price of Truth	1.50
223 Aftershocks,pt.4	4.00

223a enhanced cover	1.95
224 The Mark of Kaine,pt.4	2.50
225 SB,TDF,BSz,I:New Green Goblin, 48pg.s	3.00
225a 3-D HoloDisk Cover	5.00
226 SB,BSz,The Trial of Peter Parker,pt.4, identity revealed	3.00
227 TDF,SB,BSz,Maximum Clonage,pt.5	1.50
228 Timebomb,pt.1	1.50
229 Greatest Responsibility,pt.3	2.50
229a Special cover	4.00
230 SB,Return of Spider-Man,pt.4	2.00
231 SB,Return of Kaine,pt.1	2.00
232	2.00
233 SB,JP,Web of Carnage,pt.4	2.00
234 SB,Blood Brothers,pt.4	2.00
235	2.00
236	2.00
237 V:Lizard	2.00
238 V:Lizard	2.00
239 V:Lizard	2.00
240 TDz,LRs,"Book of Revelations," pt.1 (of 4)	2.00
241 Revelations epilogue	2.00
242 JMD,LRs,R:Chameleon, A:Kangaroo	2.00
243 JMD,LRs,R:Chameleon	2.00
244 JMD,LRs,V:Chameleon	2.00
245 JMD,LRs,V:Chameleon, A:Kangaroo	2.00
246 JMD,LRs,V:Kangaroo,Grizzly	2.00
247 JMD,LRs,F:JackO'Lantern,pt.1	2.00
248 JMD,LRs,DGr,F:Jack O' Lantern, pt.2	2.00
249 JMD,LRs,DGr, Last Temptation of Flash Thompson	2.00
250 JR, V:Original Green Goblin, double gatefold cover	3.50
251 JMD,LRs,DGr,V:Kraven the Hunter	2.00
252 JMD,LRs,DGr,V:Norman Osborn	2.00
253 JMD,LRs,DGr,V:Norman Osborn, Gibbon, Grizzly	2.00
254 JMD,LRs,DGr,V:Prof.Angst	2.00
255 JMD,LRs,DGr,Spider-Hunt,pt.4 x-over, double size	3.00
256 JMD,LRs,DGr,Identity Crisis prelude, A:Prodigy	2.00
257 JMD,LRs,DGr,Identity Crisis, as Prodigy, V:Conundrum	2.00
258 JMD,LRs,DGa,as Prodigy	2.00
259 RSt,LRs,DGa,V:Hobgoblin	2.00
260 JR,RSt,LRs,DGa,Green Goblin vs. Hobgoblin	2.00
261 RSt,LRs,AM,Goblins at the Gate,pt.3	2.00
262 JBy, AM, LRs, The Gathering of the Five, pt.4 (of 5) x-over	2.00
Ann.#8 MBa,RLm,TD,Evolutionary Wars,O:Gwen Stacy Clone	5.00
Ann.#9 DR,MG,DJu,MBa,Atlantis Attacks	4.00
Ann.#10 SLi(c),RB,MM,TM,RA	6.00
Ann.#11 EL(c),RWi,Vib.Vendetta	2.50
Ann.#12 Hero Killers#2,A:New Warriors,BU:Venom	4.50
Ann.#13 I:Noctune,w/Card	3.25
Ann.#14 V:Green Goblin	2.95
Super-Size Spec.#1 Planet of the Symbiotes,pt.4,64pg flip-book	3.95
Minus 1 Spec., JMD,LRs,DGr, flashback, F:Flash Thompson	1.95

SPEEDBALL
Sept., 1988

1 SD,JG,O:Speedball 2.00
2 SD,JG,V:Sticker,Graffiti Gorillas 1.50
3 SD,V:Leaper Logan 1.25
4 SD,DA,Ghost Springdale High . 1.25
5 SD,V:Basher 1.25
6 SD,V:Bug-Eyed Voice 1.25
7 SD,V:Harlequin Hit Man 1.25
8 SD,V:Bonehead Gang 1.25
9 SD,V:Nathan Boder 1.25
10 SD,V:Mutated Pigs,Killer
   Chickens, last issue 1.25

SPELLBOUND
Atlas March, 1952

1 'Step into my Coffin' 450.00
2 BEv,RH,'Horror Story',
   A:Edgar A. Poe 225.00
3 RH(c),OW 200.00
4 RH,Decapitation story 200.00
5 BEv,JM,'Its in the Bag' 200.00
6 BK,'The Man Who Couldn't
   be Killed' 200.00
7 BEv,JMn,'Don't Close
   the Door' 175.00
8 BEv(c),RH,JSt,DAy,
   'The Operation' 175.00
9 BEv(c),RH,'The Death of
   Agatha Slurl' 175.00
10 JMn(c),BEv,RH,'The Living
   Mummy' 175.00
11 'The Empty Coffin' 150.00
12 RH,'My Friend the Ghost' . . 150.00
13 JM,'The Dead Men' 150.00
14 BEv(c),RH,JMn,'Close Shave' 150.00
15 'Get Out of my Graveyard' . 150.00
16 RH,BEv,JF,JSt,'Behind
   the Door' 150.00
17 BEv(c),GC,BK,'Goodbye
   Forever' 150.00
18 BEv(c),JM 150.00
19 BEv(c),BP,'Witch Doctor' . . 150.00
20 RH(c),BP 150.00
21 RH(c) 125.00
22 . . . . 125.00
23 . . . . 125.00
24 JMn(c),JR 100.00
25 JO,'Look into my Eyes' . . . 100.00
26 JR,'The Things in the Box' . 100.00
27 JMn,JR,'Trap in the Mirage' 100.00
28 BEv 100.00
29 JSe(c),SD 125.00
30 BEv(c) 100.00
31 . . . . 100.00
32 BP,'Almost Human' 100.00
33 AT 100.00
34 June, 1957 . . . . 100.00

SPELLBOUND
Jan., 1988

1 thru 3 . . . . @1.50
4 A:New Mutants 2.00
5 . . . . 1.50
6 double-size 2.25

SPIDER-GIRL
August 1998

0 TDF,RF,BSz, cont. from What-If?
   #105, Peter & Mary Jane's
   daughter 3.00
1 TDF,PO,AW, F:Mayday Parker,
   V:Mr. Nobody 2.00

Spider-Man #1
© Marvel Entertainment Group

SPIDER-MAN
August, 1990

1 TM Purple Web(c),V:Lizard,
   A:Calypso,B:Torment 5.00
1a Silver Web(c) 7.00
1b Bag,Purple Web 8.00
1c Bag,Silver Web 10.00
1d 2nd print,Gold(c) 5.00
1e 2nd print Gold UPC(rare) . . . 15.00
1f Platinum Ed. 90.00
2 TM,V:Lizard,A:Calypso 5.00
3 TM,V:Lizard,A:Calypso 5.00
4 TM,V:Lizard,A:Calypso 5.00
5 TM,V:Lizard,A:Calypso,
   E:Torment 5.00
6 TM,A:Ghost Rider,V:Hobgoblin 5.00
7 TM,A:Ghost Rider,V:Hobgoblin 5.00
8 TM,B:Perceptions,A:Wolverine
   I:Wendigo IV 5.00
9 TM,A:Wolverine,Wendigo 4.00
10 TM,RLd,SW,JLe(i),A:Wolv. . . 4.00
11 TM,A:Wolverine,Wendigo. . . . 4.00
12 TM,E:Perceptions,A:Wolv.. . . 4.00
13 TM,V:Morbius,R:Black Cost. . 5.00
14 TM,V:Morbius,A:Black Cost. . 5.00
15 EL,A:Beast 3.50
16 TM,RLd,A:X-Force,V:Juggernaut,
   Black Tom,cont.in X-Force#4 . 4.00
17 RL,AW,A:Thanos,Death 3.50
18 EL,B:Return of the Sinister Six,
   A:Hulk 3.00
19 EL,A:Hulk,Deathlok 3.00
20 EL,A:Nova 2.50
21 EL,A:Hulk,Deathlok,Solo 2.50
22 EL,A:Ghost Rider,Hulk 2.50
23 EL,E:Return of the Sinister Six,
   A:Hulk,G.Rider,Deathlok,FF . 2.50
24 Infinity War,V:Hobgoblin,
   Demogoblin 2.25
25 CMa,A:Excalibur,V:Arcade . . 2.25
26 RF,MBa,Hologram(c),30th Anniv.
   I:New Burglar 4.00
27 MR,Handgun issue 2.25
28 MR,Handgun issue 2.25
29 CMa,Ret.to Mad Dog Ward#1 . 2.25
30 CMa,Ret.to Mad Dog Ward#2 . 2.25

31 CMa,Ret.to Mad Dog Ward#3 . 2.25
32 BMc,A:Punisher,V:Master of
   Vengeance 2.25
33 BMc,A:Punisher,V:Master of
   Vengeance. 2.25
34 BMc,A:Punisher,V:Master of
   Vengeance 2.25
35 TL,Total Carnage#4,V:Carnage,
   Shriek,A:Venom,Black Cat . . . 2.25
36 TL,Total Carnage#8,V:Carnage,
   A:Venom,Morbius 2.25
37 TL,Total Carnage#12,
   V:Carnage 2.25
38 thru 40 KJ,V:Electro 2.25
41 TKa(s),JaL,I:Platoon,
   A:Iron Fist 2.25
42 TKa(s),JaL,V:Platoon,
   A:Iron Fist 2.25
43 TKa(s),JaL,V:Platoon,
   A:Iron Fist 2.25
44 HMe(s),TL,V:Hobgoblin 2.25
45 HMe(s),TL,SHa,Pursuit#1,
   V:Chameleon 2.25
46 HMe(s),TL,V:Hobgoblin,w/cel . 3.25
46a Newsstand Ed. 1.75
47 TL,SHa,V:Demogoblin 2.25
48 TL,SHa,V:Hobgoblin,
   D:Demogoblin 2.25
49 TL,SHa,I:Coldheart 2.25
50 TL,SHa,I:Grim Hunter,foil(c) . . 4.25
50a newsstand ed. 2.50
51 TL,SHa,Power,pt.3,foil(c) 4.00
51a newsstand ed. 2.25
52 TL,SHa,Spide-clone,V:Venom . 2.25
53 TL,SHa,Clone,V:Venom 2.25
54 Web of Life,pt.3 . . . . 2.25
55 Web of Life,finale 2.25
56 Smoke and Mirrors 2.00
57 Aftershocks,pt.1 . . . . 2.50
57a enhanced cover 3.00
58 The Mark of Kaine,pt.3 . . . . . 2.00
59 F:Travellor,Host 2.00
60 TL,SHa,HMa,The Trial of
   Peter Parker,pt.3 . . . . 2.00
61 TL,Maximum Clonage,pt.4 . . . 2.00
62 HMe,TL,Exiled,pt.3 . . . . 2.00
63 HMe,TL,Greatest
   Responsibility,pt.2 . . . . 2.00
64 HMe,JR2,Return of
   Spider-Man,pt.3 . . . . 2.00
65 HMe,JR2,AW,Media
   Blizzard,pt.3 . . . . 2.00
66 HMe,JR2,Return of Kaine,pt.4 . 2.00
67 HMe,JR2,Web of Carnage,pt.3 2.00
68 HMe,JR2,AW,Blood
   Brothers,pt.3 . . . . 2.00
69 HMe,JR2,Blood Brothers
   aftermath 2.00
70 HMe,JR2,A:Onslaught 3.00
71 HMe,JR2, ... 2.00
72 HMe,JR2,Onslaught saga . . . 2.00
73 HMe,JR2 . . . . 2.00
74 HMe,JR2,AW,A:Daredevil,
   V:Fortunato 2.00
75 HMe,JR2,Revelations, pt.4 . . . 3.00
76 HMe,JR2,SHa,Post-Onslaught
   world,I:Shoc 2.00
77 HMe,JR2,SHa,V:Morbius 2.00
Becomes:

PETER PARKER,
SPIDER-MAN

78 HMe,SHa,F:Mary Jane
   Parker 2.00
79 HMe,JR2,SHa,V:Hydra,A:Captain

All comics prices listed are for *Near Mint* condition.

MARVEL

Arthur Stacy 2.00
80 HMe,JR2,SHa,V:S.H.O.C. . . . 2.00
81 HMe,JR2,SHa,V:Shang-Chi,pt.1 2.00
82 HMe,JR2,SHa,Anti-Mutant
   Movement 2.00
83 HMe,JR2,SHa,V:Morbius 2.00
85 HMe,JR2,SHa,V:Friends of
   Humanity 2.00
86 HMe,JR2,SHa,F:Jimmy Six,
   Hammerhead 2.00
87 HMe,JR2,SHa,A:Trapster &
   Shocker 2.00
88 HMe,JR2,SHa,Spider-Man is
   Public Enemy #1 . . . . 2.00
89 HMe,JR2,SHa,Spider-Hunt,pt.3
   x-over 2.00
90 HMe,JR2,SHa,Identity Crisis
   prelude 2.00
91 HMe,JR2,SHa,Identity Crisis,
   as Dusk 2.00
92 HMe,JR2,as Dusk, V:Trapster . 2.00
93 HMe,JS,R:Ghost Rider 2.00
94 HMe,JR2,SHa,Who wasJoeyZ? 2.00
95 HMe,JR2,SHa,Trapped in
   elevator shaft 2.00
96 HMe,JR2,SHa,The Gathering of
   the Five (pt. 3 (of 5)x-over . . . 2.00
Minus 1 Spec., HMe,JR2,SHa,
   flashback, A:Stacys 2.00
Ann.'97 Simon Garth—Zombie . . . 2.95
Ann. '98 HMe, Spider-Man/Elektra,
   V:The Silencer, 48pg. 3.00
GN Fear Itself 12.95
GN Nothing Stops Juggernaut . . 3.95
GN Parallel Lives 8.95
GN JMD,MZ,Soul of the Hunter . . 5.95
HC Kraven's Last Hunt 19.95
HC CV,Spirits of the Earth 18.95
Spec. Chaos in Calgary 1.50
Spec. Double Trouble 1.50
Spec. Hit and Run, Canadian . . . 1.50
Spec. Skating on Thin Ice 1.50
Spec. Trial of Venom,UNICEF . . 15.00
Sup.Sz.Spec#1 Planet of the
   Symbiotes, pt.2;
   flipbook F:Scarlet Spider 3.95
TPB Assasination Plot 14.95
TPB Carnage 6.95
TPB Cosmic Adventures 19.95
TPB Hooky 6.95
TPB Maximum Carnage 24.95
TPB Origin of the Hobgoblin . . . 14.95
TPB Return of the Sinister Six . . 15.95
TPB Spider-Man: Revelations,JR2,
   rep. +14 new pages (1997) . . 12.00
TPB Round Robin 15.95
TPB Saga of the Alien Costume 14.00
   2nd printing 12.95
TPB Spider-Man vs. Venom . . . 9.95
TPB Torment Rep.#1-#5 . . . . . 12.95
TPB Venom Returns 12.95
TPB Very Best of Spider-Man . . 15.95
TPB The Wedding 12.95
TPB Invasion Spider Slayers . . . 15.95
TPB Clone Genesis 16.95
TPB V:Green Goblin 15.95
TPB Spider-Man'sGreatestVillains 15.95
Holiday Spec.'95 . . . . 2.95

SPIDER-MAN ADVENTURES
1994–96
1 From animated series 1.50
1a foil (c) 2.95
2 Animated Adventures 1.50

3 V:Spider-Slayer 1.50
4 Animated Adventures 1.50
5 V:Mysterio 1.50
6 V:Kraven 1.50
7 V:Doctor Octopus 1.50
8 O:Venom,pt.1 . . . . 1.50
9 O:Venom,pt.2 . . . . 1.50
10 V:Venom 1.50
11 V:Hobgoblin 1.50
12 V:Hobgoblin 1.50
13 V:Chameleon 1.50
14 V:Doc Octopus 1.50
15 Doc Conners 1.50
TPB Rep.#1-#5, 112pg 8.95

SPIDER-MAN & AMAZING FRIENDS
Dec., 1981
1 DSp,A:Iceman,I:Firestar 5.50

SPIDER-MAN/BADROCK
Marvel/Maximum Press 1997
1 x-over, pt.1 . . . . 3.00
2 x-over, pt. 2 . . . . 3.00

SPIDER-MAN/BATMAN
1995
1 JMD,MBa,MFm,V:Carnage,Joker 5.95

SPIDER-MAN CLASSICS
1993–94
1 rep.Amazing Fantasy#15 . . . . 1.75
2 thru 11 rep.Amaz.SpM#1-#10 @1.75
12 rep.Amaz.SpM#11 . . . . 1.50
13 rep.Amaz.SpM#12 . . . . 1.50
14 rep.Amaz.SpM#13 . . . . 1.50
15 rep.Amaz.SpM#14,w/cel . . . 3.25
15a Newsstand Ed. 1.50

SPIDER-MAN COMICS MAGAZINE
Jan., 1987
1 . . . . 2.50
2 thru 13 . . . . @1.50

SPIDER-MAN: DEAD MAN'S HAND
1997
1-shot, RSt,DaR,JeM,V:Carrion . . 2.99

SPIDER-MAN: THE FINAL ADVENTURE
1995–96
1 FaN,DaR,Clv,I:Tendril 2.95
2 FaN,DaR,JAl,V:Tendril 2.95
3 FaN,DaR,JAl,V:Tendril 2.95
4 FaN,DaR,JAl,V:Tendril,concl. . . 2.95

SPIDER-MAN: FRIENDS AND ENEMIES
1995
1 V:Metahumes 1.95
2 A:Nova,Darkhawk,Speedball . . 1.95
3 V:Metahumes 1.95
4 F:Metahumes 1.95

SPIDER-MEN: FUNERAL FOR AN OCTOPUS
1995
1 Doc Oc Dead 2.50

2 A:Sinister Six 2.00
3 Final Issue 2.00

SPIDER-MAN/GEN[13]
Marvel/Wildstorm 1996
1-shot PDd,SI,CaS x-over 4.95

SPIDER-MAN: HOBGOBLIN LIVES
1997
1 (of 3) RSt,RF,GP 2.50
2 RSt,RF,GP,Who was the original
   Hobgoblin? 2.50
3 RSt,RF,GP,Original identity
   revealed 2.50
TPB RF(c), series rep. 15.00

SPIDER-MAN: MADE MEN
June 1998
GN HMe,gangster epic 6.00

SPIDER-MAN: THE MANGA
Black & White, Oct., 1997
Bi-weekly
1 imported, translated 4.00
2 . . . . 3.00
3 V:Elektro 3.00
4 V:Lizard 3.00
5 V:Lizard 3.00
6 V:Lizard, concl. 3.00
7 V:Kangaroo 3.00
8 V:Kangaroo 3.00
9 V:Kangaroo 3.00
10 Imposter Spider-Man 3.00
11 Real Spider-Man returns 3.00
12 name dragged through the mud 3.00
13 V:Mysterio 3.00
14 V:Mysterio 3.00
15 V:Mysterio, double size 4.00
16 Human side of Japanese
   Spider-Man 3.00
17 Human side cont. 3.00
18 Human side concl. 3.00
19 Spidey's vacation 3.00
20 and 21 . . . . @3.00

Spider-Man Mutant Agenda #1
© Marvel Entertainment Group

SPIDER-MAN:
MAXIMUM CLONAGE
1995
Alpha Maximum Clonage,pt.1 . . . 5.50
Omega TL,Maximum Clonage,pt.6 4.95

SPIDER-MAN MEGAZINE
1994–95
1 thru 4 rep. . . . . @2.95
5 Vision rep. 2.95
6 V:Thing & Torch, rep. 2.95

SPIDER-MAN:
MUTANT AGENDA
0 thru 2 Paste in Book . . . . . . @1.50
3 Paste in Book 1.50

SPIDER-MAN:
POWER OF TERROR
1995
1 R:Silvermane,A:Deathlok 2.00
2 V:Silvermane 2.00
3 New Scorpion 2.00
4 V:Silvermane 2.00

SPIDER-MAN/PUNISHER
Part 1 TL,A:Tombstone 3.00
Part 2 TL,A:Tombstone 3.00

SPIDER-MAN/PUNISHER/
SABERTOOTH:
DESIGNER GENES
1 SMc,Foil(c) 9.50

SPIDER-MAN:
REDEMPTION
1996
1 thru 4 JMD,MZ,BMc, Mary Jane
arrested for Murder . . . . @1.50

SPIDER-MAN SAGA
Nov., 1991
1 SLi(c),History from Amazing
Fantasy #15-Amaz.SpM#100 . 3.25
2 SLi(c),Amaz.SpM#101-#175 . 3.25
3 Amaz.SpM#176-#238 . . . . . . 3.25
4 Amaz.SpM #239-#300 . . . . . . 3.25

SPIDER-MAN
SUPER SIZE SPECIAL
1 Planet of the Symbiotes,pt.2 . 3.95

SPIDER-MAN TEAM-UP
1995–96
1 MWa,KeL,V:Hellfire Club 3.00
2 thru 4 . . . . 3.00
5 SvG,DaR,JFr,F:Gambit,
Howard the Duck 3.00
6 JMD,LHa,F:Hulk & Doctor
Strange 3.00
7 KBk,SB,F:Thunderbolts 3.00

SPIDER-MAN:
THE ARACHNIS PROJECT
1884–95
1 Wld, beginnings 1.75
2 Wld,V:Diggers 1.75
3 Wld,V:Jury 1.75
4 Wld,V:Life Foundation 1.75

5 Wld,V:Jury 1.75

SPIDER-MAN:
THE CLONE JOURNALS
One-shot (1995) 1.95

SPIDER-MAN:
THE JACKAL FILES
1 Files of the Jackal (1995) 1.95

SPIDER-MAN:
THE LOST YEARS
1995
0 JMD,JR2,LSh,64pg,rep. 4.00
1 History of Kaine,Ben 3.00
2 JMD,JR2,KJ,Kaine & Ben 3.00
3 Ben vs. Kaine 3.00

SPIDER-MAN:
THE PARKER YEARS
1995
1 JR2,JPi,F:The real Clone 2.50

SPIDER-MAN 2099
1992–96
1 RL,AW,I:Spider-Man 2099 . . . . 4.00
2 RL,AW,O:Spider-Man 2099 . . . 3.00
3 RL,AW,V:Venture 2.50
4 RL,AW,I:Specialist,
A:Doom 2099 . . . . 2.00
5 RL,AW,V:Specialist 2.00
6 RL,AW,I:New Vulture 2.00
7 RL,AW,Vulture of 2099 . . . . . . 2.00
8 RL,AW,V:New Vulture 2.00
9 KJo,V:Alchemax 2.00
10 RL,AW,O:Wellvale Home 2.00
11 RL,AW,V:S.I.E.G.E. 2.00
12 RL,AW,w/poster 2.00
13 RL,AW,V:Thanatos 1.75
14 PDd(s),RL(c),TGb,Downtown . 1.75
15 PDd(s),RL,I:Thor 2099,
Heimdall 2099 . . . . 1.75
16 PDd(s),RL,Fall of the
Hammer#1 . . . . 1.75
17 PDd(s),RL,V:Bloodsword 1.75
18 PDd(s),RLm,V:Lyla 1.75
19 PDd(s),RL,w/card 1.75
20 PDd(s),RL,Crash & Burn 1.75
21 V:Gangs 1.75
22 V:Gangs 1.75
23 RL,I:Risque 3.00
24 Kasey 1.75
25 A:Hulk 2099, dbl-size,foil(c) . . . 3.25
25a Newsstand ed. 2.25
26 V:Headhunter, Travesty 1.50
27 V:Travesty 1.50
28 V:Travesty 1.50
29 V:Foragers 1.50
30 V:Flipside 1.50
31 I:Dash 1.50

Becomes:
SPIDER-MAN 2099 A.D.
32 I:Morgue 1.95
33 One Nation Under Doom 1.95
34 V:Alchemex 1.95
35 . . . . 1.95
36a Spider-Man 2099(c) 1.95
36b Venom 2099(c) 1.95
37a Venom 2099 . . . . 1.95
37b variant cover 1.95
38 . . . . 1.95
39 A:Venom 2099 . . . . 1.95

40 V:Goblin 2099 . . . . 1.95
41 and 42 . . . . @1.95
43 V:Sub-Mariner 2099 . . . . 1.95
Ann.#1 PDd(s),RL 2.95
Spec.#1 I:3 new villains 3.95

SPIDER-MAN UNLIMITED
1993
1 RLm,Maximun Carnage#1,I:Shriek,
R:Carnage 5.00
2 RLm,Maximum Carnage#14 . . 4.50
3 RLm,O:Doctor Octopus 4.50
4 RLm,V:Mystrerio,Rhino 4.25
5 RLm,A:Human Torch,
I:Steel Spider 4.25
6 RLm,A:Thunderstrike 3.95
7 RLm,A:Clone 3.95
8 Tom Lyle 3.95
9 The Mark of Kaine,pt.5 . . . . . . 3.95
10 SwM,Exiled,pt.4 . . . . 3.95
11 FaN,V:Black Cat 3.95
12 Blood Brother tie-in 3.95
13 . . . . 3.00
14 JoB, an ally dies 3.00
15 TDF,JoB,F:Puma 3.00
16 cont. from X-Force #64 . . . . . . 3.00
17 JoB, Revelations, sequel 3.00
18 TDF,JoB,F:Doctor Octopus . . . 3.00
19 JoB,F:Lizard 3.00
20 JoB,A:Hannibal King, V:Lilith . . 3.00
21 MD2,Frankenstein Monster lives 3.00

SPIDER-MAN UNMASKED
1996
1-shot 64pg information source . . 6.00

SPIDER-MAN VS.
DRACULA
1994
1 rep. 1.75

SPIDER-MAN vs. VENOM
1990
1 TM(c) 8.95

SPIDER-MAN:
THE VENOM AGENDA
Nov., 1997
1-shot LHa,TL, J. Jonah Jameson,
V:Venom 3.00

SPIDER-MAN vs.
WOLVERINE
1990
1 MBr,AW,D:Ned Leeds(the original
Hobgoblin),V:Charlie 22.00
1a reprint 5.00

SPIDER-MAN:
WEB OF DOOM
1994
1 3-part series 1.75
2 Spidey falsely accused 1.75
3 conclusion 1.75

SPIDER-MAN &
X-FACTOR:
SHADOW GAMES
1 PB,I:Shadowforce 2.25
2 PB,V:Shadowforce 2.25
3 PB,V:Shadowforce, final issue . 2.25

Spider-Woman #25
© *Marvel Entertainment Group*

SPIDER-WOMAN
April, 1978

1 CI,TD,O:Spiderwoman	6.00
2 CI,TD,I:Morgan Le Fey	2.00
3 CI,TD,I:Brother's Grimm	2.00
4 CI,TD,V:Hangman	2.00
5 CI,TD,Nightmares	2.00
6 CI,A:Werewolf By Night	2.00
7 CI,SL,AG,V:Magnus	2.00
8 CI,AG,"Man who would not die"	2.00
9 CI,AG,A:Needle,Magnus	2.00
10 CI,AG,I:Gypsy Moth	2.00
11 CI,AG,V:Brothers Grimm	1.50
12 CI,AG,V:Brothers Grimm	1.50
13 CI,AG,A:Shroud	1.50
14 BSz(c),CI,AG,A:Shroud	1.50
15 BSz(c),CI,AG,A:Shroud	1.50
16 BSz(c),CI,AG,V:Nekra	1.50
17 CI,Deathplunge	1.50
18 CI,A:Flesh	1.50
19 CI,A:Werewolf By Night, V:Enforcer	1.75
20 FS,A:Spider-Man	1.50
21 FS,A:Bounty Hunter	1.50
22 FS,A:Killer Clown	1.50
23 TVE,V:The Gamesmen	1.50
24 TVE,V:The Gamesmen	1.50
25 SL,Two Spiderwomen	1.50
26 JBy(c),SL,V:White Gardenia	1.50
27 BSz(c),JBi,A:Enforcer	1.50
28 BSz(c),SL,A:Enforcer,Spidey	1.50
29 JR2(c),ECh,FS,A:Enforcer, Spider-Man	1.50
30 FM(c),SL,JM,I:Dr.Karl Malus	1.50
31 FM(c),SL,JM,A:Hornet	1.50
32 FM(c),SL,JM,A:Werewolf	1.75
33 SL,V:Yesterday's Villian	1.50
34 SL,AM,V:Hammer and Anvil	1.50
35 SL,AG,V:Angar the Screamer	1.50
36 SL,Spiderwoman Shot	1.50
37 SL,TA,BWi,AM,FS,A:X-Men,I: Siryn,V:Black Tom	4.00
38 SL,BWi,A:X-Men,Siryn	5.00
39 SL,BWi,Shadows	1.50
40 SL,BWi,V:The Flying Tiger	1.50
41 SL,BWi,V:Morgan LeFay	1.50
42 SL,BWi,V:Silver Samurai	1.50

43 SL,V:Silver Samurai	1.50
44 SL,V:Morgan LeFay	1.50
45 SL,Spider-Man Thief Cover	1.50
46 SL,V:Mandroids,A:Kingpin	1.50
47 V:Daddy Longlegs	1.50
48 O:Gypsy Moth	1.50
49 A:Tigra	1.50
50 PH(c),D:Spiderwoman	3.50

[Limited Series] 1993–94

1 V:Therak	2.00
2 O:Spider-Woman	2.00
3 V:Deathweb	2.00
4 V:Deathweb,Last issue	2.00

SPIDEY SUPER STORIES
Oct., 1974

1 Younger reader's series in association with the Electric Company,O:Spider-Man	12.00
2 A:Kraven	8.00
3 A:Ringleader	8.00
4 A:Medusa	8.00
5 A:Shocker	8.00
6 A:Iceman	8.00
7 A:Lizard, Vanisher	8.00
8 A:Dr. Octopus	8.00
9 A:Dr. Doom	8.00
10 A:Green Goblin	7.00
11 A:Dr. Octopus	7.00
12 A:The Cat,V:The Owl	7.00
13 A:Falcon	7.00
14 A:Shanna	7.00
15 A:Storm	8.00
16	6.00
17 A:Captain America	6.00
18 A:Kingpin	6.00
19 A:Silver Surfer,Dr. Doom	6.00
20 A;Human Torch,Invisible Girl	6.00
21 A:Dr. Octopus	5.00
22 A:Ms. Marvel,The Beetle	5.00
23 A:Green Goblin	5.00
24 A:Thundra	5.00
25 A:Dr. Doom	5.00
26 A:Sandman	5.00
27 A:Thor,Loki	5.00
28 A:Medusa	5.00
29 A:Kingpin	5.00
30 A:Kang	5.00
31 A:Moondragon,Dr. Doom	4.00
32 A:Spider-Woman,Dr. Octopus	4.00
33	4.00
34 A:Sub-Mariner	4.00
35	4.00
36 A:Lizard	4.00
37 A:White Tiger	4.00
38 A:Fantastic Four	4.00
39 A:Hellcat,Thanos	6.00
40 A:Hawkeye	4.00
41 A:Nova,Dr. Octopus	4.00
42 A:Kingpin	4.00
43 A:Daredevil,Ringmaster	4.00
44 A:Vision	4.00
45 A:Silver Surfer,Dr. Doom	6.00
46 A:Mysterio	4.00
47 A:Spider-Woman,Stilt-Man	4.00
48 A:Green Goblin	4.00
49 Spidey for President	4.00
50 A:She-Hulk	4.00
51 and 52	@4.00
53 A:Dr. Doom	4.00
54 'Attack of the Bird-Man'	4.00
55 A:Kingpin	4.00
56 A:Captain Britain,	

Jack O'Lantern	4.00
57 March, 1982	4.00

SPITFIRE AND THE TROUBLESHOOTERS
Oct., 1986

1 HT/JSt	1.00
2 HT	1.00
3 HT,Macs Armor	1.00
4 TM/BMc(Early TM work)	3.00
5 HT/TD,A:StarBrand	1.00
6 HT,Trial	1.00
7 HT	1.00
8 HT,New Armor	1.00
9	1.00

Becomes:

CODE NAME: SPITFIRE

10 MR/TD	1.00
11 thru 13	@1.00

SPOOF
Oct., 1970

1 MSe	12.00
2 MSe,'Brawl in the Family'	10.00
3 MSe,Richard Nixon cover	10.00
4 MSe,'Blechhula'	10.00
5 MSe,May, 1973	11.00

SPORT STARS
Nov., 1949

1 The Life of Knute Rockne	250.00

Becomes:

SPORTS ACTION

2 BP(c),Life of George Gipp	225.00
3 BEv,Hack Wilson	150.00

Sports Action #3
© *Marvel Entertainment Group*

4 Art Houtteman	125.00
5 Nile Kinnick	125.00
6 Warren Gun	125.00
7 Jim Konstanty	125.00
8 Ralph Kiner	150.00
9 Ed "Strangler" Lewis	125.00
10 JMn,'The Yella-Belly'	125.00
11 'The Killers'	125.00
12 'Man Behind the Mask'	125.00
13 Lew Andrews	125.00
14 MWs,Ken Roper,Sept.,1952	100.00

SPOTLIGHT
Sept., 1978
1 F:Huckleberry Hound,YogiBear		12.00
2 Quick Draw McDraw		8.00
3 The Jetsons		8.00
4 Magilla Gorilla, March, 1979		8.00

SPUMCO COMIC BOOK
1 I:Jimmy the Hapless Boy		6.95
2		6.95
3 64pgs of sick humor		6.95
4 More sick humor		6.95
TPB		24.95

SPY CASES
See: KID KOMICS

SPY FIGHTERS
March, 1951
1 GT		150.00
2 GT		75.00
3		65.00
4 thru 13		@60.00
14 thru 15 July, 1953		@65.00

SPYKE
Epic *Heavy Hitters* 1993
1 MBn,BR,I:Spyke		2.75
2 MBn,BR,V:Conita		2.75
3 thru 4 MBn,BR		@2.00

SPY THRILLERS
Atlas Nov., 1954
1 'The Tickling Death'		125.00
2 V:Communists		75.00
3		50.00
4		50.00
Becomes:

POLICE BADGE
5 Sept., 1955		75.00

SQUADRON SUPREME
Sept., 1985
1 BH,L:Nighthawk		3.00
2 BH,F:Nuke,A:Scarlet Centurion		2.50
3 BH,D:Nuke		2.50
4 BH,L:Archer		2.00
5 BH,L:Amphibian		2.00
6 PR,J:Institute of Evil		2.00
7 JB,JG,V:Hyperion		2.00
8 BH,V:Hyperion		2.00
9 BSz(c),PR,D:Tom Thumb		2.00
10 PR,V:Quagmire		2.00
11 PR,V:Redeemers		2.00
12 PR,D:Nighthawk,Foxfire,		
Black Archer		2.50
GN Death of a Universe		9.95
TPB 352 pages		15.00

STALKERS
Epic 1990–91
1 MT		1.50
2 MT		1.50
3 MT		1.50
4 MT		1.50
5 MT		1.50
6 VM,MT		1.50
7 VM,MT		1.50
8 VM,MT		1.50
9 thru 12 VM		@1.50

STARBLAST
1994
1 MGu(s),HT,After the Starbrand		2.25
2 MGu(s),HT,After the Starbrand		2.00
3 MGu(s),HT,After the Starbrand		2.00
4 MGu(s),HT,Final Issue		2.00

STARBRAND
Oct., 1986
1 JR2,O:Starbrand		1.50
2 JR2/AW		1.00
3 JR2/AW		1.00
4 JR2/AW		1.00
5 JR2/AW		1.00
6 JR2/AW		1.00
7 JR2/AW		1.00
8 JR2/AW		1.00
9 KG/BWi,A:Nightmask		1.00
10		1.00
11 JR2,TP		1.00
12 JR2,TP,X-Men X-over		1.25
13 JR2,TP		1.25
14 JR2,TP		1.25
15		1.25
16		1.25
17 JBy,TP,New Starbrand		1.50
18 JBy/TP		1.50
19 JBy/TP		1.50
Ann.#1		1.25

STAR COMICS MAGAZINE
Dec., 1986 (digest size)
1 F:Heathcliff,Muppet Babies,		
Ewoks		1.50
2 thru 13 1988		@1.50

STARJAMMERS
1995–96
1 I:The Uncreated		2.95
2 War For the Shi'ar		2.95
3 stuck in deep space		2.95
4 conclusion		2.95

STAR-LORD, SPECIAL EDITION
Feb., 1982
1 JBy reprints		6.00

STARLORD
Mini-Series 1996
1 (of 3) DLw,		2.50
2 DLw		2.50
3 DLw,V:Damyish		2.50

STARLORD MEGAZINE
TPB CCl,JBy,TA, rep., 64pg		2.95

STAR MASTER
1 MGu,Cosmic Avengers assemble		1.95
2 MGu,Worldengine saga		1.95
3 MGu,Cauldron of Conversion		2.00

STARRIORS
August, 1984
1		1.50
2		1.25
3		1.25
4 Feb., 1982		1.25

STARSTRUCK
March, 1985
1 MK		2.00
2 MK		1.75
3 thru 8 MK, Feb. 1986		@1.50

Star Trek #5
© Marvel Entertainment Group

STAR TREK
April, 1980
1 DC,KJ,rep.1st movie Adapt.		8.00
2 DC,KJ,rep.1st movie Adapt.		6.00
3 DC,KJ,rep.1st movie Adapt.		5.00
4 DC,KJ,The Weirdest Voyage		5.00
5 DC,KJ,Dr.McCoy..Killer		5.00
6 DC,KJ,A:Ambassador Phlu		5.00
7 MN,KJ,Kirk/Spock(c)		5.00
8 DC(p),F:Spock		5.00
9 DC,FS,Trapped in a Web of		
Ghostly Vengeance		5.00
10 KJ(i),Spock the Barbarian		5.00
11 TP(i),Like A Woman Scorned		5.00
12 TP(i),Trapped in a Starship		
Gone Mad		5.00
13 TP(i),A:Barbara McCoy		5.00
14 LM,GD,We Are Dying,		
Egypt,Dying		5.00
15 GK,The Quality of Mercy		5.00
16 LM,There's no Space		
like Gnomes		5.00
17 EH,TP,The Long Nights Dawn		5.00
18 A Thousand Deaths,last issue		5.00

STAR TREK: DEEP SPACE NINE
1996
1 HWe(s),TGb,AM,DS9 in the		
Gamma Quadrant,pt.1 (of 2)		2.00
2 DS9 in Gamma Quadrant,pt.2		2.00
3 TGb,AM,pt.1 (of 2)		2.00
4 TGb,AM,pt.2		2.00
5 AM,terrorist attack		2.00
6 HWe(s),TGb,AM,Shirn sentence		
Sisko to Death, "Risk," pt.1		2.00
7 HWe(s),TGb,"Risk," pt.2		2.00
8 TGb,AM,V:Maquis & Romulans		2.00
9 TGb,AM,V:Maquis & Romulans,		
pt.2		2.00
10 HWe,TGb, trapped in the		

holosuite 2.00
11 HWe,TGb, ... 2.00
12 Telepathy War x-over 2.00
13 Jem'Hadar battle 2.00
14 Why do Klingons hate tribbles? 2.00
15 The Tailor's deeds 2.00

STAR TREK: EARLY VOYAGES
Dec. 1996
1 DAn,IEd,Captain Pike's crew,
  double size premier 3.00
2 DAn,IEd,distress signal 2.00
3 DAn,IEd,on Rigel 7, prologue to
  "The Cage" 2.00
4 DAn,IEd, prologue to "The Cage" 2.00
5 DAn,IEd, V:Vulcans 2.00
6 DAn,IEd, Cloak & Dagger concl. 2.00
7 DAn,IEd, The wrath of Kaaj . . . 2.00
8 DAn,IEd,F:Dr. Boyce 2.00
9 DAn,IEd,F:Nano 2.00
10 DAn,V:Chakuun, Tholians 2.00
11 DAn,IEd,The Fallen, pt. 2 . . . . 2.00
12 DAn,IEd, ... 2.00
13 DAn,IEd,F:Yeoman Colt 2.00
14 DAn,IEd,Pike vs. Kirk 2.00
15 DAn,IEd,F:Yeoman Colt 2.00
16 . . . . 2.00
17 DAn,IEd, Pike & Kaaj 2.00

STAR TREK: FIRST CONTACT
GN Movie Adapt. 5.95

STAR TREK: MIRROR, MIRROR
1996
1-shot continuation of famous
  classic episode 3.95

STAR TREK: THE NEXT GENERATION— RIKER SPECIAL
May 1998
1-shot, DAn,IEd,Riker photo cover 3.50

STAR TREK: THE NEXT GENERATION/X-MEN: SECOND CONTACT
March 1998
1-shot, DAn,IEd,64pg 5.00
1-shot, variant CNr cover (1:5) . . . 5.00

STAR TREK: OPERATION ASSIMILATION
1-shot Borg story 2.95

STAR TREK: STARFLEET ACADEMY
1996
1 Cadets vs. Gorns 2.00
2 ALa, R&R in Australia 2.00
3 F:Decker 2.00
4 V:Klingon Bird-of-prey 2.00
5 V:Klingons 2.00
6 Funeral of Kamilah
  Goldstein,I:Edam Astrun . . . 2.00
7 ALa,F:Edam Astrun,Nog 2.00
8 ALa, Return of Charlie X 2.00
9 ALa, on Talos, V:Jem'Hadar . . 2.00

10 ALa,F:Captain Pike, Jem'Hadar 2.00
11 F:Christopher Pike 2.00
12 ALa, Telepathy War x-over . . . 2.00
13 Parent's Day 2.00
14 T'Priell revealed, pt.1 (of 3) . . . 2.00
15 T'Priell dead?, pt.2 . . . . 2.00
16 T'Priell Revealed, pt3 . . . . 2.00
17 Battle for T'Priell's mind 2.00
18 Entirely in Klingon language . . 2.00
19 Pava vs. Kovold 2.00

STAR TREK: TELEPATHY WAR
Sept., 1997
1-shot Telepathy War, pt.4
  x-over, 48pg 3.00

STAR TREK: UNLIMITED
1996
1 DAn, IEd,MBu,JeM, AW, Classic
  series & TNG 3.00
2 DAn,IEd,MBu, ... 3.00
3 DAn,IEd,MBu, ... 3.00
4 DAn,IEd,MBu,AW, 2 tales 3.00
5 DAn,IEd,TMo,RoR,AW,ANi,48pg 3.00
6 DAn, Telepathy War x-over . . . 2.00
7 DAn,IEd,F:Q & Trelane 2.00
8 DAn,IEd,Day of Honor tie-in . . . 2.00
9 DAn,IEd,V:Klingons 2.00
10 A Piece of the Action,
  conclusion of series. 2.00

STAR TREK: THE UNTOLD VOYAGES
Jan., 1998
1 (of 5) Star Trek 2nd Five Year
  Mission 2.50
2 Spock, Savik, Dr. McCoy 2.50
3 F:McCoy, McCoy's Daughter . . 2.50
4 F:Sulu 2.50
5 48pg finale 3.50

STAR TREK: VOYAGER
1996
1 F:Neelix & Talaxians, pt.1 . . . . 2.00
2 F:Neelix & Talaxians, pt.2 . . . . 2.00
3 F:Neelix & Talaxians, pt.3 . . . . 2.00
4 HWe(s),"Homeostasis," pt.1 . . . 2.00
5 HWe(s),"Homeostasis," pt.2 . . . 2.00
6 HWe(s),"Homeostasis," pt.3 . . . 2.00
7 Ancient Relic 2.00
8 Mysterious Relic encountered . 2.00
9 DAn,IEd,AM, rescue mission . . 2.00
10 The Borg are back 2.00
11 Zoological Experiment 2.00
12 Zoological Experiment 2.00
13 Crew loses a member 2.00
14 Distress Call 2.00
15 Tuvok Trapped 2.00

STAR TREK: VOYAGER: SPLASHDOWN
Jan., 1998
1 (of 4) AM,Crash landing on
  water planet 2.00
2 AM,The ship may sink 2.00
3 AM,adventure undersea 2.00
4 AM,escape from sea creatures 2.00

STAR TREK/X-MEN
1-shot SLo,MS, 64pg. 5.00
1a rep. of STAR TREK/X-MEN . . 4.95

Star Wars #30
© *Marvel Entertainment Group*

STAR WARS
July, 1977
1 HC,30 Cent,movie adaption. . 65.00
1a HC,35 Cent(square Box). . . 400.00
1b "Reprint" 7.50
2 HC,movie adaptation 25.00
2b "Reprint" 4.00
3 HC,movie adaptation 25.00
3b "Reprint" 4.00
4 HC,SL,movie adapt.(low dist.) 22.00
4b "Reprint" 4.00
5 HC,SL,movie adaptation 22.00
5b "Reprint" 3.00
6 HC,DSt,E:movie adaption . . . 22.00
6b "Reprint" 3.00
7 HC,FS,F:Luke&Chewbacca . . 20.00
7b "Reprint" 2.50
8 HC,TD,Eight against a World . 20.00
8b "Reprint" 2.50
9 HC,TP,V:Cloud Riders 20.00
9b "Reprint" 2.50
10 HC,TP,Behemoth fr.Below . . 20.00
11 CI,TP,Fate o/Luke Skywalker 18.00
12 TA,CI,Doomworld 18.00
13 TA,JBy,CI,Deadly Reunion . . 18.00
14 TA,CI 18.00
15 CI,V:Crimson Jack 18.00
16 WS,V:The Hunter 18.00
17 Crucible, Low Dist. 18.00
18 CI,Empire Strikes(Low Dist). . 18.00
19 CI,Ultimate Gamble(Low Dist) 18.00
20 CI,Death Game(Scarce) 18.00
21 TA,CI,Shadow of a Dark
  Lord(Scarce) 18.00
22 CI,Han Solo vs.Chewbacca . . 15.00
23 CI,Flight Into Fury 15.00
24 CI,Ben Kenobi Story 15.00
25 CI,Siege at Yavin 15.00
26 CI,Doom Mission 15.00
27 CI,V:The Hunter 15.00
28 CI,Cavern o/t Crawling Death 15.00
29 CI,Dark Encounter 15.00
30 CI,A Princess Alone 15.00
31 CI,Return to Tatooine 15.00
32 CI,The Jawa Express 15.00
33 CI,GD,V:Baron Tagge 15.00
34 CI,Thunder in the Stars 15.00

35 CI,V:Darth Vader 15.00
36 CI,V:Darth Vader 15.00
37 CI,V:Darth Vader 15.00
38 TA,MG,Riders in the Void . . . 15.00
39 AW,B:Empire Strikes Back . . 25.00
40 AW,Battleground Hoth 25.00
41 AW,Imperial Pursuit 25.00
42 AW,Bounty Hunters 25.00
43 AW,Betrayal at Bespin 25.00
44 AW,E:Empire Strikes Back . . 25.00
45 CI,GD,Death Probe 20.00
46 DI,TP,V:Dreamnaut Devourer 20.00
47 CI,GD,Droid World 20.00
48 CI,Leia vs.Darth Vader 20.00
49 SW,TP,The Last Jedi 20.00
50 WS,AW,TP,G-Size issue 20.00
51 WS,TP,Resurrection of Evil . . 15.00
52 WS,TP 15.00
53 CI,WS 15.00
54 CI,WS 15.00
55 thru 66 WS,TP . . . . @15.00
67 TP 15.00
68 GD,TP 20.00
69 GD,TP 20.00
70 A:Han Solo 20.00
71 A:Han Solo 20.00
72 . . . . 20.00
73 Secret of Planet Lansbane . . 20.00
74 thru 91 . . . . @20.00
92 BSz(c) 20.00
93 thru 97 . . . . @20.00
98 AW 20.00
99 . . . . 20.00
100 Painted(c),double-size 20.00
101 BSz 15.00
102 KRo's Back 15.00
103 thru 106 . . . . @15.00
107 WPo(i),last issue 50.00
Ann.#1 WS(c),V:Winged Warlords 10.00
Ann.#2 RN 8.00
Ann.#3 RN,Darth Vader(c) 8.00

STEELGRIP STARKEY
Epic July, 1986
1 . . . . 1.75
2 . . . . 1.75
3 . . . . 1.75
4 . . . . 1.75
5 . . . . 1.75
6 June, 1987 . . . . 1.75

STEELTOWN ROCKERS
April, 1990—Sept., 1990
1 SL 1.50
2 thru 6 SL . . . . @1.50

STORM
1 TyD,KIS,V:Candra 2.95
2 . . . . 2.95
3 . . . . 2.95
4 TyD,KIS, conclusion,foil cover . 2.95

STRANGE COMBAT TALES
1 thru 2 . . . . 2.75
3 Tiger by the Tail 2.50
4 Midnight Crusade 2.50

STRANGE STORIES OF SUSPENSE
See: RUGGED ACTION

STRANGE TALES
[1st Regular Series]June, 1951
1 'The Room' 2,500.00
2 'Trapped In A Tomb' 800.00
3 JMn,'Man Who Never Was' 600.00
4 BEv,'Terror in the Morgue' . 650.00
5 'A Room Without A Door' . . 650.00
6 RH(c),'The Ugly Man' 450.00
7 'Who Stands Alone' 450.00
8 BEv(c),'Something in the Fog' 450.00
9 'Drink Deep Vampire' 450.00
10 BK,'Hidden Head' 500.00
11 BEv(c),GC,'O'Malley's Friend' 300.00
12 'Graveyard At Midnight' . . . 300.00
13 BEv(c),'Death Makes A Deal' 300.00
14 GT,'Horrible Herman' 300.00
15 BK,'Don't Look Down' 325.00
16 Decapitation cover 300.00
17 DBr,JRo,'Death Feud' 300.00
18 'Witch Hunt' 300.00
19 RH(c),'The Rag Doll' 300.00
20 RH(c),GC,SMo,'Lost World' . 300.00
21 BEv 225.00

Strange Tales #72
© Marvel Entertainment Group

22 BK,JF 225.00
23 'The Strangest Tale in
    the World' 225.00
24 'The Thing in the Coffin' . . . 225.00
25 . . . . 225.00
26 . . . . 225.00
27 JF,'The Garden of Death' . . 225.00
28 'Come into my Coffin' 250.00
29 'Witch-Craft' 225.00
30 'The Thing in the Box' 225.00
31 'The Man Who Played
    with Blocks' 225.00
32 . . . . 225.00
33 JMn(c),'Step Lively Please' . 225.00
34 'Flesh and Blood' 200.00
35 'The Man in the Bottle' 200.00
36 . . . . 200.00
37 'Out of the Storm' 200.00
38 . . . . 200.00
39 'Karnoff's Plan' 200.00
40 BEv,'The Man Who Caught a
    Mermaid' 200.00
41 BEv,'Riddle of the Skull' . . . 225.00
42 DW,BEv,JMn,'Faceless One' 225.00

43 JF,'The Mysterious Machine' 200.00
44 . . . . 200.00
45 JKa,'Land of the
    Vanishing Men' 225.00
46 thru 57 . . . . @175.00
58 AW 175.00
59 BK 175.00
60 . . . . 150.00
61 BK 175.00
62 . . . . 150.00
63 . . . . 175.00
64 AW 150.00
65 . . . . 150.00
66 . . . . 150.00
67 thru 78 . . . . @200.00
79 SD,JK,Dr.Strange Prototype 200.00
80 thru 83 SD,JK . . . . @150.00
84 SD,JK,Magneto Prototype . . 175.00
85 SD,JK 150.00
86 SD,JK,'I Who
    Created Mechano' 150.00
87 SD,JK,'Return of Grogg' . . . 150.00
88 SD,JK,'Zzutak' 150.00
89 SD,JK,'Fin Fang Foom' 400.00
90 SD,JK,'Orrgo the
    Unconquerable' 150.00
91 SD,JK,'The Sacrifice' 150.00
92 SD,JK,'The Thing That Waits
    For Me' 150.00
93 SD,JK,'The Wax People' . . . 150.00
94 SD,JK,'Pildorr the Plunderer' 150.00
95 SD,JK,'Two-Headed Thing' . 150.00
96 SD,JK,'I Dream of Doom' . . 150.00
97 SD,JK,'When A Planet Dies' 350.00
98 SD,JK,'No Human Can
    Beat Me' 150.00
99 SD,JK,'Mister Morgan's
    Monster' 150.00
100 SD,JK,'I Was Trapped
    in the Crazy Maze' 150.00
101 B:StL(s),SD,JK,
    B:Human Torch 900.00
102 SD,JK,I:Wizard 300.00
103 SD,JK,I:Zemu 250.00
104 SD,JK,I:The Trapster 250.00
105 SD,JK,V:Wizard 250.00
106 SD,A:Fantastic Four 175.00
107 SD,V:Sub-Mariner 200.00
108 SD,JK,A:FF,I:The Painter . 175.00
109 SD,JK,I:Sorcerer 175.00
110 SD,I&B:Dr.Strange,
    Nightmare 1,200.00
111 SD,I:Asbestos,
    Baron Mordo 350.00
112 SD,I:The Eel 125.00
113 SD,I:Plant Man 125.00
114 SD,JK,A:Captain America . 400.00
115 SD,O:Dr.Strange 500.00
116 SD,V:Thing 125.00
117 SD,V:The Eel 100.00
118 SD,V:The Wizard 125.00
119 SD,C:Spider-Man 125.00
120 SD,1st Iceman/Torch T.U. . 135.00
121 SD,V:Plantman 75.00
122 SD,V:Dr.Doom 65.00
123 SD,A:Thor,I:Beetle 65.00
124 SD,I:Zota 65.00
125 SD,V:Sub-Mariner 65.00
126 SD,I:Dormammu,Clea 65.00
127 SD,V:Dormammu 60.00
128 SD,I:Demon 60.00
129 SD,I:Tiboro 60.00
130 SD,C:Beatles 65.00
131 SD,I:Dr.Vega 55.00
132 SD,I:Orini 55.00

MARVEL

133 SD,I:Shazana 55.00
134 SD,E:Torch,I:Merlin 55.00
135 SD,JK,I:Shield & Hydra
   B:Nick Fury 125.00
136 SD,JK,V:Dormammu 50.00
137 SD,JK,A:Ancient One 60.00
138 SD,JK,I:Eternity 45.00
139 SD,JK,V:Dormammu 45.00
140 SD,JK,V:Dormammu 45.00
141 SD,JK,I:Fixer,Mentallo 45.00
142 SD,JK,I:THEM,V:Hydra 45.00
143 SD,JK,V:Hydra 45.00
144 SD,JK,V:Druid,I:Jasper
   Sitwell 45.00
145 SD,JK,I:Mr.Rasputin 45.00
146 SD,JK,V:Dormammu,I:AIM . 45.00
147 BEv,JK,F:Wong 45.00
148 BEv,JK,O:Ancient One 75.00
149 BEv,JK,V:Kaluu 45.00
150 BEv,JK,JB(1st Marvel Art)
   I:Baron Strucker,Umar 45.00
151 JK,JSo(1st Marvel Art),
   I:Umar 60.00
152 BEv,JK,JSo,V:Umar 40.00
153 JK,JSo,MSe,V:Hydra 40.00
154 JSo,MSe,I:Dreadnought . . . 40.00
155 JSo,MSe,A:L.B.Johnson . . . 40.00
156 JSo,MSe,I:Zom 40.00
157 JSo,MSe,A:Zom,C:Living
   Tribunal 40.00
158 JSo,MSe,A:Zom,I:Living
   Tribunal(full story) 45.00
159 JSo,MSe,O:Nick Fury,A:Capt.
   America,I:Val Fontaine 50.00
160 JSo,MSe,A:Captain America
   I:Jimmy Woo. 40.00
161 JSo,I:Yellow Claw 40.00
162 JSo,DA,A:Captain America. . 40.00
163 JSo,DA,V:Yellow Claw 40.00
164 JSo,DA,V:Yellow Claw 40.00
165 JSo,DA,V:Yellow Claw 40.00
166 DA,GT,JSo,A:AncientOne . . 40.00
167 JSo,DA,V:Doctor Doom . . . 50.00
168 JSo,DA,E:Doctor Strange,Nick
   Fury,V:Yandroth 40.00
169 JSo,I&O:Brother Voodoo . . . 15.00
170 JSo,O:Brother Voodoo 12.00
171 GC,V:Baron Samed 12.00
172 GC,DG,V:Dark Lord 12.00
173 GC,DG,I:Black Talon 12.00
174 JB,JM,O:Golem 10.00
175 SD,R:Torr 10.00
176 F:Golem 10.00
177 FB,F:Golem 10.00
178 JSn,B&O:Warlock,I:Magus . 27.00
179 JSn,I:Pip,I&D:Capt.Autolycus 15.00
180 JSn,I:Gamora,Kray-tor 15.00
181 JSn,E:Warlock 15.00
182 SD,GK,rep Str.Tales
   #123,124 . . . . 10.00
183 SD,rep Str.Tales #130,131 . 10.00
184 SD,rep Str.Tales #132,133 . 10.00
185 SD,rep Str.Tales #134,135 . 10.00
186 SD,rep Str.Tales #136,137 . 10.00
187 SD,rep Str.Tales #138,139 . 10.00
188 SD,rep Str.Tales #140,141 . 10.00
Ann.#1 V:Grottu,Diablo 450.00
Ann.#2 A:Spider-Man 500.00
Marvel Milestone rep. stories from
   #110–#111, #114–#115 (1995) 2.95

[2nd Regular Series] 1987–88

1 BBl,CW,B:Cloak&Dagger,Dr.
   Strange,V:Lord of Light 1.50
2 BBl,CW,V:Lord of Light,Demon 1.25
3 BBl,AW,CW,A:Nightmare,Khat . 1.25

Strange Tales #170
© Marvel Entertainment Group

4 BBl,CW,V:Nightmare 1.25
5 BBl,V:Rodent,A:Defenders 1.25
6 BBl,BWi,V:Erlik Khan,
   A:Defenders 1.25
7 V:Nightmare,A:Defenders 1.25
8 BBl,BWi,V:Kaluu 1.25
9 BBl,BWi,A:Dazzler,I:Mr.Jip,
   V:Kaluu 1.25
10 BBl,BWi,RCa,A:Black Cat,
   V:Mr.Jip,Kaluu 1.25
11 RCa,BWi,V:Mr.Jip,Kaluu 1.25
12 WPo,BWi,A:Punisher,V:Mr.Jip . 2.00
13 JBr,BWi,RCa,Punisher,
   Power Pack 2.00
14 JBr,BWi,RCa,Punisher,P.Pack 2.00
15 RCa,BMc,A:Mayhem 1.25
16 RCa,BWi,V:Mr.Jip 1.25
17 RCa,BWi,V:Night 1.25
18 RCa,KN,A:X-Factor',V:Night . 1.50
19 MMi(c),EL,TA,RCa,A:Thing . . 1.25
TPB Fully painted 6.95

STRANGE TALES
June 1998

1 JMD,PJe,LSh,Man-Thing, 64pg. 5.00
2A JMD,PJe,LSh,Man-Thing,
   Werewolf, 64pg 5.00
2B variant cover 5.00

STRANGE TALES:
DARK CORNERS
March 1998

1-shot JEs, three stories,48pg. . . 4.00

STRANGE TALES
OF THE UNUSUAL
Dec., 1955—Aug., 1957

1 JMn(c),BP,DH,JR,'Man Lost' . 300.00
2 BEv,'Man Afraid' 150.00
3 AW,'The Invaders' 175.00
4 'The Long Wait' 100.00
5 RC,SD,'The Threat' 150.00
6 BEv 125.00
7 JK,JO 125.00

8 . . . . 100.00
9 BEv(c),BK 125.00
10 GM,AT 100.00
11 BEv(c),August, 1957 . . . . . 100.00

STRANGE WORLDS
Dec., 1958

1 JK,SD 600.00
2 SD 350.00
3 JK 275.00
4 AW 250.00
5 SD 225.00

STRAWBERRY
SHORTCAKE
Star June, 1985—April, 1986

1 . . . . 1.25
2 thru 7 . . . . @1.00

STRAY TOASTERS
Epic Jan., 1988

1 BSz 5.00
2 BSz 4.50
3 and 4 BSz . . . . @4.00

STRIKEFORCE
MORITURI
Dec., 1986

1 BA,SW,WPo(1st pencils-
   3 pages),I:Blackwatch 2.50
2 BA,SW,V:The Horde 1.50
3 BA,SW,V:The Horde 1.50
4 BA,SW,WPo,V:The Horde . . . 2.00
5 BA,SW,V:The Horde 1.50
6 BA,SW,V:The Horde 1.25
7 BA,SW,V:The Horde 1.25
8 BA,SW,V:The Horde 1.25
9 BA,SW,V:THe Horde 1.25
10 WPo,(1st pencils-full story),
   SW,R:Black Watch,O:Horde . . 3.00
11 BA,SW,V:The Horde 1.25
12 BA,SW,D:Jelene 1.25
13 BA,SW,Old V:NewTeam 1.25
14 BA,AW,V:The Horde 1.25
15 BA,AW,V:The Horde 1.25
16 WPo,SW,V:The Horde 2.50
17 WPo(c),SW,V:The Horde . . . 1.25
18 BA,SW,V:Hammersmith 1.25
19 BA,SW,V:THe Horde,D:Pilar . 1.25
20 BA,SW,V:The Horde 1.25
21 MMi(c),TD(i),V:The Horde . . 1.25
22 TD(i),V:The Horde 1.25
23 MBa,VM,V:The Horde 1.50
24 VM(i),I:Vax,V:The Horde . . . 1.75
25 TD(i),V:The Horde 1.75
26 MBa,VM,V:The Horde 1.75
27 MBa,VM,O:MorituriMaster . . . 1.75
28 MBa,V:The Tiger 1.75
29 MBa,V:Zakir Shastri 1.75
30 MBa,V:Andre Lamont,The Wind 1.75
31 MBa(c),V:The Wind,last issue . 1.75

STRONG GUY REBORN
Spec. TDz,ASm,ATi, (1997) 3.00

STRYFE'S STRIKE FILE
1 LSn,NKu,GCa,BP,C:Siena
   Blaze,Holocaust (1993) 4.00
1a 2nd Printing 1.75

MARVEL

Sub-Mariner #7
© Marvel Entertainment Group

SUB-MARINER
May, 1968

1 JB,O:Sub-Mariner	125.00
2 JB,A:Triton	40.00
3 JB,A:Triton	30.00
4 JB,V:Attuma	30.00
5 JB,I&O:Tiger Shark	30.00
6 JB,DA,V:Tiger Shark	30.00
7 JB,I:Ikthon	30.00
8 JB,V:Thing	30.00
9 MSe,DA,A:Lady Dorma	30.00
10 GC,DA,O:Lemuria	30.00
11 GC,V:Capt.Barracuda	20.00
12 MSe,I:Lyna	20.00
13 MSe,JS,A:Lady Dorma	20.00
14 MSe,V:Fake Human Torch	25.00
15 MSe,V:Dragon Man	20.00
16 MSe,I:Nekaret,Thakos	12.00
17 MSe,I:Stalker,Kormok	12.00
18 MSe,A:Triton	12.00
19 MSe,I:Stingray	15.00
20 JB,V:Dr.Doom	12.00
21 MSe,D:Lord Seth	12.00
22 MSe,A:Dr.Strange	12.00
23 MSe,I:Orka	8.00
24 JB,JM,V:Tiger Shark	8.00
25 SB,JM,O:Atlantis	8.00
26 SB,A:Red Raven	8.00
27 SB,I:Commander Kraken	9.00
28 SB,V:Brutivae	8.00
29 SB,V:Hercules	7.00
30 SB,A:Captain Marvel	8.00
31 SB,A:Triton	7.00
32 SB,JM,I&O:Llyra	7.00
33 SB,JM,I:Namora	8.00
34 SB,JM,AK,1st Defenders	12.00
35 SB,JM,A:Silver Surfer	12.00
36 BWr,SB,W:Lady Dorma	10.00
37 RA,D:Lady Dorma	8.00
38 RA,JSe,O:Rec,I:Thakorr,Fen	8.00
39 RA,JM,V:Llyra	8.00
40 GC,I:Turalla,A:Spidey	10.00
41 GT,V:Rock	6.00
42 GT,JM,V:House Named Death	6.00
43 GC,V:Tunal	6.00
44 MSe,JM,V:Human Torch	7.00

45 MSe,JM,V:Tiger Shark	6.00
46 GC,D:Namor's Father	6.00
47 GC,A:Stingray,V:Dr.Doom	6.00
48 GC,V:Dr.Doom	6.00
49 GC,V:Dr.Doom	6.00
50 BEv,I:Namorita	9.00
51 BEv,O:Namorita,C:Namora	7.00
52 GK,V:Sunfire	6.00
53 BEv,V:Sunfire	6.00
54 BEv,AW,V:Sunfire,I:Lorvex	6.00
55 BEv,V:Torg	6.00
56 DA,I:Coral	6.00
57 BEv,I:Venus	6.00
58 BEv,I:Tamara	6.00
59 BEv,V:Tamara	6.00
60 BEv,V:Tamara	6.00
61 BEv,JM,V:Dr.Hydro	6.00
62 HC,JSt,I:Tales of Atlantis.	6.00
63 HC,JSt,V:Dr.Hydro,I:Arkus	6.00
64 HC,JSe,I:Maddox	6.00
65 DH,DP,V:She-Devil,inc.BEv Eulogy Pin-up	6.00
66 DH,V:Orka,I:Raman	6.00
67 DH,A:FF,V:Triton,N:Namor I&O:Force	6.00
68 DH,O:Force	6.00
69 GT,V:Spider-Man	7.00
70 GT,I:Piranha	6.00
71 GT,V:Piranha	6.00
72 DA,V:Slime/Thing	6.00
Spec.#1 Rep. Tales to Astonish #70-#73	8.25
Spec.#2 Rep. Tales to Astonish #74-#76	8.25

[Limited Series]

1 RB,BMc,Namor's Birth	2.50
2 RB,BMc,Namor Kills Humans	2.00
3 RB,BMc,V:Surface Dwellers	2.00
4 RB,BMc,V:Human Torch	2.00
5 RB,BMc,A:Invaders	2.00
6 RB,BMc,V:Destiny	2.00
7 RB,BMc,A:Fantastic Four	2.00
8 RB,BMc,A:Hulk,Avengers	2.00
9 RB,BMc,A:X-Men,Magneto	2.00
10 RB,BMc,V:Thing	2.00
11 RB,BMc,A:Namorita,Defenders	2.00
12 RB,BMc,A:Dr.Doom, AlphaFlight	2.00

(SAGA OF THE) SUB-MARINER
[Mini-Series] Nov., 1988

1 RB,BMc,Namor's Birth	2.50
2 RB,BMc,Namor Kills Humans	1.50
3 RB,BMc,V:Surface Dwellers	1.50
4 RB,BMc,V:Human Torch	1.50
5 RB,BMc,A:Invaders	1.50
6 RB,BMc,V:Destiny	1.50
7 RB,BMc,A:Fantastic Four	1.50
8 RB,BMc,A:Hulk,Avengers	1.50
9 RB,BMc,A:X-Men,Magneto	2.00
10 RB,BMc,V:Thing	1.50
11 RB,BMc,A:Namorita,Defenders	1.50
12 RB,BMc,A:Dr.Doom,Alp.Flight	1.50

SUB-MARINER COMICS
Timely Spring, 1941

1 ASh(c),BEv,PGn,B:Sub-Mariner, The Angel	20,000.00
2 ASh(c),BEv,Nazi Submarine (c)	4,500.00
3 ASh(c),BEv	3,000.00
4 ASh(c),BEv,BW	2,500.00
5	1,800.00

6 ASh(c)	1,500.00
7	1,500.00
8 ASh(c)	1,500.00
9 ASh(c),BW	1,500.00
10 ASh(c)	1,500.00
11 ASh(c)	1,100.00
12 ASh(c)	1,100.00
13 ASh(c)	1,100.00
14 ASh(c)	1,100.00
15 ASh(c)	1,100.00
16 ASh(c)	1,100.00
17 ASh(c)	1,100.00
18 ASh(c)	1,100.00
19	1,100.00
20 ASh(c)	1,100.00
21 SSh(c),BEv	800.00
22 SSh(c),BEv	800.00
23 SSh(c),BEv	800.00
24 MSy(c),BEv,A:Namora, bondage cover	800.00
25 MSy(c),HK,B:The Blonde Phantom, A:Namora, bondage(c)	1,000.00
26 BEv,A:Namora	750.00
27 DRi(c),BEv,A:Namora	750.00
28 DRi(c),BEv,A:Namora	750.00
29 BEv,A:Namora,Human Torch	750.00
30 DRi(c),BEv,'Slaves Under the Sea'	750.00
31 BEv,'The Man Who Grew', A:Capt. America,E:Blonde Phantom	750.00
32 BEv,O:Sub-Mariner	1,300.00
33 BEv,O:Sub-Mariner,A:Human Torch,B:Namora	700.00
34 BEv,A:Human Torch,bondage cover	575.00
35 BEv,A:Human Torch	575.00
36 BEv	575.00
37 JMn(c),BEv	575.00
38 SSh(c),BEv,JMn	650.00
39 JMn(c),BEv	550.00
40 JMn(c),BEv	550.00
41 JMn(c),BEv	550.00
42 BEv,Oct., 1955	700.00

SUBURBAN JERSEY NINJA SHE-DEVILS

1 I:Ninja She-Devils	1.50

SUNFIRE & BIG HERO 6
July 1998

1 (of 3) SLo,from Alpha Flight	2.50
2 (of 3) SLo,V:Everwraith	2.50

SUPERNATURAL THRILLERS
Dec., 1972

1 JSo(c),JSe,FrG,IT!	20.00
2 VM,DA,The Invisible Man	15.00
3 GK,The Valley of the Worm	15.00
4 Dr. Jekyll and Mr. Hyde	15.00
5 RB,The Living Mummy	35.00
6 GT,JA,The Headless Horseman	8.00
7 VM,B:'The Living Mummy,' Back From The Tomb'	8.00
8 VM,'He Stalks Two Worlds'	8.00
9 GK/AM(c),VM,DA,'Pyramid of the Watery Doom'	8.00
10 VM,'A Choice of Dooms'	8.00
11 VM,'When Strikes the ASP'	8.00
12 VM,KJ,'The War That Shook the World'	8.00
13 VM,DGr,'The Tomb of the	

MARVEL

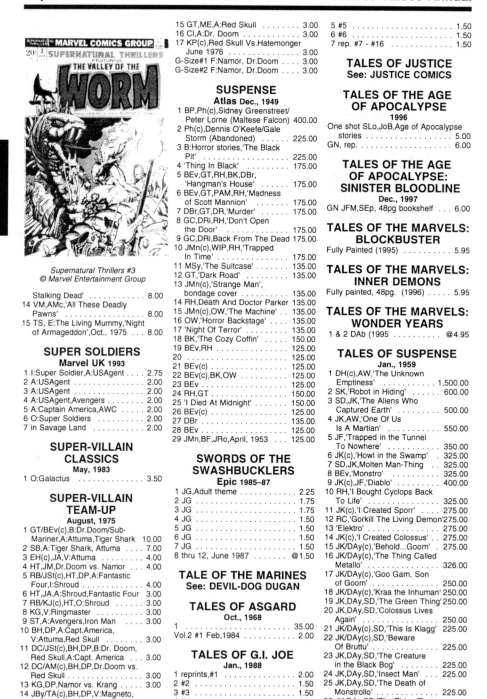

Supernatural Thrillers #3
© Marvel Entertainment Group

Stalking Dead' 8.00
14 VM,AMc,'All These Deadly
Pawns' 8.00
15 TS, E:The Living Mummy,'Night
of Armageddon',Oct., 1975 . . . 8.00

SUPER SOLDIERS
Marvel UK 1993
1 I:Super Soldier,A:USAgent 2.75
2 A:USAgent 2.00
3 A:USAgent 2.00
4 A:USAgent,Avengers 2.00
5 A:Captain America,AWC 2.00
6 O:Super Soldiers 2.00
7 in Savage Land 2.00

SUPER-VILLAIN CLASSICS
May, 1983
1 O:Galactus 3.50

SUPER-VILLAIN TEAM-UP
August, 1975
1 GT/BEv(c),B:Dr.Doom/Sub-
Mariner,A:Attuma,Tiger Shark 10.00
2 SB,A:Tiger Shark, Attuma 7.00
3 EH(c),JA,V:Attuma 4.00
4 HT,JM,Dr.Doom vs. Namor . . . 4.00
5 RB/JSt(c),HT,DP,A:Fantastic
Four,I:Shroud 4.00
6 HT,JA,A:Shroud,Fantastic Four 3.00
7 RB/KJ(c),HT,O:Shroud 3.00
8 KG,V:Ringmaster 3.00
9 ST,A:Avengers,Iron Man 3.00
10 BH,DP,A:Capt.America,
V:Attuma,Red Skull 3.00
11 DC/JSt(c),BH,DP,B:Dr. Doom,
Red Skull,A:Capt. America . . . 3.00
12 DC/AM(c),BH,DP,Dr.Doom vs.
Red Skull 3.00
13 KG,DP,Namor vs. Krang 3.00
14 JBy/TA(c),BH,DP,V:Magneto,
X-over with Champions #15 . . 5.00

15 GT,ME,A:Red Skull 3.00
16 CI,A:Dr. Doom 3.00
17 KP(c),Red Skull Vs.Hatemonger
June 1976 . . . . 3.00
G-Size#1 F:Namor, Dr.Doom 3.00
G-Size#2 F:Namor, Dr.Doom 3.00

SUSPENSE
Atlas Dec., 1949
1 BP,Ph(c),Sidney Greenstreet/
Peter Lorne (Maltese Falcon) 400.00
2 Ph(c),Dennis O'Keefe/Gale
Storm (Abandoned) 225.00
3 B:Horror stories,'The Black
Pit' 225.00
4 'Thing In Black' 175.00
5 BEv,GT,RH,BK,DBr,
'Hangman's House' 175.00
6 BEv,GT,PAM,RH,'Madness
of Scott Mannion' 175.00
7 DBr,GT,DR,'Murder' 175.00
8 GC,DRi,RH,'Don't Open
the Door' 175.00
9 GC,DRi,Back From The Dead 175.00
10 JMn(c),WIP,RH,'Trapped
In Time' 175.00
11 MSy,'The Suitcase' 135.00
12 GT,'Dark Road' 135.00
13 JMn(c),'Strange Man',
bondage cover 135.00
14 RH,Death And Doctor Parker 135.00
15 JMn(c),OW,'The Machine' . . 135.00
16 OW,'Horror Backstage' 135.00
17 'Night Of Terror' 135.00
18 BK,'The Cozy Coffin' 150.00
19 BEv,RH 125.00
20 . . . . 125.00
21 BEv(c) 125.00
22 BEv(c),BK,OW 125.00
23 BEv 125.00
24 RH,GT 150.00
25 'I Died At Midnight' 150.00
26 BEv(c) 125.00
27 DBr 135.00
28 BEv 125.00
29 JMn,BF,JRo,April, 1953 . . . 125.00

SWORDS OF THE SWASHBUCKLERS
Epic 1985–87
1 JG,Adult theme 2.25
2 JG 1.75
3 JG 1.75
4 JG 1.50
5 JG 1.50
6 JG 1.50
7 JG 1.50
8 thru 12, June 1987 . . . . . . @1.50

TALE OF THE MARINES
See: DEVIL-DOG DUGAN

TALES OF ASGARD
Oct., 1968
1 . . . . 35.00
Vol.2 #1 Feb,1984 . . . . 2.00

TALES OF G.I. JOE
Jan., 1988
1 reprints,#1 . . . . 2.00
2 #2 . . . . 1.50
3 #3 . . . . 1.50
4 #4 . . . . 1.50

5 #5 . . . . 1.50
6 #6 . . . . 1.50
7 rep. #7 - #16 . . . . 1.50

TALES OF JUSTICE
See: JUSTICE COMICS

TALES OF THE AGE OF APOCALYPSE
1996
One shot SLo,JoB,Age of Apocalypse
stories 5.00
GN, rep. 6.00

TALES OF THE AGE OF APOCALYPSE: SINISTER BLOODLINE
Dec., 1997
GN JFM,SEp, 48pg bookshelf . . . 6.00

TALES OF THE MARVELS: BLOCKBUSTER
Fully Painted (1995) 5.95

TALES OF THE MARVELS: INNER DEMONS
Fully painted, 48pg. (1996) 5.95

TALES OF THE MARVELS: WONDER YEARS
1 & 2 DAb (1995 . . . . @4.95

TALES OF SUSPENSE
Jan., 1959
1 DH(c),AW,'The Unknown
Emptiness' 1,500.00
2 SK,'Robot in Hiding' 600.00
3 SD,JK,'The Aliens Who
Captured Earth' 500.00
4 JK,AW,'One Of Us
Is A Martian' 550.00
5 JF,'Trapped in the Tunnel
To Nowhere' 350.00
6 JK(c),'Howl in the Swamp' . 325.00
7 SD,JK,Molten Man-Thing . . 325.00
8 BEv,'Monstro' 325.00
9 JK(c),JF,'Diablo' 400.00
10 RH,'I Bought Cyclops Back
To Life' 325.00
11 JK(c),'I Created Sporr' 275.00
12 RC,'Gorkill The Living Demon'275.00
13 'Elektro' 275.00
14 JK(c),'I Created Colossus' . . 275.00
15 JK/DAy(c),'Behold...Goom' . 275.00
16 JK/DAy(c),'The Thing Called
Metallo' 326.00
17 JK/DAy(c),'Goo Gam, Son
of Goom' 250.00
18 JK/DAy(c),'Kraa the Inhuman' 250.00
19 JK,DAy,SD,'The Green Thing' 250.00
20 JK,DAy,SD,'Colossus Lives
Again' 250.00
21 JK/DAy(c),SD,'This Is Klagg' 225.00
22 JK/DAy(c),SD,'Beware
Of Bruttu' 225.00
23 JK,DAy,SD,'The Creature
in the Black Bog' 225.00
24 JK,DAy,SD,'Insect Man' . . . 225.00
25 JK,DAy,SD,'The Death of
Monstrollo' 225.00
26 JK,DAy,SD,'The Thing That

Tales of Suspense #58
© Marvel Entertainment Group

Crawled By Night' 200.00
27 JK,DAy,SD,'When Oog Lives
Again' 200.00
28 JK,DAy,SD,'Back From
the Dead' 200.00
29 JK,DAy,SD,DH,'The Martian
Who Stole A City' 175.00
30 JK,DAy,SD,DH,'The Haunted
Roller Coaster' 200.00
31 JK,DAy,SD,DH,'The Monster
in the Iron Mask' 175.00
32 JK,DAy,SD,DH,'The Man in
the Bee-Hive' 300.00
33 JK,DAy,SD,DH,'Chamber of
Fear' 175.00
34 JK,DAy,SD,DH,'Inside The
Blue Glass Bottle' 175.00
35 JK,DAy,SD,DH,'The Challenge
of Zarkorr' 200.00
36 SD,'Meet Mr. Meek' 175.00
37 DH,SD,'Hagg' 175.00
38 'The Teenager who ruled
the World 175.00
39 JK,O&I:Iron Man 4,000.00
40 JK,C:Iron Man 1,400.00
41 JK,A:Iron Man,V:Dr. Strange 700.00
42 DH,SD,I:Red Pharoah . . . 325.00
43 JK,DH,I:Kala,A:Iron Man . . 325.00
44 DH,SD,V:Mad Pharoah . . . 325.00
45 DH,V:Jack Frost 325.00
46 DH,CR,I:Crimson Dynamo . 250.00
47 SD,V:Melter 200.00
48 SD,N:Iron Man 250.00
49 SD,A:Angel 200.00
50 DH,I:Manderin 150.00
51 DH,I:Scarecrow 100.00
52 DH,I:Black Widow 150.00
53 DH,O:Watcher 135.00
54 DH,V:Mandarin 75.00
55 DH,V:Mandarin 75.00
56 DH,I:Unicorn 75.00
57 DH,I&O:Hawkeye 175.00
58 DH,B:Captain America . . . 300.00
59 DH,1st S.A. Solo Captain
America,I:Jarvis 300.00

60 DH,JK,V:Assassins 125.00
61 DH,JK,V:Mandarin 75.00
62 DH,JK,O:Mandarin 75.00
63 JK,O:Captain America 225.00
64 DH,JK,A:Black Widow,
Hawkeye 85.00
65 DH,JK,I:Red Skull 150.00
66 DH,JK,O:Red Skull 150.00
67 DH,JK,V:Adolph Hitler 50.00
68 DH,JK,V:Red Skull 50.00
69 DH,JK,I:Titanium Man 50.00
70 DH,JK,V:Titanium Man 45.00
71 DH,JK,WW,V:Titanium Man . 45.00
72 DH,JK,V:The Sleeper 45.00
73 JK,GT,A:Black Knight 45.00
74 JK,GT,V:The Sleeper 45.00
75 JK,I:Batroc,Sharon Carter . . 45.00
76 JR,V:Mandarin 50.00
77 JK,JR,V:Ultimo,I:Peggy
Carter 45.00
78 GC,JK,V:Ultimo 45.00
79 GC,JK,V:Red Skull,
I:Cosmic Cube 75.00
80 GC,JK,V:Red Skull 80.00
81 GC,JK,V:Red Skull 50.00
82 GC,JK,V:The Adaptoid 50.00
83 GC,JK,V:The Adaptoid 50.00
84 GC,JK,V:Mandarin 50.00
85 GC,JK,V:Batroc 50.00
86 GC,JK,V:Mandarin 50.00
87 GC,V:Mole Man 50.00
88 JK,GC,V:Power Man 50.00
89 JK,GC,V:Red Skull 50.00
90 JK,GC,V:Red Skull 50.00
91 GC,JK,V:Crusher 50.00
92 GC,JK,A:Nick Fury 50.00
93 GC,JK,V:Titanium Man 50.00
94 GC,JK,I:Modok 50.00
95 GC,JK,V:Grey Gargoyle,
IR:Captain America 50.00
96 GC,JK,V:Grey Gargoyle . . . 50.00
97 GC,JK,I:Whiplash,
A:Black Panther 50.00
98 GC,JK,I:Whitney Frost
A:Black Panther 75.00
99 GC,JK,A:Black Panther 85.00
Marvel Milestone rep. #39 (1993) . 2.95
Becomes:

CAPTAIN AMERICA

TALES OF THE ZOMBIE
August, 1973
(black & white magazine)
1 Reprint Menace #5,O:Zombie 20.00
2 GC,GT 15.00
3 . . . . 15.00
4 'Live and Let Die' 15.00
5 BH 15.00
6 . . . . 15.00
7 thru 9 AA . . . . @15.00
10 March, 1975 . . . . 15.00

TALES TO ASTONISH
[1st Series] Jan., 1959
1 JDa,'Ninth Wonder of the
World' 1,500.00
2 SD,'Capture A Martian' 600.00
3 SD,JK,'The Giant From
Outer Space' 400.00
4 SD,JK,'The Day The
Martians Struck' 400.00
5 SD,AW,'The Things on
Easter Island' 425.00
6 SD,JK,'Invasion of the

Tales to Astonish #47
© Marvel Entertainment Group

Stone Men' 375.00
7 SD,JK,'The Thing on Bald
Mountain' 350.00
8 SD,JK,'Mummex, King of
the Mummies' 350.00
9 JK(c),SD,'Droom, the
Living Lizard' 350.00
10 JK,SD,'Titano' 350.00
11 JK,SD,'Monstrom, the Dweller
in the Black Swamp' 250.00
12 JK/DAy(c),SD,'Gorgilla' . . . 250.00
13 JK,SD,'Groot, the Monster
From Planet X' 250.00
14 JK,SD,'Krang' 250.00
15 JK,DAy,'The Blip' 400.00
16 JK,SD,'Thorr' 300.00
17 JK,SD,'Vandoom' 250.00
18 JK,SD,'Gorgilla Strikes Again' 250.00
19 JK,SD,'Rommbu' 250.00
20 JK,SD,'X, The Thing
That Lived' 250.00
21 JK,SD,'Trull the Inhuman' . . 250.00
22 JK,SD,'The Crawling
Creature' 200.00
23 JK,SD,'Moomba is Here' . . . 200.00
24 JK,SD,'The Abominable
Snowman' 200.00
25 JK,SD,'The Creature From
Krogarr' 200.00
26 JK,SD,'Four-Armed Things' . 200.00
27 StL(s),SD,JK,I:Antman 3,300.00
28 JK,SD,I Am the Gorilla Man 200.00
29 JK,SD,When the Space
Beasts Attack 200.00
30 JK,SD,Thing From the
Hidden Swamp 200.00
31 JK,SD,The Mummy's Secret 200.00
32 JK,SD,Quicksand 200.00
33 JK,SD,Dead Storage 200.00
34 JK,SD,Monster at Window . 200.00
35 StL(s),JK,SD, B:Ant Man
(2nd App.) 1,500.00
36 JK,SD,V:Comrade X 600.00
37 JK,SD,V:The Protector 375.00
38 JK,SD,Betrayed By the Ants 375.00
39 JK,DH,V:Scarlet Beetle 375.00
40 JK,SD,DH,The Day Ant-Man
Failed 375.00

MARVEL

41 DH,St,SD,V:Kulla 250.00
42 DH,JSe,SD,Voice of Doom . 250.00
43 DH,SD,Master of Time 250.00
44 JK,SD,I&O:Wasp 275.00
45 DH,SD,V:Egghead 175.00
46 DH,SD,I:Cyclops(robot) 175.00
47 DH,SD,V:Trago 175.00
48 DH,SD,I:Porcupine 175.00
49 JK,DH,AM,Ant-Man Becomes
   Giant-Man 200.00
50 JK,SD,I&O:Human Top 125.00
51 JK,V:Human Top 125.00
52 I&O:Black Knight 125.00
53 DH,V:Porcupine 125.00
54 DH,I:El Toro 125.00
55 V:Human Top 125.00
56 V:The Magician 125.00
57 A:Spider-Man 150.00
58 V:Colossus(not X-Men one) 125.00
59 V:Hulk,Black Knight 175.00
60 SD,B:Hulk,Giant Man 200.00
61 SD,I:Glenn Talbot,
   V:Egghead 75.00
62 I:Leader,N:Wasp 75.00
63 SD,O:Leader(1st full story) . . 75.00
64 SD,V:Leader 75.00
65 DH,SD,N:Giant-Man,. 75.00
66 JK,SD,V:Leader,Chameleon . 75.00
67 JK,SD,I:Kanga Khan 75.00
68 JK,N:Human Top,V:Leader . . 75.00
69 JK,V:Human Top,Leader,
   E:Giant-Man 75.00
70 JK,B:Sub-Mariner/Hulk,I:
   Neptune 100.00
71 JK,V:Leader,I:Vashti 60.00
72 JK,V:Leader 60.00
73 JK,V:Leader,A:Watcher 60.00
74 JK,V:Leader,A:Watcher 60.00
75 JK,A:Watcher 60.00
76 JK,Atlantis 60.00
77 JK,V:Executioner 60.00
78 GC,JK,Prince and the Puppet 60.00
79 JK,Hulk vs.Hercules 60.00
80 GC,JK,Moleman vs Tyrannus 60.00
81 GC,JK,I:Boomerang,Secret Empire,
   Moleman vs Tyrannus 60.00
82 GC,JK,V:Iron Man 75.00
83 JK,V:Boomerang 50.00
84 GC,JK,Like a Beast at Bay . . 50.00
85 GC,JB,Missile & the Monster . 50.00
86 JB,V:Warlord Krang 50.00
87 BEv,IR:Hulk 50.00
88 BEv,GK,V:Boomerang 50.00
89 BEv,GK,V:Stranger 50.00
90 JK,I:Abomination 50.00
91 BEv,DA,V:Abomination 50.00
92 MSe,C:Silver Surfer x-over . . 62.00
93 MSe,Silver Surver x-over . . 60.00
94 BEv,MSe,V:Dragorr,High
   Evolutionary. 50.00
95 BEv,MSe,V:High Evolutionary 50.00
96 MSe,Skull Island,High Evol. . 50.00
97 MSe,C:Kazar,X-Men 55.00
98 DA,MSe,I:Legion of the Living
   Lightning,I:Seth 50.00
99 DA,MSe,V:Legion of the Living
   Lighting 50.00
100 MSe,DA,Hulk v.SubMariner . 60.00
101 MSe,GC,V:Loki 85.00
Becomes: INCREDIBLE HULK

TALES TO ASTONISH
[2nd Series] Dec., 1979
1 JB,rep.Sub-Mariner#1 . . . . 5.00
2 JB,rep.Sub-Mariner#2 . . . . 3.00

Tales to Astonish (2nd Series) #1
© Marvel Entertainment Group

3 JB,rep.Sub-Mariner#3 . . . . . . 3.00
4 JB,rep.Sub-Mariner#4 . . . . . . 3.00
5 JB,rep.Sub-Mariner#5 . . . . . . 3.00
6 JB,rep.Sub-Mariner#6 . . . . . . 3.00
7 JB,rep.Sub-Mariner#7 . . . . . . 3.00
8 JB,rep.Sub-Mariner#8 . . . . . . 3.00
9 JB,rep.Sub-Mariner#9 . . . . . . 3.00
10 JB,rep.Sub-Mariner#10 . . . . . 3.00
11 JB,rep.Sub-Mariner#11 . . . . . 3.00
12 JB,rep.Sub-Mariner#12 . . . . . 3.00
13 JB,rep.Sub-Mariner#13 . . . . . 3.00
14 JB,rep.Sub-Mariner#14 . . . . . 3.00

TARZAN
June, 1977
1 JB,Edgar Rice Burroughs Adapt. 5.00
2 JB,O:Tarzan 4.00
3 JB,'The Alter of the Flaming
   God',I:LA 2.00
4 JB,TD,V:Leopards 2.00
5 JB,TD,'Vengeance',A:LA . . . 2.00
6 JB,TD,'Rage of Tantor,A:LA . . 2.00
7 JB,TD,'Tarzan Rescues The
   Moon' 2.00
8 JB,'Battle For The Jewel Of
   Opar' 2.00
9 JB,'Histah, the Serpent' 2.00
10 JB,'The Deadly Peril of
   Jane Clayton' 2.00
11 JB 2.00
12 JB,'Fangs of Death' 2.00
13 JB,'Lion-God' 2.00
14 JB,'The Fury of Fang and Claw' 2.00
15 JB,'Sword of the Slaver' 2.00
16 JB,'Death Rides the Jungle
   Winds' 2.00
17 JB,'The Entrance to the
   Earths Core' 2.00
18 JB,'Corsairs of the Earths Core' 2.00
19 'Pursuit' 2.00
20 'Blood Bond' 2.00
21 'Dark and Bloody Sky' 2.00
22 JM,RN,'War In Pellucidar' . . . 2.00
23 'To the Death' 2.00
24 'The Jungle Lord Returns' . . . 2.00
25 RB(c),V:Poachers 2.00
26 RB(c),'Caged' 2.00

Tarzan #16
© Marvel Entertainment Group

27 RB(c),'Chaos in the Caberet' . . 2.00
28 'A Savage Against A City' 2.00
29 Oct., 1979 . . . . 2.00
Ann.#1 JB 2.50
Ann.#2 'Drums of the
   Death-Dancers' 2.00
Ann.#3 'Ant-Men and the
   She-Devils 2.00

TARZAN OF THE APES
July, 1984
1 (movie adapt.) 1.25
2 . . . . 1.25

TEAM AMERICA
June, 1982
1 O:Team America 2.00
2 V:Marauder 1.25
3 LMc,V:Mr.Mayhem 1.25
4 Lmc,V:Arcade Assassins 1.25
5 A:Marauder 1.25
6 A:R.U. Ready 1.25
7 LMc,V:Emperor of Texas 1.25
8 DP,V:Hydra 1.25
9 A:Iron Man 1.25
10 V:Minister Ashe 1.00
11 A:Marauder,V:GhostRider 3.00
12 DP,Marauder unmasked,
   May, 1983 . . . . 2.50

TEAM HELIX
1993
1 A:Wolverine 2.00
2 A:Wolverine 2.00

TEAM X/TEAM 7
1996
1-shot LHa,SEp,MRy 4.95

TEEN COMICS
See: ALL WINNERS COMICS

TEENAGE ROMANCE
See: MY ROMANCE

TERMINATOR 2
Sept., 1991
1 KJ,movie adaption	1.25
2 KJ,movie adaption	1.25
3 KJ,movie adaption	1.25
Terminator II (bookshelf format)	4.95
Terminator II (B&W mag. size)	2.25

TERRARISTS
Epic 1993–94
1 thru 4 w/card	@2.50
5 thru 7	@2.50

TERROR INC.
1992–93
1 JZ,I:Hellfire	3.00
2 JZ,I:Bezeel,Hellfire	2.50
3 JZ,A:Hellfire	2.00
4 JZ,A:Hellfire,V:Barbatos	2.00
5 JZ,V:Hellfire,A:Dr Strange	2.00
6 JZ,MT,A:Punisher	2.00
7 JZ,V:Punisher	2.00
8 Christmas issue	2.00
9 JZ,V:Wolverine	2.25
10 V:Wolverine	2.25
11 A:Silver Sable,Cage	2.00
12 For Love Nor Money#4,A:Cage, Silver Sable	2.00
13 Inf.Crusade,A:Gh.Rider	2.00

TESSIE THE TYPIST
Timely Summer, 1944
1 BW,'Doc Rockblock'	400.00
2 BW,'Powerhouse Pepper'	225.00
3 Football cover	75.00
4 BW	125.00
5 BW	125.00
6 BW,HK,'Hey Look'	125.00
7 BW	125.00
8 BW	125.00
9 BW,HK,'Powerhouse Pepper'	150.00
10 BW,A:Rusty	150.00
11 BW,A:Rusty	150.00
12 BW,HK	150.00
13 BW,A:Millie The Model,Rusty	110.00
14 BW	100.00
15 HK,A:Millie,Rusty	100.00
16 HK	75.00
17 HK,A:Millie, Rusty	75.00
18 HK	75.00
19 Annie Oakley story	50.00
20	45.00
21 A:Lana, Millie	45.00
22	45.00
23	45.00

Becomes:
TINY TESSIE
24	45.00

Becomes:
REAL EXPERIENCES
25 Ph(c),Jan., 1950	40.00

TEXAS KID
Atlas Jan., 1951
1 GT,JMn,O:Texas Kid	125.00
2 JMn	60.00
3 JMn,'Man Who Didn't Exist'	50.00
4 JMn	50.00
5 JMn	50.00
6 JMn	50.00
7 JMn	50.00
8 JMn	50.00

9 JMn	50.00
10 JMn,July, 1952	50.00

TEX DAWSON, GUNSLINGER
Jan., 1973
1 JSo(c)	15.00

Becomes:
GUNSLINGER
2	10.00
3 June, 1973	10.00

TEX MORGAN
August, 1948
1	175.00
2 'Boot Hill Welcome For A Bad Man'	125.00
3	100.00
4 'Trapped in the Outlaws Den', A:Arizona Annie	75.00
5 'Valley of Missing Cowboys'	75.00
6 'Never Say Murder', A:Tex Taylor	75.00
7 CCB,Ph(c),'Captain Tootsie', A:Tex Taylor	125.00
8 Ph(c),'Terror Of Rimrock Valley', A:Diablo	125.00
9 Ph(c),'Death to Tex Taylor' Feb., 1950	125.00

TEX TAYLOR
Sept., 1948
1 'Boot Hill Showdown'	175.00
2 'When Two-Gun Terror Rides the Range'	125.00
3 'Thundering Hooves and Blazing Guns'	100.00
4 Ph(c),'Draw or Die Cowpoke'	125.00
5 Ph(c),'The Juggler of Yellow Valley',A:Blaze Carson	125.00
6 Ph(c),'Mystery of Howling Gap'	100.00
7 Ph(c),'Trapped in Times' Lost Land',A:Diablo	120.00
8 Ph(c),'The Mystery of Devil-Tree Plateau',A:Diablo	120.00
9 Ph(c),'Guns Along the Border', A:Nimo,March, 1950	120.00

THANOS QUEST
1990
1 JSn,RLm,V:Elders, for Soul Gems	6.00
1a 2nd printing	3.00
2 JSn,RLm,O:SoulGems,I: Infinity Gauntlet (story cont.in SilverSurfer #44)	5.00
2a 2nd printing	3.00

THING, THE
July, 1983
1 JBy,O:Thing	2.50
2 JBy,Woman from past	1.75
3 JBy,A:Inhumans	1.50
4 JBy,A:Lockjaw	1.50
5 JBy,A:Spider-Man,She-Hulk	1.50
6 JBy,V:Puppet Master	1.25
7 JBy,V:Goody Two Shoes	1.25
8 JBy,V:Egyptian Curse	1.25
9 JBy,F:Alicia Masters	1.25
10 JBy,Secret Wars	1.25
11 JBy,B:Rocky Grimm	1.25
12 JBy,F:Rocky Grimm	1.25
13 JBy,F:Rocky Grimm	1.25

Thing #35
© Marvel Entertainment Group

14 F:Rocky Grimm	1.25
15 F:Rocky Grimm	1.25
16 F:Rocky Grimm	1.25
17 F:Rocky Grimm	1.25
18 F:Rocky Grimm	1.25
19 F:Rocky Grimm	1.25
20 F:Rocky Grimm	1.25
21 V:Ultron	1.25
22 V:Ultron	1.25
23 R:Thing to Earth,A:Fant.Four	1.25
24 V:Rhino,A:Miracle Man	1.25
25 V:Shamrock	1.25
26 A:Vance Astro	1.50
27 I:Sharon Ventura	1.25
28 A:Vance Astro	1.25
29 A:Vance Astro	1.25
30 Secret Wars II,A:Vance Astro	1.25
31 A:Vance Astro	1.25
32 A:Vance Astro	1.25
33 A:Vance Astro,I:NewGrapplers	1.25
34 V:Titania,Sphinx	1.25
35 I:New Ms.Marvel,PowerBroker	1.25
36 Last Issue,A:She-Hulk	1.25

[Mini-Series]
1 rep.Marvel Two-in-One #50	1.75
2 rep Marvel Two-in-One,V:GR	1.75
3 rep Marvel Two-in-One #51	1.25
4 rep Marvel Two-in-One #43	1.25

THING/SHE-HULK
March, 1998
1-shot TDz,V:Dragon Man, 48pg	3.00

THOR, THE MIGHTY
Prev: Journey Into Mystery
March, 1966
126 JK,V:Hercules	135.00
127 JK,I:Pluto,Volla	55.00
128 JK,V:Pluto,A:Hercules	55.00
129 JK,V:Pluto,I:Ares	55.00
130 JK,V:Pluto,A:Hercules	55.00
131 JK,I:Colonizers	55.00
132 JK,A:Colonizers,I:Ego	55.00
133 JK,A:Colonizers,A:Ego	55.00
134 JK,I:High Evolutionary, Man-Beast	60.00

MARVEL

The Mighty Thor #148
© Marvel Entertainment Group

The Mighty Thor #233
© Marvel Entertainment Group

135 JK,O:High Evolutionary	. . . .	50.00
136 JK,F:Odin	. . . .	45.00
137 JK,I:Ulik	. . . .	45.00
138 JK,V:Ulik,A:Sif	. . . .	45.00
139 JK,V:Ulik	. . . .	45.00
140 JK,V:Growing Man	. . . .	45.00
141 JK,V:Replicus	. . . .	35.00
142 JK,V:Super Skrull	. . . .	35.00
143 JK,BEv,V:Talisman	. . . .	35.00
144 JK,V:Talisman	. . . .	35.00
145 JK,V:Ringmaster	. . . .	35.00
146 JK,O:Inhumans Part 1	. . . .	45.00
147 JK,O:Inhumans Part 2	. . . .	40.00
148 JK,I:Wrecker,O:Black Bolt	. .	40.00
149 JK,O:Black Bolt,Medusa	. . .	40.00
150 JK,A:Triton	. . . .	35.00
151 JK,V:Destroyer	. . . .	35.00
152 JK,V:Destroyer	. . . .	35.00
153 JK,F:Dr.Blake	. . . .	35.00
154 JK,I:Mangog	. . . .	35.00
155 JK,V:Mangog	. . . .	35.00
156 JK,V:Mangog	. . . .	35.00
157 JK,D:Mangog	. . . .	35.00
158 JK,O:Don Blake Part 1	. . . .	75.00
159 JK,O:Don Blake Part 2	. . . .	35.00
160 JK,I:Travrians	. . . .	32.00
161 JK,Shall a God Prevail	. . . .	32.00
162 JK,O:Galactus	. . . .	45.00
163 JK,I:Mutates,A:Pluto	. . . . . .	25.00
164 JK,A:Pluto,V:Greek Gods	. .	25.00
165 JK,V:Him/Warlock	. . . .	45.00
166 JK,V:Him/Warlock	. . . .	45.00
167 JK,F:Sif	. . . .	23.00
168 JK,O:Galactus	. . . .	42.00
169 JK,O:Galactus	. . . .	42.00
170 JK,BEv,V:Thermal Man	. . . .	21.00
171 JK,BEv,V:Wrecker	. . . .	21.00
172 JK,BEv,V:Ulik	. . . .	21.00
173 JK,BEv,V:Ulik,Ringmaster	.	21.00
174 JK,BEv,V:Crypto-Man	. . . .	21.00
175 JK,Fall of Asgard,V:Surtur	. .	21.00
176 JK,V:Surtur	. . . .	21.00
177 JK,I:Igon,V:Surtur	. . . .	21.00
178 JK,C:Silver Surfer	. . . .	24.00
179 JK,MSe,C:Galactus	. . . . . .	21.00
180 NA,JSi,V:Loki	. . . .	15.00
181 NA,JSi,V:Loki	. . . .	15.00
182 JB,V:Dr.Doom	. . . .	7.50

183 JB,V:Dr.Doom	. . . .	7.50
184 JB,I:The Guardian	. . . .	7.50
185 JB,JSt,V:Silent One	. . . . . .	7.50
186 JB,JSt,V:Hela	. . . .	7.50
187 JB,JSt,V:Odin	. . . .	7.50
188 JB,JM,F:Odin	. . . .	7.50
189 JB,JSt,V:Hela	. . . .	7.50
190 JB,I:Durok	. . . .	7.50
191 JB,JSt,V:Loki	. . . .	7.50
192 JB	. . . .	7.50
193 JB,SB,V:Silver Surfer	. . . . .	45.00
194 JB,SB,V:Loki	. . . .	7.50
195 JB,JR,V:Mangog	. . . .	7.50
196 JB,NR,V:Kartag	. . . .	7.50
197 JB,V:Mangog	. . . .	7.50
198 JB,V:Pluto	. . . .	7.50
199 JB,V:Pluto,Hela	. . . .	7.50
200 JB,Ragnarok	. . . .	9.00
201 JB,JM,Odin resurrected.	. . .	6.00
202 JB,V:Ego-Prime	. . . .	6.00
203 JB,V:Ego-Prime	. . . .	6.00
204 JB,JM,Demon from t/Depths	.	6.00
205 JB,V:Mephisto	. . . .	6.00
206 JB,V:Absorbing Man	. . . . .	5.00
207 JB,V:Absorbing Man	. . . . .	5.00
208 JB,V:Mercurio	. . . .	5.00
209 JB,I:Druid	. . . .	5.00
210 JB,DP,I:Ulla,V:Ulik	. . . . . .	5.00
211 JB,DP,V:Ulik	. . . .	4.00
212 JB,JSt,V:Sssthgar	. . . .	4.00
213 JB,DP,I:Gregor	. . . .	4.00
214 SB,JM,V:Dark Nebula	. . . .	4.00
215 JB,JM,J:Xorr	. . . .	4.00
216 JB,JM,V:4D-Man	. . . .	4.00
217 JB,SB,I:Krista,V:Odin	. . . .	4.00
218 JB,JM,A:Colonizers	. . . . . .	4.00
219 JB,I:Protector	. . . .	4.00
220 JB,V:Avalon	. . . .	4.00
221 JB,V:Olympus	. . . .	4.00
222 JB,JSe,A:Hercules,V:Pluto	.	4.00
223 JB,A:Hercules,V:Pluto	. . . .	4.00
224 JB,V:Destroyer	. . . .	4.00
225 JB,JSi,I:Fire Lord	. . . .	8.00
226 JB,A:Watcher,Galactus	. . .	4.00
227 JB,JSi,V:Ego	. . . .	4.00
228 JB,JSi,A:Galactus,D:Ego	. .	4.00
229 JB,JSi,A:Hercules,I:Dweller	. .	4.00
230 JB,A:Hercules	. . . .	4.00
231 JB,DG,V:Armak	. . . .	4.00
232 JB,JSi,A:Firelord	. . . .	4.00
233 JB,Asgard Invades Earth	. . .	4.00
234 JB,V:Loki	. . . .	4.00
235 JB,JSi,I:Possessor		
(Kamo Tharnn)	. . . .	4.00
236 JB,JSi,V:Absorbing Man	. . .	3.50
237 JB,JSi,V:Ulik	. . . .	3.50
238 JB,JSi,V:Ulik	. . . .	3.50
239 JB,JSi,V:Ulik	. . . .	3.50
240 SB,KJ,V:Seth	. . . .	3.50
241 JB,JGi,I:Geb	. . . .	3.50
242 JB,JSi,V:Servitor	. . . .	3.50
243 JB,JSt,V:Servitor	. . . .	3.50
244 JB,JSt,V:Servitor	. . . .	3.50
245 JB,JSt,V:Servitor	. . . .	3.50
246 JB,JSt,A:Firelord	. . . .	3.50
247 JB,JSt,A:Firelord	. . . .	3.50
248 JB,V:Storm Giant	. . . .	3.50
249 JB,V:Odin	. . . .	3.50
250 JB,D:Igron,V:Mangog	. . . .	3.50
251 JB,A:Sif	. . . .	3.50
252 JB,V:Ulik	. . . .	3.50
253 JB,I:Trogg	. . . .	3.50
254 JK,O:Dr.Blake rep	. . . .	3.50
255 Stone Men of Saturn Rep.	. .	3.50
256 JB,I:Sporr	. . . .	3.50

257 JK,JB,I:Fee-Lon	. . . .	3.50
258 JK,JB,V:Grey Gargoyle	. . . .	3.50
259 JB,A:Spider-Man	. . . .	4.00
260 WS,I:Doomsday Star	. . . . .	4.00
261 WS,I:Soul Survivors	. . . . . .	3.00
262 WS,Odin Found,I:Odin Force	3.00
263 WS,V:Loki	. . . .	3.00
264 WS,V:Loki	. . . .	3.00
265 WS,V:Destroyer	. . . .	3.00
266 WS,Odin Quest	. . . .	3.00
267 WS,F:Odin	. . . .	3.00
268 WS,V:Damocles	. . . .	3.00
269 WS,V:Stilt-Man	. . . .	3.00
270 WS,V:Blastaar	. . . .	3.00
271 Avengers,Iron Man x-over	. .	3.00
272 JB,Day the Thunder Failed	. .	3.00
273 JB,V:Midgard Serpent	. . . .	3.00
274 JB,D:Balder,I:Hermod,Hoder	.	3.00
275 JB,V:Loki,I:Sigyn	. . . .	3.00
276 JB,Trial of Loki	. . . .	3.00
277 JB,V:Fake Thor	. . . .	3.00
278 JB,V:Fake Thor	. . . .	3.00
279 A:Pluto,V:Ulik	. . . .	3.00
280 V:Hyperion	. . . .	3.00
281 O:Space Phantom	. . . . . .	3.00
282 V:Immortus,I:Tempus	. . . .	3.00
283 JB,V:Celestials	. . . .	3.00
284 JB,V:Gammenon	. . . .	3.00
285 JB,R:Karkas	. . . .	3.00
286 KP,KRo,D:Kro,I:Dragona	. . .	3.00
287 KP,2nd App & O:Forgotten		
One(Hero)	. . . .	3.00
288 KP,V:Forgotten One	. . . . . .	3.00
289 KP,V:Destroyer	. . . .	3.00
290 I:Red Bull(Toro Rojo)	. . . . .	3.00
291 KP,A:Eternals,Zeus	. . . . . .	3.00
292 KP,V:Odin	. . . .	3.00
293 KP,Door to Minds Eye	. . . .	3.00
294 KP,O:Odin & Asgard,I:Frey	. .	3.00
295 KP,I:Fafnir,V:Storm Giants	. .	3.00
296 KP,D:Siegmund	. . . .	3.00
297 KP,V:Sword of Siegfried	. . .	3.00
298 KP,V:Dragon(Fafnir)	. . . . . .	3.00
299 KP,A:Valkyrie,I:Hagen	. . . . .	3.00
300 KP,giant,O:Odin & Destroyer,		
Rindgold Ring Quest ends,D:Uni-		
Mind,I:Mother Earth	. . . .	6.00
301 KP,O:Mother Earth,V:Apollo	.	3.00

302 KP,V:Locus 3.00
303 Whatever Gods There Be . . . 3.00
304 KP,V:Wrecker 3.00
305 KP,R:Gabriel(Air Walker) . . . 3.00
306 KP,O&V:Firelord,O:AirWalker 3.00
307 KP,I:Dream Demon 3.00
308 KP,V:Snow Giants 3.00
309 V:Bomnardiers 3.00
310 KP,V:Mephisto 3.00
311 KP,GD,A:Valkyrie 3.00
312 KP,V:Tyr 3.00
313 KP,Thor Trial 3.00
314 KP,A:Drax,Moondragon 3.00
315 KP,O:Bi-Beast 3.00
316 KP,A:Iron Man,Man Thing,
    V:Man-Beast 3.00
317 KP,V:Man-Beast 3.00
318 GK,V:Fafnir 3.00
319 KP,I&D:Zaniac 3.00
320 KP,V:Rimthursar 2.75
321 I:Menagerie 2.50
322 V:Heimdall 2.50
323 V:Death 2.50
324 V:Graviton 2.50
325 JM,O:Darkoth,V:Mephisto . . 2.75
326 I:New Scarlet Scarab 2.75
327 V:Loki & Tyr 2.50
328 I:Megatak 2.75
329 HT,V:Hrungnir 2.50
330 BH,I:Crusader 2.50
331 Threshold of Death 2.50
332 V:Dracula 2.75
333 BH,V:Dracula 2.75
334 Quest For Rune Staff 2.50
335 V:Possessor 2.50
336 A:Captain Ultra 2.75
337 WS,I:Beta Ray Bill,A:Surtur . . 7.50
338 WS,O:Beta Ray Bill,I:Lorelei . 5.00
339 WS,V:Beta Ray Bill 3.50
340 WS,A:Beta Ray Bill 3.00
341 WS,V:Fafnir 2.25
342 WS,V:Fafnir,I:Eilif 2.25
343 WS,V:Fafnir 2.25
344 WS,Balder Vs.Loki,I:Malekith . 2.25
345 WS,V:Malekith 2.25
346 WS,V:Malekith 2.25
347 WS,V:Malekith,I:Algrim
    (Kurse) 2.25
348 WS,V:Malekith 2.25
349 WS,R:Beta Ray Bill,O:Odin,
    I&O:Vili & Ve(Odin's brothers) . 2.50
350 WS,V:Surtur 2.25
351 WS,V:Surtur 2.25
352 WS,V:Surtur 2.25
353 WS,V:Surtur,D:Odin 2.25
354 WS,V:Hela 2.25
355 WS,SB,A:Thor's Great
    Grandfather 2.25
356 BL,BG,V:Hercules 2.25
357 WS,A:Beta Ray Bill 2.50
358 WS,A:Beta Ray Bill 2.50
359 WS,V:Loki 2.25
360 WS,V:Hela 2.25
361 WS,V:Hela 2.25
362 WS,V:Hela 2.25
363 WS,Secret Wars II,V:Kurse . . 2.50
364 WS,I:Thunder Frog 2.25
365 WS,A:Thunder Frog 2.25
366 WS,A:Thunder Frog 2.25
367 WS,D:Malekith,A:Kurse 2.25
368 WS,F:Balder t/Brave,Kurse . . 2.25
369 WS,F:Balder the Brave 2.25
370 JB,V:Loki 2.25
371 SB,I:Justice Peace,V:Zaniac . 2.25
372 SB,V:Justice Peace 2.25

373 SB,A:X-Factor,(Mut.Mass) . . . 5.00
374 WS,SB,A:X-Factor,(Mut.Mass)
    A:Sabretooth 7.00
375 WS,SB,N:Thor(Exoskeleton) . 2.25
376 WS,SB,V:Absorbing Man . . . 2.25
377 WS,SB,N:Thor,A:Ice Man . . . 2.25
378 WS,SB,V:Frost Giants 2.25
379 WS,V:Midgard Serpent 2.25
380 WS,V:Midgard Serpent 2.25
381 WE,SB,A:Avengers 2.50
382 WS,SB,V:Frost Giants,Loki . . 2.50
383 BBr,Secret Wars story 2.50
384 RF,BBr,I:Future Thor(Dargo) . 5.00
385 EL,V:Hulk 2.00
386 RF,BBr,I:Leir 2.00
387 RF,BBr,V:Celestials 2.00
388 RF,BBr,V:Celestials 2.00
389 RF,BBr,V:Celestials 2.00
390 RF,BBr,A:Avengers,V:Seth . . 2.00
391 RF,BBr,I:Mongoose,Eric
    Masterson,A:Spider-Man 5.00
392 RF,I:Quicksand 2.00
393 RF,BBr,V:Quicksand,A:DD . . 2.00
394 RF,BBr,V:Earth Force 2.00

The Mighty Thor #338
© *Marvel Entertainment Group*

395 RF,V:Earth Force 2.00
396 RF,A:Black Knight 2.00
397 RF,A:Loki 2.00
398 RF,DH,R:Odin,V:Seth 2.00
399 RF,RT,R:Surtur,V:Seth 2.00
400 RF,JSt,CV,V:Surtur,Seth . . . 5.00
401 V:Loki 2.00
402 RF,JSt,V:Quicksand 2.00
403 RF,JSt,V:Executioner 2.00
404 RF,JSt,TD,V:Annihilus 2.00
405 RF,JSt,TD,V:Annihilus 2.00
406 RF,JSt,TD,V:Wundagore 2.00
407 RF,JSt,R:Hercules,High Evol. 2.00
408 RF,JSt,I:Eric Masterson/Thor
    V:Mongoose 3.50
409 RF,JSt,V:Dr.Doom 2.00
410 RF,JSt,V:Dr.Doom,She-Hulk . 2.00
411 RF,JSt,C:New Warriors
    V:Juggernaut,A of V 3.00
412 RF,JSt,I:New Warriors
    V:Juggernaut,A of V 4.00
413 RF,JSt,A:Dr.Strange 1.75
414 RF,JSt,V:Ulik 1.75
415 HT,O:Thor 1.75

416 RF,JSt,A:Hercules 1.75
417 RF,JSt,A:High Evolutionary . . 1.75
418 RF,JSt,V:Wrecking Crew 1.75
419 RF,JSt,B:Black Galaxy
    Saga,I:Stellaris 1.75
420 RF,JSt,A:Avengers,V:Stellaris 1.75
421 RF,JSt,V:Stellaris 1.75
422 RF,JSt,V:High Evol.,Nobilus . 1.75
423 RF,JSt,A:High Evol.,Celestials
    Count Tagar 1.75
424 RF,JSt,V:Celestials,E:Black
    Galaxy Saga 1.75
425 RF,AM,V:Surtur,Ymir 1.75
426 RF,JSt,HT,O:Earth Force . . . 1.50
427 RF,JSt,A:Excalibur 1.50
428 RF,JSt,A:Excalibur 1.50
429 RF,JSt,A:Ghost Rider 2.00
430 RF,AM,A:Mephisto,Gh.Rider . 2.00
431 HT,AM,V:Ulik,Loki 1.75
432 RF,D:Loki,Thor Banished,Eric
    Masterson becomes 2nd Thor . 4.00
433 RF,V:Ulik 5.00
434 RF,AM,V:Warriors Three 2.50
435 RF,AM,V:Annihilus 2.50
436 RF,AM,V:Titania,Absorbing
    Man,A:Hercules 1.50
437 RF,AM,V:Quasar 1.50
438 RF,JSt,A:Future Thor(Dargo) . 1.50
439 RF,JSt,A:Drago 1.50
440 RF,AM,I:Thor Corps 2.50
441 RF,AM,Celestials vs.Ego . . . 2.50
442 RF,AM,Don Blake,Beta Ray
    Bill,Mephisto 1.50
443 RF,AM,A:Dr.Strange,Silver
    Surfer,V:Mephisto 1.50
444 RF,AM,Special X-mas tale . . 1.50
445 AM,Galactic Storm,pt.7
    V:Gladiator 1.50
446 AM,Galactic Storm,pt.14
    A:Avengers 1.50
447 RF,AM,V:Absorbing Man
    A:Spider-Man 1.50
448 RF,AM,V:Titania,A:SpM 1.50
449 RF,AM,V:Ulik 1.50
450 RF,AM,V:Heimdall,A:Code Blue
    Double-Sized,Gatefold(c),rep.
    Journey Into Mystery#87 . . . . 3.00
451 RF,AM,I:Bloodaxe 1.50
452 RF,AM,V:Bloodaxe 1.50
453 RF,AM,V:Mephisto 1.50
454 RF,AM,V:Mephisto,Loki,
    Karnilla 1.50
455 AM(i),V:Loki,Karnilla,R:Odin,
    A:Dr.Strange 1.50
456 RF,AM,V:Bloodaxe 1.50
457 RF,AM,R:1st Thor 1.50
458 RF,AM,Thor vs Eric 1.50
459 RF,AM,C&I:Thunderstrike(Eric
    Masterson) 2.00
460 I:New Valkyrie 1.50
461 V:Beta Ray Bill 1.50
462 A:New Valkyrie 1.50
463 Infinity Crusade 1.50
464 Inf.Crusade,V:Loki 1.50
465 Infinity Crusade 1.50
466 Infinity Crusade 1.50
467 Infinity Crusade 1.50
468 RMz(s),Blood & Thunder#1 . . 3.00
469 RMz(s),Blood & Thunder#5 . . 1.50
470 MCW,Blood & Thunder#9 . . . 1.50
471 MCW,E:Blood & Thunder . . . 1.50
472 B:RTs(s),MCW,I:Godling,C:High
    Evolutionary 1.50
473 MCW,V:Godling,High Evolutionary
    I&C:Karnivore(Man-Beast) 1.75

MARVEL

474 MCW,C:High Evolutionary . . . 1.50
475 MCW,Foil(c),A:Donald Blake,
   N:Thor 3.00
475a Newsstand Ed. 2.00
476 V:Destroyer 1.75
477 V:Destroyer,A:Thunderstrike . 1.75
478 V:Norvell Thor 1.75
479 V:Norvell Thor 1.75
480 V:High Evolutionary 1.50
481 V:Grotesk 1.50
482 Don Blake construct 1.50
483 RTs,MCW,V:Loki 1.50
484 Badoy and Soul 1.50
485 V:The Thing 1.50
486 High Evolutionary,Godpack . . 1.50
487 V:Kurse 1.50
488 RTs,MCW,Kurse Saga concl. . 1.50
489 RTs,V:Kurse,A:Hulk 1.50
490 TDF,after Thunderstrike 1.50
491 N:Thor 7.50
492 Worldengine's Secrets 5.00
493 Worldengine trigers Ragnarok 3.00
494 Worldengine saga conclusion 3.00
495 BML,Avengers:Timeslide 2.50
496 MD2,BML 2.50
497 MD2,BML 2.50
498 BML,V:Absorbing Man 2.00
499 MD2,BML, ... 2.00
500 MD2,BML,double size,A:Dr.
   Strange 3.00
501 MD2,BML,I:Red Norvell 2.00
502 MD2,BML,Onslaught tie-in, A:Red
   Norvell, Jane Foster, Hela 2.00
Becomes:

JOURNEY INTO MYSTERY
Third Series Nov. 1996
503 TDF,MD2, The Lost Gods, New
   Norse gods? 1.50
504 TDF,Golden Realm in ruins,
   V:Ulik the Troll 1.50
505 TDF,MD2, V:Wrecker,
   A:Spider-Man 1.50
506 TDF,MD2, R:Heimdall 1.50
507 TDF,Odin kidnapped 1.50
508 TDF, ... 1.95
509 TDF,Battle for the Future
   of Asgard 1.95
510 TDF,Return of Loki,A:Seth . . 1.95
511 TDF,EBe,Lost Gods reunited
   with Odin 1.95
512 EBe, Odin vs. Seth 1.95
513 TDF,SB,AM, Odin vs. Seth, concl.
514 BRa,VRu,F:Shang Chi, Master
   of Kung Fu 2.00
515 BRa,VRu,F:Shang Chi, Master
   of Kung Fu, pt.2 . . . . 2.00
516 BRa,VRu,F:Shang Chi, Master
   of Kung Fu, pt.3 . . . . 2.00
517 SLo,RGr,F:Black Widow 2.00
518 SLo,RGr,F:Black Widow 2.00
519 SLo,RGr,F:Black Widow, concl. 2.00
520 MWn,F:Hannibal King pt.1 . . 2.00
521 MWn,F:Hannibal King, pt.2 . . 2.00
Ann.#2 JK,V:Destroyer 50.00
Ann.#3 JK,rep,Grey Gargoyle. . . 13.00
Ann.#4 JK,rep,TheLivingPlanet. . 11.00
Ann.#5 JK,JB,Hercules,O:Odin . 10.00
Ann.#6 JK,JB,A:Guardians of the
   Galaxy,V:Korvac 10.00
Ann.#7 WS,Eternals 9.00
Ann.#8 JB,V:Zeus 8.00
Ann.#9 LMc,Dormammu 7.00
Ann.#10 O:Chthon,Gaea,A:Pluto . 6.00
Ann.#11 O:Odin 6.00
Ann.#12 BH,I:Vidar(Odin's son) . . 6.00

Ann.#13 JB,V:Mephisto 6.00
Ann.#14 AM,DH,Atlantis Attacks . 5.00
Ann.#15 HT,Terminus Factor #3 . 4.00
Ann.#16 Korvac Quest,pt.2,
   Guardians of Galaxy 2.50
Ann.#17 Citizen Kang#2 . . . . 2.50
Ann.#18 TGr,I:The Flame,w/card . 3.25
Ann.#19 V:Flame 3.25
G-Size.#1 Battles,A:Hercules . . 14.00
TPB Alone Against the Celestials,
   rep.Thor#387-389 . . . . 5.95
TPB Ballad of Beta Ray Bill,rep.
   Thor#337-340 . . . . 8.95
Minus 1 Spec., TDF,EBe,flashback 1.95
1-shot, Rough Cut, DJu,JR,original
   pencils, b&w 48pg 3.00

THOR
May 1998
1 JR2,KJ,DJu,The hero returns,
   48pg 3.00
2A JR2,KJ,DJu,V:Destroyer,A:Hela,
   Marnot 2.00
2B JR2,KJ variant cover 2.00
3 DJu,JR2,KJ,A:Marnot,V:Sedna . 2.00
4 DJu,JR2,KJ,A:Namor,Sedna . . 2.00

THOR CORPS
[Limited Series]
1 TDF(s),PO,V:Demonstaff 2.00
2 TDF(s),PO,A:Invaders 2.00
3 TDF(s),PO,A:Spider-Man 2099 2.00
4 TDF(s),PO,Last Issue 2.00

THREE MUSKETEERS
1 thru 2 movie adapt. 1.25

THUNDERBOLTS
Feb. 1997
1 KBk,MBa,VRu,Post-onslaught new
   team:Citizen V, Meteorite, Techno,
   Songbird, Atlas & Mach-1, . . . 2.99
1 rep. 2.50
2 KBk,MBa,VRu,V:Mad Thinker . 1.95
2a variant cover by MBa&VRu . . 1.95
2 rep. 2.00
3 KBk,MBa,VRu,Headquarters at
   Freedom's Plaza 1.95
4 KBk,MBa,VRu,I:Jolt 1.95
5 KBk,MBa,VRu,V:Elements of
   Doom 1.95
6 KBk,MBa,VRu,V:Elements of
   Doom 1.95
7 KBk,MBa,VRu,F:Citizen V 2.00
8 KBk,MBa,VRu,Songbird fights
   alone 2.00
9 KBk,MBa,VRu,Black Widow . . . 2.00
10 KBk,MBa,VRu,Secret Identities
   discovered 2.00
11 KBk,MBa,VRu,V:Citizen V . . . 2.00
12 KBk,MBa,VRu,A:Fantastic Four,
   Avengers 2.00
13 KBk,MBa,SHa,on trial 3.00
14 KBk,MBa,VRu,V:Citizen V,
   Meteorite 2.00
15 KBk,MBa,VRu,V:S.H.I.E.L.D. . . 2.00
16 KBk,MBa,SHa,V:Lightningrods 2.00
17 KBk,MBa,SHa,V:Graviton . . . 2.00
18 KBk,MBa,SHa,villains once
   again? 2.00
19 KBk,MBa,SHa, ... 2.00
Ann. '97 KBk,MBa,TGu,GP,
   O:Thunderbolts, 48pg 2.95
TPB 176pg, secret history 12.00

THUNDERBOLTS:
DISTANT RUMBLINGS
1997
1 KBk,SEp,Flashback,F:Citizen V 2.50

THUNDERCATS
Star Dec., 1985
1 JM,TV tie-in 2.00
1a 2nd printing 1.00
2 JM,A:Berbils,V:Mumm-Ra 1.50
3 . . . . 1.50
4 JM,I:Lynxana 1.50
5 JM 1.50
6 JM 1.50
7 Return to Thundera 1.50
8 V:Monkiang 1.50
9 V:Pekmen 1.00
10 . . . . 1.00
11 I:The Molemen 1.00
12 'The Protectors' 1.00
13 EC/AW,V:Safari Joe 1.00
14 V:Snaf 1.00
15 JM,A:Spidera 1.00
16 'Time Capsule' 1.00
17 . . . . 1.00
18 EC/AW,'Doom Gaze' 1.00
19 . . . . 1.00
20 EC/AW 1.00
21 JM,A:Hercules Baby 1.00
22 I:Devious Duploids 1.00
23 V:Devious Duploids 1.00
24 June, 1988 . . . . 1.00

THUNDERSTRIKE
1993–95
1 B:TDF(s),RF,Holografx(c),
   V:Bloodaxe,I:Car Jack 3.25
2 RF,V:Juggernaut 1.50
3 RF,I:Sangre 1.50
4 RF,A:Spider-Man,I:Pandora . . 1.50
5 RF,A:Spider-Man,V:Pandora . . 1.50
6 RF,I:Blackwulf,Bristle,Schizo,Lord
   Lucian,A:SpM,Code:Blue,Stellaris,
   V:SHIELD,Pandora,C:Tantalus 1.50
7 KP,V:Tantalus,D:Jackson 1.75
8 RF,I&V:Officer ZERO 1.75
9 RF,V:Bloodaxe 1.75
10 RF,A:Thor 1.75
11 RF,A:Wildstreak 1.50
12 RF,A:Whyte Out 1.50
13 RF,Inferno 42 . . . . 1.50
13a Double Feature flip book
   with Code Blue #1 . . . . 2.50
14 RF, Inferno 42 . . . . 1.50
14a Double Feature flip book
   with Code Blue #2 . . . . 2.50
15 RF,V:Methisto 1.50
15a Double Feature flip book
   with Code Blue #3 . . . . 2.50
16 . . . . 1.50
17 V:Bloodaxe 1.50
18 V:New Villain 1.50
19 Shopping Network 1.50
20 A: Black Panther 1.50
21 A:War Machine,V:Loki 1.50
22 TDF,AM,RF,Mystery of Bloodaxe
   blows open 1.50
23 TDF,A:Avengers 1.50
24 TDF,V:Bloodaxe, final issue . . 1.50

MARVEL

TIMELY PRESENTS: HUMAN TORCH COMICS
Aug. 1998
one-shot GN 6.00

TIMESLIP: THE COMING OF THE AVENGERS
Aug. 1998
One-shot GN 6.00

TIMESPIRITS
Epic Jan., 1985
1 TY	2.00
2	1.75
3	1.75
4 AW	1.50
5	1.50
6	1.50
7	1.50
8 March, 1986	1.50

TIMESTRYKE
1	1.95
2	1.95

TINY TESSIE
See: TESSIE THE TYPIST

TOMB OF DARKNESS
See: BEWARE

TOMB OF DRACULA
April, 1972
1 GC,Night of the Vampire	85.00
2 GC,Who Stole My Coffin? . . .	50.00
3 GC,TP,I:Rachel Van Helsing .	30.00
4 GC,TP,Bride of Dracula!	30.00
5 GC,TP,To Slay A Vampire . . .	30.00
6 GC,TP,Monster of the Moors .	25.00
7 GC,TP,Child is Slayer of the Man	25.00
8 GC(p),The Hell-Crawlers	25.00
9 The Fire Cross	25.00
10 GC,I:Blade Vampire Slayer . .	28.00
11 GC,TP,Master of the Undead	

Tomb of Dracula #44
© Marvel Entertainment Group

Strikes Again!	15.00
12 GC,TP,House that Screams .	15.00
13 GC,TP,O:Blade	18.00
14 GC,TP,Vampire has Risen from the Grave	15.00
15 GC,TP,Stay Dead	15.00
16 GC,TP,Back from the Grave .	15.00
17 GC,TP,A Vampire Rides This Train!	15.00
18 GC,TP,A:Werewolf By Night .	18.00
19 GC,TP,Snowbound in Hell . .	15.00
20 GC,TP,ManhuntForAVampire	15.00
21 GC,TP,A:Blade	13.00
22 GC,TP,V:Gorna	11.00
23 GC,TP,Shadow over Haunted Castle	11.00
24 GC,TP,I am your Death	11.00
25 GC,TP,Blood Stalkers of Count Dracula	11.00
26 GC,TP,A Vampire Stalks the Night	11.00
27 GC,TP,..And the Moon Spews Death!	11.00
28 GC,TP,Five came to Kill a Vampire'	11.00
29 GC,TP,Vampire goes Mad? .	11.00
30 GC,TP,A:Blade	11.00
31 GC,TP,Child of Blood	11.00
32 GC,TP,The Vampire Walks Among Us	11.00
33 GC,TP,Blood on My Hands . .	11.00
34 GC,TP,Bloody Showdown . . .	11.00
35 GC,TP,A:Brother Voodoo . . .	11.00
36 GC,TP,Dracula in America . .	11.00
37 GC,TP,The Vampire Walks Among Us	7.00
38 GC,TP,Bloodlust for a Dying Vampire	11.00
39 GC,TP,Final Death of Dracula	11.00
40 GC,TP,Triumph of Dr.Sun . . .	11.00
41 GC,TP,A:Blade	8.00
42 GC,TP,V:Dr.Sun	7.00
43 GC,TP,A:NewYear'sNightmare	7.00
44 GC,TP,A:Dr.Strange	7.00
45 GC,TP,A:Hannibal King	8.00
46 GC,TP,W:Dracula & Domini .	7.00
47 GC,TP,Death-Bites	7.00
48 GC,TP,A:Hannibal King	8.00
49 GC,TP,A:Robin Hood, Frankenstein's Monster	7.00
50 GC,TP,A:Silver Surfer	15.00
51 GC,TP,A:Blade	7.50
52 GC,TP,V:Demon	6.50
53 GC,TP,A:Hannibal King,Blade .	7.50
54 GC,TP,Twas the Night Before Christmas	6.50
55 GC,TP,Requiem for a Vampire	6.50
56 GC,TP,A:Harold H. Harold . . .	6.50
57 GC,TP,The Forever Man	6.50
58 GC,TP,A:Blade	7.00
59 GC,TP,The Last Traitor	6.50
60 GC,TP,The Wrath of Dracula .	6.50
61 GC,TP,Resurrection	6.50
62 GC,TP,What Lurks Beneath . .	6.50
63 GC,TP,A:Janus	6.50
64 GC,TP,A:Satan	6.50
65 GC,TP,Where No Vampire Has Gone Before	6.50
66 GC,TP,Marked for Death	6.50
67 GC,TP,A:Lilith	6.50
68 GC,TP,Dracula turns Human . .	6.50
69 GC,TP,Cross of Fire	6.50
70 GC,TP,double size,last issue .	8.50
Savage Return of Dracula. rep. Tomb of Dracula #1,#2	2.00

Wedding of Dracula. rep.Tomb of Dracula #30,#45,#46	2.00
Requiem for Dracula. rep.Tomb of Dracula #69,70	2.00

TOMB OF DRACULA
[Mini-Series] Nov., 1991
1 GC,AW,Day of Blood	6.00
2 GC,AW,Dracula in DC	5.50
3 GC,AW,A:Blade	5.50
4 GC,AW,D:Dracula	5.50

TOMB OF DRACULA
(B&W Mag.) Nov., 1979
1	3.50
2 SD	5.00
3 FM	5.00
4	3.00
5	3.00
6 Sept., 1980	3.00

TOMB OF DRACULA MEGAZINE
TPB Halloween, MWn,GC,TP . . . 3.95

TOMORROW KNIGHTS
Epic June, 1990
1	1.95
2	1.50
3	1.50
4 Origin	1.50
5	2.25
6	2.25

TOP DOG
Star Comics April, 1985
1	1.25
2 thru 14, June 1987	@1.00

TOR
Epic *Heavy Hitters* 1993
1 JKu,R:Tor,Magazine Format . .	6.25
2 JKu	6.25
3 JKu,V:The Iduard Ring	6.25

TOUGH KID SQUAD COMICS
Timely March, 1942
1 O:The Human Top,Tough Kid Squad,A:The Flying Flame, V:Doctor Klutch 8,000.00

TOWER OF SHADOWS
Sept., 1969
1 JR(c),JSo,JCr,'At The Stroke of Midnight'	35.00
2 JR(c),DH,DA,NA,'The Hungry One'	22.00
3 GC,BWs,GT,'Midnight in the Wax Museum'	25.00
4 DH,Within The Witching Circle	15.00
5 DA,BWS,WW,'Demon That Stalks Hollywood'	20.00
6 WW,SD,'Pray For the Man in the Rat-Hole	25.00
7 BWS,WW,'Titano'	25.00
8 WW,SD,'Demons of Dragon-Henge'	25.00
9 BWr(c),TP,Lovecraft story . . .	25.00

MARVEL

Creatures on the Loose #27
© Marvel Entertainment Group

Becomes:

CREATURES ON THE LOOSE
March, 1971

10 BWr,A:King Kull	40.00
11 DAy,rep Moomba is Here	15.00
12 JK,'I Was Captured By Korilla'	15.00
13 RC,'The Creature From Krogarr'	15.00
14 MSe,'Dead Storage'	15.00
15 SD,Spragg the Living Mountain	15.00
16 GK,BEv,GK,B&O:Gullivar Jones, Warrior of Mars	10.00
17 GK,'Slaves o/t Spider Swarm'	10.00
18 RA,'The Fury of Phra'	10.00
19 WB,JM,GK,'Red Barbarian of Mars'	10.00
20 GK(c),GM,SD,'The Monster... And the Maiden	10.00
21 JSo(c),GM,'Two Worlds To Win',E:Guilliver	8.00
22 JSo(c),SD,VM,B:Thongor, Warrior of Lost Lemuria	8.00
23 VM,'The Man-Monster Strikes'	8.00
24 VM,'Attack of the Lizard-Hawks'	8.00
25 VM,GK(c),'Wizard of Lemuria'	8.00
26 VM,'Doom of the Serpent Gods'	8.00
27 VM,SD,'Demons Dwell in the Crypts of Yamath'	8.00
28 SD,'The Hordes of Hell'	8.00
29 GK(c),'Day of the Dragon Wings', E:Thongor,Warrior of Lost Lemuria	8.00
30 B:Man-Wolf,'Full Moon, Dark Fear'	10.00
31 GT,'The Beast Within'	8.00
32 GT,V:Kraven the Hunter	8.00
33 GK(c),GP,'The Name of the Game is Death'	8.00
34 GP,'Nightflight to Fear'	8.00
35 GK(c),GP	8.00
36 GK(c),GP,'Murder by Moonlight'	8.00
37 GP,Sept., 1975	8.00

TOXIC AVENGER
March, 1991

1 VM(i)I&O:Toxic Avenger	1.50

2 VM(i)	1.50
3 VM(i)'Night of LivingH.bodies	1.50
4 Legend of Sludgeface	1.50
5 I:Biohazard	1.50
6 V:Biohazard	1.50
7 'Sewer of Souviaki'	1.50
8 'Sewer of Souviaki' conc.	1.50
9 Abducted by Aliens	1.50
10 'Die,Yuppie Scum',pt.1	1.50

TOXIC CRUSADERS
1992

1 F:Toxic Avengers & Crusaders	1.50
2 SK(c),V:Custard-Thing	1.25
3 SK(c),V:Custard-Thing	1.25
4 V:Giant Mutant Rats	1.25
5 V:Dr.Killemoff	1.25
6 V:Dr.Killemoff	1.25
7 F:Yvonne	1.25
8 V:Psycho	1.25

[2nd Series]

1	1.25
2	1.25

TRANSFORMERS
[1st Regular Series] Sept., 1984

1 FS,Toy Comic	2.50
2 FS,OptimusPrime V:Megatron	1.75
3 FS.A:Spider-Man	1.75
4 MT(c),FS	1.50
5 Transformers Dead?	1.50
6 Autobots vs.Decepticons	1.50
7 KB,V:Megatron	1.50
8 KB,A:Dinobots	1.50
9 MM,A:Circuit Breaker	1.50
10 Dawn of the Devastator	1.50
11 HT	1.50
12 HT,V:Shockwave	1.50
13 DP,Return of Megatron	1.50
14 DP,V:Decepticons	1.50
15 DP	1.50
16 KN,A:Bumblebee	1.50
17 DP,I:New Transformers,pt.1	1.50
18 DP,I:New Transformers,pt.2	1.50
19 DP,I:Omega Supreme	1.50
20 HT,Skid vs.Ravage	1.50
21 DP,I:Aerialbots	1.25
22 DP,I:Stuntacons(Menasor)	1.25
23 DP,Return of Circuit Breaker	1.25
24 DP,D:Optimus Prime	1.25
25 DP,Decpticons (full story)	1.25
26 DP	1.25
27 DP,V:Head Hunter	1.25
28 DP	1.25
29 DP,I:Scraplets, Triplechangers	1.25
30 DP,V:Scraplets	1.25
31 DP,Humans vs. Decepticons	1.25
32 DP,I:Autobots for Sale'	1.25
33 DP,Autobots vs.Decepticons	1.25
34 V:Sky Lynx	1.25
35 JRy,I:UK.version Transformers	1.25
36	1.00
37	1.00
38	1.00
39	1.00
40 Autobots' New Leader	1.00
41	1.00
42 Return of Optimus Prime	1.00
43 Optimus Prime,Goldbug	1.00
44 FF,Return of Circuit Breaker	1.00
45 V:The Jammers	1.00
46 I:New Transformers	1.00
47 B:Underbase saga,I:Seacons	1.00
48 Optimus Prime/Megatron	

(past story)	1.00
49 Underbase saga Contd.	1.00
50 E:Underbase saga,I:New Characters	1.00
51 I:Pretender Decepticon Beasts	1.00
52 I:Mecannibles,pt.1	1.00
53 Mecannibles,pt.2	1.00
54 I:Micromasters	1.00
55 MG	1.00
56 Return of Megatron	1.00
57 Optimus Prime vs.Scraponok	1.00
58 V:Megatron	1.00
59 A:Megatron,D:Ratchet	1.00
60 Battle on Cybertron	1.00
61 O:Transformers	1.00
62 B:Matrix Quest,pt.1	1.00
63	1.00
64 I:The Klud	1.00
65 GSr	1.00
66 E:Matrix Quest,pt.5	1.00
67 V:Unicorn,Also Alternative World	1.00
68 I:Neoknights	1.00
69 Fate of Ratchet & Megatron revealed	1.00
70 Megatron/Ratchet fused together	1.00
71 Autobots Surrender to Decepticons	1.00
72 Decepticon Civil War, I:Gravitron	1.00
73 I:Unicorn,A:Neoknights	1.00
74 A:Unicron&Brothers of Chaos	1.00
75 V:Thunderwing & Dark Matrix	1.00
76 Aftermath of War	1.00
77 Unholy Alliance	1.00
78 Galvatron vs.Megatron	1.00
79 Decepticons Invade Earth	1.00
80 Return of Optimus Prime,final	1.00

[2nd Regular Series]

1 Split Foil(c),A:Dinobots	3.00
2 A:G.I.Joe,Cobra	2.00
3	2.00
4 MaG,V:Jhiaxus	2.00
5	2.00
6 V:Megatron	2.00

Transformers #8
© Marvel Entertainment Group

7 V:Darkwing	2.00
8 V:Darkwing	2.00
9	2.00
10 Total War	2.00
11	1.75

TRANSFORMERS COMICS MAGAZINE
1986–88
1 Digest Size	1.50
2 thru 11	@1.50

TRANSFORMERS, THE MOVIE
Dec., 1986–Feb. 1987
1 thru 3 Animated Movie adapt. @1.25

TRANSFORMERS UNIVERSE
Dec., 1986
1	1.25
2	1.25
3	1.25
4 March, 1987	1.25

TRANSMUTATION OF IKE GARAUDA
Epic 1991
1 JSh,I:IkeGaruda	3.95
2 JSh,conclusion	3.95

TROUBLE WITH GIRLS: NIGHT OF THE LIZARD
Epic *Heavy Hitters* 1993
1 BBI,AW,R:Lester Girls	2.75
2 BBI,AW,V:Lizard Lady	2.25
3 BBI,AW,V:Lizard Lady	2.25
4 BBI,AW,last issue	2.25

TRUE COMPLETE MYSTERY
See: COMPLETE MYSTERY

TRUE SECRETS
See: OUR LOVE

TRUE WESTERN
Dec., 1949
1 Ph(c),Billy the Kid	125.00
2 Ph(c),Alan Ladd,Badmen vs. Lawmen	125.00

Becomes:
TRUE ADVENTURES
3 BP,MSy,Boss of Black Devil	100.00

Becomes:
MEN'S ADVENTURES
4 He Called me a Coward	175.00
5 Brother Act	120.00
6 Heat of Battle	85.00
7 The Walking Death	85.00
8 RH,Journey Into Death	85.00
9 Bullets,Blades and Death	60.00
10 BEv,The Education of Thomas Dillon	60.00
11 Death of A Soldier	60.00
12 Firing Squad	60.00
13 RH(c),The Three Stripes	60.00
14 GC,BEv,Steel Coffin	60.00
15 JMn(c)	60.00

16	60.00
17	60.00
18	60.00
19 JRo	60.00
20 RH(c)	60.00
21 BEv(c),JSt,The Eye of Man	75.00
22 BEv,JR,Mark of the Witch	75.00
23 BEv(c),RC,The Wrong Body	75.00
24 RH,JMn,GT,Torture Master	75.00
25 SSh(c),Who Shrinks My Head	75.00
26 Midnight in the Morgue	75.00
27 CBu(c),A:Capt.America,Human Torch,Sub-Mariner	750.00
28 BEv,A:Capt.America,Human Torch, Sub-Mariner,July, 1954	700.00

TRY-OUT WINNER BOOK
March, 1988
1 Spider-Man vs. Doc Octopus   15.00

TV STARS
August, 1978
1 A:Great Grape Ape	12.00
2	10.00
3	10.00
4 A:Top Cat,Feb., 1979	10.00

2099: MANIFEST DESTINY
March 1998
GN LKa,MMK,F:MiguelO'Hara,48pg 6.00

2-GUN KID
See: BILLY BUCKSKIN

TWO-GUN KID
Atlas March, 1948—April, 1977
1 B:Two-Gun Kid,The Sheriff	750.00
2 Killers of Outlaw City	300.00
3 RH,A:Annie Oakley	225.00
4 RH,A:Black Rider	225.00
5	275.00
6	175.00
7 RH,Brand of a Killer	175.00
8 The Secret of the Castle of Slaves	175.00
9 JSe,Trapped in Hidden Valley A:Black Rider	175.00
10 JK(c),The Horrible Hermit of Hidden Mesa	175.00
11 JMn(c),GT,A:Black Rider	150.00
12 JMn(c),GT,A:Black Rider	150.00
13 thru 24	@125.00
25 AW	125.00
26	100.00
27	100.00
28	100.00
29	100.00
30 AW	100.00
31 thru 44	60.00
45	55.00
46	55.00
47	45.00
48	50.00
49	45.00
50	40.00
51 AW	40.00
52 thru 59	@40.00
60 DAy,New O:Two Gun Kid	25.00
61 JK,DAy,The Killer and The Kid	25.00
62 DAy,At the Mercy of Moose Morgan	25.00
63 DAy,The Guns of Wild Bill Taggert	20.00

Two-Gun Kid #83
© Marvel Entertainment Group

64 DAy,Trapped by Grizzly Gordon	20.00
65 DAy,Nothing Can Save Fort Henry	20.00
66 DAy,Ringo's Raiders	20.00
67 DAy,The Fangs of the Fox	20.00
68 DAy,The Purple Phantom	20.00
69 DAy,Badman Called Goliath	20.00
70 DAy,Hurricane	20.00
71 DAy,V:Jesse James	20.00
72 DAy,V:Geronimo	20.00
73 Guns of the Galloway Gang	20.00
74 Dakota Thompson	20.00
75 JK,Remember the Alamo	20.00
76 JK,Trapped on the Doom	20.00
77 JK,V:The Panther	20.00
78 V:Jesse James	20.00
79 The River Rats	20.00
80 V:The Billy Kid	20.00
81 The Hidden Gun	15.00
82 BEv,Here Comes the Conchos	15.00
83 Durango,Two-Gun Kid Unmasked	15.00
84 Gunslammer	15.00
85 Fury at Falcon Flats, A:Rawhide Kids	15.00
86 V:Cole Younger	15.00
87 OW,The Sidewinder and the Stallion	15.00
88 thru 100	@15.00
101	15.00
102 thru 136	@10.00

TWO-GUN KID: SUNSET RIDERS
1995
1 FaN,R:Two-Gun Kid,64pgs	6.95
2 FaN,concl. 64pgs.	6.95

TWO GUN WESTERN
See: CASEY–CRIME PHOTOGRAPHER

TWO-GUN WESTERN
See: BILLY BUCKSKIN

All comics prices listed are for *Near Mint* condition.

2001: A SPACE ODYSSEY
Oct., 1976
1 JK,FRg,Based on Movie 3.00

2001: A SPACE ODYSSEY
Dec., 1976—Sept., 1977
1 JK,Based on Movie 5.00
2 JK,Vira the She-Demon 3.00
3 JK,Marak the Merciless 3.00
4 JK,Wheels of Death 3.00
5 JK,Norton of New York 3.00
6 JK,Immortality ...Death 3.00
7 JK,The New Seed 3.00
8 JK,Capture of X-51,I&O:Mr.
 Machine(Machine-Man) 4.00
9 JK,A:Mr Machine 3.00
10 Hotline to Hades,A:Mr Machine 3.00

2010
April, 1985
1 TP,movie adapt 1.00
2 TP,movie adapt,May, 1985 ... 1.00

2099 A.D.
1995
1 Chromium cover 3.95

2099 APOCALYPSE
1995
1 .... 5.00

2099 GENESIS
1996
1 Chromium Cover 4.95

2099 SPECIAL:
THE WORLD OF DOOM
1995
1 The World of Doom 2.25

2099 UNLIMITED
1993–96
1 DT,I:Hulk 2099,A:Spider-Man 2099,
 I:Mutagen 4.50
2 DT,F:Hulk 2099,Spider-Man 2099,
 I:R-Gang 4.25
3 GJ(s),JJB,F:Hulk & SpM 2099 . 4.25
4 PR(c),GJ(s),JJB,I:Metalscream
 2099,Lachryma 2099 ...... 4.25
5 GJ(s),I:Vulx,F:Hazarrd 2099 . . 3.95
6 .... 3.95
Becomes:
2099 A.D. UNLIMITED
7 .... 3.95
8 F:Public Enemy 3.95
9 One Nation Under Doom 3.95
10 V:Chameleon 2099 .... 3.95
Spec. #1 The World of Doom ... 2.25

2099:
WORLD OF TOMORROW
1996–97
1 .... 2.50
2 .... 2.50
3 MMk,MsM,ATi,F:Spider-Man,
 X-Men 2.50
4 ATi,X-Men 2099 discover secret 2.50
5 ATi 2.50
6 PFe&ATi(c),Phalanx's final
 assault 2.50
7 Spider-Man 2099 searches for his

brother: Green Goblin 2.50
8 Phalanx invasion aftermath ... 2.50
9 Humanity vs. Lunatika 2.50

TYPHOID
1995–96
1 ANo,JVF,Painted series 3.95
2 ANo,JVF,Hunt for serial killer . . 3.95
3 ANo,JVF,sex,blood & videotapes 3.95
4 ANo,JVF,conclusion 3.95

ULTIMATE AGE
OF APOCALYPSE
Rep. #1-#4 Age of Apocalypse stories:
Ultimate Amazing X-Men 8.95
Ultimate Astonishing X-Men 8.95
Ultimate Factor X 8.95
Ultimate Gambit and the X-Ternals 8.95
Ultimate Generation Next 8.95
Ultimate Weapon X 8.95
Ultimate X-Calibre 8.95
Ultimate X-Man 8.95

ULTRAFORCE/AVENGERS
1 V:Loki,A:Malibu's Ultraforce ... 3.95

ULTRA GIRL
Mini-Series 1996
1 BKs,I&O:Ultra Girl 1.50
2 BKs, ... 1.50
3 BKs,R:New Warriors 1.50

ULTRA X-MEN
COLLECTION
1 Metallic(c), art from cards ... 2.95
2 thru 5 art from cards ..... @2.95

ULTRA X-MEN III
Preview 2.95

Uncanny Origins #2
© Marvel Entertainment Group

UNCANNY ORIGINS
Sept. 1996
1 F:Cyclops 1.00
2 F:Quicksilver 1.00
3 DHv,BAn,F:Archangel 1.00

4 F:Firelord 1.00
5 MHi,F:Hulk 1.00
6 F:Beast 1.00
7 F:Venom 1.00
8 F:Nightcrawler 1.00
9 F:Storm 1.00
10 F:Black Cat 1.00
11 F:Luke Cage 1.00
12 F:Black Knight 1.00
13 LWn,MCa,F:Doctor Strange . . 1.00
14 LWn,MCW,F:Iron Fist 1.00

UNCANNY TALES
Atlas June, 1952
1 RH,While the City Sleeps . . 600.00
2 JMn,BEv 325.00
3 Escape to What 250.00
4 JMn,Nobody's Fool 250.00
5 Fear 250.00
6 He Lurks in the Shadows . . 250.00
7 BEv,Kill,Clown,Kill 225.00
8 JMn,Bring Back My Face ... 225.00
9 RC,The Executioner 225.00
10 RH(c),JR,The Man Who Came
 Back To Life 225.00
11 GC,The Man Who Changed 200.00
12 BP,BEv,Bertha Gets Buried 200.00
13 RH,Scared Out of His Skin . 200.00
14 RH,The Victims of Vonntor . 200.00
15 JSt,The Man Who Saw Death 200.00
16 JMn,GC,Zombie at Large . . 200.00
17 GC,I Live With Corpses ... 200.00
18 JF,BP,Clock Face(c) 200.00
19 DBr,RKr,The Man Who Died
 Again 200.00
20 DBr,Ted's Head 200.00
21 thru 27 .... @150.00
28 .... 175.00
29 thru 41 .... @100.00
42 .... 125.00
43 thru 50 .... @100.00
51 .... 125.00
52 and 53 .... @100.00
54 .... 120.00
55 .... 100.00
56 Sept., 1957 .... 125.00

UNCANNY TALES
FROM THE GRAVE
Dec., 1973—Oct., 1975
1 RC,Room of no Return 15.00
2 DAy,Out of the Swamp 10.00
3 No Way Out 10.00
4 JR,SD,Vampire 10.00
5 GK,GT,Don't Go in the Cellar 10.00
6 JR,SD,The Last Kkrul 10.00
7 RH,SD,Never Dance With a
 Vampire 10.00
8 SD,Escape Into Hell 10.00
9 JA,The Nightmare Men 10.00
10 SD,DH,Beware the Power of
 Khan 10.00
11 SD,JF,RH,Dead Don't Sleep . 10.00
12 SD,Final Issue 10.00

UNCANNY X-MEN
SEE: X-MEN

UNKNOWN WORLDS OF
SCIENCE FICTION
Jan., 1975
(black & white magazine)
1 AW,RKr,AT,FF,GC 4.00

2 FB,GP 3.25
3 GM,AN,GP,GC 3.25
4 . . . . 3.25
5 GM,NC,GC 3.25
6 FB,AN,GC,Nov., 1975 . . . . . 3.25
Spec.#1 AN,NR,JB 3.50

U.S.A. COMICS
Timely Aug., 1941
1 S&K(c),BW,Bondage(c),The
  Defender(c) 9,500.00
2 S&K(c),BW,Capt.Terror(c) . 2,800.00
3 S&K(c),Capt.Terror(c) 2,100.00
4 . . . . 1,600.00
5 Hitler(c),O:AmericanAvenger 1,700.00
6 ASh(c),Capt.America(c) . . . 2,100.00
7 BW,O:Marvel Boy 1,800.00
8 Capt.America (c) 1,400.00
9 Bondage(c), Capt.America . 1,400.00
10 SSh(c),Bondage(c), Capt.
  America 1,400.00
11 SSh(c),Bondage(c), Capt.
  America 1,200.00
12 ASh(c),Capt.America 1,200.00
13 ASh(c),Capt.America 1,200.00
14 Capt.America 900.00
15 Capt.America 900.00
16 ASh(c),Bondage(c),
  Capt.America 900.00
17 Bondage(c),Capt.America . . 900.00

U.S. 1 #2
© *Marvel Entertainment Group*

U.S. 1
May, 1983–Oct. 1984
1 AM(c),HT,Trucking Down the
  Highway 1.25
2 HT,Midnight 1.00
3 FS,ME,Rhyme of the Ancient
  Highwayman 1.00
4 FS,ME 1.00
5 FS,ME,Facing The Maze 1.00
6 FS,ME 1.00
7 FS,ME 1.00
8 FS,ME 1.00
9 FS,ME,Iron Mike-King of the
  Bike 1.00
10 thru 12 FS,ME . . . . @1.00

U.S. AGENT
June – Dec. 1993
1 V:Scourge,O:U.S.Agent 2.00
2 V:Scourge 2.00
3 V:Scourge 2.00
4 last issue 2.00

UNTAMED
Epic *Heavy Hitters* 1993
1 I:Griffen Palmer 2.75
2 V:Kosansui 2.25
3 V:Kosansui 2.25

UNTOLD LEGEND OF CAPTAIN MARVEL, THE
1997
1 (of 3) Early days of Captain
  Marvel 2.50
2 Early days of Captain Marvel . . 2.50
3 V:Kree 2.50

UNTOLD TALES OF SPIDER-MAN
Sept. 1995 – Sept. 1997
1 F:Young Spider-Man 3.00
2 V:Batwing 1.50
3 V:Sandman 1.00
4 V:J.Jonah Jameson 1.00
5 V:Vulture 1.00
6 A:Human Torch 1.00
7 . . . . 1.00
8 . . . . 1.00
9 A:Batwing,Lizard 1.00
10 KBk,PO,I:Commanda 1.00
11 KBk,PO, ... 1.00
12 KBk,PO, ... 1.00
13 KBk,PO, ... 1.00
14 KBk,PO, ... 1.00
15 KBk,PO,AV,Gordon's plan to
  control the Bugle 1.00
16 Re-I:Mary Jane Watson 1.00
17 KBk,PO,AV,V:Hawkeye 1.00
18 KBk,PO,AV,A:Green Goblin,
  Headsman 1.00
19 KBk,PO,AW,F:Doctor Octopus 1.00
20 KBk,PO,AW,V:Vulture 1.00
21 KBk,PO,AW,V:Menace,A:Original
  X-Men 1.00
22 KBk,PO,AW,V:Scarecrow, . . . 1.00
23 KBk,PO,AW,V:Crime Master,
  A:Green Goblin 1.00
24 KBk,PO,BMc, Fate of Batwing . 1.00
25 LBI,PO,BMc, V:Green Goblin,
  final issue 2.00
Minus 1 Spec., RSt,JR, flashback,
  Peter's parents 1.95
Ann. '96 1 KBk,MiA,JSt,A date with
  Invisible Girl? 1.95
Ann. '97 KBk,TL,A:everyone, 48pg 2.95
TPB rep. #1–#8 . . . . 17.00
one-shot GN KBk,SL,Encounter,
  A:Dr. Strange 48pg. 6.00

VALKYRIE
1996
1-shot JMD, ... 2.50

VAMPIRE TALES
August, 1973
(black & white magazine)
1 BEv,B:Morbius the Living
  Vampire 50.00
2 JSo,I:Satana 40.00

3 A:Satana 20.00
4 GK 30.00
5 GK,O:Morbius The Living
  Vampire 35.00
6 AA,I:Lilith 30.00
7 HC,PG 30.00
8 AA,A:Blade The Vampire
  Slayer 30.00
9 RH,AA 30.00
10 . . . . 30.00
11 June, 1975 . . . . 30.00
Ann.#1 . . . . 15.00

Vault of Evil #8
© *Marvel Entertainment Group*

VAULT OF EVIL
Feb., 1973—Nov., 1975
1 B:1950's reps,Come Midnight,
  Come Monster 15.00
2 The Hour of the Witch 10.00
3 The Woman Who Wasn't . . . 10.00
4 Face that Follows 10.00
5 Ghost 10.00
6 The Thing at the Window . . . 10.00
7 Monsters 10.00
8 The Vampire is my Brother . . 10.00
9 Giant Killer 10.00
10 The Lurkers in the Caves . . . 10.00
11 Two Feasts For a Vampire . . 10.00
12 Midnight in the
  Haunted Mansion 10.00
13 Hot as the Devil 10.00
14 Midnight in the Haunted Manor 10.00
15 Don't Shake Hands with the
  Devil 10.00
16 A Grave Honeymoon 10.00
17 Grave Undertaking 10.00
18 The Deadly Edge 10.00
19 Vengeance of Ahman Ra . . . 10.00
20 . . . . 10.00
21 Victim of Valotorr 10.00
22 . . . . 10.00
23 Black Magician Lives Again . 10.00

VENOM: ALONG CAME A SPIDER
1996
1 LHA,GLz,V:New Spider-Man . . 3.00
2 LHa,JPi,V:New Spider-Man . . . 3.00

3 . . . . 3.00
4 conclusion, 48pg 3.00

VENOM:
CARNAGE UNLEASHED
1995
1 Venom vs. Carnage 3.00
2 Venom vs. Carnage 3.00
3 No Spider-Help 3.00
4 JRu,Wld,LHa,cardstock(c) 3.00

VENOM:
THE ENEMY WITHIN
1994
1 BMc,Glow-in-the-dark(C),
  A:Demogoblin,Morbius 3.25
2 BMc,A:Demogoblin,Morbius . . . 3.25
3 BMc,V:Demogoblin,A:Morbius . 3.25

VENOM: FINALE
1997–98
1 (of 3) LHa, ... 3.00
2 LJa, ... 3.00
3 LHa, finale 3.00

VENOM: FUNERAL PYRE
1993
1 TL,JRu,A:Punisher 3.50
2 TL,JRu,AM,V:Gangs 3.50
3 TL,JRu,Last issue 3.50

VENOM: THE HUNGER
1996
1 thru 4 LKa,TeH,V:Dr. Paine . @2.00

VENOM: THE HUNTED
1996
1 LHa,3 part mini-series 3.00

VENOM:
LETHAL PROTECTOR
1993
1 MBa,A:Spider-Man.holo-grafx(c) 5.00
1a Gold Ed.. . . . . 8.00
1b Black Ed.. . . . . 20.00
2 MBa,A:Spider-Man 3.50
3 MBa,Families of Venom's
  victims 3.50
4 RLm,A:Spider-Man,V:Life
  Foundation 3.50
5 RLm,V:Five Symbiotes,A:SpM . 3.50
6 RLm,V:Spider-Man 3.50
Super Size Spec.#1 Planet of
  the Symbiotes,pt.3 . . . . 3.95
Venom:Deathtrap:The Vault,RLm,
  A:Avengers,Freedom Force . . . 6.95
TPB Lethal Protector RLm,DvM . 15.95

VENOM: LICENSE TO KILL
1997
1 (of 3) LHa,KHt, sequel to Venom
  on trial 2.00
2 LHa,V:Dr. Yes 2.00
3 LHa,V:Dr. Yes 2.00

VENOM: THE MACE
1994
1 Embossed(c),CP(s),LSh,I:Mace 3.25
2 CP(s),LSh,V:Mace 3.25
3 CP(s),LSh,V:Mace,final issue . . 3.25

VENOM: THE MADNESS
1993–94
1 B:ANi(s),KJo,V:Juggernaut . . . 3.50
2 KJo,V:Juggernaut 3.25
3 E:ANi(s),KJo,V:Juggernaut . . . 3.25

VENOM:
NIGHTS OF VENGEANCE
1994
1 RLm,I:Stalkers,A:Vengeance . . 3.25
2 RLm,A:Vengeance,V:Stalkers . 3.25
3 RLm,V:Stalkers 3.25
4 RLm,final issue 3.25

VENOM: ON TRIAL
Jan.–May 1997
1 LHa,Tries to break out 2.00
2 LHa,Defended by Matt Murdock
  (Daredevil),A:Spider-Man 2.00
3 LHa,A:Spider-Man, Carnage,
  Daredevil 2.00

VENOM:
SEED OF DARKNESS
1997
1 LKa,JFy,Flashback, early Eddie
  Brock 2.00

VENOM:
SEPARATION ANXIETY
1994–95
1 Embossed(c) 3.00
2 V:Symbiotes 3.00
3 . . . . 3.00
4 . . . . 3.00
TPB Rep.#1-#4 HMe,RoR,SDR .. 9.95

VENOM:
SIGN OF THE BOSS
1997
1 (of 2) IV,TDr,V:Ghost Rider . . . 2.00
2 (of 2) IV,TDr,conclusion 2.00

VENOM:
SINNER TAKES ALL
1995
1 LHa,GLz,I:New Sin-Eater 3.00
2 V:Sineater 3.00
3 Wrong Man 3.00
4 LHa,GLz,V:Sin-Eater 3.00
5 LHa, finale 3.00

VENOM:
TOOTH AND CLAW
1996–97
1 (of 3) LHa,JPi,AM, Dirtnap usurps
  Venom's body 2.00
2 LHa,JPi,AM,V:Wolverine 2.00
3 LHa,JPi,AM,V:Wolverine,
  Chimera 2.00

VENUS
Atlas August, 1948
1 B:Venus,Hedy Devine,HK,Hey
  Look 900.00
2 Venus(c) 550.00
3 Carnival(c) 450.00
4 Cupid(c).HK,Hey Look 475.00
5 Serenade(c) 450.00
6 Wrath of a Goddess,A:Loki . 400.00

7 The Romance That Could
  Not Be 400.00
8 The Love Trap 400.00
9 Whom the Gods Destroy . . 400.00
10 B:Scince Fiction/Horror,
  Trapped On the Moon 450.00
11 The End of the World 550.00
12 GC,The Lost World 350.00
13 BEv,King of the Living Dead 550.00
14 BEv,The Fountain of Death . 550.00
15 BEv,The Empty Grave 550.00
16 BEv,Where Gargoyles Dwell 550.00
17 BEv,Tower of Death,
  Bondage(c) 550.00
18 BEv,Terror in the Tunnel . . . 550.00
19 BEv,THe Kiss Of Death . . . 550.00

VERY BEST OF
MARVEL COMICS
One Shot reps Marvel Artists
  Favorite Stories 12.95

VIDEO JACK
Nov., 1987
1 KGi,O:Video Jack 2.50
2 KGi 2.00
3 KGi 1.75
4 KGi 1.75
5 KGi 1.75
6 KGi,NA,BWr,AW 1.25

VISION, THE
1994–95
1 BHs,mini-series 1.75
2 BHs 1.75
3 BHs 1.75
4 BHs 1.75

VISION &
SCARLET WITCH
[1st Series] Nov., 1982
1 RL,V:Halloween 2.00
2 RL,V:Isbisa,D:Whizzer 1.50
3 RL,A:Wonderman,V:GrimReaper 1.50
4 RL,A:Magneto,Inhumans 1.50
[2nd Series] 1985–86
1 V:Grim Reaper 2.00
2 V:Lethal Legion,D:Grim Reaper 1.75
3 V:Salem's Seven 1.75
4 I:Glamor & Illusion 1.75
5 A:Glamor & Illusion 1.75
6 A:Magneto 1.75
7 V:Toad 1.75
8 A:Powerman 1.75
9 V:Enchantress 1.75
10 A:Inhumans 1.75
11 A:Spider-Man 1.75
12 Birth of V&S's Child 1.25

VISIONARIES
Star Nov., 1987
1 thru 5 . . . . @1.00
6 Sept., 1988 . . . . 1.00

VOID INDIGO
Epic Nov., 1984
1 VM,Epic Comics 2.00
2 VM,Epic Comics,March, 1985 . 2.00

WACKY DUCK
See: DOPEY DUCK

WALLY THE WIZARD
Star April, 1985
1	1.25
2 thru 11	@1.00
12 March, 1986	1.00

WAR, THE
1989
1 Sequel to The Draft & The Pit	3.50
2	3.50
3	3.50
4 1990	3.50

WAR ACTION
Atlas April, 1952
1 JMn,RH,War Stories, Six Dead Men	125.00
2	75.00
3 Invasion in Korea	50.00
4 thru 10	@50.00
11	65.00
12	65.00
13 BK	65.00
14 Rangers Strike,June, 1953	55.00

WAR ADVENTURES
Atlas Jan., 1952
1 GT,Battle Fatigue	100.00
2 The Story of a Slaughter	50.00
3 JRo	40.00
4 RH(c)	40.00
5 RH,Violent(c)	40.00
6 Stand or Die	40.00
7 JMn(c)	40.00
8 BK	70.00
9 RH(c)	30.00
10 JRo(c),Attack at Dawn	30.00
11 Red Trap	30.00
12	30.00
13 RH(c),The Commies Strike Feb., 1953	30.00

WAR COMBAT
Atlas March, 1952
1 JMn,Death of Platoon Leader	100.00
2	50.00
3 JMn(c)	35.00
4 JMn(c)	35.00
5 The Red Hordes	35.00
Becomes:
COMBAT CASEY
6 BEv,Combat Casey cont	100.00
7	75.00
8 JMn(c)	50.00
9	45.00
10 RH(c)	75.00
11	40.00
12	40.00
13 thru 19	@75.00
20	40.00
21 thru 33	@35.00
34 July, 1957	35.00

WAR COMICS
Atlas Dec., 1950
1 You Only Die Twice	175.00
2 Infantry's War	100.00
3	75.00
4 GC,The General Said Nuts	75.00
5	75.00
6 The Deadly Decision of General Kwang	75.00

7 RH	75.00
8 RH,No Survivors	75.00
9 RH	75.00
10	75.00
11 thru 21	@50.00
22	65.00
23 thru 37	@40.00
38 JKu	50.00
39	40.00
40	40.00
41	40.00
42	40.00
43 AT	50.00
44	40.00
45	40.00
46 RC	55.00
47	40.00
48	40.00
49 Sept., 1957	55.00

WARHEADS
Marvel UK 1992–93
1 GEr,I:Warheads,A:Wolverine,	2.25
2 GEr,V:Nick Fury	2.00
3 DTy,A:Iron Man	2.00
4 SCy,A:X-Force	2.00
5 A:X-Force,C:Deaths'Head II	2.00
6 SCy,A:Death's Head II	2.00
7 SCy,A:Death's Head II,S.Surfer	2.00
8 SCy,V:Mephisto	2.00
9 SCy,V:Mephisto	2.00
10 JCz,V:Mephisto	2.00
11 A:Death's Head II	2.00
12 V:Mechanix	2.00
13 Xenophiles Reptiles	2.00
14 last issue	2.00

WARHEADS: BLACK DAWN
1 A:Gh.Rider,Morbius	3.25
2 V:Dracula	2.00

WAR IS HELL
Jan., 1973—Oct., 1975
1 B:Reprints,Decision at Dawn	15.00
2 Anytime,Anyplace,War is Hell	9.00
3 Retreat or Die	9.00
4 Live Grenade	9.00
5 Trapped Platoon	9.00
6 We Die at Dawn	9.00
7 While the Jungle Sleeps,A:Sgt Fury	9.00
8 Killed in Action,A;Sgt Fury	9.00
9 B:Supernatural,War Stories	20.00
10 Death is a 30 Ton Tank	10.00
11 thru 15	@10.00

WARLOCK
[1st Regular Series] Aug., 1972
1 GK,I:Counter Earth,A:High Evolutionary	20.00
2 JB,TS,V:Man Beast	9.00
3 GK,TS,V:Apollo	8.00
4 JK,TS,V:Triax	7.00
5 GK,TS,V:Dr.Doom	7.00
6 TS(i),O:Brute	7.00
7 TS(i),V:Brute,D:Dr.Doom	7.00
8 TS(i),R:Man-Beast(cont in Hulk #176)	7.00
9 JSn,1st'Rebirth'Thanos,O:Magnus, N:Warlock,I:In-Betweener	9.00
10 JSn,SL,O:Thanos,V:Magus, A:In-Betweener	15.00

11 JSn,SL,D:Magus,A:Thanos, In-Betweener	10.00
12 JSn,SL,O:Pip,V:Pro-Boscis A:Starfox	6.00
13 JSn,SL,I&O:Star-Thief	6.00
14 JSn,SL,V:Star-Thief	6.00
15 JSn,A:Thanos,V:Soul-Gem	15.00
[2nd Regular Series] 1992
1 JSn,rep.Strange Tales #178-180 Baxter Paper	4.00
2 JSn,rep.Strange Tales #180 & Warlock #9	2.50
3 JSn,rep.Warlock #10–#12	2.50
4 JSn,rep.Warlock #13–#15	2.50
5 JSn,rep.Warlock #15	2.50
6 JSn,rep.	2.50

Warlock #1
© Marvel Entertainment Group

WARLOCK
[Limited Series]
1 Rep.Warlock Series	3.50
2 Rep.Warlock Series	3.00
3 Rep.Warlock Series	3.00
4 Rep.Warlock Series	3.00
5 Rep.Warlock Series	3.00
6 Rep.Warlock Series	3.00

WARLOCK AND THE INFINITY WATCH
1992–95
1 AMe,Trial of the Gods(from Infinity Gauntlet)	4.00
2 AMe,I:Infinity Watch(Gamora,Pip, Moondragon,Drax & 1 other)	3.00
3 RL,TA,A:High Evolutionary, Nobilus,I:Omega	3.00
4 RL,TA,V:Omega	2.50
5 AMe,TA,V:Omega	2.50
6 AMe,V:Omega(Man-Beast)	2.50
7 TR,TA,V:Mole Man,A:Thanos	2.50
8 TR,TA,Infinity War,A:Thanos	2.25
9 AMe,TA,Inf.War,O:Gamora	2.00
10 AMe,Inf.War,Thanos vs Doppleganger	2.50
11 O:Pip,Gamora,Drax,M'dragon	2.00
12 TR,Drax Vs.Hulk	2.00

---

13 TR,Drax vs Hulk	2.00
14 AMe,V:United Nations	2.00
15 AMe,Magnus,Him	2.00
16 TGr,I:Count Abyss	2.00
17 TGr,I:Maxam	2.00
18 AMe,Inf.Crusade,N:Pip	2.00
19 TGr,A:Hulk,Wolverine,Infinity Crusade	2.00
20 AMe,Inf.Crusade	2.00
21 V:Thor	2.00
22 AMe,Infinity Crusade	2.00
23 JSn(s),TGb,Blood & Thunder#4	2.00
24 JSn(s),TGb,V:Geirrodur	2.00
25 JSn(s),AMe,Die-Cut(c),Blood & Thunder #12	3.25
26 A:Avengers	2.00
27 TGb,V:Avengers	2.00
28 TGb,V:Man-Beast	2.00
29 A:Maya	2.25
30 PO	2.25
31	1.95
32 Heart & Soul	1.95
33 V:Count Abyss	1.95
34 V:Count Abyss	1.95
35 V:Tyrannus	1.95
36	1.95
37 A:Zaharius	1.95
38	1.95
39 V:Domitron	1.95
40 A:Thanos	1.95
41 Monster Island	1.95
42 Warlock vs. Maxam, Atlantis Rising, final issue	1.95

WARLOCK CHRONICLES
1993–94

1 TR,F:Adam Warlock,holo-grafx(c), I:Darklore,Meer'lyn	3.25
2 TR,Infinity Crusade,Thanos revealed to have the Reality Gem	2.25
3 TR,A:Mephisto	2.25
4 TR,A:Magnus	2.25
5 TR(c),Inf.Crusade	2.25
6 TR,Blood & Thunder,pt.#3	2.25
7 TR,Blood & Thunder,pt.#7	2.25
8 TR,Blood & Thunder,pt.#11	2.25
9 TR	2.00
10 TR	2.00
11 TR	2.00

WAR MACHINE
1994–96

1 GG,Foil Embossed(c),B:LKa&StB, O:War Machine,V:Cable, C:Deathlok	3.25
1a Newstand Ed.	2.25
2 GG,V:Cable,Deathlok,w/card	1.75
3 GG,V:Cable,Deathlok	1.75
4 GG,C:Force Works	1.75
5 GG,I:Deachtoll	1.50
6 GG,V:Deathtoll	1.50
7 GG,A:Hawkeye	1.50
8 reg ed.	1.50
8a neon(c),w/insert print	3.00
9 Hands of Mandarin,pt.2	1.50
10 Hands of Mandarin,pt.5	1.50
11 X-Mas Party	1.50
12 V:Terror Device	1.50
13 V:The Rush Team	1.50
14 A:Force Works	1.50
15 In The Past of WWII	2.50
16 DAn,A:Rick Fury,Cap.America	1.50
17 The Man Who Won WWII	1.50
18 DAn,N:War Machine	1.50

19 DAn,A:Hawkeye	1.50
20 DAn,The Crossing	1.50
21 DAn,The Crossing	1.50
22 DAn,V:Iron Man	1.50
23 DAn,Avengers:Timeslide	1.50

WAR MAN
Epic 1993

1 thru 2 CDi(s)	2.50

WEAPON X
1995

1 Wolverine After Xavier	4.00
2 Full Scale War	2.25
3 Jean Leaves	1.95
4 F:Gateway	1.95
TPB Rep.#1-#4	8.95

WEAVEWORLD
Epic 1991–92

1 MM, Clive Barker adaptation	4.95
2 MM,'Into the Weave'	4.95
3 MM	4.95

WEB OF SCARLET SPIDER
1995–96

1 TDF,Virtual Mortality,pt.1	1.95
2 TDF,CyberWar,pt.2	1.95
3 Nightmare in Scarlet,pt.1	1.95
4 Nightmare in Scarlet,pt.3	1.95

Web of Spider-Man #2
© Marvel Entertainment Group

WEB OF SPIDER-MAN
April, 1985

1 JM,V:New Costume	22.00
2 JM,V:Vulture	10.00
3 JM,V:Vulture	7.00
4 JM,JBy,V:Dr.Octopus	6.00
5 JM,JBy,V:Dr.Octopus	6.00
6 MZ,BL,JM,Secret Wars II	6.00
7 SB,A:Hulk,V:Nightmare, C:Wolverine	7.00
8 V:Smithville Thunder	6.00
9 V:Smithville Thunder	6.00
10 JM,A:Dominic Fortune, V:Shocker	6.00

11 BMc,V:Thugs	6.00
12 BMc,SB,V:Thugs	6.00
13 BMc,V:J.JonahJameson	6.00
14 KB,V:Black Fox	6.00
15 V:Black Fox,I:Chance	7.00
16 MS,KB,V:Magma	5.00
17 MS,V:Magma	5.00
18 MS,KB,Where is Spider-Man?	7.00
19 MS,BMc,I:Solo,Humbug	5.50
20 MS,V:Terrorists	5.00
21 V:Fake Spider-Man	5.00
22 MS,V:Terrorists	5.00
23 V:Slyde	5.00
24 SB,V:Vulture,Hobgoblin	6.00
25 V:Aliens	5.00
26 V:Thugs	5.00
27 V:Headhunter	5.00
28 BL,V:Thugs	5.00
29 A:Wolverine,2nd App:New Hobgoblin	16.00
30 KB,O:Rose,C:Daredevil,Capt. America,Wolverine,Punisher	13.00
31 MZ,BMc,V:Kraven	11.00
32 MZ,BMc,V:Kraven	10.00
33 BSz(c),SL,V:Kingpin,Mad Dog Ward,pt.#1	5.00
34 SB,A:Watcher	5.00
35 AS,V:Living Brain	5.00
36 AS,V:Phreak Out,I:Tombstone	6.00
37 V:Slasher	5.00
38 AS,A:Tombstone,V:Hobgoblin	6.00
39 AS,V:Looter(Meteor Man)	4.00
40 AS,V:Cult of Love	4.00
41 AS,V:Cult of Love	4.00
42 AS,V:Cult of Love	4.00
43 AS,V:Cult of Love	4.00
44 AS,V:Warzone,A:Hulk	3.00
45 AS,V:Vulture	3.00
46 AS:Dr.Pym,V:Nekra	3.00
47 AS,V:Hobgoblin	5.00
48 AS,O:New Hobgoblin's Demonic Power	13.00
49 VM,V:Drugs	4.00
50 AS,V:Chameleon(double size)	6.00
51 MBa,V:Chameleon,Lobo Bros.	4.00
52 FS,JR,O:J.Jonah Jameson V:Chameleon	4.00
53 MBa,V:Chameleon,C:Punisher A:Chameleon	4.50
54 AS,V:Chameleon,V:Lobo Bros.	4.00
55 AS,V:Chameleon,Hammerhead, V:Lobo Bros.	4.00
56 AS,I&O:Skin Head, A:Rocket Racer	3.50
57 AS,D:SkinHead, A:Rocket Racer	3.00
58 AS,V:Grizzly	3.00
59 AS,Acts of Vengeance,V:Titania A:Puma,Cosmic Spider-Man	8.00
60 AS,A of V,V:Goliath	5.00
61 AS,A of V,V:Dragon Man	5.00
62 AS,V:Molten Man	3.00
63 AS,V:Mister Fear	3.00
64 AS,V:Graviton,Titania,Trapster	3.00
65 AS,V:Goliath,Trapster,Graviton	3.00
66 AS,V:Tombstone,A:G.Goblin	4.00
67 AS,A:GreenGoblin, V:Tombstone	4.00
68 AS,A:GreenGoblin, V:Tombstone	3.50
69 AS,V:Hulk	5.00
70 AS,I:The Spider/Hulk	3.00
71 A:Silver Sable	2.50
72 AM,A:Silver Sable	2.50
73 AS,A:Human Torch,	

Colossus,Namor 2.50
74 AS,I:Spark,V:Bora 2.50
75 AS,C:New Warriors 2.50
76 AS,Spidey in Ice 2.50
77 AS,V:Firebrand,Inheritor 2.50
78 AS,A:Firebrand,Cloak&Dagger 2.50
79 AS,V:Silvermane 2.50
80 AS,V:Silvermane 2.50
81 I:Bloodshed 2.25
82 V:Man Mountain Marko 2.25
83 V:A.I.M. Supersuit 2.25
84 AS,B:Name of the Rose 3.00
85 AS,Name of the Rose 2.50
86 AS,I:Demogoblin 3.50
87 AS,I:Praetorian Guard 2.50
88 AS,Name of the Rose 2.50
89 AS,E:Name of the Rose,
I:Bloodrose 2.50
90 AS,30th Ann.,w/hologram,
polybagged,V:Mysterio 6.00
90a Gold 2nd printing 3.25
91 AS,V:Whisper And Pulse 2.00
92 AS,V:Foreigner 2.00
93 AS,BMc,V:Hobgoblin,A:Moon
Knight,Foreigner 2.00
94 AS,V:Hobgoblin,A:MoonKnight 2.00
95 AS,Spirits of Venom#1,A:Venom,
J.Blaze,GR,V:Hag & Troll 4.00
96 AS,Spirits of Venom#3, A:G.R,
J.Blaze,Venom,Hobgoblin 3.00
97 AS,I:Dr.Trench,V:Bloodrose . . 1.75
98 AS,V:Bloodrose,Foreigner 1.75
99 I:Night Watch,V:New Enforcer . 1.75
100 AS,JRu,V:Enforcers,Bloodrose,
Kingpin(Alfredo),I:Spider Armor,
O:Night Watch,Holografx(c) . . . 4.00
101 AS,Total Carnage,V:Carnage,
Shriek,A:Cloak and Dagger,
Venom 1.75
102 Total Carnage#6,V:Carnage,
A:Venom,Morbius 1.75
103 AS,Maximum Carnage#10,
V:Carnage 1.50
104 AS,Infinity Crusade 1.50
105 AS,Infinity Crusade 1.50
106 AS,Infinity Crusade 1.50
107 AS,A:Sandman,Quicksand . . 1.50
108 B:TKa(s),AS,I:Sandstorm,
BU:Cardiac 1.50
109 AS,V:Shocker,A:Night Thrasher,
BU:D:Calypso 1.50
110 AS,I:Warrant,A:Lizard 1.50
111 AS,V:Warrant,Lizard 1.50
112 AS,Pursuit#3,V:Chameleon,
w/card 1.75
113 AS,A:Gambit,Black Cat,w/cel . 3.50
113a Newsstand Ed. 1.75
114 AS 1.75
115 AS,V:Facade 1.75
116 AS,V:Facade 1.75
117 Foil(c), flip book with
Power & Responsibility #1 . . . 5.50
117a Newsstand ed. 2.50
118 Spider-clone, V:Venom 3.00
119 Clone,V:Venom 2.25
119a bagged with Milestone rep.
Amazing Sp-Man #150,checklist 6.50
120 Web of Life,pt.1 . . . . 2.50
121 Web of Life,pt.3 . . . . 2.50
122 Smoke and Mirrors,pt.1 . . . . 2.50
123 The Price of Truth,pt.2 . . . . . 1.50
124 The Mark of Kaine,pt.1 . . . . 1.50
125 R:Gwen Stacy 2.95
125a 3-D Holodisk cover 4.25
126 The Trial of Peter Parker,pt.1 1.50

127 Maximum Clonage,pt.2 . . . . . 1.50
128 TDF,Exiled,pt.1 . . . . 1.50
129 Timebomb,pt.2 . . . . 1.50
Ann.#1 V:Future Max 6.00
Ann.#2 AAd,MMi,A:Warlock 8.00
Ann.#3 AS,DP,JRu,JM,BL 4.50
Ann.#4 AS,TM,RLm,Evolutionary
Wars,A:Man Thing,V:Slug 5.00
Ann.#5 AS,SD,JS,Atlantis
Attacks,A:Fantastic Four 3.50
Ann.#6 SD,JBr,SB,A:Punisher . . . 4.50
Ann.#7 Vibranium Vendetta #3 . . 2.50
Ann.#8 Hero Killers#3,A:New
Warriors,BU:Venom,Black Cat . 3.00
Ann.#9 CMa,I:Cadre,w/card 3.25
Ann.#10 V:Shriek 3.75
Super Size Spec.#1 Planet of
the Symbiotes,pt.5 . . . . 3.95

Weird Wonder Tales #20
© Marvel Entertainment Group

WEIRD WONDERTALES
Dec., 1973

1 B:Reprints 15.00
2 I Was Kidnapped by a Flying
Saucer 10.00
3 The Thing in the Bog 10.00
4 It Lurks Behind the Wall 10.00
5 . . . . 10.00
6 The Man Who Owned a Ghost 10.00
7 The Apes That Walked
like Men 10.00
8 Reap A Deadly Harvest 10.00
9 The Murder Mirror 10.00
10 Mister Morgans Monster 10.00
11 Slaughter in Shrangri-La 8.00
12 The Stars Scream Murder 8.00
13 The Totem Strikes 8.00
14 Witching Circle 8.00
15 . . . . 8.00
16 The Shark 8.00
17 Creature From Krogarr 8.00
18 Krang 8.00
19 A:Dr Druid 8.00
20 The Madness 8.00
21 A:Dr Druid 8.00
22 The World Below,May, 1975 . . 8.00

WEREWOLF BY NIGHT
Sept., 1972

1 MP(cont from Marvel Spotlight)
FullMoonRise..WerewolfKill . . 50.00
2 MP,Like a Wild Beast at Bay . 20.00
3 MP,Mystery of the Mad Monk 13.00
4 MP,The Danger Game 13.00
5 MP,A Life for a Death 13.00
6 MP,Carnival of Fear 10.00
7 MP,JM,Ritual of Blood 8.00
8 MP,Krogg,Lurker from Beyond . 8.00
9 TS,V:Tatterdemalion 8.00
10 TS,bondage cover 8.00
11 GK,TS,Full Moon..Fear Moon . 6.00
12 GK,Cry Monster 6.00
13 MP,ManMonsterCalledTaboo . 5.00
14 MP,Lo,the Monster Strikes . . . 5.00
15 MP,(new)O:Werewolf,
V:Dracula 6.00
16 MP,TS,A:Hunchback of Notre
Dame 5.00
17 Behold the Behemoth 5.00
18 War of the Werewolves 5.00
19 V:Dracula 7.00
20 The Monster Breaks Free 5.00
21 GK(c),To Cure a Werewolf . . . 4.00
22 GK(c),Face of a Friend 4.00
23 Silver Bullet for a Werewolf . . 4.00
24 GK(c),V:The Brute 4.00
25 GK(c),Eclipse of Evil 4.00
26 GK(c),A Crusade of Murder . . 4.00
27 GK(c),Scourge o/t Soul-Beast . 4.00
28 GK(c),V:Dr.Glitternight 4.00
29 GK(c),V:Dr.Glitternight 4.00
30 GK(c),Red Slash across
Midnight 4.00
31 Death in White 4.00
32 I&O:Moon Knight 65.00
33 Were-Beast..Moon Knight
A:Moon Knight(2nd App) 30.00
34 GK(c),TS,House of Evil..House
of Death 4.00
35 TS,JS,BWi,Jack Russell vs.
Werewolf 4.00
36 Images of Death 4.00
37 BWr(c),BW,A:Moon Knight,
Hangman,Dr.Glitternight 7.00
38 . . . . 3.50
39 V:Brother Voodoo 3.50
40 A:Brother Voodoo,V:Dr.
Glitternight 3.50
41 V:Fire Eyes 3.50
42 A:IronMan,Birth of a Monster . 3.50
43 Tri-Animal Lives,A:Iron Man . . 3.50
G-Size#2,SD,A:Frankenstein
Monster (reprint) 3.00
G-Size#3 GK(c),Transylvania 3.50
G-Size#4 GK(c),A:Morbius 10.00
G-Size#5 GK(c),Peril of
Paingloss 3.00

WEREWOLF BY NIGHT
Dec., 1997

1 PJe,F:Jack Russell returns . . . 3.00
2 PJe,Search for wolf Amulet . . . 3.00
3 PJe,Stuck between man & wolf 3.00
4 PJe,to the depths of hell 3.00
5 PJe, confronts demon 3.00
6 PJe, visit Underworld nightclub 3.00
Storyline continues in Strange Tales

WEST COAST AVENGERS
[Limited Series] Sept., 1984
1 BH,A:Shroud,J:Hawkeye,IronMan,

West Coast Avengers #1
© Marvel Entertainment Group

#1 IN A FOUR-ISSUE LIMITED SERIES

WEST COAST AVENGERS

WonderMan,Mockingbird,Tigra 4.00
2 BH,V:Blank 3.00
3 BH,V:Graviton 2.00
4 BH,V:Graviton 2.00
[Regular Series] 1985–89
1 AM,JSt,V:Lethal Legion 4.00
2 AM,JSt,V:Lethal Legion 3.00
3 AM,JSt,V:Kraven 3.00
4 AM,JSt,A:Firebird,Thing,I:Master
   Pandemonium 3.00
5 AM,JSt,A:Werewolf,Thing 3.00
6 AM,KB,A:Thing 3.00
7 AM,JSt,V:Ultron 3.00
8 AM,JSt,V:Rangers,A:Thing . . . 3.00
9 AM,JSt,V:Master Pandemonium 3.00
10 AM,JSt,V:Headlok,Griffen 3.00
11 AM,JSt,A:Nick Fury 2.50
12 AM,JSt,V:Graviton 2.50
13 AM,JSt,V:Graviton 2.50
14 AM,JSt,V:Pandemonium 2.50
15 AM,JSt,A:Hellcat 2.50
16 AM,JSt,V:Tiger Shark,
   Whirlwind 2.50
17 AM,JSt,V:Dominus' Minions . . 2.50
18 AM,JSt,V:The Wild West 2.50
19 AM,JSt,A:Two Gun Kid 2.50
20 AM,JSt,A:Rawhide Kid 2.50
21 AM,JSt,A:Dr.Pym,Moon Knight 2.50
22 AM,JSt,A:Fant.Four,Dr.Strange,
   Night Rider 2.00
23 AM,RT,A:Phantom Rider 2.00
24 AM,V:Dominus 2.00
25 AM,V:Abomination 2.00
26 AM,V:Zodiac 2.00
27 AM,V:Zodiac 1.75
28 AM,V:Zodiac 1.75
29 AM,V:Taurus,A:Shroud 1.75
30 AM,C:Composite Avenger . . . 1.75
31 AM,V:Arkon 1.75
32 AM,TD,V:Yetrigar,J:Wasp . . . 1.75
33 AM,O:Ant-Man,Wasp;
   V:Madam X,El Toro 1.75
34 AM,V:Quicksilver,J:Vision &
   Scarlet Witch 1.75
35 AM,V:Dr.Doom,Quicksilver . . . 1.75
36 AM,V:The Voice 1.75
37 V:The Voice,A:Mantis 1.75
38 AM,TMo,V:Defiler 1.50

39 AM,V:Swordsman 1.50
40 AM,MGu,V:NightShift,
   A:Shroud 1.50
41 TMo,I:New Phantom Rider,
   L:Moon Knight 1.50
42 JBy,Visionquest#1,V:Ultron . . . 2.50
43 JBy,Visionquest#2, ... 2.25
44 JBy,Visionquest#3,J:USAgent . 2.00
45 JBy,Visionquest#4,
   I:New Vision 2.25
46 JBy,I:Great Lakes Avengers . . 2.00
Ann. #1 MBr,GI,V:Zodiak 2.25
Ann. #2 AM,A:SilverSurfer,V:Death,
   Collector,R:Grandmaster 2.00
Ann. #3 AM,RLm,TD,Evolutionary
   Wars,R:Giant Man 3.50
Becomes:
AVENGERS WEST COAST

WESTERN GUNFIGHTERS
[2nd series] August, 1970
1 JK,JB,DAy,B:Ghost Rider
   A:Fort Rango,The Renegades
   Gunhawk 12.00
2 HT(c),DAy,JMn,O:Nightwind,
   V:Tarantula 7.00
3 DAy,V:Hurricane(reprint) 7.00
4 HT(c),DAy,TS,B:Gunhawk,
   Apache Kid,A:Renegades . . . 7.00
5 DAy,FrG,A:Renegades 7.00
6 HT(c),DAy,SSh,Death of
   Ghost Rider 8.00
7 HT(c),DAy,SSh,O:Ghost Rider
   retold,E:Ghost Rider,Gunhawk 10.00
8 DAy,SSh,B:Black Rider,Outlaw
   Kid(rep) 6.00
9 DW,Revenge rides the Range . 6.00
10 JK,JMn,O:Black Rider,B:Matt
   Slade,E:Outlaw Kid 6.00
11 JK,Duel at Dawn 6.00
12 JMn,O:Matt Slade 6.00
13 Save the Gold Coast Expires . 6.00
14 JSo(c),Outlaw Town 6.00
15 E:Matt Slade,Showdown in
   Outlaw Canyon 6.00
16 B:Kid Colt,Shoot-out in Silver
   City 6.00
17 thru 20 . . . . @6.00
21 thru 24 . . . . @5.00
25 . . . . 5.00
26 F:Kid Colt,Gun-Slinger,Apache
   Kid 5.00
27 thru 32 . . . . @5.00
33 Nov., 1975 . . . . 5.00

WESTERN KID
[1st Series] Dec., 1954
1 JR,B:Western Kid,O:Western Kid
   (Tex Dawson) 150.00
2 JMn,JR,Western Adventure . . 75.00
3 JMn(c),JR,Gunfight(c) 60.00
4 JMn(c),JR,The Badlands . . . 60.00
5 JR 60.00
6 JR 60.00
7 JR 60.00
8 JR 60.00
9 JR,AW 75.00
10 JR,AW,Man in the Middle . . 75.00
11 thru 16 . . . . @50.00
17 August, 1957 . . . . 50.00
[2nd Series] Dec., 1971–Aug. 1972
1 Reprints 10.00
2 . . . . 7.00
3 . . . . 7.00

4 . . . . 7.00
5 . . . . 7.00

WESTERN OUTLAWS
Atlas Feb., 1954—Aug., 1957
1 JMn(c),RH,BP,The Greenville
   Gallows,Hanging(c) 125.00
2 . . . . 65.00
3 thru 10 . . . . @50.00
11 AW 50.00
12 . . . . 50.00
13 MB 50.00
14 AW 55.00
15 AT,GT 50.00
16 BP 40.00
17 . . . . 45.00
18 . . . . 40.00
19 . . . . 50.00
20 and 21 . . . . @45.00

**WESTERN OUTLAWS
& SHERIFFS**
See: BEST WESTERN

**WESTERN TALES
OF BLACK RIDER**
See: ALL WINNERS COMICS

WESTERN TEAM-UP
Nov., 1973
1 Rawhide Kid/Dakota Kid 2.00

WESTERN THRILLERS
Nov., 1954
1 JMn,Western tales 100.00
2 . . . . 50.00
3 . . . . 50.00
4 . . . . 50.00
Becomes:
COWBOY ACTION
5 JMn(c),The Prairie Kid 60.00
6 . . . . 40.00
7 . . . . 40.00
9 . . . . 40.00
10 . . . . 40.00
11 MN,AW,Ther Manhunter March,
   1956 . . . . 60.00
Becomes:
**QUICK-TRIGGER
WESTERN**
12 Bill Larson Strikes 75.00
13 The Man From Cheyenne . . . 85.00
14 BEv,RH(c) 60.00
15 AT 50.00
16 JK 45.00
17 GT 45.00
18 GM 45.00
19 JSe 40.00

WESTERN WINNERS
See: ALL WINNERS COMICS

WHAT IF?
[1st Regular Series] Feb., 1977
1 Spider-Man joined Fant.Four . 18.00
2 GK(c),Hulk had Banner brain . . 9.00
3 GK,KJ,F:Avengers 6.00
4 GK(c),F:Invaders 6.00
5 F:Captain America 6.00
6 F:Fantastic Four 6.00

7 GK(c),F:Spider-Man	6.00
8 GK(c),F:Daredevil	5.50
9 JK(c),F:Avengers of the '50s	6.00
10 JB,F:Thor	5.00
11 JK,F:FantasticFour	5.00
12 F:Hulk	5.00
13 JB,Conan Alive Today	6.00
14 F:Sgt. Fury	5.00
15 CI,F:Nova	5.00
16 F:Master of Kung Fu	5.00
17 CI,F:Ghost Rider	5.00
18 TS,F:Dr.Strange	4.00
19 PB,F:Spider-Man	5.00
20 F:Avengers	4.00
21 GC,F:Sub-Mariner	4.00
22 F:Dr.Doom	4.00
23 JB,F:Hulk	4.00
24 GK,RB,Gwen Stacy had lived	5.00
25 F:Thor,Avengers,O:Mentor	4.00
26 JBy(c),F:Captain America	4.00
27 FM(c),Phoenix hadn't died	7.00
28 FM,F:Daredevil,Ghost Rider.	6.00
29 MG(c),F:Avengers	4.00
30 RB,F:Spider-Man	10.00
31 Wolverine killed the Hulk	15.00
32 Avengers lost to Korvac	3.50
33 BL,Dazzler herald of Galactus	3.50
34 FH,FM,JBy,BSz:Humor issue	3.50
35 FM,Elektra had lived	6.00
36 JBy,Fant.Four had no powers	3.00

What If? #35
© Marvel Entertainment Group

37 F:Thing,Beast,Silver Surfer	3.50
38 F:Daredevil,Captain America	3.00
39 Thor had fought Conan	3.00
40 F:Dr.Strange	3.00
41 F:Sub-Mariner	3.50
42 F:Fantastic Four	3.00
43 F:Conan	3.00
44 F:Captain America	3.00
45 F:Hulk,Berserk	3.50
46 Uncle Ben had lived	5.00
47 F:Thor,Loki	3.00
Spec.#1 F:Iron Man,Avengers	4.00
Best of What IF? rep.#1,#24,	
#27,#28	12.95

[2nd Regular Series]

1 RWi,MG,The Avengers had lost	
the Evolutionary War	5.00
2 GCa,Daredevil Killed Kingpin,	

A:Hobgoblin, The Rose	4.00
3 Capt.America Hadn't Given Up	
Costume,A:Avengers	3.50
4 MBa,Spider-Man kept Black	
Costume,A:Avengers,Hulk	4.50
5 Vision Destroyed Avengers,	
A:Wonder Man	3.50
6 RLm,X-Men Lost Inferno,	
A:Dr.Strange	6.00
7 RLd,Wolverine Joined Shield,	
A:Nick Fury,Black Widow	7.00
8 Iron Man Lost The Armor Wars,	
A:Ant Man	3.50
9 RB,New X-Men Died	6.00
10 MZ(c),BMc,Punisher's Family	
Didn't Die,A:Kingpin	3.00
11 TM(c),JV,SM,Fant.Four had the	
Same Powers,A:Nick Fury	3.50
12 JV,X-Men Stayed in Asgard,	
A:Thor,Hela	3.00
13 JLe(c),Prof.X Became	
Juggernaut,A:X-Men	3.50
14 RLm(c),Capt.Marvel didn't die	
A:Silver Surfer	3.00
15 GCa,Fant.Four Lost Trial of	
Galactus,A:Gladiator	3.00
16 Wolverine Battled Conan,	
A:X-Men,Red Sonja	5.00
17 Kraven Killed Spider-Man,	
A:Daredevil,Captain America	3.00
18 LMc,Fant.Four fought Dr.Doom	
before they gained powers	2.50
19 RW,Vision took over Earth,	
A:Avengers,Dr.Doom	2.50
20 Spider-Man didn't marry Mary	
Jane,A:Venom,Kraven	3.00
21 Spider-Man married Black Cat,	
A:Vulture,Silver Sable	2.50
22 RLm,Silver Surfer didn't escape	
Earth,A:F.F,Mephisto,Thanos	4.00
23 New X-Men never existed,	
A:Eric the Red,Lilandra	2.50
24 Wolverine Became Lord of	
Vampires,A:Punisher	3.00
25 Marvel Heroes lost Atlantis	
Attacks,double size	3.25
26 LMc,Punisher Killed Daredevil,	
A:Spider-Man	2.50
27 Submariner Joined Fantastic	
Four,A:Dr. Doom	2.00
28 RW,Capt.America led Army of	
Super-Soldiers,A:Submariner	2.00
29 RW,Capt.America formed the	
Avengers	2.00
30 Inv.Woman's 2nd Child had	
lived,A:Fantastic Four	2.00
31 Spider-Man/Captain Universe	
Powers	2.00
32 Phoenix Rose Again,pt.1	2.00
33 Phoenix Rose Again,pt.2	2.00
34 Humor Issue	1.75
35 B:Time Quake,F.F. vs.Dr. Doom	
& Annihilus	1.75
36 Cosmic Avengers,V:Guardians	
of the Galaxy	1.75
37 X-Vampires,V:Dormammu	1.75
38 Thor was prisoner of Set	1.75
39 E:Time Quake,Watcher saved the	
Universe	1.75
40 Storm remained A thief?	1.75
41 JV,Avengers fought Galactus	2.00
42 KWe,Spidey kept extra arms	1.75
43 Wolverine married Mariko	1.75
44 Punisher possessed by Venom	1.75
45 Barbara Ketch became G.R.	1.75

46 Cable Killed Prof.X,Cyclops &	
Jean Grey	1.75
47 Magneto took over USA	1.75
48 Daredevil Saved Nuke	1.50
49 Silver Surfer had Inf.Gauntlet?	1.50
50 Hulk killed Wolverine	4.00
51 PCu,Punisher is Capt.America	1.50
52 BHi,Wolverine led Alpha Flight	2.00
53 F:Iron Man,Hulk	1.50
54 F:Death's Head	1.50
55 LKa(s),Avengers lose G.Storm	1.50
56 Avengers lose G.Storm#2	1.50
57 Punisher a member of SHIELD	1.50
58 Punisher kills SpM	1.50
59 Wolverine lead Alpha Flight	2.00
60 RoR,Scott & Jean's Wedding	1.50
61 Spider-Man's Parents	1.95
62 Woverine vs Weapon X	2.25
63 F:War Machine,Iron Man	1.95
64 Iron Man sold out	2.25
65 Archangel fell from Grace	1.50
66 Rogue and Thor	1.50
67 Cap.America returns	1.50
68 Captain America story	1.50
69 Stryfe Killed X-Men	1.50
70 Silver Surfer	1.50
71 The Hulk	1.50
72 Parker Killed Burglar	1.50
73 Daredevil,Kingpin	1.50
74 Sinister Formed X-Men	1.50
75 Gen-X's Blink had lived	1.50
76 Flash Thompson Spider-Man	1.50
77 Legion had killed Magneto	1.50
78 FF had stayed together	1.50
79 Storm had Phoenix's Power	1.50
80 KGa,Hulk was Cured	1.50
81 Age of Apocalypse didn't end	1.50
82 WML,J.JonahJameson	
adopted Spider-Man	1.50
83	1.50
84	1.50
85 Magneto Ruled all mutants	1.50
86	1.50
87	1.50
88	1.50
89	1.50
90	1.50
91 F:Hulk, nice guy, Banner violent	1.50
92 F:Cannonball,Husk	1.50
93 F:Wolverine	1.50
94 JGz,F:Juggernaut	1.50
95 IV,F:Ghost Rider	1.50
96 CWo,F:Quicksilver,	2.00
97 F:Black Knight	2.00
98 F:Nightcrawler & Rogue	2.00
99 F:Black Cat	2.00
100 IV,KJ,F:Gambit & Rogue, 48pg	3.00
101 ATi,F:Archangel	2.00
102 F:Daredevil's Dad	2.00
103 DaF,F:Captain America	2.00
104 F:Silver Surver,ImpossibleMan	2.00
105 TDF,RF,F:Spider-Man and	
Mary Jane's Daughter	2.00
106 TDF,F:X-Men,Gambit	
sentenced to death	2.00
107 TDF,RF,BSz,F:Thor	2.00
108 TDF,F:The Avengers	2.00
109 TA,F:Fantastic Four	2.00
110 TDF,F:Wolverine	2.00
111 TDF,F:Wolverine	2.00
112 F:Ka-Zar	2.00
113 F:Iron Man, Dr. Strange,	2.00
Minus 1 Spec., AOI, flashback,	
F:Bishop	1.95
TPB Best of What If?	12.95

WHAT THE -?!
[Parodies]
August, 1988

1	5.00
2 JBy,JOy,AW,	4.00
3 TM,	5.00
4	3.00
5 EL,JLe,WPo,Wolverine	5.00
6 Wolverine,Punisher	3.00
7	2.50
8 DK	2.50
9	1.75
10 JBy,X-Men,Dr.Doom, Cap. America	1.75
11 DK,RLd(part)	2.00
12 Conan, F.F.,Wolverine.	1.50
13 Silver Burper,F.F.,Wolverine.	1.50
14 Spittle-Man	1.50
15 Capt.Ultra,Wolverina	1.50
16 Ant Man,Watcher	1.25
17 Wulverean/Pulverizer,Hoagg/Spider-Ham,SleepGawker,F.F.	1.25
18	1.25
19	1.25
20 Infinity Wart Crossover	1.25
21 Weapon XX,Toast Rider	1.25
22 F:Echs Farce	1.25
23	1.25
24 Halloween issue	1.25

What The-?! #6
© Marvel Entertainment Group

25	1.25
26 Spider-Ham 2099	1.25
Summer Spec.	2.50
Fall Spec.	2.50

WHERE CREATURES ROAM
July, 1970—Sept., 1971

1 JK,SD,DAy,B:Reprints The Brute That Walks	25.00
2 JK,SD,Midnight/Monster	15.00
3 JK,SD,DAy,Thorg	15.00
4 JK,SD,Vandoom	15.00
5 JK,SD,Gorgilla	15.00
6 JK,SD,Zog	15.00

7 SD	15.00
8 The Mummy's Secret,E:Reprints	15.00

WHERE MONSTERS DWELL
Jan., 1970

1 B:Reprints,Cyclops	25.00
2 Sporr	15.00
3 Grottu	15.00
4	15.00
5 Taboo	15.00
6 Groot	15.00
7 Rommbu	15.00
8 The Four-Armed Men	15.00
9 Bumbu	15.00
10 Monster That Walks Like A Man	15.00
11 Gruto	12.00
12 Orogo	12.00
13 The Thing That Crawl	12.00
14 The Green Thing	12.00
15 Kraa- The Inhuman	12.00
16 Beware the Son Of Goom	12.00
17 The Hidden Vampires	12.00
18 The Mask of Morghum	12.00
19 The Insect Man	12.00
20 Klagg	12.00
21 Fin Fang Foom	12.00
22 Elektro	12.00
23 The Monster Waits For Me	12.00
24 The Things on Easter Island	12.00
25 The Ruler of the Earth	12.00
26	12.00
27	12.00
28 Droom,The Living Lizard	12.00
29 thru 37 Reprints	@12.00
38 Reprints,Oct., 1975	12.00

WHIP WILSON
See: BLAZE CARSON

WILD
Atlas Feb., 1954

1 BEv,JMn,Charlie Chan Parody	175.00
2 BEv,RH,JMn,Witches(c)	125.00
3 CBu(c),BEv,RH,JMn,	100.00
4 GC,Didja Ever See a Cannon Brawl	100.00
5 RH,JMn,August, 1954	100.00

WILD CARDS
Epic Sept., 1990

1 JG	5.50
2 JG,V:Jokers	4.50
3 A:Turtle	4.50

WILDC.A.T.S/X-MEN: THE DARK AGE
Dec., 1997

1-shot MtB,WEI,V:Daemonites & Sentinels, 48pg	4.50
1a variant cover MGo	4.50

WILD THING
Marvel UK 1993

1 A:Virtual Reality Venom and Carnage	3.00
2 A:VR Venom and Carnage	2.00
3 A:Shield	2.00
4	2.00
5 Virtual Reality Gangs	2.00

6 Virtual Reality Villians	2.00
7 V:Trask	2.00
8	1.75
9	1.75
10	1.75
11	1.75
12	1.75
13	1.75

WILD WEST
Spring, 1948

1 SSh(c),B:Two Gun Kids,Tex Taylor,Arizona Annie	225.00
2 SSh(c),CCb, Captain Tootsie	175.00

Becomes:

WILD WESTERN

3 SSh(c),B:Tex Morgan,Two Gun Kid,Tex Taylor,Arizona Annie	200.00
4 Rh,SSh,CCB,Capt. Tootsie. A:Kid Colt,E:Arizona Annie	150.00
5 RH,CCB,Captain Tootsie A;Black Rider,Blaze Carson	150.00
6 A:Blaze Carson,Kid Colt	100.00
7	100.00
8 RH	100.00
9 Ph(c),B:Black Rider	150.00
10 Ph(c)	175.00
11	100.00
12	80.00
13	80.00
14	80.00
15	90.00
16 thru 20	@75.00
21 thru 29	@70.00
30 JKa	75.00
31 thru 40	@50.00
41 thru 47	@40.00
48 AW	45.00
49 thru 53	@40.00
54 AW	60.00
55 AW	60.00
56 and 57 Sept. 1957	@40.00

WILLIAM SHATNER'S TEK WORLD
1992–94

1 LS,Novel adapt.	2.25

William Shatner's Tek World #12
© Marvel Entertainment Group

2 LS,Novel adapt.cont.	2.00
3 LS,Novel adapt.cont.	2.00
4 LS,Novel adapt.cont.	2.00
5 LS,Novel adapt.concludes	2.00
6 LS,V:TekLords	2.00
7 E:The Angel	2.00
8	2.00
9	2.00
10	2.00
11 thru 17	2.00
18	2.00
19 Sims of the Father#1	1.75
20 Sims of the Father#2	1.75
21 Who aren't in Heaven	1.75
22 Father and Guns	1.75
23 We'll be Right Back	2.00
24	1.75

WILLIE COMICS
See: IDEAL COMICS

WILLOW
August, 1988

1 Movie adapt.	1.00
2 Movie adapt.	1.00
3 Movie adapt,Oct., 1988.	1.00

WITNESS, THE
Sept., 1948

1	1,000.00

WOLFPACK
August, 1988

1 I:Wolfpack	1.00
2 thru 11	@1.00
12 July, 1988	1.00

Wolverine #1
© Marvel Entertainment Group

WOLVERINE
[Limited Series] Sept., 1982

1 B:CCl(s),FM,JRu,A:Mariko, I:Shingen	42.00
2 FM,JRu,A:Mariko,I:Yukio	30.00
3 FM,JRu,A:Mariko,Yukio	30.00
4 B:CCl(s),FM,JRu,A:Mariko, D:Shingen	32.00

[Regular Series] 1988

1 JB,AW,V:Banipur	40.00
2 JB,KJ,V:Silver Samurai	20.00
3 JB,AW,V:Silver Samurai	15.00
4 JB,AW,I:Roughouse, Bloodsport	14.00
5 JB,AW,V:Roughouse, Bloodsport	14.00
6 JB,AW,V:Roughouse, Bloodsport	13.00
7 JB,A:Hulk	12.00
8 JB,A:Hulk	12.00
9 GC,Old Wolverine Story	12.00
10 JB,BSz,V:Sabretooth (1st battle)	37.00
11 JB,BSz,B:Gehenna Stone	8.00
12 JB,BSz,Gehenna Stone	8.00
13 JB,BSz,Gehenna Stone	8.00
14 JB,BSz,Gehenna Stone	8.00
15 JB,BSz,Gehenna Stone	8.00
16 JB,BSz,E:Gehenna Stone	8.00
17 JBy,KJ,V:Roughouse	7.00
18 JBy,KJ,V:Roughouse	7.00
19 JBy,KJ,A of V,I:La Bandera	7.00
20 JBy,KJ,A of V,V:Tigershark	6.00
21 JBy,KJ,V:Geist	6.00
22 JBy,KJ,V:Geist,Spore	6.00
23 JBy,KJ,V:Geist,Spore	6.00
24 GC,'Snow Blind'	5.00
25 JB,O:Wolverine(part)	5.00
26 KJ,Return to Japan	4.50
27 thru 30 Lazarus Project	4.50
31 MS,DGr,A:Prince o'Mandripoor	4.50
32 MS,DGr,V:Ninjas	4.50
33 MS,Wolverine in Japan	4.50
34 MS,DGr,Wolverine in Canada	4.50
35 MS,DGr,A:Puck	4.50
36 MS,DGr,A:Puck,Lady D'strike	4.50
37 MS,DGr,V:Lady Deathstrike	4.50
38 MS,DGr,A:Storm,I:Elsie Dee	4.50
39 MS,DGr,Wolverine Vs. Clone	4.50
40 MS,DGr,Wolverine Vs. Clone	4.50
41 MS,DGr,R:Sabretooth, A:Cable	12.00
41a 2nd printing	2.25
42 MS,DGr,A:Sabretooth,Cable	7.00
42a 2nd printing	2.25
43 MS,DGr,A:Sabretooth,C:Cable	5.00
44 LSn,DGr	4.00
45 MS,DGr,A:Sabretooth	5.00
46 MS,DGr,A:Sabretooth	4.50
47 V:Tracy	4.00
48 LHa(s),MS,DGr,B:Shiva Scenario	4.00
49 LHa(s),MS,DGr,	4.00
50 LHa(s),MS,DGr,A:X-Men,Nick Fury, I:Shiva,Slash-Die Cut(c)	8.00
51 MS,DGr,A:Mystique,X-Men	3.50
52 MS,DGr,A:Mystique,V:Spiral	3.50
53 MS,A:Mystique,V:Spiral,Mojo	3.50
54 A:Shatterstar	3.50
55 MS,V:Cylla,A:Gambit,Sunfire	3.50
56 MS,A:Gambit,Sunfire,V:Hand, Hydra	3.50
57 MS,D:Lady Mariko,A:Gambit	4.00
58 A:Terror	3.00
59 A:Terror	3.00
60 Sabretooth vs.Shiva, I:John Wraith	3.50
61 MT,History of Wolverine and Sabretooth,A:John Wraith	3.50
62 MT,A:Sabretooth,Silver Fox	3.00
63 MT,V:Ferro,D:Silver Fox	3.00
64 MPa,V:Ferro,Sabretooth	3.00
65 MT,A:Professor X	3.00
66 MT,A:X-Men	3.00

67 MT,A:X-Men	3.00
68 MT,V:Epsilon Red	3.00
69 DT,A:Rogue,V:Sauron,tie-in to X-Men#300	2.75
70 DT,Sauron,A:Rogue,Jubilee	2.75
71 DT,V:Sauron,Brain Child, A:Rogue, Jubilee	2.75
72 DT,Sentinels	2.75
73 DT,V:Sentinels	2.75
74 ANi,V:Sentinels	2.50
75 AKu,Hologram(c),Wolv.has Bone Claws,leaves X-Men	9.00
76 DT(c),B:LHa(s),A:Deathstrike, Vindicator,C:Puck	2.25
77 AKu,A:Vindicator,Puck,V:Lady Deathstrike	2.25
78 AKu,V:Cylla,Bloodscream	2.25
79 AKu,V:Cyber,I:Zoe Culloden	2.25
80 IaC,V:Cyber,	2.25
81 IaC,V:Cyber,A:Excalibur	2.25
82 AKu,BMc,A:Yukio,Silver Samurai	2.25
83 AKu,A:Alpha Flight	2.25
84 A:Alpha Flight	1.95
85 Phalanx Covenant, Final Sanction, V:Phalanx,holografx(c)	4.50
85a newsstand ed.	5.50
86 AKu,V:Bloodscream	2.50
87 AKu,deluxe,V:Juggernaut	3.25
87a newsstand ed.	1.50
88 AKu,deluxe ed.	3.25
88a newsstand ed.	1.50
89 deluxe ed.	3.25
89a newsstand ed.	1.50
90 V:Sabretooth, deluxe ed.	5.00
90a newsstand ed.	1.50
91 LHa,Logan's future unravels	4.00
92 LHa,AKu,DGr,A:Sabretooth	4.00
93 R:Cyber	4.00
94 Feral Wolverine	4.00
95 LHa,AKu,DGr,V:Dark Riders	4.00
96 LHa,AKu,DGr,Death of Cyber	4.00
97 LHa,AKu,DGr,A:Genesis	3.50
98 LHa,AKu,F:Genesis	3.50
99	3.50
100 LHa,AKu,DG,A:Elektra;double-size, Foil Hologram cover	12.00
100a regular edition	6.00
101 LHa,AKu,A:Elektra	4.00
102 LHa	3.50
103 LHa,Elektra,A:Onslaught	5.00
104 LHa,Gateway, Onslaught	2.50
105 LHa,Gateway, Elektra	2.25
106 LHa	2.25
107 LHa,VS,prologue to Elektra#1	2.25
108 LHa,back to Tokyo,A:Yukio	2.25
109 LHa,DG,	2.25
110 LHa,DG,Who's spying on Logan	2.25
111 LHa,DG,Logan moves to NYC	2.25
112 LHa,DG,Logan in NYC	2.25
113 LHa,R:Ogun,A:Lady Deathstrike & Spiral	2.00
114 LHa,back in costume,V:Cyborg Donald Pierce	2.00
115 LHa,Zero Tolerance,V:Bastion	2.00
116 LHa,Zero Tolerance,	2.00
117 LHa,Zero Tolerance, V:Prime Sentinels	2.00
118 LHa,Zero Tolerance aftermath	2.00
119 WEI,Pt.1 (of 4)	2.00
120 WEI,The White Ghost	2.00
121 WEI,Not Yet Dead, pt.3	2.00
122 WEI,Not Yet Dead, pt.4	2.00
123 TDF,DCw,R:Roughouse,	

MARVEL

Bloodscream 2.00
124 TDF,DCw,A:Captain America,
  V:Rascal 2.00
125 CCI,V:Viper,48pg 3.00
126 CCI,V:Sabretooth 2.00
127 CCI,Sabretooth takes over . . 2.00
128 CCI,V:Hydra, The Hand 2.00
129 TDz,A:Wendigo 2.00
TPB Wolverine rep Marvel Comics
  Presents #1-#10 . . . . 2.95
Jungle Adventure MMi,(Deluxe) . . 5.50
SC Acts of Vengeance, rep. 6.95
Bloodlust (one shot),AD
  V:Siberian Were-Creatures . . . 6.00
Global Jeapordy,PDd(s) 2.95
Killing, KSW,JNR 5.95
Rahne of Terror, C:Cable 8.00
Save the Tiger,rep. 2.95
GNv Bloody ChoicesJB,A:N.Fury 12.95
Typhoid's Kiss,rep. 6.95
Inner Fury,BSz,V:Nanotech
  Machines 6.25
GN Scorpio Rising, T.U.Fury . . . 5.95
HC Weapon X 19.95
Spec. '95 LHa,F:Nightcrawler . . . 3.95
Minus 1 Spec., LHa,CNn, flashback,
  F:Weapon X 1.95
Ann. '97 JOs,V:Volk 3.00
TPB Triumphs & Tragedies 16.95

**WOLVERINE & PUNISHER:
DAMAGING EVIDENCE**
1993
1 B:CP(s),GEr,A:Kingpin 2.25
2 GEr,A:Kingpin,Sniper 2.25
3 GEr,Last issue 2.25

**WOLVERINE: DAYS
OF FUTURE PAST**
Oct., 1997
1 (of 3) JFM,JoB,JHo, Logan &
  Magneto in far future 2.50
2 JFM,JoB,JHo,with Jubilee 2.50
3 JFM,JoB,JHo,V:Council of the
  Chosen, concl. 2.50

**WOLVERINE:
DOOMBRINGER**
Nov., 1997
1-shot DgM,JP,F:Silver Samurai . 3.00

**WOLVERINE
ENCYCLOPEDIA**
Vol. 1 AKu(c) 48pg. 5.95
Vol. 2 48pg 5.95
Vol. 3 48pg 5.95

**WOLVERINE/GAMBIT:
VICTIMS**
1995
1 Takes Place in London 3.00
2 Is Wolverine the Killer? 3.00
3 V:Mastermind 3.00
4 conclusion 3.00

WOLVERINE SAGA
Sept., 1989
1 RLd(c), ... 6.50
2 . . . . 5.00
3 . . . . 5.00
4 Dec., 1989 . . . . 5.00

WONDER DUCK
Sept., 1949
1 Whale(c) 50.00
2 . . . . 33.00
3 March, 1950 . . . . 33.00

WONDERMAN
March, 1986
1 KGa,one-shot special 3.00

WONDER MAN
Sept., 1991
1 B:GJ(s),JJ,V:Goliath 2.50
2 JJ,A:West Coast Avengers . . . 1.50
3 JJ,V:Abominatrix,I:Spider 1.50
4 JJ,I:Splice,A:Spider 1.50
5 JJ,A:Beast,V:Rampage 1.50
6 JJ,A:Beast,V:Rampage 1.50
7 JJ,Galactic Storm,pt.4,
  A:Hulk & Rich Jones 1.50
8 JJ,GalacticStorm,pt.11,A:Vision 1.50
9 JJ,GalacticStorm,pt.18,A:Vision 1.50
10 JJ,V:Khmer Rouge 1.50
11 V:Angkor 1.50
12 V:Angkor 1.50
13 Infinity War 1.50
14 Infinity War,V:Warlock 1.50

Wonder Man Annual #2
© *Marvel Entertainment Group*

15 Inf.War,V:Doppleganger 1.50
16 JJ,I:Armed Response,
  A:Avengers West Coast 1.50
17 JJ,A:Avengers West Coast . . . 1.50
18 V:Avengers West Coast 1.50
19 . . . . 1.50
20 V:Splice,Rampage 1.50
21 V:Splice, Rampage 1.50
22 JJ,V:Realm of Death 1.50
23 JJ,A:Grim Reaper,Mephisto . . 1.50
24 JJ,V:Grim Reaper,Goliath . . . 1.50
25 JJ,N:Wonder Man,D:Grim Reaper,
  V:Mephisto 3.25
26 A:Hulk,C:Furor,Plan Master . . 1.50
27 A:Hulk 1.50
28 RoR,A:Spider-Man 1.50
29 RoR,A:Spider-Man 1.50
30 V:Hate Monger 1.25
31 . . . . 1.25
32 . . . . 1.25

33 . . . . 1.25
Spec.#1 (1985),KGa 3.00
Ann.#1 System Bytes #3 . . . . . . 2.25
Ann.#2 I:Hit-Maker,w/card 2.95

**WORLD CHAMPIONSHIP
WRESTLING**
1 F:Lex Luger,Sting 1.50
2 . . . . 1.25
3 . . . . 1.25
4 Luger Vs El Gigante 1.25
5 Rick Rude Vs. Sting 1.25
6 F:Dangerous Alliance,R.Rude . 1.25
7 F:Steiner Brothers 1.25
8 F:Sting,Dangerous Alliance . . . 1.25
9 Bunkhouse Brawl 1.25
10 Halloween Havoc 1.25
11 Sting vs Grapplers 1.25
12 F:Ron Simmons 1.25

WORLD OF FANTASY
Atlas May, 1956
1 The Secret of the Mountain . 300.00
2 AW,Inside the Tunnel 175.00
3 DAy,SC, The Man in the Cave160.00
4 BEv(c),Back to the Lost City 125.00
5 BEv(c),BP,In the Swamp . . . 125.00
6 BEv(c),The Strange Wife of
  Henry Johnson 125.00
7 BEv(c),GM,Man in Grey . . . 125.00
8 GM,JO,MF,The Secret of the
  Black Cloud 135.00
9 BEv,BK 125.00
10 . . . . 100.00
11 AT 125.00
12 BEv(c) 100.00
13 BEv,JO 100.00
14 JMn(c),GM,JO 100.00
15 JK(c) 100.00
16 AW,SD,JK 150.00
17 JK(c),SD 135.00
18 JK(c) 135.00
19 JK(c),SD,August, 1959 . . . 135.00

WORLD OF MYSTERY
Atlas June, 1956
1 BEv(c),AT,JO,The Long Wait 300.00
2 BEv(c),The Man From
  Nowhere 125.00
3 SD,AT,JDa, The Bugs 150.00
4 SD(c),BP,What Happened in
  the Basement 150.00
5 JO,She Stands in Shadows . 125.00
6 AW,SD,Sinking Man 150.00
7 Pick A Door July, 1957 . . . . 125.00

WORLD OF SUSPENSE
Atlas April, 1956
1 JO,BEv,A Stranger Among Us 225.00
2 SD,When Walks the Scarecrow 125.00
3 AW,The Man Who Couldn't
  Be Touched 135.00
4 Something is in This House . 100.00
5 BEv,DH,JO 100.00
6 BEv(c),BP 100.00
7 AW,The Face 110.00
8 Prisoner of the Ghost Ship . 100.00

WORLDS UNKNOWN
May, 1973
1 GK,AT,The Coming of the
  Martians,Reprints 15.00
2 GK,TS,A Gun For A Dinosaur 10.00

3 The Day the Earth Stood
  Still 10.00
4 JB,Arena 10.00
5 DA,JM,Black Destroyer 10.00
6 GK(c),The Thing Called It . . . 10.00
7 GT,The Golden Voyage of
  Sinbad,Part 1 . . . . 10.00
8 The Golden Voyage of
  Sinbad,Part 2, August, 1974   10.00

WYATT EARP
Atlas Nov., 1955
1 JMn,F:Wyatt Earp 150.00
2 AW,Saloon(c) 90.00
3 JMn(c),The Showdown,
  A:Black Bart 75.00
4 Ph(c),Hugh O'Brian,JSe,
  India Sundown 75.00
5 Ph(c),Hugh O'Brian,DW,
  Gun Wild Fever 75.00
6 . . . . 75.00
7 AW 75.00
8 . . . . 75.00
9 and 10 . . . . @75.00
11 . . . . 75.00
12 AW 75.00
13 thru 20 . . . . @60.00
21 JDa(c) 50.00
22 thru 29 . . . . @35.00
30 Reprints 15.00
31 thru 33 Reprints . . . . @10.00
34 June, 1973 . . . . 10.00

XAVIER INSTITUTE
ALUMNI YEARBOOK
GN 48pg (1996) 5.95

X-CALIBRE
1995
1 Excaliber After Xavier 5.00
2 V:Callisto & Morlock Crew . . . 3.50
3 D:Juggernaut 3.00
4 Secret Weapon 3.00
TPB Rep.#1-#4 . . . . 8.95

X-FACTOR
Feb., 1986
1 WS(c),JG,BL,JRu,I:X-Factor,
  Rusty 10.00
2 JG,BL,I:Tower 6.00
3 JG,BL,V:Tower 5.00
4 KP,JRu,V:Frenzy 5.00
5 JG,JRu,I:Alliance of Evil,
  C:Apocalypse 6.00
6 JG,BMc,I:Apocalypse 17.00
7 JG,JRu,V:Morlocks,I:Skids . . . 5.00
8 MS,JRu,V:Freedom Force . . . 5.00
9 JRu(i),V:Freedom Force
  (Mutant Massacre) 6.00
10 WS,BWi,V:Marauders(Mut.Mass),
  A:Sabretooth 7.00
11 WS,BWi,A:Thor(Mutant Mass) . 6.00
12 MS,BWi,V:Vanisher 5.00
13 WS,DGr,V:Mastermold 5.00
14 WS,BWi,V:Mastermold 5.00
15 WS,BWi,D:Angel 6.00
16 DM,JRu,V:Masque 5.00
17 WS,BWi,I:Rictor 6.00
18 WS,BWi,V:Apocalypse 5.00
19 WS,BWi,V:Horsemen of
  Apocalypse 4.00
20 JBr,A:X-Terminators 3.00
21 WS,BWi,V:The Right 3.00

X-Factor #18
© Marvel Entertainment Group

22 SB,BWi,V:The Right 3.00
23 WS,BWi,C:Archangel 11.00
24 WS,BWi,Fall of Mutants,
  I:Archangel 16.00
25 WS,BWi,Fall of Mutants 4.00
26 WS,BWi,Fall of Mutants,
  N:X-Factor 4.00
27 WS,BWi,Christmas Issue 3.50
28 WS,BWi,V:Ship 3.00
29 WS,BWi,V:Infectia 3.00
30 WS,BWi,V:Infectia,Free.Force . 3.00
31 WS,BWi,V:Infectia,Free.Force . 3.00
32 SLi,A:Avengers 3.00
33 WS,BWi,V:Tower & Frenzy,
  R:Furry Beast 3.00
34 WS,BWi,I:Nanny,
  Orphan Maker 3.00
35 JRu(i),WS(c),V:Nanny,
  Orphan Maker 3.00
36 WS,BWi,Inferno,V:Nastirh . . . 3.50
37 WS,BWi,Inferno,V:Gob.Queen . 3.50
38 WS,AM,Inferno,A:X-Men,D:
  MadelynePryor(GoblinQueen) . 3.50
39 WS,AM,Inferno,A:X-Men,
  V:Mr.Sinister 3.50
40 RLd,AM,O:Nanny,Orphan Maker
  1st Liefeld Marvel work 8.00
41 AAd,AM,I:Alchemy 3.50
42 AAd,AM,A:Alchemy 3.50
43 PS,AM,V:Celestials 3.00
44 PS,AM,V:Rejects 2.50
45 PS,AM,V:Rask 2.50
46 PS,AM,V:Rejects 2.50
47 KD,AM,V:Father 2.50
48 thru 49 PS,AM,V:Rejects . . . 2.50
50 RLd&TM(c),RB,AM,A:Prof.X
  (double sized),BU:Apocalypse . 4.00
51 AM,V:Sabretooth,Caliban 5.00
52 RLd(c),AM,V:Sabretooth,
  Caliban 4.00
53 AM,V:Sabretooth,Caliban 4.00
54 MS,AM,A:Colossus,I:Crimson . 2.00
55 MMi(c),CDo,AM,V:Mesmero . . 2.00
56 AM,V:Crimson 2.00
57 NKu,V:Crimson 2.00
58 JBg,AM,V:Crimson 2.00
59 AM,V:Press Gang 2.00
60 JBg,AM,X-Tinction Agenda#3 . 4.00

60a 2nd printing(gold) 3.00
61 JBg,AM,X-Tinction Agenda#6 . 4.00
62 JBg,AM,JLe(c),E:X-Agenda . . 4.00
63 WPo,I:Cyberpunks 4.00
64 WPo,ATb,V:Cyberpunks 4.00
65 WPo,ATb,V:Apocalypse 4.00
66 WPo,ATb,I:Askani,
  V:Apocalypse 4.00
67 WPo,ATb,V:Apocalypse,I:Shinobi
  Shaw,D:Sebastian Shaw . . . 3.00
68 WPo,ATb,JLe(c),V:Apocalypse,
  L:Nathan,(taken into future) . . . 4.00
69 WPo,V:Shadow King 3.00
70 MMi(c),JRu,Last old team . . . 3.00
71 LSn,AM,New Team 5.00
71a 2nd printing 1.50
72 LSn,AM,Who shot Madrox
  revealed 3.00
73 LSn,AM,Mob Chaos in D.C.. . . 3.00
74 LSn,AM,I:Slab 2.50
75 LSn,AM,I:Nasty Boys(doub.sz) 3.25
76 LSn,AM,A:Hulk,Pantheon . . . 2.50
77 LSn,AM,V:Mutant Lib. Front. . 2.25
78 LSn,AM,V:Mutant Lib. Front . . 2.25
79 LSn,AM,V:Helle's Belles 2.25
80 LSn,AM,V:Helle's Belles,
  C:Cyber 2.25
81 LSn,AM,V:Helle's Belles,Cyber 2.25
82 JQ(c),LSn,V:Brotherhood of Evil
  Mutants,I:X-iles 2.25
83 MPa,A:X-Force,X-iles 2.25
84 JaL,X-Cutioners Song #2,
  V:X-Force,A:X-Men 3.00
85 JaL,X-Cutioners Song #6,
  Wolv.& Bishop,V:Cable 3.00
86 JaL,AM,X-Cutioner's Song#10,
  A:X-Men,X-Force,V:Stryfe . . . 3.00
87 JQ,X-Cutioners Song
  Aftermath 3.00
88 JQ,AM,V:2nd Genegineer,
  I:Random 5.00
89 JQ,V:Mutates,Genosha 2.00
90 JQ,AM,Genosha vs. Aznia . . . 2.00
91 AM,V:Armageddon 1.75
92 JQ,AM,V:Fabian Cortez,
  Acolytes,hologram(c) 6.00
93 Magneto Protocols 3.00
94 PR,J:Forge 3.00
95 B:JMD(s),AM,Polaris
  Vs. Random 1.75
96 A:Random 1.75
97 JD,I:Haven,A:Random 1.75
98 GLz,A:Haven,A:Random 1.50
99 JD,A:Haven,Wolfsbane returns
  to human 1.50
100 JD,Red Foil(c),V:Haven,
  D:Madrox 3.25
100a Newstand Ed. 2.00
101 JD,AM,Aftermath 1.50
102 JD,AM,V:Crimson Commando,
  Avalanche 1.50
103 JD,AM,A:Malice 1.75
104 JD,AM,V:Malice,
  C:Mr. Sinister 1.75
105 JD,AM,V:Malice 1.75
106 Phalanx Covenant,Life Signs
  Holografx(c) 3.25
106a newsstand ed 2.00
107 A:Strong Guy 1.75
108 A:Mystique, deluxe ed. 2.50
108a newsstand ed. 1.50
109 A:Mystique,V:Legion, deluxe . 2.00
109a newsstand ed. 1.50
110 Invasion 2.00
110a deluxe ed. 2.00

X-Factor #103
© Marvel Entertainment Group

111 Invasion	1.50
111a deluxe ed.	2.00
112 AM,JFM,SEp,F:Guido,Havok	2.00
113 A:Mystique	2.00
114 AM,Wild Child & Mystique	2.00
115 F:Wild Child,Havok	2.00
116 F:Wild Child	2.00
117 HMe,AM,F:Cyclops	2.00
118 HMe,AM,A:Random,Shard	2.00
119 HMe,AM,F:Sabretooth	2.00
120	2.00
121	2.00
122 HMe,SEp,AM,J:Sabretooth	2.00
123	2.00
124 A:Onslaught	3.00
125 Onslaught saga, double size	3.00
126 Beast vs. Dark Beast	2.00
127 Mystique	2.00
128 HMe,JMs,AM,Hound Program	2.00
129 HMe,JMs,AM,Graydon Creed's campaign	2.00
130 HMe,JMs,AM,Assassination of Graydon Creed	2.50
131 HMe,JMs,ATi,Havok strikes back	2.00
132 HMe,JMs,ATi,Break away from government	2.00
133 HMe,JMs,ATi,A:Multiple Man & Strong Guy	2.00
134 HMe,JMs,Ati,"Operation X-Factor Underground," cont.	2.00
135 HMe,JMs,Strong Guy awakes	2.00
136 HMe,JMs,ATi, A:Sabretooth	2.00
137 HMe,JMs,ATi, Final fate of Shard and Polaris	2.00
138 HMe,JMs,ATi,Sabertooth, V:Maberick	2.00
139 HMe,ATi,Who killed Graydon Creed	2.00
140 HMe,ATi,Who killed Graydon Creed, A:Mystique	2.00
141 HMe,ATi,Shard's Plan	2.00
142 ATi,F:Wild Child	2.00
143 HMe,ATi,Havok vs.DarkBeast	2.00
144 HMe,ATi,V:Brotherhood, Dark Beast	2.00
145 HMe,ATi,Havok vs. X.U.E.	2.00
146 HMe,ATi,Havok, Multiple	

Man,V:Polaris	2.00
147 HMe,Havok v. Mandroids	2.00
148 F:Shard	2.00
149 HMe,Polaris & Madrox rejoin	2.00
Spec #1 JG,Prisoner of Love	5.00
Ann.#1 BL,BBr,V:CrimsonDynamo	5.00
Ann.#2 TGr,JRu,A:Inhumans	4.00
Ann.#3 WS(c),AM,JRu,PC,TD, Evolutionary War	3.50
Ann.#4 JBy,WS,JRu,MBa,Atlantis Attacks,BU:Doom & Magneto	3.50
Ann.#5 JBg,AM,DR,GI,Days of Future Present,A:Fant.Four,V:Ahab	4.00
Ann.#6 Flesh Tears Saga,pt.4, A:X-Force, New Warriors	4.00
Ann #7 JQ,JRu,Shattershot,pt.3	4.00
Ann.#8 I:Charon,w/card	3.25
Ann.#9 JMD(s),MtB,V:Prof.Power, A:Prof.X,O:Haven	3.25
Minus 1 Spec., HMe,JMs,ATi, flashback,F:Havok	1.95
GN X-Men: Wrath of Apocalypse, rep.X-Factor#65-#68	4.95

X-Force #1
© Marvel Entertainment Group

X-FORCE
August, 1991

1 RLd,V:Stryfe,Mutant Liberation Front,bagged, white on black graphics with X-Force Card	5.00
1a with Shatterstar Card	4.00
1b with Deadpool Card	4.00
1c with Sunspot & Gideon Card	4.00
1d with Cable Card	5.00
1e Unbagged Copy	1.75
1f 2nd Printing	1.75
2 RLd,I:New Weapon X,V: Deadpool	4.50
3 RLd,C:Spider-Man, V:Juggernaut,Black Tom	3.00
4 RLd,SpM/X-Force team-up, V:Juggernaut(cont.from SpM#16) Sideways format	3.00
5 RLd,A:Brotherhood Evil Mutants	3.00
6 RLd,V:Bro'hood Evil Mutants	3.00
7 RLd,V:Bro'hood Evil Mutants	3.00
8 MMi,O:Cable(Part)	3.00
9 RLd,D:Sauron,Masque	3.00

10 MPa,V:Mutant Liberation Front	2.00
11 MPa,Deadpool Vs Domino	2.00
12 MPa,A:Weapon Prime,Gideon	2.00
13 MPa,V:Weapon Prime	2.00
14 TSr,V:Weapon Prime,Krule	2.00
15 GCa,V:Krule,Deadpool	2.00
16 GCa,X-Cutioners Song #4, X-Factor V:X-Force	3.00
17 GCa,X-Cutioners Song#8, Apocalypse V:Stryfe	3.00
18 GCa,X-Cutioners Song#12, Cable vs Stryfe	3.00
19 GCa,X-Cutioners Song Aftermath,N:X-Force	2.00
20 GCa,O:Graymalkin	2.00
21 GCa,V:War Machine,SHIELD	2.00
22 GCa,V:Externals	2.00
23 GCa,V:Saul,Gigeon,A:Six Pack	2.00
24 GCa,A:Six Pack,A:Deadpool	1.50
25 GCa,A:Mageneto,Exodus, R:Cable	5.00
26 GCa(c),MtB,I:Reignfire	4.00
27 GCa(c),MtB,V:Reignfire,MLF, I:Moonstar,Locus	1.50
28 MtB,V:Reignfire,MLF	1.50
29 MtB,V:Arcade,C:X-Treme	1.50
30 TnD,V:Arcade,A:X-Treme	1.50
31 F:Siryn	1.50
32 Child's Play#1,A:New Warriors	1.50
33 Child's Play#3,A:New Warriors, V:Upstarts	1.50
34 F:Rictor,Domino,Cable	4.00
35 TnD,R:Nimrod	1.50
36 TnD,V:Nimrod	1.75
37 PaP,I&D:Absalom	1.50
38 TaD,Life Signs,pt.2, I:Generation X, foil(c)	3.50
38a newsstand ed.	2.00
39 TaD	1.50
40 TaD, deluxe	2.00
40a newsstand ed.	1.50
41 TaD,O:feral,deluxe	2.00
41a newsstand ed.	1.50
42 Emma Frost, deluxe	2.00
42a newsstand ed.	1.50
43 Home is Where Heart	1.50
43a deluxe ed.	2.00
44 AdP,Prof.X,X-Mansion	2.00
45 AdP,Caliban vs. Sabretooth	2.00
46 R:The Mimic	3.25
47 A:Deadpool	2.00
48 AdP,Siryn Takes Charge	2.00
49 ADp,MBu,Holocaust is here	2.00
50 AdP,MPn,F:Sebastian Shaw	2.00
50a prismatic foil cover	4.00
51 AdP,MPn,V:Risque	2.00
52 A:Onslaught	3.50
53	2.00
54 AdP, Can X-Force protect X-Ternals?	2.00
55	2.00
56 Deadpool, A:Onslaught	3.50
57 Onslaught saga	2.50
58 Onslaught saga	2.50
59	2.50
60 JLb,,F:Shatterstar,A:Long Shot	2.50
61 JLb,R:Longshot,O:Shatterstar	2.50
62 JLb,F:Sunspot	2.50
63 JFM,AdP,F:Risque,Cannonball	2.50
64 JFM,AdP,In Latveria, searching for Doctor Doom's weapons	2.50
65 JFM,AdP,Warpath follows Risque to Florida	2.50
66 JFM,AdP,A:Risque,James Proudstar	2.50

MARVEL

67 JFM,AdP,F:Warpath, Risque . . 2.50
68 JFM,AdP,Zero Tolerance 2.50
69 JFM,AdP,Zero Tolerance
aftermath 2.50
70 JFM,AdP,new direction starts . 2.00
71 JFM,AdP,new direction 2.00
72 JFM,AdP,on the road 2.00
73 JFM,AdP,in New Orleans 2.00
74 JFM,ASm,Skids is back 2.00
75 JFM,AdP,A:Reignfire,
double size 3.00
76 JFM,AdP,F:Shatterstar 2.00
77 JFM,AdP,F:Sunfire & Meltdown 2.00
78 JFM,AdP,Reignfire makes his
move 2.00
79 JFM,AdP,O:Reignfire 2.00
80 JFM,AdP,V:Reignfire 2.00
81 JFM,AdP,trip to Hawaii,
V:Lava Men, AdP Poster 2.00
82 JFM,V:Griffin, Damocles
Foundation 2.00
Ann.#1 Shattershot,pt1 .... 2.75
Ann.#2 JaL,LSn,I:X-Treme,w/card 3.25
Ann.#3 .... 2.95
Minus 1 Spec., JFM,AdP, flashback,
F:John Proudstar 1.95
TPB X-Force & Spider-Man: Sabotage,
rep.X-Force #3 & #4 and
Spider-Man #16 .... 6.95

X-FORCE MEGAZINE
TPB LSi,RLd, rep. New Mutants
#99–#100 .... 3.95

X-MAN
March 1995
1 Cable after Xavier 6.00
2 Sinister's Plan 4.00
3 V:Domino 3.00
4 V:Sinister 3.00
5 Into this World 3.00
6 V:X-Men 2.50
7 Evil from Age of Apocalypse . 2.25
8 Crossover Adventure 2.00
9 F:Nate's Past 2.00
10 Nate's Past 2.00
11 Young Nate seeks out X-Men . 2.00
12 F:Excalibur 2.00
13 .... 2.00
14 .... 2.00
15 JOs,X-Men/Cable war aftermath 6.00
16 Holocaust,A:Onslaught 4.00
17 Holocaust,Quicksilver,Scarlet
Witch, A:Onslaught 3.50
18 Onslaught saga 2.50
19 Onslaught saga 2.50
20 .... 2.50
21 TKa,RCz,F:Nate 2.50
22 TKa,RCz,F:Threnody,A:Madelyne
Pryor 2.50
23 TKa,RCz,F:Bishop 2.50
24 TKa,RCz,Spider-Man vs. Nate 2.50
25 TKa,RCz,Madelyne Pryor,
double size 3.50
26 TKa,RCz,Nate limps to Muir
Isle,A:Moira Mactaggert 2.50
27 TKa,RCz,Hellfire Club, concl. . 2.50
28 TKa,RCz,Dark Beast's offer . 2.50
29 TKa,RCz,Back in New York, . 2.50
30 TKa,RCz,F:Nate Grey 2.50
31 RL,DGr,F:Nate Grey 2.00
32 TKa,V:Jacknife 2.00
33 TKa,V:Jacknife 2.00
34 TKa,Secret of Nate's popularity 2.00
35 TKa,Terrorists Strike 2.00

36 TKa,V:Purple Man 2.00
37 TKa,Nate leaves N.Y.,
A:Spider-Man 2.00
38 TKa,A:Spider-Man, Gwen Stacy 2.00
39 TKa,AOl,Nate & Madeline Pryor 2.00
40 TKa,RPc,V:Great Beasts 2.00
41 TKa,RCz,Madelyne Pryor 2.00
42 TKa,RCz,hunted by leprechauns 2.00
43 TKa,RCz,Nate Grey–murderer?! 2.00
Minus 1 Spec., TKa,RCz,
flashback,O:Nate Grey 1.95
Spec.#1 X-Man '96 .... 2.95
Ann. '97 RBe, Nate, Sugar Man,
Dark Beast, Holocaust 3.00
Ann. '98 X-Man, The Hulk, Thanos,
48pg 3.00
GNv X-Man,BRa,TyD, 48pg 6.00

X-MEN
Sept., 1963
1 JK,O:X-Men,I:Professor X,Beast
Cyclops,Marvel Girl,Iceman
Angel,Magneto 5,600.00
2 JK,I:Vanisher 1,750.00
3 JK,I:Blob 675.00
4 JK,I:Quicksilver,Scarlet Witch
Mastermind,Toad 600.00
5 JK,V:Broth. of Evil Mutants . 450.00
6 JK,V:Sub-Mariner 350.00
7 JK,V:Broth. of Evil Mutants,

X-Men #19
© *Marvel Entertainment Group*

Blob 300.00
8 JK,I:Unus,1st Ice covered
Iceman 300.00
9 JK,A:Avengers,I:Lucifer 300.00
10 JK,I:Modern Kazar 300.00
11 JK,I:Stranger 250.00
12 JK,O:Prof.X,I:Juggernaut . 325.00
13 JK,JSt,V:Juggernaut 250.00
14 JK,I:Sentinels 250.00
15 JK,O:Beast,V:Sentinels 250.00
16 JK,V:Mastermold,Sentinels . 250.00
17 JK,V:Magneto 150.00
18 V:Magneto 150.00
19 I:Mimic 150.00
20 V:Lucifer 150.00

21 V:Lucifer,Dominus 110.00
22 V:Maggia 110.00
23 V:Maggia 110.00
24 I:Locust(Prof.Hopper) 110.00
25 JK,I:El Tigre 110.00
26 V:El Tigre 100.00
27 C:Fant.Four,V:Puppet Master 100.00
28 I:Banshee 150.00
29 V:Super-Apaptoid 100.00
30 JK,I:The Warlock 100.00
31 JK,I:Cobalt Man 75.00
32 V:Juggernaut 75.00
33 GK,A:Dr.Strange,Juggernaut . 75.00
34 V:Tyrannus,Mole Man 75.00
35 JK,A:Spider-Man,Banshee . 100.00
36 V:Mekano 75.00
37 DH,V:Blob,Unus 75.00
38 DH,A:Banshee,O:Cyclops .. 100.00
39 DH,GT,A:Banshee,V:Mutant
Master,O:Cyclops 75.00
40 DH,GT,V:Frankenstein,
O:Cyclops 75.00
41 DH,GT,I:Grotesk,O:Cyclops . 65.00
42 DH,GT,JB,V:Grotesk,
O:Cyclops,D:Prof.X 65.00
43 GT,JB,V:Magneto,Quicksilver,
Scarlet Witch,C:Avengers ... 75.00
44 V:Magneto,Quicksilver,Sc.Witch,
R:Red Raven,O:Iceman 75.00
45 PH,JB,V:Magneto,Quicksilver,
Scarlet Witch,O:Iceman 75.00
46 DH,V:Juggernaut,O:Iceman .. 65.00
47 DH,I:Maha Yogi 65.00
48 DH,JR,V:Quasimodo 65.00
49 JSo,DH,C:Magneto,I:Polaris,
Mesmero,O:Beast 65.00
50 JSo,V:Magneto,O:Beast 70.00
51 JSo,V:Magneto,Polaris,
Erik the Red,O:Beast 65.00
52 DH,MSe,JSt,O:Lorna Dane
V:Magneto,O:Beast 55.00
53 1st BWS,O:Beast 75.00
54 BWS,DH,I:Havok,O:Angel .. 70.00
55 BWS,DH,O:Havok,Angel 65.00
56 NA,V:LivingMonolith,O:Angel . 65.00
57 NA,V:Sentinels,A:Havok 65.00
58 NA,A:Havoc,V:Sentinels 80.00
59 NA,V:Sentinels,A:Havoc 65.00
60 NA,I:Sauron 70.00
61 NA,V:Sauron 60.00
62 NA,A:Kazar,Sauron,Magneto . 60.00
63 A:Ka-Zar,V:Magneto 60.00
64 DH,A:Havok,I:Sunfire 55.00
65 NA,MSe,A:Havok,Shield,
Return of Prof.X 60.00
66 SB,MSe,V:Hulk,A:Havok 60.00
67 rep.X-Men #12,#13 .... 30.00
68 rep.X-Men #14,#15 .... 30.00
69 rep.X-Men #16,#19 .... 30.00
70 rep.X-Men #17,#18 .... 30.00
71 rep.X-Men #20 .... 30.00
72 rep.X-Men #21,#24 .... 30.00
73 thru 93 rep.X-Men #25-45 . @30.00
94 GK(c),B:CCl(s),DC,BMc,B:2nd
X-Men,V:Count Nefaria 450.00
95 GK(c),DC,V:Count Nefaria,
Ani-Men,D:Thunderbird 95.00
96 DC,I:Moira McTaggert,
Kierrok 75.00
97 DC,V:Havok,Polaris,Eric
the Red,I:Lilandra 65.00
98 DC,V:Sentinels,Stephen Lang 75.00
99 DC,V:Sentinels,S.Lang 80.00
100 DC,V:Stephen Lang 75.00
101 DC,I:Phoenix,Black Tom,

MARVEL

A:Juggernaut 75.00
102 DC,O:Storm,V:Juggernaut,
Black Tom 35.00
103 DC,V:Juggernaut,Bl.Tom . . . 40.00
104 DC,V:Magneto,I:Star
Jammers,A:Lilandra 30.00
105 DC,BL,V:Firelord 30.00
106 DC,TS,V:Firelord 30.00
107 DC,DGr,I:Imperial Guard,Star
Jammers,Gladiator,Corsair . . 40.00
108 JBy,TA,A:Star Jammers,
C:Fantastic Four,Avengers. . . 80.00
109 JBy,TA,I:Vindicator 45.00
110 TD,DC,V:Warhawk 28.00
111 JBy,TA,V:Mesmero,A:Beast,
Magneto 28.00
112 GP(c),JBy,TA,V:Magneto,
A:Beast 28.00
113 JBy,TA,V:Magneto,A:Beast . 28.00
114 JBy,TA,A:Beast,R:Sauron . . 28.00
115 JBy,TA,V:Sauron,Garokk,
A:Kazar,I:Zaladane 26.00
116 JBy,TA,V:Sauron,Garokk,
A:Kazar 26.00

X-Men #91
© Marvel Entertainment Group

117 JBy,TA,O:Prof.X,I:Amahl
Farouk (Shadow King) 35.00
118 JBy,I:Moses Magnum,A:Sunfire
C:Iron Fist,I:Mariko 30.00
119 JBy,TA,V:Moses Magnum,
A:Sunfire 30.00
120 JBy,TA,I:AlphaFlight (Shaman,
Sasquatch,Northstar,Snowbird,
Aurora) 40.00
121 JBy,TA,V:Alpha Flight 45.00
122 JBy,TA,A:Juggernaut,Black
Tom,Arcade,Power Man 25.00
123 JBy,TA,V:Arcade,A:SpM . . . 22.00
124 JBy,TA,V:Arcade 22.00
125 JBy,TA,A:Beast,Madrox the
Multiple Man,Havok,Polaris . . 22.00
126 JBy,TA,I:Proteus,
A:Havok,Madrox 22.00
127 JBy,TA,V:Proteus,A:Havok,
Madrox 22.00
128 GP(c),JBy,TA,V:Proteus,

A:Havok,Madrox 22.00
129 JBy,TA,I:Shadow Cat,White
Queen,C:Hellfire Club 30.00
130 JR2(c),JBy,TA,I:Dazzler
V:White Queen 25.00
131 JBy,TA,V:White Queen,
A:Dazzler 22.00
132 JBy,TA,I:Hellfire Club,
V:Mastermind 22.00
133 JBy,TA,V:Hellfire Club,
Mastermind,F:Wolverine . . . 22.00
134 JBy,TA,V:Hellfire Club,Master
mind,I:Dark Phoenix,A:Beast . 22.00
135 JBy,TA,V:Dark Phoenix,C:SpM,
Fant.Four,Silver Surfer 22.00
136 JBy,TA,V:Dark Phoenix,
A:Beast 22.00
137 JBy,TA,D:Phoenix,V:Imperial
Guard,A:Beast 28.00
138 JBy,TA,History of X-Men,
L:Cyclops,C:Shadow Cat . . . 22.00
139 JBy,TA,A:Alpha Flight,R:Wendigo,
N:Wolverine,J:Shadowcat . . . 35.00
140 JBy,TA,V:Wendigo,A:Alpha
Flight 25.00
141 JBy,TA,I:2nd Brotherhood of Evil
Mutants,I:Rachel (Phoenix II) . 35.00
Becomes: UNCANNY X-MEN
142 JBy,TA,V:Evil Mutants,
A:Rachel (Phoenix II) 25.00
143 JBy,TA,V:N'Garai,I:Lee
Forrester 10.00
144 BA,JRu,A:Man-Thing,
O:Havok, V:D'Spayre 9.00
145 DC,JRu,V:Arcade,A:DrDoom . 9.00
146 DC,JRu,V:Dr.Doom,Arcade . . 9.00
147 DC,JRu,V:Dr.Doom,Arcade . . 9.00
148 DC,JRu,I:Caliban,A:Dazzler
Spiderwoman 9.00
149 DC,JRu,A:Magneto 9.00
150 DC,JRu,BWi,V:Magneto . . . 11.00
151 JSh,BMc,JRu,V:Sentinels . . . 7.00
152 BMc,JRu,V:White Queen . . . 7.00
153 DC,JRu,I:Bamf 7.00
154 DC,JRu,BWi,I:Sidrian Hunters
A:Corsair,O:Cyclops(part) . . . 7.00
155 DC,BWi,V:Deathbird,I:Brood . 7.00
156 DC,BWi,V:Death Bird,
A:Tigra, Star Jammers 7.00
157 DC,BWi,V:Deathbird 7.00
158 DC,BWi,2nd A:Rogue,
Mystique 10.00
159 BSz,BWi,V:Dracula 7.00
160 BA,BWi,V:Belasco,I:Magik . . . 7.00
161 DC,BWi,I:Gabrielle Haller,
O:Magneto,Professor X 8.00
162 DC,BWi,V:Brood 11.00
163 DC,BWi,V:Brood 7.00
164 DC,BWi,V:Brood,I:Binary 7.00
165 PS,BWi,V:Brood 8.00
166 PS,BWi,V:Brood,A:Binary,
I:Lockheed 8.00
167 PS,BWi,V:Brood,A:N.Mutants 8.00
168 PS,BWi,I:Madelyne Pryor . . . 7.00
169 PS,BWi,I:Morlocks 7.00
170 PS,BWi,A:Angel,V:Morlocks . 7.00
171 WS,BWi,J:Rogue,V:Binary . . 11.00
172 PS,BWi,V:Viper,Silver
Samurai, ... 8.00
173 PS,BWi,V:Viper,Silver
Samurai, ... 6.00
174 PS,BWi,A:Mastermind 6.00
175 PS,JR2,BWi,W:Cyclops and
Madelyne,V:Mastermind 9.00
176 JR2,BWi,I:Val Cooper 6.00

177 JR2,JR,V:Brotherhood of
Evil Mutants 6.00
178 JR2,BWi,BBr,V:Brotherhood
of Evil Mutants 6.00
179 JR2,DGr,V:Morlocks 6.00
180 JR2,DGr,BWi,Secret Wars . 6.00
181 JR2,DGr,A:Sunfire 6.00
182 JR2,DGr,V:S.H.I.E.L.D. 6.00
183 JR2,DGr,V:Juggernaut 6.00
184 JR2,DGr,V:Selene,I:Forge . . . 8.00
185 JR2,DGr,V:Shield,U.S.
Govt.,Storm loses powers 6.00
186 BWS,TA,Lifedeath,
V:Dire Wraiths 7.00
187 JR2,DGr,V:Dire Wraiths 6.00
188 JR2,DGr,V:Dire Wraiths 6.00
189 JR2,SL,V:Selene,A:Magma . . 6.00
190 JR2,DGr,V:Kulan Gath,A:SpM,
Avengers,New Mutants 6.00
191 JR2,DGr,A:Avengers,Spider-Man,
New Mutants,I:Nimrod 6.00
192 JR2,DGr,V:Magus 6.00
193 JR2,DGr,V:Hellions,I:Firestar
Warpath,20th Anniv. 8.00

Uncanny X-Men #195
© Marvel Entertainment Group

194 JR2,DGr,SL,V:Nimrod 6.00
195 BSz(c),JR2,DGr,A:Power
Pack,V:Morlocks 6.00
196 JR2,DGr,J:Magneto 7.00
197 JR2,DGr,V:Arcade 6.00
198 BWS,F:Storm,'Lifedeath II' . . 6.00
199 JR2,DGr,I:Freedom Force,
Rachel becomes 2nd Phoenix . 6.00
200 JR2,DGr,A:Magneto,I:Fenris 11.00
201 RL,WPo(i),I:Nathan
Christopher (Cyclops son) . . . 15.00
202 JR2,AW,Secret Wars II 7.00
203 JR2,AW,Secret Wars II 7.00
204 JBr,WPo,V:Arcade 8.00
205 BWS,A:Lady Deathstrike . . . 18.00
206 JR2,DGr,V:Freedom Force . . 7.00
207 JR2,DGr,V:Selene 7.00
208 JR2,DGr,V:Nimrod,
A:Hellfire Club 7.00
209 JR2,CR,V:Nimrod,A:Spiral . . . 7.00
210 JR2,DGr,I:Marauders,

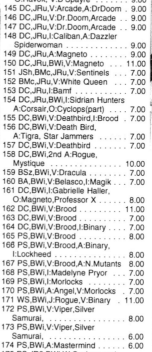

(Mutant Massacre) 18.00
211 JR2,BBI,AW,V:Marauders,
  (Mutant Massacre) 18.00
212 RL,DGr,V:Sabretooth,
  (Mutant Massacre) 24.00
213 AD,V:Sabretooth (Mut.Mass) 24.00
214 BWS,BWi,V:Malice,A:Dazzler 6.00
215 AD,DGr,I:Stonewall,Super
  Sabre,Crimson Commando . . . 6.00
216 BWS(c),JG,DGr,V:Stonewall . 6.00
217 WS(c),JG,SL,V:Juggernaut . . 6.00
218 AAD(c),MS,DGr,V:Juggernaut 6.00
219 BBI,DGr,V:Marauders,Polaris
  becomes Malice,A:Sabretooth . 7.00
220 MS,DGr,A:Naze 6.00
221 MS,DGr,I:Mr.Sinister,
  V:Maruaders 15.00
222 MS,DGr,V:Marauders,Eye
  Killers,A:Sabertooth 17.00
223 KGa,DGr,A:Freedom Force . . 6.00
224 MS,DGr,V:Adversary 6.00
225 MS,DGr,Fall of Mutants
  I:1st US App Roma 9.00
226 MS,DGr,Fall of Mutants 9.00
227 MS,DGr,Fall of Mutants 9.00
228 RL,TA,A:OZ Chase 6.00
229 MS,DGr,I:Reavers,Gateway . 6.00
230 RL,DGr,Xmas Issue 6.00
231 RL,DGr,V:Limbo 6.00
232 MS,DGr,V:Brood 6.00
233 MS,DGr,V:Brood 6.00
234 MS,JRu,V:Brood 6.00
235 RL,CR,V:Magistrates 6.00
236 MS,DGr,V:Magistrates 6.00
237 RL,TA,V:Magistrates 6.00
238 MS,DGr,V:Magistrates 6.00
239 MS,DGr,Inferno,A:Mr.Sinister 7.00
240 MS,DGr,Inferno,V:Marauders 7.50
241 MS,DGr,Inferno,O:Madeline
  Pryor,V:Marauders 7.50
242 MS,DGr,Inferno,D:N'Astirh,
  A:X-Factor,Double-sized 7.50
243 MS,Inferno,A:X-Factor. 7.50
244 MS,DGr,I:Jubilee 25.00
245 RLd,DGr,Invasion Parody . . . 6.00
246 MS,DGr,V:Mastermold,
  A:Nimrod 6.00
247 MS,DGr,V:Mastermold 5.00
248 JLe(1st X-Men Art),DGr,
  V:Nanny & Orphan Maker . . . 28.00
248a 2nd printing 2.00
249 MS,DGr,C:Zaladane,
  V:Savage Land Mutates. 5.00
250 MS,SL,I:Zaladane. 5.00
251 MS,DGr,V:Reavers 5.00
252 JLe,BSz(c),RL,SW,V:Reavers 5.00
253 MS,SL,V:Amahl Farouk 5.00
254 JLe(c),MS,DGr,V:Reavers . . . 5.00
255 MS,DGr,V:Reavers,D:Destiny 5.00
256 JLe,SW,Acts of Vengeance,
  V:Manderin,A:Psylocke 16.00
257 JLe,JRu,AofV,V:Manderin . . 14.00
258 JLe,SW,AofV,V:Manderin . . 15.00
259 MS,DGr,V:Magistrates, ... 7.00
260 JLe(c),MS,DGr,A:Dazzler . . 5.50
261 JLe(c),MS,DGr,V:Hardcase &
  Harriers 5.50
262 KD,JRu,V:Masque,Morlocks . 5.50
263 JRu(i),O:Forge,V:Morlocks . . 5.50
264 JLe(c),MC,JRu,V:Magistrate . 5.50
265 JRu(i),V:Shadowking 5.50
266 NKu(c),MC,JRu,I:Gambit . . . 45.00
267 JLe,WPo,SW,V:Shadowking 16.00
268 JLe,SW,A:Captain America,
  Black Widow,V:The Hand,

Baron Strucker 24.00
269 JLe,ATi,Rogue V:Ms.Marvel . 9.00
270 JLe,ATi,SW,X-Tinction Agenda
  #1, A:Cable,New Mutants . . . 13.00
270a 2nd printing(Gold) 4.00
271 JLe,SW,X-Tinction Agenda
  #4,A:Cable,New Mutants 9.00
272 JLe,SW,X-Tinction Agenda
  #7,A:Cable,New Mutants 9.00
273 JLe,WPo,JBy,KJ,RL,MS,MGo,
  LSn,SW,A:Cable,N.Mutants . . . 8.50
274 JLe,SW,V:Zaladane,A:Magneto,
  Nick Fury,Kazar 7.00
275 JLe,SW,R:Professor X,A:Star
  Jammers,Imperial Guard 10.00
275a 2nd Printing (Gold) 3.00
276 JLe,SW,V:Skrulls,Shi'ar 6.00
277 JLe,SW,V:Skrulls,Shi'ar 6.00
278 PS,Professor X Returns to
  Earth,V:Shadowking 4.00
279 NKu,SW,V:Shadowking 4.00
280 E:CCl(s),NKu,A:X-Factor,
  D:Shadowking,Prof.X Crippled . 4.00

Uncanny X-Men #200
© Marvel Entertainment Group

281 WPo,ATi,new team (From X-Men
  #1),D:Pierce,Hellions,V:Sentinels,
  I:Trevor Fitzroy,Upstarts 10.00
281a 2nd printing,red(c) 1.25
282 WPo,ATi,V:Fitzroy,C:Bishop 15.00
282a 2nd printing,gold(c) of #281
  inside 1.25
283 WPo,ATi,I:Bishop,Malcolm,
  Randall 15.00
284 WPo,ATi,SOS from USSR. . . 4.00
285 WPo,I:Mikhail(Colossus'
  brother from Russia) 3.25
286 JLe,WPo,ATi,A:Mikhail 3.25
287 JR2,O:Bishop,
  D:Malcolm,Randall 5.00
288 NKu,BSz,A:Bishop 3.00
289 WPo,ATi,Forge proposes
  to Storm 3.00
290 WPo,SW,V:Cyberpunks,
  L:Forge 3.00
291 TR,V:Morlocks 2.50
292 TR,V:Morlocks 2.50

293 TR,D:Morlocks,Mikhail 2.50
294 BP,TA,X-Cutioner's Song#1,
  Stryfe shoots Prof X,A:X-Force,
  X-Factor,polybag.w/ProfX card 4.00
295 BP,TA,X-Cutioners Song #5,
  V:Apocalypse 3.00
296 BP,TA,X-Cutioners Song #9,
  A:X-Force,X-Factor,V:Stryfe . . 3.00
297 BP,X-Cutioners Song
  Aftermath 2.00
298 BP,TA,V:Acolytes 2.00
299 BP,A:Forge,Acolytes,I:Graydon
  Creed (Sabretooth's son) 2.00
300 JR2,DGr,BP,V:Acolytes,A:Forge,
  Nightcrawler,Holografx(c) . . . 6.00
301 JR2,DGr,I:Sienna Blaze,
  V:Fitzroy 2.00
302 JR2,V:Fitzroy 2.00
303 JR2,V:Upstarts,D:Illyana . . . 2.00
304 JR2,JaL,PS,L:Colossus,
  V:Magneto,Holo-grafx(c) 6.50
305 JD,F:Rogue,Bishop 2.00
306 JR2,V:Hodge 2.00
307 JR2,Bloodties#4,A:Avengers,
  V:Exodus,Cortez 2.00
308 JR2,Scott & Jean announce
  impending marriage 2.00
309 JR2,O:Professor X & Amelia . 2.00
310 JR2,DG,A:Cable,V:X-Cutioner,
  w/card 5.00
311 JR2,DG,AV,V:Sabretooth,
  C:Phalanx 2.00
312 JMd,DG,A:Yukio,I:Phalanx,
  w/card 2.00
313 JMd,DG,V:Phalanx 2.00
314 LW,BSz,R:White Quen 2.00
315 F:Acolytes 2.00
316 V:Phalanx,I:M,Phalanx Covenant
  Generation Next,pt.1, holo(c) . . 5.00
316a newsstand ed. 2.00
317 JMd,V:Phalanx,prism(c) 5.00
317a newsstand ed. 2.00
318 JMd,L:Jubilee, deluxe 2.25
318a newsstand ed. 2.00
319 R:Legion, deluxe 2.25
319a newsstand ed. 2.00
320 deluxe ed. 4.00
320 newsstand ed. 2.00
321 R:Lilandra, deluxe ed. 2.25
321 newsstand ed. 2.00
322 SLo,TGu,Rogue,Iceman run from
  Gambit's Secret 6.00
323 I:Onslaught 2.25
324 SLo,F:Cannonball 2.25
325 R:Colossus 4.00
326 SLo,JMd,F:Gambit,Sabretooth 2.00
327 SLo,JMd,Magneto's Fate . . . 2.00
328 SLo,JMd,Sabretooth freed . . . 2.00
329 SLo,JMd,A:Doctor Strange . . 2.00
330 . . . . 2.00
331 . . . . 2.00
332 SLo,JMd, cont from
  Wolverine #100 . . . . 2.00
333 SLo,JMd, Operation: Zero
  Tolerance, Onslaught saga . . . 3.00
334 SLo,JMd, Onslaught saga . . . 3.00
335 SLo,JMd, Onslaught saga . . . 3.00
336 Apocalypse vs. Onslaught . . 2.50
337 Operation: Zero Tolerance . . 2.50
338 SLo,JMd,R:Angel 2.50
339 SLo,JMd,F:Cyclops, J.J.
  Jameson, Havok 2.50
340 SLo,JMd,F:Iceman 2.50
341 SLo,JMd,Rogue gets gift 2.50
342 SLo,JMd, Shi'ar Empire, pt.1 . 2.50

Uncanny X-Men #217
© Marvel Entertainment Group

342a Rogue cover 17.00
343 SLo,JMd, Shi'ar Empire, pt.2 . 2.50
344 SLo,JMd, Shi'ar Empire, pt.3 . 2.50
345 SLo,JMd, trip home, A:Akron . 2.50
346 SLo,JMd,Zero Tolerance,
　A:Spider-Man 4.00
347 SLo,JMd,Zero Tolerance . . . 2.00
348 SLo,JMd,at Magneto's base . 2.00
349 SLo,JMd,Maggot vs. Psylocke
　& Archangel 2.00
350 SSe,JMd,Trial of Gambit,
　double-sized 3.50
350a Gambit (c) 7.00
351 SSe,JMd,Dr. Cecilia Reyes . 2.50
352 SSe,EBe,Cyclops & Phoenix
　leave, Facade arrives 2.50
353 SSe,CBa,Rogues Anguish . . 2.00
354 SSe,CBa,F:Rogue 2.00
354a Jean Gray (c) 6.00
355 SSe,CBa, North & South
　pt.2 x-over 5.00
356 SSe,CBa, originals V:Phoenix 2.00
357 SSe,Cyclops & Phoenix . . . 2.00
358 SSe,CBa,Phoenix collapses . 2.00
359 SSe,CBa,Rogue 2.00
360A SSe,CBa, I:New X-Men, foil
　etched cover 4.00
360B regular cover 3.00
Ann.#1 rep.#9,#11 . . . . 75.00
Ann.#2 rep.#22,#23 . . . . 65.00
Ann.#3 GK(c),GP,TA,A:Arkon . . 20.00
Ann.#4 JR2,BMc,A:Dr.Strange . 15.00
Ann.#5 BA,BMc,A:F.F. 12.00
Ann.#6 BSz,BWi,Dracula 13.00
Ann.#7 MGo,TMd,BWi,TA,BBr,
　BA,JRu,BBl,SL,AM,
　V:Impossible Man 10.00
Ann.#8 SL,Kitty's story 10.00
Ann.#9 AAd,AG,MMi,Asgard,V:Loki,
　Enchantress,A:New Mutants . 15.00
Ann.#10 AAd,TA,V:Mojo,
　J:Longshot,A:New Mutants . 13.00
Ann.#11 AD,V:Horde,A:CaptBrit . 6.00
Ann.#12 AAd,BWi,RLm,TD,Evol.
　War,V:Terminus,Savage Land . 6.00

Ann.#13 MBa,JRu,Atlantis Attacks 5.00
Ann.#14 AAd,DGr,BWi,AM,ATi,
　V:Ahab,A:X-Factor, ... 14.00
Ann.#15,TR,JRu,MMi(c),Flesh Tears,
　Pt.3,A:X-Force,New Warriors . . 5.00
Ann.#16 JaL,JRu,Shattershot
　Part.2 . . . . 8.00
Ann.#17 JPe,MFm,I:X-Cutioner,
　D:Mastermind,w/card 4.00
Ann.#18 JR2,V:Caliban,
　BU:Bishop 3.25
Marvel Milestone rep. #1 (1991) . . 2.95
Marvel Milestone rep. #9 (1993) . . 2.95
Marvel Milestone rep. #28 (1994) . 2.95
G-Size #1,GK,DC,I:New X-Men
　(Colossus,Storm,Nightcrawler,
　Thunderbird,3rd A:Wolv.) . . 475.00
G-Size #2,rep.#57-59 . . . . 50.00
Marvel Milestone rep. Giant
　Size #1 (1991) 3.95
Spec.#1 X-Men: Earth Fall,
　rep. #232–#234 (1996) 2.95
Spec.#1 X-Men vs. Dracula, rep.
　X-Men Ann.#6 (1993) 2.00
GNv X-Men: Days of Future Past
　rep. X-Men #141-142 . . . . . . 5.00
GNv Pryde of the X-Men 10.95
GNv God Loves,Man Kills,
　(1994) prestige 6.95
GN X-Men Firsts, I:Wolverine,Rogue,
　Gambit & Mr. Sinister, rep. Avengers
　Ann.#10, Uncanny X-Men #221,#266
　& Incredible Hulk #181 (1996) . 5.00
GNv X-Men Rarities,F:Classic
　Stories (1995) 5.95
TPB Asgardian Wars 15.95
TPB Bloodties V:Exodus 15.95
TPB The Coming of Bishop, rep.
　#282–#285,#287–#288 (1995) 12.95
TPB Dark Phoenix Saga 12.95
TPB X-Men: Days of Future Present,
　MMi(c),Rep.F.F.Ann.#23,X-Men
　Ann.#14,X-Factor Ann.#5,
　New Mutant Ann.#10 . . . . . . 14.95
TPB Essential X-Men
　collection, rep. 12.95
TPB Fatal Attractions (1994) . . . 17.95
TPB From the Ashes 16.95
TPB Greatest Battles 15.95
TPB X-Men: Inferno, 352pg 19.95
TPB X-Men Magazine, CCI,JLe, rep.
　Uncanny X-Men #273–#275 . . 3.95
TPB X-Men: Mutant Massacre,
　rep. 256pg. 24.95
TPB Savage Land 9.95
TPB X-Cutioner's Song 24.95
TPB X-Tinction Agenda, rep.X-Men
　#270-272,X-Factor #60-62,
　New Mutants #95-97 . . . . . . 19.95
X-Men Survival Guide to the
　Mansion, NKu(c) (1993) 6.95

X-MEN
[2nd Regular Series] Oct., 1991
1A(c);Storm,Beast,B:CCI(s),JLe,SW
　I:Fabian Cortez,Acolytes,
　V:Magneto 3.00
1B(c);Colossus,Psylocke 3.00
1C(c);Cyclops,Wolverine 3.00
1D(c);Magneto 3.00
1E(c);Gatefold w/pin-ups 6.50
2 JLe,SW,V:Magneto 5.00
3 E:CCI(s),JLe,SW,V:Magneto . 4.00
4 JBy(s),JLe,SW,I:Omega Red,
　V:Hand 6.00

Uncanny X-Men (2nd Series) #8
© Marvel Entertainment Group

5 B:SLo(s),JLe,SW,V:Hand,
　Omega Red,I:Maverick 6.00
6 JLe,SW,V:Omega Red, Hand,
　Sabretooth 6.00
7 JLe,SW,V:Omega Red,Hand,
　Sabretooth 5.00
8 JLe,SW,Bishop vs. Gambit . . 5.00
9 JLe,SW,A:Ghost Rider,V:Brood 5.00
10 JLe,SW,MT,Longshot Vs. Mojo,
　BU:Maverick 5.00
11 E:SLo(s)JLe,MT,V:Mojo,
　BU:Maverick 3.00
12 B:FaN(s),ATb,BWi,I:Hazard . . 3.00
13 ATb,BWi,V:Hazard 3.00
14 NKu,X-Cutioners Song#3,A:X-Fact.
　X-Force,V:Four Horsemen . . . 3.00
15 NKu,X-Cutioners Song #7,
　V:Mutant Liberation Front . . . 3.00
16 NKu,MPn,X-Cutioners Song #11,
　A:X-Force,X-Factor,V:Dark Riders,
　Apocalypse Vs.Archangel,IR:Stryfe
　is Nathan Summers 3.00
17 NKu,MPn,R:Illyana,A:Darkstar . 2.50
18 NKu,MPn,R:Omega Red,V:Soul
　Skinner 2.50
19 NKu,MPn,V:Soul Skinner,
　Omega Red 2.50
20 NKu,MPn,J.Grey vs Psylocke . 2.50
21 NKu,V:Silver Samurai,Shinobi . 2.50
22 BPe,V:Silver Samurai,Shinobi . 2.50
23 NKu,MPn,V:Dark Riders,
　Mr.Sinister 2.50
24 NKu,BSz,A Day in the Life . . 2.50
25 NKu,Hologram(c),V:Magneto,
　Wolverine's Adamantium skeleton
　pulled out 14.00
26 NKu,Bloodties#2,A:Avengers,
　I:Unforgiven 3.00
27 RiB,I:Threnody 2.50
28 NKu,MRy,F:Sabretooth 2.50
29 NKu,MRy,V:Shinobi 2.50
30 NKu,MRy,W:Cyclops&Jean Grey,
　w/card 6.00
31 DKu,MRy,A:Spiral,Matsuo,
　D:Kwannon 2.50

32 NKu,MRy,A:Spiral,Matsuo 2.25
33 NKu,MRy,F:Gambit &
    Sabretooth 2.25
34 NKu,MRy,A:Riptide 2.25
35 LSh,A:Nick Fury 2.25
36 NKu,MRy,I:Synch,PhalanxCovenant
    Generation Next,pt.2, deluxe .. 5.00
36a Newsstand ed. 1.75
37 NKu,MRy,Generation Next,pt.3
    foil(c) 5.00
37a newsstand ed. 1.75
38 NKu,MRy,F:Psylocke 2.50
38a newsstand ed. 1.50
39 X-Treme, deluxe 2.50
39a newsstand ed. 1.50
40 deluxe 3.00
40a newsstand ed. 1.50
41 V:Legion, deluxe 2.50
41a newsstand ed. 1.50
42 PS,PaN,Mysterious Visitor ... 2.50
43 Rogue and Iceman 2.50
44 FaN,Mystery of Magneto 2.50
45 20th Anniv.pt.2 .... 4.00
46 FaN,Aku,V:Comcast 2.00
47 SLo,AKu,CaS,F:Dazzler 2.00
48 SLo,AKu,CaS,F:Sabretooth .. 2.00
49 SLo,AKu,Bishop wanted 5.00
50 Onslaught(c) 8.00
50a regular edition 5.00
51 MWa,Onslaught 3.00
52 MWa,AKu,CaS,V:Sinister 3.00
53 Onslaught saga 7.00
54 Onslaught saga 5.00
55 Onslaught saga 4.00
56 Onslaught saga 5.00
57 Operation: Zero Tolerance ... 3.00
58 SLo,NKu 3.00
59 .... 3.00
60 SLo,NKu,F:Ororo, V:Candra . 3.00
61 SLo,CNn,F:Storm, V:Candra . 3.00
62 SLo,CPa,F:Sebastian Shaw,
    Shang Chi 3.00
62A variant Storm/Wolverine(c) . 11.00
63 SLo,CPa,ATi,A:Sebastian Shaw,
    Inner Circle 2.50
64 SLo,CPa,ATi,V:Hellfire Club . 2.50
65 SLo,CPa,ATi, No Exit prelude . 2.50
66 SLo,CPa,ATi, Zero Tolerance,
    A:Bastion 2.00
67 SLo,CPa,ATi, Zero Tolerance,
    F:Iceman, Cecilia Reyes 2.00
68 SLo,CPa,ATi, Operation: Zero
    Tolerance 2.00
69 SLo,CPa, Operation: Zero Tolerance,
    concl. 2.00
70 ATi,Who will join X-Men?,
    double-sized 4.00
71 ATi,Cyclops banished 3.50
72 ATi,Professor Logan's School of
    Hard Knocks 2.50
73 ATi,Marrow visits Callisto ... 2.00
74 ATi,Terror in Morlock Tunnels . 2.00
75 ATi,V:N'Garai, double size ... 3.00
76 CCI,V:Sabretooth, 35th anniv
    kickoff 2.00
77 ATi,A:Black Panther,Maggott .. 2.00
78 Return of Professor X 2.00
79 ATi,Cannonball must leave team 2.00
80A BPe, ATi, cont. from Uncanny X-
    Men #360, etched foil (c) 4.00
80B regular cover 3.00
Ann.#1 JLe,Shattershot,pt.1,
    I:Mojo II 3.50
Ann.#2 I:Empyrean,w/card 3.25
Ann.#3 F:Storm 3.50

Ann. Uncanny X-Men '97, V:Brother-
    hood, 48pg. 3.00
Ann. '98 RMz, F:X-Men & Doctor
    Doom 3.00
Ann. '98 X-Men/Fantastic Four, JoC,
    PaP, 48pg 3.00
Uncanny X-Men'95 Spec. F:Husk . 3.95
Spec.X-Men '95, F:Mr.Sinister ... 3.95
Spec.X-Men'96 LHa, 64pg., F:Gambit,
    Rogue, Magneto, Jubilee
    & Wolverine 2.95
Spec. X-Men'97,JFM,SEp,F:Gambit,
    Joesph & Phoenix 3.00
Minus 1 Spec., SLo,JMd,, flashback,
    discovery of mutants 1.95
Spec.#1 X-Men: Road to Onslaught
    (1996) 2.50
GN TKa,AD,MFm, Age of
    Apocalypse 2.95
TPB Legion Quest 8.95
TPB Magneto Returns 15.95
TPB Dawn of the Age of
    Apocalypse, gold foil cover ... 8.95
TPB Rise of Apocalypse 9.00
TPB Twilight of the Age of
    Apocalypse, gold foil cover ... 8.95

X-MEN ADVENTURES
[1st Season] 1992–94
1 V:Sentinals, Based on TV
    Cartoon 6.00
2 V:Sentinals,D:Morph 5.00
3 V:Magneto,A:Sabretooth 4.00
4 V:Magneto 4.00
5 V:Morlocks 4.00
6 V:Sabretooth 3.50
7 V:Cable,Genosha,Sentinels ... 3.00
8 A:Colossus,A:Juggernaut 3.00
9 I:Colussus(on cartoon),
    V:Juggernaut 3.00
10 A:Angel,V:Mystique 3.00
11 I:Archangel(on cartoon) 2.00
12 V:Horsemen of Apocalypse ... 2.00
13 RMc(s),I:Bishop(on cartoon) . 2.00
14 V:Brotherhood of Evil Mutants . 2.00
15 .... 2.00
TPB Vol.1 .... 4.95
TPB Vol.2 .... 4.95
TPB Vol.3 .... 5.95
TPB Vol.4 rep. Days of Future Past
    and Final Conflict 6.95
[2nd Season] 1994–95
1 R:Morph,I:Mr. Sinister
    (on cartoon) 3.00
2 I:Nasty Boys (on cartoon) 2.00
3 I:Shadow King (on cartoon) ... 2.00
4 I:Omega Red (on cartoon) 2.00
5 I:Alpha Flight (on cartoon) 2.00
6 F:Gambit 2.00
7 A:Cable,Bishop,Apocalypse ... 1.75
8 A:Cable,Bisiph,Apocalypse ... 1.75
9 O:Rogue 1.75
10 .... 1.75
11 F:Mojo,Longshot 1.75
12 Reunions,pt.1 .... 1.75
13 Reunions,pt.1 .... 1.75
[3rd Season] 1995–96
1 Out of the Past,pt.1 .... 3.00
2 V:Spirit Drinker 1.75
3 Phoenix Saga,pt.1 .... 1.75
4 Phoenix Saga,pt.2 .... 1.75
5 Phoenix Saga,pt.3 .... 1.75
6 Phoenix Saga,pt.4 .... 1.75
7 Phoenix Saga,pt.5 .... 1.50

8 War in The Savage Land 1.50
9 F:Ka-Zar 1.50
10 Dark Phoenix,Saga,pt.1 .... 1.50
11 Dark Phoenix Saga,pt.2 .... 1.50
12 Dark Phoenix Saga,pt.3 .... 1.50
13 Dark Phoenix Saga,pt.4 .... 1.50

X-MEN: ALPHA
1994
1 Age of Apocalypse, double size 8.00
1a gold edition, 48pp 45.00

X-Men/Alpha Flight #1
© *Marvel Entertainment Group*

X-MEN/ALPHA FLIGHT
Jan., 1986
1 PS,BWi,V:Loki 5.00
2 PS,BWi,V:Loki 4.00

X-MEN/ALPHA FLIGHT: THE GIFT
Jan. 1998
1-shot CCI,PS, rep. of limited series 6.00

X-MEN/ ANIMATION SPECIAL
TV Screenplay Adapt 10.95

X-MEN ARCHIVES: CAPTAIN BRITAIN
1995
1 AMo,AD,Secret History 3.00
2 AMo,AD,F:Captain Britain 3.00
3 AMo,AD,Trial of Captain Britain 3.00
4 AMo,AD,Trial cont. 3.00
5 AD,AMo,F:Captain Britain ... 3.00
6 AMo,AD,Final Apocalypse? ... 3.00
7 AMo,AD,conclusion 3.00

X-MEN: ASKANI'SON
1 SLo,GeH,sequel to Adventures of
    Cyclops & Phoenix 3.00
2 SLo,GeH,A:Stryfe 3.00
3 SLo,GeH 3.00
4 SLo,GeH,conclusion 3.00
Books of Askani, portraits (1995) . 3.00

X-MEN AT STATE FAIR
1 KGa,Dallas Times Herald . . . 40.00

X-MEN CHRONICLES
1995
1 X-Men Unlimited AX 4.00
2 V:Abbatoir 4.00

X-MEN/CLANDESTINE
1996
1 & 2 AD,MFm,48pg . . . . @3.00

X-MEN CLASSICS
Dec., 1983
1 NA,rep. 3.50
2 NA,rep. 3.50
3 NA,rep. 3.50

CLASSIC X-MEN
Sept., 1986
1 AAd(c),JBo,New stories, rep.
  giant size X-Men 1 . . . . 9.00
2 rep.#94,JBo/AAd(c),BU:
  Storm & Marvel Girl 6.00
3 rep.#95,JBo/AAd(c),BU:
  I:Thunderbird II 4.00
4 rep.#96,JBo/AAd(c),BU:
  Wolverine & N.Crawler 3.50
5 rep.#97,JBo/AAd(c),BU:
  Colossus 3.00
6 rep.#98,JBo/AAd(c),BU:
  JeanGrey,I:Seb.Shaw 3.00
7 rep.#99,JBo/AAd(c),BU:
  HellfireClub,W.Queen 3.00
8 rep.#100,JBo/AAd(c),BU:
  O:Jean Grey/Phoenix 3.00
9 rep.#101,JBo/AAd(c),BU:
  Nightcrawler 3.00
10 rep.#102,JBo/AAd(c),BU:
  Wolverine,A:Sabretooth 8.00
11 rep.#103,JBo/BL(c),BU:Storm . 2.50
12 rep.#104,JBo/AAd(c),BU:
  O:Magneto 7.00
13 rep.#105,JBo/AAd(c),BU:
  JeanGrey & Misty Knight 3.00
14 rep.#107,JBo/AAd(c),BU:
  Lilandra 3.00
15 rep.#108,JBo/AAd(c),BU:
  O:Starjammers 3.00
16 rep.#109,JBo/AAd(c),BU:
  Banshee 3.00
17 rep.#111,JBo/TA(c),BU:
  Mesmero 5.00
18 rep.#112,JBo/AAd(c),BU:
  Phoenix 4.00
19 rep.#113,JBo/AAd(c),BU:
  Magnetoo 4.00
20 rep.#114,JBo/AAd(c),
  BU:Storm 3.00
21 rep.#115,JBo/AAd(c),
  BU:Colossus. 3.00
22 rep.#116,JBo/AAd(c),
  BU:Storm 3.00
23 rep.#117,JBo/KGa(c),BU:
  Nightcrawler 3.00
24 rep.#118,JBo/KGa(c),BU:
  Phoenix 3.00
25 rep.#119,JBo/KGa(c),BU:Wolv. 3.00
26 rep.#120,JBo/KGa(c),BU:Wolv. 4.00
27 rep.#121,JBo/KD(c),BU:
  Wolverine & Phoenix 3.00
28 rep.#122,JBo/KD(c),BU:X-Men 3.00
29 rep.#123,JBo/KD(c),BU:
  Colossus 3.00

Classic X-Men #9
© Marvel Entertainment Group

30 rep.#124,JBo/SLi(c),BU:
  O:Arcade 3.00
31 rep.#125,JBo/SLi(c),BU:
  Professor.X 3.00
32 rep.#126,JBo/SLi(c),BU:
  Wolverine. 3.00
33 rep.#127,JBo/SLi(c),BU:
  Havok 3.00
34 rep.#128,JBo/SLi(c),BU:
  W.Queen,M.Mind 3.00
35 rep.#129,JBo/SLi(c),BU:
  K.Pryde 3.00
36 rep.#130,MBr(c),BU:
  Banshee & Moira 3.00
37 rep.#131,RL/SLi(c),BU:
  Dazzler 3.00
38 rep.#132,KB/SLi(c),BU:
  Dazzler 3.00
39 rep.#133,2nd JLe X-Men/SLi(c),
  BU:Storm 11.00
40 rep.#134,SLi(c),BU:N.Crawler . 2.00
41 rep.#135,SLi(c),BU:
  Mr. Sinister,Cyclops 2.00
42 rep.#136,SLi(c),BU:
  Mr. Sinister,Cyclops 2.00
43 rep.#137,JBy(c),BU:
  Phoenix,Death 2.50
Becomes:

X-MEN CLASSICS
1990
44 rep.#138,KD/SLi(c) 2.00
45 thru 49 rep.#139-#145,SLi(c) @2.00
50 thru 69 rep.#146-#165 . . . . @1.50
70 rep.#166 . . . . 1.75
71 thru 99 rep.#167-#195 . . . . @1.50
100 thru 105 rep. #196-#201 . . @1.50
106 Phoenix vs. Beyonder 1.50
107 F:Rogue 1.50
108 F:Nightcrawler 1.50
109 Rep. Uncanny X-Men #205 . . 1.50
110 Rep. Uncanny X-Men #206 . . 1.50

X-MEN: EARLY YEARS
1 rep. X-Men (first series) #1 . . . 1.75
2 rep. X-Men (first series) #2 . . . 1.75
3 rep. X-Men (first series) #3 . . . 1.75
4 thru 16 rep. X-Men (first series)

#4 to #16 . . . . @1.50
17 Rep. X-Men #17 & #18 . . . . . 2.50

X-MEN INDEX
**SEE: OFFICIAL MARVEL
INDEX TO THE X-MEN**

X-MEN: LOST TALES
1997
1 CCI,JBo,rep. from Classic X-Men 3.00
2 CCI,JBo,rep. from Classic X-Men 3.00

X-MEN/MICRONAUTS
Jan., 1984
1 JG,BWi,Limited Series 3.50
2 JG,BWi,KJo,V:Baron Karza . . . 2.50
3 JG,BWi,V:Baron Karza 2.50
4 JG,BWi,V:Baron Karza,Apr.1984 2.50

X-MEN: THE MANGA
Jan. 1998
1 b&w,translated,F:Jubilee 3.00
2 Jubilee joins, V:Sentinels 3.00
3 Agent Gyrich strikes 3.00
4 Beast captured, morph dead . . 3.00
5 Magneto attempts to rescue
  Beast 3.00
6 Beast on trial, A:Sabretooth . . . 3.00
7 V:Magneto 3.00
8 V:Magneto 3.00
9 V:Morlocks 3.00
10 V:Morlocks, 40pg finale 3.00
11 Wolverine vs. Sabretooth 3.00
12 Wolverine vs. Sabretooth 3.00
13 F:Storm, Jubilee & Gambit . . . 3.00
14 . . . . 3.00

X-MEN OMEGA
1995
1 FaN,Slo,After Xavier, concl. . . 10.00
1a Gold ed. Chromium(c) 48pg. 45.00

X-MEN PRIME
1995
1 SLo,FaN,BHi,major plotlines for
  all X books begin, chromium(c) 10.00

X-MEN: PRYDE & WISDOM
1 WEI,TyD,KIS 2.00
2 & 3 WEI,TyD,KIS . . . . @2.00

X-MEN: THE RISE OF APOCALYPSE
1 TKa,AdP, ancient history of
  X-Men 1.95
2 thru 4 TKa,AdP, ... @1.95
TPB 10.00

X-MEN SPOTLIGHT ON STARJAMMERS
1990
1 DC,F:Starjammers,A:Prof.X . . . 5.00
2 DC,F:Starjammers,A:Prof.X . . . 5.00

X-MEN 2099
1993-96
1 B:JFM(s),RLm,JP,I:X-Men 2099 4.00
1a Gold Ed. 11.00
2 RLm,JP,V:Rat Pack 3.00
3 RLm,JP,D:Serpentina 2.50
4 RLm,JP,I:Theatre of Pain 2.00

MARVEL

5 RLm,JP,Fall of the Hammer#3 .	2.00
6 RLm,JP,I:Freakshow	2.00
7 RLm,JP,V:Freakshow	2.00
8 RLm(c),JS3,JP,N;Metalhead, I:2nd X-Men 2099	1.75
9 RLm,JP,V:2nd X-Men 2099	1.75
10 RLm,JP,A:La Lunatica	1.75
11 RLm,JP,V:2nd X-Men 2099	1.75
12 RLm,JP,A:Junkpile	1.75
13 RLm,JP	1.75
14 RLm,JP,R:Loki	1.75
15 RLm,JP,F:Loki,I:Haloween Jack	1.50
16	1.50
17 X'ian	1.50
18 Haloween Jack	1.50
19 Conclusion Halloween Jack	1.50

Becomes:

X-MEN 2099 A.D.

20 F:Bloodhawk	1.95
21 Doom Factor	1.95
22 One Nation Under Doom	1.95
23 V:Junkpile	1.95
24	1.95
25 X-Men Reunited	2.50
25a variant cover	4.25
26 V:Graverobber	1.95
27	1.95
28 X-Nation x-over	1.95
29 X-Nation x-over	1.95
30	1.95
31	1.95
32 V:Foolkiller	1.95
Spec.#1 Bros.Hildebrandt(c)	3.95
GN X-Men 2099: Oasis, rep., Greg Hildebrandt(c) 64pg, (1998)	6.00

X-MEN UNLIMITED
1993

1 CBa,BP,O:Siena Blaze	8.00
2 JD,O:Magneto	7.00
3 FaN(s),BSz(c),MMK,Sabretooth joins X-Men,A:Maverick	8.00
4 SLo(s),RiB,O:Nightcrawler,Rogue, Mystique,IR:Mystique is Nightcrawler's mother	6.00
5 JFM(s),LSh,After Shi'ar/ Kree War	5.00
6 JFM(s),PS,Sauron	5.00
7 JR2,HMe,O:Storm	5.00
8 Legacy Virus Victim	4.00
9 LHa,Wolverine & Psylocke	4.00
10 MWa,Dark Beast,Beast, double-size	10.00
11 Rogue & Magneto, double-size	10.00
12 Onslaught x-over,A:Juggernaut	3.00
13 GP,Binary gone berserk	3.00
14 TKa, Onslaught fallout	3.00
15 HMe,F:Wolverine, Iceman & Maverick	3.00
16 MvR,F:Banshee, White Queen, I:Primal	3.00
17 TKa,Wolverine vs. Sabretooth, minds are switched	3.00
18 TDF,V:Hydro Man	3.00
19 BRa,Nightcrawler v. Belasco	3.00
20 F:Generation X	3.00

X-MEN VS. AVENGERS
April, 1987

1 MS,JRu,V:Soviet SuperSoldiers	4.50
2 MS,JRu,V:Sov.Super Soldiers	3.50
3 MS,JRu,V:Sov.Super Soldiers	3.50
4 KP,JRu,BMc,AW,AM,V:Magneto July 1987	3.00

TPB	12.95

X-MEN VS. THE BROOD
1996

1 and 2 Day of Wrath	@3.00
TPB rep. #1,#2 and Unc.X-Men #232–#234	17.00

X-NATION 2099
1996

1	1.95
2	1.95
3 At Herod's Themepark	1.95

X.S.E.
Mini-Series 1996

1 (of 4) JOs,Bishop & Shard's secrets	2.00
2 JOs, How did Shard die	2.00
3 JOs, How Shard died	2.00
4 JOs, conclusion	2.00

X-TERMINATORS
Oct., 1988—Jan., 1989

1 JBg,AW,AM,I:N'astirh	4.00
2 JBg,AM,V:N'astirh	3.50
3 JBg,AM,V:N'astirh	3.00
4 JBg,AM,A:New Mutants	3.00

X-UNIVERSE
1995

1 The Other Heroes	3.50
2 F:Ben Grimm,Tony Stark	3.50

YOGI BEAR
Nov., 1977

1 A:Flintstones	9.00
2	7.00
3	7.00
4	7.00
5	7.00
6	7.00
7	7.00
8	7.00
9 March, 1979	7.00

YOUNG ALLIES COMICS
Timely Summer, 1941—Oct., 1946

1 S&K,Hitler(c),I&O:Young Allies 1st meeting Capt. America & Human Torch,A:Red Skull	10,000.00
2 S&K,A;Capt.America,Human Torch	2,500.00
3 Remember Pearl Harbor(c)	1,800.00
4 A;Capt. America,Torch,Red Skull ASh(c),Horror In Hollywood A:Capt.America,Torch	2,800.00
5 ASh(c)	1,200.00
6 ASh(c)	800.00
7 ASh(c)	800.00
8 ASh(c)	800.00
9 ASh(c),Axis leaders(c), B:Tommy Type	900.00
10 ASh(c)	800.00
11 ASh(c)	650.00
12 ASh(c)	650.00
13 ASh(c)	650.00
14	650.00
15 ASh(c)	650.00
16 ASh(c)	650.00
17 ASh(c)	650.00
18 ASh(c)	650.00
19 ASh(c),E:Tommy Type	650.00

20	650.00

YOUNG HEARTS
Nov., 1949—Feb., 1950

1	50.00
2 Feb., 1950	40.00

YOUNG MEN
See: COWBOY ROMANCES

YUPPIES FROM HELL
1989

1 Satire	2.95
2	2.95
3	2.95

ZORRO
Marvel UK 1990

1 Don Diego	1.00
2 thru 12	@1.00

GOLDEN AGE

A-1 COMICS
Magazine Enterprises
1944

N# F:Kerry Drake,BU:Johnny
  Devildog & Streamer Kelly . 175.00
1 A:Dotty Driple,Mr. EX,Bush
  Berry and Lew Loyal 90.00
2 A:Texas Slim & Dirty Dalton,
  The Corsair,Teddy Rich, Dotty
  Dripple,Inca Dinca,Tommy Tinker
  Little Mexico and Tugboat . . . 50.00
3 same 30.00
4 same 30.00
5 same 30.00
6 same 28.00
7 same 25.00

A-1 Comics #124
© Magazine Enterprises

8 same 25.00
9 Texas Slim Issue 28.00
10 Same characters as
  issues #2–#8 . . . . 25.00
11 Teena 40.00
12 Teena 30.00
13 JCr,Guns of Fact and Fiction,
  narcotics & junkies featured 150.00
14 Tim Holt WesternAdventures 375.00
15 Teena 35.00
16 Vacation Comics 28.00
17 Jim Holt #2, E:A-1 on cover 200.00
18 Jimmy Durante, Ph(c) 175.00
19 Tim Holt #3 . . . . 150.00
20 Jimmy Durante Ph(c) 150.00
21 OW,Joan of Arc movie adapt. 135.00
22 Dick Powell (1949) 150.00
23 Cowboys N' Indians #6 . . . . 35.00
24 FF(c),LbC,Trail Colt #2 . . . . 250.00
25 Fibber McGee & Molly (1949) 45.00
26 LbC, Trail Colt #2 . . . . 185.00
27 Ghost Rider#1,O:GhostRider 500.00
28 Christmas (Koko & Kola) . . . 20.00
29 FF(c), Ghost Rider #2 . . . . . 450.00
30 BP, Jet Powers #1 . . . . 225.00
31 FF,Ghost Rider#3,O:Ghost

Rider 450.00
32 AW,GE,Jet Powers #2 . . . 165.00
33 Muggsy Mouse #2 . . . . 28.00
34 FF(c),Ghost Rider #4 . . . . . 425.00
35 AW,Jet Powers 250.00
36 Muggsy Mouse 35.00
37 FF(c),Ghost Rider 450.00
38 AW,WW,Jet Powers 275.00
39 Muggsy Mouse 20.00
40 Dogface Dooley 28.00
41 Cowboys N' Indians 22.00
42 BP,Best of the West 300.00
43 Dogface Dooley 20.00
44 Ghost Rider 175.00
45 American Air Forces 25.00
46 Best of the West 125.00
47 FF,Thunda 900.00
48 Cowboys N' Indians 22.00
49 Dogface Dooley 15.00
50 BP,Danger Is Their Busines . 50.00
51 Ghost Rider 175.00
52 Best of the West 100.00
53 Dogface Dooley 15.00
54 BP,American Air Forces 25.00
55 BP,U.S. Marines 25.00
56 BP,Thunda 130.00
57 Ghost Rider 150.00
58 American Air Forces 25.00
59 Best of the West 100.00
60 The U.S. Marines 25.00
61 Space Ace 350.00
62 Starr Flagg 250.00
63 Manhunt 175.00
64 Dogface Dooley 15.00
65 BP,American Air Forces 25.00
66 Best of the West 100.00
67 American Air Forces 25.00
68 U.S. Marines 25.00
69 Ghost Rider 160.00
70 Best of the West 75.00
71 Ghost Rider 150.00
72 U.S. Marines 25.00
73 BP,Thunda 75.00
74 BP,American Air Forces 20.00
75 Ghost Rider 150.00
76 Best of the West 75.00
77 Manhunt 110.00
78 BP,Thunda 80.00
79 American Air Forces 28.00
80 Ghost Rider 150.00
81 Best of the West 75.00
82 BP,Cave Girl 275.00
83 BP,Thunda 75.00
84 Ghost Rider 150.00
85 Best of the West 75.00
86 BP,Thunda 70.00
87 Best of the West 75.00
88 Bobby Benson's B-Bar-B . . . 45.00
89 BP,Home Run,Stan Musial . 175.00
90 Red Hawk 60.00
91 BP,American Air Forces 20.00
92 Dream Book of Romance . . . 30.00
93 BP,Great Western 100.00
94 FF,White Indian 150.00
95 BP,Muggsy Mouse 15.00
96 BP,Cave Girl 200.00
97 Best of the West 70.00
98 Undercover Girl 275.00
99 Muggsy Mouse 12.00
100 Badmen of the West 125.00

101 FF,White Indian 135.00
101(a) FG, Dream Book of
  Romance, Marlon Brando . . 100.00
103 BP,Best of the West 75.00
104 FF,White Indian 125.00
105 Great Western 60.00
106 Dream Book of Love 40.00
107 Hot Dog 25.00
108 BP,BC,Red Fox 75.00
109 Dream Book of Romance . . 25.00
110 Dream Book of Romance . . 25.00
111 I'm a Cop 65.00
112 Ghost Rider 110.00
113 BP,Great Western 60.00
114 Dream Book of Love 40.00
115 Hot Dog 18.00
116 BP,Cave Girl 170.00
117 White Indian 55.00
118 BP(c),Undercover Girl 250.00
119 Straight Arrow's Fury 75.00
120 Badmen of the West 75.00
121 Mysteries of the
  Scotland Yard 75.00
122 Black Phantom 275.00
123 Dream Book of Love 25.00
124 Hot Dog 18.00
125 BP,Cave Girl 175.00
126 BP,I'm a Cop 55.00
127 BP,Great Western 60.00
128 BP,I'm a Cop 50.00
129 The Avenger 200.00
130 BP,Strongman 100.00
131 BP,The Avenger 150.00
132 Strongman 80.00
133 BP,The Avenger 150.00
134 Strongman 75.00
135 White Indian 50.00
136 Hot Dog 15.00
137 BP,Africa 125.00
138 BP,Avenger 150.00
139 BP,Strongman, 1955 . . . . . 85.00

ABBIE AN' SLATS
United Features Syndicate
March–Aug., 1948

1 RvB(c) 225.00
2 RvB(c) 175.00
3 RvB(c) 100.00
4 August, 1948 . . . . 100.00
N# 1940,Earlier Issue 275.00
N# 225.00

ABBOTT AND COSTELLO
St. John Publishing Co.
February, 1948

1 PP(c), Waltz Time 400.00
2 Jungle Girl and Snake(c) . . . 175.00
3 Outer Space cover 150.00
4 MD, Circus cover 100.00
5 MD,Bull Fighting cover 100.00
6 MD,Harem cover 100.00
7 MD,Opera cover 100.00
8 MD,Pirates cover 100.00
9 MD,Polar Bear cover 100.00
10 MD,PP(c),Son of Sinbad tale 170.00
11 MD 75.00
12 PP(c), Movie issue 70.00
13 Fire fighters cover 70.00
14 Bomb cover 70.00

All comics prices listed are for *Near Mint* condition.

15 Bubble Bath cover 70.00
16 thru 29 MD . . . . @60.00
30 thru 39 MD . . . . @50.00
40 MD,September, 1956 . . . . . . 50.00
3-D #1, Nov. 1953 . . . . 230.00

ACE COMICS
David McKay Publications
April, 1937

1 JM, F:Katzenjammer Kids . 2,500.00
2 JM, A:Blondie 725.00
3 JM, A:Believe It Or Not 500.00
4 JM, F:Katzenjammer Kids . . 475.00
5 JM, A:Believe It Or Not 475.00
6 JM, A:Blondie 365.00
7 JM, A:Believe It Or Not 365.00
8 JM, A:Jungle Jim 365.00
9 JM, A:Blondie 365.00
10 JM, F:Katzenjammer Kids . . 350.00
11 I:The Phantom series 500.00
12 A:Blondie, Jungle Jim 275.00
13 A:Ripley's Believe It Or Not . 260.00
14 A:Blondie, Jungle Jim 260.00
15 A:Blondie 250.00
16 F:Katzenjammer Kids 250.00
17 A:Blondie 250.00
18 A:Ripley's Believe It Or N8t . 250.00
19 F:Katzenjammer Kids 250.00
20 A:Jungle Jim 250.00
21 A:Blondie 235.00
22 A:Jungle Jim 235.00
23 F:Katzenjammer Kids 235.00
24 A:Blondie 235.00
25 . . . . 200.00
26 O:Prince Valiant 650.00
27 thru 36 . . . . @235.00
37 Krazy Kat Ends 175.00
38 thru 49 . . . . @150.00
50 thru 59 . . . . @125.00
60 thru 69 . . . . @120.00
70 thru 79 . . . . @110.00
80 thru 89 . . . . @100.00
90 thru 99 . . . . @75.00
100 . . . . 100.00
101 thru 109 . . . . @75.00
110 thru 119 . . . . @65.00
120 thru 143 . . . . @60.00
144 Phantom covers begin . . . 100.00
145 thru 150 . . . . @75.00
151 October-November, 1949 . 100.00

ACES HIGH
E.C. Comics
March-April, 1955

1 GE(c) 200.00
2 GE(c) 125.00
3 GE(c) 100.00
4 GE(c) 100.00
5 GE(c)Nov.-Dec., 1955 . . . . . 100.00

ADVENTURES INTO DARKNESS
Standard Publications
August, 1952

5 JK(c), ATh 200.00
6 GT, JK 125.00
7 JK(c) 150.00
8 ATh 160.00
9 JK,ATh 175.00
10 JK,ATh,MSy 110.00
11 JK,ATh,MSy 110.00
12 JK,ATh,MYs 110.00
13 Cannibalism feature 125.00

Adventures into the Unknown #14
© American Comics Group

14 . . . . 85.00

ADVENTURES INTO THE UNKNOWN!
American Comics Group
Fall 1948

1 FG, Haunted House cover . 1,400.00
2 Haunted Island cover 550.00
3 AF, Sarcophagus cover 600.00
4 Monsters cover 250.00
5 Monsters cover 250.00
6 Giant Hands cover 200.00
7 Skeleton Pirate cover 200.00
8 Horror 200.00
9 Snow Monster 200.00
10 Red Bats 200.00
11 Death Shadow 200.00
12 OW(c) 200.00
13 OW(c),Dinosaur 175.00
14 OW(c),Cave 175.00
15 Red Demons 175.00
16 . . . . 150.00
17 OW(c),The Thing Type 200.00
18 OW(c),Wolves 175.00
19 OW(c),Graveyard 150.00
20 OW(c),Graveyard 150.00
21 Bats and Dracula 150.00
22 Death 150.00
23 Bats 150.00
24 . . . . 150.00
25 . . . . 150.00
26 . . . . 150.00
27 AW 200.00
28 thru 39 . . . . @125.00
40 thru 49 . . . . @100.00
50 . . . . 100.00
51 Lazarus 225.00
52 Lazarus 225.00
53 . . . . 200.00
54 . . . . 200.00
55 . . . . 200.00
56 Lazarus 200.00
57 . . . . 200.00
58 Lazarus 200.00
59 . . . . 175.00
60 . . . . 75.00
61 . . . . 75.00

62 thru 69 . . . . @60.00
70 thru 79 . . . . @40.00
80 thru 89 . . . . @30.00
90 thru 99 . . . . @35.00
100 . . . . 32.00
101 thru 115 . . . . @30.00
116 AW,AT 28.00
117 thru 127 . . . . @25.00
128 AW,Forbidden Worlds . . . 30.00
129 thru 152 . . . . @25.00
153 A:Magic Agent 25.00
154 O:Nemesis 30.00
155 . . . . 25.00
156 A:Magic Agent 25.00
157 thru 174, Aug. 1967 . . . . @25.00

ADVENTURES IN WONDERLAND
Lev Gleason Publications
April, 1955

1 . . . . 40.00
2 . . . . 30.00
3 . . . . 25.00
4 . . . . 25.00
5 . . . . 28.00

Adventures of Mighty Mouse #6
© St. John Publishing Co.

ADVENTURES OF MIGHTY MOUSE
St. John Publishing Co.
November, 1951

1 Mighty Mouse Adventures . . 175.00
2 Menace of the Deep 135.00
3 Storm Clouds of Mystery . . . 100.00
4 Thought Control Machine . . . 85.00
5 Jungle Peril 75.00
6 'The Vine of Destruction' . . . 65.00
7 Space Ship(c) 65.00
8 Charging Alien(c) 65.00
9 Meteor(c) 60.00
10 Revolt at the Zoo" 60.00
11 Jungle(c) 60.00
12 A:Freezing Terror 60.00
13 A:Visitor from Outer Space . . 60.00
14 V:Cat 55.00
15 . . . . 55.00

GOLDEN AGE

16 . . . . 55.00
17 . . . . 55.00
18 May, 1955 . . . . 55.00

AGGIE MACK
Four Star Comics/
Superior Comics
January, 1948
1 AF,HR(c) 200.00
2 JK(c) 100.00
3 AF,JK(c) 90.00
4 AF 125.00
5 AF,JK(c) 100.00
6 AF,JK(c) 90.00
7 AF,Burt Lancaster on cover . 100.00
8 AF,JK(c), August 1949 . . . . . 80.00

BILL BARNES,
AMERICA'S AIR ACE
Street and Smith Publications
July, 1940
1 (Bill Barnes Comics) 650.00
2 Second Battle Valley Forge . 350.00
3 A:Aviation Cadets 300.00
4 Shotdown(c) 275.00
5 A:Air Warden, Danny Hawk . 225.00
6 A:Danny Hawk,RocketRodney 200.00
7 How to defeat the Japanese . 200.00
8 Ghost Ship 200.00
9 Flying Tigers, John Wayne . 210.00
10 I:Roane Waring 200.00
11 Flying Tigers 200.00
12 War Workers 200.00
Becomes:

AIR ACE
2-1 Invades Germany 175.00
2-2 Jungle Warfare 100.00
2-3 A:The Four Musketeers . . . 90.00
2-4 A:Russell Swann 90.00
2-5 A:The Four Musketeers . . . 90.00
2-6 Raft(c) 75.00
2-7 BP, What's New In Science 75.00
2-8 XP-59 . . . . 75.00
2-9 The Northrop P-61 . . . . . . 75.00
2-10 NCG-14 . . . . 75.00
2-11 Whip Lanch 75.00
2-12 PP(c) 75.00
3-1 . . . . 60.00
3-2 Atom and It's Future 60.00
3-3 Flying in the Future 60.00
3-4 How Fast Can We Fly 60.00
3-5 REv(c) 60.00
3-6 V:Wolves 60.00
3-7 BP(c), Vortex of Atom Bomb 150.00
3-8 February-March, 1947 . . . . 75.00

AIRBOY
(see AIR FIGHTERS
COMICS)

AIR FIGHTERS COMICS
Hillman Periodicals
November, 1941
1 I:BlackCommander
(only App) 1,500.00
2 O:Airboy A:Sky Wolf 2,500.00
3 O:Sky Wolf and Heap 1,200.00
4 A:Black Angel, Iron Ace . . . 900.00
5 A:Sky Wolf and Iron Ace . . . 650.00
6 Airboy's Bird Plane 600.00
7 Airboy battles Kultur 550.00
8 A:Skinny McGinty 525.00

Air Fighters #13 (2/1)
© Hillman Periodicals

9 A:Black Prince, Hatchet Man 500.00
10 I:The Stinger 500.00
11 Kida(c) 500.00
12 A:Misery 500.00
2-1 A:Flying Dutchman 475.00
2-2 I:Valkyrie 650.00
2-3 Story Panels cover 475.00
2-4 V:Japanese 475.00
2-5 Air Boy in Tokyo 475.00
2-6 'Dance of Death' 475.00
2-7 A:Valkyrie 475.00
2-8 Airboy Battles Japanese . . 475.00
2-9 Airboy Battles Japanese . . 475.00
2-10 O:Skywolf 600.00
Becomes:

AIRBOY
2-11 . . . . 550.00
2-12 A:Valykrie 350.00
3-1 . . . . 300.00
3-2 . . . . 275.00
3-3 Never published
3-4 I:The Heap 250.00
3-5 Airboy 225.00
3-6 A:Valykrie 225.00
3-7 AMc,Witch Hunt 225.00
3-8 A:Condor 235.00
3-9 O:The Heap 250.00
3-10 . . . . 200.00
3-11 . . . . 200.00
3-12 Airboy missing 250.00
4-1 Elephant in chains cover . 235.00
4-2 I:Rackman 150.00
4-3 Airboy profits on name . . . 150.00
4-4 S&K 160.00
4-5 S&K,The American Miracle 180.00
4-6 S&K,A:Heap and
Flying Fool 180.00
4-7 S&K 180.00
4-8 S&K,Girlfriend captured . . 180.00
4-9 S&K,Airboy in quick sand . 180.00
4-10 S&K,A:Valkyrie 180.00
4-11 S&K,A:Frenchy 180.00
4-12 FBe 200.00
5-1 LSt 125.00
5-2 I:Wild Horse of Calabra . . 125.00
5-3 . . . . 125.00

5-4 CI 125.00
5-5 Skull on cover 125.00
5-6 . . . . 125.00
5-7 . . . . 125.00
5-8 Bondage Cover 150.00
5-9 Zoi,Row 125.00
5-10 A:Valykrie,O:The Heap . 135.00
5-11 Airboy vs. The Rats 125.00
5-12 BK,Rat Army captures
Airboy 125.00
6-1 . . . . 125.00
6-2 . . . . 125.00
6-3 . . . . 125.00
6-4 Airboy boxes 135.00
6-5 A:The Ice People 125.00
6-6 . . . . 125.00
6-7 Airboy vs. Chemical Giant 125.00
6-8 O:The Heap 150.00
6-9 . . . . 125.00
6-10 . . . . 125.00
6-11 . . . . 125.00
6-12 . . . . 125.00
7-1 . . . . 120.00
7-2 BP 120.00
7-3 BP 120.00
7-4 I:Monsters of the Ice 120.00
7-5 V:Monsters of the Ice 120.00
7-6 . . . . 120.00
7-7 Mystery of the Sargasso
Sea 120.00
7-8 A:Centaur 120.00
7-9 I:Men of the StarlightRobot 120.00
7-10 O:The Heap 120.00
7-11 . . . . 120.00
7-12 Airboy visits India 120.00
8-1 BP,A:Outcast and Polo
Bandits 100.00
8-2 BP,Suicide Dive cover . . . 100.00
8-3 I:The Living Fuse 100.00
8-4 A:Death Merchants o/t Air . 100.00
8-5 A:Great Plane from Nowhere 100.00
8-6 . . . . 100.00
8-7 . . . . 100.00
8-8 . . . . 100.00
8-9 . . . . 100.00
8-10 A:Mystery Walkers 100.00
8-11 . . . . 100.00
8-12 . . . . 120.00
9-1 . . . . 100.00
9-2 A:Valykrie 90.00
9-3 A:Heap (cover) 90.00
9-4 A:Water Beast, Frog Headed
Riders 100.00
9-5 A:Heap vs.Man of Moonlight 90.00
9-6 Heap cover 90.00
9-7 Heap cover 90.00
9-8 Heap cover 100.00
9-9 . . . . 100.00
9-10 Space cover 100.00
9-11 . . . . 90.00
9-12 Heap cover 90.00
10-1 Heap cover 90.00
10-2 Ships on Space 90.00
10-3 . . . . 90.00
10-4 May, 1953 . . . . 90.00

AL CAPP'S
DOG PATCH COMICS
Toby Press
June, 1949
1 . . . . 175.00
2 A:Daisy 125.00
3 . . . . 110.00
4 December, 1949 . . . . 110.00

GOLDEN AGE

AL CAPP'S SHMOO
Toby Press
July, 1949
1 100 Trillion Schmoos 250.00
2 Super Shmoo(c) 175.00
3 . . . . 175.00
4 . . . . 150.00
5 April, 1950 . . . . 150.00

AL CAPP'S WOLF GAL
Toby Press
1951
1 Pin-Up 225.00
2 1952 . . . . 200.00

ALL-FAMOUS CRIME
Star Publications
May, 1951
8 LbC(c) 100.00
9 LbC(c) 200.00
10 LbC(c) 100.00
4 LbC(c) 100.00
5 LbC(c) 100.00
Becomes:

ALL-FAMOUS POLICE CASES
6 LbC(c) 100.00
7 LbC(c) 90.00
8 LbC(c) 75.00
9 LbC(c) 75.00
10 thru 15 LbC(c) . . . . @75.00
16 September, 1954 . . . . 75.00

ALL GOOD COMICS
R. W. Voight/Fox Publ. /St. John Publ.
1 1944 . . . . 125.00
1 1946 . . . . 100.00
N# 1949 . . . . 450.00

ALL GREAT COMICS
(see DAGGER, DESERT HAWK)

ALL HERO COMICS
Fawcett Publications
March, 1943
1 A:Capt. Marvel Jr.,Capt.
Midnight,Ibis, Golden Arrow
and Spy Smasher 1,200.00

ALL HUMOR COMICS
Comic Favorites, Inc. (Quality Comics)
Spring 1946
1 . . . . 125.00
2 PG 65.00
3 I:Kelly Poole 40.00
4 thru 7 . . . . @35.00
8 PG 40.00
9 . . . . 40.00
10 . . . . 40.00
11 thru 17 . . . . @30.00

ALL LOVE ROMANCES
(see SCREAM COMICS)

ALL NEGRO COMICS
1 . . . . 2,500.00

All-New Comics #12
© Family Comics/Harvey Publ.

ALL-NEW COMICS
Family Comics (Harvey Publ.)
January, 1943
1 A:Steve Case, Johnny Rebel
I:Detective Shane 2,000.00
2 JKu,O:Scarlet Phantom 750.00
3 . . . . 550.00
4 AdH 550.00
5 Flash Gordon 500.00
6 I:Boy Heroes and Red Blazer 500.00
7 JKu,AS(c),A:Black Cat &
Zebra 500.00
8 JKu,A:Shock Gibson 500.00
9 JKu,A:Black Cat 500.00
10 JKu,A:Zebra 450.00
11 A:Man in Black, Girl
Commandos 450.00
12 JKu 450.00
13 Stuntman by S&K,
A:Green Hornet&cover . . . 475.00
14 A:Green Hornet 450.00
15 Smaller size, Distributed
by Mail, March-April, 1947 . 400.00

ALL TOP COMICS
William H. Wise Co.
1944
N# 132pgs.,A:Capt.
V,Red Robbins 225.00

ALL TOP COMICS
Fox Features Syndicate
Spring 1946
1 A:Cosmo Cat, Flash Rabbit . 100.00
2 . . . . 50.00
3 . . . . 40.00
4 . . . . 40.00
5 . . . . 40.00
6 . . . . 40.00
7 . . . . 40.00
7a 85.00
8 JKa(c),I:Blue Beetle 1,600.00
9 JKa(c),A:Rulah 900.00
10 JKa(c),A:Rulah 1,000.00
11 A:Rulah,Blue Beetle 750.00

12 A:Rulah,Jo Jo,Blue Beetle . 750.00
13 A:Rulah 700.00
14 A:Rulah,Blue Beetle 900.00
15 A:Rulah 700.00
16 A:Rulah,Blue Beetle 650.00
17 A:Rulah,Blue Beetle 650.00
18 A:Dagar,Jo Jo 500.00
Green Publ.
6 1957 . . . . 20.00
6 1958 . . . . 20.00
6 1959 . . . . 20.00
6 1959 . . . . 20.00
6 Supermouse cover 20.00

ALLEY OOP
Argo Publications
November, 1955
1 . . . . 125.00
2 . . . . 100.00
3 March, 1956 . . . . 100.00

AMAZING ADVENTURES
Ziff-Davis Publ. Co.
1950
1 WW, Asteroid Witch 500.00
2 Masters of Living Flame . . . 225.00
3 The Evil Men Do 225.00
4 Invasion of the Love Robots 225.00
5 Secret of the Crater-Men . . . 225.00
6 Man Who Killed a World . . . 250.00

AMAZING GHOST STORIES
(See: WEIRD HORRORS)

AMAZING-MAN COMICS
Centaur Publications
September, 1939
5 BEv,O:Amazing Man 15,000.00
6 BEv,B:The Shark 2,700.00
7 BEv,I:Magician From Mars . 1,600.00
8 BEv 1,200.00
9 BEv 1,200.00
10 BEv 1,100.00
11 BEv,I:Zardi 1,000.00
12 SG(c) 900.00
13 SG(c) 900.00
14 B:Reef Kinkaid, Dr. Hypo . . 750.00
15 A:Zardi 600.00
16 Mighty Man's powers
revealed 650.00
17 A:Dr. Hypo 600.00
18 BLb(a),SG(c) 600.00
19 BLb(a),SG(c) 600.00
20 BLb(a),SG(c) 600.00
21 O:Dash Dartwell 625.00
22 A:Silver Streak, The Voice . 600.00
23 I&O:Tommy the Amazing Kid 600.00
24 B:King of Darkness,Blue Lady550.00
25 A:Meteor Marvin 900.00
26 A:Meteor Marvin,Electric Ray
February, 1942 . . . . 850.00

AMAZING MYSTERY FUNNIES
Centaur Publications
1938
1 Skyrocket Steele in the
Year X 2,700.00
2 WE,Skyrocket Steele 1,400.00
3 . . . . 500.00
(#4) WE,bondage (c) 700.00

Amazing Mystery Funnies #8
© Centaur Publications

2-1(#5) 650.00
2-2(#6) Drug use 550.00
2-3(#7) Air Sub DX 550.00
2-4(#8) 550.00
2-5(#9) 700.00
2-6(#10) 550.00
2-7(#11) scarce 2,700.00
2-8(#12) Speed Centaur 1,000.00
2-9(#13) 600.00
2-10(#14) 600.00
2-11(#15) 600.00
2-12(#16) BW,I:Space Patrol . 1,500.00
3-1(#17) I:Bullet 600.00
18 . . . . 600.00
19 BW,Space Patrol 750.00
20 . . . . 600.00
21 BW,Space Patrol 750.00
22 BW,Space Patrol 750.00
23 BW,Space Patrol 750.00
24 BW,Space Patrol 750.00

AMAZING WILLIE MAYS
Famous Funnies
1954
1 Willie Mays(c) 550.00

AMERICAN LIBRARY
David McKay Publ.
1943
(#1) Thirty Seconds Over
  Tokyo, movie adapt. 250.00
(#2) Guadalcanal Diary 175.00
3 Look to the Mountain 100.00
4 The Case of the Crooked
  Candle (Perry Mason) 100.00
5 Duel in the Sun 100.00
6 Wingate's Raiders 110.00

AMERICA'S BEST
COMICS
Nedor/Better/Standard
Publications
February 1942
1 B:Black Terror, Captain Future,
  The Liberator,Doc Strange   1,700.00
2 O:American Eagle 650.00

3 B:Pyroman 500.00
4 A:Doc Strange, Jimmy Cole . 400.00
5 A:Lone Eagle, Capt. Future . 375.00
6 A:American Crusader 350.00
7 A:Hitler,Hirohito 500.00
8 The Liberator ends 350.00
9 ASh(c) 425.00
10 ASh(c) 350.00
11 ASh(c) 350.00
12 Red Cross cover 350.00
13 . . . . 350.00
14 Last American Eagle app . . 350.00
15 ASh(c) 325.00
16 ASh(c) 335.00
17 Doc Strange carries football 325.00
18 Bondage cover 325.00
19 ASh(c) 325.00
20 vs. the Black Market 325.00
21 Infinity cover 300.00
22 A:Captain Future 300.00
23 B:Miss Masque 350.00
24 Bondage cover 350.00
25 A:Sea Eagle 300.00
26 A:The Phantom Detective . . 300.00
27 ASh(c) 300.00
28 A:Commando Cubs,
  Black Terror 300.00
29 A:Doc Strange 300.00
30 ASh(c) 300.00
31 July, 1949 . . . . 300.00

AMERICA'S BIGGEST
COMICS BOOK
William H. Wise
1944
1 196 pgs. A:Grim Reaper, Zudo,
  Silver Knight, Thunderhoof,
  Jocko and Socko,Barnaby
  Beep,Commando Cubs 300.00

AMERICA'S GREATEST
COMICS
Fawcett Publications
Fall 1941
1 MRa(c),A:Capt. Marvel,
  Bulletman,Spy Smasher and
  Minute Man 2,200.00
2 F:Capt. Marvel 1,200.00
3 F:Capt. Marvel 800.00
4 B:Commando Yank 600.00
5 Capt.Marvel in "Lost Lighting" 600.00
6 Capt.Marvel fires Machine
  Gun 500.00
7 A:Balbo the Boy Magician . . 500.00
8 A:Capt.Marvel Jr.,Golden
  Arrow,Summer 1943 . . . . . . 500.00

AMERICA IN ACTION
Dell Publishing Co.
1942
1 . . . . 125.00

ANDY COMICS
(see SCREAM COMICS)

ANGEL
Dell Publishing Co.
August, 1954
(1) *see Dell Four Color #576*
2 . . . . 20.00
3 thru 16 . . . . @15.00

ANIMAL ANTICS
Dell Publishing Co.
1946
1 B:Racoon Kids 350.00
2 . . . . 200.00
3 thru 10 . . . . @125.00
11 thru 23 . . . . @75.00

ANIMAL COMICS
Dell Publishing Co.
1942
1 WK,Pogo 1,000.00
2 Uncle Wiggily(c),A:Pogo . . . 450.00
3 Muggin's Mouse(c),A:Pogo . 325.00
4 Uncle Wiggily(c) 250.00
5 Uncle Wiggily(c) 325.00
6 Uncle Wiggily 200.00
7 Uncle Wiggily 200.00
8 Pogo 250.00
9 War Bonds(c),A:Pogo 250.00
10 Pogo 250.00
11 Pogo 175.00
12 Pogo 175.00
13 Pogo 175.00
14 Pogo 175.00
15 Pogo 175.00
16 Uncle Wiggily 100.00
17 Pogo(c) 125.00
18 Pogo(c) 125.00
19 Pogo(c) 125.00
20 Pogo 100.00
21 Pogo(c) 125.00
22 Pogo 75.00
23 Pogo 75.00
24 Pogo(c) 85.00
25 Pogo(c) 85.00
26 Pogo(c) 85.00
27 Pogo(c) 75.00
28 Pogo(c) 75.00
29 Pogo(c) 75.00
30 Pogo(c) 75.00

ANIMAL FABLES
E.C. Comics
July-August 1946
1 B:Korky Kangaroo,Freddy Firefly
  Petey Pig and Danny Demon 275.00
2 B:Aesop Fables 200.00
3 . . . . 150.00
4 . . . . 150.00
5 Firefly vs. Red Ants 150.00
6 . . . . 150.00
7 O:Moon Girls,Nov.-Dec.1947 450.00

ANIMAL FAIR
Fawcett Publications
March 1946
1 B:Captain Marvel Bunny,
  Sir Spot 150.00
2 A:Droopy, Colonel Walrus . . 75.00
3 . . . . 35.00
4 A:Kid Gloves, Cub Reporter . 35.00
5 thru 7 . . . . 35.00
8 . . . . 25.00
9 . . . . 25.00
10 . . . . 25.00
11 February 1947 . . . . 25.00

ANNIE OAKLEY & TAGG
Dell Publishing Co.
1953
(1) *see Dell Four Color #438*
(2) *see Dell Four Color #481*

GOLDEN AGE

(3) *see Dell Four Color #575*
4	125.00
5	90.00
6 thru 10	@75.00
11 thru 18	@50.00

Archie Comics #26
© *Archie Publications*

ARCHIE COMICS
MLJ Magazines
Winter, 1942-43

1 I:Jughead & Veronica	10,000.00
2	2,200.00
3	1,600.00
4	900.00
5	850.00
6	650.00
7 thru 11	@600.00
12 thru 15	@450.00
16 thru 19	@400.00

Archie Publications

20	400.00
21	300.00
22 thru 31	@275.00
32 thru 42	@150.00
43 thru 50	@100.00
51 thru 60	@75.00
61 thru 70	@50.00
71 thru 80	@40.00
81 thru 99	@30.00
100	50.00
101	25.00
102 thru 115	@15.00
116 thru 130	@12.00
131 thru 145	@10.00
146 thru 160	@7.50
161 thru 180	@5.00
181 thru 200	@4.00
201 thru 250	@3.00
251 thru 280	@3.00
281 thru 389	@3.00

ARCHIE'S GIANT SERIES MAGAZINE
Archie Publications
1954

1	900.00
2	550.00

3	400.00
4	350.00
5	350.00
6 thru 10	@250.00
11 thru 20	@200.00
21 thru 29	@125.00
30 thru 35	@45.00
136 thru 141	@45.00
142	32.00
143 thru 160	@12.00
161 thru 199	@8.00
200	5.00
201 thru 250	@2.50
251 thru 299	@2.00
300 thru 500	@2.00

ARCHIE'S GIRLS BETTY AND VERONICA
Archie Publications
1950

1	1,100.00
2	500.00
3	350.00
4	250.00
5	240.00
6 thru 10	@200.00
11 thru 15	@150.00
16 thru 20	@100.00
21	90.00
22 thru 29	@85.00
30 thru 40	@60.00
41 thru 50	@50.00
51 thru 60	@40.00
61 thru 70	@35.00
71 thru 80	@30.00
81 thru 90	@25.00
91 thru 99	@20.00
100	25.00
101 thru 120	@12.00
121 thru 140	@10.00
141 thru 160	@7.00
161 thru 180	@3.00
181 thru 199	@2.00
200	3.00
201 thru 220	@2.00
221 thru 240	@2.00
241 thru 347	@2.00

ARCHIE'S JOKE BOOK MAGAZINE
Archie Publications
1953

1	650.00
2	350.00
3	250.00
15 thru 19	@165.00
20 thru 25	@120.00
26 thru 35	@90.00
36 thru 40	@60.00
41 1st NA art	125.00
42 & 43	60.00
44 thru 48 NA	@70.00
49 thru 60	@20.00
61 thru 70	@15.00
71 thru 80	@10.00
81 thru 100	@5.00
101 thru 200	@2.50
201 thru 288	@2.00

ARCHIE'S MECHANICS
Archie Publications
September, 1954

1	550.00

2	400.00
3	300.00

ARCHIE'S PAL, JUGHEAD
Archie Publications
1949

1	900.00
2	450.00
3	275.00
4	250.00
5	250.00
6	200.00
7 thru 10	@175.00
11 thru 15	@125.00
16 thru 20	@85.00
21 thru 30	@65.00
31 thru 39	@50.00
40 thru 50	@35.00
51 thru 60	@30.00
61 thru 70	@25.00
71 thru 80	@20.00
81 thru 99	@15.00
100	17.00
101 thru 126	@10.00

Archie's Pals 'N' Gals #4
© *Archie Publications*

ARCHIE'S PALS 'N' GALS
Archie Publications
1952 thru 53

1	550.00
2	300.00
3	200.00
4	135.00
5	135.00
6	80.00
7	80.00
8 thru 10	@75.00
11 thru 15	@50.00
16 thru 20	@35.00
21 thru 30	@20.00
31 thru 40	@20.00
41 thru 50	@12.00
51 thru 60	@10.00
61 thru 70	@7.00
71 thru 80	@5.00
81 thru 99	@2.50

GOLDEN AGE (side tab)

100	3.00
101 thru 120	@2.00
121 thru 160	@2.00
161 thru 224	@2.00

ARCHIE'S RIVAL REGGIE
Archie Publications
1950

1	550.00
2	275.00
3	200.00
4	175.00
5	175.00
6	150.00
7 thru 10	@125.00
11 thru 13	@75.00
14 thru 15	@65.00
16 August, 1954	70.00

ARMY & NAVY COMICS
(see SUPERSNIPE COMICS)

ARROW, THE
Centaur Publications
October 1940

1 B:Arrow	2,200.00
2 BLB(c)	900.00
3 O:Dash Dartwell,Human Meteor, Rainbow, Bondage cover, October, 1941	850.00

ATOMAN
Spark Publications
February 1946

1 JRo,MMe,O:Atoman,A:Kid Crusaders	400.00
2 JRo,MMe	300.00

ATOMIC COMICS
Green Publishing Co.
January, 1946

1 S&S,A:Radio Squad, Barry O'Neal	1,100.00
2 MB,A:Inspector Dayton, Kid Kane	500.00
3 MB,A:Zero Ghost Detective	350.00
4 JKa(c), July-August, 1946	325.00

ATOMIC COMICS
Daniels Publications
1946 (Reprints)

1 A:Rocketman,Yankee Boy, Bondage cover,rep.	225.00

ATOMIC MOUSE
Capital Stories/ Charlton Comics
March, 1953

1 AFa,O:Atomic Mouse	150.00
2 AFa,Ice Cream cover	65.00
3 AFa,Genie and Magic Carpet cover	50.00
4 AFa	50.00
5 AFa,A:Timmy the Timid Ghost	50.00
6 thru 10 Funny Animal	@40.00
11 thru 14 Funny Animal	@25.00
15 A:Happy the Marvel Bunny	30.00
16 Funny Animal,Giant	32.00
17 thru 30 Funny Animal	@25.00
31 thru 36 Funny Animal	@20.00
37 A:Atom the Cat	20.00

38 thru 40 Funny Animal	@15.00
41 thru 53 Funny Animal	@10.00
54 June, 1963	10.00

ATOMIC THUNDER BOLT, THE
Regor Company
February, 1946

1 I:Atomic Thunderbolt, Mr. Murdo	375.00

AUTHENTIC POLICE CASES
St. John Publ. Co.
1948

1 Hale the Magician	275.00
2 Lady Satan, Johnny Rebel	150.00
3 A:Avenger	300.00
4 Masked Black Jack	175.00
5 JCo	175.00
6 JCo,MB(c)	300.00
7 thru 10	@125.00
11 thru 15	@100.00
16 thru 23	@75.00
24 thru 28	@125.00
29 thru 38	@45.00

AVIATION AND MODEL BUILDING
(see TRUE AVIATION PICTURE STORIES)

AVON ONE-SHOTS
Avon Periodicals
1949-1953
{Listed in Alphabetical Order}

1 Atomic Spy Cases	200.00
N# WW,Attack on Planet Mars	550.00
1 Batchelor's Diary	150.00
1 Badmen of the West	200.00
N# Badmen of Tombstone	75.00
1 Behind Prison Bars	150.00
2 Betty and Her Steady	35.00
N# Blackhawk Indian Tomahawk War	75.00
1 Blazing Sixguns	75.00
1 Butch Cassidy	80.00
N# Chief Crazy Horse	100.00
N# FF,Chief Victorio's Apache Massacre	300.00
N# City of the Living Dead	300.00
1 Complete Romance	150.00
N# Custer's Last Fight	75.00
1 Dalton Boys	70.00
N# Davy Crockett	70.00
N# The Dead Who Walk	350.00
1 Diary of Horror,Bondage(c)	275.00
N# WW,An Earth Man on Venus	900.00
1 Eerie, bondage (c)	650.00
1 Escape from Devil's Island	250.00
N# Fighting Daniel Boone	80.00
N# For a Night of Love	125.00
1 WW,Flying Saucers	600.00
N# Flying Saucers.	400.00
1 Going Steady with Betty	60.00
N# Hooded Menace	350.00
N# King of the Badmen of Deadwood	100.00
1 King Solomon's Mines	225.00
N# Kit Carson & the Blackfeet Warriors	50.00
N# Last of the Comanches	75.00

N# Masked Bandit	100.00
1 WW,Mask of Dr. Fu Manchu	700.00
N# Night of Mystery	275.00
1 Outlaws of the Wild West	175.00
1 Out of this World	475.00
N# Pancho Villa	125.00
1 Phantom Witch Doctor	325.00
1 Pixie Puzzle Rocket to Adventureland	75.00
1 Prison Riot,drugs	175.00
N# Red Mountain Featuring Quantrell's Raiders	150.00
N# Reform School Girl	950.00
1 Robotmen of the Lost Planet	750.00
N# WW(c),Rocket to the Moon	800.00
N# JKu,Secret Diary of Eerie Adventures	1,100.00
1 Sheriff Bob Dixon's Chuck Wagon	65.00
1 Sideshow	135.00
1 JKu,Sparkling Love	80.00
N# Speedy Rabbit	30.00
1 Teddy Roosevelt & His Rough Riders	110.00
N# The Underworld Story	200.00
N# The Unknown Man	175.00
1 War Dogs of the U.S. Army	100.00
N# White Chief of the Pawnee Indians	75.00
N# Women to Love	150.00

Babe #6
© *Prize/Headline Feature*

BABE
Prize/Headline Feature
June-July 1948

1 BRo,A;Boddy Rogers	120.00
2 BRo,same	75.00
3 Bro,same	50.00
4 thru 9 BRo,same	@35.00

BABE RUTH SPORTS COMICS
Harvey Publications
April, 1949

1 BP	350.00
2 BP	250.00
3 BP,Joe Dimaggio(c)	200.00
4 BP,Bob Feller(c)	175.00

5 BP,Football(c)	175.00
6 BP,Basketball(c)	175.00
7 BP	175.00
8 BP	175.00
9 BP, Stan Musial(c)	150.00
11 February, 1951	150.00

BANNER COMICS
Ace Magazines
September, 1941

3 B:Captain Courageous, Lone Warrior	750.00
4 JM(c),Flag(c)	500.00
5	450.00

Becomes:
CAPTAIN COURAGEOUS COMICS

6 I:The Sword	600.00

BARNYARD COMICS
Animated Cartoons
June, 1944

1 (fa)	80.00
2 (fa)	40.00
3 (fa)	25.00
4 (fa)	25.00
5 (fa)	25.00
6 thru 12 (fa)	@22.00
13 FF(ti)	30.00
14 FF(ti)	30.00
15 FF(ti)	30.00
16	35.00
17 FF(ti)	30.00
18 FF,FF(ti)	75.00
19 FF,FF(ti)	75.00
20 FF(ti)	75.00
21 FF(ti)	30.00
22 FF,FF(ti)	75.00
23 FF(ti)	30.00
24 FF,FF(ti)	75.00
25 FF(ti)	75.00
26 FF(ti)	30.00
27 FF(ti)	30.00
28	20.00
29 FF(ti)	30.00
30 and 31	@20.00

Becomes:
DIZZY DUCK

32 thru 39	@15.00

BASEBALL COMICS
Will Eisner Productions
Spring, 1949

1 A:Rube Rocky	600.00

BASEBALL HEROS
Fawcett Publications
1952

N# Babe Ruth cover	650.00

BASEBALL THRILLS
Ziff-Davis Publ. Co.
Summer 1951

10 Bob Feller Predicts Pennant Winners	300.00
2 BP, Yogi Berra story	225.00
3 EK, Joe DiMaggio story, Summer 1952	250.00

BATTLEFIELD ACTION
(see DYNAMITE)

BEANY & CECIL
Dell Publishing Co.
January, 1952

1	140.00
2	100.00
3	100.00
4	100.00
5	100.00

BEN BOWIE & HIS MOUNTAIN MEN
Dell Publishing Co.
1952

(1) *see Dell Four Color #443*
(2 thru 6) *see Dell Four Color*

7	15.00
8 thru 10	@15.00
11 I:Yellow Hair	17.00
12	12.00
13	12.00
14	12.00
15	12.00
16	12.00
17	12.00

BEST COMICS
Better Publications
November, 1939

1 B:Red Mask	600.00
2 A:Red Mask, Silly Willie	375.00
3 A:Red Mask	375.00
4 Cannibalism story, February, 1940	400.00

BEWARE
(see CAPTAIN SCIENCE)

BIG CHIEF WAHOO
Eastern Color Printing
July, 1942

1	300.00
2 BWa(c),Three Ring Circus	150.00
3 BWa(c)	100.00
4 BWa(c)	100.00
5 BWa(c),Wild West Rodeo	100.00
6 A:Minnie-Ha-Cha	75.00
7	50.00
8	50.00
9	50.00
10	60.00
11 thru 22	@40.00
23 1943	40.00

BIG SHOT COMICS
Columbia Comics Group
May, 1940

1 MBI,OW,Skyman,B:The Face, Joe Palooka, Rocky Ryan	1,500.00
2 MBi,OW,Marvelo cover	550.00
3 MBi,Skyman cover	450.00
4 MBi,OW,Joe Palooka cover	400.00
5 MBi,Joe Palooka cover	375.00
6 MBi,Joe Palooka cover	325.00
7 MBi,Elect Joe Palooka and Skyman	300.00
8 MBi,Joe Palooka and Skyman dress as Santa	300.00
9 MBi,Skyman	325.00
10 MBi,Skyman	325.00
11 MBi	275.00
12 MBi,OW	275.00
13 MBi,OW	275.00

Big Shot Comics #19
© Columbia Comics Group

14 MBi,OW,O:Sparky Watts	275.00
15 MBi,OW,O:The Cloak	300.00
16 MBi,OW	200.00
17 MBi(c),OW	200.00
18 MBi,OW	200.00
19 MBi,OW,The Face cover	210.00
20 MBi,OW,OW(c),Skyman cov.	210.00
21 MBi,OW,A:Raja the Arabian Knight	175.00
22 MBi,OW,Joe Palooka cover	175.00
23 MBi,OW,Sparky Watts cover	150.00
24 MBi,OW,Uncle Sam cover	175.00
25 MBi,OW,Sparky Watts cover	150.00
26 MBi,OW,Devildog cover	175.00
27 MBi,OW,Skyman cover	185.00
28 MBi,OW,Hitler cover	225.00
29 MBi,OW,I:Captain Yank	185.00
30 MBi,OW,Santa cover	150.00
31 MBi,OW,Sparky Watts cover	125.00
32 MBi,OW,B:The Face Jordan newspaper reps	150.00
33 MBi,OW,Sparky Watts cover	125.00
34 MBi,OW	135.00
35 MBi,OW	135.00
36 MBi,OW,Sparky Watts cover	125.00
37 MBi,OW	135.00
38 MBi,Uncle Slap Happy cover	125.00
39 MBi,Uncle Slap Happy cover	125.00
40 MBi,Joe Palooka Happy cover	125.00
41 MBi,Joe Palooka	100.00
42 MBi,Joe Palooka parachutes	100.00
43 MBi,V:Hitler	110.00
44 MBi,Slap Happy cover	100.00
45 MBi,Slap Happy cover	100.00
46 MBi,Uncle Sam cover,V:Hitler	110.00
47 MBi,Uncle Slap Happy cover	100.00
48 MBi	100.00
49 MBi	75.00
50 MBi,O:The Face	75.00
51 MBi	75.00
52 MBi,E:Vic Jordan (Hitler cov) newspaper reps	100.00
53 MBi,Uncle Slap Happy cover	75.00
54 MBi,Uncle Slap Happy cover	75.00
55 MBi,Happy Easter cover	75.00
56 MBi	75.00
57 MBi	75.00
58 MBi	75.00

All comics prices listed are for *Near Mint* condition.

GOLDEN AGE

59 MBi,Slap Happy	75.00
60 MBi,Joe Palooka	60.00
61 MBi	55.00
62 MBi	55.00
63 MBi	55.00
64 MBi,Slap Happy	50.00
65 MBi,Slap Happy	50.00
66 MBi,Slap Happy	50.00
67 MBi	50.00
68 MBi,Joe Palooka	50.00
69 MBi	50.00
70 MBi,OW,Joe Palooka cover	50.00
71 MBi,OW	55.00
72 MBi,OW	55.00
73 MBi,OW,The Face cover	55.00
74 MBi,OW	55.00
75 MBi,OW,Polar Bear swim club cover	55.00
76 thru 80 MBi,OW	@45.00
81 thru 84 MBi,OW	@40.00
85 MBi,OW,Dixie Dugan cover	42.00
86 thru 95 MBi,OW	@40.00
96 MBi,OW,X-Mas cover	40.00
97 thru 99 MBi,OW	@40.00
100 MBi,OW,Special issue	45.00
101 thru 103 MBi,OW	@40.00
104 MBi, August, 1949	45.00

BIG-3
Fox Features Syndicate
Fall 1940

1 B:BlueBeetle,Flame,Samson	1,500.00
2 A:BlueBeetle,Flame,Samson	650.00
3 same	500.00
4 same	450.00
5 same	450.00
6 E:Samson, bondage cover	400.00
7 A:V-Man, January, 1942	375.00

BILL BARNES, AMERICA'S AIR ACE
(see AIR ACE)

BILL BOYD WESTERN
Fawcett Publications
February, 1950

1 B:Bill Boyd, MidnitePh(c)	375.00
2 P(c)	200.00
3 B:Ph(c)	150.00
4	100.00
5	100.00
6	100.00
7	90.00
8	90.00
9	90.00
10	90.00
11	75.00
12	75.00
13	75.00
14	75.00
15 thru 21	@70.00
22 E:Ph(c)	70.00
23 June, 1952	85.00

BILL STERN'S SPORTS BOOK
Approved Comics
Spring-Summer, 1951

1 Ewell Blackwell	150.00
2	100.00
2-2 EK Giant	125.00

BILLY THE KID ADVENTURE MAGAZINE
Toby Press
October, 1950

1 AW,FF,AW(c),FF(c)	225.00
2 Photo cover	50.00
3 AW,FF	250.00
4	40.00
5	40.00
6 FF,Photo cover	60.00
7 Photo cover	40.00
8	40.00
9 HK Pot-Shot Pete	60.00
10	40.00
11	40.00
12	40.00
13 HK	50.00
14 AW,FF	60.00
15 thru 21	@35.00
22 AW,FF	40.00
23 thru 29	@30.00
30 1955	35.00

BINGO COMICS
Howard Publications
1945

1	165.00

Black Cat #4 © Harvey Publications

BLACK CAT COMICS
Harvey Publications
(Home Comics)
June-July, 1946

1 JKu	450.00
2 JKu,JSm(c)	250.00
3 JSm(c)	225.00
4 B:Red Demon	200.00
5 S&K	250.00
6 S&K,A:Scarlet Arrow, O:Red Demon	250.00
7 S&K	250.00
8 S&K,B:Kerry Drake	225.00
9 S&K,O:Stuntman	250.00
10 JK,JSm	175.00
11	175.00
12 "Ghost Town Terror"	175.00
13 thru 16 LEI	@150.00
17 A:Mary Worth, Invisible	

Scarlet	150.00
18 LEI	150.00
19 LEI	150.00
20 A:Invisible Scarlet	150.00
21 LEI	150.00
22 LEI thru 26	@150.00
27 X-Mas issue	150.00
28 I:Kit,A:Crimson Raider	150.00
29 Black Cat bondage cover	150.00
Becomes:

BLACK CAT MYSTERY

30 RP,Black Cat(c)	165.00
31 RP	125.00
32 BP,RP,Bondage cover	135.00
33 BP,RP,Electrocution cover	150.00
34 BP,RP	125.00
35 BP,RP,OK, Atomic Storm	150.00
36 RP	175.00
37 RP	125.00
38 RP	125.00
39 RP	150.00
40 RP	125.00
41	125.00
42	125.00
43 BP	125.00
44 BP,HN,JkS,Oil Burning cover	150.00
45 BP,HN,Classic cover	175.00
46 BP,HN	125.00
47 BP,HN	125.00
48 BP,HN	125.00
49 BP,HN	125.00
50 BP,Rotting Face	300.00
51 BP,HN,MMe	125.00
52 BP	75.00
53 BP	75.00
Becomes:

BLACK CAT WESTERN

54 A:Black Cat & Story	100.00
55 A:Black Cat	75.00
56 same	75.00
Becomes:

BLACK CAT MYSTIC

58 JK,Starts Comic Code	125.00
59 KB	100.00
60 JK	100.00
61 HN	90.00
62	75.00
63 JK	75.00
64 JK	90.00
65 April, 1963	90.00

BLACK DIAMOND WESTERN
(see DESPERADO)

UNCLE SAM QUARTERLY
Quality Comics Group
Fall, 1941

1 BE,LF(c),JCo	2,800.00
2 LG(c),BE	1,000.00
3 GT,GT(c)	750.00
4 GT,GF(c)	650.00
5 RC,GT	650.00
6 GT	550.00
7 Hitler, Tojo, Mussolini	700.00
8	@525.00
Becomes:

BLACKHAWK
Comic Magazines
Winter, 1944

9 Bait for a Death Trap	2,600.00
10 RC	850.00

11 RC 600.00
12 Flies to thrilling adventure . . 550.00
13 Blackhawk Stalks Danger . . 550.00
14 BWa 525.00
15 Patrols the Universe 525.00
16 RC,BWa,Huddles for Action 450.00
17 BWa,Prepares for Action . . 450.00
18 RC,RC(c),BWa,One for All
   and All for One 425.00
19 RC,RC(c),BWa,Calls
   for Action 425.00
20 RC,RC(c),BWa,Smashes
   Rugoth the ruthless God . . . 425.00
21 BWa,Battles Destiny
   Written n Blood 350.00
22 RC,RC(c),BWa,Fear battles
   Death and Destruction 350.00
23 RC,RC(c),BWa,Batters
   Down Oppression 350.00
24 RC,RC(c),BWa 350.00
25 RC,RC(c),BWa,V:The Evil
   of Mung 350.00
26 RC,RC(c),V:Menace of a
   Sunken World 325.00
27 BWa,Destroys a War-Mad
   Munitions Magnate 325.00
28 BWa,Defies Destruction in the
   Battle of the Test Tube 325.00
29 BWa,Tale of the Basilisk
   Supreme Chief 325.00
30 BWa,RC,RC(c),The Menace
   of the Meteors 325.00
31 BWa,RC,RC(c),JCo,Treachery
   among the Blackhawks 250.00
32 BWa,RC,RC(c),A:Delya,
   Flying Fish 250.00
33 RC,RC(c),BWa,
   A:The Mockers 250.00
34 BWa,A:Tana,Mavis 250.00
35 BWa,I:Atlo,Strongest Man
   on Earth 250.00
36 RC,RC(c),BWa,V:Tarya . . . 225.00
37 RC,RC(c),BWa,V:Sari,The
   Rajah of Ramastan 225.00
38 BWa 225.00
39 RC,RC(c),BWa,V:Lilith 225.00
40 RC,RC(c),BWa,Valley of
   Yesterday 225.00
41 RC,RC(c),BWa 200.00
42 RC,RC(c),BWa,
   V:Iron Emperor 200.00
43 RC,RC(c),BWa,Terror
   from the Catacombs 200.00
44 RC,RC(c),BWa,The King
   of Winds 200.00
45 BWa,The Island of Death . . 200.00
46 RC,RC(c),BWa,V:DeathPatrol 200.00
47 RC,RC(c),BWa,War! 200.00
48 RC,RC(c),BWa,A:Hawks of
   Horror,Port of Missing Ships 200.00
49 RC,RC(c),BWa,A:Valkyrie,
   Waters of Terrible Peace . . 200.00
50 RC,RC(c),BWa,I:Killer Shark,
   Flying Octopus 225.00
51 BWa,V:The Whip, Whip of
   Nontelon 175.00
52 RC,RC(c),BWa,Traitor in
   the Ranks 175.00
53 RC,RC(c),BWa,V:Golden
   Mummy 175.00
54 RC,RC(c),BWa,V:Dr. Deroski,
   Circles of Suicide 175.00
55 RC,RC(c),BWa,V:Rocketmen 175.00
56 RC,RC(c),BWa,V:The Instructor,
   School for Sabotage 175.00

57 RC,RC(c),BWa,Paralyzed City
   of Armored Men 175.00
58 RC,RC(c),BWa,V:King Cobra,
   The Spider of Delanza 175.00
59 BWa,V:Sea Devil 175.00
60 RC,RC(c),BWa,V:Dr. Mole and
   His Devils Squadron 175.00
61 V:John Smith, Stalin's
   Ambassador of Murder 165.00
62 V:General X, Return of
   Genghis Kahn 165.00
63 RC,RC(c),The Flying
   Buzz-Saws 165.00
64 RC,RC(c),V:Zoltan Korvas,
   Legion of the Damned 165.00
65 Olaf as a Prisoner in Dungeon
   of Fear 165.00
66 RC,RC(c),V:The Red
   Executioner, Crawler 165.00
67 RC,RC(c),V:Future Fuehrer . 165.00
68 V:Killers of the Kremlin 150.00
69 V:King of the Iron Men,
   Conference of the Dictators . 150.00
70 V:Killer Shark 150.00

Blackhawk #13 © Comic Magazines

71 V:Von Tepp, The Man Who
   could Defeat Blackhawk
   O:Blackhawk 200.00
72 V:Death Legion 150.00
73 V:Hangman,The Tyrannical
   Freaks 150.00
74 Plan of Death 150.00
75 V:The Mad Doctor Baroc,
   The Z Bomb Menace 150.00
76 The King of Blackhawk Island 150.00
77 V:The Fiendish
   Electronic Brain 150.00
78 V:The Killer Vulture,
   Phantom Raider 150.00
79 V:Herman Goering, The
   Human Bomb 150.00
80 V:Fang, the Merciless,
   Dr. Death 150.00
81 A:Killer Shark, The Sea
   Monsters of Killer Shark . . . 150.00
82 V:Sabo Teur, the Ruthless
   Commie Agent 150.00
83 I:Hammmer & Sickle, V:Madam
   Double Cross 150.00
84 V:Death Eye,Dr. Genius,

   The Dreaded Brain Beam . . 150.00
85 V:The Fiendish Impersonator 150.00
86 V:The Human Torpedoes . . 150.00
87 A:Red Agent Sovietta,V:Sea
   Wolf, Le Sabre,Comics Code 125.00
88 V:Thunder the Indestructible,
   The Phantom Sniper 125.00
89 V:The Super Communists . . 125.00
90 V:The Storm King, Villainess
   who smashed the Blackhawk
   team 125.00
91 Treason in the Underground 125.00
92 V:The World Traitor 125.00
93 V:Garg the Destroyer,
   O:Blackhawk 135.00
94 V:Black Widow, Darkk the
   Destroyer 125.00
95 V:Madam Fury, Queen of the
   Pirates 125.00
96 Doom in the Deep 125.00
97 Revolt of the Slave Workers 125.00
98 Temple of Doom 125.00
99 The War That Never Ended 125.00
100 The Delphian Machine . . . 150.00
101 Satan's Paymaster 100.00
102 The Doom Cloud 100.00
103 The Super Race 100.00
104 The Jet Menace 100.00
105 The Red Kamikaze Terror 100.00
106 The Flying Tank Platoon . 100.00
107 The Winged Menace 100.00
   (Please see DC Listings)

BLACK HOOD
(see LAUGH COMICS)

BLACK TERROR
Better Publications/
Standard
Winter, 1942-43
1 Bombing cover 2,100.00
2 V:Arabs,Bondage(c) 750.00
3 V:Nazis,Bondage(c) 550.00
4 V:Sub Nazis 475.00
5 V:Japanese 475.00
6 Air Battle 400.00
7 Air Battle,V:Japanese,
   A:Ghost 400.00
8 V:Nazis 400.00
9 V:Japanese,Bondage(c) . . . 425.00
10 V:Nazis 400.00
11 thru 16 . . . . @300.00
17 Bondage(c) 325.00
18 ASh 300.00
19 ASh 300.00
20 ASh 300.00
21 ASh 325.00
22 FF,ASh 300.00
23 ASh 300.00
24 Bondgae(c) 325.00
25 ASh 300.00
26 GT,ASh 300.00
27 MME,GT,ASh 300.00

BLAZING COMICS
Enwil Associates/Rural Home
June, 1944
1 B:Green Turtle, Red Hawk,
   Black Buccaneer 400.00
2 Green Turtle cover 250.00
3 Green Turtle cover 225.00
4 Green Turtle cover 225.00
5 March, 1945 . . . . 225.00
5a Black Buccaneer(c),1955 . . . 75.00

GOLDEN AGE

All comics prices listed are for _Near Mint_ condition.   CVA Page 311

6 Indian-Japanese(c), 1955 ... 75.00

BLONDIE COMICS
David McKay
Spring, 1947

1		150.00
2		75.00
3		50.00
4		50.00
5		50.00
6 thru 10		@30.00
11 thru 15		@25.00

Harvey Publications

16		30.00
17 thru 20		@20.00
21 thru 30		@15.00
31 thru 50		@12.00
51 thru 80		@10.00
81 thru 99		@7.50
100		10.00
101 thru 124		@7.50
125 Giant		10.00
126 thru 135		@7.00
136 thru 140		@6.00
141 thru 163		@10.00

Blondie #167
© *King Publications*

King Publications

164 thru 167		@10.00
168 thru 174		@4.00

Charlton Comics

175 thru 200		@3.00
201 thru 220		@3.00

BLUE BEETLE, THE
Fox Features Syndicate/
Holyoke Publ.
Winter 1939

1 O:Blue Beetle,A:Master Magician		3,500.00
2		1,100.00
3 JSm(c)		800.00
4 Mentions marijuana		550.00
5 A:Zanzibar the Magician		500.00
6 B:Dynamite Thor, O:Blue Beetle		500.00
7 A:Dynamo		425.00
8 E:Thor,A:Dynamo		425.00

9 A:Black Bird,Gorilla		425.00
10 A:Black Bird, bondage cover	425.00
11 A:Gladiator		375.00
12 A:Black Fury		375.00
13 B:V-Man		450.00
14 JKu,I:Sparky		450.00
15 JKu		450.00
16		325.00
17 A:Mimic		300.00
18 E:V-Man,A:Red Knight		300.00
19 JKu,A:Dascomb Dinsmore	325.00
20 I&O:The Flying Tiger Squadron		350.00
21		225.00
22 A:Ali-Baba		225.00
23 A:Jimmy DooLittle		225.00
24 I:The Halo		225.00
25		225.00
26 General Patton story		235.00
27 A:Tamoa		225.00
28		200.00
29		200.00
30 L:Holyoke		200.00
31 F:Fox		175.00
32 Hitler cover		225.00
33 Fight for Freedom		175.00
34 A:Black Terror,Menace of K-4	175.00
35		175.00
36 The Runaway House		175.00
37 Inside the House		175.00
38 Revolt of the Zombies		175.00
39		175.00
40		175.00
41 A:O'Brine Twins		150.00
42		150.00
43		150.00
44		150.00
45		150.00
46 A:Puppeteer		175.00
47 JKa,V:Junior Crime Club	850.00
48 JKa,A:Black Lace		700.00
49 JKa		700.00
50 JKa,The Ambitious Bride	650.00
51 JKa, Shady Lady		575.00
52 JKa(c),Bondage cover		900.00
53 JKa,A:Jack "Legs" Diamond,Bondage(c)	600.00
54 JKa,The Vanishing Nude	1,000.00
55 JKa		550.00
56 JKa,Tri-State Terror		550.00
57 JKa,The Feagle Bros.		550.00
58		100.00
59		100.00
60 August, 1960		100.00

BLUE BEETLE
(see THING!, THE)

BLUE BOLT
Funnies, Inc./Novelty Press/
Premium Service Co
June, 1940

1 JSm,PG,O:Blue Bolt		2,300.00
2 JSm		1,100.00
3 S&K,A:Space Hawk		900.00
4 PG		800.00
5 BEv,B:Sub Zero		750.00
6 JK,JSm		750.00
7 S&K,BEv		800.00
8 S&K(c)		750.00
9		725.00
10 S&K(c)		725.00
11 BEv(c)		775.00
12		775.00

2-1 BEv(c),PG,O:Dick Cole & V:Simba		250.00
2-2 BEv(c),PG		200.00
2-3 PG,Cole vs Simba		175.00
2-4 BD		175.00
2-5 I:Freezum		175.00
2-6 O:Sgt.Spook, Dick Cole	150.00
2-7 BD		125.00
2-8 BD		125.00
2-9 JW		125.00
2-10 JW		125.00
2-11 JW		125.00
2-12 E:Twister		125.00
3-1 A:115th Infantry		100.00
3-2 A:Phantom Sub		100.00
3-3		100.00
3-4 JW(c)		75.00
3-5 Jor		75.00
3-6 Jor		75.00
3-7 X-Mas cover		75.00
3-8		75.00
3-9 A:Phantom Sub		75.00
3-10 DBa		75.00
3-11 April Fools cover		75.00
3-12		75.00
4-1 Hitler,Tojo,Mussolini cover	100.00
4-2 Liberty Bell cover		50.00
4-3 What are You Doing for Your Country		50.00
4-4 I Fly for Vengence		50.00
4-5 TFH(c)		50.00
4-6 HcK		50.00

Blue Bolt Vol. 5 #6
© *Funnies, Inc./Novelty Press*

4-7 JWi(c)		50.00
4-8 E:Sub Zero		50.00
4-9		50.00
4-10		50.00
4-11		50.00
4-12		50.00
5-1 thru 5-12		@50.00
6-1		50.00
6-2 War Bonds (c)		60.00
6-3		50.00
6-4 Racist(c)		75.00
6-5 Soccer cover		50.00
6-6 thru 6-12		@50.00
7-1 thru 7-12		@50.00
8-1 Baseball cover		50.00
8-2 JHa		50.00

All comics prices listed are for *Near Mint* condition.

8-3 JHe	50.00
8-4 JHa	50.00
8-5 JHe	50.00
8-6 JDo	50.00
8-7 LbC(c).	60.00
8-8	50.00
8-9 AMc(c)	50.00
8-10	50.00
8-11 Basketball cover	55.00
8-12	50.00
9-1 AMc,Baseball cover	50.00
9-2 AMc	45.00
9-3	45.00
9-4 JHe	45.00
9-5 JHe	45.00
9-6 LbC(c),Football cover	60.00
9-7 JHe	45.00
9-8 Hockey cover	50.00
9-9 LbC(c),3-D effect	70.00
9-10	40.00
9-11	40.00
9-12	40.00
10-1 Baseball cover,3-D effect	50.00
10-2 3-D effect	45.00

Star Publications

102 LbC(c),Chameleon	225.00
103 LbC(c),same	200.00
104 LbC(c),same	200.00
105 LbC(c),O:Blue Bolt Space, Drug Story	350.00
106 S&K,LbC(c),A:Space Hawk	300.00
107 S&K,LbC(c),A:Space Hawk	300.00
108 S&K,LbC(c),A:Blue Bolt	300.00
109 BW,LbC(c)	300.00
110 B:Horror covers,A:Target	300.00
111 Weird Tales of Horror, A:Red Rocket	300.00
112 JyD,WiP	275.00
113 BW,JyD,A:Space Hawk	275.00
114 LbC(c),JyD	275.00
115 LbC(c),JyD,A:Sgt.Spook	300.00
116 LbC(c),JyD,A:Jungle Joe	300.00
117 LbC(c),A:Blue Bolt,Jo-Jo	300.00
118 WW,LbC(c),A:White Spirit	300.00
119 LbC(c)	300.00

Becomes:

GHOSTLY WEIRD STORIES
Star Publications
September, 1953

120 LbC,A:Jo-Jo	225.00
121 LbC,A:Jo-Jo	200.00
122 LbC,A:The Mask	200.00
123 LbC,A:Jo-Jo	200.00
124 LbC, September, 1954	200.00

BLUE CIRCLE COMICS
Enwil Associates/Rural Home
June, 1944

1 B:Blue Circle,O:Steel Fist	175.00
2	125.00
3 Hitler parody cover	135.00
4	75.00
5 E:Steel Fist,A:Driftwood Davey	75.00
6	75.00

BLUE RIBBON COMICS
MLJ Magazines
November, 1939

1 JCo,B:Dan Hastings, Richy-Amazing Boy	2,600.00
2 JCo,B:Bob Phantom, Silver Fox	1,000.00

3 JCo,A:Phantom,Silver Fox	650.00
4 O:Fox,Ty Gor,B:Doc Strong, Hercules	700.00
5 Gattling Gun cover	500.00
6 Amazing Boy Richy cover	475.00
7 A:Fox cover,Corporal Collins V:Nazis	475.00
8 E:Hercules	475.00
9 O&I:Mr. Justice	2,200.00
10 Mr. Justice cover	750.00
11 SCp(c)	750.00
12 E:Doc Strong	750.00
13 B:Inferno	750.00
14 A:Inferno	650.00
15 A:Inferno,E:Green Falcon	650.00
16 O:Captain Flag	1,400.00
17 Captain Flag V:Black Hand	675.00
18 Captain Flag-Black Hand	650.00
19 Captain Flag cover	650.00
20 Captain Flag V:Nazis cover	700.00
21 Captain Flag V:Death	650.00
22 Circus Cover, March, 1942	650.00

BLUE RIBBON COMICS
St. John Publications
February, 1949

1 Heckle & Jeckle	40.00
2 MB(c),Diary Secrets	80.00
3 MB,MB(c),Heckle & Jeckle	35.00
4 Teen-age Diary Secrets	80.00
5 MB,Teen-age Diary Secrets	75.00
6 Dinky Duck	15.00

BO
Charlton Comics
June, 1955

1	40.00
2	30.00
3 October, 1955	30.00

BOB COLT
Fawcett Publications
November, 1950

1 B:Bob Colt,Buck Skin	350.00
2 Death Round Train	200.00
3 Mysterious Black Knight of the Prairie	175.00
4 Death Goes Downstream	175.00
5 The Mesa of Mystery	175.00
6 The Mysterious Visitors	175.00
7 Dragon of Disaster	150.00
8 Redman's Revenge	150.00
9 Hidden Hacienda	150.00
10 Fiend from Vulture Mountain	150.00

BOLD STORIES
Kirby Publishing Co.
March, 1950

1 WW,Near nudity cover	1,000.00
2 GI,Cobra's Kiss	800.00
3 WW,Orge of Paris,July, 1950	700.00
4 Case of the Winking Buddha	300.00
5 It Rhymes with Lust	300.00
6 Candid Tales, April 1950	300.00

BOMBER COMICS
Elliot Publishing Co.
March, 1944

1 B:Wonder Boy,Kismet, Eagle Evans	450.00
2 Wonder Boy cover	275.00
3 Wonder Boy-Kismet cover	250.00

4 Hitler,Tojo, Mussolini cover	300.00

BOOK OF ALL COMICS
William H. Wise
1945

1 A:Green Mask,Puppeteer	300.00

BOOK OF COMICS, THE
William H. Wise
1945

N# A:Captain V	300.00

Boy Comics #11 © Lev Gleason Publ.

BOY COMICS
Comic House, Inc.
(Lev Gleason Publ.)
April, 1942

3 O:Crimebuster,Bombshell,Young Robin, B:Yankee Longago, Swoop Storm	2,400.00
4 Hitler,Tojo,Mussolini cover	900.00
5 Crimebuster saves day cover	700.00
6 O:Iron Jaw & Death of Son, B:Little Dynamite	1,700.00
7 Hitler,Tojo,Mussolini cover	650.00
8 D:Iron Jaw	675.00
9 I:He-She	600.00
10 Iron Jaw returns	900.00
11 Iron Jaw falls in love	550.00
12 Crimebuster V:Japanese	500.00
13 V:New,more terrible Iron Jaw	500.00
14 V:Iron Jaw	500.00
15 I:Rodent,D:Iron Jaw	550.00
16 Crimebuster V:Knight	250.00
17 Flag cover,Crimebuster V:Moth	275.00
18 Smashed car cover	250.00
19 Express train cover	250.00
20 Coffin cover	250.00
21 Boxing cover	175.00
22 Under Sea cover	175.00
23 Golf cover	175.00
24 County insane asylum cover	175.00
25 52 pgs	175.00
26 68 pgs	175.00
27 Express train cover	200.00
28 E:Yankee Longago	200.00

GOLDEN AGE

29 Prison break cover	200.00
30 O:Crimebuster,Murder cover	250.00
31 68 pgs	175.00
32 E:Young Robin Hood	175.00
33	175.00
34 Suicide cover & story	135.00
35	125.00
36	125.00
37	125.00
38	125.00
39 E:Little Dynamite	125.00
40	125.00
41 thru 50	@110.00
51 thru 56	@100.00
57 B:Dilly Duncan	125.00
58	100.00
59	100.00
60 Iron Jaw returns	125.00
61 O:Iron Jaw,Crimebuster	135.00
62 A:Iron Jaw	125.00
63 thru 70	@75.00
71 E:Dilly Duncan	75.00
72	75.00
73	75.00
74 thru 79	@75.00
80 I:Rocky X	60.00
81 thru 88	@60.00
89 A:The Claw	65.00
90 same	65.00
91 same	65.00
92 same	65.00
93 The Claw(c),A:Rocky X	65.00
94	55.00
95	55.00
96	55.00
97	55.00
98 A:Rocky X	65.00
99	55.00
100	65.00
101	65.00
102	65.00
103 thru 118	@65.00
119 March, 1956	65.00

BOY EXPLORERS
(see TERRY AND
THE PIRATES)

BRENDA STARR
Four Star Comics Corp./
Superior Comics Ltd.
September, 1947

13(1)	600.00
14(2) JKa,Bondage cover	650.00
2-3	500.00
2-4 JKa,Operating table cover	600.00
2-5 Swimsuit cover	500.00
2-6	500.00
2-7	500.00
2-8 Cosmetic cover	500.00
2-9 Giant Starr cover	500.00
2-10 Wedding cover	500.00
2-11	500.00
2-12	500.00

BRICK BRADFORD
Best Books
(Standard Comics)
July, 1949

5	150.00
6 Robot cover	175.00
7 AS	100.00
8	100.00

BROADWAY ROMANCES
Quality Comics Group
January, 1950

1 PG,BWa&(c)	225.00
2 BWa,Glittering Desire	175.00
3 BL,Stole My Love	75.00
4 Enslaved by My Past	85.00
5 Flame of Passion,Sept.,1950	85.00

BRONCHO BILL
Visual Editions
(Standard Comics)
January, 1948

5	75.00
6 AS(c)	45.00
7 AS(c)	35.00
8 ASh	35.00
9 AS(c)	35.00
10 AS(c)	35.00
11 AS(c)	25.00
12 AS(c)	25.00
13 AS(c)	25.00
14 ASh	25.00
15 ASh	25.00
16 AS(c)	25.00

BRUCE GENTRY
Four Star Publ./
Visual Editions/
Superior
January, 1948

1 B:Ray Bailey reprints	300.00
2 Plane crash cover	225.00
3 E:Ray Bailey reprints	200.00
4 Tiger attack cover	150.00
5	150.00
6 Help message cover	150.00
7	150.00
8 End of Marriage cover, July, 1949	150.00

BUCCANEERS
(see KID ETERNITY)

BUCK JONES
Dell Publishing Co.
October, 1950

1	150.00
2	75.00
3	60.00
4	60.00
5	60.00
6	60.00
7	60.00
8	60.00

BUCK ROGERS
Eastern Color Printing
Winter 1940

1 Partial Painted(c)	2,700.00
2	1,000.00
3 Living Corpse from Crimson Coffin	850.00
4 One man army of greased lightning	800.00
5 Sky Roads	750.00
6 September, 1943	750.00

Toby Press

100 Flying Saucers	200.00
101	175.00
9	175.00

BUG MOVIES
Dell Publishing Co.
1931

1	100.00

Bugs Bunny County Fair #1
© Dell Publishing Co.

BUGS BUNNY
DELL GIANT EDITIONS
Dell Publishing Co.
Christmas

1 Christmas Funnies (1950)	300.00
2 Christmas Funnies (1951)	250.00
3 Christmas Funnies (1952)	200.00
4 Christmas Funnies (1953)	200.00
5 Christmas Funnies (1954)	200.00
6 Christmas Party (1955)	175.00
7 Christmas Party (1956)	185.00
8 Christmas Funnies (1957)	185.00
9 Christmas Funnies (1958)	185.00
1 County Fair (1957)	200.00

Halloween

1 Halloween Parade (1953)	200.00
2 Halloween Parade (1954)	175.00
3 Trick 'N' Treat Halloween Fun (1955)	185.00
4 Trick 'N' Treat Halloween Fun (1956)	185.00

Vacation

1 Vacation Funnies (1951)	300.00
2 Vacation Funnies (1952)	275.00
3 Vacation Funnies (1953)	250.00
4 Vacation Funnies (1954)	200.00
5 Vacation Funnies (1955)	200.00
6 Vacation Funnies (1956)	175.00
7 Vacation Funnies (1957)	175.00
8 Vacation Funnies (1958)	175.00
9 Vacation Funnies (1959)	175.00

BUGS BUNNY
Dell Publishing Co.
1942
see Four Color for early years

28 thru 30	@40.00
31 thru 50	@30.00
51 thru 70	@25.00
71 thru 85	@20.00
86 Giant-Show Time	75.00

87 thru 100 . . . . @10.00
101 thru 120 . . . . @7.00
121 thru 140 . . . . @5.00
141 thru 190 . . . . @4.00
191 thru 245 . . . . @3.00

BULLETMAN
Fawcett Publications
Summer, 1941

1 I:Bulletman & Bulletgirl . . . 2,800.00
2 MRa(c) 1,200.00
3 MRa(c) 900.00
4 V:Headless Horror,
   Guillotine cover 850.00
5 Riddle of Dr. Riddle 800.00
6 V:Japanese 650.00
7 V:Revenge Syndicate 625.00
8 V:Mr. Ego 600.00
9 V:Canine Criminals 600.00
10 I:Bullet Dog 625.00
11 V:Fiendish Fiddler 550.00
12 . . . . 500.00
13 . . . . 500.00
14 V:Death the Comedian 500.00
15 V:Professor D 500.00
16 VanishingElephant,Fall 1946 500.00

Buster Crabbe #6 © Famous Funnies

BUSTER CRABBE
Famous Funnies
November, 1951

1 The Arrow of Death 225.00
2 AW&GE(c) 250.00
3 AW&GE(c) 275.00
4 FF(c) 300.00
5 AW,FF,FF,(c) 800.00
6 Sharks cover 100.00
7 FF 125.00
8 Gorilla cover 100.00
9 FF 100.00
10 . . . . 100.00
11 Snakes cover 75.00
12 September, 1953 . . . . 75.00

BUSTER CRABBE
Lev Gleason Pub. 1953

1 Ph(c) 150.00
2 ATh 150.00
3 ATh 150.00

4 F. Gordon(c) 125.00

BUZ SAWYER
Standard Comics
June, 1948

1 . . . . 150.00
2 I:Sweeney 100.00
3 . . . . 75.00
4 . . . . 75.00
5 June, 1949 . . . . 75.00

CALLING ALL BOYS
Parents Magazine Institute
January, 1946

1 Skiing 75.00
2 . . . . 30.00
3 Peril Out Post 25.00
4 Model Airplane 25.00
5 Fishing 25.00
6 Swimming 25.00
7 Baseball 25.00
8 School 25.00
9 The Miracle Quarterback . . 25.00
10 Gary Cooper cover 35.00
11 Rin-Tin-Tin cover 25.00
12 Bob Hope cover 50.00
13 Bing Cosby cover 40.00
14 J. Edgar Hoover cover 25.00
15 Tex Granger cover 20.00
16 . . . . 20.00
17 Tex Granger cover, May, 1948 20.00
Becomes:

TEX GRANGER

18 Bandits of the Badlands 55.00

19 The Seven Secret Cities 45.00
20 Davey Crockett's Last Fight . 35.00
21 Canyon Ambush 35.00
22 V:Hooded Terror 35.00
23 V:Billy the Kid 35.00
24 A:Hector, September, 1949 . . 40.00

CALLING ALL GIRLS
Parent Magazine Press, Inc.
September, 1941

1 . . . . 85.00
2 Virginia Weidler cover 40.00
3 Shirley Temple cover 55.00
4 Darla Hood cover 30.00
5 Gloria Hood cover 30.00
6 . . . . 25.00
7 . . . . 25.00
8 . . . . 25.00
9 Flag cover 28.00
10 . . . . 25.00
11 thru 20 . . . . @25.00
21 thru 39 . . . . @15.00
40 Liz Taylor 70.00
41 . . . . 15.00
42 . . . . 15.00
43 October, 1945 . . . . 15.00

CALLING ALL KIDS
Quality Comics, Inc.
December/January, 1946

1 Funny Animal stories 50.00
2 . . . . 25.00
3 . . . . 20.00
4 . . . . 15.00
5 . . . . 15.00
6 . . . . 15.00
7 . . . . 15.00
8 . . . . 15.00

9 . . . . 15.00
10 . . . . 15.00
11 thru 25 . . . . @10.00
26 August, 1949 . . . . 10.00

CAMERA COMICS
U.S. Camera Publishing Corp.
July-September, 1944

1 Airfighter,Grey Comet 150.00
2 How to Set Up a Darkroom . 125.00
3 Linda Lens V:Nazi cover 80.00
4 Linda Lens cover 60.00
5 Diving cover 60.00
6 Jim Lane cover 60.00
7 Linda Lens cover 60.00
8 Linda Lens cover 60.00
9 Summer, 1946 . . . . 60.00

CAMP COMICS
Dell Publishing Co.
February, 1942

1 Ph(c),WK,A:Bugs Bunny . . 400.00
2 Ph(c),WK,A:Bugs Bunny . . 300.00
3 Ph(c),Wk 400.00

Captain Aero #7 © Holyoke Publishing

CAPTAIN AERO COMICS
Holyoke Publishing Co.
December, 1941

1 B:Flag-Man&Solar,Master
   of Magic Captain Aero,
   Captain Stone 1,200.00
2 A:Pals of Freedom 600.00
3 JKu,B:Alias X,A:Pals of
   Freedom 600.00
4 JKu,O:Gargoyle,
   Parachute jump 600.00
5 JKu 500.00
6 JKu,Flagman,A:Miss Victory 400.00
7 Alias X 250.00
8 O:Red Cross,A:Miss Victory 250.00
9 A:Miss Victory,Alias X 200.00
10 A:Miss Victory,Red Cross . . 175.00
11 A:Miss Victory 150.00
12 same 150.00
13 same 150.00
14 same 150.00
15 AS(c),A:Miss Liberty 150.00
16 AS(c),Leather Face 125.00

GOLDEN AGE

17 LbC(c)	225.00
21 LbC(c)	225.00
22 LbC(c),I:Mighty Mite	225.00
23 LbC(c)	225.00
24 LbC(c) American Planes Dive Bomb Japan	250.00
25 LbC(c),Science Fiction(c)	250.00
26 LbC(c)	225.00

CAPTAIN BATTLE
**New Friday Publ./
Magazine Press**
Summer, 1941

1 B:Captain Battle,O:Blackout	900.00
2 Pirate Ship cover	650.00
3 Dungeon cover	550.00
4	400.00
5 V:Japanese, Summer, 1943	400.00

CAPTAIN BATTLE, Jr.
Comic House
Fall, 1943

1 Claw V:Ghost, A:Sniffer	850.00
2 Man who didn't believe in Ghosts	600.00

CAPTAIN COURAGEOUS
(see BANNER COMICS)

CAPTAIN EASY
Standard Comics
1939

N# Swash Buckler	750.00
10	80.00
11	60.00
12	60.00
13 ASh(c)	60.00
14	60.00
15	60.00
16 ASh(c)	60.00
17 September, 1949	60.00

CAPTAIN FEARLESS COMICS
Helnit Publishing Co.
August, 1941

1 O:Mr. Miracle,Alias X,Captain Fearless Citizen Smith, A:Miss Victory	600.00
2 A:Border Patrol, Sept.,1941	400.00

CAPTAIN FLASH
Sterling Comics
November, 1954

1 O:Captain Flash	275.00
2 V:Black Knight	150.00
3 Beasts from 1,000,000 BC	150.00
4 Flying Saucer Invasion	150.00

CAPTAIN FLEET
Approved Comics
Fall, 1952

1 Storm and Mutiny ...Typhoon	100.00

CAPTAIN FLIGHT COMICS
Four Star Publications
March, 1944

N# B:Captain Flight,Ace Reynolds Dashthe Avenger,Professor X	275.00
2	150.00

3	125.00
4 B:Rock Raymond Salutes America's Wartime Heroines	150.00
5 Bondage cover,B:Red Rocket A:The Grenade	375.00
6 Girl tied at the stake	150.00
7 Dog Fight cover	250.00
8 B:Yankee Girl,A:Torpedoman	300.00
9 Dog Fight cover	300.00
10 Bondage cover	300.00
11 LBc(c),Future(c), Feb-March, 1947	400.00

CAPTAIN GALLANT
Charlton Comics
1955

1 Ph(c),Buster Crabbe	55.00
2	45.00
3	45.00
4 September, 1956	45.00

CAPTAIN JET
Four Star Publ.
May, 1952

1 Factory bombing cover	150.00
2 Parachute jump cover	90.00
3 Tank bombing cover	75.00
4 Parachute cover	75.00
5	50.00

CAPTAIN KIDD
(see ALL GREAT COMICS)

Captain Marvel #23
© Fawcett Publications

CAPTAIN MARVEL ADVENTURES
Fawcett Publications
Spring, 1941

N# JK, B:Captain Marvel & Sivana	28,000.00
2 GT,JK(c),Billy Batson (c)	3,500.00
3 JK(c),Thunderbolt (c)	2,000.00
4 Shazam(c)	1,300.00
5 V:Nazis	1,000.00
6 Solomon, Hercules, Atlas, Zeus, Achilles & Mercury cover	800.00
7 Ghost of the White Room	800.00

8 Forward America	800.00
9 A:Ibac the Monster, Nippo the Nipponese, Relm of the Subconscious	800.00
10 V:Japanese	800.00
11 V:Japanese and Nazis	650.00
12 Joins the Army	650.00
13 V:Diamond-Eyed Idol of Doom	650.00
14 Nippo meets his Nemesis	650.00
15 Big "Paste the Axis" contest	650.00
16 Uncle Sam cover, Paste the Axis	650.00
17 P(c), Paste the Axis	600.00
18 P(c), O:Mary Marvel	1,500.00
19 Mary Marvel & Santa cover	500.00
20 Mark of the Black Swastika	3,100.00
21 Hitler cover	3,000.00
22 B:Mr. Mind serial, Shipyard Sabotage	650.00
23 A:Steamboat	450.00
24 Minneapolis Mystery	450.00
25 Sinister Faces cover	450.00
26 Flag cover	450.00
27 Joins Navy	375.00
28 Uncle Sam cover	375.00
29 Battle at the China Wall	350.00
30 Modern Robinson Crusoe	350.00
31 Fights his own Conscience	350.00
32 V:Mole Men, Dallas	350.00
33 Mt. Rushmore parody cover, Omaha	325.00
34 Oklahoma City	325.00
35 O:Radar the International Policeman, Indianapolis	300.00
36 Missing face contest, St. Louis	300.00
37 V:Block Busting Bubbles, Cincinnati	300.00
38 V:Chattanooga Ghost, Rock Garden City	300.00
39 V:Mr. Mind's Death Ray, Pittsburgh	300.00
40 V:Ghost of the Tower,Boston	300.00
41 Runs for President, Dayton	250.00
42 Christmas special, St. Paul	250.00
43 V:Mr. Mind,I:Uncle Marvel, Chicago	250.00
44 OtherWorlds,Washington,D.C.	250.00
45 V:Blood Bank Robbers	250.00
46 E: Mr. Mind Serial, Tall Stories of Jonah Joggins	250.00
47	235.00
48 Signs Autographs cover	225.00
49 V: An Unknown Killer	225.00
50 Twisted Powers	225.00
51 Last of the Batsons	175.00
52 O&I:Sivana Jr.,V:Giant Earth Dreamer	200.00
53 Gets promoted	175.00
54 Marooned in the Future, Kansas City	200.00
55 Endless String, Columbus	175.00
56 Goes Crazy, Mobile	175.00
57 A:Haunted Girl, Rochester	175.00
58 V:Sivana	175.00
59	175.00
60 Man who made Earthquakes	175.00
61 I&V: Oggar, the Worlds Mightiest Immortal	225.00
62 The Great Harness Race	175.00
63 Stuntman	175.00
64	175.00
65 V:Invaders from Outer Space	175.00

All comics prices listed are for _Near Mint_ condition.

66 Atomic War cover 200.00	141 Horror 150.00	31 . . . . 200.00
67 Hartford 175.00	142 . . . . 150.00	32 Keeper of the Lonely Rock . 200.00
68 Scenes from the Past,	143 Great Stone Face	33 . . . . 200.00
Baltimore 175.00	on the Moon 150.00	34/35 I&O:Sivana Jr. 200.00
69 Gets Knighted 175.00	144 thru 147 . . . . @150.00	36 Underworld Tournament . . . 200.00
70 Horror in the Box 175.00	148 V:The World 150.00	37 FreddyFreeman'sNews-stand 200.00
71 Wheel of Death 175.00	149 . . . . 150.00	38 A:Arabian Knight 200.00
72 . . . . 175.00	150 Captains Marvel's Wedding,	39 V:Sivana Jr., Headline
73 Becomes a Petrophile 175.00	November, 1953 . . . . 200.00	Stealer 200.00
74 Who is the 13th Guest 175.00		40 Faces Grave Situation 200.00
75 V:Astonishing Yeast Menace 175.00		41 I:The Acrobat 150.00
76 V:Atom Ambassador 175.00		42 V:Sivana Jr. 150.00
77 The Secret Life 175.00		43 V:Beasts on Broadway 150.00
78 O:Mr. Tawny 200.00		44 Key to the Mystery 150.00
79 O:Atom,A:World's Worst		45 A:Icy Fingers 150.00
Actor 250.00		46 . . . . 150.00
80 Twice told story 350.00		47 V:Giant of the Beanstalk . . 150.00
81 A:Mr. Atom 150.00		48 Whale of a Fish Story 150.00
82 A:Mr. Tawny 150.00		49 V:Dream Recorder 150.00
83 Indian Chief 150.00		50 Wanted: Freddy Freeman . 150.00
84 V:Surrealist Imp 150.00		51 The Island Riddle 125.00
85 Freedom Train 185.00		52 A:Flying Postman 125.00
86 A:Mr. Tawny 150.00		53 Atomic Bomb on the Loose . 175.00
87 V:Electron Thief 150.00		54 V:Man with 100 Heads 150.00
88 Billy Batson's Boyhood 150.00		55 Pyramid of Eternity 150.00
89 V:Sivana 150.00		56 Blue Boy's Black Eye 150.00
90 A:Mr. Tawny 150.00		57 Magic Ladder 150.00
91 A:Chameleon Stone 150.00		58 Amazing Mirror Maze 150.00
92 The Land of Limbo 150.00		59 . . . . 150.00
93 Book of all Knowledge 150.00		60 V:Space Menace 150.00
94 Battle of Electricity 150.00		61 V:Himself 125.00
95 The Great Ice Cap 150.00		62 . . . . 125.00
96 V:Automatic Weapon 150.00		63 V:Witch of Winter 125.00
97 Wiped Out 150.00		64 thru 70 . . . . @125.00
98 United Worlds 150.00		71 thru 74 . . . . @125.00
99 Rain of Terror 150.00		75 V:Outlaw of Crooked Creek 125.00
100 V:Sivana,Plot against		76 thru 85 . . . . @125.00
the Universe 300.00		86 Defenders of time 125.00
101 Invisibility Trap 150.00		87 thru 89 . . . . @125.00
102 Magic Mix-up 150.00		90 The Magic Trunk 100.00
103 Ice Covered World of		91 thru 99 . . . . @100.00
1,000,000 AD 150.00		100 V:Sivana Jr 125.00
104 Mr. Tawny's Masquerade . 150.00		101 thru 106 . . . . @100.00
105 The Dog Catcher 150.00		107 The Horror Dimension . . . 100.00
106 V:Menace of the Moon . . . 150.00		108 thru 118 . . . . @100.00
107 V:Space Hunter 150.00		119 Condemned to Die,
108 V:Terrible Termites 150.00		June, 1953 . . . . 100.00
109 The Invention Inventor . . . 150.00		
110 V:Sivana 150.00		
111 The Eighth Sea 150.00		**CAPTAIN MIDNIGHT**
112 . . . . 150.00		**Fawcett Publications**
113 Captain Marvel's Feud . . . 150.00		**September, 1942**
114 V:The Ogre 150.00		1 O:Captain Midnight,
115 . . . . 150.00		Capt. Marvel cover 2,200.00
116 Flying Saucer 175.00		2 Smashes Jap Juggernaut . 1,000.00
117 . . . . 135.00		3 Battles the Phantom Bomber 700.00
118 V:Weird Water Man 150.00		4 Grapples the Gremlins 600.00
119 . . . . 150.00		5 Double Trouble in Tokyo . . 600.00
120 . . . . 150.00		6 Blasts the Black Mikado . . . 500.00
121 . . . . 150.00		7 Newspaper headline cover . 500.00
122 . . . . 150.00		8 Flying Torpedoes
123 . . . . 150.00		Berlin-Bound 500.00
124 V:Discarded Instincts 150.00		9 MRa(c), Subs in Mississippi 500.00
125 V:Ancient Villain 150.00		10 MRa(c), Flag cover 500.00
126 thru 130 . . . . @150.00		11 MRa(c), Murder in Mexico . 375.00
131 . . . . 150.00		12 V:Sinister Angels 375.00
132 V:Flood 150.00		13 Non-stop Flight around
133 . . . . 150.00		the World 375.00
134 . . . . 150.00		14 V:King of the Villains 375.00
135 Perplexing Past Puzzle . . . 150.00		15 V:Kimberley Killer 375.00
136 . . . . 150.00		16 Hitler's Fortress Breached . . 375.00
137 . . . . 150.00		17 MRa(c), Hello Adolf 350.00
138 V:Haunted Horror 150.00		18 Death from the Skies 350.00
139 . . . . 150.00		19 Hour of Doom for the Axis . 350.00
140 Hand of Horror 150.00		20 Brain and Brawn against Axis 350.00
		21 Trades with Japanese 300.00

Captain Marvel Jr. #2
© Fawcett Publications

CAPTAIN MARVEL JR.
Fawcett Publications
November, 1952

1 O:Captain Marvel, Jr.,	
A:Capt. Nazi 4,500.00	
2 O:Capt.Nippon,V:Capt. Nazi 1,500.00	
3 Parade to Excitement 800.00	
4 V:Invisible Nazi 800.00	
5 V:Capt. Nazi 700.00	
6 Adventure of Sabbac 600.00	
7 City under the Sea 600.00	
8 Dangerous Double 550.00	
9 Independence cover 550.00	
10 Hitler cover 575.00	
11 . . . . 450.00	
12 Scuttles the Axis Isle in the	
Sky 500.00	
13 V:The Axis,Hitler,cover 475.00	
14 X-Mas cover, Santa wears	
Capt. Marvel uniform 400.00	
15 . . . . 450.00	
16 A:Capt. Marvel, Sivana, Pogo 400.00	
17 Meets his Future self 400.00	
18 V:Birds of Doom 400.00	
19 A:Capt. Nazi & Capt. Nippon 400.00	
20 Goes on the Warpath 375.00	
21 Buy War Stamps 300.00	
22 Rides World's oldest	
steamboat 300.00	
23 . . . . 300.00	
24 V:Weather Man 300.00	
25 Flag cover 300.00	
26 Happy New Year 300.00	
27 Jungle Thrills 300.00	
28 V:Sivana's Crumbling Crimes 300.00	
29 Blazes a Wilderness Trail . . 300.00	
30 . . . . 300.00	

GOLDEN AGE

Captain Midnight #10
© Fawcett Publications

22 Plea for War Stamps	300.00
23 Japanese Prison cover	300.00
24 Rising Sun Flag cover	300.00
25 Amusement Park Murder	300.00
26 Hotel of Horror	300.00
27 Death Knell for Tyranny	300.00
28 Gliderchuting to Glory	300.00
29 Bomb over Nippon	300.00
30	300.00
31	200.00
32	200.00
33 V:Shark	200.00
34	200.00
35 thru 40	@200.00
41 thru 50	@150.00
51 thru 63	@150.00
64 V:XOG, Ruler of Saturn	150.00
65	150.00
66 V:XOG	150.00
67 Fall, 1948	150.00

Becomes:

SWEET HEART

68 Robert Mitchum	75.00
69 thru 118	@25.00
111 Ronald Reagan story	30.00
119 Marilyn Monroe	150.00
120 Atomic Bomb story	@35.00
121	20.00
122 1954	15.00

CAPTAIN SCIENCE
Youthful Magazines
November, 1950

1 WW,O:Captain Science, V:Monster God of Rogor	600.00
2 WW,V:Cat Men of Phoebus, Space Pirates	300.00
3 Ghosts from the Underworld	300.00
4 WW,Vampires	600.00
5 WW,V:Shark Pirates of Pisces	600.00
6 WW,V:Invisible Tyrants, bondage cover	500.00
7 WW,Bondage(c) Dec., 1951	500.00

Becomes:

FANTASTIC

8 Isle of Madness	250.00

9 Octopus cover	200.00

Becomes:

BEWARE

10 SHn,Doll of Death	250.00
11 SHn,Horror Head	200.00
12 SHn,Body Snatchers	175.00

Becomes:

CHILLING TALES

13 MF,Screaming Skull	350.00
14 SHn,Smell of Death	225.00
15 SHn,Curse of the Tomb	225.00
16 HcK,Mark of the Beast Bondage(c)	225.00
17 MFc(c),Wandering Willie, Oct.,1953	250.00

CAPTAIN STEVE SAVAGE
[1st Series]
Avon Periodicals
1950

N# WW	275.00
2 EK(c),The Death Gamble	125.00
3 EK(c),Crash Landing in Manchuria	75.00
4 EK(c),V:Red Raiders from Siang-Po	50.00
5 EK(c),Rockets of Death	50.00
6 Operation Destruction	50.00
7 EK(c),Flight to Kill	50.00
8 EK(c),V:Red Mystery Jet	50.00
9 EK(c)	50.00
10	50.00
11 EK(c)	55.00
12 WW	75.00
13	65.00

[2nd Series]
September/October, 1954

5	35.00
6 WW	50.00
7 thru 13	@20.00

CAPTAIN VIDEO
Fawcett Publications
February, 1951

1 GE,Ph(c)	800.00
2 Time when Men could not Walk	550.00
3 GE,Indestructible Antagonist	450.00
4 GE,School of Spies	450.00
5 GE,Missiles of Doom, Photo cover	450.00
6 GE,Island of Conquerors, Photo cover; Dec. 1951	450.00

CASPER, THE FRIENDLY GHOST
St. John Publishing
September, 1949

1 O:Baby Huey	1,200.00
2	500.00
3	450.00
4	350.00
5	350.00

Harvey Publications

7	275.00
8 thru 9	@150.00
10 I:Spooky	175.00
11 A:Spooky	100.00
12 thru 18	@75.00
19 I:Nightmare	85.00
20 I:Wendy the Witch	85.00
21 thru 30	@50.00

Casper, The Friendly Ghost #9
© St. John Publishing

31 thru 40	@40.00
41 thru 50	@30.00
51 thru 60	@25.00
61 thru 69	@20.00
70 July, 1958	22.00

CAT MAN COMICS
Helnit Publ. Co./
Holyoke Publ. Co./
Continental Magazine
May, 1941

1 O:Deacon&Sidekick Mickey, Dr. Diamond & Ragman,A:Black Widow, B:Blaze Baylor	2,500.00
2 Ragman	800.00
3 B:Pied Piper	600.00
4 CQ	550.00
5 I&O: The Kitten	500.00
6 CQ	450.00
7 CQ	450.00
8 JKa, I:Volton	600.00
9 JKa	400.00
10 JKa,O:Blackout, B:Phantom Falcon	375.00
11 JKa,DRi,BF	410.00
12	350.00
13	350.00
14 CQ	350.00
15 Rajah of Destruction	350.00
16 Bye-Bye Axis	425.00
17 Buy Bonds and Stamps	400.00
18 Buy Bonds and Stamps	400.00
19 CQ,Hitler,Tojo and Mussolini cover	425.00
20 CQ,Hitler,Tojo and Mussolini cover	425.00
21 CQ	300.00
22 CQ	300.00
23 CQ	300.00
N# V:Japanese,Bondage(c)	310.00
N# V:Demon	300.00
N# A:Leather Face	300.00
27 LbC(c),Flag cover,O:Kitten	500.00
28 LbC(c),Horror cover	500.00
29 LbC(c),BF	500.00
30 LbC(c),Bondage(c)	550.00
31 LbC(c)	500.00

32 August, 1946 . . . . 400.00

CHALLENGER, THE
Interfaith Publications
1945
N# O:The Challenger Club . . 225.00
2 JKa 200.00
3 JKa 200.00
4 JKa,BF 200.00

Chamber of Chills #24
© Harvey Publications

CHAMBER OF CHILLS
Harvey Publications/
Witches Tales
June, 1951
21 . . . . 300.00
22 . . . . 175.00
23 Eyes Ripped Out 175.00
24 Bondage cover 200.00
5 Shrunken Skull,
　Operation Monster 200.00
6 Seven Skulls of Magondi . . 175.00
7 Pit of the Damned 175.00
8 Formula for Death 175.00
9 Bondage cover 150.00
10 Cave of Death 150.00
11 Curse of Morgan Kilgane . . 125.00
12 Swamp Monster 125.00
13 The Lost Race 150.00
14 Down to Death 125.00
15 Nightmare of Doom 150.00
16 Cycle of Horror 150.00
17 Amnesia 150.00
18 Hair cut-Atom Bomb 175.00
19 Happy Anniversary 150.00
20 Shock is Struck 150.00
21 BP,Nose for News 160.00
22 Is Death the End? 125.00
23 BP,Heartline 125.00
24 BP,Bondage(c) 175.00
25 . . . . 75.00
26 HN,Captains Return 75.00
Becomes:
CHAMBER OF CLUES
27 BP,A:Kerry Drake 100.00
28 A:Kerry Drake 50.00

CHAMPION COMICS
Worth Publishing Co.
December, 1939
2 B:Champ, Blazing Scarab, Neptina,
　Liberty Lads, Jingleman . . 1,100.00
3 . . . . 600.00
4 Bailout(c) 625.00
5 Jungleman(c) 625.00
6 MNe 625.00
7 MNe,Human Meteor 650.00
8 . . . . 900.00
9 . . . . 900.00
10 Bondage cover 1,000.00
Becomes:
CHAMP COMICS
11 Human Meteor 650.00
12 Human Heteor 500.00
13 Dragon's Teeth 450.00
14 Liberty Lads 450.00
15 Liberty Lads 450.00
16 Liberty Lads 450.00
17 Liberty Lads 450.00
18 Liberty Lads 600.00
19 A:The Wasp 625.00
20 A:The Green Ghost 450.00
21 . . . . 350.00
22 A:White Mask 425.00
23 Flag cover 425.00
24 . . . . 350.00
25 . . . . 350.00
26 thru 29 . . . . 350.00

CHARLIE McCARTHY
Dell Publishing Co.
November, 1947
1 . . . . 150.00
2 . . . . 75.00
3 . . . . 75.00
1 . . . . 75.00
2 . . . . 75.00
3 . . . . 75.00
4 . . . . 75.00
5 . . . . 75.00
6 . . . . 75.00
7 . . . . 75.00
8 . . . . 75.00
9 . . . . 75.00

CHIEF, THE
Dell Publishing Co.
August, 1950
(1) see Dell Four Color #290
2 . . . . 30.00

CHILLING TALES
(see CAPTAIN SCIENCE)

CHUCKLE THE GIGGLY
BOOK OF COMIC ANIMALS
R. B. Leffing Well Co.
1944
1 . . . . 125.00

CINEMA COMICS
HERALD
Paramount/Universal/RKO/
20th Century Fox
Giveaways 1941-43
N# Mr. Bug Goes to Town 75.00
N# Bedtime Story 75.00
N# Lady for a Night,J.Wayne . 100.00

N# Reap the Wild Wind 75.00
N# Thunderbirds 75.00
N# They All Kissed Me 75.00
N# Bombardier 75.00
N# Crash Dive 75.00
N# Arabian Nights 75.00

CIRCUS THE
COMIC RIOT
Globe Syndicate
June, 1938
1 BKa,WE,BW 4,500.00
2 BKa,WE,BW 2,500.00
3 BKa,WE,BW, August, 1938 2,500.00

CISCO KID, THE
Dell Publishing Co.
(1) See Dell Four Color #292
2 January, 1951 . . . . 250.00
3 thru 5 . . . . @125.00
6 thru 10 . . . . @90.00
11 thru 20 . . . . @75.00
21 thru 36 . . . . @60.00
37 thru 41 Ph(c)'s . . . . @100.00

CLAIRE VOYANT
Leader Publ./Visual Ed./
Pentagon Publ.
1946-47
N# 425.00
2 JKa(c) 350.00
3 Case of the Kidnapped Bride 325.00
4 Bondage cover 375.00

CLOAK AND DAGGER
Approved Comics
(Ziff-Davis)
Fall, 1952
1 NS(c),Al Kennedy of the Secret
　Service 175.00

CLUE COMICS
Hillman Periodicals
January, 1943
1 O:Boy King,Nightmare,Micro-Face,
　Twilight,Zippo. 800.00
2 . . . . 375.00
3 Boy King V:The Crane 350.00
4 V:The Crane 275.00
5 V:The Crane 250.00
6 Hells Kitchen 175.00
7 V:Dr. Plasma,Torture(c) . . . 200.00
8 RP,A:The Gold Mummy King 250.00
9 I:Paris 175.00
10 O:Gun Master 175.00
11 A:Gun Master 125.00
12 O:Rackman 175.00
2-1 S&K,O:Nightro,A:Iron Lady 325.00
2-2 S&K,Bondage(c) 350.00
2-3 S&K 300.00
Becomes:
REAL CLUE
CRIME STORIES
2-4 DBw,S&K,True Story of
　Ma Barker 350.00
2-5 S&K, Newface surgery cover 250.00
2-6 S&K, Breakout cover 225.00
2-7 S&K, Stick up cover 225.00
2-8 Kidnapping cover 75.00
2-9 DBa,Boxing fix cover 75.00
2-10 DBa,Murder cover 75.00
2-11 Attempted bank

All comics prices listed are for _Near Mint_ condition.

robbery cover 75.00
2-12 Murder cover 75.00
3-1 thru 3-12 . . . . @50.00
4-1 thru 4-12 . . . . @75.00
5-1 thru 5-12 . . . . @40.00
6-1 thru 6-12 . . . . @40.00
6-10 Bondage(c) 70.00
7-1 thru 7-12 . . . . @30.00
8-1 thru 8-4 . . . . @30.00
8-5 May, 1953 . . . . 30.00

C-M-O COMICS
Comic Corp. of America
(Centaur)
May, 1942
1 Invisible Terror 700.00
2 Super Ann 450.00

COCOMALT BIG BOOK
OF COMICS
Harry A. Chesler
1938
1 BoW,PGn,FG,JCo,(Give away)
  Little Nemo 1,700.00

COLOSSUS COMICS
Sun Publications
March, 1940
1 A:Colossus 2,700.00

COLUMBIA COMICS
William H. Wise Co.
1944
1 Joe Palooka,Charlie Chan . 200.00

COMICS, THE
Dell Publishing Co.
March, 1937
1 I:Tom Mix & Arizona Kid . . 1,400.00
2 A:Tom Mix & Tom Beaty . . . 650.00
3 A:Alley Oop 500.00
4 same 500.00
5 same 500.00
6 thru 11 same . . . . @500.00

COMICS ON PARADE
United Features Syndicate
April 1938–Feb. 1955
1 B:Tarzan,Captain and the Kids,
  Little Mary, Mixup,Abbie & Slats,
  Broncho Bill,Li'l Abner . . . 3,000.00
2 Circus Parade of all 1,100.00
3 . . . . 800.00
4 On Rocket 750.00
5 All at the Store 750.00
6 All at Picnic 450.00
7 Li'l Abner(c) 450.00
8 same 450.00
9 same 450.00
10 same 450.00
11 same 350.00
12 same 350.00
13 same 350.00
14 Abbie n' Slats (c) 350.00
15 Li'l Abner(c) 350.00
16 Abbie n' Slats(c) 350.00
17 Tarzan,Abbie n' Slats(c) . . 375.00
18 Li'l Abner(c) 350.00
19 same 350.00
20 same 300.00
21 Li'l Abner(c) 300.00
22 Tail Spin Tommy(c) 300.00

23 Abbie n' Slats(c) 300.00
24 Tail Spin Tommy(c) 300.00
25 Li'l Abner(c) 300.00
26 Abbie n' Slats(c) 300.00
27 Li'l Abner(c) 300.00
28 Tail Spin Tommy(c) 300.00
29 Abbie n' Slats(c) 300.00
30 Li'l Abner(c) 200.00
31 The Captain & the Kids(c) . . 175.00
32 Nancy and Fritzi Ritz(c) . . . 125.00
33 Li'l Abner(c) 150.00
34 The Captain & the Kids(c) . . 125.00
35 Nancy and Fritzi Ritz(c) . . . 125.00
36 Li'l Abner(c) 145.00
37 The Captain & the Kids(c) . . 125.00
38 Nancy and Fritzi Ritz(c) . . . 110.00
39 Li'l Abner(c) 135.00
40 The Captain & the Kids(c) . . 125.00
41 Nancy and Fritzi Ritz(c) 75.00
42 Li'l Abner(c) 125.00
43 The Captain & the Kids(c) . . 125.00
44 Nancy and Fritzi Ritz(c) 75.00
45 Li'l Abner(c) 125.00

Comics on Parade #10
© United Features Syndicate

46 The Captain & the Kids(c) . . . 90.00
47 Nancy and Fritzi Ritz(c) 75.00
48 Li'l Abner(c) 125.00
49 The Captain & the Kids(c) . . . 90.00
50 Nancy and Fritzi Ritz(c) 75.00
51 Li'l Abner(c) 125.00
52 The Captain & the Kids(c) . . . 75.00
53 Nancy and Fritzi Ritz(c) 75.00
54 Li'l Abner(c) 125.00
55 Nancy and Fritzi Ritz(c) 75.00
56 The Captain & the Kids(c) . . . 75.00
57 Nancy and Fritzi Ritz(c) 70.00
58 Li'l Abner(c) 125.00
59 The Captain & the Kids(c) . . . 70.00
60 Nancy and Fritzi Ritz(c) 55.00
61 thru 76 same . . . . @55.00
77 Nancy & Sluggo(c) 50.00
78 thru 104 same . . . . @50.00

COMPLETE BOOK OF
COMICS AND FUNNIES
William H. Wise & Co.
1945
1 Wonderman-Magnet 300.00

CONFESSIONS OF LOVE
Artful Publications
April, 1950
1 . . . . 200.00
2 July, 1950 . . . . 125.00

CONFESSIONS OF LOVE
Star Publications
July, 1952
11 AW,LbC(c)Intimate Secrets of
  Daring Romance 75.00
12 AW,LbC(c),I Couldn't Say No 75.00
13 AW,LbC(c),Heart Break . . . 75.00
14 AW,LbC(c),My Fateful Love . 50.00
4 JyD,AW,LbC(c),The Longing
  Heart 50.00
5 AW,LbC(c),I Wanted Love . . . 50.00
6 AW,LbC(c),My Jealous Heart . 50.00
Becomes:

CONFESSIONS OF
ROMANCE
7 LbC(c)Too Good 100.00
8 AW,LbC(c),I Lied About Love . 60.00
9 WW,AW,LbC(c),I Paid
  Love's Price 100.00
10 JyD,AW,LbC(c),My Heart Cries
  for Love 60.00
11 JyD,AW,LbC(c),Intimate
  Confessions, November, 1954 60.00

CONFESSIONS OF
LOVELORN
(see LOVELORN)

CONQUEROR COMICS
Albrecht Publications
Winter, 1945
1 . . . . 125.00

CONTACT COMICS
Aviation Press
July, 1944
N# LbC(c),B:Black Venus,
  Golden Eagle 350.00
2 LbC(c),Peace Jet 250.00
3 LbC(c),LbC,E:Flamingo . . . 225.00
4 LbC(c),LbC 225.00
5 LbC(c),A:Phantom Flyer . . . 250.00
6 LbC(c),HK 275.00
7 LbC(c),Flying Tigers 225.00
8 LbC(c),Peace Jet 225.00
9 LbC(c),LbC,A:Marine Flyers 225.00
10 LbC(c),A:Bombers of the AAF 225.00
11 LbC(c),HK,AF,Salutes Naval
  Aviation 300.00
12 LbC(c),A:Sky Rangers, Air Kids,
  May, 1946 . . . . 225.00

COO COO COMICS
Nedor/Animated Cartoons
(Standard)
October, 1942
1 O&I:Super Mouse 200.00
2 . . . . 100.00
3 . . . . 50.00
4 . . . . 50.00
5 . . . . 50.00
6 . . . . 40.00
7 thru 10 . . . . @35.00
11 thru 33 . . . . @35.00
34 thru 40 FF illustration . . . @50.00

41 FF	125.00
42 FF	125.00
43 FF illustration	75.00
44 FF illustration	75.00
45 FF illustration	75.00
46 FF illustration	45.00
47 FF	75.00
48 FF illustration	50.00
49 FF illustration	60.00
50 FF Illustration	60.00
51 thru 61	@25.00
62 April, 1952	25.00

"COOKIE"
Michel Publ./Regis Publ.
(American Comics Group)
April, 1946

1	125.00
2	50.00
3	40.00
4	40.00
5	40.00
6 thru 20	@35.00
21 thru 30	@30.00
31 thru 54	@25.00
55 August, 1955	25.00

COSMO CAT
Fox Features Syndicate
July/August, 1946

1	175.00
2	85.00
3 O:Cosmo Cat	65.00
4 thru 10	@35.00

COURAGE COMICS
J. Edward Slavin
1945

1	75.00
2 Boxing cover	80.00
77 Naval rescue, PT99 cover	80.00

COWBOY COMICS
(see STAR RANGER)

COWBOYS 'N' INJUNS
Compix
(M.E. Enterprises)
1946-47

1 Funny Animal Western	40.00
2 thru 8	@25.00

COWBOY WESTERN
COMICS/HEROES
(see YELLOWJACKET
COMICS)

COWGIRL ROMANCES
Fiction House Magazine
1952

1 The Range of Singing Guns	225.00
2 The Lady of Lawless Range	125.00
3 Daughter of the Devil's Band	100.00
4 Bride Wore Buckskin	90.00
5 Taming of Lone-Star Lou	90.00
6 Rose of Mustang Mesa	85.00
7 Nobody Loves a Gun Man	85.00
8 Wild Beauty	85.00
9 Gun-Feud Sweethearts	85.00
10 JKa,AW,No Girl of Stampede Valley	90.00

11 Love is Where You Find It	85.00
12 December, 1952	85.00

COW PUNCHER
Avon Periodicals/
Realistic Publ.
January, 1947

1 JKu	275.00
2 JKu,JKa(c),Bondage cover	225.00
3 AU(c)	150.00
4	150.00
5	150.00
6 WJo(c),Drug story	200.00
7	150.00
1 JKu	150.00

Crack Comics #39
© Quality Comics Group

CRACK COMICS
Comic Magazines
(Quality Comics Group)
May, 1940

1 LF,O:Black Condor,Madame Fatal, Red Torpedo, Rock Bradden, Space Legion, B:The Clock,Wizard Wells	4,000.00
2 Black Condor cover	1,700.00
3 The Clock cover	1,200.00
4 Black Condor cover	1,000.00
5 LF,The Clock cover	800.00
6 PG,Black Condor cover	750.00
7 Clock cover	750.00
8 Black Condor cover	750.00
9 Clock cover	750.00
10 Black Condor cover	750.00
11 LF,PG,Clock cover	650.00
12 LF,PG,Black Condor cover	650.00
13 LF,PG,Clock cover	650.00
14 AMc,LF,PG,Clack Condor(c)	650.00
15 AMc,LF,PG,Clock cover	650.00
16 AMc,LF,PG,Black Condor(c)	650.00
17 FG,AMc,LF,PG,Clock cover	650.00
18 AMc,LF,PG,Black Condor(c)	650.00
19 AMc,LF,PG,Clock cover	650.00
20 AMc,LF,PG,Black Condor(c)	650.00
21 AMc,LF,PG,same	500.00
22 LF,PG,same	500.00
23 AMc,LF,PG,same	500.00
24 AMc,LF,PG,same	500.00

25 AMc,same	450.00
26 AMc,same	450.00
27 AMc,I&O:Captain Triumph	750.00
28 Captain Triumph cover	450.00
29 A:Spade the Ruthless	450.00
30 I:Biff	400.00
31 Helps Spade Dig His Own Grave	200.00
32 Newspaper cover	200.00
33 V:Men of Darkness	200.00
34	200.00
35 V:The Man Who Conquered Flame	200.00
36 Good Neighbor Tour	200.00
37 V:The Tyrant of Toar Valley	200.00
38 Castle of Shadows	200.00
39 V:Crime over the City	200.00
40 Thrilling Murder Mystery	125.00
41	125.00
42 All that Glitters is Not Gold	125.00
43 Smashes the Evil Spell of Silent	125.00
44 V:Silver Tip	125.00
45 V:King-The Jack of all Trades	125.00
46 V:Mr. Weary	125.00
47 V:Hypnotic Eyes Khor	135.00
48 Murder in the Sky	135.00
49	135.00
50 A Key to Trouble	135.00
51 V:Werewolf	135.00
52 V:Porcupine	135.00
53 V:Man Who Robbed the Dead	135.00
54 Shoulders the Troubles of the World	135.00
55 Brain against Brawn	135.00
56 Gossip leads to Murder	135.00
57 V:Sitok–Green God of Evil	135.00
58 V:Targets	125.00
59 A Cargo of Mystery	125.00
60 Trouble is no Picnic	125.00
61 V:Mr. Pointer-Finger of Fear	125.00
62 V:The Vanishing Vandals	125.00

Becomes:
CRACK WESTERN

63 PG, I&O:Two-Gun Lil, B:Frontier Marshal,Arizona Ames,	150.00
64 RC,Arizona AmesV:Two-Legged Coyote	100.00
65 RC,Ames Tramples on Trouble	100.00
66 Arizona Ames Arizona Raines, Tim Holt,Ph(c)	90.00
67 RC, Ph(c)	100.00
68	75.00
69 RC	75.00
70 O&I:Whip and Diablo	90.00
71 RC(c)	100.00
72 RC,Tim Holt,Ph(c)	72.00
73 Tim Holt,Ph(c)	55.00
74 RC(c)	60.00
75 RC(c)	60.00
76 RC(c),Stage Coach to Oblivion	60.00
77 RC(c),Comanche Terror	60.00
78 RC(c),Killers of Laurel Ridge	60.00
79 RC(c),Fires of Revenge	60.00
80 RC(c),Mexican Massacre	60.00
81 RC(c),Secrets of Terror Canyon	60.00
82 The Killer with a Thousand Faces	40.00
83 Battlesnake Pete's Revenge	40.00
84 PG(c),Revolt at Broke Creek May,1951	40.00

All comics prices listed are for *Near Mint* condition.

CRACKAJACK FUNNIES
Dell Publishing Co.
June, 1938
1 AMc,A:Dan Dunn,The Nebbs,
  Don Winslow 2,000.00
2 AMc,same 750.00
3 AMc,same 600.00
4 AMc,same 400.00
5 AMc,Naked Women(c) 450.00
6 AMc,same 350.00
7 AMc,same 350.00
8 AMc,same 350.00
9 AMc,A:Red Ryder 1,000.00
10 AMc,A:Red Ryder 350.00
11 AMc,A:Red Ryder 300.00
12 AMc,A:Red Ryder 300.00
13 AMc,A:Red Ryder 300.00
14 AMc,A:Red Ryder 300.00
15 AMc,A:Tarzan 350.00
16 AMc 250.00
17 AMc 250.00
18 AMc 250.00
19 AMc 250.00
20 AMc 250.00
21 AMc 250.00
22 AMc 250.00
23 AMc 250.00
24 AMc 250.00
25 AMc,I:The Owl 550.00
26 AMc 400.00
27 AMc 400.00
28 AMc,A:The Owl 400.00
29 AMc,A:Ellery Queen 400.00
30 AMc,A:Tarzan 400.00
31 AMc,A:Tarzan 400.00
32 AMc,O:Owl Girl 450.00
33 AMc,A:Tarzan 300.00
34 AMc,same 300.00
35 AMc,same 300.00
36 AMc,same 300.00
37 AMc 300.00
38 AMc 300.00
39 AMc,I:Andy Panada 400.00
40 AMc,A:Owl(c) 300.00
41 AMc 300.00
42 AMc 300.00
43 AMc,A:Owl(c) 275.00

CRASH COMICS
Tem Publishing Co.
May, 1940
1 S&K,O:Strongman, B:Blue Streak,
  Perfect Human, Shangra . . 2,400.00
2 S&K 1,100.00
3 S&K 1,000.00
4 S&K,O&I:Catman 2,000.00
5 S&K, November, 1940 . . . 1,000.00

CRIME AND PUNISHMENT
Lev Gleason Publications
April, 1948
1 CBi(c),Mr.Crime(c) 200.00
2 CBi(c) 100.00
3 CBi(c),BF 125.00
4 CBi(c),BF 75.00
5 CBi(c) 75.00
6 thru 10 CBi(c) . . . . @65.00
11 thru 15 CBi(c) . . . . @50.00
16 thru 27 CBi(c) . . . . @40.00
28 thru 38 . . . . @35.00
39 Drug issue 60.00
40 thru 44 . . . . @35.00

Crime and Punishment #6
© Lev Gleason Publications

45 Drug issue 60.00
46 thru 73 . . . . @35.00
66 ATh 250.00
67 Drug Storm 200.00
68 ATh(c) 175.00
69 Drug issue 55.00
74 August, 1955 . . . . 30.00

CRIME DETECTIVE COMICS
Hillman Publications
March-April, 1948
1 BFc(c),A:Invisible 6 . . . . . . 175.00
2 Jewel Robbery cover 75.00
3 Stolen cash cover 60.00
4 Crime Boss Murder cover . . . 60.00
5 BK,Maestro cover 60.00
6 AMc,Gorilla cover 50.00
7 GMc,Wedding cover 50.00
8 . . . . 40.00
9 Safe Robbery cover
  (a classic) 225.00
10 . . . . 60.00
11 BP 60.00
12 BK 60.00
2-1 Bluebird captured 75.00
2-2 . . . . 40.00
2-3 . . . . 40.00
2-4 BK 45.00
2-5 . . . . 40.00
2-6 . . . . 40.00
2-7 BK,GMc 45.00
2-8 . . . . 40.00
2-9 . . . . 40.00
2-10 . . . . 40.00
2-11 . . . . 40.00
2-12 . . . . 40.00
3-1 Drug Story 40.00
3-2 thru 3-7 . . . . @40.00
3-8 May/June, 1953 . . . . 30.00

CRIME DOES NOT PAY
(see SILVER STREAK COMICS)

CRIME ILLUSTRATED
E.C. Comics
November-December, 1955
1 Grl,RC,GE,JO 125.00
2 Grl,RC,JCr,JDa,JO 100.00

CRIME MUST STOP
Hillman Periodicals
October, 1952
1 BK 450.00

CRIME MYSTERIES
Ribage Publishing Corp.
May, 1952
1 Transvestism,Bondage(c) . . 375.00
2 A:Manhunter, Lance Storm,
  Drug 250.00
3 FF-one page, A:Dr. Foo . . . 200.00
4 A:Queenie Star, Bondage Star 300.00
5 Claws of the Green Girl . . . 175.00
6 . . . . 175.00
7 Sons of Satan 175.00
8 Death Stalks the Crown,
  Bondage(c) 200.00
9 You are the Murderer 175.00
10 The Hoax of the Death . . . 175.00
11 The Strangler 175.00
12 Bondage(c) 190.00
13 AT,6 lives for one 200.00
14 Painted in Blood 175.00
15 Feast of the Dead,Acid Face 250.00
Becomes:

SECRET MYSTERIES
16 Hiding Place,Horror 150.00
17 The Deadly Diamond,Horror 100.00
18 Horror 125.00
19 Horror,July, 1955 . . . . . . 125.00

CRIMES ON THE WATERFRONT
(see FAMOUS GANGSTERS)

INTERNATIONAL COMICS
E.C. Publ. Co.
Spring, 1947
1 KS,I:Manhattan's Files 600.00
2 KS,A: Van Manhattan &
  Madelon 450.00
3 KS,same 300.00
4 KS,same 300.00
5 I:International Crime-Busting
  Patrol 300.00
Becomes:

INTERNATIONAL CRIME PATROL
6 A:Moon Girl & The Prince . . 550.00
Becomes:

CRIME PATROL
7 SMo,A:Capt. Crime Jr.,Field
  Marshall of Murder 450.00
8 JCr,State Prison cover 400.00
9 AF,JCr,Bank Robbery 400.00
10 AF,JCr,Wanted:James Dore 400.00
11 AF,JCr 400.00
12 AF,Grl,JCr,Interrogation(c) . 400.00
13 AF,JCr 400.00
14 AF,JCr,Smugglers cover . . 400.00
15 AF,JCr,Crypt of Terror . . . 1,900.00
16 AF,JCr,Crypt of Terror . . . 1,400.00
Becomes:

CRYPT OF TERROR
E.C. Comics
April, 1950
17 JCr&(c),AF,'Werewolf
   Strikes Again' 2,200.00
18 JCr&(c),AF,WW,HK
   'The Living Corpse' 1,200.00
19 JCr&(c),AF,Grl,
   'Voodoo Drums' 1,200.00
Becomes:

TALES FROM
THE CRYPT
October, 1950
20 JCr&(c),AF,GI,JKa
   'Day of Death' 1,000.00
21 AF&(c),WW,HK,GI,'Cooper
   Dies in the Electric Chair . . 750.00
22 AF, JCr(c) 750.00
23 AF&(c),JCr,JDa,Grl
   'Locked in a Mauseleum' . 450.00
24 AF(c),WW,JDa,JCr,Grl
   'Danger...Quicksand' 450.00
25 AF(c),WW,JDa,JKa,Grl
   'Mataud Waxworks' 450.00

Tales From the Crypt #43
© E.C. Comics

26 WW(c),JDa,Grl,
   'Scared Graveyard' 350.00
27 JKa, WW(c), Guillotine cover 350.00
28 AF(c),JDa,JKa,Grl,JO
   'Buried Alive' 350.00
29 JDa&(c),JKa,Grl,JO
   'Coffin Burier' 350.00
30 JDa&(c),JO,JKa,Grl
   'Underwater Death' 350.00
31 JDa&(c),JKa,Grl,AW
   'Hand Chopper' 400.00
32 JDa&(c),GE,Grl,'Woman
   Crushed by Elephant' 300.00
33 JDa&(c),GE,JKa,Grl,'Lower
   Berth',O:Crypt Keeper 500.00
34 JDa&(c),JKa,GE,Grl,'Jack the
   Ripper,'Ray Bradbury adapt. 300.00
35 JDa&(c),JKa,JO,Grl,
   'Werewolf' 300.00
36 JDa&(c),JKa,GE,Grl, Ray
   Bradbury adaptation 300.00
37 JDa(c),JO,BE 300.00
38 JDa(c),BE,RC,Grl,'Axe Man' 300.00

39 JDa&(c),JKa,JO,Grl,'Children
   in the Graveyard' 300.00
40 JDa&(c),GE,BK,Grl,
   'Underwater Monster' 300.00
41 JDa&(c),JKa,GE,Grl,
   'Knife Thrower' 275.00
42 JDa(c),JO,Vampire cover . . 275.00
43 JDa(c),JO,GE 275.00
44 JO,RC,Guillotine cover 275.00
45 JDa&(c),JKa,BK,GI,'Rat
   Takes Over His Life' 275.00
46 JDa&(c),GE,JO,GI,'Werewolf
   man being hunted,Feb.1955 350.00

CRIME REPORTER
St. John Publishing Co.
August, 1948
1 Death Makes a Deadline . . 300.00
2 GT,MB(c),Matinee Murders . 500.00
3 GT,MB(c),December, 1948 . 250.00

CRIMES BY WOMEN
Fox Features Syndicate
June, 1948
1 Bonnie Parker 900.00
2 Vicious Female 500.00
3 Prison break cover 425.00
4 Murder cover 400.00
5 . . . . 400.00
6 Girl Fight cover 500.00
7 . . . . 400.00
8 . . . . 400.00
9 . . . . 400.00
10 . . . . 400.00
11 . . . . 400.00
12 . . . . 400.00
13 ACME jewelry robbery cover 400.00
14 Prison break cover 400.00
15 August, 1951 . . . . 400.00

CRIME SMASHER
Fawcett Publications
Summer, 1948
1 The Unlucky Rabbit's Foot . 300.00

CRIME SMASHERS
Ribage Publishing Corp.
October, 1950
1 Girl Rape 600.00
2 JKu,A:Sally the Sleuth, Dan Turner,
   Girl Friday, Rat Hale 300.00
3 MFa 200.00
4 Zak(c) 200.00
5 WW 250.00
6 . . . . 150.00
7 Bondage cover,Drugs 175.00
8 . . . . 150.00
9 Bondage cover 175.00
10 . . . . 150.00
11 . . . . 150.00
12 FF 175.00
13 . . . . 165.00
14 . . . . 150.00
15 . . . . 150.00

CRIME SUSPENSTORIES
L.L. Publishing Co.
(E.C. Comics)
October-November, 1950
1a JCr,Grl 1,000.00
1 JCr,WW,Grl 800.00
2 JCr,JKa,Grl 450.00
3 JCr,WW,Grl 350.00

4 JCr,Gln,Grl,JDa 325.00
5 JCr,JKa,Grl,JDa 300.00
6 JCr,JDa,Grl 250.00
7 JCr,Grl 250.00
8 JCr,Grl 250.00
9 JCr,Grl 250.00
10 JCr,Grl 250.00
11 JCr,Grl 200.00
12 JCr,Grl 200.00
13 JCr,AW 225.00
14 JCr 200.00
15 JCr 200.00
16 JCr,AW 225.00
17 JCr,FF,AW, Ray Bradbury . 250.00
18 JCr,RC,BE 200.00
19 JCr,RC,GE,AF(c) 200.00
20 RC,JCr, Hanging cover . . . 250.00
21 JCr 150.00
22 RC,JO,JCr(c),
   Severed head cover 175.00
23 JKa,RC,GE 175.00
24 BK,RC,JO 150.00
25 JKa,(c),RC 150.00
26 JKa,(c),RC,JO 150.00
27 JKa,(c),GE,Grl,March, 1955 150.00

CRIMINALS ON
THE RUN
Premium Group of Comics
August, 1948
4-1 LbC(c) 175.00
4-2 LbC(c), A:Young King Cole 150.00
4-3 LbC(c), Rip Roaring Action
   in Alps 150.00
4-4 LbC(c), Shark cover 150.00
4-5 AMc 150.00
4-6 LbC 125.00
4-7 LbC 325.00
5-1 LbC 125.00
5-2 LbC 125.00
10 LbC 150.00
Becomes:

CRIME-FIGHTING
DETECTIVE
11 LbC, Brodie Gang Captured 100.00
12 LbC(c), Jail Break Genius . 100.00
13 . . . . 50.00
14 LbC(c), A Night of Horror . . . 75.00
15 LbC(c) 75.00
16 LbC(c), Wanton Murder 75.00
17 LbC(c), The Framer
   was Framed 75.00
18 LbC(c), A Web of Evil 75.00
19 LbC(c), Lesson of the Law . . 75.00
Becomes:

SHOCK DETECTIVE
CASE
20 LbC(c), The Strangler 100.00
21 LbC(c), Death Ride 100.00
Becomes:

SPOOK DETECTIVE
CASES
22 Headless Horror 225.00
Becomes:

SPOOK SUSPENSE
AND MYSTERY
23 LbC,Weird Picture of Murder 150.00
24 LbC(c),Mummy's Case 175.00
25 LbC(c),Horror Beyond Door 150.00
26 LbC(c),JyD,Face of Death . 150.00
27 LbC(c),Ship of the Dead . . . 150.00

GOLDEN AGE

28 LbC(c),JyD,Creeping Death   150.00
29 LbC(c),Solo for Death 150.00
30 LbC(c),JyD,Nightmare,
   Oct.,1954 . . . . 150.00

CROWN COMICS
Golfing/McCombs Publ.
Winter 1944
1 Edgar Allen Poe adapt. 250.00
2 MB,I:Mickey Magic 175.00
3 MB,Jungle adventure cover   175.00
4 MB(c) 175.00
5 MB(c),Jungle adventure cover 175.00
6 MB(c),Jungle adventure cover 175.00
7 JKa,AF,MB(c),Race Car driving
   cover 175.00
8 MB 135.00
9 . . . . 85.00
10 Plane crash cover 85.00
11 LSt 75.00
12 LSt 75.00
13 LSt 75.00
14 . . . . 95.00
15 FBe 75.00
16 FBe,Jungle adventure(c) . . . 75.00
17 FBe 75.00
18 FBe 75.00
19 BP,July, 1949 . . . . 75.00

CRUSADER FROM MARS
Approved Publ.
(Ziff-Davis)
January-March, 1952
1 Mission Thru Space, Death in
   the Sai 550.00
2 Beachhead on Saturn's Ring,
   Bondage(c),Fall, 1952 . . . . . 400.00

CRYIN' LION, THE
William H. Wise Co.
Fall, 1944
1 . . . . 75.00
2 . . . . 60.00
3 Spring, 1945 . . . . 60.00

CRYPT OF TERROR
(see CRIME PATROL)

CYCLONE COMICS
Bibara Publ. Co.
June, 1940
1 O:Tornado Tom 1,000.00
2 . . . . 550.00
3 . . . . 500.00
4 Voltron 450.00
5 A:Mr. Q,October, 1940 . . . . 450.00

ALL GREAT COMICS
Fox Features Syndicate
October, 1947
12 A:Brenda Starr 400.00
13 JKa,O:Dagger, Desert Hawk 350.00
Becomes:

DAGAR, DESERT HAWK
14 JKa,Monster of Mura 550.00
15 JKa,Curse of the Lost
   Pharaoh 350.00
16 JKa,Wretched Antmen 300.00
19 Pyramid of Doom 275.00
20 . . . . 275.00
21 JKa(c),The Ghost of Fate . . 300.00

Dagar, Desert Hawk #21
© *Fox Features Syndicate*

22 . . . . 275.00
23 Bondage cover 300.00
Becomes:

CAPTAIN KIDD
24 Blackbeard the Pirate 100.00
25 Sorceress of the Deep 100.00
Becomes:

MY SECRET STORY
26 He Wanted More Than Love . 85.00
27 My Husband Hated Me 50.00
28 I Become a Marked Women . . 50.00
29 My Forbidden Rapture,
   April, 1950 . . . . 50.00

DAFFY
Dell Publishing Co.
March, 1953
(1) *see Dell Four Color #457*
(2) *see Dell Four Color #536*
(3) *see Dell Four Color #615*
4 thru 7 . . . . @25.00
8 thru 11 . . . . @20.00
12 thru 17 . . . . @15.00
Becomes:

DAFFY DUCK
18 . . . . 15.00
19 . . . . 15.00
20 . . . . 15.00
21 thru 30 . . . . @10.00
Gold Key
31 thru 40 . . . . @8.00
41 thru 59 . . . . @6.00
60 B&A:Road Runner 3.00
61 thru 90 same . . . . @3.00
91 thru 127 . . . . @2.00
Whitman
128 thru 145 . . . . @2.00

DAGWOOD
Harvey Publications
September, 1950
1 . . . . 100.00
2 . . . . 50.00
3 thru 10 . . . . @35.00
11 thru 20 . . . . @30.00

21 thru 30 . . . . @20.00
31 thru 50 . . . . @15.00
51 thru 70 . . . . @10.00
71 thru 109 . . . . @8.00
110 thru 140 . . . . @7.00

DANGER AND ADVENTURE
(see THIS MAGAZINE IS HAUNTED)

DANGER IS OUR BUSINESS
Toby Press/
I.W. Enterprises
1953
1 AW,FF,Men who Defy Death
   for a Living 325.00
2 Death Crowds the Cockpit . . 75.00
3 Killer Mountain 60.00
4 . . . . 60.00
5 thru 9 . . . . @50.00
10 June, 1955 . . . . 60.00

DAREDEVIL COMICS
Lev Gleason Publications
July, 1941
1 Daredevil Battles Hitler, A:Silver
   Streak, Lance Hale, Dickey Dean,
   Cloud Curtis,V:The Claw,
   O:Hitler 9,000.00
2 I:The Pioneer, Champion of
   American,B:London,Pat
   Patriot,Pirate Prince 2,500.00
3 CBi(c),O:Thirteen 1,500.00
4 CBi(c),Death is the Refere . 1,200.00
5 CBi(c),I:Sniffer&Jinx, Claw
   V:Ghost,Lottery of Doom . . 1,000.00
6 CBi(c) 850.00
7 CBi(c), What Ghastly Sight Lies
   within the Mysterious Trunk . 750.00
8 V:Nazis cover, E:Nightro . . 700.00
9 V:Double 700.00
10 America will Remember
   Pearl Harbor 700.00
11 Bondage cover, E:Pat
   Patriot, London 750.00
12 BW,CBi(c), O:The Law . . . 1,100.00
13 BW,I:Little Wise Guys 1,000.00
14 BW,CBi(c) 500.00
15 BW,CBi(c), D:Meatball 700.00
16 BW,CBi(c) 475.00
17 BW,CBi(c), Into the Valley
   of Death 450.00
18 BW,CBi(c), O:Daredevil,
   double length story 1,000.00
19 BW,CBi(c), Buried Alive . . . 375.00
20 BW,CBi(c), Boxing cover . . 375.00
21 CBi(c), Can Little Wise Guys
   Survive Blast of Dynamite? . 650.00
22 CBi(c) 300.00
23 CBi(c), I:Pshyco 300.00
24 CBi(c), Punch and Judy
   Murders 300.00
25 CBi(c), baseball cover 325.00
26 CBi(c) 275.00
27 CBi(c), Bondage cover 300.00
28 CBi(c) 275.00
29 CBi(c) 275.00
30 CBi(c), Ann Hubbard White
   1922-1943 . . . . 275.00
31 CBi(c), D:The Claw 600.00
32 V:Blackmarketeers 200.00

Daredevil #36
© Lev Gleason Publications

33 CBi(c) 200.00
34 CBi(c) 200.00
35 B:Two Daredevil stories
  every issue 175.00
36 CBi(c) 175.00
37 CBi(c) 175.00
38 CBi(c), O:Daredevil 350.00
39 CBi(c) 175.00
40 CBi(c) 175.00
41 . . . . 150.00
42 thru 50 CBi(c) . . . . @150.00
51 CBi(c) 125.00
52 CBi(c),Football cover 150.00
53 thru 57 . . . . @125.00
58 Football cover 150.00
59 . . . . 125.00
60 . . . . 125.00
61 thru 68 . . . . @125.00
69 E:Daredevil 125.00
70 . . . . 100.00
71 thru 78 . . . . @75.00
79 B:Daredevil 85.00
80 . . . . 80.00
81 . . . . 55.00
82 . . . . 55.00
83 thru 99 . . . . @55.00
100 . . . . 75.00
101 thru 133 . . . . @50.00
134 September, 1956 . . . . 50.00

DARING CONFESSIONS
(see YOUTHFUL HEART)

DARING LOVE
(see YOUTHFUL ROMANCES)

DARK MYSTERIES
Merit Publications
June-July, 1951
1 WW, WW(c), Curse of the
  Sea Witch 700.00
2 WW, WW(c), Vampire Fangs
  of Doom 450.00
3 Terror of the Unwilling
  Witch 225.00
4 Corpse that Came Alive . . . 225.00

5 Horror of the Ghostly Crew . 200.00
6 If the Noose Fits Wear It! . . 200.00
7 Terror of the Cards of Death 200.00
8 Terror of the Ghostly Trail . 200.00
9 Witch's Feast at Dawn 200.00
10 Terror of the Burning Witch . 250.00
11 The River of Blood 175.00
12 Horror of the Talking Dead . 175.00
13 Terror of the Hungry Cats . . 175.00
14 Horror of the Fingers of Doom 185.00
15 Terror of the Vampires Teeth 175.00
16 Horror of the Walking Dead 175.00
17 Terror of the Mask of Death 175.00
18 Terror of the Burning Corpse 175.00
19 The Rack of Terror 225.00
20 Burning Executioner 200.00
21 The Sinister Secret 125.00
22 The Hand of Destiny 125.00
23 The Mardenburg Curse 100.00
24 Give A Man enough Rope,
  July, 1955 . . . . 100.00

DAVY CROCKETT
Avon Periodicals
1951
1 . . . . 125.00

DEAD END
CRIME STORIES
Kirby Publishing Co.
April, 1949
N# BP 400.00

DEAD-EYE
WESTERN COMICS
Hillman Periodicals
November-December, 1948
1 BK 125.00
2 . . . . 60.00
3 . . . . 50.00
4 thru 12 . . . . @35.00
2-1 . . . . 30.00
2-2 . . . . 30.00
2-3 . . . . 45.00
2-4 . . . . 45.00
2-5 thru 2-12 . . . . @25.00
3-1 . . . . 25.00

DEADWOOD GULCH
Dell Publishing Co.
1931
1 . . . . 125.00

DEAR BEATRICE
FAIRFAX
Best Books
(Standard Comics)
November, 1950
5 . . . . 40.00
6 thru 9 . . . . @25.00

DEAR LONELY HEART
Artful Publications
March, 1951
5 . . . . 100.00
6 . . . . 35.00
7 MB,Jungle Girl 75.00
8 . . . . 30.00
9 . . . . 30.00

DEAR LONELY HEARTS
Comic Media
August, 1953
1 Six Months to Live 38.00
2 Date Hungry, Price of Passion 22.00
3 thru 8 . . . . @22.00

DEARLY BELOVED
Approved Comics
(Ziff-Davis)
Fall, 1952
1 Ph(c) 100.00

DEBBIE DEAN,
CAREER GIRL
Civil Service Publishing
April, 1945
1 . . . . 75.00
2 . . . . 70.00

DELL GIANT EDITIONS
Dell Publishing Co.
1953-58
Abe Lincoln Life Story 125.00
Cadet Gray of West Point 100.00
Golden West Rodeo Treasury . 150.00
Life Stories of
  American Presidents 90.00
Lone Ranger Golden West . . . 300.00
Lone Ranger Movie Story 500.00
Lone Ranger Western
  Treasury('53) 275.00
Lone Ranger Western
  Treasury('54) 175.00
Moses & Ten Commandments . . 75.00
Nancy & Sluggo Travel Time . . 100.00
Pogo Parade 450.00
Raggedy Ann & Andy 275.00
Santa Claus Funnies 150.00
Tarzan's Jungle Annual #1 . . . 200.00
Tarzan's Jungle Annual #2 . . . 150.00
Tarzan's Jungle Annual #3 . . . 125.00
Tarzan's Jungle Annual #4 . . . 125.00
Tarzan's Jungle Annual #5 . . . 125.00
Tarzan's Jungle Annual #6 . . . 125.00
Tarzan's Jungle Annual #7 . . . 125.00
Treasury of Dogs 100.00
Treasury of Horses 100.00
Universal Presents-Dracula-
  The Mummy & Other Stories 300.00
Western Roundup #1 . . . . 350.00
Western Roundup #2 . . . . 200.00
Western Roundup #3 . . . . 175.00
Western Roundup #4 thru #5 @150.00
Western Roundup #6 thru #10 @140.00
Western Roundup #11 thru #17@135.00
Western Roundup #18 . . . . . . 125.00
Western Roundup #19 thru #25 125.00
Woody Woodpecker Back
  to School #1 . . . . 165.00
Woody Woodpecker Back
  to School #2 . . . . 120.00
Woody Woodpecker Back
  to School #3 . . . . 90.00
Woody Woodpecker Back
  to School #4 . . . . 90.00
Woody Woodpecker County
  Fair #5 . . . . 90.00
Woody Woodpecker Back
  to School #6 . . . . 80.00
Woody Woodpecker County
  Fair #2 . . . . 75.00
Also See:

DELL GIANT COMICS
Bugs Bunny
Marge's Little Lulu
Tom and Jerry, and
Walt Disney Dell Giant Editions

DELL GIANT COMICS
Dell Publishing Co.
September 1959

21 M.G.M. Tom & Jerry Picnic Time	200.00
22 W.Disney's Huey, Dewey & Louie Back to School (Oct 1959)	135.00
23 Marge's Little Lulu & Tubby Halloween Fun	200.00
24 Woody Woodpeckers Family Fun	125.00
25 Tarzan's Jungle World	175.00
26 W.Disney's Christmas Parade,CB	375.00
27 W.Disney's Man in Space (1960)	200.00
28 Bugs Bunny's Winter Fun	175.00
29 Marge's Little Lulu & Tubby in Hawaii	200.00
30 W.Disney's DisneylandU.S.A.	175.00
31 Huckleberry Hound Summer Fun	225.00
32 Bugs Bunny Beach Party	100.00
33 W.Disney's Daisy Duck & Uncle Scrooge Picnic Time	175.00
34 Nancy&SluggoSummerCamp	120.00
35 W.Disney's Huey, Dewey & Louie Back to School	150.00
36 Marge's Little Lulu & Witch Hazel Halloween Fun	200.00
37 Tarzan, King of the Jungle	150.00
38 W.Disney's Uncle Donald and his Nephews Family Fun	125.00
39 W.Disney's Merry Christmas	125.00
40 Woody Woodpecker Christmas Parade	100.00
41 Yogi Bear's Winter Sports	225.00
42 Marge's Little Lulu & Tubby in Australia	100.00
43 Mighty Mouse in OuterSpace	400.00
44 Around the World with Huckleberry & His Friends	225.00
45 Nancy&SluggoSummerCamp	100.00
46 Bugs Bunny Beach Party	100.00
47 W.Disney's Mickey and Donald in Vacationland	175.00
48 The Flintstones #1 (Bedrock Bedlam)	275.00
49 W.Disney's Huey, Dewey & Louie Back to School	150.00
50 Marge's Little Lulu & Witch Hazel Trick 'N' Treat	225.00
51 Tarzan, King of the Jungle	150.00
52 W.Disney's Uncle Donald & his Nephews Dude Ranch	150.00
53 W.Disney's Donald Duck Merry Christmas	135.00
54 Woody Woodpecker Christmas Party	120.00
55 W.Disney's Daisy Duck & Uncle Scrooge Show Boat (1961)	075.00

DELL JUNIOR TREASURY
Dell Publishing Co.
June, 1955

1 Alice in Wonderland	100.00
2 Aladdin	65.00
3 Gulliver's Travels	50.00
4 Adventures of Mr. Frog	55.00

5 Wizard of Oz	60.00
6 Heidi	65.00
7 Santa & the Angel	65.00
8 Raggedy Ann	65.00
9 Clementina the Flying Pig	60.00
10 Adventures of Tom Sawyer	60.00

Dennis the Menace #93
© Fawcett Publications

DENNIS THE MENACE
Visual Editions/Literary Ent.
(Standard, Pines)
August, 1953

1	425.00
2	200.00
3	125.00
4	125.00
5 thru 10	@100.00
11 thru 20	@75.00
21 thru 31	@50.00

Hallden (Fawcett)

32 thru 40	@30.00
41 thru 50	@25.00
51 thru 60	@20.00
61 thru 70	@15.00
71 thru 90	@10.00
91 thru 140	@5.00
141 thru 166	@4.00

DESPERADO
Lev Gleason Publications
June, 1948

1 CBi(c)	75.00
2 CBi(c)	40.00
3 CBi(c)	30.00
4 CBi(c)	25.00
5 CBi(c)	25.00
6 CBi(c)	25.00
7 CBi(c)	25.00
8 CBi(c)	25.00

Becomes:

BLACK DIAMOND WESTERN

9 CBi(c)	125.00
10 CBi(c)	60.00

Black Diamond Western #37
© Fawcett Publications

11 CBi(c)	50.00
12 CBi(c)	50.00
13 CBi(c)	50.00
14 CBi(c)	50.00
15 CBi(c)	50.00
16 thru 28 BW,Big Bang Buster	@65.00
29 thru 40	@30.00
41 thru 52	@25.00
53 3-D	60.00
54 3-D	50.00
55 thru 60	@25.00

DETECTIVE EYE
Centaur Publications
November, 1940

1 B:Air Man, The Eye Sees, A:Masked Marvel	1,700.00
2 O:Don Rance, Mysticape, December, 1940	1,200.00

DETECTIVE PICTURE STORIES
Comics Magazine Co.
December, 1936

1 The Phantom Killer	3,500.00
2	1,500.00
3	1,000.00
4 WE, Muss Em Up	900.00
5 Trouble, April, 1937	1,100.00

DEXTER COMICS
Dearfield Publications
Summer, 1948–July 1949

1	40.00
2	30.00
3 thru 5	@20.00

DIARY CONFESSIONS
(see TENDER ROMANCE)

DIARY LOVES
Comic Magazines
(Quality Comics Group)
September, 1949

1 BWa	100.00

2 BWa	80.00
3	30.00
4 RC	45.00
5	25.00
6	25.00
7	25.00
8 BWa	75.00
9 BWa	60.00
10 BWa	75.00
11	25.00
12	25.00
13	25.00
14	25.00
15 BWa	50.00
16 BWa	50.00
17	25.00
18	25.00
19	25.00
20	25.00
21 BWa	40.00
22 thru 31	@15.00

Becomes:

G.I. SWEETHEARTS
32 Love Under Fire	25.00
33	25.00
34	25.00
35	25.00
36 Lend Lease Love Affair	25.00
37 thru 45	@25.00

Becomes:

GIRLS IN LOVE
46 Somewhere I'll Find You	30.00
47 thru 56	@20.00
57 MB,MB(c), Can Love Really Change Him, Dec., 1956	40.00

DIARY SECRETS
(see TEEN-AGE DIARY SECRETS)

DICK COLE
**Curtis Publ./
Star Publications**
December-January, 1949
1 LbC,LbC(c),CS,All sports(c)	175.00
2 LbC	90.00
3 LbC, LbC(c)	100.00
4 LbC, LbC(c),Rowing cover	100.00
5 LbC,LbC(c)	100.00
6 LbC,LbC(c), Rodeo cover	100.00
7 LbC,LbC(c)	100.00
8 LbC,LbC(c), Football cover	100.00
9 LbC,LbC(c), Basketball cover	100.00
10 Joe Louis	100.00

Becomes:

SPORTS THRILLS
11 Ted Williams & Ty Cobb	250.00
12 LbC, Joe Dimaggio & Phil Rizzuto, Boxing cover	175.00
13 LbC(c),Basketball cover	150.00
14 LbC(c),Baseball cover	150.00
15 LbC(c),Baseball cover, November, 1951	150.00

DICKIE DARE
Eastern Color Printing Co.
1941
1 BEv(c)	250.00
2	175.00
3	175.00
4 1942	200.00

Dick Tracy Monthly #39 © Dell Publ. Co.

DICK TRACY MONTHLY
Dell Publishing Co.
January, 1948
1 ChG,Dick Tracy & the Mad Doctor'	450.00
2 ChG,A:MarySteele,BorisArson	250.00
3 ChG,A:Spaldoni,Big Boy	250.00
4 ChG,A:Alderman Zeld	200.00
5 ChG,A:Spaldoni,Mrs.Spaldoni	200.00
6 ChG,A:Steve the Tramp	200.00
7 ChG,A:Boris Arson,Mary Steele	200.00
8 ChG,A:Boris & Zora Arson	200.00
9 ChG,A:Chief Yellowpony	200.00
10 ChG,A:Cutie Diamond	200.00
11 ChG,A:Toby Townly, Bookie Joe	150.00
12 ChG,A:Toby Townly, Bookie Joe	150.00
13 ChG,A:Toby Townly, Blake	160.00
14 ChG,A:Mayor Waite Wright	150.00
15 ChG,A:Bowman Basil	150.00
16 ChG,A:Maw,'Muscle' & 'Cut' Famon	150.00
17 ChG,A:Jim Trailer, Mary Steele	150.00
18 ChG,A:Lips Manlis, Anthel Jones	150.00
19 'Golden Heart Mystery'	200.00
20 'Black Cat Mystery'	200.00
21 'Tracy Meets Number One'	200.00
22 'Tracy and the Alibi Maker'	150.00
23 'Dick Tracy Meets Jukebox'	150.00
24 'Dick Tracy and Bubbles'	150.00

Becomes:

DICK TRACY COMICS MONTHLY
Harvey
25 ChG,A:Flattop	175.00
26 ChG,A:Vitamin Flintheart	150.00
27 ChG,'Flattop Escapes Prision'	150.00
28 ChG,'Case o/t Torture Chamber'	160.00
29 ChG,A:Brow,Gravel Gertie	150.00
30 ChG,'Blackmail Racket'	150.00
31 ChG,A:Snowflake Falls	125.00
32 ChG,A:Shaky,Snowflake Falls	125.00

33 ChG,'Strange Case of Measles'	150.00
34 ChG,A:Measles,Paprika	125.00
35 ChG,'Case of Stolen $50,000'	125.00
36 ChG,'Case of the Runaway Blonde'	150.00
37 ChG,'Case of Stolen Money'	125.00
38 ChG,A:Breathless Mahoney	125.00
39 ChG,A:Itchy,B.O.Pleanty	125.00
40 ChG,'Case of Atomic Killer'	125.00
41 ChG,Pt.1'Murder by Mail'	100.00
42 ChG,Pt.2'Murder by Mail'	100.00
43 ChG,'Case of the Underworld Brat'	100.00
44 ChG,'Case of the Mouthwash Murder'	100.00
45 ChG,'Case of the Evil Eyes'	100.00
46 ChG,'Case of the Camera Killers'	100.00
47 ChG,'Case of the Bloodthirsty Blonde'	100.00
48 ChG,'Case of the Murderous Minstrel'	100.00
49 ChG,Pt.1'Killer Who Returned From the Dead	100.00
50 ChG,Pt.2'Killer Who Returned From the Dead'	100.00
51 ChG,'Case of the High Tension Hijackers'	75.00
52 ChG,'Case of the Pipe-Stem Killer	75.00
53 ChG,Pt.1'Dick Tracy Meets the Murderous Midget'	75.00
54 ChG,Pt.2'Dick Tracy Meets the Murderous Midget'	75.00
55 ChG,Pt.3'Dick Tracy Meets the Murderous Midget'	75.00
56 ChG,'Case of the Teleguard Terror'	75.00
57 ChG,Pt.1'Case of the Ice Cold Killer'	100.00
58 ChG,Pt.2'Case of the Ice Cold Killer'	75.00
59 ChG,Pt.1'Case of the Million Dollar Murder'	75.00
60 ChG,Pt.2'Case of the Million Dollar Murder'	65.00
61 ChG,'Case of the Murderers Mask'	65.00
62 ChG,Pt.1'Case of the White Rat Robbers'	65.00
63 ChG,Pt.2'Case of the White Rat Robbers'	65.00
64 ChG,Pt.1'Case of the Interrupted Honeymoon'	65.00
65 ChG,Pt.2'Case of the Interrupted Honeymoon'	65.00
66 ChG,Pt.1'Case of the Killer's Revenge'	65.00
67 ChG,Pt.2'Case of the Killer's Revenge'	65.00
68 ChG,Pt.1'Case of the TV Terror'	65.00
69 ChG,Pt.2'Case of the TV Terror'	65.00
70 ChG,Pt.3'Case of the TV Terror'	65.00
71 ChG,A:Mrs. Forchune,Opal	65.00
72 ChG,A:Empty Wiliams,Bonny	65.00
73 ChG,A:Bonny Braids	65.00
74 ChG,A:Mr. & Mrs. Fortson Knox	65.00
75 ChG,A:Crewy Lou, Sphinx	65.00
76 ChG,A:Diet Smith,Brainerd	65.00
77 ChG,A:Crewy Lou,	

Bonny Braids 65.00
78 ChG,A:Spinner Records 65.00
79 ChG,A:Model Jones,
Larry Jones 65.00
80 ChG,A:Tonsils,Dot View . . . 65.00
81 ChG,A:Edward Moppet,Tonsils 65.00
82 ChG,A:Dot View,Mr. Crime . . 65.00
83 ChG,A:Rifle Ruby,Newsuit Nan 65.00
84 ChG,A:Mr. Crime,Newsuit Nan 65.00
85 ChG,A:Newsuit Nan, Mrs.Lava 65.00
86 ChG,A:Mr. Crime, Odds Zonn 65.00
87 ChG,A:Odds Zonn,Wingy . . . 65.00
88 ChG,A:Odds Zonn,Wingy . . . 65.00
89 ChG,Pt.1'Canhead' 65.00
90 ChG,Pt.2'Canhead' 65.00
91 ChG,Pt.3'Canhead' 65.00
92 ChG,Pt.4'Canhead' 65.00
93 ChG,Pt.5'Canhead' 65.00
94 ChG,Pt.6'Canhead' 65.00
95 ChG,A:Mrs. Green,Dewdrop . 65.00
96 ChG,A:Dewdrop,Sticks 65.00
97 ChG,A:Dewdrop,Sticks 65.00
98 ChG,A:Open-Mind Monty,
Sticks 65.00
99 ChG,A:Open-Mind Monty,
Sticks 70.00
100 ChG,A:Half-Pint,Dewdrop . . 75.00
101 ChG,A:Open-Mind Monty . . 65.00
102 ChG,A:Rainbow Reiley,Wingy 65.00
103 ChG,A:Happy,Rughead 65.00
104 ChG,A:Rainbow Reiley,Happy 65.00
105 ChG,A:Happy,Rughead 65.00
106 ChG,A:Fence,Corny,Happy . 65.00
107 ChG,A:Rainbow Reiley 65.00
108 ChG,A:Rughead,Corny,Fence 65.00
109 ChG,A:Rughead,Mimi,Herky 65.00
110 ChG,A:Vitamin Flintheart . . . 65.00
111 ChG,A:Shoulders,Roach . . . 65.00
112 ChG,A:Brilliant,Diet Smith . . 65.00
113 ChG,A:Snowflake Falls 65.00
114 ChG,A:'Sketch'Paree, ... 65.00
115 ChG,A:Rod & Nylon Hoze . . 65.00
116 ChG,A:Empty Williams 65.00
117 ChG,A:Spinner Records . . . 65.00
118 ChG,A:Sleet 65.00
119 ChG,A:Coffyhead 65.00
120 ChG,'Case Against
Mumbles Quartet' 60.00
121 ChG,'Case of the Wild Boys' 60.00
122 ChG,'Case of the
Poisoned Pellet' 60.00
123 ChG,'Case of the Deadly
Treasure Hunt' 60.00
124 ChG,'Case of Oodles
Hears Only Evil 60.00
125 ChG,'Case of the Desparate
Widow' 60.00
126 ChG,'Case of Oodles'
Hideout' 60.00
127 ChG,'Case Against
Joe Period' 60.00
128 ChG,'Case Against Juvenile
Delinquent' 60.00
129 ChG,'Case of Son of Flattop' 60.00
130 ChG,'Case of Great
Gang Roundup' 60.00
131 ChG,'Strange Case of
Flattop's Conscience' 65.00
132 ChG,'Case of Flattop's
Big Show' 65.00
133 ChG,'Dick Tracy Follows Trail
of Jewel Thief Gang' 60.00
134 ChG,'Last Stand of
Jewel Thieves' 60.00
135 ChG,'Case of the

Rooftop Sniper' 60.00
136 ChG,'Mystery of the
Iron Room' 60.00
137 ChG,'Law Versus Dick Tracy' 60.00
138 ChG,'Mystery of Mary X' . . . 60.00
139 ChG,'Yogee the Merciless' . 60.00
140 ChG,'The Tunnel Trap' 60.00
141 ChG,'Case of Wormy &
His Deadly Wagon 60.00
142 ChG,'Case of the
Killer's Revenge' 60.00
143 ChG,'Strange Case of
Measles' 60.00
144 ChG,'Strange Case of
Shoulders' 60.00
145 ChG,'Case of the Feindish
Photo-graphers';April, 1961 . . 60.00

DIME COMICS
Newsbook Publ. Corp.
1945
1 LbC,A:Silver Streak 350.00

DING DONG
Compix
(Magazine Enterprises)
1947
1 (fa) 90.00
2 (fa) 50.00
3 thru 5 (fa) . . . . @40.00

DINKY DUCK
St. John Publ. Co./Pines
November, 1951
1 . . . . 50.00
2 . . . . 30.00
3 thru 10 . . . . @20.00
11 thru 15 . . . . @15.00
16 thru 18 . . . . @10.00
19 Summer, 1958 . . . . 10.00

DIXIE DUGAN
Columbia Publ./
Publication Enterprises
July, 1942
1 Boxing cover,Joe Palooka . . 200.00
2 . . . . 125.00
3 . . . . 85.00
4 . . . . 60.00
5 . . . . 60.00
6 thru 12 . . . . @45.00
13 1949 . . . . 45.00

DIZZY DAMES
B&M Distribution Co.
(American Comics)
September-October, 1952
1 . . . . 60.00
2 . . . . 40.00
3 thru 6 July-Aug., 1953 . . . @25.00

DIZZY DON COMICS
Howard Publications/
Dizzy Dean Ent.
1943
1 B&W interior 45.00
2 B&W Interior 20.00
3 B&W Interior 15.00
4 B&W Interior 15.00
5 thru 21 . . . . @15.00
22 October, 1946 . . . . 40.00
1a thru 3a . . . . @30.00

DIZZY DUCK
(see BARNYARD COMICS)

DOC CARTER
V.D. COMICS
Health Publ. Inst.
1949
N# 150.00
N# 100.00

Doc Savage Comics #3
© Street & Smith Publications

DOC SAVAGE COMICS
Street & Smith Publications
May, 1940
1 B:Doc Savage, Capt. Fury, Danny
Garrett, Mark Mallory, Whisperer,
Capt. Death, Treasure
Island, A: The Magician . . 4,000.00
2 O:Ajax,The Sun Man,E:The
Whisperer 1,200.00
3 Artic Ice Wastes 900.00
4 E:Treasure Island, Saves
U.S. Navy 750.00
5 O:Astron, the Crocodile
Queen, Sacred Ruby 600.00
6 E: Capt. Fury, O:Red Falcon,
Murderous Peace Clan . . . 500.00
7 V:Zoombas 500.00
8 Finds the Long Lost Treasure 500.00
9 Smashes Japan's Secret Oil
Supply 500.00
10 O:Thunder Bolt, The Living
Dead A:Lord Manhattan . . . 500.00
11 V:Giants of Destruction 400.00
12 Saves Merchant Fleet from
Complete Destruction 400.00
2-1 The Living Evil 400.00
2-2 V:Beggar King 400.00
2-3 . . . . 400.00
2-4 Fight to Death 400.00
2-5 Saves Panama Canal from
Blood Raider 400.00
2-6 . . . . 400.00
2-7 V:Black Knight 400.00
2-8 October, 1943 . . . . 400.00

All comics prices listed are for *Near Mint* condition.

DR. ANTHONY KING HOLLYWOOD LOVE DOCTOR
Harvey, Publ.
1952

1	75.00
2	40.00
3	40.00
4 BP,May, 1954	40.00

DOLL MAN
Comic Favorites
(Quality Comics Group)
Fall, 1941

1 RC,B:Doll Man & Justine Wright	2,500.00
2 B:Dragon	1,000.00
3 Five stories	700.00
4 Dolls of Death, Wanted: The Doll Man	600.00
5 RC,Four stories	550.00
6 Buy War Stamps cover	450.00
7 Four stories	450.00
8 BWa,Three stories,A:Torchy	750.00
9	400.00
10 RC,V:Murder Marionettes, Grim, The Good Sport	300.00
11 Shocks Crime Square in the Eye	300.00
12	300.00
13 RC,Blows Crime Sky High	300.00
14 Spotlight on Comics	300.00
15 Faces Danger	300.00
16	300.00
17 Deals out Punishment for Crime	300.00
18 Redskins Scalp Crime	300.00
19 Fitted for a Cement Coffin	300.00
20 Destroys the Black Heart of Nemo Black	300.00
21 Problem of a Poison Pistol	225.00
22 V:Tom Thumb	225.00
23 V:Minstrel, musician of menace	225.00
24 V:Elixir of Youth	225.00
25 V:Thrawn, Lord of Lightning	225.00
26 V:Sultan of Satarr & Wonderous Runt	225.00
27 Space Conquest	225.00
28 V:The Flame	225.00
29 V:Queen MAB	225.00
30 V:Lord Damion	225.00
31 I:Elmo, the Wonder Dog	200.00
32 A:Jeb Rivers	200.00
33	200.00
34	200.00
35 Prophet of Doom	200.00
36 Death Trap in the Deep	200.00
37 V:The Skull,B:Doll Girl, Bondage(c)	275.00
38 The Cult of Death	200.00
39 V:The Death Drug	225.00
40 Giants of Crime	175.00
41 The Headless Horseman	175.00
42 Tale of the Mind Monster	175.00
43 The Thing that Kills	175.00
44 V:Radioactive Man	175.00
45 What was in the Doom Box?	175.00
46 Monster from Tomorrow	175.00
47 V:Mad Hypnotist, October, 1953	175.00

FAMOUS GANG, BOOK OF COMICS
Firestone Tire & Rubber Co.
1942

N#	750.00

Becomes:
DONALD AND MICKEY MERRY CHRISTMAS

N# (2),CB, 1943	700.00
N# (3),CB, 1944	700.00
N# (4),CB, 1945	950.00
N# (5),CB, 1946	750.00
N# (6),CB, 1947	650.00
N# (7),CB, 1948	650.00
N# (8),CB, 1949	675.00

DONALD DUCK
Whitman

W.Disney's Donald Duck ('35)	2,200.00
W.Disney's Donald Duck ('36)	2,000.00
W.Disney's Donald Duck ('38)	2,200.00

DONALD DUCK GIVEAWAYS

Donald Duck Surprise Party (Icy Frost Ice Cream 1948)WK	900.00
Donald Duck (Xmas Giveaway 1944)	350.00
Donald Duck Tells About Kites (P.G.&E., Florida 1954)	2,000.00
Donald Duck Tells About Kites (S.C.Edison 1954)	1,800.00
Donald Duck and the Boys (Whitman 1948)	125.00
Donald Ducks Atom Bomb (Cherrios 1947)	275.00

Donald Duck #48
© Dell Publishing Co.

(WALT DISNEY'S) DONALD DUCK
Dell Publishing Co.
November 1952
(#1-#25) See Dell Four Color

26 CB;"Trick or Treat" (1952)	350.00
27 CB(c);"Flying Horse"('53)	150.00
28 CB(c); Robert the Robot	125.00
29 CB(c)	125.00
30 CB(c)	125.00
31 thru 39	@65.00
40 thru 44	@60.00
45 CB	160.00
46 CB; "Secret of Hondorica"	250.00
47 thru 51	@60.00
52 CB; "Lost Peg-Leg Mine"	150.00
53	40.00
54 CB; "Forbidden Valley"	150.00
55 thru 59	@40.00
60 CB; "Donald Duck & the Titanic Ants"	150.00
61 thru 67	@40.00
68 CB	125.00
69 thru 78	@35.00
79 CB (1 page)	45.00
80	30.00
81 CB (1 page)	35.00
82	30.00
83	30.00
84	30.00

See: Independent Color Listings

DON FORTUNE MAGAZINE
Don Fortune Publ. Co.
August, 1946

1 CCB	150.00
2 CCB	100.00
3 CCB,Bondage(c)	75.00
4 CCB	75.00
5 CCB	75.00
6 CCB, January, 1947	75.00

DON NEWCOMBE
Fawcett Publications
1950

1 Baseball Star	300.00

DON WINSLOW OF THE NAVY
Fawcett Publ./ Charlton Comics
February, 1943

1 Captain Marvel cover	800.00
2 Nips the Nipponese in the Solomons	400.00
3 Single-Handed invasion of the Philippines	300.00
4 Undermines the Nazis!	250.00
5 Stolen Battleship Mystery	250.00
6 War Stamps for Victory cover	250.00
7 Coast Guard	150.00
8 U.S. Marines	150.00
9 Fighting Marines	150.00
10 Fighting Seabees	150.00
11	125.00
12 Tuned for Death	125.00
13 Hirohito's Hospitality	135.00
14 Catapults against the Axis	135.00
15 Fighting Merchant Marine	120.00
16 V:The Most Diabolical Villain of all Time	120.00
17 Buy War Stamps cover	120.00
18 The First Underwater Convoy	100.00
19 Bonape Excersion	100.00
20 The Nazi Prison Ship	100.00
21 Prisoner of the Nazis	90.00
22 Suicide Football	90.00
23 Peril on the High Seas	90.00
24 Adventures on the High Seas	90.00
25 Shanghaied Red Cross Ship	90.00

GOLDEN AGE

Don Winslow of the Navy #8
© Fawcett Publications

26 V:The Scorpion 90.00
27 Buy War Stamps 90.00
28 . . . . 90.00
29 Invitation to Trouble 90.00
30 . . . . 90.00
31 Man or Myth? 75.00
32 Return of the Renegade 75.00
33 Service Ribbons 75.00
34 Log Book 75.00
35 . . . . 75.00
36 . . . . 75.00
37 V: Sea Serpent 75.00
38 Climbs Mt. Everest 75.00
39 Scorpion's Death Ledger . . . 75.00
40 Kick Off! 75.00
41 Rides the Skis! 70.00
42 Amazon Island 70.00
43 Ghastly Doll Murder Case . . 70.00
44 The Scorpions Web 70.00
45 V:Highwaymen of the Seas . . 70.00
46 Renegades Jailbreak 70.00
47 The Artic Expedition 70.00
48 Maelstrom of the Deep 70.00
49 The Vanishing Ship! 70.00
50 V:The Snake 70.00
51 A:Singapore Sal 60.00
52 Ghost of the Fishing Ships . . 60.00
53 . . . . 60.00
54 . . . . 60.00
55 . . . . 60.00
56 Far East 60.00
57 A:Singapore Sal 60.00
58 . . . . 60.00
59 . . . . 60.00
60 . . . . 60.00
61 . . . . 60.00
62 . . . . 60.00
63 . . . . 60.00
64 MB 70.00
65 Ph(c) 75.00
66 Ph(c) 75.00
67 Ph(c) 75.00
68 Ph(c) 75.00
69 Ph(c), Jaws of Destruction . . 75.00
70 . . . . 50.00
71 . . . . 50.00
72 . . . . 50.00
73 September, 1955 . . . . 50.00

DOPEY DUCK
Non-Pareil Publ. Corp.
Fall, 1945
1 A:Krazy Krow,Casper Cat . . 125.00
2 same 100.00
Becomes:
WACKY DUCK
3 . . . . 65.00
4 . . . . 50.00
5 . . . . 50.00
6 Summer, 1947 . . . . 50.00

DOROTHY LAMOUR
(see JUNGLE LIL)

DOTTY DRIPPLE
Magazine Enterprises/
Harvey Publications
1946
1 . . . . 60.00
2 . . . . 30.00
3 thru 10 . . . . @15.00
11 thru 20 . . . . @10.00
21 thru 23 . . . . @8.00
24 June, 1952 . . . . 8.00
Becomes:
HORACE &
DOTTY DRIPPLE
25 thru 42 . . . . @6.00
43 October, 1955 . . . . 6.00

DOUBLE COMICS
Elliot Publications
1 ('40),Masked Marvel 1,600.00
2 ('41),Tornado Tim 1,200.00
3 ('42) 1,000.00
4 ('43) 750.00
5 ('44) 750.00

DOUBLE UP
Elliot Publications
1941
1 . . . . 600.00

DOWN WITH CRIME
Fawcett Publications
November, 1951
1 A:Desarro 200.00
2 BP, A:Scanlon Gang 125.00
3 H-is for Heroin 100.00
4 BP, A:Desarro 75.00
5 No Jail Can Hold Me 100.00
6 The Puncture-Proof Assassin . 75.00
7 The Payoff, November, 1952 . 75.00

DUDLEY
Prize Publications
November-December, 1952
1 . . . . 100.00
2 . . . . 75.00
3 March-April, 1950 . . . . 65.00

DUMBO WEEKLY
The Walt Disney Co.
1942
1 Gas giveaways 400.00
2 . . . . 125.00
3 . . . . 125.00
4 . . . . 125.00
5 thru 16 . . . . @125.00

DURANGO KID
Magazine Enterprises
October-November, 1949
1 FF, Charles Starrett photo cover
  B:Durango Kid & Raider . . 550.00
2 FF, Charles Starrett Ph(c) . . 300.00
3 FF, Charles Starrett Ph(c) . . 275.00
4 FF, Charles Starrett Ph(c),
  Two-Timing Guns 250.00
5 FF, Charles Starrett Ph(c),
  Tracks Across the Trail . . . 250.00
6 FF 150.00
7 FF,Atomic(c) 165.00
8 FF thru 10 . . . . @150.00
11 FF 125.00
12 FF 125.00
13 FF 125.00
14 thru 16 FF . . . . @125.00
17 O:Durango Kid 150.00
18 FMe,DAy(c) 75.00
19 FMe,FG 60.00
20 FMe,FG 60.00
21 FMe,FG 60.00
22 FMe,FG 65.00
23 FMe,FG,I:Red Scorpion 65.00
24 thru 30 FMe,FG . . . . @65.00
31 FMe,FG 65.00
32 thru 40 FG . . . . @60.00
41 FG,October, 1941 . . . . 70.00

DYNAMIC COMICS
Dynamic Publications
(Harry 'A' Chesler)
October, 1941
1 EK,O:Major Victory, Dynamic Man,
  Hale the Magician, A:Black
  Cobra 1,300.00
2 O:Dynamic Boy & Lady
  Satan,I:Green Knight,
  Lance Cooper 600.00
3 GT 500.00
8 Horror cover 500.00
9 MRa,GT,B:Mr.E 500.00
10 . . . . 400.00
11 GT 325.00
12 GT 300.00
13 GT 325.00
14 . . . . 300.00
15 . . . . 300.00
16 GT,Bondage(c),Marijuana . . 325.00
17 . . . . 425.00
18 Ric 250.00
19 A:Dynamic Man 235.00
20 same,Nude Woman 350.00
21 same 225.00
22 same 225.00
23 A:Yankee Girl,1.0948 . . . . 225.00

DYNAMITE
Comic Media/Allen Hardy Publ.
May, 1953
1 DH(c),A:Danger#6 . . . . 120.00
2 . . . . 75.00
3 PAM,PAM(c),B:Johnny
  Dynamite,Drug 75.00
4 PAM,PAM(c),Prostitution . . . 100.00
5 PAM,PAM(c) 75.00
6 PAM,PAM(c) 75.00
7 PAM,PAM(c) 75.00
8 PAM,PAM(c) 75.00
9 PAM,PAM(c) 75.00
Becomes:

JOHNNY DYNAMITE
Charlton Comics
10 PAM(c) 50.00
11 . . . . 35.00
12 . . . . 40.00
Becomes:
FOREIGN INTRIGUES
13 A:Johnny Dynamite 35.00
14 same 30.00
15 same 30.00
Becomes:
BATTLEFIELD ACTION
16 . . . . 25.00
17 . . . . 15.00
18 . . . . 15.00
19 . . . . 15.00
20 . . . . 15.00
21 thru 30 . . . . @10.00
31 thru 70 . . . . @5.00
71 thru 84 October 1984 . . . . . @2.00

EAGLE, THE
Fox Features Syndicate
July, 1941
1 B:The Eagle,A:Rex Dexter
of Mars 1,500.00
2 B:Spider Queen 700.00
3 B:Joe Spook 550.00
4 January, 1942 . . . . 500.00

EAGLE
Rural Home Publ.
February-March, 1945
1 LbC 250.00
2 LbC,April-May, 1945 . . . . . 150.00

EAT RIGHT
TO WORK AND WIN
Swift Co.
1942
N# Flash Gordon,Popeye . . . 250.00

EDDIE STANKY
Fawcett Publications
1951
N# New York Giants 250.00

EERIE
Avon Periodicals
May-June, 1951–Aug.-Sept. 1954
1 JKa,Horror from the Pit,
Bondage(c) 2,200.00
2 WW,WW(c), Chamber
of Death 450.00
3 WW,WW(c),JKa,JO
Monster of the Storm 500.00
4 WW(c),Phantom of Reality . 400.00
5 WW(c), Operation Horror . . 350.00
6 Devil Keeps a Date 200.00
7 WW(c),JKa,JO,Blood for
the Vampire 300.00
8 EK, Song of the Undead . . 200.00
9 JKa, Hands of Death 200.00
10 Castle of Terror 200.00
11 Anatomical Monster 175.00
12 Dracula 225.00
13 . . . . 200.00
14 Master of the Dead 200.00
15 . . . . 125.00
16 WW, Chamber of Death . . . 150.00
17 WW(c),JO,JKa, ... 200.00

Eerie #16 © Avon Periodicals

EERIE ADVENTURES
Approved Comics
(Ziff-Davis)
Winter, 1951
1 BP,JKa,Bondage 250.00

EGBERT
Arnold Publications/
Comic Magazine
Spring, 1946
1 I:Egbert & The Count 150.00
2 . . . . 75.00
3 . . . . 40.00
4 . . . . 40.00
5 . . . . 40.00
6 . . . . 50.00
7 . . . . 40.00
8 . . . . 40.00
9 . . . . 40.00
10 . . . . 40.00
11 thru 17 . . . . @25.00
18 1950 . . . . 25.00

EH!
Charlton Comics
December, 1953
1 DAy(c),DG 200.00
2 DAy(c) 150.00
3 DAy(c) 125.00
4 DAy(c) 125.00
5 DAy(c) 125.00
6 DAy(c) 125.00
7 DAy(c),November, 1954 . . . 125.00

EL BOMBO COMICS
Frances M. McQueeny
1945
1 . . . . 50.00

ELLERY QUEEN
Superior Comics
May–Nov., 1949
1 LbC(c),JKa,Horror 400.00
2 . . . . 300.00
3 Drug issue 275.00
4 The Crooked Mile 250.00

ELLERY QUEEN
Approved Comics
(Ziff-Davis)
January-March, 1952
1 NS(c),The Corpse the Killed 350.00
2 NS,Killer's Revenge,
Summer, 1952 . . . . 275.00

ELSIE THE COW
D.S. Publishing Co.
October-November, 1949
1 P(c) 175.00
2 Bondage(c) 200.00
3 July-August, 1950 . . . . 175.00

ENCHANTING LOVE
Kirby Publishing Co.
October, 1949
1 Branded Guilty, Ph(c) 100.00
2 Ph(c),BP 50.00
3 Ph(c),Utter Defeat was our
Victory; Jan.-Feb., 1950 . . . . 40.00

ETTA KETT
Best Books, Inc.
(Standard Comics)
December, 1948
11 . . . . 75.00
12 . . . . 40.00
13 . . . . 40.00
14 September, 1949 . . . . 40.00

ERNIE COMICS
(see SCREAM COMICS)

EXCITING COMICS
Better Publ./Visual Editions
(Standard Comics)
April, 1940
1 O:Mask, Jim Hatfield,
Dan Williams 3,000.00
2 B:Sphinx 1,200.00
3 V;Robot 800.00
4 V:Sea Monster 550.00
5 V:Gargoyle 550.00
6 . . . . 650.00
7 AS(c) 450.00
8 . . . . 450.00
9 O:Black Terror & Tim,
Bondage(c) 6,200.00
10 A:Black Terror 2,000.00
11 same 1,000.00
12 Bondage(c) 650.00
13 Bondage(c) 650.00
14 O:Sphinx 450.00
15 O:Liberator 475.00
16 Black Terror 400.00
17 same 400.00
18 same 400.00
19 same 400.00
20 E:Mask,Bondage(c) 375.00
21 A:Liberator 350.00
22 O:The Eaglet,B:American
Eagle 400.00
23 Black Terror 300.00
24 Black Terror 300.00
25 Bondage(c) 325.00
26 ASh(c) 300.00
27 ASh(c) 300.00
28 ASh(c) 350.00
29 ASh(c) 350.00
30 ASh(c),Bondage(c) 375.00

GOLDEN AGE

GOLDEN AGE

Exciting Comics #3
© Better Publ./Visual Editions

31 ASh(c) 350.00
32 ASh(c) 350.00
33 ASh(c) 350.00
34 ASh(c) 350.00
35 ASh(c),E:Liberator 350.00
36 ASh(c) 350.00
37 ASh(c) 350.00
38 ASh(c) 350.00
39 ASh(c)O:Kara, Jungle
   Princess 450.00
40 ASh(c) 400.00
41 ASh(c) 400.00
42 ASh(c),B:Scarab 450.00
43 ASh(c) 400.00
44 ASh(c) 400.00
45 ASh(c),V:Robot 400.00
46 ASh(c) 400.00
47 ASh(c) 400.00
48 ASh(c) 400.00
49 ASh(c),E:Kara &
   American Eagle 400.00
50 ASh(c),E:American Eagle . 400.00
51 ASh(c),B:Miss Masque . . . 450.00
52 ASh(c),Miss Masque 375.00
53 ASh(c),Miss Masque 375.00
54 ASh(c),E:Miss Masque 375.00
55 ASh(c),O&B:Judy o/t Jungle 400.00
56 ASh(c) 375.00
57 ASh(c) 375.00
58 ASh(c) 375.00
59 ASh(c),FF,Bondage(c) 400.00
60 ASh(c),The Mystery Rider . 350.00
61 ASh(c) 325.00
62 ASh(c) 325.00
63 thru 65 ASh(c) . . . . @350.00
66 . . . . 325.00
67 GT 325.00
68 . . . . 325.00
69 September, 1949 . . . . 325.00

EXCITING ROMANCES
Fawcett Publications
1949
1 Ph(c) 75.00
2 thru 3 . . . . @40.00
4 Ph(c) 45.00
5 thru 14 . . . . @30.00

EXOTIC ROMANCE
(see TRUE WAR ROMANCES)

EXPLORER JOE
Approved Comics
(Ziff-Davis)
Winter, 1951
1 NS,The Fire Opal
   of Madagscar 75.00
2 BK, October-November, 1952 85.00

EXPOSED
D.S. Publishing Co.
March-April, 1948
1 Corpses Cash and Carry . . 150.00
2 Giggling Killer 175.00
3 One Bloody Night 75.00
4 JO,Deadly Dummy 75.00
5 Body on the Beach 75.00
6 Grl,The Secret in the Snow 250.00
7 The Gypsy Baron,
   July-August, 1949 . . . . 275.00

EXTRA
Magazine Enterprises
1947
1 . . . . 400.00

EXTRA!
E.C. Comics
March-April, 1955
1 JCr,RC,JSe 150.00
2 JCr,RC,JSe 100.00
3 JCr,RC,JSe 100.00
4 JCr,RC,JSe 100.00
5 November-December, 1955 100.00

FACE, THE
Publication Enterprises
(Columbia Comics)
1942
1 MBi(c),The Face 650.00
2 MBi(c) 400.00
Becomes:

TONY TRENT
3 MBi,A:The Face 75.00
4 1949 . . . . 55.00

FAIRY TALE PARADE
Dell Publishing Co.
1942
1 WK,Giant 1,400.00
2 WK,Flying Horse 600.00
3 WK 425.00
4 WK 400.00
5 WK 400.00
6 WK 300.00
7 WK 300.00
8 WK 300.00
9 WK 300.00

FAMOUS COMICS
Zain-Eppy Publ.
N# Joe Palooka 350.00

FAMOUS CRIMES
Fox Features Syndicate
June, 1948
1 Cold Blooded Killer 350.00
2 Near Nudity cover 250.00

3 Crime Never Pays 300.00
4 . . . . 125.00
5 . . . . 125.00
6 . . . . 125.00
7 Drug issue 250.00
8 thru 19 . . . . @100.00
20 August, 1951 . . . . 100.00
51 1952 . . . . 50.00

FAMOUS FAIRY TALES
K.K. Publication Co.
1942
N# WK, Giveaway 325.00
N# WK, Giveaway 250.00
N# WK, Giveaway 250.00

FAMOUS FEATURE STORIES
Dell Publishing Co.
1938
1 A:Tarzan, Terry and the Pirates
   Dick Tracy,Smilin' Jack 550.00

FAMOUS FUNNIES
Eastern Color Printing Co.
1933
N# A Carnival of Comics . . . 8,000.00
N# February, 1934,
   1st 10¢ comic 22,000.00
1 July, 1934 . . . . 15,000.00
2 . . . . 3,000.00
3 B:Buck Rogers 3,800.00
4 Football cover 1,200.00
5 . . . . 1,000.00
6 . . . . 700.00
7 . . . . 700.00
8 . . . . 700.00
9 . . . . 700.00
10 . . . . 700.00
11 Four pages of Buck Rogers 650.00
12 Four pages of Buck Rogers 650.00
13 . . . . 550.00
14 . . . . 475.00
15 Football cover 475.00
16 . . . . 475.00
17 Christmas cover 475.00
18 Four pages of Buck Rogers 650.00

Famous Funnies #22
© Eastern Color Printing Co.

19	475.00	166	40.00	Smith & Capt. Kid	3,800.00
20	475.00	167	40.00	2 BP,LFc(c),Samson destroyed the	
21 Baseball	375.00	168	40.00	Battery and Routed the Foe	1,600.00
22 Buck Rogers	400.00	169 AW	75.00	3 BP,LF(c),Slays the Iron	
23	350.00	170 AW	75.00	Monster	4,000.00
24 B: War on Crime	350.00	171 thru 190	@40.00	4 GT,LFc(c),Demolishes the	
25	350.00	191 thru 203	@35.00	Closing Torture Walls	1,300.00
26	350.00	204 War cover	32.00	5 GT,LFc(c),Crumbles the	
27 G-Men cover	350.00	205 thru 208	@30.00	Mighty War Machine	1,300.00
28	350.00	209 FF(c),Buck Rogers	650.00	6 JSm(c),Bondage(c)	1,000.00
29	350.00	210 FF(c),Buck Rogers	650.00	7 JSm(c)	1,000.00
30	350.00	211 FF(c),Buck Rogers	650.00	8 GT,Destroys the Mask of	
31	300.00	212 FF(c),Buck Rogers	650.00	Fire,Bondage(c)	700.00
32	300.00	213 FF(c),Buck Rogers	650.00	9 Mighty Muscles saved the	
33 A:Baby Face Nelson &		214 FF(c),Buck Rogers	650.00	Drowning Girl	700.00
John Dillinger	300.00	215 FF(c),Buck Rogers	650.00	10 I&O:David	700.00
34	300.00	216 FF(c),Buck Rogers	650.00	11 Wrecks the Torture Machine	
35 Buck Rogers	325.00	217	40.00	to save his fellow American .	600.00
36	275.00	218 July, 1955	40.00	12 Heaved the Huge Ship high	
37	275.00			into the Air	600.00
38 Portrait,Buck Rogers	300.00			13	600.00
39	275.00			14	600.00
40	275.00			15	600.00

41 thru 50	@200.00
51 thru 57	@175.00
58 Baseball cover	175.00
59	175.00
60	175.00
61	150.00
62	150.00
63	150.00
64	150.00
65 JK	150.00
66	150.00
67	150.00
68 JK	150.00
69	150.00
70	150.00
71 BEv	125.00
72 BEv,B:Speed Spaulding	125.00
73 BEv	125.00
74 BEv	125.00
75 BEv	125.00
76 BEv	125.00
77 BEv,Merry Christmas cover	125.00
78 BEv	125.00
79 BEv	125.00
80 BEv,Buck Rogers	125.00
81 O:Invisible Scarlet O'Neil	100.00
82 Buck Rogers cover	125.00
83 Dickie Dare	100.00
84 Scotty Smith	100.00
85 Eagle Scout,Roy Rogers	100.00
86 Moon Monsters	100.00
87 Scarlet O'Neil	100.00
88	100.00
89 O:Fearless Flint	100.00
90 Bondage cover	110.00
91	75.00
92	75.00
93	75.00
94 War Bonds	85.00
95 Invisible Scarlet O'Neil	75.00
96	75.00
97 War Bonds Promo	75.00
98	75.00
99	75.00
100 Anniversary issue	75.00
101 thru 110	@75.00
111 thru 130	@60.00
131 thru 150	@50.00
151 thru 162	@50.00
163 Valentine's Day cover	45.00
164	40.00
165	40.00

FAMOUS GANG, BOOK OF COMICS
(see DONALD AND MICKEY MERRY CHRISTMAS)

FAMOUS GANGSTERS
Avon Periodicals
April, 1951

1 Al Capone, Dillinger, Luciano & Shultz	250.00
2 WW(c),Dillinger Machine-Gun Killer	250.00
3 Lucky Luciano & Murder Inc.	250.00

Becomes:

CRIME ON THE WATERFRONT

4 Underworld Gangsters who Control the Shipment of Drugs!, May, 1952	225.00

FAMOUS STARS
Ziff-Davis Publ. Co.
August, 1950

1 OW,Shelley Winter,Susan Peters & Shirley Temple	225.00
2 BEv,Betty Hutton, Bing Crosby	150.00
3 OW,Judy Garland, Alan Ladd	165.00
4 RC,Jolson, Bob Mitchum	125.00
5 BK,Elizabeth Taylor, Esther Williams	150.00
6 Gene Kelly, Spring, 1952	125.00

FAMOUS STORIES
Dell Publishing Co.
1942

1 Treasure Island	200.00
2 Tom Sawyer	200.00

FAMOUS WESTERN BADMEN
(see REDSKIN)

FANTASTIC
(see CAPTAIN SCIENCE)

FANTASTIC COMICS
Fox Features Syndicate
December, 1939

1 LFc(c),I&O:Samson,B:Star Dust, Super Wizard, Space

Fantastic #16 © Fox Features Syndicate

16 E:Stardust	600.00
17	600.00
18 I:Black Fury & Chuck	650.00
19	600.00
20	600.00
21 B&I: The Banshee,Hitler(c)	625.00
22	500.00
23 O:The Gladiator, Nov., 1941	625.00

FARGO KID
(see JUSTICE TRAPS OF THE GUILTY)

FAST FICTION
Seaboard Publ./ Famous Author Illustrated
October, 1949

1 Scarlet Pimpernel	275.00
2 HcK,Captain Blood	250.00
3 She	350.00
4 The 39 Steps	200.00
5 HcK,Beau Geste	200.00

Becomes:

STORIES BY FAMOUS

GOLDEN AGE

AUTHORS ILLUSTRATED

1a Scarlet Pimpernel		250.00
2a Captain Blood		250.00
3a She		300.00
4a The 39 Steps		200.00
5a Beau Geste		175.00
6 HcK,MacBeth		200.00
7 HcK,Window		165.00
8 HcK,Hamlet		175.00
9 Nicholas Nickleby		150.00
10 HcK,Romeo & Juliet		150.00
11 GS,Ben Hur		165.00
12 GS,La Svengali		165.00
13 HcK,Scaramouche		165.00

FAWCETT FUNNY ANIMALS
Fawcett Publications
December, 1942

1 I:Hoppy the Marvel, Captain Marvel cover	450.00
2 X-Mas Issue	225.00
3 Spirit of '43	150.00
4 and 5	@150.00
6 Buy War Bonds and Stamps	100.00
7	100.00
8 Flag cover	100.00
9 and 10	@100.00
11 thru 20	@75.00
21 thru 30	@50.00
31 thru 40	@35.00
41 thru 83	@25.00

Charlton Comics

84	25.00
85 thru 91 Feb. 1956	@20.00

FAWCETT MOVIE COMICS
Fawcett Publications
1949

N# Dakota Lil	250.00
N#a Copper Canyon	200.00
N# Destination the Moon	600.00
N# Montana	175.00
N# Pioneer Marshal	175.00
N# Powder River Rustlers	200.00
N# Singing Guns	160.00
7 Gunmen of Abilene	175.00
8 King of the Bull Whip	275.00
9 BP,The Old Frontier	160.00
10 The Missourians	160.00
11 The Thundering Trail	225.00
12 Rustlers on Horseback	165.00
13 Warpath	125.00
14 Last Outpost,RonaldReagan	300.00
15 The Man from Planet-X	1,700.00
16 10 Tall Men	100.00
17 Rose Cimarron	55.00
18 The Brigand	65.00
19 Carbine Williams	75.00
20 Ivan hoe, December, 1952	150.00

FEATURE BOOKS
David McKay Publications
May, 1937

N# Dick Tracy	7,000.00
N# Popeye	7,000.00
1 Zane Grey's King of the Royal Mounted	650.00
2 Popeye	650.00
3 Popeye and the "Jeep"	600.00
4 Dick Tracy	1,000.00
5 Popeye and his Poppa	600.00

6 Dick Tracy	800.00
7 Little Orphan Annie	900.00
8 Secret Agent X-9	500.00
9 Tracy & the Famon Boys	800.00
10 Popeye & Susan	600.00
11 Annie Rooney	250.00
12 Blondie	600.00
13 Inspector Wade	200.00
14 Popeye in Wild Oats	700.00
15 Barney Baxter in the Air	250.00
16 Red Eagle	275.00
17 Gang Busters	500.00
18 Mandrake the Magician	400.00
19 Mandrake	400.00
20 The Phantom	750.00
21 Lone Ranger	600.00
22 The Phantom	600.00
23 Mandrake in Teibe Castle	400.00
24 Lone Ranger	600.00
25 Flash Gordon on the Planet Mongo	750.00
26 Prince Valiant	750.00
27 Blondie	125.00
28 Blondie and Dagwood	100.00
29 Blondie at the Home Sweet Home	100.00
30 Katzenjammer Kids	125.00
31 Blondie Keeps the Home Fires Burning	100.00
32 Katzenjammer Kids	100.00
33 Romance of Flying	85.00
34 Blondie Home is Our Castle	90.00
35 Katzenjammer Kids	100.00
36 Blondie on the Home Front	100.00
37 Katzenjammer Kids	100.00
38 Blondie the ModelHomemaker	80.00
39 The Phantom	400.00
40 Blondie	80.00
41 Katzenjammer Kids	90.00
42 Blondie in Home-Spun Yarns	80.00
43 Blondie Home-Cooked Scraps	80.00
44 Katzenjammer Kids in Monkey Business	80.00
45 Blondie in Home of the Free and the Brave	75.00
46 Mandrake in Fire World	275.00
47 Blondie is Eaten out of House and Home	80.00
48 The Maltese Falcon	450.00
49 Perry Mason - The Case of the Lucky Legs	175.00
50 The Shoplifters Shoe, P. Mason	175.00
51 Rip Kirby - Mystery of the Mangler	250.00
52 Mandrake in the Land of X	275.00
53 Phantom in Safari Suspense	350.00
54 Rip Kirby - Case of the Master Menace	250.00
55 Mandrake in 5-numbers Treasue Hunt	275.00
56 Phantom Destroys the Sky Band	300.00
57 Phantom in the Blue Gang, 1948	300.00

FEATURE FUNNIES
Harry A. Chesler Publ./ Comic Favorites
October, 1937–May 1950

1 RuG,RuG(c),A:Joe Palooka, Mickey Finn, Bungles, Dixie Dugan, Big Top, Strange as It Seems, Off the Record	2,200.00
2 A: The Hawk	1,000.00

Feature Funnies #7
© Harry A. Chesler Publ.

3 WE,Joe Palooka,The Clock	750.00
4 RuG,WE,RuG(c),Joe Palooka	550.00
5 WE, Joe Palooka drawing	550.00
6 WE, Joe Palooka cover	550.00
7 WE,LLe, Gallant Knight story by Vernon Henkel	450.00
8 WE	375.00
9 WE, Joe Palooka story	400.00
10 WE,Micky Finn(c)	375.00
11 WE,LLe,The Bungles(c)	375.00
12 WE, Joe Palooka(c)	400.00
13 WE,LLe, World Series(c)	450.00
14 WE,Ned Brant(c)	325.00
15 WE,Joe Palooka(c)	350.00
16 Mickey Finn(c)	325.00
17 WE	325.00
18 Joe Palooka cover	350.00
19 WE,LLe,Mickey Finn(c)	325.00
20 WE,LLe	325.00

Becomes:
FEATURE COMICS

21 Joe Palooka(c)	450.00
22 LLe(c),Mickey Finn(c)	350.00
23 B:Charlie Chan	375.00
24 AAr,Joe Palooka(c)	325.00
25 AAr,The Clock(c)	325.00
26 AAr,The Bundles(c)	325.00
27 WE,AAr,I:Doll Man	3,000.00
28 LF,AAr,The Clock(c)	1,200.00
29 LF,AAr,The Clock(c)	700.00
30 LF,AAr,Doll Man(c)	700.00
31 LF,AAr,Mickey Finn(c)	600.00
32 PGv,LF,GFx,Doll Man(c)	425.00
33 PGv,LF,GFx,Bundles(c)	400.00
34 PGv,LF,GFx,Doll Man(c)	425.00
35 PGv,LF,GFx,Bundles(c)	400.00
36 PGv,LF,GFx,Doll Man(c)	425.00
37 PGv,LF,GFx,Bundles(c)	400.00
38 PGv,GFx,Doll Man(c)	325.00
39 PGv,GFx,Bundles(c)	350.00
40 PGv,GFx,WE(c),Doll Man(c)	325.00
41 PGv,GFx,WE(c),Bundles(c)	350.00
42 GFx,Doll Man(c)	250.00
43 RC,GFx,Bundles(c)	225.00
44 RC,GFx,Doll Man(c)	325.00
45 RC,GFx,Bundles(c)	225.00
46 RC,PGv,GFx,Doll Man(c)	250.00

47 RC,GFx,Bundles(c) 225.00
48 RC,GFx,Doll Man(c) 250.00
49 RC,GFx,Bundles(c) 225.00
50 RC,GFx,Doll Man(c) 250.00
51 RC,GFx,Bundles(c) 225.00
52 RC,GFx,Doll Man(c) 225.00
53 RC,GFx,Bundles(c) 200.00
54 RC,GFx,Doll Man(c) 225.00
55 RC,GFx,Bundles(c) 200.00
56 RC,GFx,Bundles(c) 250.00
57 RC,GFx,Bundles(c) 200.00
58 RC,GFx,Doll Man cover ... 225.00
59 RC,GFx,Mickey Finn(c) ... 200.00
60 RC,GFx,Doll Man(c) 225.00
61 RC,GFx,Bundles(c) 185.00
62 RC,GFx,Doll Man(c) 190.00
63 RC,GFx,Bundles(c) 175.00
64 BP,GFx,Doll Man(c) 185.00
65 BP,GFx(c),Bundles(c) 175.00
66 BP,GFx,Doll Man(c) 175.00
67 BP 150.00
68 BP,Doll Man vs.BeardedLady 175.00
69 BP,GFx(c),Devil cover 165.00
70 BP,Doll Man(c) 175.00
71 BP,GFx(c) 125.00
72 BP,Doll Man(c) 125.00
73 BP,GFx(c),Bundles(c) 110.00
74 Doll Man(c) 125.00
75 GFx(c) 100.00
76 GFx(c) 100.00
77 Doll Man cover until #140 .. 110.00
78 Knows no Fear but the
   Knife Does 100.00
79 Little Luck God 100.00
80 .... 100.00
81 Wanted for Murder 100.00
82 V:Shawunkas the Shaman . 100.00
83 V:Mechanical Man 100.00
84 V:Masked Rider, Death
   Goes to the Rodeo 100.00
85 V:King of Beasts 100.00
86 Is He A Killer? 100.00
87 The Maze of Murder 100.00
88 V:The Phantom Killer 100.00
89 Crook's Goose 100.00
90 V:Whispering Corpse 100.00
91 V:The Undertaker 100.00
92 V:The Image 100.00
93 .... 100.00
94 V:The Undertaker 100.00
95 Flatten's the Peacock's Pride 100.00
96 Doll Man Proves
   Justice is Blind 100.00
97 V:Peacock 100.00
98 V:Master Diablo 100.00
99 On the Warpath Again! ... 100.00
100 Crushes the City of Crime . 125.00
101 Land of the Midget Men! ... 75.00
102 The Angle 75.00
103 V:The Queen of Ants 75.00
104 V:The Botanist 75.00
105 Dream of Death 75.00
106 V:The Sword Fish 75.00
107 Hand of Horror! 75.00
108 V:Cateye 75.00
109 V:The Brain 75.00
110 V:Fat Cat 75.00
111 V:The Undertaker 75.00
112 I:Mr. Curio & His Miniatures 75.00
113 V:Highwayman 75.00
114 V:Tom Thumb 75.00
115 V:The Sphinx 75.00
116 V:Elbows 75.00
117 Polka Dot on the Spot 75.00
118 thru 144 .... @75.00

FEDERAL MEN COMICS
Gerard Publ. Co.
1942
2 S&S,Spanking 250.00

Felix the Cat #36
© Dell Publishing Co./Toby Press

FELIX THE CAT
Dell Publishing Co.
Feb.-March 1948
1 .... 250.00
2 .... 150.00
3 .... 100.00
4 .... 100.00
5 .... 100.00
6 .... 75.00
7 .... 75.00
8 .... 75.00
9 .... 75.00
10 .... 75.00
11 thru 19 .... @65.00
Toby Press
20 thru 30 .... @125.00
31 .... 25.00
32 .... 60.00
33 .... 60.00
34 .... 25.00
35 .... 25.00
36 thru 59 .... @60.00
60 .... 55.00
61 .... 55.00
Harvey
62 thru 80 .... @18.00
81 thru 99 .... @15.00
100 .... 20.00
101 thru 118 .... @12.00
Spec., 100 pgs, 1952 .... 175.00
Summer Ann., 100 pgs. 1953 . 150.00
Winter Ann.,#2 100 pgs, 1954.. 125.00

FERDINAND THE BULL
Dell Publishing Co.
1938
1 .... 140.00

FIGHT AGAINST CRIME
Story Comics May, 1951
1 Scorpion of Crime Inspector

"Brains" Carroway 200.00
2 Ganglands Double Cross .. 100.00
3 Killer Dolan's Double Cross . 75.00
4 Hopped Up Killers - The
   Con's Slaughter,Drug issue . 80.00
5 Horror of the Avenging Corpse 75.00
6 Terror of the Crazy Killer ... 75.00
7 .... 75.00
8 Killer with the Two-bladed
   Knife 65.00
9 Rats Die by Gas,Horror 175.00
10 Horror of the Con's Revenge 175.00
11 Case of the Crazy Killer ... 175.00
12 Horror,Drug issue 200.00
13 The Bloodless Killer 175.00
14 Electric Chair cover 200.00
15 .... 150.00
16 RA,Bondage(c) 200.00
17 Knife in Neck(c) 200.00
18 Attempted hanging cover . 225.00
19 Bondage(c) 225.00
20 Severed Head cover 300.00
21 .... 150.00
Becomes:

FIGHT AGAINST
THE GUILTY
22 RA,Electric Chair 175.00
23 March, 1955 .... 125.00

FIGHT COMICS
Fight Comics Inc.
(Fiction House Magazines)
January, 1940
1 LF,GT,WE(c),O:Spy Fighter 2,200.00
2 GT,WE(c),Joe Lewis ... 900.00
3 WE(c),GT,B:Rip Regan,
   The Powerman 650.00
4 GT,LF(c) 550.00
5 WE(c) 550.00
6 GT,BP(c) 400.00
7 GT,BP(c),Powerman-Blood
   Money 400.00
8 GT,Chip Collins-Lair of
   the Vulture 400.00
9 GT,Chip Collins-Prey of the
   War Eagle 400.00
10 GT,Wolves of the Yukon ... 400.00
11 .... 350.00
12 RA,Powerman-Monster of
   Madness 350.00
13 Shark Broodie-Legion
   of Satan 350.00
14 Shark Broodie-Lagoon
   of Death 350.00
15 Super-American-Hordes of
   the Secret Dicator 500.00
16 B:Capt.Fight,SwastikaPlague 500.00
17 Super-American-Blaster of
   the Pig-Boat Pirates 400.00
18 Shark Broodie-Plague of
   the Yellow Devils 400.00
19 E:Capt. Fight 400.00
20 .... 300.00
21 Rip Carson-Hell's Sky-Riders 250.00
22 Rip Carson-Sky Devil's
   Mission 250.00
23 Rip Carson-Angels of
   Vengeance 250.00
24 Baynonets for the Banzai
   Breed! Bondage(c) 200.00
25 Rip Carson-Samurai
   Showdown 175.00
26 Rip Carson-Fury of

the Sky-Brigade 175.00
27 War-Loot for the Mikado,
Bondage(c) 175.00
28 Rip Carson 175.00
29 Rip Carson-Charge of the
Lost Region 175.00
30 Rip Carson-Jeep-Raiders of
the Torture Jungle 175.00
31 Gangway for the Gyrenes,
Decapitation cover 185.00
32 Vengeance of the Hun-
Hunters,Bondage(c) 185.00
33 B:Tiger Girl 150.00
34 Bondage(c) 165.00
35 MB 150.00
36 MB 150.00
37 MB 150.00
38 MB,Bondage(c) 165.00
39 MB,Senorita Rio-Slave Brand
of the Spider Cult 150.00
40 MB,Bondage cover 165.00
41 MB,Bondage cover 165.00
42 MB 150.00

Fight Comics #10
© *Fiction House Magazines*

43 MB,Senorita Rio-The Fire-Brides
o/t Lost Atlantis,Bondage(c)   165.00
44 MB,R:Capt. Fight 150.00
45 MB,Tonight Don Diablo Rides 150.00
46 MB 150.00
47 MB,SenoritaRio-Horror's
Hacienda 150.00
48 MB 150.00
49 MB,JKa,B:Tiger Girl(c) 150.00
50 MB 150.00
51 MB,O:Tiger Girl 300.00
52 MB,Winged Demons of Doom 125.00
53 MB,Shadowland Shrine . . . 125.00
54 MB,Flee the Cobra Fury . . . 125.00
55 MB,Jungle Juggernaut 125.00
56 MB 125.00
57 MB,Jewels of Jeopardy 125.00
58 MB 125.00
59 MB,Vampires ofCrystalCavern125.00
60 MB,Kraal of DeadlyDiamonds 125.00
61 MB,Seekers of the Sphinx,
O:Tiger Girl 175.00
62 MB,Graveyard if the
Tree Tribe 110.00
63 MB 110.00

64 MB,DawnBeast from
Karama-Zan! 110.00
65 Beware the Congo Girl 110.00
66 Man or Ape! 100.00
67 Head-Hunters of Taboo Trek 100.00
68 Fangs of Dr. Voodoo 100.00
69 Cage of the Congo Fury . . . 100.00
70 Kraal of Traitor Tusks 100.00
71 Captives for the Golden
Crocodile 100.00
72 Land of the Lost Safaris . . . 100.00
73 War-Gods of the Jungle . . . 100.00
74 Advengers of the Jungle . . . 100.00
75 Perils of Momba-Kzar 100.00
76 Kraal of Zombi-Zaro 100.00
77 Slave-Queen of the Ape Man 100.00
78 Great Congo Diamond
Robbery 125.00
79 A:Space Rangers 125.00
80 . . . . 100.00
81 E:Tiger Girl(c) 100.00
82 RipCarson-CommandoStrike 100.00
83 NobodyLoves a Minesweeper 100.00
84 Rip Carson-Suicide Patrol . . 100.00
85 . . . . 100.00
86 GE,Tigerman,Summer,1954 110.00

FIGHTING AMERICAN
Headline Publications
(Prize)
April-May, 1954
1 S&K,O:Fighting American &
Speedboy 1,400.00
2 S&K,S&K(c) 600.00
3 S&K,S&K(c) 500.00
4 S&K,S&K(c) 500.00
5 S&K,S&K(c) 500.00
6 S&K,S&K(c),O:Fighting
American 475.00
7 S&K,S&K(c), April-May, 1955 425.00

FIGHTING DAVY
CROCKETT
(see KIT CARSON)

FIGHTING INDIANS OF
THE WILD WEST
Avon Periodicals
March, 1952
1 EK,EL,Geronimo, Crazy Horse,
Chief Victorio 100.00
2 EK,Same, November, 1952 . 75.00

FIGHTING
LEATHERNECKS
Toby Press
February, 1952
1 JkS,Duke's Diary 100.00
2 . . . . 65.00
3 . . . . 50.00
4 . . . . 50.00
5 . . . . 45.00
6 December, 1952 . . . . 40.00

FIGHTIN' TEXAN
(see TEXAN, THE)

FIGHTING YANK
Nedor Publ./Better Publ.
(Standard Comics) Sept., 1942
1 B:Fighting Yank, A:Wonder Man,

Mystico, Bondage cover . . 1,500.00
2 JaB 650.00
3 . . . . 500.00
4 AS(c) 400.00
5 AS(c) 400.00
6 AS(c) 400.00
7 AS(c),A:Fighting Yank . . . 350.00
8 AS(c) 350.00
9 AS(c) 350.00
10 AS(c) 350.00
11 AS(c), A:Grim Reaper, Nazis
bomb Washington cover . . 300.00
12 AS(c), Hirohito bondage cover300.00
13 AS(c) 275.00
14 AS(c) 275.00
15 AS(c) 275.00
16 AS(c) 275.00
17 AS(c) 275.00
18 AS(c), A:American Eagle . . 275.00
19 AS(c) 275.00
20 AS(c) 275.00
21 AS(c) A:Kara,Jungle
Princess 300.00
22 AS(c) A:Miss Masque-
cover story 325.00
23 AS(c) Klu Klux Klan
parody cover 325.00
24 A:Miss Masque 300.00
25 JRo,MMe,A:Cavalier 350.00
26 JRo,MMe,A:Cavalier 300.00
27 JRo,MMe,A:Cavalier 300.00
28 JRo,MMe,AW,A:Cavalier . . 325.00
29 JRo,MMe,August, 1949 . . . 325.00

FILM STAR ROMANCES
Star Publications
January-February, 1950
1 LbC(c), Rudy Valentino story 300.00
2 Liz Taylor & Robert Taylor,
photo cover 250.00
3 May-June, 1950, photo(c) . . 175.00

FIREHAIR COMICS
Flying Stories, Inc.
(Fiction House Magazine)
Winter, 1948
1 I:Firehair, Riders on the
Pony Express 450.00
2 Bride of the Outlaw Guns . . 200.00
3 Kiss of the Six-Gun Siren! . . 150.00
4 . . . . 150.00
5 . . . . 150.00
6 . . . . 125.00
7 War Drums at Buffalo Bend 125.00
8 Raid on the Red Arrows . . . 125.00
9 French Flags and Tomahawks 125.00
10 Slave Maiden of the Crees . 125.00
11 Wolves of the Overland
Trail,Spring, 1952 . . . . 125.00

FLAME, THE
Fox Feature Syndicate
Summer, 1940
1 LF,O:The Flame 2,700.00
2 GT,LF 1,000.00
3 BP 750.00
4 . . . . 700.00
5 GT 700.00
6 GT 700.00
7 A:The Yank 700.00
8 The Finger of the Frozen
Death!, January, 1942 . . . . 700.00

FLAMING LOVE
Comic Magazines
(Quality Comics Group)
December, 1949
1 BWa,BWa(c),The Temptress
  I Feared in His Arms 250.00
2 Torrid Tales of Turbulent
  Passion 100.00
3 BWa,RC,My Heart's at Sea 175.00
4 One Women who made a
  Mockery of Love, Ph(c) 75.00
5 Bridge of Longing, Ph(c) 75.00
6 Men both Loved & Feared Me,
  October, 1950 . . . . 75.00

FLASH GORDON
Harvey Publications
October, 1950
1 AR,Bondage(c) 200.00
2 AR 150.00
3 AR Bondage(c) 165.00
4 AR, April, 1951 . . . . 150.00

FLIP
Harvey Publications
April, 1954
1 HN 150.00
2 HN,BP,June, 1954 . . . . 150.00

FLY BOY
Approved Comics
(Ziff-Davis)
Spring, 1952
1 NS(c),Angels without Wings 125.00
2 NS(c),Flyboy's Flame-Out,
  October-November, 1952 . . . 75.00

THE FLYING A'S
RANGE RIDER
Dell Publishing Co.
June-August, 1953
(1) = Dell Four Color #404
2 Ph(c) all 75.00
3 . . . . 50.00
4 . . . . 50.00
5 . . . . 50.00
6 . . . . 50.00
7 . . . . 50.00
8 . . . . 50.00
9 . . . . 50.00
10 . . . . 50.00
11 . . . . 40.00
12 . . . . 40.00
13 . . . . 40.00
14 . . . . 40.00
15 . . . . 40.00
16 . . . . 40.00
17 ATh 55.00
19 . . . . 40.00
20 . . . . 40.00
21 . . . . 40.00
22 . . . . 40.00
23 . . . . 40.00
24 . . . . 40.00

FOODINI
Continental Publications
March, 1950
1 . . . . 90.00
2 . . . . 50.00
3 . . . . 40.00
4 August, 1950 . . . . 40.00

FOOTBALL THRILLS
Approved Comics
(Ziff-Davis)
Fall-Winter, 1952
1 BP,NS(c),Red Grange story   200.00
2 NS(c),Bronko Nagurski,
  Spring,1952 . . . . 150.00

FORBIDDEN LOVE
Comic Magazine
(Quality Comics Group)
March, 1950
1 RC,Ph(c),Heartbreak Road . 550.00
2 Ph(c),I loved a Gigolo 225.00
3 Kissless Bride 225.00
4 BWa,Brimstone Kisses,
  September, 1950 . . . . 250.00

Forbidden Worlds #13
© American Comics Group

FORBIDDEN WORLDS
American Comics Group
July-August, 1951
1 AW,FF 1,000.00
2 . . . . 500.00
3 AW,WW,JD 500.00
4 Werewolf cover 250.00
5 AW 400.00
6 AW,King Kong cover 350.00
7 . . . . 200.00
8 . . . . 200.00
9 Atomic Bomb 225.00
10 JyD 175.00
11 The Mummy's Treasure . . 150.00
12 Chest of Death 150.00
13 Invasion from Hades 150.00
14 Million-Year Monster 150.00
15 The Vampire Cat 150.00
16 The Doll 150.00
17 . . . . 150.00
18 The Mummy 150.00
19 Pirate and the Voodoo Queen 150.00
20 Terror Island 150.00
21 The Ant Master 100.00
22 The Cursed Casket 100.00
23 Nightmare for Two 100.00
24 . . . . 100.00
25 Hallahan's Head 100.00

26 The Champ 100.00
27 SMo,The Thing with the
  Golden Hair 100.00
28 Portrait of Carlotta 100.00
29 The Frogman 100.00
30 The Things on the Beach   . 100.00
31 SMo,The Circle of the Doomed 80.00
32 The Invasion of the
  Dead Things 80.00
33 . . . . 80.00
34 Atomic Bomb 110.00
35 Comics Code 75.00
36 thru 62 . . . . @50.00
63 AW 75.00
64 . . . . 45.00
65 . . . . 45.00
66 . . . . 45.00
67 . . . . 45.00
68 OW(c) 45.00
69 AW 75.00
70 . . . . 45.00
71 . . . . 45.00
72 OW,I:Herbie 150.00
73 . . . . 45.00
74 . . . . 45.00
75 JB 40.00
76 AW 60.00
77 . . . . 40.00
78 AW,OW(c) 60.00
79 thru 85 JB . . . . @40.00
86 Flying Saucer 50.00
87 . . . . 40.00
88 . . . . 40.00
89 . . . . 40.00
90 . . . . 40.00
91 . . . . 40.00
92 . . . . 40.00
93 . . . . 40.00
94 OW(c),A:Herbie 75.00
95 . . . . 30.00
96 AW 50.00
97 thru 115 . . . . @30.00
116 OW(c)A:Herbie 35.00
117 . . . . 30.00
118 . . . . 30.00
119 . . . . 30.00
120 thru 124 . . . . @30.00
125 I:O:Magic Man 35.00
126 A:Magic Man 25.00
127 same 25.00
128 same 25.00
129 same 25.00
130 same 25.00
131 same 25.00
132 same 25.00
133 I:O:Dragona 25.00
134 A:Magic Man 25.00
135 A:Magic Man 25.00
136 A:Nemesis 25.00
137 A:Magic Man 25.00
138 A:Magic Man 25.00
139 A:Magic Man 25.00
140 SD,A:Mark Midnight 25.00
141 thru 145 . . . . @15.00

FOREIGN INTRIGUES
(see DYNAMITE)

FOUR COLOR
Dell Publishing Co.
1939
N# Dick Tracy 7,000.00
N# Don Winslow of the Navy 1,400.00
N# Myra North 800.00

Dell Four Color #40
© Dell Publishing Co.

4 Disney'sDonaldDuck(1940) 11,000.00
5 Smilin' Jack 600.00
6 Dick Tracy 1,500.00
7 Gang Busters 400.00
8 Dick Tracy 800.00
9 Terry and the Pirates 650.00
10 Smilin' Jack 600.00
11 Smitty 400.00
12 Little Orphan Annie 500.00
13 Walt Disney's Reluctant
   Dragon (1941) 1,700.00
14 Moon Mullins 400.00
15 Tillie the Toiler 400.00
16 W.Disney's Mickey Mouse Outwits
   the Phantom Blob (1941) . 9,000.00
17 W.Disney's Dumbo the Flying
   Elephant (1941) 2,000.00
18 Jiggs and Maggie 450.00
19 Barney Google and
   Snuffy Smith 450.00
20 Tiny Tim 350.00
21 Dick Tracy 675.00
22 Don Winslow 350.00
23 Gang Busters 300.00
24 Captain Easy 450.00
25 Popeye 750.00
[Second Series]
1 Little Joe 500.00
2 Harold Teen 300.00
3 Alley Oop 500.00
4 Smilin' Jack 475.00
5 Raggedy Ann and Andy . . . 550.00
6 Smitty 250.00
7 Smokey Stover 350.00
8 Tillie the Toiler 250.00
9 Donald Duck finds Pirate
   Gold! 8,000.00
10 Flash Gordon 800.00
11 Wash Tubs 350.00
12 Bambi 600.00
13 Mr. District Attorney 350.00
14 Smilin' Jack 400.00
15 Felix the Cat 750.00
16 Porky Pig 850.00
17 Popeye 600.00
18 Little Orphan Annie's
   Junior Commandos 450.00
19 W.Disney's Thumper meets

the Seven Dwarfs 600.00
20 Barney Baxter 275.00
21 Oswald the Rabbit 550.00
22 Tillie the Toiler 225.00
23 Raggedy Ann and Andy . . . 400.00
24 Gang Busters 300.00
25 Andy Panda 500.00
26 Popeye 600.00
27 Mickey Mouse and the
   Seven Colored Terror 1,000.00
28 Wash Tubbs 250.00
29 CB,Donald Duck and the
   Mummy's Ring 7,000.00
30 Bambi's Children 600.00
31 Moon Mullins 200.00
32 Smitty 175.00
33 Bugs Bunny 1,200.00
34 Dick Tracy 475.00
35 Smokey Stover 175.00
36 Smilin' Jack 250.00
37 Bringing Up Father 200.00
38 Roy Rogers 2,200.00
39 Oswald the Rabbit 400.00
40 Barney Google and Snuffy
   Smith 250.00
41 WK,Mother Goose 250.00
42 Tiny Tim 175.00
43 Popeye 350.00
44 Terry and the Pirates 450.00
45 Raggedy Ann 350.00
46 Felix the Cat and the
   Haunted House 450.00
47 Gene Autry 450.00
48 CB,Porky Pig o/t Mounties 1,100.00
49 W.Disney's Snow White and
   the Seven Dwarfs 700.00
50 WK,Fairy Tale Parade 325.00
51 Bugs Bunny Finds the
   Lost Treasure 400.00
52 Little Orphan Annie 350.00
53 Wash Tubbs 150.00
54 Andy Panda 300.00
55 Tillie the Toiler 125.00
56 Dick Tracy 350.00
57 Gene Autry 375.00
58 Smilin' Jack 250.00
59 WK,Mother Goose 200.00
60 Tiny Folks Funnies 150.00
61 Santa Claus Funnies 250.00
62 CB,Donald Duck in
   Frozen Gold 2,300.00
63 Roy Rogers-photo cover . . . 600.00
64 Smokey Stover 150.00
65 Smitty 125.00
66 Gene Autry 400.00
67 Oswald the Rabbit 200.00
68 WK,Mother Goose 225.00
69 WK,Fairy Tale Parade 275.00
70 Popeye and Wimpy 300.00
71 WK,Walt Disney's
   Three Caballeros 850.00
72 Raggedy Ann 250.00
73 The Grumps 125.00
74 Marge's Little Lulu 1,000.00
75 Gene Autry and the Wildcat 300.00
76 Little Orphan Annie 275.00
77 Felix the Cat 450.00
78 Porky Pig & the Bandit Twins 275.00
79 Mickey Mouse in the Riddle
   of the Red Hat 1,200.00
80 Smilin' Jack 175.00
81 Moon Mullins 125.00
82 Lone Ranger 450.00
83 Gene Autry in Outlaw Trail . 325.00
84 Flash Gordon 450.00

Dell Four Color #62
© Dell Publishing Co.

85 Andy Panda and the
   Mad Dog Mystery 175.00
86 Roy Rogers-photo cover . . 400.00
87 WK,Fairy Tale Parade 275.00
88 Bugs Bunny 250.00
89 Tillie the Toiler 150.00
90 WK,Christmas with
   Mother Goose 200.00
91 WK,Santa Claus Funnies . . 200.00
92 WK,W.Disney's Pinocchio . . 700.00
93 Gene Autry 250.00
94 Winnie Winkle 125.00
95 Roy Rogers,Ph(c) 400.00
96 Dick Tracy 275.00
97 Marge's Little Lulu 500.00
98 Lone Ranger 325.00
99 Smitty 100.00
100 Gene Autry Comics-photo
   cover 275.00
101 Terry and the Pirates 300.00
102 WK,Oswald the Rabbit . . . 175.00
103 WK,Easter with
   Mother Goose 200.00
104 WK,Fairy Tale Parade 225.00
105 WK,Albert the Aligator . . . 700.00
106 Tillie the Toiler 100.00
107 Little Orphan Annie 250.00
108 Donald Duck in the
   Terror of the River 1,600.00
109 Roy Rogers Comics 300.00
110 Marge's Little Lulu 350.00
111 Captain Easy 150.00
112 Porky Pig's Adventure in
   Gopher Gulch 150.00
113 Popeye 150.00
114 WK,Fairy Tale Parade 200.00
115 Marge's Little Lulu 350.00
116 Mickey Mouse and the
   House of Many Mysteries . 275.00
117 Roy Rogers Comics,
   Ph(c) 250.00
118 Lone Ranger 325.00
119 Felix the Cat 300.00
120 Marge's Little Lulu 300.00
121 Fairy Tale Parade 100.00
122 Henry 125.00
123 Bugs Bunny's Dangerous
   Venture 165.00

124 Roy Rogers Comics,Ph(c) . 250.00
125 Lone Ranger 225.00
126 WK,Christmas with
   Mother Goose 175.00
127 Popeye 150.00
128 WK,Santa Claus Funnies . 150.00
129 W.Disney's Uncle Remus
   & his tales of Brer Rabbit . . 300.00
130 Andy Panda 100.00
131 Marge's Little Lulu 300.00
132 Tillie the Toiler 100.00
133 Dick Tracy 250.00
134 Tarzan and the Devil Ogre 650.00
135 Felix the Cat 250.00
136 Lone Ranger 225.00
137 Roy Rogers Comics 250.00
138 Smitty 75.00
139 Marge's Little Lulu 275.00
140 WK,Easter with
   Mother Goose 175.00
141 Mickey Mouse and the
   Submarine Pirates 250.00
142 Bugs Bunny and the
   Haunted Mountain 175.00
143 Oswald the Rabbit & the
   Prehistoric Egg 100.00
144 Poy Rogers Comics,Ph(c) . 250.00
145 Popeye 150.00
146 Marge's Little Lulu 275.00
147 W.Disney's Donald Duck
   in Volcano Valley 1,100.00
148 WK,Albert the Aligator
   and Pogo Possum 650.00
149 Smilin' Jack 125.00
150 Tillie the Toiler 100.00
151 Lone Ranger 200.00
152 Little Orphan Annie 150.00
153 Roy Rogers Comics 200.00
154 Andy Panda 100.00
155 Henry 75.00
156 Porky Pig and the Phantom 100.00
157 W.Disney's Mickey Mouse
   and the Beanstalk 250.00
158 Marge's Little Lulu 275.00
159 CB,W.Disney's Donald Duck
   in the Ghost of the Grotto . . 900.00
160 Roy Rogers Comics,Ph(c) . 175.00
161 Tarzan & the Fires of Tohr 600.00
162 Felix the Cat 175.00
163 Dick Tracy 175.00
164 Bugs Bunny Finds the
   Frozen Kingdom 175.00
165 Marge's Little Lulu 275.00
166 Roy Rogers Comics,Ph(c) . 200.00
167 Lone Ranger 175.00
168 Popeye 150.00
169 Woody Woodpecker,Drug . 165.00
170 W.Disney's Mickey Mouse
   on Spook's Island 200.00
171 Charlie McCarthy 250.00
172 WK,Christmas with
   Mother Goose 150.00
173 Flash Gordon 150.00
174 Winnie Winkle 75.00
175 WK,Santa Claus Funnies . 150.00
176 Tillie the Toiler 75.00
177 Roy Rogers Comics,Ph(c) . 175.00
178 CB,W.Disney's Donald Duck
   Christmas on Bear Mountain1,400.00
179 WK,Uncle Wiggly 150.00
180 Ozark the Ike 85.00
181 W.Disney's Mickey Mouse
   in Jungle Magic 200.00
182 Porky Pig in Never-
   Never Land 125.00

183 Oswald the Rabbit 75.00
184 Tillie the Toiler 75.00
185 WK,Easter with
   Mother Goose 150.00
186 W.Disney's Bambi 175.00
187 Bugs Bunny and the
   Dreadful Bunny 125.00
188 Woody Woodpecker 125.00
189 W.Disney's Donald Duck in
   The Old Castle's Secret . . . 800.00
190 Flash Gordon 150.00
191 Porky Pig to the Rescue . 125.00
192 WK,The Brownies 135.00
193 Tom and Jerry 150.00
194 W.Disney's Mickey Mouse
   in the World Under the Sea . 200.00
195 Tillie the Toiler 50.00
196 Charlie McCarthy in The
   Haunted Hide-Out 175.00
197 Spirit of the Border 125.00
198 Andy Panda 100.00

Dell Four Color #130
© Dell Publishing Co.

199 W.Disney's Donald Duck in
   Sheriff of Bullet Valley 875.00
200 Bugs Bunny, Super Sleuth 125.00
201 WK,Christmas with
   Mother Goose 125.00
202 Woody Woodpecker 75.00
203 CB,W.Disney's Donald Duck in
   The Golden Christmas Tree 650.00
204 Flash Gordon 100.00
205 WK,Santa Claus Funnies . 150.00
206 Little Orphan Funnies 75.00
207 King of the Royal Mounted 175.00
208 W.Disney's Brer Rabbit
   Does It Again 125.00
209 Harold Teen 50.00
210 Tippe and Cap Stubbs . . . 45.00
211 Little Beaver 60.00
212 Dr. Bobbs 40.00
213 Tillie the Toiler 50.00
214 W.Disney's Mickey Mouse
   and his Sky Adventure 175.00
215 Sparkle Plenty 100.00
216 Andy Panda and the
   Police Pup 75.00
217 Bugs Bunny in Court Jester 125.00
218 W.Disney's 3 Little Pigs . . 150.00
219 Swee'pea 120.00

220 WK,Easter with
   Mother Goose 150.00
221 WK,Uncle Wiggly 125.00
222 West of the Pecos 75.00
223 CB,W.Disney's Donald Duck in
   Lost in the Andes 850.00
224 Little Iodine 75.00
225 Oswald the Rabbit 50.00
226 Porky Pig and Spoofy 75.00
227 W.Disney's Seven Dwarfs . 125.00
228 The Mark of Zorro 250.00
229 Smokey Stover 50.00
230 Sunset Press 60.00
231 W.Disney's Mickey Mouse
   and the Rajah's Treasure . . 150.00
232 Woody Woodpecker 75.00
233 Bugs Bunny 125.00
234 W.Disney's Dumbo in Sky
   Voyage 125.00
235 Tiny Tim 45.00
236 Heritage of the Desert . . . 75.00
237 Tillie the Toiler 50.00
238 CB,W.Disney's Donald Duck
   in Voodoo Hoodoo 600.00
239 Adventure Bound 50.00
240 Andy Panda 60.00
241 Porky Pig 75.00
242 Tippie and Cap Stubbs 35.00
243 W.Disney's Thumper
   Follows His Nose 125.00
244 WK,The Brownies 125.00
245 Dick's Adventures in
   Dreamland 40.00
246 Thunder Mountain 45.00
247 Flash Gordon 125.00
248 W.Disney's Mickey Mouse
   and the Black Sorcerer 150.00
249 Woody Woodpecker 65.00
250 Bugs Bunny in
   Diamond Daze 135.00
251 Hubert at Camp Moonbeam 50.00
252 W.Disney's Pinocchio 125.00
253 WK,Christmas with
   Mother Goose 140.00
254 WK,Santa Claus Funnies,
   A:Pogo 140.00
255 The Ranger 45.00
256 CB,W.Disney's Donald Duck in
   Luck of the North 450.00
257 Little Iodine 50.00
258 Andy Panda and the
   Ballon Race 75.00
259 Santa and the Angel 50.00
260 Porky Pig, Hero of the
   Wild West 75.00
261 W.Disney's Mickey Mouse
   and the Missing Key 150.00
262 Raggedy Ann and Andy . . . 60.00
263 CB,W.Disney's Donald Duck in
   Land of the Totem Poles . . . 450.00
264 Woody Woodpecker in
   the Magic Lantern 60.00
265 King of the Royal Mountain . 85.00
266 Bugs Bunny on the Isle of
   Hercules 125.00
267 Little Beaver 40.00
268 W.Disney's Mickey Mouse's
   Surprise Visitor 150.00
269 Johnny Mack Brown,Ph(c) . 200.00
270 Drift Fence 40.00
271 Porky Pig 75.00
272 W.Disney's Cinderella . . . 125.00
273 Oswald the Rabbit 45.00
274 Bugs Bunny 125.00
275 CB,W.Disney's Donald Duck

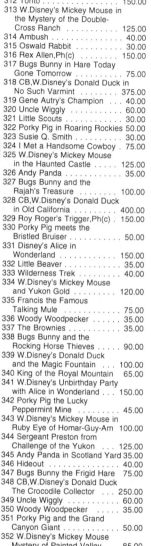

Dell Four Color #251
© Dell Publishing Co.

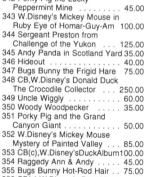

Dell Four Color #384
© Dell Publishing Co.

in Ancient Persia 425.00
276 Uncle Wiggly 75.00
277 PorkyPig in DesertAdventure 75.00
278 Bill Elliot Comics,Ph(c) . . . 150.00
279 W.Disney's Mickey Mouse &
   Pluto Battle the Giant Ants . 125.00
280 Andy Panda in the Isle
   of the Mechanical Men 60.00
281 Bugs Bunny in The Great
   Circus Mystery 125.00
282 CB,W.Disney's Donald Duck in
   The Pixilated Parrot 450.00
283 King of the Royal Mounted 100.00
284 Porky Pig in the Kingdom
   of Nowhere 75.00
285 Bozo the Clown 200.00
286 W.Disney's Mickey Mouse
   and the Uninvited Guest . . . 125.00
287 Gene Autry's Champion in the
   Ghost of BlackMountain,Ph(c) 100.00
288 Woody Woodpecker 75.00
289 BugsBunny in IndianTrouble 120.00
290 The Chief 50.00
291 CB,W.Disney's Donald Duck in
   The Magic Hourglass 450.00
292 The Cisco Kid Comics . . . 150.00
293 WK,The Brownies 125.00
294 Little Beaver 45.00
295 Porky Pig in President Pig . 75.00
296 W.Disney's Mickey Mouse
   Private Eye for Hire 125.00
297 Andy Panda in The
   Haunted Inn 50.00
298 Bugs Bunny in Sheik
   for a Day 125.00
299 Buck Jones & the Iron Trail 175.00
300 CB,W.Disney's Donald Duck in
   Big-Top Bedlam 450.00
301 The Mysterious Rider 40.00
302 Santa Claus Funnies 35.00
303 Porky Pig in The Land of
   the Monstrous Flies 65.00
304 W.Disney's Mickey Mouse
   in Tom-Tom Island 100.00
305 Woody Woodpecker 30.00
306 Raggedy Ann 35.00
307 Bugs Bunny in Lumber
   Jack Rabbit 85.00

308 CB,W.Disney's Donald Duck in
   Dangerous Disguise 375.00
309 Dollface and Her Gang 40.00
310 King of the Rotal Mounted . 55.00
311 Porky Pig in Midget Horses
   of Hidden Valley 55.00
312 Tonto 150.00
313 W.Disney's Mickey Mouse in
   the Mystery of the Double-
   Cross Ranch 125.00
314 Ambush 40.00
315 Oswald Rabbit 30.00
316 Rex Allen,Ph(c) 150.00
317 Bugs Bunny in Hare Today
   Gone Tomorrow 75.00
318 CB,W.Disney's Donald Duck in
   No Such Varmint 375.00
319 Gene Autry's Champion . . . 40.00
320 Uncle Wiggly 60.00
321 Little Scouts 30.00
322 Porky Pig in Roaring Rockies 50.00
323 Susie Q. Smith 30.00
324 I Met a Handsome Cowboy . 75.00
325 W.Disney's Mickey Mouse
   in the Haunted Castle 125.00
326 Andy Panda 35.00
327 Bugs Bunny and the
   Rajah's Treasure 100.00
328 CB,W.Disney's Donald Duck
   in Old California 400.00
329 Roy Roger's Trigger,Ph(c) . 150.00
330 Porky Pig meets the
   Bristled Bruiser 50.00
331 Disney's Alice in
   Wonderland 150.00
332 Little Beaver 35.00
333 Wilderness Trek 40.00
334 W.Disney's Mickey Mouse
   and Yukon Gold 120.00
335 Francis the Famous
   Talking Mule 75.00
336 Woody Woodpecker 35.00
337 The Brownies 35.00
338 Bugs Bunny and the
   Rocking Horse Thieves 90.00
339 W.Disney's Donald Duck
   and the Magic Fountain . . . 100.00
340 King of the Royal Mountain 65.00
341 W.Disney's Unbirthday Party
   with Alice in Wonderland . . . 150.00
342 Porky Pig the Lucky
   Peppermint Mine 45.00
343 W.Disney's Mickey Mouse in
   Ruby Eye of Homar-Guy-Am 100.00
344 Sergeant Preston from
   Challenge of the Yukon . . . 125.00
345 Andy Panda in Scotland Yard 35.00
346 Hideout 40.00
347 Bugs Bunny the Frigid Hare 75.00
348 CB,W.Disney's Donald Duck
   The Crocodile Collector . . . 250.00
349 Uncle Wiggly 60.00
350 Woody Woodpecker 35.00
351 Porky Pig and the Grand
   Canyon Giant 50.00
352 W.Disney's Mickey Mouse
   Mystery of Painted Valley . . . 85.00
353 CB(c),W.Disney'sDuckAlbum100.00
354 Raggedy Ann & Andy 45.00
355 Bugs Bunny Hot-Rod Hair . . 75.00
356 CB(c),W.Disney's Donald
   Duck in Rags to Riches . . . 250.00
357 Comeback 35.00
358 Andy Panada 35.00
359 Frosty the Snowman 60.00

360 Porky Pig in Tree Fortune . 45.00
361 Santa Claus Funnies 35.00
362 W.Disney's Mickey Mouse &
   the Smuggled Diamonds . . . 100.00
363 King of the Royal Mounted . 60.00
364 Woody Woodpecker 35.00
365 The Brownies 30.00
366 Bugs Bunny Uncle
   Buckskin Comes to Town . . . 75.00
367 CB,W.Disney's Donald Duck in
   A Christmas for Shacktown . 375.00
368 Bob Clampett's
   Beany and Cecil 300.00
369 Lone Ranger's Famous
   Horse Hi-Yo Silver 75.00
370 Porky Pig in Trouble
   in the Big Trees 45.00
371 W.Disney's Mickey Mouse
   the Inca Idol Case 85.00
372 Riders of the Purple Sage . . 30.00
373 Sergeant Preston 75.00
374 Woody Woodpecker 30.00
375 John Carter of Mars 275.00
376 Bugs Bunny 75.00
377 Susie Q. Smith 30.00
378 Tom Corbett, Space Cadet 200.00
379 W.Disney's Donald Duck in
   Southern Hospitality 100.00
380 Raggedy Ann & Andy 40.00
381 Marge's Tubby 150.00
382 W.Disney's Show White and
   the Seven Dwarfs 150.00
383 Andy Panda 25.00
384 King of the Royal Mounted . 50.00
385 Porky Pig 45.00
386 CB,W.Disney's Uncle Scrooge
   in Only A Poor Old Man . . 1,000.00
387 W.Disney's Mickey Mouse
   in High Tibet 85.00
388 Oswald the Rabbit 45.00
389 Andy Hardy Comics 30.00
390 Woody Woodpecker 35.00
391 Uncle Wiggly 60.00
392 Hi-Yo Silver 50.00
393 Bugs Bunny 75.00
394 CB(c),W.Disney's Donald Duck
   in Malayalaya 250.00
395 Forlorn River 35.00

396 Tales of the Texas Rangers,
Ph(c) 100.00
397 Sergeant Preston o/t Yukon 75.00
398 The Brownies 30.00
399 Porky Pig in the Lost
Gold Mine 45.00
400 AMc,Tom Corbett 125.00
401 W.Disney's Mickey Mouse &
Goofy's Mechanical Wizard .. 75.00
402 Mary Jane and Sniffles .. 75.00
403 W.Disney's Li'l Bad Wolf .. 100.00
404 The Ranger Rider,Ph(c) .. 100.00
405 Woody Woodpecker 30.00
406 Tweety and Sylvester 75.00
407 Bugs Bunny, Foreign-
Legion Hare 65.00
408 CB,W.Disney's Donald Duck
and the Golden Helmet 400.00
409 Andy Panda 25.00
410 Porky Pig in the
Water Wizard 40.00
411 W.Disney's Mickey Mouse
and the Old Sea Dog 75.00
412 Nevada 35.00
413 Disney's Robin Hood(movie),
Ph(c) 125.00
414 Bob Clampett's Beany
and Cecil 175.00
415 Rootie Kazootie 125.00
416 Woody Woodpecker 30.00
417 Double Trouble with Goober 25.00
418 Rusty Riley 40.00
419 Sergeant Preston 75.00
420 Bugs Bunny 65.00
421 AMc,Tom Corbett 125.00
422 CB,W.Disney's Donald Duck
and the Gilded Man 375.00
423 Rhubarb 30.00
424 Flash Gordon 150.00
425 Zorro 140.00
426 Porky Pig 35.00
427 W.Disney's Mickey Mouse &
the Wonderful Whizzix .. 65.00
428 Uncle Wiggily 35.00
429 W.Disney's Pluto in
Why Dogs Leave Home ... 100.00
430 Marge's Tubby 100.00
431 Woody Woodpecker 30.00
432 Bugs Bunny and the
Rabbit Olympics 60.00
433 Wildfire 35.00
434 Rin Tin Tin,Ph(c) 165.00
435 Frosty the Snowman 35.00
436 The Brownies 30.00
437 John Carter of Mars 175.00
438 W.Disney's Annie
Oakley (TV) 150.00
439 Little Hiawatha 50.00
440 Black Beauty 30.00
441 Fearless Fagan 25.00
442 W.Disney's Peter Pan 100.00
443 Ben Bowie and His
Mountain Men 50.00
444 Marge's Tubby 75.00
445 Charlie McCarthy 40.00
446 Captain Hook and Peter Pan 100.00
447 Andy Hardy Comics 25.00
448 Beany and Cecil 175.00
449 Tappan's Burro 35.00
450 CB(c),W.Disney's DuckAlbum 75.00
451 Rusty Riley 30.00
452 Raggedy Ann and Andy .. 40.00
453 Susie Q. Smith 30.00
454 Krazy Kat Comics 35.00
455 Johnny Mack Brown Comics,

Ph(c) 50.00
456 W.Disney's Uncle Scrooge
Back to the Klondike 650.00
457 Daffy 75.00
458 Oswald the Rabbit 35.00
459 Rootie Kazootie 75.00
460 Buck Jones 75.00
461 Marge's Tubby 75.00
462 Little Scouts 15.00
463 Petunia 30.00
464 Bozo 100.00
465 Francis the Talking Mule ... 50.00
466 Rhubarb, the Millionaire Cat 30.00
467 Desert Gold 30.00
468 W.Disney's Goofy 125.00
469 Beetle Bailey 110.00
470 Elmer Fudd 35.00
471 Double Trouble with Goober 20.00
472 Wild Bill Elliot,Ph(c) 55.00
473 W.Disney's Li'l Bad Wolf ... 65.00
474 Mary Jane and Sniffles 70.00
475 M.G.M.'s the Two
Mouseketeers 75.00

Dell Four Color #408
© Dell Publishing Co.

476 Rin Tin Tin,Ph(c) 60.00
477 Bob Clampett's Beany and
Cecil 150.00
478 Charlie McCarthy 40.00
479 Queen o/t West Dale Evans 150.00
480 Andy Hardy Comics 25.00
481 Annie Oakley and Tagg ... 65.00
482 Brownies 30.00
483 Little Beaver 30.00
484 River Feud 30.00
485 The Little People 40.00
486 Rusty Riley 35.00
487 Mowgli, the Jungle Book .. 35.00
488 John Carter of Mars 175.00
489 Tweety and Sylvester 30.00
490 Jungle Jim 50.00
491 EK,Silvertip 75.00
492 W.Disney's Duck Album ... 65.00
493 Johnny Mack Brown,Ph(c) .. 45.00
494 The Little King 125.00
495 CB, W.Disney's Uncle
Scrooge 500.00
496 The Green Hornet 275.00
497 Zorro, (Sword of) 150.00
498 Bugs Bunny's Album 45.00

499 M.G.M.'s Spike and Tyke .. 25.00
500 Buck Jones 65.00
501 Francis the Famous
Talking Mule 35.00
502 Rootie Kazootie 60.00
503 Uncle Wiggily 40.00
504 Krazy Kat 35.00
505 W.Disney's the Sword and
the Rose (TV),Ph(c) 100.00
506 The Little Scouts 20.00
507 Oswald the Rabbit 25.00
508 Bozo 100.00
509 W.Disney's Pluto 65.00
510 Son of Black Beauty 35.00
511 EK,Outlaw Trail 40.00
512 Flash Gordon 60.00
513 Ben Bowie and His
Mountain Men 30.00
514 Frosty the Snowman 30.00
515 Andy Hardy 25.00
516 Double Trouble With Goober 20.00
517 Walt Disney's Chip 'N' Dale 100.00
518 Rivets 25.00
519 Steve Canyon 100.00
520 Wild Bill Elliot,Ph(c) 50.00
521 Beetle Bailey 40.00
522 The Brownies 25.00
523 Rin Tin Tin,Ph(c) 75.00
524 Tweety and Sylvester 25.00
525 Santa Claus Funnies 30.00
526 Napoleon 20.00
527 Charlie McCarthy 35.00
528 Queen o/t West Dale Evans,
Ph(c) 75.00
529 Little Beaver 25.00
530 Bob Clampett's Beany
and Cecil 150.00
531 W.Disney's Duck Album .. 55.00
532 The Rustlers 35.00
533 Raggedy Ann and Andy ... 40.00
534 EK,Western Marshal 40.00
535 I Love Lucy,Ph(c) 500.00
536 Daffy 35.00
537 Stormy, the Thoroughbred . 25.00
538 EK,The Mask of Zorro ... 165.00
539 Ben and Me 25.00
540 Knights of the Round Table,
Ph(c) 75.00
541 Johnny Mack Brown,Ph(c) . 50.00
542 Super Circus Featuring
Mary Hartline 50.00
543 Uncle Wiggily 35.00
544 W.Disney's Rob Roy(Movie),
Ph(c) 100.00
545 The Wonderful Adventures
of Pinocchio 100.00
546 Buck Jones 75.00
547 Francis the Famous
Talking Mule 40.00
548 Krazy Kat 30.00
549 Oswald the Rabbit 25.00
550 The Little Scouts 15.00
551 Bozo 100.00
552 Beetle Bailey 45.00
553 Susie Q. Smith 30.00
554 Rusty Riley 30.00
555 Range War 30.00
556 Double Trouble with Goober 20.00
557 Ben Bowie and His
Mountain Men 30.00
558 Elmer Fudd 30.00
559 I Love Lucy,Ph(c) 350.00
560 W.Disney's Duck Album ... 60.00
561 Mr. Magoo 125.00
562 W.Disney's Goofy 85.00

563 Rhubarb, the Millionaire Cat 30.00
564 W.Disney's Li'l Bad Wolf . . . 60.00
565 Jungle Jim 30.00
566 Son of Black Beauty 30.00
567 BF,Prince Valiant,Ph(c) . . . 125.00
568 Gypsy Cat 35.00
569 Priscilla's Pop 25.00
570 Bob Clampett's Beany
    and Cecil 150.00
571 Charlie McCarthy 40.00
572 EK,Silvertip 40.00
573 The Little People 30.00
574 The Hand of Zorro 150.00
575 Annie and Oakley and Tagg,
    Ph(c) 60.00
576 Angel 25.00
577 M.G.M.'s Spike and Tyke . . 25.00
578 Steve Canyon 55.00
579 Francis the Talking Mule . . . 40.00
580 Six Gun Ranch 30.00
581 Chip 'N' Dale 55.00
582 Mowgli, the Jungle Book . . . 30.00
583 The Lost Wagon Train 35.00
584 Johnny Mack Brown,Ph(c) . . 40.00
585 Bugs Bunny's Album 50.00
586 W.Disney's Duck Album . . . 60.00
587 The Little Scouts 15.00
588 MB,King Richard and the
    Crusaders,Ph(c) 125.00
589 Buck Jones 60.00
590 Hansel and Gretel 50.00
591 EK,Western Marshal 50.00
592 Super Circus 45.00
593 Oswald the Rabbit 25.00
594 Bozo 100.00
595 Pluto 50.00
596 Turok, Son of Stone 600.00
597 The Little King 75.00
598 Captain Davy Jones 30.00
599 Ben Bowie and His
    Mountain Men 25.00
600 Daisy Duck's Diary 65.00
601 Frosty the Snowman 30.00
602 Mr. Magoo and the Gerald
    McBoing-Boing 125.00
603 M.G.M.'s The Two
    Mouseketeers 30.00
604 Shadow on the Trail 35.00
605 The Brownies 25.00
606 Sir Lancelot 100.00
607 Santa Claus Funnies 30.00
608 EK,Silver Tip 40.00
609 The Littlest Outlaw,Ph(c) . . . 60.00
610 Drum Beat,Ph(c) 100.00
611 W.Disney's Duck Album . . . 60.00
612 Little Beaver 25.00
613 EK,Western Marshal 50.00
614 W.Disney's 20,000 Leagues
    Under the Sea (Movie) . . . 100.00
615 Daffy 40.00
616 To The Last Man 30.00
617 The Quest of Zorro 125.00
618 Johnny Mack Brown,Ph(c) . . 50.00
619 Krazy Kat 30.00
620 Mowgli, Jungle Book 30.00
621 Francis the Famous
    Talking Mule 35.00
622 Beetle Bailey 40.00
623 Oswald the Rabbit 20.00
624 Treasure Island,Ph(c) 100.00
625 Beaver Valley 75.00
626 Ben Bowie and His
    Mountain Men 30.00
627 Goofy 100.00
628 Elmer Fudd 25.00

629 Lady & The Tramp with Jock 75.00
630 Priscilla's Pop 30.00
631 W.Disney's Davy Crockett
    Indian Fighter (TV),Ph(c) . . . 150.00
632 Fighting Caravans 30.00
633 The Little People 25.00
634 Lady and the Tramp Album . 60.00
635 Bob Clampett's Beany
    and Cecil 150.00
636 Chip 'N' Dale 55.00
637 EK,Silvertip 45.00
638 M.G.M.'s Spike and Tyke . . 20.00
639 W.Disney's Davy Crockett
    at the Alamo (TV),Ph(c) . . . 125.00
640 EK,Western Marshal 50.00
641 Steve Canyon 75.00
642 M.G.M.'s The Two
    Mouseketeers 30.00
643 Wild Bill Elliott,Ph(c) 35.00
644 Sir Walter Raleigh,Ph(c) . . . 75.00
645 Johnny Mack Brown,Ph(c) . . 50.00
646 Dotty Dripple and Taffy 30.00
647 Bugs Bunny's Album 50.00

THE HAND OF
ZORRO

Dell Four Color #574
© Dell Publishing Co.

648 Jace Pearson of the
    Texas Rangers,Ph(c) 50.00
649 Duck Album 60.00
650 BF,Prince Valiant 75.00
651 EK,King Colt 35.00
652 Buck Jones 45.00
653 Smokey the Bear 120.00
654 Pluto 50.00
655 Francis the Famous
    Talking Mule 35.00
656 Turok, Son of Stone 350.00
657 Ben Bowie and His
    Mountain Men 30.00
658 Goofy 75.00
659 Daisy Duck's Diary 60.00
660 Little Beaver 25.00
661 Frosty the Snowman 30.00
662 Zoo Parade 50.00
663 Winky Dink 60.00
664 W.Disney's Davy Crockett in
    the Great Keelboat
    Race (TV),Ph(c) 125.00
665 The African Lion 50.00
666 Santa Claus Funnies 35.00
667 EK,Silvertip and the Stolen

    Stallion 40.00
668 W.Disney's Dumbo 100.00
668a W.Disney's Dumbo 75.00
669 W.Disney's Robin Hood
    (Movie),Ph(c) 60.00
670 M.G.M.'s Mouse Musketeers 25.00
671 W.Disney's Davey Crockett &
    the River Pirates(TV),Ph(c) . 125.00
672 Quentin Durward,Ph(c) 60.00
673 Buffalo Bill Jr.,Ph(c) 60.00
674 The Little Rascals 75.00
675 EK,Steve Donovan,Ph(c) . . 60.00
676 Will-Yum! 30.00
677 Little King 75.00
678 The Last Hunt,Ph(c) 60.00
679 Gunsmoke 150.00
680 Out Our Way with the
    Worry Wart 25.00
681 Forever, Darling,Lucile
    Ball Ph(c) 125.00
682 When Knighthood Was
    in Flower,Ph(c) 60.00
683 Hi and Lois 25.00
684 SB,Helen of Troy,Ph(c) . . . 125.00
685 Johnny Mack Brown,Ph(c) . . 50.00
686 Duck Album 50.00
687 The Indian Fighter,Ph(c) . . . 50.00
688 SB,Alexander the Great,
    Ph(c) 75.00
689 Elmer Fudd 25.00
690 The Conqueror,
    John Wayne Ph(c) 175.00
691 Dotty Dripple and Taffy 25.00
692 The Little People 30.00
693 W.Disney's Brer Rabbit
    Song of the South 125.00
694 Super Circus,Ph(c) 50.00
695 Little Beaver 25.00
696 Krazy Kat 30.00
697 Oswald the Rabbit 20.00
698 Francis the Famous
    Talking Mule 30.00
699 BA,Prince Valiant 75.00
700 Water Birds and the
    Olympic Elk 50.00
701 Jimmy Cricket 100.00
702 The Goofy Success Story . . 100.00
703 Scamp 100.00
704 Priscilla's Pop 30.00
705 Brave Eagle,Ph(c) 50.00
706 Bongo and Lumpjaw 40.00
707 Corky and White Shadow,
    Ph(c) 60.00
708 Smokey the Bear 60.00
709 The Searchers,John
    Wayne Ph(c) 275.00
710 Francis the Famous
    Talking Mule 30.00
711 M.G.M.'s Mouse Musketeers 25.00
712 The Great Locomotive
    Chase, Ph(c) 75.00
713 The Animal World 40.00
714 W.Disney's Spin
    & Marty (TV) 100.00
715 Timmy 30.00
716 Man in Space 100.00
717 Moby Dick,Ph(c) 100.00
718 Dotty Dripple and Taffy 25.00
719 BF,Prince Valiant 75.00
720 Gunsmoke,Ph(c) 100.00
721 Captain Kangaroo,Ph(c) . . . 150.00
722 Johnny Mack Brown,Ph(c) . . 40.00
723 EK,Santiago 85.00
724 Bugs Bunny's Album 45.00

GOLDEN AGE

725 Elmer Fudd 20.00
726 Duck Album 40.00
727 The Nature of Things 60.00
728 M.G.M.'s Mouse Musketeers 20.00
729 Bob Son of Battle 30.00
730 Smokey Stover 30.00
731 EK,Silvertip and The
     Fighting Four 40.00
732 Zorro, (the Challenge of) . . 150.00
733 Buck Rogers 35.00
734 Cheyenne,C.Walker Ph(c) . 175.00
735 Crusader Rabbit 350.00
736 Pluto 45.00
737 Steve Canyon 55.00
738 Westward Ho, the Wagons,
     Ph(c) 90.00
739 MD,Bounty Guns 30.00
740 Chilly Willy 30.00
741 The Fastest Gun Alive,Ph(c) 60.00
742 Buffalo Bill Jr.,Ph(c) 55.00
743 Daisy Duck's Diary 45.00
744 Little Beaver 25.00
745 Francis the Famous
     Talking Mule 30.00
746 Dotty Dripple and Taffy 25.00
747 Goofy 90.00
748 Frosty the Snowman 30.00
749 Secrets of Life,Ph(c) 50.00
750 The Great Cat 50.00
751 Our Miss Brooks,Ph(c) 75.00
752 Mandrake, the Magician . . . 125.00
753 Walt Scott's Little People . . 30.00
754 Smokey the Bear 60.00
755 The Littlest Snowman 30.00
756 Santa Claus Funnies 30.00
757 The True Story of
     Jesse James,Ph(c) 90.00
758 Bear Country 45.00
759 Circus Boy,Ph(c) 100.00
760 W.Disney's Hardy Boys(TV) 125.00
761 Howdy Doody 125.00
762 SB,The Sharkfighters,Ph(c) 100.00
763 GrandmaDuck'sFarmFriends 75.00
764 M.G.M.'s Mouse Musketeers 20.00
765 Will-Yum! 20.00
766 Buffalo Bill,Ph(c) 35.00
767 Spin and Marty 75.00
768 EK,Steve Donovan, Western
     Marshal,Ph(c) 45.00
769 Gunsmoke 75.00
770 Brave Eagle,Ph(c) 30.00
771 MD,Brand of Empire 30.00
772 Cheyenne,C.Walker Ph(c) . 65.00
773 The Brave One,Ph(c) 35.00
774 Hi and Lois 25.00
775 SB,Sir Lancelot and
     Brian,Ph(c) 85.00
776 Johnny Mack Brown,Ph(c) . 40.00
777 Scamp 75.00
778 The Little Rascals 50.00
779 Lee Hunter, Indian Fighter . 40.00
780 Captain Kangaroo,Ph(c) . . 150.00
781 Fury,Ph(c) 75.00
782 Duck Album 50.00
783 Elmer Fudd 20.00
784 Around the World in 80
     Days,Ph(c) 75.00
785 Circus Boys,Ph(c) 100.00
786 Cinderella 50.00
787 Little Hiawatha 40.00
788 BF,Prince Valiant 75.00
789 EK,Silvertip-Valley Thieves . 45.00
790 ATh,The Wings of Eagles,
     J.Wayne Ph(c) 175.00
791 The 77th Bengal Lancers,

Ph(c) 65.00
792 Oswald the Rabbit 20.00
793 Morty Meekle 25.00
794 SB,The Count of Monte
     Cristo 85.00
795 Jiminy Cricket 65.00
796 Ludwig Bemelman's
     Madeleine and Genevieve . . . 35.00
797 Gunsmoke,Ph(c) 75.00
798 Buffalo Bill,Ph(c) 40.00
799 Priscilla's Pop 30.00
800 The Buccaneers,Ph(c) 50.00
801 Dotty Dripple and Taffy 25.00
802 Goofy 75.00
803 Cheyenne,C.Walker Ph(c) . 60.00
804 Steve Canyon 50.00
805 Crusader Rabbit 250.00
806 Scamp 65.00
807 MB,Savage Range 30.00
808 Spin and Marty,Ph(c) 75.00
809 The Little People 30.00
810 Francis the Famous
     Talking Mule 25.00

Dell Four Color #719
© Dell Publishing Co.

811 Howdy Doody 100.00
812 The Big Land,A.Ladd Ph(c) 100.00
813 Circus Boy,Ph(c) 100.00
814 Covered Wagon,A:Mickey
     Mouse 80.00
815 Dragoon Wells Massacre . . 75.00
816 Brave Eagle,Ph(c) 30.00
817 Little Beaver 25.00
818 Smokey the Bear 60.00
819 Mickey Mouse in Magicland 45.00
820 The Oklahoman,Ph(c) 120.00
821 Wringle Wrangle,Ph(c) 75.00
822 ATh,W.Disney's Paul Revere's
     Ride (TV) 125.00
823 Timmy 25.00
824 The Pride and the Passion,
     Ph(c) 100.00
825 The Little Rascals 50.00
826 Spin and Marty and Annette,
     Ph(c) 150.00
827 Smokey Stover 30.00
828 Buffalo Bill, Jr,Ph(c). 35.00
829 Tales of the Pony Express,
     Ph(c) 40.00
830 The Hardy Boys,Ph(c) . . . 100.00

831 No Sleep 'Til Dawn,Ph(c) . . 60.00
832 Lolly and Pepper 30.00
833 Scamp 75.00
834 Johnny Mack Brown,Ph(c) . 50.00
835 Silvertip- The Fake Rider . . 40.00
836 Man in Fight 75.00
837 All-American Athlete
     Cotton Woods 40.00
838 Bugs Bunny's Life
     Story Album 60.00
839 The Vigilantes 50.00
840 Duck Album 55.00
841 Elmer Fudd 20.00
842 The Nature of Things 70.00
843 The First Americans 85.00
844 Gunsmoke,Ph(c) 100.00
845 ATh,The Land Unknown . . 150.00
846 ATh,Gun Glory 125.00
847 Perri 65.00
848 Marauder's Moon 40.00
849 BF,Prince Valiant 75.00
850 Buck Jones 30.00
851 The Story of Mankind,
     V.Price Ph(c) 60.00
852 Chilly Willy 30.00
853 Pluto 50.00
854 Hunchback of Notre Dame,
     Ph(c) 125.00
855 Broken Arrow,Ph(c) 45.00
856 Buffalo Bill, Jr.,Ph(c) 40.00
857 The Goofy Adventure Story . 75.00
858 Daisy Duck's Diary 50.00
859 Topper and Neil 30.00
860 Wyatt Earp,Ph(c) 100.00
861 Frosty the Snowman 30.00
862 Truth About Mother Goose . 65.00
863 Francis the Famous
     Talking Mule 30.00
864 The Littlest Snowman 30.00
865 Andy Burnett,Ph(c) 75.00
866 Mars and Beyond 100.00
867 Santa Claus Funnies 30.00
868 The Little People 30.00
869 Old Yeller,Ph(c) 75.00
870 Little Beaver 25.00
871 Curly Kayoe 25.00
872 Captain Kangaroo,Ph(c) . . 150.00
873 Grandma Duck's
     Farm Friends 50.00
874 Old Ironsides 60.00
875 Trumpets West 30.00
876 Tales of Wells Fargo,Ph(c) . 75.00
877 ATh,Frontier Doctor,Ph(c) . 100.00
878 Peanuts 150.00
879 Brave Eagle,Ph(c) 30.00
880 MD,Steve Donovan,Ph(c) . . 40.00
881 The Captain and the Kids . . 25.00
882 ATh,W.DisneyPresentsZorro 200.00
883 The Little Rascals 50.00
884 Hawkeye and the Last
     of the Mohicans,Ph(c) 75.00
885 Fury,Ph(c) 60.00
886 Bongo and Lumpjaw 30.00
887 The Hardy Boys,Ph(c) 75.00
888 Elmer Fudd 20.00
889 ATh,W.Disney's Clint
     & Mac(TV),Ph(c) 100.00
890 Wyatt Earp,Ph(c) 60.00
891 Light in the Forest,
     C.Parker Ph(c) 75.00
892 Maverick,J.Garner Ph(c) . . 300.00
893 Jim Bowie,Ph(c) 50.00
894 Oswald the Rabbit 20.00
895 Wagon Train,Ph(c) 150.00
896 Adventures of Tinker Bell . . 60.00

All comics prices listed are for *Near Mint* condition.

897 Jiminy Cricket 50.00
898 EK,Silvertip 45.00
899 Goofy 60.00
900 BF,Prince Valiant 75.00
901 Little Hiawatha 60.00
902 Will-Yum! 25.00
903 Dotty Dripple and Taffy ... 25.00
904 Lee Hunter, Indian Fighter . 30.00
905 W.Disney's Annette (TV),
   Ph(c) 250.00
906 Francis the Famous
   Talking Mule 30.00
907 Ath,Sugarfoot,Ph(c) 150.00
908 The Little People
   and the Giant 30.00
909 Smitty 25.00
910 ATh,The Vikings,
   K.Douglas Ph(c) 100.00
911 The Gray Ghost,Ph(c) ... 100.00
912 Leave it to Beaver,Ph(c) . 200.00
913 The Left-Handed Gun,
   Paul Newman Ph(c) 100.00
914 ATh,No Time for Sergeants,
   Ph(c) 125.00
915 Casey Jones,Ph(c) 50.00
916 Red Ryder Ranch Comics . 25.00
917 The Life of Riley,Ph(c) .. 125.00
918 Beep Beep, the Roadrunner 100.00
919 Boots and Saddles,Ph(c) . 75.00
920 Ath,Zorro,Ph(c) 150.00
921 Wyatt Earp.Ph(c) 60.00
922 Johnny Mack Brown,Ph(c) . 50.00
923 Timmy 20.00
924 Colt .45,Ph(c) 75.00
925 Last of the Fast Guns,Ph(c) 60.00
926 Peter Pan 35.00
927 SB,Top Gun 30.00
928 Sea Hunt,L.Bridges Ph(c) . 125.00
929 Brave Eagle,Ph(c) 30.00
930 Maverick,J. Garner Ph(c) . 125.00
931 Have Gun, Will Travel,Ph(c) 125.00
932 Smokey the Bear 60.00
933 ATh,W.Disney's Zorro 150.00
934 Restless Gun 100.00
935 King of the Royal Mounted . 30.00
936 The Little Rascals 50.00
937 Ruff and Ready 125.00
938 Elmer Fudd 20.00
939 Steve Canyon 60.00
940 Lolly and Pepper 25.00
941 Pluto 40.00
942 Pony Express 40.00
943 White Wilderness 60.00
944 SB,7th Voyage of Sinbad . 150.00
945 Maverick,J.Garner Ph(c) . 125.00
946 The Big Country,Ph(c) ... 60.00
947 Broken Arrow,Ph(c) 40.00
948 Daisy Duck's Diary 50.00
949 High Adventure,Ph(c) 45.00
950 Frosty the Snowman 30.00
951 ATh,Lennon Sisters
   Life Story,Ph(c) 150.00
952 Goofy 60.00
953 Francis the Famous
   Talking Mule 30.00
954 Man in Space 75.00
955 Hi and Lois 25.00
956 Ricky Nelson,Ph(c) 225.00
957 Buffalo Bee 75.00
958 Santa Claus Funnies 30.00
959 Christmas Stories 30.00
960 ATh,W.Disney's Zorro 150.00
961 Jace Pearson's Tales of
   Texas Rangers,Ph(c) 40.00
962 Maverick,J.Garner Ph(c) . 125.00

963 Johnny Mack Brown,Ph(c) . 40.00
964 The Hardy Boys,Ph(c) ... 85.00
965 GrandmaDuck'sFarmFriends 55.00
966 Tonka,Ph(c) 75.00
967 Chilly Willy 25.00
968 Tales of Wells Fargo,Ph(c) . 75.00
969 Peanuts 125.00
970 Lawman,Ph(c) 125.00
971 Wagon Train,Ph(c) 75.00
972 Tom Thumb 85.00
973 SleepingBeauty & the Prince 150.00
974 The Little Rascals 50.00
975 Fury,Ph(c) 50.00
976 ATh,W.Disney's Zorro,Ph(c) 150.00
977 Elmer Fudd 20.00
978 Lolly and Pepper 20.00
979 Oswald the Rabbit 20.00
980 Maverick,J.Garner Ph(c) . . 125.00
981 Ruff and Ready 100.00
982 The New Adventures of
   Tinker Bell 65.00
983 Have Gun, Will Travel,Ph(c) 100.00
984 Sleeping Beauty's Fairy

WALT DISNEY'S
ZORRO

Dell Four Color #976
© Dell Publishing Co.

Godmothers 75.00
985 Shaggy Dog,Ph(c) 75.00
986 Restless Gun,Ph(c) 75.00
987 Goofy 60.00
988 Little Hiawatha 30.00
989 Jimmy Cricket 50.00
990 Huckleberry Hound 125.00
991 Francis the Famous
   Talking Mule 30.00
992 ATh,Sugarfoot,Ph(c) 100.00
993 Jim Bowie,Ph(c) 50.00
994 Sea Hunt,L.Bridges Ph(c) . 100.00
995 Donald Duck Album 55.00
996 Nevada 30.00
997 Walt Disney Presents,Ph(c) . 65.00
998 Ricky Nelson,Ph(c) 225.00
999 Leave It To Beaver,Ph(c) . 175.00
1000 The Gray Ghost,Ph(c) .. 100.00
1001 Lowell Thomas' High
   Adventure,Ph(c) 45.00
1002 Buffalo Bee 50.00
1003 ATh,W.Disney's Zorro,Ph(c)150.00
1004 Colt .45,Ph(c) 60.00
1005 Maverick,J.Garner Ph(c) . 125.00
1006 SB,Hercules 100.00

1007 John Paul Jones,Ph(c) ... 45.00
1008 Beep, Beep, the
   Road Runner 50.00
1009 CB,The Rifleman,Ph(c) . 250.00
1010 Grandma Duck's Farm
   Friends 125.00
1011 Buckskin,Ph(c) 75.00
1012 Last Train from Gun
   Hill,Ph(c) 75.00
1013 Bat Masterson,Ph(c) ... 135.00
1014 ATh,The Lennon Sisters,
   Ph(c) 150.00
1015 Peanuts 100.00
1016 Smokey the Bear 50.00
1017 Chilly Willy 25.00
1018 Rio Bravo,J.Wayne Ph(c) 225.00
1019 Wagoon Train,Ph(c) ... 75.00
1020 Jungle 25.00
1021 Jace Pearson's Tales of
   the Texas Rangers,Ph(c) . 45.00
1022 Timmy 25.00
1023 Tales of Wells Fargo,Ph(c) 75.00
1024 ATh,Darby O'Gill and
   the Little People,Ph(c) ... 100.00
1025 CB,W.Disney's Vacation in
   Disneyland 225.00
1026 Spin and Marty,Ph(c) ... 60.00
1027 The Texan,Ph(c) 60.00
1028 Rawhide,
   Clint Eastwood Ph(c) 250.00
1029 Boots and Saddles,Ph(c) . 50.00
1030 Spanky and Alfalfa, the
   Little Rascals 50.00
1031 Fury,Ph(c) 60.00
1032 Elmer Fudd 20.00
1033 Steve Canyon,Ph(c) ... 60.00
1034 Nancy and Sluggo
   Summer Camp 25.00
1035 Lawman,Ph(c) 75.00
1036 The Big Circus,Ph(c) ... 60.00
1037 Zorro,Ph(c) 175.00
1038 Ruff and Ready 75.00
1039 Pluto 40.00
1040 Quick Draw McGraw ... 150.00
1041 ATh,Sea Hunt,
   L.Bridges Ph(c) 100.00
1042 The Three Chipmunks ... 40.00
1043 The Three Stooges,Ph(c) . 225.00
1044 Have Gun,Will Travel,Ph(c) 100.00
1045 Restless Gun,Ph(c) 75.00
1046 Beep Beep, the
   Road Runner 50.00
1047 CB,W.Disney's
   GyroGearloose 200.00
1048 The Horse Soldiers
   J.Wayne Ph(c) 165.00
1049 Don't Give Up the Ship
   J.Lewis Ph(c) 60.00
1050 Huckleberry Hound 75.00
1051 Donald in Mathmagic Land 100.00
1052 RsM,Ben-Hur 125.00
1053 Goofy 60.00
1054 Huckleberry Hound
   Winter Fun 75.00
1055 CB,Daisy Duck's Diary . 125.00
1056 Yellowstone Kelly,
   C.Walker Ph(c) 50.00
1057 Mickey Mouse Album ... 40.00
1058 Colt .45,Ph(c) 60.00
1059 Sugarfoot 75.00
1060 Journey to the Center of the
   Earth, P.Boone Ph(c) 125.00
1061 Buffalo Bill 50.00
1062 Christmas Stories 35.00
1063 Santa Claus Funnies ... 35.00

GOLDEN AGE

1064 Bugs Bunny's Merry
   Christmas 55.00
1065 Frosty the Snowman 30.00
1066 ATh,77 Sunset Strip,Ph(c) 150.00
1067 Yogi Bear 120.00
1068 Francis the Famous
   Talking Mule 30.00
1069 ATh,The FBI Story,Ph(c) . 125.00
1070 Soloman and Sheba,Ph(c) 75.00
1071 ATh,TheRealMcCoys,Ph(c) 125.00
1072 Blythe 40.00
1073 CB,Grandma Duck's Farm
   Friends 150.00
1074 Chilly Willy 25.00
1075 Tales of Wells Fargo,Ph(c) 75.00
1076 MSy,The Rebel,Ph(c) . . . 125.00
1077 SB,The Deputy,
   H.Fonda Ph(c) 150.00
1078 The Three Stooges,Ph(c) 125.00
1079 The Little Rascals 50.00
1080 Fury,Ph(c) 60.00
1081 Elmer Fudd 20.00
1082 Spin and Marty 60.00
1083 Men into Space,Ph(c) 75.00
1084 Speedy Gonzales 35.00
1085 ATh,The Time Machine . . 175.00
1086 Lolly and Pepper 25.00
1087 Peter Gunn,Ph(c) 110.00
1088 A Dog of Flanders,Ph(c) . . 35.00
1089 Restless Gun,Ph(c) 70.00
1090 Francis the Famous
   Talking Mule 30.00
1091 Jacky's Diary 40.00
1092 Toby Tyler,Ph(c) 50.00
1093 MacKenzie's Raiders,Ph(c) 60.00
1094 Goofy 55.00
1095 CB,W.Disney's
   GyroGearloose 125.00
1096 The Texan,Ph(c) 60.00
1097 Rawhide,C.Eastwood Ph(c) 175.00
1098 Sugarfoot,Ph(c) 75.00
1099 CB(c),Donald Duck Album . 75.00
1100 W.Disney's Annette's
   Life Story (TV),Ph(c) 225.00
1101 Robert Louis Stevenson's
   Kidnapped,Ph(c) 60.00
1102 Wanted: Dead or Alive,
   Ph(c) 150.00
1103 Leave It To Beaver,Ph(c) . 175.00
1104 Yogi Bear Goes to College 75.00
1105 ATh,Gale Storm,Ph(c) . . . 125.00
1106 ATh,77 Sunset Strip,Ph(c) 125.00
1107 Buckskin,Ph(c) 60.00
1108 The Troubleshooters,Ph(c) 50.00
1109 This Is Your Life, Donald
   Duck,O:Donald Duck 175.00
1110 Bonanza,Ph(c) 400.00
1111 Shotgun Slade 50.00
1112 Pixie and Dixie
   and Mr. Jinks 60.00
1113 Tales of Wells Fargo,Ph(c) 75.00
1114 Huckleberry Finn,Ph(c) . . . 40.00
1115 Ricky Nelson,Ph(c) 165.00
1116 Boots and Saddles,Ph(c) . . 50.00
1117 Boy and the Pirate,Ph(c) . . 50.00
1118 Sword and the Dragon,Ph(c) 60.00
1119 Smokey and the Bear
   Nature Stories 50.00
1120 Dinosaurus,Ph(c) 75.00
1121 RC,GE,HerculesUnchained 120.00
1122 Chilly Willy 25.00
1123 Tombstone Territory,Ph(c) . 75.00
1124 Whirlybirds,Ph(c) 60.00
1125 GK,RH,Laramie,Ph(c) . . . 125.00
1126 Sundance,Ph(c) 75.00

Dell Four Color #1028
© Dell Publishing Co.

1127 The Three Stooges,Ph(c) 125.00
1128 Rocky and His Friends . . 425.00
1129 Pollyanna,H.Mills Ph(c) . . . 85.00
1130 SB,The Deputy,
   H.Fonda Ph(c) 125.00
1131 Elmer Fudd 20.00
1132 Space Mouse 30.00
1133 Fury,Ph(c) 50.00
1134 ATh,Real McCoys,Ph(c) . . 110.00
1135 M.G.M.'s Mouse Musketeers 60.00
1136 Jungle Cat,Ph(c) 45.00
1137 The Little Rascals 50.00
1138 The Rebel,Ph(c) 100.00
1139 SB,Spartacus,Ph(c) 150.00
1140 Donald Duck Album 65.00
1141 Huckleberry Hound for
   President 75.00
1142 Johnny Ringo,Ph(c) 65.00
1143 Pluto 40.00
1144 The Story of Ruth,Ph(c) . . 110.00
1145 GK,The Lost World,Ph(c) . 125.00
1146 Restless Gun,Ph(c) 65.00
1147 Sugarfoot,Ph(c) 75.00
1148 I aim at the Stars,Ph(c) . . . 75.00
1149 Goofy 55.00
1150 CB,Daisy Duck's Diary . . . 125.00
1151 Mickey Mouse Album 40.00
1152 Rocky and His Friends . . 275.00
1153 Frosty the Snowman 30.00
1154 Santa Claus Funnies 30.00
1155 North to Alaska 175.00
1156 Walt Disney Swiss
   Family Robinson 65.00
1157 Master of the World 50.00
1158 Three Worlds of Gulliver . . 50.00
1159 ATh,77 Sunset Strip 125.00
1160 Rawhide 175.00
1161 CB,Grandma Duck's
   Farm Friends 150.00
1162 Yogi Bera joins the Marines 75.00
1163 Daniel Boone 50.00
1164 Wanted: Dead or Alive . . 100.00
1165 Ellery Queen 125.00
1166 Rocky and His Friends . . 275.00
1167 Tales of Wells Fargo,Ph(c) . 65.00
1168 The Detectives,
   R.Taylor Ph(c) 125.00
1169 New Adventures of

Sherlock Holmes 150.00
1170 The Three Stooges,Ph(c) 125.00
1171 Elmer Fudd 20.00
1172 Fury,Ph(c) 50.00
1173 The Twilight Zone 235.00
1174 The Little Rascals 40.00
1175 M.G.M.'s Mouse Musketeers 25.00
1176 Dondi,Ph(c) 45.00
1177 Chilly Willy 25.00
1178 Ten Who Dared 60.00
1179 The Swamp Fox,
   L.Nielson Ph(c) 75.00
1180 The Danny Thomas Show 165.00
1181 Texas John Slaughter,Ph(c) 60.00
1182 Donald Duck Album 45.00
1183 101 Dalmatians 125.00
1184 CB,W.Disney's
   Gyro Gearloose 125.00
1185 Sweetie Pie 30.00
1186 JDa,Yak Yak 100.00
1187 The Three Stooges,Ph(c) 125.00
1188 Atlantis the Lost
   Continent,Ph(c) 110.00
1189 Greyfriars Bobby,Ph(c) . . . 50.00
1190 CB(c),Donald and
   the Wheel 75.00
1191 Leave It to Beaver,Ph(c) . 175.00
1192 Rocky Nelson,Ph(c) 175.00
1193 The Real McCoys 100.00
1194 Pepe,Ph(c) 45.00
1195 National Velvet,Ph(c) 65.00
1196 Pixie and Dixie
   and Mr. Jinks 40.00
1197 The Aquanauts,Ph(c) 60.00
1198 Donald in Mathmagic Land 75.00
1199 Absent-Minded Professor,
   Ph(c) 75.00
1200 Hennessey,Ph(c) 60.00
1201 Goofy 55.00
1202 Rawhide,C.Eastwood Ph(c) 175.00
1203 Pinocchio 60.00
1204 Scamp 40.00
1205 David & Goliath,Ph(c) 50.00
1206 Lolly and Pepper 25.00
1207 MSy,The Rebel,Ph(c) . . . 100.00
1208 Rocky and His Friends . . 275.00
1209 Sugarfoot,Ph(c) 75.00
1210 The Parent Trap,
   H.Mills Ph(c) 85.00
1211 RsM,77 Sunset Strip,Ph(c) 100.00
1212 Chilly Willy 25.00
1213 Mysterious Island,Ph(c) . . 100.00
1214 Smokey the Bear 50.00
1215 Tales of Wells Fargo,Ph(c) 65.00
1216 Whirlybirds,Ph(c) 75.00
1218 Fury,Ph(c) 50.00
1219 The Detectives,
   Robert Taylor Ph(c) 85.00
1220 Gunslinger,Ph(c) 75.00
1221 Bonanza,Ph(c) 200.00
1222 Elmer Fudd 20.00
1223 GK,Laramie,Ph(c) 75.00
1224 The Little Rascals 40.00
1225 The Deputy,H.Fonda Ph(c) 85.00
1226 Nikki, Wild Dog of the North 50.00
1227 Morgan the Pirate,Ph(c) . . 75.00
1229 Thief of Bagdad,Ph(c) 70.00
1230 Voyage to the Bottom
   of the Sea,Ph(c) 125.00
1231 Danger Man,Ph(c) 125.00
1232 On the Double 40.00
1233 Tammy Tell Me True 60.00
1234 The Phantom Planet 75.00
1235 Mister Magoo 125.00
1236 King of Kings,Ph(c) 100.00

GOLDEN AGE

1237 ATh,The Untouchables, Ph(c)	250.00
1238 Deputy Dawg	125.00
1239 CB(c),Donald Duck Album	65.00
1240 The Detectives, R.Taylor Ph(c)	85.00
1241 Sweetie Pies	30.00
1242 King Leonardo and His Short Subjects	150.00
1243 Ellery Queen	75.00
1244 Space Mouse	30.00
1245 New Adventures of Sherlock Holmes	150.00
1246 Mickey Mouse Album	40.00
1247 Daisy Duck's Diary	45.00
1248 Pluto	40.00
1249 The Danny Thomas Show, Ph(c)	175.00
1250 Four Horseman of the Apocalypse,Ph(c)	75.00
1251 Everything's Ducky	60.00
1252 The Andy Griffith Show, Ph(c)	325.00
1253 Spaceman	100.00
1254 "Diver Dan"	50.00
1255 The Wonders of Aladdin	50.00
1256 Kona, Monarch of Monster Isle	50.00
1257 Car 54, Where Are You?, Ph(c)	100.00
1258 GE,The Frogmen	60.00
1259 El Cid,Ph(c)	60.00
1260 The Horsemasters,Ph(c)	125.00
1261 Rawhide,C.Eastwood Ph(c)	175.00
1262 The Rebel,Ph(c)	100.00
1263 RsM,77 Sinset Strip,Ph(c)	100.00
1264 Pixie & Dixie & Mr.Jinks	40.00
1265 The Real McCoys,Ph(c)	100.00
1266 M.G.M.'s Spike and Tyke	15.00
1267 CB,GyroGearloose	75.00
1268 Oswald the Rabbit	20.00
1269 Rawhide,C.Eastwood Ph(c)	175.00
1270 Bullwinkle and Rocky	225.00
1271 Yogi Bear Birthday Party	50.00
1272 Frosty the Snowman	25.00
1273 Hans Brinker,Ph(c)	60.00
1274 Santa Claus Funnies	30.00
1275 Rocky and His Friends	225.00
1276 Dondi	30.00
1278 King Leonardo and His Short Subjects	150.00
1279 Grandma Duck's Farm Friends	55.00
1280 Hennessey,Ph(c)	50.00
1281 Chilly Willy	25.00
1282 Babes in Toyland,Ph(c)	100.00
1283 Bonanza,Ph(c)	200.00
1284 RH,Laramie,Ph(c)	75.00
1285 Leave It to Beaver,Ph(c)	175.00
1286 The Untouchables,Ph(c)	175.00
1287 Man from Wells Fargo,Ph(c)	40.00
1288 RC,GE,The Twilight Zone	150.00
1289 Ellery Queen	75.00
1290 M.G.M.'s Mouse Musketeers	25.00
1291 RsM,77 Sunset Strip,Ph(c)	100.00
1293 Elmer Fudd	20.00
1294 Ripcord	60.00
1295 Mr. Ed, the Talking Horse, Ph(c)	100.00
1296 Fury,Ph(c)	50.00
1297 Spanky, Alfalfa and the Little Rascals	40.00
1298 The Hathaways,Ph(c)	35.00
1299 Deputy Dawg	125.00

1300 The Comancheros	175.00
1301 Adventures in Paradise	40.00
1302 JohnnyJason,TeenReporter	25.00
1303 Lad: A Dog,Ph(c)	30.00
1304 Nellie the Nurse	75.00
1305 Mister Magoo	125.00
1306 Target: The Corruptors, Ph(c)	55.00
1307 Margie	45.00
1308 Tales of the Wizard of Oz	75.00
1309 BK,87th Precinct,Ph(c)	85.00
1310 Huck and Yogi Winter Sports	75.00
1311 Rocky and His Friends	275.00
1312 National Velvet,Ph(c)	35.00
1313 Moon Pilot.Ph(c)	75.00
1328 GE,The Underwater City,Ph(c)	60.00
1330 GK,Brain Boy	100.00
1332 Bachelor Father	75.00
1333 Short Ribs	40.00
1335 Aggie Mack	30.00
1336 On Stage	40.00
1337 Dr. Kildare,Ph(c)	100.00
1341 The Andy Griffith Show, Ph(c)	300.00
1348 JDa,Yak Yak	100.00
1349 Yogi Berra Visits the U.N.	100.00
1350 Commanche,Ph(c)	50.00
1354 Calvin and the Colonel	60.00

FOUR FAVORITES
Ace Magazines
September, 1941

1 B:Vulcan, Lash Lighting, Magno the Magnetic Man, Raven, Flag cover,Hitler	1,000.00
2 A: Black Ace	400.00
3 E:Vulcan	350.00
4 E:Raven,B:Unknown Soldiers	350.00
5 B:Captain Courageous	325.00
6 A: The Flag, B: Mr. Risk	325.00
7 JM	300.00
8	300.00
9 RP,HK	300.00
10 HK	350.00
11 HK,LbC,UnKnown Soldier	325.00
12 LbC	225.00
13 LbC	175.00
14 Fer	175.00
15 Fer	175.00
16 Bondage(c)	200.00
17 Magno Lighting	150.00
18 Magno Lighting	150.00
19 RP,RP(c)	150.00
20 RP,RP(c)	150.00
21 RP,RP(c)	125.00
22 RP(c)	125.00
23 RP(c)	125.00
24 RP(c)	125.00
25 RP(c)	125.00
26 RP(c)	125.00
27 RP(c)	110.00
28	100.00
29	100.00
30	100.00
31	100.00
32	100.00

FRANKENSTEIN COMICS
Crestwood Publications
(Prize Publ.)
Summer, 1945

1 B:Frankenstein,DBr, DBr(c)	800.00

2 DBr,DBr(c)	400.00
3 DBr,DBr(c)	275.00
4 DBr,DBr(c)	275.00
5 DBr,DBr(c)	275.00
6 DBr,DBr(c),S&K	250.00
7 DBr,DBr(c),S&K	250.00
8 DBr,DBr(c),S&K	250.00
9 DBr,DBr(c),S&K	250.00
10 DBr,DBr(c),S&K	250.00
11 DBr,DBr(c)A:Boris Karloff	200.00
12 DBr,DBr(c)	200.00
13 DBr,DBr(c).	200.00
14 DBr,DBr(c)	200.00
15 DBr,DBr(c)	200.00
16 DBr,DBr(c)	200.00

Frankenstein #23
© Crestwood/Prize Publications

17 DBr,DBr(c)	200.00
18 B:Horror	300.00
19	175.00
3-4	150.00
3-5	150.00
3-6	150.00
4-1 thru 4-6	@150.00
5-1 thru 5-4	@150.00
5-5 October-November, 1954	150.00

FRISKY FABLES
Novelty Press/Premium Group
Spring, 1945

1 AFa	75.00
2 AFa	40.00
3 AFa	35.00
4 AFa	28.00
5 AFa	28.00
6 AFa	28.00
7 AFa,Flag (c)	30.00
2-1 AFa,Rainbow(c)	25.00
2-2 AFa	20.00
2-3 AFa	20.00
2-4 AFa	20.00
2-5 AFa	20.00
2-6 AFa	20.00
2-7 AFa	20.00
2-8 AFa,Halloween (c)	20.00
2-9 AFa,Thanksgiving(c)	18.00
2-10 AFa,Christmas cover	20.00
2-11 AFa	20.00
2-12 AFa,Valentines Day cover	18.00

3-1 AFa	15.00
3-2 AFa	15.00
3-3 AFa	18.00
3-4 AFa	15.00
3-5 AFa	15.00
3-6 AFa	15.00
3-7 AFa	15.00
3-8 AFa,Turkey (c)	15.00
3-9 AFa	15.00
3-10 AFa	15.00
3-11 AFa,1948(c)	15.00
3-12 AFa	15.00
4-1 thru 4-7 AFa	@15.00
5-1 AFa	15.00
5-2 AFa	15.00
5-3	15.00
5-4 Star Publications	15.00
39 LbC(c)	50.00
40 LbC(c)	50.00
41 LbC(c)	50.00
42 LbC(c)	50.00
43 LbC(c)	20.00

Becomes:

FRISKY ANIMALS
Star Publications

44 LbC	70.00
45 LbC	100.00
46 LbC,Baseball	60.00
47 LbC	60.00
48 LbC	60.00
49 LbC	60.00
50 LbC	60.00
51 LbC(c)	60.00
52 LbC(c)	75.00
53 LbC(c)	55.00
54 LbC(c),Supercat(c)	55.00
55 LbC(c),same	55.00
56 LbC(c),same	55.00
57 LbC(c),same	55.00
58 LbC(c),same,July, 1954	55.00

FRITZI RITZ
United Features Syndicate/
St. John Publications
Fall, 1948

N# Special issue	100.00
2	50.00
3	40.00
4 thru 7	@30.00
6 A:Abbie & Slats	35.00
8 thru 10	@25.00
11 1958	25.00

FROGMAN COMICS
Hillman Periodicals
Jan.-Feb., 1952–May 1953

1	75.00
2	40.00
3	40.00
4 MMe	30.00
5 BK,AT	40.00
6	25.00
7	25.00
8 thru 11	@25.00

FRONTIER ROMANCES
Avon Periodicals
November-December, 1949

1 She Learned to Ride and Shoot, and Kissing Came Natural	400.00
2 Bronc-Busters Sweetheart, January-February, 1950	250.00

FRONTLINE COMBAT
Tiny Tot Publications
(E.C. Comics)
July-August, 1951

1 HK(c),WW, JSe,JDa,Hanhung Changjn cover	500.00
2 HK(c),WW,Tank Battle cover	300.00
3 HK(c),WW,Naval Battleship fire cover	275.00
4 HK(c),WW, Bazooka cover	225.00
5 HK(c),JSe	200.00
6 HK(c),WW,JSe	175.00
7 HK(c),WW,JSe,Document of the Action at Iwo Jima	175.00
8 HK(c),WW,ATh	175.00
9 HK(c),WW,JSe,Civil War iss.	175.00
10 GE,HK(c),WW, Crying Child cover	225.00
11 GE	150.00
12 GE,Air Force issue	150.00
13 JSe,GE,WW(c), Bi-Planes cover	150.00
14 JKu,GE,WW(c)	150.00
15 JSe,GE,WW(c), Jan., 1954	150.00

FRONT PAGE COMIC BOOK
Front Page Comics
1945

1 JKu,BP,BF(c),I:Man in Black	275.00

FUGITIVES FROM JUSTICE
St. John Publishing Co.
February, 1952

1	125.00
2 MB, Killer Boomerang	150.00
3 GT	125.00
4	50.00
5 Bondage cover, October, 1952	70.00

FUNNIES, THE
(1ST SERIES)
Dell Publishing Co.
1929-30

1 B:Foxy Grandpa, Sniffy	600.00
2 thru 21	@250.00
N#(22)	225.00
N#(23) thru (36)	@200.00

FUNNIES, THE
(2ND SERIES)
Dell Publishing Co.
October, 1936

1 Tailspin Tommy,Mutt & Jeff, Capt. Easy,D.Dixon	2,200.00
2 Scribbly	1,000.00
3	700.00
4 Christmas issue	550.00
5	550.00
6 thru 22	@400.00
23 thru 29	@300.00
30 B:John Carter of Mars	900.00
31 inc. Dick Tracy	550.00
32	550.00
33	550.00
34	550.00
35 John Carter (c)	550.00
36 John Carter (c)	550.00
37 John Carter (c)	550.00
38 Rex King of the Deep (c)	550.00
39 Rex King (c)	550.00

40 John Carter (c)	550.00
41 Sky Ranger (c)	550.00
42 Rex King (c)	550.00
43 Rex King (c)	550.00
44 Rex King (c)	550.00
45 I&O:Phantasmo:Master of the World	450.00
46 Phantasmo (c)	450.00
47 Phantasmo (c)	350.00
48 Phantasmo (c)	325.00
49 Phantasmo (c)	325.00
50 Phantasmo (c)	325.00
51 Phantasmo (c)	325.00
52 Phantasmo (c)	350.00
53 Phantasmo (c)	350.00
54 Phantasmo (c)	350.00
55 Phantasmo (c)	350.00
56 Phantasmo (c) E:John Carter	350.00
57 I&O:Captain Midnight	1,200.00
58 Captain Midnight (c)	550.00
59 Captain Midnight (c)	500.00
60 Captain Midnight (c)	500.00
61 Captain Midnight (c)	475.00
62 Captain Midnight (c)	450.00
63 Captain Midnight (c)	450.00
64 B: Woody Woodpecker	650.00

New Funnies #70 © Dell Publishing Co.

Becomes:

NEW FUNNIES
Dell Publishing Co.
July, 1942

65 Andy Panda, Ragady Ann & Andy, Peter Rabbit	650.00
66 same	350.00
67 Felix the Cat	350.00
68	350.00
69 WK, The Brownies	350.00
70	350.00
71	200.00
72 WK	200.00
73	200.00
74	200.00
75 WK,Brownies	200.00
76 CB,Andy Panda, Woody Woodpecker	1,100.00
77 same	200.00
78 Andy Panda	200.00
79	150.00
80	150.00

81 . . . . 150.00
82 WK,Brownies 175.00
83 WK,Brownies 175.00
84 WK,Brownies 150.00
85 WK,Brownies 175.00
86 . . . . 125.00
87 Woody Woodpecker 100.00
88 same 100.00
89 same 100.00
90 same 100.00
91 thru 99 . . . . @75.00
100 . . . . 85.00
101 thru 110 . . . . @50.00
111 thru 118 . . . . @40.00
119 Christmas 35.00
120 thru 142 . . . . @30.00
143 Christmas cover 35.00
144 thru 149 . . . . @30.00
150 thru 154 . . . . @20.00
155 Christmas cover 22.00
156 thru 167 . . . . @20.00
168 Christmas cover 22.00
169 thru 181 . . . . @20.00
182 I&O:Knothead & Splinter . . . 20.00
183 thru 200 . . . . @20.00
201 thru 240 . . . . @15.00
241 thru 288 . . . . @10.00

FUNNY BOOK
Funny Book Publ. Corp.
(Parents Magazine)
December, 1952
1 Alec, the Funny Bunny,
   Alice in Wonderland 100.00
2 Gulliver in Giant-Land 45.00
3 . . . . 35.00
4 Adventures of Robin Hood . . 30.00
5 . . . . 30.00
6 . . . . 30.00
7 . . . . 30.00
8 . . . . 30.00
9 . . . . 30.00

FUNNY FILMS
Best Syndicated Features
(American Comics Group)
September-October, 1949
1 B:Puss An' Boots,
   Blunderbunny 125.00
2 . . . . 75.00
3 . . . . 40.00
4 . . . . 35.00
5 . . . . 35.00
6 . . . . 35.00
7 . . . . 35.00
8 . . . . 35.00
9 . . . . 35.00
10 . . . . 35.00
11 thru 20 . . . . @25.00
21 thru 28 . . . . @22.00
29 May-June, 1954 . . . . 22.00

FUNNY FUNNIES
Nedor Publ. Co.
April, 1943
1 Funny Animals 135.00

FUNNYMAN
Magazine Enterprises of
Canada
December, 1947
1 S&K,S&K(c) 300.00
2 S&K,S&K(c) 175.00

3 S&K,S&K(c) 150.00
4 S&K,S&K(c) 150.00
5 S&K,S&K(c) 150.00
6 S&K,S&K(c), August, 1948 . 150.00

FUTURE COMICS
David McKay Publications
June, 1940
1 Lone Ranger,Phantom . . . 2,000.00
2 Lone Ranger 950.00
3 Lone Ranger 800.00
4 Lone Ranger,Sept., 1940 . . 750.00

FUTURE WORLD COMICS
George W. Dougherty
Summer, 1946
1 . . . . 165.00
2 Fall, 1946 . . . . 150.00

GABBY HAYES WESTERN
Fawcett Publ./Charlton Comics
November, 1948
1 Ph(c) 350.00
2 Ph(c) 150.00
3 The Rage of the Purple Sage,
   Ph(c) 100.00
4 Ph(c) 100.00
5 Ph(c) 85.00
6 Ph(c) 85.00
7 Ph(c) 75.00
8 Ph(c) 75.00
9 Ph(c),V:The Kangaroo Crook . 75.00
10 Ph(c) 75.00
11 Ph(c), Chariot Race 75.00
12 V:Beaver Ben, The Biting Bandit,
   Ph(c) 65.00
13 thru 15 . . . . @65.00
16 . . . . 50.00
17 . . . . 50.00
18 thru 20 . . . . @50.00
21 thru 51 . . . . @35.00
51 thru 59 December, 1954 . . @20.00

GANGSTERS AND GUN MOLLS
Realistic Comics
(Avon)
September, 1951
1 WW,A:Big Jim Colosimo,
   Evelyn Ellis 325.00
2 JKa, A:Bonnie Parker, The
   Kissing Bandit 250.00
3 EK, A:Juanita Perez, Crimes
   Homicide Squad 225.00
4 A:Mara Hite, Elkins Boys,
   June, 1952 . . . . 175.00

GANGSTERS CAN'T WIN
D.S. Publishing Co.
February-March, 1948
1 Shot Cop cover 200.00
2 A:Eddie Bentz 100.00
3 Twin Trouble Trigger Man . . 75.00
4 Suicide on SoundStageSeven . 75.00
5 Trail of Terror 75.00
6 Mystery at the Circus 75.00
7 Talisman Trail 60.00
8 . . . . 60.00
9 Suprise at Buoy 13,
   June-July, 1949 . . . . 60.00

GANG WORLD
Literary Enterprises
(Standard Comics)
October, 1952
5 Bondage cover 125.00
6 Mob Payoff, January, 1953 . 100.00

GASOLINE ALLEY
Star Publications
October, 1950
1 . . . . 150.00
2 LBc 90.00
3 LBc(c), April, 1950 . . . . 125.00

GEM COMICS
Spotlight Publ.
April, 1945
1 A:Steve Strong,Bondage(c) . 175.00

Gene Autry Comics #2
© Fawcett Publications

GENE AUTRY COMICS
Fawcett Publications
January, 1942
1 The Mark of Cloven Hoof . 6,000.00
2 . . . . 1,200.00
3 Secret of the Aztec Treasure 1,000.00
4 . . . . 650.00
5 Mystery of PaintRockCanyon 700.00
6 Outlaw Round-up 650.00
7 Border Bullets 650.00
8 Blazing Guns 600.00
9 Range Robbers 600.00
10 Fightin' Buckaroo, Danger's
   Trail, Sept., 1943 . . . . 600.00
11 . . . . 625.00
12 . . . . 600.00

GENE AUTRY COMICS
Dell Publishing Co.
May/June 1946
1 . . . . 450.00
2 Ph(c) 250.00
3 Ph(c) 175.00
4 Ph(c),I:Flap Jack 175.00
5 Ph(c), all 150.00
6 thru 10 . . . . @135.00

GOLDEN AGE

11 thru 19	@125.00
20	135.00
21 thru 29	@100.00
30 thru 40, B:Giants	@75.00
41 thru 56 E:Giants	@60.00
57	35.00
58 Christmas cover	40.00
59 thru 66	@35.00
67 thru 80, B:Giant	@40.00
81 thru 90, E:Giant	@30.00
91 thru 93	@25.00
94 Christmas cover	28.00
95 thru 99	@25.00
100	30.00
101 thru 111	@25.00
112 thru 121	@20.00

GENE AUTRY'S CHAMPION
Dell Publishing Co.
August, 1950

(1) *see Dell Four Color #287*	
(2) *see Dell Four Color #319*	
3	35.00
4	35.00
5 thru 19	@35.00

GEORGE PAL'S PUPPETOON'S
Fawcett Publications
December, 1945

1 Captain Marvel (c)	300.00
2	150.00
3	100.00
4 thru 17	@90.00
18 December, 1947	90.00

GERALD McBOING-BOING AND THE NEARSIGHTED MR. MAGOO
Dell Publishing Co.
August-October, 1952

1	100.00
2	75.00
3	75.00
4	75.00
5	75.00

GERONIMO
Avon Periodicals
1950

1 Massacre at San Pedro Pass	125.00
2 EK(c), Murderous Battle at Kiskayah	75.00
3 EK(c)	75.00
4 EK(c),Apache Death Trap, February, 1952	75.00

GET LOST
Mikeross Publications
February-March, 1954

1	175.00
2	125.00
3 June-July, 1954	100.00

GHOST
Fiction House Magazine
Winter, 1951

1 The Banshee Bells	500.00
2 I Woke In Terror	225.00
3 The Haunted Hand of X	200.00

Ghost #4 © Fiction House Magazine

4 Flee the Mad Furies	200.00
5 The Hex of Ruby Eye	200.00
6 The Sleepers in the Crypt	225.00
7 When Dead Rogues Ride	225.00
8 Curse of the Mist-Thing	225.00
9 It Crawls by Night,Bondage(c)	250.00
10 Halfway to Hades	225.00
11 GE, The Witch's Doll, Summer, 1954	225.00

GHOST BREAKERS
Street & Smith Publications
September, 1948

1 BP,BP(c), A:Dr. Neff	275.00
2 BP,BP(c), Breaks the Voodoo Hoodoo,December, 1948	225.00

GHOSTLY WEIRD STORIES
(see BLUE BOLT)

GIANT BOY BOOK OF COMICS
Newsbook Publ.
(Lev Gleason)
1945

1 A:Crime Buster & Young Robin Hood	700.00

GIANT COMICS EDITION
St. John Publ.
1948

1 Mighty Mouse	450.00
2 Abbie and Slats	200.00
3 Terry Toons	350.00
4 Crime Comics	500.00
5 MB, Police Case Book	500.00
6 MB,MB(c), Western Picture Story	475.00
7 May not exist	
8 The Adventures of Mighty Mouse	300.00
9 JKu,MB,Romance & Confession Stories,Ph(c)	450.00
10 Terry Toons	300.00
11 MB,MB(c),JKu,Western	

Picture Stories	450.00
12 MB,MB(c),Diary Secrets, Prostitute	750.00
13 MB,JKu, Romances	425.00
14 Mighty Mouse Album	350.00
15 MB(c),Romance	425.00
16 Little Audrey	300.00
N#, Mighty Mouse Album	300.00

GIANT COMICS EDITION
United Features Syndicate
1945

1 A:Abbie & Slats, Jim Hardy, Ella Cinders,Iron Vic	275.00
2 Elmo, Jim Hardy, Abbie & Slats, 1945	200.00

G.I. COMBAT
Quality Comics Group
October, 1952

1 RC(c), Beyond the Call of Duty	400.00
2 RC(c), Operation Massacre	175.00
3 An Indestructible Marine	165.00
4 Bridge to Blood Hill	165.00
5 Hell Breaks loose on Suicide Hill	165.00
6 Beachhead Inferno	150.00
7 Fire Power Assault	125.00
8 RC(c),Death-trap Hill	125.00
9 Devil Riders	125.00
10 RC(c), Two-Ton Booby Trap	150.00
11 Hell's Heroes	100.00
12 Hand Grenade Hero	100.00
13 Commando Assault	100.00
14 Spear Head Assault	100.00
15 Vengeance Assault	100.00
16 Trapped Under Fire	90.00
17 Attack on Death Mountain	90.00
18 Red Battle Ground	90.00
19 Death on Helicopter Hill	90.00
20 Doomed Legion-Death Trap	90.00
21 Red Sneak Attack	75.00
22 Vengeance Raid	75.00
23 No Grandstand in Hell	75.00
24 Operation Steel Trap,Comics Code	75.00
25 Charge of the CommieBrigade	70.00
26 Red Guerrilla Trap	70.00
27 Trapped Behind Commie Lines	70.00
28 Atomic Battleground	70.00
29 Patrol Ambush	70.00
30 Operation Booby Trap	70.00
31 Human Fly on Heartbreak Hill	70.00
32 Atomic Rocket Assault	90.00
33 Bridge to Oblivion	70.00
34 RC,Desperate Mission	85.00
35 Doom Patrol	70.00
36 Fire Power Assault	70.00
37 Attack at Dawn	70.00
38 Get That Tank	70.00
39 Mystery of No Man's Land	70.00
40 Maneuver Battleground	70.00
41 Trumpet of Doom	70.00
42 March of Doom	70.00
43 Operation Showdown	70.00
See DC Comics for 44-120	

GIFT COMICS
Fawcett Publications
March, 1942

1 A:Captain Marvel, Bulletman, Golden Arrow,Ibis, the Invincible, Spy Smasher	2,400.00

GOLDEN AGE

GOLDEN AGE *(vertical side tab)*

2	1,650.00
3	1,000.00
4 A:Marvel Family, 1949	650.00

GIGGLE COMICS
Creston Publ./
American Comics Group
October, 1943

1 (fa)same	175.00
2 KHu	90.00
3 KHu	55.00
4 KHu	50.00
5 KHu	50.00
6 KHu	45.00
7 KHu	45.00
8 KHu	45.00
9 I:Super Katt	50.00
10 KHu	45.00
11 thru 20 KHu	@30.00
21 thru 30 KHu	@25.00
31 thru 40 KHu	@20.00
41 thru 94 KHu	@18.00
95 A:Spencer Spook	20.00
96 KHu	18.00
97 KHu	18.00
98 KHu	18.00
99 KHu	18.00
100 and 101 March-April,1955	@18.00

G.I. JANE
Stanhall Publ.
May, 1953

1	60.00
2 thru 6	@25.00
7 thru 9	@20.00
10 December, 1954	18.00

G.I. JOE
Ziff-Davis Publication Co.
1950

10 NS(c),Red Devils of Korea, V:Seoul City Lou	75.00
11 NS(c),The Guerrilla's Lair	50.00
12 NS(c)	50.00
13 NS(c),Attack at Dawn	50.00
14 NS(c),Temple of Terror, A:Peanuts the Great	45.00
2-6 It's a Foot Soldiers Job, I:Frankie of the Pump	45.00
2-7 BP,NS(c),The Rout at Sugar Creek	45.00
8 BP,NS(c),Waldo'sSqueezeBox	45.00
9 NS(c),Dear John	45.00
10 NS(c),Joe Flies the Payroll	45.00
11 NS(c),For the Love of Benny	45.00
12 NS(c),Patch work Quilt	45.00
13 NS(c)	45.00
14 NS(c),The Wedding Ring	45.00
15 The Lacrosse Whoopee	45.00
16 Mamie's Mortar	45.00
17 A Time for Waiting	45.00
18 Giant	125.00
19 Old Army Game..Buck Passer	40.00
20 General Confusion	40.00
21 Save 'Im for Brooklyn	40.00
22 Portrait of a Lady	40.00
23 Take Care of My Little Wagon	40.00
24 Operation 'Operation'	40.00
25 The Two-Leaf Clover	40.00
26 NS(c),Nobody Flies Alone Mud & Wings	40.00
27 "Dear Son...Come Home"	40.00
28 They Alway's Come Back Bondage cover	40.00

G.I. Joe #15
© Ziff-Davis Publication Co.

29 What a Picnic	35.00
30 NS(c),The One-Sleeved Kimono	35.00
31 NS(c),Get a Horse	30.00
32 thru 47	@30.00
48 Atom Bomb	35.00
49 thru 51 June, 1957	@30.00

GINGER
Close-Up Publ.
(Archie Publications)
January, 1951

1 GFs	75.00
2	40.00
3	30.00
4	30.00
5	25.00
6	25.00
7 thru 9	@35.00
10 A:Katy Keene,Summer,1954	40.00

GIRLS IN LOVE
Fawcett Publications
May, 1950

1	55.00
2 Ph(c),July, 1950	50.00

GIRLS IN LOVE
(see DIARY LOVES)

G.I. SWEETHEARTS
(see DIARY LOVES)

G.I. WAR BRIDES
Superior Publ. Ltd.
April, 1954

1	30.00
2	25.00
3 thru 7	@15.00
8 June, 1955	15.00

GOING STEADY
(see TEEN-AGE TEMPTATIONS)

GOLDEN ARROW
Fawcett Publications
Spring, 1942

1 B:Golden Arrow	650.00
2	300.00
3	250.00
4	225.00
5 Spring, 1947	225.00
6 BK	250.00
6a 1944 Well Known Comics (Giveaway)	275.00

GOLDEN LAD
Spark Publications
July, 1945

1 MMe,MMe(c),A:Kid Wizards, Swift Arrow,B:Golden Ladd	550.00
2 MMe,MMe(c)	250.00
3 MMe,MMe(c)	250.00
4 MMe,MMe(c), The Menace of the Minstrel	250.00
5 MMe,MMe(c),O:Golden Girl, June, 1946	250.00

GOLDEN WEST LOVE
Kirby Publishing Co.
September-October, 1949

1 BP,I Rode Heartbreak Hill, Ph(c)	125.00
2 BP	85.00
3 BP,Ph(c)	85.00
4 BP,April, 1950	85.00

GOLD MEDAL COMICS
Cambridge House
1945

N# Captain Truth	200.00

GOOFY COMICS
Nedor Publ. Co./
Animated Cartoons
(Standard Comics)
June, 1943

1 (fa)	135.00
2	70.00
3 VP	45.00
4 VP	35.00
5 VP	35.00
6 thru 10 VP	@35.00
11 thru 15	@30.00
15 thru 19	@25.00
20 thru 35 FF	@40.00
36 thru 48	@25.00

GREAT AMERICAN COMICS PRESENTS– THE SECRET VOICE
4 Star Publ.
1944

1 Hitler,Secret Weapon	175.00

GREAT COMICS
Novak Publ. Co.
1945

1 LbC(c)	275.00

GREAT COMICS
Great Comics Publications
November, 1941

1 I:The Great Zorro	1,000.00
2 Buck Johnson	500.00

3 The Lost City, Jan., 1942 .. 950.00

GREAT LOVER ROMANCES
Toby Press
March, 1951

1 Jon Juan,A:Dr. King 100.00
2 Hollywood Girl 50.00
3 Love in a Taxi 30.00
4 The Experimental Kiss 30.00
5 After the Honeymoon 30.00
6 HK,The Kid Sister Falls
   in Love 50.00
7 Man Crazy 25.00
8 Stand-in Boyfriend 25.00
9 The Cheat 25.00
10 Heart Breaker 25.00
11 .... 25.00
12 .... 25.00
13 Powerhouse of Deciet 25.00
14 .... 25.00
15 Ph(c),Still Undecided,
   Liz Taylor 60.00
16 thru 21 .... @25.00
22 May, 1955 .... 25.00

GREEN GIANT COMICS
Pelican Publications
1941

1 Black Arrow, Dr. Nerod
   O:Colossus 8,500.00

Green Hornet #23
© Helnit Publ./Family Comics

GREEN HORNET COMICS
Helnit Publ. Co./
Family Comics
(Harvey Publ.)
December, 1940

1 B:Green Hornet,P(c) 4,000.00
2 .... 1,200.00
3 BWh(c) 1,000.00
4 BWh(c) 750.00
5 BWh(c) 750.00
6 .... 750.00
7 BP, O:Zebra, B:Robin

Hood & Spirit of 76 ...... 650.00
8 BP,Bondage cover 550.00
9 BP, Behind the Cover 550.00
10 BP 550.00
11 Who is Mr. Q? 550.00
12 BP,A:Mr.Q 550.00
13 Hitler cover 500.00
14 BP,Spirit of 76-Twinkle
   Twins, Bondage(c) 450.00
15 ASh(c),Nazi Ghost Ship ... 425.00
16 BP,Prisoner of War 425.00
17 ASh(c),Nazis' Last Stand 425.00
18 BP,ASh(c),Jap's Treacherous
   Plot,Bondage cover 450.00
19 BP,ASh(c),Clash with the
   Rampaging Japs 425.00
20 BP,ASh(c),Tojo's
   Propaganda Hoax 450.00
21 BP,ASh(c),Unwelcome Cargo 350.00
22 ASh(c),Rendezvous with
   Jap Saboteurs 350.00
23 BF,ASh(c),Jap's Diabolical
   Plot #B2978 .... 350.00
24 BF,Science Fiction cover . 375.00
25 thru 29 .... @350.00
30 BP,JKu 350.00
31 BP,JKu 375.00
32 BP,JKu 300.00
33 BP,JKu 300.00
34 BP,JKu 300.00
35 BP,JKu 300.00
36 BP,JKu,Bondage cover ... 325.00
37 BP,JKu 300.00
38 BP,JKu 300.00
39 S&K 300.00
40 thru 45 .... @225.00
46 Drug 250.00
47 September, 1949 .... 225.00

GREEN LAMA
Spark Publications/Prize Publ.
December, 1944

1 I:Green Lama, Lt. Hercules
   & Boy Champions 1,000.00
2 MRa,Forward to Victory
   in 1945 .... 600.00
3 MRa,The Riddles of Toys .. 500.00
4 MRa,Dive Bombs Japan ... 475.00
5 MRa,MRa(c),Fights for
   the Four Freedoms 475.00
6 MRa,Smashes a Plot
   against America 475.00
7 MRa,Merry X-Mas 400.00
8 MRa,Smashes Toy Master
   of Crime, March, 1946 .... 400.00

GREEN MASK, THE
Fox Features Syndicate
Summer, 1940

1 O:Green Mask & Domino . 2,800.00
2 A:Zanzibar 1,000.00
3 BP 650.00
4 B:Navy Jones 500.00
5 .... 400.00
6 B:Nightbird,E:Navy Jones,
   Bondage cover 350.00
7 B:Timothy Smith &
   The Tumbler 275.00
8 JSs 250.00
9 E:Nightbird, Death Wields
   a Scalpel! 275.00
10 .... 225.00
11 The Banshee of Dead
   Man's Hill 225.00

The Green Mask #11
© Fox Feature Syndicate

2-1 Election of Skulls 175.00
2-2 Pigeons of Death 175.00
2-3 Wandering Gold Brick ... 150.00
2-4 Time on His Hands 150.00
2-5 JFe,SFd 175.00
2-6 Adventure of the Disappearing
   Trains, Oct.-Nov., 1946 .... 175.00

GUMPS, THE
Dell Publishing Co.
1945

1 .... 100.00
2 .... 75.00
3 .... 50.00
4 .... 50.00
5 .... 50.00

GUNS AGAINST GANGSTERS
Curtis Publ./Novelty Press
September-October, 1948

1 LbC,LbC(c),B:Toni Gayle .. 225.00
2 LbC,LbC(c) 175.00
3 LbC,LbC(c) 150.00
4 LbC,LbC(c) 150.00
5 LbC,LbC(c) 150.00
6 LbC,LbC(c),Shark 150.00
2-1 LbC,LbC(c),
   September-October, 1949 . 150.00

GUNSMOKE
Western Comics, Inc.
April-May, 1949

1 GRi,GRi(c),Gunsmoke & Masked
   Marvel,Bondage cover 300.00
2 GRi,GRi(c) 200.00
3 GRi,GRi(c) 150.00
4 GRi(c),Bondage(c) 125.00
5 GRi(c) 125.00
6 .... 65.00
7 .... 65.00
8 .... 65.00
9 .... 65.00
10 .... 65.00
11 thru 15 .... @50.00
16 Jan., 1952 .... 50.00

GOLDEN AGE

HA HA COMICS
Creston Publ.
(American Comics Group)
October, 1943

1 Funny Animal, all		175.00
2		75.00
3		55.00
4		55.00
5		55.00
6 thru 10		@40.00
11		30.00
12 thru 15 KHu		@30.00
16 thru 20 KHu		@28.00
21 thru 30 KHu		@25.00
31 thru 101		@20.00
102 February-March, 1955		20.00

MISTER RISK
Humor Publ.
(Ace Magazines)
October, 1950

1 (7) B:Mr. Risk		30.00
2		25.00

Becomes:

MEN AGAINST CRIME

3 A:Mr. Risk, Case of the Carnival Killer	60.00
4 Murder-And the Crowd Roars	35.00
5	35.00
6	35.00
7 Get Them!	35.00

Becomes:

HAND OF FATE
Ace Magazines

8	250.00
9 LC	175.00
10 LC	150.00
11 Genie(c)	125.00
12	125.00
13 Hanging(c)	135.00
14	125.00
15	125.00
16	100.00
17	100.00
18	100.00
19 Drug issue,Quicksand(c)	125.00
20	100.00
21 Drug issue	125.00
22	100.00
23 Graveyard(c)	100.00
24 LC,Electric Chair	175.00
25 November, 1954	75.00
25a December, 1954	100.00

HANGMAN COMICS
(see LAUGH COMICS)

HAP HAZARD COMICS
A.A. Wyn/Red Seal Publ./
Readers Research
Summer, 1944

1 Funny Teen		60.00
2 Dog Show		30.00
3 Sgr,		28.00
4 Sgr,		28.00
5 thru 10 Sgr,		@20.00
11 thru 13 Sgr,		@15.00
14 AF(c)		35.00
15		15.00
16 thru 24		@15.00

Becomes:

REAL LOVE

25 Dangerous Dates		50.00
26		25.00
27 LbC(c), Revenge Conquest		35.00
28 thru 40		@18.00
41 thru 66		@15.00
67 Comics code		12.00
68 thru 76, Nov. 1956		@12.00

HAPPY COMICS
Nedor Publications/
Animated Cartoons
(Standard Comics)
August, 1943

1 Funny Animal in all		125.00
2		75.00
3		45.00
4		40.00
5 thru 10		@40.00
11 thru 20		@35.00
21 thru 30		@30.00
31 and 32		@50.00
33 FF		125.00
34 thru 37 FF		@50.00
38 thru 40		@20.00

Becomes:

HAPPY RABBIT

41 Funny Animal in all		25.00
42 thru 50		@15.00

Becomes:

HARVEY COMIC HITS

51 Phantom	200.00
52 Steve Canyon's Air Power	85.00
53 Mandrake	150.00
54 Tim Tyler's Tales of Jungle Terror	75.00
55 Love Stories of Mary Worth	30.00
56 Phantom, Bondage cover	175.00
57 AR,Kidnap Racket	110.00
58 Girls in White	30.00
59 Tales of the Invisible	75.00
60 Paramount Animated Comics	275.00
61 Casper the Friendly Ghost	300.00
62 Paramount Animated Comics, April, 1953	100.00

HAPPY HOULIHANS
(see SADDLE JUSTICE)

HAUNTED THRILLS
Four Star Publ.
(Ajax/Farrell)
June, 1952

1 Ellery Queen		275.00
2 LbC,Ellery Queen		200.00
3 Drug Story		175.00
4 Ghouls Castle		150.00
5 Fatal Scapel		150.00
6 Pit of Horror		125.00
7 Trail to a Tomb		125.00
8 Vanishing Skull		125.00
9 Madness of Terror		125.00
10		125.00
11 Nazi Concentration Camp		150.00
12 RWb		100.00
13		100.00
14 RWb		125.00
15 The Devil Collects		100.00
16		100.00
17 Mirror of Madness		100.00
18 No Place to Go, November-December, 1954		110.00

Haunted Thrills #18 © Four Star Publ.

HAUNT OF FEAR
Fables Publ.
(E.C. Comics)
May-June, 1950

15 JCr,JCr(c),AF,WW	2,200.00
16 JCr,JCr(c),AF,WW	850.00
17 JCr,JCr(c),AF,WW,O:Crypt of Terror,Vault of Horror & Haunt of Fear	850.00
4 AF(c),WW,JDa	600.00
5 JCr,JCr(c),WW,JDa,Eye Injury	500.00
6 JCr,JCr(c),WW,JDa	325.00
7 JCr,JCr(c),WW,JDa	325.00
8 AF(c),JKa,JDa, Shrunken Head	325.00
9 AF(c),JCr,JDa	325.00
10 AF(c),Grl,JDa	300.00
11 JKa,Grl,JDa	275.00
12 JCr,Grl,JDa	275.00
13 Grl,JDa	275.00
14 Grl,Grl(c),JDa,O:Old Witch	325.00
15 JDa	275.00
16 GRi(c),JDa,Ray Bradbury adaptation	275.00
17 JDa,Grl(c),Classic Ghastly (c)	275.00
18 JDa,Grl(c),JKa,Ray Bradbury adaptation	300.00
19 JDa,Guillotine (c), Bondage cover	300.00
20 RC,JDa,Grl,Grl(c)	250.00
21 JDa,Grl,Grl(c)	200.00
22 same	200.00
23 same	200.00
22 same	200.00
23 same	200.00
24 same	200.00
25 same	200.00
26 RC,same	250.00
27 same, Cannibalism	225.00
28 December, 1954	225.00

HAWK, THE
Approved Comics
(Ziff-Davis)
Winter, 1951

1 MA,The Law of the Colt,P(c)	150.00
2 JKu,Iron Caravan of the	

Mojave, P(c)	100.00
3 Leverett's Last Stand,P(c) ..	75.00
4 Killer's Town,P(c)	60.00
5	50.00
6	50.00
7	50.00
8 MB(c),Dry River Rampage .	60.00
9 MB,MB(c),JKu	75.00
10 MB(c)	60.00
11 MB(c)	60.00
12 MB,MB(c), May, 1955	60.00

HEADLINE COMICS
American Boys Comics/
Headline Publ. (Prize Publ.)
February, 1943

1 B:Jr. Rangers	350.00
2 JaB,JaB(c)	150.00
3 JaB,JaB(c)	110.00
4	100.00
5 HcK	100.00
6 HcK	100.00
7 HcK,Jr. Rangers	100.00
8 HcK,Hitler cover	250.00
9 HcK	100.00
10 HcK,Hitler story,Wizard(c) ..	150.00
11	65.00
12 HcK,Heroes of Yesterday ...	65.00
13 HcK,A:Blue Streak	75.00
14 HcK,A:Blue Streak	75.00
15 HcK,A:Blue Streak	75.00
16 HcK,O:Atomic Man	175.00
17 Atomic Man(c)	100.00
18 Atomic Man(c)	100.00
19 S&K,Atomic Man(c)	200.00
20 Atomic Man(c)	100.00
21 E:Atomic Man	100.00
22 HcK	50.00
23 S&K,S&K(c),Valentines Day Massacre	175.00
24 S&K,S&K(c),You can't Forget a Killer	175.00
25 S&K,S&K(c),CrimeNeverPays	175.00
26 S&K,S&K(c),CrimeNeverPays	175.00
27 S&K,S&K(c),CrimeNeverPays	175.00
28 S&K,S&K(c),CrimeNeverPays	175.00
29 S&K,S&K(c),CrimeNeverPays	175.00
30 S&K,S&K(c),CrimeNeverPays	175.00
31 S&K,S&K(c),CrimeNeverPays	175.00
32 S&K,S&K(c),CrimeNeverPays	175.00
33 S&K,S&K(c),Police and FBI heroes	175.00
34 S&K,S&K(c),same	175.00
35 S&K,S&K(c),same	175.00
36 S&K,S&K(c),same,Ph(c) ..	100.00
37 S&K,S&K(c),MvS,same,Ph(c)	125.00
38 S&K,S&K(c),same,Ph(c) ..	40.00
39 S&K,S&K(c),same,Ph(c) ..	40.00
40 S&K,S&K(c),Ph(c)Violent Crime	40.00
41 Ph(c),J.Edgar Hoover(c) ...	40.00
42 Ph(c)	30.00
43 Ph(c)	30.00
44 MMe,MvS,WE,S&K	50.00
45 JK	25.00
46	20.00
47	20.00
48	20.00
49 MMe	20.00
50	20.00
51 JK	22.00
52	20.00
53	20.00
54	20.00
55	20.00

56 S&K	40.00
57	20.00
58	20.00
59	20.00
60 MvS(c)	20.00
61 MMe,MvS(c)	20.00
62 MMe,MMe(c)	20.00
63 MMe,MMe(c)	20.00
64 MMe,MMe(c)	20.00
65 MMe,MMe(c)	20.00
66 MMe,MMe(c)	20.00
67 MMe,MMe(c)	20.00
68 MMe,MMe(c)	20.00
69 MMe,MMe(c)	20.00
70 MMe,MMe(c)	20.00
71 MMe,MMe(c)	20.00
72 MMe,MMe(c)	20.00
73 MMe,MMe(c)	20.00
74 MMe,MMe(c)	20.00
75 MMe,MMe(c)	20.00
76 MMe,MMe(c)	20.00
77 MMe,MMe(c),October, 1956 .	20.00

HEART THROBS
Comics Magazines
(Quality)
August, 1949

1 BWa(c),PG,Spoiled Brat ...	275.00
2 BWa(c),PG,Siren of the Tropics	175.00
3 PG	50.00
4 BWa(c),Greed Turned Me into a Scheming Vixen,Ph(c) ...	100.00
5 Ph(c)	30.00
6 BWa	85.00
7	30.00
8 BWa	85.00
9 I Hated Men,Ph(c)	45.00
10 BWa,My Secret Fears	50.00
11	18.00
12	15.00
13	18.00
14 BWa	18.00
15 My Right to Happiness,Ph(c) .	45.00
16	16.00
17	16.00
18	16.00
19	16.00
20	16.00
21 BWa	35.00
22 BWa	30.00
23 BWa	30.00
24 thru 30	@15.00
31 thru 33	@15.00
34 thru 39	@15.00
40 BWa	25.00
41	15.00
42	15.00
43 thru 45	@15.00
(Please see DC listings)	

HECKLE AND JECKLE
St. John Publ./Pines
November, 1951

1 Blue Ribbon Comics	200.00
2 Blue Ribbon Comics	125.00
3	85.00
4	75.00
5	75.00
6	75.00
7	55.00
8	50.00
9	50.00
10	50.00

Heckle and Jeckle #17
© St. John Publications

11 thru 15	@40.00
16 thru 20	@35.00
21 thru 33	@30.00
34 June, 1959	32.00

HELLO PAL COMICS
Harvey Publications
January, 1943

1 B:Rocketman & Rocket Girl, Mickey Rooney cover, Ph(c) all	500.00
2 Charlie McCarthy cover	400.00
3 Bob Hope cover, May, 1943	375.00

HENRY
Dell Publishing Co.
October, 1946

1	100.00
2	50.00
3 thru 10	@35.00
11 thru 20	@25.00
21 thru 30	@20.00
31 thru 40	@15.00
41 thru 50	@12.00
51 thru 65	@10.00

HENRY ALDRICH COMICS
Dell Publishing Co.
August-September, 1950

1	90.00
2	45.00
3	30.00
4	30.00
5	30.00
6 thru 10	@25.00
11 thru 22	@20.00

HEROIC COMICS
Eastern Color Printing Co./
Famous Funnies
August, 1940

1 BEv,BEv(c),O:Hydroman,Purple Zombie, B:Man of India ..	1,200.00
2 BEv,BEv(c),B:Hydroman covers	600.00
3 BEv, BEv(c)	375.00

GOLDEN AGE

4 BEv,BEv(c)	350.00
5 BEv,BEv(c)	325.00
6 BEv,BEv(c)	300.00
7 BEv,BEv(c),O:Man O'Metal	350.00
8 BEv,BEv(c)	200.00
9 BEv	200.00
10 BEv	200.00
11 BEv,E:Hydroman covers	200.00
12 BEv,B&O:Music Master	225.00
13 BEv,RC,LF	200.00
14 BEv	225.00
15 BEv,I:Downbeat	225.00
16 BEv,CCB(c),A:Lieut Nininger, Major Heidger,Lieut Welch,B:P(c)	150.00
17 BEv,A:JohnJames Powers,Hewitt T.Wheless, Irving Strobing	150.00
18 HcK,BEv,Pass the Ammunition	150.00
19 HcK,BEv,A:Barney Ross	150.00
20 HcK,BEv	135.00
21 HcK,BEv	100.00
22 HcK,BEv,Howard Gilmore	100.00
23 HcK,BEv	100.00
24 HcK,BEv	100.00
25 HcK,BEv	100.00
26 HcK,BEv	100.00
27 HcK,BEv	100.00
28 HcK,BEv,E:Man O'Metal	100.00
29 HcK,BEv,E:Hydroman	100.00
30 BEv	100.00
31 BEv,CCB,Capt. Tootsie	25.00
32 ATh,CCB,WWII(c), Capt. Tootsie	45.00
33 ATh	45.00
34 WWII(c)	25.00
35 Ath,B:Rescue(c)	45.00
36 HcK,ATh	45.00
37 same	45.00
38 ATh	45.00
39 HcK,ATh	45.00
40 ATh,Boxing	45.00
41 Grl(c),ATh	45.00
42 ATh	45.00
43 ATh	35.00
44 HcK,ATh	35.00
45 HcK	35.00
46 HcK	35.00
47 HcK	35.00
48 HcK	35.00
49 HcK	35.00
50 HcK	35.00
51 HcK,ATh,AW	40.00
52 HcK,AW	40.00
53 HcK	35.00
54	25.00
55 ATh	25.00
56 ATh(c)	30.00
57 ATh(c)	25.00
58 ATh(c)	25.00
59 ATh(c)	25.00
60 ATh(c)	25.00
61 BEv(c)	20.00
62 BEv(c)	20.00
63 BEv(c)	20.00
64 GE,BEv(c)	22.00
65 HcK(c),FF,ATh,AW,GE	50.00
66 HcK(c),FF	35.00
67 HcK(c),FF,Korean War(c)	35.00
68 HcK(c),FF,Korean War(c)	35.00
69 HcK(c),FF	50.00
70 HcK(c),FF,B:Korean War(c)	35.00
71 HcK(c),FF	35.00
72 HcK(c),FF	50.00
73 HcK(c),FF	35.00

74 HcK(c)	35.00
75 HcK(c),FF	35.00
76 HcK,HcK(c)	20.00
77 same	20.00
78 same	20.00
79 same	20.00
80 same	20.00
81 FF,HcK(c)	22.00
82 FF,HcK(c)	22.00
83 FF,HcK(c)	22.00
84 HcK(c)	22.00
85 HcK(c)	22.00
86 FF,HcK(c)	25.00
87 FF,HcK(c)	25.00
88 HcK(c),E:Korean War covers	20.00
89 HcK(c)	20.00
90 HcK(c)	20.00
91 HcK(c)	20.00
92 HcK(c)	20.00
93 HcK(c)	20.00
94 HcK(c)	20.00
95 HcK(c)	20.00
96 HcK(c)	20.00
97 HcK(c),E:P(c),June, 1955	20.00

HICKORY
Comic Magazine
(Quality Comics Group)
October, 1949

1 ASa,	75.00
2 ASa,	35.00
3 ASa,	25.00
4 ASa,	25.00
5 ASa,	25.00
6 ASa,August, 1950	25.00

HI-HO COMICS
Four Star Publications
1946

1 LbC(c)	200.00
2 LbC(c)	100.00
3 1946	100.00

HI-JINX
B & I Publ. Co.
(American Comics Group)
July-August, 1947

1 (fa) all	100.00
2	60.00
3	60.00
4 thru 7	@40.00
N#	75.00

HI-LITE COMICS
E.R. Ross Publ.
Fall, 1945

1	100.00

HIT COMICS
Comics Magazine
(Quality Comics Group)
July, 1940

1 LF(c),O:Neon,Hercules,I:The Red Bee, B:Bob & Swab, Blaze Barton Strange Twins,X-5 Super Agent Casey Jones,Jack & Jill	5,500.00
2 GT,LF(c),B:Old Witch	2,000.00
3 GT,LF(c),E:Casey Jones	1,800.00
4 GT,LF(c),B:Super Agent & Betty Bates,E:X-5	1,500.00
5 GT,LF(c),B:Red Bee cover	4,400.00

6 GT,LF(c)	1,500.00
7 GT,LF(c),E:Red Bee cover	1,550.00
8 GT,LF(c),B:Neon cover	1,500.00
9 JCo,LF(c),E:Neon cover	1,500.00
10 JCo,RC,LF(c),B:Hercules(c)	1,500.00
11 JCo,RC,LF(c),A:Hercules	950.00
12 JCo,RC,LF(c),A:Hercules	950.00
13 JCo,RC,LF(c),A:Hercules	950.00
14 JCo,RC,LF(c),A:Hercules	950.00
15 JCo,RC,A:Hercules	900.00
16 JCo,RC,LF(c),A:Hercules	900.00
17 JCo,RC,LF(c),E:Hercules(c)	900.00
18 JCo,RC,RC(c),O:Stormy Foster,B:Ghost of Flanders	1,000.00
19 JCo,RC(c),B:StormyFoster(c)	800.00
20 JCo,RC(c),A:Stormy Foster	800.00
21 JCo,RC(c)	775.00
22 JCo	775.00
23 JCo,RC,RC(c)	725.00
24 JCo,E:Stormy Foster cover	725.00
25 JCo,RP,O:Kid Eternity	1,200.00
26 JCo,RP,A:Black Hawk	800.00
27 JCo,RP,B:Kid Eternity covers	400.00

Hit Comics #40
© Quality Comics Group

28 JCo,RP,A:Her Highness	400.00
29 JCo,RP	400.00
30 JCo,RP,HK,V:Julius Caesar and his Legion of Warriors	350.00
31 JCo,RP	350.00
32 JCo,RP,V:Merlin the Wizard	200.00
33 JCo,RP	175.00
34 JCo,RP,E:Stormy Foster	175.00
35 JCo,Kid Eternity accused of Murder	175.00
36 JCo,The Witch's Curse	175.00
37 JCo,V:Mr. Silence	175.00
38 JCo	175.00
39 JCo,Runaway River Boat	175.00
40 PG,V:Monster from the Past	175.00
41 PG,Did Kid Eternity Lose His Power?	125.00
42 PG,Kid Eternity Loses Killer Cronson	125.00
43 JCo,PG,V:Modern Bluebeard	125.00
44 JCo,PG,Trips up the Shoe	125.00
45 JCo,PG,Pancho Villa against Don Pablo	125.00
46 JCo,V:Mr. Hardeel	125.00
47 A Polished Diamond can be	

Rough on Rats 125.00
48 EhH,A Treasure Chest
  of Trouble 125.00
49 EhH,V:Monsters from
  the Mirror 125.00
50 EhH,Heads for Trouble . . . 125.00
51 EhH,Enters the Forgotten
  World 100.00
52 EhH,Heroes out of the Past 100.00
53 EhH,V:Mr. Puny 100.00
54 V:Ghost Town Killer 100.00
55 V:The Brute 100.00
56 V:Big Odds 100.00
57 Solves the Picture in
  a Frame 100.00
58 Destroys Oppression! 100.00
59 Battles Tomorrow's Crimes
  Today! 100.00
60 E:Kid Eternity covers,
  V:The Mummy 100.00
61 RC,RC(c),I:Jeb Rivers 125.00
62 RC(c) 100.00
63 RC(c),A:Jeb Rivers 125.00
64 RC,A:Jeb Rivers 125.00
65 Bondage cover,RC,July, 1950 135.00

HOLIDAY COMICS
Fawcett Publ.
November, 1942
1 Captain Marvel (c) 1,400.00

HOLIDAY COMICS
Star Publ.
January, 1951
1 LbC(c),(fa),Christmas cover . 200.00
2 LbC(c),Parade(c) 250.00
3 LbC(c),July 4th(c) 150.00
4 LbC(c),Vacation(c) 150.00
5 LbC(c),Christmas(c) 150.00
6 LbC(c),Birthday(c) 150.00
7 LbC(c) 125.00
8 LbC(c),Christmas(c) 150.00

HOLLYWOOD COMICS
New Age Publishers
Winter, 1944
1 (fa) 125.00

HOLLYWOOD
CONFESSIONS
St. John Publ. Co.
October, 1949
1 JKu,JKu(c) 175.00
2 JKu,JKu(c), December, 1949 225.00

HOLLYWOOD DIARY
Comics Magazine
(Quality Comics)
December, 1949
1 . . . . 125.00
2 Photo cover 75.00
3 Photo cover 60.00
4 . . . . 60.00
5 Photo cover, August, 1950 . . 60.00

HOLLYWOOD FILM
STORIES
Feature Publications
(Prize)
April, 1950
1 June Allison,Ph(c) 125.00
2 Lizabeth Scott,Ph(c) 75.00

3 Barbara Stanwick,Ph(c) 75.00
4 Beth Hutton, August, 1950 . . 75.00

HOLLYWOOD SECRETS
Comics Magazine
(Quality Comics Group)
November, 1949
1 BWa,BWa(c) 200.00
2 BWa,BWa(c),RC 125.00
3 Ph(c) 60.00
4 Ph(c),May, 1950 . . . . 60.00
5 Ph(c) 60.00
6 Ph(c) 60.00

HOLYOKE ONE-SHOT
Tem Publ.
(Holyoke Publ. Co.)
1944
1 Grit Grady 75.00
2 Rusty Dugan 65.00
3 JK,Miss Victory,O:Cat Woman 150.00
4 Mr. Miracle 55.00
5 U.S. Border Patrol 50.00
6 Capt. Fearless 50.00
7 Strong Man 55.00
8 Blue Streak 50.00
9 S&K, Citizen Smith 80.00
10 S&K, Capt. Stone 75.00

HONEYMOON
ROMANCE
Artful Publications
(Digest Size)
April, 1950
1 . . . . 250.00
2 July, 1950 . . . . 225.00

HOODED HORSEMAN
(see OUT OF THE NIGHT)

HOPALONG CASSIDY
Fawcett Publications
February, 1943
1 B:Hopalong Cassidy & Topper,
  Captain Marvel cover 4,500.00
2 . . . . 650.00
3 Blazing Trails 300.00
4 5-full length story 275.00
5 Death in the Saddle, Ph(c) . . 250.00
6 . . . . 200.00
7 . . . . 200.00
8 Phantom Stage Coach 200.00
9 The Last Stockade 200.00
10 4-spine tingling adventures . 200.00
11 Desperate Jetters! Ph(c) . . . 150.00
12 The Mysterious Message . . 150.00
13 The Human Target, Ph(c) . . 150.00
14 Land of the Lawless, Ph(c) . 150.00
15 Death holds the Reins, Ph(c) 150.00
16 Webfoot's Revenge, Ph(c) . . 150.00
17 The Hangman's Noose, Ph(c) 150.00
18 The Ghost of Dude Ranch,
  Ph(c) 150.00
19 A:William Boyd,Ph(c) 150.00
20 The Notorious Nellie Blaine!,
  B:P(c) 125.00
21 V:Arizona Kid 125.00
22 V:Arizona Kid 125.00
23 Hayride Horror 125.00
24 Twin River Giant 125.00
25 On the Trails of the Wild
  and Wooly West 125.00

26 thru 30 . . . . @100.00
31 52 pages 75.00
32 36 pages 75.00
33 thru 35, 52 pages . . . . @75.00
36 36 pages 60.00
37 thru 40, 52 pages . . . . @75.00
40 36 pages 60.00
41 E:P(c) 40.00
42 B:Ph(c) 75.00
43 . . . . 75.00
44 . . . . 50.00
45 . . . . 60.00
46 thru 51 . . . . @50.00
52 . . . . 45.00
53 . . . . 50.00
54 . . . . 50.00
55 . . . . 45.00
56 . . . . 50.00
57 . . . . 50.00
58 thru 70 . . . . @50.00
71 thru 84 . . . . @40.00
85 E:Ph(c),January, 1954 . . . . . 50.00
(Please see DC listings)

Hoppy the Marvel Bunny #2
© Fawcett Publications

HOPPY THE
MARVEL BUNNY
Fawcett Publications
December, 1945
1 A:Marvel Bunny 150.00
2 . . . . 75.00
3 . . . . 50.00
4 . . . . 50.00
5 . . . . 50.00
6 thru 14 . . . . @40.00
15 September, 1947 . . . . 40.00

HORRIFIC
Artful/Comic Media/
Harwell Publ./Mystery
September, 1952
1 Conductor in Flames(c) 250.00
2 Human Puppets(c) 125.00
3 DH(c),Bullet hole in
  head(c) 225.00
4 DH(c),head on a stick (c) . . 100.00
5 DH(c) 125.00

GOLDEN AGE

6 DH(c),Jack the Ripper 100.00
7 DH(c),Shrunken Skulls 100.00
8 DH(c),I:The Teller 125.00
9 DH(c),Claws of Horror, Wolves
   of Midnight 100.00
10 DH(c),The Teller-four
   eerie tales of Horror 100.00
11 DH(c),A:Gary Ghoul,Freddie,
   Demon,Victor Vampire,
   Walter Werewolf 75.00
12 DH(c),A:Gary Ghoul,Freddie
   Demon,Victor Vampire,
   Walter Werewolf 75.00
13 DH(c),A:Gary Ghoul,Freddie
   Demom,Victor Vampire,
   Walter Werewolf 75.00
Becomes:
TERRIFIC COMICS
14 .... 175.00
15 .... 125.00
16 B:Wonderboy 125.00
Becomes:
WONDERBOY
17 The Enemy's Enemy 350.00
18 Success is No Accident,
   July, 1955 .... 300.00

HORROR FROM THE TOMB
(see MYSTERIOUS STORIES)

HORRORS, THE
Star Publications
January, 1953
11 LbC(c),JyD,of War 200.00
12 LbC(c),of War 175.00
13 LbC(c),of Mystery 150.00
14 LbC(c),of the Underworld .. 175.00
15 LbC(c),of the Underworld,
   April, 1954 .... 175.00

HORSE FEATHER COMICS
Lev Gleason Publications
November, 1947
1 BW 135.00
2 .... 55.00
3 .... 50.00
4 Summer, 1948 .... 50.00

HOT ROD AND SPEEDWAY COMICS
Hillman Periodicals
February-March, 1952
1 .... 150.00
2 BK 100.00
3 .... 50.00
4 .... 50.00
5 April-May, 1953 .... 50.00

HOT ROD COMICS
Fawcett Publications
Feb., 1952–53
N# BP,BP(c),F:Clint Curtis ... 200.00
2 BP,BP(c),Safety comes First 125.00
3 BP,BP(c),The Racing Game 100.00
4 BP,BP(c),Bonneville National
   Championships 100.00
5 BP,BP(c), ... 100.00
6 BP,BP(c),Race to Death ... 100.00

HOT ROD KING
Approved Comics
(Ziff-Davis)
Fall, 1952
1 P(c) 175.00

HOWDY DOODY
Dell Publishing Co.
January, 1950
1 Ph(c) 850.00
2 Ph(c) 400.00
3 Ph(c) 225.00
4 Ph(c) 225.00
5 Ph(c) 225.00
6 P(c) 150.00
7 .... 135.00
8 .... 135.00
9 .... 135.00
10 .... 135.00
11 .... 125.00
12 .... 125.00
13 Christmas (c) 125.00
14 thru 20 .... @125.00
21 thru 38 .... @100.00

Howdy Doody Comics #10
© Dell Publishing Co.

HOW STALIN HOPES WE WILL DESTROY AMERICA
Pictorial News
1951
N# (Giveaway) 400.00

HUMBUG
Harvey Kurtzman
1957
1 JDa,WW,WE,End of the World 200.00
2 JDa,WE,Radiator 100.00
3 JDa,WE 75.00
4 JDa,WE,Queen Victoria(c) ... 75.00
5 JDa,WE 75.00
6 JDa,WE 75.00
7 JDa,WE,Sputnik(c) 80.00
8 JDa,WE,Elvis/George
   Washington(c) 75.00
9 JDa,WE 75.00

10 JDa,Magazine 100.00
11 JDw,WE,HK,Magazine 100.00

HUMDINGER
Novelty Press/
Premium Service
May-June, 1946
1 B:Jerkwater Line,Dink,
   Mickey Starlight 225.00
2 .... 100.00
3 .... 75.00
4 .... 75.00
5 .... 75.00
6 .... 75.00
2-1 .... 60.00
2-2 July-August, 1947 .... 60.00

HUMPHREY COMICS
Harvey Publications
October, 1948
1 BP,Joe Palooka 80.00
2 BP 35.00
3 BP 30.00
4 BP,A:Boy Heroes 40.00
5 BP 25.00
6 BP 25.00
7 BP,A:Little Dot 25.00
8 BP,O:Humphrey 30.00
9 BP 20.00
10 BP 20.00
11 thru 21 .... @20.00
22 April, 1952 .... 20.00

HYPER MYSTERY COMICS
Hyper Publications
May, 1940
1 B:Hyper 1,500.00
2 June, 1940 .... 800.00

IBIS, THE INVINCIBLE
Fawcett Publications
January, 1942
1 MRa(c),O:Ibis 1,400.00
2 Bondage cover 700.00
3 BW 600.00
4 BW,A:Mystic Snake People 400.00
5 BW,Bondage cover,The
   Devil's Ibistick 425.00
6 BW, The Book of Evil,
   Spring, 1948 .... 425.00

IDEAL ROMANCE
(see TENDER ROMANCE)

IF THE DEVIL WOULD TALK
Catechetical Guild
1950
N# Rare 600.00
N#, 1958 Very Rare 450.00

ILLUSTRATED STORIES OF THE OPERA
B. Bailey Publ. Co.
1943
N# Faust 500.00
N# Aida 450.00
N# Carman 450.00
N# Rigoletto 450.00

I LOVED
(see ZOOT COMICS)

I LOVE LUCY COMICS
Dell Publishing Co.
February, 1954
(1) see Dell Four Color #535
(2) see Dell Four Color #559
3 Lucile Ball Ph(c) all 225.00
4 . . . . 200.00
5 . . . . 200.00
6 thru 10 . . . . @175.00
11 thru 20 . . . . 125.00
21 thru 35 . . . . 100.00

IMPACT
E.C. Comics
March-April, 1955
1 RC,GE,BK,Grl 125.00
2 RC,JDu,Grl,BK,JO 100.00
3 JO,RC,JDU,Grl,JKa,BK 80.00
4 RC,JO,JDa,GE,Grl,BK 80.00
5 November-December, 1955 . 80.00

INCREDIBLE
SCIENCE FANTASY
(see WEIRD SCIENCE)

INCREDIBLE
SCIENCE FICTION
E.C. Comics
July-August, 1955
30 . . . . 250.00
31 . . . . 275.00
32 January-February, 1956 . . . 275.00
33 . . . . 250.00

INDIAN CHIEF
Dell Publishing Co.
July-September, 1951
3 P(c) all 30.00
4 . . . . 15.00
5 . . . . 15.00
6 A:White Eagle 15.00
7 . . . . 15.00
8 . . . . 15.00
9 . . . . 15.00
10 . . . . 15.00
11 . . . . 15.00
12 I:White Eagle 25.00
13 thru 29 . . . . @10.00
30 SB 15.00
31 SB 15.00
32 SB 15.00
33 SB 15.00

INDIAN FIGHTER
Youthful Magazines
May, 1950
1 Revenge of Chief Crazy Horse 60.00
2 Bondage cover 35.00
3 . . . . 20.00
4 Cheyenne Warpath 20.00
5 . . . . 20.00
6 Davy Crockett in Death Stalks
   the Alamo 20.00
7 Tom Horn-Bloodshed at
   Massacre Valley 20.00
8 Tales of Wild Bill Hickory,
   January, 1952 . . . . 20.00

INDIANS
Wings Publ. Co.
(Fiction House)
Spring, 1950
1 B:Long Bow, Manzar, White
   Indian & Orphan 150.00
2 B:Starlight 75.00
3 Longbow(c) 60.00
4 Longbow(c) 50.00
5 Manzar(c) 60.00
6 Captive of the Semecas 50.00
7 Longbow(c) 50.00
8 A:Long Bow 50.00
9 A:Long Bow 50.00
10 Manzar(c) 50.00
11 thru 16 . . . . @40.00
17 Spring, 1953,Longbow(c) . . . 40.00

Indians on the Warpath #1
© St. John Publishing Co.

INDIANS ON
THE WARPATH
St. John Publ. Co.
1950
N# MB(c) 200.00

INFORMER, THE
Feature Television
Productions
April, 1954
1 MSy,The Greatest Social
   Menace of our Time! 65.00
2 MSy 35.00
3 MSy 30.00
4 MSy 30.00
5 December, 1954 . . . . 30.00

IN LOVE
Mainline/Charlton Comics
August, 1954
1 S&K,Bride of the Star 225.00
2 S&K,Marilyn's Men 125.00
3 S&K 100.00
4 S&K,Comics Code 60.00
5 S&K(c) 60.00
6 30.00
Becomes:

I LOVE YOU
7 JK(c),BP 75.00
8 . . . . 25.00
9 . . . . 25.00
10 . . . . 25.00
11 thru 16 . . . . @20.00
17 . . . . 15.00
18 . . . . 10.00
19 . . . . 10.00
20 . . . . 10.00
21 thru 50 . . . . @7.00
51 thru 59 . . . . @5.00
60 Elvis 85.00
61 thru 100 . . . . @4.00
101 thru 130 . . . . @3.00

INTERNATIONAL COMICS
(see CRIME PATROL)

INTERNATIONAL
CRIME PATROL
(see CRIME PATROL)

INTIMATE
CONFESSIONS
Fawcett Publ./
Realistic Comics
1951
1a P(c) all, Unmarried Bride . 550.00
1 EK,EK(c),Days of Temptation...
   Nights of Desire 150.00
2 Doomed to Silence 135.00
3 EK(c), The Only Man For Me 125.00
3a Robert Briffault 125.00
4 EK(c),Tormented Love 125.00
5 Her Secret Sin 125.00
6 Reckless Pick-up 125.00
7 A Love Like Ours,Spanking . 150.00
8 Fatal Woman, March, 1953 . 125.00

INTIMATE LOVE
Standard Magazines
January, 1950
5 Wings on My Heart,Ph(c) . . . 40.00
6 WE,JSe,Ph(c) 45.00
7 WE,JSe,Ph(c),I Toyed
   with Love 45.00
8 WE,JSe,Ph(c) 45.00
9 Ph(c) 25.00
10 Ph(c),My Hopeless Heart . . . 35.00
11 . . . . 15.00
12 . . . . 15.00
13 thru 18 . . . . @15.00
19 ATh 35.00
20 . . . . 15.00
21 ATh 35.00
22 ATh 35.00
23 ATh 15.00
24 ATh 35.00
25 ATh 15.00
26 ATh 35.00
27 ATh 15.00
28 ATh,August, 1954 . . . . 15.00

INTIMATE SECRETS
OF ROMANCE
Star Publications
September, 1953
1 LbC(c) 100.00
2 LbC(c) 85.00

INVISIBLE SCARLET O'NEIL
Harvey Publications
December, 1950

1	....	100.00
2	....	75.00
3 April, 1951	....	75.00

IT REALLY HAPPENED
William H. Wise/
Visual Editions
1945

1 Benjamin Franklin, Kit Carson 125.00
2 The Terrible Tiddlers 75.00
3 Maid of the Margiris 50.00
4 Chaplain Albert J. Hoffman .. 50.00
5 AS(c),Monarchs of the Sea,Lou
 Gehrig, Amelia Earhart .. 100.00
6 AS(c),Ernie Pyle 50.00
7 FG,Teddy Roosevelt,Jefferson
 Davis, Story of the Helicopter 50.00
8 FG,Man O' War,Roy Rogers 125.00
9 AS(c),The Story of
 Old Ironsides 50.00
10 AS(c),Honus Wagner, The
 Story of Mark Twain 75.00
11 AS(c),MB,Queen of the Spanish
 Main, October, 1947 ...... 65.00

JACK ARMSTRONG
Parents' Institute
November, 1947

1 Artic Mystery 350.00
2 Den of the Golden Dragon . 150.00
3 Lost Valley of Ice 125.00
4 Land of the Leopard Men .. 125.00
5 Fight against Racketeers of
 the Ring 125.00
6 .... 75.00
7 Baffling Mystery on the
 Diamond 80.00
8 .... 80.00
9 Mystery of the Midgets 80.00
10 Secret Cargo 80.00
11 .... 75.00
12 Madman's Island, rare 125.00
13 September, 1949 .... 75.00

JACE PEARSON OF THE TEXAS RANGERS
Dell Publishing Co.
May, 1952

(1) see Dell Four Color #396
2 Ph(c),Joel McRae 50.00
3 Ph(c),Joel McRae 50.00
4 Ph(c),Joel McRae 50.00
5 Ph(c),Joel McRae 50.00
6 Ph(c),Joel McRae 50.00
7 Ph(c),Joel McRae 50.00
8 Ph(c),Joel McRae 50.00
9 Ph(c),Joel McRae 50.00
(10) see Dell Four Color #648
Becomes:

TALES OF JACE PEARSON OF THE TEXAS RANGERS

11 .... 30.00
12 .... 30.00
13 .... 30.00
14 .... 30.00
15 ATh 40.00

16 ATh 40.00
17 .... 30.00
18 .... 30.00
19 .... 30.00
20 .... 30.00

JACKIE GLEASON
St. John Publishing Co.
September, 1955

1 Ph(c) 700.00
2 .... 500.00
3 .... 400.00
4 December, 1955 .... 375.00

Jackie Robinson N#
© St. John Publishing Co.

JACKIE ROBINSON
Fawcett Publications
May, 1950

N# Ph(c) all issues 700.00
2 .... 500.00
3 thru 5 .... @400.00
6 May, 1952 .... 350.00

JACK IN THE BOX
(see YELLOW JACKET COMICS)

JACKPOT COMICS
MLJ Magazines
Spring, 1941

1 CBi(c),B:Black Hood,Mr.Justice,
 Steel Sterling,Sgt.Boyle .. 2,200.00
2 SCp(c), ... 1,000.00
3 Bondage cover 750.00
4 First Archie 2,000.00
5 Hitler(c) 1,000.00
6 Son of the Skull v:Black
 Hood, Bondage(c) 850.00
7 Bondage (c) 850.00
8 Sal(c), ... 750.00
9 Sal(c), ... 800.00
Becomes:

JOLLY JINGLES
10 Super Duck,(fa) 250.00
11 Super Duck 135.00
12 Hitler parody cover,A:Woody

Woodpecker 75.00
13 Super Duck 50.00
14 Super Duck 50.00
15 Super Duck 50.00
16 December, 1944 .... 50.00

JACK THE GIANT KILLER
Bimfort & Co.
August-September, 1953
1 HcK,HcK(c) 135.00

JAMBOREE
Round Publishing Co.
February, 1946
1 .... 125.00
2 March, 1946 .... 75.00

JANE ARDEN
St. John Publ. Co.
March, 1948
1 .... 120.00
2 June, 1948 .... 70.00

JEEP COMICS
R.B. Leffingwell & Co.
Winter, 1944
1 B;Captain Power 300.00
2 .... 200.00
3 LbC(c),March-April, 1948 .. 250.00

JEFF JORDAN, U.S. AGENT
D.S. Publ. Co.
December, 1947
1 .... 55.00

JESSE JAMES
Avon Periodicals/ Realistic Publ.
August, 1950

1 JKu,The San Antonio Stage
 Robbery 125.00
2 JKu,The Daring Liberty Bank
 Robbery 100.00
3 JKu,The California Stagecoach
 Robberies 75.00
4 EK(c),Deadliest Deed! ... 35.00
5 JKu,WW,Great Prison Break 100.00
6 JKu,Wanted Dead or Alive . 100.00
7 JKu,Six-Gun Slaughter at
 San Romano! 75.00
8 EK,Daring Train Robbery! ... 50.00
9 EK 25.00
10 thru 14 {Do not exist}
15 .... 40.00
16 .... 30.00
17 .... 25.00
18 JKu 25.00
19 JKu 25.00
20 AW,FF,A:Chief Vic,Kit West 100.00
21 .... 25.00
22 .... 25.00
23 .... 25.00
24 EK,B:New McCarty 25.00
25 EK 25.00
26 EK 25.00
27 EK,E:New McCarty 25.00
28 .... 25.00
29 August, 1956 .... 25.00

JEST
Harry 'A' Chesler
1944
10 J. Rebel,Yankee Boy	100.00
11 1944,Little Nemo	125.00

JET ACES
Real Adventure Publ. Co.
(Fiction House)
1952
1 Set 'em up in MIG Alley	100.00
2 Kiss-Off for Moscow Molly	60.00
3 Red Task Force Sighted	60.00
4 Death-Date at 40,000, 1953	60.00

JET FIGHTERS
Standard Magazines
November, 1953
5 ATh,Korean War Stories	85.00
6 Circus Pilot	35.00
7 ATh, Iron Curtains for Ivan, March, 1953	50.00

JETTA OF THE 21st CENTURY
Standard Comics
December, 1952
5 Teen Stories	150.00
6	100.00
7 April, 1953	100.00

JIGGS AND MAGGIE
Best Books (Standard)/
Harvey Publ.
June, 1949
11	60.00
12 thru 21	@30.00
22 thru 26	@22.00
27 February-March, 1954	22.00

JIM HARDY
Spotlight Publ.
1944
N# Dynamite Jim,Mirror Man	300.00

JIM RAY'S AVIATION SKETCH BOOK
Vital Publishers
February, 1946
1 Radar, the Invisible eye	175.00
2 Gen.Hap Arnold, May, 1946	150.00

JINGLE JANGLE COMICS
Eastern Color Printing Co.
February, 1942
1 B:Benny Bear,Pie Face Prince, Jingle Jangle Tales,Hortense	350.00
2 GCn	175.00
3 GCn	150.00
4 GCn,Pie Face cover	150.00
5 GCn,B:Pie Face	150.00
6 GCn,	125.00
7	125.00
8	125.00
9	125.00
10	125.00
11 thru 15 E:Pie Face	@100.00
16 thru 20	@75.00
21 thru 25	@60.00

26 thru 30	@50.00
31 thru 41	@40.00
42 December, 1949	40.00

JING PALS
Victory Publ. Corp.
February, 1946
1 Johnny Rabbit	60.00
2	30.00
3	30.00
4 August, 1948	30.00

JOE COLLEGE
Hillman Periodicals
Fall, 1949
1 BP,DPr	50.00
2 BP, Winter, 1949	45.00

JOE LOUIS
Fawcett Periodicals
September, 1950
1 Ph(c),Life Story	450.00
2 Ph(c),November, 1950	300.00

JOE PALOOKA
Publication Enterprises
(Columbia Comics Group)
1943
1 Lost in the Desert	600.00
2 Hitler cover	400.00
3 KO's the Nazis!	250.00
4 Eiffel tower cover, 1944	225.00

Joe Palooka #39 © Harvey Comics

JOE PALOOKA
Harvey Publications
Nov., 1954–March 1961
1 Joe Tells How he became World Champ	350.00
2 Skiing cover	175.00
3	100.00
4 Welcome Home Pals!	100.00
5 S&K,The Great Carnival Murder Mystery	150.00
6 Classic Joe Palooka (c)	100.00
7 BP,V:Grumpopski	100.00
8 BP,Mystery of the Ghost Ship	75.00
9 Drooten Island Mystery	75.00

10 BP	75.00
11	65.00
12 BP,Boxing Course	65.00
13	60.00
14 BP,Palooka's Toughest Fight	60.00
15 BP,O:Humphrey	100.00
16 BP,A:Humphrey	60.00
17 BP,A:Humphrey	60.00
18	60.00
19 BP,Freedom Train(c)	75.00
20 Punch Out(c)	60.00
21	50.00
22 V:Assassin	50.00
23 Big Bathing Beauty Issue	50.00
24	50.00
25	50.00
26 BP,Big Prize Fight Robberies	50.00
27 BP,Mystery of Bal Eagle Cabin	50.00
28 BP,Fights out West	50.00
29 BP,Joe Busts Crime Wide Open	50.00
30 BP,V:Hoodlums	40.00
31 BP	40.00
32 BP,Fight Palooka was sure to Lose	40.00
33 BP,Joe finds Ann	40.00
34 BP,How to Box like a Champ	40.00
35 BP,More Adventures of Little Max	40.00
36 BP	40.00
37 BP,Joe as a Boy	40.00
38 BP	40.00
39 BP,Original Hillbillies with Big Leviticus	40.00
40 BP,Joe's Toughest Fight	40.00
41 BP,Humphrey's Grudge Fight	40.00
42 BP	40.00
43 BP	40.00
44 BP,M:Ann Howe	50.00
45 BP	35.00
46 Champ of Champs	35.00
47 BreathtakingUnderwaterBattle	35.00
48 BP,Exciting Indian Adventure	35.00
49 BP	35.00
50 BP,Bondage(c)	35.00
51 BP	35.00
52 BP,V:Balonki	35.00
53 BP	35.00
54 V:Bad Man Trigger McGehee	35.00
55	35.00
56 Foul Play on the High Seas	35.00
57 Curtains for the Champ	35.00
58 V:The Man-Eating Swamp Terror	35.00
59 The Enemy Attacks	35.00
60 Joe Fights Escaped Convict	35.00
61	30.00
62 S&K	45.00
63	30.00
64	30.00
65	30.00
66	30.00
67	30.00
68	30.00
69 A Package from Home	30.00
70 BP	30.00
71	30.00
72	30.00
73 BP	30.00
74 thru 118	@30.00
Giant 1 Body Building	65.00
Giant 2 Fights His Way Back	125.00
Giant 3 Visits Lost City	60.00
Giant 4 All in Family	65.00

JOE YANK
Visual Editions
(Standard Comics)
March, 1952

5 ATh,WE,Korean Jackpot! ... 60.00
6 Bacon and Bullets,
G.I.Renegade 40.00
7 Two-Man War,A:Sgt. Glamour 30.00
8 ATh(c),Miss Foxhole of 1952, 30.00
9 G.I.'s and Dolls,Colonel Blood 25.00
10 A Good Way to Die,
A:General Joe 25.00
11 .... 25.00
12 RA 25.00
13 .... 25.00
14 .... 25.00
15 .... 25.00
16 July, 1954 .... 25.00

JOHN HIX SCRAPBOOK
Eastern Color Printing Co.
1937

1 Strange as It Seems 250.00
2 Strange as It Seems 200.00

JOHNNY DANGER
Toby Press
August, 1954

1 Ph(c),Private Detective 125.00

JOHNNY DYNAMITE
(see DYNAMITE)

JOHNNY HAZARD
Best Books
(Standard Comics)
August, 1948

5 FR 100.00
6 FR,FR(c) 75.00
7 FR(c) 60.00
8 FR,FR(c), May, 1949 ...... 60.00

JOHNNY LAW,
SKY RANGER
Good Comics (Lev Gleason)
April, 1955

1 .... 50.00
2 .... 30.00
3 .... 30.00
4 November, 1955 .... 30.00

JOHN WAYNE
ADVENTURE
COMICS
Toby Press
Winter, 1949

1 Ph(c),The Mysterious Valley
of Violence 1,200.00
2 AW,FF,Ph(c) 500.00
3 AW,FF,Flying Sheriff 500.00
4 AW,FF,Double-Danger,Ph(c) 500.00
5 Volcano of Death,Ph(c) ... 450.00
6 AW,FF,Caravan of Doom,
Ph(c) 450.00
7 AW,FF,Ph(c) 400.00
8 AW,FF,Duel of Death,Ph(c) 425.00
9 Ghost Guns,Ph(c) 250.00
10 Dangerous Journey,Ph(c) . 250.00
11 Manhunt!,Ph(c) 250.00
12 HK,Joins the Marines,Ph(c) . 275.00
13 V:Frank Stacy 225.00

14 Operation Peeping John ... 225.00
15 Bridge Head 250.00
16 AW,FF,Golden Double-Cross 250.00
17 Murderer's Music 250.00
18 AW,FF,Larson's Folly 275.00
19 .... 200.00
20 Whale Cover 200.00
21 .... 200.00
22 Flash Flood! 200.00
23 Death on Two Wheels 200.00
24 Desert 200.00
25 AW,FF,Hondo!,Ph(c) 275.00
26 Ph(c) 225.00
27 Ph(c) 225.00
28 Dead Man's Boots! 225.00
29 AW,FF,Ph(c),Crash in
California Desert 275.00
30 The Wild One, Ph(c) 225.00
31 AW,FF,May, 1955 .... 250.00

Jo-Jo #6 © Fox Feature Syndicate

JO-JO COMICS
Fox Features Syndicate
Spring, 1946

N# (fa) 50.00
2 (fa) 25.00
3 (fa) 25.00
4 (fa) 25.00
5 (fa) 25.00
6 (fa) 25.00
7 B:Jo-Jo Congo King 650.00
8 (7)B:Tanee,V:The
Giant Queen 450.00
9 (8)The Mountain of Skulls .. 400.00
10 (9)Death of the Fanged Lady 375.00
11 (10) 375.00
12 (11)Bondage(c),
Water Warriors 325.00
13 (12) Jade Juggernaut 300.00
14 The Leopards of Learda ... 300.00
15 The Flaming Fiend 300.00
16 Golden Gorilla,bondage(c) . 300.00
17 Stark-Mad Thespian,
bondage(c) 325.00
18 The Death Traveler 300.00
19 Gladiator of Gore 300.00
20 .... 300.00
21 .... 300.00
22 .... 300.00
23 .... 300.00

24 .... 300.00
25 Bondage(c) 325.00
26 .... 300.00
27 .... 300.00
28 .... 300.00
29 July, 1949 .... 325.00

JOURNEY INTO FEAR
Superior Publications
May, 1951

1 MB,Preview of Chaos 400.00
2 Debt to the Devil 250.00
3 Midnight Prowler 225.00
4 Invisible Terror 225.00
5 Devil Cat 150.00
6 Partners in Blood 150.00
7 The Werewolf Lurks 150.00
8 Bells of the Damned 150.00
9 Masked Death 150.00
10 Gallery of the Dead 150.00
11 Beast of Bedlam 125.00
12 No Rest for the Dead 125.00
13 Cult of the Dead 125.00
14 Jury of the Undead 125.00
15 Corpse in Make-up 135.00
16 Death by Invitation 125.00
17 Deadline for Death 125.00
18 Here's to Horror 125.00
19 This Body is Mine! 125.00
20 Masters of the Dead 125.00
21 Horror in the Clock,
September, 1954 .... 125.00

JUDO JOE
Jay-Jay Corp.
August, 1952

1 Drug 50.00
2 .... 35.00
3 Drug, December, 1953 .... 35.00

JUDY CANOVA
Fox Features Syndicate
May, 1950

23 (1)WW,WW(c) 125.00
24 (2)WW,WW(c) 120.00
3 JO,WW,WW(c)
September, 1950 .... 150.00

JUKE BOX
Famous Funnies
March, 1948

1 ATh(c),Spike Jones 300.00
2 Dinah Shore,Transvestitism . 200.00
3 Vic Damone 150.00
4 Jimmy Durante 150.00
5 .... 125.00
6 January, 1949,Desi Arnaz . 175.00

JUMBO COMICS
Real Adventure Publ. Co.
(Fiction House)
September, 1938

1 LF,BKa,JK,WE,WE(c),B:Sheena
Queen of the Jungle,The Hunchback 17,000.00
2 LF,JK,WE,BKa,BP,
O:Sheena 5,500.00
3 JK,WE,WE(c),BP,LF,BKa . 4,000.00
4 WE,WE(c),MMe,LF,BKa,
O:The Hawk 3,500.00
5 WE,WE(c),BP,BKa 3,000.00
6 WE,WE(c),BP,BKa 2,700.00
7 WE,BKa,BP 2,600.00

8 LF(c),BP,BKa,World of
   Tommorow 2,600.00
9 LF(c),BP 2,400.00
10 WE,LF(c),BKa,Regular size
   issues begin 1,300.00
11 LF(c),WE&BP,War of the
   Emerald Gas 1,000.00
12 WE(c),WE&BP,Hawk in Buccaneer
   Vengeance,Bondage(c) . . . 1,100.00
13 WE(c),BP,Sheena in The
   Thundering Herds 1,000.00
14 WE(c),LF,BP,Hawk in Siege
   of Thunder Isle,B:Lightning 1,200.00
15 BP(c),BP,Sheena(c) 650.00
16 BP(c),BP,The Lightning
   Strikes Twice 750.00
17 BP(c), all Sheena covers
   and lead stories 650.00
18 BP 600.00
19 BP(c),BKa,Warriors of
   the Bush 600.00
20 BP,BKa,Spoilers of
   the Wild 600.00
21 BP,BKa,Prey of the
   Giant Killers 500.00
22 BP,BKa,Victims of the
   Super-Ape,O:Hawk 550.00
23 BP,BKa,Swamp of the
   Green Terror 550.00
24 BP,BKa,Curse of the Black
   Venom 550.00
25 BP,BKa,Bait for the Beast . . 500.00
26 BP,BKa,Tiger-Man Terror . . 500.00
27 BP,BKa,Sabre-Tooth Terror 500.00
28 BKa,RWd,The Devil of
   the Congo 500.00
29 BKa,RWd,Elephant-Scourge 500.00
30 BKa,RWd,Slashing Fangs . 500.00
31 BKa,RWd,Voodoo Treasure
   of Black Slave Lake 450.00
32 BKa,RWd,AB,Captives of
   the Gorilla-Men 450.00
33 BKa,RWd,AB,Stampede
   Tusks 450.00
34 BKa,RWd,AB,Claws of the
   Devil-Cat 450.00
35 BKa,RWd,AB,Hostage of the
   Devil Apes 450.00
36 BKa,RWd,AB,Voodoo Flames 450.00
37 BKa,RWd,AB,Congo Terror . 450.00
38 BKa,RWd,ABDeath-Trap of
   the River Demons 450.00
39 BKa,RWd,AB,Cannibal Bait . 450.00
40 BKa,RWd,AB,
   Assagai Poison 450.00
41 BKa,RWd,AB,Killer's Kraal,
   Bondage(c) 350.00
42 BKa,RWd,AB,Plague of
   Spotted Killers 350.00
43 BKa,RWd,AB,Beasts of the
   Devil Queen 350.00
44 BKa,RWd,AB,Blood-Cult of
   K'Douma 350.00
45 BKa,RWd,AB,Fanged
   Keeper of the Fire-Gem . . . 350.00
46 BKa,RWd,AB,Lair of the
   Armored Monsters 350.00
47 BKa,RWd,AB,The Bantu
   Blood-Monster 350.00
48 BKa,RWd,AB,Red Meat for
   the Cat-Pack 350.00
49 BKa,RWd,AB,Empire of the
   Hairy Ones 350.00
50 BKa,RWd,AB,Eyrie of the
   Leopard Birds 350.00

51 BKa,RWd.AB,Monsters with
   Wings 275.00
52 BKa,RWd,AB,Man-Eaters
   Paradise 275.00
53 RWd,AB,Slaves of the
   Blood Moon 275.00
54 RWd,AB,Congo Kill 275.00
55 RWd,AB,Bait for the Silver
   King Cat 275.00
56 RWd,AB,Sabre Monsters of
   the Aba-Zanzi,Bondage(c) . . 275.00
57 RWd,AB,Arena of Beasts . . 275.00
58 RWd,AB,Sky-Atlas of the
   Thunder-Birds 275.00
59 RWd,AB,Kraal of Shrunken
   Heads 275.00
60 RWd,AB,Land of the
   Stalking Death 200.00
61 RWd,AB,King-Beast of
   the Masai 200.00
62 RWd,AB,Valley of Golden
   Death 200.00
63 RWd,AB,The Dwarf Makers 200.00

Jumbo Comics #26
© Real Adventure Publ./Fiction House

64 RWd,The Slave-Brand of Ibn
   Ben Satan,Male Bondage . . 200.00
65 RWd,The Man-Eaters of
   Linpopo 200.00
66 RWd,Valley of Monsters . . . 200.00
67 RWd,Land of Feathered Evil 200.00
68 RWd,Spear of Blood Ju-Ju . 200.00
69 RWd,AB,MB,Slaves for the
   White Sheik 200.00
70 RWd,AB,MB,The Rogue
   Beast's Prey 200.00
71 RWd,AB,MB,The Serpent-
   God Speaks 175.00
72 RWd,AB,MB,Curse of the
   Half-Dead 175.00
73 RWd,AB,MB,War Apes of
   the T'Kanis 175.00
74 RWd,AB,MB,Drums of the
   Voodoo God 175.00
75 RWd,AB,MB,Terror Trail of
   the Devil's Horn 175.00
76 RWd,AB,MB,Fire Gems of
   Skull Valley 175.00
77 RWd,AB,MB,Blood Dragons
   from Fire Valley 175.00

78 RWd,AB,MB,Veldt of the
   Vampire Apes 175.00
79 RWd,AB,MB,Dancing
   Skeletons 175.00
80 RWd,AB,MB,Banshee Cats 175.00
81 RWd,AB,MB,JKa,Heads for
   King' Hondo's Harem 160.00
82 RWd,MB,AB,JKa,Ghost Riders
   of the Golden Tuskers 160.00
83 RWd,MB,AB,JKa,Charge of
   the Condo Juggernauts 160.00
84 RWd,MB,AB,JKa,Valley of
   the Whispering Fangs 160.00
85 RWd,MB,AB,JKa,Red Tusks
   of Zulu-Za'an 160.00
86 RWd,MB,AB,JKa,Witch-Maiden
   of the Burning Blade 160.00
87 RWd,AB,MB,JKa,Sargasso of
   Lost Safaris 160.00
88 RWd,AB,MB,JKa,Kill-Quest
   of the Ju-Ju Tusks 160.00
89 RWd,AB,MB,JKa,Ghost Slaves
   of Bwana Rojo 160.00
90 RWd,AB,MB,JKa,Death Kraal
   of the Mastadons 160.00
91 RWd,AB,MB,JKa,Spoor of
   the Sabre-Horn Tiger 150.00
92 RWd,MB,JKa,Pied Piper
   of the Congo 150.00
93 RWd,MB,JKa,The Beasts
   that Dawn Begot 150.00
94 RWd,MB,JKa,Wheel of a
   Thousand Deaths 150.00
95 RWd,MB,JKa,Flame Dance
   of the Ju-Ju Witch 150.00
96 RWd,MB,JKa,Ghost Safari . 150.00
97 RWd,MB,JKa,Banshee Wail
   of the Undead,Bondage(c) . 150.00
98 RWd,MB,JKa,Seekers of
   the Terror Fangs 150.00
99 RWd,MB,JKa,Shrine of
   the Seven Souls 150.00
100 RWd,MB,Slave Brand
   of Hassan Bey 175.00
101 RWd,MB,Quest of the
   Two-Face Ju Ju 135.00
102 RWd,MB,Viper Gods of
   Vengeance Veldt 135.00
103 RWd,MB,Blood for the
   Idol of Blades 135.00
104 RWd,MB,Valley of Eternal
   Sleep 135.00
105 RWd,MB,Man Cubs from
   Momba-Zu 200.00
106 RWd,MB,The River of
   No-Return 200.00
107 RWd,MB,Vandals of
   the Veldt 135.00
108 RWd,MB,The Orphan of
   Vengeance Vale 135.00
109 RWd,MB,The Pygmy's Hiss
   is Poison 135.00
110 RWd,MB,Death Guards the
   Congo Keep 135.00
111 RWd,MB,Beware of the
   Witch-Man's Brew 135.00
112 RWd,MB,The Blood-Mask
   from G'Shinis Grave 125.00
113 RWd,MB,The Mask's of
   Zombi-Zan 125.00
114 RWd,MB 125.00
115 RWd,MB,Svengali of
   the Apes 125.00
116 RWd,MB,The Vessel of
   Marbel Monsters 125.00

GOLDEN AGE

GOLDEN AGE

117 RWd,MB,Lair of the Half-
   Man King 125.00
118 RWd,MB,Quest of the
   Congo Dwarflings 125.00
119 RWd,MB,King Crocodile's
   Domain 125.00
120 RWd,MB,The Beast-Pack
   Howls the Moon 125.00
121 RWd,MB,The Kraal of
   Evil Ivory 125.00
122 RWd,MB,Castaways of
   the Congo 125.00
123 RWd,MB, ... 125.00
124 RWd,MB,The Voodoo Beasts
   of Changra-Lo 125.00
125 RWd,MB,JKa(c),The Beast-
   Pack Strikes at Dawn 125.00
126 RWd,MB,JKa(c),Lair of the
   Swamp Beast 125.00
127 RWd,MB,JKa(c),The Phantom
   of Lost Lagoon 125.00
128 RWd,MB,JKa(c),Mad Mistress
   of the Congo-Tuskers 125.00
129 RWd,MB,JKa(c),Slaves of
   King Simbas Kraal 125.00
130 RWd,MB,JKa(c),Quest of
   the Pharaoh's Idol 125.00
131 RWd,JKa(c),Congo Giants
   at Bay 125.00
132 RWd,JKa(c),The Doom of
   the Devil's Gorge 125.00
133 RWd,JKa(c),Blaze the
   Pitfall Trail 125.00
134 RWd,JKa(c),Catacombs of
   the Jackal-Men 125.00
135 RWd,JKa(c),The 40 Thieves
   of Ankar-Lo 125.00
136 RWd,JKa(c),The Perils of
   Paradise Lost 125.00
137 RWd,JKa(c),The Kraal of
   Missing Men 125.00
138 RWd,JKa(c),The Panthers
   of Kajo-Kazar 125.00
139 RWd,JKa(c),Stampede of
   the Congo Lancers 125.00
140 RWd,JKa(c),The Moon
   Beasts from Vulture Valley . 125.00
141 RWd,JKa(c),B:Long Bow . . 135.00
142 RWd,JKa(c),Man-Eaters
   of N'Gamba 135.00
143 RWd,JKa(c),The Curse of
   the Cannibal Drum 135.00
144 RWd,JKa(c),The Secrets of
   Killers Cave 135.00
145 RWd,JKa(c),Killers of
   the Crypt 135.00
146 RWd,JKa(c),Sinbad of the
   Lost Lagoon 135.00
147 RWd,JKa(c),The Wizard of
   Gorilla Glade 135.00
148 RWd,JKa(c),Derelict of
   the Slave King 135.00
149 RWd,JKa(c),Lash Lord of
   the Elephants 135.00
150 RWd,JKa(c),Queen of
   the Pharaoh's Idol 125.00
151 RWd,The Voodoo Claws
   of Doomsday Trek 125.00
152 RWd,Red Blades of Africa 125.00
153 RWd,Lost Legions of the Nile 125.00
154 RWd,The Track of the
   Black Devil 125.00
155 RWd,The Ghosts of
   Blow- Gun Trail 125.00
156 RWd,The Slave-Runners

of Bambaru 125.00
157 RWd,Cave of the
   Golden Skull 125.00
158 RWd,Gun Trek to
   Panther Valley 125.00
159 RWd,A:Space Scout 110.00
160 RWd,Savage Cargo,
   E:Sheena covers 110.00
161 RWd,Dawns of the Pit . . . 110.00
162 RWd,Hangman's Haunt . . 110.00
163 RWd,Cagliostro Cursed
   Thee 110.00
164 RWd,Death Bars the Door 110.00
165 RWd,Day off from a Corpse 110.00
166 RWd,The Gallows Bird . . . 110.00
167 RWd,Cult of the Clawmen,
   March, 1953 . . . . 110.00

Jungle Comics #31
© Glen Kel. Publ./Fiction House

JUNGLE COMICS
Glen Kel Publ./Fiction House
January, 1940
1 HcK,DBr,LF(c),O:The White
   Panther,Kaanga,Tabu, B:The
   Jungle Boy,Camilla, all
   Kaanga covers & stories . . 3,500.00
2 HcK,DBr,WE(c),B:Fantomah 1,200.00
3 HcK,DBr,GT,The Crocodiles
   of Death River 1,000.00
4 HcK,DBr,Wambi in
   Thundering Herds 950.00
5 WE(c),GT,HcK,DBr,Empire
   of the Ape Men 1,100.00
6 WE(c),GT,DBr,HcK,Tigress
   of the Deep Jungle Swamp . 600.00
7 BP(c),DBr,GT,HcK,Live
   Sacrifice,Bondage(c) 550.00
8 BP(c),GT,HcK,Safari into
   Shadowland 550.00
9 GT,HcK,Captive of the
   Voodoo Master 550.00
10 GT,HcK,BP,Lair of the
   Renegade Killer 550.00
11 GT,HcK,V:Beasts of Africa's Ancient
   Primieval Swamp Land 400.00
12 GT,HcK,The Devil's
   Death-Trap 400.00
13 GT(c),GT,HcK,Stalker of

the Beasts 425.00
14 HcK,Vengeance of the
   Gorilla Hordes 400.00
15 HcK,Terror of the Voodoo
   Cauldron 400.00
16 HcK,Caveman Killers 400.00
17 HcK,Valley of the Killer-Birds 400.00
18 HcK,Trap of the Tawny
   Killer, Bondage(c) 425.00
19 HcK,Revolt of the Man-Apes 400.00
20 HcK,One-offering to
   Ju-Ju Demon 400.00
21 HcK,Monster of the Dismal
   Swamp, Bondage(c) 375.00
22 HcK,Lair o/t Winged Fiend . 350.00
23 HcK,Man-Eater Jaws 350.00
24 HcK,Battle of the Beasts . . 350.00
25 HcK,Kaghis the Blood God,
   Bondage(c) 375.00
26 HcK,Gorillas of the
   Witch-Queen 350.00
27 HcK,Spore o/t Gold-Raiders . 350.00
28 HcK,Vengeance of the Flame
   God, Bondage(c) 375.00
29 HcK,Juggernaut of Doom . 350.00
30 HcK,Claws o/t Black Terror . 350.00
31 HcK,Land of Shrunken Skulls 350.00
32 HcK,Curse of the King-Beast 350.00
33 HcK,Scaly Guardians of
   Massacre Pool,Bondage(c) . 350.00
34 HcK,Bait of the Spotted
   Fury,Bondage(c) 350.00
35 HcK,Stampede of the
   Slave-Masters 350.00
36 HcK,GT,The Flame-Death of
   Ju Ju Mountain 350.00
37 HcK,GT,Scaly Sentinel of
   Taboo Swamp 350.00
38 HcK,GT,Duel of the Congo
   Destroyers 350.00
39 HcK,Land of Laughing Bones 350.00
40 HcK,Killer Plague 350.00
41 Hck,The King Ape
   Feeds at Dawn 250.00
42 Hck,RC,Master of the
   Moon-Beasts 250.00
43 HcK,The White Shiek 250.00
44 HcK,Monster of the
   Boiling Pool 255.00
45 HcK,The Bone-Grinders of
   B'Zambi, Bondage(c) 250.00
46 HcK,Blood Raiders of
   Tree Trail 250.00
47 HcK,GT,Monsters of the Man
   Pool, Bondage(c) 250.00
48 HcK,GT,Strangest Congo
   Adventure 200.00
49 HcK,GT,Lair of the King
   -Serpent 200.00
50 HcK,GT,Juggernaut of
   the Bush 200.00
51 HcK,GT,The Golden Lion of
   Genghis Kahn 200.00
52 HcK,Feast for the River
   Devils, Bondage(c) 225.00
53 HcK,GT,Slaves for Horrors
   Harem 225.00
54 HcK,GT,Blood Bride of
   the Crocodile 200.00
55 HcK,GT,The Tree Devil . . . 200.00
56 HcK,Bride for the
   Rainmaker Raj 200.00
57 HcK,Fire Gems of T'ulaki . . 200.00
58 HcK,Land of the
   Cannibal God 200.00

59 HcK,Dwellers of the Mist
Bondage(c) 225.00
60 HcK,Bush Devil's Spoor . . . 200.00
61 HcK,Curse of the Blood
Madness 200.00
62 Bondage(c) 210.00
63 HcK,Fire-Birds for the
Cliff Dwellers 175.00
64 Valley of the Ju-Ju Idols . . . 175.00
65 Shrine of the Seven Ju Jus,
Bondage(c) 185.00
66 Spoor of the Purple Skulls . 175.00
67 Devil Beasts of the Golden
Temple 175.00
68 Satan's Safari 175.00
69 Brides for the Serpent King . 175.00
70 Brides for the King Beast,
Bondage(c) 185.00
71 Congo Prey,Bondage(c) . . . 185.00
72 Blood-Brand o/t Veldt Cats . 150.00
73 The Killer of M'omba Raj,
Bondage(c) 175.00
74 AgF,GoldenJaws,Bondage(c) 175.00
75 AgF,Congo Kill 150.00
76 AgF,Blood Thrist of the
Golden Tusk 150.00
77 AgF,The Golden Gourds
Shriek Blood,Bondage(c) . . 175.00
78 AgF,Bondage(c) 175.00
79 AgF,Death has a
Thousand Fangs 150.00
80 AgF,Salome of the
Devil-Cats Bondage(c) 175.00
81 AgF,Colossus of the Congo 150.00
82 AgF,Blood Jewels of the
Fire-Bird 150.00
83 AgF,Vampire Veldt,
Bondage(c) 175.00
84 AgF,Blood Spoor of the
Faceless Monster 150.00
85 AgF,Brides for the Man-Apes
Bondage(c) 175.00
86 AgF,Firegems of L'hama
Lost, Bondage(c) 175.00
87 AgF,Horror Kraal of the
Legless One,Bondage(c) . . . 150.00
88 AgF,Beyond the Ju-Ju Mists 165.00
89 AgF,Blood-Moon over the
Whispering Veldt 150.00
90 AgF,The Skulls for the
Altar of Doom,Bondage(c) . 165.00
91 AgF,Monsters from the Mist
Lands, Bondage(c) 165.00
92 AgF,Vendetta of the
Tree Tribes 150.00
93 AgF,Witch Queen of the
Hairy Ones 150.00
94 AgF,Terror Raid of
the Congo Caesar 150.00
95 Agf,Flame-Tongues of the
Sky Gods 150.00
96 Agf,Phantom Guardians of the
Enchanted Lake,Bondage(c) 135.00
97 AgF,Wizard of the Whirling
Doom,Bondage(c) 165.00
98 AgF,Ten Tusks of Zulu Ivory 175.00
99 AgF,Cannibal Caravan,
Bondage(c) 150.00
100 AgF,Hate has a
Thousand Claws 150.00
101 AgF,The Blade of
Buddha, Bondage(c) 150.00
102 AgF,Queen of the
Amazon Lancers 135.00
103 AgF,The Phantoms of

Lost Lagoon 135.00
104 AgF 135.00
105 AgF,The Red Witch
of Ubangi-Shan 135.00
106 AgF,Bondage(c) 150.00
107 Banshee Valley 150.00
108 HcK,Merchants of Murder . 150.00
109 HcK,Caravan of the
Golden Bones 135.00
110 HcK,Raid of the Fire-Fangs 135.00
111 HcK,The Trek of the
Terror-Paws 135.00
112 HcK,Morass of the
Mammoths 135.00
113 HcK,Two-Tusked Terror . . 135.00
114 HcK,Mad Jackals Hunt
by Night 135.00
115 HcK,Treasure Trove in
Vulture Sky 135.00
116 HcK,The Banshees of
Voodoo Veldt 135.00
117 HcK,The Fangs of the
Hooded Scorpion 135.00

Jungle Comics #34
© Glen Kel. Publ./Fiction House

118 HcK,The Muffled Drums
of Doom 135.00
119 HcK,Fury of the Golden
Doom 135.00
120 HcK,Killer King Domain . . 135.00
121 HcK,Wolves of the
Desert Night 135.00
122 HcK,The Veldt of
Phantom Fangs 135.00
123 HcK,The Ark of the
Mist-Maids 135.00
124 HcK,The Trail of the
Pharaoh's Eye 135.00
125 HcK,Skulls for Sale on
Dismal River 135.00
126 HcK,Safari Sinister 150.00
127 Hck,Bondage(c) 150.00
128 HcK,Dawn-Men of the Congo 125.00
129 Hck,The Captives of
Crocodile Swamp 125.00
130 HcK,Phantoms of the Congo 125.00
131 HcK,Treasure-Tomb of the
Ape-King 125.00
132 HcK,Bondage(c) 150.00
133 HcK,Scourge of the Sudan

Bondage(c) 150.00
134 HcK,The Black Avengers of
Kaffir Pass 125.00
135 Hck 125.00
136 HcK,The Death Kraals
of Kongola 125.00
137 BWg(c),HcK,The Safari of
Golden Ghosts 125.00
138 BWg(c),HcK,Track of the
Black Terror Bondage(c) . . . 125.00
139 BWg(c),HcK,Captain Kidd
of the Congo 125.00
140 BWg(c),HcK,The Monsters
of Kilmanjaro 125.00
141 BWg(c)HcK,The Death Hunt
of the Man Cubs 125.00
142 BWg(c),Hck,Sheba of the
Terror Claws,Bondage(c) . . 150.00
143 BWg(c)Hck,The Moon of
Devil Drums 150.00
144 BWg(c)Hck,Quest of the
Dragon's Claw 150.00
145 BWg(c)Hck,Spawn of the
Devil's Moon 150.00
146 BWg(c),HcK,Orphans of
the Congo 150.00
147 BWG(c),HcK,The Treasure
of Tembo Wanculu 150.00
148 BWg(c),HcK,Caged Beasts
of Plunder-Men,Bondage(c) . 150.00
149 BWg(c),HcK 125.00
150 BWg(c),HcK,Rhino Rampage,
Bondage(c) 150.00
151 BWg(c),HcK 125.00
152 BWg(c),HcK,The Rogue of
Kopje Kull 125.00
153 BWg(c),HcK,The Wild Men
of N'Gara 125.00
154 BWg(c),HcK,The Fire Wizard 125.00
155 BWg(c),HcK,Swamp of
the Shrieking Dead 125.00
156 BWg(c),HcK 125.00
157 BWg(c),HcK 125.00
158 BWg(c),HcK,A:Sheena . . . 125.00
159 BWg(c),HcK,The Blow-Gun
Kill 125.00
160 BWg,HcK,King Fang 125.00
161 BWg(c),HcK,The Barbarizi
Man-Eaters 125.00
162 BWg(c) 125.00
163 BWg(c),Jackals at the
Kill, Summer,1954 . . . . . . 125.00

JUNGLE JIM
Best Books
(Standard Comics)
January, 1949

11 . . . . 40.00
12 Mystery Island 25.00
13 Flowers of Peril 25.00
14 . . . . 25.00
15 . . . . 25.00
16 . . . . 25.00
17 . . . . 25.00
18 . . . . 25.00
19 . . . . 25.00
20 1951 . . . . 25.00

JUNGLE JIM
Dell Publishing Co.
August, 1953

(1) *see Dell Four Color #490*
(1) *see Dell Four Color #565*
3 P(c) all 30.00

GOLDEN AGE

GOLDEN AGE

4	25.00
5	25.00
6	20.00
7	20.00
8	20.00
9	20.00
10	20.00
11	20.00
12	20.00
13 'Mystery Island'	20.00
14 'Flowers of Peril'	20.00
15 thru 20	@20.00

JUNGLE JO
Hero Books
(Fox Features Syndicate)
March, 1950

N#	275.00
1 Mystery of Doc Jungle	300.00
2	250.00
3 The Secret of Youth, September, 1950	225.00

JUNGLE LIL
Hero Books
(Fox Features Syndicate)
April, 1950

1 Betrayer of the Kombe Dead	250.00

Becomes:

DOROTHY LAMOUR

2 WW,Ph(c)The Lost Safari	175.00
3 WW,Ph(c), August, 1950	125.00

JUNGLE THRILLS
(see TERRORS OF THE JUNGLE)

JUNIE PROM
Dearfield Publishing Co.
Winter, 1947

1 Teenage Stories	50.00
2	25.00
3	20.00
4	20.00
5	20.00
6 June, 1949	20.00

Junior Comics #16
© Fox Feature Syndicate

JUNIOR COMICS
Fox Features Syndicate
September, 1947

9 AF,AF(c) ,Teenage Stories	550.00
10 AF,AF(c)	500.00
11 AF,AF(c)	500.00
12 AF,AF(c)	500.00
13 AF,AF(c)	500.00
14 AF,AF(c)	500.00
15 AF,AF(c)	500.00
16 AF,AF(c),July,1948	500.00

JUNIOR HOOP COMICS
Stanmor Publications
January, 1952

1	40.00
2	20.00
3 July, 1952	20.00

JUSTICE TRAPS THE GUILTY
Headline Publications
(Prize)
October-November, 1947

2-1 S&K,S&K(c),Electric chair cover	375.00
2 S&K,S&K(c)	225.00
3 S&K,S&K(c)	200.00
4 S&K,S&K(c),True Confession of a Girl Gangleader	200.00
5 S&K,S&K(c)	200.00
6 S&K,S&K(c)	200.00
7 S&K,S&K(c)	200.00
8 S&K,S&K(c)	200.00
9 S&K,S&K(c)	200.00
10 S&K,S&K(c)	200.00
11 S&K,S&K(c)	75.00
12	35.00
13	50.00
14	35.00
15	35.00
16	35.00
17	50.00
18 S&K,S&K(c)	50.00
19 S&K,S&K(c)	50.00
20	30.00
21 S&K	40.00
22 S&K(c)	30.00
23 S&K(c)	30.00
24	20.00
25	25.00
26	20.00
27 S&K(c)	30.00
28	20.00
29	20.00
30 S&K	40.00
31 thru 50	@20.00
51	20.00
52	20.00
53	20.00
54	20.00
55	20.00
56	20.00
57	20.00
58 Drug	150.00
59 thru 92	@20.00

Becomes:

FARGO KID
Headline Publications
(Prize)

93 AW,JSe,O:Kid Fargo	120.00
94 JSe	75.00
95 June-July, 1958,JSe	75.00

KA'A'NGA COMICS
Glen-Kel Publ.
(Fiction House)
Spring, 1949

1 Phantoms of the Congo	400.00
2 V:The Jungle Octopus	200.00
3	150.00
4 The Wizard Apes of Inkosi-Khan	135.00
5	100.00
6 Captive of the Devil Apes	75.00
7 GT,Beast-Men of Mombassa	85.00
8 The Congo Kill-Cry	75.00
9	75.00
10 Stampede for Congo Gold	75.00
11 Claws of the Roaring Congo	60.00
12 Bondage(c)	75.00
13 Death Web of the Amazons	60.00
14 Slave Galley of the Lost Nile Bondage(c)	75.00
15 Crocodile Moon,Bondage(c)	75.00
16 Valley of Devil-Dwarfs	70.00
17 Tembu of the Elephants	60.00
18 The Red Claw of Vengeance	60.00
19 The Devil-Devil Trail	60.00
20 The Cult of the Killer Claws, Summer, 1954	60.00

KASCO COMICS
Kasco Grainfeed
(Giveaway)
1945

1 BWo	85.00
2 1949,BWo	75.00

KATHY
Standard Comics
September, 1949

1 Teen-Age Stories	40.00
2 ASh	22.00
3 thru 6	@15.00
7 thru 17	@12.00

KATY KEENE
Archie Publications/Close-Up Radio Comics
1949

1 BWo	750.00
2 BWo	400.00
3 BWo	300.00
4 BWo	300.00
5 BWo	275.00
6 BWo	250.00
7 BWo	250.00
8 thru 12 BWo	@225.00
13 thru 20 BWo	@200.00
21 thru 29 BWo	@150.00
30 thru 38 BWo	@125.00
39 thru 62 BWo	@100.00
Ann.#1	375.00
Ann.#2 thru #6	225.00

KEEN DETECTIVE FUNNIES
Centaur Publications
July, 1938

1-8 B:The Clock,	1,500.00
1-9 WE	600.00
1-10	550.00
1-11 Dean Denton	550.00
2-1 The Eye Sees	500.00
2-2 JCo	500.00

2-3 TNT 500.00
2-4 Gabby Flynn 500.00
5 . . . . 525.00
6 . . . . 500.00
7 Masked Marvel 1,500.00
8 PGn,Gabby Flynn,Nudity
  Expanded 16 pages 600.00
9 Dean Denton 525.00
10 . . . . 525.00
11 BEv,Sidekick 500.00
12 Masked Marvel(c) 650.00
3-1 Masked Marvel(c) 500.00
3-2 Masked Marvel(c) 500.00
3-3 BEv 500.00
16 BEv 500.00
17 JSm 500.00
18 The Eye Sees,Bondage(c) . 550.00
19 LFe 500.00
20 BEv,The Eye Sees 500.00
21 Masked Marvel(c) 500.00
22 Masked Marvel(c) 500.00
23 B:Airman 600.00
24 Airman 600.00

KEEN KOMICS
Centaur Publications
May, 1939
1 Teenage Stories 750.00
2 PGn,JaB,CBu 500.00
3 JCo 500.00

KEEN TEENS
Life's Romances Publ./Leader/
Magazine Enterprises
1945
N# P(c) 175.00
N# Ph(c),Van Johnson 150.00
3 Ph(c), ... 50.00
4 Ph(c),Glenn Ford 50.00
5 Ph(c),Perry Como 50.00
6 . . . . 50.00

KEN MAYNARD
WESTERN
Fawcett Publications
September, 1950
1 B:Ken Maynard & Tarzan

Ken Manyard Western #1
© Fawcett Publications

(horse) The Outlaw
  Treasure Trail 400.00
2 Invasion of the Badmen . . . 250.00
3 Pied Piper of the West 200.00
4 Outlaw Hoax 200.00
5 Mystery of Badman City . . . 200.00
6 Redwood Robbery 200.00
7 Seven Wonders of the West 200.00
8 Mighty Mountain Menace,
  Feb.,1952 . . . . 200.00

KEN SHANNON
Quality Comics Group
October, 1951
1 RC, Evil Eye of Count Ducrie 250.00
2 RC, Cut Rate Corpses 200.00
3 RC, Corpse that Wouldn't
  Sleep 150.00
4 RC, Stone Hatchet Murder . 125.00
5 RC, Case of the Carney Killer 125.00
6 Weird Vampire Mob 150.00
7 RC,Ugliest Man in the World 125.00
8 Chinatown Murders,Drug . . . 150.00
9 RC, Necklace of Blood 100.00
10 RC, Shadow of the Chair,
  Apr. 1953 . . . . 100.00

KERRY DRAKE
DETECTIVE CASES
Life's Romances/M.E./
1944
(1) see N# A-1 Comics 175.00
2 A:The Faceless Horror 125.00
3 . . . . 100.00
4 A:Squirrel, Dr. Zero, Caresse 100.00
5 Bondage cover 110.00
Harvey Publ.
6 A:Stitches 50.00
7 A:Shuteye 60.00
8 Bondage cover 65.00
9 Drug 100.00
10 BP,A:Meatball,Drug 100.00
11 BP,I:Kid Gloves 40.00
12 BP 40.00
13 BP,A:Torso 35.00
14 BP,Bullseye Murder Syndicate 35.00
15 BP,Fake Mystic Racket 35.00
16 BP,A:Vixen 30.00
17 BP,Case of the $50,000
  Robbery 30.00
18 BP,A:Vixen 30.00
19 BP,Case of the Dope
  Smugglers 35.00
20 BP,Secret Treasury Agent . . 30.00
21 BP,Murder on Record 25.00
22 BP,Death Rides the Air Waves 25.00
23 BP,Blackmailer's Secret
  Weapon 25.00
24 Blackmailer's Trap 25.00
25 Pretty Boy Killer 25.00
26 . . . . 25.00
27 . . . . 25.00
28 BP 25.00
29 BP 25.00
30 Mystery Mine,Bondage(c) . . 35.00
31 . . . . 25.00
32 . . . . 25.00
33 August, 1952 . . . . 25.00

KEWPIES
Will Eisner Publications
Spring, 1949
1 . . . . 350.00

KEY COMICS
Consolidated Magazines
January, 1944
1 B:The Key, Will-O-The-Wisp 250.00
2 . . . . 125.00
3 . . . . 100.00
4 O:John Quincy,B:The Atom 110.00
5 HoK,August, 1946 . . . . 100.00

KID COWBOY
Approved Comics/
St. John Publ. Co.
1950
1 B:Lucy Belle & Red Feather . 65.00
2 Six-Gun Justice 35.00
3 Shadow on Hangman's Bridge 30.00
4 Red Feather V:Eagle of Doom 25.00
5 Killers on the Rampage 25.00
6 The Stovepipe Hat 25.00
7 Ghost Town of Twin Buttes . 25.00
8 Thundering Hoofs 25.00
9 Terror on the Salt Flats 25.00
10 Valley of Death 25.00
11 Vanished Herds,Bondage(c) . 35.00
12 . . . . 25.00
13 . . . . 25.00
14 1954 . . . . 25.00

KIDDIE KARNIVAL
Approved Comics
1952
N# 250.00

KID ETERNITY
Comics Magazine
(Quality Comics Group)
Spring, 1946
1 . . . . 650.00
2 . . . . 300.00
3 Follow Him Out of This World 200.00
4 Great Heroes of the Past . . 200.00
5 Don't Kid with Crime 175.00
6 Busy Battling Crime 175.00
7 Protects the World 175.00
8 Fly to the Rescue 175.00
9 Swoop Down on Crime 175.00
10 Golden Touch from Mr. Midas 175.00
11 Aid the Living by Calling
  the Dead 150.00
12 Finds Death 150.00
13 Invades General Poschka . . 150.00
14 Battles Death 150.00
15 A: Master Man 150.00
16 Balance Scales of Justice . . 125.00
17 A:Baron Roxx 125.00
18 A:Man with Two Faces 125.00
Becomes:
BUCCANEERS
19 RC,Sword Fight(c) 400.00
20 RC,Treasure Chest 275.00
21 RC,Death Trap 325.00
22 A:Lady Dolores,Snuff,
  Bondage(c) 225.00
23 RC,V:Treasure Hungry
  Plunderers of the Sea 250.00
24 A:Adam Peril,Black Roger,
  Eric Falcon 175.00
25 V:Clews 175.00
26 V:Admiral Blood 175.00
27 RC,RC(c)May, 1951 . . . . . . 275.00

KID ZOO COMICS
Street & Smith Publications
July, 1948
1 (fa) 125.00

KILLERS, THE
Magazine Enterprises
1947
1 LbC(c),Thou Shall Not Kill . . 700.00
2 Grl,OW,Assassins Mad Slayers
  of the East,Hanging(c),Drug 650.00

KILROYS, THE
B&L Publishing Co./
American Comics
June-July, 1947
1 Three Girls in Love(c) 125.00
2 Flat Tire(c) 60.00
3 Right to Swear(c) 45.00
4 Kissing Booth(c) 45.00
5 Skiing(c) 45.00
6 Prom(c) 30.00
7 To School 30.00
8 . . . . 30.00
9 . . . . 30.00
10 B:Solid Jackson solo 30.00
11 . . . . 25.00
12 Life Guard(c) 25.00
13 thru 21 . . . . @25.00
22 thru 30 . . . . @20.00
31 thru 40 . . . . @18.00
41 thru 47 . . . . @15.00
48 3-D effect 100.00
49 3-D effect 100.00
50 thru 54, July 1954 . . . . . . @15.00

KING COMICS
David McKay Publications
April, 1936
(all have Popeye covers)
1 AR,EC,B:Popeye,Flash Gordon,B:
  Henry,Mandrake 8,000.00
2 AR,EC,Flash Gordon 2,400.00
3 AR,EC,Flash Gordon 1,500.00
4 AR,EC,Flash Gordon 1,200.00
5 AR,EC,Flash Gordon 800.00
6 AR,EC,Flash Gordon 600.00
7 AR,EC,King Royal Mounties 575.00
8 AR,EC,Thanksgiving(c) 550.00
9 AR,EC,Christmas(c) 550.00
10 AR,EC,Flash Gordon 550.00
11 AR,EC,Flash Gordon 500.00
12 AR,EC,Flash Gordon 500.00
13 AR,EC,Flash Gordon 500.00
14 AR,EC,Flash Gordon 500.00
15 AR,EC,Flash Gordon 500.00
16 AR,EC,Flash Gordon 500.00
17 AR,EC,Flash Gordon 475.00
18 AR,EC,Flash Gordon 475.00
Covers say: "Starring Popeye"
19 AR,EC,Flash Gordon 475.00
20 AR,EC,Football(c) 475.00
21 AR,EC,Flash Gordon 350.00
22 AR,EC,Flash Gordon 350.00
23 AR,EC,Flash Gordon 350.00
24 AR,EC,Flash Gordon 350.00
25 AR,EC,Flash Gordon 350.00
26 AR,EC,Flash Gordon 325.00
27 AR,EC,Flash Gordon 325.00
28 AR,EC,Flash Gordon 325.00
29 AR,EC,Flash Gordon 325.00
30 AR,EC,Flash Gordon 325.00
31 AR,EC,Flash Gordon 325.00

32 AR,EC,Flash Gordon 325.00
33 AR,EC,Skiing(c) 325.00
34 AR,Ping Pong(c) 275.00
35 AR,Flash Gordon 275.00
36 AR,Flash Gordon 275.00
37 AR,Flash Gordon 275.00
38 AR,Flash Gordon 275.00
39 AR,Baseball(c) 275.00
40 AR,Flash Gordon 275.00
41 AR,Flash Gordon 250.00
42 AR,Flash Gordon 250.00
43 AR,Flash Gordon 250.00
44 AR,Popeye golf(c) 250.00
45 AR,Flash Gordon 250.00
46 AR,B:Little Lulu 250.00
47 AR,Flash Gordon 250.00
48 AR,Flash Gordon 250.00
49 AR,Weather Vane 250.00
50 AR,B:Love Ranger 250.00
51 AR,Flash Gordon 250.00
52 AR,Flash Gordon 175.00
53 AR,Flash Gordon 175.00
54 AR,Flash Gordon 175.00

King Comics #44
© *David McKay Publications*

55 AR,Magic Carpet 175.00
56 AR,Flash Gordon 175.00
57 AR,Cows Over Moon(c) . . . 175.00
58 AR,Flash Gordon 175.00
59 AR,Flash Gordon 175.00
60 AR,Flash Gordon 175.00
61 AR,B:Phantom,Baseball(c) . 175.00
62 AR,Flash Gordon 175.00
63 AR,Flash Gordon 150.00
64 AR,Flash Gordon 150.00
65 AR,Flash Gordon 150.00
66 AR,Flash Gordon 150.00
67 AR,Sweet Pea 150.00
68 AR,Flash Gordon 150.00
69 AR,Flash Gordon 150.00
70 AR,Flash Gordon 150.00
71 AR,Flash Gordon 150.00
72 AR,Flash Gordon 125.00
73 AR,Flash Gordon 125.00
74 AR,Flash Gordon 125.00
75 AR,Flash Godron 125.00
76 AR,Flag(c) 135.00
77 AR,Flash Gordon 125.00
78 AR,Popeye,Olive Oil(c) . . . 125.00
79 AR,Sweet Pea 125.00

80 AR,Wimpy(c) 125.00
81 AR,B:Blondie(c) 125.00
82 thru 91 AR . . . . @100.00
92 thru 98 AR . . . . @85.00
99 AR,Olive Oil(c) 100.00
100 . . . . 125.00
101 thru 116 AR . . . . @85.00
117 O:Phantom 75.00
118 Flash Gordon 85.00
119 Flash Gordon 75.00
120 Wimpy(c) 60.00
121 thru 140 . . . . @75.00
141 Flash Gordon 60.00
142 Flash Gordon 60.00
143 Flash Gordon 60.00
144 Flash Gordon 60.00
145 Prince Valiant 55.00
146 Prince Valiant 55.00
147 Prince Valiant 55.00
148 thru 154 . . . . @45.00
155 E:Flash Gordon 45.00
156 Baseball(c) 45.00
157 thru 159 . . . . @35.00

KING OF THE ROYAL MOUNTED
Dell Publishing Co.
Dec., 1948–1958
(1) *see Dell Four Color #207*
(2) *see Dell Four Color #265*
(3) *see Dell Four Color #283*
(4) *see Dell Four Color #310*
(5) *see Dell Four Color #340*
(6) *see Dell Four Color #363*
(7) *see Dell Four Color #384*
8 Zane Grey adapt. 40.00
9 . . . . 40.00
10 . . . . 40.00
11 thru 28 . . . . @30.00

KIT CARSON
Avon Periodicals
1950
N# EK(c) Indian Scout 75.00
2 EK(c),Kit Carson's Revenge,
  Doom Trail 50.00
3 EK(c),V:Comanche Raiders . 35.00
4 . . . . 30.00
5 EK(c),Trail of Doom 30.00
6 EK(c) 30.00
7 EK(c) 35.00
8 EK(c) 30.00
Becomes:

FIGHTING DAVY CROCKETT
9 EK(c),October/Nov., 1955 . . . 35.00

KOKO AND KOLA
Compix/Magazine Enterprises
Fall, 1946
1 (fa) 40.00
2 X-Mas Issue 20.00
3 . . . . 15.00
4 . . . . 15.00
5 . . . . 15.00
6 May, 1947 . . . . 15.00

KO KOMICS
Gerona Publications
October, 1945
1 . . . . 400.00

KOMIK PAGES
Harry 'A' Chestler
April, 1945
1 JK,Duke of Darkness 375.00

KRAZY KAT COMICS
Dell Publishing Co.
May-June, 1951
1 .... 60.00
2 .... 40.00
3 .... 40.00
4 .... 40.00
5 .... 40.00

KRAZY LIFE
(See PHANTOM LADY)

LABOR IS A PARTNER
Catechetical Guild
Educational Society
1949
1 .... 175.00

LAFFY-DAFFY COMICS
Rural Home Publ. Co.
February, 1945
1 (fa) 30.00
2 .... 30.00

LANCE O'CASEY
Fawcett
1946–47
1 High Seas Adventure
from Whiz comics 250.00
2 thru 4 .... @150.00

LAND OF THE LOST
EC Comics
July-Aug. 1946–Spring 1948
1 Radio show adapt. 225.00
2 .... 150.00
3 thru 9 .... @125.00

LARGE FEATURE COMICS
Dell Publishing Co.
1939
1 Dick Tracy vs. the Blank . 1,500.00
2 Terry and the Pirates 700.00
3 Heigh-Yo Silver!
the Lone Ranger 900.00
4 Dick Tracy gets his man ... 700.00
5 Tarzan of the Apes 1,300.00
6 Terry and the Pirates 650.00
7 Lone Ranger to the rescue . 800.00
8 Dick Tracy, Racket Buster . 675.00
9 King of the Royal Mounted . 450.00
10 Gang Busters 600.00
11 Dick Tracy, Mad Doc Hump 800.00
12 Smilin' Jack 550.00
13 Dick Tracy and Scottie
of Scotland Yard 800.00
14 Smilin' Jack helps G-Men .. 575.00
15 Dick Tracy and
the kidnapped princes 800.00
16 Donald Duck, 1st Daisy. . 5,500.00
17 Gang Busters 425.00
18 Phantasmo The Master
of the World 325.00
19 Walt Disney's Dumbo 2,400.00
20 Donald Duck 5,500.00

BRINGING UP FATHER
10¢

Large Feature Comics #9
© Dell Publishing Co.

21 Private Buck 100.00
22 Nuts and Jolts 100.00
23 The Nebbs 125.00
24 Popeye in 'Thimble Theatre' 450.00
25 Smilin'Jack 500.00
26 Smitty 225.00
27 Terry and the Pirates 550.00
28 Grin and Bear It 75.00
29 Moon Mullins 200.00
30 Tillie the Toiler 175.00
[Series 2]
1 Peter Rabbit 350.00
2 Winnie Winkle 150.00
3 Dick Tracy 600.00
4 Tiny Tim 250.00
5 Toots and Casper 100.00
6 Terry and the Pirates 550.00
7 Pluto saves the Ship ... 1,200.00
8 Bugs Bunny 750.00
9 Bringing Up Father 150.00
10 Popeye 400.00
11 Barney Google&SnuffySmith 200.00
12 Private Buck 100.00
13 1001 Hours of Fun 150.00

LARRY DOBY, BASEBALL HERO
Fawcett Publications
1950
1 Ph(c),BW 575.00

LARS OF MARS
Ziff-Davis Publishing Co.
April-May, 1951
10 MA,'Terror from the Sky' ... 600.00
11 GC, The Terror Weapon ... 500.00

LASH LARUE WESTERN
Fawcett Publications
Summer, 1949
1 Ph(c),The Fatal Roundups .. 750.00
2 Ph(c),Perfect Hide Out 325.00
3 Ph(c),The Suspect 275.00
4 Ph(c),Death on Stage 275.00
5 Ph(c),Rustler's Haven 275.00
6 Ph(c) 250.00

7 Ph(c),Shadow of the Noose . 200.00
8 Ph(c),Double Deadline 200.00
9 Ph(c),Generals Last Stand .. 200.00
10 Ph(c) 200.00
11 Ph(c) 175.00
12 thru 20 Ph(c) .... @125.00
21 thru 29 Ph(c) .... @100.00
30 thru 46 Ph(c) .... @75.00
46 Ph(c),Lost Chance 75.00

LASSIE
(& SEVERAL SPECIAL ISSUES)
Dell Publishing Co.
October-December, 1950
1 Ph(c) all 125.00
2 .... 50.00
3 .... 35.00
4 .... 35.00
5 .... 35.00
6 .... 35.00
7 .... 35.00
8 .... 35.00
9 .... 35.00
10 .... 35.00
11 .... 25.00
12 Rocky Langford 27.00
13 .... 25.00
14 .... 25.00
15 I:Timbu 27.00
16 .... 25.00
17 .... 25.00
18 .... 25.00
19 .... 25.00
20 MB 30.00
21 MB 30.00
22 MB 30.00
23 thru 38 .... @20.00
39 I:Timmy 22.00
40 thru 62 .... @18.00
63 E:Timmy 12.00
64 thru 70 .... @10.00

LATEST COMICS
Spotlight Publ./ Palace Promotions
March, 1945
1 Funny Animal-Super Duper .. 60.00
2 .... 40.00

SPECIAL COMICS
MLJ Magazines (Archie Publ.)
Winter, 1941
1 O:Boy Buddies & Hangman,
D:The Comet 2,000.00
Becomes:

HANGMAN COMICS
2 B:Hangman & Boy Buddies 1,300.00
3 V:Nazis cover,Bondage(c) . 800.00
4 V:Nazis cover 750.00
5 Bondage cover 700.00
6 .... 675.00
7 BF,Graveyard cover 675.00
8 BF 675.00
Becomes:

BLACK HOOD
9 BF 750.00
10 BF,A:Dusty, the
Boy Detective 400.00
11 Here lies the Black Hood . 300.00
12 .... 275.00
13 EK(c) 275.00

GOLDEN AGE

14 EK(c)	275.00
15 EK	275.00
16 EK(c)	275.00
17 Bondage cover	300.00
18	275.00
19 I.D. Revealed	400.00

Becomes:

LAUGH COMICS

20 BWo,B:Archie,Katy Keene	500.00
21 BWo	225.00
22 BWo	225.00
23 Bwo	225.00
24 BWo,JK,Pipsy	250.00
25 BWo	225.00
26 BWo	125.00
27 BWo	125.00
28 BWo	125.00
29 BWo	125.00
30 BWo	125.00
31 thru 40 BWo	@75.00
41 thru 50 BWo	@55.00
51 thru 60 BWo	@50.00
61 thru 80 BWo	@25.00
81 thru 99 BWo	@20.00
100 BWo	30.00
101 thru 126 BWo	@20.00
127 A:Jaguar	22.00
128 A:The Fly	22.00
129 A:The Fly	22.00
130 A:Jaguar	22.00
131 A:Jaguar	22.00
132 A:The Fly	22.00
133 A:Jaguar	22.00
134 A:The Fly	22.00
135 A:Jaguar	22.00
136 A:Fly Girl	22.00
137 A:Fly Girl	22.00
138 A:The Fly	22.00
139 A:The Fly	22.00
140 A:Jaguar	22.00
141 A:Jaguar	22.00
142 thru 144	@22.00
145 A:Josie	15.00
146 thru 165	@10.00
166 Beatles cover	15.00
167 thru 220	@5.00
221 thru 250	@2.50
251 thru 300	@2.00
301 thru 400	@1.00

LAUGH COMIX
(see TOP-NOTCH COMICS)

LAUREL AND HARDY
St. John Publishing Co.
March, 1949

1	500.00
2	300.00
3	200.00
26 Rep #1	125.00
27 Rep #2	125.00
28 Rep #3	125.00

LAWBREAKERS
Law & Order Magazines
(Charlton)
March, 1951

1	200.00
2	100.00
3	75.00
4 Drug	85.00
5	75.00
6 LM(c)	85.00

7 Drug	85.00
8	75.00
9 StC(c)	75.00

Becomes:

LAWBREAKERS SUSPENSE STORIES
January, 1953

10 StC(c)	175.00
11 LM(c),Negligee(c)	550.00
12 LM(c)	75.00
13 DG(c)	75.00
14 DG(c),Sharks	75.00
15 DG(c),Acid in Face(c)	250.00

Becomes:

STRANGE SUSPENSE STORIES

16 DG(c); January, 1954	175.00
17 DG(c)	150.00

Lawbreakers Suspense Stories #11
© Law & Order Magazines/Charlton

18 SD,SD(c)	112.00
19 SD,SD(c),Electric Chair	300.00
20 SD,SD(c)	225.00
21 SD,SD(c)	150.00
22 SD,SD(c)	200.00

Becomes:

THIS IS SUSPENSE

23 WW; February, 1955 Comics Code	135.00
24 GE,DG(c)	70.00
25 DG(c)	50.00
26 DG(c)	50.00

Becomes:

STRANGE SUSPENSE STORIES

27 October, 1955	100.00
28	50.00
29	50.00
30	50.00
31 SD	125.00
32 SD	125.00
33 SD	125.00
34 SD	125.00
35 SD	125.00
36 SD	125.00
37 SD	125.00
38	50.00

39 SD	150.00
40 SD	150.00
41 SD	150.00
42	40.00
43	40.00
44	40.00
45	40.00
46	40.00
47 SD	100.00
48 SD	100.00
49	40.00
50 SD	100.00
51 SD	100.00
52 SD	100.00
53 SD	100.00
54 thru 60	@35.00
61 thru 74	@20.00
75 SD,SD(c)	150.00
77 Oct 1965	50.00

LAWBREAKERS ALWAYS LOSE
Crime Bureau Stories
Spring, 1948

1 HK; FBI Reward Poster Photo	200.00
2	100.00
3	75.00
4 Vampire	100.00
5	75.00
6 Anti Wertham Edition	75.00
7 Drug	200.00
8	75.00
9 Ph(c)	75.00
10 Ph(c), October 1949	75.00

LAW-CRIME
Essenkay Publications
April, 1948

1 LbC,LbC-(c);Raymond Hamilton Dies In The Chair	500.00
2 LbC,LbC-(c);Strangled Beauty Puzzles Police	350.00
3 LbC,LbC-(c);Lipstick Slayer Sought; August '43	450.00

LEROY
Visual Editions
(Standard Comics)
November, 1949

1 FunniestTeenager of them All	25.00
2	20.00
3 thru 6	@15.00

LET'S PRETEND
D.S. Publishing Company
May–June, 1950

1 From Radio Nursery Tales	100.00
2	75.00
3 November, 1950	75.00

MISS LIBERTY
Burten/Green Publishing
Circa 1944

1 Reprints-Shield,Wizard	300.00

Becomes:

LIBERTY COMICS

10 Reprints,Hangman	125.00
11	90.00
12 Black Hood	90.00
14	90.00
15	75.00

LIBERTY GUARDS
Chicago Mail Order
(Comic Corp of America)
Circa 1942
1 PG(c),Liberty Scouts 225.00
Becomes:

LIBERTY SCOUTS
June, 1941
2 PG,PG(c)O:Fireman,Liberty
Scouts 1,000.00
3 PG,PG(c) August,1941
O:Sentinel 750.00

LIFE STORY
Fawcett Publications
April, 1949
1 Ph(c) 75.00
2 Ph(c) 35.00
3 Ph(c) 30.00
4 Ph(c) 30.00
5 Ph(c) 30.00
6 Ph(c) 30.00
7 Ph(c) 25.00
8 Ph(c) 25.00
9 Ph(c) 25.00
10 Ph(c) 25.00
11 . . . . 20.00
12 . . . . 20.00
13 WW,Drug 100.00
14 thru 21 . . . . @20.00
22 Drug 35.00
23 thru 35 . . . . @20.00
36 Drug 25.00
37 thru 42 . . . . @18.00
43 GE 25.00
44 . . . . 18.00
45 1952 . . . . 18.00

LIFE WITH
SNARKY PARKER
Fox Feature Syndicate
August, 1950
1 . . . . 150.00

LI'L ABNER
Harvey Publications
December, 1947
61 BP,BW,Sadie Hawkins Day . 250.00
62 . . . . 150.00
63 . . . . 150.00
64 . . . . 150.00
65 BP 150.00
66 . . . . 100.00
67 . . . . 100.00
68 FearlessFosdick V:Any Face 125.00
69 . . . . 100.00
70 . . . . 100.00
Toby Press
71 . . . . 100.00
72 . . . . 100.00
73 . . . . 100.00
74 . . . . 100.00
75 HK 125.00
76 . . . . 100.00
77 HK 125.00
78 HK 125.00
79 HK 125.00
80 . . . . 100.00
81 . . . . 75.00
82 . . . . 75.00
83 Baseball 85.00
84 . . . . 75.00

Li'l Abner #63 © Harvey Publications

85 . . . . 75.00
86 HK 125.00
87 . . . . 75.00
88 . . . . 75.00
89 . . . . 75.00
90 . . . . 75.00
91 Rep. #77 . . . . 80.00
92 . . . . 75.00
93 Rep. #71 . . . . 80.00
94 . . . . 75.00
95 Fearless Fosdick 100.00
96 . . . . 75.00
97 January, 1955 . . . . 75.00

LI'L GENIUS
Charlton Comics
1955
1 . . . . 50.00
2 . . . . 20.00
3 thru 15 . . . . @15.00
16 Giants 25.00
17 Giants 25.00
18 Giants,100 pages 30.00
19 thru 40 . . . . @10.00
41 thru 54 . . . . @7.00
55 1965 . . . . 7.00

LI'L PAN
Fox Features Syndicate
December-January, 1946-47
6 . . . . 35.00
7 . . . . 25.00
8 April-May, 1947 . . . . 25.00

LINDA
(see PHANTOM LADY)

LITTLE AUDREY
St. John Publ. Co./
Harvey Comics
April, 1948
1 . . . . 300.00
2 . . . . 150.00
3 thru 6 . . . . @100.00
7 thru 10 . . . . @60.00
11 thru 20 . . . . @35.00
21 thru 24 . . . . @25.00

Little Audrey #11 © Harvey Comics

25 B:Harvey Comics 85.00
26 A: Casper 50.00
27 A: Casper 50.00
28 A: Casper 50.00
29 thru 31 . . . . @30.00
32 A: Casper 35.00
33 A: Casper 35.00
34 A: Casper 35.00
35 A: Casper 35.00
36 thru 53 . . . . @20.00

LITTLE BIT
Jubilee Publishing Company
March, 1949
1 . . . . 30.00
2 June, 1949 . . . . 30.00

LITTLE DOT
Harvey Publications
September, 1953
1 I: Richie Rich & Little Lotta . 750.00
2 . . . . 350.00
3 . . . . 200.00
4 . . . . 150.00
5 O:Dots on Little Dot's Dress 200.00
6 1st Richie Rich(c) 175.00
7 . . . . 135.00
8 . . . . 75.00
9 . . . . 75.00
10 . . . . 75.00
11 thru 20 . . . . @60.00
21 thru 30 . . . . @35.00
31 thru 38 . . . . @30.00
39 . . . . 50.00
40 thru 50 . . . . @20.00
51 thru 60 . . . . @15.00
61 thru 70 . . . . @12.00
71 thru 80 . . . . @10.00
81 thru 100 . . . . @8.00
101 thru 130 . . . . @7.00
131 thru 140 . . . . @7.00
141 thru 145, 52 pages . . . . . . @7.00
146 thru 163 . . . . @3.00

LITTLE EVA
St. John Publishing Co.
May, 1952
1 . . . . 60.00

GOLDEN AGE

2	30.00
3	18.00
4	18.00
5 thru 10	@12.00
11 thru 30	@10.00
31 November, 1956	10.00

LITTLE GIANT COMICS
Centaur Publications
July, 1938

1 PG, B&W with Color(c)	450.00
2 B&W with Color(c)	400.00
3 B&W with Color(c)	425.00
4 B&W with Color(c)	425.00

LITTLE GIANT DETECTIVE FUNNIES
Centaur Publications
October, 1938

1 B&W	550.00
2 B&W	400.00
3 B&W	400.00
4 January 1939	400.00

LITTLE GIANT MOVIE FUNNIES
Centaur Publications
August, 1938

1 Ed Wheelan-a	550.00
2 Ed Wheelan-a, Oct., 1938	400.00

LITTLE IKE
St. John Publishing Co.
April, 1953

1	50.00
2	25.00
3	20.00
4 October, 1953	20.00

LITTLE IODINE
Dell Publishing Co.
April, 1949

1	75.00
2	30.00
3	30.00
4	30.00
5	30.00
6 thru 10	@20.00
11 thru 30	@15.00
31 thru 50	@10.00
51 thru 56	@8.00

LITTLE JACK FROST
Avon Periodicals
1951

1	35.00

LITTLE LULU
(see MARGE'S LITTLE LULU)

LITTLE MAX COMICS
Harvey Publications
October, 1949

1 I: Little Dot,Joe Palooka	125.00
2 A: Little Dot	60.00
3 A: Little Dot,Joe Palooka(c)	40.00
4	25.00
5 C: Little Dot	25.00
6 thru 10	@20.00
11 thru 22	@18.00
23 A: Little Dot	12.00

24 thru 37	@10.00
38 Rep. #20	10.00
39 thru 72	@10.00
73 A: Richie Rich; Nov.'61	10.00

LITTLE MISS MUFFET
Best Books
(Standard Comics)
December, 1948

11 Strip Reprints	45.00
12 Strip Reprints	30.00
13 Strip Reprints; Mar.'49	30.00

LITTLE MISS SUNBEAM COMICS
Magazine Enterprises
June-July, 1950

1	75.00
2	40.00
3	40.00
4 December-January, 1951	40.00

LITTLE ORPHAN ANNIE
Dell Publishing Co.
1941

1	150.00
2 Orphan Annie and the Rescue	100.00
3	100.00

Little Roquefort #2
© St. John Publishing Co.

LITTLE ROQUEFORT
St. John Publishing Co.
June,1952

1	40.00
2	20.00
3 thru 9	@15.00

Pines

10 Summer 1958	18.00

LITTLE SCOUTS
Dell Publishing Co.
March, 1951

(1) see Dell Four Color #321	
2	20.00
3	20.00
4	20.00

5	20.00
6	20.00

LITTLEST SNOWMAN
Dell Publishing Co.
December, 1956

1	20.00

LIVING BIBLE, THE
Living Bible Corp.
Autumn, 1945

1 LbC-(c) Life of Paul	300.00
2 LbC-(c) Joseph &His Brethren	150.00
3 LbC-(c) Chaplains At War	250.00

LONE EAGLE
Ajax/Farrell
April-May, 1954

1	50.00
2	30.00
3 Bondage(c)	35.00
4 October-November, 1954	30.00

LONE RANGER
Dell Publishing Co.
January-February 1948

1 B:Lone Ranger & Tonto B:Strip Reprint	650.00
2	300.00
3	250.00
4	250.00
5	250.00
6	200.00
7	200.00
8 O:Retold	250.00
9	200.00
10	200.00
11 B:Young Hawk	125.00
12 thru 20	@125.00
21	100.00
22	100.00
23 O:Retold	125.00
24 thru 30	@100.00
31 (1st Mask Logo)	110.00
32 thru 36	@75.00
37 (E:Strip reprints)	75.00
38 thru 50	@60.00
51 thru 75	@50.00
76 thru 99	@45.00
100	75.00
101 thru 111	@40.00
112 B:Clayton Moore Ph(c)	135.00
113 thru 117	@75.00
118 O:Lone Ranger & Tonto retold, Anniv. issue	150.00
119 thru 144	@75.00
145 final issue,May/July 1962	75.00

THE LONE RANGER'S COMPANION TONTO
Dell Publishing Co.
January, 1951

(1) see Dell Four Color #312	
2 P(c) all	60.00
3	60.00
4	50.00
5	50.00
6 thru 10	@50.00
11 thru 20	@40.00
21 thru 25	@30.00
26 thru 33	@25.00

THE LONE RANGER'S FAMOUS HORSE HI-YO SILVER
Dell Publishing Co.
January, 1952
(1) see Dell Four Color #369
(1) see Dell Four Color #392
3 P(c) all 35.00
4 . . . . 35.00
5 . . . . 35.00
6 thru 10 . . . . @35.00
11 thru 36 . . . . @30.00

Lone Rider #1 © Superior Comics

LONE RIDER
Farrell
(Superior Comics)
April, 1951
1 . . . . 125.00
2 I&O: Golden Arrow; 52 pgs. . 60.00
3 . . . . 50.00
4 . . . . 50.00
5 . . . . 50.00
6 E: Golden Arrow 60.00
7 G. Arrow Becomes Swift Arrow 65.00
8 O: Swift Arrow 70.00
9 thru 14 . . . . @30.00
15 O: Golden Arrow Rep. #2 . . . 35.00
16 thru 19 . . . . @25.00
20 . . . . 20.00
21 3-D (c) 75.00
22 . . . . 20.00
23 A: Apache Kid 25.00
24 . . . . 20.00
25 . . . . 20.00
26 July, 1955 . . . . 20.00

LONG BOW
Real Adventures Publ.
(Fiction House)
Winter, 1950
1 . . . . 100.00
2 . . . . 50.00
3 "Red Arrows Means War" . . . 45.00
4 "Trial of Tomahawk" 45.00
5 . . . . 45.00
6 "Rattlesnake Raiders" 35.00
7 . . . . 35.00

8 . . . . 35.00
9 Spring, 1953 . . . . 35.00

LOONEY TUNES AND MERRIE MELODIES
Dell Publishing Co.
1941
1 B:&1st Comic App. Bugs Bunny
  Daffy Duck,Elmer Fudd . . 10,000.00
2 Bugs/Porky(c) 1,500.00
3 Bugs/Porky(c) B:WK,
  Kandi the Cave 1,200.00
4 Bugs/Porky(c),WK 1,000.00
5 Bugs/Porky(c),WK,
  A:Super Rabbit 1,000.00
6 Bugs/Porky/Elmer(c),E:WK,
  Kandi the Cave 700.00
7 Bugs/Porky(c) 500.00
8 Bugs/Porky swimming(c),F:WK,
  Kandi the Cave 700.00
9 Porky/Elmer car painted(c) . 500.00
10 Porky/Bugs/Elmer Parade(c) 500.00
11 Bugs/Porky(c),F:WK,
  Kandi the Cave 500.00
12 Bugs/Porky rollerskating(c) . 400.00
13 Bugs/Porky(c) 400.00
14 Bugs/Porky(c) 400.00
15 Bugs/Porky X-Mas(c),F:WK
  Kandi the Cave 350.00
16 Bugs/Porky ice-skating(c) . 350.00
17 Bugs/Petunia Valentines(c) . 350.00
18 Sgt.Bugs Marine(c) 350.00
19 Bugs/Painting(c) 350.00
20 Bugs/Porky/ElmerWarBonds(c),
  B:WK,Pat,Patsy&Pete 350.00
21 Bugs/Porky 4th July(c) 300.00
22 Porky(c) 300.00
23 Bugs/Porky Fishing(c) 300.00
24 Bugs/Porky Football(c) 300.00
25 Bugs/Porky/Petunia
  Halloween(c),E:WK,Pat,
  Patsy & Pete 300.00
26 Bugs Thanksgiving(c) 250.00
27 Bugs/Porky New Years(c) . . 250.00
28 Bugs/Porky Ice-Skating(c) . . 250.00
29 Bugs Valentine(c) 250.00
30 Bugs(c) 250.00
31 Bugs(c) 200.00
32 Bugs/Porky Hot Dogs(c) . . . 200.00
33 Bugs/Porky War Bonds(c) . . 210.00
34 Bugs/Porky Fishing(c) 200.00
35 Bugs/Porky Swimming(c) . . 200.00
36 Bugs/Porky(c) 200.00
37 Bugs Hallowean(c) 200.00
38 Bugs Thanksgiving(c) 200.00
39 Bugs X-Mas(c) 200.00
40 Bugs(c) 200.00
41 Bugs Washington's
  Birthday(c) 150.00
42 Bugs Magician(c) 150.00
43 Bugs Dream(c) 150.00
44 Bugs/Porky(c) 150.00
45 Bugs War Bonds(c) 150.00
46 Bugs/Porky(c) 125.00
47 Bugs Beach(c) 125.00
48 Bugs/Porky Picnic(c) 125.00
49 Bugs(c) 125.00
50 Bugs(c) 125.00
51 thru 60 . . . . @100.00
61 thru 80 . . . . @75.00
81 thru 86 . . . . @50.00
87 Bugs X-Mas(c) 55.00
88 thru 99 . . . . @50.00
100 . . . . 55.00

*Looney Tunes & Merrie Melodies #20
© Dell Publ. Co.*

101 thru 110 . . . . @35.00
111 thru 125 . . . . @30.00
126 thru 150 . . . . @25.00
151 thru 165 . . . . @20.00
Becomes:

LOONEY TUNES
August, 1955
166 thru 200 . . . . @15.00
201 thru 245 . . . . @12.00
246 final issue,Sept.1962 . . . . . 12.00

LOST WORLD
Literacy Enterprises
(Standard Comics)
October, 1952
5 ATh, Alice in Terrorland . . . 275.00
6 ATh 250.00

LOVE AND MARRIAGE
Superior Comics Ltd.
March, 1952
1 . . . . 50.00
2 . . . . 25.00
3 . . . . 20.00
4 . . . . 20.00
5 . . . . 20.00
6 . . . . 20.00
7 . . . . 20.00
8 thru 15 . . . . @20.00
16 September, 1954 . . . . 20.00

LOVE AT FIRST SIGHT
Periodical House
(Ace Magazines)
October, 1949
1 P(c) 60.00
2 P(c) 25.00
3 . . . . 15.00
4 P(c) 15.00
5 thru 10 . . . . @15.00
11 thru 33 . . . . @10.00
34 1st Edition Under Code 7.00
35 thru 41 . . . . @7.00
42 1956 . . . . 7.00

LOVE CONFESSIONS
Comics Magazine
(Quality Comics Group)
October, 1949

1 PG,BWa(c)& Some-a	200.00
2 PG	65.00
3	40.00
4 RC	60.00
5 BWa	65.00
6 Ph(c)	20.00
7 Ph(c) Van Johnson	20.00
8 BWa	60.00
9 Ph(c)Jane Russell/Robert Mitchum	20.00
10 BWa	60.00
11 thru 18 Ph(c)	@35.00
19	25.00
20 BWa	60.00
21	20.00
22 BWa	22.00
23 thru 28	@15.00
29 BWa	35.00
30 thru 38	@15.00
39 MB	20.00
40	15.00
41	15.00
42	15.00
43 1st Edition Under Code	15.00
44 thru 46	@15.00
47 BWa(c)	20.00
48 thru 54 December, 1956	@15.00

LOVE DIARY
Our Publishing Co./Toytown
July, 1949

1 BK,Ph(c)	100.00
2 BK,Ph(c)	75.00
3 BK,Ph(c)	75.00
4 thru 9 Ph(c)	@30.00
10 BEv, Ph(c)	25.00
11 thru 24 Ph(c)	@22.00
25	20.00
26	20.00
27 Ph(c)	22.00
28	20.00
29 Ph(c)	22.00
30	20.00
31 JB(c)	20.00
32 thru 41	@20.00
42 MB(c)	20.00
43 thru 47	@20.00
48 1st Edition Under Code, Oct.'55	20.00

LOVE DIARY
Quality Comics Group
September, 1949

1 BWa(c)	200.00

LOVE LESSONS
Harvey Publications
October, 1949

1	65.00
2	30.00
3 Ph(c)	20.00
4	20.00
5 June, 1950	20.00

LOVE LETTERS
Comic Magazines
(Quality Comics Group)
November, 1949

1 PG,BWa(c)	150.00

2 PG,BWa(c)	125.00
3 PG	75.00
4 BWa	125.00
5	25.00
6	25.00
7	25.00
8	25.00
9 Ph(c) of Robert Mitchum	35.00
10	25.00
11 BWa	45.00
12	20.00
13	20.00
14	20.00
15	20.00
16 Ph(c) of Anthony Quinn	22.00
17 BWa, Ph(c) of Jane Russell	22.00
18 thru 30	@15.00
31 BWa	25.00

Becomes:

LOVE SECRETS

32	32.00
33	15.00
34 BWa	35.00
35 thru 39	@15.00
40 MB(c)1st Edition Under Code	25.00
41 thru 50	@12.00
50 MB	12.00
51 MB(c)	12.00
52 thru 56	@10.00

LOVELORN
Best Syndicated/Michel Publ.
(American Comics Group)
August-September, 1949

1	75.00
2	35.00
3 thru 10	@25.00
11 thru 17	@18.00
18 2pgs. MD-a	15.00
19	12.00
20	12.00
21 Prostitution Story	30.00
22 thru 50	@12.00
51 July, 1954 3-D	75.00

Becomes:

CONFESSIONS OF LOVELORN

52 3-D	125.00
53	35.00
54 3-D	125.00
55	25.00
56 Communist Story	40.00
57 Comics Code	15.00
58 thru 90	@15.00
91 AW	35.00
92 thru 105	@10.00
106 P(c)	10.00
107 P(c)	10.00
108 thru 114	@10.00

LOVE MEMORIES
Fawcett Publications
Autumn, 1949

1 Ph(c)	50.00
2 Ph(c)	25.00
3 Ph(c)	25.00
4 Ph(c)	25.00

LOVE MYSTERY
Fawcett Publications
June, 1950

1 GE, Ph(c)	150.00

2 GE, Ph(c)	125.00
3 GE & BP, Ph(c); Oct., 1950	125.00

LOVE PROBLEMS AND ADVICE ILLUSTRATED
McCombs/Harvey Publications
Home Comics
June, 1949

1 BP	85.00
2 BP	35.00
3	25.00
4	25.00
5 L. Elias(c)	22.00
6	20.00
7 BP	20.00
8 BP	20.00
9 BP	20.00
10 BP	20.00
11 BP	18.00
12 BP	18.00
13 BP	18.00
14 BP	18.00
15	15.00

Love Problems & Advice #1
© McCombs/Harvey Publ.

16	15.00
17 thru 23 BP	@15.00
24 BP, Rape Scene	20.00
25 BP	12.00
26	12.00
27	12.00
28 BP	12.00
29 BP	12.00
30	12.00
31	12.00
32 Comics Code	8.00
33 BP	8.00
34	8.00
35	8.00
36	8.00
37	8.00
38 S&K (c)	8.00
39	8.00
40 BP	8.00
41 BP	8.00
42	8.00
43	8.00
44 March, 1957	8.00

LOVERS LANE
Lev Gleason Publications
October, 1949

1 CBi (c),FG-a	50.00
2 P(c)	35.00
3 P(c)	18.00
4 P(c)	18.00
5 P(c)	18.00
6 GT,P(c),	18.00
7 P(c),	18.00
8 P(c),	18.00
9 P(c),	18.00
10 P(c)	18.00
11 thru 19 P(c)	@15.00
20 Ph(c); FF 1 page Ad,	20.00
21 Ph(c)	10.00
22 Ph(c)	10.00
23	10.00
24	10.00
25	10.00
26 Ph(c)	10.00
27 Ph(c)	10.00
28 Ph(c)	10.00
29 thru 38	@10.00
39 Story Narrated by Frank Sinatra	30.00
40	9.00
41 June, 1954	9.00

LOVE SCANDALS
Comic Magazines
(Quality Comics Group)
February, 1950

1 BW(c)&a	175.00
2 PG-a, Ph(c)	65.00
3 PG-a, Ph(c)	65.00
4 BWa(c)&a 18Pgs.; GFx-a	135.00
5 Ph(c), October, 1950	50.00

LOVE STORIES OF MARY WORTH
Harvey Publications
September, 1949

1 Newspaper Reprints	40.00
2 Newspaper Reprints	25.00
3 Newspaper Reprints	20.00
4 Newspaper Reprints,	20.00
5 May, 1950	20.00

LUCKY COMICS
Consolidated Magazines
January, 1944

1 Lucky Star	125.00
2 Henry C. Kiefer(c)	75.00
3	75.00
4	75.00
5 Summer, 1946,Devil(c)	75.00

LUCKY DUCK
Standard Comics
(Literary Enterprises)
January, 1953

5 IS (c)&a	40.00
6 IS (c)&a	30.00
7 IS (c)&a	30.00
8 IS (c)&a, September, 1953	30.00

LUCKY FIGHTS IT THROUGH
Educational Comics
1949

N# HK-a, V.D. Prevention	1,300.00

LUCKY "7" COMICS
Howard Publications
1944

1 Bondage(c) Pioneer	225.00

LUCKY STAR
Nationwide Publications
1950

1 JDa,B:52 pages western	75.00
2 JDa	40.00
3 JDa	40.00
4 JDa	35.00
5 JDa	35.00
6 JDa	35.00
7 JDa	35.00
8 thru 13	@25.00
14 1955,E:52 pages western	25.00

LUCY, THE REAL GONE GAL
St. John Publishing Co.
June, 1953

1 Negligee Panels,Teenage	65.00
2	35.00
3 MD-a	25.00
4 February, 1954	22.00

Becomes:

MEET MISS PEPPER
St. John Publishing Co.
April, 1954

5 JKu-a	100.00
6 JKu (c)&a, June,1954	90.00

MAD
E.C. Comics
October-November, 1952

1 JSe,HK(c),JDa,WW	5,000.00
2 JSe,JDa(c),JDa,WW	1,200.00
3 JSe,HK(c),JDa,WW	650.00
4 JSe,HK(c),JDa-Flob Was A Slob,JDa,WW	650.00
5 JSe,BE(c).JDa,WW	1,200.00
6 JSe,HK(c),Jda,WW	525.00
7 HK(c),JDa,WW	525.00
8 HK(c),JDa,WW	525.00
9 JSe,HK(c),JDa,WW	525.00
10 JSe,HK(c),JDa,WW	525.00
11 BW,BW(c),JDa,WW,Life(c)	525.00
12 BK,JDa,WW	425.00
13 HK(c),JDa,WW,Red(c)	425.00
14 RH,HK(c),JDa,WW, Mona Lisa(c)	425.00
15 JDa,WW,Alice in Wonderland(c)	425.00
16 HK(c),JDa,WW,Newspaper(c)	425.00
17 BK,BW,JDa,WW	425.00
18 HK(c),JDa,WW	425.00
19 JDa,WW,Racing Form(c)	350.00
20 JDa,WW,Composition(c)	350.00
21 JDa,WW,1st A.E.Neuman(c)	350.00
22 BE,JDa,WW,Picasso(c)	350.00
23 Last Comic Format Edition, JDa,WW Think(c)	350.00
24 BK,WW, HK Logo & Border; 1st Magazine Format	750.00
25 WW, Al Jaffee Sterts As Reg.	325.00
26 BK,WW,WW(c)	275.00
27 WWa,RH,JDa(c)	250.00
28 WW,BE(c),RH Back(c)	250.00
29 JKa,BW,WW,WW(c); 1st Don Martin Artwork	250.00
30 BE,WW,RC; 1st A.E. Neuman(c) By Mingo	400.00
31 JDa,WW,BW,Mingo(c)	200.00
32 MD,JO 1st as reg.;Mingo(c); WW-Back(c)	175.00
33 WWa,Mingo(c);JO-Back(c)	175.00
34 WWa,Mingo(c);1st Berg as Reg.	150.00
35 WW,RC,Mingo Wraparound(c)	150.00
36 WW,BW,Mingo(c),JO,MD	100.00
37 WW,Mingo(c)JO,MD	100.00
38 WW,JO,MD	100.00
39 WW,JO,MD	100.00
40 WW,BW,JO,MD	100.00
41 WW,JO,MD	75.00
42 WW,JO,MD	75.00
43 WW,JO,MD	75.00
44 WW,JO,MD	75.00
45 WW,JO,MD	75.00
46 JO,MD	75.00
47 JO,MD	75.00
48 JO,MD	75.00
49 JO,MD	75.00
50 JO,MD	75.00

Mad #7 © E.C. Comics

51 JO,MD	65.00
52 JO,MD	65.00
53 JO,MD	65.00
54 JO,MD	65.00
55 JO,MD	65.00
56 JO,MD	60.00
57 JO,MD	60.00
58 JO,MD	60.00
59 WW,JO,MD	65.00
60 JO,MD	60.00
61 JO,MD	50.00
62 JO,MD	50.00
63 JO,MD	50.00
64 JO,MD	50.00
65 JO,MD	50.00
66 JO,MD	45.00
67 JO,MD	45.00
68 Don Martin(c),JO,MD	45.00
69 JO,MD	45.00
70 JO,MD	45.00
71 JO,MD	45.00
72 JO,MD	45.00
73 JO,MD	45.00
74 JO,MD	45.00
75 Mingo(c),JO,MD	40.00
76 Mingo(c),SA,JO,MD	40.00

77 Mingo(c),SA,JO,MD	40.00
78 Mingo(c),SA,JO,MD	40.00
79 Mingo(c),SA,JO,MD	40.00
80 Mingo(c),SA,JO,MD	40.00
81 Mingo(c),SA,JO,MD	40.00
82 BW,Mingo(c),SA,JO,MD	40.00
83 Mingo(c),SA,JO,MD	40.00
84 Mingo(c),SA,JO,MD	40.00
85 Mingo(c)SA,JO,MD	40.00
86 Mingo(c);1st Fold-in Back(c), SA,JO,MD	40.00
87 Mingo(c),JO,MD	35.00
88 Mingo(c),JO,MD	35.00
89 WK,Mingo(c),JO,MD	40.00
90 Mingo(c); FF-Back(c),JO,MD	35.00
91 Mingo(c),JO,MD	30.00
92 Mingo(c),JO,MD	30.00
93 Mingo(c),JO,MD	30.00
94 Mingo(c),JO,MD	30.00
95 Mingo(c),JO,MD	30.00
96 Mingo(c),JO,MD	30.00
97 Mingo(c),JO,MD	30.00
98 Mingo(c),JO,MD	30.00
99 JDa,Mingo(c),JO,MD	40.00
100 Mingo(c),JO,MD	30.00
101 Infinity(c) by Mingo,JO,MD	25.00
102 Mingo(c)JO,MD	25.00
103 Mingo(c)JO,MD	25.00
104 Mingo(c)JO,MD	25.00
105 Mingo(c);Batman TV Spoof ,JO,MD	30.00
106 Mingo(c);FF-Back(c),JO,MD	30.00
107 Mingo(c),JO,MD	25.00
108 Mingo(c),JO,MD	25.00
109 Mingo(c),JO,MD	25.00
110 Mingo(c),JO,MD	25.00
111 Mingo(c),JO,MD	25.00
112 JO,MD	25.00
113 JO,MD	25.00
114 JO,MD	25.00
115 JO,MD	25.00
116 JO,MD	25.00
117 JO,MD	25.00
118 JO,MD	25.00
119 JO,MD	25.00
120 JO,MD	25.00
121 Beatles,JO,MD	25.00
122 MD & Mingo(c),JO,MD, Reagan	20.00
123 JO,MD	18.00
124 JO,MD	18.00
125 JO,MD	18.00
126 JO,MD	18.00
127 JO,MD	18.00
128 Last JO;MD.	18.00
129 MD	18.00
130 MD	18.00
131 MD	18.00
132 MD	18.00
133 MD	18.00
134 MD	18.00
135 JDa(c),MD	17.00
136 MD	15.00
137 BW,MD	15.00
138 MD	15.00
139 JDa(c),MD	16.00
140 thru 153 MD	@16.00
154 Mineo(c),MD	16.00
155	16.00
156	16.00
157	16.00
158	16.00
159	16.00
160 Mingo(c),JDa,AT	16.00
161	14.00

162 Mingo(c),MD,AT	14.00
163	14.00
164 Mingo,PaperMoon(c),AT, MD,SA	14.00
165 Don Martin(c),At,MD	14.00
166	14.00
167	14.00
168 Mingo(c),AT,MD	14.00
169 MD(c)	14.00
170	14.00
171 Mingo(c)	12.00
172 Mingo(c)	12.00
173 JDa(c)	12.00
174	12.00
175	12.00
176 MD(c)	12.00
177	12.00
178 JDa(c)	12.00
179	12.00
180 Jaws(c),SA,MD,JDA,AT	12.00
181 G.Washington(c),JDa	12.00
182	12.00
183 Mingo(c),AT,SA,MD	12.00
184 Mingo(c),Md,AT	12.00
185	12.00
186 Star Trek Spoof	14.00
187	12.00
188	12.00
189	12.00
190	12.00
191 Clark(c),JDa,MD,AT	12.00
192	12.00
193 Charlies Angels(c), Rickart,JDa,SA,MD	12.00
194 Rocky(c),Rickart,AT,MD	12.00
195	12.00
196 Star Wars Spoof, Rickart,AT,JDa	18.00
197	12.00
198 UPC(c),AT,MD	12.00
199 Jaffee(c),AT,JDa,SA,MD	12.00
200 Rickart(c),Close Encounters	15.00
201 Rickart(c),Sat.Night Fever	7.50
202	7.50
203 Star Wars Spoof,Rickart(c)	8.50
204 Hulk TV Spoof,JawsII(c)	7.50
205 Rickart(c),Grease	7.50
206 Mingo,(c),AT,JDa,Md	7.50
207 Jones(c),Animal House(c)	7.50
208 Superman Movie Spoof, Rickart(c)	7.50
209 Mingo(c),AT,MD	7.50
210 Mingo,Lawn Mower,AT, JDa,MD	7.50
211 Mingo(c)	7.50
212 Jda(c),AT,MD	8.00
213 JDa(c),SA,AT,JDa	8.00
214	7.00
215 Jones(c),MD,AT,JDa	7.00
216	7.00
217 Jaffee(c),For Pres,AT,MD	7.00
218 Martin(c),AT,MD	7.00
219 thru 250	@7.00
251 thru 260	@5.00
261 thru 299	@4.00
300 thru 303	6.00
304 thru 330	3.00

MAGIC COMICS
David McKay Publications
August, 1939

1 Mandrake the Magician, Henry,Popeye,Blondie, Barney Baxter,Secret Agent X-9, Bunky,Henry on(c)	2,200.00

Magic Comics #8
© David McKay Publications

2 Henry on(c)	700.00
3 Henry on(c)	550.00
4 Henry on(c),Mandrake-Logo	450.00
5 Henry on(c),Mandrake-Logo	350.00
6 Henry on(c),Mandrake-Logo	300.00
7 Henry on(c),Mandrake-Logo	300.00
8 B:Inspector Wade,Tippie	275.00
9 Henry-Mandrake Interact(c)	275.00
10 Henry-Mandrake Interact(c)	275.00
11 Henry-Mandrake Interact(c)	250.00
12 Mandrake on(c)	250.00
13 Mandrake on(c)	250.00
14 Mandrake on(c)	250.00
15 Mandrake on(c)	250.00
16 Mandrake on(c)	250.00
17 B:Lone Ranger	275.00
18 Mandrake/Robot on(c)	250.00
19 Mandrake on(c)	250.00
20 Mandrake on(c)	250.00
21 Mandrake on(c)	175.00
22 Mandrake on(c)	175.00
23 Mandrake on(c)	175.00
24 Mandrake on(c)	175.00
25 B:Blondie; Mandrake in Logo for Duration	175.00
26 Blondie (c)	150.00
27 Blondie (c); High School Heroes	150.00
28 Blondie (c); High School Heroes	150.00
29 Blondie (c); High School Heroes	150.00
30 Blondie (c)	150.00
31 Blondie(c);High School Sports Page	125.00
32 Blondie (c);Secret Agent X-9	125.00
33 C.Knight's-Romance of Flying	125.00
34 ClaytonKnight's-War in the Air	125.00
35 Blondie (c)	125.00
36 July'42; Patriotic-(c)	125.00
37 Blondie (c)	125.00
38 ClaytonKnight's-Flying Tigers	125.00
39 Blondie (c)	125.00
40 Jimmie Doolittle bombs Tokyo	125.00
41 How German Became British Censor	100.00
42 Joe Musial's-Dollar-a-Dither	100.00
43 Clay Knight's-War in the Air	100.00
44 Flying Fortress in Action	100.00
45 Clayton Knight's-Gremlins	100.00

GOLDEN AGE

46 Adventures of Aladdin Jr. . . . 100.00
47 Secret Agent X-9 . . . . 100.00
48 General Arnold U.S.A.F. 100.00
49 Joe Musial's-Dollar-a-Dither . 100.00
50 The Lone Ranger 100.00
51 Joe Musial's-Dollar-a-Dither . 75.00
52 C. Knights-Heroes on Wings . 75.00
53 C. Knights-Heroes on Wings . 75.00
54 High School Heroes 75.00
55 Blondie (c) 80.00
56 High School Heroes 75.00
57 Joe Musial's-Dollar-a-Dither . 75.00
58 Private Breger Abroad 75.00
59 . . . . 75.00
60 . . . . 75.00
61 Joe Musial's-Dollar-a-Dither . 60.00
62 . . . . 60.00
63 B:Buz Sawyer, Naval Pilot . . 60.00
64 thru 70 . . . . @60.00
71 thru 80 . . . . @45.00
80 thru 90 . . . . @40.00
91 thru 99 . . . . @40.00
100 . . . . 50.00
101 thru 108 . . . . @35.00
108 Flash Gordon 40.00
109 Flash Gordon 40.00
110 thru 113 . . . . @30.00
114 The Lone Ranger 30.00
115 thru 119 . . . . @30.00
120 Secret Agent X-9 . . . . 35.00
121 Secret Agent X-9 . . . . 35.00
122 Secret Agent X-9 . . . . 35.00
123 Sec. Agent X-9;Nov-Dec.'49 35.00

MAJOR HOOPLE COMICS
Nedor Publications
1942
1 Mary Worth,Phantom Soldier;
   Buy War Bonds On(c) 275.00

MAJOR VICTORY COMICS
H. Clay Glover Svcs./ Harry A. Chestler
1944
1 O:Major Victory,I:Spider
   Woman 450.00
2 A: Dynamic Boy 275.00
3 A: Rocket Boy 225.00

MAN HUNT!
Magazine Enterprises
October, 1953
1 LbC,FG,OW(c);B:Red Fox,
   Undercover Girl, Space Ace 350.00
2 LbC,FG,OW(c);
   Electrocution(c) 250.00
3 LbC,FG,OW,OW(c) 225.00
4 LbC,FG,OW,OW(c) 225.00
5 LbC,FG,OW,OW(c) 225.00
6 LbC,OW,OW(c) 200.00
7 LbC,OW; E:Space Ace 200.00
8 LbC,OW,FG(c);B:Trail Colt . 200.00
9 LbC,OW 200.00
10 LbC,OW,OW(c),Gwl 200.00
11 LbC,FF,OW;B:The Duke,
   Scotland Yard 275.00
12 LbC,OW 150.00
13 LbC,FF,OW;Rep.Trail Colt #1 250.00
14 LbC,OW;Bondage,
   Hypo-(c);1953 . . . . 225.00

MAN OF WAR
Comic Corp. of America (Centaur Publ.)
November, 1941
1 PG,PG(c);Flag(c);B:The Fire-
   Man,Man of War,The Sentinel,
   Liberty Guards,Vapoman . 1,200.00
2 PG,PG(c);I: The Ferret . . . 1,000.00

MAN O'MARS
Fiction House/ I.W. Enterprises
1953
0
1 MA, Space Rangers . . . .
   .00.00
1 MA, Rep. Space Rangers . . . 50.00

March of Comics #36
© K.K. Publications/Western Publ.

MARCH OF COMICS
K.K. Publications/ Western Publ.
1946
(All were Giveaways)
N# WK back(c),Goldilocks . . . 300.00
N# WK,How Santa got His
   Red Suit 300.00
N# WK,Our Gang 400.00
N# CB,Donald Duck;
   "Maharajah Donald" 7,500.00
5 Andy Panda 150.00
6 WK,Fairy Tales 200.00
7 Oswald the Lucky Rabbit . . 150.00
8 Mickey Mouse 550.00
9 Gloomey Bunny 75.00
10 Santa Claus 65.00
11 Santa Claus 50.00
12 Santa's Toys 50.00
13 Santa's Suprise 50.00
14 Santa's Kitchen 50.00
15 Hip-It-Ty Hop 75.00
16 Woody Woodpecker 150.00
17 Roy Rogers 225.00
18 Fairy Tales 90.00
19 Uncle Wiggily 75.00
20 CB,Donald Duck 4,500.00
21 Tom and Jerry 100.00
22 Andy Panda 65.00

23 Raggedy Ann and Andy . . . 125.00
24 Felix the Cat; By
   Otto Messmer 200.00
25 Gene Autrey 200.00
26 Our Gang 200.00
27 Mickey Mouse 400.00
28 Gene Autry 200.00
29 Easter 30.00
30 Santa 25.00
31 Santa 25.00
32 Does Not Exist
33 A Christmas Carol 25.00
34 Woody Woodpecker 75.00
35 Roy Rogers 225.00
36 Felix the Cat 175.00
37 Popeye 150.00
38 Oswald the Lucky Rabbit . . 50.00
39 Gene Autrey 185.00
40 Andy and Woody 50.00
41 CB,DonaldDuck,SouthSeas 3,600.00
42 Porky Pig 60.00
43 Henry 40.00
44 Bugs Bunny 75.00
45 Mickey Mouse 300.00
46 Tom and Jerry 70.00
47 Roy Rogers 175.00
48 Santa 20.00
49 Santa 20.00
50 Santa 20.00
51 Felix the Cat 150.00
52 Popeye 125.00
53 Oswald the Lucky Rabbit . . 50.00
54 Gene Autrey 150.00
55 Andy and Woody 45.00
56 CB back(c),Donald Duck . . 275.00
57 Porky Pig 55.00
58 Henry 30.00
59 Bugs Bunny 70.00
60 Mickey Mouse 275.00
61 Tom and Jerry 50.00
62 Roy Rogers 175.00
63 Santa 20.00
64 Santa 20.00
65 Jingle Bells 20.00
66 Popeye 100.00
67 Oswald the Lucky Rabbit . . 30.00
68 Roy Rogers 175.00
69 Donald Duck 250.00
70 Tom and Jerry 40.00
71 Porky Pig 55.00
72 Krazy Kat 50.00
73 Roy Rogers 150.00
74 Mickey Mouse 250.00
75 Bugs Bunny 65.00
76 Andy and Woody 35.00
77 Roy Rogers 100.00
78 Gene Autrey; last regular
   sized issue 100.00
79 Andy Panda,5"x7" format . . . 25.00
80 Popeye 65.00
81 Oswald the Lucky Rabbit . . . 25.00
82 Tarzan 150.00
83 Bugs Bunny 50.00
84 Henry 25.00
85 Woody Woodpecker 25.00
86 Roy Rogers 125.00
87 Krazy Kat 25.00
88 Tom and Jerry 30.00
89 Porky Pig 25.00
90 Gene Autrey 90.00
91 Roy Rogers and Santa . . . 125.00
92 Christmas w/Santa 15.00
93 Woody Woodpecker 25.00
94 Indian Chief 65.00
95 Oswald the Lucky Rabbit . . . 20.00

96 Popeye 60.00	171 Oswald the Lucky Rabbit . . 20.00	219 Journey to the Sun 30.00
97 Bugs Bunny 40.00	172 Tarzan 100.00	220 Bugs Bunny 20.00
98 Tarzan,Lex Barker Ph(c) . . . 150.00	173 Tom and Jerry 15.00	221 Roy and Dale,Ph(c) 60.00
99 Porky Pig 25.00	174 The Lone Ranger 60.00	222 Woody Woodpecker 15.00
100 Roy Rogers 100.00	175 Porky Pig 20.00	223 Tarzan 75.00
101 Henry 20.00	176 Roy Rogers 60.00	224 Tom and Jerry 15.00
102 Tom Corbet,P(c) 135.00	177 Woody Woodpecker 15.00	225 The Lone Ranger 40.00
103 Tom and Jerry 25.00	178 Henry 15.00	226 Christmas Treasury 10.00
104 Gene Autrey 75.00	179 Bugs Bunny 20.00	227 Not Published
105 Roy Rogers 100.00	180 Rin Tin Tin 25.00	228 Letters to Santa 10.00
106 Santa's Helpers 15.00	181 Happy Holiday 10.00	229 The Flintstones 100.00
107 Not Published	182 Happi Tim 10.00	230 Lassie 20.00
108 Fun with Santa 15.00	183 Welcome Santa 10.00	231 Bugs Bunny 20.00
109 Woody Woodpecker 20.00	184 Woody Woodpecker 15.00	232 The Three Stooges 75.00
110 Indian Chief 30.00	185 Tarzan, Ph(c) 100.00	233 Bullwinkle 75.00
111 Oswald the Lucky Rabbit . . 20.00	186 Oswald the Lucky Rabbit . . 12.00	234 Smokey the Bear 20.00
112 Henry 20.00	187 Indian Chief 25.00	235 Huckleberry Hound 35.00
113 Porky Pig 25.00	188 Bugs Bunny 25.00	236 Roy and Dale 50.00
114 Tarzan,RsM 150.00	189 Henry 15.00	237 Mighty Mouse 20.00
115 Bugs Bunny 40.00	190 Tom and Jerry 18.00	238 The Lone Ranger 40.00
116 Roy Rogers 100.00	191 Roy Rogers 60.00	239 Woody Woodpecker 15.00
117 Popeye 60.00	192 Porky Pig 20.00	240 Tarzan 60.00
118 Flash Gordon, P(c) 120.00	193 The Lone Ranger 60.00	241 Santa Around the World . . . 10.00
119 Tom and Jerry 20.00	194 Popeye 25.00	242 Santa Toyland 10.00
120 Gene Autrey 65.00	195 Rin Tin Tin 30.00	243 The Flintstones 100.00
121 Roy Rogers 100.00	196 Not Published	244 Mr.Ed,Ph(c) 25.00
122 Santa's Suprise 15.00	197 Santa is Coming 10.00	245 Bugs Bunny 20.00
123 Santa's Christmas Book . . . 15.00	198 Santa's Helper 10.00	246 Popeye 20.00
124 Woody Woodpecker 20.00	199 Huckleberry Hound 50.00	247 Mighty Mouse 20.00
125 Tarzan, Lex Barker Ph(c) . 150.00	200 Fury 30.00	248 The Three Stooges 75.00
126 Oswald the Lucky Rabbit . . 20.00	201 Bugs Bunny 25.00	249 Woody Woodpecker 10.00
127 Indian Chief 20.00	202 Space Explorer 50.00	250 Roy and Dale 50.00
128 Tom and Jerry 20.00	203 Woody Woodpecker 15.00	251 Little Lulu & Witch Hazel . . 100.00
129 Henry 20.00	204 Tarzan 55.00	252 P(c),Tarzan 45.00
130 Porky Pig 25.00	205 Mighty Mouse 35.00	253 Yogi Bear 25.00
131 Roy Rogers 100.00	206 Roy Rogers,Ph(c) 60.00	254 Lassie 20.00
132 Bugs Bunny 30.00	207 Tom and Jerry 15.00	255 Santa's Christmas List . . . 10.00
133 Flash Gordon,Ph(c) 100.00	208 The Lone Ranger,Ph(c) . . . 90.00	256 Christmas Party 10.00
134 Popeye 45.00	209 Porky Pig 15.00	257 Mighty Mouse 20.00
135 Gene Autrey 60.00	210 Lassie 30.00	258 The Sword in the Stone
136 Roy Rogers 75.00	211 Not Published	(Disney Version) 50.00
137 Gifts from Santa 10.00	212 Christmas Eve 10.00	259 Bugs Bunny 20.00
138 Fun at Christmas 10.00	213 Here Comes Santa 10.00	260 Mr. Ed 20.00
139 Woody Woodpecker 20.00	214 Huckleberry Hound 50.00	261 Woody Woodpecker 15.00
140 Indian Chief 25.00	215 Hi Yo Silver 35.00	262 Tarzan 55.00
141 Oswald the Lucky Rabbit . . 15.00	216 Rocky & His Friends 75.00	263 Donald Duck 75.00
142 Flash Gordon 80.00	217 Lassie 20.00	264 Popeye 25.00
143 Porky Pig 20.00	218 Porky Pig 20.00	265 Yogi Bear 30.00
144 RsM,Ph(c),Tarzan 135.00		266 Lassie 20.00
145 Tom and Jerry 20.00		267 Little Lulu 90.00
146 Roy Rogers,Ph(c) 100.00		268 The Three Stooges 75.00
147 Henry 15.00		269 A Jolly Christmas 10.00
148 Popeye 35.00		270 Santa's Little Helpers 10.00
149 Bugs Bunny 25.00		271 The Flintstones 75.00
150 Gene Autrey 60.00		272 Tarzan 45.00
151 Roy Rogers 75.00		273 Bugs Bunny 20.00
152 The Night Before Christmas 12.00		274 Popeye 20.00
153 Merry Christmas 12.00		275 Little Lulu 75.00
154 Tom and Jerry 20.00		276 The Jetsons 100.00
155 Tarzan,Ph(c) 125.00		277 Daffy Duck 15.00
156 Oswald the Lucky Rabbit . . 15.00		278 Lassie 20.00
157 Popeye 30.00		279 Yogi Bear 30.00
158 Woody Woodpecker 20.00		280 Ph(c),The Three Stooges . 75.00
159 Indian Chief 20.00		281 Tom & Jerry 15.00
160 Bugs Bunny 20.00		282 Mr. Ed 20.00
161 Roy Rogers 75.00		283 Santa's Visit 10.00
162 Henry 15.00		284 Christmas Parade 10.00
163 Rin Tin Tin 32.00		285 Astro Boy 225.00
164 Porky Pig 20.00		286 Tarzan 40.00
165 The Lone Ranger 65.00		287 Bugs Bunny 20.00
166 Santa & His Reindeer 12.00		288 Daffy Duck 15.00
167 Roy Rogers and Santa . . . 75.00		289 The Flintstones 65.00
168 Santa Claus' Workshop . . . 12.00		290 Ph(c), Mr. Ed. 18.00
169 Popeye 30.00		291 Yogi Bear 25.00
170 Indian Chief 25.00		292 Ph(c), The Three Stooges . . 70.00

March of Comics #70
© K.K. Publications/Western Publ.

GOLDEN AGE

293 Little Lulu 55.00	365 Tom & Jerry 12.00	440 Bugs Bunny 7.00
294 Popeye 20.00	366 Tarzan 25.00	441 The Pink Panther 5.00
295 Tom & Jerry 15.00	367 Bugs Bunny & Porky Pig . . . 15.00	442 The Road Runner 5.00
296 Lassie 20.00	368 Scooby Doo 20.00	443 Baby Snoots 3.00
297 Christmas Bells 10.00	369 Little Lulu 20.00	444 Tom & Jerry 3.00
298 Santa's Sleigh 10.00	370 Ph(c), Lassie 12.00	445 Tweety & Sylvester 3.00
299 The Flintstones 60.00	371 Baby Snoots 9.00	446 Wacky Witch 2.00
300 Tarzan 40.00	372 Smokey The Bear 11.00	447 Mighty Mouse 5.00
301 Bugs Bunny 15.00	373 The Three Stooges 50.00	448 Cracky 2.00
302 Ph(c), Laurel & Hardy 30.00	374 Wacky Witch 8.00	449 The Pink Panther 5.00
303 Daffy Duck 10.00	375 Beep-Beep & Daffy Duck . . 12.00	450 Baby Snoots 3.00
304 Ph(c), The Three Stooges . . 70.00	376 The Pink Panther 15.00	451 Tom & Jerry 4.00
305 Tom & Jerry 10.00	377 Baby Snoots 9.00	452 Bugs Bunny 4.00
306 Ph(c), Daniel Boone 40.00	378 Turok, Son of Stone 95.00	453 Popeye 3.00
307 Little Lulu 45.00	379 Heckle & Jeckle 8.00	454 Woody Woodpecker 4.00
308 Ph(c), Lassie 15.00	380 Bugs Bunny & Yosemite Sam 15.00	455 The Road Runner 4.00
309 Yogi Bear 25.00	381 Lassie 12.00	456 Little Lulu 3.00
310 Ph(c) of Clayton Moore;	382 Scooby Doo 18.00	457 Tweety & Sylvester 3.00
The Lone Ranger 75.00	383 Smokey the Bear 9.00	458 Wacky Witch 2.00
311 Santa's Show 8.00	384 The Pink Panther 12.00	459 Mighty Mouse 5.00
312 Christmas Album 8.00	385 Little Lulu 15.00	460 Daffy Duck 3.00
313 Daffy Duck 12.00	386 Wacky Witch 7.00	461 The Pink Panther 4.00
314 Laurel & Hardy 25.00	387 Beep-Beep & Daffy Duck . . 10.00	462 Baby Snoots 2.00
315 Bugs Bunny 15.00	388 Tom & Jerry 10.00	463 Tom & Jerry 4.00
316 The Three Stooges 60.00	389 Little Lulu 15.00	464 Bugs Bunny 5.00
317 The Flintstones 30.00	390 The Pink Panther 12.00	465 Popeye 4.00
318 Tarzan 35.00	391 Scooby Doo 18.00	466 Woody Woodpecker 4.00
319 Yogi Bear 20.00	392 Bugs Bunny & Yosemite Sam 15.00	467 Underdog 8.00
320 Space Family Robinson . . 100.00	393 Heckle & Jeckle 8.00	468 Little Lulu 4.00
321 Tom & Jerry 12.00	394 Lassie 10.00	469 Tweety & Sylvester 3.00
322 The Lone Ranger 40.00	395 Woodsy the Owl 6.00	470 Wacky Witch 3.00
323 Little Lulu 30.00	396 Baby Snoots 6.00	471 Mighty Mouse 5.00
324 Ph(c), Lassie 12.00	397 Beep-Beep & Daffy Duck . . . 7.00	472 Heckle & Jeckle 4.00
325 Fun With Santa 9.00	398 Wacky Witch 6.00	473 The Pink Panther 5.00
326 Christmas Story 9.00	399 Turok, Son of Stone 65.00	474 Baby Snoots 2.00
327 The Flintstones 55.00	400 Tom & Jerry 8.00	475 Little Lulu 3.00
328 Space Family Robinson . . . 55.00	401 Baby Snoots 6.00	476 Bugs Bunny 5.00
329 Bugs Bunny 15.00	402 Daffy Duck 8.00	477 Popeye 3.00
330 The Jetsons 75.00	403 Bugs Bunny 10.00	478 Woody Woodpecker 5.00
331 Daffy Duck 12.00	404 Space Family Robinson . . . 40.00	479 Underdog 10.00
332 Tarzan 35.00	405 Cracky 6.00	480 Tom & Jerry 8.00
333 Tom & Jerry 12.00	406 Little Lulu 15.00	481 Tweety & Sylvster 3.00
334 Lassie 15.00	407 Smokey the Bear 6.00	482 Wacky Witch 3.00
335 Little Lulu 25.00	408 Turok, Son of Stone 45.00	483 Mighty Mouse 5.00
336 The Three Stooges 55.00	409 The Pink Panther 10.00	484 Heckle & Jeckle 3.00
337 Yogi Bear 20.00	410 Wacky Witch 6.00	485 Baby Snoots 3.00
338 The Lone Ranger 35.00	411 Lassie 10.00	486 The Pink Panther 5.00
339 *Not Published*	412 New Terrytoons 4.00	487 Bugs Bunny 5.00
340 Here Comes Santa 9.00	413 Daffy Duck 4.00	
341 The Flintstones 55.00	414 Space Family Robinson . . . 35.00	
342 Tarzan 30.00	415 Bugs Bunny 10.00	
343 Bugs Bunny 20.00	416 The Road Runner 6.00	
344 Yogi Bear 23.00	417 Little Lulu 15.00	
345 Tom & Jerry 12.00	418 The Pink Panther 10.00	
346 Lassie 15.00	419 Baby Snoots 4.00	
347 Daffy Duck 12.00	420 Woody Woodpecker 4.00	
348 The Jetsons 65.00	421 Tweety & Sylvester 4.00	
349 Little Lulu 25.00	422 Wacky Witch 4.00	
350 The Lone Ranger 30.00	423 Little Monsters 4.00	
351 Beep-Beep, The	424 Cracky 4.00	
Road Runner 20.00	425 Daffy Duck 4.00	
352 Space Family Robinson . . . 75.00	426 Underdog 18.00	
353 Beep-Beep, The Road	427 Little Lulu 10.00	
Runner 20.00	428 Bugs Bunny 6.00	
354 Tarzan 25.00	429 The Pink Panther 6.00	
355 Little Lulu 25.00	430 The Road Runner 7.00	
356 Scooby Doo, Where Are You 22.00	431 Baby Snoots 4.00	
357 Daffy Duck & Porky Pig . . . 12.00	432 Lassie 5.00	
358 Lassie 15.00	433 Tweety & Sylvester 4.00	
359 Baby Snoots 12.00	434 Wacky Witch 4.00	
360 Ph(c), H.R. Pufnstuf 15.00	435 New Terrytoons 4.00	
361 Tom & Jerry 12.00	436 Cracky 4.00	
362 Smokey the Bear 15.00	437 Daffy Duck 4.00	
363 Bugs Bunny & Yosemite Sam 15.00	438 Underdog 10.00	
364 Ph(c), The Banana Splits . . 11.00	439 Little Lulu 10.00	

Marge's Little Lulu #8
© *Dell Publishing Co.*

GOLDEN AGE

---

488 April, 1982; Little Lulu 3.00

MARGE'S LITTLE LULU
Dell Publishing Co.
1 B:Lulu's Diary	600.00
2 I:Gloria,Miss Feeny	300.00
3	275.00
4	275.00
5	275.00
6	200.00
7 I:Annie,X-Mas Cover	200.00
8	200.00
9	200.00
10	200.00
11 thru 18	@175.00
19 I:Wilbur	175.00
20 I:Mr.McNabbem	175.00
21 thru 25	@150.00
26 rep.Four Color#110	150.00
27 thru 29	@150.00
30 Christmas cover	150.00
31 thru 34	@125.00
35 B:Mumday Story	125.00
36 thru 38	@125.00
39 I:Witch Hazel	150.00
40 Halloween Cover	125.00
41	125.00
42 Christmas Cover	125.00
43 Skiing Cover	125.00
44 Valentines Day Cover	125.00
45 2nd A:Witch Hazel	125.00
46 thru 60	@125.00
61	75.00
62	75.00
63 I:Chubby	75.00
64 thru 67	@75.00
68 I:Professor Cleff	75.00
69 thru 77	@75.00
78 Christmas Cover	75.00
79	75.00
80	75.00
81 thru 89	@60.00
90 Christmas Cover	60.00
91 thru 99	@60.00
100	75.00
101 thru 122	@60.00
123 I:Fifi	50.00
124 thru 164	@40.00
165 giant sized	150.00
166 giant sized	150.00
167 thru 169	@35.00
170	15.00
171	15.00
172	18.00
173	15.00
174	15.00
175	18.00
176	18.00
177	15.00
178 thru 196	@18.00
197	15.00
198 thru 200	@18.00
201	8.00
202	12.00
203	8.00
204	12.00
205	12.00
206	8.00

MARMADUKE MOUSE
Quality Comics Group
(Arnold Publications)
Spring, 1946
1 Funny Animal	85.00

2 Funny Animal	32.00
3 thru 8 Funny Animal	@25.00
9 Funny Animal	22.00
10 Funny Animal	22.00
11 thru 20 Funny Animal	@20.00
21 thru 30 Funny Animal	@18.00
31 thru 40 Funny Animal	@15.00
41 thru 50 Funny Animal	@12.00
51 thru 65 Funny Animal	@10.00

MARTIN KANE
Hero Books
(Fox Features syndicate)
June, 1950
1 WW,WW-(c)	200.00
2 WW,JO, Auguat, 1950	150.00

Marvel Family #6
© Fawcett Publications

MARVEL FAMILY, THE
Fawcett Publications
December, 1945
1 O:Captain Marvel,Captain Marvel Jr., Mary Marvel,Uncle Marvel; V:Black Adam	1,200.00
2	550.00
3	400.00
4 The Witch's Tale	350.00
5 Civilization of a Prehistoric Race	325.00
6	275.00
7 The Rock of Eternity	250.00
8 The Marvel Family Round Table	250.00
9 V: The Last Vikings	250.00
10 V: The Sivana Family	250.00
11 V: The Well of Evil	225.00
12 V: The Iron Horseman	225.00
13	225.00
14 Captain Marvel Invalid	225.00
15 V: Mr. Triangle	200.00
16 World's Mightiest Quarrell	200.00
17	200.00
18	200.00
19 V: The Monster Menace	200.00
20 The Marvel Family Feud	200.00
21 V: The Trio of Terror	160.00
22 V: The Triple Threat	160.00
23 March of Independence (c)	175.00

24 V: The Fighting Xergos	160.00
25 Trial of the Marvel Family	160.00
26 V: Mr. Power	150.00
27 V: The Amoeba Men	150.00
28	150.00
29 V: The Monarch of Money	150.00
30 A:World's Greatest Magician	150.00
31 V:Sivana & The Great Hunger	125.00
32 The Marvel Family Goes Into Buisness	125.00
33 I: The Hermit Family	125.00
34 V: Sivana's Miniature Menace	125.00
35 V: The Berzerk Machines	125.00
36 V: The Invaders From Infinity	125.00
37 V: The Earth Changer	125.00
38 V: Sivana's Instinct Exterminator Gun	125.00
39 The Legend of Atlantis	125.00
40 Seven Wonders of the Modern World	125.00
41 The Great Oxygen Theft	125.00
42 V: The Endless Menace	100.00
43	100.00
44 V: The Rust That Menaced the World	100.00
45 The Hoax City	100.00
46 The Day Civilization Vanished	100.00
47 V: The Interplanetary Thieves	150.00
48 V: The Four Horsemen	100.00
49 ...Proves Human Hardness	100.00
50 The Speech Scrambler Machine	100.00
51 The Living Statues	120.00
52 The School of Witches	100.00
53 V: The Man Who Changed the World	100.00
54	100.00
55	100.00
56 The World's Mightiest Project	100.00
57	100.00
58 The Triple Time Plot	100.00
59	100.00
60	100.00
61	90.00
62	90.00
63 V: The Pirate Planet	90.00
64	90.00
65	90.00
66 The Miracle Stone	90.00
67	90.00
68	90.00
69 V: The Menace of Old Age	90.00
70 V: The Crusade of Evil	90.00
71	90.00
72	90.00
73	90.00
74	90.00
75 The Great Space Struggle	90.00
76	125.00
77 Anti-Communist	150.00
78 V: The Red Vulture	125.00
79	90.00
80	90.00
81	90.00
82	90.00
83 V: The Flying Skull	90.00
84 thru 87	@90.00
88 Jokes of Jeopardy	90.00
89 And Then There Were None; January, 1954	90.00

MARVELS OF SCIENCE
Charlton Comics
March, 1946
1 1st Charlton Book; Atomic	

GOLDEN AGE

GOLDEN AGE

Bomb Story	150.00
2	100.00
3	100.00
4 President Truman(c); Jun.'6	100.00

MARY MARVEL COMICS
Fawcett Publications/
Charlton Comics
December, 1945

1 Intro: Mary Marvel	1,300.00
2	600.00
3	400.00
4 On a Leave of Absence . . .	350.00
5 Butterfly (c)	250.00
6 A:Freckles,Teenager of Mischief	250.00
7 The Kingdom Undersea . . .	250.00
8 Holiday Special Issue	250.00
9 Air Race (c)	225.00
10 A: Freckles	225.00
11 A: The Sad Dryads	175.00
12 Red Cross Appeal on(c) . . .	175.00
13 Keep the Homefires Burning	175.00
14 Meets Ghosts (c)	175.00

Mary Marvel #16 © Fawcett
Publications/Charlton Comics

15 A: Freckles	175.00
16 The Jukebox Menace	150.00
17 Aunt Agatha's Adventures . .	150.00
18	150.00
19 Witch (c)	150.00
20	150.00
21 V: Dice Head	125.00
22 The Silver Slippers	125.00
23 The Pendulum Strikes	125.00
24 V: The Nightowl	125.00
25 A: Freckles	125.00
26 A:Freckles dressed as Clown	125.00
27 The Floating Oceanliner . . .	125.00
28 September, 1948	125.00

Becomes:
MONTE HALE WESTERN

29 Ph(c),B:Monte Hale & His Horse Pardner	350.00
30 Ph(c),B:Big Bow-Little Arrow; CCB,Captain Tootsie	225.00
31 Ph(c),Giant	175.00
32 Ph(c),Giant	175.00
33 Ph(c),Giant	175.00

34 Ph(c),E:Big Bow-Little Arrow;B:Gabby Hayes,Giant	175.00
35 Ph(c),Gabby Hayes, Giant .	175.00
36 Ph(c),Gabby Hayes, Giant .	175.00
37 Ph(c),Gabby Hayes	125.00
38 Ph(c),Gabby Hayes, Giant .	150.00
39 Ph(c),CCB, Captain Tootsie; Gabby Hayes, Giant	150.00
40 Ph(c),Gabby Hayes, Giant .	150.00
41 Ph(c),Gabby Hayes	75.00
42 Ph(c),Gabby Hayes, Giant .	90.00
43 Ph(c),Gabby Hayes, Giant .	90.00
44 Ph(c),Gabby Hayes, Giant .	90.00
45 Ph(c),Gabby Hayes, Giant .	75.00
46 Ph(c),Gabby Hayes, Giant .	75.00
47 Ph(c),A:Big Bow-Little Arrow; Gabby Hayes, Giant	75.00
48 Ph(c),Gabby Hayes, Giant .	75.00
49 Ph(c),Gabby Hayes	75.00
50 Ph(c),Gabby Hayes, Giant .	75.00
51 Ph(c),Gabby Hayes, Giant .	70.00
52 Ph(c),Gabby Hayes, Giant .	70.00
53 Ph(c),A:Slim Pickens; Gabby Hayes	50.00
54 Ph(c),Gabby Hayes, Giant .	70.00
55 Ph(c),Gabby Hayes, Giant .	70.00
56 Ph(c),Gabby Hayes, Giant .	70.00
57 Ph(c),Gabby Hayes	50.00
58 Ph(c),Gabby Hayes, Giant .	60.00
59 Ph(c),Gabby Hayes, Giant .	60.00
60 thru 79 Ph(c),Gabby Hayes @	45.00
80 Ph(c),E: Gabby Hayes	45.00
81 Ph(c)	45.00
82 Final Ph(c), Last Fawcett Edition	45.00
83 1st Charlton Edition, R:G. Hayes Back B&W Ph(c)	45.00
84	45.00
85	42.00
86 E: Gabby Hayes	42.00
87	42.00
88 January, 1956	42.00

MASK COMICS
Rural Home Publications
February-March, 1945

1 LbC,LbC-(c), Evil (c)	2,000.00
2 LbC-(c),A:Black Rider,The Collector The Boy Magician; Apr-May'45, Devil (c)	1,400.00

MASKED MARVEL
Centaur Publications
September, 1940

1 I: The Masked Marvel . . .	1,300.00
2 PG, ...	900.00
3 December, 1940	850.00

MASKED RANGER
Premier Magazines
April, 1954

1 FF,O&B:The Masked Ranger, Streak the Horse,The Crimson Avenger	250.00
2	75.00
3	75.00
4 B: Jessie James,Billy the Kid, Wild Bill Hickock, Jim Bowie's Life Story	90.00
5	90.00
6	90.00
7	90.00
8	90.00
9 AT,E:All Features; A:Wyatt	

Earp August, 1955	100.00

MASTER COMICS
Fawcett Publications
March, 1940
1-6 Oversized,7-Normal Format

1 O:Master Man; B:The Devil's Dagger, El Carin-Master of Magic, Rick O'Say, Morton Murch, White Rajah, Shipwreck Roberts, Frontier Marshall, Mr. Clue, Streak Sloan . . .	7,000.00
2 Master Man (c)	1,800.00
3 Master Man (c) Bondage . .	1,500.00
4 Master Man (c)	1,400.00
5 Master Man (c)	1,400.00
6 E: All Above Features . . .	1,500.00
7 B:Bulletman,Zorro,The Mystery Man, Lee Granger, Jungle King,Buck Jones	2,200.00
8 B:The Red Gaucho,Captain Venture, Planet Princess .	1,200.00
9 Bulletman & Steam Roller . .	900.00
10 E: Lee Granger	900.00

Master Comics #7
© Fawcett Publications

11 O: Minute Man	2,000.00
12 Minute Man (c)	1,100.00
13 O:Bulletgirl; E:Red Gaucho	1,600.00
14 B: The Companions Three .	800.00
15 MRa, Bulletman & Girl (c) . .	800.00
16 MRa, Minute Man (c)	800.00
17 B:MRa on Bulletman	750.00
18 MRa, ...	750.00
19 MRa, Bulletman & Girl (c) . .	750.00
20 MRa,C:Cap.Marvel-Bulletman	750.00
21 MRa-(c),Capt. Marvel in Bulletman,I&O:CaptainNazi	4,500.00
22 MRa-(c),E:Mystery Man,Captain Venture; Bondage(c);Capt. Marvel Jr. X-Over In Bulletman; A:Capt. Nazi . .	4,000.00
23 MRa,MRa(c),B:Capt. Marvel Jr. V:Capt. Nazi . . .	2,200.00
24 MRa,MRa(c),Death By Radio	775.00
25 MRa,MRa(c),The Jap Invasion	775.00
26 MRa,MRa(c),Capt. Marvel Jr. Avenges Pearl Harbor	700.00

27 MRa.MRa(c),V For Victory(c) 700.00
28 MRa,MRa(c)Liberty Bell(c) . 700.00
29 MRa,MRa(c),Hitler & Hirohito(c) 700.00
30 MRa,MRa(c),Flag (c);Capt. Marvel Jr, V: Capt. Nazi ... 700.00
31 MRa,MRa(c),E:Companions Three,Capt.Marvel Jr, V:Mad Dr. Macabre 500.00
32 MRa,MRa(c),E: Buck Jones; CMJr Strikes Terror Castle . 500.00
33 MRa,MRa(c),B:Balbo the Boy Magician, Hopalong Cassidy 500.00
34 MRa,MRa(c),Capt.Marvel Jr V: Capt.Nazi 500.00
35 MRa,MRa(c),CMJr Defies the Flame 500.00
36 MRa,MRa(c),Statue Of Liberty(c) 500.00
37 MRa,MRa(c),CMJr Blasts the Nazi Raiders 450.00
38 MRa,MRa(c),CMJr V: the Japs 450.00
39 MRa,MRa(c),CMJr Blasts Nazi Slave Ship 450.00
40 MRa,MRa(c),Flag (c) 450.00
41 MRa,MRa(c),Bulletman,Bulletgirl, CMJr X-Over In Minuteman . 500.00
42 MRa,MRa(c),CMJr V: Hitler's Dream Soldier 300.00
43 MRa(c),CMJr Battles For Stalingrad 300.00
44 MRa(c),CMJr In Crystal City of the Peculiar Penguins ... 300.00
45 MRa(c), ... 300.00
46 MRa(c) 300.00
47 MRa(c),A:Hitler; E: Balbo .. 325.00
48 MRa(c),I:Bulletboy;Capt. Marvel A: in Minuteman ... 350.00
49 MRa(c),E: Hopalong Cassidy, Minuteman 300.00
50 I&O: Radar,A:Capt. Marvel, B:Nyoka the Jungle Girl ... 250.00
51 MRa(c),CMJr V: Japanese . 175.00
52 MRa(c),CMJr & Radar Pitch War Stamps on (c) 175.00
53 CMJR V: Dr. Sivana 175.00
54 MRa(c),Capt.Marvel Jr Your Pin-Up Buddy 175.00
55 .... 175.00
56 MRa(c) 150.00
57 CMJr V: Dr. Sivana 150.00
58 MRA,MRa(c), ... 150.00
59 MRa(c),A:The Upside Downies 165.00
60 MRa(c) 165.00
61 CMJr Meets Uncle Marvel .. 165.00
62 Uncle Sam on (c) 165.00
63 W/ Radar (c) 125.00
64 W/ Radar (c) 125.00
65 .... 125.00
66 CMJr & Secret Of the Sphinx 125.00
67 Knight (c) 125.00
68 CMJr in the Range of the Beasts 125.00
69 .... 125.00
70 .... 125.00
71 CMJr,V:Man in Metal Mask . 110.00
72 CMJr V: Sivana & The Whistle That Wouldn't Stop 110.00
73 CMJr V: The Ghost of Evil . 110.00
74 CMJr & The Fountain of Age 110.00
75 CMJr V: The Zombie Master 110.00
76 .... 110.00
77 Pirate Treasure (c) 110.00

78 CMJr in Death on the Scenic Railway 110.00
79 CMJr V: The Black Shroud . 110.00
80 CMJr-The Land of Backwards 110.00
81 CMJr & The Voyage 'Round the Horn 100.00
82 CMJr,IN,Death at the Launching 100.00
83 .... 100.00
84 CMJr V: The Human Magnet 100.00
85 CMJr-Crime on the Campus 100.00
86 CMJr V: The City of Machines 100.00
87 CMJr & The Root of Evil ... 100.00
88 CMJr V: The Wreckers; B: Hopalong Cassidy 100.00
89 .... 100.00
90 CMJr V: The Caveman ... 100.00
91 CMJr V: The Blockmen ... 100.00
92 CMJr V: The Space Slavers 100.00
93 BK,CMJr,V:TheGrowingGiant 125.00
94 E: Hopalong Cassidy 100.00
95 B: Tom Mix; CMJr Meets the Skyhawk 100.00
96 CMJr Meets the Worlds Mightiest Horse 100.00

Master Comics #95
© Fawcett Publications

97 CMJr Faces the Doubting Thomas 100.00
98 KKK Type 100.00
99 Witch (c) 100.00
100 CMJr V: The Ghost Ship . 120.00
101 thru 105 .... @100.00
106 E: Bulletman 100.00
107 CMJr Faces the Disappearance of the Statue of Liberty 100.00
108 .... 80.00
109 .... 80.00
110 CMJr & The Hidden Death . 80.00
111 thru 122 .... @80.00
123 CMJr V: The Flying Desperado 80.00
124 .... 80.00
125 CMJr & The Bed of Mystery 80.00
126 thru 131 .... @80.00
132 V: Migs 90.00
133 E: Tom Mix; April, 1953 .. 100.00

MD
E.C. Comics
April 1955-Jan. 1956
1 RC,GE,Grl,JO,JCr(c) 100.00
2 thru 5 RC,GE,Grl,JO,JCr(c) @75.00

MEDAL OF HONOR COMICS
Stafford Publication
Spring, 1947
1 True Stories of Medal of Honor Recipants 55.00

MEET CORLISS ARCHER
Fox Features Syndicate
March, 1948
1 AF,AF(c), Teenage 450.00
2 AF(c) 400.00
3 .... 300.00

My Life #10 © Fox Features Syndicate

Becomes:
MY LIFE
4 JKa,AF, ... 225.00
5 JKa, ... 150.00
6 JKa,AF, ... 150.00
7 Watercolor&Ink Drawing on(c) 75.00
8 .... 50.00
9 .... 50.00
10 WW, July, 1950 .... 85.00

MEET MERTON
Toby Press
December, 1953
1 Dave Berg-a,Teen Stories ... 30.00
2 Dave Berg-a 15.00
3 Dave Berg-a 12.00
4 Dave Berg-a; June, 1954 ... 12.00

MEET THE NEW POST GAZETTE SUNDAY FUNNIES
Pitsberg Post Gazette
N# One Shot Insert F: Several Syndicated Characters in Stories Exclusive to This Edition ... 750.00

MEL ALLEN
SPORTS COMICS
Visual Editions
1949

1 GT	175.00
2 Lou Gehrig	125.00

MEN AGAINST CRIME
(see HAND OF FATE)

MERRY-GO-ROUND
COMICS
LaSalle/Croyden/
Rotary Litho.
1944

1 LaSalle Publications Edition	100.00
1a 1946, Croyden Edition	35.00
1b Sept-Oct.'47,Rotary Litho Ed	50.00
2	50.00

MERRY MOUSE
Avon Periodicals
June, 1953

1 (fa),F. Carin (c)&a	35.00
2 (fa),F. Carin (c)&a	20.00
3 (fa),F. Carin (c)&a	20.00
4 (fa),F. Carin (c)&a;Jan.'54	20.00

METEOR COMICS
Croyden Publications
November, 1945

1 Captain Wizard & Baldy Bean	250.00

MICKEY FINN
Eastern Color/
Columbia Comics Group
1942

1	225.00
2	125.00
3 A: Charlie Chan	75.00
4	60.00
5 thru 9	@40.00
10 thru 15	@30.00

(WALT DISNEY'S)
MICKEY MOUSE
Dell Publishing Co.
December 1952
#1-#27 Dell Four Color

28	40.00
29	35.00
30	35.00
31	35.00
32 thru 34	@35.00
35 thru 50	@25.00
51 thru 73	@15.00
74	20.00
75 thru 99	@15.00
100 thru 105 rep.	@20.00
106 thru 120	@15.00
121 thru 130	@10.00
131 thru 146	@10.00
147 rep,Phantom Fires	15.00
148 rep.	15.00
149 thru 158	@8.00
159 rep.	12.00
160 thru 170	@7.00
171 thru 199	@3.00
200 rep.	5.00
201 thru 218	@3.00
See: Independent Color Comics	

MICKEY MOUSE MAGAZINE
Kay Kamen

1 (1933) scarce	3,200.00
2	1,000.00
3 thru 8	@950.00
9	900.00

MICKEY MOUSE MAGAZINE
Kay Kamen

1 digest size (1933)		1,200.00
2 dairy give-away promo(1933)	400.00	
3 dairy give-away promo(1934)	350.00	
4 dairy give-away promo(1934)	350.00	
5 dairy give-away promo(1934)	350.00	
6 dairy give-away promo(1934)	350.00	
7 dairy give-away promo(1934)	350.00	
8 dairy give-away promo(1934)	350.00	
9 dairy give-away promo(1934)	350.00	
10 dairy give-away promo(1934)	350.00	
11 dairy give-away promo(1934)	350.00	
12 dairy give-awaypromo(1934)	350.00	
Volume II		
1 dairy give-away promo(1934)	250.00	
2 dairy give-away promo(1934)	250.00	
3 dairy give-away promo(1935)	250.00	
4 dairy give-away promo(1935)	250.00	
5 dairy give-away promo(1935)	250.00	
6 dairy give-away promo(1935)	250.00	
7 dairy give-away promo(1935)	250.00	
8 dairy give-away promo(1935)	250.00	
9 dairy give-away promo(1935)	250.00	
10 dairy give-awaypromo(1935)	250.00	
11 dairy give-awaypromo(1935)	250.00	
12 dairy give-awaypromo(1935)	250.00	

Mickey Mouse Magazine #46
© Kay Kamen

MICKEY MOUSE MAGAZINE
K.K. Pub./Westen Pub

1 (1935) 13¼"x10¼"	12,000.00
2	1100.00
3	600.00
4	600.00
5 (1936) Donald Duck solo	700.00
6 Donald Duck editor	600.00
7	600.00
8 Donald Duck solo	600.00
9	600.00
10	600.00
11 Mickey Mouse, editor	550.00

12	550.00
Volume II	
1	550.00
2	550.00
3 Christmas issue, 100pg	2,500.00
4 (1937) Roy Ranger adv.strip	500.00
5 Ted True strip	400.00
6 Mickey Mouse cut-outs	375.00
7 Mickey Mouse cut-outs	375.00
8 Mickey Mouse cut-outs	375.00
9 Mickey Mouse cut-outs	375.00
10 Full color	550.00
11	400.00
12 Hiawatha	400.00
13	400.00
Volume III	
2 Big Bad Wolf (c)	450.00
3 First Snow White	750.00
4 (1938) Snow White	600.00
5 Snow White (c)	700.00
6 Snow White ends	500.00
7 7 Dwarfs Easter (c)	375.00
8	350.00
9 Dopey(c)	350.00
10 Goofy(c)	350.00
11 Mickey Mouse Sheriff	350.00
12 A:Snow White	350.00
Volume IV	
1 Practile Pig	350.00
2 I:Huey,Louis & Dewey(c)	400.00
3 Ferdinand the Bull	350.00
4 (1939),B:Spotty	325.00
5 Pluto solo	350.00
7 Ugly Duckling	325.00
7a Goofy & Wilber	350.00
8 Big Bad Wolf(c)	350.00
9 The Pointer	350.00
10 July 4th	450.00
11	300.00
12 Donald's Penguin	400.00
Volume V	
1 Black Pete	400.00
2 Goofy(c)	600.00
3 Pinochio	600.00
4 (1940)	350.00
5 Jimmy Crickett(c)	375.00
6 Tugboat Mickey	375.00
7 Huey, Louis & Dewey(c)	400.00
8 Figaro & Cleo	375.00
9 Donald(c),J.Crickett	450.00
10 July 4th	425.00
11 Mickey's Tailor	450.00
12 Change of format	3,500.00
{becomes:	
Walt Disney Comics & Stories}	

MICKEY MOUSE
Whitman

904 W.Disney's Mickey Mouse and his friends (1934)	1,100.00
948 Disney'sMickeyMouse('34)	1,100.00

MIDGET COMICS
St. John Publishing Co.
February, 1950

1 MB(c),Fighting Indian Stories	100.00
2 April, 1950;Tex West-Cowboy Marshall	50.00

MIGHTY ATOM, THE
(see PIXIES)

GOLDEN AGE

GOLDEN AGE

MIGHTY MIDGET COMICS
Samuel E. Lowe & Co.
1942-43
4"x5" Format
1 Bulletman 125.00
2 Captain Marvel 125.00
3 Captain Marvel Jr. 100.00
4 Golden Arrow 100.00
5 Ibis the Invincible 100.00
6 Spy Smasher 100.00
7 Balbo, The Boy magician . . . 40.00
8 Bulletman 75.00
9 Commando Yank 50.00
10 Dr. Voltz, The Human
    Generator 40.00
11 Lance O'Casey 40.00
12 Leatherneck the Marine 40.00
13 Minute Man 75.00
14 Mister Q 40.00
15 Mr. Scarlet & Pinky 60.00
16 Pat Wilson & His
    Flying Fortress 40.00
17 Phantom Eagle 50.00
18 State Trooper Stops Crime . . 40.00
19 Tornado Tom 40.00

MIGHTY MOUSE
Fall, 1946
[1st Series]
1 Terytoons Presents 900.00
2 . . . . 400.00
3 . . . . 275.00
4 Summer, 1947 . . . . 275.00

MIGHTY MOUSE
St. John Publishing
August, 1947
5 . . . . 275.00
6 thru 10 . . . . @150.00
11 thru 20 . . . . @100.00
21 thru 25 . . . . @75.00
26 thru 30 . . . . @60.00
31 thru 34 . . . . @50.00
35 Flying Saucer 65.00
36 . . . . 50.00
37 . . . . 50.00
38 thru 45 Giant 100 pgs . . @150.00
46 thru 66 . . . . @50.00
67 P(c), ... 50.00
Pines
68 thru 81 Funny Animal . . . . @40.00
82 Infinity (c) 40.00
83 June, 1959 . . . . 40.00

MIGHTY MOUSE ADVENTURE STORIES
St. John Publishing Co.
1953
N# 384 Pages,Rebound 350.00

MIKE BARNETT, MAN AGAINST CRIME
Fawcett Publications
December, 1951
1 The Mint of Dionysosi 125.00
2 Mystery of the Blue Madonna . 75.00
3 Revenge Holds the Torch . . . 50.00
4 Special Delivery 50.00
5 Market For Morphine 75.00
6 October, 1952 . . . . 50.00

MILITARY COMICS
Comics Magazines (Quality Comics Group)
August, 1941
1 JCo,CCu,FG,BP,WE(c),O:Blackhawk,
   Miss America, Death Patrol,
   Blue Tracer; B:X of the Underground, Yankee Eagle,Q-Boat,
   Shot & Shell, Archie Atkins,
   Loops & Banks 8,000.00
2 JCo,FG,BP,CCu,CCu(c),B:
   Secret War News 2,000.00
3 JCo,FG,BP,AMc,CCu,CCu(c),
   I&O:Chop Chop 1,800.00
4 FG,BP,AMc,CCu,CCu(c), . 1,400.00
5 FG,BP,AMc,CCu,CCu(c),
   B: The Sniper 1,200.00
6 FG,BP,AMc,CCu,CCu(c) . . 900.00
7 FG,BP,AMc,CCu,CCu(c)
   E:Death Patrol 900.00
8 FG,BP,AMc,CCu,CCu(c) . . 900.00
9 FG,BP,AMc,CCu,CCu(c),
   B: The Phantom Clipper . . 900.00
10 FG,BP,CCu,AMc,WE(c) . . 1,000.00
11 FG,BP,CCu,AMc,
   WE(c),Flag(c) 750.00
12 FG,BP,AMc,RC,RC(c) 900.00
13 FG,BP,AMc,RC,RC(c),E:X of
   the Underground 700.00
14 FG,AMc,RC,RC(c),B:Private
   Dogtag 700.00
15 FG,AMc,RC,RC(c), ... 700.00
16 FG,AMc,RC,RC(c),E:The
   Phantom Clipper,Blue Tracer 600.00
17 FG,AMc,RC,RC(c),
   B:P.T. Boat 600.00
18 FG,AMc,RC,RC(c), V:
   The Thunderer 600.00
19 FG,RC,RC(c), V:King Cobra 600.00
20 GFx,RC,RC(c), Death Patrol 600.00
21 FG,GFx 550.00
22 FG,GFx 550.00
23 FG,GFx 550.00
24 FG,GFx,V: Man-Heavy
   Glasses 550.00
25 FG,GFx,V: Wang The Tiger 550.00
26 FG,GFx,V: Skull 500.00
27 FG,JCo,R:The Death Patrol 500.00
28 FG,JCo, Dungeon of Doom . 500.00
29 FG,JCo,V: Xanukhara 500.00
30 FG,JCo,BWa,BWa(c),B.Hwk
   V: Dr. Koro 500.00
31 FG,JCo,BWa,E:Death
   Patrol; I: Captain Hitsu . . . 500.00
32 JCo,A: Captain Hitsu 450.00
33 W/ Civil War Veteran 450.00
34 A: Eve Rice 450.00
35 Shipwreck Island 450.00
36 Cult of the Wailing Tiger . . 450.00
37 Pass of Bloody Peace 450.00
38 B.Hwk Faces Bloody Death 450.00
39 A: Kwan Yin 450.00
40 V: Ratru 425.00
41 W/ Chop Chop (c) 425.00
42 V: Jap Mata Hari 425.00
43 . . . . 425.00
Becomes:
MODERN COMICS
44 Duel of Honor 450.00
45 V: Sakyo the Madman 350.00
46 RC, Soldiers of Fortune . . . 350.00
47 RC,PG,V:Count Hokoy 350.00
48 RC,PG,V:Pirates of Perool . 350.00
49 RC,PG,I:Fear,Lady

Adventuress 350.00
50 RC,PG 350.00
51 RC,PG, Ancient City of Evil . 300.00
52 PG,BWa,V: The Vulture . . . 300.00
53 PG,BWa,B: Torchy 350.00
54 PG,RC,RC/CCu,BWa 275.00
55 PG,RC,RC/CCu,BWa 275.00
56 PG,RC/CCu,BWa 275.00
57 PG,RC/CCu,BWa 275.00
58 PG,RC,RC/CCu,BWa,
   V:The Grabber 275.00
59 PG,RC,RC/CCu,BWa 275.00
60 PG,RC/CCu,BWa,RC(c),
   V:Green Plague 275.00
61 PG,RC/CCu,BWa,RC(c) . . 275.00
62 PG,RC/CCu,BWa,RC(c) . . 275.00
63 PG,RC/CCu,BWa,RC(c) . . 250.00
64 PG,RC,CCu,BWa,RC(c) . . 250.00
65 PG,RC/CCu,BWa,RC(c) . . 250.00
66 PG,RC/CCu,BWa 250.00
67 PG,RC,CCu,BWa,RC(c) . . 250.00
68 PG,RC,RC/CCu,BWa,RC(c);
   I:Madame Butterfly 250.00
69 PG,RC/CCu,BWa,RC(c) . . 250.00
70 PG,RC/CCu,BWa,RC(c) . . 250.00
71 PG,RC/CCu,BWa,RC(c) . . 250.00
72 PG,RC/CCu,BWa,RC(c) . . 225.00
73 PG,RC/CCu,BWa,RC(c) . . 225.00
74 PG,RC/CCu,BWa,RC(c) . . 225.00
75 PG,RC/CCu,BWa,RC(c) . . 225.00
76 PG,RC/CCu,BWa,RC(c) . . 225.00
77 PG,RC/CCu,BWa,RC(c) . . 225.00
78 PG,RC/CCu,BWa,JCo,RC(c) 250.00
79 PG,RC/CCu,BWa,JCo,RC(c) 225.00
80 PG,RC/CCu,BWa,JCo,RC(c) 225.00
81 PG,RC/CCu,BWa,JCo,RC(c) 225.00
82 PG,RC/CCu,BWa,JCo,RC(c) 225.00
83 PG,RC/CCu,BWa,JCo,RC(c);
   E: Private Dogtag 225.00
84 PG,RC/CCu,BWa,RC(c) . . 225.00
85 PG,RC/CCu,BWa,RC(c) . . 225.00
86 PG,RC/CCu,BWa,RC(c) . . 225.00
87 PG,RC/CCu,BWa,RC(c) . . 225.00
88 PG,RC/CCu,BWa,RC(c) . . 225.00
89 PG,RC/CCu,BWa,RC(c) . . 225.00
90 PG,RC/CCu,GFx,RC(c) . . 225.00
91 RC/CCu,GFx,RC(c) 225.00
92 RC/CCu,GFx,RC(c) 225.00

Modern Comics #57
© Quality Comics Group

93 RC/CCu,GFx,RC(c) 225.00	12 Flaming Object to Eye (c) . . 750.00
94 RC/CCu,GFx,RC(c) 225.00	13 . . . . 200.00
95 RC/CCu,GFx,RC(c) 225.00	14 . . . . 200.00
96 RC/CCu,GFx,RC/CCu(c) . . . 225.00	15 The Coffin & Medusa's Head 225.00
97 RC/CCu,GFx,RC/CCu(c) . . . 225.00	16 Bondage(c) 225.00
98 RC/CCu,GFx,RC/CCu(c) . . . 225.00	17 . . . . 200.00
99 RC/CCu,GFx,JCo,RC/CCu(c) 225.00	18 BW,Bondage(c) 400.00

2 Gag Oriented Caricature . . . 25.00

100 GFx,JCo,RC/CCu(c) 225.00
101 GFx,JCo,RC/CCu(c) 225.00
102 GFx,JCo,WE,BWa,
RC/CCu(c) 250.00

MILT GROSS FUNNIES
Milt Gross, Inc.
August, 1947
1 Gag Oriented Caricature 50.00
2 Gag Oriented Caricature 45.00

MINUTE MAN
Fawcett Publications
Summer, 1941
1 V: The Nazis 1,300.00
2 V: The Mongol Horde 900.00
3 V: The Black Poet;Spr'42 . . 800.00

MIRACLE COMICS
Hillman Periodicals
February,1940
1 B:Sky Wizard,Master of Space,
Dash Dixon,Man of Might,Dusty
Doyle,Pinkie Parker, The Kid
Cop,K-7 Secret Agent,Scorpion
& Blandu,Jungle Queen . . 1,300.00
2 . . . . 700.00
3 B:Bill Colt,The Ghost Rider . 650.00
4 A:The Veiled Prophet,
Bullet Bob; Mar'41 . . . . . . 600.00

MISS CAIRO JONES
Croyden Publishers
1944
1 BO,Rep. Newspaper Strip . . 150.00

MR. ANTHONY'S
LOVE CLINIC
Hillman Periodicals
1945
1 Ph(c) 75.00
2 . . . . 50.00
3 . . . . 40.00
4 . . . . 40.00
5 Ph(c),Apr/May'50 . . . . 40.00

MR. MUSCLES
(see THING, THE)

MISTER MYSTERY
Media Publ./SPM Publ./
Aragon Publ.
September, 1951
1 HK,RA,Horror 550.00
2 RA,RA(c) 350.00
3 RA(c) 350.00
4 Bondage(c) 350.00
5 Lingerie(c) 300.00
6 Bondage(c) 350.00
7 BW,Bondage(c);The Brain
Bats of Venus 750.00
8 Lingerie(c) 300.00
9 HN 275.00
10 . . . . 275.00
11 BW,Robot Woman 500.00

MISTER RISK
(see HAND OF FATE)

Mister Universe #1
© Mr. Publ./Media Publ.

MISTER UNIVERSE
Mr. Publ./Media Publ./
Stanmore
July, 1951
1 . . . . 150.00
2 RA(c);Jungle That time Forgot 125.00
3 Marijuana Story 100.00
4 Mr. Universe Goes to War . . . 50.00
5 Mr. Universe Goes to War;
April, 1952 . . . . 60.00

MODERN COMICS
(see MILITARY COMICS)

MODERN LOVE
Tiny Tot Comics
(E.C. Comics)
June-July, 1949
1 Stolen Romance 450.00
2 JcR,AF(c),I Craved
Excitement 350.00
3 AF(c);Our Families Clashed 300.00
4 AF(c);I Was a B Girl 400.00
5 AF(c);Saved From Shame . 400.00
6 AF(c);The Love That
Might Have Been 400.00
7 AF(c);They Won't Let Me
Love Him 300.00
8 AF(c);Aug-Sept'50 . . . . 300.00

MOE & SHMOE COMICS
O.S. Publishing Co.
Spring, 1948
1 Gag Oriented Caricature . . . 35.00

MOLLY O'DAY
Avon Periodicals
February, 1945
1 GT;The Enchanted Dagger . 350.00

MONKEYSHINES COMICS
Publ. Specialists/Ace/
Summer, 1944
1 (fa),Several Short Features . . 50.00
2 (fa),Same Format Throughout
Entire Run 25.00
3 thru 16 Funny Animal . . . . @20.00
Ace
17 Funny Animal 20.00
18 thru 21 . . . . @15.00
Unity Publ.
22 (fa) 15.00
23 (fa) 15.00
24 (fa),AFa,AFa(c) 15.00
25 (fa) 15.00
26 (fa) 15.00
27 (fa),July, 1949 . . . . 15.00

MONSTER
Fiction House Magazines
1953
1 Dr. Drew 350.00
2 . . . . 275.00

MONSTER CRIME
COMICS
Hillman Periodicals
October, 1952
1 52 Pgs,15 Cent Cover Price   700.00

MONTE HALL
WESTERN
(see MARY MARVEL COMICS)

MONTY HALL OF
THE U.S. MARINES
Toby Press
August, 1951
1 B:Monty Hall,Pin-Up Pete;
(All Issues) 50.00
2 . . . . 30.00
3 thru 5 . . . . @25.00
6 . . . . 20.00
7 The Fireball Express 20.00
8 . . . . 20.00
9 . . . . 20.00
10 The Vial of Death 20.00
11 Monju Island Prison Break . . 20.00

MOON GIRL AND
THE PRINCE
E.C. Comics
Autumn, 1947
1 JCr(c),O:Moon Girl 650.00
2 JCr(c),Battle of the Congo . 350.00
3 . . . . 300.00
4 V: A Vampire 325.00
5 1st E.C. Horror-Zombie Terror 800.00
6 . . . . 400.00
7 O:Star;The Fient Who
Fights With Fire 400.00
8 True Crime Feature 400.00
Becomes:

GOLDEN AGE

A MOON, A GIRL ...ROMANCE
9 AF,Grl,AF(c),C:Moon Girl;
 Spanking Panels 500.00
10 AF,Grl,WW,AF(c),Suspicious
 of His Intentions 450.00
11 AF,Grl,WW,AF(c),Hearts
 Along the Ski Trail 450.00
12 AF,Grl,AF(c),
 March-April, 1950 . . . . 550.00

MOPSY
St. John Publishing Co.
February, 1948
1 Paper Dolls Enclosed 100.00
2 . . . . 55.00
3 . . . . 50.00
4 Paper Dolls Enclosed 50.00
5 Paper Dolls Enclosed 50.00
6 Paper Dolls Enclosed 50.00
7 . . . . 40.00
8 Paper Dolls Enclosed;
 Lingerie Panels 45.00
9 . . . . 40.00
10 . . . . 40.00

Mopsy #4 © St. John's Publishing Co.
11 . . . . 30.00
12 . . . . 30.00
13 Paper Dolls Enclosed 35.00
14 thru 18 . . . . @30.00
19 Lingerie(c);Paper
 Dolls Enclosed 35.00

MORTIE
Magazine Publishers
December, 1952
1 ...Mazie's Friend 30.00
2 . . . . 18.00
3 . . . . 15.00

MOTION PICTURE COMICS
Fawcett Publications
November, 1950
101 Ph(c),Monte Hale's-
 Vanishing Westerner 225.00
102 Ph(c),Rocky Lane's-Code
 of the Silver Sage 200.00
103 Ph(c),Rocky Lane's-Covered
 Wagon Raid 200.00
104 BP,Ph(c),Rocky Lane's-
 Vigilante Hideout 200.00
105 BP,Ph(c),Audie Murphy's-
 Red Badge of Courage 250.00
106 Ph(c),George Montgomery's-
 The Texas Rangers 200.00
107 Ph(c),Rocky Lane's-Frisco
 Tornado 200.00
108 Ph(c),John Derek's-Mask
 of the Avenger 150.00
109 Ph(c),Rocky Lane's-Rough
 Rider of Durango 200.00
110 GE,Ph(c), When Worlds
 Collide 700.00
111 Ph(c),Lash LaRue's-The
 Vanishing Outpost 225.00
112 Ph(c),Jay Silverheels'-
 Brave Warrior 125.00
113 KS,Ph(c),George Murphy's-
 Walk East on Beacon 100.00
114 Ph(c),George Montgomery's-
 Cripple Creek;Jan, 1953 . . . 100.00

MOTION PICTURES FUNNIES WEEKLY
1st Funnies Incorporated
1939
1 BEv,1st Sub-Mariner . . . 18,000.00
2 Cover Only 250.00
3 Cover Only 250.00
4 Cover Only 250.00

MOVIE CLASSICS
(NO #S)
Dell Publishing Co.
January, 1953
1 Around the World Under
 the Sea 30.00
2 Bambi 35.00
3 Battle of the Buldge 25.00
4 Ph(c),Beach Blanket Bingo . . 50.00
5 Ph(c),Bon Voyage 25.00
6 Castilian 30.00
7 Cat 20.00
8 Cheyenne Autumn 45.00
9 Ph(c),Circus World,
 John Wayne (c) 100.00
10 Ph(c),Countdown,J.Caan(c) . 30.00
11 Creature 50.00
12 Ph(c),David Ladd's Life Story 75.00
13 Ph(c),Die Monster Die 50.00
14 Dirty Dozen 40.00
15 Ph(c),Dr. Who & the Daleks 125.00
16 Dracula 40.00
17 El Dorado,J.WaynePh(c) . . . 125.00
18 Ensign Pulver 25.00
19 Frankenstein 40.00
20 Ph(c),Great Race 40.00
21 B.LancasterPh(c) 40.00
22 Hatari 65.00
23 Horizontal Lieutenant 25.00
24 Ph(c) Mr. Limpet 25.00
25 Jack the Giant Killer 60.00
26 Ph(c),Jason & the Argonauts 100.00
27 Lancelot & Guinevere 55.00
28 Lawrence 55.00
29 Lion of Sparta 25.00
30 Mad Monster Party 55.00
31 Magic Sword 45.00
32 Ph(c),Masque of Red Death . 40.00
33 Maya 35.00
34 McHale's Navy 40.00
35 Ph(c) Merrills' Marauders . . . 25.00
36 Ph(c),Mouse on the Moon . . 20.00
37 Mummy 40.00
38 Music Man 30.00
39 Ph(c),Naked Prey 50.00
40 Ph(c),Night of the Grizzly . . 35.00
41 None but the Brave 55.00
42 Ph(c),Operation Bikini 30.00
43 Operation Cross Bold 30.00
44 Prince & the Pauper 30.00
45 Raven,V.Price(c) 45.00
46 Ring of Bright Water 35.00
47 Runaway 20.00
48 Ph(c),Santa Claus Conquers
 the Martians 65.00
49 Ph(c),Six Black Horses 30.00
50 Sky Party 35.00
51 Smoky 25.00
52 Ph(c),Sons of Katie Elder . . 125.00
53 GE,Tales of Terror 30.00
54 Ph(c),3 Stooges meet
 Hercules 75.00
55 Tomb of Legeia 25.00
56 Treasure Island 25.00
57 Twice Told Tales(V.Price) . . . 35.00
58 Two on a Guillotine 25.00
59 Valley of Gwangi 45.00
60 War Gods of the Deep 20.00
61 War Wagon (John Wayne) . . 85.00
62 Who's Minding the Mint . . . 25.00
63 Wolfman 35.00
64 Ph(c),Zulu 30.00
65 . . . . 25.00

MOVIE COMICS
Fiction House Magazines
December, 1946
1 Big Town on(c) 450.00
2 MB,White Tie & Tails 325.00
3 MB,Andy Hardy Laugh Hit . 325.00
4 MB,Slave Girl 375.00

MOVIE LOVE
Famous Funnies Publications
February, 1950
1 Ph(c),Dick Powell(c) 100.00
2 Ph(c),Myrna Loy(c) 50.00
3 Ph(c),Cornell Wilde(c) 35.00
4 Ph(c),Paulette Goddard(c) . 35.00
5 Ph(c),Joan Fontaine(c) 35.00
6 Ph(c),Ricardo Montalban(c) . 35.00
7 Ph(c),Fred Astaire(c) 35.00
8 AW,FF,Ph(c),Corinne
 Calvert(c) 250.00
9 Ph(c),John Lund(c) 35.00
10 Ph(c),Mona Freeman(c) . . 275.00
11 Ph(c),James Mason(c) 35.00
12 Ph(c),Jerry Lewis &
 Dean Martin(c) 50.00
13 Ph(c),Ronald Reagan(c) . . . 150.00
14 Ph(c),Janet Leigh,Gene Kelly 40.00
15 Ph(c), ... 35.00
16 Ph(c),Angela Lansbury 60.00
17 FF,Ph(c),Leslie Caron 30.00
18 Ph(c),Cornel Wilde 30.00
19 Ph(c),John Derek 30.00
20 Ph(c),Debbie Reynolds 35.00
21 Ph(c),Patricia Medina 30.00
22 Ph(c),John Payne 30.00

MOVIE THRILLERS
Magazine Enterprises 1949
1 Ph(c),Burt Lancaster's-
 Rope of Sand 200.00

MR. MUSCLES
(see THING!, THE)

MUGGY-DOO, BOY CAT
Stanhall Publications
July, 1953

1	30.00
2 and 3	@20.00
4 January, 1954	20.00

MURDER, INCORPORATED
Fox Features Incorporated
January, 1948

1 For Adults Only-on(c)	350.00
2 For Adults Only-on(c);Male Bondage(c),Electrocution sty	275.00
3 Dutch Schultz-Beast of Evil	150.00
4 The Ray Hamilton Case, Lingerie(c)	150.00
5 thru 8	@150.00
9 Bathrobe (c)	165.00
9a Lingerie (c)	175.00
10	125.00
11	110.00
12	110.00
13	125.00
14 Bill Hale-King o/t Murderers	110.00
15	110.00
16(5),Second Series	90.00
17(2)	90.00
18(3), Bondage(c) w/Lingerie, August, 1951	125.00

MURDEROUS GANGSTERS
Avon Periodicals/Realistic
July, 1951

1 WW,Pretty Boy Floyd, Leggs Diamond	300.00
2 WW,Baby Face Nelson,Mad Dog Esposito	200.00
3 P(c),Tony & Bud Fenner, Jed Hawkins	175.00
4 EK(c),Murder By Needle-Drug Story, June, 1952	200.00

MUTINY
Aragon Magazines
October, 1954

1 AH(c),Stormy Tales of the Seven Seas	100.00
2 AH(c)	75.00
3 Bondage(c),February, '55 . . .	75.00

MY CONFESSIONS
(see WESTERN TRUE CRIME)

MY DATE COMICS
Hillman Periodicals
July, 1944

1 S&K,S&K (c), Teenage	225.00
2 S&K,DB,S&K(c)	150.00
3 S&K,DB,S&K(c)	150.00
4 S&K,DB,S&K(c)	150.00

MY DESIRE
Fox Features Syndicate
October, 1949

1 Intimate Confessions	100.00
2 WW,They Called Me Wayward	60.00

3 I Hid My Lover	40.00
4 WW, April, 1950	125.00

MY GREAT LOVE
Fox Features Syndicate
October, 1949

1 Reunion In a Shack	75.00
2 My Crazy Dreams	40.00
3 He Was Ashamed of Me . . .	35.00
4 My Two Wedding Rings;Apr'50	40.00

MY INTIMATE AFFAIR
Fox Features Syndicate
March, 1950

1 I Sold My Love	75.00
2 I Married a Jailbird;May'50 . .	45.00

MY LIFE
(see MEET CORLISS ARCHER)

MY LOVE AFFAIR
Fox Features Syndicate
July, 1949

1 Truck Driver's Sweetheart . .	75.00
2 My Dreadful Secret	50.00
3 WW,I'll Make Him Marry Me	100.00
4 WW,They Called Me Wild . .	100.00
5 WW,Beauty Was My Bait . .	100.00
6 WW,The Man Downstairs . .	100.00

MY LOVE MEMORIES
(see WOMEN OUTLAWS)

MY LOVE LIFE
(see TEGRA, JUNGLE EMPRESS)

MY LOVE STORY
Fox Features Syndicate
September, 1949

1 Men Gave Me Jewels	75.00
2 He Dared Me	50.00
3 WW,I Made Love a Plaything	100.00
4 WW,I Tried to Be Good . . .	100.00

© Fox Features Syndicate

My Private Life #16
© Fox Features Syndicate

MY PAST CONFESSIONS
(see WESTERN THRILLERS)

MY PRIVATE LIFE
Fox Features Syndicate
February, 1950

16 My Friendship Club Affair . . .	75.00
17 My Guilty Kisses;April'50 . .	50.00

MY SECRET
Superior Comics
August, 1949

1 True Love Stories	75.00
2 I Was Guilty of Being a Cheating Wife	50.00
3 Was I His Second Love?; . . .	50.00

Becomes:

OUR SECRET

4 JKa,She Loves Me,She Loves Me Not; November, 1949 . .	60.00
5	40.00
6	40.00
7 How Do You Fall In Love? . . .	45.00
8 His Kiss Tore At My Heart; June, 1950	40.00

MY SECRET AFFAIR
Hero Books
(Fox Features Syndicate)
December, 1949

1 WW,SHn,My Stormy Love Affair	125.00
2 WW,I Loved a Weakling	75.00
3 WW, April, 1950	100.00

MY SECRET LIFE
Fox Features Syndicate
July, 1949

22 I Loved More Than Once . . .	75.00
23 WW	100.00
24 Love Was a Habit	30.00
25	30.00

Becomes:

ROMEO TUBBS

26 WW,That Lovable Teen-ager	100.00

MY SECRET LOVE
(see PHANTOM LADY)

MY SECRET MARRIAGE
Superior Comics
May, 1953

1 I Was a Cheat	75.00
2	30.00
3 We Couldn't Wait	20.00
4	20.00
5	20.00
6	20.00
7 thru 23	@20.00
24 1956	20.00

MY SECRET ROMANCE
Hero Books
(Fox Features Syndicate)
January, 1950

1 WW,They Called Me 'That' Woman	85.00
2 WW,They Called Me Cheap .	75.00

GOLDEN AGE

MYSTERIES WEIRD AND STRANGE
Superior Comics/ Dynamic Publ.
May, 1953
1 The Stolen Brain 200.00
2 The Screaming Room, Atomic Bomb 125.00
3 The Avenging Corpse 100.00
4 Ghost on the Gallows 100.00
5 Horror a la Mode 100.00
6 Howling Horror 100.00
7 Demon in Disguise 100.00
8 The Devil's Birthmark 100.00
9 . . . . 100.00
10 . . . . 110.00
11 . . . . 100.00

MYSTERIOUS ADVENTURES
Story Comics
March, 1951
1 Wild Terror of the Vampire Flag 350.00
2 Terror of the Ghoul's Corpse 175.00
3 Terror of the Witche's Curse 150.00
4 The Little Coffin That Grew . 150.00
5 LC,Curse of the Jungle, Bondage(c) 165.00
6 LC,Ghostly Terror in the Cave 135.00
7 LC,Terror of the Ghostly Castle 250.00
8 Terror of the Flowers of Deat 250.00
9 The Ghostly Ghouls- Extreme Violence 200.00
10 Extreme Violence 150.00
11 The Trap of Terror 200.00
12 SHn,Vultures of Death- Extreme Violence 200.00
13 Extreme Violence 200.00
14 Horror of the Flame Thrower Extreme Violence 200.00
15 DW,Ghoul Crazy 250.00
16 Chilling Tales of Horror . . . 250.00
17 DW,Bride of the Dead 250.00
18 Extreme Violence 250.00

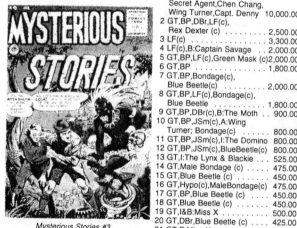

Mysterious Stories #3
© Premier Magazines

19 The Coffin 250.00
20 Horror o/t Avenging Corpse 250.00
21 Mother Ghoul's Nursery Tales, Bondage (c) 250.00
22 RA,Insane 150.00
23 RA,Extreme Violence 175.00
24 KS, ... 125.00
25 KS,August, 1955 . . . . 125.00

HORROR FROM THE TOMB
Premier Magazines
September, 1954
1 AT,GWb,The Corpse Returns 225.00
Becomes:
MYSTERIOUS STORIES
2 GWb(c),Eternal Life 250.00
3 GWb,The Witch Doctor . . . 175.00
4 That's the Spirit 150.00
5 King Barbarossa 150.00
6 GWb,Strangers in the Night . 175.00
7 KS,The Pipes of Pan;Dec'55 150.00

MYSTERIOUS TRAVELER COMICS
Trans-World Publications
November, 1948
1 BP,BP(c),Five Miles Down . . 400.00

MYSTERY COMICS
William H. Wise & Co.
1944
1 AS(c),B:Brad Spencer-Wonderman, King of Futeria,The Magnet, Zudo-Jungle Boy,The Silver Knight 800.00
2 AS(c),Bondage (c) 550.00
3 AS(c),Robot(c),LanceLewis,B 500.00
4 AS(c),E:All Features, KKK Type(c) 500.00

MYSTERY MEN COMICS
Fox Features Syndicate
August, 1939
1 GT,DBr,LF(c),Bondage(c);I:Blue Beetle,Green Mask,Rex Dexter of Mars,Zanzibar,Lt.Drake,D-13 Secret Agent,Chen Chang, Wing Turner,Capt. Denny 10,000.00
2 GT,BP,DBr,LF(c), Rex Dexter (c) 2,500.00
3 LF(c) 3,300.00
4 LF(c),B:Captain Savage . . 2,000.00
5 GT,BP,LF(c),Green Mask (c) 2,000.00
6 GT,BP 1,800.00
7 GT,BP,Bondage(c), Blue Beetle(c) 2,000.00
8 GT,BP,LF(c),Bondage(c), Blue Beetle 1,800.00
9 GT,BP,DBr(c),B:The Moth . . 900.00
10 GT,BP,JSm(c),A:Wing Turner; Bondage(c) 800.00
11 GT,BP,JSm(c),I:The Domino 800.00
12 GT,BP,JSm(c),BlueBeetle(c) 800.00
13 GT,I:The Lynx & Blackie . . 525.00
14 GT,Male Bondage (c) 475.00
15 GT,Blue Beetle (c) 450.00
16 GT,Hypo(c),MaleBondage(c) 475.00
17 GT,BP,Blue Beetle (c) 450.00
18 GT,Blue Beetle (c) 450.00
19 GT,I&B:Miss X 500.00
20 GT,DBr,Blue Beetle (c) . . . 425.00
21 GT,E:Miss X 425.00

Mystery Men Comics #10
© Fox Features Syndicate

22 GT,CCu(c),Blue Beetle (c) . 425.00
23 GT,Blue Beetle (c) 425.00
24 GT,BP,DBr, Blue Beetle (c) . 425.00
25 GT,Bondage(c);
A:Private O'Hara 450.00
26 GT,Bondage(c);B:The Wraith 450.00
27 GT,Bondage(c),BlueBeetle(c) 450.00
28 GT,Bondage(c);Satan's Private Needlewoman 450.00
29 GT,Bondage(c),Blue Beetle (c) 450.00
30 Holiday of Death 425.00
31 Bondage(c);Feb'42 . . . . 450.00

MY STORY
(see ZAGO, JUNGLE PRINCE)

NATIONAL COMICS
Comics Magazines (Quality Comics Group)
July, 1940
1 GT,HcK,LF(c),B:Uncle Sam,Wonder Boy,Merlin the Magician,Cyclone, Kid Patrol,Sally O'Neil-Police-woman, Pen Miller,Prop Powers, Paul Bunyan . . 4,500.00
2 WE,GT,HcK,LF&RC(c) . . . 1,750.00
3 GT,HcK,WE&RC(c) 1,200.00
4 GT,HcK,LF&RC(c),E:Cyclone; Torpedo Islands of Death . 1,000.00
5 GT,LF&RC(c),B:Quicksilver; O:Uncle Sam 1,100.00
6 GT,LF&RC(c) 1,000.00
7 GT,LF&RC(c) 1,100.00
8 GT,LF&RC(c) 1,000.00
9 JCo,LF&RC(c) 1,000.00
10 RC,JCo,LF&RC(c) 1,000.00
11 RC,JCo,LF&RC(c) 1,000.00
12 RC,JCo,LF&RC(c) 750.00
13 RC,JCo,LF,LF&RC(c) 650.00
14 RC,JCo,LF,PG,LF&RC(c) . . 650.00
15 RC,JCo,LF,PG,LF&RC(c) . . 650.00
16 RC,JCo,LF,PG,LF&RC(c) . . 650.00
17 RC,JCo,LF,PG,LF&RC(c) . . 475.00
18 JCo,LF,PG,LF&RC(c), Pearl Harbor 850.00
19 JCo,LF,PG,RC(c),The Black

Fog Mystery	475.00
20 JCo,LF,PG,LF&RC(c)	475.00
21 LF,JCo,PG,LF(c)	475.00
22 JCo,LF,PG,FG,GFx,LF(c),	
E:Jack & Jill,Pen Miller,	
Paul Bunyan	475.00
23 JCo,PG,FG,GFx,AMc,LF	
& GFx(c),B:The Unknown,	
Destroyer 171	500.00
24 JCo,PG,RC,AMc,FG,	
GFx,RC(c)	475.00
25 AMc,RC,JCo,PG,FG,	
GFx,RC(c)	350.00
26 AMc,Jco,RC,PG,RC(c),	
E:Prop Powers,WonderBoy	350.00
27 JCo,AMc	350.00
28 JCo,AMc	350.00
29 JCo,O:The Unknown;U.Sam	
V:Dr. Dirge	375.00
30 JCo,RC(c)	365.00
31 JCo,RC(c)	350.00
32 JCo,RC(c)	350.00
33 JCo,GFx,RC(c),B:Chic Carter;	
U.Sam V:Boss Spring	350.00

National Comics #57
© Comics Mag./Quality Comics Group

34 JCo,GFx,U.Sam V:Big John	
Fales	350.00
35 JCo,GFx,E:Kid Patrol	250.00
36 JCo	250.00
37 JCo,FG,A:The Vagabond	250.00
38 JCo,FG,Boat of the Dead	250.00
39 JCo,FG,Hitler(c);U.Sam	
V:The Black Market	250.00
40 JCo,FG,U.Sam V:The	
Syndicate of Crime	175.00
41 JCo,FG	175.00
42 JCo,FG,JCo(c),B:The Barker	150.00
43 JCo,FG,JCo(c)	150.00
44 JCo,FG	150.00
45 JCo,FG,E:Merlin the Magician	150.00
46 JCo,JCo(c),Murder is no Joke	150.00
47 JCo,JCo(c),E:Chic Carter	150.00
48 JCo,O:The Whistler	150.00
49 JCo,JCo(c),A Corpse	
for a Cannonball	150.00
50 JCo,JCo(c),V:Rocks Myzer	150.00
51 JCo,BWa,JCo(c),	
A:Sally O'Neil	200.00
52 JCo,A Carnival of Laughs	125.00

53 PG,V:Scramolo	125.00
54 PG,V:Raz-Ma-Taz	125.00
55 JCo,AMc,V:The Hawk	125.00
56 GFx,JCo,AMc,V:The Grifter	125.00
57 GFX,JCo,AMc,V:Witch Doctor	125.00
58 GFz,JCo,AMc,Talking Animals	125.00
59 GFx,JCo,AMc,V:The Birdman	125.00
60 GFx,JCo,AMc,V:Big Ed Grew	125.00
61 GFx,AMc,Trouble Comes in	
Small Packages	90.00
62 GFx,AMc,V:Crocodile Man	90.00
63 GFx,AMc,V:Bearded Lady	90.00
64 GFx,V:The Human Fly	90.00
65 GFx,GFx(c)V:The King	90.00
66 GFx,GFx(c)V:THe Man Who	
Hates the Circus	90.00
67 GFx,Gfx(c),A:Quicksilver;	
V:Ali Ben Riff Raff	90.00
68 GFx,GFx(c),V:Leo the LionMan	90.00
69 GFx,Gfx(c),A:Percy the	
Powerful	90.00
70 GFx,GFx(c),Barker Tires	
of the Big Top	90.00
71 PG,GFx(c),V:SpellbinderSmith	90.00
72 PG,GFx(c),The Oldest Man	
in the World	90.00
73 PG,GFx(c),V:A CountrySlicker	90.00
74 PG,GFx(c),V:Snake Oil Sam	90.00
75 PG,GFx(c),Barker Breaks the	
Bank at Monte Marlo;Nov'49	90.00

NEBBS, THE
Dell Publishing Co.
1941

1 rep.	60.00

NEGRO ROMANCE
Fawcett Publications
June, 1950

1 GE,Ph(c), Love's Decoy	900.00
2 GE,Ph(c), A Tragic Vow	650.00
3 GE,Ph(c), My Love	
Betrayed Me	650.00

Charlton Comics

4 Rep.FawcettEd.#2;May,1955	500.00

NEW ROMANCES
Standard Comics
May, 1951

5 Ph(c), The Blame I Bore	75.00
6 Ph(c), No Wife Was I	40.00
7 Ph(c), My Runaway Heart,	
Ray Miland	35.00
8 Ph(c)	35.00
9 Ph(c)	35.00
10 ATh,Ph(c)	50.00
11 ATh,Ph(c) of Elizabeth Taylor	80.00
12 Ph(c)	25.00
13 Ph(c)	25.00
14 ATh,Ph(c)	40.00
15 Ph(c)	25.00
16 ATh,Ph(c)	40.00
17 Ath	40.00
18 and 19	@25.00
20 GT,	30.00
21 April, 1954	25.00

NICKEL COMICS
Dell Publishing Co.
1938

1 Bobby & Chip	500.00

NICKEL COMICS
Fawcett Publications
May, 1940

1 JaB(c),O&I: Bulletman	3,200.00
2 JaB(c),	950.00
3 JaB(c),	700.00
4 JaB(c), B: Red Gaucho	650.00
5 CCB(c),Bondage(c)	650.00
6 and 7 CCB(c)	@550.00
8 CCB(c),August 23, 1940,	
World's Fair	600.00

NIGHTMARE
(see WEIRD HORRORS)

NIGHTMARE
Ziff-Davis Publishing Co.

1 EK,GT,P(c),The Corpse That	
Wouldn't Stay Dead	375.00
2 EK,P(c),Vampire Mermaid	300.00

St. John Publishing Co.

3 EK,P(c),The Quivering Brain	200.00
4 P(c),1953	175.00

NORTHWEST MOUNTIES
Jubilee Publications/
St. John Publ. Co.
October, 1948

1 MB,BLb(c),Rose of the Yukon	350.00
2 MB,BLb(c),A:Ventrilo	275.00
3 MB, Bondage(c)	250.00
4 MB(c),A:Blue Monk,July'49	250.00

NURSERY RHYMES
Ziff-Davis Publishing Co.
1950

1 How John Came Clean	75.00
2 The Old Woman Who	
Lived in a Shoe	50.00

NUTS!
Premere Comics Group
March, 1954

1	200.00
2	150.00
3 Mention of "Reefers"	165.00
4	150.00
5 Captain Marvel Spoof;Nov.'54	150.00

NUTTY COMICS
Fawcett Publications
Winter, 1946

1 (fa),F:Capt. Kid,Richard Richard,	
Joe Miller...Among others	100.00

NUTTY LIFE
(see PHANTOM LADY)

NYOKA THE
JUNGLE GIRL
Fawcett Publications
Winter, 1945

1 Bondage(c);Partial Ph(c) of	
Kay Aldridge as Nyoka	450.00
2	225.00
3	225.00
4 Bondage(c)	225.00
5 Barbacosi Madness;	
Bondage(c)	225.00
6	175.00

Nyoka the Jungle Girl #14
© Fawcett Publications

7 North Pole Jungle;Bondage(c) 165.00
8 Bondage(c) 165.00
9 . . . . 150.00
10 . . . . 150.00
11 Danger! Death! in an
  Unexplored Jungle 125.00
12 . . . . 90.00
13 The Human Leopards 125.00
14 The Mad Witch Doctor;
  Bondage(c) 125.00
15 Sacred Goat of Kristan 125.00
16 BK,The Vultures of Kalahari 150.00
17 BK 150.00
18 BK,The Art of Murder 150.00
19 The Elephant Battle 150.00
20 Explosive Volcano Action . . 150.00
21 . . . . 75.00
22 The Weird Monsters 75.00
23 Danger in Duplicate 75.00
24 The Human Jaguar;
  Bondage(c) 80.00
25 Hand Colored Ph(c) 60.00
26 A Jungle Stampede 60.00
27 Adventure Laden 60.00
28 The Human Statues of
  the Jungle 60.00
29 Ph(c) 60.00
30 Ph(c) 60.00
31 thru 40 Ph(c) . . . . @50.00
41 thru 50 Ph(c) . . . . @40.00
51 thru 59 Ph(c) . . . . @35.00
60 Ph(c) 30.00
61 Ph(c),The Sacred Sword of
  the Jungle 30.00
62 & 63 Ph(c) . . . . @30.00
64 Ph(c), The Jungle Idol 30.00
65 Ph(c) 30.00
66 Ph(c) 30.00
67 Ph(c), The Sky Man 30.00
68 thru 74 Ph(c) . . . . @30.00
75 Ph(c), The Jungle Myth
  of Terror 30.00
76 Ph(c) 30.00
77 Ph(c),The Phantoms of the
  Elephant Graveyard;Jun'53 . . 30.00

OAKY DOAKS
Eastern Color Printing Co.
July, 1942
1 Humor Oriented 225.00

OH, BROTHER!
Stanhall Publications
January, 1953
1 Bill Williams-a 25.00
2 thru 5 . . . . @15.00

OK COMICS
United Features Syndicate
July, 1940
1 B:Pal Peyton,Little Giant, Phantom
  Knight,Sunset Smith,Teller Twins,
  Don Ramon, Jerrry Sly,Kip Jaxon,
  Leatherneck,Ulysses 600.00
2 October, 1940 . . . . 575.00

100 PAGES OF COMICS
Dell Publishing Co.
1937
101 Alley Oop,OG,Wash Tubbs,
  Tom Mix,Dan Dunn 1,200.00

ON THE AIR
NBC Network Comics
1947
1 Giveaway, no cover 175.00

ON THE SPOT
Fawcett Publications
Autumn, 1948
N# Bondage(c),PrettyBoyFloyd 200.00

Operation Peril #3
© American Comics Group/Michel Publ.

OPERATION PERIL
American Comics Group
(Michel Publ.)
October-November, 1950
1 LSt,OW,OW(c),B:TyphoonTyler,
  DannyDanger,TimeTravellers 250.00
2 OW,OW(c) 150.00
3 OW,OW(c),Horror 125.00

4 OW,OW(c), Flying Saucers . 125.00
5 OW,OW(c), Science Fiction . 125.00
6 OW, Tyr. Rex 125.00
7 OW,OW(c) 100.00
8 OW,OW(c) 100.00
9 OW,OW(c) 100.00
10 OW,OW(c) 100.00
11 OW,OW(c), War 100.00
12 OW,OW(c),E:Time Travellers 100.00
13 OW,OW(c),War Stories 50.00
14 OW,OW(c),War Stories 50.00
15 OW,OW(c),War Stories 50.00
16 OW,OW(c),April-May,1953,
  War Stories 50.00

OUR FLAG COMICS
Ace Magazines
August, 1941
1 MA,JM,B:Capt.Victory,Unknown
  Soldier,The Three Cheers 1,700.00
2 JM,JM(c),O:The Flag 900.00
3 Tank Battle (c) 700.00
4 MA 700.00
5 I:Mr. Risk;April, 1942,
  Male Bondage 725.00

OUR GANG COMICS
Dell Publishing Co.
September-October, 1942
1 WK,Barney Bear, Tom & Jerry 900.00
2 WK 500.00
3 WK,Benny Burro 350.00
4 WK 350.00
5 WK 350.00
6 WK 500.00
7 WK 250.00
8 WK,CB,Benny Burro 600.00
9 WK,CB,Benny Burro 550.00
10 WK,CB,Benny Burro 400.00
11 WK,I:Benny Bear 550.00
12 thru 20 WK . . . . @250.00
21 thru 29 WK . . . . @175.00
30 WK,Christmas(c) 150.00
31 thru 34 WK . . . . @125.00
35 WK,CB 125.00
36 WK,CB 125.00
37 thru 40 WK . . . . @60.00
41 thru 50 WK . . . . @50.00
51 thru 56 WK . . . . @35.00
57 . . . . 30.00
58 Our Gang 30.00
59 Our Gang 30.00
Becomes:

TOM AND JERRY
July, 1949
60 . . . . 60.00
61 . . . . 50.00
62 . . . . 45.00
63 . . . . 45.00
64 . . . . 45.00
65 . . . . 45.00
66 Christmas (c) 50.00
67 thru 70 . . . . @45.00
71 thru 76 . . . . @35.00
77 Christmas (c) 40.00
78 thru 80 . . . . @35.00
81 thru 89 . . . . @30.00
90 Christmas (c) 35.00
91 thru 99 . . . . @30.00
100 . . . . 35.00
101 thru 120 . . . . @25.00
121 thru 150 . . . . @20.00
151 thru 212 . . . . @12.00

GOLDEN AGE

OUR SECRET
(see MY SECRET)

OUTLAWS
D.S. Publishing Co.
February-March, 1948

1 HcK,Western Crime Stories	225.00
2 Grl,Doc Dawson's Dilema	200.00
3 Cougar City Cleanup	100.00
4 JO,Death Stakes A Claim	125.00
5 RJ,RJ(c),Man Who Wanted Mexico	100.00
6 AMc,RJ,RJ(c),The Ghosts of	

Outlaws #1 © D.S. Publishing Co.

Crackerbox Hill	100.00
7 Grl,Dynamite For Boss Cavitt	150.00
8 Grl,The Gun & the Pen	150.00
9 FF,Shoot to Kill;June-July, 1949	325.00

WHITE RIDER AND SUPER HORSE
Star Publications
September, 1950

1 LbC(c)	75.00
2 LbC(c)	30.00
3 LbC(c)	30.00
4 LbC(c)	35.00
5 LbC(c),Stampede of Hard Riding Thrills	35.00
6 LbC(c),Drums of the Sioux	35.00

Becomes:

INDIAN WARRIORS

7 LbC(c),Winter on the Great Plains	50.00
8 LbC(c)	30.00

Becomes:

WESTERN CRIME CASES

9 LbC(c),The Card Sharp Killer	60.00

Becomes:

OUTLAWS, THE

10 LbC(c),Federated Express	75.00
11 LbC(c),Frontier Terror!!!	50.00
12 LbC(c),Ruthless Killer!!!	50.00
13 LbC(c),The Grim Avengers	50.00
14 AF,JKa,LbC(c),Trouble in	

Dark Canyon,April'54	50.00

OUT OF THE NIGHT
American Comics Group/ Best Synd. Feature
February-March, 1952

1 AW	500.00
2 AW	400.00
3	175.00
4 AW	325.00
5	175.00
6 The Ghoul's Revenge	175.00
7	175.00
8 The Frozen Ghost	175.00
9 Death Has Wings, Science Fiction	175.00
10 Ship of Death	175.00
11	150.00
12 Music for the Dead	150.00
13 HN,From the Bottom of the Well	150.00
14 Out of the Screen	150.00
15 The Little Furry Thing	125.00
16 Nightmare From the Past	125.00
17 The Terror of the Labyrinth	125.00

Becomes:

HOODED HORSEMAN

18 B: The Hooded Horseman	75.00
19 The Horseman's Strangest Adventure	100.00
20 OW,O:Johnny Injun	65.00
21 OW,OW(c)	50.00
22 OW	50.00
23	50.00
24	50.00
25	50.00
26 O&I:Cowboy Sahib	70.00
27 January-February, 1953	60.00

OUT OF THE SHADOWS
Visual Editions (Standard Comics)
July, 1952

5 ATh,GT,The Shoremouth Horror	325.00
6 ATh,JKz,Salesman of Death	225.00
7 JK,Plant of Death	150.00
8 Mask of Death	125.00
9 RC,Till Death Do Us Part	150.00
10 MS,We Vowed,Till Death Do Us Part	100.00
11 ATh,Fountain of Fear	150.00
12 ATh,Hand of Death	225.00
13 MS,The Cannibal	175.00
14 ATh,The Werewolf, August, 1954	185.00

OXYDOL-DREFT
Giveaways
1950
The Set is More Valuable if the Original Envelope is Present

1 L'il Abner	75.00
2 Daisy Mae	75.00
3 Shmoo	80.00
4 AW&FF(c),John Wayne	135.00
5 Archie	65.00
6 Terry Toons Comics	75.00

OZZIE AND BABS
Fawcett Publications
Winter, 1946

1 Humor Oriented, Teenage	45.00

2 Humor Oriented	20.00
3 Humor Oriented	15.00
4 Humor Oriented	15.00
5 Humor Oriented	15.00
6 Humor Oriented	15.00
7 Humor Oriented	15.00
8 Humor Oriented	15.00
9 Humor Oriented	15.00
10 Humor Oriented	15.00
11 Humor Oriented	15.00
12 Humor Oriented	15.00
13 Humor Oriented;1949	15.00

PAGEANT OF COMICS
St. John Publishing Co.
September, 1947

1 Rep. Mopsy	75.00
2 Rep. Jane Arden,Crime Reporter	75.00

PANHANDLE PETE AND JENNIFER
J. Charles Lave Publishing Co.
July, 1951

1 (fa)	40.00
2 (fa)	30.00
3 (fa),November'51	30.00

Panic #10 © E.C. Comics

PANIC
Tiny Tot Publications (E.C. Comics)
March, 1954
"Humor in a Jugular Vein"

1 BE,JKa,JO,JDa,AF(c)	200.00
2 BE,JO,WW,JDa,A:Bomb	125.00
3 BE,JO,BW,WW,JDa,AF(c)	110.00
4 BE,JO,WW,JDa,BW(c), Infinity(c)	110.00
5 BE,JO,WW,JDa,AF(c)	90.00
6 BE,JO,WW,JDa,Blank (c)	90.00
7 BE,JO,WW,JDa	90.00
8 BE,JO,WW,JDa,Eye Chart (c)	90.00
9 BE,JO,WW,JDa,Ph(c), Confidential(c)	90.00
10 BE,JDa, Postal Package(c)	90.00
11 BE,WW,JDa,Wheaties parody	

All comics prices listed are for *Near Mint* condition.

as Weedies (c) 90.00
12 BE,WW,JDa,JDa(c);
    December-January 1955-56 110.00

PARAMOUNT ANIMATED COMICS
Family Publications
(Harvey Publ.) June, 1953
1 (fa),B:Baby Herman & Katnip,
    Baby Huey,Buzzy the Crow   110.00
2 (fa) 60.00
3 (fa) 45.00
4 (fa) 45.00
5 (fa) 45.00
6 (fa) 45.00
7 (fa), Baby Huey (c) 120.00
8 (fa), Baby Huey (c) 50.00
9 (fa), Infinity(c),Baby Huey (c) . 50.00
10 thru 21 (fa),Baby Huey(c) . @30.00
22 (fa), July, 1956, Baby Huey (c) 30.00

PAROLE BREAKERS
Avon Periodicals/Realistic
December, 1951
1 P(c),Hellen Willis,Gun
    Crazed Gun Moll 300.00
2 JKu,P(c),Vinnie Sherwood,
    The Racket King 200.00
3 EK(c),John "Slicer" Berry,
    Hatcheman of Crime;
    July,1952 . . . . 175.00

PATCHES
Rural Home Publ./
Patches Publ.
March-April, 1945
1 LbC(c),Imagination In Bed(c) 225.00
2 Dance (c) 100.00
3 Rocking Horse (c) 75.00
4 Music Band (c) 75.00
5 LbC(c),A:Danny Kaye,Football 125.00
6 A: Jackie Kelk 75.00
7 A: Hopalong Cassidy 125.00
8 A: Smiley Burnettte 75.00
9 BK,A: Senator Claghorn 75.00
10 A: Jack Carson 75.00
11 A: Red Skeleton; Dec'47 . . . 100.00

PAWNEE BILL
Story Comics
Feb.–July, 1951
1 A:Bat Masterson,Wyatt Earp,
    Indian Massacre
    at Devil's Gulch 55.00
2 Blood in Coffin Canyon 35.00
3 LC,O:Golden Warrior,Fiery
    Arrows at Apache Pass; 35.00

PAY-OFF
D.S. Publishing Co.
July-Aug., 1948–March-April, 1949
1 . . . . 150.00
2 The Pennsylvania Blue-Beard 100.00
3 The Forgetful Forger 75.00
4 RJ(c),Lady and the Jewels . . 75.00
5 The Beautiful Embezzeler . . . 75.00

PEDRO
Fox Features Syndicate
January, 1950
1 WW,WW(c),Humor Oriented 165.00
2 August, 1950 . . . . 110.00

PENNY
Avon Publications
1947
1 The Slickest Chick of 'em All   60.00
2 . . . . 30.00
3 America's Teen-age
    Sweetheart 30.00
4 . . . . 30.00
5 . . . . 30.00
6 Perry Como Ph(c),September-
    October, 1949 . . . . 35.00

Pep Comics #46
© MJL Magazines/Archie Publ.

PEP COMICS
MJL Magazines/
Archie Publications
January, 1940
1 IN,JCo,MMe,IN(c),I:Shield,
    O:Comet,Queen of Diamonds,
    B:The Rocket,Press Guardian,
    Sergeant Boyle Chang,Bently
    of Scotland Yard 7,000.00
2 CBi,JCo,IN,IN(c),O:Rocket . 1,700.00
3 JCo,IN,IN(c),Shield (c) 1,200.00
4 Cbi,JCo,MMe,IN,IN(c),
    C:Wizard(not Gareb) 900.00
5 Cbi,JCo,MMe,IN,IN(c),
    C:Wizard 900.00
6 IN,IN(c), Shield (c) 750.00
7 IN,IN(c),Bondage(c),Shield(c) 750.00
8 JCo,IN, Shield (c) 725.00
9 IN, Shield (c) 725.00
10 IN,IN(c), Shield (c) 725.00
11 MMe,IN,IN(c),I:Dusty,
    Boy Detective 725.00
12 IN,IN(c),O:Fireball
    Bondage(c), E:Rocket,
    Queen of Diamonds 1,000.00
13 IN,IN(c),Bondage(c) 625.00
14 IN,IN(c) 600.00
15 IN,Bondage(c) 625.00
16 IN,O:Madam Satan 1,000.00
17 IN,IN(c),O:Hangman,
    D:Comet 2,700.00
18 IN,IN(c),Bondage(c) 600.00
19 IN 575.00
20 IN,IN(c),E:Fireball 575.00
21 IN,IN(c),Bondage(c),

E: Madam Satan 600.00
22 IN,IN(c)I:Archie,
    Jughead, Betty 9,200.00
23 IN,IN(c) 1,000.00
24 IN,IN(c) 900.00
25 IN,IN(c) 900.00
26 IN,IN(c),I:Veronica 1,200.00
27 IN,IN(c),Bill of Rights (c) . . . 700.00
28 IN,IN(c), V:Capt. Swastika . 700.00
29 ASH (c) 700.00
30 B:Capt.Commando 700.00
31 Bondage(c) 700.00
32 Bondage(c) 550.00
33 . . . . 500.00
34 Bondage(c) 550.00
35 . . . . 500.00
36 1st Archie(c) 1,200.00
37 Bondage(c) 425.00
38 ASH(c) 400.00
39 ASH(c), Human Shield 400.00
40 . . . . 400.00
41 2nd Archie; I:Jughead 275.00
42 F:Archie & Jughead 250.00
43 F:Archie & Jughead 250.00
44 . . . . 250.00
45 . . . . 250.00
46 . . . . 250.00
47 E:Hangman,Infinity(c) 250.00
48 B:Black Hood 250.00
49 . . . . 250.00
50 . . . . 250.00
51 . . . . 200.00
52 B:Suzie 200.00
53 . . . . 200.00
54 E:Captain Commando 200.00
55 . . . . 200.00
56 thru 58 . . . . @175.00
59 E:Suzie 175.00
60 B:Katy Keene 175.00
61 . . . . 150.00

Pep Comics #50
© MJL Magazines/Archie Publ.

62 I L'il Jinx 150.00
63 . . . . 150.00
64 . . . . 150.00
65 E:Shield 150.00
66 thru 71 . . . . @100.00
72 thru 80 . . . . @85.00
81 thru 90 . . . . @65.00
91 thru 99 . . . . @50.00

100	85.00
101 thru 110	@40.00
111 thru 120	@35.00
121 thru 130	@30.00
131 thru 140	@25.00
141 thru 150	@20.00
151 thru 160, A:Super Heroes	@18.00
161 thru 200	@10.00
201 thru 250	@5.00
251 thru 300	@5.00
301 thru 350	@4.00
351 thru 411	@3.00

Perfect Crime #31
© Cross Publications

PERFECT CRIME, THE
Cross Publications
October, 1949

1 BP,DW	200.00
2 BP	125.00
3	100.00
4 BP	100.00
5 DW	100.00
6	100.00
7 B:Steve Duncan	100.00
8 Drug Story	125.00
9	100.00
10	100.00
11 Bondage (c)	125.00
12	75.00
13	75.00
14 Poisoning (c)	75.00
15 "The Most Terrible Menace", Drug	100.00
16	75.00
17	75.00
18 Drug (c)	125.00
19	75.00
20 thru 25	@50.00
26 Drug w/ Hypodermic (c)	150.00
27	75.00
28	75.00
29	75.00
30 E:Steve Duncan, Rope Strangulation (c)	125.00
31	60.00
32	60.00
33	60.00

PERFECT LOVE
Approved Comics(Ziff-Davis)/
St. John Publ. Co.
August-September, 1951

1 (10),P(c),Our Kiss was a Prelude to Love Adrift	125.00
2	75.00
3 P(c)	50.00
4	50.00
5	50.00
6	50.00
7	50.00
8 EK	55.00
9 EK,P(c)	40.00
10 Ph(c), Dec '53	40.00

PERSONAL LOVE
Famous Funnies
January, 1950

1 Ph(c) Are You in Love	100.00
2 Ph(c) Serenade for Suzette Mario Lanzo	50.00
3 Ph(c)	40.00
4 Ph(c)	40.00
5 Ph(c)	40.00
6 Ph(c) Be Mine Forever	45.00
7 Ph(c) You'll Always Be Mine, Robert Walker	45.00
8 EK,Ph(c),Esther Williams & Howard Keel	50.00
9 EK,Ph(c),Debra Paget & Louis Jordan	50.00
10 Ph(c),Loretta Young Joseph Cotton	45.00
11 ATh, Ph(c),Gene Tierney & Glenn Ford	75.00
12 Ph(c) Jane Greer & William Lundigan	40.00
13 Ph(c) Debra Paget & Louis Jordan	35.00
14 Ph(c) Kirk Douglas & Patrice Wymore	50.00
15 Ph(c) Dale Robertson & Joanne Dru	35.00
16 Ph(c) Take Back Your Love	35.00
17 Ph(c) My Cruel Deception	35.00
18 Ph(c) Gregory Peck & Susan Hayward	45.00
19 Ph(c) Anthony Quinn	45.00
20 Ph(c) The Couple in the Next Apartment, Bob Wagner	40.00
21 Ph(c) I'll Make You Care	35.00
22 Ph(c) Doorway To Heartbreak	35.00
23 Ph(c) SaveMe from that Man	35.00
24 FF, Ph(c) Tyrone Power	300.00
25 FF, Ph(c) The Dark Light	300.00
26 Ph(c) Love Needs A Break	35.00
27 FF, Ph(c) Champ or Chump?	300.00
28 FF, Ph(c) A Past to Forget	300.00
29 Ph(c) Charlton Heston	45.00
30 Ph(c) The Lady is Lost	35.00
31 Ph(c) Marlon Brando	60.00
32 FF, Ph(c) The Torment, Kirk Douglas	350.00
33 Ph(c) June ,1955	35.00

PETER COTTONTAIL
Key Publications
January, 1954

1 No 3-D (fa)	40.00
1 Feb '54 3-D (fa)	100.00
2 Rep of 3-D #1,not in 3-D	30.00

PETER PAUL'S 4 IN 1 JUMBO COMIC BOOK
Capitol Stories
1953

1 F: Racket Squad in Action, Space Adventures,Crime & Justice,Space Western	300.00

PETER PENNY AND HIS MAGIC DOLLAR
American Bakers Association
1947

1 History from Colonial America to the 1950's	125.00
2	75.00

PETER RABBIT
Avon Periodicals
1947

1 H. Cady art	225.00
2 H. Cady art	175.00
3 H. Cady art	150.00
4 H. Cady art	150.00
5 H. Cady art	150.00
6 H. Cady art	150.00
7 thru 10	@30.00
11	15.00

KRAZY LIFE
Fox Features Syndicate
1945

1 (fa)	55.00

Becomes:

NUTTY LIFE

2 (fa)	45.00

Becomes:

WOTALIFE
Fox Features Synd./
Green Publ.
August-September, 1946

3 (fa)B:L'il Pan,Cosmo Cat	35.00
4	25.00
5 thru 11	@20.00
12 July, 1947	20.00

Becomes:

Phantom Lady #17
© Fox Features Syndicate

GOLDEN AGE

PHANTOM LADY
Fox Features Syndicate
August, 1947
13(#1) MB,MB(c) Knights of
  the Crooked Cross 3,000.00
14(#2) MB,MB(c) Scoundrels
  and Scandals 1,800.00
15 MB,MB(c) The Meanest
  Crook In the World 1,700.00
16 MB,MB(c) Claa Peete The
  Beautiful Beast, Negligee . 1,700.00
17 MB.MB(c) The Soda Mint
  Killer, Bondage (c) 4,200.00
18 MB,MB(c) The Case of
  Irene Shroeder 1,300.00
19 MB,MB(c) The Case of
  the Murderous Model ... 1,300.00
20 MB,MB(c) Ace of Spades . 1,000.00
21 MB,MB(c) 1,000.00
22 MB,JKa 1,000.00
23 MB,JKa Bondage (c) 1,100.00
Becomes:

MY LOVE SECRET
24 JKa, My Love Was For Sale . 90.00
25 Second Hand Love 50.00
26 WW I Wanted Both Men 100.00
27 I Was a Love Cheat 40.00
28 WW, I Gave Him Love 100.00
29 .... 40.00
30 Ph(c) 40.00

LINDA
Ajax/Farrell
April-May, 1954
1 .... 75.00
2 Lingerie section 55.00
3 .... 40.00
4 October-November,1954 ... 40.00
Becomes:

PHANTOM LADY
5(1) MB,Dec-Jan'54-55 ..... 800.00
2 Last Pre-Code Edition 650.00
3 Comics Code 500.00
4 Red Rocket,June, 1955 ... 500.00

PHIL RIZZUTO
Fawcett Publications
1951
Ph(c) The Sensational Story of
The American Leagues MVP 500.00

PICTORIAL CONFESSIONS
St. John Publishing Co.
September, 1949
1 MB,MB(c),I Threw Away My Reputation on a Worthless Love 200.00
2 MB,Ph(c) I Tried to be a
  Hollywood Glamour Girl ... 125.00
3 JKY,MB,MB(c),They Caught
  Me Cheating 125.00
Becomes:
PICTORIAL ROMANCES
4 Ph(c) MB, Trapped By Kisses
  I Couldn't Resist 200.00
5 MB,MB(c) 150.00
6 MB,MB(c) I Was Too Free
  With Boys 100.00
7 MB,MB(c) 100.00
8 MB,MB(c) I Made a
  Sinful Bargain 100.00
9 MB,MB(c) Dishonest Love .. 100.00

10 MB,MB(c) I Was The
  Other Woman 75.00
11 MB,MB(c) The Worst
  Mistake A Wife Can Make ... 85.00
12 MB,MB(c) Love Urchin ... 60.00
13 MB,MB(c) Temptations of a
  Hatcheck Girl 60.00
14 MB,MB(c) I Was A
  Gamblers Wife 60.00
15 MB,MB(c) Wife Without
  Pride or Principles 60.00
16 MB,MB(c) The Truth of My
  Affair With a Farm Boy 60.00
17 MB,MB(c) True Confessions
  of a Girl in Love 175.00
18 MB,MB(c) 175.00
20 MB,MB(c) 175.00
21 MB,MB(c) 50.00
22 MB,MB(c) 50.00
23 MB,MB(c) 50.00
24 MB,MB(c) March,1954 ..... 50.00

PICTORIAL LOVE STORIES
St. John Publishing Co.
October, 1952
1 MB,MB(c) I Lost My Head, My
  Heart and My Resistance .. 175.00

PICTURE NEWS
299 Lafayette Street Corp.
January, 1946
1 Will The Atom Blow The
  World Apart 275.00
2 Meet America's 1st Girl Boxing
  Expert,Atomic Bomb 150.00
3 Hollywood's June Allison Shows
  You How to be Beautiful,
  Atomic Bomb 100.00
4 Amazing Marine Who Became
  King of 10,000 Voodoos,
  Atomic Bomb 125.00
5 G.I.Babies,Hank Greenberg .. 90.00
6 Joe Louis(c) 125.00
7 Lovely Lady, Englands
  Future Queen 80.00
8 Champion of them All 75.00
9 Bikini Atom Bomb,
  Joe DiMaggio 100.00
10 Dick Quick, Ace Reporter,
  Atomic Bomb
  January/February 1947 .... 100.00

PICTURE STORIES FROM SCIENCE
Educational Comics
Spring, 1947
1 Understanding Air and Water 200.00
2 Fall '47 Amazing Discoveries
  About Food & Health 175.00

PICTURE STORIES FROM WORLD HISTORY
E.C. Comics
Spring, 1947
1 Ancient World to the
  Fall of Rome 200.00
2 Europes Struggle for
  Civilization 175.00

YOUR FAVORITE TELEVISION PUPPETS
PINHEAD and **FOODINI**

FOR REAL KICKS READ FOODINI'S TALKING CAMEL

Pinhead and Foodini #4
© Fawcett Publications

PINHEAD AND FOODINI
Fawcett Publications
July, 1951–Jan. 1952
1 Ph(c) 175.00
2 Ph(c) 100.00
3 Ph(c) Too Many Pinheads ... 60.00
4 Foodini's Talking Camel 60.00

PIN-UP PETE
Minoan Magazine Publishers
1952
1 Loves of a GI Casanova ... 100.00

PIONEER PICTURE STORIES
Street & Smith Publications
December, 1941
1 Red Warriors in Blackface .. 200.00
2 Life Story of Errol Flynn ... 100.00
3 Success Stories of Brain
  Muscle in Action 75.00
4 Legless Ace & Boy Commando
  Raid Occupied France 75.00
5 How to Tell Uniform and
  Rank of Any Navy Man 75.00
6 General Jimmy Doolittle 85.00
7 Life Story of Admiral Halsey . 85.00
8 Life Story of Timoshenko ... 75.00
9 Dec. '43,Man Who Conquered
  The Wild Frozen North 75.00

PIRACY
E.C. Comics Oct.-Nov., 1954
1 WW,JDa,AW,WW(c),RC,AT 225.00
2 RC,JDa(c),WW,AW,AT 175.00
3 RC,GE, RC(c),Grl 150.00
4 RC,GE,RC(c),Grl 125.00
5 RC,GE,BK(c),Grl 125.00
6 JDa,RC,GE,BK(c),Grl 125.00
7 Oct Nov GE(c),RC,GE,Grl . 125.00

PIRATE COMICS
Hillman Periodicals Feb., 1950
1 .... 175.00

2 . . . . 120.00
3 . . . . 100.00
4 Aug–Sept., 1950 . . . . 90.00

PIXIES, THE
Magazine Enterprises
Winter, 1946
1 Mighty Atom 45.00
2 . . . . 25.00
3 . . . . 20.00
4 . . . . 20.00
5 . . . . 25.00
Becomes:
MIGHTY ATOM, THE
6 . . . . 25.00

Planet Comics #49
© Fiction House Magazines

PLANET COMICS
Love Romance Publ.
(Fiction House Magazines)
January, 1940
1 AB,DBR,HCk, Planet Comics,
WE&LF,O:Aura,B:Flint Baker,
Red Comet,Spurt Hammond,
Capt. Nelson Cole 10,000.00
2 HcK,LF(c) 3,500.00
3 WE(c),HcK 2,500.00
4 HcK,B:Gale Allan and
the Girl Squad 2,000.00
5 BP,HcK 1,900.00
6 BP,HcK,BP(c),The Ray
Pirates of Venus 2,000.00
7 BP,AB,HcK,BP(c) B:Buzz
Crandall Planet Payson . . 1,600.00
8 BP,AB HcK 1,500.00
9 BP,AB,GT,HcK,B:Don
Granville Cosmo Corrigan . 1,500.00
10 BP,AB,GT HcK 1,500.00
11 HcK, B:Crash Parker 1,500.00
12 Dri,B:Star Fighter 1,500.00
13 Dri,B:Reef Ryan 1,200.00
14 Dri B:Norge Benson 1,100.00
15 B: Mars,God of War 2,300.00
16 Invasion From The Void . . 1,100.00
17 Warrior Maid of Mercury . . 1,100.00
18 Bondage(c) 1,200.00
19 Monsters of the Inner World 1,100.00

20 RP, Winged Man Eaters
of the Exile Star 1,100.00
21 RP,B:Lost World
Hunt Bowman 1,200.00
22 Inferno on the Fifth Moon . 1,100.00
23 GT,Lizard Tyrant of
the Twilight World 1,000.00
24 GT,Grl Raiders From
The Red Moon 1,000.00
25 Grl,B:Norge Benson 1,000.00
26 Grl,B:The Space Rangers
Bondage(c) 1,100.00
27 Grl, The Fire Eaters of
Asteroid Z 800.00
28 Grl, Bondage (c) 850.00
29 Grl,Dragon Raiders of Aztla 800.00
30 GT,Grl City of Lost Souls . . 800.00
31 Grl,Fire Priests of Orbit6X . . 675.00
32 Slaver's Planetoid 800.00
33 MA 675.00
34 MA,Bondage 850.00
35 MA B:Mysta of The Moon . . 700.00
36 MA Collosus of the
Blood Moon 700.00
37 MA, Behemoths of the
Purple Void 700.00
38 MA 600.00
39 MA. Death Webs Of Zenith 3 600.00
40 Chameleon Men from
Galaxy 9 . . . . 600.00
41 MA,Aaf,New O: Auro
Bondage (c) 650.00
42 MA,AaF,E:Gale Allan 600.00
43 MA,AaF Death Rays
From the Sun. 600.00
44 MA,Bbl,B:Futura 600.00
45 Ma,Bbl,Her Evilness
from Xanado 600.00
46 MA,Bbl,GE The Mecho-Men
From Mars 600.00
47 MA,Bbl,GE,The Great
Green Spawn 550.00
48 MA,GE 550.00
49 MA,GE, Werewolves From
Hydra Hell 550.00
50 MA,GE,The Things of Xeves 550.00
51 MA, GE, Mad Mute X-Adapts 500.00
52 GE,Mystery of the Time
Chamber 500.00
53 MB,GE,Bondage(c)
Dwarflings From Oceania . . 500.00
54 MB,GE,Robots From Inferno 500.00
55 MB,GE,Giants of the
Golden Atom 500.00
56 MB,GE,Grl 450.00
57 MB,GE,Grl 450.00
58 MB,GE,Grl 450.00
59 MB,GE,Grl,LSe 450.00
60 GE,Grl,Vassals of Volta . . . 450.00
61 GE,Grl, The Brute in the
Bubble 350.00
62 GE,Musta,Moon Goddess . . 350.00
63 GE,Paradise or Inferno 350.00
64 GE,Monkeys From the Blue 350.00
65 The Lost World 350.00
66 The Plague of the
Locust Men 350.00
67 The Nymphs of Neptune . . . 350.00
68 Synthoids of the 9th Moon . 350.00
69 The Mentalists of Mars 350.00
70 Cargo For Amazonia 350.00
71 Sandhogs of Mars 250.00
72 Last Ship to Paradise 250.00
73 The Martian Plague,
Winter 1953 . . . . 250.00

Plastic Man #44
© Comics Magazines/Quality Comics

PLASTIC MAN
Comics Magazines
(Quality Comics Group)
Summer, 1943
1 JCo,JCo(c)Game of Death . 3,000.00
2 JCo,JCo(c)The Gay Nineties
Nightmare 1,200.00
3 JCo,JCo(c) 800.00
4 JCo,JCo(c) 650.00
5 JCo,JCo(c) 550.00
6 JCo,JCo(c) 450.00
7 JCo,JCo(c) 450.00
8 JCo,JCo(c) 450.00
9 JCo,JCo(c) 450.00
10 JCo,JCo(c) 450.00
11 JCo,JCo(c) 400.00
12 JCo,JCo(c),V:Spadehead . 400.00
13 JCo,JCo(c),V:Mr.Hazard . . . 400.00
14 JCo,JCo(c),Words,Symbol
of Crime 400.00
15 JCo,JCo(c),V:BeauBrummel 400.00
16 JCo,JCo(c),Money
Means Trouble 400.00
17 JCo,JCo(c),A:The Last
Man on Earth 400.00
18 JCo,JCo(c),Goes Back
to the Farm 400.00
19 JCo,JCo(c),V:Prehistoric
Plunder 400.00
20 JCo,JCo(c),A:Sadly,Sadly . . 400.00
21 JCo,JCo(c),V:Crime Minded
Mind Reader 300.00
22 JCo,JCo(c), Which Twin
is the Phony 300.00
23 JCo,JCo(c),The Fountain
of Age 300.00
24 JCo,JCo(c),The Black Box
of Terror 300.00
25 JCo,JCo(c),A:Angus
MacWhangus 300.00
26 JCo,JCo(c),On the Wrong
Side of the Law? 300.00
27 JCo,JCo(c),V:The Leader . . 300.00
28 JCo,JCo(c),V:Shasta 300.00
29 JCo,JCo(c),V:Tricky Toledo . 300.00
30 JCo,JCo(c),V:Weightless
Wiggins 300.00

31 JCo,JCo(c),V:Raka the
   Witch Doctor 225.00
32 JCo,JCo(c),V:Mr.Fission . . . 225.00
33 JCo,JCo(c),V:The Mad
   Professor 225.00
34 JCo,JCo(c),Smuggler'sHaven 225.00
35 JCo,JCo(c),V:The Hypnotist 225.00
36 JCo,JCo(c),The Uranium
   Underground 225.00
37 JCo,JCo(c),V:Gigantic Ants . 225.00
38 JCo,JCo(c),The Curse of
   Monk Mauley 225.00
39 JCo,JCo(c),The Stairway
   to Madness 225.00
40 JCo,JCo(c),The Ghoul of
   Ghost Swamp 225.00
41 JCo,JCo(c),The Beast with
   the Bloody Claws 200.00
42 JCo,JCo(c),The King of
   Thunderbolts 200.00
43 JCo,JCo(c),The Evil Terror . 200.00
44 JCo,JCo(c),The Magic Cup . 200.00
45 The Invisible Raiders 200.00
46 V:The Spider 200.00
47 The Fiend of a
   Thousand Faces 200.00
48 Killer Crossbones 200.00
49 JCo,The Weapon for Evil . . 200.00
50 V:Iron Fist 200.00
51 Incredible Sleep Weapon . 175.00
52 V:Indestructible Wizard . . 185.00
53 V:Dazzia,Daughter of
   Darkness 185.00
54 V:Dr.Quomquat 185.00
55 The Man Below Zero 185.00
56 JCo, The Man Who Broke
   the Law of Gravity 185.00
57 The Chemist's Cauldron . . 185.00
58 JCo,The Amazing
   Duplicating Machine 185.00
59 JCo,V:The Super Spy 185.00
60 The Man in the Fiery
   Disguise 175.00
61 V:King of the Thunderbolts . 175.00
62 V:The Smokeweapon 175.00
63 V:Reflecto 175.00
64 Nov'56 The Invisible
   Raiders 175.00

POCAHONTAS
Pocahontas Fuel Co.
October, 1941
N# 65.00
2 . . . . 50.00

POCKET COMICS
Harvey Publications
August, 1941
1 100 pages,O:Black Cat,Spirit
of '76,Red Blazer Phantom
Sphinx & Zebra,B:Phantom
Ranger,British Agent #99,
Spin Hawkins,Satan 750.00
2 . . . . 500.00
3 . . . . 400.00
4 Jan.'42,All Features End . . . 350.00

POGO POSSUM
Dell Publishing Co.
1 WK,A:Swamp Land Band . . 550.00
2 WK 400.00
3 WK 375.00
4 WK 375.00
5 WK 375.00

6 thru 10 WK . . . . @250.00
11 WK, Christmas cover . . . @300.00
12 thru 16 WK . . . . @200.00

POLICE COMICS
Comic Magazines
(Quality Comics Group)
August, 1941
1 GFx,JCo,WE.PGn,RC,FG,AB,
GFx(c),B&O:Plastic Man
The Human Bomb,#711,I&B,
Chic Canter,The Firebrand
Mouthpiece,Phantom Lady
The Sword 6,500.00
2 JCo,GFx,PGn,WE,RC,FG,
GFx(c) 2,200.00
3 JCo,GFx,PGn,WE,RC,FG,
GFx(c) 1,600.00
4 JCo,GFx,PGn,WE,RC,FG,
GFx&WEC(c) 1,500.00
5 JCo,GFx,PGn,WE,RC,FG,
GFx(c) 1,300.00
6 JCo,GFx,PGn,WE,RC,FG,
GFx(c) 1,200.00
7 JCo,GFx,PGn,WE,RC,FG,
GFx(c) 1,100.00
8 JCo,GFx,PGn,WE,RC,FG,
GFx(c),B&O:Manhunter . . 1,500.00
9 JCo,GFx,PGn,WE,RC,FG,
GFx(c) 1,100.00
10 JCo,GFx,PGn,WE,RC,FG,
GFx(c) 1,000.00
11 JCo,GFx,PGn,WE,RC,FG,
GFx(c),B:Rep:Rep.Spirit
Strips 1,700.00
12 JCo,GFX,PGn,WE,FG,AB,
RC(c) I:Ebony 1,000.00
13 JCo,GFx,PGn,WE,FG,AB,RC(c)
E:Firebrand,I:Woozy Winks 1,000.00
14 JCo,GFx,PGn,WE,Jku,GFX(c) 750.00
15 JCo,GFx,PGn,WE,Jku,GFX(c)
E#711,B:Destiny 750.00
16 JCo,PGn,WE,JKu 750.00
17 JCo,PGn,WE,JKu,JCo(c) . . 750.00
18 JCo,PGN,WE,JCo(c) 750.00
19 JCo,PGn,WE,JCo(c) 750.00
20 JCo,PGn,WE,JCo(c),A:Jack
Cole in Phantom Lady 750.00

Police Comics #23
© *Quality Comics Group*

21 JCo,PGn,WE,JCo(c) 600.00
22 JCo,PGn,WE,RP,JCo(c)
The Eyes Have it 600.00
23 JCo,WE,RP,JCo(c),E:Phantom
Lady 550.00
24 JCo,WE,HK,JCo(c),B:Flatfoot
Burns 550.00
25 JCo,WE,HK,RP,JCo(c),The
Bookstore Mysrery 550.00
26 JCo,WE,Hk,JCo,(c)E:Flatfoot
Burns 550.00
27 JCo,WE,JCo(c) 550.00
28 JCo,WE,JCo(c) 550.00
29 JCo,WE,JCo(c) 550.00
30 JCo,WE,JCo(c),A Slippery
Racket 550.00
31 JCo,WE,JCo(c),Is Plastic
Man Washed Up? 400.00
32 JCo,WE,JCo(c),Fiesta Turns
Into a Fracas 400.00
33 JCo,WE 400.00
34 JCo,WE,JCO(c) 400.00
35 JCo,WE,JCO(c) 400.00
36 JCo,WE,JCO(c),Rest
In Peace 400.00
37 JCo,WE,PGn,JCo(c),Love
Comes to Woozy 400.00
38 JCo,WE,PGn,JCo(c) 400.00
39 JCo,WE,PGn,JCo(c) 400.00
40 JCo,WE,PGn,JCo(c) 400.00
41 JCo,WE,PGn,JCo(c),E:Reps.
of Spirit Strip 300.00
42 JCo,LF&WE,PGn,JCo(c),
Woozy Cooks with Gas . . . 300.00
43 JCo,LF&WE,PGn,JCo(c) . . 300.00
44 JCo,PGn,LF,JCo(c) 275.00
45 JCo,PGn,LF,JCo(c) 275.00
46 JCo,PGn,LF,JCo(c) 275.00
47 JCo,PGn,LF,JCo(c),
V:Dr.Slicer 275.00
48 JCo,PGn,LF,JCo(c),V:Big
Beaver 275.00
49 JCo,PGn,LF,JCo(c),V:Thelma
Twittle 275.00
50 JCo,PGn,LF,JCo(c) 275.00
51 JCo,PGn,LF,JCo(c),V:The
Granite Lady 225.00
52 JCo,PGn,LF,JCo(c) 225.00
53 JCo,PGn,LF,JCo(c),
V:Dr.Erudite 225.00
54 JCo,PGn,LF,JCo(c) 225.00
55 JCo,PGn,LF,JCo(c),V:The
Sleepy Eyes 225.00
56 JCo,PGn,LF,JCo(c),V:The
Yes Man 225.00
57 JCo,PGn,LF,JCo(c),
V:Mr.Misfit 225.00
58 JCo,PGn,LF,JCo(c),E:The
Human Bomb 225.00
59 JCo,PGn,LF,JCo(c),A:Mr.
Happiness 225.00
60 JCo,PGn,LF,JCo(c) 175.00
61 JCo,PGn,LF,JCo(c) 175.00
62 JCo,PGn,LF,JCo(c) 175.00
63 JCo,PGn,LF,JCo(c),
V:The Crab 175.00
64 JCo,PGn,LF,HK,JCo(c) . . . 175.00
65 JCo,PGn,LF,JCo(c) 175.00
66 JCo,PGn,LF,JCo(c) Love
Can Mean Trouble 175.00
67 JCo,LF,JCo(c),
V:The Gag Man 175.00
68 JCo,LF,JCo(c) 175.00
69 JCo,LF,JCo(c),V:Strecho . . 175.00
70 JCo,LF,JCo(c) 175.00

71 JCo,LF,JCo(c)	175.00
72 JCo,LF,JCo(c),V:Mr.Cat . .	175.00
73 JCo,LF,JCo(c)	175.00
74 JCo,LF,JCo(c),V:Prof.Dimwit	175.00
75 JCo,LF,JCo(c)	175.00
76 JCo,LF,JCo(c),V:Mr.Morbid .	175.00
77 JCo,LF,JCo(c),V:Skull Face & Eloc	175.00
78 JCo,LF,JCo(c),A Hot Time In Dreamland	175.00
79 JCo,LF,JCo(c),V:Eaglebeak	175.00
80 JCo,LF,JCo(c),V:Penetro	175.00
81 JCo,LF,JCo(c),V:A Gorilla . .	175.00
82 JCo,LF,JCo(c)	175.00
83 JCo,LF,JCo(c)	175.00
84 JCo,LF,JCo(c)	175.00
85 JCo,LF,JCo(c),V:Lucky 7 . .	175.00
86 JCo,LF,JCo(c),V:The Baker	175.00
87 JCo,LF,JCo(c)	175.00
88 JCo,LF,JCo(c),V:The Seen .	175.00
89 JCo,JCo(c),V:The Vanishers	150.00
90 JCo,JCo(c),V:Capt.Rivers	150.00
91 JCo,JCo(c),The Forest Primeval	160.00
92 JCo,LF,JCo(c),V:Closets Kennedy	160.00
93 JCo,JCo(c),V:The Twinning Terror	160.00
94 JCo,JCo(c),WE	250.00
95 JCo,JCo(c),WE,V:Scowls . .	250.00
96 JCo,JCo(c),WE,V:Black Widow	250.00
97 JCo,JCo(c),WE,V:The Mime	250.00
98 JCo,JCo(c),WE	250.00
99 JCo,JCo(c),WE	250.00
100 JCo,JCo(c)	300.00
101 JCo,JCo(c)	300.00
102 JCo,JCo(c),E:Plastic Man .	300.00
103 JCo,LF,B&I:Ken Shannon; Bondage(c)	175.00
104 The Handsome of Homocide	150.00
105 Invisible Hands of Murder .	150.00
106 Museum of Murder	150.00
107 Man with the ShrunkenHead	150.00
108 The Headless Horse Player	150.00
109 LF,Bondage(c),Blood on the Chinese Fan	150.00
110 Murder with a Bang	150.00
111 Diana, Homocidal Huntress	150.00
112 RC,The Corpse on the Sidewalk	165.00
113 RC,RC(c), The Dead Man with the Size 13 Shoe	165.00
114 The Terrifying Secret of the Black Bear	150.00
115 Don't Let Them Kill Me . . .	150.00
116 Stage Was Set For Murder	150.00
117 Bullet Riddled Bookkeeper	150.00
118 Case of the Absent Corpse	150.00
119 A Fast & Bloody Buck	150.00
120 Death & The Derelict	150.00
121 Curse of the Clawed Killer	150.00
122 The Lonely Hearts Killer . .	150.00
123 Death Came Screaming . .	150.00
124 Masin Murder	150.00
125 Bondage(c),The Killer of King Arthur's Court	165.00
126 Hit & Run Murders	150.00
127 Oct'53,Death Drivers	150.00

POLICE LINE-UP
**Avon Periodicals/
Realistic Comics
August, 1951**

1 WW,P(c)	250.00

2 P(c),Drugs	175.00
3 JKu,EK,P(c)	125.00
4 July '52;EK	125.00

POLICE TRAP
Mainline Sept., 1954

1 S&K(c)	200.00
2 S&K(c)	100.00
3 S&K(c)	100.00
4 S&K(c)	100.00

Charlton Comics

5 S&K,S&K(c)	150.00
6 S&K,S&K(c)	150.00

Becomes:

PUBLIC DEFENDER IN ACTION

7	50.00
8 thru 12, Oct. 1957	@40.00

POLLY PIGTAILS
**Parents' Magazine Institute
January, 1946**

1 Ph(c)	55.00
2 Ph(c)	25.00
3 Ph(c)	20.00
4 Ph(c)	20.00
5 Ph(c)	20.00
6 Ph(c)	20.00
7 Ph(c)	15.00
8	15.00
9	15.00
10	15.00
11 thru 22	@10.00
22 Ph(c)	10.00
23 Ph(c)	10.00
34 thru 43	@10.00

Popeye #10 © King Features

POPEYE
**Dell Publishing Co.
1948**

1	325.00
2	150.00
3 'Welcome to Ghost Island' . .	125.00
4	125.00
5	125.00
6	125.00
7	125.00

8	125.00
9	125.00
10	125.00
11	100.00
12	100.00
13	100.00
14 thru 20	@100.00
21 thru 30	@75.00
31 thru 40	@65.00
41 thru 45	@50.00
46 O:Sweat Pea	65.00
47 thru 50	@45.00
51 thru 60	@35.00
61 thru 65	@25.00

POPULAR COMICS
**Dell Publishing Co.
February, 1936**

1 Dick Tracy, Little Orphan Annie	3,800.00
2 Terry Pirates	1,300.00
3 Terry,Annie,Dick Tracy . . .	1,000.00
4	800.00
5 B:Tom Mix	800.00
6	650.00
7	650.00
8	650.00
9	650.00
10 Terry,Annie,Tracy	650.00
11 Terry,Annie,Tracy	500.00
12 Christmas(c)	500.00
13 Terry,Annie,Tracy	500.00
14 Terry,Annie,Tracy	500.00
15 same	500.00
16 same	500.00
17 same	500.00
18 same	500.00
19 same	500.00
20 same	500.00
21 same	400.00
22 same	400.00
23 same	400.00
24 same	400.00
25 same	400.00
26 same	400.00
27 E:Terry,Annie,Tracy	400.00
28 A:Gene Autry	300.00
29	300.00
30	300.00
31 A:Jim McCoy	300.00
32 A:Jim McCoy	300.00
33	300.00
34	300.00
35 Christmas(c),Tex Ritter . . .	300.00
36	300.00
37	300.00
38 B:Gang Busters	325.00
39	300.00
40	300.00
41	300.00
42	300.00
43 F:Gang Busters	325.00
44	225.00
45 Tarzan(c)	225.00
46 O:Martan the Marvel Man .	350.00
47 F:Martan the Marvel Man . .	225.00
48 F:Martan the Marvel Man . .	225.00
49 F:Martan the Marvel Man . .	225.00
50	225.00
51 B&O:Voice	225.00
52 A:Voice	175.00
53 F:The Voice	175.00
54 F:Gang Busters,A:Voice . . .	175.00
55 F:Gang Busters	185.00
56 F:Gang Busters	175.00

GOLDEN AGE

All comics prices listed are for *Near Mint* condition.

GOLDEN AGE

57 F:The Marvel Man 175.00
58 F:The Marvel Man 175.00
59 F:The Marvel Man 175.00
60 O:Prof. Supermind 185.00
61 Prof. Supermind & Son 150.00
62 Supermind & Son 150.00
63 B:Smilin' Jack 150.00
64 Smilin'Jack,Supermind 150.00
65 Professor Supermind 150.00
66 . . . . 150.00
67 Gasoline Alley 150.00
68 F:Smilin' Jack 150.00
69 F:Smilin' Jack 150.00
70 F:Smilin' Jack 150.00
71 F:Smilin' Jack 150.00
72 B:Owl,Terry & the Pirates . . . 300.00
73 F:Terry and the Pirates 175.00
74 F:Smilin' Jack 175.00
75 F:Smilin'Jack,A:Owl 175.00
76 Captain Midnight 250.00
77 Captain Midnight 250.00
78 Captain Midnight 250.00
79 A:Owl 175.00

Popular Comics #41
© Dell Publishing Co.

80 F:Smilin' Jack,A:Owl 175.00
81 F: Terry&thePirates,A:Owl . . 175.00
82 F:Smilin' Jack,A:Owl 175.00
83 F:Smilin' Jack,A:Owl 175.00
84 F:Smilin' Jack,A:Owl 175.00
85 F:ThreeLittleGremlins,A:Owl 175.00
86 F:Three Little Gremlins 125.00
87 F:Smilin' Jack 125.00
88 F:Smilin' Jack 125.00
89 F:Smokey Stover 125.00
90 F:Terry and the Pirates 125.00
91 F:Smokey Stover 125.00
92 F:Terry and the Pirates 125.00
93 F:Smilin' Jack 125.00
94 F:Terry and the Pirates 125.00
95 F:Smilin' Jack 125.00
96 F:Gang Busters 125.00
97 F:Smilin' Jack 125.00
98 B:Felix Cat 135.00
99 F:Bang Busters 125.00
100 . . . . 150.00
101 thru 141 . . . . 75.00
142 E:Terry & the Pirates 70.00
143 . . . . 70.00
144 . . . . 70.00

145 F:Harold Teen 70.00

POPULAR ROMANCES
Better Publications
(Standard Comics)
December, 1949

5 B:Ph(c) 40.00
6 Ph(c) 25.00
7 RP 25.00
8 Ph(c) 25.00
9 Ph(c) 25.00
10 WW 40.00
11 thru 16 . . . . @20.00
17 WE 25.00
18 thru 21 . . . . @25.00
22 thru 27 ATh,Ph(c) . . . . . . @50.00

SCHOOL DAY ROMANCES
Star Publications
November-December, 1949

1 LbC(c),Teen-Age 125.00
2 LbC(c) 85.00
3 LbC(c),Ph(c) 85.00
4 LbC(c),JyD,RonaldReagan . 135.00
Becomes:
POPULAR TEEN-AGERS

5 LbC(c),Toni Gay,
    Eve Adams 175.00
6 LbC(c),Ginger Bunny,
    Midge Martin 150.00
7 LbC(c) 150.00
8 LbC(c) 150.00
9 LbC(c) 75.00
10 LbC(c) 75.00
11 LbC(c) 50.00
12 LbC(c) 50.00
13 LbC(c),JyD 50.00
14 LbC,WW,Spanking 125.00
15 LbC(c),JyD 40.00
16 . . . . 35.00
17 LbC(c),JyD 35.00
18 LbC(c) 35.00
19 LbC(c) 35.00
20 LbC(c),JyD 45.00
21 LbC(c),JyD 45.00
22 LbC(c) 30.00
23 LbC(c) 30.00

POWER COMICS
Holyoke/Narrative Publ.
1944

1 LbC(c) 1,100.00
2 B:Dr.Mephisto,Hitler(c) . . . 1,200.00
3 LbC(c) 1,200.00
4 LbC(c) 1,100.00

PRIDE OF THE YANKEES
Magazine Enterprises
1949

1 N#,OW,Ph(c),The Life
    of Lou Gehrig 650.00

PRISON BREAK
Avon Periodicals/Realistic
September, 1951

1 WW(c),WW 300.00
2 WW(c),WW,JKu 200.00
3 JD,JO 175.00
4 EK 150.00
5 EK,CI 150.00

PRIZE COMICS
Feature Publications
(Prize Publ.)
March, 1940

1 O&B:Power Nelson,Jupiter.
    B:Ted O'Neil,Jaxon of
    the Jungle,Bucky Brady,
    Storm Curtis, Rocket(c) . . 1,700.00
2 B:The Owl 750.00
3 Power Nelson(c) 700.00
4 Power Nelson(c) 700.00
5 A:Dr.Dekkar 650.00
6 A:Dr.Dekkar 650.00
7 S&K,DBr,JK(c),O&B DR Frost,
    Frankenstein,B:GreenLama,
    Capt Gallant,Voodini
    Twist Turner 1,400.00
8 S&K,DBr 750.00
9 S&K,DBr,Black Owl(c) 700.00
10 DBr,Black Owl(c) 600.00
11 DBr,O:Bulldog Denny 550.00
12 DBr 550.00

Prize Comics #50
© Feature Publications

13 DBR,O&B:Yank and
    Doodle,Bondage(c) 600.00
14 DBr,Black Owl(c) 550.00
15 DBr,Black Owl(c) 550.00
16 DBr,JaB,B:Spike Mason . . . 550.00
17 DBr,Black Owl(c) 550.00
18 DBr,Black Owl(c) 550.00
19 DBr,Yank&Doodle(c) 550.00
20 DBr,Yank&Doodle(c) 550.00
21 DBr,JaB(c),Yank&Doodle(c) 350.00
22 DBr,Yank&Doodle(c) 350.00
23 DBr,Uncle Sam(c) 350.00
24 DBr,Abe Lincoln(c) 350.00
25 DBr,JaB, Yank&Doodle(c) . . 350.00
26 DBr,JaB,JaB(c),Liberty
    Bell(c) 350.00
27 DBr,Yank&Doodle(c) 225.00
28 DBr,Yank&Doodle(c) 200.00
29 DBr,JaB(c)Yank&Doodle(c) . 200.00
30 DBr,Yank&Doodle(c) 225.00
31 DBr,Yank&Doodle(c) 200.00
32 DBr,Yank&Doodle(c) 200.00
33 DBr,Bondage(c),Yank
    & Doodle 225.00
34 DBr,O:Airmale;New

Black Owl 225.00
35 DBr,B:Flying Fist & Bingo . . 125.00
36 DBr,Yank&Doodle(c) 125.00
37 DBr,I:Stampy,Hitler(c) 200.00
38 DBr,B.Owl,Yank&Doodle(c) . 125.00
39 DBr,B.Owl,Yank&Doodle(c) . 125.00
40 DBr,B.Owl,Yank&Doodle(c) . 125.00
41 DBr,B.Owl,Yank&Doodle(c) . 125.00
42 DBr,B.Owl,Yank&Doodle(c) . 100.00
43 DBr,B.Owl,Yank&Doodle(c) . 100.00
44 DBr, B&I:Boom Boom
    Brannigan 100.00
45 DBr 100.00
46 DBr 100.00
47 DBr 100.00
48 DBr,B:Prince Ra;Bondage(c) 125.00
49 DBr,Boom Boom(c) 90.00
50 DBr,Farnkenstein(c) 100.00
51 DBr 90.00
52 DBr, B:Sir Prize 90.00
53 DBr, The Man Who Could
    Read Features 100.00
54 DBr 90.00
55 DBr,Yank&Doodle(c) 90.00
56 DBr,Boom Boom (c) 90.00
57 DBr,Santa Claus(c) 90.00
58 DBr,The Poisoned Punch . . . 90.00
59 DBr,Boom Boom(c) 90.00
60 DBr,Sir Prise(c) 90.00
61 DBr,The Man wih the
    Fighting Feet 90.00
62 DBr,Hck(c),Yank&Doodle(c) . 90.00
63 DBr,S&K,S&K(c),Boom
    Boom(c) 100.00
64 DBr,Blackowl Retires 90.00
65 DBr,DBr(c),Frankenstein . . . 90.00
66 DBr,DBr(c),Frankenstein . . . 90.00
67 DBr,B:Brothers in Crime 90.00
68 DBr,RP(c) 90.00
Becomes:

PRIZE COMICS
WESTERN

69 ACa(c),B:Dusty Ballew . . 100.00
70 ACa(c) 75.00
71 ACa(c) 75.00
72 ACa(c),JSe 75.00
73 ACa(c) 75.00
74 ACa(c) 75.00
75 JSe,S&K(c),6-Gun Showdown
    at Rattlesnake Gulch 80.00
76 Ph(c),Randolph Scott 100.00
77 Ph(c),JSe,Streets of
    Laredo,movie 75.00
78 Ph(c),JSe,HK,Bullet
    Code,movie 120.00
79 Ph(c),JSe,Stage to
    China, movie 120.00
80 Ph(c),Gunsmoke Justice 75.00
81 Ph(c),The Man Who Shot
    Billy The Kid 75.00
82 Ph(c),MBi,JSe&BE,Death
    Draws a Circle 75.00
83 JSe,S&K(c) 70.00
84 JSe 50.00
85 JSe,B:American Eagle 150.00
86 JSe 60.00
87 JSe&BE 65.00
88 JSe&BE 65.00
89 JSe&BE 65.00
90 JSe&Be 65.00
91 JSe&BE,JSe&BE(c) 65.00
92 JSe,JSe&BE(c) 65.00
93 JSe&BE(c), ... 65.00
94 JSe&BE,JSe&BE(c) 65.00

Prize Comics Western #93
© Feature Publications

95 JSe&BE(c) 65.00
96 JSe,JSe&BE, JSe&BE(c) 65.00
97 JSe,JSe&BE,JSeBE(c) 65.00
98 JSe&BE,JSe&BE(c) 65.00
99 JSe&BE,JSe&BE(c) 65.00
100 JSe,JSe(c) 85.00
101 JSe 65.00
102 JSe 65.00
103 JSe 65.00
104 JSe 65.00
105 JSe 65.00
106 JSe 50.00
107 JSe 50.00
108 JSe 70.00
109 JSe&AW 80.00
110 JSe&BE 75.00
111 JSe&BE 75.00
112 . . . . 50.00
113 AW&JSe 75.00
114 MMe,B:The Drifter 35.00
115 MMe 35.00
116 MMe 35.00
117 MMe 35.00
118 MMe,E:The Drifter 35.00
119 Nov/Dec'56 . . . . 35.00

PSYCHOANALYSIS
E.C. Comics
March-April, 1955

1 JKa,JKa(c) 125.00
2 JKa,JKa(c) 100.00
3 JKa,JKa(c) 100.00
4 JKa,JKa(c) Sept.-Oct. 1955 100.00

PUBLIC ENEMIES
D.S. Publishing Co.
1948

1 AMc 150.00
2 AMc 150.00
3 AMc 75.00
4 AMc 75.00
5 AMc 75.00
6 AMc 75.00
7 AMc,Eye Injury 90.00
8 . . . . 75.00
9 . . . . 75.00

PUNCH AND JUDY
COMICS
Hillman Periodicals
1944

1 (fa) 100.00
2 . . . . 50.00
3 . . . . 40.00
4 thru 12 . . . . @35.00
2-1 . . . . 30.00
2-2 JK 100.00
2-3 . . . . 30.00
2-4 . . . . 30.00
2-5 . . . . 30.00
2-6 . . . . 30.00
2-7 . . . . 30.00
2-8 . . . . 30.00
2-9 . . . . 30.00
2-10 JK 100.00
2-11 JK 100.00
2-12 JK 100.00
3-1 JK 100.00
3-2 . . . . 90.00
3-3 . . . . 25.00
3-4 . . . . 25.00
3-5 . . . . 25.00
3-6 . . . . 25.00
3-7 . . . . 25.00
3-8 . . . . 25.00
3-9 . . . . 25.00

PUNCH COMICS
Harry 'A' Chesler
December, 1941

1 B:Mr.E,The Sky Chief,Hale
    the Magician,Kitty Kelly . . . 1,000.00
2 A:Capt.Glory 650.00
3-8 Do Not Exist
9 B:Rocket Man & Rocket
    girl,Master Ken 550.00
10 JCo,A:Sky Chief 500.00
11 JCo,O:Master Key,A:Little
    Nemo 500.00
12 A:Rocket Boy,Capt.Glory . 650.00
13 Ric(c) 500.00
14 GT 400.00
15 FSm(c) 400.00
16 . . . . 400.00
17 . . . . 400.00
18 FSm(c),Bondage(c),Drug . 500.00
19 FSm(c) 400.00
20 Women semi-nude(c) 650.00
21 Drug 400.00
22 I:Baxter,Little Nemo 200.00
23 A:Little Nemo 200.00

PUPPET COMICS
Dougherty, Co.
Spring, 1946

1 Funny Animal 35.00
2 . . . . 30.00

PURPLE CLAW, THE
Minoan Publishing Co./
Toby Press
January, 1953

1 O:Purple Claw 200.00
2 and 3 . . . . @150.00

PUZZLE FUN COMICS
George W. Dougherty Co.
Spring, 1946

1 PGn 150.00

---

2 . . . . 125.00

QUEEN OF THE WEST, DALE EVANS
Dell Publishing Co.
July, 1953
(1) see Dell Four Color #479
(1) see Dell Four Color #528
3 ATh, Ph(c) all 75.00
4 ATh,RsM 65.00
5 RsM 45.00
6 RsM 45.00
7 RsM 45.00
8 RsM 45.00
9 RsM 45.00
10 RsM 45.00
11 . . . . 32.00
12 RsM 40.00
13 RsM 40.00
14 RsM 40.00
15 RsM 40.00
16 RsM 40.00
17 RsM 40.00
18 RsM 40.00
19 . . . . 30.00
20 RsM 40.00
21 . . . . 30.00
22 RsM 40.00

RACKET SQUAD IN ACTION
Capitol Stories/ Charlton Comics
May-June, 1952
1 Carnival(c) 200.00
2 . . . . 100.00
3 Roulette 100.00
4 FFr(c) 100.00
5 Just off the Boat 125.00
6 The Kidnap Racket 85.00
7 . . . . 75.00
8 . . . . 75.00
9 2 Fisted fix 75.00
10 . . . . 75.00
11 SD,SD(c),Racing(c) 175.00
12 JoS,SD(c),Explosion(c) 325.00
13 JoS(c),The Notorious Modelling
   Agency Racket,Acid 75.00
14 DG(c),Drug 100.00
15 Photo Extortion Racket 60.00
16 thru 28 . . . . @60.00
29,March, 1958 . . . . 75.00

RAGGEDY ANN AND ANDY
Dell Publishing Co.
1942
1 Billy & Bonnie Bee 250.00
2 . . . . 125.00
3 DNo,B:Egbert Elephant . . . 125.00
4 DNo,WK 150.00
5 DNo 100.00
6 DNo 100.00
7 Little Black Sambo 100.00
8 . . . . 100.00
9 . . . . 100.00
10 . . . . 100.00
11 . . . . 75.00
12 . . . . 75.00
13 . . . . 75.00
14 . . . . 75.00
15 . . . . 75.00
16 thru 20 . . . . @75.00

21 Alice in Wonderland 65.00
22 thru 27 . . . . @45.00
28 WK 50.00
29 thru 39 . . . . @45.00

RALPH KINER HOME RUN KING
Fawcett Publications
1950
1 N#, Life Story of the
   Famous Pittsburgh Slugger . 450.00

RAMAR OF THE JUNGLE
Toby Press/ Charlton Comics
1954
1 Ph(c),TV Show 125.00
2 Ph(c) 75.00
3 . . . . 75.00
4 . . . . 75.00
5 Sept '56 . . . . 75.00

RANGE ROMANCES
Comics Magazines (Quality Comics)
December, 1949
1 PGn(c),PGn 150.00
2 RC(c),RC 175.00
3 RC,Ph(c) 125.00
4 RC,Ph(c) 125.00
5 RC,PGn,Ph(c) 125.00

RANGERS OF FREEDOM
Flying Stories, Inc. (Fiction House)
October, 1941
1 I:Ranger Girl & Rangers
   of Freedom;V:Super-Brain . 1,700.00
2 V:Super -Brain 700.00
3 Bondage(c) The Headsman
   of Hate 550.00
4 Hawaiian Inferno 500.00
5 RP,V:Super-Brain 500.00
6 RP,Bondage(c);Bugles
   of the Damned 500.00
7 RP,Death to Tojo's
   Butchers 400.00
Becomes:

RANGERS COMICS
8 RP,B:US Rangers 400.00
9 GT,BLb,Commando Steel
   for Slant Eyes 400.00
10 BLb,Bondage (c) 425.00
11 Raiders of the
   Purple Death 350.00
12 A:Commando Rangers 350.00
13 Grl,B:Commando Ranger . . 350.00
14 Grl,Bondage(c) 350.00
15 GT,Grl,Bondage(c) 350.00
16 Grl,GT;Burma Raid 375.00
17 GT,GT,Bondage(c),Raiders
   of the Red Dawn 375.00
18 GT 375.00
19 GE,Blb,GT,Bondage(c) 300.00
20 GT 275.00
21 GT,Bondage(c) 300.00
22 GT,B&O:Firehair 225.00
23 GT,BLb,B:Kazanda 200.00
24 Bondage(c) 225.00
25 Bondage(c) 225.00
26 Angels From Hell 200.00

Rangers Comics #2 © Fiction House

27 Bondage(c) 225.00
28 BLb,E:Kazanda;B&O Tiger
   Man 225.00
29 Bondage(c) 225.00
30 BLb,B:Crusoe Island 235.00
31 BLb,Bondage(c) 200.00
32 BLb 175.00
33 BLb,Drug 175.00
34 BLb 175.00
35 BLB,Bondage(c) 200.00
36 BLb,MB 175.00
37 BLb,Mb 175.00
38 BLb,MB,GE,Bondage(c) . . . 200.00
39 BLb,GE 175.00
40 BLb,GE,BLb(c) 175.00
41 BLb,GE 150.00
42 BLb,GE 150.00
43 BLb,GE 150.00
44 BLb,GE 150.00
45 BLb,GEl 150.00
46 BLb,GE 135.00
47 BLb,JGr 135.00
48 BLb,JGr 135.00
49 BLb,JGr 135.00
50 BLb,JGr,Bondage(c) 150.00
51 BLb,JGr 135.00
52 BLb,JGr,Bondage(c) 150.00
53 BLb,JGr,Prisoners of
   Devil Pass 135.00
54 JGr,When The Wild
   Commanches Ride 135.00
55 JGr,Massacre Guns at
   Pawnee Pass 135.00
56 JGr, Gun Smuggler of
   Apache Mesa 135.00
57 JGr,Redskins to the
   Rescue 135.00
58 JGr,Brides of the
   Buffalo Men 135.00
59 JGr,Plunder Portage 135.00
60 JGr, Buzzards of
   Bushwack Trail 135.00
61 BWh(c)Devil Smoke at
   Apache Basin 100.00
62 BWh(c)B:Cowboy Bob 100.00
63 BWh(c) 100.00
64 BWh(c)B:Suicide Smith . . . 100.00
65 BWh(c):Wolves of the
   Overland Trail,Bondage(c) . 110.00

66 BWh(c) 100.00
67 BWh(c)B:Space Rangers . . . 100.00
68 BWh(c);Cargo for Coje 100.00
69 BWh(c);Great Red Death
    Ray 100.00

REAL CLUE
CRIME STORIES
(see CLUE COMICS)

REAL FUNNIES
Nedor Publishing Co.
January, 1943
1 (fa) 135.00
2 and 3 (fa) . . . . @65.00

REAL HEROES COMICS
Parents' Magazine Institiute
September, 1941
1 HcK,Franklin Roosevelt 225.00
2 J, Edgar Hoover 100.00
3 General Wavell 75.00
4 Chiang Kai Shek 75.00
5 Stonewall Jackson 90.00
6 Lou Gehrig 150.00
7 Chennault and his
    Flying Tigers 75.00
8 Admiral Nimitz 75.00
9 The Panda Man 60.00
10 Carl Akeley-Jungle
    Adventurer 60.00
11 Wild Jack Howard 55.00
12 General Robert L
    Eichelberger 50.00
13 HcK,Victory at Climback 50.00
14 Pete Gray 50.00
15 Alexander Mackenzie 50.00
16 Balto of Nome Oct '46 . . . . . 50.00

REAL LIFE STORY
OF FESS PARKER
Dell Publishing Co.
1955
1 . . . . 75.00

REALISTIC ROMANCES
Avon Periodicals/
Realistic Comics
July-August, 1951
1 Ph(c) 125.00
2 Ph(c) 75.00
3 P(c) 50.00
4 P(c) 50.00
5 thru 14 . . . . @60.00
15 . . . . 40.00
16 Drug 75.00
17 . . . . 40.00

REAL LIFE COMICS
Visual Editions/Better/
Standard/Nedor
September, 1941
1 ASh(c),Lawrence of
    Arabia,Uncle Sam(c) 400.00
2 ASh(c),Liberty(c) 175.00
3 Adolph Hitler(c) 350.00
4 ASh(c)Robert Fulton,
    Charles DeGaulle 125.00
5 ASh(c)Alexander the Great . 125.00
6 ASh(c)John Paul Jones,CDR 100.00
7 ASh(c)Thomas Jefferson . . . 100.00
8 Leonardo Da Vinci 100.00

9 US Coast Guard Issue 100.00
10 Sir Hubert Wilkens 100.00
11 Odyssey on a Raft 75.00
12 ImpossibleLeatherneck 75.00
13 ASh(c)The Eternal Yank 75.00
14 Sir Isaac Newton 75.00
15 William Tell 75.00
16 Marco Polo 75.00
17 Albert Einstein 85.00
18 Ponce De Leon 75.00
19 The Fighting Seabees 75.00
20 Joseph Pulitzer 75.00
21 Admiral Farragut 50.00
22 Thomas Paine 50.00
23 Pedro Menendez 50.00
24 Babe Ruth 125.00
25 Marcus Whitman 50.00
26 Benvenuto Cellini 50.00
27 A Bomb Story 125.00
28 Robert Blake 50.00
29 Daniel DeFoe 50.00
30 Baron Robert Clive 50.00
31 Anthony Wayne 50.00

Real Life Comics #14
© Visual Editions/Better/Standard

32 Frank Sinatra 75.00
33 Frederick Douglas 50.00
34 Paul Revere,Jimmy Stewart . 60.00
35 Rudyard Kipling 50.00
36 Story of the Automobile 50.00
37 Francis Manion 50.00
38 Richard Henry Dana 45.00
39 Samuel FB Morse 40.00
40 FG,ASh(c),Hans Christian
    Anderson 45.00
41 Abraham Lincoln,Jimmy Foxx 60.00
42 Joseph Conrad,Fred Allen . . 50.00
43 Louis Braille,O.W.Holmes . . . 45.00
44 Citizens of Tomorrow 45.00
45 ASh(c),Francois Villon 65.00
46 The Pony Express 65.00
47 ASh(c),Montezuma 45.00
48 . . . . 45.00
49 ASh(c),Gene Bearden,
    Baseball 50.00
50 FF,ASh(c),Lewis & Clark . . . 175.00
51 GE,ASh(c),Sam Houston . . . 125.00
52 GE,FF,ASh(c),JSe&BE
    Leif Erickson 160.00
53 JSe&BE,Henry Wells &

    William Fargo 65.00
54 GT,Alexander Graham Bell . . 65.00
55 ASh(c),JSe&BE, The James
    Brothers 65.00
56 JSe&BE 65.00
57 JSe&BE 65.00
58 JSe&BE,Jim Reaves 75.00
59 FF,JSe&BE,Battle Orphan
    Sept '52 . . . . 65.00

REAL LOVE
(see HAP HAZARD COMICS)

REAL WEST ROMANCES
Crestwoood Publishing Co./
Prize Publ.
April-May, 1949
1 S&K,Ph(c) 125.00
2 Ph(c),Spanking 90.00
3 JSe,BE,Ph(c) 40.00
4 S&K,JSe,BE,Ph(c) 75.00
5 S&K,MMe,JSe,Audie
    Murphy Ph(c) 65.00
6 S&K,JSe,BE,Ph(c) 50.00

RECORD BOOK OF
FAMOUS POLICE
CASES
St. John Publishing Co.
1949
1 N#,JKu,MB(c) 250.00

Red Arrow #1 © P.L. Publishing Co.

RED ARROW
P.L. Publishing Co.
May,1951
1 Bondage(c) 75.00
2 . . . . 50.00
3 P(c) 40.00

RED BAND COMICS
Enwil Associates
November, 1944
1 The Bogeyman 250.00
2 O:Bogeyman,same(c)as#1 . . 200.00
3 A:Captain Wizard 175.00
4 May '45,Repof#3,Same(c) . . 175.00

GOLDEN AGE

RED CIRCLE COMICS
Enwil Associates
(Rural Home Public)
January, 1945
1 B:Red Riot,The Prankster . . 225.00
2 LSt,A:The Judge 175.00
3 LSt,LSt(c) 150.00
4 LSt,LSt(c) covers of #4
   stapled over other comics . . 150.00

TRAIL BLAZERS
Street & Smith Publications
January, 1942
1 Wright Brothers 150.00
2 Benjamin Franklin,Dodgers . 175.00
3 Red Barber,Yankees 255.00
4 Famous War song 125.00
Becomes:

RED DRAGON COMICS
5 JaB(c),B&O:Red Rover:
   B:Capt.Jack Comkmando
   Rex King&Jet,Minute Man . . 750.00
6 O:Red Dragon 1,400.00
7 The Curse of the
   Boneless Men 900.00
8 China V:Japan 500.00
9 The Reducing Ray,Jan '44 . 500.00
November, 1947
(2nd Series)
1 B:Red Dragon 700.00
2 BP 500.00
3 BP,BP(c),I:Dr Neff 450.00
4 BP,BP(c) 550.00
5 BP,BP(c) 400.00
6 BP,BP(c) 400.00
7 BP,BP(c),May 49 . . . . 400.00

RED MASK
(see TIM HOLT)

RED RABBIT
Dearfield/
J. Charles Lave Publ. Co.
January, 1941
1 (fa) 55.00
2 . . . . 30.00
3 thru 10 . . . . @20.00
11 thru 22 . . . . @18.00

RED SEAL COMICS
Harry 'A' Chesler, Jr./Superior
October, 1945
14 GT,Bondage(c),Black Dwarf 500.00
15 GT,Torture 325.00
16 GT 450.00
17 GT,Lady Satan,Sky Chief . 325.00
18 Lady Satan,Sky Chief 325.00
19 Lady Satan,Sky Chief 300.00
20 Lady Satan,Sky Chief 300.00
21 Lady Satan,Sky Chief 300.00
22 Rocketman 200.00

REDSKIN
Youthful Magazines
September, 1950
1 Redskin,Bondage(c) 75.00
2 Apache Dance of Death 50.00
3 Daniel Boone 35.00
4 Sitting Bull- Red Devil
   of the Black Hills 35.00
5 . . . . 35.00
6 Geronimo- Terror of the

Desert,Bondage 45.00
7 Firebrand of the Sioux 35.00
8 . . . . 35.00
9 . . . . 35.00
10 Dead Man's Magic 35.00
11 . . . . 35.00
12 Quanah Parker,Bondage(c) . . 45.00
Becomes:

FAMOUS WESTERN BADMEN
13 Redskin- Last of the
   Comanches 40.00
14 . . . . 25.00
15 The Dalton Boys Apr '52 . . . . 25.00

REMEMBER PEARL HARBOR
Street & Smith Publications
1942
1 N# JaB,Battle of the
   Pacific,Uncle Sam(c) 350.00

RETURN OF THE OUTLAW
Minoan Publishing Co.
February, 1953
1 Billy The Kid 50.00
2 . . . . 30.00
3 thru 11 . . . . @20.00

REVEALING ROMANCES
A.A. Wyn
(Ace Magazines)
September, 1949
1 . . . . 40.00
2 . . . . 20.00
3 thru 6 . . . . @15.00

REX ALLEN COMICS
Dell Publishing Co.
February, 1951
(1) see Four Color #316
2 Ph(c) all 75.00
3 thru 10 . . . . @60.00
11 thru 23 . . . . @40.00
24 ATh 50.00
25 thru 31 . . . . @40.00

REX DEXTER OF MARS
Fox Features Syndicate
Autumn, 1940
1 DBr,DBr(c) Battle ofKooba . 1,500.00

RIBTICKLER
Fox Features Syndicate
1945
1 . . . . 70.00
2 . . . . 35.00
3 Cosmo Cat 25.00
4 thru 6 . . . . @20.00
7 Cosmo Cat 22.00
8 thru 9 . . . . @20.00

RIN TIN TIN
Dell Publishing Co.
November, 1952
(1) see Dell Four Color #434
(1) see Dell Four Color #476
(1) see Dell Four Color #523
4 thru 10 Ph(c) all . . . . @50.00

11 thru 20 . . . . @70.00

Rocket Comics #2 © Hillman Periodicals

ROCKET COMICS
Hillman Periodicals
March, 1940
1 O:Red Roberts;B:Rocket
   Riley,Phantom Ranger,Steel
   Shank,Buzzard Baynes,Lefty
   Larson,The Defender,Man
   with 1,000 Faces 1,800.00
2 . . . . 600.00
3 May '40 E:All Features . . . 1,000.00

ROCKET KELLY
Fox Features Syndicate
Autumn, 1945–Oct. Nov. 1946
N# 200.00
1 . . . . 200.00
2 A:The Puppeteer 150.00
3 thru 6 . . . . @125.00

ROCKETMAN
Ajax/Farrell Publications
June, 1952
1 Space Stories of the Future . 300.00

ROCKET SHIP X
Fox Features Syndicate
September, 1951
1 . . . . 450.00
2 N# Variant of Original 300.00

ROCKY LANE WESTERN
Fawcett/Charlton Comics
May, 1949
1 Ph(c)B:Rocky Lane,Slim
   Pickins 750.00
2 Ph(c) 300.00
3 Ph(c) 200.00
4 Ph(c)CCB,Rail Riders
   Rampage,F Capt Tootsie . . 200.00
5 Ph(c)The Missing
   Stagecoaches 200.00
6 Ph(c)Ghost Town Showdown 150.00
7 Ph(c)The Border Revolt 175.00
8 Ph(c)The Sunset Feud 175.00
9 Ph(c)Hermit of the Hills 175.00

All comics prices listed are for *Near Mint* condition.

10 Ph(c)Badman's Reward ...	150.00
11 Ph(c)Fool's Gold Fiasco ...	125.00
12 Ph(c),CCB,Coyote Breed F:Capt Tootsie,Giant	125.00
13 Ph(c),Giant	125.00
14 Ph(c)	100.00
15 Ph(c)B:Black Jacks Hitching Post,Giant	110.00
16 Ph(c),Giant	100.00
17 Ph(c),Giant	100.00
18 Ph(c)	110.00
19 Ph(c),Giant	115.00
20 Ph(c)The Rodeo Rustler E:Slim Pickens	115.00
21 Ph(c)B: Dee Dickens	100.00
22 Ph(c)	90.00
23 thru 30	@100.00
31 thru 40	@90.00
41 thru 55	@90.00
56 thru 60	@65.00
61 thru 70	@60.00
71 thru 87	@50.00

ROD CAMERON WESTERN
Fawcett Publications
February, 1950

1 Ph(c)	400.00
2 Ph(c)	175.00
3 Ph(c),Seven Cities of Cipiola	150.00
4 Ph(c),Rip-Roaring Wild West	125.00
5 Ph(c),Six Gun Sabotage ...	125.00
6 Ph(c),Medicine Bead Murders	125.00
7 Ph(c),Wagon Train Of Death	125.00
8 Ph(c),Bayou Badman	125.00
9 Ph(c),Rustlers Ruse	125.00
10 Ph(c),White Buffalo Trail ...	125.00
11 Ph(c),Lead Poison	100.00
12 thru 19 Ph(c)	@100.00
20 Phc(c),Great Army Hoax ...	100.00

ROLY-POLY COMICS
Green Publishing Co.
1945

1 B:Red Rube&Steel Sterling .	200.00
6 A:Blue Cycle	100.00

Roly-Poly Comics #15
© Green Publishing

10 A:Red Rube	100.00
11	100.00
12	100.00
13	100.00
14 A:Black Hood	100.00
15 A:Steel Fist;1946	225.00

ROMANCE AND CONFESSION STORIES
St. John Publishing Co.
1949

1 MB(c),MB	250.00

ROMANTIC LOVE
Avon Periodicals/Realistic
September-October, 1949

1 P(c)	135.00
2 P(c)	85.00
3 P(c)	75.00
4 Ph(c)	75.00
5 P(c)	75.00
6 Ph(c),Drug,Thrill Crazy	100.00
7 P(c)	75.00
8 P(c)	75.00
9 EK,P(c)	85.00
10 thru 11 P(c)	@80.00
12 EK	85.00
20	75.00
21	75.00
22 EK	75.00
23 EK	75.00

ROMANTIC MARRIAGE
Ziff-Davis/ St. John Publishing Co.
November-December, 1950

1 Ph(c),Selfish wife	125.00
2 P(c),Mother's Boy	60.00
3 P(c),Hen Peck House	50.00
4 P(c)	50.00
5 Ph(c)	50.00
6 Ph(c)	40.00
7 Ph(c)	40.00
8 P(c)	40.00
9 P(c)	40.00
10 P/PH(c)	100.00
11	40.00
12	40.00
13 Ph(c)	40.00
14 thru 20	@40.00
20 Ph(c)	40.00
21	40.00
22	40.00
23 MB	45.00
24	40.00

ROMANTIC PICTURE NOVELETTES
Magazine Enterprises
1946

1 Mary Wothr adventure	100.00

ROMANTIC SECRETS
Fawcett Publ./Charlton Comics
September, 1949

1 Ph(c)	100.00
2 MSy(c)	50.00
3 MSy(c)	50.00
4 GE	60.00
5 BP	55.00
6	25.00
7 BP	25.00

8	25.00
9 GE	35.00
10 BP	30.00
11	25.00
12 BP	30.00
13	25.00
14	25.00
15	25.00
16 BP,MSy	30.00
17 BP	30.00
18	25.00
19	25.00
20 BP.MBi	30.00
21	20.00
22	20.00
23	18.00
24 GE	40.00
25 MSy	18.00
26 BP,MSy	20.00
27 MSy	18.00
28	18.00
29 BP	20.00
30 thru 32	@18.00
33 MSy	20.00
34 BP	20.00
35	18.00
36 BP	20.00
37 BP	20.00
38 thru 52	@18.00

ROMANTIC STORY
Fawcett Publ./Charlton Comics
November, 1949

1 Ph(c)	75.00
2 Ph(c)	40.00
3 Ph(c)	30.00
4 Ph(c)	30.00
5 Ph(c)	30.00
6 Ph(c)	30.00
7 BP,Ph(c)	25.00
8 BP,Ph(c)	25.00
9 Ph(c)	22.00
10 Ph(c)	22.00
11 Ph(c)	22.00
12 Ph(c)	22.00
13 Ph(c)	22.00
14 Ph(c)	22.00
15 GE,Ph(c)	35.00
16 BP,Ph(c)	25.00
17 Ph(c)	20.00
18 Ph(c)	20.00
19 Ph(c)	20.00
20 BP,Ph(c)	22.00
22 ATh,Ph(c)	18.00

Charlton Comics

23	15.00
24 Ph(c)	15.00
25 thru 29	@15.00
30 BP	20.00
31 thru 39	@15.00

ROMANTIC WESTERN
Fawcett Publications
Winter, 1949

1 Ph(c)	125.00
2 Ph(c),AW,AMc	135.00
3 Ph(c)	100.00

ROMEO TUBBS
(see MY SECRET LIFE)

GOLDEN AGE

ROUNDUP
D.S. Publishing Co.
July-August, 1948
1 HcK	125.00
2 Drug	100.00
3	75.00
4	75.00
5 Male Bondage	85.00

ROY CAMPANELLA, BASEBALL HERO
Fawcett Publications
1950
N# Ph(c),Life Story of the Battling Dodgers Catcher	500.00

ROY ROGERS
Dell Publishing Co.
1 photo (c)	750.00
2	300.00
3	200.00
4	200.00
5	200.00
6 thru 10	@150.00
11 thru 20	@125.00
21 thru 30	@100.00
31 thru 46	@75.00
47 thru 50	@65.00
51 thru 56	@50.00
57 Drug	65.00
58 thru 70	@50.00
71 thru 80	@40.00
81 thru 91	@35.00
Becomes:

ROY ROGERS AND TRIGGER
92 thru 99	@35.00
100	50.00
101 thru 118	@35.00
119 thru 125 ATn	@50.00
126 thru 131	@40.00
132 thru 144 RsM	@45.00
145	50.00

ROY ROGER'S TRIGGER
Dell Publishing Co.
May, 1951
(1) see Dell Four Color #329	
2 Ph(c)	125.00
3 P(c)	40.00
4 P(c)	40.00
5 P(c)	40.00
6 thru 17 P(c)	@30.00

RULAH, JUNGLE GODDESS
(see ZOOT COMICS)

SAARI, THE JUNGLE GODDESS
P.L. Publishing Co.
November, 1951
1 The Bantu Blood Curse	300.00

SABU, ELEPHANT BOY
Fox Features Syndicate
June, 1950
1(30) WW,Ph(c)	175.00
2 JKa,Ph(c),August'50	125.00

HAPPY HOULIHANS
Fables Publications
(E.C. Comics)
Autumn, 1947
1 O:Moon Girl	400.00
2	250.00
Becomes:

SADDLE JUSTICE
3 HcK,JCr,AF	300.00
4 AF,JCr	275.00
5 AF,Grl,WI	250.00
6 AF,Grl	250.00
7 AF,Grl	250.00
8 AF,Grl,WI	250.00
Becomes:

SADDLE ROMANCES
9 Grl(c),Grl	300.00
10 AF(c),WW	325.00
11 AF(c),Grl	275.00

SAD SACK
Harvey Publications
Sept. 1949
1 I:Little Dot	400.00
2	200.00
3	100.00
4 thru 10	@75.00
11 thru 21	50.00
22 Back in the Army Again, The Specialist	35.00
23 thru 50	@20.00
51 thru 100	@15.00
100 thru 150	@7.50
151 thru 200	@5.00
200 thru 287	@4.00
See also Other Pub. (Color)	

The Saint #2 © Avon Periodicals

SAINT, THE
Avon Periodicals
August, 1947
1 JKa,JKa(c),Bondage(c)	550.00
2	300.00
3 Rolled Stocking Leg(c)	225.00
4 MB(c)	200.00
5 Spanking Panel	275.00
6 B:Miss Fury	325.00

7 P(c),Detective Cases(c)	175.00
8 P(c),Detective Cases"(c)	150.00
9 EK(c),The Notorious Murder Mob	150.00
10 WW,P(c),V:The Communist Menace	175.00
11 P(c),Wanted For Robbery	100.00
12 P(c),The Blowpipe Murders March, 1952	125.00

SAM HILL PRIVATE EYE
Close-Up Publications
1950
1 The Double Trouble Caper	100.00
2	55.00
3	50.00
4 Negligee panels	65.00
5 thru 7	@40.00

SAMSON
Fox Features Syndicate
Autumn, 1940
1 BP,GT,A:Wing Turner	1,600.00
2 BP,A:Dr. Fung	700.00
3 JSh(c),A:Navy Jones	500.00
4 WE,B:Yarko	450.00
5 WE	450.00
6 WE,O:The Topper;Sept'41	450.00

SAMSON
Ajax Farrell Publ (Four Star)
April, 1955
12 The Electric Curtain	200.00
13 Assignment Danger	175.00
14 The Red Raider;Aug'55	175.00

SANDS OF THE SOUTH PACIFIC
Toby Press
January, 1953
1 2-Fisted Romantic Adventure	150.00

SCHOOL DAY ROMANCES
(see POPULAR TEEN-AGERS)

SCIENCE COMICS
Fox Features Syndicate
February, 1940
1 GT,LF(c),O&B:Electro,Perisphere Payne,The Eagle,Navy Jones; B:Marga,Cosmic Carson, Dr. Doom; Bondage(c)	3,500.00
2 GT,LF(c)	1,600.00
3 GT,LF(c),Dynamo	1,300.00
4 JK,Cosmic Carson	1,200.00
5 Giant Comiscope Offer Eagle(c)	700.00
6 Dynamop(c)	700.00
7 Bondage(c),Dynamo	700.00
8 September, 1940 Eagle(c)	650.00

SCIENCE COMICS
Humor Publications
January, 1946
1 RP(c),Story of the A-Bomb	100.00
2 RP(c),How Museum Pieces Are Assembled	45.00
3 AF,RP(c),How Underwater Tunnels Are Made	75.00

GOLDEN AGE

4 RP(c),Behind the Scenes at
  A TV Broadcast 30.00
5 The Story of the World's
  Bridges; September, 1946 . . 35.00

SCIENCE COMICS
Ziff-Davis Publ. Co.
May, 1946
N# Used For A Mail Order
  Test Market 250.00

SCIENCE COMICS
Export Publication Enterprises
March, 1951
1 How to resurrect a dead rat . . 50.00

SCOOP COMICS
Harry 'A' Chesler Jr.
November, 1941
1 I&B:Rocketman&Rocketgirl;B:Dan
  Hastings;O&B:Master Key . 1,000.00
2 A:Rocketboy,Eye Injury 950.00
3 Partial rep. of #2 . . . . 500.00
4 thru 7 do not exist
8 1945 . . . . 300.00

SCREAM COMICS
Humor Publ./Current Books
(Ace Magazines)
Autumn, 1944
1 . . . . 100.00
2 . . . . 50.00
3 . . . . 40.00
4 thru 15 . . . . @40.00
16 I:Lily Belle 45.00
17 . . . . 30.00
18 Drug 40.00
19 . . . . 30.00
Becomes:

ANDY COMICS
20 Teenage 25.00
21 . . . . 25.00
Becomes:

ERNIE COMICS
22 Teenage 30.00
23 thru 25 . . . . @20.00
Becomes:

ALL LOVE ROMANCES
26 Ernie 25.00
27 LbC 32.00
28 thru 32 . . . . @15.00

(Capt. Silvers Log of...) SEA HOUND, THE
Avon Periodicals
1945
N# The Esmerelda's Treasure . 90.00
2 Adventures in Brazil 70.00
3 Louie the Llama 70.00
4 In Greed & Vengence;
  Jan-Feb, 1946 . . . . 70.00

SECRET LOVES
Comics Magazines
(Quality Comics)
November, 1949
1 BWa(c) 150.00
2 BWa(c),Lingerie(c) 125.00
3 RC 75.00
4 . . . . 50.00
5 Boom Town Babe 75.00

6 . . . . 50.00

SECRET MYSTERIES
(see CRIME MYSTERIES)

SELECT DETECTIVE
D.S. Publishing Co.
August-September, 1948
1 MB,Exciting New Mystery
  Cases 150.00
2 MB,AMc,Dead Men.... . . . . . 100.00
3 Face in theFrame;Dec-Jan'48 75.00

SERGEANT PRESTON OF THE YUKON
Dell Publishing Co.
August, 1951
(1 thru 4) see Dell Four Color #344;
  #373, 397, 419
5 thru 10 P(c) . . . . @65.00
11 P(c) 50.00
12 P(c) 50.00
13 P(c),O:Sergeant Preston 55.00
14 thru 17 P(c) . . . . @50.00
18 P(c) 55.00
19 thru 29 Ph(c) . . . . @55.00

Seven Seas Comics #6 © Universal Phoenix Features/Leader Publ

SEVEN SEAS COMICS
Universal Phoenix Features/ Leader Publ.
April, 1946
1 MB,RWb(c),B:South Sea
  Girl, Captain Cutlass 600.00
2 MB,RWb(c) 500.00
3 MB,AF,MB(c) 450.00
4 MB,MB(c) 450.00
5 MB,MB(c),Hangman's Noose 450.00
6 MB,MB(c);1947 . . . . 450.00

SHADOW COMICS
Street & Smith Publications
March, 1940
1-1 P(c),B:Shadow,Doc Savage,
  Bill Barnes,Nick Carter,
  Frank Merriwell,Iron Munro 4,000.00

1-2 P(c),B: The Avenger 1,500.00
1-3 P(c),A: Norgill the
  Magician 1,000.00
1-4 P(c),B:The Three
  Musketeers 850.00
1-5 P(c),E: Doc Savage 850.00
1-6 A: Captain Fury 700.00
1-7 O&B: The Wasp 750.00
1-8 A:Doc Savage 700.00
1-9 A:Norgill the Magician 700.00
1-10 O:Iron Ghost;B:The Dead
  End Kids 650.00
1-11 O:Hooded Wasp 700.00
1-12 Crime Does Not pay 550.00
2-1 . . . . 550.00
2-2 Shadow Becomes Invisible 500.00
2-3 O&B:supersnipe;
  F:Little Nemo 725.00
2-4 F:Little Nemo 500.00
2-5 V:The Ghost Faker 500.00
2-6 A:Blackstone the Magician . 400.00
2-7 V:The White Dragon 400.00
2-8 A:Little Nemo 400.00
2-9 The Hand of Death 400.00
2-10 A:Beebo the WonderHorse 400.00
2-11 V:Devil Kyoti 400.00
2-12 V:Devil Kyoti 375.00
3-1 JaB(c),V:Devil Kyoti 375.00

Shadow Comics #65 (6/5)
© Street & Smith Publications

3-2 Red Skeleton Life Story . . 375.00
3-3 V:Monstrodamus 375.00
3-4 V:Monstrodamus 375.00
3-5 V:Monstrodamus 375.00
3-6 V:Devil's of the Deep 375.00
3-7 V: Monstrodamus 375.00
3-8 E: The Wasp 375.00
3-9 The Stolen Lighthouse . . . 375.00
3-10 A:Doc Savage 375.00
3-11 P(c),V: Thade 375.00
3-12 V: Thade 375.00
4-1 Red Cross Appeal on (c) . 350.00
4-2 V:The Brain of Nippon . . . 350.00
4-3 Little Men in Space 350.00
4-4 ...Mystifies Berlin 350.00
4-5 ...Brings Terror to Tokio . . 350.00
4-6 V:The Tarantula 350.00
4-7 Crypt of the Seven Skulls . 350.00
4-8 V:the Indigo Mob 350.00
4-9 Ghost Guarded Treasure

GOLDEN AGE

of the Haunted Glen 350.00
4-10 V:The Hydra 350.00
4-11 V:The Seven Sinners 350.00
4-12 Club Curio 300.00
5-1 A:Flatty Foote 300.00
5-2 Bells of Doom 300.00
5-3 The Circle of Death 300.00
5-4 The Empty Safe Riddle . . . 300.00
5-5 The Mighty Master Nomad . 300.00
5-6 ...Fights Piracy Among
   the Golden Isles 300.00
5-7 V:The Talon 300.00
5-8 V:The Talon 300.00
5-9 V:The Talon 300.00
5-10 V:The Crime Master 300.00
5-11 The Clutch of the Talon . . 300.00
5-12 Most Dangerous Criminal . 300.00
6-1 Double Z 300.00
6-2 Riddle of Prof.Mentalo . . . 300.00
6-3 V:Judge Lawless 300.00
6-4 V:Dr. Zenith 300.00
6-5 . . . . 300.00
6-6 ...Invades the
   Crucible of Death 300.00
6-7 Four Panel Cover 300.00
6-8 Crime Among the Aztecs . 300.00
6-9 I:Shadow Jr. 350.00
6-10 Devil's Passage 300.00
6-11 The Black Pagoda 300.00
6-12 BP,BP(c),Atomic Bomb
   Secrets Stolen 325.00
7-1 The Yellow Band 325.00
7-2 A:Shadow Jr. 325.00
7-3 BP,BP(c),Crime Under
   the Border 350.00
7-4 BP,BP(c),One Tree Island,
   Atomic Bomb 375.00
7-5 A:Shadow Jr. 325.00
7-6 BP,BP(c),The Sacred Sword
   of Sanjorojo 350.00
7-7 Crime K.O. 350.00
7-8 ...Raids Crime Harbor . . . 350.00
7-9 BP.BP(c),Kilroy Was Here 350.00
7-10 BP,BP(c),The Riddle of
   the Flying Saucer 400.00
7-11 BP,BP(c),Crime
   Doesn't Pay 350.00
7-12 BP,BP(c)Back From
   the Grave 350.00
8-1 BP,BP(c),Curse of the Cat 350.00
8-2 BP,BP(c),Decay,Vermin &
   Murder in the Bayou 350.00
8-3 BP,BP(c),The Spider Boy . 350.00
8-4 BP,BP(c),Death Rises
   Out of the Sea 350.00
8-5 BP,BP(c),Jekyll-
   Hyde Murders 350.00
8-6 Secret of Valhalla Hall . . . 350.00
8-7 BP,BP(c),Shadow in Danger 350.00
8-8 BP,BP(c),...Solves a
   Twenty Year Old Crime . . . 350.00
8-9 BP,BP(c),3-D Effect(c) 350.00
8-10 BP,BP(c),Up&Down(c) . . . 350.00
8-11 BP,BP(c) 350.00
8-12 BP,BP(c),Arabs,Boat(c) . . 350.00
9-1 Airport(c) 350.00
9-2 BP,BP(c),Flying Cannon(c) 350.00
9-3 BP,BP(c),Shadow's Shadow 350.00
9-4 BP,BP(c) 350.00
9-5 Death in the Stars;Aug'49 . 350.00

SHARP COMICS
H.C. Blackerby
Winter, 1945
1 O:Planetarian(c) 300.00

2 O:The Pioneer 250.00

Sheena, Queen of the Jungle #10
© Real Adventures

SHEENA, QUEEN OF THE JUNGLE
Real Adventures
(Fiction House)
Spring, 1942
1 Blood Hunger 1,800.00
2 Black Orchid of Death 800.00
3 Harem Shackles 600.00
4 The Zebra Raiders 400.00
5 War of the Golden Apes . . . 350.00
6 . . . . 325.00
7 They Claw By Night 300.00
8 The Congo Colossus 300.00
9 and 10 . . . . @275.00
11 Red Fangs of the Tree Tribe 275.00
12 . . . . 225.00
13 Veldt o/t Voo Doo Lions . . . 225.00
14 The Hoo Doo Beasts of
   Mozambique 225.00
15 . . . . 225.00
16 Black Ivory 225.00
17 Great Congo Treasure Trek 225.00
18 Doom of the Elephant Drum
   Winter, 1952 . . . . 225.00

SHIELD-WIZARD COMICS
MLJ Magazines
Summer, 1940
1 IN,EA,O:Shield 3,400.00
2 O:Shield;I:Roy 1,500.00
3 Roy,Child Bondage(c) 900.00
4 Shield,Roy,Wizard 900.00
5 B:Dusty-Boy Dectective,Child
   Bondage 800.00
6 B:Roy the Super Boy,Child
   Bondage 750.00
7 Shield(c),Roy Bondage(c) . . 770.00
8 Bondage(c) 750.00
9 Shield/Roy(c) 650.00
10 Shield/Roy(c) 650.00
11 Shield/Roy(c) 650.00
12 Shield/Roy(c) 650.00
13 Bondage (c);Spring'44 . . . . 675.00

SHIP AHOY
Spotlight Publishers
November, 1944
1 LbC(c) 75.00

SHOCK DETECTIVE CASE
(see CRIMINALS ON THE RUN)

SHOCK DETECTIVE CASES
(see CRIMINALS ON THE RUN)

SHOCK SUSPENSTORIES
Tiny Tot Comics
(E.C. Comics)
February-March, 1952
1 JDa,JKa,AF(c),ElectricChair . 650.00
2 WW,JDa,Grl,JKa,WW(c) . . . 350.00
3 WW,JDa,JKa,WW(c) 300.00
4 WW,JDa,JKa,WW(c) 300.00
5 WW,JDa,JKa,WW(c),Hanging 250.00
6 WW,AF,JKa,WW(c),
   Bondage(c) 300.00
7 JKa,WW,GE,AF(c),Face
   Melting 300.00
8 JKa,AF,AW,GE,WW,AF(c) . . 300.00
9 JKa,AF,RC,WW,AF(c) 300.00
10 JKa,WW,RC,JKa(c),Drug . . 300.00
11 JCr,JKa,WW,RC,JCr(c) . . . 275.00
12 AF,JKa,WW,RC,AF(c)Drug(c) 300.00
13 JKa,WW,FF,JKa(c) 350.00
14 JKa,WW,BK,WW(c) 275.00
15 JKa,WW,RC,JDa(c)
   Strangulation 225.00
16 GE,RC,JKa,GE(c),Rape . . . 225.00
17 GE,RC,JKa,GE(c) 200.00
18 GE,RC,JKa,GE(c);Jan'55 . . 200.00

SHOCKING MYSTERY CASES
(see THRILLING CRIME CASES)

SILVER STREAK COMICS
Your Guide/New Friday/
Comic House/Newsbrook
Publications/Lev Gleason
December, 1939
1 JCo,JCo(c),I&B:The Claw,Red
   Reeves Capt.Fearless;B:Mr.
   Midnight,Wasp;A:Spiritman 11,000.00
2 JSm,JCo,JSm(c) 3,500.00
3 JaB(c),I&O:Silver Streak;
   B:Dickie Dean,Lance Hale,
   Ace Powers,Bill Wayne,
   Planet Patrol 2,800.00
4 JCo,JaB(c)B:Sky Wolf;
   N:Silver Streak,I:Lance
   Hale's Sidekick-Jackie . . . 1,300.00
5 JCo,JCo(c),Dickie Dean
   V:The Raging Flood 1,500.00
6 JCo,JaB,JCo(c),O&I:Daredevil
   [Blue & Yellow Costume];
   R:The Claw 11,000.00
7 JCo,N: Daredevil 7,200.00
8 JCo,JCo(c) 2,300.00
9 JCo,BoW(c) 1,500.00
10 BoW,BoW(c) 1,300.00

Silver Streak #13
© Your Guide/New Friday

11 DRi(c) I:Mercury 900.00
12 DRi(c) 700.00
13 JaB,JaB(c),O:Thun-Dohr . . . 700.00
14 JaB,JaB(c),A:Nazi
   Skull Men 700.00
15 JaB,DBr,JaB(c),
   B:Bingham Boys 600.00
16 DBr,BoW(c),Hitler(c) 650.00
17 DBr,JaB(c),E:Daredevil 600.00
18 DBr,JaB(c),B:The Saint 500.00
19 DBr,EA 400.00
20 BW,BEv,EA 400.00
21 BW,BEv 400.00
Becomes:

CRIME DOES NOT PAY

22(23) CBi(c),The Mad Musician
   & Tunes of Doom 1,600.00
23 CBi(c),John Dillinger-One
   Man Underworld 1,000.00
24 CBi(c),The Mystery of the
   Indian Dick 700.00
25 CBi(c),Dutch Shultz-King
   of the Underworld 450.00
26 CBi(c),Lucky Luciano-The
   Deadliest of Crime Rats . . . 450.00
27 CBi(c),Pretty Boy Floyd . . . 450.00
28 CBi(c), ... 450.00
29 CBi(c),Two-Gun Crowley-The
   Bad Kid with the Itchy
   Trigger Finger 350.00
30 CBi(c),"Monk"Eastman
   V:Thompson's Mob 350.00
31 CBi(c) The Million Dollar
   Bank Robbery 250.00
32 CBi(c),Seniorita of Sin 250.00
33 CBi(c),Meat Cleaver Murder 250.00
34 CBi(c),Elevator Shaft 250.00
35 CBi(c),Case o/t MissingToe . 250.00
36 CBi(c) 225.00
37 CBi(c) 225.00
38 CBi(c) 225.00
39 FG,CBi(c) 225.00
40 FG,CBi(c) 225.00
41 FG,RP,CBi(c),The Cocksure
   Counterfeiter 175.00
42 FG,RP,CBi(c) 200.00
43 FG,RP,CBi(c) 150.00

44 FG,CBi(c),The Most Shot
   At Gangster 150.00
45 FG,CBi(c) 150.00
46 FG,CBi(c),ChildKidnapping(c) 160.00
47 FG,CBi(c),ElectricChair 200.00
48 FG,CBi(c) 150.00
49 FG,CBi(c) 150.00
50 FG,CBi(c) 150.00
51 FG,GT,CBi(c),1st Monthly Iss.125.00
52 FG,GT,CBi(c) 125.00
53 FG,CBi(c) 125.00
54 FG,CBi(c) 125.00
55 FG,CBi(c) 125.00
56 FG,GT,CBi(c) 125.00
57 FG,CBi(c) 125.00
58 FG,CBi(c) 125.00
59 FG,Cbi(c) 125.00
60 FG,CBi(c) 125.00
61 FG,GT,CBi(c) 100.00
62 FG,CBi(c),Bondage(c) 125.00
63 FG,GT,CBi(c) 100.00
64 FG,GT,CBi(c) 100.00
65 FG,CBi(c) 100.00
66 FG,GT,CBi(c) 100.00
67 FG,GT,CBi(c) 100.00
68 FG,CBi(c) 100.00
69 FG,CBi(c) 100.00
70 FG,Cbi(c) 100.00
71 FG,CBi(c) 75.00
72 FG,CBi(c) 75.00
73 FG,CBi(c) 75.00
74 FG,CBi(c) 75.00
75 FG,CBi(c) 75.00
76 FG,CBi(c) 75.00
77 FG,CBi(c),Electrified Safe . . 100.00
78 FG,CBi(c) 75.00
79 FG 75.00
80 FG 75.00
81 FG 75.00
82 FG 75.00
83 FG 75.00
84 FG 75.00
85 FG 75.00
86 FG 70.00
87 FG,P(c),The Rock-A-Bye
   Baby Murder 70.00
88 FG,P(c),Death Carries a Torch 70.00
89 FG,BF,BF P(c),The Escort
   Murder Case 70.00
90 FG,BF P(c),The Alhambra
   Club Murders 70.00
91 FG,AMc,BF P(c),Death
   Watches The Clock 70.00
92 BF,FG,BF P(c) 70.00
93 BF,FG,AMc,BF P(c) 70.00
94 BF,FG,BF P(c) 70.00
95 FG,AMc,BF P(c) 70.00
96 BF,FG,BF P(c),The Case of
   the Movie Star's Double . . . 70.00
97 FG,BF P(c) 70.00
98 BF,FG,BF P(c),Bondage(c) . . 70.00
99 BF,FG,BF P(c) 70.00
100 FG,BF,AMc,P(c),The Case
   of the Jittery Patient 100.00
101 FG,BF,AMc,P(c) 60.00
102 FG,BF,AMc,BF P(c) 60.00
103 FG,BF,AMc,BF P(c) 60.00
104 thru 110 FG . . . . @60.00
111 thru 120 . . . . @60.00
121 thru 140 . . . . @45.00
141 JKu 40.00
142 JKu,CBi(c) 40.00
143 JKu,Comic Code 40.00
144 I Helped Capture"Fat Face"
   George Klinerz 35.00

145 RP,Double Barreled Menace 35.00
146 BP,The Con & The Canary . 35.00
147 JKu,BP,A Long Shoe On the
   Highway;July, 1955 . . . . . . 50.00

SINGLE SERIES
United Features Syndicate
1938
1 Captain & The Kids 550.00
2 Bronco Bill 300.00
3 Ella Cinders 250.00
4 Li'l Abner 500.00
5 Fritzi Ritz 175.00
6 Jim Hardy 225.00
7 Frankie Doodle 175.00
8 Peter Pat 175.00
9 Strange As it Seems 200.00
10 Little Mary Mixup 165.00
11 Mr. & Mrs. Beans 165.00
12 Joe Jinx 165.00
13 Looy Dot Dope 165.00
14 Billy Make Believe 165.00
15 How It Began 175.00
16 Illustrated Gags 125.00
17 Danny Dingle 125.00
18 Li'l Abner 400.00
19 Broncho Bill 225.00
20 Tarzan 1,200.00
21 Ella Cinders 200.00
22 Iron Vic 175.00
23 Tailspin Tommy 200.00
24 Alice In Wonderland 250.00
25 Abbie an' Slats 200.00
26 Little Mary Mixup 150.00
27 Jim Hardy 175.00
28 Ella Cinders & Abbie AN'
   Slats 1942 . . . . 175.00

SKELETON HAND
American Comics Group
September-October, 1952
1 . . . . 300.00
2 The Were-Serpent of Karnak 200.00
3 Waters of Doom 175.00
4 Black Dust 175.00
5 The Rise & Fall of the
   Bogey Man 175.00
6 July-August, 1953 . . . . 175.00

SKY BLAZERS
Hawley Publications
September, 1940
1 Flying Aces,Sky Pirates 450.00
2 November, 1940 . . . . 300.00

SKYMAN
Columbia Comics Group
1941
1 OW,OW(c),O:Skyman,Face . 800.00
2 OW,OW(c),Yankee Doodle . 450.00
3 OW,OW(c) 300.00
4 OW,OW(c),Statue of
   Liberty(c) 1948 . . . . 300.00

SKY PILOT
Ziff-Davis Publishing Co.
1950
10 NS P(c),Lumber Pirates . . . 100.00
11 Ns P(c),The 2,00 Foot Drop;
   April-May, 1951 . . . . 75.00

GOLDEN AGE

SKY ROCKET
Home Guide Publ.
(Harry 'A' Chesler)
1944
1 Alias the Dragon,Skyrocket . 200.00

SKY SHERIFF
D.S. Publishing
Summer, 1948
1 I:Breeze Lawson & the Prowl
Plane Patrol 75.00

SLAM BANG COMICS
Fawcett Publications
January, 1940
1 B:Diamond Jack,Mark Swift,
Lee Granger,Jungle King . 1,500.00
2 F:Jim Dolan Two-Fisted
Crime Buster 650.00
3 A: Eric the Talking Lion . . . 900.00
4 F: Hurricane Hansen-Sea
Adventurer 550.00
5 . . . . 550.00
6 I: Zoro the Mystery Man;
Bondage(c) 550.00
7 Bondage(c);Sept., 1940 . . . 550.00

SLAPSTICK COMICS
Comic Magazine Distrib., Inc.
1945
N# Humorous Parody 150.00

SLAVE GIRL COMICS
Avon Periodicals
February, 1949
1 . . . . 650.00
2 April, 1949 . . . . 500.00

SLICK CHICK COMICS
Leader Enterprises, Inc.
1947
1 Teen-Aged Humor 65.00
2 Teen-Aged Humor 45.00
3 1947 . . . . 45.00

SMASH COMICS
Comics Magazine, Inc.
(Quality Comics Group)
August, 1939
1 WE,O&B:Hugh Hazard, Bozo
the Robot,Black X, Invisible
Justice: B:Wings Wendall,
Chic Carter 2,000.00
2 WE,A:Lone Star Rider 800.00
3 WE,B:Captain Cook,JohnLaw 500.00
4 WE,PGn,B:Flash Fulton . . . 450.00
5 WE,PGn,Bozo Robot 450.00
6 WE,PGn,GFx,Black X(c) . . . 450.00
7 WE,PGn,GFx,Wings
Wendell(c) 400.00
8 WE,PGn,GFx,Bozo Robot . . 400.00
9 WE,PGn,GFx,Black X(c) . . . 400.00
10 WE,PGn,GFx,Bozo robot(c) 400.00
11 WE,PGn,GFx,BP,Black X(c) 400.00
12 WE,PGn,GFx,BP,Bozo(c) . . 400.00
13 WE,PGn,GFx,AB,BP,B:Mango,
Purple Trio,BlackX(c) . . . 400.00
14 BP,LF,AB,PGn,I:The Ray . 2,200.00
15 BP,LF,AB,PGn,The Ram(c) 1,000.00
16 BP,LF,AB,PGn,Bozo(c) . . . 1,000.00
17 BP,LF,AB,PGn,JCo,
The Ram(c) 1,000.00

Smash Comics #35
© Comics Magazine/Quality Comics

18 BP,LF,AB,JCo,PGn,
B&O:Midnight 1,200.00
19 BP,LF,AB,JCo,PGn,Bozo(c) 650.00
20 BP,LF,AB,JCo,PGn,
The Ram(c) 650.00
21 BP,LF,AB,JCo,PGn 650.00
22 BP,LF,AB,JCo,PGn,
B:The Jester 650.00
23 BP,AB,JCo,RC,PGn,
The Ram(c) 500.00
24 BP,AB,JCo,RC,PGn,A:Sword,
E:ChicCarter,
N:WingsWendall 500.00
25 AB,JCo,RC,PGn,O:Wildfire . 600.00
26 AB,JCo,RC,PGn,Bozo(c) . . 500.00
27 AB,JCo,RC,PGn,The Ram(c) 500.00
28 AB,JCo,RC,PGn,
1st Midnight (c) 500.00
29 AB,JCo,Rc,PGn,B:Midnight(c) 450.00
30 AB,JCo,PGn 450.00
31 AB,JCo,PGn 400.00
32 AB,JCo,PGn 400.00
33 AB,JCo,PGn,O:Marksman . . 500.00
34 AB,JCo,PGn 400.00
35 AB,JCo,RC,PGn 400.00
36 AB,JCo,PGn,E:Midnight(c) 400.00
37 AB,JCo,RC,PGn,Doc
Wacky becomes Fastest
Human on Earth 400.00
38 JCo,RC,PGn,B:Yankee Eagle 450.00
39 PGn,B:Midnight(c) 350.00
40 PGn,E:Ray 350.00
41 PGn 225.00
42 PGn,B:Lady Luck 250.00
43 PGn 250.00
44 PGn 225.00
45 PGn,E:Midnight(c) 225.00
46 RC,Twelve Hours to Live . . 225.00
47 Wanted Midnight,
Dead or Alive 225.00
48 Midnight Meets the
Menace from Mars 225.00
49 PGn,FG,Mass of Muscle . . . 225.00
50 I:Hyram the Hermit 225.00
51 A:Wild Bill Hiccup 175.00
52 PGn,FG,Did Ancient Rome Fall,
or was it Pushed? 175.00
53 Is ThereHonorAmongThieves 175.00

54 A:Smear-Faced Schmaltz . . 175.00
55 Never Trouble Trouble until
Trouble Troubles You 175.00
56 The Laughing Killer 175.00
57 A Dummy that Turns Into
A Curse 175.00
58 . . . . 175.00
59 A Corpse that Comes Alive . 175.00
60 The Swooner & the Trush . . 175.00
61 . . . . 150.00
62 V:The Lorelet 150.00
63 PGn 150.00
64 PGn,In Search of King Zoris 150.00
65 PGn,V:Cyanide Cindy 150.00
66 Under Circle's Spell 150.00
67 A Living Clue 150.00
68 JCo,Atomic Dice 150.00
69 JCo,V:Sir Nuts 150.00
70 . . . . 150.00
71 . . . . 125.00
72 JCo,Angela,the Beautiful
Bovine 125.00
73 . . . . 125.00
74 . . . . 125.00
75 The Revolution 125.00
76 Bowl Over Crime 125.00
77 Who is Lilli Dilli? 125.00
78 JCo,Win Over Crime 125.00
79 V:The Men From Mars 125.00
80 JCo,V:Big Hearted Bosco . . 125.00
81 V:Willie the Kid 125.00
82 V:Woodland Boy 125.00
83 JCo,Quizmaster 125.00
84 A Date With Father Time . . 125.00
85 JCo,A Singing Swindle 125.00

SMASH HITS SPORTS COMICS
Essankay Publications
January, 1949
1 LbC,LbC(c) 200.00

SMILEY BURNETTE WESTERN
Fawcett Publications
March, 1950
1 Ph(c),B:Red Eagle 350.00
2 Ph(c) 250.00
3 Ph(c) 250.00
4 Ph(c) 250.00

SMILIN' JACK
Dell Publishing Co.
1940
1 . . . . 125.00
2 . . . . 65.00
3 thru 8 . . . . @40.00

SMITTY
Dell Publishing Co.
1940
1 . . . . 100.00
2 . . . . 50.00
3 . . . . 40.00
4 thru 7 . . . . @30.00

SNAP
Harry 'A' Chesler Jr.
Publications
1944
N# Humorous 100.00

Smilin' Jack #12 © Dell Publishing Co.

SNAPPY COMICS
Cima Publications
(Prize)
1945
1 A:Animale 175.00

SNIFFY THE PUP
Animated Cartoons
(Standard Comics)
November, 1949
5 FF,Funny Animal 45.00
6 thru 9 Funny Animal . . . . @20.00
10 thru 17 Funny Animal . . . @15.00
18 September, 1953 . . . . 15.00

SOLDIER COMICS
Fawcett Publications
January, 1952
1 Fighting Yanks on Flaming
  Battlefronts 70.00
2 Blazing Battles Exploding
  with Combat 35.00
3 . . . . 30.00
4 A Blow for Freedom . . . 25.00
5 Only The Dead Are Free . . . 25.00
6 Blood & Guts 18.00
7 The Phantom Sub 18.00
8 More Plasma! 18.00
9 Red Artillery 18.00
10 . . . . 18.00
11 September, 1953 . . . . 18.00

SOLDIERS OF FORTUNE
Creston Publications
(American Comics Group)
February-March, 1952
1 OW(c),B:Ace Carter,
  Crossbones, Lance Larson . 150.00
2 OW(c) 75.00
3 OW(c) 60.00
4 . . . . 60.00
5 OW(c) 60.00
6 OW(c),OW,Bondage(c) . . . 65.00
7 . . . . 60.00
8 OW thru 10 . . . . @60.00
11 OW,Format Change to War . 30.00

12 . . . . 30.00
13 OW,February-March, 1953 . . 30.00

SON OF SINBAD
St. John Publishing Co.
February, 1950
1 JKu,JKu(c),The Curse of the
  Caliph's Dancer 300.00

SPACE ACTION
Junior Books
(Ace Magazines)
June, 1952
1 Invaders from a Lost Galaxy 550.00
2 The Silicon Monster from
  Galaxy X 450.00
3 Attack on Ishtar,
  October., 1952 . . . . 450.00

Space Adventures #18
© Charlton Comics

SPACE ADVENTURES
Capitol Stories/
Charlton Comics
July, 1952
1 AFa&LM(c) 325.00
2 . . . . 150.00
3 DG(c) 135.00
4 DG(c) 125.00
5 StC(c) 125.00
6 StC(c),Two Worlds 100.00
7 DG(c),Transformation 125.00
8 DG(c),All For Love 100.00
9 DG(c) 100.00
10 SD,SD(c) 250.00
11 SD,JoS 275.00
12 SD(c) 275.00
13 A:Blue Beetle 125.00
14 A:Blue Beetle 125.00
15 Ph(c) of Rocky Jones 125.00
16 BKa,A:Rocky Jones 150.00
17 A:Rocky Jones 125.00
18 A:Rocky Jones 125.00
19 . . . . 100.00
20 First Trip to the Moon 175.00
21 . . . . 100.00
22 Does Not Exist
23 SD,Space Trip to the Moon . 150.00

24 . . . . 125.00
25 Brontosaurus 125.00
26 SD,Flying Saucers 150.00
27 SD,Flying Saucers 150.00
28 Moon Trap 45.00
29 Captive From Space 45.00
30 Peril in the Sky 45.00
31 SD,SD(c),Enchanted Planet 125.00
32 SD,SD(c),Last Ship
  from Earth 125.00
33 Galactic Scourge,
  I&O:Captain Atom 375.00
34 SD,SD(c),A:Captain Atom . . 150.00
35 thru 40 SD,SD(c),
  A:Captain Atom . . . . @150.00
41 . . . . 25.00
42 SD,A:Captain Atom 25.00
43 . . . . 25.00
44 A:Mercury Man 25.00
45 A:Mercury Man 25.00
46 thru 58 . . . . @25.00
59 November, 1964 . . . . 25.00

SPACE BUSTERS
Ziff-Davis Publishing Co.
Spring, 1952
1 BK,NS(c),Ph(c),Charge of
  the Battle Women 600.00
2 EK,BK,MA,NS(c),
  Bondage(c),Ph(c) 500.00
3 Autumn, 1952 . . . . 450.00

SPACE COMICS
Avon Periodicals
March-April, 1954
4 (fa),F:Space Mouse 30.00
5 (fa),F:Space Mouse,
  May-June, 1954 . . . . 25.00

SPACE DETECTIVE
Avon Periodicals
July, 1951
1 WW,WW(c),Opium Smugglers
  of Venus 800.00
2 WW,WW(c),Batwomen of
  Mercury 500.00
3 EK(c),SeaNymphs ofNeptune 300.00
4 EK,Flame Women of Vulcan,
  Bondage(c) 325.00

SPACE MOUSE
Avon Periodicals
April, 1953
1 Funny Animal 45.00
2 Funny Animal 35.00
3 thru 5 Funny Animal . . . . @20.00

SPACE PATROL
Approved Comics
(Ziff-Davis)
Summer, 1952
1 BK,NS,Ph(c), The Lady of
  Diamonds 700.00
2 BK,NS,Ph(c),Slave King of
  Pluto,Oct.-Nov., 1952 . . . . 500.00

SPACE THRILLERS
Avon Periodicals
1954
N# Contents May Vary 850.00

SPACE WESTERN COMICS
(see YELLOWJACKET COMICS)

SPARKLER COMICS
United Features Syndicate
July, 1940

1 Jim Handy	300.00
2 Frankie Doodle,August, 1940	225.00

Sparkler Comics #12
© United Features Syndicate

SPARKLER COMICS
United Features Syndicate
July, 1941

1 BHg,O:Sparkman;B:Tarzan,Captain & the Kids,Ella Cinders,Danny Dingle,Dynamite Dunn, Nancy, Abbie an' Slats, Frankie Doodle,Broncho Bill	1,700.00
2 BHg, The Case of Poisoned Fruit	600.00
3 BHg	500.00
4 BHg,Case of Sparkman & the Firefly	500.00
5 BHg,Sparkman,Natch	425.00
6 BHg,Case o/t Bronze Bees .	400.00
7 BHg,Case o/t Green Raiders	400.00
8 BHg,V:River Fiddler	400.00
9 BHg,N:Sparkman	400.00
10 BHg,B:Hap Hopper, Sparkman's ID revealed . .	400.00
11 BHg,V:Japanese	350.00
12 BHg,Another N:Sparkman .	350.00
13 BHg,Hap Hopper Rides For Freedom	350.00
14 BHg,BHg(c),Tarzan V:Yellow Killer	400.00
15 BHg	350.00
16 BHg,Sparkman V:Japanese	350.00
17 BHg,Nancy(c)	350.00
18 BHg,Sparkman in Crete . .	350.00
19 BHg,I&B:Race Riley, Commandos	350.00
20 BHg,Nancy(c)	350.00
21 BHg,Tarzan(c)	350.00
22 BHg,Nancy(c)	275.00

23 BHg,Capt&Kids(c)	275.00
24 BHg,Nancy(c)	275.00
25 BHg,BHg(c),Tarzan(c) . . .	300.00
26 BHg,Capt&Kids(c)	275.00
27 BHg,Nancy(c)	275.00
28 BHg,BHg(c),Tarzan(c) . . .	300.00
29 BHg,Capt&Kids(c)	275.00
30 BHg,Nancy(c)	275.00
31 BHg,BHg(c),Tarzan(c) . . .	300.00
32 BHg,Capt&Kids(c)	125.00
33 BHg,Nancy(c)	125.00
34 BHg,BHg(c),Tarzan(c) . . .	250.00
35 BHg,Capt&Kids(c)	125.00
36 BHg,Nancy(c)	125.00
37 BHg,BHg(c),Tarzan(c) . . .	250.00
38 BHg,Capt&Kids(c)	125.00
39 BHg,BHg(c),Tarzan(c) . . .	250.00
40 BHg,Nancy(c)	125.00
41 BHg,Capt&Kids(c)	100.00
42 BHg,BHg,Tarzan(c)	200.00
43 BHg,Nancy(c)	100.00
44 BHg,Tarzan(c)	200.00
45 BHg,Capt&Kids(c)	100.00
46 BHg,Nancy(c)	100.00
47 BHg,Tarzan(c)	200.00
48 BHg,Nancy(c)	100.00
49 BHg,Capt&Kids(c)	100.00
50 BHg,BHg(c),Tarzan(c) . . .	165.00
51 BHg,Capt&Kids(c)	100.00
52 BHg,Nancy(c)	100.00
53 BHg,BHg(c),Tarzan(c) . . .	150.00
54 BHg,Capt&Kids(c)	75.00
55 BHg,Nancy(c)	75.00
56 BHg,Capt&Kids(c)	75.00
57 BHg,F:Li'l Abner	75.00
58 BHg,A:Fearless Fosdick . .	90.00
59 BHg,B:Li'l Abner	90.00
60 BHg,Nancy(c)	75.00
61 BHg,Capt&Kids(c)	75.00
62 BHg,Li'L Abner(c)	75.00
63 BHg,Capt&Kids(c)	75.00
64 BHg,Valentines (c)	75.00
65 BHg,Nancy(c)	75.00
66 BHg,Capt&Kids(c)	75.00
67 BHg,Nancy(c)	75.00
68 BHg, ...	75.00
69 BHg,B:Nancy (c)	75.00
70 BHg	75.00
71 thru 80 BHg	@60.00
81 BHg,E:Nancy(c)	60.00
82 BHg	60.00
83 BHg,Tarzan(c)	50.00
84 BHg	50.00
85 BHg,E:Li'l Abner	50.00
86 BHg	50.00
87 BHg,Nancy(c)	50.00
88 thru 96 BHg	@50.00
97 BHg,O:Lady Ruggles	100.00
98 BHg	50.00
99 BHg,Nancy(c)	50.00
100 BHg,Nancy(c)	60.00
101 thru 108 BHg	@35.00
109 BHg,ATh	40.00
110 BHg	35.00
111 BHg	35.00
112 BHg	35.00
113 BHg,ATh	60.00
114 thru 120 BHg	@35.00

SPARKLING STARS
Holyoke Publishing Co.
June, 1944

1 B:Hell's Angels,Ali Baba,FBI, Boxie Weaver,Petey & Pop	125.00
2	75.00

3	50.00
4 thru 12	@45.00
13 O&I:Jungo, The Man-Beast .	50.00
14 thru 19	@45.00
20 I:Fangs the Wolfboy	45.00
21 thru 28	@45.00
29 Bondage(c)	35.00
30 thru 32	@30.00
33 March, 1948	30.00

SPARKMAN
Frances M. McQueeny
1944

1 O:Sparkman	225.00

SPARKY WATTS
Columbia Comics Group
1942

1 A:Skyman,Hitler(c)	350.00
2	200.00
3	125.00
4 O:Skyman	125.00
5 A:Skyman	100.00
6	75.00
7	75.00
8	75.00
9	75.00
10 1949	75.00

[STEVE SAUNDERS] SPECIAL AGENT
Parents Magazine/ Commended Comics
December, 1947

1 J. Edgar Hoover, Ph(c)	60.00
2	30.00
3 thru 7	@25.00
8 September, 1949	25.00

SPECIAL COMICS
(see LAUGH COMICS)

SPECIAL EDITION COMICS
Fawcett Publications
August, 1940

1 CCB,CCB(c),F:Captain Marvel	8,500.00

SPEED COMICS
Brookwood/Speed Publ.
Harvey Publications
October, 1939

1 BP,B&O:Shock Gibson,B:Spike Marlin,Biff Bannon	2,500.00
2 BP ,B:Shock Gibson(c)	800.00
3 BP,GT	450.00
4 BP	400.00
5 BP,DBr	400.00
6 BP,GT	350.00
7 GT,JKu,B:Mars Mason	350.00
8 JKu	325.00
9 JKu	325.00
10 JKu,E:Shock Gibson(c) . . .	325.00
11 JKu,E:Mars Mason	325.00
12 B:The Wasp	400.00
13 I:Captain Freedom;B:Girls Commandos,Pat Parker . . .	450.00
14 Pocket sized format-100pgs.	450.00
15 Pocket size	450.00
16 JKu,Pocket size	450.00
17 O:Black Cat	550.00

Speed Comics #10
© Brookwood/Speed Publ./Harvey Publ.

18 B:Capt.Freedom,Bondage(c)	425.00
19	400.00
20	400.00
21 JKu(c)	400.00
22 JKu(c)	400.00
23 JKu(c),O:Girl Commandos	425.00
24	300.00
25	275.00
26 Flag (c)	275.00
27	275.00
28 E:Capt Freedom	275.00
29 Case o/t Black Marketeers	275.00
30 POW Death Chambers	275.00
31 ASh(c),Nazi Thrashing(c)	350.00
32 ASh(c)	325.00
33 ASh(c)	325.00
34 ASh(c)	325.00
35 ASh(c),BlackCat'sDeathTrap	350.00
36 ASh(c)	325.00
37 RP(c)	325.00
38 RP(c),War Bond Plea with Iwo Jima flag allusion(c)	325.00
39 RP(c),B:Capt Freedom(c)	275.00
40 RP(c)	275.00
41 RP(c)	275.00
42 JKu,RP(c)	275.00
43 JKu,E:Capt Freedom(c)	275.00
44 BP,JKu,Four Kids on a raft, January-February, 1947	300.00

SPEED SMITH THE HOT ROD KING
Ziff-Davis Publishing Co.
Spring, 1952

1 INS,Ph(c),A:Roscoe the Rascal	125.00

SPIRIT, THE
Will Eisner
(Weekly Coverless Comic Book)
June, 1940

WE,O:SPirit	550.00
6/9/40 WE	250.00
6/16/40 WE,Black Queen	175.00
6/23/40 WE,Mr Mystic	150.00

6/30/40 WE	150.00
7/7/40 WE,Black Queen	150.00
7/14/40 WE	100.00
7/21/40 WE	100.00
7/28/40 WE	100.00
8/4/40 WE	100.00
7/7/40-11/24/40,WE	70.00
12/1/40 WE,Ellen Spanking(c)	125.00
12/8/40-12/29/40	60.00
1941 WE Each	50.00
3/16 WE I:Silk Satin	95.00
6/15 WE I Twilight	60.00
6/22 WE Hitler	60.00
1942 WE Each	40.00
2-1	60.00
2-15	45.00
2-23	65.00
1943 WE Each,LF,WE scripts	30.00
1944 JCo,LF	15.00
1945 LF Each,	15.00
1946 WE Each	30.00
1/13 WE,O:The Spirit	50.00
1/20 WE,Satin	50.00
3/17 WE,I:Nylon	50.00
4/21 WE,I:Mr.Carrion	55.00
7/7 WE,I:Dulcet Tone&Skinny	50.00
10/6 WE,I:F:Gell	60.00
1947 WE Each	30.00
7/13..,WE,Hansel &Gretel	45.00
7/20,WE,A:Bomb	50.00
9/28,WE,Flying Saucers	65.00
10/5,WE, Cinderella	32.00
12/7,WE,I:Power Puff	32.00
1948 WE Each	30.00
1/11,WE,Sparrow Fallon	35.00
1/25,WE,I:Last A Net	40.00
3/14,WE,A:Kretuama	35.00
4/4,WE,A:Wildrice	35.00
7/25,The Thing	60.00
8/22,Poe Tale,Horror	65.00
9/18, A:Lorelei	35.00
11/7,WE,A:Plaster of Paris	40.00
1949 WE Each	30.00
1/23 WE,I:Thorne	40.00
8/21 WE,I:Monica Veto	40.00
9/25 WE,A;Ice	40.00
12/4 WE,I:Flaxen	35.00
1950 WE Each	30.00
1/8 WE,I:Sand Saref	70.00
2/10, Horror Issue	35.00
1951 WE(Last WE 8/12/51)	@30.00
Non-Eisners	@12.00
1952 Non-Eisners	@12.00
7/27 WW,Denny Colt	350.00
8/3 WW,Moon	350.00
8/10 WW,Moon	350.00
8/17 WW,WE,Heart	300.00
8/24 WW,Rescue	300.00
8/31 WW,Last Man	300.00
9/7 WW,Man Moon	380.00
9/14 WE	80.00
9/21 WE Space	250.00
9/28 WE Moon	300.00
10/5 WE Last Story	125.00

SPIRIT, THE
Quality Comics Group/ Vital Publ.
1944

N# Wanted Dead or Alive!	500.00
N# ...in Crime Doesn't Pay	300.00
N# ...In Murder Runs Wild	225.00
4 ...Flirts with Death	200.00
5 ...Wanted Dead or Alive	175.00
6 ...Gives You Triple Value	150.00

The Spirit #19 © Quality Comics

7 ...Rocks the Underworld	150.00
8	150.00
9 ...Throws Fear Into the Heart of Crime	150.00
10 ...Stalks Crime	150.00
11 ...America's Greatest Crime Buster	150.00
12 WE(c),...The Famous Outlaw Who Smashes Crime	225.00
13 WE(c),...and Ebony Cleans Out the Underworld;Bondage(c)	225.00
14 WE(c)	225.00
15 WE(c),Bank Robber at Large	225.00
16 WE(c),The Caase of the Uncanny Cat	225.00
17 WE(c),The Organ Grinding Bank Robber	225.00
18 WE,WE(c),'The Bucket of Blood	275.00
19 WE,WE(c),'The Man Who Murdered the Spirit'	275.00
20 WE,WE(c),'The Vortex'	275.00
21 WE,WE(c),'P'Gell of Paris'	275.00
22 WE(c),TheOctopus,Aug.1950	400.00

SPIRIT, THE
Fiction House Magazines
1952

1 Curse of Claymore Castle	225.00
2 WE,WE(c),Who Says Crime Doesn't Pay	250.00
3 WE/JGr(c),League of Lions	150.00
4 WE,WE&JGr(c),Last Prowl of Mr. Mephisto;Bondage (c)	225.00
5 WE,WE(c),Ph(c)1954	225.00

SPIRITMAN
Will Eisner
1944

1 3 Spirit Sections from 1944 Bound Together	150.00
2 LF, 2 Spirit Sections from 1944 Bound Together	125.00

SPITFIRE COMICS
Harvey Publ.
August, 1941

1 MKd(c), 100pgs., Pocket size	500.00

GOLDEN AGE

2 100 pgs.,Pocket size,
October, 1941 .... 425.00

SPOOK COMICS
Baily Publications
1946
1 A:Mr. Lucifer 200.00

SPOOK DETECTIVE CASES
(see CRIMINALS ON THE RUN)

SPOOKY
Harvey Publications
November, 1955
1 Funny Apparition 225.00
2 same 100.00
3 thru 10 same .... @45.00
11 thru 20 same .... @25.00
21 thru 30 same .... @20.00
31 thru 40 same .... @15.00
41 thru 70 same .... @9.00
71 thru 90 same .... @5.00
91 thru 120 same .... @3.00
121 thru 160 same .... @2.50
161 same,September, 1980 ..... 2.50

SPOOKY MYSTERIES
Your Guide Publishing Co.
1946
1 Rib-Tickling Horror 75.00

SPORT COMICS
(see TRUE SPORT PICTURE STORIES)

SPORTS THRILLS
(see DICK COLE)

SPOTLIGHT COMICS
Harry 'A' Chesler Jr. Publications
November, 1944
1 GT,GT(c),B:Veiled Avenger,
Black Dwarf,Barry Kuda ... 450.00
2 .... 375.00
3 1945,Eye Injury 400.00

SPUNKY
Standard Comics
April, 1949
1 FF,Adventures of a Junior
Cowboy 40.00
2 FF 25.00
3 .... 20.00
4 .... 20.00
5 .... 20.00
6 .... 20.00
7 November, 1951 .... 20.00

SPY AND COUNTER SPY
Best Syndicated Features (American Comics Group)
August-September, 1949
1 I&O:Jonathan Kent 175.00
2 .... 100.00
Becomes:

SPY HUNTERS
3 Jonathan Kent 135.00

4 J.Kent 75.00
5 J.Kent 75.00
6 J.Kent 75.00
7 OW(c),J.Kent 75.00
8 OW(c),J.Kent 75.00
9 OW(c),J.Kent 75.00
10 OW(c),J.Kent 75.00
11 .... 50.00
12 OW(c),MD 50.00
13 and 14 .... @45.00
15 OW(c) 50.00
16 AW 100.00
17 .... 35.00
18 War (c) 45.00
19 and 20 .... @45.00
21 B:War Content 45.00
22 .... 45.00
23 Torture 125.00
24 'BlackmailBrigade',July,1953 . 45.00

SPY SMASHER
Fawcett Publications
Autumn, 1941
1 B;Spy Smasher 2,800.00
2 Mra(c) 1,300.00
3 Bondage (c) 900.00
4 .... 800.00
5 Mra,Mt. Rushmore(c) 900.00
6 Mra,Mra(c),V:The Sharks
of Steel 750.00
7 Mra 750.00
8 AB 600.00
9 AB,Hitler,Tojo, Mussolini(c) . 650.00
10 AB,Did Spy Smasher
Kill Hitler? 650.00
11 AB,February, 1943 .... 600.00

SQUEEKS
Lev Gleason Publications
October, 1953
1 CBi(c),(fa) 30.00
2 CBi(c),(fa) 15.00
3 CBi(c),(fa) 12.00
4 (fa) 12.00
5 (fa),January, 1954 .... 12.00

STAMP COMICS
Youthful Magazines/Stamp Comics, Inc.
October, 1951
1 HcK,Birth of Liberty 250.00
2 HcK,RP,Battle of White Plains 125.00
3 HcK,DW,RP,Iwo Jima 100.00
4 HcK,DW,RP 100.00
5 HcK,Von Hindenberg disaster 110.00
6 HcK,The Immortal Chaplains 100.00
7 HcK,RKr,RP,B&O:Railroad . 150.00
Becomes:

THRILLING ADVENTURES IN STAMPS
8 HcK, 100 Pgs.,Jan.,1953 .. 500.00

STAR COMICS
Comic Magazines/Ultem Publ./Chesler Centaur Publications
February, 1937
1 B:Dan Hastings 1,100.00
2 .... 550.00
3 .... 500.00
4 WMc(c) 525.00
5 WMc(c),A:Little Nemo 525.00

Star Comics #14
© Chester Centaur Publications

6 CBi(c),FG 475.00
7 FG 425.00
8 BoW,BoW(c),FG,A:Little
Nemo,Horror 450.00
9 FG,CBi(c) 425.00
10 FG,CBi(c),BoW,A:Impyk . 600.00
11 FG,BoW,JCo 450.00
12 FG,BoW,B:Riders of the
Golden West 400.00
13 FG,BoW 375.00
14 FG,GFx(c) 375.00
15 CBu,B:The Last Pirate 400.00
16 CBu,B:Phantom Rider 400.00
2-1 CBu,B:Phantom Rider(c) . 400.00
2-2 CBu,A:Diana Deane 375.00
2-3 GFx(c),CBu 325.00
2-4 CBu 325.00
2-5 CBu 325.00
2-6 CBu,E:Phantom Rider ... 325.00
2-7 CBu,August, 1939 ..... 325.00

STARLET O'HARA IN HOLLYWOOD
Standard Comics
December, 1948
1 The Terrific Tee-Age Comic . 100.00
2 Her Romantic Adventures in
Movie land 75.00
3 and 4, Sept., 1949 ...... @50.00

STAR RANGER
Comics Magazines/Ultem/ Centaur Publ.
February, 1937
1 FG,I:Western Comic 1,200.00
2 .... 500.00
3 FG 450.00
4 .... 450.00
5 .... 375.00
6 FG 375.00
7 FG 350.00
8 GFx,FG,PGn,BoW 350.00
9 GFx,FG,PGn,BoW 350.00
10 JCo,GFx,FG,PGn,BoW ... 600.00
11 .... 450.00
12 JCo,JCo(c),FG,PGn 450.00

All comics prices listed are for *Near Mint* condition.

Becomes:
COWBOY COMICS
13 FG,PGn 750.00
14 FG,PGn 600.00

Becomes:
STAR RANGER FUNNIES
15 WE,PGn 700.00
2-1(16) JCo,JCo(c) 500.00
2-2(17) PGn,JCo,A:Night Hawk 425.00
2-3(18) JCo,FG 400.00
2-4(19) A:Kit Carson 400.00
2-5(20) October, 1939 . . . . . 400.00

STARS AND STRIPES COMICS
Comic Corp of America (Centaur Publications)
May, 1941
2 PGn,PGn(c),'Called to Colors',
The Shark,The Voice 1,700.00
3 PGn,PGn(c),O:Dr.Synthe . 1,000.00
4 PGn,PGn(c),I:The Stars
& Stripes 875.00
5 . . . . 600.00
6(5), December, 1941 . . . . . . 600.00

STAR STUDDED
Cambridge House
1945
N# 25 cents (c) price;128 pgs.;
32 F:stories 200.00
N# The Cadet,Hoot Gibson,
Blue Beetle 150.00

STARTLING COMICS
Better Publ./Nedor Publ.
June, 1940
1 WE,LF,B&O:Captain Future,
Mystico, Wonder Man;
B:Masked Rider 1,700.00
2 Captain Future(c) 700.00
3 same 550.00
4 same 450.00
5 same 350.00
6 same 325.00
7 same 325.00
8 ASh(c) 350.00
9 Bondage(c) 2,500.00
10 O:Fighting Yank 2,500.00
11 Fighting Yank(c) 775.00
12 Hitler,Mussolini,Tojo cover . 550.00
13 JBi 450.00
14 JBi 450.00
15 Fighting Yank (c) 450.00
16 Bondage(c),O:FourComrades 500.00
17 Fighting Yank (c),
E:Masked Rider 325.00
18 JBi,B&O:Pyroman 700.00
19 Pyroman(c) 325.00
20 Pyroman(c),B:Oracle 325.00
21 HcK,ASh(c)Bondage(c)O:Ape 350.00
22 HcK,ASh(c),Fighting Yank(c) 325.00
23 HcK,BEv,ASh(c),Pyroman(c) 325.00
24 HcK,BEv,ASh(c),Fighting
Yank(c) 325.00
25 HcK,BEv,ASh(c),Pyroman(c) 325.00
26 BEv,ASh(c),Fighting Yank(c) 325.00
27 BEv,ASh(c),Pyroman(c) . . . 325.00
28 BEv,ASh(c),Fighting Yank(c) 325.00
29 BEv,ASh(c),Pyroman(c) . . . 325.00
30 ASh(c),Fighting Yank(c) . . . 325.00

31 ASh(c),Pyroman(c) 325.00
32 ASh(c),Fighting Yank(c) . . . 325.00
33 ASh(c),Pyroman(c) 325.00
34 ASh(c),Fighting Yank(c),
O:Scarab 325.00
35 ASh(c),Pyroman(c) 335.00
36 ASh(c),Fighting Yank(c) . . . 300.00
37 ASh(c),Bondage (c) 300.00
38 ASh(c),Bondage(c) 300.00
39 ASh(c),Pyroman(c) 300.00
40 ASh(c),E:Captain Future . . 300.00
41 ASh(c),Pyroman(c) 300.00
42 ASh(c),Fighting Yank(c) . . . 300.00
43 ASh(c),Pyroman(c),
E:Pyroman 300.00
44 Grl(c),Lance Lewis(c) 450.00
45 Grl(c),I:Tygra 450.00
46 Grl,Grl(c),Bondage(c) 450.00
47 ASh(c),Bondage(c) 450.00
48 ASh(c),Lance Lewis(c) . . . 400.00
49 ASh(c),Bondage(c),
E:Fighting Yank 2,000.00
50 ASh(c),Lance Lewis(c),
Sea Eagle 350.00
51 ASh(c),Sea Eagle 350.00
52 ASh(c) 350.00
53 ASh(c),September, 1948 . . . 350.00

STARTLING TERROR TALES
Star Publications
May, 1952
10 WW,LbC(c),The Story Starts 500.00
11 LbC(c),The Ghost Spider
of Death 400.00
12 LbC(c),White Hand Horror . 150.00
13 JyD,LbC(c),Love From
a Gorgor 150.00
14 LbC(c),Trapped by the
Color of Blood 150.00
4 LbC(c),Crime at the Carnival 135.00
5 LbC(c),The Gruesome
Demon of Terror 135.00
6 LbC(c),Footprints of Death . 135.00
7 LbC(c),The Case of the
Strange Murder 150.00
8 RP,LbC(c),Phantom Brigade 150.00
9 LbC(c),The Forbidden Tomb 125.00

Steve Canyon Comics #5
© Star Publications

10 LbC(c),The Horrible Entity . . 150.00
11 RP,LbC(c),The Law Will
Win, July, 1954 . . . . 150.00

STEVE CANYON COMICS
Harvey Publications
February, 1948
1 MC,BP,O:Steve Canyon . . . 150.00
2 MC,BP 125.00
3 MC,BP,Canyon's Crew 100.00
4 MC,BP,Chase of Death . . . 100.00
5 MC,BP,A:Happy Easter . . . 100.00
6 MC,BP,A:Madame Lynx,
December, 1948 . . . . 110.00

STEVE ROPER
Famous Funnies
April, 1948
1 Reprints newspaper strips . . 65.00
2 . . . . 35.00
3 . . . . 25.00
4 . . . . 25.00
5 December, 1948 . . . . 25.00

STORIES BY FAMOUS AUTHORS ILLUSTRATED
(see FAST FICTION)

STORY OF HARRY S. TRUMAN, THE
Democratic National Committee
1948
N# Giveaway-The Life of Our
33rd President 85.00

STRAIGHT ARROW
Magazine Enterprises
February-March, 1950
1 OW,B:Straight Arrow & his
Horse Fury 300.00
2 BP,B&O:Red Hawk 150.00
3 BP,FF(c) 200.00
4 BP,Cave(c) 150.00
5 BP,StraightArrow'sGreatLeap 150.00
6 BP 125.00
7 BP,The Railroad Invades
Comanche Country 125.00
8 BP 125.00
9 BP 125.00
10 BP 125.00
11 BP,The Valley of Time 150.00
12 thru 19 BP . . . . @100.00
20 BP,Straight Arrow's
Great War Shield 125.00
21 BP,O:Fury 150.00
22 BP,FF(c) 150.00
23 BP 75.00
24 BP,The Dragons of Doom . . 75.00
25 BP 75.00
26 BP 75.00
27 BP 75.00
28 BP,Red Hawk 50.00
29 thru 35 BP . . . . @50.00
36 BP Drug 55.00
37 BP 55.00
38 BP 55.00
39 BP,The Canyon Beasts . . . 60.00
40 BP,Secret of the
Spanish Specters 60.00
41 BP 40.00

42 BP 40.00
43 BP,I:Blaze 55.00
44 BP 40.00
45 BP 40.00
46 thru 53 BP . . . . @40.00
54 BP,March, 1956 . . . . 40.00

STRANGE CONFESSIONS
Approved Publications
(Ziff-Davis)
Spring, 1952
1 EK,Ph(c) 300.00
2 . . . . 200.00
3 EK,Ph(c),Girls reformatory . . 200.00
4 Girls reformatory 200.00

STRANGE FANTASY
Farrell Publications/
Ajax Comics
August, 1952
(2)1 . . . . 275.00
2 . . . . 225.00
3 The Dancing Ghost 225.00
4 Demon in the Dungeon,
  A:Rocketman 200.00
5 Visiting Corpse 150.00
6 . . . . 150.00
7 A:Madam Satan 200.00
8 A:Black Cat 150.00
9 S&K,SD 175.00
10 . . . . 150.00
11 Fearful Things Can Happen
   in a Lonely Place 150.00
12 The Undying Fiend 150.00
13 Terror in the Attic,
   Bondage(c) 200.00
14 Monster in the Building,
   October-November, 1954 . . 150.00

UNKNOWN WORLD
Fawcett Publications
June, 1952
1 NS(c),Ph(c),Will You Venture
  to Meet the Unknown 300.00
Becomes:
STRANGE STORIES
FROM ANOTHER
WORLD
2 NS(c),Ph(c),Will You?
  Dare You 325.00
3 NS(c),Ph(c),The Dark Mirror   250.00
4 NS(c),Ph(c),Monsters of
  the Mind 250.00
5 NS(c),Ph(c),Dance of the
  Doomed February, 1953 . . 250.00

STRANGE SUSPENSE
STORIES
Fawcett Publications
June, 1952
1 BP,MSy,MBi 500.00
2 MBi,GE 300.00
3 MBi,GE(c) 275.00
4 BP 275.00
5 MBi(c),Voodoo(c) 275.00
6 BEv 125.00
7 BEv 150.00
8 AW 150.00
9 . . . . 125.00
10 . . . . 150.00
11 . . . . 100.00
12 . . . . 100.00

Strange Suspense Stories #18
© Charlton Comics

13 . . . . 100.00
14 . . . . 125.00
15 AW,BEv(c) 125.00

Charlton Comics
16 . . . . 175.00
17 . . . . 125.00
18 SD,SD(c) 225.00
19 SD,SD(c) 300.00
20 SD,SD(c) 225.00
21 . . . . 125.00
22 SD(c) 200.00
Becomes:
THIS IS SUSPENSE!
23 WW 200.00
24 . . . . 75.00
25 . . . . 50.00
26 . . . . 50.00
Becomes:
STRANGE SUSPENSE
STORIES
27 . . . . 75.00
28 . . . . 50.00
29 . . . . 50.00
30 . . . . 50.00
31 SD(c) 125.00
32 SD 125.00
33 SD 125.00
34 SD,SD(c) 200.00
35 SD 125.00
36 SD,SD(c) 125.00
37 SD 135.00
38 . . . . 125.00
39 SD 150.00
40 SD 125.00
41 SD 125.00
42 . . . . 35.00
43 . . . . 35.00
44 . . . . 35.00
45 SD 75.00
46 . . . . 35.00
47 SD 75.00
48 SD 75.00
49 . . . . 35.00
50 SD 90.00
51 thru 53 SD . . . . @50.00
54 thru 60 . . . . @30.00
61 thru 74 . . . . @15.00

75 . . . . 100.00
76 . . . . 30.00
77 . . . . 30.00

STRANGE SUSPENSE
STORIES
(see LAWBREAKERS)

STRANGE TERRORS
St. John Publishing Co.
June, 1952
1 The Ghost of Castle
  Karloff, Bondage(c) 350.00
2 UnshackledFlight intoNowhere 175.00
3 JKu,Ph(c),The Ghost Who
  Ruled Crazy Heights 235.00
4 JKu,Ph(c),Terror from
  the Tombs 275.00
5 JKu,Ph(c),No Escaping
  the Pool of Death 225.00
6 LC,PAM,Bondage(c),Giant . . 300.00
7 JKu,JKu(c),Cat's Death,Giant 325.00

STRANGE WORLD OF
YOUR DREAMS
Prize Group
August, 1952
1 S&K(c),What Do They Mean–
  Messages Rec'd in Sleep . 450.00
2 MMe,S&K(c),Why did I Dream
  That I Was Being Married
  to a Man without a Face? . . 350.00
3 S&K(c) 300.00
4 MMe,S&K(c),The Story of
  a Man Who Dreamed a Murder
  that Happened 275.00

STRANGE WORLDS
Avon Periodicals
November, 1950
1 JKu,Spider God of Akka . . . 650.00
2 WW,Dara of the Vikings . . . 600.00
3 AW&FF,EK(c),WW,JO . . . 1,200.00
4 JO,WW,WW(c),The
  Enchanted Dagger 550.00
5 WW,WW(c),JO,Bondage(c);
  Sirens of Space 400.00
6 EK,WW(c),JO,SC,
  Maid o/t Mist 300.00
7 EK, Sabotage on
  Space Station 1 . . . . 225.00
8 JKu,EK,The Metal Murderer 225.00
9 The Radium Monsters 225.00
18 JKu 225.00
19 Astounding Super
   Science Fantasies 225.00
20 WW(c),Fighting War Stories . 50.00
21 EK(c) 40.00
22 EK(c),Sept.-Oct., 1955 . . . . 40.00

STRICTLY PRIVATE
Eastern Color Printing
July, 1942
1 You're in theArmyNow-Humor 150.00
2 F:Peter Plink, 1942 . . . . . . 150.00

STUNTMAN COMICS
Harvey Publications
April-May, 1946
1 S&K,O:Stuntman 800.00
2 S&K,New Champ of Split-
  Second Action 550.00

3 S&K,Digest sized,Mail Order
Only, B&W interior,
October-November, 1946 .. 550.00

SUGAR BOWL COMICS
Famous Funnies
May, 1948

1 ATh,ATh(c),The Newest in
Teen Age! 80.00
2 .... 30.00
3 ATh 60.00
4 .... 30.00
5 January, 1949 .... 30.00

SUN FUN KOMIKS
Sun Publications
1939

1 F:Spineless Sam the
Sweetheart 200.00

SUNNY, AMERICA'S SWEETHEART
Fox Features Syndicate
December, 1947

11 AF,AF(c) 550.00
12 AF,AF(c) 450.00
13 AF,AF(c) 450.00
14 AF,AF(c) 450.00

SUNSET CARSON
Charlton Comics
February, 1951

1 Painted, Ph(c);Wyoming
Mail 650.00
2 Kit Carson-Pioneer 500.00
3 .... 375.00
4 Panhandle Trouble,
August, 1951 .... 375.00

SUPER BOOK OF COMICS
Western Publishing Co. 1943

N# Dick Tracy 300.00
1 Dick Tracy 250.00
2 Smitty,Magic Morro 80.00

PAN·AM
SUPER BOOK
OF COMICS
featuring
SMITTY
ALSO IN THIS ISSUE   MAGIC MORRO
BOOK NUMBER TWO

Super Book of Comics #2
© Western Publishing Co.

---

3 Capt. Midnight 135.00
4 Red Ryder,Magic Morro 70.00
5 Don Winslow,Magic Morro ... 70.00
5 Dom Winslow,Stratosphere Jim 70.00
5 Terry & the Pirates 80.00
6 Don Winslow 75.00
7 Little Orphan Annie 70.00
8 Dick Tracy 100.00
9 Terry & the Pirates 100.00
10 Red Ryder, Magic Morro ... 70.00

SUPER-BOOK OF COMICS
Western Publishing Co.
1944

1 Dick Tracy (Omar) 135.00
1 Dick Tracy (Hancock) 100.00
2 Bugs Bunny (Omar) 40.00
2 Bugs Bunny (Hancock) 30.00
3 Terry & the Pirates (Omar) .. 75.00
3 Terry & the Pirates (Hancock) 65.00
4 Andy Panda (Omar) 35.00
4 Andy Panda (Hancock) 30.00
5 Smokey Stover (Omar) 30.00
5 Smokey Stover (Hancock) .. 20.00
6 Porky Pig (Omar) 35.00
6 Porky Pig (Hancock) 30.00
7 Smilin' Jack (Omar) 40.00
7 Smilin' Jack (Hancock) 35.00
8 Oswald the Rabbit (Omar) ... 30.00
8 Oswald the Rabbit (Hancock) 20.00
9 Alley Oop (Omar) 80.00
9 Alley Oop (Hancock) 70.00
10 Elmer Fudd (Omar) 30.00
10 Elmer Fudd (Hancock) 20.00
11 Little Orphan Annie (Omar) .. 45.00
11 Little Orphan Amnie (Hancock) 35.00
12 Woody Woodpecker (Omar) . 35.00
12 WoodyWoodpecker(Hancock) 25.00
13 Dick Tracy (Omar) 80.00
13 Dick Tracy (Hancock) 75.00
14 Bugs Bunny (Omar) 30.00
14 Bugs Bunny (Hanock) 25.00
15 Andy Panda (Omar) 20.00
15 Andy Panda (Hancock) 15.00
16 Terry & the Pirates (Omar) .. 70.00
16 Terry & the Pirates (Hancock) 50.00
17 Smokey Stover (Omar) 30.00
17 Smokey Stover (Hancock) .. 30.00
18 Porky Pig (Omar) 25.00
18 Smokey Stover (Hancock) .. 20.00
19 Smilin' Jack (Omar) 35.00
N# Smilin' Jack (Hancock) 20.00
20 Oswald the Rabbit (Omar) .. 25.00
N# Oswald the Rabbit (Hancock) 15.00
21 Gasoline Alley (Omar) 45.00
N# Gasoline Alley (Hancock) ... 35.00
22 Elmer Fudd (Omar) 25.00
N# Elmer Fudd (Hancock) 30.00
23 Little Orphan Annie (Omar) .. 30.00
N# Little Orphan Annie (Hancock) 25.00
24 Woody Woodpecker (Omar) .. 22.00
N# WoodyWoodpecker(Hancock) 18.00
25 Dick Tracy (Omar) 70.00
N# Dick Tracy (Hancock) 50.00
26 Bugs Bunny (Omar) 25.00
N# Bugs Bunny (Hancock) 20.00
27 Andy Panda (Omar) 20.00
27 Andy Panda (Hancock) 15.00
28 Terry & the Pirates (Omar) .. 70.00
28 Terry & the Pirates (Hancock) 50.00
29 Smokey Stover (Omar) 25.00
29 Smokey Stover (Hancock) .. 20.00
30 Porky Pig (Omar) 25.00

---

30 Porky Pig (Hancock) 20.00
N# Bugs Bunny (Hancock) 20.00

SUPER CIRCUS
Cross Publishing Co.
January, 1951

1 Partial Ph(c) 55.00
2 .... 40.00
3 .... 30.00
4 .... 30.00
5 1951 .... 30.00

SUPER COMICS
Dell Publishing Co.
May 1938

1 Dick Tracy,Terry and the
Pirates,Smilin'Jack,Smokey
Stover,Orphan Annie,etc. . 2,000.00
2 .... 700.00
3 .... 650.00
4 .... 550.00
5 Gumps(c) 500.00
6 .... 400.00
7 Smokey Stover(c) 400.00
8 Dick Tracy(c) 375.00
9 .... 375.00
10 Dick Tracy(c) 375.00
11 .... 325.00
12 .... 325.00
13 .... 325.00
14 .... 325.00
15 .... 325.00
16 Terry & the Pirates 300.00
17 Dick Tracy(c) 300.00
18 .... 300.00
19 .... 300.00
20 Smilin'Jack(c) 325.00
21 B:Magic Morro 275.00
22 Magic Morro(c) 300.00
23 all star(c) 275.00
24 Dick Tracy(c) 300.00
25 Magic Morro(c) 275.00
26 .... 275.00
27 Magic Morro(c) 275.00
28 Jim Ellis(c) 300.00
29 Smilin'Jack(c) 275.00
30 inc.The Sea Hawk 300.00
31 Dick Tracy(c) 225.00
32 Smilin' Jack(c) 235.00
33 Jim Ellis(c) 225.00
34 Magic Morro(c) 225.00
35 thru 40 Dick Tracy(c) ... @225.00
41 B:Lightning Jim 200.00
42 thru 50 Dick Tracy(c) ... @200.00
51 thru 54 Dick Tracy(c) ... @150.00
55 .... 150.00
56 .... 150.00
57 Dick Tracy(c) 150.00
58 Smitty(c) 150.00
59 .... 150.00
60 Dick Tracy(c) 175.00
61 .... 135.00
62 Flag(c) 135.00
63 Dick Tracy(c) 135.00
64 Smitty(c) 125.00
65 Dick Tracy(c) 135.00
66 Dick Tracy(c) 135.00
67 Christmas(c) 135.00
68 Dick Tracy(c) 135.00
69 Dick Tracy(c) 135.00
70 Dick Tracy(c) 100.00
71 Dick Tracy(c) 100.00
72 Dick Tracy(c) 100.00
73 Smitty(c) 100.00

All comics prices listed are for *Near Mint* condition.

74 War Bond(c)	100.00	
75 Dick Tracy(c)	100.00	
76 Dick Tracy(c)	100.00	
77 Dick Tracy(c)	100.00	
78 Smitty(c)	90.00	
79 Dick Tracy(c)	90.00	
80 Smitty(c)	90.00	
81 Dick Tracy(c)	90.00	
82 Dick Tracy(c)	90.00	
83 Smitty(c)	85.00	
84 Dick Tracy(c)	90.00	
85 Smitty(c)	85.00	
86 All on cover	90.00	
87 All on cover	90.00	
88 Dick Tracy(c)	90.00	
89 Smitty(c)	75.00	
90 Dick Tracy(c)	85.00	
91 Smitty(c)	75.00	
92 Dick Tracy(c)	85.00	
93 Dick Tracy(c)	85.00	
94 Dick Tracy(c)	85.00	
95 thru 99	@75.00	
100	90.00	
101 thru 115	@50.00	
116 Smokey Stover(c)	40.00	
117 Gasoline Alley(c)	40.00	
118 Smokey Stover(c)	40.00	
119 Terry and the Pirates(c)	45.00	
120	45.00	
121	45.00	

SUPER-DOOPER COMICS
Able Manufacturing Co.
1946

1 A:Gangbuster	125.00
2	75.00
3 & 4	@50.00
5 A:Captain Freedom,Shock Gibson	50.00
6 & 7 same	@50.00
8 A:Shock Gibson, 1946	50.00

SUPER DUCK COMICS
MLJ Magazines/Close-Up (Archie Publ.)
Autumn, 1944

1 O:Super Duck	350.00

Super Duck Comics #16
© MLJ Magazines

2	200.00	
3 I:Mr. Monster	150.00	
4 & 5	@125.00	
6 thru 10	@100.00	
11 thru 20	@75.00	
21 thru 40	@60.00	
41 thru 60	@40.00	
61 thru 94	@30.00	

Super Western Funnies #4
© Superior Comics Publishers

SUPER FUNNIES
Superior Comics Publishers
March, 1954

1 Dopey Duck	275.00
2 Out of the Booby-Hatch	50.00

Becomes:

SUPER WESTERN FUNNIES

3 F:Phantom Ranger	30.00
4 F:Phantom Ranger,Sept. 1954	30.00

SUPER MAGICIAN COMICS
Street & Smith Publications
May, 1941

1 B:The Mysterious Blackstone	400.00
2 V:Wild Tribes of Africa	275.00
3 V:Oriental Wizard	250.00
4 V:Quetzal Wizard,O:Transo	225.00
5 A:The Moylan Sisters	225.00
6 JaB,JaB(c),The Eddie Cantor story	225.00
7 In the House of Skulls	250.00
8 A:Abbott & Costello	250.00
9 V:Duneen the Man-Ape	250.00
10 V:Pirates o/t Sargasso Sea	250.00
11 JaB(c),V:Fire Wizards	250.00
12 V:Baal	250.00
2-1 A:The Shadow	225.00
2-2 In the Temple of the 10,00 Idols	100.00
2-3 Optical Illusion on (c)-Turn Jap into Monkey	100.00
2-4 V:Cannibal Killers	100.00
2-5 V:The Pygmies of Lemuria	100.00
2-6 V:Pirates & Indians	100.00
2-7 Can Blackstone Catch the	

Cannonball?	100.00	
2-8 V:Marabout,B:Red Dragon	100.00	
2-9	100.00	
2-10 Pearl Dives Swallowed By Sea Demons	100.00	
2-11 Blackstone Invades Pelican Islands	100.00	
2-12 V:Bubbles of Death	100.00	
3-1	100.00	
3-2 Bondage(c),Midsummers Eve	90.00	
3-3 The Enchanted Garden	90.00	
3-4 Fabulous Aztec Treasure	90.00	
3-5 A:Buffalo Bill	90.00	
3-6 Magic Tricks to Mystify	90.00	
3-7 V:Guy Fawkes	90.00	
3-8 V:Hindu Spook Maker	90.00	
3-9	90.00	
3-10 V:The Water Wizards	90.00	
3-11 V:The Green Goliath	90.00	
3-12 Lady in White	90.00	
4-1 Cannibal of Crime	85.00	
4-2 The Devil's Castle	85.00	
4-3 V:Demons of Golden River	85.00	
4-4 V:Dr. Zero	85.00	
4-5 Bondage(c)	85.00	
4-6 V:A Terror Gang	85.00	
4-7	85.00	
4-8 Mystery of the Disappearing Horse	85.00	
4-9 A Floating Light?	85.00	
4-10 Levitation	85.00	
4-11 Lost, Strange Land of Shangri	85.00	
4-12 I:Nigel Elliman	85.00	
5-1 V:Voodoo Wizards of the Everglades,Bondage (c)	90.00	
5-2 Treasure of the Florida Keys; Bondage (c)	85.00	
5-3 Elliman Battles Triple Crime	85.00	
5-4 Can A Human Being Really Become Invisible	85.00	
5-5 Mystery of the Twin Pools	85.00	
5-6 A:Houdini	85.00	
5-7 F:Red Dragon	125.00	
5-8 F:Red Dragon, Feb.-March, 1947	125.00	

SUPERMOUSE
Standard Comics/Pines
December, 1948

1 FF,(fa)	150.00	
2 FF,(fa)	85.00	
3 FF,(fa)	65.00	
4 FF,(fa)	70.00	
5 FF,(fa)	65.00	
6 FF,(fa)	65.00	
7 thru 10 (fa)	@25.00	
11 thru 20 (fa)	@20.00	
21 thru 44 (fa)	@15.00	
45 (fa),Autumn, 1958	15.00	

SUPER-MYSTERY COMICS
Periodical House (Ace Magazines)
July, 1940

1 B:Magno,Vulcan,Q-13,Flint of the Mountes	1,300.00
2 Bondage (c)	625.00
3 JaB,B:Black Spider	550.00
4 O:Davy;A:Captain Gallant	450.00
5 JaB,JM(c),I&B:The Clown	450.00
6 JM,JM(c),V:The Clown	350.00
2-1 JM,JM(c),O:Buckskin,	

GOLDEN AGE

Super-Mystery Comics #19 (4/1)
© *Periodical House/Ace Magazines*

Bondage(c) 350.00
2-2 JM,JM(c),V:The Clown . . . 325.00
2-3 JM,JM(c),V:The Clown . . . 325.00
2-4 JM,JM(c),V:The Nazis . . . 325.00
2-5 JM,JM(c),Bondage(c) 350.00
2-6 JM,JM(c),Bondage(c),
  'Foreign Correspondent' . . . 350.00
3-1 B:Black Ace 375.00
3-2 A:Mr, Risk, Bondage(c) . . 375.00
3-3 HK,HK(c),I:Lancer;B:Dr.
  Nemesis, The Sword 350.00
3-4 HK 350.00
3-5 HK,LbC,A:Mr. Risk 375.00
3-6 HK,LbC,A:Paul Revere Jr. . 375.00
4-1 HK,LbC,A:Twin Must Die . . 325.00
4-2 A:Mr. Risk 225.00
4-3 Mango out to Kill Davey! . 225.00
4-4 Danger Laughs at Mr. Risk . 225.00
4-5 A:Mr. Risk 225.00
4-6 RP,A:Mr. Risk 225.00
5-1 RP 200.00
5-2 RP,RP(c),The Riddle of the
  Swamp-Land Spirit 200.00
5-3 RP,RP(c),The Case of the
  Whispering Death 200.00
5-4 RP,RP(c) 200.00
5-5 RP,Harry the Hack 200.00
5-6 . . . . 175.00
6-1 . . . . 175.00
6-2 RP,A:Mr. Risk 175.00
6-3 Bondage (c) 175.00
6-4 E:Mango;A:Mr. Risk 175.00
6-5 Bondage(c) 175.00
6-6 A:Mr. Risk 175.00
7-1 . . . . 175.00
7-2 KBa(c) 175.00
7-3 Bondage(c) 175.00
7-4 . . . . 175.00
7-5 . . . . 175.00
7-6 . . . . 175.00
8-1 The Riddle of the Rowboat . 150.00
8-2 Death Meets a Train 150.00
8-3 The Man Who Couldn't Die . 150.00
8-4 RP(c) 150.00
8-5 GT,MMe,Staged for Murder . 150.00
8-6 Unlucky Seven,July, 1949 . 150.00

ARMY AND NAVY COMICS
Street & Smith Publications
May, 1941
1 Hawaii is Calling You,Capt.
  Fury,Nick Carter 400.00
2 Private Rock V;Hitler 250.00
3 The Fighting Fourth 250.00
4 The Fighting Irish 250.00
5 I:Super Snipe 350.00
Becomes:
SUPERSNIPE COMICS
6 A "Comic" With A Sense
  of Humor 600.00
7 A:Wacky, Rex King 375.00
8 Axis Powers & Satan(c),
  Hitler(c) 400.00
9 Hitler Voodoo Doll (c) 500.00
10 Lighting (c) 350.00
11 A:Little Nemo 350.00
12 Football(c) 350.00
2-1 B:Huck Finn 250.00
2-2 Battles Shark 250.00
2-3 Battles Dinosaur 250.00
2-4 Baseball(c) 250.00
2-5 Battles Dinosaur 250.00
2-6 A:Pochontas 250.00
2-7 A:Wing Woo Woo 250.00
2-8 A:Huck Finn 250.00
2-9 Dotty Loves Trouble 250.00
2-10 Assists Farm Labor
  Shortage 250.00
2-11 Dotty & the Jelly Beans . . 250.00
2-12 Statue of Liberty 250.00
3-1 Ice Skating(c) 225.00
3-2 V:Pirates(c) 225.00
3-3 Baseball(c) 225.00
3-4 Jungle(c) 225.00
3-5 Learn Piglatin 225.00
3-6 Football Hero 225.00
3-7 Saves Girl From Grisley . . 225.00
3-8 Rides a Wild Horse 225.00
3-9 Powers Santa's Sleigh . . . 225.00
3-10 Plays Basketball 225.00
3-11 Is A Baseball Pitcher . . . 225.00
3-12 Flies with the Birds 225.00
4-1 Catches A Whale 175.00
4-2 Track & Field Athlete 175.00
4-3 Think Machine(c) 175.00
4-4 Alpine Skiier 175.00
4-5 Becomes a Boxer 175.00
4-6 Race Car Driver 175.00
4-7 Bomber(c) 175.00
4-8 Baseball Star 175.00
4-9 Football Hero 175.00
4-10 Christmas(c) 175.00
4-11 Artic Adventure 175.00
4-12 The Ghost Remover 175.00
5-1 August-September, 1949 . 175.00

SUPER SPY
Centaur Publications
Oct.–Nov., 1940
1 O:Sparkler 900.00
2 A:Night Hawk, Drew Ghost, Tim
  Blain, S.S. Swanson the Inner
  Circle, Duke Collins, Gentlemen
  of Misfortune 550.00

SUPER WESTERN COMICS
Youthful Magazines Aug., 1950
1 BP,BP,(c),B:Buffalo Bill,Wyatt

Earp,CalamityJane,SamSlade 55.00
2 thru 4 March, 1951 . . . . . @35.00

SUPER WESTERN FUNNIES
(see SUPER FUNNIES)

Superworld Comics #3
© *Komos Publications*

SUPERWORLD COMICS
Komos Publications
(Hugo Gernsback)
April, 1940
1 FP,FP(c),B:MilitaryPowers,BuzzAllen
  Smarty Artie, Alibi Alige . . 4,500.00
2 FP,FP(c),A:Mario 2,700.00
3 FP,FP(c),V:Vest Wearing
  Giant Grasshoppers 1,900.00

SUSPENSE COMICS
Et Es Go Mag. Inc.
(Continental Magazines)
December, 1945
1 LbC, Bondage(c),B:Grey
  Mask 3,000.00
2 DRi,I:The Mask 2,200.00
3 LbC,ASh(c),Bondage(c) . . 6,000.00
4 LbC,LbC(c),Bondage(c) . . 1,600.00
5 LbC,LbC(c) 1,600.00
6 LbC,LbC(c),The End of
  the Road 1,600.00
7 LbC,LbC(c) 1,300.00
8 LbC,LbC(c) 3,200.00
9 LbC,LbC(c) 1,300.00
10 RP,LbC,LbC(c) 1,300.00
11 RP,LbC,LbC(c),Satan(c) . 3,200.00
12 LbC,LbC(c),Dec., 1946 . . 1,300.00

SUSPENSE DETECTIVE
Fawcett Publications
June, 1952
1 GE,MBi,MBi(c),Death Poised
  to Strike 300.00
2 GE,MSy 175.00
3 A Furtive Footstep 150.00
4 MBi,MSy,Bondage(c),A Blood
  Chilling Scream 135.00

GOLDEN AGE

5 MSy,MSy(c),MBi,A Hair-Trigger
from Death, March, 1953 . . 150.00

SUZIE COMICS
(see TOP-NOTCH COMICS)

SWEENEY
Standard Comics
June, 1949
4 Buzz Sawyer's Pal 45.00
5 September, 1949 . . . . 40.00

SWEETHEART DIARY
Fawcett
Winter, 1949
1 . . . . 75.00
2 . . . . 40.00
3 and 4 WW . . . . @75.00
5 thru 10 . . . . @30.00
11 thru 14 . . . . @20.00

SWEETHEART DIARY
Charlton Comics
January 1953
32 . . . . 22.00
33 thru 40 . . . . @10.00
41 thru 65 . . . . @6.00

SWEET HEART
(see CAPTAIN MIDNIGHT)

SWEET LOVE
Harvey Publications
(Home Comics)
September, 1949
1 Ph(c) 35.00
2 Ph(c) 20.00
3 BP 20.00
4 Ph(c) 15.00
5 BP,JKa,Ph(c) 30.00

SWEET SIXTEEN
Parents' Magazine Group
August-September, 1946
1 Van Johnson story 125.00
2 Alan Ladd story 100.00
3 Rip Taylor 60.00
4 E:Taylor 60.00
5 Gregory Peck story (c) 55.00
6 Dick Hammes(c) 50.00
7 Ronald Reagan(c) 125.00
8 Shirley Jones(c) 50.00
9 William Holden(c) 50.00
10 James Stewart(c) 55.00
11 . . . . 50.00
12 Bob Cummings(c) 50.00
13 Robert Mitchum(c) 60.00

SWIFT ARROW
Farrell Publications(Ajax)
February-March, 1954
1 Lone Rider's Redskin Brother 60.00
2 . . . . 35.00
3 . . . . 30.00
4 . . . . 30.00
5 October-November, 1954 . . . 30.00
2nd Series
April, 1957
1 . . . . 30.00
2 B:Lone Rider 20.00
3 September, 1957 . . . . 20.00

TAFFY
Orbit Publications/Rural Home/
Taffy Publications
March-April, 1945
1 LbC(c),(fa),Bondage(c) 200.00
2 LbC(c),(fa) 100.00
3 (fa) 50.00
4 (fa) 45.00
5 LbC(c),A:Van Johnson 60.00
6 A:Perry Como 50.00
7 A:Dave Clark 55.00
8 A:Glen Ford 50.00
9 A:Lon McCallister 50.00
10 A:John Hodiak 50.00
11 A:Mickey Rooney 50.00
12 February, 1948 . . . . 50.00

TAILSPIN
Spotlight Publications
November, 1944
N# LbC(c),A:Firebird 175.00

TALES FROM
THE CRYPT
(see CRIME PATROL)

TALES FROM THE TOMB
(see Dell Giants)

TALES OF HORROR
Toby Press/Minoan Publ. Corp
June, 1952
1 Demons of the Underworld . 250.00
2 What was the Thing in
the Pool?,Torture 200.00
3 The Big Snake 125.00
4 The Curse of King Kala! . . . 125.00
5 Hand of Fate 125.00
6 The Fiend of Flame 125.00
7 Beast From The Deep 125.00
8 The Snake that Held A
City Captive 125.00
9 It Came From the Bottom
of the World 150.00
10 The Serpent Strikes 150.00
11 Death Flower? 150.00
12 Guaranteed to Make Your
Hair Stand on End 165.00
13 Ghost with a Torch;
October, 1954 . . . . 135.00

TALES OF TERROR
Toby Press
1952
1 Just A Bunch of Hokey
Hogwash 150.00

TALES OF TERROR
ANNUAL
E.C. 1951
N# AF 3,400.00
2 AF 1,500.00
3 . . . . 1,100.00

TALLY-HO COMICS
Baily Publishing Co.
December, 1944
N# FF,A:Snowman 250.00

Target Comics #9/11
© Funnies Inc./Novelty Publ.

TARGET COMICS
Funnnies Inc./Novelty Publ./
Premium Group/Curtis
Circulation Co./Star
Publications
February, 1940
1 BEv,JCo,CBu,JSm;B,O&I:Manowar,
White Streak,Bull's-Eye;B:City
Editor,High Grass Twins,T-Men,
Rip Rory,Fantastic Feature
Films, Calling 2-R 3,700.00
2 BEv,JSm,JCo,CBu,White
Streak(c) 1,800.00
3 BEv,JSm,JCo,CBu 1,000.00
4 JSm,JCo 1,000.00
5 CBu,BW,O:White Streak . . 3,200.00
6 CBu,BW,White Streak(c) . . 1,300.00
7 CBu,BW,BW(c),V:Planetoid
Stories,Space Hawk(c) . . . 3,700.00
8 CBu,BW,White Shark(c) . . 1,000.00
9 CBu,BW,White Shark(c) . . 1,000.00
10 CBu,BW,JK(c),The
Target(c) 1,300.00
11 BW,The Target(c) 1,100.00
12 BW,same 1,000.00
2-1 BW,CBu 600.00
2-2 BW,BoW(c) 550.00
2-3 BW,BoW(c),The Target(c) . 450.00
2-4 BW,B:Cadet 450.00
2-5 BW,BoW(c),The Target(c) . 400.00
2-6 BW,The Cadet(c) 400.00
2-7 BW,The Cadet(c) 400.00
2-8 BW,same 400.00
2-9 BW,The Target(c) 400.00
2-10 BW,same 700.00
2-11 BW,The Cadet(c) 400.00
2-12 BW,same 400.00
3-1 BW,same 375.00
3-2 BW 375.00
3-3 BW,The Target(c) 375.00
3-4 BW,The Cadet(c) 375.00
3-5 BW 375.00
3-6 BW,War Bonds(c) 375.00
3-7 BW 375.00
3-8 BW,War Bonds(c) 375.00
3-9 BW 375.00
3-10 BW 375.00

3-11	90.00
3-12	90.00
4-1 JJo(c)	65.00
4-2 ERy(c)	65.00
4-3 AVi	65.00
4-4	65.00
4-5 API(c),Statue of Liberty(c)	75.00
4-6 BW	65.00
4-7 AVi	65.00
4-8,Christmas(c)	65.00
4-9	65.00
4-10	65.00
4-11	65.00
4-12	65.00
5-1	50.00
5-2 The Target	55.00
5-3 Savings Checkers(c)	50.00
5-4 War Bonds Ph(c)	50.00
5-5 thru 5-12	@50.00
6-1 The Target(c)	55.00
6-2	50.00
6-3 Red Cross(c)	50.00
6-4	50.00
6-5 Savings Bonds(c)	50.00
6-6 The Target(c)	50.00
6-7 The Cadet(c)	50.00
6-8 AFa	50.00
6-9 The Target(c)	50.00
6-10	50.00
6-11	50.00
6-12	50.00
7-1	50.00
7-2 Bondage(c)	50.00
7-3 The Target(c)	50.00
7-4 DRi,The Cadet(c)	50.00
7-5	50.00
7-6 DRi(c)	50.00
7-7 The Cadet(c)	50.00
7-8 DRi(c)	50.00
7-9 The Cadet(c)	50.00
7-10 DRi,DRi(c)	50.00
7-11	50.00
7-12 JH(c)	50.00
8-1	50.00
8-2 DRi,DRi(c),BK	50.00
8-3 DRi,The Cadet(c)	50.00
8-4 DRi,DRi(c)	50.00
8-5 DRi,The Cadet(c)	50.00
8-6 DRi,DRi(c)	50.00
8-7 BK,DRi,DRi(c)	50.00
8-8 DRi,The Cadet(c)	50.00
8-9 DRi,The Cadet(c)	50.00
8-10 DRi,KBa,LbC(c)	200.00
8-11 DRi,The Cadet	50.00
8-12 DRi,The Cadet	50.00
9-1 DRi,LbC(c)	200.00
9-2 DRi	50.00
9-3 DRi,Bondage(c),The Cadet(c)	50.00
9-4 DRi,LbC(c)	200.00
9-5 DRi,Baseball(c)	50.00
9-6 DRi,LbC(c)	200.00
9-7 DRi	50.00
9-8 DRi,LbC(c)	200.00
9-9 DRi,Football(c)	50.00
9-10 DRi,LbC(c)	200.00
9-11,The Cadet	50.00
9-12 LbC(c),Gems(c)	200.00
10-1,The Cadet	50.00
10-2 LbC(c)	200.00
10-3 LbC(c)	200.00

Becomes:

TARGET WESTERN ROMANCES
Star Publications

October-November, 1949

106 LbC(c),The Beauty Scar	200.00
107 LbC(c),The Brand Upon His Heart	175.00

Tarzan #8 © Dell Publishing Co.

TARZAN
Dell Publishing Co.
January-February 1948

1 V:White Savages of Vari	1,000.00
2 Captives of Thunder Valley	550.00
3 Dwarfs of Didona	400.00
4 The Lone Hunter	400.00
5 The Men of Greed	400.00
6 Outlwas of Pal-ul-Don	300.00
7 Valley of the Monsters	300.00
8 The White Pygmies	300.00
9 The Men of A-Lur	300.00
10 Treasure of the Bolgani	300.00
11 The Sable Lion	250.00
12 The Price of Peace	250.00
13 B:Lex Barker photo(c)	225.00
14	225.00
15	225.00
16	200.00
17	200.00
18	200.00
19	200.00
20	200.00
21 thru 30	@150.00
31 thru 54 E:L.Barker Ph(c)	@75.00
55 thru 70	@75.00
71 thru 79	@50.00
80 thru 90 B:ScottGordonPh(c)	@30.00
91 thru 99	@28.00
100	40.00
101 thru 110 E:S.GordonPh(c)	@25.00
111 thru 120	@20.00
121 thru 131	@20.00

TEEN-AGE DIARY SECRETS
St. John Publishing Co.
October, 1949

6 MB,PH(c)	75.00
7 MB,PH(c)	85.00
8 MB,PH(c)	75.00
9 MB,PH(c)	85.00

Becomes:

DIARY SECRETS

10 MB	65.00
11 MB	55.00
12 thru 19 MB	@50.00
20 MB,JKu	55.00
21 thru 28 MB	@30.00
29 MB,Comics Code	25.00
30 MB	25.00

TEEN-AGE ROMANCES
St. John Publishing Co.
January, 1949

1 MB(c),MB	250.00
2 MB(c),MB	150.00
3 MB(c),MB	175.00
4 Ph(c)	150.00
5 MB,Ph(c)	150.00
6 MB,Ph(c)	150.00
7 MB,Ph(c)	150.00
8 MB,Ph(c)	150.00
9 MB,MB(c),JKu	160.00
10 thru 27 MB,MB(c),JKu	@125.00
28 thru 30	@50.00
31 thru 34 MB(c)	@50.00
35 thru 42 MB(c),MB	@60.00
43 MB(c),MB,Comics Code	40.00
44 MB(c),MB	40.00
45 MB(c),MB	40.00

TEEN-AGE TEMPTATIONS
St. John Publishing Co.
October, 1952

1 MB(c),MB	300.00
2 MB(c),MB	100.00
3 MB(c),MB	140.00
4 MB(c),MB	140.00
5 MB(c),MB	140.00
6 MB(c),MB	140.00
7 MB(c),MB	140.00
8 MB(c),MB,Drug	150.00
9 MB(c),MB	135.00

Becomes:

GOING STEADY

10 MB(c),MB	85.00
11 MB(c),MB	60.00
12 MB(c),MB	60.00
13 MB(c),MB	60.00
14 MB(c),MB	60.00

TEENIE WEENIES, THE
Ziff-Davis Publishing Co.
1951

10	85.00
11	80.00

TEEN LIFE
(see YOUNG LIFE)

TEGRA, JUNGLE EMPRESS
(see ZEGRA, JUNGLE EMPRESS)

TELEVISION COMICS
Animated Cartoons
(Standard Comics)
February, 1950

5 Humorous Format,I:Willie Nilly	50.00
6	35.00
7	35.00
8 May, 1950	35.00

GOLDEN AGE

TELEVISION PUPPET SHOW
Avon Periodicals
1950
1 F:Sparky Smith,Spotty,
Cheeta, Speedy 80.00
2 November, 1950 .... 75.00

TELL IT TO THE MARINES
Toby Press
March, 1952
1 I:Spike & Pat 125.00
2 A:Madame Cobra 60.00
3 Spike & Bat on a
Commando Raid! 40.00
4 Veil Dancing(c) 42.00
5 .... 42.00
6 To Paris 35.00
7 Ph(c),The Chinese Bugle ... 30.00
8 Ph(c),V:Communists in
South Korea 30.00
9 Ph(c) 30.00
10 .... 30.00
11 .... 30.00
12 .... 30.00
13 John Wayne Ph(c) 75.00
14 Ph(c) 30.00
15 Ph(c),July, 1955 ...... 30.00

Tender Romance #2
© Key Publications

TENDER ROMANCE
Key Publications
December, 1953
1 .... 65.00
2 .... 35.00
Becomes:

IDEAL ROMANCE
3 .... 35.00
4 thru 8 .... @20.00
Becomes:

DIARY CONFESSIONS
9 .... 25.00
10 .... 15.00

TERRIFIC COMICS
(see HORRIFIC)

TERRIFIC COMICS
Et Es Go Mag. Inc./
Continental Magazines
January, 1944
1 LbC,DRi(c),F:Kid
Terrific Drug 2,500.00
2 LcC,ASh(c),B:Boomerang,
'Comics' McCormic,
..... 1,800.00
3 LbC,LbC(c) 1,500.00
4 LbC,RP(c) 1,800.00
5 LbC,BF,ASh(c),Bondage(c) 2,000.00
6 LbC,LbC(c),BF,Nov.,1944 . 1,500.00

TERROR ILLUSTRATED
E.C. Comics
November-December, 1955
1 JCr,GE,Grl,JO,RC(c) 75.00
2 Spring, 1956 .... 60.00

TERRIFYING TALES
Star Publications
January, 1953
11 LbC,LbC(c),'TyrantsofTerror' 350.00
12 LbC,LbC(c),'Bondage(c),
'Jungle Mystery' 300.00
13 LbC(c),Bondage(c),'The
Death-Fire,Devil Head(c) ... 350.00
14 LbC(c),Bondage(c),'The
Weird Idol' 300.00
15 LbC(c),'The Grim Secret',
April, 1954 .... 300.00
Becomes:

JUNGLE THRILLS
Star Publications
February, 1952
16 LbC(c),'Kingdom of Unseen
Terror' 300.00
Becomes:

TERRORS OF THE JUNGLE
17 LbC(c),Bondage(c) 300.00
18 LbC(c),Strange Monsters .. 225.00
19 JyD,LbC(c),Bondage(c),The
Golden Ghost Gorilla 225.00
20 JyD,LbC(c),The Creeping
Scourge 225.00
21 LbC(c),Evil Eyes of Death! . 250.00
4 JyD,LbC(c),Morass of Death 175.00
5 JyD,LbC(c),Bondage(c),
Savage Train 200.00
6 JyD,LbC(c),Revolt of the
Jungle Monsters 200.00
7 JyD,LbC(c) 175.00
8 JyD,LbC(c),Death's Grim
Reflection 175.00
9 JyD,LbC(c),Doom to
Evil-Doers 175.00
10 JyD,LbC(c),Black Magic,
September, 1954 .... 175.00

BOY EXPLORERS
1 S&K(c),S&K,The Cadet 650.00
2 S&K(c),S&K 750.00
Becomes:

TERRY AND THE PIRATES
3 S&K,MC(c),MC,Terry and
Dragon Lady 300.00
4 S&K,MC(c),MC 175.00

5 S&K,MC(c),MC,BP,
Chop-Chop(c) 100.00
6 S&K,.MC(c),MC 100.00
7 S&K,MC(c),MC,BP 100.00
8 S&K,MC(c),MC,BP 100.00
9 S&K,MC(c),MC,BP 100.00
10 S&K,MC(c),MC,BP 100.00
11 S&K,MC(c),MC,BP,
A:Man in Black 75.00
12 S&K,MC(c),MC,BP 75.00
13 S&K,MC(c),MC,Belly Dancers 75.00
14 thru 20 S&K,MC(c),MC ... @60.00
22 thru 26 S&K,MC(c),MC ... @55.00
27 Charlton Comics 50.00
28 .... 50.00

TERRY-BEARS COMICS
St. John Publishing Co.
June, 1952
1 .... 20.00
2 & 3 .... @15.00

Terry-Toons Comics #50
© Select Comics/Timely Comics

TERRY-TOONS COMICS
Select,Timely,Marvel,St. Johns
1942
1 Paul Terry (fa) 1,200.00
2 .... 500.00
3 thru 6 .... @350.00
7 Hitler,Hirohito,Mussolini(c) .. 300.00
8 thru 20 .... @225.00
21 thru 37 .... @150.00
38 I&(c):Mighty Mouse 850.00
39 Mighty Mouse 250.00
40 thru 49 All Mighty Mouse @125.00
50 I:Heckle & Jeckle 250.00
51 thru 60 .... @75.00
61 thru 70 .... @65.00
71 thru 86 .... @60.00

TEXAN, THE
St. John Publishing Co.
August, 1948
1 GT,F:Buckskin Belle,The Gay
Buckaroo,Mustang Jack 80.00
2 GT 40.00
3 BLb(c) 35.00

GOLDEN AGE

4 MB,MB(c) 60.00
5 MB,MB(c),Mystery Rustlers
   of the Rio Grande 60.00
6 MB(c),Death Valley
   Double-Cross 50.00
7 MB,MB(c),Comanche Justice
   Strikes at Midnight 60.00
8 MB,MB(c),Scalp Hunters
   Hide their Tracks 60.00
9 MB(c),Ghost Terror of
   the Blackfeet 60.00
10 MB,MB(c),Treason Rides
   the Warpath 50.00
11 MB,MB(c),Hawk Knife 60.00
12 MB 60.00
13 MB,Doublecross at Devil'sDen 60.00
14 MB,Ambush at Buffalo Trail . 60.00
15 MB,Twirling Blades Tame
   Treachery 60.00
Becomes:

FIGHTIN' TEXAN
16 GT,Wanted Dead or Alive . . 45.00
17 LC,LC(c);Killers Trail,
   December, 1952 . . . . 40.00

TEX FARRELL
D.S. Publishing Co.
March-April, 1948
1 Pride of the Wild West 75.00

TEX GRANGER
(see CALLING ALL BOYS)

TEX RITTER WESTERN
Fawcett Publications/
Charlton Comics
Oct., 1950–May 1959
1 Ph(c),B:Tex Ritter, his Horse
   White Flash, his dog Fury, and
   his mom Nancy 500.00
2 Ph(c),Vanishing Varmints . . 250.00
3 Ph(c),Blazing Six-Guns . . . 175.00
4 Ph(c),The Jaws of Terror . . 150.00
5 Ph(c),Bullet Trail 150.00
6 Ph(c),Killer Bait 150.00
7 Ph(c),Gunsmoke Revenge . 125.00
8 Ph(c),Lawless Furnace Valley 125.00
9 Ph(c),The Spider's Web . . . 125.00
10 Ph(c),The Ghost Town 125.00
11 Ph(c),Saddle Conquest 125.00
12 Ph(c),Prairie Inferno 75.00
13 Ph(c) 75.00
14 Ph(c) 75.00
15 Ph(c) 75.00
16 thru 19 Ph(c) . . . . @75.00
20 Ph(c),Stagecoach To Danger 75.00
21 . . . . 75.00
22 Panic at Diamond B 60.00
23 A:Young Falcon 50.00
24 A:Young Falcon 50.00
25 A:Young Falcon 50.00
26 thru 38 . . . . @45.00
39 AW,AW(c) 45.00
40 thru 46 . . . . @40.00

THING!, THE
Song Hits/Capitol Stories/
Charlton Comics
February, 1952
1 Horror 550.00
2 Crazy King(c) 400.00
3 . . . . 400.00
4 AFa(c),I Was A Zombie . . . 325.00

5 LM(c),Severed Head(c) 350.00
6 . . . . 325.00
7 Fingenail to Eye(c) 500.00
8 . . . . 325.00
9 Severe 550.00
10 Devil(c) 325.00
11 SC,Cleaver 425.00
12 SD,SD(c),Neck Blood
   Sucking 550.00
13 SD,SD(c) 550.00
14 SD,SD(c) 550.00
15 SD,SD(c) 550.00
16 Eye Torture 350.00
17 BP,SD(c) 500.00
Becomes:

BLUE BEETLE
18 America's Fastest Moving
   Crusader Against Crime . . . 125.00
19 JKa,Lightning Fast 150.00
20 JKa 150.00
21 The Invincible 100.00
Becomes:

MR. MUSCLES
22 World's Most Perfect Man . . . 30.00
23 August, 1956 . . . . 20.00

THIS IS SUSPENSE
(see LAWBREAKERS)

THIS IS WAR
Standard Comics
July, 1952
5 ATh,Show Them How To Die 80.00
6 ATh,Make Him A Soldier . . . 75.00
7 One Man For Himself 25.00
8 Miracle on Massacre Hill . . . 25.00
9 ATh,May, 1953 . . . . 60.00

THIS IS SUSPENSE!
(see STRANGE SUSPENSE
STORIES)

THIS MAGAZINE IS
HAUNTED
Fawcett Publications/
Charlton Comics
October, 1951
1 MBi,F:Doctor Death 450.00
2 GE 300.00
3 MBi,Quest of the Vampire . 200.00
4 BP,The Blind, The Doomed
   and the Dead 200.00
5 BP,GE,The Slithering Horror
   of Skontong Swamp! 300.00
6 Secret of the Walking Dead . 150.00
7 The Man Who Saw Too Much 150.00
8 The House in the Web 150.00
9 The Witch of Tarlo 150.00
10 I Am Dr Death,
   Severed Head(c) 225.00
11 BP,Touch of Death 125.00
12 BP 125.00
13 BP,Severed Head(c) 200.00
14 BP,Horrors of the Damned . 125.00
15 DG(c) 100.00
16 SD(c) 250.00
17 SD,SD(c) 265.00
18 SD,SD(c) 265.00
19 SD(c) 225.00
20 SMz(c) 125.00
21 SD(c) 200.00
Becomes:

DANGER AND
ADVENTURE
22 The Viking King,F:Ibis the
   Invincible 50.00
23 F:Nyoka the Jungle Girl
   Comics Code 45.00
24 DG&AA(c) 35.00
25 thru 27 . . . . @30.00
Becomes:

ROBIN HOOD AND HIS
MERRY MEN
28 . . . . 40.00
29 thru 37 . . . . @30.00
38 SD,August, 1958 . . . . 75.00

3-D-ELL
Dell Publishing Co.
1953
1 Rootie Kazootie 300.00
2 Rootie Kazootie 250.00
3 Flunkey Louise 225.00

THREE RING COMICS
Spotlight Publishers
March, 1945
1 Funny Animal 50.00

THREE STOOGES
Jubilee Publ.
February, 1949
1 JKu,Infinity(c) 750.00
2 JKu,On the Set of the
   'The Gorilla Girl' 600.00
   St. John Publishing Co.
1 JKu,'Bell Bent for
   Treasure, Sept., 1953 . . . . . 500.00
2 JKu 350.00
3 JKu,3D 350.00
4 JKu,Medical Mayhem 250.00
5 JKu,Shempador-Matador
   Supreme 250.00
6 JKu, ... 250.00
7 JKu,Ocotber, 1954 . . . . 250.00

Thrilling Comics #9
© Better Publ./Nedor/Standard Comics

THRILLING COMICS
Better Publ./Nedor/ Standard Comics
February, 1940

1 B&O:Doc Strange,B:Nickie Norton	2,000.00
2 B:Rio Kid,Woman in Red Pinocchio	900.00
3 B:Lone Eagle,The Ghost	550.00
4 Dr Strange(c)	500.00
5 Bondage(c)	450.00
6 Dr Strange(c)	450.00
7 Dr Strange(c)	450.00
8 V:Pirates	450.00
9 Bondage(c)	450.00
10 V:Nazis	450.00
11 ASh(c),V:Nazis	425.00
12 ASh(c)	400.00
13 ASh(c),Bondage(c)	450.00
14 ASh(c)	425.00
15 ASh(c),V:Nazis	425.00
16 Bondage(c)	450.00
17 Dr Strange(c)	450.00
18 Dr Strange(c)	450.00
19 I&O:American Crusader	450.00
20 Bondage(c)	450.00
21 American Crusader(c)	325.00
22 Bondage(c)	350.00
23 American Crusader	325.00
24 I:Mike in Doc Strange	325.00
25 DR Strange(c)	325.00
26 Dr Strange(c)	325.00
27 Bondage(c)	350.00
28 Bondage(c)	350.00
29 E:Rio Kid;Bondage(c)	350.00
30 Bondage(c)	350.00
31 Dr Strange(c)	300.00
32 Dr Strange(c)	275.00
33 Dr Strange(c)	275.00
34 Dr Strange(c)	275.00
35 Dr Strange	275.00
36 ASh(c),B:Commando	300.00
37 BO,ASh(c)	275.00
38 ASh(c)	275.00
39 ASh(c),E:American Crusader	275.00
40 ASh(c)	275.00
41 ASh(c),F:American Crusader	275.00
42 ASh(c)	200.00
43 ASh(c)	200.00
44 ASh(c),Hitler(c)	300.00
45 EK,ASh(c)	210.00
46 ASh(c)	210.00
47 ASh(c)	200.00
48 EK,ASh(c)	200.00
49 ASh(c)	200.00
50 ASh(c)	200.00
51 ASh(c)	200.00
52 ASh(c),E:Th Ghost; Peto-Bondage(c)	225.00
53 ASh(c),B:Phantom Detective	200.00
54 ASh(c),Bondage(c)	225.00
55 ASh(c),E:Lone Eagle	200.00
56 ASh(c),B:Princess Pantha	325.00
57 ASh(c)	250.00
58 ASh(c)	250.00
59 ASh(c)	250.00
60 ASh(c)	250.00
61 ASh(c),GRi,A:Lone Eagle	250.00
62 ASh(c)	250.00
63 ASh(c),GT	250.00
64 ASh(c)	250.00
65 ASh(c),E:Commando Cubs, Phantom Detective	250.00
66 ASh(c)	250.00
67 FF,ASh(c)	325.00

Thrilling Comics #18
© Standard Comics

68 FF,ASh(c)	325.00
69 FF,ASh(c)	325.00
70 FF,ASh(c)	325.00
71 FF,ASh(c)	325.00
72 FF,ASh(c)	325.00
73 FF,ASh(c)	325.00
74 E:Princess Pantha; B:Buck Ranger	200.00
75 B:Western Front	100.00
76	100.00
77 ASh(c)	100.00
78 Bondage(c)	110.00
79 BK	100.00
80 JSe,BE,April, 1951	110.00

THRILLING CRIME CASES
Star Publications
June-July, 1950

41 LbC(c),The Unknowns	175.00
42 LbC(c),The Gunmaster	150.00
43 LbC,LbC(c),The Chameleon	175.00
44 LbC(c),Sugar Bowl Murder	175.00
45 LbC(c),Maze of Murder	175.00
46 LbC,LbC(c),Modern Communications	125.00
47 LbC(c),The Careless Killer	125.00
48 LbC(c),Road Black	125.00
49 LbC(c),The Poisoner	225.00

Becomes:

SHOCKING MYSTERY CASES

50 JyD,LbC(c),Dead Man's Revenge	275.00
51 JyD,LbC(c),A Murderer's Reward	150.00
52 LbC(c),The Carnival Killer	150.00
53 LbC(c),The Long Shot of Evil	150.00
54 LbC(c),Double-Cross of Death	150.00
55 LbC(c),Return from Death	150.00
56 LbC(c),The Chase	175.00
57 LbC(c),Thrilling Cases	125.00
58 LbC(c),Killer at Large	125.00
59 LbC(c),Relentless Huntdown	125.00
60 LbC(c),Lesson of the Law, October, 1954	125.00

THRILLING ROMANCES
Standard Comics
December, 1949

5 Ph(c)	55.00
6 Ph(c)	25.00
7 Ph(c),JSe,BE	35.00
8 Ph(c)	25.00
9 Ph(c),GT	30.00
10 Ph(c),JSe,BE	30.00
11 Ph(c),JSe,BE	30.00
12 Ph(c),WW	45.00
13 Ph(c),JSe	25.00
14 Ph(c),Danny Kaye	18.00
15 Ph(c),Tony Martin,Ph(c)	18.00
16 Ph(c)	15.00
17 Ph(c)	15.00
18 Ph(c)	15.00
19 Ph(c)	15.00
20 Ph(c)	15.00
21 Ph(c)	15.00
22 Ph(c),ATn	35.00
23 Ph(c),ATn	35.00
24 Ph(c),ATn3	35.00
25 Ph(c),ATn	35.00

THRILLING TRUE STORY OF THE BASEBALL GIANTS
Fawcett Publications
1952

N# Partial Ph(c),Famous Giants of the Past	550.00
2 Yankees Ph(c),Joe DiMaggio, Yogi Berra,Mickey Mantle, Casey Stengel	550.00

TICK TOCK TALES
Magazine Enterprises
January, 1946

1 (fa) Koko & Kola	65.00
2 (fa) Calender	35.00
3 thru 10 (fa)	@25.00
11 thru 18 (fa)	@20.00
19 (fa),Flag(c)	20.00
20 (fa)	20.00
21 (fa)	15.00
22 (fa)	15.00
23 (fa),Mugsy Mouse	15.00
24 thru 33 (fa)	@15.00
34 (fa), 1951	15.00

TIM HOLT
Magazine Enterprises
January-February, 1949

4 FBe,Ph(c)	350.00
5 FBe,Ph(c)	200.00
6 FBe,Ph(c),I:Calico Kid	225.00
7 FBe,Ph(c),Man-Killer Mustang	175.00
8 FBe,Ph(c)	175.00
9 FBe,DAy(c),TerribleTenderfoot	175.00
10 FBe,DAy(c),The Devil Horse	175.00
11 FBe,DAy(c),O&I:Ghost Rider	275.00
12 FBe,DAy(c),Battle at Bullock Gap	80.00
13 FBe,DAy(c),Ph(c)	80.00
14 FBe,DAy(c),Ph(c),The Honest Bandits	80.00
15 FBe,DAy,Ph(c)	80.00
16 FBe,DAy,Ph(c)	80.00
17 FBe,DAy,Ph(c)	250.00
18 FBe,DAy,Ph(c)	75.00
19 FBe,DAy,They Dig By Night	60.00
20 FBe,DAy,O:Red Mask	90.00

21 FBe,DAy,FF(c)	225.00
22 FBe,DAy	55.00
23 FF,FBe,DAy	175.00
24 FBe,DAy,FBe(c)	55.00
25 FBe,DAy,FBe(c)	100.00
26 FBe,DAy,FBe(c)	50.00
27 FBe,DAy,FBe(c),V:Straw Man	50.00
28 FBe,DAy,FBe(c),Ph(c)	50.00
29 FBe,DAy,FBe,Ph(c), ...	50.00
30 FBe,DAy,FBe(c),Lady Doom	
& The Death Wheel	45.00
31 FBe,DAy,FBe(c)	45.00
32 FBe,DAy,FBe(c)	45.00
33 FBe,DAy,FBe(c)	45.00
34 FBe,DAy,FBe(c)	60.00
35 FBe,DAy,FBe(c)	60.00
36 FBe,DAy,FBe(c),Drugs	65.00
37 FBe,DAy,FBe(c)	65.00
38 FBe,DAy,FBe(c)	65.00
39 FBe,DAy,FBe(c),3D Effect . .	70.00
40 FBe,DAy,FBe(c)	70.00
41 FBe,DAy,FBe(c)	70.00

Becomes:

RED MASK

42 FBe,DAy,FBe(c),3D	125.00
43 FBe,DAy,FBe(c),3D	100.00
44 FBe,DAy,FBe(c),Death at	
Split Mesa,3D	90.00
45 FBe,DAy,FBe(c),V:False Red	
Mask	90.00
46 FBe,DAy,FBe(c)	90.00
47 FBe,DAy,FBe(c)	90.00
48 FBe,DAy,FBe(c),Comics Code	85.00
49 FBe,DAy,FBe(c)	85.00
50 FBe,DAy	85.00
51 FBe,DAy,The Magic of 'The	
Presto Kid'	85.00
52 FBe,DAy,O:Presto Kid	90.00
53 FBe,DAy	70.00
54 FBe,DAy,September, 1957 . .	90.00

TIM TYLER COWBOY
Standard Comics
November, 1948

11	40.00
12	30.00
13 The Doll Told the Secret	30.00
14 Danger at Devil's Acres	30.00
15 Secret Treasure	30.00
16	30.00
17	30.00
18 1950	30.00

TINY TOTS COMICS
Dell Publishing Co.
1943

1	300.00

TINY TOTS COMICS
E.C. Comics
March, 1946

N# Your First Comic Book	
B:Burton Geller(c) and art . .	225.00
2	125.00
3 Celebrate the 4th	100.00
4 Go Back to School	120.00
5 Celebrate the Winter	100.00
6 Do Their Spring Gardening . .	90.00
7 On a Thrilling Ride	100.00
8 On a Summer Vacation . . .	100.00
9 On a Plane Ride	100.00
10 Merry X-Mas Tiny Tots	
E:Burton Geller(c)and art . .	100.00

TIP TOP COMICS
United Features,St. John,Dell
1930

1 HF,Li'l Abner	6,200.00
2 HF	1,400.00
3 HF,Tarzan(c)	1,300.00
4 HF,Li'l Abner(c)	750.00
5 HF,Capt&Kids(c)	600.00
6 HF	550.00
7 HF	550.00
8 HF,Li'l Abner(c)	550.00
9 HF,Tarzan(c)	675.00
10 HF,Li'l Abner(c)	600.00
11 HF,Tarzan(c)	550.00
12 HF,Li'l Abner	500.00
13 HF,Tarzan(c)	525.00
14 HF,Li'l Abner(c)	500.00
15 HF,Capt&kids(c)	500.00
16 HF,Tarzan(c)	525.00
17 HF,Li'l Abner(c)	500.00
18 HF,Tarzan(c)	525.00
19 HF,Football(c)	450.00

Tip Top Comics #33
© United Features/St. John/Dell

20 HF,Capt&Kids(c)	450.00
21 HF,Tarzan(c)	450.00
22 HF,Li'l Abner(c)	350.00
23 HF,Capt&Kids(c)	350.00
24 HF,Tarzan(c)	450.00
25 HF,Capt&Kids(c)	350.00
26 HF,Li'L Abner(c)	350.00
27 HF,Tarzan(c)	450.00
28 HF,Li'l Abner(c)	350.00
29 HF,Capt&Kids(c)	350.00
30 HF,Tarzan(c)	450.00
31 HFCapt&Kids(c)	350.00
32 HF Tarzan(c)	350.00
33 HF,Tarzan(c)	400.00
34 HF,Capt&Kids(c)	400.00
35 HF	300.00
36 HF,HK,Tarzan(c)	400.00
37 HF,Tarzan	400.00
38 HF	300.00
39 HF,Tarzan	400.00
40 HF	300.00
41 Tarzan(c)	450.00
42	300.00
43 Tarzan(c)	325.00
44 HF	300.00

45 HF,Tarzan(c)	325.00
46 HF	300.00
47 HF,Tarzan(c)	325.00
48 HF	300.00
49 HF	300.00
50 HF,Tarzan(c)	325.00
51	250.00
52 Tarzan(c)	300.00
53	250.00
54	325.00
55	250.00
56	250.00
57 BHg	250.00
58	225.00
59 BHg	250.00
60	200.00
61 and 62 BHg	@250.00
63 thru 90	@125.00
91 thru 99	@100.00
100	125.00
101 thru 150	@65.00
151 thru 188	@40.00
189 thru 225	@40.00

T-Man #21 © Quality Comics Group

T-MAN
Comics Magazines
(Quality Comics Group)
September, 1951

1 JCo,Pete Trask-the	
Treasury Man	275.00
2 RC(c),The Girl with Death	
in Her Hands	150.00
3 RC,RC(c),Death Trap in Iran	125.00
4 RC,RC(c),Panama Peril . . .	125.00
5 RC,RC(c),Violence in Venice	125.00
6 RC(c),The Man Who	
Could Be Hitler	125.00
7 RC(c),Mr. Murder & The	
Black Hand	110.00
8 RC(c),Red Ticket to Hell . . .	110.00
9 RC(c),Trial By Terror	110.00
10	110.00
11 The Voice of Russia	75.00
12 Terror in Tokyo	75.00
13 Mind Assassins	75.00
14 Trouble in Bavaria	75.00
15 The Traitor,Bondage(c)	75.00
16 Hunt For a Hatchetman	75.00

17 Red Triggerman 75.00
18 Death Rides the Rails 75.00
19 Death Ambush 75.00
20 The Fantastic H-Bomb Plot . . 90.00
21 The Return of Mussolini 75.00
22 Propaganda for Doom 50.00
23 Red Intrigue in Parid,H-Bomb 75.00
24 Red Sabotage 50.00
25 RC,The Ingenious Red Trap . 75.00
26 . . . . 50.00
27 . . . . 50.00
28 . . . . 50.00
29 . . . . 50.00
30 thru 37 . . . . @50.00
38 December, 1956 . . . . 50.00

TNT COMICS
Charles Publishing Co.
February, 1946
1 FBI story,YellowJacket 175.00

TODAY'S BRIDES
Ajax/Farrell Publishing Co.
November, 1955
1 . . . . 35.00
2 . . . . 20.00
3 . . . . 20.00
4 November, 1956 . . . . 20.00

TODAY'S ROMANCE
Standard Comics
March, 1952
5 . . . . 35.00
6 ATh 40.00
7 . . . . 20.00
8 . . . . 20.00

TOM AND JERRY
DELL GIANT EDITIONS
Dell Publishing Co.
1952–58
Back to School 200.00
Picnic Time 150.00
Summer Fun 1 . . . . 250.00
Summer Fun 2 . . . . 100.00
Winter Carnival 1 . . . . 350.00
Winter Carnival 2 . . . . 175.00
Winter Fun 3 . . . . 100.00
Winter Fun 4 . . . . 90.00
Winter Fun 5 . . . . 80.00
Winter Fun 6 . . . . 75.00
Winter Fun 7 . . . . 75.00

TOMB OF TERROR
Harvey Publications
June, 1952
1 BP,The Thing From the
  Center of the Earth 250.00
2 RP,The Quagmire Beast . . 135.00
3 BP,RP,Caravan of the
  Doomed, Bondage(c) 150.00
4 RP,I'm Going to Kill You,
  Torture 135.00
5 RP 125.00
6 RP,Return From the Grave . 125.00
7 RP,Shadow of Death 125.00
8 HN,The Hive 125.00
9 BP,HN,The Tunnel 125.00
10 BP,HN,The Trial 125.00
11 BP,HN,The Closet 125.00
12 BP,HN,Tale of Cain 135.00
13 BP,What Was Out There . . 150.00
14 BP,SC,End Result 150.00

15 BP,HN,Break-up 200.00
16 BP,Going,Going,Gone 150.00
Becomes:

THRILLS OF TOMORROW
17 RP,BP,The World of Mr. Chatt 40.00
18 RP,BP,The Dead Awaken . . 30.00
19 S&K,S&K(c),A:Stuntman . . . 250.00
20 S&K,S&K(c),A:Stuntman . . . 200.00

Tom Corbett, Space Cadet #2
© Dell Publishing Co.

TOM CORBETT SPACE CADET
Dell Publishing Co.
Jan., 1952
See also Dell Four Color
4 based on TV show 100.00
5 . . . . 75.00
6 . . . . 70.00
7 . . . . 60.00
8 . . . . 50.00
9 . . . . 50.00
10 . . . . 50.00
11 . . . . 50.00

TOM CORBETT SPACE CADET
Prize Publications
May-June, 1955
1 . . . . 200.00
2 . . . . 175.00
3 September-October, 1955 . 175.00

TOM MIX
Ralston-Purina Co.
September, 1940
1 O:Tom Mix 2,800.00
2 . . . . 850.00
3 . . . . 550.00
4 thru 9 . . . . @500.00
Becomes:

TOM MIX COMMANDOS COMICS
10 . . . . 450.00
11 Invisible Invaders 450.00
12 Terrible Talons Of Tokyo . . 450.00

Tom Mix Western #4
© Fawcett Publications

TOM MIX WESTERN
Fawcett Publications
January, 1948
1 Ph(c),Two-Fisted
  Adventures 800.00
2 Ph(c),Hair-Triggered Action 350.00
3 Ph(c),Double Barreled Action 250.00
4 Ph(c),Cowpunching 250.00
5 Ph(c),Two Gun Action 250.00
6 CCB,Most Famous Cowboy 200.00
7 CCB,A Tattoo of Thrills . . . 200.00
8 EK,Ph(c),Gallant Guns . . . 185.00
9 CCB,Song o/t Deadly Spurs 175.00
10 CCB,Crack Shot Western . . 175.00
11 CCB,EK(C),Triple Revenge . 175.00
12 King of the Cowboys 150.00
13 Ph(c),Leather Burns 150.00
14 Ph(c),Brand of Death 150.00
15 Ph(c),Masked Treachery . . 150.00
16 Ph(c),Death Spurting Guns . 150.00
17 Ph(c),Trail of Doom 150.00
18 Ph(c),Reign of Terror 100.00
19 Hand Colored Ph(c) 125.00
20 Ph(c),CCB,F:Capt Tootsie . . 100.00
21 Ph(c) 100.00
22 Ph(c),The Human Beast . . . 100.00
23 Ph(c),Return of the Past . . . 100.00
24 Hand Colored Ph(c),
  The Lawless City 100.00
25 Hand Colored Ph(c),
  The Signed Death Warrant . 100.00
26 Hand Colored Ph(c),
  Dangerous Escape 100.00
27 Hand Colored Ph(c),
  Hero Without Glory 100.00
28 Ph(c),The Storm Kings 100.00
29 Hand Colored Ph(c),The
  Case of the Rustling Rose . 100.00
30 Ph(c),Disappearance
  in the Hills 100.00
31 Ph(c) 80.00
32 Hand Colored Ph(c),
  Mystery of Tremble Mountain 75.00
33 . . . . 75.00
34 . . . . 65.00
35 Partial Ph(c),The Hanging
  at Hollow Creek 75.00

36 Ph(c)	75.00	
37 Ph(c)	75.00	
38 Ph(c),36 pages	65.00	
39 Ph(c)	75.00	
40 Ph(c)	75.00	
41 Ph(c)	70.00	
42 Ph(c)	75.00	
43 Ph(c)	50.00	
44 Ph(c)	50.00	
45 Partial Ph(c),The Secret Letter	50.00	
46 Ph(c)	50.00	
47 Ph(c)	50.00	
48 Ph(c)	50.00	
49 Partial Ph(c),Blind Date With Death	50.00	
50 Ph(c)	50.00	
51 Ph(c)	50.00	
52 Ph(c)	50.00	
53 Ph(c)	50.00	
54 Ph(c)	50.00	
55 Ph(c)	50.00	
56 Partial Ph(c),Deadly Spurs	50.00	
57 Ph(c)5	50.00	
58 Ph(c)	50.00	
59 Ph(c)	50.00	
60 Ph(c)	50.00	
61 Partial Ph(c),Lost in the Night,May 1953	75.00	

TOMMY OF THE BIG TOP
King Features/ Standard Comics
1948

10 Thrilling Circus Adventures	30.00
11	20.00
12 March, 1949	20.00

TOM-TOM THE JUNGLE BOY
Magazine Enterprises
1946

1 (fa)	40.00
2 (fa)	30.00
3 Winter 1947,(fa),X-mas issue	15.00
1	15.00

TONTO
(See LONE RANGER'S COMPANION TONTO)

TONY TRENT
(see FACE, THE)

TOP FLIGHT COMICS
Four Star/St. John Publ. Co.
July, 1949

1	60.00
1 Hector the Inspector	40.00

TOP LOVE STORIES
Star Publications
May, 1951

3 LbC(c)	125.00
4 LbC(c)	100.00
5 LbC(c)	100.00
6 LbC(c),WW	150.00
7 LbC(c)	100.00
8 LbC(c)	100.00
9 LbC(c)	100.00
10 thru 16 LbC(c)	@100.00

17 LbC(c),WW	125.00	
18 LbC(c)	100.00	
19 LbC(c),JyD	100.00	

Top-Notch Comics #15
© MLJ Magazines

TOP-NOTCH COMICS
MLJ Magazines
December, 1939

1 JaB,JCo,B&O:The Wizard, B:Kandak,Swift of the Secret Service,The Westpointer, Mystic, Air Patrol,Scott Rand, Manhunter	4,700.00
2 JaB,JCo,B:Dick Storm, E:Mystic, B:Stacy Knight	1,700.00
3 JaB,JCo,EA(c),E:Swift of the Secret Service,Scott Rand	1,200.00
4 JCo,EA(c),MMe,O&I:Streak, Chandler	1,000.00
5 Ea(c),MMe,O&I:Galahad, B:Shanghai Sheridan	1,000.00
6 Ea(c),MMe,A:The Sheild	900.00
7 Ea(c),MMe,N:The Wizard	1,000.00
8 E:Dick Sorm,B&O:Roy The Super Boy,The Firefly	1,000.00
9 O&I:Black Hood, B:Fran Frazier	4,400.00
10	1,200.00
11	700.00
12	700.00
13	700.00
14 Bondage(c)	750.00
15 MMe	700.00
16	650.00
17 Bondage(c)	675.00
18	625.00
19 Bondage(c)	675.00
20	625.00
21	500.00
22	500.00
23 Bondage(c)	525.00
24 Black Hood Smashes Murder Ring	500.00
25 E:Bob Phantom	500.00
26	500.00
27 E:The Firefly	500.00
28 B:Suzie,Pokey Okay, Gag Oriented	500.00

29 E:Kandak	500.00
30	500.00
31	300.00
32	300.00
33 BWo,B:Dotty&Ditto	300.00
34 BWo	300.00
35 BWo	300.00
36 BWo	300.00
37 thru 40 BWo	@300.00
41	300.00
42 BWo	300.00
43	300.00
44 EW:Black Hood,I:Suzie	275.00
45 Suzie(c)	275.00

Becomes:
LAUGH COMIX

46 Suzie & Wilbur	100.00
47 Suzie & Wilbur	85.00
48 Suzie & Wilbur	85.00

Becomes:
SUZIE COMICS

49 B:Ginger	150.00
50 AFy(c)	90.00
51 AFy(c)	90.00
52 AFy(c)	90.00
53 AFy(c)	90.00
54 AFy(c)	100.00
55 AFy(c)	110.00
56 BWo,B:Katie Keene	65.00
57 thru 70 BWo	@65.00
71 thru 79 BWo	@55.00
80 thru 99 BWo	@45.00
100 August, 1954, BWo	45.00

TOPS
Tops Mag. Inc.
(Lev Gleason)
July, 1949

1 RC&BLb,GT,DBa,CBi(c),I'll Buy That Girl,Our Explosive Children	800.00
2 FG,BF,CBi(c),RC&BLb	750.00

TOPS COMICS
Consolidated Book Publishers
1944

2000 Don on the Farm	200.00
2001 The Jack of Spades V:The Hawkman	100.00
2002 Rip Raiders	75.00
2003 Red Birch	20.00

TOP SECRET
Hillman Publications
January, 1952

1 The Tricks of the Secret Agent Revealed	150.00

TOP SECRETS
Street & Smith Publications
November, 1947

1 BP,BP(c),Of the Men Who Guard the U.S. Mail	225.00
2 BP,BP(c),True Story of Jim the Penman	175.00
3 BP,BP(c),Crime Solved by Mental Telepathy	150.00
4 Highway Pirates	150.00
5 BP,BP(c),Can Music Kill	150.00
6 BP,BP(c),The Clue of the Forgotten Film	150.00
7 BP,BP(c),Train For Sale	225.00

GOLDEN AGE

8 BP,BP(c) 150.00
9 BP,BP(c) 150.00
10 BP,BP(c),July-August, 1949 225.00

TOPS IN ADVENTURE
Approved Comics
(Ziff-Davis)
Autumn, 1952
1 BP,Crusaders From Mars .. 350.00

TOP SPOT COMICS
Top Spot Publishing Co.
1945
1 The Duke Of Darkness 200.00

TOPSY-TURVY
R.B. Leffingwell Publ.
April, 1945
1 I:Cookie 50.00

TOR
St. John Publishing Co.
September, 1953
1 JKu,JKu(c),O;Tor,One Million
  Years Ago 85.00
2 JKu,JKu(c),3-D Issue 75.00
3 JKu,JKu(c),ATh,historic life .. 80.00
4 JKu,JKu(c),ATh 80.00
5 JKu,JKu(c),ATh,October, 1954 80.00

Torchy #4 © Quality Comics Group

TORCHY
Quality Comics Group
November, 1949
1 GFx,BWa(c),The Blonde
  Bombshell 1,000.00
2 GFx,GFx(c),Beauty at
  its' Best 500.00
3 GFX,GFx(c),You Can't
  Beat Nature 500.00
4 GFx,GFx(c),The Girl to
  Keep Your Eye On 600.00
5 BWa,GFx,BWa(c),At the
  Masquerade Party 800.00
6 September, 1950,BWa,GFx,
  BWa(c),The Libido Driven
  Boy Scout 800.00

TORMENTED, THE
Sterling Comics
July, 1954
1 Buried Alive 150.00
2 September, 1954,The Devils
  Circus 125.00

TOYLAND COMICS
Fiction House Magazines
January, 1947
1 Wizard of the Moon 175.00
2 Buddy Bruin & Stu Rabbit .. 125.00
3 GT,The Candy Maker 150.00
4 July, 1947 .... 125.00

TOY TOWN COMICS
Toytown Publ./Orbit Publ.
February, 1945
1 LbC,LbC(c)(fa) 225.00
2 LbC,(fa) 150.00
3 LbC,LbC(c),(fa) 125.00
4 LbC,(fa) 125.00
5 LbC,(fa) 125.00
6 LbC,(fa) 125.00
7 LbC,(fa),May, 1947 ..... 125.00

TRAIL BLAZERS
(see RED DRAGON COMICS)

TREASURE COMICS
Prize Comics Group
1943
1 S&K,Reprints of Prize Comics
  #7 through #11 .... 1,600.00

TREASURE COMICS
American Boys Comics
(Prize Publications)
June-July, 1945
1 HcK,B:PaulBunyan,MarcoPolo 200.00
2 HcK,HcK(c),B:Arabian Knight,
  Gorilla King,Dr.Styx 100.00
3 HcK 75.00
4 HcK 75.00
5 HcK,JK 125.00
6 HcK,BK,HcK(c) 100.00
7 HcK,FF,HcK(c) 225.00
8 HcK,FF 225.00
9 HcK,DBa 75.00
10 JK,DBa,JK(c) 200.00
11 BK,HcK,DBa,The Weird
  Adventures of Mr. Bottle ... 125.00
12 DBa,DBa(c),Autumn, 1947 .. 90.00

TREASURY OF COMICS
St. John Publishing Co.
1947
1 RvB,RvB(c),Abbie an' Slats 125.00
2 Jim Hardy 75.00
3 Bill Bimlin 75.00
4 RvB,RvB(c),Abbie an' Slats .. 75.00
5 Jim Hardy,January, 1948 ... 70.00

TRIPLE THREAT
Gerona Publications
Winter, 1945
1 F:King O'Leary,The Duke of
  Darkness,Beau Brummell .. 150.00

TRUE AVIATION PICTURE STORIES
Parents' Institute/P.M.I.
August, 1942
1 How Jimmy Doolittle
  Bombed Tokyo 100.00
2 Knight of the Air Mail 50.00
3 The Amazing One-Man
  Air Force 40.00
4 Joe Foss America's No. 1
  Air Force 40.00
5 Bombs over Germany 40.00
6 Flight Lt. Richard
  Hillary R.A.F. 40.00
7 "Fatty" Chow China's
  Sky Champ 40.00
8 Blitz over Burma 40.00
9 Off the Beam 40.00
10 "Pappy" Boyington 40.00
11 Ph(c) 40.00
12 .... 40.00
13 Ph(c),Flying Facts 40.00
14 .... 40.00
15 .... 40.00
Becomes:

AVIATION AND MODEL BUILDING
16 .... 45.00
17 February, 1947 .... 50.00

True Comics #15
© True Comics/Parents' Magazine

TRUE COMICS
True Comics/
Parents' Magazine Press
April, 1941
1 My Greatest Adventure-by
  Lowell Thomas 225.00
2 BEv,The Story of the
  Red Cross 125.00
3 Baseball Hall of Fame 135.00
4 Danger in the Artic 100.00
5 Father Duffy-the Fighting
  Chaplin 120.00
6 The Capture of Aquinaldo .. 120.00
7 JKa,Wilderness Adventures of
  George Washington 120.00
8 U.S. Army Wings 75.00

9 A Pig that Made History 75.00
10 Adrift on an Ice Pan 75.00
11 Gen. Douglas MacArthur ... 65.00
12 Mackenzie-King of Cananda . 60.00
13 The Real Robinson Crusoe .. 65.00
14 Australia war base of
   the South Pacific 65.00
15 The Story of West Point 75.00
16 How Jimmy Doolittle
   Bombed Tokyo 70.00
17 The Ghost of Captain Blig,
   B.Feller 75.00
18 Battling Bill of the
   Merchant Marine 80.00
19 Secret Message Codes 50.00
20 The Story of India 45.00
21 Timoshenko the Blitz Buster . 50.00
22 Gen, Bernard L. Montgomery 45.00
23 The Story of Steel 45.00
24 Gen. Henri Giraud-Master
   of Escape 45.00
25 Medicine's Miracle Men 45.00
26 Hero of the Bismarck Sea ... 45.00
27 Leathernecks have Landed . 50.00
28 The Story of Radar 40.00
29 The Fighting Seabees 40.00
30 Dr. Norman Bethune-Blood
   Bank Founder 40.00
31 Our Good Neighbor Bolivia,
   Red Grange 50.00
32 Men against the Desert ... 35.00
33 Gen. Clark and his Fighting
   5th 40.00
34 Angel of the Battlefield ... 35.00
35 Carlson's Marine Raiders ... 35.00
36 Canada's Sub-Busters 35.00
37 Commander of the Crocodile
   Fleet 35.00
38 Oregon Trailblazer 35.00
39 Saved by Sub 35.00
40 Sea Furies 35.00
41 Cavalcade of England ... 30.00
42 Gen. Jaques Le Clerc-Hero
   of Paris 30.00
43 Unsinkable Ship 35.00
44 El Senor Goofy 30.00
45 Tokyo Express 25.00
46 The Magnificent Runt 30.00
47 Atoms Unleashed,
   Atomic Bomb 75.00
48 Pirate Patriot 30.00
49 Smiking Fists 30.00
50 Lumber Pirates 30.00
51 Exercise Musk-Ox 30.00
52 King of the Buckeneers 30.00
53 Baseline Booby 30.00
54 Santa Fe Sailor 30.00
55 Sea Going Santa 30.00
56 End of a Terror 30.00
57 Newfangled Machines 30.00
58 Leonardo da Vinci-500 years
   too Soon 30.00
59 Pursuit of the Pirates 35.00
60 Emmett Kelly-The World's
   Funniest Clown 30.00
61 Peter Le Grand-
   Bold Buckaneer 30.00
62 Sutter's Gold 30.00
63 Outboard Outcome 30.00
64 Man-Eater at Large 30.00
65 The Story of Scotland Yard .. 30.00
66 Easy Guide to Football
   Formations 35.00
67 The Changing Zebra 30.00
68 Admiral Byrd 25.00

69 FBI Special Agent Steve
   Saunders 35.00
70 The Case of the Seven
   Hunted Men 30.00
71 Story of Joe DiMaggio 150.00
72 FBI,Jackie Robinson 60.00
73 The 26 Mile Dash-Story of
   the Marathon 35.00
74 A Famous Coach's Special
   Football Tips 35.00
75 King of Reporters 35.00
76 The Story of a Buried
   Treasure 35.00
77 France's Greatest Detective . 35.00
78 Cagliostro-Master Rogue .. 50.00
79 Ralph Bunche-Hero of Peace 35.00
80 Rocket Trip to the Moon ... 150.00
81 Red Grange 150.00
82 Marie Celeste Ship of
   Mystery 125.00
83 Bullfighter from Brooklyn ... 125.00
84 King of the Buckaneers,
   August, 1950 .... 125.00

TRUE CONFIDENCES
Fawcett Publications
Autumn, 1949

1 .... 75.00
2 and 3 .... @45.00
4 DP 45.00

True Crime Comics #2
© Magazine Village, Inc.

TRUE CRIME COMICS
Magazine Village, Inc.
May, 1947

2 JCo(c),JCo(c),James Kent-
   Crook,Murderer,Escaped
   Convict; Drug 1,000.00
3 JCo,JCo(c),Benny Dickson-
   Killer;Drug 750.00
4 JCo,JCo(c),Little Jake-
   Big Shot 700.00
5 JCo(c),The Rat & the Blond
   Gun Moll;Drug 450.00
6 Joseph Metley-Swindler,
   Jailbird, Killer 350.00
2-1(7) ATh,WW,Ph(c),Phil
   Coppola,September, 1949 . 600.00

TRUE LIFE SECRETS
**Romantic Love Stories/
Charlton Comics**
March-April, 1951

1 .... 70.00
2 .... 40.00
3 .... 30.00
4 .... 30.00
5 thru 20 .... @30.00
21 thru 25 .... @20.00
26 Comics Code 15.00
27 thru 29 .... @15.00

TRUE LIFE ROMANCES
Ajax/Farrell Publications
December, 1955

1 .... 50.00
2 .... 30.00
3 August, 1956 .... 35.00

TRUE LOVE PICTORIAL
St. John Publishing Co.
1952

1 Ph(c) 100.00
2 MB 65.00
3 MB(c),MB,JKu 200.00
4 MB(c),MB,JKu 200.00
5 MB(c),MB,JKu 200.00
6 MB(c) 100.00
7 MB(c) 100.00
8 MB(c) 75.00
9 MB(c) 75.00
10 MB(c),MB 75.00
11 MB(c),MB 75.00

TRUE MOVIE AND TELEVISION
Toby Press
August, 1950

1 Liz Taylor, Ph(c) 275.00
2 FF,Ph(c),John Wayne,
   L.Taylor 200.00
3 June Allyson,Ph(c) ... 175.00
4 Jane Powell,Ph(c),Jan.,1951 100.00

SPORT COMICS
Street & Smith Publications
October, 1940

1 F:Lou Gehrig 400.00
2 F:Gene Tunney 200.00
3 F:Phil Rizzuto 250.00
4 F:Frank Leahy 200.00
Becomes:
TRUE SPORT PICTURE STORIES

5 Joe DiMaggio 250.00
6 Billy Confidence 125.00
7 Mel Ott 150.00
8 Lou Ambers 125.00
9 Pete Reiser 125.00
10 Frankie Sinkwich 125.00
11 Marty Serfo 125.00
12 JaB(c),Jack Dempsey ... 135.00
2-1 JaB(c),Willie Pep 125.00
2-2 JaB(c) 125.00
2-3 JaB(c),Carl Hubbell ... 135.00
2-4 Advs. in Football & Battle 150.00
2-5 Don Hutson 150.00
2-6 Dixie Walker 150.00
2-7 Stan Musial 175.00

GOLDEN AGE

2-8 Famous Ring Champions	
of All Time	150.00
2-9 List of War Year Rookies	175.00
2-10 Connie Mack	150.00
2-11 Winning Basketball Plays	125.00
2-12 Eddie Gottlieb	125.00
3-1 Bill Conn	125.00
3-2 Philadelphia Athletics	100.00
3-3 Leo Durocher	125.00
3-4 Rudy Dusek	100.00
3-5 Ernie Pyle	100.00
3-6 Bowling with Ned Day	100.00
3-7 Return of the Mighty (Home	
from War);Joe DiMaggio(c)	250.00
3-8 Conn V:Louis	200.00
3-9 Reuben Shark	100.00
3-10 BP,BP(c),Don "Dopey"	
Dillock	100.00
3-11 BP,BP(c),Death	
Scores a Touchdown	100.00
3-12 Red Sox V:Senators	100.00
4-1 Spring Training in	
Full Spring	100.00
4-2 BP,BP(c),How to Pitch 'Em	
Where They Can't Hit 'Em	100.00
4-3 BP,BP(c),1947 Super Stars	125.00
4-4 BP,BP(c),Get Ready for	
the Olympics	125.00
4-5 BP,BP(c),Hugh Casey	100.00
4-6 BP,BP(c),Phantom Phil	
Hergesheimer	100.00
4-7 BP,BP(c),How to Bowl Better	100.00
4-8 Tips on the Big Fight	125.00
4-9 BP,BP(c),Bill McCahan	100.00
4-10 BP,BP(c),Great Football	
Plays	100.00
4-11 BP,BP(c),Football	100.00
4-12 BP,BP(c),Basketball	100.00
5-1 Satchel Paige	150.00
5-2 History of Boxing,	
July-August, 1949	100.00

TRUE SWEETHEART SECRETS
Fawcett Publications
May, 1950

1 Ph(c)	75.00
2 WW	125.00
3 BD	50.00
4 BD	50.00
5 BD	50.00
6 thru 11	@40.00

TRUE-TO-LIFE ROMANCES
Star Publications
November-December, 1949

3 LbC(c),GlennFord/JanetLeigh	150.00
4 LbC(c)	100.00
5 LbC(c)	100.00
6 LbC(c)	100.00
7 LbC(c)	100.00
8 LbC(c)	100.00
9 LbC(c)	100.00
10 LbC(c)	100.00
11 LbC(c)	100.00
12 LbC(c)	100.00
13 LbC(c),JyD	100.00
14 LbC(c),JyD	100.00
15 LbC(c),WW,JyD	125.00
16 LbC(c),WW,JyD	125.00
17 LbC(c),JyD	100.00
18 LbC(c),JyD	100.00
19 LbC(c),JyD	100.00

20 LbC(c),JyD	100.00
21 LbC(c),JyD	100.00
22 LbC(c)	90.00
23 LbC(c)	90.00

TRUE WAR ROMANCES
Comic Magazines, Inc.
(Quality Comics)
September, 1952

1 Ph(c)	75.00
2	40.00
3 thru 10	@20.00
11 thru 20	@15.00
21 Comics Code	15.00

Becomes:
EXOTIC ROMANCES

22	35.00
23 thru 26	@20.00
27 MB	35.00
28 MB	35.00
29	20.00
30 MB	35.00
31 MB	35.00

TUROK, SON OF STONE
Dell Publishing Co.
December, 1954

(1) see Dell Four Color #596	
(2) see Dell Four Color #656	
3	250.00
4 and 5	@225.00
6 thru 10	@150.00
11 thru 20	@90.00
21 thru 29	@60.00

See Other Color section

TWEETY AND SYLVESTER
Dell Publishing Co.
June, 1952

(1) see Dell Four Color #406	
(2) see Dell Four Color #489	
(3) see Dell Four Color #524	
4 thru 20	@20.00
21 thru 37	@10.00

TWINKLE COMICS
Spotlight Publications
May, 1945

1 Humor Format	70.00

TWO-FISTED TALES
Fables Publications
(E.C. Comics)
November-December, 1950

18 HK,JCr,WW,JSe,HK(c)	750.00
19 HK,JCr,WW,JSe,HK(c)	500.00
20 JDa,HK,WW,JSe,HK(c)	300.00
21 JDa,HK,WW,JSe,HK(c)	250.00
22 JDa,HK,WW,JSe,HK(c)	250.00
23 JDa,HK,WW,JSe,HK(c)	225.00
24 JDa,HK,WW,JSe,HK(c)	200.00
25 JDa,HK,WW,JSe,HK(c)	200.00
26 JDa,JSe,HK(c),Action at	
the Changing Reservoir	150.00
27 JDa,JSe,HK(c)	150.00
28 JDa,JSe,HK(c)	150.00
29 JDa,JSe,HK(c)	200.00
30 JDa,JSe,JDa(c)	200.00
31 JDa,JSe,HK(c),Civil	
War Story	160.00
32 JDa,JKu,WW(c)	160.00
33 JDa,JKu,WW(c)	175.00

Two-Fisted Tales #36 © E.C. Comics

34 JDa,JSe,JDa(c)	160.00
35 JDa,JSe,JDa(c),Civil	
War Story	175.00
36 JDa,JSe,JSe(c),A	
Difference of Opinion	100.00
37 JSe,JSe(c),Bugles &	
Battle Cries	100.00
38 JSe,JSe(c)	100.00
39 JSe,JSe(c)	100.00
40 JDa,JSe,GE,GE(c)	150.00
41 JSe,GE,JDa(c),March, 1955	100.00

UNCLE CHARLIE'S FABLES
Lev Gleason Publications
January, 1952

1 CBi(c),Ph(c)	55.00
2 BF,CBi(c),Ph(c)	30.00
3 CBi(c),Ph(c)	35.00
4 CBi(c),Ph(c)	35.00
5 CBi,Ph(c),September, 1952	30.00

UNCLE SAM
(see BLACKHAWK)

UNCLE SCROOGE
Dell Publishing Co.
March, 1952

(1) see Dell Four Color #386	
(2) see Dell Four Color #456	
(3) see Dell Four Color #495	
4	400.00
5	300.00
6	250.00
7 CB	225.00
8	200.00
9	200.00
10	200.00
11 thru 20	@175.00
21 thru 30	@150.00
31 thru 39	@100.00

See Other Pub. section

UNDERWORLD
D.S. Publishing Co.
February-March, 1948

1 SMo(c),Violence	300.00

2 SMo(c),Electrocution	300.00
3 AMc,AMc(c),The Ancient Club	275.00
4 Grl,The Beer Baron Murder	200.00
5 Grl,The Postal Clue	175.00
6 The Polka Dot Gang	125.00
7 Mono-The Master	125.00
8 The Double Tenth	125.00
9 Thrilling Stories of the Fight against Crime,June, 1953	125.00

UNDERWORLD CRIME
Fawcett Publications
June, 1952

1 The Crime Army	225.00
2 Jailbreak	150.00
3 Microscope Murder	125.00
4 Death on the Docks	125.00
5 River of Blood	125.00
6 The Sky Pirates	125.00
7 Bondage & Torture(c)	175.00
8	125.00
9 June, 1953	125.00

UNITED COMICS
United Features Syndicate
1950

8 thru 26 Bushmiller(c), Fritzi Ritz	@25.00

UNITED STATES FIGHTING AIR FORCE
Superior Comics, Ltd.
September, 1952

1 Coward's Courage	50.00
2 Clouds that Killed	25.00
3 Operation Decoy	15.00
4 thru 28	@15.00
29 October, 1959	15.00

UNITED STATES MARINES
Wm. H. Wise/Magazine Ent/ Toby Press
1943

N# MBi,MBi(c),Hellcat out of Heaven	50.00
2 MBi,Drama of Wake Island	35.00

The Unseen #8
© Standard Comics

3 A Leatherneck Flame Thrower	30.00
4 MBi	30.00
5 BP	25.00
6 BP	25.00
7 BP	20.00
8 thru 10	@20.00
11 1952	20.00

UNKEPT PROMISE
Legion of Truth
1949

1 Anti:Alcoholic Drinking	50.00

UNKNOWN WORLDS
(see STRANGE STORIES FROM ANOTHER WORLD)

UNSEEN, THE
Visual Editions
(Standard Comics)
1952

5 ATh,The Hungry Lodger	250.00
6 JKa,MSy,Bayou Vengeance	200.00
7 JKz,MSy,Time is the Killer	175.00
8 JKz,MSy,The Vengance Vat	175.00
9 JKz,MSy,Your Grave is Ready	175.00
10 JKz,MSy	175.00
11 JKz,MSy	175.00
12 ATh,GT,Till Death Do Us Part	175.00
13	125.00
14	125.00
15 ATh,The Curse of the Undead!, July, 1954	175.00

UNTAMED LOVE
Comic Magazines
(Quality Comics Group)
January, 1950

1 BWa(c),PGn	175.00
2 Ph(c)	100.00
3 PGn	100.00
4	100.00
5 PGn	100.00

USA IS READY
Dell Publishing Co.
1941

1 Propaganda WWII	300.00

U.S. JONES
Fox Features Syndicate
November, 1941

1 Death Over the Airways	1,000.00
2 January, 1942	700.00

U.S. MARINES IN ACTION!
Avon Periodicals
Aug.–Dec., 1952

1 On Land,Sea & in the Air	50.00
2 The Killer Patrol	20.00
3 EK(c),Death Ridge	22.00

U.S. TANK COMMANDOS
Avon Periodicals
June, 1952

1 EK(c),Fighting Daredevils of the USA	50.00
2 EK(c)	25.00
3 EK,EK(c),Robot Armanda	25.00

4 EK,EK(c),March, 1953	25.00

VALOR
E.C. Comics
March, 1955

1 AW,AT,WW,WW(c),Grl,BK	250.00
2 AW(c),AW,WWGrl,BK	200.00
3 AW,RC,BK,JOc(c)	150.00
4 WW(c),RC,Grl,BK,JO	150.00
5 WW(c),WW,AW,GE,Grl,BK	125.00

VARIETY COMICS
Rural Home Publ./ Croyden Publ. Co.
1944

1 MvS,MvS(c),O:Capt, Valiant	125.00
2 MvS,MvS(c)	75.00
3 MvS,MvS(c)	50.00
4	50.00
5 1946	50.00

VAULT OF HORROR
(see WAR AGAINST CRIME)

V...COMICS
Fox Features Syndicate
January, 1942

1 V:V-Man	1,000.00
2 The Horror of the Dungeons, March, 1942	750.00

VERI BEST SURE SHOT COMICS
Holyoke Publishing Co. 1945

1 reprint Holyoke One-Shots	250.00

VIC FLINT
St. John Publishing Co.
August, 1948

1 ...Crime Buster	60.00
2	40.00
3	35.00
4	35.00
5 April, 1949	35.00

VIC JORDAN
Civil Service Publications
April, 1945

1 Escape From a Nazi Prison	75.00

VIC TORRY AND HIS FLYING SAUCER
Fawcett Publications
1950

1 Ph(c),Revealed at Last	450.00

VICTORY COMICS
Hillman Periodicals
August, 1941

1 BEv,BEv(c),F:TheConqueror	2,200.00
2 BEv,BEv(c)	1,000.00
3 The Conqueror(c)	650.00
4 December, 1941	600.00

VIC VERITY MAGAZINE
Vic Verity Publications
1945

1 CCB,CCB(c),B:Vic Verity,Hot- Shot Galvan, Tom Travis	125.00
2 CCB,CCB(c),Annual Classic	

GOLDEN AGE

Dance Recital	75.00
3 CCB	60.00
4 CCB,I:Boomer Young;The Bee-U-TiFul Weekend	60.00
5 CCB,Championship Baseball Game	60.00
6 CCB,High School Hero	60.00
7 CCB,CCB(c),F:Rocket Rex	60.00

Voodoo #18
© Four Star Publ./Farrell/Ajax Comics

VOODOO
Four Star Publ./Farrell/ Ajax Comics May, 1952

1 MB,South Sea Girl	400.00
2 MB	300.00
3 Face Stabbing	200.00
4 MB,Rendezvous	200.00
5 Ghoul For A Day,Nazi	175.00
6 The Weird Dead, Severed Head	185.00
7 Goodbye World	175.00
8 MB, Revenge	200.00
9 Will this thing Never Stew?	175.00
10 Land of Shadows & Screams	175.00
11 Human Harvest	150.00
12 The Wazen Taper	150.00
13 Bondage(c),Caskets to Fit Everybody	165.00
14 Death Judges the Beauty Contest	150.00
15 Loose their Heads	165.00
16 Fog Was Her Shroud	150.00
17 Apes Laughter,Electric Chair	165.00
18 Astounding Fantasy	150.00
19 MB,Bondage(c); Destination Congo	200.00
Ann.#1	475.00

Becomes:
VOODA
20 MB,MB(c),Echoes of an A-Bomb	225.00
21 MB,MB(c),Trek of Danger	200.00
22 MB,MB(c),The Sun Blew Away, August, 1955	200.00

WACKY DUCK
(see DOPEY DUCK)

WALT DISNEY'S COMICS & STORIES
Dell Publishing Co.
N# 1943 dpt.store giveway	400.00
N# 1945 X-mas giveaway	150.00

WALT DISNEY'S COMICS & STORIES
Dell Publishing Co. October, 1940
1 (1940)FG,Donald Duck & Mickey Mouse	17,000.00
2	6,500.00
3	2,000.00
4 Christmas(c)	1,400.00
4a Promo issue	1,500.00
5	1,100.00
6	900.00
7	900.00
8	900.00
9	900.00
10	900.00
11 1st Huey,Louie,Dewey	750.00
12	800.00
13	750.00
14	750.00
15 3 Little Kittens	700.00
16 3 Little Pigs	650.00
17 The Ugly Ducklings	700.00
18	550.00
19	525.00
20	525.00
21	550.00
22	500.00
23	475.00
24	475.00
25	475.00
26	475.00
27	500.00
28	475.00
29	475.00
30	475.00
31 CB; Donald Duck	3,000.00
32 CB	1,400.00
33 CB	1,000.00
34 CB;WK; Gremlins	800.00
35 CB;WK; Gremlins	750.00
36 CB;WK; Gremlins	750.00
37 CB;WK; Gremlins	375.00
38 CB;WK; Gremlins	475.00
39 CB;WK; Gremlins	475.00
40 CB;WK; Gremlins	475.00
41 CB;WK; Gremlins	425.00
42 CB	425.00
43 CB	400.00
44 CB	400.00
45 CB	400.00
46 CB	400.00
47 CB	375.00
48 CB	375.00
49 CB	375.00
50 CB	375.00
51 CB	300.00
52 CB; Li'l Bad Wolf begins	300.00
53 CB	300.00
54 CB	300.00
55 CB	300.00
56 CB	300.00
57 CB	300.00
58 CB	300.00
59 CB	300.00
60 CB	300.00
61 CB; Dumbo	225.00
62 CB	225.00

63 CB; Pinocchio	225.00
64 CB; Pinocchio	225.00
65 CB; Pluto	225.00
66 CB	225.00
67 CB	225.00
68 CB	225.00
69 CB	225.00
70 CB	225.00
71 CB	175.00
72 CB	175.00
73 CB	175.00
74 CB	175.00
75 CB; Brer Rabbit	175.00
76 CB; Brer Rabbit	175.00
77 CB; Brer Rabbit	175.00
78 CB	175.00
79 CB	175.00
80 CB	175.00
81 CB	150.00
82 CB;Bongo	175.00
83 CB;Bongo	175.00
84 CB;Bongo	175.00
85 CB	175.00
86 CB; Goofy & Agnes	175.00
87 CB;Goofy & Agnes	150.00
88 CB;Goofy & Agnes, I:Gladstone Gander	175.00
89 CB;Goofy&Agnes,Chip'n'Dale	150.00
90 CB;Goofy&Agnes	150.00
91 CB	125.00
92 CB	125.00
93 CB	125.00
94 CB	125.00
95	125.00
96 Little Toot	125.00
97 CB; Little Toot	125.00
98 CB; Uncle Scrooge	275.00
99 CB	125.00
100 CB	175.00
101 CB	125.00
102 CB	125.00
103 CB	110.00
104	110.00
105 CB	125.00
106 CB	125.00
107 CB	125.00
108	110.00
109	110.00
110 CB	125.00
111 CB	125.00
112 CB; drugs	125.00
113 CB	125.00
114 CB	125.00
115	40.00
116	40.00
117	40.00
118	40.00
119	40.00
120	40.00
121 Grandma Duck begins	40.00
122	40.00
123	40.00
124 CB	110.00
125 CB;I:Junior Woodchucks	125.00
126 CB	75.00
127 CB	75.00
128 CB	75.00
129 CB	75.00
130 CB	75.00
131 CB	75.00
132 CB A:Grandma Duck	75.00
133 CB	75.00
134 I:The Beagle Boys	175.00
135 CB	75.00
136 CB	75.00

Walt Disney's Comics and Stories #116
© Dell Publ. Co.

137 CB 75.00
138 CB 75.00
139 CB 75.00
140 CB; I:Gyro Gearloose 175.00
141 CB 60.00
142 CB 60.00
143 CB; Little Hiawatha 60.00
144 CB; Little Hiawatha 60.00
145 CB; Little Hiawatha 60.00
146 CB; Little Hiawatha 60.00
147 CB; Little Hiawatha 60.00
148 CB; Little Hiawatha 60.00
149 CB; Little Hiawatha 60.00
150 CB; Little Hiawatha 60.00
151 CB; Little Hiawatha 60.00
152 thru 200 CB . . . . @50.00
201 CB 40.00
202 CB 40.00
203 CB 40.00
204 CB, Chip 'n' Dale & Scamp . 40.00
205 thru 240 CB . . . . @40.00
241 CB; Dumbo x-over 30.00
242 CB 30.00
243 CB 30.00
244 CB 30.00
245 CB 30.00
246 CB 30.00
247 thru 255 CB;GyroGearloose@30.00
256 thru 263 CB;Ludwig Von
Drake & Gearloose . . . . . . @30.00
See: Independent Color Comics

WALT DISNEY ANNUALS
Walt Disney's Autumn Adventure . 4.00
Walt Disney's Holiday Parade . . . 3.50
Walt Disney's Spring Fever 3.25
Walt Disney's Summer Fun 3.25

WALT DISNEY DELL GIANT EDITIONS
Dell Publishing Co.
1 CB,W.Disney'sXmas
Parade('49) 900.00
2 CB,W.Disney'sXmas
Parade('50) 700.00
3 W.Disney'sXmas Parade('51) 225.00
4 W.Disney'sXmas Parade('52) 200.00

5 W.Disney'sXmas Parade('53) 200.00
6 W.Disney'sXmas Parade('54) 200.00
7 W.Disney'sXmas Parade('55) 200.00
8 CB,W.Disney'sXmas
Parade('56) 350.00
9 CB,W.Disney'sXmas
Parade('57) 300.00
1 CB,W.Disney's Christmas in
Disneyland (1957) 400.00
1 CB,W.Disney's Disneyland
Birthday Party (1958) 400.00
1 W.Disney's Donald and Mickey
in Disneyland (1958) 175.00
1 W.Disney's Donald Duck
Beach Party (1954) 225.00
2 W.Disney's Donald Duck
Beach Party (1955) 175.00
3 W.Disney's Donald Duck
Beach Party (1956) 175.00
4 W.Disney's Donald Duck
Beach Party (1957) 175.00
5 W.Disney's Donald Duck
Beach Party (1958) 175.00
6 W.Disney's Donald Duck
Beach Party (1959) 175.00
1 W.Disney's Donald Duck
Fun Book (1954) 600.00
2 W.Disney's Donald Duck
Fun Book (1954) 550.00
1 W.Disney's Donald Duck
in Disneyland (1955) 200.00
1 W.Disney's Huey, Dewey
and Louie (1958) 150.00
1 W.Disney's DavyCrockett('55) 135.00
1 W.Disney's Lady and the
Tramp (1955) 275.00
1 CB,W.Disney's Mickey Mouse
Almanac (1957) 400.00
1 W.Disney's Mickey Mouse
Birthday Party (1953) 500.00
1 W.Disney's Mickey Mouse
Club Parade (1955) 400.00
1 W.Disney's Mickey Mouse
in Fantasyland (1957) 200.00
1 W.Disney's Mickey Mouse
in Frontierland (1956) 200.00
1 W.Disney's Summer Fun('58) 200.00
2 CB,W.Disney'sSummer
Fun('59) 200.00
1 W.Disney's Peter Pan
Treasure Chest (1953) . . . 1,500.00
1 Disney Silly Symphonies('52) 450.00
2 Disney Silly Symphonies('53) 400.00
3 Disney Silly Symphonies('54) 350.00
4 Disney Silly Symphonies('54) 350.00
5 Disney Silly Symphonies('55) 300.00
6 Disney Silly Symphonies('56) 300.00
7 Disney Silly Symphonies('57) 300.00
8 Disney Silly Symphonies('58) 300.00
9 Disney Silly Symphonies('59) 300.00
1 Disney SleepingBeauty('59) . 450.00
1 CB,W.Disney's Uncle Scrooge
Goes to Disneyland (1957) . 400.00
1 W.Disney's Vacation in
Disneyland (1958) 175.00
1 CB,Disney's Vacation
Parade('50) 1,300.00
2 Disney'sVacation Parade('51) 450.00
3 Disney'sVacation Parade('52) 225.00
4 Disney'sVacation Parade('53) 225.00
5 Disney'sVacation Parade('54) 225.00
6 Disney's Picnic Party (1955) 175.00
7 Disney's Picnic Party (1956) 175.00
8 CB,Disney's Picnic
Party (1957) 350.00

DELL JUNIOR TREASURY
1 W.Disney's Alice in Wonderland
(1955) 85.00

WALT DISNEY PRESENTS
Dell Publishing Co.
June-August, 1952
1 Ph(c), Four Color 60.00
2 Ph(c) 50.00
3 Ph(c) 50.00
4 Ph(c) 50.00
5 and 6 Ph(c) . . . . @50.00

WAMBI JUNGLE BOY
Fiction House Magazines
Spring, 1942
1 HcK,HcK(c),Vengence of
the Beasts 700.00
2 HcK,HcK(c),Lair of the
Killer Rajah 400.00
3 HcK,HcK(c) 250.00
4 HcK,HcK(c),The Valley of
the Whispering Drums 150.00
5 HcK,HcK(c),Swampland Safari 150.00
6 Taming of the Tigress 100.00
7 Duel of the Congo Kings . . . 100.00
8 AB(c),Friend of the Animals . 100.00
9 Quest of the Devils Juju . . . 100.00
10 Friend of the Animals 75.00
11 . . . . 75.00
12 Curse of the Jungle Jewels . 75.00
13 New Adventures of Wambi . . 75.00
14 . . . . 75.00
15 The Leopard Legions 75.00
16 . . . . 75.00
17 Beware Bwana! 75.00
18 Ogg the Great Bull Ape,
Winter, 1952 . . . . 75.00

WANTED COMICS
Toytown Comics/ Orbit Publications
September-October, 1947
9 Victor Everhart 125.00
10 Carlo Banone 75.00
11 Dwight Band 75.00
12 Ralph Roe 80.00
13 James Spencer;Drug 80.00
14 John "Jiggs" Sullivan;Drug . . 80.00
15 Harry Dunlap;Drug 50.00
16 Jack Parisi;Drug 50.00
17 Herber Ayers;Drug 50.00
18 Satan's Cigarettes;Drug . . . 135.00
19 Jackson Stringer 45.00
20 George Morgan 45.00
21 BK,Paul Wilson 50.00
22 . . . . 50.00
23 George Elmo Wells 40.00
24 BK,Bruce Cornett;Drug 65.00
25 Henry Anger 30.00
26 John Wormly 30.00
27 Death Always Knocks Twice . 30.00
28 Paul H. Payton 30.00
29 Hangmans Holiday 30.00
30 George Lee 30.00
31 M Consolo 30.00
32 William Davis 30.00
33 The Web of Davis 30.00
34 Dead End 30.00
35 Glen Roy Wright 50.00
36 SSh,SSh(c),Bernard Lee

GOLDEN AGE

Wanted #27 © Toytown Comics

Vault of Horror #30 © E.C. Comics

Thomas	30.00
37 SSh,SSh(c),Joseph M. Moore	30.00
38 SSh,SSh(c)	30.00
39 The Horror Weed;Drug	75.00
40	30.00
41	30.00
42	30.00
43	30.00
44	30.00
45 Killers on the Loose;Drug	50.00
46 Chalres Edward Crews	30.00
47	30.00
48 SSh,SSh(c)	30.00
49	30.00
50 JB(c),Make Way for Murder	75.00
51 JB(c),Dope Addict on a Holiday of Murder;Drug	65.00
52 The Cult of Killers; Classic Drug	65.00
53 April, 1953	30.00

WAR AGAINST CRIME
L.L. Publishing Co.
(E.C. Comics)
Spring, 1948

1 Grl	500.00
2 Grl,Guilty of Murder	300.00
3 JCr(c)	300.00
4 AF,JCr(c)	250.00
5 JCr(c)	250.00
6 AF,JCr(c)	250.00
7 AF,JCr(c)	250.00
8 AF,JCr(c)	250.00
9 AF,JCr(c),The Kid	250.00
10 JCr(c),I:Vault Keeper	1,500.00
11 JCr(c)	1,000.00

Becomes:

VAULT OF HORROR

12 AF,JCr,JCr(c),Wax Museum	3,800.00
13 AF,WW,JCr(c),Grl,Drug	800.00
14 AF,WW,JCr(c),Grl	750.00
15 AF,JCr,JCr(c),Grl,JKa	600.00
16 Grl,JKa,JCr(c)	550.00
17 JDa,Grl,JKa,JCr,JCr(c)	400.00
18 JDa,Grl,JKa,JCr,JCr(c)	400.00
19 JDa,Grl,JKa,JCr,JCr(c)	400.00
20 JDa,Grl,JKa,JCr,JCr(c)	275.00
21 JDa,Grl,JKa,JCr,JCr(c)	275.00

22 JDa,JKa,JCr,JCr(c)	275.00
23 JDa,Grl,JCr,JCr(c)	275.00
24 JDa,Grl,JO,JCr,JCr(c)	275.00
25 JDa,Grl,JKa,JCr,JCr(c)	275.00
26 JDa,Grl,JCr,JCr(c)	275.00
27 JDa,Grl,GE,JCr(c)	200.00
28 JDa,Grl,JCr,JCr(c)	200.00
29 JDa,Grl,JCr,JKa,JCr(c), JDa,Grl,JCr,JCr(c) Bradbury Adapt	200.00
30 JDa,Grl,JCr,JCr(c)	200.00
31 JDa,Grl,JCr,JCr(c), Bradbury Adapt	175.00
32 JDa,Grl,JCr,JCr(c)	175.00
33 JDa,Grl,RC,JCr(c)	175.00
34 JDa,Grl,JCr,RC,JCr(c)	175.00
35 JDa,Grl,JCr,JCr(c)	175.00
36 JDa,Grl,JCr,BK,JCr(c),Drug	175.00
37 JDa,Grl,JCr,AW,JCr(c) Hanging	175.00
38 JDa,Grl,JCr,BK,JCr(c)	175.00
39 GRi,JCr,BK,RC,JCr(c) Bondage(c)	200.00
40 January, 1955, Grl,JCr,BK,JO JCr(c)	175.00

WAR BATTLES
Harvey Publications
February, 1952

1 BP,Devils of the Deep	75.00
2 BP,A Present From Benny	40.00
3 BP	30.00
4	30.00
5	30.00
6 HN	30.00
7 BP	35.00
8	30.00
9 December, 1953	30.00

WAR BIRDS
Fiction House Magazines
1952

1 Willie the Washout	100.00
2 Mystery MIGs of Kwanjamu	50.00
3 thru 6	@40.00
7 Winter, 1953,Across the Wild Yalu	40.00

WAR COMICS
Dell Publishing Co.
May, 1940

1 AMc,Sky Hawk	450.00
2 O:Greg Gildam	250.00
3	150.00
4 O:Night Devils	200.00

WAR HEROES
Dell Publishing Co.
July-September, 1942

1 Gen. Douglas MacArthur (c)	175.00
2	100.00
3	75.00
4 A:Gremlins	125.00
5	45.00
6 thru 11	@40.00

WAR HEROES
Ace Magazines
May, 1952

1 Always Comin'	50.00
2 LC,The Last Red Tank	30.00
3 You Got it	20.00
4 A Red Patrol	20.00
5 Hustle it Up	20.00
6 LC,Hang on Pal	25.00
7	25.00
8 LC,April, 1953	25.00

WARPATH
Key Publications/ Stanmore
November, 1954

1 Red Men Raid	50.00
2 AH(c),Braves Battle	30.00
3 April, 1955	30.00

WARRIOR COMICS
H.C. Blackerby
1944

1 Ironman wing Brady	150.00

WAR SHIPS
Dell Publishing Co.
1942

1 AMc	75.00

WAR STORIES
Dell Publishing Co.
1942

5 O:The Whistler	175.00
6 A:Night Devils	125.00
7 A:Night Devils	125.00
8 A:Night Devils	125.00

WARTIME ROMANCES
St. John Publishing Co.
July, 1951

1 MB(c),MB	175.00
2 MB(c),MB	125.00
3 MB(c),MB	100.00
4 MB(c),MB	100.00
5 MB(c),MB	75.00
6 MB(c),MB	100.00
7 MB(c),MB	75.00
8 MB(c),MB	75.00
9 MB(c),MB	50.00
10 MB(c),MB	50.00
11 MB(c),MB	50.00

12 Mb(c),MB	50.00
13 MB(c)	40.00
14 MB(c)	40.00
15 MB(c)	40.00
16 MB(c),MB	40.00
17 MB(c)	40.00
18 MB(c),MB	40.00

WAR VICTORY COMICS
U.S. Treasury/War Victory/
Harvey Publ.
Summer, 1942

1 Savings Bond Promo with
Top Syndicated Cartoonists,
benefit USO 275.00
Becomes:

WAR VICTORY
ADVENTURES

2 BP,2nd Front Comics 150.00
3 BP,F:Capt Cross of the
Red Cross 125.00

Web of Evil #4
© Quality Comics Group

WEB OF EVIL
Comic Magazines, Inc.
(Quality Comics Group)
November, 1952

1 Custodian of the Dead 375.00
2 JCo,Hangmans Horror 250.00
3 JCo 250.00
4 JCo,JCo(c),Monsters of
the Mist 250.00
5 JCo,JCo(c),The Man who Died
Twice,Electric Chair(c) 275.00
6 JCo,JCo(c),Orgy of Death . 250.00
7 JCo,JCo(c),The Strangling
Hands 250.00
8 JCo,Flaming Vengeance .. 225.00
9 JCo,The Monster in Flesh . 225.00
10 JCo,Brain that Wouldn't Die 225.00
11 JCo,Buried Alive 225.00
12 Phantom Killer 125.00
13 Demon Inferno 125.00
14 RC(c),The Monster Genie .. 125.00
15 Crypts of Horror 125.00
16 Hamlet of Horror 125.00
17 Terror in Chinatown 135.00

18 Scared to Death,Acid Face .	150.00
19 Demon of the Pit	125.00
20 Man Made Terror	125.00
21 December, 1954, Death's	
Ambush	125.00

WEB OF MYSTERY
A.A. Wyn Publ.
(Ace Magazines)
February, 1951

1 MSy,Venom of the Vampires 350.00
2 MSy,Legacy of the Accursed 175.00
3 MSy,The Violin Curse 150.00
4 GC 150.00
5 .... 150.00
6 LC 150.00
7 MSy 150.00
8 LC,LC(c),MSy,The Haunt of
Death Lake 150.00
9 LC,LC(c) 150.00
10 .... 150.00
11 MSy 150.00
12 LC 125.00
13 LC,LC(c) 125.00
14 MSy 125.00
15 .... 125.00
16 .... 125.00
17 LC,LC(c) 125.00
18 LC 125.00
19 LC 125.00
20 LC 125.00
21 MSy 125.00
22 .... 125.00
23 .... 125.00
24 LC 125.00
25 LC 125.00
26 .... 125.00
27 LC 125.00
28 RP,1st Issue under Comics
Code Authority 100.00
29 MSy,September, 1955 .... 100.00

WEDDING BELLS
Quality Comics Group
February, 1954

1 OW 100.00
2 .... 45.00
3 .... 25.00
4 .... 25.00
5 .... 25.00
6 .... 25.00
7 .... 25.00
8 .... 25.00
9 Comics Code 25.00
10 BWa 75.00
11 .... 25.00
12 .... 20.00
13 .... 20.00
14 .... 20.00
15 MB(c) 25.00
16 MB(c),MB 35.00
17 .... 20.00
18 MB 25.00
19 MB 25.00

WEEKENDER, THE
Rucker Publishing Co.
September, 1945

3 .... 125.00
4 .... 100.00
2-1(5)JCo,WMc,January, 1946 145.00

WEIRD ADVENTURES
P.L. Publishing
May, 1951

1 MB,Missing Diamonds 350.00
2 Puppet Peril 300.00
3 Blood Vengeance,
October 1951 .... 250.00

WEIRD ADVENTURES
Approved Comics
(Ziff-Davis)
July-August, 1951

10 P(c),Seeker from Beyond .. 250.00

WEIRD CHILLS
Key Publications
July, 1954

1 MBi(c),BW 500.00
2 Eye Torture(c) 450.00
3 Bondage(c),November, 1954 300.00

WEIRD COMICS
Fox Features Syndicate
April, 1940

1 LF(c),Bondage(c),B:Birdman,
Thor,Sorceress of Doom,
Blast Bennett,Typhon,Voodoo
Man, Dr.Mortal 3,700.00
2 LF(c),Mummy(c) 1,600.00
3 JSm(c) 900.00
4 JSm(c) 900.00
5 Bondage(c),I:Dart,Ace;E:Thor 900.00
6 Dart & Ace(c) 750.00
7 Battle of Kooba 750.00
8 B:Panther Woman,Dynamo,
The Eagle 750.00
9 V:Pirates 650.00
10 A:Navy Jones 650.00
11 Dart & Ace(c) 450.00
12 Dart & Ace(c) 450.00
13 Dart & Ace(c) 450.00
14 The Rage(c) 450.00
15 Dart & Ace (c) 450.00
16 Flag,The Encore(c) 450.00
17 O:Black Rider 475.00
18 .... 450.00
19 .... 450.00
20 January, 1941,I'm The Master
of Life and Death 450.00

WEIRD FANTASY
I.C. Publishing Co.
(E.C. Comics)
May-June, 1950

13(1)AF,HK,JKa,WW,AF(c),
Roger Harvey's Brain 1,500.00
14(2)AF,HK,JKa,WW,AF(c),
Cosmic Ray Brain Explosion 600.00
15(3)AF,HK,JKa,WW,AF(c),Your
Destination is the Moon 450.00
16(4)AF,HK,JKa,WW,AF(c) ... 450.00
17(5)AF,HK,JKa,WW,AF(c),Not
Made by Human Hands ... 400.00
6 AF,HK,JKa,WW,AF(c) ... 300.00
7 AF,JKa,WW,AF(c) 300.00
8 AF,JKa,WW,AF(c) 300.00
9 AF,Jka,WW,JO,AF(c) ... 300.00
10 AF,Jka,WW,JO,AF(c) ... 350.00
11 AF,Jka,WW,JO,AF(c) ... 250.00
12 AF,Jka,WW,JO,AF(c) ... 250.00
13 AF,Jka,WW,JO,AF(c) 250.00
14 AF,JKa,WW,JO,AW&FF,AF(c) 350.00

15 AF,JKa,JO,AW&RKr,AF(c),
     Bondage(c) 250.00
16 AF,JKa,JO,AW&RKr,AF(c) . 225.00
17 AF,JOP,JKa,AF(c),Bradbury 225.00
18 AF,JO,JKa,AF(c),Bradbury . 225.00
19 JO,JKa,JO(c),Bradbury 225.00
20 JKa,FF,AF(c) 225.00
21 JO,JKa,AW&FF(c) 350.00
22 JO,JKa,JO(c),Nov.,1953 . . . 195.00

WEIRD HORRORS
St. John Publishing Co.
June, 1952

1 GT,Dungeon of the Doomed 350.00
2 Strangest Music Ever 300.00
3 PAM,Strange Fakir From
     the Orient 300.00
4 Murderers Knoll 175.00
5 Phantom Bowman 175.00
6 Monsters from Outer Space 275.00
7 LC,Deadly Double 300.00
8 JKu,JKu(c),Bloody Yesterday 250.00
9 JKu,JKu(c),Map Of Doom . . 250.00
Becomes:

NIGHTMARE

10 JKu(c),The Murderer's Mask 350.00
11 BK,Ph(c),Fangs of Death . . 250.00
12 JKu(c),The Forgotten Mask . 225.00
13 BP,Princess of the Sea 200.00
Becomes:

AMAZING GHOST STORIES

14 EK,MB(c), ... 150.00
15 BP 125.00
16 February, 1955, EK,JKu . . . 150.00

WEIRD MYSTERIES
Gilmore Publications
October, 1952

1 BW(c) 500.00
2 BWi 700.00
3 Severed Heads(c) 350.00
4 BW,Human headed ants(c) . 600.00
5 BW,Brains From Head(c) . . . 600.00
6 Severed Head(c) 350.00
7 Used in "Seduction" 550.00
8 The One That Got Away . . 350.00
9 Epitaph,Cyclops 350.00
10 The Ruby 300.00
11 Voodoo Dolls 300.00
12 September, 1954 . . . . 300.00

WEIRD SCIENCE
E.C. Comics
1950

1 AF(c),AF,JKu,HK,WW 1,500.00
2 AF(c),AF,JKu,HK,WW,Flying
     Saucers(c) 700.00
3 AF(c),AF,JKu,HK 650.00
4 AF(c),AF,JKu,HK 550.00
5 AF(c),AF,JKu,HK,WW,
     Atomic Bomb(c) 400.00
6 AF(c),AF,JKu,HK 350.00
7 AF(c),AF,JKu,HK,Classic(c) . 400.00
8 AF(c),AF,JKu 350.00
9 WW(c),JKu,Classic(c) 400.00
10 WW(c),JKu,JO,Classic(c) . . 400.00
11 AF,JKu,Space war 275.00
12 WW(c),JKu,Classic(c) 275.00
13 WW(c),JKu,JO 300.00
14 WW(c),WW,JO 300.00
15 WW(c),WW,JO,GRi,AW,
     RKr,JKa 300.00

Weird Science #11
© E.C. Comics

16 WW(c),WW,JO,AW,RKr,JKa 300.00
17 WW(c),WW,JO,AW,RKr,JKa 300.00
18 WW(c),WW,JO,AW,RKr,
     JKa,Atomic Bomb 250.00
19 WW(c),WW,JO,AW,
     FF,Horror(c) 400.00
20 WW(c),WW,JO,AW,FF,JKa . 400.00
21 WW(c),WW,JO,AW,FF,JKa . 400.00
22 WW(c),WW,JO,AW,FF 400.00
Becomes:

WEIRD SCIENCE FANTASY

23 WW(c),WW,AW,BK 250.00
24 WW,AW,BK,Classic(c) 225.00
25 WW,AW,BK,Classic(c) 250.00
26 AF(c),WW,RC,
     Flying Saucer(c) 250.00
27 WW(c),WW,RC 250.00
28 AF(c),WW 250.00
29 AF(c),WW,Classic(c) 450.00
Becomes:

INCREDIBLE SCIENCE FANTASY

30 WW,JDa(c),BK,AW,RKr,JO 250.00
31 WW,JDa(c),BK,AW,RKr . . . 300.00
32 JDa(c),BK,WW,JO 300.00
33 WW(c),BK,WW,JO 300.00

WEIRD TALES OF THE FUTURE
S.P.M. Publ./ Aragon Publications
March, 1952

1 RA 600.00
2 BW,BW(c) 900.00
3 BW,BW(c) 850.00
4 BW,BW(c) 600.00
5 BW,BW(c),Jumpin' Jupiter
     Lingerie(c) 850.00
6 Bondage(c) 350.00
7 BW,Devil(c) 550.00
8 July-August 1953 . . . . 450.00

WEIRD TERROR
Allen Hardy Associates (Comic Media)
September, 1952

1 RP,DH,DH(c),Dungeon of the
     Doomed;Hitler 300.00
2 HcK(c),PAM 200.00
3 PAM,DH,DH(c) 200.00
4 PAM,DH,DH(c) 250.00
5 PAM,DH,RP,DH(c),Hanging(c) 200.00
6 DH,RP,DH(c),Step into
     My Parlour 225.00
7 DH,PAM,DH(c),Blood o/t Bats 175.00
8 DH,RP,DH(c),Step into
     My Parlour 200.00
9 DH,PAM,DH(c),The Fleabite 175.00
10 DH,BP,RP,DH(c) 175.00
11 DH,DH(c),Satan's Love Call 200.00
12 DH,DH(c),King Whitey 175.00
13 DH,DH(c),September, 1954,
     Wings of Death 175.00

WEIRD THRILLERS
Approved Comics (Ziff-Davis)
September-October, 1951

1 Ph(c),Monsters & The Model 500.00
2 AW,P(c),The Last Man 400.00
3 AW,P(c),Princess o/t Sea . . 500.00
4 AW,P(c),The Widows Lover . 350.00
5 BP,October, 1952,AW,P(c),
     Wings of Death 300.00

WESTERN ACTION THRILLERS
Dell Publishing Co.
April, 1937

1 . . . . 600.00

WESTERN ADVENTURES COMICS
A.A. Wyn, Inc. (Ace Magazines)
October, 1948

N#(1)Injun Gun Bait 150.00
N#(2)Cross-Draw Kid 75.00
N#(3)Outlaw Mesa 75.00
4 Sheriff 50.00
5 . . . . 50.00
6 Rip Roaring Adventure 50.00
Becomes:

WESTERN LOVE TRAILS

7 . . . . 75.00
8 Maverick Love 50.00
9 March, 1950 . . . . 40.00

WESTERN BANDIT TRAILS
St. John Publishing Co.
January, 1949

1 GT,MB(c) 150.00
2 GT,MB(c) 100.00
3 GT,MB,MB(c),Gingham Fury 125.00

WESTERN CRIME-BUSTERS
Trojan Magazines
September, 1950

1 Gunslingin' Galoots 200.00
2 K-Bar Kate 100.00

3 Wilma West	100.00
4 Bob Dale	100.00
5 Six-Gun Smith	100.00
6 WW	200.00
7 WW,Wells Fargo Robbery	200.00
8	100.00
9 WW,Lariat Lucy	200.00
10 WW,April 1952;Tex Gordon	200.00

WESTERN CRIME CASES
(see WHITE RIDER)

WESTERNER, THE
Wanted Comics Group/
Toytown Publ.
June, 1948

14 F:Jack McCall	75.00
15 F:Bill Jamett	35.00
16 F:Tom McLowery	35.00
17 F:Black Bill Desmond	35.00
18 BK,F:Silver Dollar Dalton	50.00
19 MMe,F:Jess Meeton	30.00
20	25.00
21 BK,MMe	50.00
22 BK,MMe	50.00
23 BK,MMe	50.00
24 BK,MMe	50.00
25 O,I,B:Calamity Jane	50.00
26 BK,F:The Widowmaker	65.00
27	75.00
28 thru 31	@25.00
32 E:Calamity Jane	25.00
33 A:Quest	25.00
34	25.00
35 SSh(c)	25.00
36	25.00
37 Lobo-Wolf Boy	25.00
38	25.00
39	25.00
40 SSh(c)	25.00
41 December, 1951	25.00

WESTERN FIGHTERS
Hillman Periodicals
April-May, 1948

1 S&K(c)	250.00
2 BF(c)	60.00

Western Fighters #2
© Hillman Periodicals

3 BF(c)	50.00
4 BK,BF	55.00
5	35.00
6	34.00
7 BK	60.00
8	35.00
9	35.00
10 BK	60.00
11 AMC&FF	200.00
2-1 BK	60.00
2-2 BP	40.00
2-3 thru 2-12	@20.00
3-1 thru 3-11	@20.00
3-12 BK	40.00
4-1	20.00
4-2 BK	50.00
4-3 BK	50.00
4-4 BK	50.00
4-5 BK	50.00
4-6 BK	50.00
4-7 March-April 1953	20.00

WESTERN FRONTIER
P.L. Publishers
(Approved Comics)
May, 1951

1 Flaming Vengeance	75.00
2	35.00
3 Death Rides the Iron Horse	25.00
4 thru 6	@25.00
7 1952	25.00

WESTERN HEARTS
Standard Magazine, Inc.
December, 1949

1 Ph(c),JSe	125.00
2 Ph(c),AW,FF	150.00
3 Ph(c)	65.00
4 Ph(c),JSe,BE	65.00
5 Ph(c),JSe,BE	65.00
6 Ph(c),JSe,BE	65.00
7 Ph(c),JSe,BE	65.00
8 Ph(c)	75.00
9 Ph(c),JSe,BE	75.00
10 Ph(c),JSe,BE	50.00

WESTERN LOVE
Feature Publications
(Prize Comics Group)
July-August, 1949

1 S&K	200.00
2 S&K	150.00
3 JSE,BE	100.00
4 JSE,BE	100.00
5 JSE,BE	100.00

WESTERN PICTURE STORIES
Comics Magazine Co.
February, 1937

1 WE,Treachery Trail, 1st Western	1,400.00
2 WE,Weapons of the West	850.00
3 WE,Dragon Pass	650.00
4 June, 1937,CavemanCowboy	650.00

WESTERN THRILLERS
Fox Features Syndicate
August, 1948

1	350.00
2	125.00
3 GT,RH(c)	100.00

4	125.00
5	125.00
6 June, 1949	100.00

Becomes:
MY PAST CONFESSIONS

7	60.00
8	40.00
9	40.00
10	40.00
11	75.00
12	20.00

WESTERN TRUE CRIME
Fox Features Syndicate
August, 1948

1	175.00
2	150.00
3	125.00
4 JCr	150.00
5	100.00
6	100.00

Becomes:
MY CONFESSION

7 WW	150.00
8 WW,My Tarnished Reputation	125.00
9 I:Tormented Men	40.00
10 February, 1950,I Am Damaged Goods	40.00

WHACK
St. John Publishing Co.
December, 1953

1 Steve Crevice,Flush Jordan V:Bing(Crosby)The Merciful	225.00
2	125.00
3 F:Little Awful Fannie	125.00

WHAM COMICS
Centaur Publications
November, 1940

1 PG,The Sparkler & His Disappearing Suit	1,200.00
2 December, 1940,PG,PG(C), Men Turn into Icicles	850.00

WHIRLWIND COMICS
Nita Publications
June, 1940

1 F:The Cyclone	1,200.00
2 A:Scoops Hanlon,Cyclone(c)	800.00
3 September, 1940,A:Magic Mandarin,Cyclone(c)	750.00

WHITE PRINCESS OF THE JUNGLE
Avon Periodicals
July, 1951

1 EK(c),Terror Fangs	400.00
2 EK,EK(c),Jungle Vengeance	300.00
3 EK,EK(c),The Blue Gorilla	250.00
4 Fangs of the Swamp Beast	225.00
5 EK,Coils of the Tree Snake November, 1952	225.00

WHIZ COMICS
Fawcett Publications
February, 1940

1 O:Captain Marvel,B:Spy Smasher,Golden Arrow,Dan Dare, Scoop Smith,Ibis the Invincible, Sivana	65,000.00

GOLDEN AGE

2 . . . . 4,500.00
3 Make way for
   Captain Marvel 4,000.00
4 Captain Marvel
   Crashes Through 2,500.00
5 Captain Marvel
   Scores Again! 2,000.00
6 Circus of Death 1,800.00
7 B:Dr Voodoo,Squadron
   of Death 1,500.00
8 Saved by Captain Marvel! 1,200.00
9 MRa,Captain Marvel
   on the Job 1,200.00
10 Battles the Winged Death . 1,200.00
11 Hurray for Captain Marvel . 1,000.00
12 Captain Marvel rides
   the Engine of Doom 1,000.00
13 Worlds Most Powerful Man! . 900.00
14 Boomerangs the Torpedo . . 900.00
15 O:Sivana 1,000.00
16 . . . . 1,000.00
17 Knocks out a Tank 1,000.00
18 V:Spy Smasher 1,000.00

Whiz Comics #24
© Fawcett Publications

19 Crushes the Tiger Shark . . . 650.00
20 V:Sivana 650.00
21 O:Lt. Marvels 700.00
22 Mayan Temple 550.00
23 GT,A:Dr. Voodoo 550.00
24 . . . . 550.00
25 O&I:Captain Marvel Jr.,
   Stops the Turbine of Death 5,000.00
26 . . . . 475.00
27 V:Death God of the Katonkas 500.00
28 V:Mad Dervish of Ank-Har . 500.00
29 Three Lt. Marvels (c), Pan
   American Olympics 500.00
30 . . . . 450.00
31 Douglass MacArthur&Spy
   Smasher(c) 400.00
32 Spy Smasher(c) 400.00
33 Spy Smasher(c) 450.00
34 Three Lt. Marvels (c) 350.00
35 Capt. Marvel and the
   Three Fates 375.00
36 Haunted Hallowe'en Hotel . . 325.00
37 Return of the Trolls 325.00
38 Grand Steeplechase 325.00
39 A Nazi Utopia 325.00

40 A:Three Lt. Marvels, The
   Earth's 4 Corners 325.00
41 Captain Marvel 1,000 years
   from Now 250.00
42 Returns in Time Chair 250.00
43 V:Sinister Spies,
   Spy Smasher(c) 250.00
44 Life Story of Captain Marvel 275.00
45 Cures His Critics 250.00
46 . . . . 250.00
47 Captain Marvel needs
   a Birthday 250.00
48 . . . . 250.00
49 Writes a Victory song 250.00
50 Captain Marvel's most
   embarrassing moment 250.00
51 Judges the Ugly-
   Beauty Contest 200.00
52 V:Sivana, Chooses
   His Birthday 200.00
53 Captain Marvel fights
   Billy Batson 200.00
54 Jack of all Trades 200.00
55 Family Tree 200.00
56 Tells what the Future Will Be 200.00
57 A:Spy Smasher,Golden Arrow,
   Ibis 200.00
58 . . . . 200.00
59 V:Sivana's Twin 200.00
60 Missing Person's Machine . 200.00
61 Gets a first name 175.00
62 Plays in a Band 175.00
63 Great Indian Rope Trick . . . 175.00
64 Suspected of Murder 175.00
65 Lamp of Diogenes 175.00
66 The Trial of Mr. Morris! . . . 175.00
67 . . . . 175.00
68 Laugh Lotion, V:Sivana . . . 175.00
69 Mission to Mercury 175.00
70 Climbs the World's Mightiest
   Mountain 175.00
71 Strange Magician 150.00
72 V:The Man of the Future . . . 150.00
73 In Ogre Land 150.00
74 Old Man River 150.00
75 The City Olympics 150.00
76 Spy Smasher become
   Crime Smasher 150.00
77 . . . . 150.00
78 . . . . 150.00
79 . . . . 150.00
80 . . . . 150.00
81 . . . . 150.00
82 The Atomic Ship 150.00
83 Magic Locket 150.00
84 . . . . 150.00
85 The Clock of San Lojardo . . 150.00
86 V:Sinister Sivanas 150.00
87 The War on Olympia 150.00
88 The Wonderful Magic Carpet 150.00
89 Webs of Crime 150.00
90 . . . . 150.00
91 Infinity (c) 150.00
92 . . . . 150.00
93 Captain America become
   a Hobo? 150.00
94 V:Sivana 150.00
95 Captain Marvel is grounded 150.00
96 The Battle Between Buildings 150.00
97 Visits Mirage City 150.00
98 . . . . 150.00
99 V:Menace in the Mountains . 150.00
100 . . . . 200.00
101 . . . . 150.00
102 A:Commando Yank 150.00

103 . . . . 150.00
104 . . . . 150.00
105 . . . . 150.00
106 A:Bulletman 150.00
107 The Great Experiment . . . 175.00
108 thru 114 . . . . @150.00
115 The Marine Invasion 150.00
116 . . . . 150.00
117 V:Sivana 150.00
118 . . . . 150.00
119 . . . . 150.00
120 . . . . 150.00
121 . . . . 150.00
122 V:Sivana 150.00
123 . . . . 150.00
124 . . . . 150.00
125 Olympic Games of the Gods 150.00
126 . . . . 150.00
127 . . . . 150.00
128 . . . . 150.00
129 . . . . 150.00
130 . . . . 150.00
131 The Television Trap 150.00

Whiz Comics #47
© Fawcett Publications

132 thru 142 . . . . @150.00
143 Mystery of the Flying Studio 150.00
144 V:The Disaster Master . . . 150.00
145 . . . . 150.00
146 . . . . 150.00
147 . . . . 150.00
148 . . . . 150.00
149 . . . . 150.00
150 V:Bug Bombs 150.00
151 . . . . 150.00
152 . . . . 150.00
153 V:The Death Horror 200.00
154 Horror Tale, I:Dr.Death . . . 200.00
155 V:Legend Horror,Dr.Death . 225.00

WHODUNIT?
D.S. Publishing Co.
August-September, 1948

1 MB,Weeping Widow 150.00
2 Diploma For Death 100.00
3 December-January, 1949 . . . 100.00

WHO IS NEXT?
Standard Comics
January, 1953
5 ATh,RA,Don't Let Me Kill .. 125.00

WILD BILL ELLIOT
Dell Publishing Co.
May, 1950
(1) *see Dell Four Color #278*
2 . . . . 45.00
3 thru 5 . . . . @35.00
6 thru 10 . . . . @35.00
(11-12) *see Four Color #472, 520*
13 thru 17 . . . . @30.00

WILD BILL HICKOK
AND JINGLES
(see YELLOWJACKET
COMICS)

WILBUR COMICS
MLJ Magazines
(Archie Publications)
Summer, 1944
1 F:Wilbur Wilkin-America's Song
  of Fun 400.00
2 . . . . 200.00
3 . . . . 150.00
4 . . . . 135.00
5 I:Katy Keene 500.00
6 . . . . 125.00
7 . . . . 125.00
8 . . . . 125.00
9 . . . . 125.00
10 . . . . 125.00
11 thru 20 . . . . @75.00
21 thru 30 . . . . @45.00
31 thru 40 . . . . @35.00
41 thru 50 . . . . @25.00
51 thru 89 . . . . @20.00
90 October, 1965 . . . . 20.00

WILD BILL HICKOK
Avon Periodicals
September-October, 1949
1 GRI(c),Frontier Fighter 150.00
2 Ph(c),Gambler's Guns 60.00
3 Ph(c),Great Stage Robbery . 30.00
4 Ph(c),Guerilla Gunmen 30.00
5 Ph(c),Return of the Renegade 30.00
6 EK,EK(c),Along the Apache
  Trail 30.00
7 EK,EK(c)Outlaws of
  Hell's Bend 30.00
8 Ph(c),The Border Outlaws . . 30.00
9 PH(c),Killers From Texas . . 30.00
10 Ph(c) 30.00
11 EK,EK(c),The Hell Riders . . 30.00
12 EK,EK(c),The Lost Gold Mine 35.00
13 EK,EK(c),Bloody Canyon
  Massacre 35.00
14 . . . . 35.00
15 . . . . 20.00
16 JKa 30.00
17 thru 23 . . . . @25.00
24 EK,EK(c) 30.00
25 EK,EK(c) 30.00
26 EK,EK(c) 30.00
27 EK,EK(c) 30.00
28 EK,EK(c),May-June, 1956 . . 30.00

Wild Boy of the Congo #15
© Approved/Ziff-Davis/St. Johns

WILD BOY OF
THE CONGO
Approved(Ziff-Davis)/
St. John Publ. Co.
February-March, 1951
10(1)NS,PH(c),Bondage(c),The
  Gorilla God 150.00
11(2)NS,Ph(c),Star of the Jungle 75.00
12(3)NS,Ph(c),Ice-Age Men . . . 75.00
4 NS.Ph(c),Tyrant of the Jungle 85.00
5 NS,Ph(c),The White Robe
  of Courage 50.00
6 NS,Ph(c) 50.00
7 MB,EK.Ph(c) 60.00
8 Ph(c),Man-Eater 50.00
9 Ph(c),Killer Leopard 50.00
10 . . . . 50.00
11 MB(c) 60.00
12 MB(c) 60.00
13 MB(c) 60.00
14 MB(c) 60.00
15 June, 1955 . . . . 40.00

WINGS COMICS
Wings Publ.
(Fiction House Magazines)
September, 1940
1 HcK,AB,GT,Ph(c),B:Skull Squad,
  Clipper Kirk,Suicide Smith,
  War Nurse,Phantom Falcons,
  Greasemonkey Griffin,Parachute
  Patrol,Powder Burns 1,800.00
2 HcK,AB,GT,Bomber Patrol . 750.00
3 HcK,AB,GT 500.00
4 HcK,AB,GT,B:Spitfire Ace . 500.00
5 HcK,AB,GT,Torpedo Patrol . 500.00
6 HcK,AB,GT,Bombs for Berlin 425.00
7 HcK,AB 425.00
8 HcK,AB,The Wings of Doom 425.00
9 Sky-Wolf 400.00
10 The Upside Down 400.00
11 . . . . 350.00
12 Fury of the fire Boards 350.00
13 Coffin Slugs For The
  Luftwaffe 350.00
14 Stuka Buster 350.00

15 Boomerang Blitz 350.00
16 O:Capt.Wings 400.00
17 Skyway to Death 300.00
18 Horsemen of the Sky 300.00
19 Nazi Spy Trap 300.00
20 The One Eyed Devil 300.00
21 Chute Troop Tornado 275.00
22 TNT for Tokyo 275.00
23 RP,Battling Eagles of Bataan 275.00
24 RP,The Death of a Hero . . . 275.00
25 RP,Suicide Squeeze 275.00
26 Tojo's Eagle Trap 275.00
27 Blb,Mile High Gauntlet . . . 275.00
28 Blb,Tail Gun Tornado 275.00
29 Blb,Buzzards from Berlin . . 275.00
30 Blb,Monsters of the
  Stratosphere 225.00
31 BLb,Sea Hawks away 225.00
32 BLb,Sky Mammoth 225.00
33 BLb,Roll Call of the Yankee
  Eagles 225.00
34 BLb,So Sorry,Mr Tojo 225.00
35 BLb,RWb,Hell's Lightning . . 225.00
36 RWb,The Crash-Master . . . 225.00
37 RWb,Sneak Blitz 225.00
38 RWb,Rescue Raid of the
  Yank Eagle 225.00
39 RWb,Sky Hell/Pigboat Patrol 225.00
40 RWb,Luftwaffe Gamble 225.00
41 RWb,.50 Caliber Justice . . . 175.00
42 RWb,PanzerMeat forMosquito 175.00
43 RWb,Suicide Sentinels 175.00
44 RWb,Berlin Bombs Away . . 175.00
45 RWb,Hells Cargo 175.00
46 RWb,Sea-Hawk Patrol 175.00
47 RWb,Tojo's Tin Gibraltar . . . 175.00
48 RWb 175.00
49 RWb,Rockets Away 175.00
50 RWb,Mission For a Madman 175.00
51 RWb,Toll for a Typhoon . . . 150.00
52 MB,Madam Marauder 150.00
53 MB,Robot Death Over
  Manhattan 150.00
54 MB,Juggernauts of Death . . 150.00
55 MB 150.00
56 MB,Sea Raiders Grave 150.00
57 MB,Yankee Warbirds over
  Tokyo 150.00
58 MB 150.00
59 MB,Prey of the Night Hawks 150.00
60 MB,E:Skull Squad,
  Hell's Eyes 150.00
61 MB,Raiders o/t Purple Dawn 135.00
62 Twilight of the Gods 135.00
63 Hara Kiri Rides the Skyways 135.00
64 Taps For Tokyo 135.00
65 AB,Warhawk for the Kill . . . 135.00
66 AB,B:Ghost Patrol 135.00
67 AB 125.00
68 AB,ClipperKirkBecomesPhantom
  Falcon;O:Phantom Falcon . . 125.00
69 AB,O:cont,Phantom Falcon . 125.00
70 AB,N:Phantom Falcon;
  O:Final Phantom Falcon . . . 125.00
71 Ghost Patrol becomes
  Ghost Squadron 125.00
72 V:Capt. Kamikaze 125.00
73 Hell & Stormoviks 125.00
74 BLb(c),Loot is What She
  Lived For 125.00
75 BLb(c),The Sky Hag 125.00
76 BLb(c),Temple of the Dead . 125.00
77 BLb(c),Sky Express to Hell . 125.00
78 BLb(c),Loot Queen of
  Satan's Skyway 125.00

GOLDEN AGE

GOLDEN AGE

Wings Comics #58
© Fiction House Magazines

79 BLb(c),Buzzards of
  Plunder Sky 125.00
80 BLb(c),Port of Missing Pilots 125.00
81 BLb(c),Sky Trail of the
  Terror Tong 125.00
82 BLb(c),Bondage(c),Spider &
  The Fly Guy 135.00
83 BLb(c),GE,Deep Six For
  Capt. Wings 125.00
84 BLb(c),GE,Sky Sharks to
  the Kill 125.00
85 BLb(c),GE 125.00
86 BLb(c),GE,Moon Raiders .. 125.00
87 BLb(c),GE 125.00
88 BLb(c),GE,Madmans Mission 125.00
89 BLb(c),GE,Bondage(c),
  Rockets Away 135.00
90 BLb(c),GE,Bondage(c),The
  Radar Rocketeers 135.00
91 BLb(c),GE,Bondage(c),V-9 for
  Vengeance 135.00
92 BLb(c),GE,Death's red Rocket125.00
93 BLb(c),GE,Kidnap Cargo .. 125.00
94 BLb(c),GE,Bondage(c),Ace
  of the A-Bomb Patrol 135.00
95 BLb(c),GE,The Ace of
  the Assassins 125.00
96 BLb(c),GE 125.00
97 BLb(c),GE,The Sky Octopus 125.00
98 BLb(c),GE,The Witch Queen
  of Satan's Skyways 125.00
99 BLb(c),GE,The Spy Circus . 125.00
100 BLb(c),GE,King o/t Congo . 150.00
101 BLb(c),GE,Trator of
  the Cockpit 125.00
102 BLb(c),GE,Doves of Doom 125.00
103 BLb(c),GE 125.00
104 BLb(c),GE,Fireflies of Fury 125.00
105 BLb(c),GE 125.00
106 BLb(c),GE,Six Aces & A
  Firing Squad 125.00
107 BLb(c),GE,Operation Satan 125.00
108 BLb(c),GE,The Phantom
  of Berlin 125.00
109 GE,Vultures of
  Vengeance Sky 125.00
110 GE,The Red Ray Vortex .. 125.00
111 GE,E:Jane Martin 100.00

112 The Flight of the
  Silver Saucers 100.00
113 Suicide Skyways 100.00
114 D-Day for Death Rays ... 100.00
115 Ace of Space 100.00
116 Jet Aces of Korea 100.00
117 Reap the Red Wind 100.00
118 Vengeance Flies Blind ... 100.00
119 The Whistling Death 100.00
120 Doomsday Mission 100.00
121 Ace of the Spyways 100.00
122 Last Kill Korea 100.00
123 The Cat & the Canaries .. 100.00
124 Summer, 1954, Death
  Below Zero 100.00

WINNIE WINKLE
Dell Publishing Co.
1941

1 .... 45.00
2 .... 30.00
3 .... 20.00
4 thru 7 .... @20.00

WITCHCRAFT
Avon Periodicals
March-April, 1952
1 SC,JKu,Heritage of Horror . 500.00
2 SC,JKu,The Death Tattoo .. 350.00
3 EK,Better off Dead 225.00
4 Claws of the Cat,
  Boiling Humans 250.00
5 Ph(c),Where Zombies Walk 300.00
6 March, 1953 Mysteries of the
  Moaning Statue 225.00

Witches Tales #26
© Harvey Publications

WITCHES TALES
Harvey Publications
January, 1951
1 RP,Bondage(c),Weird Yarns
  of Unseen Terror 350.00
2 RP,We Dare You 175.00
3 RP,Bondage(c)Forest of
  Skeletons 125.00
4 BP 125.00
5 BP,Bondage(c),Share

  My Coffin 135.00
6 BP,Bondage(c),Servants of
  the Tomb 135.00
7 BP,Screaming City 135.00
8 Bondage(c) 150.00
9 Fatal Steps 125.00
10 BP,.....,IT! 125.00
11 BP,Monster Maker 100.00
12 Bondage(c);The Web
  of the Spider 125.00
13 The Torture Jar 100.00
14 Transformation 125.00
15 Drooling Zombie 100.00
16 Revenge of a Witch 100.00
17 Dimension IV 135.00
18 HN,Bird of Prey 125.00
19 HN,The Pact 125.00
20 HN,Kiss & Tell 125.00
21 HN,The Invasion 125.00
22 HN,A Day of Panic 125.00
23 HN,The Wig Maker 125.00
24 HN,The Undertaker 125.00
25 What Happens at 8:30 PM?
  Severed Heads(c) 125.00
26 Up There 100.00
27 The Thing That Grew 100.00
28 Demon Flies 100.00
Becomes:

**WITCHES WESTERN
TALES**
29 S&K,S&K(c),F:Davy Crockett 125.00
30 S&K.S&K(c) 150.00
Becomes:

WESTERN TALES
31 S&K,S&K(c),F:Davy Crockett 100.00
32 S&K,S&K(c) 100.00
33 S&K,S&K(c),July-Sept.,1956 100.00

**WITH THE MARINES
ON THE BATTLEFRONTS
OF THE WORLD**
Toby Press
June, 1953
1 Ph(c),Flaming Soul 250.00
2 Ph(c),March, 1954 .... 50.00

WITTY COMICS
**Irwin H. Rubin/Chicago Nite
Life News**
1945
1 .... 100.00
2 1945 .... 50.00
3 thru 7 .... @40.00

WOMEN IN LOVE
**Fox Features Synd./
Hero Books/
Ziff-Davis**
August, 1949
1 .... 400.00

WOMEN OUTLAWS
Fox Features Syndicate
July, 1948
1 .... 550.00
2 .... 450.00
3 .... 450.00
4 .... 450.00
5 thru 8 .... @350.00
Becomes:

MY LOVE MEMORIES
9	75.00
10	35.00
11	70.00
12 WW	75.00

WONDERBOY
(see HORRIFIC)

WONDER COMICS
**Great Publ./Nedor/
Better Publications
May, 1944**

1 SSh(c),B:Grim Reaper, Spectro Hitler(c)	900.00
2 ASh(c),O:Grim Reaper,B:Super Sleuths,Grim Reaper(c)	500.00
3 ASh(c),Grim Reaper(c)	450.00
4 ASh(c),Grim Reaper(c)	425.00
5 ASh(c),Grim Reaper(c)	425.00
6 ASh(c),Grim Reaper(c)	350.00
7 ASh(c),Grim Reaper(c)	350.00
8 ASh(c),E:Super Sleuths, Spectro	350.00
9 ASh(c),B:Wonderman	350.00
10 ASh(c),Wonderman(c)	400.00
11 Grl(c),B:Dick Devins	400.00
12 Grl(c),Bondage(c)	400.00
13 ASh(c),Bondage(c)	400.00
14 ASh(c),Bondage(c) E:Dick Devins	400.00
15 ASh(c),Bondage(c),B:Tara	500.00
16 ASh(c),A:Spectro, E:Grim Reaper	425.00
17 FF,ASh(c),A:Super Sleuth	450.00
18 ASh(c),B:Silver Knight	425.00
19 ASh(c),FF	400.00
20 FF,October, 1948	450.00

WONDERLAND COMICS
**Feature Publications
(Prize Comics Group)
Summer, 1945**

1 (fa),B:Alex in Wonderland	60.00
2	35.00
3 thru 8	@25.00
9 1947	25.00

WONDER COMICS
**Fox Features Syndicate
May, 1930–Jan. 1942**

1 BKa,WE,WE(c),B:Wonderman, DR,Kung,K-51	15,000.00
2 WE,BKa,LF(c),B:Yarko the Great,A:Spark Stevens	4,500.00

Becomes:
WONDERWORLD COMICS

3 WE,LF,BP,LF&WE,I:Flame	6,000.00
4 WE,LF,BP,LF(c)	2,400.00
5 WE,LF,BP,GT,LF(c),Flame	1,500.00
6 WE,LF,BP,GT,LF(c),Flame	1,300.00
7 WE,LF,BP,GT,LF(c),Flame	1,300.00
8 WE,LF,BP,GT,LF(c),Flame	1,400.00
9 WE,LF,BP,GT,LF(c),Flame	1,300.00
10 WE,LF,BP,LF(c),Flame	1,300.00
11 WE,LF,BP,LF(c),O:Flame	1,100.00
12 BP,LF(c),Bondage(c),Flame	900.00
13 E:Dr Fung,Flame	850.00
14 JoS,Bondage(c),Flame	900.00
15 JoS&LF(c),Flame	800.00
16 Flame(c)	650.00

17 Flame(c)	650.00
18 Flame(c)	650.00
19 Male Bondage(c),Flame	675.00
20 Flame(c)	650.00
21 O:Black Club &Lion,Flame	600.00
22 Flame(c)	550.00
23 Flame(c)	500.00
24 Flame(c)	500.00
25 A:Dr Fung,Flame	500.00
26 Flame(c)	500.00
27 Flame(c)	450.00
28 Bondage(c)I&O:US Jones, B:Lu-nar,Flame	650.00
29 Bondage(c),Flame	400.00
30 O:Flame(c),Flame	700.00
31 Bondage(c),Flame	400.00
32 Hitler(c),Flame	450.00
33 Male Bondage(c)	400.00

WORLD FAMOUS HEROES MAGAZINE
**Comic Corp. of America
(Centaur)
October, 1941**

1 BLb,Paul Revere	1,000.00
2 BLb,Andrew Jackson,V: Dickinson	450.00
3 BLb,Juarez-Mexican patriot	400.00
4 BLb,Canadian Mounties	400.00

WORLD'S GREATEST STORIES
**Jubilee Publications
January, 1949**

1 F:Alice in Wonderland	200.00
2 F:Pinocchio	175.00

World War III #2 © Ace Periodicals

WORLD WAR III
**Ace Periodicals
March–May, 1953**

1 Atomic Bomb cover	450.00
2 The War That Will Never Happen	400.00

WOTALIFE COMICS
(see PHANTOM LADY)

WOW COMICS
**David McKay/Henle Publ.
July, 1936**

1 WE,DBr(c),Fu Manchu, Buck Jones	2,000.00
2 WE,Little King	1,400.00
3 WE,WE(c)	1,400.00
4 WE,BKa,AR,DBr(c),Popeye, Flash Gordon,Nov.,1936	1,700.00

Wow Comics #37 © Fawcett Publ.

WOW COMICS
**Fawcett Publications
Winter, 1940**

N#(1)S&K,CCB(c),B&O:Mr Scarlett; B:Atom Blake,Jim Dolan,Rick O'Shay,Bondage(c)	14,000.00
2 B:Hunchback	1,800.00
3 V:Mummy Ray Gun	800.00
4 O:Pinky	900.00
5 F:Pinky the Whiz Kid	600.00
6 O:Phantom Eagle; B:Commando Yank	550.00
7 Spearhead of Invasion	500.00
8 All Three Heroes	500.00
9 A:Capt Marvel,Capt MarvelJr. Shazam,B:Mary Marvel	1,000.00
10 The Sinister Secret of Hotel Hideaway	450.00
11	350.00
12 Rocketing adventures	350.00
13 Thrill Show	350.00
14 V:Mr Night	350.00
15 The Shazam Girl of America	325.00
16 Ride to the Moon	325.00
17 V:Mary Batson,Alter Ego Goes Berserk	325.00
18 I:Uncle Marvel,Infinity(c) V is For Victory	325.00
19 A Whirlwind Fantasy	325.00
20 Mary Marvel's Magic Carpet	325.00
21 Word That Shook the World	200.00
22 Come on Boys- Everybody Sing	200.00
23 Trapped by the Terror of the Future	200.00
24 Mary Marvel	200.00
25 Mary Marvel Crushes Crime	200.00
26 Smashing Star-	

GOLDEN AGE

Studded Stories	175.00
27 War Stamp Plea(c)	175.00
28	175.00
29	175.00
30 In Mirror Land	175.00
31 Stars of Action	175.00
32 The Millinery Marauders	125.00
33 Mary Marvel(c)	125.00
34 A:Uncle Marvel	125.00
35 I:Freckles Marvel	125.00
36 Secret of the Buried City	125.00
37 7th War loan plea	125.00
38 Pictures That Came to Life	125.00
39 The Perilous Packages	125.00
40 The Quarrel of the Gnomes	125.00
41 Hazardous Adventures	100.00
42	100.00
43 Curtain Time	100.00
44 Volcanic Adventure	100.00
45	100.00
46	100.00
47	100.00
48	100.00
49	100.00
50 Mary Marvel/Commando Yank	100.00
51	75.00
52	75.00
53 Murder in the Tall Timbers	75.00
54 Flaming Adventure	75.00
55 Earthquake!	75.00
56 Sacred Pearls of Comatesh	75.00
57	75.00
58 E:Mary Marvel;The Curse of the Keys	75.00
59 B:Ozzie the Hilarious Teenager	75.00
60 thru 64	@75.00
65 A:Tom Mix	75.00
66 A:Tom Mix	75.00
67 A:Tom Mix	75.00
68 A:Tom Mix	75.00
69 A:Tom Mix,Baseball	75.00

Becomes:
REAL WESTERN HERO

70 It's Round-up Time	250.00
71 CCB,P(c),A Rip Roaring Rodeo	150.00
72 w/Gabby Hayes	150.00
73 thru 75	@150.00

Becomes:
WESTERN HERO

76 Partial Ph(c)&P(c)	200.00
77 Partial Ph(c)&P(c)	125.00
78 Partial Ph(c)&P(c)	125.00
79 Partial Ph(c)&P(c), Shadow of Death	100.00
80 Partial Ph(c)&P(c)	125.00
81 CCB,Partial Ph(c)&P(c), F:Tootsie	125.00
82 Partial Ph(c)&P(c), A:Hopalong Cassidy	125.00
83 Partial Ph(c)&P(c)	125.00
84 Ph(c)	100.00
85 Ph(c)	100.00
86 Ph(c),The Case of the Extra Buddy, giant	100.00
87 Ph(c),The Strange Lands	100.00
88 Ph(c),A:Senor Diablo	100.00
89 Ph(c),The Hypnotist	100.00
90 Ph(c),The Menace of the Cougar, giant	90.00
91 Ph(c),Song of Death	90.00
92 Ph(c),The Fatal Hide-out, giant	90.00

Western Hero #97 © Fawcett Publ.

93 Ph(c),Treachery at Triple T, giant	90.00
94 Ph(c),Bank Busters,giant	90.00
95 Ph(c),Rampaging River	80.00
96 Ph(c),Range Robbers,giant	90.00
97 Ph(c),Death on the Hook,giant	90.00
98 Ph(c),Web of Death,giant	90.00
99 Ph(c),The Hidden Evidence	80.00
100 Ph(c),A:Red Eagle,Giant	90.00
101 Ph(c)	90.00
102 thru 111 Ph(c)	@80.00
112 Ph(c),March, 1952	100.00

YANKEE COMICS
Chesler Publications
(Harry A. Chesler)
September, 1941

1 F:Yankee Doodle Jones	1,100.00
2 The Spirit of '41	600.00
3 Yankee Doodle Jones	450.00
4 JCo,Yankee Doodle Jones March, 1942	450.00

YELLOWJACKET COMICS
Levy Publ./Frank Comunale/ Charlton
September, 1944

1 O&B:Yellowjackets,B:Diana the Huntress	450.00
2 Rosita &The Filipino Kid	250.00
3	225.00
4 Fall of the House of Usher	250.00
5 King of Beasts	250.00
6	225.00
7 I:Diane Carter;The Lonely Guy	225.00
8 The Buzzing Bee Code	225.00
9	225.00
10 Capt Grim V:The Salvage Pirates	225.00

Becomes:
JACK IN THE BOX

11 Funny Animal,Yellow Jacket	55.00
12 Funny Animal	25.00
13 BW,Funny Animal	80.00

14 thru 16 Funny Animal	@30.00

Becomes:
COWBOY WESTERN COMICS

17 Annie Oakley,Jesse James	75.00
18 JO,JO(c)	50.00
19 JO,JO(c),Legends of Paul Bunyan	50.00
20 JO(c),Jesse James	35.00
21 Annie Oakley VisitsDryGulch	35.00
22 Story of the Texas Rangers	35.00
23	35.00
24 Ph(c),F:James Craig	35.00
25 Ph(c),F:Sunset Carson	35.00
26 Ph(c)	65.00
27 Ph(c),Sunset Carson movie	150.00
28 Ph(c),Sunset Carson movie	100.00
29 Ph(c),Sunset Carson movie	100.00
30 Ph(c),Sunset Carson movie	150.00
31 Ph(c)	30.00
32 thru 34 Ph(c)	@25.00
35 thru 37 Sunset Carson	@75.00
38 and 39	@25.00

Becomes:
SPACE WESTERN COMICS

40 Spurs Jackson,V:The Saucer Men	450.00
41 StC(c),Space Vigilantes	300.00
42 StC(c)	350.00
43 StC(c),Battle of Spacemans Gulch	300.00
44 StC(c),The Madman of Mars	300.00
45 StC(c),The Moon Bat	300.00

Becomes:
COWBOY WESTERN COMICS

46	70.00

Becomes:
COWBOY WESTERN HEROES

47	25.00
48	25.00

Becomes:
COWBOY WESTERN

49	25.00
50 F:Jesse James	20.00
51 thru 56	@20.00
58, giant	25.00
59 thru 66	@20.00
67 AW&AT	50.00

Becomes:
WILD BILL HICKOK AND JINGLES

68 AW	50.00
69 AW	35.00
70 AW	30.00
71 thru 73	@20.00
74 1960	20.00

YOGI BERRA
Fawcett
1957

1 Ph(c)	550.00

YOUNG BRIDES
Feature Publications
(Prize Comics) Sept.-Oct., 1952

1 S&K,Ph(c)	200.00
2 S&K,Ph(c)	100.00

3 S&K,Ph(c)	75.00
4 S&K	75.00
5 S&K	75.00
6 S&K	75.00
2-1 S&K	50.00
2-2 S&K	35.00
2-3 S&K	40.00
2-4 S&K	40.00
2-5 S&K	40.00
2-6 S&K	40.00
2-7 S&K	40.00
2-8 S&K	25.00
2-9 S&K	25.00
2-10 S&K	40.00
2-11 S&K	40.00
2-12 S&K	40.00
3-1	15.00
3-2	18.00
3-3	18.00
3-4	18.00
3-5	18.00
3-6	18.00
4-1	18.00
4-2 S&K	50.00
4-3	18.00
4-4 S&K	40.00
4-5	18.00

YOUNG EAGLE
Fawcett Publications/
Charlton Comics
December, 1950

1 Ph(c)	125.00
2 Ph(c),Mystery of Thunder Canyon	60.00
3 Ph(c),Death at Dawn	50.00
4 Ph(c)	50.00
5 Ph(c),The Golden Flood	50.00
6 Ph(c),The Nightmare Empire	50.00
7 Ph(c),Vigilante Veangeance	50.00
8 Ph(c),The Rogues Rodeo	50.00
9 Ph(c),The Great Railroad Swindle	50.00
10 June, 1952, Ph(c),Thunder Rides the Trail,O:Thunder	30.00

YOUNG KING COLE
Novelty Press/Premium
Svcs. Co.
Autumn, 1945

1-1 Detective Toni Gayle	200.00
1-2	100.00
1-3	75.00
1-4	50.00
2-1	50.00
2-2	50.00
2-3	50.00
2-4	50.00
2-5	50.00
2-6	50.00
2-7	45.00
3-1	45.00
3-2 LbC	45.00
3-3 The Killer With The Hat	40.00
3-4 The Fierce Tiger	40.00
3-5 AMc	40.00
3-6	50.00
3-7 LbC(c),Case of the Devil's Twin	75.00
3-8	60.00
3-9 The Crime Fighting King	60.00
3-10 LbC(c)	75.00
3-11 LbC(c)	75.00
3-12 July, 1948,AMc(c)	40.00

YOUNG LIFE
New Age Publications
Summer, 1945

1 Partial Ph(c),Louis Palma	75.00
2 Partial Ph(c),Frank Sinatra	80.00

Teen Life #4 © New Age Publications

Becomes:
TEEN LIFE

3 Partial Ph(c),Croon without Tricks,June Allyson(c)	50.00
4 Partial Ph(c),Atom Smasher Blueprints,Duke Ellington(c)	45.00
5 Partial Ph(c), Build Your Own Pocket Radio, Jackie Robinson(c)	60.00

YOUNG LOVE
Feature Publ.
(Prize Comics Group)
February-March, 1949

1 S&K,S&K(c)	300.00
2 S&K,Ph(c)	150.00
3 S&K,JSe,BE,Ph(c)	125.00
4 S&K,Ph(c)	75.00
5 S&K,Ph(c)	75.00
2-1 S&K,Ph(c)	125.00
2-2 Ph(c)	50.00
2-3 Ph(c)	50.00
2-4 Ph(c)	50.00
2-5 Ph(c)	50.00
2-6 S&K(c)	75.00
2-7 S&K(c),S&K	75.00
2-8 S&K	75.00
2-9 S&K(c),S&K	75.00
2-10 S&K(c),S&K	75.00
2-11 S&K(c),S&K	75.00
2-12 S&K(c),S&K	75.00
3-1 S&K(c),S&K	75.00
3-2 S&K(c),S&K	75.00
3-3 S&K(c),S&K	75.00
3-4 S&K(c),S&K	75.00
3-5 Ph(c)	50.00
3-6 BP,Ph(c)	50.00
3-7 Ph(c)	50.00
3-8 Ph(c)	50.00
3-9 MMe,Ph(c)	50.00
3-10 Ph(c)	50.00
3-11 Ph(c)	50.00

3-12 Ph(c)	50.00
4-1 S&K	50.00
4-2 Ph(c)	40.00
4-3 Ph(c)	40.00
4-4 Ph(c)	40.00
4-5 Ph(c)	40.00
4-6 S&K,Ph(c)	40.00
4-7 thru 4-12 Ph(c)	@35.00
5-1 thru 5-12 Ph(c)	@25.00
6-1 thru 6-9	@20.00
6-10 thru 6-12	@20.00
7-1 thru 7-7	@15.00
7-8 thru 7-11	@15.00
7-12 thru 8-5	@15.00
8-6 thru 8-12	@20.00

YOUNG ROMANCE
COMICS
Feature Publ./Headline/
Prize Publ.
September-October, 1947

1 S&K(c),S&K	300.00
2 S&K(c),S&K	200.00
3 S&K(c),S&K	175.00
4 S&K(c),S&K	175.00
5 S&K(c),S&K	175.00
6 S&K(c),S&K	150.00
2-1 S&K(c),S&K	150.00
2-2 S&K(c),S&K	150.00
2-3 S&K(c),S&K	150.00
2-4 S&K(c),S&K	150.00
2-5 S&K(c),S&K	150.00
2-6 S&K(c),S&K	100.00
3-1 thru 3-12 S&K(c),S&K	@100.00
4-1 thru 4-12 S&K	@100.00
5-1 ATh,S&K	100.00
2	100.00
3	100.00
5-4 thru 5-12 S&K	@100.00
6-1 thru 6-3	@35.00

YOUR UNITED STATES
Lloyd Jacquet Studios
1946

1N# Teeming nation of Nations	175.00

YOUTHFUL HEART
Youthful Magazines
May, 1952

1 Frankie Lane(c)	175.00
2 Vic Damone	125.00
3 Johnnie Ray	125.00

Becomes:
DARING CONFESSIONS

4 DW,Tony Curtis	50.00
5	35.00
6 DW	40.00
7	35.00
8 DW	40.00

YOUTHFUL ROMANCES
Pix Parade/Ribage/
Trojan
August-September, 1949

1	150.00
2	75.00
3 Tex Beneke	50.00
4	50.00
5	35.00
6	35.00
7 Tony Martin(c)	40.00
8 WW(c)	125.00

GOLDEN AGE

9 thru 14 . . . . @35.00
Becomes:

DARLING LOVE

15 WD 40.00
16 . . . . 30.00
17 DW,Ph(c) 30.00

ZAGO, JUNGLE PRINCE
Fox Features Syndicate
September, 1948

1 A:Blue Beetle 450.00
2 JKa 350.00
3 JKa 300.00
4 MB(c) 300.00
Becomes:

MY STORY

5 JKa,Too Young To Fall in Love 75.00
6 I Was A She-Wolf 35.00
7 I Lost My Reputation 35.00
8 My Words Condemned Me . . 35.00
9 WW,Wayward Bride 85.00
10 WW,March, 1950,Second
    Rate Girl 85.00
11 . . . . 35.00
12 . . . . 35.00

TEGRA, JUNGLE EMPRESS
Fox Features Syndicate
August, 1948

1 Blue Bettle,Rocket Kelly . . . 375.00
Becomes:

ZEGRA, JUNGLE EMPRESS

2 JKa 450.00
3 . . . . 325.00
4 . . . . 325.00
5 . . . . 325.00
Becomes:

MY LOVE LIFE

6 I Put A Price Tag On Love . . 65.00
7 An Old Man's Fancy 35.00
8 My Forbidden Affair 35.00
9 I Loved too Often 35.00
10 My Secret Torture 35.00
11 I Broke My Own Heart 35.00
12 I Was An Untamed Filly 35.00
13 I Can Never Marry You,
    August 1950 . . . . 30.00

ZIP COMICS
MLJ Magazines
February, 1940

1 MMe,O&B:Kalathar,The Scarlet
    Avenger,Steel Sterling,B:Mr
    Satan,Nevada Jones,War Eagle
    Captain Valor 3,500.00
2 MMe,CBi(c)B:Steel
    Sterling(c) 1,500.00
3 CBi,MMe,CBi(c) 1,100.00
4 CBi,MMe,CBi(c) 900.00
5 CBi,MMe,CBi(c) 900.00
6 CBi,MMe,CBi(c) 750.00
7 CBi,MMe,CBi(c) 750.00
8 CBi,MMe,CBi(c),Bondage(c) 750.00
9 CBi,MMe,CBi(c)E:Kalathar,
    Mr Satan;Bondage(c) . . . 750.00
10 CBi,MMe,CBi(c),B:Inferno . . 800.00
11 CBi,MMe,CBi(c) 625.00
12 CBi,MMe,CBi(c),Bondage(c) 625.00
13 CBi,MMe,CBi(c)E:Inferno,

Bondage(c),Woman in
    Electric Chair 650.00
14 CBi,MMe,CBi(c),Bondage(c) 625.00
15 CBi,MMe,CBi(c),Bondage(c) 625.00
16 CBi,MMe,CBi(c),Bondage(c) 625.00
17 CBi,CBi(c),E:Scarlet
    Avenger Bondage(c) 625.00
18 IN(c),B:Wilbur 650.00
19 IN(c),Steel Sterling(c) 625.00
20 IN(c),O&I:Black Jack
    Hitler(c) 1,000.00
21 IN(c),V:Nazis 600.00
22 IN(c) 550.00
23 IN(c),Flying Fortress 550.00
24 IN(c),China Town Exploit . . 550.00
25 IN(c),E:Nevada Jones 550.00
26 IN(c),B:Black Witch,
    E:Capt Valor 575.00
27 IN(c),I:Web,V:Japanese . . . 950.00
28 IN(C),O:Web,Bondage(c) . 1,000.00
29 Steel Sterling & Web 450.00
30 V:Nazis 450.00
31 IN(c) 350.00

Zip Comics #42
© MLJ Magazines/Archie Comics

32 . . . . 350.00
33 Bondage(c) 375.00
34 I:Applejack;Bondage(c) . . . 375.00
35 E:Zambini 350.00
36 I:Senor Banana 350.00
37 . . . . 350.00
38 E:Web 350.00
39 O&B:Red Rule 350.00
40 . . . . 250.00
41 . . . . 250.00
42 . . . . 250.00
43 . . . . 250.00
44 . . . . 250.00
45 E:Wilbur 250.00
46 . . . . 250.00
47 Crooks Can't Win,
    Summer, 1944 . . . . 250.00

ZIP-JET
St. John Publishing Co.
February, 1953

1 Rocketman 500.00
2 April,May, 1953, Assassin
    of the Airlanes 350.00

ZOOM COMICS
Carlton Publishing Co.
December, 1945

N# O:Captain Milksop 300.00

ZOOT COMICS
Fox Features Syndicate
Spring, 1946

N#(1)(fa) 100.00
2 A:Jaguar(fa) 85.00
3 (fa) 50.00
4 (fa) 50.00
5 (fa) 35.00

Zoot Comics #3
© Fox Features Syndicate

6 (fa) 35.00
7 B:Rulah 650.00
8 JKa(c),Fangs of Stone 450.00
9 JKa(c),Fangs of Black Fury . 450.00
10 JKa(c),Inferno Land 450.00
11 JKa,The Purple Plague,
    Bondage(c) 475.00
12 JKa(c),The Thirsty Stone,
    Bondage(c) 325.00
13 Bloody Moon 300.00
14 Pearls of Pathos,Woman
    Carried off by Bird 400.00
15 Death Dancers 300.00
16 . . . . 300.00
Becomes:

RULAH, JUNGLE GODDESS

17 JKa(c),Wolf Doctor 650.00
18 JKa(c),Vampire Garden . . . 500.00
19 JKa(c) 450.00
20 . . . . 450.00
21 JKa(c) 450.00
22 JKa(c) 450.00
23 . . . . 375.00
24 . . . . 350.00
25 . . . . 350.00
26 . . . . 350.00
27 . . . . 375.00
Becomes:

I LOVED

28 . . . . 35.00
29 thru 31 . . . . @25.00
32 My Poison Love, March, 1950 25.00

GOLDEN AGE

ACCLAIM

ACCLAIM ADVENTURE ZONE
Acclaim Young Readers 1997
Digest Size

Ninjak
Spec. "The Boss" 4.50

Turok
Spec. "Extinction" 4.50
Spec. "Dinosaur Rodeo" 4.50
Spec. "Scrounge Rules" 4.50

Archer & Armstrong #22 © Valiant

ARCHER & ARMSTRONG
Valiant 1992

0 JiS(s),BWS,BL,I&O:Archer,
   I:Armstrong,The Sec 3.00
0 Gold Ed. 5 .... 5.00
1 FM(c),B:JiS(s),BWS,BL,Unity #3,
   A:Eternal Warrior 2.50
2 WS(c),E:JiS(s),BWS,BL,Unity
   #11,2nd A:Turok,A:X-O 2.50
3 B:BWS(a&s), BWi, V:Sect in
   Rome 2.50
4 BWS,BWi,V:Sect in Rome 2.50
5 BWS,BWi,I:Andromeda 2.50
6 BWS,BWi, A:Andromeda,
   V:Medoc 2.50
7 BWS,ANi,BWi,V:Sect in England 2.50
8 BWS,as Eternal Warrior #8,
   Three Musketeers,I:Ivan 2.50
9 BCh,BWi,in Britain 2.25
10 BWS,A:Ivar 2.25
11 BWS,A:Solar,Ivar 2.25
12 BWS,V:The Avenger 2.25
13 B:MBn(s),RgM,In Los Angeles 2.25
14 In Los Angeles 2.25
15 E:MBn(s),In LasVegas, I:Duerst 2.25
16 V:Sect 2.25
17 B:MBn(s),In Florida 2.25
18 MV,in Heaven 2.25
19 MV,V:MircobotieCult,D:Duerst . 2.25
20 MV,Chrismas Issue 2.25
21 MV,A:Shadowman,Master

Darque 2.25
22 MV,A:Shadowman,Master
   Darque,w/Valiant Era card ... 2.25
23 MV, ... 2.25
24 MV, ... 2.25
25 MV,A:Eternal Warrior 2.25
26 Chaos Effect-Gamma #4, A:Ivar,
   Et. Warrior 2.25

ARMED & DANGEROUS
Valiant (B&W) 1995

1 thru 4 .... @2.95
Spec.#1 .... 2.95

ARMED & DANGEROUS
Acclaim (B&W) 1996

1 BH,"Hell's Slaughterhouse" Pt.1 2.95
2 BH,"Hell's Slaughterhouse" Pt.2 2.95
3 BH,"Hell's Slaughterhouse" Pt.3 2.95
4 BH,"Hell's Slaughterhouse" Pt.4 2.95

ARMED & DANGEROUS No. 2
Acclaim (B&W) Dec. 1996

1 BH,"When Irish Eyes are Dying,"
   pt.1 .... 2.95
2 BH,"When Irish Eyes are Dying,"
   pt.2 .... 2.95
3 BH,"When Irish Eyes are Dying,"
   pt.3 .... 2.95
4 BH,"When Irish Eyes are Dying,"
   pt.4 concl. 2.95

ARMORINES
Valiant 1994

0 (from X-O #25),Card Stock (c),
   Diamond Distributors "Fall Fling"
   Retailer Meeting 2.50
0a Gold Ed. 3.00
1 JGz(s),JCf,B:White Death 2.50
2 JGz(s),JCf,E:White Death 2.50
3 JGz(s),JCf,V:Spider Aliens ... 2.50
4 JCf, V: Spider Aliens 2.25
5 JCf, Chaos Effect-Delta #2,
   A:H.A.R.D. Corp 2.25
6 Spider Alien Mothership 2.25
7 Rescue 2.25
8 Rescue in Iraq 2.25
9 .... 2.25
10 Protect Fidel Castro 2.25
11 V: Spider Super Suit 2.25
12 F: Sirot 2.25
Yearbook I:Linoff 2.95

BAD EGGS
Acclaim 1996

1 thru 4 BL,DP,"That Dirty Yellow
   Mustard" .... @2.95

BAR SINISTER
Windjammer 1995

1 From Shaman's Tears 2.50
2 V:SWAT Team 2.50
3 F: Animus Prime 2.50
4 MGe,RHo,V:Jabbersnatch 2.50

BART SEARS' X-O MANOWAR
Valiant 1995
HC Bart Sears' Artwork 17.95

BLOODSHOT
Valiant 1992

0 KVH(a&s),DG(i),Chromium (c),
   O:Bloodshot,A:Eternal Warrior . 3.00
0a Gold Ed.,w/Diamond "Fall Fling"
   logo 5.00
1 BWS(c),B:KVH(s),DP,BWi,I:Carbo
   ni, V:Mafia,1st Chromium(c) .. 3.00
2 DP,I:Durkins,V:Ax 3.00
3 DP,V:The Mob 3.00
4 DP,A:Eternal Warrior 2.50
5 DP,A:Eternal Warrior,Rai 2.50
6 DP,I:Ninjak (Not in Costume) .. 2.50
7 DP,JDx,A:Ninjak (1st appearance
   in costume) 2.50
8 DP,JDx,A:Geoff 2.50
9 DP,JDx,V:Slavery Ring 2.50
10 DP,JDx,V:Tunnel Rat 2.50
11 DP,JDx,V:Iwatsu 2.50
12 DP,JDx,Day Off 2.50
13 DP,JDx,V:Webnet 2.50
14 DP,JDx,V:Carboni 2.50
15 DP,JDx,V:Cinder 2.50
16 DP,JDx,w/Valiant Era Card .. 2.50
17 DP,JDx,A:H.A.R.D.Corps ... 2.50
18 DP,KVH,After the Missile 2.50
19 DP,I:Uzzi the Clown 2.25
20 DP,KVH, Chaos Effect-Gamma
   #1, V:Immortal Enemy 2.25
21 DP,V: Immortal Enemy, Ax .. 2.25
22 Immortal Enemy 2.25
23 Cinder 2.25
24 Geomancer, Immortal Enemy . 2.25
25 V:Uzzi the Clown 2.25
26 V:Uzzi the Clown 2.25
27 Rampage Pt. 1 .... 2.25
28 Rampage Pt. 3 .... 2.25
29 Rampage Conc. A:Ninjak 2.25
30 V:Shape Shifter 2.25
31 Nanite Killer 2.25
32 KVH,SCh,V: Vampires 2.25
33 KVH,SCh,V: Vampires 2.25
34 NBy,KVH,new villains spawned 2.50
35 NBY,KVH,attempts to control . 2.50
36 V:Voodoo Drug Dealer 2.50
37 V:Voodoo Drug Dealer 2.50
38 V:Rampage 2.50
39 V:Rampage 2.50
40 USA wants Bloodshot 2.50
41 F:Jillian Alcott 2.50
42 Virtual Nightmare 2.50
43 V:U.S. Troops 2.50
44 I:Deathangel, V:Speedshots . 2.50
45 thru 51 .... @2.50
Yearbook #1 KVH,briefcase bomb 4.25
Yearbook 1995 Villagers 2.95
Spec.GN Last Stand 5.95

BLOODSHOT Series Two
Acclaim March 1997

1 LKa(s),SaV "Behold, a Pale
   Horseman" 2.50
1a variant cover 3.00

All comics prices listed are for *Near Mint* condition.

Bloodshot #17 © Valiant

2 LKa(s),SaV "Dead Man Walking" 2.50
3 LKa(s),SaV "ChainsawMassacre" 2.50
4 LKa(s),SaV Search for Identity . 2.50
5 LKa(s),SaV V:Simon Oreck . . . 2.50
6 LKa(s),SaV "Bloodwhispers" . . 2.50
7 LKa(s),SaV "To the Bitter End..",
pt.1 . . . . 2.50
8 LKa(s),SaV "To the Bitter End..",
pt.2 . . . . 2.50
9 LKa(s),SaV "Suicide" 2.50
10 LKa(s),SaV "Dreamland" 2.50
11 LKa(s),SaV 2.50
12 LKa(s),SaV "Cat Scratch Fever" 2.50
13 LKa(s),SaV in Russia 2.50
14 LKa(s),SaV to the Vatican 2.50
15 LKa(s),SaV DOA Headquarters 2.50
16 LKa(s),SaV final issue 2.50

CAPTAIN JOHNER
& THE ALIENS
Valiant May 1995
1 Rep. Magnus Robot Fighter #1–7
(Gold Key 1963–64) 2.95

CHAOS EFFECT
Valiant 1994
Alpha DJ(c), BCh, JOy, A:All Valiant
Characters 2.25
Alpha Red (c) 4.00
Omega DJ(c), BCh, JOy, A:All
Valiant Characters 2.25
Omega Gold(c) 4.00
Epilogue pt.1 . . . . 2.95
Epilogue pt.2 . . . . 2.95

CITY KNIGHTS, THE
Windjammer 1995
1 I:Michael Walker 2.50
2 I:Herald 2.50
3 & 4 V:Herald . . . . @2.50

CONCRETE JUNGLE:
THE LEGEND OF
THE BLACK LION
Acclaim 1998
1 (of 6) CPr,JFy,F:Terry Smalls . 2.50

2 CPr,JFy,Black Lion Order 2.50
3 CPr,JFy,The Man 2.50
4 CPr,JFy 2.50
5 CPr,JFy 2.50

DARQUE PASSAGES
Acclaim 1997
1 (of 4) sequal to Master Darque 2.50
1 signed edition 6.00
2 . . . . 2.50
3 A:Pere Jean, Voodoo King . . . 2.50
4 conclusion 2.50

DEATHMATE
Valiant/Image 1993
Preview (Advanced Comics) . . . 2.00
Preview (Previews) 2.00
Preview (Comic Defense Fund) . 5.00
Prologue BL,JLe,RLd,Solar meets
Void 3.25
Prologue Gold 5.00
Blue SCh, HSn, F:Solar, Magnus,
Battlestone, Livewire, Stronghold,
Impact, Striker, Harbinger,
Brigade, Supreme 4.00
Blue Gold Ed. 5.00
Yellow BCh,MLe,DP,F:Armstrong,
H.A.R.D.C.A.T.S.,Ninjak,Zealot,
Shadowman,Grifter,Ivar 4.00
Yellow Gold Ed. 5.00
Black JLe,MS,F:Warblade,Ripclaw,
Turok,X-O Manowar 5.25
Black Gold Ed. 8.00
Red RLd,JMs, ... 5.25
Red Gold Ed. 5.00
Epilogue 3.25
Epilogue Gold 5.00

DESTROYER
Valiant 1994
0 MM 41st Century 2.95

DR. TOMORROW
Acclaim May 1997
1 (of 12) BL,Bart Simms finds
Angel Computer 2.50
2 BL,V:Teutonic Knight 2.50
3 BL,V:Teutonic Knight concl. . . . 2.50
4 BL,V:Joe McCarthy 2.50
5 BL,V:J. Edgar Hoover 2.50
6 BL,DG,V:Mushroom Cloud . . . 2.50
7 BL,DG,A:Mushroom Cloud 2.50
8 BL,GK,Vietnam 2.50
9 BL, ... 2.50
10 BL,SMc,on *Oprah* 2.50
11 BL,the time capsule 2.50
12 BL,MBu(c),final issue 2.50

DISNEY'S ACTION CLUB
Acclaim Young Readers 1997
Digest Size
Aladdin
Spec."An Imp-Perfect Day" . . . 4.50
Spec."Monkey Business" 4.50
Buzz Lightyear
Spec."Antique Attack" 4.50
Hercules
Spec."My Fill of Phil" 4.50
The Lion King
Spec."Lurkers in the Water" . . . 4.50
Mighty Ducks
Spec."Puck Power" 4.50
Spec."Rough Stuff" 4.50

DISNEY'S
BEAUTY AND THE BEAST
Acclaim Young Readers 1997
Spec. Holiday Special, digest size 4.50

DISNEY'S
ENCHANTING STORIES
Acclaim Young Readers 1997
Digest Size
Beauty and the Beast
Spec."The Book Crook" 4.50
Hercules
Spec."A Torch for Meg" 4.50
Hunchback of Notre Dame
Spec."Veiled Beauty" 4.50
The Little Mermaid
Spec."Seal of Approval" 4.50
101 Dalmatians
Spec."Star Search" 4.50
Pocahontas
Spec."River of Youth" 4.50
Snow White and the Seven Dwarfs
Spec."Mirror,Mirror,on the Floor" . 4.50
Spec."Dopey the Genius" 4.50

DISNEY'S HERCULES
Acclaim Young Readers 1997
1-shot Movie adaptation, 64pg . . 4.50
Spec. Making of a Hero 6.00

DISNEY'S HERCULES:
THE GREATEST BATTLES
Acclaim Young Readers 1997
HC 96pg 24.00
TPB 13.00

DISNEY'S
THE LITTLE MERMAID
Acclaim 1997
Spec. Underwater Engagements flip
book, digest size 4.50

DISNEY'S
101 DALMATIANS
Acclaim 1997
HC Bad to the Bone 24.00
TPB Bad to the Bone 13.00

ETERNAL WARRIOR
Valiant 1992
1 FM(c),JDx,Unity #2,O:Eternal
Warrior,Armstrong 4.00
1a Gold Ed. 6.00
1b Gold Foil Logo 8.00
2 WS(c),JDx,Unity #10,A:Solar,
Harbinger,Eternal Warrior of
4001 . . . . 3.00
3 JDx,V:Armstrong,I:Astrea 2.50
4 JDx(i),I:Caldone, C:Bloodshot . 4.00
5 JDx,I:Bloodshot,V:Iwatsu's Men 3.00
6 BWS,JDx,V:Master Darque . . . 3.00
7 BWS,V:Master Darque, D:Uncle
Buck 3.00
8 BWS,as Archer & Armstrong #8
Three Musketeers,I:Ivar 3.00
9 MMo,JDx,B:Book of the
Geomancer 3.00
10 JDx,E:Bk. o/t Geomancer . . . 3.00
11 B:KVH(s),JDx(i), V:Neo-Nazis . 3.00
12 JDx(i),V:Caldone 3.00

ACCLAIM

13 MMo,JDx(i),V:Caldone,
  A:Bloodshot 2.75
14 E:KVH(s),MMo,V:Caldone,
  A:Geoff 2.50
15 YG,A:Bloodshot,V:Tanaka 2.50
16 YG,A:Bloodshot 2.50
17 A:Master Darque 2.50
18 C:Doctor Mirage 2.50
19 KVH(s),TeH,A:Doctor Mirage . 2.50
20 KVH(s),Access Denied 2.50
21 KVH(s),TeH,V:Dr. Steiner 2.50
22 V:Master Darque,w/Valiant Era
  Card 2.50
23 KVH(s),TeH,Blind Fate 2.50
24 KVH(s),TeH,V:Immortal Enemy 2.50
25 MBn(s),A:Archer,Armstrong . . 2.50
26 Double(c), Chaos Effect-Gamma
  #4, A:Archer, Armstrong, Ivar . 3.00
27 JOs(s) 2.25
28 War on Drugs 2.25
29 Immortal Enemy 2.25
30 Lt. Morgan 2.25
31 JD,JOs 2.25
32 . . . . 2.25
33 Mortal Kin Pt.1 . . . . 2.25
34 Mortal Kin Pt.2 . . . . 2.25
35 Mortal Kin Finale 2.50
36 Fenris League 2.50
37 Youthful Tale 2.50
38 V:Niala, The Dead Queen 2.50
39 JOs,JG,PG(c),V:body thieves . 2.50
40 JOs,JG,PG(c),finds organ farm 2.50
41 War in Herznia 2.50
42 I: Brisbane 2.50
43 V:Neo Nazi 2.50
44 V:Neo Nazi 2.50
45 R:Fenris Society 2.50
46 V:Fenris Society 2.50
47 Jihad 2.50
48 Immortal Life in Danger 2.50
49 JOs,JG,Hallucinations 2.50
50 . . . . 2.50
Yearbook #1 . . . . 4.25
Yearbook #2 . . . . 4.00
Wings of Justice WWI 2.50
Quarterly
Time and Treachery 3.95
Digital Alchemy 3.95
Spec. Blackworks AHo, ... 4.00

ETERNAL WARRIORS
Acclaim 1997
Quarterly
Archer & Armstrong AHo 3.95
Mog AHo 3.95
The Immortal Enemy AHo 3.95

FOX FUNHOUSE
Acclaim Young Readers 1997
Digest Size, Featuring The Tick
Spec. "Spoo-o-o-o-nn" 4.50
Spec. "A World of Pain(t)" 4.50
Spec. "Raw, Uncooked Justice" . 4.50
Spec. "Way Out of Tuna" 4.50
Spec. "Tick vs. the Entire Ocean . 4.50
Spec. Neato-Keen Holiday Special 4.50

FOX PRESENTS
Acclaim Young Readers 1997
The Tick "No Time For Sanity" . . 10.00

GEOMANCER
Valiant 1994
1 RgM, I:Geomancer 3.50
2 RgM, Eternal Warrior 2.25
3 RgM, Darque Elementals 2.25
4 RgM 2.25
5 Riot Gear pt. 1 . . . . 2.25
6 Riot Gear pt. 2 . . . . 2.25
7 F:Zorn 2.25
8 v:Zorn 2.25

GOAT, THE: H.A.E.D.U.S.
Acclaim 1998
Spec. CPr,KG,F:Vincent Van Goat 3.95

GRACKLE, THE
Acclaim (B&W) Sept. 1996
1 MBn,PG,"Double Cross" Pt.1 . 2.95
2 MBn,PG,"Double Cross" Pt.2 . 2.95
3 MBn,PG,"Double Cross" Pt.3 . 2.95
4 MBn,PG,"Double Cross" Pt.4 . 2.95

GRAVEDIGGERS
Acclaim (B&W) 1996
1 (of 4) 2.95
2 thru 4 . . . . @2.95

HARBINGER
Valiant 1992
0 DL,O:Sting,V:Harada, from TPB
  (Blue Bird Ed.) 2.00
0 from coupons 5.00
1 DL,JDx,I:Sting,Torque,
  Zeppelin,Flamingo,Kris 4.00
1a w/o coupon 1.00
2 DL,JDx,V:Harbinger Foundation,
  I:Dr.Heyward 2.00
2a w/o coupon 1.00
3 DL,JDx,I:Ax,Rexo, V:Spider
  Aliens 2.00
3a w/o coupon 1.00
4 DL,JDx,V:Ax,I:Fort,
  Spikeman,Dog,Bazooka 2.00
4a w/o coupon 1.00
5 DL,JDx,I:Puff,Thumper,
  A:Solar,V:Harada 2.00
5a w/o coupon 1.00
6 DL,D:Torque,A:Solar,
  V:Harada,Eggbreakers 2.00
6a w/o coupon 1.00
7 DL,Torque's Funeral 2.00
8 FM(c),DL,JDx,Unity#8,
  A:Magnus,Eternal Warrior 2.00
9 WS(c),DL,Unity #16,
  A:Magnus,Armstrong,Rai,
  Archer,Eternal Warrior 2.00
10 DL,I:H.A.R.D.Corps, Daryl,
  Shetiqua 2.00
11 DL,V:H.A.R.D.Corps 2.00
12 DL,F:Zeppelin,A:Elfquest . . . 2.00
13 Flamingo Vs. Rock 2.00
14 A:Magnus(Dream Sequence),
  C:Stronghold 2.00
15 I:Livewire,Stronghold 2.00
16 A:Livewire,Stronghold 2.00
17 HSn,I:Simon 2.00
18 HSn,I:Screen 2.00
19 HSn,I:Caliph 2.00
20 HSn,V:Caliph 2.00
21 I:Pete's Father 2.00
22 HSn,A:Archer & Armstrong . . . 2.00
23 HSn,B:Twilight of the
  Eighth Day 2.00

Harbinger #30 © Valiant

24 HSn,V:Eggbreakers 2.00
25 HSn,V:Harada,E:Twilight of the
  Eighth Day 2.50
26 SCh,AdW,I:Jolt,Amazon,
  Mircowave,Anvil,Sonix 2.00
27 SCh,AdW,Chrismas issue 2.00
28 SCh,AdW,O:Sonix,J:Tyger . . . 2.00
29 SCh,AdW,A:Livewire,Stronghold,
  w/Valiant Era card 2.00
30 SCh,AdW,A:Livewire,Stronghold 2.00
31 SCh,AdW,V:H.A.R.D.Corps . . . 2.00
32 SCh,AdW,A:Eternal Warrior . . 2.00
33 SCh, V:Dr. Eclipse 2.00
34 SCh,Chaos Effect-Delta#1, A:X-
  O, Dr. Eclipse 2.00
35 Zephyr 2.00
36 Zephyr, Magnus 2.00
37 Magnus, Harada 2.00
38 A:Spikeman 2.00
39 Zepplin vs. Harada 2.00
40 V:Harbinger 2.00
41 V:Harbinger 2.00
TPB w/#0,rep#1-4 . . . . 25.00
TPB 2nd Printing w/o #0 . . . . . . 9.95
TPB #2, Rep. 6-7,10-11 . . . . 9.95

HARBINGER FILES: HARADA
Valiant 1994
1 BL,DC,O:Harada 2.75
2 Harada's ultimate weapon 2.50

H.A.R.D. CORPS
Valiant 1992
1 JLe(c),DL,BL,V:Harbinger
  Foundation,I:Flatline,D:Maniac . 2.50
1a Gold Ed. 3.00
2 DL,BL,V:Harb.Foundation 2.50
3 DL,BL,J:Flatline 2.50
4 BL 2.50
5 BCh,BL(i),A:Bloodshot 2.50
5a Comic Defense System Ed. . . 2.50
6 MLe,A:Spider Aliens 2.50
7 MLe,V:Spider Aliens, I:Hotshot . 2.50
8 MLe,V:Harada,J:Hotshot 2.50
9 MLe,V:Harada,A:Turok 2.00
10 MLe,A:Turok,V:Dinosaurs 2.00

ACCLAIM

ACCLAIM

H.A.R.D. Corps #18 © Valiant

11 YG,I:Otherman 2.00
12 MLe,V:Otherman 2.00
13 YG,D:Superstar 2.50
14 DvM(s),YG,V:Edie Simkus . . . 2.00
15 DvM(s),YG,V:Edie Simkus . . . 2.00
16 DvM(s),YG, ... 2.00
17 DvM(s),RLe,V:Armorines 2.00
18 DvM(s),RLe,V:Armorines,
    w/Valiant Era card 2.00
19 RLe,A:Harada 2.00
20 RLe,V:Harbingers 2.00
21 RLe,New Direction 2.00
22 RLe,V:Midnight Earl 2.00
23 RLe,Chaos Effect-Delta #4,
    A:Armorines, X-O 2.00
24 Ironhead 2.00
25 Midnight Earl 2.00
26 Heydrich, Omen 2.00
27 Heydrich shows evil 2.00
28 New Hardcorps 2.00
29 V:New Guard 2.00
30 Final Issue 2.00

KILLER INSTINCT
1 thru 3 . . . . @2.50
Spec. Brothers by Art Holcomb . . 2.50

KNIGHTHAWK
Windjammer 1995
1 NA(c&a),I:Knighthawk the
    Protector,V:Nemo 2.75
2 NA(c&a),Birth of Nemo 2.50
3 NA,V:Nemo 2.50
4 NA,V:Nemo 2.50
5 I:Cannon, Brick 2.50
6 V:Cannon, Brick 2.50

MAGIC THE GATHERING: ANTIQUITIES WAR
Armada 1995
1 Based on the Antiquities Set . 2.75
2 F:Urza, Mishra 2.50
3 I:Tawnos, Ashod 2.50
4 The War Begins 2.50

MAGIC THE GATHERING: ARABIAN KNIGHTS
Armada 1995
1 Based on Rare Card set 2.75
2 V:Queen Nailah 2.50

MAGIC THE GATHERING: CONVOCATIONS
Armada 1995
1 Gallery of Art from Game 2.50

MAGIC THE GATHERING: FALLEN EMPIRES
[Mini-series]
Armada
1 with pack of cards 2.75
2 F:Tymolin 2.50
TPB Rep. #1-#2 . . . . 4.95

MAGIC THE GATHERING: HOMELANDS
Armada 1995
1 I:Feroz, Serra 5.95

MAGIC THE GATHERING: ICE AGE
Armada 1995
1 Dominaia, from card game . . . 3.00
2 Ice Age Adventures 2.50
3 CV(c) Planeswalker battles . . 2.50
4 final issue 2.50
TPB Rep. #1-#2 . . . . 4.95
TPB Rep. #3-#4 . . . . 4.95

MAGIC THE GATHERING: SHADOW MAGE
Armada 1995
1 I:Jared 3.00
2 F:Hurloon the Minotaur 2.75
3 VMk(c&a),V:Juggernaut 2.50
4 Final issue 2.50
TPB Rep. #1-#2 . . . . 4.95
TPB Rep. #3-#4 . . . . 4.95

MAGIC THE GATHERING: THE URZA-MISHRA WAR
Armada
1 & 2 with Ice Age II card 5.95

MAGIC THE GATHERING: WAYFARER
Armada 1995
1 R:Jared 2.75
2 I:New Land 2.50
3 R:Liana, Ravidel 2.50
4 I:Golthonor 2.50
5 . . . . 2.50

MAGIC THE GATHERING: THE LEGENDS OF:
THE ELDER DRAGONS
1 & 2 . . . . @2.50
JEDIT OJANEN
1 & 2 . . . . @2.50
SHANDALAR
1 & 2 . . . . @2.50

[ON THE WORLD OF] MAGIC THE GATHERING
GN Serra Angel + card 5.95
GN Legend of the Fallen Angel +
    card 5.95
GN Dakkon Blackblade + card . . . 5.95

MAGNUS: ROBOT FIGHTER
Valiant 1991
0 PCu,BL,"Emancipator",w/ BWS
    card 7.00
0a PCu,BL,w/o card 3.00
1 ANi,BL,B:Steel Nation 4.00
1a w/o coupon 1.00
2 ANi,BL,Steel Nation #2 . . . . . 3.00
2a w/o coupon 1.00
3 ANi,BL,Steel Nation #3 . . . . . 3.00
3a w/o coupon 1.00
4 ANi,BL,E:Steel Nation 3.00
4a w/o coupon 1.00
5 DL,BL(i),I:Rai(#1),V:Slagger
    Flipbook format 3.00
5a w/o coupon 1.00
6 DL,A:Solar,V:Grandmother
    A:Rai(#2) 2.50
6a w/o coupon 1.00
7 DL,EC,V:Rai(#3) 2.50
7a w/o coupon 1.00
8 DL,A:Rai(#4),Solar,X-O
    Armor.E:Flipbooks 2.50
8a w/o coupon 1.00
9 EC,V:Xyrkol,E-7 . . . . 2.50
10 V:Xyrkol 2.50
11 V:Xyrkol. 2.50
12 I:Turok,V:Dr. Noel,
    I:Asylum,40pgs 7.00
13 EC,Asylum Pt 1 . . . . 2.50
14 EC,Asylum Pt2 . . . . 2.50
15 FM(c),EC,Unity#4,I:Eternal
    Warrior of 4001, O:Unity 2.50
16 WS(c),EC,Unity#12,A:Solar,
    Archer,Armstrong,Harbinger, X-
    O,Rai,Eternal Warrior 2.50
17 JaB,V:Talpa 2.50
18 SD,R:Mekman,V:E-7 . . . . . . 2.50
19 SD,V:Mekmen 2.50
20 EC,Tale of Magnus' past 2.50
21 JaB,R:Malevalents, Grand-
    mother 3.00
21a Gold Ed. 4.00
22 JaB,D:Felina,V:Malevalents,
    Grandmother 2.50
23 V:Malevolents 2.50
24 V:Malevolents 2.50
25 N:Magnus,R:1-A,silver-foil(c) . 3.00
26 I:Young Wolves 2.50
27 V:Dr.Lazlo Noel 2.50
28 V:The Malevs 2.25
29 JCf,A:Eternal Warrior 2.25
30 JCf,V:The Malevs 2.25
31 JCf,V:The Malevs 2.25
32 JCf,Battle for South Am 2.25
33 B:JOs(s),JCf,A:Ivar 2.25
34 JCf,Captured 2.25
35 JCf,V:Mekman 2.25
36 JCf,w/Valiant Era Card 2.25
37 JCf,A:Starwatchers 2.25
38 JCf, ... 2.25
39 JCf,F:Torque 2.25
40 JCf,F:Torque, A:Rai 2.25
41 JCf,Chaos Effect-Epsilon#4
    A:Solar, Psi-Lords,Rai 2.50
42 JCf, F:Torque,A:Takashi 2.25

Magnus: Robot Fighter #34
© Voyager Communications, Inc.

43 JCf,F:Torque,Immortal E	2.25
44 JCf,F:Torque,Stagger	2.25
45 V:Immortal Enemy	2.25
46 V:Immortal Enemy	2.25
47 Cold Blooded,pt.1	2.25
48 Cold Blooded,pt.2	2.25
49 F:Slagger	2.25
50 V:Invisible Legion	2.25
51 KoK,RyR,Return of the Robots,pt.1	2.25
52 KoK,RyR,Return of the Robots,pt.2	2.25
53 KoK,RyR,Return of the Robots,pt.3	2.25
54 KoK,RyR,Return of the Robots,pt.4	2.25
55 KG,A:Rai	2.50
56 Magnus in Japan	2.50
57	2.50
58	2.50
59 V:Rai	2.50
60 R:The Malevs	2.50
61 Secrets of the Malevs	2.50
62 V:Leeja	2.50
63 R:Destroyer	2.50
64 Ultimatum, F:Destroyer	2.50
Yearbook #1	3.95
TPB 1-4	9.95

MAGNUS
(ROBOT FIGHTER)
Acclaim Jan. 1997

1 Magnus back from the future	2.50
2 "Tomorrow Never Knows"	2.50
3 "Tomorrow Never Knows"	2.50
4 "Tomorrow Never Knows"	2.50
5 "Tomorrow Never Knows"	2.50
6 A:Janice Whitcraft	2.50
7 "When Titans Clash"	2.50
8 TPe,DdB,"When Titans Clash"	2.50
9 TPe,"See Tirana and Die"	2.50
10 TPe,"The Memory"	2.50
11 TPe,"Where Angels Fear"	2.50
12 TPe,"Showdown"	2.50
13 TPe,	2.50
14 TPe,"Wild in the Streets"	2.50

15 TPe,Magnus stands alone	2.50
16 TPe,"Hart's Home"	2.50
17 TPe,"Invasive Procedures"	2.50
18 TPe,"Welcome to Salvation"	2.50

MAN OF THE ATOM
Valiant Heroes Special Project
Acclaim Jan 1997

Spec.	3.95
TPB The Rebirth of Solar	8.00

MASTER DARQUE
Acclaim 1997

Spec. F:Brixton Sound, 48pg	4.00

MUTANT CHRONICLES— GOLGOTHA
Valiant

1 thru 4 + game trading card	@2.95
TPB, Vol. 1 rep. Pt.#1–#4	10.95

NINJAK
Valiant 1994

0: O:Ninjak, Pt. 1	2.50
00: O:Ninjak, Pt.2	2.50
1 B:MMo(s),JQ,JP,Chromium(c), I:Dr.Silk,Webnet	3.00
1a Gold Ed	4.00
2 JQ,JP,V:Dr.Silk,Webnet	2.50
3 JQ,JP,I:Seventh Dragon	2.25
4 MMo(a&s),V:Seventh Dragon, w/Valiant Era card	2.25
5 MMo(a&s),A:X-O Manowar	2.25
6 MMo(a&s),A:X-O Manowar, V:Dr.Silk,Webnet	2.25
7 MMo(a&s),I:Rhaman	2.25
8 MMo(a&s),Chaos Effect-Gamma #3, A:Madame Noir	2.25
9 Dogs of War	2.00
10 Cantebury Tale #1	2.00
11 Cantebury Tale #2	2.00
12	2.00
13 Mad Dogs and English	2.00
14 Cry Wolf pt. 1	2.00
15 Cry Wolf pt. 2	2.25
16 Plague Pt. 1	2.25
17 Plague Pt. 2	2.25
18 Computer Virus	2.25
19 DAn,ALa,MM,Breaking the Web,pt.1	2.25
20 DAn,ALa,MM,Breaking the Web,pt.2	2.25
21 DAn,ALa,MM,Breaking the Web,pt.3	2.25
22 Bitter Wind	2.25
23 w/o arsenal	2.25
24 Unusual sidekick	2.25
25	2.25
26	2.25
27 Diamond Smugglers	2.25
28 F:Sister Gabriela	2.25
Yearbook #1, Dr. Silk	3.95

NINJAK
Acclaim 1996

1 KBk(s), Denny Meechum becomes Ninjak	2.50
2 KBk(s) video game spin-off	2.50
3 KBk(s) video game spin-off	2.50
4 KBk(s) video game spin-off	2.50
5 KBk(s) video game spin-off	2.50
6 KBk(s) "The World's Finest"	2.50
7 KBk(s) video game spin-off	2.50

Ninjak #2 © Valiant

8 KBk(s) video game spin-off	2.50
9 KBk(s) video game spin-off	2.50
10 KBk(s) F:Maria Barbella	2.50
11 KBk(s) Trial Continues	2.50
12 KBk(s) final issue	2.50

OPERATION: STORMBRINGER
Acclaim Special Event, April 1997

Spec. F:Teutonic Knight	3.95

ORIGINAL CAPTAIN JOHNAR AND THE ALIENS
Valiant 1995

1 Reprint from Magnus	2.95
2 Russ Manning rep.	2.95

ORIGINAL DR. SOLAR MAN OF THE ATOM
Valiant 1995

1 Reprint	2.95
2 Reprints	2.95
3 Reprints	2.95

ORIGINAL MAGNUS ROBOT FIGHTER
Valiant 1995

1 Reprint	2.95
2 Russ Manning Art	2.95
3 Russ Manning	2.95

ORIGINAL TUROK, SON OF STONE
Valiant 1995

1 Reprint	2.95
2 Alberto Gioletti art	2.95
3 Alberto Gioletti	2.95
4 Reprints	2.95

OUTCAST SPECIAL
Valiant 1995

1 R:The Outcast	2.50

ACCLAIM

All comics prices listed are for _Near Mint_ condition.

PLANESWALKER WAR
Acclaim Aug. 1996
GN #1 Magic: The Gathering tie-in 5.95

PSI-LORDS: REIGN OF THE STARWATCHERS
Valiant 1994
1 MLe,DG,Chromium(c),Valiant
　Vision,V:Spider Aliens 3.00
2 MLe,DG,V:Spider Aliens 2.25
3 MLe,DG,Chaos Effect-Epsilon#2,
　A:Solar 2.25
becomes:

PSI-LORDS
4 V:Ravenrok 2.25
5 V:Ravenrok 2.25
6 .... 2.25
7 Micro-Invasion 2.25
8 A:Solar the Destroyer 2.25
9 Frozen Harbingers 2.25
10 F:Ravenrok 2.25

PUNX
Windjammer 1995
1 KG,I:Punx 2.50
2 KG,A:Harbinger 2.50
3 KG,F:P.M.S 2.50
4 KG,final issue 2.50
Spec.#1 .... 2.50

PUNX REDUX
1 thru 4 .... @2.50

PUNX
Acclaim Jan. 1997
One Shot Spec. F:Big Max 2.50

QUANTUM LEAP
Acclaim Jan. 1997
1 BML(s),"Into the Void," pt.1 . 2.50
2 BML(s),"Into the Void," pt.2 . 2.50
3 BML(s),"Into the Void," pt.3 . 2.50
Spec. "The Leaper Before 3.95

QUANTUM & WOODY
Acclaim Feb. 1997
1 CPr(s),MBr Woodrow Van
　Chelton & Eric Henderson
　become unlikely superheros .. 6.00
1a Variant (c) 7.00
2 CPr(s),MBr,World's worst
　superhero team 5.00
3 CPr(s),MBr,Woody buys a goat 5.00
4 CPr(s),MBr, ... 4.00
5 CPr(s),MBr, ... 3.00
6 CPr(s),MBr, ... 3.00
7 CPr(s),MBr, ... 3.00
8 CPr(s),MBr,R:Warrant 3.00
9 CPr(s),DCw,Woody is dying .. 3.00
10 CPr(s),MBr,trapped in each
　other's bodies, Goat month ... 3.00
11 CPr(s),MBr,switched body
　delimma 2.50
12 CPr(s),MBr,switched bodies . 2.50
13 CPr(s),MBr,back in own bodies 2.50
14 CPr(s),MBr,Magnum Force,pt.1 2.50
15 CPr(s),MBr,Magnum Force,pt.2 2.50
16 CPr(s),MBr,Magnum Force,pt.3 2.50
17 CPr(s),MBr,Magnum Force,pt.4 2.50
TPB Director's Cut, rep.#1–#4 ... 8.00
TPB Kiss Your Ass Goodbye 8.00

RAI
Valiant 1991
0 DL,O:Bloodshot,I:2nd Rai,D:X-O,
　Archer,Shadowman,F:all Valiant
　heroes,bridges Valiant Universe
　1992-4001 .... 4.00
1 V:Grandmother 6.00
2 V:Icespike 3.00
3 V:Humanists,Makiko 4.00
4 V:Makiko,rarest Valiant ... 5.00
5 Rai leaves earth, C:Eternal
　Warrior 3.00
6 FM(c),Unity#7,V:Pierce ... 2.50
7 WS(c),Unity#15,V:Pierce,
　D:Rai,A:Magnus 2.50
8 Epilogue of Unity in 4001 ... 2.50
Becomes:

RAI AND THE FUTURE FORCE
Valiant 1993
9 F:Rai,E.Warrior of 4001,Tekla, X-
　O Commander,Spylocke 2.50
9a Gold Ed. 4.00
10 Rai vs. Malev Emperor 2.25
11 SCh,V:Malevolents 2.25
12 V:Cyber Raiders 2.25
13 Spylocke Revealed 2.25
14 SCh,D:M'Ree 2.25
15 SCh,V:X-O 2.25
16 SCh,V:Malevs 2.25
17 .... 2.25
18 JOs(s),Spk,V:Malevs 2.25
19 JCf,V:Malves 2.25
20 JOs(s),DR,V:Malves,Spylocke
　realed to be Spider Alien ... 2.25
21 DR,I:Starwatchers,b:Torque,
　w/Valiant Era card 2.25
22 DR,D:2nd Rai, A:Starwatchers 2.25
23 DR,A:Starwatchers, ... 2.25
24 DR,in Tibet 2.00
25 DR,F:Spylocke 2.00
26 DR,Chaos Effect-Epsilon#3,
　A:Solar Magnus,Psi-Lords 2.00
Becomes:

RAI
Valiant 1994
27 "Rising Son" 2.00
28 V:Takashi 2.00
29 A:Rentaro Nakadai 2.00
30 Splocke 2.00
31 Bad Penny pt. 1 .... 2.00
32 Bad Penny pt. 2, F:Axscan . 2.00
33 F:Spylocke, Rentaro 2.00
TPB #0-#4 .... 11.95
TPB Star System ed. 11.95

REVELATIONS
one-shot by Jim Krueger 3.95

SABAN POWERHOUSE
Acclaim Young Readers 1997
Digest Size, F: Power Rangers Turbo
Spec. "Simple Simon Says" 4.50
Spec. "Into the Fire" 4.50
Spec. "Mystery of the Phantom
　Ranger" 4.50

SABAN PRESENTS
Acclaim 1997
Spec. Power Rangers Turbo vs. Big
　Bad Beetleborgs 4.50

SAMUREE
Windjammer 1995
1 I:Samuree 2.50
2 V: The Dragon 2.50
3 V: The Dragon 2.50

The Second Life of Dr. Mirage #9
© Voyager Communications, Inc.

THE SECOND LIFE OF DR. MIRAGE
Valiant 1993
1 B:BL(s),BCh,V:Mast.Darque ... 2.50
1a Gold Ed. 4.00
2 BCh,V:Master Darque 2.50
3 BCh 2.50
4 BCh,V:Bhrama 2.50
5 BCh,A:Shadowman,V:Master
　Darque 2.50
6 BCh,V:Dr.Eclipse 2.50
7 BCh,V:Dr.Eclipse,w/card ... 2.50
8 BCh, ... 2.50
9 BCh,A:Otherman 2.50
10 BCh,V:Otherman 2.50
11 BCh,Chaos Effect-Beta#2, . 2.50
12 BCh 2.25
13 BCh 2.25
14 .... 2.25
15 Chaos Effect 2.25
16 .... 2.25
17 .... 2.25
18 F:Deathsmith 2.25
19 R:Walt Wiley 2.25

SECRETS OF THE VALIANT UNIVERSE
Valiant 1994
1 from Wizard 2.50
2 BH,Chaos Effect-Beta#4,A:Master
　Darque,Dr.Mirage,Max St.James,
　Dr. Eclipse 2.25

SECRET WEAPONS
Valiant 1993
1 JSP(a&s),BWi(i),I:Dr.Eclipse,
　A:Master Darque,A:Geoff,
　Livewire,Stronghold,Solar,X-O,

Bloodshot,Shadowman 2.75
1a Gold Ed. 5.00
2 JSP(a&s),V:Master Darque,
Dr.Eclipse 2.25
3 JSP(a&s),V:Speedshots 2.25
4 JSP(a&s),V:Scatterbrain 2.25
5 JSP(a&s),A:Ninjak 2.25
6 JPS(s),JPh(pl),TeH, V:Spider
Aliens 2.25
7 JPS(s),V:Spider Aliens 2.25
8 JSP(a&pl),V:Harbingers 2.25
9 JSP(a&s),V:Webnet, w/Valiant
Era card 2.25
10 JSP(a&s),V:Webnet 2.25
11 PGr,New Line-up 2.25
12 PGr,A:Bloodshot 2.25
13 PGr,Chaos Effect-Gamma#2 . . 2.25
14 PGr,F:Bloodshot 2.00
15 . . . . 2.00
16 . . . . 2.00
17 V:Dr. Silk 2.00
18 Gigo 2.00
19 A:Ninjak 2.00
20 Bloodshot Rampage Pt.2 . . . . 2.00
21 Bloodshot Rampage Pt.4 . . . . 2.00
22 I:Gestalt, Pyroclast 2.00
23 A:Bloodshot 2.00

SECRET WEAPONS: PLAYING WITH FIRE
Valiant
1 & 2 . . . . @2.50

SHADOW MAN
Valiant 1992
0 BH,TmR,Chromium (c),O:Maxim
St.James,Shadowman 3.00
0a Newstand ed. 2.50
0b Gold Ed. 5.00
1 DL,JRu,I&O:Shadowman 6.00
2 DL,V:Serial Killer 3.00
3 V:Emil Sosa 3.00
4 DL,FM(c),Unity#6,A:Solar 2.50
5 DL,WS(c),Unity#14, A:Archer &
Armstrong 2.50
6 SD,L:Lilora 2.50
7 DL,V:Creature 2.50
8 JDx(i),I:Master Darque 3.00
9 JDx(i),V:Darque's Minions 3.00
10 BH,I:Sandria 2.50
11 BH,N:Shadowman 2.50
12 BH,V:Master Darque 2.50
13 BH,V:Rev.Shadow Man 2.50
14 BH,JDx,V:Bikers 2.50
15 BH,JDx,V:JB,Fake Shadow
Man,C:Turok 2.50
16 BH,JDx,I:Dr.Mirage, Carmen . . 4.00
17 BH,JDx,A:Archer & Armstrong . . 2.25
18 BH,JDx,A:Archer & Armstrong . . 2.25
19 BH,A:Aerosmith 2.25
20 BH,A:Master Darque,
V:Shadowman's Father 2.25
21 BH,I:Maxim St.James (1895
Shadowman) 2.25
22 V:Master Darque 2.25
23 BH(a&s),A:Doctor Mirage,
V:Master Darque 2.25
24 BH(a&s),V:H.A.T.E. 2.25
25 RgM,w/Valiant Era card 2.25
26 w/Valiant Era card 2.50
27 BH,V:Drug Lord 2.25
28 BH,A:Master Darque 2.25
29 Chaos Effect-Beta#1,V:Master
Darque 2.25

30 R:Rotwak 2.25
31 thru 33 . . . . @2.25
34 Voodoo in Carribean 2.25
35 A:Ishmael 2.25
36 F:Ishmael 2.25
37 A:X-O, V:Blister 2.25
38 V:Ishmael, Blister 2.25
39 BH,TmR,Explores Powers 2.25
40 BH,TmR,I,Vampire! 2.25
41 A:Steve Massarsky 2.25
42 . . . . 2.25
43 V:Smilin Jack 2.25
TPB rep.#1-#3,#6 . . . . 9.95

SHADOWMAN
Acclaim Nov. 1996
1 GEn(s),"Deadside," pt.1 . . . . . 2.50
2 GEn(s),"Deadside," pt.2 . . . . . 2.50
3 GEn(s),"Deadside," pt.3 . . . . . 2.50
4 GEn(s),"Deadside," pt.4 . . . . . 2.50
5 JaD,CAd,"Nothing is True," pt.1 2.50
6 JaD,CAd,"Nothing is True," pt.2 2.50
7 JaD,CAd,"Nothing is True," pt.3 2.50
8 JaD,CAd,"Nothing is True," pt.4 2.50
9 JaD, CAd,"The Buzz," pt.1 . . . . 2.50
10 JaD, CAd,"The Buzz," pt.2 . . . . 2.50
11 JaD,CAd,"ClearBlueSkies,"pt.1 2.50
12 JaD,CAd,"ClearBlueSkies,"pt.2 2.50
13 JaD,CAd,"Hoodoo Bash,"pt.1 . 2.50
14 JaD,CAd,"Hoodoo Bash,"pt.2 . 2.50
15 JaD,CAd,"Hoodoo Bash,"pt.3 . 2.50
16 Mask of Shadows ripped out . . 2.50
17 Mask of Shadows, pt.2 . . . . . 2.50
18 Claudine kidnapped? 2.50
19 pursuit of Mah 2.50
20 Deadside vortes 2.50

SLIDERS
Valiant 1996
1 & 2 . . . . @2.50

SLIDERS: DARKEST HOUR
1 DGC,DG. 2.50
2 DGC,DG 2.50
3 DGC,DG, Concl. 2.50
Spec. RgM, Montezuma IV rules the
world 3.95
Spec. #2 "Secrets" 3.95
TPB from TV show 9.00

SLIDERS: ULTIMATUM
Valiant 1996
1 & 2 . . . . @2.50

SOLAR: HELL ON EARTH
Acclaim 1997
1 (of 4) CPr,DCw,Seleski twins
have power of God 2.50
2 CPr,Goat Month prelude 2.50
3 CPr,RT,V:Jimmy Six 2.50
4 CPr, ... 2.50

SOLAR: MAN OF THE ATOM
Valiant 1991
1 BWS,DP,BL,B:2nd Death B:Alpha
& Omega 5.00
2 BWS,DP,BL,V:Dr Solar 3.00
3 BWS,DP,BL,V:Harada I:Harbinger
Foundation 3.00
4 BWS,DP,BL,E:2nd Death V:Dr

Solar 2.50
5 BWS,EC,V:Alien Armada 2.50
6 BWS,DP,SDr, V:Alien Armada X-
O Armor 2.50
7 BWS,DP,SDr, V:Alien Armada X-
O Armor 2.50
8 BWS,V:Dragon of Bangkok . . . 2.50
9 BWS,DP,SDr, V:Erica's Baby . . 2.50
10 BWS,DP,SDr,JDx,I:Eternal
Warrior,E:Alpha&Omega 4.00
10a 2nd printing 2.00
11 SDr,A:Eternal Warrior, Prequel
to Unity #0 . . . . 3.00
12 SDr,FM(c),Unity#9,O:Pierce,
Albert 2.50
13 DP,SDr,WS(c),Unity #17,
V:Pierce 2.50
14 DP,SDr,I:Bender (becomes
Dr.Eclipse) 3.00
15 SD,V:Bender 3.00
16 Solar moves to California 2.50
17 SDr(i),V:X-O Manowar 2.50
18 SDr(i),A:X-Manowar 2.50
19 SDr(i),V:Videogame 2.50
20 SDr(i),Dawn of the Malevolence 2.50
21 SDr(i),Master Darque 2.50
22 SDr(i),V:Master Darque,A:
Bender(Dr.Eclipse) 2.50
23 SDr(i),JQ(c),V:Master
Darque,I:Solar War God 2.50
24 SDr(i),A:Solar War God 2.50
25 V:Dr.Eclipse 2.25
26 Phil and Gayle on vaction 2.25
27 in Austrialia 2.25
28 A:Solar War God 2.25
29 KVH(s),JP(i),Valiant Vision,
A:Solar War God 2.50
30 KVH(s),JP,V:Energy Parasite . 2.25
31 KVH(s),JP,Chrismas Issue . . . 2.25
32 KVH(s),JP,Parent's Night 2.25
33 KVH(s),PGr,JP,B:Solar the
Destroyer,w/Valiant Era card . 2.25
34 KVH(s),PGr,V:Spider Alien . . . 2.25
35 KVH(s),PGr,JP,E:Solar the
Destroyer,Valiant Vision 2.25
36 KVH(s),PGr,JP,B:Revenge times
two,V:Doctor Eclipse, Ravenus 2.25
37 PGr,JP,E:Revenge times two,

Solar: Man of the Atom #28,
© Voyager Communications, Inc.

V:Doctor Eclipse,Ravenus	2.00
38 PGr,JP,Chaos Effect-Epsilon#1	2.00
39	2.00
40	2.00
41	2.00
42 Elements of Evil pt.1	2.00
43 Elements of Evil pt.2	2.00
44 I:New Character	2.00
45 Explores Powers	2.00
46 I:The Sentry	2.25
47 DJu,DG,Brave New World,pt.2	2.25
48 DJu,DG,Brave New World,pt.3	2.25
49 DJu,DG,Brave New World,pt.4	2.25
50 DJu,DG,Brave New World,pt.5	2.25
51 I:Aliens on the Moon	2.25
52 Solar Saves Earth	2.25
53 I:Marauder	2.25
54 V:Marauder	2.25
55 I:Black Star	2.25
56 V:Black Star	2.25
57 A:Armorines	2.25
58 I:Atman, The Inquisitor	2.25
59 and 60 KG	@2.25
TPB #0 JiS,BWS,BL,Alpha and Omega rep. from Solar #1–#10	9.95
TPB #1 JiS,BWS,GL,V:Doctor Solar rep. from Solar #1–#4	9.95

STARSLAYER DIRECTORS CUT
Windjammer 1995

1 R:Starslayer, Mike Grell	2.50
2 I:New Star Slayer	2.50
3 Jolly Rodger	2.50
4 V:Battle Droids	2.50
5 I:Baraka Kuhi	2.50
6 V:Valkyrie	2.50
7 MGr(c&a),Can Torin destroy?	2.50
8 MGr(c&a),JAl, Can Torin live with his deeds?,final issue	2.50

STARWATCHERS
Valiant

1 MLe,DG,Chromium(c),Valiant Vision,	3.50

SUPER MARIO BROS.
Valiant 1991

1 thru 6	@1.95
Spec. #1	1.95

TICK, THE

Spec. digest size	4.50

TIMEWALKER
Valiant 1994

0 BH,DP,O:3 Immortals	2.95
1 DP, BH	2.50
2 DP,BH	2.50
3 DP BH	2.50
4 Ten Commandments	2.50
5 DP,BH	2.50
6 Harbinger Wars Pt.1	2.50
7 Harbinger Wars Pt.2	2.50
8 Harbinger Wars Pt.3	2.50
9 V:Jahk rt	2.50
10 Last God of Dura-Europus,pt.1 time: 260 A.D.	2.50
11 Last God of Dura-Europus,pt.2	2.50
12 3RW,DP,Ashes to Ashes,pt.1	2.50
13 3RW,DP,Ashes to Ashes,pt.2	2.50
14 Meets Mozart	2.50
15 26th Century	2.50

Yearbook F:Harada	2.95
TPB F:Archer & Armstrong	9.95

TRINITY ANGELS
Acclaim March 1997

1 KM,DPs, Maria, Gianna & Theresa Barbella become Trinity Angels	2.50
2 KM,DPs, V:The 99	2.50
3 KM,DPs, looking for a little head	2.50
4 KM,DPs, V:Flaming Queen	2.50
5 KM, New costumes	2.50
6 KM, in Las Vegas	2.50
7 KM, in Las Vegas	2.50
8 KM, "A Woman Scorned"	2.50
9 KM, A:Rumblin' Guys	2.50
10 KM, Mad Cow	2.50
11 KM,	2.50
12 KM, Final issue	2.50

TROUBLEMAKERS
Acclaim Dec. 1996

1 FaN(s)	2.50
2 FaN(s) go back in time	2.50
3 FaN(s) Jane has a big problem	2.50
4 FaN(s) Can Blur prevent parents divorce?	2.50
5 FaN(s) A:Ninjak	2.50
6 FaN(s) in outer space	2.50
7 FaN(s) I:The Rabble Rousers	2.50
8 FaN(s) Rabble Rousers,pt.2	2.50
9 FaN(s) F:Christine	2.50
10 FaN(s) F:Zach	2.50
11 FaN(s) F:Calamity Jane	2.50
12 FaN(s) a Troublemaker dead	2.50
13 FaN(s) F:XL	2.50
14 FaN(s)	2.50
15 FaN(s) Is Parker alive?	2.50
16 FaN(s) Andrew Chase	2.50
17 FaN(s) V:Turnabout	2.50
18 FaN(s) Jacinda Monroe	2.50
19 FaN(s) V:Rabblerousers	2.50

TUROK: CHILD OF BLOOD
Acclaim 1997

1-shot FaN, 48pg	4.00

TUROK: DINOSAUR HUNTER
Valiant 1993

1 BS,Chromium(c),O:Turok retold,V:Monark	3.00
1a Gold Ed.	5.00
2 BS,V:Monark	2.75
3 BCh,V:Monark	2.75
4 TT(s),RgM,O:Turok	2.75
5 TT(s),RgM,V:Dinosaurs	2.75
6 TT(s),RgM,V:Longhunter	2.75
7 TT(a&s),B:People o/t Spider	2.75
8 TT(a&s),V:T-Rex	2.75
9 TT(a&s),E:People o/t Spider	2.75
10 MBn,RgM,A:Bile	2.75
11 MBn,RgM,V:Chun Yee,w/card	2.75
12 MBn,RgM,V:Dinosaur	2.75
13 B:TT(c&s),RgM,	2.75
14 V:Dino-Pirate	2.50
15 RgM,V:Dino-Pirate	2.25
16 Chaos Effect-Beta#3, V:Evil Shaman	2.75
17 V:C.I.A.	2.50
18 V:Bionosaurs	2.50
19 A:Manowar	2.50
20 Chichak	2.50

Turok: Dinosaur Hunter #8 © Valiant

21 Ripsaw	2.50
22	2.50
23 A:Longhunter	2.50
24 R:To The Lost Land	2.50
25 I:Warrior of Mother God	2.50
26 V:Overlord	2.50
27 TT,RgM,Lost Land,pt.4	2.50
28 MBn,DEA hunts rogue T-Rex	2.50
29 SFu,Manhunt,pt.1	2.50
30 SFu,Manhunt,pt.2	2.50
31 F:Darwin Challenger	2.50
32 V:Special Effects	2.50
33 V:Aliens	2.50
34 V:Alien Ooze	2.50
35 Early Years	2.50
36 Confronts Past	2.50
37 V:Nazi Women	2.50
38 V:Bigfoot	2.50
39 TT,Shainer Silver	2.50
40 A:Longhunter	2.50
41 Church of the Poison Mind	2.50
42 Church of the Poison Mind	2.50
43 thru 47	@2.50
Yearbook #1 MBn(s),DC, N&V:Mon Ark	4.25
Yearbook 1995 MGr,The Hunted	2.95
Spec. Tales of the Lost Land	4.00
TPB FaN 112pgs.rep. game	10.00

TUROK
Acclaim 1998

1 FaN 3-D cover	2.50
2 FAn,A:Armorines	2.50
3 FAn,Lazarus Concordance	2.50
4 FAn, real President?	2.50

TUROK: THE HUNTED
Valiant

1 & 2	2.50

TUROK QUARTERLY— REDPATH

March 1997, FaN(s),"Spring Break in the Lost Land"	3.95
June 1997, FaN(s), Killer loose in Oklahoma City	3.95

TUROK/SHAMAN'S TEARS
Valiant 1995
1 MGr,Ghost Dance Pt. 1 . . . . . . 2.50
2 MGr,JAI,White Buffalo
   kidnapped,V:Bar Sinister 2.50
3 V:Supremeists/Circle Sea 2.50

TUROK/TIMEWALKER
Acclaim 1997
1 of 2 FaN(s),"Seventh Sabbath"   2.50
2 of 2 FaN(s),"Seventh Sabbath"   2.50

UNITY
Valiant 1992
0 BWS,BL,Chapter#1,A:All Valiant
   Heroes,V:Erica Pierce 3.00
0a Red ed.,w/red logo 4.00
1 BWS,BL,Chapter#18,A:All Valiant
   Heroes,D:Erica Pierce 3.00
1a Gold logo 4.00
1b Platinum 4.00
TPB Previews Exclusive,Vol.I
   Chap.#1-9 . . . . 8.00
TPB Previews Exclusive,Vol.II
   Chap.#10-18 . . . . 3.00
TPB #1 rep Chapters #1-4 . . . . 10.95
TPB #2 rep Chapters #5-9 . . . . 9.95
TPB #3 rep Chapters #10-14 . . 9.95

VALERIA, THE SHE-BAT
Windjammer 1995
1 (of 2) NA,Valeria & 'Rilla 2.50
2 (of 2) NA,BSz, final issue 2.50

VALIANT ERA
Valiant
TPB rep.Magnus #12,Shadowman
   #8, Solar #10-11,Eternal
   Warrior#4-5 . . . . 13.95

VALIANT READER: GUIDE TO THE VALIANT UNIVERSE
1 O:Valiant Universe 1.00

VALIANT VISION STARTER KIT
Valiant
1 w/3-D Glasses 2.95
2 F:Starwatchers 2.95

VINTAGE MAGNUS ROBOT FIGHTER
Valiant
1 rep. Gold Key Magnus #22
   (which is #1) 6.00
2 rep. Gold Key Magnus #3 . . . . 4.50
3 rep. Gold Key Magnus #13 . . . 3.50
4 rep. Gold Key Magnus #15 . . . 3.50

VISITOR
Valiant 1994
1 New Series 2.50
2 F:The Harbinger 2.50
3 The Bomb 2.50
4 V:F/X Specialists 2.50
5 R:Harbinger 2.50
6 KVH,BS(c),V:Men in Black . . . 2.50
7 KVH,BS(c),V:Men in Black,pt.2   2.50
8 KVH,V:Harbinger identity 2.50

9 KVH,A:Harbinger,Flamingo . . . 2.50
10 Weather Problems 2.50
11 V:Cannibals 2.50
12 V:Harada, Men in Black 2.50
13 Visitor is the Future Harbinger . 2.50

VISITOR VS. VALIANT
Valiant 1994
1 V:Solar 2.95
2 . . . . 2.95

WATERWORLD
Acclaim 1997
1 of 4 V:Leviathan 2.50
2 of 4 "Children of Leviathan" . . . 2.50
3 of 4 KoK 2.50
4 of 4 KoK "Children of Leviathan" 2.50

WWF BATTLEMANIA
Valiant
1 WWF Action 2.50
2 thru 5 . . . . @2.50

X-O Manowar #23
© *Voyager Communications, Inc.*

X-O MANOWAR
Valiant 1992
0 JQ,O:Aric,1st Full Chromium(c)   3.00
0a Gold Ed. 4.00
1 BL,BWS,I:Aric,Ken 5.00
2 BL(i),V:Lydia,Wolf-Class Armor   3.50
3 I:X-Caliber,A:Solar 3.50
4 MM,A:Harbinger,C:Shadowman
   (Jack Boniface) 3.50
5 BWS(c),V:AX 3.50
5a w/Pink logo 3.50
6 SD,V:Ax(X-O Armor) 3.50
7 FM(c),Unity#5,V:Pierce 3.00
8 WS(c),Unity#13,V:Pierce 3.00
9 Aric in Italy,408 A.D. 3.00
10 N:X-O Armor 3.00
11 V:Spider Aliens 2.50
12 A:Solar 2.50
13 V:Solar 2.50
14 BS,A:Turok,I:Randy Cartier . . 3.00
15 BS,A:Turok 2.50
15a Red Ed. 4.00

16 V:The Mob 2.50
17 BL 2.50
18 JCf,V:CIA,A:Randy,I:Paul . . . 2.50
19 JCf,V:US Government 2.50
20 A:Toyo Harada 2.50
21 V:Ax 2.50
22 Aria in S.America 2.50
23 Aria in S.America 2.50
24 Aria comes back 2.50
25 JCf,JGz,PaK,I:Armories,
   BU:Armories#0 . . . . 3.50
26 JGz(s),RLv,F:Ken 2.50
27 JGz,RLe,A:Turok,Geomancer,
   Stronghold,Livewire 2.50
28 JGz,RLe,D:X-O,V:Spider
   Aliens,w/Valiant Era card 2.75
29 JGz,RLe,A:Turok,V:SpiderAliens 2.50
30 JGz,RLe,A:Solar 2.50
31 JGz,RLe, ... 2.50
32 JGz,RLe,at Orb,Inc. 2.25
33 JGz,RLe,Chaos Effect-Delta#3,
   A:Armorines,H.A.R.D. Corps . . 2.25
34 thru 36 . . . . @2.25
37 Wolfbridge Affair pt.1 . . . . . . 2.25
38 Wolfbridge Affair pt.2 . . . . . . 2.25
39 Wolfbridge Affair pt.3 . . . . . . 2.25
40 Wolfbridge Affair pt.4 . . . . . . 2.25
41 Aftermath 2.25
42 A:Shadowman Surprise 2.25
43 Chasitty's Boys 2.25
44 Bart Sears New Direction 2.50
45 RMz,V:Crescendo 2.50
46 RMz,V:Crescendo 2.50
47 RMz,V:Crescendo 2.50
48 RMz,BS,A:Turok 2.50
49 RMz,loses control of armor . . . 2.50
50-X R:Paul, I:Alloy 2.50
50-O V:Alloy 2.50
51 V:Lummox 2.50
52 V:A Blast From the Past 2.50
53 Returns To Space 2.50
54 I:New Aliens 2.50
55 V:Aliens 2.50
56 V:Aliens 2.50
57 I:Gamin 2.50
58 I:Volt 2.50
59 thru 67 . . . . @2.50
TPB rep.#1-4,w/X-O Manual . . . 11.00

X-O MANOWAR
Series Two
Acclaim Oct. 1997
1 Rand Banion v. R.A.G.E. 2.50
2 v. R.A.G.E. 2.50
3 . . . . 2.50
4 R.A.G.E. is back 2.50
5 Donovan Wylie vs. Internaut . . 2.50
6 Internaut controls X-O suit . . . 2.50
7 SEa, Donovan wears his armor   2.50
8 SEa, V:Basilisk 2.50
9 SEa, A: new Hard Corps 2.50
10 SEa, R:Bravado 2.50
11 BAu,MWa,SEa,alien creators . 2.50
12 BAu,MWa,SEa,O:armor 2.50
13 BAu,SEa,V:Alien creators . . . 2.50
14 BAu,SEa,V:Aliens of Unity . . . 2.50
15 BAu,SEa,out of armor 2.50
16 BAu,SEa, ... 2.50
17 DMD,SEa,civil war 2.50
18 DMD,SEa,Rand Banion 2.50
19 DMD,SEa,V:Master Blaster . . 2.50
20 DMD,trapped in a sleep-state . 2.50
TPB MWa,BAu rep. #1–#4 . . . . 10.00

All comics prices listed are for *Near Mint* condition.   CVA Page 449

DARK HORSE

ABE SAPIEN: DRUMS OF THE DEAD
March 1998
1-shot Hellboy spin-off 2.95

ABYSS, THE
1 MK,Movie Adaptation pt.1 . . . . 2.50
2 MK,Movie Adaptation pt.2 . . . . 2.50

Accident Man #2 © Dark Horse Comics

ACCIDENT MAN
(B&W)
1 I:Accident Man 2.50
2 and 3 . . . . @2.50

ADVENTURES OF LUTHER ARKWRIGHT
Valkyrie Press/Dark Horse
(B&W) 1987–89
1 thru 9 . . . . @2.00
(B&W) 1990
1 thru 9 Rep. . . . . @1.95
TPB 14.95

ADVENTURES OF THE MASK
1996
1 thru 12 by Michael Eury & Marc
Campos, TV cartoon adapt. . @2.50

AGENTS OF LAW
Comics' Greatest World 1995
1 KG, I:Law 2.50
2 A:Barb Wire 2.50
3 KG,DLw,The Judgment Gate . . 2.50
4 Open Golden City 2.50
5 Who is the Mystery figure 2.50
6 V:Predator 2.50

AGE OF REPTILES
1993–94
1 DRd,Story on Dinosaurs 3.00
2 DRd,Story on Dinosaurs 3.00
3 DRd,Story on Dinosaurs 3.00
4 DRd,Story on Dinosaurs 3.00
TPB Tribal Warfare 14.95

AGE OF REPTILES: THE HUNT
1996
1 thru 5 by Ricardo Delgado . . @2.95
TPB The Hunt 17.95

ALIENS
(B&W) 1988
1 Movie Sequel,R:Hicks,Newt . . 18.00
1a 2nd printing 3.00
1b 3rd printing 2.00
1c 4th printing 1.50
2 Hicks raids Mental Hospital . . . 8.00
2a 2nd printing 2.50
2a 3rd printing 1.50
3 Realize Queen is on Earth 4.00
3a 2nd printing 1.50
4 Queen is freed, Newton on Aliens
World 3.00
5 All out war on Aliens World . . . 3.00
6 Hicks & Newt return to Earth . . 3.00
TPB rep.#1–#6 & DHP #24 . . . . 11.00
TPB 2nd printing, DvD(c) 11.00
HC rep..#1–#6 & DHP #24 . . . . 25.00

Aliens: Colonial Marines #2
© Dark Horse Comics

ALIENS (II)
[Mini-Series] 1989
1 DB,Hicks,Newt hijack ship 5.00
1a 2nd Printing 3.00
2 DB,Crazed general trains aliens 3.00
2a 2nd Printing 3.00

3 DB,HicksV:General Spears . . . 3.00
3a 2nd Printing 2.50
4 DB,Heroes reclaim earth from
aliens 3.00
HC, 2,500 made 80.00
HC, 1,000 made 100.00

ALIENS
1-shot Earth Angel, JBy 3.00
HC rep. Earth Angel 21.00
1-shot Glass Corridor, DvL 2.95
1-shot Mondo Heat, I:Herk Mondo 2.50
1-shot Mondo Pest 2.95
1-shot Purge, IEd,PhH 2.95
1-shot Pig, CDi,FH 2.95
1-shot Sacrifice, rep.Aliens UK . . 4.95
1-shot Salvation DGb,MMi,KN,
F:Selkirk 4.95
1-shot Special 2.50
1-shot Stalker 2.50
1-shot Wraith 2.95
GN Female War, remastered . . . 16.95
GN Genocide, remastered 16.95
GN Labyrinth, remastered 17.95
GN Nightmare Asylum, remaster 16.95
GN Outbreak, remastered 17.95
GN Rogue, Remastered 16.95

ALIENS: ALCHEMY
Sept. 1997
1 (of 3) JAr,RCo 2.95
2 thru 3 . . . . @2.95

ALIENS: BERSERKER
1 I:Crew of the Nemesis 2.50
2 Terminall 949 . . . . 2.50
3 Traitor 2.50
4 Finale 2.50

ALIENS: COLONIAL MARINES
1 I: Lt. Joseph Henry 3.00
2 I: Pvt. Carmen Vasquez 2.75
3 V:Aliens 2.75
4 F:Lt.Henry 2.75
5 V:Aliens 2.75
6 F:Herk Mondo 2.75
7 A:Beliveau 2.75
8 F:Lt.Joseph Henry 2.75
9 F:Lt.Henry 2.75
10 final issue 2.50

ALIENS: EARTH WAR
1 SK,JBo(c),Alien's War renewed 5.00
1a 2nd Printing 2.50
2 SK,JBo(c),To trap the Queen . . 5.00
3 SK,JBo(c) Stranded on Alien's
planet 4.00
4 SK,JBo(c),Resolution,final 4.00
HC Earth War, rep. #1–#4, signed
and numbered edition 60.00

ALIENS: GENOCIDE
1 Aliens vs. Aliens 3.50
2 Alien Homeworld 3.00
3 Search for Alien Queen 3.00
4 Conclusion, inc. poster 3.00
TPB Genocide rep. #1–#4 . . . . 13.95

All comics prices listed are for *Near Mint* condition.

ALIENS: HIVE
1 KJo,I:Stanislaw Mayakovsky	4.00
2 KJo,A:Norbert	3.50
3 KJo,A:Julie,Gill	3.25
4 KJo,A:Stan,Final	3.00
TPB Hive rep. #1–#4	14.00

ALIENS: HAVOC
1 (of 2) "over 40 creators"	2.95
2	2.95

ALIENS: KIDNAPPED
Dec. 1997–Feb. 1998
1 (of 3)	2.50
2 thru 3	@2.50

ALIENS: LABYRINTH
1 F:Captured Alien	3.00
2	2.50
3 O:Dr.Church	2.50
4 D:Everyone	2.50
TPB rep. #1–#4	17.95

ALIENS: MUSIC OF THE SPEARS
1 I:Damon Eddington	3.00
2 TBd(c),A:Damon Eddington	2.75
3 TBd(c),A:Damon Eddington	2.75
4 TBd(c),last issue	2.75

ALIENS: NEWT'S TALE
1 How Newt Survived	5.50
2 JBo(c),Newt's point of view on how 'Aliens' ended	4.95

ALIEN RESURRECTION
Oct. 1997
1 (of 2) movie adaptation	2.50
2 DMc(c)	2.50

ALIENS: ROGUE
1 F:Mr.Kay	3.00
2 V:Aliens	3.00
3 V:Aliens	3.00
4 V:Aliens King	3.00
TPB Nel(c),rep.#1–#4	14.95

ALIENS: STRONGHOLD
1 DoM,JP	2.50
2 DoM,JP	2.50
3 DoM,JP	2.50
4 DoM,JP	2.50
TPB	16.95

ALIENS: SURVIVAL
Feb.–Apr. 1998
1 (of 3) TyH(c)	2.95
2 thru 3	@2.95

ALIENS: TRIBES
HC DvD(c)	24.95
TPB	11.95
HC SBi,DvD	24.95

ALIENS/PREDATOR: DEADLIEST OF THE SPECIES
1 B:CCl(s),JG,F:Caryn Delacroix	3.75
2 JG,V:Predator	3.00
3 JG,F:Caryn Delacroix	3.00
4 JG,V:Predator	3.00

5 JG,Roadtrip	3.00
6 JG,in Space Station	3.00
7 JG,EB	2.50
8 JG,EB	2.50
9 JG,EB	2.50
10 CCl(s), Human Predators	2.50
11 CCl,EB,JBo(c),Delacroix vs. DeMatier	2.50
12 Caryn's Fate	2.50
TPB	29.95
Lim. Ed. hc	99.95

ALIENS VS. PREDATOR
0 PN,KS,Rep.DHP#34-36,(B&W)	6.00
1 Duel to the Death	4.00
1a 2nd Printing	3.00
2 Dr. Revna missing	3.00
3 Predators attack Aliens	3.00
4 CW,F:Machiko & Predator	3.00
TPB Rep.#1–#4	19.95
TPB PN,KS,rep.DHP#34-36	19.95
HC PN,KS,rep.DHP#34-36	79.95

ALIENS VS. PREDATOR: BOOTY
1-shot Rep. Diamond Previews	2.50

ALIENS VS. PREDATOR: DUEL
1 Trap, JS	2.50
2 War	2.50

ALIENS VS. PREDATOR: ETERNAL
June 1998
1 (of 4) IEd,GF(c)	2.50
2 thru 4 IEd,GF(c)	@2.50

ALIENS VS. PREDATOR: WAR
0 Prelude to New Series	2.50
1 RSd,MM,RCo(c) F:Machiko	2.50
2 I:Machiko Naguchi	2.50
3 F:Machiko Naguchi	2.50
4 final issue	2.50
TPB	19.95

ALIEN 3
1 thru 3 Movie Adaptation	@2.50

AMERICAN, THE
(B&W)
1 CW,'Chinese Boxes,'D:Gleason	5.00
2 CW,'Nightmares	4.00
3 CW,Secrets of the American	4.00
4 CW,American vs.Kid America	4.00
5 A:Kiki the Gorilla	4.00
6 Rashomon-like plot	3.50
7 Pornography business issue	3.50
8 Deals with violence issue	3.50
9 American Falls into a cult	3.50

THE AMERICAN: LOST IN AMERICA
1 CMa, American joins a cult	2.50
2 CMa, V:"Feel-Good" cult	2.50
3 CMa, "ApeMask" cult	2.50
4 CMa, Final issue	2.50
ColorSpec.#1	2.95

AMERICAN SPLENDOR
1-shot Letterman by Harvey Pekar	2.95
1-shot A Step Out of the Nest	2.95
1-shot On the Job	2.95
1-shot Comics Con, JZe	2.95
1-shot Music Comics	2.95
1-shot Odds & Ends	2.95
1-shot Transatlantic Comics	2.95

AMERICAN SPLENDOR WINDFALL
(B&W) 1995
1 Windfall Gained,pt.1	3.95
2 Windfall Lost	3.95

ANOTHER CHANCE TO GET IT RIGHT
1 B&W	14.95
TPB AVs, GfD(c)	9.95

APPLESEED
(B&W) Manga
TPB Book One: The Promethean Challenge	14.95
TPB Book Two: Prometheus Unbound	14.95
TPB Book Three: The Scales of Prometheus	14.95
TPB Book Four: The Promethean Balance	14.95

APPLESEED DATABOOK
(B&W) Manga
1 Flip Book, by Masamune Shirow	5.00
1a 2nd printing	3.50
2 Flip Book	3.50
TPB Rep. #1–#2	12.95

ARZACH
TPB by Moebius	6.95

A SMALL KILLING
GN by Alan Moore & Oscar Zarate	11.95

Atlas #2 © Dark Horse Comics

All comics prices listed are for *Near Mint* condition.

ATLAS
1 BZ,I:Atlas 2.75
2 BZ,V:Sh'en Chui 2.75
3 BZ,V:Sh'en Chui 2.50
4 BZ, final issue 2.50

BABE
Legend 1994
1 JBy(a&s) 3.00
2 thru 4 JBy(a&s) . . . . @2.50

BABE 2
Legend 1995
1 V:Shrewmanoid 2.50
2 A:Abe Sapien 2.50

BACCHUS
COLOR SPECIAL
1 A:Thor 2.95
2 A:Abe Sapien 2.50

BADGER:
SHATTERED MIRROR
1 R:Badger 2.50
2 R:Badger 2.50
3 Badger 2.50
4 Phantom, final issue 2.50

BADGER: ZEN POP
FUNNY ANIMAL VERSION
1 MBn,R:Badger 2.50
2 Ham 2.50

BADLANDS
(B&W)
1 I:Connie Bremen 3.50
2 Anne Peck, C.I.A. 3.00
3 Assassination Rumor 2.50
4 Connie heads South 2.50
5 November 22, 1963, Dallas . . . 2.25
6 . . . . 2.25

BARB WIRE
Comics' Greatest World
1 Foil(c),I:Deathcard 2.25

Barb Wire #2 © Dark Horse Comics

---

2 DLw,I:Hurricane Max 2.25
3 V:Mace Blitzkrieg 2.00
4 Ghost pt.1 . . . . 2.00
5 Ghost pt.2 . . . . 2.00
6 Hardhide, Ignition 2.50
7 A:Motorhead 2.50
8 V:Ignition 2.50
9 A:Mecha, V:Ignition 2.50
Movie Spec. 3.95
TPB 8.95

BARB WIRE:
ACE OF SPADES
1 thru 4 by CW, TBd & DoM . . @2.95

BARRY WINDSOR-SMITH:
STORYTELLER
Oct. 1996
TPBs 1 thru 9 9"x12½" . . . . . @4.95

BASEBALL GREATS
1 Jimmy Piersall story 3.25

BASIL WOLVERTON'S
FANTASIC FABLES
(B&W)
1 BW 2.50
2 BW 2.50

BATMAN/ALIENS
Dark Horse/DC March 1997
1 (of 2) RMz,BWr 4.95
2 conclusion 4.95
TPB 14.95

BETTIE PAGE
1-shot, some nudity 3.95

BETTIE PAGE COMICS:
SPICY ADVENTURE
1-shot by Jim Silke 2.95

BETTIE PAGE:
QUEEN OF HEARTS
1 Movie adaptation 2.00
TPB 19.95

BIG
1 Movie Adaptation 2.00

BIG BLOWN BABY
(B&W) Aug. 1996
1 thru 4 by Bill Wray . . . . @2.95

BIG GUY AND
RUSTY THE ROBOT BOY
1 V:Monster 4.95
2 V:Monster 4.95
TPB FM & GfD 14.95
TPB King Size 29.95

BILLI 99
(B&W)
1 'Pray for us Sinners' 4.50
2 'Trespasses' 4.00
3 'Daily Bread' 4.00

BLACK CROSS:
DIRTY WORK
April 1997
1-shot by Chris Warner 2.95

BLACK DRAGON, THE
(B&W)
TPB Chris Claremont & John Bolton 7.95

BLACK PEARL, THE
Sept. 1996
1 by Mark Hamill 2.95
2 thru 5 . . . . @2.95
TPB by Mark Hamill 16.95

BLADE OF THE
IMMORTAL
(B&W) Manga
Call of the Worm, April 1997
9 pt. 1 by Hiroaki Samura 3.95
10 pt. 2 . . . . 3.95
11 pt. 3 . . . . 3.95
TPB Cry of the Worm 12.95
Dreamsong, July 1997
12 pt. 1 (of 7) by Hiroaki Samura . 2.95
13 pt. 2 F:Makie, Manji 2.95
14 pt. 3 . . . . 2.95
15 pt. 4 . . . . 2.95
16 pt. 5 . . . . 2.95
17 pt. 6 . . . . 2.95
18 pt. 7 . . . . 2.95
Rin's Bane, March 1998
19 pt.1, by Hiroaki Samura 2.95
20 pt.2 . . . . 2.95
On Silent Wings, May 1998
21 pt. 1 (of 8) 2.95
22 pt. 2 . . . . 2.95
23 pt. 3 . . . . 2.95
24 pt. 4 . . . . 2.95
TPB Blood of a Thousand 12.95

BLADE OF THE
IMMORTAL: CONQUEST
(B&W) Manga
1 by Hiroaki Samura 3.50
2 and 3 . . . . @3.50

BLADE OF THE
IMMORTAL: FANATIC
(B&W) Manga
1 by Hiroaki Samura 2.95
2 . . . . 2.95

BLADE OF THE
IMMORTAL: GENIUS
(B&W) Manga Oct. 1996
1 by Hiroaki Samura 3.50
2 . . . . 3.50

BLANCHE GOES TO
NEW YORK
1 Turn of the Century N.Y. 2.95

BLUE LILY
1 thru 3 . . . . @4.00

BODY BAGS
Aug. 1996
1 (of 4) by Jason Pearson and Ken

DARK HORSE

Bruzinak 2.95
2 and 3 . . . . @2.95
TPB 12.95

BOOK OF NIGHT
(B&W)
1 CV 2.50
2 CV 2.00
TPB Children of the Stars 12.95

BOOK OF NIGHT
1 thru 3 . . . . 3.95

Slaughters the Teenage
Radioactive Black Belt
Mutant Ninja Critters

Boris The Bear #1
© Dark Horse Comics

BORIS THE BEAR
(B&W)
1 V:Funny Animals 3.00
1a 2nd printing 2.00
2 V:Robots 2.00
3 V:Super Heroes 2.00
4 Bear of Steel 2.00
5 Dump Thing 2.00
6 Bat Bear 2.00
7 Elves 2.00
8 LargeSize 2.50
9 Awol 2.00
10 thru 12 . . . . @2.00
See: B & W Pub. section

BORIS THE BEAR
Color Classics
1 thru 7 . . . . @1.95

BRAVE
March 1997
1 by Cully Hamner & Jason Martin 2.95

BUBBLE GUM CRISIS:
GRAND MAL
Manga
1 . . . . 2.75
2 and 3 . . . . @2.75
4 final issue 2.50
TPB Rep.#1–#4 . . . . 14.95

BY BIZARRE HANDS
(B&W)
1 JLd(s) 2.50
2 JLd(s) 2.50
3 JLd(s) 2.50

CARAVAN KIDD
(B&W) Manga
1 thru 10 by Johji Manabe . . . @2.50
[2nd Series]
1 thru 10 F:Miam . . . . @2.50
TPB Rep. #1–#10 . . . . 19.95
Holiday Spec. 2.50
Valentine's Day Spec. 2.50
[3rd Series]
1 thru 8 . . . . @2.50
Christmas Special 2.50
TPB Vol. 2 . . . . 19.95

CATALYST: AGENTS
OF CHANGE
Comics' Greatest World
1 JPn(c),V:US Army 2.25
2 JPn(c),I:Grenade 2.25
3 JPn(c),Rebel vs. Titan 2.25
4 JPn(c),Titan vs. Grace 2.00
5 JPn(c),V:Ape 2.00
6 and 7 . . . . @2.00

CHEVAL NOIR
(B&W)
1 DSt(c) 4.00
2 thru 6 . . . . @3.50
7 DSt(c) 3.50
8 . . . . 3.50
9 . . . . 3.50
10 80 page 4.50
11 80 page 4.50
12 MM(c) 3.95
13 thru 15 . . . . @3.95
16 thru 19 with 2-card strip . . @3.95
20 Great Power o/t Chninkel . . . 4.50
21 Great Power o/t Chninkel 3.95
22 Great Power o/t Chninkel,concl. 4.50
23 inc.'Rork','Forever War' concl. . 3.95
24 In Dreams, Pt.1 . . . . 3.95
25 In Dreams, Pt.2 . . . . 3.95
26 In Dreams, Pt.3 . . . . 3.95
27 I:The Man From Ciguri (Airtight
   Garage sequel) Dreams Pt.4 . 2.95
28 Ciguri cont. 2.95
29 Ciguri cont. 2.95
30 Ciguri,cont. 2.95
31 Angriest Dog in the World . . . 2.95
32 thru 38 . . . . @2.95
39 In Search of Peter Pan 2.95
40 . . . . 2.95
41 F:Demon 2.95
42 F:Demon 2.95
43 F:Demon 2.95
44 F:Demon 2.95
45 . . . . 2.95
46 . . . . 2.95
47 . . . . 2.95
48 SwM(c) 2.95
49 F:Rork 2.95
50 F:Rork 2.95

CHRONOWAR
(B&W) Aug. 1996
1 (of 9) by Kazumasa Takayama 2.95
2 thru 9 . . . . @2.95

Classic Star Wars #20
© Dark Horse Comics

CLASSIC STAR WARS
1 AW,newspaper strip reps. 6.00
2 AW,newspaper strip reps. 4.00
3 AW,newspaper strip reps. 4.00
4 AW,newspaper strip reps. 4.00
5 AW,newspaper strip reps. 4.00
6 AW newspaper strip reps. 4.00
7 AW,newspaper reps. 4.00
8 AW,newspaper reps. w/card . . 4.00
9 AW,newspaper reps. 3.50
10 AW,newspaper reps. 3.50
11 thru 19 AW,newspaper reps. @3.00
20 AW,newspaper strip reps., with
   trading card, final issue 4.00
TPB Vol. 1, "In Deadly Pursuit,"
   rep.#1–#7 . . . . 15.99
TPB Vol. 1, rep. 2nd edition 16.95
TPB Vol. 2, "Rebel Storm," rep.
   #8–#14 . . . . 16.95
TPB Vol. 3, "Escape to Hoth," rep.
   #15–#20 . . . . 16.95

CLASSIC STAR WARS:
A NEW HOPE
1 AAd(c), rep. 4.25
2 AH(c), rep. 3.95
TPB Rep. #1–#2 . . . . 9.95

CLASSIC STAR WARS:
DEVILWORLDS
Aug. 1996
1 (of 2) by Alan Moore 2.50
2 . . . . 2.50

CLASSIC STAR WARS:
EARLY ADVENTURES
Aug. 1994–April 1995
1 MiA(c), Gambler's World 3.00
2 RHo&MGr(c),Blackhole 2.50
3 EiS(c),Rebels of Vorzyd-5 . . . . 2.50
3 bagged with trading card DH2 . 5.00
4 RHo(c),Tatooine 2.50
5 RHo(c),A:Lady Tarkin 2.50
6 Weather Dominator 2.50

DARK HORSE

7 RHo(c),V:Darth Vader 2.50
8 KPI(c),X-Wing Secrets 2.50
9 KPI(c),A:Boba Fett 2.50
TPB RsM & AGw, AW(c) 19.95

CLASSIC STAR WARS: EMPIRE STRIKES BACK
1 Movie Adaptation 4.00
2 Movie Adaptation 4.00
TPB Rep.#1–#2 AW&CG(c) 9.95
TPB reprint, Hildebrandt(c) 9.95

CLASSIC STAR WARS: HAN SOLO AT STAR'S END
March 1997
1 (of 3) by Alfredo Alcala 2.95
2 thru 3 . . . . @2.95
TPB rep. AW(c) 6.95

Classic Star Wars: Return of the Jedi #1
© Dark Horse Comics

CLASSIC STAR WARS: RETURN OF THE JEDI
1 Movie Adaptation 4.00
2 Movie Adaptation 3.50
TPB Rep.#1–#2 . . . . 9.95
TPB rep. Hildebrandt(c) 9.95

CLASSIC STAR WARS: VANDELHELM MISSION
1995
1-shot F:Han Solo, Lando 3.95

CLONEZONE
(B&W)
Spec #1 . . . . 2.00

CLOWNS, THE (PAGLIACCI)
April 1998
1-shot B&W, CR 2.95

COLORS IN BLACK
Comics From Spike
1 B:Passion Play 2.95
2 Images 2.95
3 Back on the Bus 2.95
4 final issue 2.95

COMIC BOOK
1 thru 4 9"x12" John Kricfalusi @5.95

COMICS AND STORIES
4 (of 4) by Martin & Millionaire . . 2.95

COMICS' GREATEST WORLD
(Arcadia)
1 B:MRi(s),FM(c),B:LW,B:O:Vortex,
 F:X,I:Seekers 3.00
1a B&W proof ed. (1,500 made) 10.00
1b Hologram(c), with cards 10.00
2 JoP,I:Pit Bulls 1.50
3 AH,I:Ghost 7.00
4 I:Monster 1.50
TPB Arcadia 25.00
(Golden City)
1 B:BKs(s),JOy(c),I:Rebel,
 Amaz.Grace,V:WarMaker 1.25
1a Gold Ed. 8.00
2 I:Mecha 1.25
3 WS(c),I:Titan 1.25
4 E:BKs(s),GP(c),JD,I:Catalyst . 1.25
TPB Golden City 11.00
(Steel Harbor)
1 B:CW(s),PG,I:Barb Wire,
 V:Ignition 1.25
2 MMi(c),TNa,I:Machine 1.25
3 CW(a&s),I:Wolf Gang 1.25
4 E:CW(s),VGi,I:Motorhead 1.25
TPB Steel Harbor 11.00
(Vortex)
1 B:RSd(s),LW,DoM,I:Division 13 1.25
2 I:Hero Zero 1.25
3 PC,I:King Tiger 1.25
4 B:RSd(s),E:MRi(s)BMc,E:LW,
 E:O:Vortex,C:Vortex 1.25
TPB Vortex 11.00
Sourcebook 10.00

Golden City #1 © Dark Horse Comics

Concrete #1 © Dark Horse Comics

CONCRETE
(B&W)
1 PC,R:Concrete, A Stone among
 Stones 8.00
1a 2nd printing 3.00
2 PC,'Transatlantic Swim' 5.00
3 PC 4.00
4 PC 3.50
5 PC,'An Armchair Stuffed with
 Dynamite' 3.50
6 PC,Concrete works on farm . . . 3.50
7 PC,Concrete grows horns 3.50
8 PC,Climbs Mount Everest 3.50
9 PC,Mount Everest Pt.2 . . . . . . 3.50
10 PC,last Issue 3.50
TPB The Complete Concrete . . 25.00

CONCRETE
1 PC,ColorSpec. 4.00
EarthDay Spec. PC,Moebius 4.00

CONCRETE: A NEW LIFE
1 . . . . 3.50
Spec.Land & Sea,rep. 3.25

CONCRETE CELEBRATES EARTH DAY 1990
1-shot 2.50

CONCRETE: ECLECTICA
1 PC,The Ugly Boy 3.25
2 PC 3.25

CONCRETE: FRAGILE CREATURE
1 PC,'Rulers o/t Omniverse'Pt.1 . 4.00
2 PC,'Rulers o/t Omniverse'Pt.2 . 3.00
3 PC,'Rulers o/t Omniverse'Pt.3 . 3.00
4 PC,'Rulers o/t Omniverse'Pt.3 . 3.00
TPB 15.95

CONCRETE: KILLER SMILE
Dark Horse-Legend 1994
1 PC 3.50
2 PC 2.95

3 PC 2.95
4 PC, final issue 2.95
TPB Rep.#1–#4 . . . . 16.95

CONCRETE: ODD JOBS
(B&W)
1-shot 3.50

[PAUL CHADWICK'S] CONCRETE: STRANGE ARMOR
Dec. 1997–Apr. 1998
1 (of 5) 2.95
2 thru 5 . . . . @2.95

CONCRETE: THINK LIKE A MOUNTAIN
1 thru 6 PC,GfD(c) . . . . @2.95
TPB PC,GfD(c) 17.95

CORMAC MAC ART
1 Robert E. Howard adapt. 2.25
2 . . . . 2.25
3 . . . . 2.25

CORNY'S FETISH
April 1998
GN by Renee French, 64pg. 4.95

COUTOO
1 Lt. Joe Kraft 3.50

CREEPY
(B&W)
1 KD,TS,GC,SL,Horror 3.95
2 TS,CI,DC,Demonic Baby 3.95
3 JM,TS,JG,V:Killer Clown 3.95
4 TS,Final issue 3.95

CREATURE FROM THE BLACK LAGOON
1 Movie Adaptation 4.95

CRITICAL ERROR
1 rep.Classic JBy story 2.75

[ANDREW VACHSS'] CROSS
0 GfD(c),I:Cross,Rhino,Princess . 2.50
1 thru 7 . . . . @2.95

CUD COMICS
(B&W) 1995
1 thru 8 by Terry LaBan . . . . @2.95

THE CURSE OF DRACULA
July 1998
1 (of 3) MWn,GC 2.95
2 thru 3 . . . . @2.95

CYBERANATICS
HC by Jerry Prosser & Rick Geary 14.95

DANGER UNLIMITED
Dark Horse-Legend
1 JBy(a&s),KD,I:Danger Unlimited,
   B:BU:Torch of Liberty 2.50
2 JBy(a&s),KD,O:DangerUnlimited 2.25
3 JBy(a&s),KD,O:Torch of Liberty 2.25

Danger Unlimited #3
© Dark Horse Comics

4 JBy(a&s),KD,Final Issue 2.25
TPB rep. #1–#4 . . . . 14.95

DARK HORSE CLASSICS
(B&W)
1 Last of the Mohicans 3.95
2 20,000 Leagues Under the Sea 3.95

DARK HORSE CLASSICS: ALIENS VS. PREDATOR
Feb. 1997
1 thru 6 Rep. . . . . @2.95

DARK HORSE CLASSICS: GODZILLA, KING OF THE MONSTERS
July 1998
1 RSd,SBi,now color 2.95
2 rep. from 1995 . . . . 2.95

DARK HORSE CLASSICS: PREDATOR: JUNGLE TALES
1-shot Rep. 2.95

DARK HORSE CLASSICS: STAR WARS— DARK EMPIRE
1997
1 rep. by Tom Veitch,CK,DvD(c) . 2.95
2 thru 6 rep., DvD(c) . . . . @2.95

DARK HORSE CLASSICS: TERROR OF GODZILLA
Aug. 1998
1 by Kazuhisa Iwata, AAd(c) 2.95

DARK HORSE COMICS
1 RL,CW,F:Predator,Robocop,
   I:Renegade,Time Cop,(double
   gatefold cover) 4.00
2 RL,CW,F:Predator,Robocop,
   Renegade,Time Cop 3.00

3 CW,F:Robocop,Time Cop,Aliens,
   Indiana Jones 3.00
4 F:Predator,Aliens,Ind.Jones . . 2.75
5 F:Predator,E:Aliens 2.75
6 F:Robocop,Predator, E:Indiana
   Jones 2.75
7 F:Robocop,Predator,B:StarWars 6.00
8 B&I:X,Robocop 8.00
9 F:Robocop,E:Star Wars 4.00
10 E:X,B:Godzilla,Predator, James
   Bond 3.50
11 F:Godzilla,Predator,James
   Bond,B:Aliens 2.75
12 F:Predator 2.75
13 F:Predator,B:Thing 2.75
14 MiB(s),B:The Mark 2.75
15 MiB(s),E:The Mark,B:Aliens . . 2.75
16 B:Predator,E:Thing,Aliens 2.75
17 B:Aliens,Star Wars:Droids 2.75
18 E:Predator 2.75
19 RL(c),B:X,E:Star Wars:Droids,
   Aliens 2.75
20 B:Predator 2.75
21 F:Mecha 2.75
22 B:Aliens, E:Mecha 2.75
23 B:The Machine 2.50

Dark Horse Comics #9
© Dark Horse Comics

24 The Machine 2.50
25 Final issue 2.50

DARK HORSE DOWNUNDER
(B&W)
1 F:Australian Writers 2.50
2 Australian Writers 2.50
3 Australian Writers, finale 2.50

DARK HORSE MONSTERS
Feb. 1997
1-shot 2.95

DARK HORSE PRESENTS
(B&W)
1 PC,I:Concrete 12.00

DARK HORSE

1a 2nd printing	2.50
2 PC,Concrete	8.00
3 Boris theBear,Concrete	5.00
4 PC,Concrete	4.00
5 PC,Concrete	4.00
6 PC,Concrete	4.00
7 I:MONQ	3.50
8 PC,Concrete	3.50
9	3.50
10 PC,Concrete, I:Masque	8.00
11 Masque	7.00
12 PC,Concrete, Masque	5.00
13 Masque	5.00
14 PC,Concrete, Masque	5.00
15 Masque	5.00
16 PC,Concrete, Masque	5.00
17	3.00
18 PC,Concrete, Mask	5.00
19 Masque	5.00
20 double,Flaming Carrot	6.00
21 Masque	5.00
22	3.00
23	3.00
24 PC,I:Aliens	12.00
25 thru 31	@3.00
32	4.00
33	3.00
34 Aliens	4.00
35 Predator	4.00
36 Aliens vs.Predator	4.00
36a painted cover	5.00
37	2.50
38	2.50
39	2.50
40 I:The Aerialist	2.50
41	2.50
42 Aliens	5.00
43 Aliens	4.00
44	2.50
45	2.50
46 Predator	4.00
47	2.50
48 with 2-card strip	2.50
49 with 2-card strip	2.50
50 inc.'Heartbreakers', with 2-card strip	2.50
51 FM(c),inc.'Sin City'	5.00

52 FM,inc. 'Sin City'	3.00
53 FM,inc. 'Sin City'	3.00
54 FM,Sin City;JBy Preview of Next Men Pt.1	5.00
55 FM,Sin City;JBy Preview of Next Men (JBy) Pt.2	4.00
56 FM,Sin City, JBy, Next MenPt.3 Aliens Genocide(prologue)	3.00
57 FM,SinCity;JBy Next Men Pt.4	3.00
58 FM, Sin City,Alien Fire	2.50
59 FM, Sin City,Alien Fire	2.50
60 FM,Sin City	2.50
61 FM,Sin City	2.50
62 FM,E:Sin City	2.50
63 Moe,Marie Dakar	2.50
64 MWg,R:The Aerialist	2.50
65 B:Accidental Death	2.50
66 PC,inc.Dr.Giggles	2.50
67 B:Predator story (lead in to "Race War"),double size	3.95
68 F:Predator,Swimming Lessons (Nestrobber tie-in)	2.50
69 F:Predator	2.50
70 F:Alec	2.50
71 F:Madwoman	2.50
72 F:Eudaemon	2.50
73 F:Eudaemon	2.50
74	2.50
75 F:Chairman	2.50
76 F:Hermes Vs.the Eye,Ball Kid	2.50
77 F:Hermes Vs.the Eye,Ball Kid	2.50
78 F:Hermes Vs.the Eye,Ball Kid	2.50
79 B:Shadow Empires Slaves	2.50
80 AAd,I:Monkey Man & O'Brien	6.00
81 B:Buoy	2.50
82 B:Just Folks	2.50
83 Last Impression	2.50
84 MBn,F:Nexus,E:Hermes Vs.the Eye Ball Kid	2.50
85 Winner Circle	2.50
86	2.50
87 F:Concrete	2.50
88 Hellboy	3.00
89 Hellboy	3.00
90 Hellboy	3.00
91 Blackheart, Baden	3.00
92 Too Much Coffee Man	7.00
93 Cud, Blackheart,Coffee Man	9.00
94 A:Eyeball Kid,Coffee Man	7.00
95 Too Much Coffee Man	8.00
96 Kabuli Kid	2.50
97 F:Kabuki Kid	2.50
98 Pot Full of Noodles	2.50
99 Anthology title	2.50
100–#1 Lance Blastoff	2.50
100–#2 Hellboy	2.50
100–#3 Concrete	2.50
100–#4 Black Cross	2.50
100–#5 Pan Fried Girl	2.50
101 BW,F:Aliens	2.50
102 F:Mr. Painter	2.50
103 F:The Pink Tornado	3.00
104 F:The Pink Tornado	3.00
105 F:The Pink Tornado	3.00
106 F:Godzilla	3.00
107 F:Rusty Razorclam	3.00
108	2.95
109	2.95
110	2.95
111	2.95
112 three stories, concl.	2.95
113	2.95
114 F:Star Slammers	2.95
115 flip-book	2.95
116	2.95

117 F:Aliens	2.95
118	2.95
119	2.95
120 "One Last Job"	2.95
121 F: Jack Zero	2.95
122 "Lords of Misrule"	2.95
123 F: Jack Zero	2.95
124 F:Predator	2.95
125 F:Nocturnals	2.95
126 flip book, 48pg	3.95
127 F:The Nocturnals	2.95
128	2.95
129 F:Hammer	2.95
130 F:Zombie Worl	2.95
131 F:Girl Crazy	2.95
132 flip book	2.95
133 F:Tarzan	2.95
134 F:The Dirty Pair	2.95
135	2.95
Fifth Anniv. Special DGi,PC, SBi,CW,MW,FM,Sin City, Aliens,Give Me Liberty	8.00
Milestone Ed.#1,rep.DHP#1	2.25
TPB rep.Sin City	6.00
TPB Best of DHP #1–#20	9.95
TPB Best of DHP #1–#20 2nd edition	9.95
TPB Best of DHP #21–#30	8.95
TPB Best of DHP #31–#50	8.95
Ann. 1997	4.95
Ann. 1998	4.95

DARK HORSE PRESENTS: ALIENS

1 Rep.	4.95
1a Platinum Edition	8.00

DEADFACE: DOING ISLANDS WITH BACCHUS
(B&W)

1 rep. Bacchus apps.	2.95
2 rep. inc.'Book-Keeper of Atlantis	2.95

DEADFACE: EARTH, WATER, AIR & FIRE
(B&W)

1 Bacchus & Simpson in Sicily	2.50
2 A:Don Skylla	2.50
3 Mafia/Kabeirol-War prep.	2.50
4 Last issue	2.50

DEAD IN THE WEST
(B&W)

1 TT,Joe Landsdale adapt.	5.00
2 TT,adapt.	5.00

DEAD IN THE WEST

1 TT(c)	3.95

DEAD OR ALIVE— A CYBERPUNK WESTERN
April 1998

1 (of 4) by Tatjana and Alberto Ponticelli	2.50
2 thru 4	@2.50

DEADLINE USA
(B&W)

1 rep. Deadline UK,Inc. Tank Girl Johnny Nemo	9.95
2 inc. Tank Girl,Johnny Nemo	9.95

Dark Horse Presents #26
© Dark Horse Comics

DECADE OF
DARK HORSE, A
1 (of 4) inc. Star Wars, Nexus,
   Ghost 2.95
2 thru 4 . . . . @2.95

[RANDY BOWEN'S]
DECAPITATOR
June 1998
1 (of 4) GEr,DoM 2.95
2 GEr, ... 2.95
3 MMi,KJo,AAl 2.95
4 . . . . 2.95

DEVIL CHIEF
1 I:Devil Chief 2.50

DIRTY PAIR
(B&W) Manga
TPB Book 3 A Plague of Angels by
  Adam Warren & Toren Smith 12.95
TPB Dangerous Acquaintances . 12.95
TPB Biohazards 12.95

DIRTY PAIR: FATAL
BUT NOT SERIOUS
Manga
1 R:Kei,Yuri 2.95
2 V:Kevin Sleet,Yuri 2.95
3 Anti Yuri 2.95
4 V:Terrorists 2.95
5 conclusion 2.95

DIRTY PAIR: SIM HELL
(B&W) Manga
1 thru 4 by Adam Warren . . . . @3.25
TPB rep. #1–#4 . . . . 13.95

DIVISION 13
1 . . . . 2.50
2 . . . . 2.50
3 A:Payback 2.50
4 Carnal Genesis 2.50

Dr. Giggles #2 © Dark Horse Comics

DOC SAVAGE: CURSE
OF THE FIRE GOD
1 R:Man of Bronze 2.95
2 Exploding Plane 2.95
3 & 4 . . . . @2.95

DR. GIGGLES
1 Horror movie adapt. 2.50
2 Movie adapt.contd. 2.50

DOMINION
(B&W) Manga
TPB 1 by Masamune Shirow . . . 15.00
TPB 2nd printing 14.95

DOMINION: CONFLICT 1
— NO MORE NOISE
(B&W) Manga 1996
1 thru 6 by Masamune Shirow   @2.95
TPB series rep. 14.95

DOMINION SPECIAL:
PHANTOM OF
THE AUDIENCE
(B&W) Manga
1-shot by Masamune Shirow 2.50

DOMU:
A CHILD'S DREAMS
(B&W) Manga
1 Psychic Warfare 5.95
2 Murders Continue 5.95
3 Psychic war conclusion 5.95
TPB by Katsuhiro Otomo 17.95

DRACULA
1 Movie Adaptation 4.95

DRAKUUN: RISE OF
THE DRAGON PRINCESS
(B&W) Feb. 1997
1 by Johji Manabe 2.95
2 thru 6 (of 6) . . . . @2.95
TPB rep. 12.95

DRAKUUN: THE REVENGE
OF GUSTAV
(B&W) Aug. 1997
1 by Johji Manabe 2.95
2 thru 6 (of 6) F:Karula . . . . . . @2.95

DRAKUUN: SHADOW
OF THE WARLOCK
Feb. 1998
1 (of 6) by Johji Manabe 2.95
2 thru 6 . . . . @2.95

EDGAR RICE
BURROUGHS'
RETURN OF TARZAN
April 1997
1 adapted by Thomas Yeates &
  John Totleben 2.95
2 thru 3 . . . . @2.95

EDGAR RICE
BURROUGHS' TARZAN:
CARSON OF VENUS
May 1998
1 (of 4) by Darko Macan and Igor
  Kordey, adaptation of novels,
  F:Carson Napier 2.95
2 thru 4 . . . . @2.95

EDGAR RICE
BURROUGHS' TARZAN:
THE LOST ADVENTURE
1 Lost Manuscript 2.95
2 V:Gorgo the Buffalo 2.95
3 V:Bandits 2.95
4 V:Bandits 2.95
HC 19.95
HC lim. ed. 100.00

EDGAR RICE
BURROUGHS' TARZAN
Mugambi
1 by Bruce Jones, Christopher
   Schenck & Thomas Yeates,
   Betrayed by 3 man-beasts . . . 2.95
2 "Tarzan's Jungle Fury" 2.95
3 "Tarzan's Jungle Fury" 2.95
4 vs. the Tara virus 2.95
5 Cure to the Tara virus 2.95
6 . . . . 2.95
Tarzan and the Legion of Hate
7 by Allan Gross, Christopher
   Schenck, George Freeman . . . 2.95
8 pt.2 . . . . 2.95
9 pt.3 . . . . 2.95
10 pt.4, concl.. . . . . 2.95
Le Monstre, June 1997
11 pt.1 . . . . 2.95
12 pt.2 Bernie Wrightson(c) 2.95
Modern Prometheus, Aug. 1997
13 pt.1 MK(c) in New York 2.95
14 pt.2 MK(c) 2.95
Tooth and Nail, Oct. 1997
15 pt.1 MSh(c) 2.95
16 pt.2 . . . . 2.95
TPB adapts #11–#16 . . . . 16.95
Tarzan vs. the Moon Men
17 pt.1 TT,AW,TY 2.95
18 pt.2 TT,AW,TY 2.95
19 pt.3 TT,AW,TY 2.95
20 pt.4 TT,AW,TY 2.95
Primeval
21 pt.1 MGr 2.95
22 pt.2 MGr 2.95
23 pt.3 MGr 2.95
24 pt.4 MGr 2.95
GN RsM The Land That Time
  Forgot 12.95

EGON
Jan.–Feb. 1998
1 and 2 . . . . @2.95

EIGHTH WONDER, THE
Nov. 1997
1-shot by Peter Janes & Killian
  Plunkett 2.95

ELRIC: STORMBRINGER
Dark Horse/Topps 1996
1 by Michael Moorcock & CR . . . 2.95
2 thru 7 (of 7) . . . . @2.95

All comics prices listed are for *Near Mint* condition.

TPB rep. series 17.95

ENEMY
1 MZ(c),StG(s),I:Enemy 2.75
2 MZ(c),StG(s),F:Heller 2.75
3 MZ(c),StG(s),A:Heller 2.50
4 . . . . 2.50
5 final issue 2.95
TPB 14.95

ENO AND PLUM
Sept. 1997
TPB 12.95

EUDAEMON, THE
1 Nel,I:New Eudaemon 3.00
2 Nel,V:Mordare 2.75
3 Nel,V:Mordare 2.75

EVIL DEAD III: ARMY OF DARKNESS
1 JBo,Movie adaptation 4.00
2 JBo,Movie adaptation 3.50
3 JBo,Movie adaptation 3.00

EXOTICS, THE
TPB by Moebius 7.95

EYEBALL KID
(B&W)
1 I:Eyeball Kid 2.25
2 V:Stygian Leech 2.25
3 V:Telchines Brothers,last iss. . . 2.25

FAT DOG MENDOZA
(B&W)
1 I&O:Fat Dog Mendoza 2.50

FAX FROM SARAJEVO
Oct. 1996
GN JKu, 224 pg. 24.95

FLAMING CARROT
(B&W)
18 . . . . 3.50

*Flaming Carrot #25
© Dark Horse Comics*

18a Ash-Can-Limited 5.00
19 . . . . 2.00
20 . . . . 2.00
21 . . . . 2.00
22 . . . . 2.00
23 . . . . 2.00
24 . . . . 3.00
25 F:TMNT,Mysterymen, with 2-card
  strip 3.00
26 A:TMNT 2.50
27 TM(c),A:TMNT conclusion 2.50
28 . . . . 2.50
29 Man in the Moon,Iron City 2.50
30 V:Man in the Moon 2.50
31 A:Fat Fury 2.50
Ann. 1 by Bob Burden 5.00
TPB Man of Mystery, B&W 12.95
TPB The Wild Shall Wild Remain 17.95
TPB Flaming Carrot's Greatest Hits,
  rep. #12–#18 . . . . 17.95

FLAXEN
1 Based on Model,w/poster 2.95

FLOATERS
(B&W)
1 thru 6 From Spike Lee 2.50

FOOT SOLDIERS, THE
1 thru 4 by Jim Krueger 2.95
TPB 14.95
See also Image Comics

FRANKENSTEIN
1 Movie Adaptation 3.95

FREAKSHOW
1 JBo,DMc,KB, "Wanda the Worm
Woman," "Lillie" 9.95

GAMERA
Aug. 1996
1 (of 4) by Dave Chipps & Mozart
  Couto 2.95
2 thru 4 . . . . @2.95

GHOST
Comics' Greatest World
Spec. AH(c) 3.95

GHOST
1 by Eric Luke, R:Ghost 2.50
2 AH,MfM,Arcadia Nocturne,pt.2 . 2.50
3 Arcadia Nocturn,pt.3 . . . . 2.50
4 . . . . 2.50
5 V:Predator 2.50
6 . . . . 2.50
7 Hell Night 2.50
8 thru 20 . . . . @2.50
21 Two heroes, one room 2.50
22 "The key is forever beyond your
  reach" 2.50
23 I: The Goblins 2.50
24 X is dead 2.50
25 double size 3.95
26 Fairytale version 2.95
27 . . . . 2.95
28 CW(c),Painful Music, pt.1 . . . 2.95
29 CW(c),Painful Music, pt.2 . . . 2.95
30 CW(c),Painful Music, pt.3 . . . 2.95
31 CW(c),Painful Music, pt.4 . . . 2.95
32 A Pathless Land 2.95
33 Jade Cathedral, pt.1 . . . . 2.95

Ghost #15 © Dark Horse

34 Jade Cathedral, pt.2 . . . . 2.95
35 Jade Cathedral, pt.3 . . . . 2.95
36 Jade Cathedral, pt.4 . . . . 2.95
Spec.#2 Immortal Coil 3.95
TPB Ghost Stories 8.95
TPB Ghost: Nocturnes 9.95
TPB Exhuming Elisa 17.95

GHOST/HELLBOY COLLECTION
TPB 4.95

GHOST AND THE SHADOW
Spec. 1-shot 2.95

GHOST IN THE SHELL
Manga
1 Manga Style 3.95
2 Wetware Virus 3.95
3 Killer Robots 3.95
4 Rookie Cop Killed 3.95
5 F:Major Kusangi 3.95
6 . . . . 3.95
7 Kusanagi in Jail 3.95
8 final issue 3.95
TPB by Masamune Shirow 24.95

G.I. JOE
1 by Mike Barr & Tatsuya Ishida . 1.95
2 thru 4 . . . . @2.50

GIRL CRAZY
TPB by Gilbert Hernandez,
  rep.#1–#3 . . . . 9.95

GIVE ME LIBERTY
1 FM/DGb, Homes & Gardens . . 6.00
2 FM/DGb 5.00
3 and 4 FM/DGb . . . . @5.00
TPB 16.00

GODZILLA
(B&W) 1988
1 Japanese Manga 3.50
2 thru 6 . . . . @2.25
Spec #1 . . . . 1.50
TPB 2nd printing 17.95

GODZILLA
COLOR SPECIAL
1 AAd,R:Godzilla,V:Gekido-Jin . . 4.00
1a rep (1998) 2.95

GODZILLA
1995
0 RSd,The King of Monsters is
  back! 3.00
1 R:Godzill 2.50
2 V:Cybersaur 2.50
3 I:Bagorah the Bat Creature . . . 2.50
4 V:Bagorah,Cybersaur 2.50
5 V:U.S. Army 2.50
6 thru 14 . . . . @2.50
15 "Thunder Downunder" 2.95
16 "Thunder in the Past" 2.95
TPB Past, Present, Future 17.95

GODZILLA VS. BARKLEY
1 MBn(s),JBt,DvD 3.50

GODZILLA VS.
HERO ZERO
1 Tatsuya Ishida 2.50

GRENDEL CLASSICS
1 Rep.#18–#19 Comico series . . 3.95

GRENDEL CYCLE
1 Grendel History 5.95

GRENDEL: DEVIL BY
THE DEED
1993
1 MWg,RRa 3.95
1 representation (1997) 3.95

GRENDEL:
DEVIL'S LEGACY
Aug. 1996
1 (of 12) by Matt Wagner 2.75
2 thru 3 . . . . @2.75
TPB Devils and Deaths 16.95

GRENDEL: HOMECOMING
1 Babylon Crash 2.95
2 Babylon Crash pt. 2 . . . . 2.95
3 Too Dead To Die 2.95

GRENDEL: WAR CHILD
1 MWg 4.00
2 thru 9 MWg 3.00
10 MWg, final issue, dbl.size 4.00
TPB 18.95
HC signed and numbered 100.00

GRENDEL TALES:
DEVIL'S APPRENTICE
Sept. 1997
1 (of 3) 2.95
2 thru 3 . . . . @2.95

GRENDEL TALES:
DEVILS AND DEATHS
1 . . . . 2.95
2 . . . . 2.95
TPB rep. Devils and Deaths plus
  Devil's Choices 16.95

GRENDEL TALES:
DEVIL'S CHOICES
1 F:Goran 2.95
2 Marica 2.95
3 Marica vs. Goran 2.95
4 conclusion 2.95

GRENDEL TALES:
FOUR DEVILS, ONE HELL
1 MWg(c),F:Four Grendels 3.50
2 MWg(c),F:Four Grendels 3.50
3 MWg(c),F:Four Grendels 3.50
4 MWg(c),F:Four Grendels 3.50
5 MWg(c),F:Four Grendels 3.50
6 MWg(c),last issue 3.25
TPB Rep. #1–#6 . . . . 17.95

Grendel Tales: The Devil in our
Midst #2 © Dark Horse Comics

GRENDEL TALES:
THE DEVIL IN
OUR MIDST
1 MWg(c) 3.50
2 MWg(c) 3.25
3 MWg(c) 2.95
4 & 5 . . . . @2.95
TPB series rep. 15.95

GRENDEL TALES:
THE DEVIL MAY CARE
1 thru 6 mini-series 2.95

GRENDEL TALES:
THE DEVIL'S HAMMER
1 MWg(a&s),I:Petrus Christus . . . 3.50
2 MWg(a&s),A:P.Christus 3.25
3 MWg(a&s),last issue 3.25

GRIFTER AND THE MASK
Sept. 1996
1 by Seagle, Lima & Pimentel . . . 2.50
2 . . . . 2.50

GUFF
April 1998
1-shot by Sergio Aragones, flip
  book, with Meanie Babies card,
  B&W 1.95

GUNSMITH CATS
(B&W) Manga
1 I:Rally & Mini May 2.95
2 Revolver Freak 2.50
3 . . . . 2.95
4 V:Bonnie and Clyde 2.95
5 V:Bonnie and Clyde 2.95
6 Hostage Situation 2.95
7 thru 10 (10 part series) 2.95
TPB Misfire rep. #7–#10 &
  Return of Gray #1–#3 . . . . . . 12.95

GUNSMITH CATS:
BAD TRIP
(B&W) June 1998
1 (of 6) by Kenichi Sonoda 2.95
2 thru 3 . . . . @2.95

GUNSMITH CATS:
BONNIE & CLYDE
TPB by Kenichi Sonoda 12.95

GUNSMITH CATS:
GOLDIE VS. MISTY
(B&W) Nov. 1997
1 (of 7) by Kenichi Sonoda 2.95
2 thru 7 . . . . @2.95

GUNSMITH CATS:
SHADES OF GRAY
(B&W) May 1997
1 (of 5) by Kenichi Sonoda 2.95
2 thru 5 (of 5) . . . . @2.95

GUNSMITH CATS:
THE RETURN OF GRAY
(B&W) Aug. 1996
1 thru 7 by Kenichi Sonoda . . @2.95
TPB rep. series 17.95

HAMMER OF
GOD: PENTATHLON
1 MiB(s),NV 2.50

HAMMER OF GOD:
BUTCH
1 MBn 2.50
2 and 3 MBn . . . . @2.50

THE HAMMER:
UNCLE ALEX
Aug. 1998
1-shot KJo 2.95

HAPPY BIRTHDAY
MARTHA WASHINGTON
1 Frank Miller 2.95

HARD BOILED
1 GfD 6.00
2 and 3 . . . . @5.00
TPB 14.95
HC 99.95
TPB Big Damn Hard Boiled 29.95

HARD LOOKS
(B&W)
1 thru 10 AVs Adaptations . . . @2.50
Book One 14.95
TPB AVs 17.95

HARLAN ELLISON'S DREAM CORRIDOR
1 Various stories 2.95
2 Various stories 2.95
3 JBy, I Have No Mouth and I Must
   Scream and other stories . . . 2.95
4 Catman 2.95
5 . . . . 2.95
6 Opposites Attract 2.95
Spec.#1 Various stories 4.95
TPB 18.95
HC, vol. 1 limited 70.00

HARLAN ELLISON'S DREAM CORRIDOR QUARTERLY
Aug. 1996
1 . . . . 5.95
2 . . . . 5.95

HEARTBREAKERS
1 . . . . 2.95

HELLBOY
Christmas Special (1997) MMi,
   48pg. 3.95
Hellboy, Jr. Halloween Special . . . 3.95
TPB The Lost Army 14.95
TPB The Chained Coffin & Others 17.95

HELLBOY: ALMOST COLOSSUS
1 (of 2) MMi, sequel to *Wake the
   Devil* 2.95
2 (of 2) 2.95

HELLBOY: SEEDS OF DESTRUCTION
Legend/Dark Horse
1 JBy,MMi,AAd,V:Vampire Frog,
   BU:Monkeyman & O'Brien . . . 4.00
2 MMi(c),JBy,AAd,BU:Monkeyman
   & O'Brien 3.00
3 MMi(c),JBy,AAd,BU:Monkeyman
   & O'Brien 3.00
4 MMi(c),JBy,AAd,BU:Monkeyman
   & O'Brien 3.00
TPB Seed of Destruction 17.95

HELLBOY: WAKE THE DEVIL
Legend
1 (of 5) MMi 2.95
2 thru 5 . . . . @2.95
TPB Wake The Devil 17.95

HELLHOUNDS
(B&W)
1 I:Hellhounds 2.50
2 thru 6 A:Hellhounds . . . . . . @2.50

HELLHOUNDS: PANZER CORPS
(B&W) 1994
1 thru 6 . . . . @2.95
TPB 14.95

HERBIE
1 JBy,reps.& new material 2.50
2 Reps.& new material 2.50

HERETIC, THE
Nov. 1996
1 (of 4) by Rich DiLeonardo, Joe
   Phillips & Dexter Vines 2.95
2 thru 4 . . . . @2.95

HERMES VS. THE EYEBALL KID
1 thru 3 Symphony of Blood 2.95

HERO ZERO
1 First and last issue 2.50

H.P.'S ROCK CITY
TPB by Moebius 7.95

HYPERSONIC
Nov. 1997
1 (of 4) DAn,GEr 2.95
2 thru 4 . . . . @2.95

INDIANA JONES AND THE ARMS OF GOLD
1 In South America 2.75
2 In South America 2.75
3 V:Incan Gods 2.75
4 . . . . 2.50

Indiana Jones and the Fate of Atlantis #2 © Dark Horse Comics

INDIANA JONES AND THE FATE OF ATLANTIS
1 DBa,Search for S.Hapgood with
   2-card strip 5.00
1a 2nd printing 3.00
2 DBa,Lost Dialogue of Plato with
   2-card strip 3.00
3 Map Room of Atlantis 3.00
4 Atlantis, Last issue 3.00
TPB 13.95

INDIANA JONES AND THE GOLDEN FLEECE
1 SnW 2.75
2 SnW 2.50

INDIANA JONES AND THE IRON PHOENIX
1 . . . . 2.50
2 V:Nazis 2.50
3 A:Nadia Kirov 2.50
4 V:Undead 2.50

INDIANA JONES AND THE SARGASSO PIRATES
1 thru 4 . . . . @2.50

INDIANA JONES AND THE SHRINE OF THE SEA DEVIL
1 . . . . 2.50

INDIANA JONES AND THE SPEAR OF DESTINY
1 I:Spear T/Pierced Christ 2.50
2 DSp, with Henry Jones 2.50
3 Search for the Shaft 2.50

INDIANA JONES: THUNDER IN THE ORIENT
1 DBa(a&s),in Tripoli 2.75
2 DBa(a&s),Muzzad Ram 2.75
3 DBa(a&s),V:Sgt.Itaki 2.75
4 DBa(a&s),In Hindu Kush 2.75
5 DBa(a&s),V:Japanese Army . . 2.75
6 DBa(a&s),last issue 2.75

INSTANT PIANO
1 Offbeat humor 3.95
2 . . . . 3.95
3 Various stories 3.95
4 Devil Puppet 3.95

IRON HAND OF ALMURIC
(B&W)
1 Robert E. Howard adaption . . 2.00
2 A:Cairn,V:Yagas 2.25
3 V:Yasmeena,The Hive Queen . 2.00
4 Conclusion 2.25
GN 10.95

JAMES BOND 007: QUASIMODO GAMBIT
1 I:Maximillion Quasimodo 3.95
2 V:Fanatical Soldiers 3.95
3 V:Steel 3.95

JAMES BOND 007: SERPENT'S TOOTH
1 PG,DgM,V:Indigo 5.50
2 PG,DgM,V:Indigo 5.00
3 PG,DgM 5.25
TPB 15.95

JAMES BOND 007: SHATTERED HELIX
1 V:Cerberus 2.50
2 V:Cerberus 2.50

JAMES BOND 007: A SILENT ARMAGEDDON
1 V:Troy 3.25
2 V:Omega 3.25
3 V:Omega 3.25

JOHN BOLTON'S STRANGE WINK
March 1998
1 (of 3) 2.95
2 thru 3 .... @2.95

JOHNNY DYNAMITE
1 .... 2.95
2 .... 2.95
3 V:Faust 2.95
4 Last issue 2.95

JONNY DEMON
1 SL(c),KBk,NV 2.75
2 SL(c),KBk,NV 2.75
2 SL(c),KBk,NV, final issue 2.50

JUNIOR CARROT PATROL
(B&W)
1 .... 2.00
2 .... 2.00

KELLY JONES' THE HAMMER
Sept. 1997
1 (of 4) KJo, horror series 2.95
2 KJo, ... 2.95

KINGS OF THE NIGHT
1 .... 2.25
2 end Mini-Series 2.25

KING TIGER/MOTORHEAD
1 (of 2) by D.G. Chichester, Karl
  Waller & Eric Shanower 2.95
2 .... 2.95

KLING KLANG KLATCH
GN 11.95

LAND OF NOD
(B&W) July 1997
1 (of 4) by Jay Stephens 2.95
2 thru 4 .... 2.95

THE LEGEND OF MOTHER SARAH
B&W, Manga
1 I:Mother Sarah 2.50
2 Sarah and Tsutsu 2.50
3 Firing Squad 2.50

4 F:Toki 2.50
5 Yunnel Town 2.50
6 Kill or Be Killed 2.95
7 Firing Squad 2.95
8 Conclusion 2.95
TPB The Tunnel Town 18.95

THE LEGEND OF MOTHER SARAH: CITY OF THE ANGELS
(B&W) Oct. 1996
1 (of 9) by Katsuhiro Otomo and
  Takumi Nagayasu 3.95
1 rep. (1997) 3.95
2 thru 4 .... 3.95
2 thru 4 rep. (1997) 3.95
5 Tsue a victim 3.95
6 Mother Teres questioned 3.95
7 put in front trenches 3.95
8 Teres suicide run 3.95
9 .... 3.95

THE LEGEND OF MOTHER SARAH: CITY OF THE CHILDREN
(B&W) 1995
1 thru 4 (7 part mini-series) .. @3.95

LORDS OF MISRULE
(B&W) Jan. 1997
1 by Dan Abnett, John Tomlinson,
  Steve White & Peter Snejbjerg 2.95
2 thru 6 .... @2.95

LOST IN SPACE
April 1998
1 (of 3) sequel to film 2.95
2 thru 3 GEr(c) .... @2.95
TPB rep. series, GEr(c) 7.95

THE LUCK IN THE HEAD
TPB 11.95

THE MACHINE
Comics Greatest World 1994
1 (a) The Barb Wire spin 2.50
2 V:Salvage 2.50
3 Freak Show 2.50
4 I:Skion 2.50

MADMAN
Legend 1994
1 MiA(s) 10.00
2 MiA(s) 9.00
3 MiA(s) 8.00
4 MiA(s),Muscleman 8.00
5 MiA(s),I:The Blast 7.00
6 MiA(s),A:Big Guy, Big Brain-o-
  rama,pt.1 .... 25.00
7 MiA(s),FM,A:Big Guy, Big Brain-
  o-rama,pt.2 .... 9.00
8 MiA(s) 5.00
9 Micro Madman 5.00
10 .... 5.00
11 .... 5.00
12 thru 14 .... @6.00
15 .... 12.00
Yearbook '95 TPB 17.95
Yearbook '96 TPB 17.95
TPB Vol. 1 .... 17.95
TPB Vol. 2 .... 17.95

HC Vol. 1 & Vol. 2, set 100.00

MADMAN/THE JAM
July 1998
1 (of 2) MiA 2.95
2 MiA 2.95

MADWOMAN OF THE SACRED HEART, THE
(B&W)
TPB by Alexandro Jodorowsky and
  Moebius 12.95

MAGIC: THE GATHERING
March 1998
1 (of 4) MGr,Initiation 2.95
2 MGr, Legacy 2.95
3 MGr, Crucible 2.95
4 MGr, Destiny 2.95

MAGNUS/NEXUS
Dark Horse/Valiant
1 MBn(s), SR 3.25
2 MBn(s), SR 3.25

MAN FROM THE CIGUIRI
TPB by Moebius 7.95

MARK, THE
1 LSn, in America 1.75
2 LSn 1.95
3 LSn 1.95
4 .... 1.95

MARK, THE
(B&W)
1 .... 1.95
2 thru 7 .... @1.75

MARK, THE
1 MiB(s),V:Archon 2.75
2 MiB(s),V:Archon 2.75
3 MiB(s),V:Archon,A:Pierce 2.75
4 MiB(s),last issue 2.75

The Mark #1 © Dark Horse Comics

MARK, THE
1 I:The Mark 2.50
2 V:Child Killer 2.50

MARSHALL LAW: BLOOD, SWEAT, AND FEARS
Feb. 1998
TPB 15.95

MARSHALL LAW: CAPE FEAR
1 KON 2.95

MARSHALL LAW: SECRET TRIBUNAL
1 KON 2.95
2 KON 2.95

MARSHALL LAW: SUPER BABYLON
1 KON 4.95

Martha Washington Goes To War #3
© Dark Horse Comics

MARTHA WASHINGTON GOES TO WAR
Dark Horse-Legends
1 FM(s),DGb, V:Fat Boys Corp. . 3.25
2 FM(s),DGb, V:Fat Boys Corp. . 3.25
3 FM(s),DGb, V:Fat Boys Corp. . 3.25
4 FM(s),DGb, V:Fat Boys Corp. . 3.25
5 FM(s),DBb, final issue 3.25
TPB Rep.#1–#5 . . . . 17.95

MARTHA WASHINGTON SAVES THE WORLD
Dec. 1997
1 (of 3) FM,DGb 2.95
2 thru 3 . . . . @2.95

MARTHA WASHINGTON STRANDED IN SPACE
1 . . . . 2.95

MASK, THE
0 . . . . 3.00
1 I:Lt.Kellaway Mask 6.00
2 V:Rapaz & Walter 5.00
3 O:Mask 5.00
4 final issue 5.00
TPB 14.95

MASK, THE
1 Movie Adaptation 3.00
2 Movie Adaptation 2.50

MASK, THE
(B&W)
0 'Who's Laughing Now' 6.00

MASK/MARSHALL LAW
Feb. 1998
1 (of 2) by Pat Mills and Kevin
O'Neill 2.95
2 concl. 2.95

MASK RETURNS, THE
1 inc.cut-out Mask 6.00
2 Mask's crime spree 4.00
3 . . . . 4.00
4 . . . . 4.00
TPB by John Arcudi & Doug
Mahnke 14.95

MASK STRIKES BACK, THE
[Mini-series]
1 Mask Strikes Back pt.1 . . . . . 2.50
2 Mask Strikes Back pt.2 . . . . . 2.50
3 Mask Strikes Back pt.3 . . . . . 2.50
4 DoM,Mask Strikes Back pt.4 . . 2.50
5 Mask Strikes Back,pt.5 . . . . . 2.50
TPB by John Arcudi, Doug Mahnke
& Keith Williams 14.95

MASK, THE: THE HUNT FOR GREEN OCTOBER
1 . . . . 2.50
2 Kellaway vs. Ray Tuttle 2.50
3 F:Emily Tuttle 2.50
4 final issue 2.50

MASK, THE: SOUTHERN DISCOMFORT
1 Mardi Gras time 2.50

MASK, THE: VIRTUAL SURREALITY
1-shot F: MMi,SA 2.95

MASK, THE: WORLD TOUR
1 thru 4 . . . . @2.50

MASK: TOYS IN THE ATTIC
Aug. 1998
1 (of 4) 2.95

MAXIMUM OVERLOAD
1 Masque (Mask) 15.00
2 thru 4 Mask . . . . @10.00

MAXIMUM OVERLOAD
1 thru 5 . . . . @3.95

MECHA
Comics Greatest World 1995
1 color 1.75
2 color 1.75
3 thru 6 B&W . . . . @1.75
Spec.(#1) CW(c),color 2.95

MEDAL OF HONOR
1 Ace of Aces 2.50
2 . . . . 2.50
3 Andrew's Raid 2.50
4 Frank Miller(c) 2.50
5 final issue 2.50

MEDAL OF HONOR SPECIAL
1 JKu 2.50

MEZZ GALACTIC TOUR
1 MBn,MV 2.50

THE MINOTAUR'S TALE
TPB by Al Davison 11.95

MR. MONSTER
(B&W)
1 . . . . 3.50
2 . . . . 2.50
3 Alan Moore story 2.50
4 . . . . 2.50
5 I:Monster Boy 2.00
6 . . . . 2.00
7 . . . . 2.00
8 V:Vampires (giant size) 4.95

MONKEYMAN & O'BRIEN
Legend
1 by Arthur Adams 2.95
2 and 3 . . . . @2.95
Spec. 2.95
TPB 16.95

MOTORHEAD
Comics Greatest World 1995
1 V:Predator 2.50
2 Laughing Wolf Carnival 2.50
3 V:Jackboot 2.50

MOTORHEAD SPECIAL
1 JLe(c),V:Mace Blitzkrieg 3.95

MYST: THE BOOK OF THE BLACK SHIPS
Aug. 1997
1 (of 4) from CD-Rom game . . . 2.95
2 thru 4 . . . . @2.95

NEW FRONTIER
(B&W)
1 From series in Heavy Metal . . . 2.75
2 Who Killed Ruby Fields? 2.75
3 Conclusion 2.75

NEW TWO FISTED TALES: VOL II
1 War stories 4.95

DARK HORSE

Next Men #10 © Dark Horse Comics

[JOHN BYRNE'S] NEXT MEN
0 Rep Next Men from Dark Horse
Presents 3.00
1 JBy,'Breakout'inc.trading card
certificate 5.00
1a 2nd Printing Blue 3.00
2 JBy,World View 4.00
3 JBy,A:Sathanis 4.00
4 JBy,A:Sathanis 4.00
5 JBy,A:Sathanis 4.00
6 JBy,O:Senator Hilltop,
Sathanis,Project Next Men . . . 3.50
7 JBy,I:M-4,Next Men Powers
explained 3.50
8 JBy,I:Omega Project,A:M-4 . . . 3.00
9 JBy,A:Omega Project,A:M-4 . . . 3.00
10 JBy,V:OmegaProject,A:M-4 . . . 3.00
11 JBy,V:OmegaProject,A:M-4 . . . 3.00
12 JBy,V:Dr.Jorgenson 3.00
13 JBy,Nathan vs Jack 3.00
14 JBy,I:Speedboy 2.75
15 JBy,in New York 2.75
16 JBy,Jasmine's Pregnant 2.75
17 FM(c),JBy,Arrested 2.75
18 JBy,On Trial 2.75
TPB rep.#1-6 . . . . 16.95
TPB Parallel Collection 16.95

NEXT MEN: FAITH
Dark Horse-Legend 1993
1 JBy(a&s),V:Dr.Trogg, Blue Dahlia 3.25
2 JBy,(a&s),F:Jack 2.75
3 MMi(c),JBy(a&s),I:Hellboy 3.50
4 JBy(a&s),Last issue 2.75
TPB Book Four 14.95

NEXT MEN: LIES
Dark Horse-Legend 1994
1 JBy 2.50
2 JBy 2.50
3 JBy 2.50
4 JBy 2.50
Book 6 TPB Lies 16.95

NEXT MEN: POWER
Dark Horse-Legend 1994
1 JBy(a&s) 2.75
2 JBy(a&s) 2.75
3 JBy(a&s) 2.75
4 JBY(a&s), final issue 2.50

NEXUS: ALIEN JUSTICE
1 . . . . 4.25
2 . . . . 4.25
3 . . . . 3.95
TPB 16.95

NEXUS: EXECUTIONER'S SONG
1 (of 4) by Mike Baron, Steve Rude
& Gary Martin 2.95
2 thru 4 . . . . @2.95

NEXUS: GOD CON
April 1997
1 (of 2) by Mike Baron, Steve Rude
& Gary Martin 2.95
2 . . . . 2.95

NEXUS: THE LIBERATOR
1 "Waking Dreams" 2.75
2 Civil War,D:Gigo 2.75
3 Civil War contd. 2.75
4 Last issue 2.75

NEXUS MEETS MADMAN
1-shot 2.95

NEXUS: NIGHTMARE IN BLUE
(B&W) July 1997
1 (of 4) MBn,SR,GyM 2.95
2 thru 4 . . . . @2.95

NEXUS: THE ORIGIN
1 SR,O:Nexus 4.95

NEXUS: OUT OF THE VORTEX
1 R:Nexus 2.50
2 Zolot & Nexus Together 2.50
3 O:Vortex 2.50

NEXUS: THE WAGES OF SIN
1 The Client 2.95
2 V:Munson 2.95
3 SR(c&a) Murders in New Eden 2.95

NIGHT BEFORE CHRISTMASK
1 Rick Geary 9.95

NINA'S NEW AND IMPROVED ALL-TIME GREATEST
1 Anthology: Nina Paley 2.50

NINTH GLAND, THE
(B&W) March 1997
1-shot by Renee French 3.95

NOCTURNALS: WITCHING HOUR
May 1998
1-shot by Dan Brereton 4.95

NOSFERATU
(B&W)
1 The Last Vampire 3.95
2 . . . . 2.95

OH MY GODDESS!
(B&W) Manga
1 . . . . 7.00
2 and 3 . . . . @5.00
4 thru 6 . . . . @4.00
Part 2
1 F:Keiichi 5.00
2 thru 8 . . . . @4.00
Part 3
1 Wishes are Granted 5.00
2 Love Potion Number 9 . . . . . . 4.00
3 thru 11 . . . . @3.50
TPB 1-555-Goddess 12.95
TPB Love Potion Number 9 . . . . 12.95
TPB Sympathy for the Devil 12.95
Spec. The Forgotten Promise . . 2.95
Spec. The Lunchbox of Love . . . 2.95
Spec. On a Wing and a Prayer . . 2.95
Spec. Meet Me by the Seashore . 3.95
Spec. The Queen of Vengeance . 2.95
Spec. You're So Bad 3.95
Spec. It's Lonely at the Top 3.50
Spec. Fallen Angel 3.95
Spec. Play the Game 3.95

OH MY GODDESS!: MARA STRIKES BACK
(B&W) Manga May 1997
1 (of 3) by Kosuke Fujishima . . . 3.50
2 & 3 . . . . @2.95

OH MY GODDESS!: MISS KEIICHI
(B&W) Manga March 1998
1 (of 2) by Kosuke Fujishima . . . 4.00
2 . . . . 4.00

OH MY GODDESS!: NINJA MASTER
(B&W) Jan.–Feb. 1998
1 & 2 by Kosuke Fujishima . . . @4.00

OH MY GODDESS!: TERRIBLE MASTER URD
(B&W)
1 (of 6) by Kosuke Fujishima . . . 3.00
2 thru 6 . . . . @3.00

OH MY GODDESS!: THE TRIALS OF MORISATO
(B&W) Jan. 1997
1 thru 3 by Kosuke Fujishima . @3.00

OH MY GODDESS: VALENTINE RHAPSODY
(B&W)
1 thru 5 (8 part mini-series) . . @3.00

DARK HORSE

OKTANE
1 R:Oktane 2.50
2 V:God Zero 2.50
3 V:God Zero 2.50
4 conclusion 2.50

ONE BAD RAT
1 BT 2.95
2 thru 4 . . . . @2.95

ONE-TRICK RIP-OFF
TPB by Paul Pope 12.95

ORION
(B&W) Manga
1 SF by Masamune Shirow 2.50
2 F:Yamata Empire 2.95
3 thru 6 . . . . @2.95
TPB 15.95

OTIS GOES HOLLYWOOD
(B&W) April 1997
1 (of 2) by Bob Fingerman 2.95
2 . . . . 2.95

OUTLANDERS
(B&W) Manga
1 . . . . 3.00
2 . . . . 2.50
3 thru 7 . . . . @2.00
8 thru 20 . . . . @2.25
21 Operation Phoenix 2.25
22 thru 24 . . . . @2.50
25 thru 29 with 2-card strip . . @2.50
30 . . . . 2.50
31 Tetsua dying 2.50
32 D:The Emperor 2.50
33 Story finale 2.50
#0 The Key of Graciale 2.75
TPB Vol. 1 by Johji Manabe . . 13.95
TPB Vol. 1 2nd edition 13.95
TPB Vol. 2 . . . . 13.95
TPB Vol. 2 2nd edition 13.95
TPB Vol. 3 . . . . 13.95
TPB Vol. 4 . . . . 12.95

Out of the Vortex #10
© Dark Horse Comics

TPB Vol. 5 . . . . 14.95

OUTLANDERS: EPILOGUE
(B&W)
1 . . . . 2.75

OUT OF THE VORTEX
Comics' Greatest World 1993
1 B:JOs(s),V:Seekers 2.25
2 MMi(c),DaW,A:Seekers 2.25
3 WS(c),E:JOs(s),DaW,A:Seeker,
　C:Hero Zero 2.25
4 DaW,A:Catalyst 2.25
5 V:Destroyers,A:Grace 2.25
6 V:Destroyers,A:Hero Zero . . . 2.25
7 AAd(c),DaW,V:Destroyers,
　A:Mecha 2.25
8 DaW,A:Motorhead 2.25
9 DaW,V:Motorhead 2.25
10 MZ(c), A:Division 13 . . . . . . 2.25
11 V:Reaver Swarm 2.50
12 Final issue 2.50

OZ
by Eric Shanower
TPB The Blue Witch of Oz 9.95
TPB The Forgotten Forest of Oz . 8.95
TPB The Ice King of Oz 8.95
TPB The Secret Island of Oz . . . 8.95

PETE & MOE VISIT PROFESSOR SWIZZLE'S ROBOTS
HC 14.95

PREDATOR
1 CW,Mini Series 7.00
1a 2ndPrinting 3.00
1b 3rdPrinting 2.50
2 CW 5.00
2a 2ndPrinting 3.00
3 CW 4.00
3a 2ndPrinting 2.50
4 CW 3.00
4a 2ndPrinting 2.50

PREDATOR: BAD BLOOD
1 CW,I:John Pulnick 2.75
2 CW,V:Predator 2.75
3 CW,V:Predator,C.I.A. 2.75
4 Last issue 2.50

PREDATOR: BIG GAME
1 Corp.Nakai Meets Predator . . . 3.50
2 Army Base Destroyed, with 2-
　card strip 3.50
3 Corp.Nakai Arrested, with 2-card
　strip 3.50
4 Nakai vs. Predator 3.50
TPB rep. #1–#4 . . . . 13.95
TPB rep. #1–#4, 2nd edition . . . 14.95

PREDATOR: BLOODY SANDS OF TIME
1 DBa,CW,Predator in WWI 3.50
2 DBa,CW, WWII cont'd. 3.25

PREDATOR: CAPTIVE
April 1998
1-shot 2.95

PREDATOR: COLD WAR
1 Predator in Siberia 3.50
2 U.S. Elite Squad in Siberia . . . 3.25
3 U.S. vs. USSR commandos . . . 3.25
4 U.S. vs. USSR in Siberia 3.00
TPB 13.95
TPB 2nd printing 13.95

PREDATOR: CONCRETE JUNGLE
TPB 14.95

PREDATOR: DARK RIVER
1 thru 4 by Verheiden,RoR,RM @2.95

PREDATOR: HELL & HOT WATER
1 thru 3 MSh, GC & GWt . . . . @2.95

PREDATOR: HELL COME A WALKIN'
Feb. 1998
1 (of 2) by Nancy Collins, Dean
　Ormston 2.95
2 concl. 2.95

PREDATOR: INVADERS FROM THE FOURTH DIMENSION
1 . . . . 3.95

PREDATOR JUNGLE TALES
1 Rite of Passage 2.95

PREDATOR: KINDRED
1 . . . . 2.50
2 thru 4 . . . . @2.95
TPB Kindred 14.95

PREDATOR: NEMESIS
Dec. 1997
1 (of 2) TTg(c) 2.95
2 . . . . 2.95

PREDATOR: PRIMAL
1997
1 (of 2) Kevin J. Anderson(s),
　ScK,Low 2.95
2 (of 2) 2.95

PREDATOR: RACE WAR
0 F:Serial Killer 2.75
1 V:Serial Killer 2.75
2 D:Serial Killer 2.75
3 in Prison 2.75
4 Last Issue 2.75
TPB Race War, serie rep. 17.95

PREDATOR: STRANGE ROUX
1-shot 2.95

PREDATOR 2
1 DBy, Movie Adapt Pt1 . . . . . . 3.50
2 MBr, Movie Adapt. Pt2 with 2-
　card strip 3.00

PREDATOR VS. JUDGE DREDD
Sept. 1997
1 (of 3) by John Wagner and
Enrique Alcatena 2.50
2 thru 3 . . . . @2.50

PREDATOR VS. MAGNUS ROBOT FIGHTER
Valiant/Dark Horse 1992
1 LW,A:Tekla 3.00
1a Platinum Ed. 5.00
1b Gold Ed. 3.00
2 LW,Magnus Vs. Predator, with 2-
card strip 3.00
TPB Rep. #1–#2 . . . . 7.95

PRIMAL
1 Contd.from Primal:from the
Cradle to the Grave 2.95
2 A:TJ Cyrus 2.50

PRIMAL FROM THE CRADLE TO THE GRAVE
GN 9.95

PROPELLER MAN
1 I:Propeller Man 2.95
2 O:Propeller Man,w/2 card strip . 2.95
3 V:Manipulator 2.95
4 V:State Police,w/2 card strip . . 2.95
5 V:Manipulator 2.95
6 V:Thing, w/2 card strip 2.95
7 . . . . 2.95
8 Last issue,w/2 card strip 2.95

PUMPKINHEAD
1 Based on the movie 2.50

RACE OF SCORPIONS
(B&W)
1 A:Argos,Dito,Alma,Ka 2.25

RACE OF SCORPIONS
Book 1 short stories 5.00
Book 2 . . . . 4.95
Book 3 . . . . 2.50
Book 4 Final issue 2.50

RACK & PAIN
1 GCa(c),I:Rack,Pain 2.50
2 GCa(c),V:Web 2.50
3 GCa(c),V:Web 2.50
4 GCa(c),Final Issue 2.50

RASCALS IN PARADISE
1 I:Spicy Sanders 3.95
2 . . . . 3.95
3 last issue 3.95
TPB Rep.#1–#3 . . . . 16.95

REAL ADVENTURES OF JONNY QUEST, THE
Sept. 1996
1 . . . . 2.95
3 thru 12 . . . . @2.95

REBEL SWORD
(B&W) Manga
1 by Yoshikazu Yashiko 2.50

2 . . . . 2.50
3 . . . . 2.50
4 V:Ruken 2.50
5 Choice of Jiro 2.50
6 R:Ruken 2.50

REDBLADE
1 V:Demons 2.50
2 V:Tull 2.50
3 Last Issue 2.50

RED ROCKET 7
Aug. 1997
1 (of 7) MiA 3.95
2 thru 7 . . . . @3.95
TPB rep. series, 208 pg 29.95

RING OF ROSES
(B&W)
1 Alternate world,1991 . . . . 2.50
2 Plague in London 2.50
3 Plague cont.A:Secret Brotherhood
of the Rosy Cross 2.50
4 Conclusion 2.50

RIO AT BAY
1 F:Doug Wildey art 2.95
2 F:Doug Wildey art 2.95
TPB 6.95

ROACHMILL
(B&W)
1 thru 8 . . . . @3.50
9 and 10 . . . . @2.00

GRANT • GNAZZO • PATTERSON
Robocop: Mortal Coils #2
© *Dark Horse Comics*

ROBOCOP: MORTAL COILS
1 V:Gangs 2.75
2 V:Gangs 2.75
3 V:Coffin,V:Gangs 2.75

ROBOCOP VERSUS TERMINATOR
1 FM(s),WS,w/Robocop cut-out . 3.50
2 FM(s),WS,w/Terminator cut-out 3.00

3 FM(s),WS,w/cut-out 3.00
4 FM(s),WS,Conclusion 3.00

ROBOCOP: PRIME SUSPECT
1 Robocop framed 2.75
2 thru 4 V:ZED-309s . . . . @2.50
Collected 13.95

ROBOCOP: ROULETTE
1 V:ED-309s 2.75
2 I:Philo Drut 2.75
3 V:Stealthbot 2.75
4 last issue 2.75

ROBOCOP 3
1 B:StG(s),Movie Adapt 2.75
2 V:Aliens,OCP 2.75
3 HNg,ANi(i) 2.75

ROCCO VARGAS
HC by Daniel Torres 30.00

ROCKETEER ADVENTURE MAGAZINE
1988–95
1 and 2 . . . . @4.00
3 . . . . 2.95
TPB Cliff's New York Adventure by
Dave Stevens 9.95

THE SAFEST PLACE
SC, SD 2.50

SCATTERBRAIN
June 1998
1 (of 4) MMi, ... 2.95
2 thru 4 . . . . @2.95

SECRET OF THE SALAMANDER
(B&W)
1 Jacquestardi, rep 2.95

SERGIO ARAGONES' BOOGEYMAN
(B&W) June 1998
1 (of 4) 2.95
2 thru 4 . . . . @2.95

SERGIO ARAGONES' GROO
Jan.–April 1998
1 (of 4) 2.95
2 thru 4 . . . . @2.95

SERGIO ARAGONES' LOUDER THAN WORDS
(B&W) July–Dec. 1997
1 (of 6) SA 2.95
2 thru 6 . . . . @2.95
TPB rep. series 12.95

SEX WARRIORS
1 I:Dakini 2.50
2 V:Steroids 2.50

THE SHADOW
1 MK 2.75

DARK HORSE

2 MK 2.50

THE SHADOW AND DOC SAVAGE

1 . . . . 2.95
2 The Shrieking Skeletons 2.95

THE SHADOW: HELL'S HEAT WAVE

1 Racial War 2.95
2 MK,V:Ghost 2.95
3 Final issue 2.95

THE SHADOW: IN THE COILS OF LEVIATHAN

1 MK,V:Monster 3.25
2 MK 3.25
3 MK,w/ GfD poster 3.25
4 MK,Final issue 3.25
TPB, reprints #1–#4 . . . . 13.95

THE SHADOW AND THE MYSTERIOUS 3

1 Three stories 2.95

SHADOW EMPIRE: FAITH CONQURES

1 CsM 2.95
2 CsM,V:Vaylen 2.95
3 CsM 2.95
4 CsM, final issue 2.95

- SIN CITY: A DAME TO KILL FOR
Dark Horse-Legend (B&W)

1 FM(a&s),I:Dwight,Ava 4.00
1a 2nd printing 3.00
2 FM(a&s),A:Ava 3.00
2a 2nd printing 2.50
3 FM(a&s),D:Ava's Husband . . . 3.00
3a 2nd printing 2.95
4 FM(a&s) 3.00
5 FM(a&s) 3.00
6 FM(a&s),Final issue 3.00
TPB rep. #1–#6, new pages . . 15.00
HC rep. #1–#6, new pages . . . 25.00
HC signed, limited 90.00

SIN CITY: A SMALL KILLING
Dark Horse-Legend

1 GN 14.00

SIN CITY: FAMILY VALUES
(B&W) 1997

GN 128pg by Frank Miller 10.00

SIN CITY: LOST, LONELY, AND LETHAL
Dark Horse–Legend

1-shot, two color 2.95

SIN CITY: SEX AND VIOLENCE
(B&W)

1-shot by Frank Miller 3.00

SIN CITY: SILENT NIGHT
Dark Horse-Legend (B&W) 1995

1-Shot 2.95

SIN CITY: THAT YELLOW BASTARD
(B&W)

1 F.Miller 4.00
2 . . . . 3.00
3 thru 6 . . . . @3.00
TPB by Frank Miller 15.00
HC 25.00
HC limited 90.00

SIN CITY: THE BABE WORE RED
Dark Horse-Legend 1994

1 PM 3.50

SIN CITY: THE BABE WORE RED AND OTHER STORIES
(B&W) 1996

1-shot, some nudity 3.00

SIN CITY: THE BIG FAT KILL
Dark Horse-Legend 1994

1 FM 4.00
2 FM 3.50
3 FM, Dump the Stiffs 3.50
4 FM, Town Without Pity 3.50
5 FM, final issue 3.50
TPB 15.00
HC 25.00

SOLO

1 and 2 . . . . @.50

SPACEHAWK
(B&W)

1 BW reps. 2.25
2 thru 4 BW . . . . @2.00
5 BW 2.50

SPACE USAGI

1 thru 3 Stan Sakai . . . . @2.95

SPECIES

1 Alien Human Hybrid 2.50
2 thru 4 SIL . . . . @2.50

SPECIES: HUMAN RACE

1 PhH 2.95
2 . . . . 2.95
3 SBi 2.95
4 (of 4) 2.95
TPB 11.95

SPIRIT OF WONDER
(B&W)

1 thru 5 by Kenji Tsuruia . . . . @2.95
TPB 12.95

STAN SHAW'S BEAUTY & THE BEAST

1 Based on the book 4.95

STARSTRUCK: THE EXPANDING UNIVERSE
(B&W)

1 Pt1 . . . . 2.95
2 Pt2, with 2-card strip 2.95

STAR WARS: A NEW HOPE— SPECIAL EDITION
Jan.–April 1997

1 EB, AW 2.95
2 thru 4 . . . . @2.95
TPB Rep. #1–#4 Hildebrandt(c) . . 9.95
Spec. Edition boxed set 30.00

STAR WARS: A NEW HOPE
(B&W) Manga July 1998

1 (of 4) by Tamaki Hisao, 96pg. . 9.95

Star Wars: Battle of the Bounty Hunters, © Dark Horse Comics

STAR WARS: BATTLE OF THE BOUNTY HUNTERS
July 1996

Pop-up Comic 17.95

STAR WARS: BOBA FETT—

1-shot Bounty on Bar-Kooda,48pg 3.95
1-shot When the Fat Lady Swings 3.95
1-shot Murder Most Foul 3.95
1-shot Twin Engins of Destruction 2.95
TPB Death, Lies & Treachery . . 12.95

STAR WARS: CRIMSON EMPIRE
Dec. 1997–May 1998

1 thru 5 PG,CR,DvD(c) . . . . . @2.95

STAR WARS: DARK EMPIRE

1 CK,Destiny of a Jedi 18.00
1a 2nd Printing 5.00
1b Gold Ed. 15.00

DARK HORSE

2 CK,Destroyer of worlds, very low
  print run 18.00
2a 2nd Printing 5.00
2b Gold Ed. 15.00
3 CK,V:The Emperor 10.00
3a 2nd printing 4.00
3b Gold Ed. 10.00
4 CK,V:The Emperor 7.00
4a Gold Ed. 7.00
5 CK,V:The Emperor 7.00
5a Gold Ed. 10.00
6 CK,V:Emperor,last issue 5.00
6a Gold Ed. 9.00
Gold editions, foil logo set 75.00
Platinum editions, embossed set 135.00
TPB Preview 32pg. 1.00
TPB rep.#1–#6 . . . . 19.95
TPB CK & Tom Veitch 2nd ed. . 17.95
HC leather bound 125.00

STAR WARS DARK EMPIRE II
1 2nd chapter 6.00
2 F:Boba Fett 4.00
3 V:Darksiders 4.00
4 Luke Vs. Darksiders 3.50
5 Creatures 3.50
6 CK,DvD(c), save the twins 3.50
Platinum editions, set 50.00
TPB CK & Tom Veitch rep.#1–#6 17.95
HC Leather bound 100.00

STAR WARS: DARK FORCE RISING
May–Oct. 1997
1 thru 6 (of 6) MBn,TyD,KN . . @2.95
TPB series rep 17.95

STAR WARS: DARK FORCES— REBEL AGENT
March 1998
HC by William C. Dietz & Dean
  Williams 24.95

STAR WARS: DARK FORCES— SOLDIER FOR THE EMPIRE
HC by William C. Dietz and Dean
  Williams 24.95
TPB 14.95

STAR WARS: DROIDS
April–Sept. 1994
1 F:C-3PO,R2-D2 . . . . 3.50
2 V:Thieves 2.75
3 on the Hosk moon 2.75
4 . . . . 2.75
5 A meeting 2.50
6 final issue 2.50
Spec.#1 I:Olag Greck 2.50
TPB The Kalarba Adventures, rep.17.95
2nd Series
1 Deputized Droids 3.00
2 Marooned on Nar Shaddaa . . . 2.50
3 C-3PO to the Rescue 2.50
4 . . . . 2.50
5 Caretaker virus 2.50
6 Revolution 2.50
7 & 8 . . . . @2.50

Star Wars Droids #3
© Dark Horse Comics

TPB Droids—Rebellion, rep. . . . 17.95

STAR WARS: EMPIRE'S END
Oct.–Nov. 1995
1 R:Emperor Palpatine 2.95
2 conclusion 2.95
TPB rep. 5.95

STAR WARS HANDBOOK
July 1998
1 X-Wing Rogue Squadron 2.95

STAR WARS: HEIR TO THE EMPIRE
Oct. 1995–April 1996
1 I:Grand Admiral Thrawn 2.95
2 thru 6 . . . . 2.95
TPB from novel by Timothy Zahn 19.95
HC signed, slipcase 100.00

STAR WARS: JABBA THE HUTT—
1995–1996
1-shot The Garr Suppoon Hit . . . 2.50
1-shot Hunger of Princess Nampi . 2.50
1-shot The Dynasty Trap 2.50
1-shot Betrayal 2.50

STAR WARS: THE LAST COMMAND
Nov. 1997–July 1998
1 thru 6 MBn . . . . @2.95

STAR WARS: MARA JADE— BY THE EMPEROR'S HAND
Aug. 1998
1 (of 6) by Timothy Zahn 2.95

STAR WARS: THE PROTOCOL OFFENSIVE
Sept. 1997
1-shot written by Anthony Daniels 4.95

STAR WARS: RETURN OF THE JEDI—SPECIAL EDITION
TPB Hildebrandt(c) 9.95

STAR WARS: RIVER OF CHAOS
May–Nov. 1995
1 LSi,JBr,Emperor sends spies . . 2.50
2 Imperial in Allies Clothing 2.50
3 . . . . 2.50
4 F:Ranulf 2.50

STAR WARS: SHADOWS OF THE EMPIRE
1 (of 6) by John Wagner, Kilian
  Plunkett & P. Craig Russell . . 2.95
2 thru 6 . . . . @2.95
TPB 17.95
HC 80.00

STAR WARS: SHADOWS OF THE EMPIRE — EVOLUTION
Feb.–June 1998
1 thru 5 . . . . @2.95

STAR WARS: SHADOW STALKER
Nov. 1997
1-shot from Galaxy Mag. 2.95

STAR WARS: SPLINTER OF THE MIND'S EYE
Dec. 1995–June 1996
1 thru 4 A.D.Foster novel adapt. @2.95
TPB 14.95

STAR WARS: TALES FROM MOS EISLEY
1-shot, from Star Wars Galaxy Mag.
  #2–#4 . . . . 2.95

STAR WARS: TALES OF THE JEDI
1 RV,I:Ulic Qel-Droma 6.00
2 RV,A:Ulic Qel-Droma 5.00
3 RV,D:Andur 4.00
4 RV,A:Jabba the Hut 3.50
5 RV,last issue 3.50
TPB 14.95
TPB 2nd printing 14.95

STAR WARS: TALES OF THE JEDI: DARK LORDS OF THE SITH
Oct. 1994–March 1995
1 Bagged with card 3.00
2 . . . . 2.50
3 Krath Attack 2.50
4 F:Exar Kun 2.50
5 V:TehKrath 2.50
6 Final battle 2.50
TPB 17.95

STAR WARS: TALES OF THE JEDI: THE FREEDON NADD UPRISING
Aug.–Sept. 1997
1 and 2 . . . . @2.75
2 . . . . 2.50
TPB series rep. 5.95

STAR WARS: TALES OF THE JEDI: THE SITH WAR
Aug. 1995–Jan. 1996
1 F:Exar Kun 2.50
2 F:Ulic Qel-Droma 2.50
3 F:Exar Kun 2.50
4 thru 6 (6 part mini-series) . . @2.50
TPB 17.95

STAR WARS: TALES OF THE JEDI—THE FALL OF THE SITH EMPIRE
June–Oct. 1997
1 (of 5) 2.95
2 thru 5 . . . . @2.95

STAR WARS: TALES OF THE JEDI—THE GOLDEN AGE OF THE SITH
Oct. 1996–Feb. 1997
1 thru 5 . . . . @2.95
TPB 16.95

STAR WARS: TALES OF THE JEDI— THE REDEMPTION OF ULIC QEL-DROMA
July 1998
1 (of 5) by Kevin J. Anderson . . . 2.95
2 . . . . 2.95

STAR WARS: THE EMPIRE STRIKES BACK
TPB Hildebrandt(c) 9.95

STAR WARS: X-WING ROGUE SQUADRON
July 1995
The Rebel Opposition
1 F:Wedge Antilles 4.00
2 . . . . 3.00
3 F:Tycho Clehu 3.00
4 F:Tycho Clehu 3.00
½ Wizard limited exclusive 15.00
The Phantom Affair
5 thru 8 . . . . @3.00
TPB rep. 12.95
Battleground Tatooine
9 thru 12 . . . . @3.00
TPB rep. 12.95
The Warrior Princess
13 thru 16 . . . . @3.00
Requiem for a Rogue
17 thru 20 . . . . @3.00
In the Empire's Service
21 thru 24 . . . . @3.00
Making of Baron Fell
25 . . . . 3.00
Family Ties
26 thru 27 . . . . @3.00
Masquerade

Star Wars: X-Wing Rogue Squadron #4
© Dark Horse Comics

28 thru 31 . . . . @3.00
Mandatory Retirement
32 thru 35 . . . . @2.95

STARSHIP TROOPERS
Sept. 1997
1 (of 2) movie adaptation 2.95
2 movie adaptation, concl. 2.95
TPB rep., inc. Brute Creations,
Insect Touch, & movie 152 pg. 14.95

STARSHIP TROOPERS: BRUTE CREATIONS
1997
1-shot 2.95

STARSHIP TROOPERS: DOMINANT SPECIES
Aug. 1998
1 (of 4) 2.95

STARSHIP TROOPERS: INSECT TOUCH
1 by Warren Ellis & Paolo Parente 2.95
2 and 3 (of 3) . . . . @2.95

SUPERMAN/MADMAN HULLABALOO
June–Aug. 1997
1 (of 3) MiA 2.95
2 and 3 (of 3) . . . . @2.95

SUPERMAN VS. ALIENS
DC/Dark Horse
1 DJu,KN 6.00
2 V:Queen Alien 5.00
TPB 14.95

TALE OF ONE BAD RAT
1 BT 2.95
2 thru 4 . . . . 2.95
TPB Rep.#1–#4 . . . . 14.95

TALES OF ORDINARY MADNESS
(B&W)
1 JBo(c),Paranoid 3.00
2 JBo(c),Mood 2.50
3 JBo(c),A Little Bit of Neurosis . 2.50

TALES TO OFFEND
July 1997
1-shot by Frank Miller 2.95

TANK GIRL
(B&W) 1991
1 Rep. from U.K.Deadline Mag. with
2-card strip 4.00
2 V:Indiana Potato Jones 3.00
3 On the Run 3.00
4 . . . . 3.00
TPB colorized 14.95
[2nd Series]
1 . . . . 3.50
2 . . . . 3.00
3 and 4 . . . . @3.00

TANK GIRL
1 and 2 . . . . @3.00

TARZAN/JOHN CARTER: WARLORDS OF MARS
1 thru 4 E.R.Burroughs adapt. @2.50

TARZAN VS. PREDATOR AT THE EARTH'S CORE
1 Tarzan vs. Predator 2.50
2 V:Predator 2.50
3 Tarzan on the Hunt 2.50
4 . . . . 2.50
TPB series rep. 12.95

TERMINAL POINT
1 . . . . 2.50
2 . . . . 2.50

TERMINATOR
1 CW,Tempest 4.00
2 CW,Tempest 3.00
3 CW 3.00
4 CW, conclusion 3.00

TERMINATOR
1-shot MW,3-D const(c2,pop-up
inside 5.00
Spec. AlG,GyD,GeD(1998) 2.95

TERMINATOR: END GAME
1 JG,Final *Terminator* series 3.00
2 JG,Cont.last Term.story 2.75
3 JG,(Conclusion of Dark Horse
Terminator stories) 2.75

TERMINATOR: ENEMY WITHIN
1 cont. from Sec.Objectives . . . 4.00
2 C890.L.threat contd. 3.00
3 Secrets of Cyberdyne 3.00
4 Conclusion 3.00
SC rep #1–#4 . . . . 13.95

Terminator: End Game #3
© Dark Horse Comics

TERMINATOR: HUNTERS & KILLERS
1 V:Russians 3.00
2 V:Russians 2.75
3 V:Russians 2.75

TERMINATOR: SECONDARY OBJECTIVES
1 cont. 1st DH mini-series 4.00
2 PG,A:New Female Terminator . 3.00
3 PG,Terminators in L.A.&Mexico 3.00
4 PG,Terminator vs Terminator
concl. 3.00

TEX AVERY'S DROOPY
1 Dr. Droopenstein 2.50
2 & 3 . . . . @2.50

TEX AVERY'S SCREWBALL SQUIRREL
1 I:Screwball Squirrel 2.50
2 Cleaning House 2.50
3 School of Hard Rocks 2.50

THING, THE
1 JHi, Movie adaptation 4.00
2 JHi, Movie adaptation 3.50

THE THING: COLD FEAR
1 R:Thing 3.00
2 . . . . 2.75

THING FROM ANOTHER WORLD: CLIMATE OF FEAR
1 Argentinian Military Base
(Bahiathetis) 2.75
2 Thing on Base 2.75
3 Thing/takeover 2.75
4 Conclusion 2.75
TPB 15.95

THING FROM ANOTHER WORLD: ETERNAL VOWS
1 PG,I:Sgt. Rowan 2.75
2 PG 2.75
3 PG,in New Zealand 2.75
4 PG,Last issue 2.75

THIRTEEN O'CLOCK
(B&W)
1 Mr.Murmer,from Deadline USA 2.95

3 X 3 EYES
(B&W) Manga
1 I:Pai,Yakumo, (Manga) 2.95
2 & 3 (5-part mini-series) . . . . @2.95
TPB Curse of the Gesu, by Yuzo
Takada 12.95
TPB House of Demons 12.95

300
May 1998
1 (of 5) FM & Lynn Varley 2.95
2 thru 5 F:Spartans . . . . @2.95

TIME COP
1 Movie Adaptation 2.75
2 Movie Adaptation 2.50

TITAN
Spec.#1 BS(c),I:Inhibitors 4.25

TONGUE*LASH
Aug. 1996
1 by Randy and Jean-Marc Lofficier
& Dave Taylor 2.95
2 . . . . 2.95

TOO MUCH COFFEE MAN
(B&W) July 1997
1-shot by Shannon Wheeler . . . 2.95
TPB Guide for the Perplexed . . . 10.95
HC lim. Guide for the Perplexed 50.00

TREKKER
(B&W)
1 thru 4 . . . . @1.50
5 thru 7 . . . . @1.75
8 O:Trekker 1.50
9 . . . . 1.50

TREKKER
1 . . . . 2.95

TRIPLE•X
(B&W)
TPB by Arnold & Jacob Pander . 24.95

TWO FACES OF TOMORROW, THE
(B&W) Manga Aug. 1997
1 (of 13) from James P. Hogan
novel, by Yukinobu Hoshino . . 2.95
2 thru 4 . . . . @2.95
5 thru 13 . . . . @3.95

TWO FISTED TALES
Spec. WW,WiS 4.95

2112
GN JBy,A:Next Men 2.00
2nd Printing 5.00
TPB GNv, JBy,A:Next Men 10.00
2nd & 3rd printing 9.95

[ANDREW VACHSS'] UNDERGROUND
(B&W)
1 AVs(s) 4.25
2 thru 4 AVs(s) . . . . @3.95

UNIVERSAL MONSTERS
1 AAd,Creature From The Black
Lagoon 5.50
2 The Mummy 5.50

USAGI YOJIMBO
(B&W)
1 by Stan Sakai 2.95
2 thru 9 . . . . 2.95
10 with Sergio Aragones 2.95
11 "The Lord of Owls" 2.95
12 "Vampire Cat of the Geishu" . . 2.95
13 thru 22 "Grasscutter," pt.1
thru pt. #10 . . . . 2.95
TPB Shades of Death, rep. of
Mirage series 14.95
HC Shades of Death, lim. 50.00
TPB Daisho, rep. Mirage 14.95
HC Daisho, 200 pg. signed . . . 50.00
TPB The Brink of Life & Death . . 14.95

USAGI YOJIMBO
1996
1 SS,color spec 4.00
2 SS,color spec. 3.00
3 SS,color spec. 3.00
4 thru 6 . . . . @3.00

USAGI YOJIMBO COLOR SPECIAL: GREEN PERSIMMON
1-shot by Stan Sakai 2.95

VAMPIRELLA
(B&W)
1 'The Lion and the Lizard'Pt.1 . . 4.50
2 'The Lion and the Lizard'Pt.2 . . 3.95
3 'The Lion and the Lizard'Pt.3 . . 3.95
4 'The Lion and the Lizard'Pt.3 . . 3.95

VENUS WARS
(B&W) Manga
1 Aphrodia V:Ishtar, with 2-card
strip 3.00
2 I: Ken Seno 2.50
3 Aphrodia V:Ishtar 2.50
4 Seno Joins Hound Corps. 2.50
5 SenoV:Octopus Supertanks . . 2.50
6 Chaos in Aphrodia 2.50
7 All Out Ground War 2.50
8 Ishtar V:Aphrodia contd. 2.50
9 Ishtar V:Aphrodia contd. 2.50
10 Supertanks of Ishtar Advance . 2.50
11 Aphrodia Captured 2.50
12 A:Miranda,48pgs 2.75
13 Hound Brigade-Suicide Assault 2.25
14 V:Army 2.50
15 . . . . 2.50
TPB Vol. 1 . . . . 13.95

VENUS WARS II
1 V:Security Police 2.75
2 Political Unrest 2.25
3 Conspiracy 2.25
4 A:Lupica 2.25
5 Love Hotel 2.25
6 Terran Consulate 2.25
7 Doublecross 2.25
8 D:Lupisa 2.95
9 A:Matthew 2.95
10 A:Mad Scientist 2.95
11 thru 15 V:Troopers . . . . @2.95

VIRUS
1 MP(c),F:The Wan Xuan & the
crew of the Electra 3.00
2 MP(c),V:Captian Powell 3.00
3 MP(c),V:Virus 3.00
4 MP(c),Last issue 3.00
TPB rep.#1–#4 . . . . 16.95

VERSION
(B&W) Manga
1.1 by Hisashi Sakaguchi 2.50
1.2 thru 1.8 . . . . @2.50

VERSION II
(B&W) Manga
1.1 by Hisashi Sakaguchi 2.50
1.2 thru 1.6 . . . . @2.50

VORTEX, THE
1 . . . . 2.00

WALTER:
CAMPAIGN OF TERROR
1 thru 3 . . . . @2.50

WARRIOR OF
WAVERLY STREET, THE
Nov. 1996
1 (of 2) by Manny Coto and John
Stokes 2.95

WARRIOR OF WAVERLY
STREET, THE:
BROODSTORM
March 1997
1-shot Manny Coto & John Stokes 2.95

WARWORLD!
(B&W)
1 . . . . 1.75

WHAT'S MICHAEL?
(B&W) Manga
TPB by Makoto Kobayashi 5.95
TPB Living Together 5.95
TPB Off the Deep End 5.95

WHITE LIKE SHE
(B&W)
1 thru 4 by Bob Fingerman 2.95

WILL TO POWER
Comics' Greatest World 1994
1 BS, A:X 1.25
2 BS, A:X,Monster 1.25

Will to Power #9 © Dark Horse Comics

3 BS, A:X 1.25
4 BS, In Steel Harbor 1.25
5 V:Wolfgang 1.00
6 V:Motorhead 1.00
7 JOy(c),V:Amazing Grace 1.00
8 V:Catalyst 1.00
9 Titan, Grace 1.00
10 Vortex alien, Grace 1.00
11 Vortex alien, King Titan 1.00
12 Vortex alien 1.00

WIZARD OF
FOURTH STREET
(B&W)
1 thru 4 . . . . @1.75

WOLF & RED
1 Looney Tunes 2.50
2 Watchdog Wolf 2.50
3 Red Hot Riding Hood 2.50

WOLVERTON IN SPACE
(B&W) April 1997
TPB by Basil Wolverton 16.95

X
Comics' Greatest World 1994
1 B:StG(s),DoM,JP,I:X-Killer 3.00
2 DoM,JP,V:X-Killer 2.25
3 DoM,JP,A:Pit Bulls 2.25
4 DoM,JP 2.25
5 DoM,JP,V:Chaos Riders 2.00
6 Cyberassassins 2.00
7 Alamout 2.00
8 A:Ghost 2.50
9 War for Arcadia 2.50
10 War for Arcadia 2.50
11 I:Coffin, War 2.50
12 V:Coffin, A:Monster 2.50
13 D:X 2.50
14 conclusion to War 2.50
15 JS,SiG,war survivors 2.50
16 V:Headhunter 2.50
17 . . . . 2.50
18 V:Predator 2.50

19 V:Challenge 2.50
20 thru 24 . . . . @2.50

X: ONE SHOT
TO THE HEAD
1 . . . . 2.50

XXX
1 . . . . 3.95
2 V:Dr. Zemph 3.95
3 . . . . 3.95
4 V:Rhine Lords 3.95
5 I:Klaar 3.95
6 Klaar captured 4.95
7 Revolution Consequences 4.95

YOUNG CYNICS CLUB
(B&W)
1 . . . . 2.50

THE YOUNG INDIANA
JONES CHRONICLES
1 DBa,FS,TV Movie Adapt 3.25
2 DBa,TV Movie Adapt 2.75
3 thru 5 DBa,GM . . . . @2.75
6 BBa,GM,WW1,French Army . . . 2.75
7 The Congo 2.75
8 Africa,A:A.Schweitzer 2.50
9 Vienna,Sophie-daughter of Arch-
Duke Ferdinand 2.50
10 In Vienna continued 2.50
11 Far East 2.50
12 Fever Issue 2.50

YOU'RE UNDER ARREST!
(B&W) Manga 1995–96
1 by Kosuke Fujishima 2.95
2 thru 8 (mini-series) . . . . @2.95
TPB rep. 12.95

ZOMBIEWORLD:
1-shot Eat Your Heart Out, KJo . 2.95
1-shot Home for the Holidays . . . 2.95

ZOMBIEWORLD:
DEAD END
Jan. 1998
1 (of 2) by Stephen Blue 2.95
2 . . . . 2.95

ZOMBIEWORLD:
CHAMPION
OF THE WORMS
Sept. 1997
1 (of 3) MMi 2.95
2 thru 3 . . . . @2.95
Spec. Home for the Holidays . . . 2.95
TPB 8.95

ZOMBIEWORLD:
WINTER'S DREGS
May 1998
1 (of 4) by Bob Fingerman and
Tommy Lee Edwards 2.95
2 thru 4 . . . . @2.95

IMAGE

AARON STRIPS
Image (B&W) April 1997
1 thru 4 rep. from Sunday comic
strips, by Aaron Warner ... @2.95

ACTION PLANET
Image (B&W) Sept. 1997
Prev. ?
3 . . . . 3.95

ADVENTURES OF AARON
Image March 1997
(B&W) by Aaron Warner
1 "Baby-sitter Gone Bad" 2.95
2 "Thunder Thighs of the
Terrordome" 2.95
3 Babysitter Gone Bad, concl. . . 2.95
100 Super Special 2.95
Christmas Spectacular #1 . . . . . 2.95

ADVENTURE STRIP DIGEST
Image (B&W) April 1998
1 by Randy Reynaldo 2.95
2 F:Rob Hanes, detective 2.95

AGE OF HEROES, THE
Image/Halloween 1996
(B&W)
1 JHI & JRy 2.95
2 JHI & JRy 2.95
3 JHI & JRy,Luko,Trickster &
Aerwyn try to steal treasure of
the gods 2.95
4 JHI & JRy,Drake, the blind
swordsman returns 2.95
Spec. #1 rep. #1 & #2 . . . . 4.95

AGE OF HEROES: WEX
Image (B&W) Aug. 1998
1 by JHI,Vurtex 2.95

ALLEGRA
Image/Wildstorm 1996
1 ScC,SSe 2.50
2 thru 4 . . . . @2.50

ALLIANCE, THE
Image/Shadowline 1995
1 I:The Alliance 2.50
1a variant cover 2.50
2 Team Comes Together 2.50
2a variant cover 2.50
3 I:Slash C 2.50
3a variant cover 2.50
4 . . . . 2.50
4a variant cover 2.50

ALLIES, THE
Image/Extreme 1995
1 thru 4 mini-series . . . . @2.50

ALTERED IMAGE
Image April 1998
1 JV,The Day Reality Went Wild . 2.50
2 JV,F:Everybody smooshed . . . 2.50
3 JV,Middle Age Crisis, concl. . . 2.50

AMANDA AND GUNN
Image (B&W) April 1997
1 JeR, Montana 2036 . . . . 2.95
2 (of 4) JeR 2.95
3 (of 4) JeR 2.95
4 (of 4) JeR, conclusion 2.95

ANGELA
Image/TMP 1994–95
1 NGa(s),GCa,A:Spawn 15.00
2 NGa(s),GCa,Angela's trial . . 14.00
3 NGa(s),GCa,In Hell 12.00
Spec. Pirate Spawn(c) 32.00
Spec. Pirate Angela(c) 30.00
TPB Rep.#1–#3 . . . . 9.95

ANGELA/GLORY: RAGE OF ANGELS
Image/TMP/Extreme 1996
1 x-over begins 5.00

ARCANUM
Image/Top Cow March 1997
Mini-series
1 BPe, from Medieval
Spawn/Witchblade 2.50
1a variant MS(s) (1:4) 2.50
2 BPe, Chi in Asylum 2.50
3 BPe, Ming Chang captive in
Atlantis 2.50
4 BPe,"The End?" 2.50
5 BPe,Royale's secret journal . . 2.50
6 BPe,Safe Haven? 2.50
7 BPe,Egypt 2.50

ARKAGA
Image Sept. 1997
1 by Arnie Tang Jorgensen 2.95
2 Desire for revenge 2.95

ART OF ERIK LARSEN
1 Sketchbook 4.95

ART OF HOMAGE STUDIOS
1 Various Pin-ups 4.95

ASCENSION
Image/Top Cow Sept. 1997
1 by David Finch, F:Angels 2.50
2 Andromeda fights alone 2.50
3 reunited with Lucien 2.50
4 . . . . 2.50
5 Gregorieff and Dayak Army . . . 2.50
6 Voivodul returns, concl. 2.50
7 Andy's problems worsen 2.50
8 revenge on Dayaks & Mineans 2.50
9 Andy exiled 2.50
Coll.Ed.#1, rep.#1–#2 . . . . 4.95

ASTRO CITY
**See: KURT BUSIEK'S
ASTRO CITY**

THE AWAKENING
Image (B&W) Oct. 1997
1 (of 4) by Stephen Blue 2.95
2 thru 4 . . . . @2.95

Backlash #11 © Image/Wildstorm

BACKLASH
Image/Wildstorm 1994
1 Taboo, 2 diff. covers 4.00
1a variant edition, 2 covers 3.00
2 Savage Dragon 2.50
3 V:Savage Dragon 2.50
4 SRf,A:Wetworks 2.50
5 SRf,A:Dane 2.50
6 BBh,SRf,A:Wetworks 2.50
7 BBh,SRf,V:Bounty Hunters . . . 2.50
8 RMz,BBh,BWS(c),WildStorm
Rising,pt.8,w/2 cards 2.50
8a Newsstand ed. 1.95
9 F:Dingo,V:Chasers 2.50
10 I:Crimson 2.50
11 R:Bloodmoon 2.50
12 R:Taboo,Crimson's Costume . . 3.00
13 Taboo to the Rescue 2.50
14 A:Deathblow 2.50
15 F:Cyberjack 2.50
16 thru 18 . . . . @2.50
19 Fire From Heaven,pt.2 . . . . . . 2.50
20 SRf,BBh 2.50
21 SRf,BBh 2.50
22 SRf,BBh 2.50
23 SRf,BBh 2.50
24 SRf,BBh,return of Dingo 2.50
25 SRf,BBh,56pg. special 4.00
26 SRf,BBh,Gramalkin identity
revealed 2.50
27 SRf,BBh, ... 2.50
28 SRf,BBh,Backlash leads PSI
team to Europe 2.50

All comics prices listed are for *Near Mint* condition.

29 SRf,BBh,Haroth raises the
 remnants of Atlantis 2.50
30 SRf,BBh,Backlash confronts
 Kherubim lords 2.50
31 SRf,BBh,team returns to PSI . . 2.50
32 SRf,BBh,earth-shattering final
 issue 2.50
TPB Backlash/Spider-Man, Webs &
 Whips, crossover 4.95
TPB The Drahn War, rep.#27–#3215.00

BACKLASH/SPIDER-MAN
Image/Wildstorm/Marvel 1996
1 . . . . 2.50
1a variant cover 3.00
2 . . . . 2.50

BADGER
Image (B&W) May 1997
1 MBn,"Betelgeuse" 2.95
2 MBn,"Beefalo don't like fences" 2.95
3 MBn,"Loose Eel" 2.95
4 MBn,"Hot House" 2.95
5 MBn,Octopi in the hot tub 2.95
6 MBn,Prime Minister of
 Klactoveedesteen 2.95
7 MBn,Crime Comics 2.95
8 MBn,Root 2.95
9 MBn, ... 2.95
10 MBn,Tuesday Ruby 2.95
11 MBn,Watch the Skies 2.95
12 MBn,The Lady Cobras 2.95
13 MBn,Horse Police 2.95
14 MBn,Badger Sells Out 2.95

BADROCK
Image/Extreme 1995
1a RLd(p),TM(c), A:Dragon . . . 1.75
1b SPa(ic),A:Savage Dragon . . 1.75
1c DF(ic) 1.75
2 RLd,ErS(s),V:Girth,A:Savage
 Dragon 2.50
3 RLd,ErS,V:The Overlord 2.50
Ann.#1 I:Gunner 2.95
Super-Spec. #1 A:Grifter & The
 Dragon 2.50

BADROCK
AND COMPANY
Image/Extreme 1994–95
1 KG(s), ... 2.50
1a San Diego Comic Con Ed. . . 3.00
2 RLd(c),Fuji 2.50
3 Overtkill 2.50
4 TBm,MBm,TNu,A:Velocity . . . 2.50
5 A:Grifter 2.50
6 Finale, A:ShadowHawk 2.50

BALLISTIC
Image/Top Cow 1995
1 A:Wetworks 2.50
2 Jesters Transformation 2.50
3 final issue 2.50

BALLISTIC ACTION
Image/Top Cow 1996
1 MSi(c) pin-ups 2.95

BALLISTIC IMAGERY
Image/Top Cow 1995
1 anthology 2.50

BALLISTIC/WOLVERINE
Image/Top Cow 1996
1 Devil's Reign, pt.4 . . . . 4.00

BATTLESTONE
Image/Extreme 1994
1 New Series 2.50
1a variant cover 3.00
2 RLd,ErS,MMy,AV,I&D:Roarke,
 finale 2.50

BATTLE CHASERS
Image/Cliffhanger April 1998
1 JMd, fantasy, team-up 2.50
1a Chromium edition (5,000 made)3.00
2 JMd,F:Gully 2.50
3 JMd,new ally 2.50
4 JMd,Red Monika 2.50
4a,b,c JMd variant covers . . . . @2.50
Prelude #1, JMd, 16pg 10.00

BEETLEBORGS
Image/Extreme Nov. 1996
1 from TV show 2.50

BERZERKERS
Image/Extreme 1995
1 From Youngblood #2 . . . . 2.50
2 Escape from Darkthorne 2.50
3 In the Darklands 2.50
4 final issue 2.50

BIG BANG COMICS
Image/Big Bang Studios 1996
(B&W) Prev. Caliber
1 F:Mighty Man 2.00
2 Silver Age Shadowhawk 2.00
3 . . . . 2.00
4 . . . . 2.50
5 Top Secret Origins 2.95
6 Round Table of America and
 Knights of Justice meet, orig.
 mini-series #3 (color) 2.95
7 . . . . 2.95
8 F:Mister U.S. 2.95
9 I:Peter Chefren 2.95
10 F:Galahad 2.95
11 Faulty Towers is destroying
 Midway City 2.95
12 F:The Savage Dragon 2.95
13 by Jeff Weigel, 40pg spec. . . 2.95
14 RB,A:The Savage Dragon . . 2.95
15 SBi(c),F:Dr. Weird 2.95
16 F:Thunder Girl 2.95
17 . . . . 2.95
18 Savage Dragon on Trial 2.95
19 O:Beacon,Hummingbird 2.95
20 F:Knight Watchman,Blitz . . . 2.95
21 F:Shadow Lady 2.95
22 The Bird-Man of Midway City . 2.95
TPB rep. 1994 mini-series 11.00

BLACK AND WHITE
Image/Hack Studios 1996
1 New heroes 1.95
2 ATi(p),apparent death 1.95
3 V:Chang 1.95
Ashcan 5.00

BLACK ANVIL
Image/Top Cow 1996
1 & 2 . . . . 2.50

BLACK FLAG
Image/Extreme 1994
1 B&W Preview 3.00

BLACK OPS
Image/Wildstorm 1996
1 thru 5 . . . . @2.50
TPB 14.95

BLINDSIDE
Image/Extreme Aug. 1996
1 MMy & AV, F:Nucgaek Jeno . . 2.50
2 MMy & AV, Origin continues . . 2.50

BLISS ALLEY
Image (B&W) July 1997
1 BML 2.95
2 BML,F:Wizard Walker 2.95
3 BML,Inky-Dinks 2.95

BLOODHUNTER
Image/Extreme Nov. 1996
1 RV, Cabbot Stone rises from the
 slab 2.95

BLOODPOOL
Image/Exteme 1995
1 I:Seoul,Rubbe,Wylder 2.50
1a variant cover 2.50
2 New Neighborhood 2.50
3 The Mummy's Curse 2.50
4 final issue 2.50
TPB Rep. #1–#4 . . . . 12.95

[Regular Series] 1996
1 thru 3 JDy . . . . @2.50

Bloodstrike #3 © Rob Liefeld

BLOODSTRIKE
Image/Extreme 1993
1 A:Brigade,Rub the Blood(c) . . . 3.00
2 V:Brigade,B:BU:Knight 2.50
3 B:ErS(s),ATi(c),V:Coldsnap . . 2.25
4 ErS(s), ... 2.25
5 KG,A:Supreme, ... 2.25
6 KG(s),CAx,C&J:Chapel 2.25
7 KG,RHe,A:Badrock 2.25
8 RHe,A:Spawn 2.25

All comics prices listed are for *Near Mint* condition.

9 RHe,Extreme Prejudice #3,
  I:Extreme Warrior,ATh,BU: Black
  & White 2.25
10 V:Brigade, B:BU:Knight 1.95
25 I:Cabbot Bloodstrike 2.50
11 ErS(s),ATi(c),V:Coldsnap . . . 1.95
12 ErS(s) 1.95
13 KG,A:Supreme 2.50
14 KG(s),CAx,C&J:Chapel 2.50
15 KG,RHe,A:Badrock 1.95
16 KG,RHe 1.95
17 KIA,V:The Horde 2.50
18 ExtremeSacrifice x-over,pt.2 . . 2.50
19 V:The Horde 2.50
20 R:Deadlock New Order 2.50
21 KA,V:Epiphany New Order . . . 2.50
22 V:The Horde, last issue 2.50
25 see above, after #10
Ashcan 5.00

BLOODSTRIKE: ASSASSIN
Image/Extreme 1995
0 R:Battlestone 2.50
1 Debut new series 2.50
1a alternate cover 2.50
2 V:M.D.K. Assassins 2.50
3 V:Persuasion 2.50

BLOODWULF
[Miniseries]
1 RLd,R:Bloodwulf 2.50
1b Run OJ Run 2.50
1c Alternate cover 2.50
1d Alternate cover 2.50
2 A:Hot Blood 2.50
3 Slippery When Wet 2.50
4 final issue 2.50
Spec.#1 V:Supreme Freeferall . . . 2.50

BODY COUNT
1 & 2 . . . . @2.50

BOHOS
Image/Flypaper (B&W) 1998
1 by Maggie Whorf & B.Penaranda 2.95
2 F:teenage bohemians 2.95
3 concl 2.95

BONE
(B & W)
[Previously by Cartoon Books]
21 thru 25 . . . . @2.95
26 The Turning 2.95
27 end of dragonslayer storyline . 2.95
Bone Sourcebook 25
HC#1 Out of Boneville, rep. 19.95
HC#2 The Great Cow Race, rep. 19.95
HC#3 Gran'ma's Story, rep. 19.95
Image reprints with new covers
#1 thru #9 . . . . @2.95
10 rep. "Great Cow Race" 2.95
Image/Cartoon Books
11 Aftermath of the Great Cow
   Race 2.95
12 . . . . 2.95
13 Thar she blows 2.95
14 . . . . 2.95
15 Double or nothing 2.95
16 hiding from the Rat Creatures . 2.95
17 with 5 new pages 2.95
18 Betrayed 2.95
19 three cheers for dragon-slayer

Phoney Bone 2.95
20 Phoney Bone vs. Lucius 2.95

BOOF
1 . . . . 1.95
2 Meathook 1.95
3 Joyride 1.95
4 Beach 1.95
5 Down on the Farm 1.95
6 V:Gangster Chimps 1.95

BOOF AND THE BRUISE CREW
1 thru 4 . . . . @1.95
5 Supermarket 1.95
6 I:Mortar, O:Bruise Crew 1.95

BRASS
Image/Wildstorm
1 Rib,AWa,Folio Edition 3.50
2 Rib,AWa, ... 2.50
3 Rib,AWa,concl. 2.50

Brigade #9 © Rob Liefeld

BRIGADE
Image/Extreme 1993
[1st Series]
1 RLd(s),MMy,I:Brigade 3.50
1a Gold Ed. 5.00
2 RLd(s),V:Genocide,w/coupon#4 4.00
2a w/o coupon 1.00
2b Gold Ed. 5.00
3 V:Genocide 2.00
4 CyP,Youngblood#5 flip 2.00
[2nd Series]
0 RLd(s),ATi(c),JMs,NRd,I:Warcry,
  A:Emp,V:Youngblood 2.25
1 V:Bloodstrike 2.75
1a Gold Ed. 3.00
2 C:Coldsnap 3.00
3 ErS(s),GP(c),MMy,NRd(i),
  V:Bloodstrike 2.25
4 Rip(s),MMy,RHe,I:Roman,
  BU:Lethal 2.25
5 Rip(s),MMy, ... 2.25
6 Rip(s),MMy,I:Coral,BU:Hackers
  Tale 2.25
7 Rip(s),MMy,V:Worlok 2.25

8 ErS(s),MMy,Extreme Prejudice
  #2,BU:Black & White 2.25
9 ErS(s),MMy,Extreme Prejudice
  #6,ATh,BU:Black & White 2.25
25 ErS(s),MMy,D:Kayo,Coldsnap,
   Thermal, ... 2.25
26 Images of Tomorrow 2.25
10 Extreme Prejudice 1.95
11 WildC.A.T.S 2.50
12 Battlestone 2.50
13 Thermal 1.95
14 Teamate deaths 1.95
15 MWm,R:Roman Birds of Prey . 1.95
16 ExtremeSacrifice x-over,pt.3 . . 2.50
17 MWn,I:New Team 2.50
18 I:The Shape New Order 2.50
19 MWn,F:Troll 2.50
20 MWn,alien cult saga,concl. . . . 2.50
21 F:ShadowHawk 2.50
22 F:Brigade Team 2.50
23 & 24 . . . . @2.50
25 & 26 see above
27 Extreme Babewatch 2.50
Sourcebook 2.95

BUGBOY
Image (B&W) June 1998
1-shot, by Mark Lewis, 48pg 3.95

CASUAL HEROES
1 thru 5 . . . . @2.50

CATHEDRAL CHILD
Image 1998
GN by Lea Hernandez 9.95

CELESTINE
Image/Extreme 1996
1 . . . . 2.50
2 . . . . 2.50

CHANNEL ZERO
Image (B&W) 1998
1 by Brian Wood 2.95
2 . . . . 2.95
3 gone global 2.95
4 Filter 2.95

CHAPEL
Image/Extreme 1995
1 BWn,F:Chapel 3.50
2 V:Colonel Black 3.00
2a variant cover 2.50
[Regular Series]
1 BWn,F:Chapel 2.50
1a variant cover 2.50
2 V:Giger 2.50
3 V:Giger 2.50
4 Extreme Babewatch 2.50
5 Hell on Earth,pt.1 . . . . 2.50
6 Hell on Earth,pt.2 . . . . 2.50
7 Shadowhunt x-over,pt.2 . . . . . . 2.50

CHILDHOOD'S END
Image (B&W) Oct. 1997
1 (of 5) JCf, comunity playground 2.95

THE C.H.I.X. THAT TIME FORGOT
Image/Studiosaurus Aug. 1998
1 F:Good Girl 2.95

CODE BLUE
Image (B&W) April 1998
1 by Jimmie Robinson 2.95
2 F.I.T.E. creates havoc 2.95

CODENAME: STYKE FORCE
Image/Top Cow 1994
1A MS(s),BPe,JRu(i), ... 3.50
1B Gold Embossed Cover 6.00
1C Blue Embossed Cover 9.00
2 MS(s),BPe,JRu(i), ... 2.50
3 MS(s),BPe,JRu(i), ... 2.50
4 MS(s),BPe,JRu(i), ... 2.50
5 MS(s),BPe,JRu(i), ... 2.50
6 MS(s),BPe,JRu(i), ... 2.25
7 MS(s),BPe,JRu(i), ... 2.25
8A Cyblade poster (Tucci) 4.00
8B Shi poster (Silvestri) 4.00
8C Tempest poster (Tan) 2.25
9 New Teamate 2.25
10 SvG, B:New Adventure 2.25
11 F:Bloodbow 1.95
12 F:Stryker 1.95
13 SvG(s),F:Strkyer 2.25
14 New Jobs 2.25
Spec.#0 O:Stryke Force 2.50
TPB Rep. Death's Angel Saga . . . 9.95

COMBAT
1 . . . . 2.50

CREECH, THE
Image/TMP Oct. 1997
1 GCa,DaM,F:Chirs Rafferty 1.95
2 GCa,DaM,F:Dennis Dross 1.95

CRIMSON
Image/Cliffhanger May 1998
1 BAu,HuR,F:Alex Elder, vampire 2.50
1a variant AWa(c) 2.50
1b Chromium Edition 3.00
2 BAu,HuR,V:Jelly-Bats 2.50
2a variant AAd(c) 2.50
3 BAu,HuR,V:Rose 2.50
4 BAu,HuR,F:Red Hood 2.50

CRUSH, THE
Image/Motown Jan. 1996
1 thru 5 mini-series . . . . @2.50

CRYPT
Image/Extreme 1995
1 A:Prophet 2.50
1a Variant cover 2.50
2 A:Prophet 2.50

CURSE OF THE SPAWN
Image/TMP Sept. 1996
1 DT,DaM,F:Daniel Lianso 8.00
1a B&W Variant 15.00
2 DT,DaM,Dark Future, Pt. 2: Blood
   Lust 5.00
3 DT,DaM,Dark Future, Pt. 3:
   Corpse Candles 5.00
4 DT,DaM, ... 4.00
5 DT,DaM,Sam & Twitch search for
   Gretchen Culver 3.00
6 DT,DaM,Sam & Twitch pursue
   Suture 3.00
7 DT,DaM,Suture is captured . . 2.50

8 DT,DaM,Suture escapes police
   custody 2.50
9 DT,DaM,Angela's secret origin . 4.00
10 DT,DaM,Angela, Spawn Slayer 3.00
11 DT,DaM,Angela's story, concl. 2.50
12 DT,DaM,Jessica Priest, movie
   photo(c) 2.00
13 DT,DaM "Heart of Darkness" . . 2.00
14 DT,DaM,Jessica, concl. 2.00
15 DT,DaM,Tempt an Angel,pt.1 . 2.00
16 DT,DaM,Tempt an Angel,pt.2 . 2.00
17 DT,DaM 2.00
18 DT,DaM,F:Tony Twist 2.00
19 DT,Curse & Tony Twist 2.00
20 DT,DaM,Monsters & Mythology 2.00
21 DT,DaM,Zeus Must Die 2.00
22 DT,F:Ryan Hatchett 2.00
23 DT,TM,R:Overtkill 2.00
24 DT,TM,Pandemic 2.00

CYBERFORCE
Image/Top Cow
[Limited Series] 1992–93
0 WS,O:Cyber Force 2.50
1 MS,I:Cyberforce,w/coupon#3 . 4.00
1a w/o coupon 3.00
2 MS,V:C.O.P.S. 3.50
3 MS 2.50
4 MS,V:C.O.P.S,BU:Codename
   Styke Force. 2.50
TPB Rep. mini-series 12.95
[Regular Series] 1993
1 EcS(s),MS,SW, ... 2.50
1B Gold Foil Logo 6.00
2 EcS(s),MS,SW,Killer Instinct
   #2,A:Warblade 2.25
2B Silver Embossed Cover 6.00
3 EcS(s),MS,SW,Killer Instinct #4,
   A:WildC.A.T.S. 2.25
3B Gold Embossed Cover 6.00
4 EcS(s),MS,Ballistic 2.00
5 EcS(s),MS 2.00
6 EcS(s),MS,Ballistic's Past . . . 2.00
7 S.H.O.Cs 2.00
8 . . . . 2.50
9 A:Huntsman 2.00
10 A:Huntsman 2.00
10a Alternate Cover 4.00
10b Silver Seal Oz-Con 500c 9.00

Cyberforce #4 © Top Cow

11 . . . . 2.00
12 T.I.M.M.I.E. goes wild 2.00
13 EcS,MS,O:Cyberdata 2.25
14 EcS,MSI,V:T.I.M.M.I.E. 2.25
15 New Cyberdata Threat 2.25
16 O:Ripclaw 2.25
17 Regrouping 2.25
18 thru 25 . . . . @2.50
26 KWo 2.50
27 F:Ash 2.50
27a variant cover by JQ&JP (1:4) 4.00
Top Cow 1996
28 A:Gabriel 2.50
29 . . . . 2.50
30 ScL,"Devil's Reign" tie-in 2.50
31 The team in conflict 2.50
32 Cyblade leads rejuvenated team 2.50
33 KWo, Cheleene in midst of civil
   war 2.50
34 KWo,Royal Blood, pt.3 . . . . . . 2.50
35 BTn,Royal Blood, concl. 2.50
Ashcan 1 (San Diego) 4.00
Ashcan 1 (signed) 6.00
Sourcebook 1 . . . . 2.50
Sourcebook 2 I:W.Zero 2.50
Ann.#1 O:Velocity 2.50
Ann.#2 . . . . 2.95
TPB new art 12.95
TPB EcS,MS,SW,Assault with a
   Deadly Woman 9.95

CYBERFORCE/ CODENAME STRYKEFORCE: OPPOSING FORCES
1 V:Dangerous Threat 2.50
2 Team Vs. Team 2.50

CYBERFORCE ORIGINS
Image/Top Cow 1995
1 O:Cyblade 2.50
1B Gold Seal 1000c 6.00
2 O:Stryker 2.50
3 O:Impact 2.50
4 Misery 3.00

CYBERFORCE UNIVERSE SOURCEBOOK
Image/Top Cow 1994–95
1 and 2 . . . . @2.50

CYBERNARY
Image/Wildstorm 1995–96
1 thru 5 mini-series . . . . @2.50

CYBERPUNX
Image/Extreme 1996
1 & 2 . . . . @2.50
3 RLe & Ching Lau,F:Drake 2.50

DAMNED
Image/Homage June 1997
1 (of 4) StG, MZ & DRo 2.50
2 StG, MZ & DRo,F:Mick Thorne 2.50
3 StG, MZ & DRo 2.50
4 StG, MZ & DRo 2.50

DANGER GIRL
Wildstorm/Cliffhanger 1998
1 JSC,AGo, spy, 40 pg 2.95
1a chromium edition, 40pg 5.00

IMAGE

2 I:Johnny Barracuda 2.50
3 in Switzerland 2.50
3a variant AH(c) 2.50
3b variant TC(c) 2.50
4 I:Major Maxim 2.50
TPB The Dangerous Collection . . 5.95

DARKCHYLD/GLORY
Image/Extreme
one-shot, four variant covers, by
RLd, RQu, JDy & PtL 2.95

DARKCHYLDE
Image/TMP
1 . . . . 4.00
1a remastered, RLd(c) 6.00
1b American Entertainment 4.00
2 . . . . 3.00
2a Variant cover 3.00
3 . . . . 3.00
4 RQu,Ariel & Kauldron's past . . 2.50
5 RQu,No one here gets out alive 2.50
TPB Rep. #1–#5 . . . . 12.95
Series Two, March 1998
0 RQu,Ariel's back, Ariel's past . . 2.50

DARKCHYLDE:
THE DIARY
Image May 1997
one-shot, RQu et al,diary excerpts 2.50

DARKCHYLDE:
THE LEGACY
Image/Majesty Aug. 1998
1 RQu,F:Ariel 2.50

DARKER IMAGE
1 BML,BCi(s),RLd,SK,JLe,I:Blood
  Wulf,Deathblow,Maxx 4.00
1a Gold logo(c) 8.00
1b White(c) 6.00
Ashcan 1 . . . . 4.00

DARKMINDS
Image 1998
1 PtL,cyberpunk,detective 2.50
2 Neon Dragon 2.50
2a variant cover 2.50

DARKNESS, THE
Image/Top Cow 1996
0 Preview Edition, B&W 20.00
½ 15.00
½ variant cover 35.00
1 GEn, MS 15.00
1a Dark cover 20.00
1b Platinum cover 150.00
2 GEn, MS 10.00
3 GEn,MS,Jackie pursued by many
  foes 8.00
4 GEn,MS,Jackie explores
  Darkness power 6.00
5 GEn,MS,New York gangs on
  verge of all-out war 5.00
6 GEn,MS,F:JackieEstacado,concl.4.00
7 MS 3.00
7a variant (c) 18.00
8 JBz,retribution 3.50
8a MS(c)(1:4) 7.50
9 Family Ties,pt.2,x-over 2.50
10 Family Ties,pt.3,x-over 2.50

11 GEn,MS,Hearts of Darkness . 3.00
11a Chromium (c) 25.00
11b variant (c) 4.00
12 GEn,Hearts of Darkness 2.50
13 GEn,Hearts of Darkness 2.50
14 GEn,JBz,Hearts of Darkness,
  concl. 2.50
15 JBz,Spear of Destiny,pt.1 . . 2.50
16 JBz,Spear of Destiny,pt.2 . . 2.50
17 JBz,Spear of Destiny,pt.3 . . 2.50
GN rep. #1–#2 . . . . 4.95
GN rep. #3–#4, 56 pg. 4.95
GN rep. #5–#6, 56 pg. 4.95
GN rep. #5–#6, with slipcase. . . 10.00
GN rep. #7–#8 . . . . 4.95
Slipcase and all 3 GNs 25.00
Signed Slipcase and all 3 GNs . 50.00

DART
Image 1996
1 thru 3 Jozef Szekeres . . . . . @2.50

Deadly Duo #4 © Erik Larsen

DEADLY DUO, THE
Image/Highbrow 1994–95
1 A:Kill-Cat 2.50
2 A:Pitt, O:Kid Avenger 2.50
3 A:Roman, O:Kill-Cat 2.50
[Second Series] 1995
1 A:Spawn 2.50
2 A:Savage Dragon 2.50
3 A:Grunge, Gen[13] 2.50
4 Movie Mayhem 2.50

DEATHBLOW
Image/Wildstorm 1993
1 JLe,MN,I:Cybernary 3.00
2 JLe,BU:Cybernary 2.50
3 JLe(a&s),BU:Cybernary 3.00
4 JLe(s),TSe,BU:Cybernary . . . 2.50
5 JLe(s),TSe,BU:Cybernary . . . 2.50
5a different cover 5.00
6 Black Angel 2.00
7 . . . . 2.00
8 Black Angel 2.00
9 The Four Horseman 2.00
10 Michael Cray, Sister Mary . . . 2.00
11 A:Four Horseman 2.00
12 Final Battle 2.50

13 New Story Arc 2.50
14 A:Johnny Savoy 2.50
15 F:Michael Cray 2.50
16 TvS,BWS(c),WildStorm
  Rising,pt.6,w/2 cards 2.50
16a Newsstand ed. 2.00
17 V:Gammorran Hunter Killers . 2.50
18 F:Cybernary 2.50
19 F:Cybernary 2.50
20 A:Gen 13 . . . . 3.50
21 Brothers in Arms,pt.2,A:Gen13 3.50
22 Brothers in Arms,pt.3 . . . . . . 2.50
23 Brothers in Arms,pt.4 . . . . . . 2.50
24 Brothers in Arms,pt.5 . . . . . . 3.00
25 Brothers in Arms,pt.6 . . . . . . 2.50
26 Fire From Heaven prelude . . . 2.50
27 Fire From Heaven,pt.8 . . . . . 3.00
28 . . . . 2.50
29 . . . . 2.50
Ashcan 1 . . . . 4.00
TPB Dark Angel Saga,rep.,216pg 29.95

DEATHBLOW/WOLVERINE
Image/Wildstorm
1 RiB, AWs,crossover, set in San
  Francisco's Chinatown 2.50
2 RiB, AWs,concl 2.50
TPB rep. series 8.95

DEFCON 4
Image/Wildstorm 1996
1 thru 4 mini-series . . . . @2.50

DESPERADOS
Image/Homage Sept. 1997
1 by JMi & John Cassaday 8.00
2 V:Leander Peik 4.00
2a 2nd printing 2.50
3 V:Leander Peik 3.00
4 V:Leander Peik, concl. 3.00
5 V:Gideon Brood, pt.1. . . . . . . 3.00
TPB A Moment's Sunlight,rep.
  #1–#5 . . . . 16.95

DESPERATE TIMES
Image (B&W) June 1998
1 by Chris Eliopoulos 2.95
2 Strip joint 2.95

DEVASTATOR
Image (B&W) April 1998
1 JHI and Greg Horn 2.95
2 book 1, pt.2 . . . . 2.95
3 concl to book 1 . . . . 2.95

A DISTANT SOIL
Image/Highbrow
(B&W) Prev: Warp Graphics
15 CDo, ... 3.00
16 CDo,A:Bast, Avatar 3.00
17 CDo,D'mer & Bast conflict . . . 3.00
18 CDo,"Ascension" finale 3.00
19 CDo,"Spires of Heaven" pt.1 . 3.00
20 CDo,Lord Merai's suicide
  weakens Hierachy 3.00
21 CDo,"Exile for D'mer?" 3.00
22 CDo,Avatar's secrets,32pg . . 3.00
23 CDo,three stories 3.00
24 CDo,malfunctioning spacesuit . 3.00
25 CDo,NGa,Troll Bridge,48pg . . 3.95
Images of A Distant Soil 3.00
Images of A Distant Soil, signed,

IMAGE

limited 34.95
GN The Gathering, rep.#1–#11 . 18.95
TPB The Ascendant, rep.#13–#24 18.95

DIVINE RIGHT:
THE ADVENTURES OF
MAX FARADAY
Image/Wildstorm Sept. 1997
1 JLe,SW 7.00
1a variant cover 7.50
1b variant, signed 29.95
1c Voyager pollybaged pack 8.00
1d Spanish edition 5.00
2 JLe,SW,search for lost love .. 4.00
2a variant (c) 7.00
3 JLe,SW,F:Christie Blaze 4.00
4 JLe,SW,F:Lynch 2.50
4a variant (c) 5.00
5 JLe,SW,V:Dominique Faust ... 2.50
6 JLe,SW,Susanna Chaste located2.50
7 JLe,SW,Into the Hollow Realm . 2.50
8 JLe,SW,Tobru,V:Acheron ... 2.50
8a variant SW(c) 2.50

DOOM'S IV
Image/Extreme 1994
1 I:Doom's IV 2.50
1a Variant(c) 2.50
2 MECH-MAX 2.50
2a variant cover 2.50
3 Dr. Lychee, Brick 2.50
4 Dr. Lyche, Syber-idol 2.50
Sourcebook 2.50

DRAGON, THE
1 Rep. of Savage Dragon 0.99
2 Rep. of Savage Dragon 0.99

THE DRAGON:
BLOOD AND GUTS
Image/Highbrow 1995
1 I:Grip 2.50
2 and 3 JPn,KIS .... @2.50

DUSTY STAR
Image (B&W) April 1997
0 sci-fi,western,adventure 2.95
1 thru 3 .... @2.95

DV8
Image/Wildstorm 1996
1 WEI(s),HuR 4.00
1a JLe(c) 5.00
1b Kevin Nowlan(c) 4.00
2 WEI(s),HuR,Gen-active serial
  killers are reported 3.00
3 WEI(s), Evo & Frostbite go for a
  walk 2.50
4 Ivana tries to tighten her control
  on Threshold 2.50
5 Ivana sends DV8 to Japan .. 2.50
6 idle hands are the devil's tools . 2.50
7 Sideways Bob's bedtime story . 2.50
8 Sublime, Evo & Frostbite
  abandoned 2.50
9 "Ivana Dead?!" 2.50
10 "A Team Divided," pt.2 ..... 2.50
11 F:Copycat 2.50
12 F:Freestyle,V:Sen.Killory ... 2.50
13 MHs,prelude to New Horizons 2.50
14 MHs,TR,New Horizon,TR(c) .. 2.50
14a TC(c) 2.50

14b Voyager bagged pack 3.50
15 MHs,F:Ivana Baiul 2.50
16 MHs,V:Dominique Faust ... 2.50
17 MHs, ... 2.50
18 MHs,Team 7 .... 2.50
19 MHs,First Mision,pt.1 ..... 2.50
20 MHs,First Mision,pt.2 ..... 2.50
21 MHs,First Mision,pt.3,Arthrax . 2.50

DV8 VS. BLACK OPS
Image/Wildstorm (Oct. 1997)
1 Techromis Design, pt.1 ..... 2.50
2 Techromis Design, pt.2 ..... 2.50
3 Techromis Design, pt.3 ..... 2.50

ELEKTRA/CYBLADE
Image/Top Cow Jan 1997
1-shot "Devil's Reign" pt.7 (of 8) . 2.95

ESPERS
Image April 1997
(B&W) Vol. 3
1 JHI,A:Brian Marx,V:Architects . 2.95
1a 2nd printing 2.95
2 JHI, ... 2.95
3 JHI,Black Magic 2.95
4 JHI,Black Magic, concl. 2.95
5 JHI,two stories 2.95
6 JHI,F:Simon Ashley,Alan Black 2.95
7 JHI,Feel the Rapture 2.95
TPB Undertow, rep.Halloween
  Comics series 14.95

EXTREME ANTHOLOGY
1 .... 2.50

EXTREME
CHRISTMAS SPECIAL
Various artists, new work 2.95

EXTREME HERO
1 .... 2.95

EXTREME PREJUDICE
0 Prelude to X-over 2.50

EXTREME SACRIFICE
Prelude A:Everyone + card 2.50
Epiloque, conclusion + card 2.50
TPB Rep. whole x-over series .. 16.95

EXTREME 3000
Prelude 2.50

EXTREME TOUR BOOK
Tour Book 1992 .... 3.00
Tour Book 1994 .... 25.00

EXTREMELY
YOUNGBLOOD
Image/Extreme Sept 1997
1 TBm&MBm(s) 3.50

EXTREME ZERO
0 RLd,CYp,ATi(i),I:Cybrid, Law &
  Order, Risk, Code 9, Lancers,
  Black Flag 2.75
0a Variant cover 2.75

FALLING MAN
Image (B&W) Dec. 1997
1 (of 3) BMC,PhH 2.95
2 thru 3 Floyd vs. Duncan ... @2.95

FATHOM
Image/Top Cow 1998
1 by Michael Turner,F:Aspen ... 2.50
2 war beneath the waves 2.50

FIRE FROM HEAVEN
1 x-over 3.50

FIRSTMAN
Image April 1997
1 ASm,LukeHenry becomesApollo 2.50

FOOT SOLDIERS, THE
Image (B&W) Sept. 1997
Prev. Dark Horse
1 by Jim Krueger, Graveyard of
  Forgotten Heroes 2.95
2 Tragedy o/t Travesty Tapestry . 2.95
3 Arch enemies, pt.3 .... 2.95
4 It's a Wicker World Afterall ... 2.95
5 Loose Ends 2.95

Freak Force #7 © Highbrow

FREAK FORCE
Image/Highbrow 1993–95
1 EL(s),KG 2.25
2 EL(s),KG 2.25
3 EL(s),KG 2.25
4 EL(s),KG,A:Vanguard 2.25
5 EL(s),KG 2.25
6 EL(s),KG 2.25
7 EL(s),KG 2.25
8 EL(s),space ants 2.25
9 EL(s),Cyberforce 2.25
10 EL(s),Savage Dragon 2.25
11 EL(s),Invasion pt.1 ...... 2.50
12 EL(s),Invasion pt.2 ...... 2.50
13 EL(s),Invasion pt.3 ...... 2.50
14 EL(s),Team Defeated 2.50
15 EL(s),F:Barbaric 2.50
16 KG,EL(s),V:Chelsea Nirvana . 2.50
17 EL,KG,major plots converge .. 2.50

18 Final Issue 2.50
TPB 448pg 29.95

Series Two
Image March 1997
1 EL,Star joins team,V:The
  Frightening Force 2.95
2 EL,Dart quits team 2.95
3 EL,"Lo there shall come..an
  ending" 2.95

FRIENDS OF MAXX
Image/I Before E
1 WML&SK 2.95
2 MHs&SK 2.95

GEN¹³
Image/Wildstorm
0 Individual Hero Stories 4.00
1 JLe(s),BCi(s),I:Fairchild,Grunge,
  Freefall,Burnout 22.00
1a 2nd printing 4.00
2 JLe(s),BCi(s), ... 20.00
3 JLe(s),BCi(s),A:Pitt 10.00
4 JLe(s),BCi(s) 8.00
5 Final issue 5.00
5a WP variant cover 10.00
TPB 12.95
HC 1,000 copies 40.00

Gen¹³ #0 © Jim Lee

Regular Series 1995
1a BCi(s),V:Mercenaries 5.00
1b Common Cover 2 . . . . 5.00
1c Heavy Metal Gen 10.00
1d Pulp Fiction Parody 12.00
1e Gen 13 Bunch 10.00
1f Lin-Gen-re 12.00
1g Lil Gen 13 . . . . 10.00
1h Friendly Neighbor Grunge . . 10.00
1i Gen 13 Madison Ave 10.00
1j Gen-Et Jackson 10.00
1k Gen Dress Up cover 10.00
1l Verti-Gen 10.00
1m Do It Yourself Cover 10.00
2 BCi,BWS(c),WildStorm Rising,
  pt.4, w/2 cards 3.00
2a Newstand Edition 2.25
3 Coda Island 3.00
4 Coda Island 2.50
5 I:New Member 2.50

6 I:The Deviants 3.00
7 European Vacation,pt.2 . . . . . 3.00
8 . . . . 2.50
9 . . . . 2.50
10 Fire From Heaven, pt.3 . . . . 2.50
11 . . . . 2.50
12 . . . . 2.50
13 A, B & C, each . . . . @1.30
14 back to school 2.50
15 Fraternity and Sorority rush . . . 2.50
16 . . . . 2.50
17 BCi,JSC,AGo,battle royale in
  Tower of Luv 2.50
18 BCi,JSC,AGo,V:Keepers 2.50
19 BCi,JSC,AGo,Lynch & kids flee
  to Antarctica 2.50
20 BCi,JSC,AGo,"Spaced Out" . . 2.50
21 BCi,JSC,AGo,V:D'Rahn 2.50
22 BCi,global civil war 2.50
23 BCi,21st century 2.50
24 BCi,V:D'Rahn 2.50
25 BCi,Homecoming,JsC(c) 3.50
25a TC(c) 3.50
25b Voyager bagged pack 3.50
26 JAr,GFr,CaS,back in NYC . . . 2.50
27 JAr,GFr,CaS,bailed out of jail . 2.50
28 JAr,GFr,CaS, new villain 2.50
29 JAr,GFr,CaS,I:Tindalos 2.50
30 JAr,GFr,CaS,to Florida Keys . . 2.50
31 JAr,GFr,CaS,Roxy's Big Score 2.50
32 JAr,GFr,CaS,Hard Wind 2.50
College Yearbook 1997 . . . . 2.50
Ann. #1 WEI,SDi"London'sBrilliant" 2.95
3-D Spec. #1, with glasses 4.95
3-D Spec. #1, variant cover 4.95
TPB rep.1–#5 of original mini-series,
  3rd printing 12.95
TPB Lost in Paradise, rep. #3–#5 6.95
TPB EuropeanVacation,rep.#6–#7 6.95
TPB rep. #13 A, B & C 6.95
TPB Ordinary Heroes 12.95
TPB Wildstorm Archives, rep. mini-
  series, #0–#13, covers, etc. . 13.00

GEN 13 BOOTLEG
Image/Wildstorm Nov. 1996
1 MFm&AD,lost in the "Linquist
  Fault" 2.50
1a signed 15.00
2 . . . . 2.50
3 On the banks of the River Plin . 2.50
4 WS&LSi,F:Valaria 2.50
5 Fairchild looses 30 minutes of her
  life 2.50
6 Fairchild goes back in time,pt.2 2.50
7 Day before a big exam 2.50
8 AWa, pt.1 (of 3) 2.50
9 AWa, pt.2 (of 3) 2.50
10 AWa, pt.3 (of 3) 2.50
11 AaL,WS,Chupacabra,pt.1 . . . . 2.50
12 AaL,WS,Chupacabra,pt.2 . . . . 2.50
13 F:Grunge 2.50
14 JMi,JoP,GL,bad neighbors . . 2.50
15 KNo,V:Trance, pt.1 . . . . 2.50
16 KNo,V:Trance, pt.2 . . . . 2.50
17 Video arcade challenge 2.50
18 MFm,Grunge-mania 2.50
19 BKs,JhB,Satyr 2.50
20 CAd,F:John Lynch 2.50
21 StG,DdW,Grunge, Gorilla Guy . 2.50
Ann.#1 WEI,SDi, to NYC 2.95
TPB Grunge: The Movie,AWa . . 9.95

GEN¹³: INTERACTIVE
Image/Wildstorm Oct. 1997
1 vote via internet 2.50
2 MHs,vote via internet 2.50
3 MHs,conclusion 2.50
TPB Gen¹³ Interactive Plus, rep. 11.95

GEN¹³/ GENERATION X
Image/Wildstorm July 1997
1 BCi&AAd 2.95
1 variant cover by JSC 2.95
3-D Edition, with glasses 4.95
3-Da variant cover, with glasses . 4.95

GEN¹³/MAXX
1 . . . . 4.00

GEN¹³/MONKEY MAN
& O'BRIEN
Image/Wildstorm June 1998
1 (of 2) AAd 2.50
1a chromium edition 4.50
2 AAd,alternate universe, concl. . 2.50
2a variant AAd(c) 2.50

GEN¹³:
ORDINARY HEROES
1 . . . . 2.50
2 . . . . 2.50

GEN¹²
Image/Wildstorm Feb. 1998
1 BCi,Team 7 tie-in 2.50
2 BCi,F:Morgan of I.O. 2.50
3 BCi,Dominique Faust 2.50
4 BCi,F:Miles Craven 2.50
5 BCi,Team 7 re-unites 2.50

Glory #15 © Extreme

GLORY
Image/Extreme 1995
0 JDy 2.50
1 JDy,F:Glory 4.00
1a variant cover 4.00
2 JDy,V:Demon Father 3.00
3 JDy,A:Rumble & Vandal 2.50

IMAGE

4 Vandal vs. Demon Horde 2.50
4a JDy variant cover 3.00
5 F:Vandal 2.50
6 Drug Problem 2.50
7 F:Superpatriot 2.50
8 Extreme Babewatch 2.50
9 thru 11 .... @2.50
12 JDy, EBe & JSb 3.50
13 JDy, EBe & JSb 2.50
14 JDy, EBe & JSb 2.50
15 JDy, EBe & JSb, Out for
   vengeance 2.50
continued: see Color Comics section
TPB Rep.#1–#4 .... 9.95

GLORY/ANGELA HELL'S ANGELS
1 .... 4.00

GLORY/AVENGELYNE
1 V:B'lial,I:Faith 4.00
1a no chrome (c) 3.00

GLORY/AVENGELYNE: THE GODYSSEY
Image/Extreme
1 RLd & JDy 3.00
1a photo (c) 4.00

GLORY/CELESTINE: DARK ANGEL
Image/Extreme Sept. 1996
1 (of 3) JDy,PtL,sequel to Rage of
   Angels, A:Maximage 2.50
2 JDy,PtL,"Doomsday+1" 2.50

GLORY & FRIENDS BIKINI FEST
1 Nuff said 2.50

GOLDFISH
Image (B&W) 1998
TPB by Brian Michael Bendis .. 16.95

GREASE MONKEY
Image March 1998
1 TEl..................... 2.95
2 TEl..................... 2.95
3 TEl, The Calling; Rewards 2.95

GRIFTER
Image/Wildstorm 1995
1 BWS(c), WildStorm
   Rising,pt.5,w/2 cards 2.50
1a Newsstand Ed. 1.95
2 City of Angels,pt.1 .... 2.50
3 City of Angels,pt.2 .... 2.50
4 R:Forgotten Hero 2.50
5 Rampage of a Fallen Hero ... 2.50
6 V:Poerhouse 2.50
7 & 8 .... @2.50

GRIFTER/BADROCK
1 To Save Badrock's Mom 3.00
1a Variant cover 2.50
2 .... 3.00
3 double size 3.50

GRIFTER-ONE SHOT
1 SS,DN 4.00

GRIFTER
Image/Wildstorm
1 StG 4.00
2 StG 3.00
3 StG,captured by MadJackPower 3.00
4 StG,vs. Condition Red 2.50
5 StG,Grifter gambles his soul .. 2.50
6 StG, ... 2.50
7 StG,MtB,I:Charlatan 2.50
8 StG,MtB,Zealot
   disappears,V:Soldier 2.50
9 StG,Zealot captured?, secret
   history of Quiet Men 2.50
10 StG,Grifter & Soldier go to
   rescue Zealot 2.50
11 StG, renegade former agent .. 2.50
12 StG,"Who is Tanager?" 2.50
13 StG,"Family Feud" 2.50
14 StG,V:Joe the Dead 2.50

GRIFTER/SHI
1 & 2 .... 3.00
HC 29.95
HC signed & numbered(Lee) ... 50.00
HC signed & numbered(Tucci) .. 50.00
HC signed & numbered(Charest) 35.00
HC signed & numbered(Hubbs) . 25.00

GROO
1 SA 2.25
2 A:Arba, Dakarba 2.00
3 The Generals Hat 2.00
4 A Drink of Water 2.00
5 SA,A Simple Invasion 2.00
6 SA,A Little Invention 2.00
7 The Plight of the Drazils 2.00
8 .... 2.25
9 I:Arfetto 2.25
10 The Sinkes 2.25
11 The Gamblers 2.25
12 .... 2.25

HAZARD
Image/Wildstorm 1996
1 JMi,RMr 2.50
2 JMi,RMr 1.75
3 JMi,RMr 1.75
4 JMi,RMr 1.75
5 JMi,RMr,Hazard finds Dr. D'Oro 1.75
6 JMi,RMr 2.25
7 JMi,RMr,Hazard meets Prism . 2.25

HEADHUNTERS
Image April 1997 (B&W)
1 ChM,V:Army of Wrath 2.95
2 ChM,V:undead militia 2.95
3 ChM,"Slaughterground" 2.95

HEARTBREAKERS
Image July 1998 Superdigest, 6"x9"
1 B&W and color 104pg 9.95

HEARTBREAKERS VERSUS BIOVOC
Image
TPB "Bust Out" 9.95
TPB PGn 14.95

HELLSHOCK
Image 1994
1 I:Hellshock 3.50
2 Powers & Origin 3.50
3 New foe 3.50
4 .... 3.50

HELLSHOCK
Image Jan. 1997
1 JaL,Something wrong with Daniel,
   48pg. 3.00
2 JaL,Daniel learns to control
   powers 2.50
3 JaL,Daniel free of madness ... 2.50
4 JaL,Daniel searches for his
   mother, Jonakand plans escape
   from Hell 2.50
5 JaL,Jonakand and fallen angels
   tear hell apart 2.50
6 JaL,"The Milk of Paradise" ... 2.50
7 JaL,"A Mother's Story", double
   size 3.95
8 JaL,House of Torture 2.50

HOMAGE STUDIOS
Swimsuit Spec.#1 JLe,WPo, MS . 2.25

HONG ON THE RANGE
Image/Matinee Entertainment/Flypaper
1 (of 3) by William Wu & Jeff
   Lafferty 2.50
2 in Washout 2.50
3 Duke Goslin 2.50

IMAGE ZERO
Image 1993
0 I:Troll,Deathtrap,Pin-ups,rep.
   Savage Dragon #4,O:Stryker,
   F:ShadowHawk 15.00

IMAGES OF SHADOWHAWK
Image 1993–94
1 KG,V:Trencher 2.25
2 thru 3 V:Trencher 2.25

IMMORTAL TWO
Image May 1997 (B&W) Half-Tone
1 MsM,F:Gaijin & Gabrielle 2.50
2 MsM 2.50
3 MsM 2.50
4 MsM,V:Okami Red 2.50
5 MsM,new drug epidemic 2.50
6 MsM,First Order, cont. 2.50
7 MsM,vs. impossible odds 2.50
7 MsM,flip photo cover 2.50

JACKIE CHAN'S SPARTAN X
Image (B&W) March 1998
1 MGo,RM,Hell-Bent Hero for Hire 2.95
2 MGo,to Russia 2.95
3 MGo,V:Kenshi 2.95
4 MGo,RM, in Istanbul 2.95
5 MGo,RM, Mind of God 2.95
5a MGo,RM, photo cover 2.95
6 MGo,RM, The Armor of Heaven 2.95
6a MGo,RM, photo cover 2.95

JIM LEE'S C-23
Image/Wildstorm April 1998
1 BCi,JMi,F:Corben Helix 2.50
2 JMi,TC(c),V:Angelans 2.50
3 JMi,TC(c),with trading card . . . 2.50
4 JMi,Corbin, banished 2.50
5 JMi,RCo(c),Queen Mother 2.50
5a variant JLe(c) (1:4) 2.50

JINX
Image (B&W) June 1997
1 by Brian Michael Bendis 2.95
1a 2nd printing 2.95
2 F:Jinx, female bounty hunter . . 2.95
3 thru 5 . . . . @3.95
TPB rep. prev. #1–#4 . . . . 9.95
Spec.#1 Buried Treasure 3.95
Spec.#1 True Crime Confessions . 3.95

JINX: TORSO
Image (B&W) Aug. 1998
1 by Brian Michael Bendis, 48pg . 3.95

KABUKI
Image Sept. 1997
1 DMk,O:Kabuki 4.00
1a variant JSo(c) 7.00
2 DMk,O:Kabuki, pg.2 . . . . 3.00
3 DMk,surprise visitor 3.00
4 DMk,Akemi, romance 3.00
5 DMk,action 3.00
TPB Circle of Blood, rep. orig. series
  plus "Fear the Reaper," B&W 17.95
TPB Dreams 10.00
TPB Masks of the Noh 10.95
TPB Skin Deep 9.95
TPB Images, part rep. #1, 48pg. . 4.95
Reflections #1, 48pg 4.95

KID SUPREME
Image/Supreme 1996–97
1 & 2 . . . . 2.50
3 DaF,ErS 2.50
4 DaF,ErS,Party time 2.50
5 DaF,ErS,"Birds of a Feather" . . 2.50
6 DaF,ErS,I: The Sensational
  Spinner 2.50
7 DaF,ErS,Everything falls apart . 2.50

KILLER INSTINCT
TOUR BOOK
1 All Homage Artist,I:Crusade . . . 5.00
1a signed 45.00

KILLRAZOR SPECIAL
1 O:Killrazor 2.50

KINDRED
Image/Wildstorm 1994
1 JLe,BCi(s),BBh,I:Knindred 5.00
2 JLe,BCi(s),BBh,V:Kindred 3.50
3 JLe,BCi(s),BBh,V:Kindred 3.00
3a WPo(c),Alternate(c) 6.00
4 JLe,BCi(s),BBh,V:Kindred 3.00
TPB rep. #1-#4 . . . . 9.95

KISS:
THE PSYCHO CIRCUS
Image/TMP July 1997
1 SvG,AMe 7.00
2 AMe, unearthly origins 6.00

3 AMe, Judgment o/t Elementals 5.00
4 AMe,Smoke and Mirrors, pt.1 . 3.00
5 AMe,Smoke and Mirrors, pt.2 . 2.00
6 AMe,Smoke and Mirrors, concl. 2.00
7 AMe,Creatures of the Night . . . 2.25
8 AMe,Forever 2.25
9 AMe,Four Sides to Every Story 1.95
10 AMe,Destroyer, pt.1 . . . . 2.25
11 AMe,Destroyer, pt.2 . . . . 2.25
12 AMe,Destroyer,pt.3 (of 4) . . . 2.25

KNIGHTMARE
Image/Extreme 1995
0 O:Knightmare 2.50
1 I:Knightmare MMy 2.50
2 I:Caine 2.50
3 RLd,AV,The New Order,
  F:Detective Murtaugh 2.50
4 RLd,AV,MMy,I:Thrillkill 2.50
5 V:Thrillkill 2.50
6 Extreme Babewatch 2.50
7 . . . . 2.50
8 I:Acid 2.50

KNIGHT WATCHMAN
Image (B&W) May 1998
1 by Gary Carlson & Chris Ecker 2.95
2 Graveyard Shift, pt.2 . . . . 2.95
3 Graveyard Shift, pt.3 . . . . 2.95
4 Graveyard Shift, concl. 2.95

KURT BUSIEK'S
ASTRO CITY
1 I:Samaritan 11.00
1a 2nd printing 2.00
2 V:Shirak the Devourer 6.00
3 F:Jack in the Box 5.00
4 thru 6 . . . . @7.00
TPB 19.95
HC 39.95

KURT BUSIEK'S
ASTRO CITY VOL.2
Homage Comics 1996–97
½ 5.00
1 KBk(s),BA 7.00
1a Trunk(c) 10.00
1b 2nd printing 2.50
2 KBk(s),BA,F:Astra 6.00
2b 2nd printing 2.50
3 KBk(s),BA, ... 5.00
Image/Homage Comics
4 KBk,BA,Teenager seeks to
  become teen sidekick,pt.1 (of 6) 5.00
5 . . . . 5.00
6 V: creatures of Shadow Hill . . . 5.00
7 Aliens invade Astro City 3.00
8 The aliens are out there 2.50
9 Honor Guard vs. Aliens finale . 2.50
10 meet the junkman 2.50
11 . . . . 2.50
12 F:Jack-In-The-Box 2.50
13 F:Looney Leo 2.50
14 F:Steeljack 2.50
15 F:supervillains 2.50
16 F:El Hombre 2.50
17 F:Steeljack, staying straight . 2.50
TPB Confession, rep.#4–#9 . . . 19.95
HC Confession 50.00
3-D #1 . . . . 4.95
TPB Life in the Big City 19.95
HC Life in the Big City 34.95

LABMAN
1 . . . . 3.50
1a variant cover 3.50
2 and 3 . . . . @2.95

LADY SUPREME
Image/Extreme
1 TMr 2.50
2 TMr 2.50
3 TMr,V:Manassa 2.50
4 TMr,"Lady Supreme goes
  undercover" 2.50

LEAVE IT TO CHANCE
Homage Comics Sept. 1996
1 JeR,PS,I:Chance Falconer 2.50
2 . . . . 2.50
Image/Homage Comics
3 Chance and St. George race
  against time 2.50
4 . . . . 2.50
5 Halloween Night in Devil's Echo 2.50
6 Chance sent to private school . 2.50
7 Falconer's battle with Captain
  Hitch, pt.2 . . . . 2.50
8 "The Phantom of the Mall" 2.50
9 Menace from the Matinee 2.50
10 Terror off the silver screen . . 2.50
11 Sudden Death 2.50
TPB rep. #1–#4 . . . . 9.95
HC Shaman's Rain 24.95
HC Shaman's Rain, signed 34.95

LEGEND OF SUPREME
1 KG(s),JJ,DPs,Revelations pt.1 . 2.50
2 Revelations pt.2 . . . . 2.50
3 Conclusion 2.50

LETHAL
Image 1996
1 and 2 . . . . @2.50

LITTLE-GREYMAN
Image (B&W)
TPB by C. Scott Morse 6.95

Mars Attacks #1 © Image

All comics prices listed are for *Near Mint* condition.

LYNCH
Image/Wildstorm June 1997
1 TVs,"Terror in the Jungle" 2.50

MAN AGAINST TIME
1 .... 2.50
2 .... 2.50

MAGE:
THE HERO DEFINED
Image 1997
1 MWg,F:Kevin Matchstick 4.00
2 MWg,Kirby Hero, V:harpies ... 3.00
3 MWg,Isis, Gretch 3.00
4 MWg,Isis, drug 3.00
5 MWg,into Canada 3.00
6 MWg,V:Dragonslayer 2.50
7 MWg, ... 2.50
8 MWg,V:Red Caps 2.50
9 MWg,Sibling Trio 2.50
10 MWg,enchanted by a succubus 2.50
11 MWg,Joe Phat, missing 2.50
Spec. 3-D #1 .... 4.95
TPB Vol. 1 rep. 9.95

MARS ATTACKS
Image 1996
1 KG,BSz(of 4) 2.50
2 .... 2.50
3 .... 2.50
4 End of their world as they
 knew it 2.50

MASK OF ZORRO, THE
Image July 1998
1 (of 4) DMG,RoW,RM,MGo(c),
 movie adapt. 2.95
2 DMG,RoW,RM,MGo(c) 2.95

MAXIMAGE
1 thru 8 .... @2.50
9 BML, Sex Slaves of Bomba
 Island 2.50
10 BML, The King of Emotion is
 back 2.50

MAXX, THE
1/2 SK,from Wizard 5.00
1 SK,I:The Maxx 4.00
1a glow in the dark(c) 8.00
2 SK,V:Mr.Gone 4.00
3 SK,V:Mr.Gone 4.00
4 SK, ... 4.00
5 SK, ... 3.00
6 SK, ... 3.00
7 SK,A:Pitt 3.50
8 SK,V:Pitt 3.50
9 SK 3.00
10 SK 3.00
11 SK 2.50
12 SK 2.50
13 Maxx Wanders in Dreams 2.50
14 R:Julie 2.50
15 Julia's Pregnant 2.50
16 SK,Is Maxx in Danger? 2.50
17 Gardener Maxx 2.25
18 .... 1.95
19 V:Hooley 1.95
20 Questions are answered ... 2.25
21 AM story 1.95
22 SK 1.95
23 SK 1.95

The Maxx #24 © Image

24 SK 1.95
25 SK 1.95
26 SK 1.95
27 V:Iago the Killer Slug 1.95
28 Sara and Norberg look for Julie 1.95
29 Sara and Gone defeat Iago the
 Slug 1.95
30 Lil' Sara faces her fears 1.95
31 F:The Library girl 1.95
32 F:The Library girl,pt.2 ...... 1.95
33 Sara's back 1.95
34 Mark and Julia 1.95
35 who knows? 1.95
36 bumfuzzled 1.95
37 Megan's story concl 1.95
38 Mark,Julie,Larry, pt.1 (of 4) ... 1.95
Spec. Friends of Maxx 2.95
TPB Rep. #1-#5 .... 12.95
TPB Vol. 2 .... 12.95

MECHANIC, THE
Image/Homage Aug. 1998
GN JCh,JPe,time travel 5.95

MEDIEVAL SPAWN/
WITCHBLADE
1 .... 11.00
2 .... 9.00
3 .... 7.00
TPB collected 9.95

MEGAHURTZ
Image (B&W) Aug. 1997
1 JPi,I:Megahurtz 2.95
2 JPi,visit to Wonderland 2.95
3 JPi,V:N-Filtraitors 2.95
4 JPi,Liberaiders 2.95

MIKE GRELL'S
MAGGIE THE CAT
1 thru 4 .... @2.50

MISERY SPECIAL
1 Cyberforce Origins 2.95

MONSTERMAN
Image (B&W) Sept. 1997
1 MM,from Action Planet 2.95
2 MM,Inhuman monsters 2.95
3 MM,King of Monsters 2.95
4 MM, conclusion 2.95

MR. MONSTER
VS. GORZILLA
Image (2 color) July 1998
1-shot, MGi 2.95

MS. FORTUNE
Image (B&W) 1998
1 by Chris Marrinan 2.95
2 Carnage in the Caribbean ... 2.95
3 Doom at the Dawn of Time ... 2.95

MYSTERY, INC.
Ashcan 1 .... 4.00

NAMELESS, THE
Image May 1997
1 PhH,I:The Nameless, protector of
 Mexico City's lost children 2.95
2 .... 2.95
3 .... 2.95
4 .... 2.95
5 V:Huitzilopochtili 2.95

NEW ADVENTURES OF
ABRAHAM LINCOLN
Image/Homage Feb. 1998
TPB SMI, 144pg. 19.95

NEW FORCE
1 thru 4 mini-series .... @2.50

THE NEW ORDER
HANDBOOK
Various artists 1.50

NEW MAN
1 thru 3 .... @2.50
4 Shadowhunt x-over,pt.5 ...... 2.50

NEWMEN
Image/Extreme 1994
1 JMs, ... 3.00
2 JMs,I:Girth 2.25
3 JMs,V:Girth,I:Ikonna 2.25
4 JMs,A:Ripclaw 1.95
5 JMs,Ripclaw,V:Ikonn 2.50
6 JMs 2.50
7 JMs 2.50
8 JMs,Team Youngblood 2.50
9 ErS(s),JMs,Kodiak Kidnapped . 2.50
10 ExtremeSacrifice x-over,pt.4 .. 2.50
11 F:Reign 2.50
12 R:Elemental 2.50
13 ErS,I:Bootleg 2.50
14 ErS,Dominion's Secret 2.50
15 I:Time Guild 2.50
16 .... 2.50
16a variant cover 3.00
17 R:Girth 2.50
18 F:Byrd 2.50
19 I:Bordda Khan,Shepherd 2.50
20 Extreme Babewatch 2.50
21 ErS,CSp,(1 of 5) 2.50

IMAGE

22 ErS,CSp, Who Needs the
   Newmen? 2.50
23 ErS,CSp,Who are the Newmen?2.50

NEW SHADOWHAWK, THE
1 I:New ShadowHawk 2.50
2 V:Mutants 2.50
3 I:Trophy 2.50
4 V:Blowfish 2.50
5 thru 7 .... @2.50

1963
1 AnM(s),RV,DGb,I:Mystery, Inc. 2.50
1a Gold Ed. 4.00
1b Bronze Ed. 3.00
2 RV,SBi,DGb,JV,I:The Fury 2.25
3 RV,SBi,I:U.S.A. 2.25
4 JV,SBi,I:N-Man, Johnny Beyond 2.25
5 JV,SBi,I:Horus 2.25
6 JV,SBi,I:Tommorrow Synicate,
   C:Shaft 2.25
Ashcan #1 .... 3.00
Ashcan #2 .... 2.50
Ashcan #4 .... 2.00

NINE VOLT
Image/Top Cow 1997
1 ACh 4.00
1a Variant (c) 7.00
2 ACh 4.00
3 ACh,V:crazed junkie terrorists . 2.50
4 ACh,V:Rev. Cyril Gibson 2.50

NORMAL MAN/ MEGATON MAN SPECIAL
1 .... 2.50

OPERATION KNIGHTSTRIKE
1 RHe,A:Chapel,Bravo,Battlestone 2.50
2 In Afganistan 2.50
3 final issue 2.50

THE OTHERS
0 JV(s),From ShadowHawk 2.50
1 JV(s)V:Mongrel 2.50
2 JV,Mongrel takes weapons ... 2.50
3 War 2.50
4 O:Clone 2.50

PACT
Image 1994
1 JV(s),WMc,I:Pact, C:Youngblood 2.25
2 JV(s),V:Youngblood 1.95
3 JV(s),V:Atrocity 1.95

PHANTOM FORCE
1 RLd,JK,w/card 2.75
2 JK,V:Darkfire 1.95
See also Color Comics section

PHANTOM GUARD
Image/Wildstorm Oct. 1997
1 by Sean Ruffner, Ryan Benjamin2.50
1a variant cover 2.50
1b Voyager bagged pack 3.50
2 Martian wasteland 2.50
3 Lowell Zerium Mines 2.50
4 .... 2.50
5 V:Vanox, ... 2.50
6 Countdown to Armageddon .. 2.50

PITT
Image/Top Cow 1993–95
1 DK,I:Pitt,Timmy 4.00
2 DK,V:Quagg 3.00
3 DK,V:Zoyvod 4.00
4 DK,V:Zoyvod 3.00
5 DK 2.50
6 DK 2.50
7 DK 2.50
8 Ransom 2.50
9 DK,Artic Adventures 2.00
Ashcan 1 .... 3.00

POWER OF THE MARK
1 I:Ted Miller 2.50
2 V:The Fuse 2.50
3 TMB(s), The Mark 2.50
4 TMB,Mark's secrets revealed .. 2.50

POWER RANGERS ZEO
Image/Extreme Sept. 1997
1 thru 3 TBm&MBm(s),TNu,NRd @2.50

POWER RANGERS ZEO YOUNGBLOOD
Image/Extreme Oct. 1997
1 thru 2 RLd,TBm,MBm ..... @2.95

Prophet #10 © Rob Liefeld

PROPHET
Image/Extreme 1993–95
0 San Diego Comic-Con Ed. 4.00
1 RLd(s)DPs,O:Prophet 3.00
1a Gold Ed. 4.00
2 RLd(s),DPs,C:Bloodstrike 2.50
3 RLd(s),DPs, V:Bloodstrike,
   I:Judas 2.50
4 RLd(s),DPs,A:Judas 2.50
4a SPa(c),Limited Ed. 3.00
5 SPa 3.00
6 SPa 2.50
7 SPa War Games pt.1 .... 2.25
8 SPa War Games pt.2 .... 2.50
9 SPa,Extreme Sacrifice Prelude 2.50
10 ExtremeSacrifice x-over,pt.6 .. 2.50
Sourcebook 2.95
Ashcan #1 .... 3.00
Ashcan #2 .... 3.00

[Regular Series]
1 SPI, New Series 2.75
2 SPI, New Direction 2.50
2a variant cover 2.50
3 True Nature 2.50
4 The Dying Factor 2.50
5 and 6 .... @2.50
7 CDi,SPa 2.50
8 and 9 .... @2.50
TPB 12.95
Ann.#1 Supreme Apocalypse 2.50
Spec.#1 Babewatch special 2.50

PROPHET/AVENGELYNE
1 .... 3.00

RAGMOP
Image (B&W)
Vol.2 #1 by Rob Walton 2.95
Vol.2 #2 .... 2.95

Regulators #1 © Image

REGULATORS
June 1995
1 F:Blackjack,"Touch of Scandal" 2.50
2 F:Vortex 2.50
3 F:Arson 2.50
4 F:Scandal 2.50

REPLACEMENT GOD AND OTHER STORIES, THE
Image (B&W) May 1997
1 Knute vs. King Ursus 2.95
2 by Zander Cannon 2.95
3 thru 4 .... @2.95

RESIDENT EVIL
Image/Wildstorm March 1998
1 comic/game magazine 56pg .. 4.95
2 comic/game magazine 56pg .. 4.95

RIPCLAW
Image/Top Cow 1995
1/2 Prelude to Series (Wizard) .. 3.00
1/2a Con versions 10.00
1 A:Killjoy, I:Shadowblade 3.00
2 Cyblade, Heatwave 2.50

IMAGE

3 EcS,BPe,AV,Alliance with
   S.H.O.C.s 2.50
4 conclusion 2.50
Spec.#1 I:Ripclaw's Brother 3.00
   [1st Regular Series]
1 thru 5 .... @2.50

RIPTIDE
Image 1995
1 O:Riptide 2.50
2 O:Riptide 2.50

Savage Dragon #28 © Erik Larsen

SAVAGE DRAGON
Image/Highbrow
1 EL,I:Savage Dragon 3.00
2 EL,I:Superpatriot 3.50
3 EL,V:Bedrock,w'coupon#6 .. 2.50
3a EL,w/o coupon 2.50
Spec. Savage Dragon Versus Savage
   Megaton Man #1 EL,DSm .. 2.50
Gold Ed. 12.00
TPB 9.95
   [2nd Series] 1993
1 EL,I:Freaks 2.50
2 EL,V:Teen.Mutant Ninja Turtles,
   Flip book Vanguard #0 .... 2.50
3 EL,A:Freaks 2.25
4 EL,A:Freaks 2.25
5 EL,Might Man flip book ... 2.25
6 EL,A:Freaks 2.25
7 EL,Overlord 2.25
8 EL,V:Cutthroat,Hellrazor .. 2.25
9 thru 10 EL, ... 2.25
11 EL,A:Overlord 1.95
12 EL 1.95
13 EL,Mighty Man,Star,I:Widow
   (appeared after issue #20) .. 2.50
13a Larsen version of 13 .... 2.50
14 Possessed pt.1 .... 2.50
15 Possessed pt.2 .... 2.50
16 Possessed pt.3,V:Mace ... 2.50
17 V:Dragonslayer 2.50
18 R:The Fiend 2.50
19 V:The Fiend 2.50
20 Rematch with Ovrlord 2.50
21 V:Overlord 2.50
22 A:Teenage Mutant Turtles .. 2.50
23 Rapture vs. SheDragon ... 2.50

24 Gang War pt.1 .... 2.50
25 Gang War,pt.2 double size ... 4.00
26 .... 2.50
27 .... 2.50
28 .... 2.50
29 .... 2.50
30 .... 2.50
31 "The Dragon is trapped in Hell" 2.50
32 Kill-Cat vs. Justice 2.50
33 fatherhood 2.50
34 F:Hellboy, pt.1 .... 3.00
35 F:Hellboy, pt.2 .... 2.50
36 Dragon & Star try to rescue Peter
   Klaptin 2.50
37 mutants struggle in ruins of
   Chicago 2.50
38 Dragon vs. Cyberface 2.50
39 Dragon vs. Dung 2.50
40 "G-Man" 2.50
41 Wedding issue 2.50
42 V:Darklord 2.50
43 Stranded on another world .. 2.50
44 in flying saucer, ... 2.50
45 .... 2.50
46 She-Dragon vs. Vicious Circle 2.50
47 A knight and a mummy 2.50
48 Unfinished Business, pt.1 .. 2.50
49 Unfinished Business, pt.2 ... 2.50
50 Unfinished Business, pt.3, some
   reps., 96pg 5.95
51 F:She-Dragon 2.50
52 F:She-Dragon,V:Hercules ... 2.50
TPB A Talk With God 17.95
HC A Talk With God, signed ... 74.95
TPB The Fallen, rep.#7–#11 .. 12.95
HC The Fallen 29.95
TPB Possessed, rep.#12–#16 .. 12.95

SAVAGE DRAGON DESTROYER DUCK
Image Comics
1 SvG,ChM,EL 3.95

SAVAGE DRAGON, THE: RED HORIZON
Image Comics Feb. 1997
1 MsM 2.50
2 MsM,Dragon in the ER,A:Freak
   Force 2.50
3 (of 3) MsM,Freak Force beaten 2.50

SAVAGE DRAGON: MARSHAL LAW
Image July 1997
(B&W)
1 (of 2) PMs,KON,F:Marshal Law 2.50
2 PMs,KON, concl. 2.95

SAVAGE DRAGON: SEX & VIOLENCE
Image July 1997
1 (of 2) TBm,MBm 2.50
2 TBm,MBm,AH, concl. 2.50

SAVANT GARDE
Image/Wildstorm March 1997
1 "A team without a rule book" .. 2.50
2 Between killer & killer cat 2.50
3 V: strange Tapestry 2.50
4 "Any super-villain can take over
   the world" 2.50
5 "The Final Showdown" 2.50

6 BKs,Guilty until proven innocent 2.50
7 BKs,death of John Colt 2.50

Shadowhawk #3 © Shadowline

SHADOWHAWK
Image/Shadowline
1 JV,I:ShadowHawk,Black Foil(c),
   Pin-up of The Others,w/
   coupon#1 .... 3.00
1a w/o coupon 2.00
2 JV,V:Arsenal,A:Spawn, I:Infiniti 3.00
3 JV,V:Arsenal,w/glow-in-the-
   dark(c) 2.50
4 V:Savage Dragon 2.50
TPB rep.#1-4 .... 19.95
Ashcan #1 .... 2.00
Ashcan #2 .... 2.00
Ashcan #3 .... 2.00
Ashcan #4 .... 2.00
   [2nd Series] 1993
1 JV,Die Cut(c) 2.50
1a Gold Ed. 3.00
2 JV,ShadowHawk I.D. 2.50
2a Gold Ed. 2.50
3 Poster(c),JV,w/Ash Can 2.50
TPB 19.95
   [3rd Series] 1993
0 Zero issue 2.25
1 JV,CWf,V:Vortex,Hardedge, Red
   Foil(c) 2.50
1a Gold Ed. 3.00
1b signed 6.00
2 JV,CWf,MA,I:Deadline, BU&I:US
   Male 2.50
3 JV(a&s),ShadowHawk has AIDS,
   V:Hardedge,Blackjak 2.25
4 JV(a&s),V:Hardedge, ... 2.25
*Note: #5 to #11 not used; #12 below
   is the next issue, and the 12th
   overall.*
12 Monster Within, pt.1 ...... 1.95
13 Monster Within, pt.2 ...... 1.95
14 Monster Within, pt.3 ...... 2.50
15 Monster Within, pt.4 ...... 2.50
16 Monster Within, pt.5 ...... 2.50
17 Monster Within, pt.6 ...... 2.50
18 JV,D:ShadowHawk 2.50
Spec.#1 .... 3.50
Gallery#1 .... 1.95

SHADOWHAWK/ VAMPIRELLA

Book 2 V:Kaul 4.95
Book #1: see Vampi/ShadowHawk

SHADOWHUNT SPECIAL

1 Shadowhunt x-over, pt.1 . . . . . 2.50

SHAMAN'S TEARS

0 . . . . 2.50
1 MGr,I:Shaman,B:Origin 3.00
1a Siver Prism Ed. 5.00
2 MGr,Poster(c) 2.50
3 MGr,V:Bar Sinister 2.50
4 MGr,V:Bar Sinister,E:Origin . 1.95
5 MGr,R:Jon Sable 1.95
6 MGr,V:Jon Sable 1.95
7 MGr,V:Rabids 1.95
8 MGr,A:Sable 1.95
9 MGr,Becoming of Broadarrow . 1.95
10 Becoming of Broadarrow,pt.2 . 2.50
11 Becoming of Broadarrow,pt.3 . 2.50
12 Becoming of Broadarrow,pt.4 . 2.50
13 The Offspring,pt.1 . . . . 2.50

SHARKY
Image 1998

1 by Dave Elliott & Alex Horley . . 2.50
1a variant cover (5,000 made) . . 2.95
2 coma over 2.50
2a variant cover 2.95
3 R:Blazin' Glory 2.50
3a variant SBi(c) 2.50
4 tons of guest stars, concl 2.50
4a variant DAy (c) 2.50

SHATTERED IMAGE
Image/Wildstorm

1 KBk,TnD,crossover 2.50
2 KBk,TnD, ... 2.50
3 KBk,TnD, ... 2.50
4 KBk,TnD,concl. 2.50

SHIP OF FOOLS
Image (B&W) Sept. 1997

0 Bryan J.L. Glass, Michael Avon
Oeming 2.95
1 Death & Taxes, pt.1 . . . . 2.95
2 Death & Taxes, pt.2 . . . . 2.95
3 Death & Taxes, pt.3 . . . . 2.95
4 Death & Taxes, pt.4 . . . . 2.95

SHUT UP & DIE
Image (B&W) 1998

1 JHi and Kevin Stokes 2.95
2 JHi,Angry White Man 2.95
3 JHi,Wife abducted 2.95
4 JHi 2.95

SIEGE
Image/Wildstorm Jan. 1997

1 JPe,AV,Nothing you believe is
real 2.50
2 JPe,AV,Omega goes to Hawaii
for funeral 2.50
3 JPe,AV,Zontarian Crab Ships vs.
Drop Ship 2.50
4 JPe,AV,Raid to rescue Omega
Squad 2.50

SIGMA

1 Fire From Heaven prelude 2.50
2 Fire From Heaven, pt.6 . . . . . . 2.50

SIREN
Image (B&W) May 1998

1 by J. Torres & Tim Levins 2.95

SOULWIND
Image (B&W) March 1997

1 quest for Soulwind begins 2.95
2 Nick becomes "Captain Crash" 2.95
3 Captain Crash & Poke pursue
Soulwind info 2.95
4 concl. of story arc 2.95
5 The Day I Tried to Live,pt.1 . . . 2.95
6 The Day I Tried to Live,pt.2 . . . 2.95
7 The Day I Tried to Live,pt.3 . . . 2.95
8 The Day I Tried to Live,pt.4 . . . 2.95
TPB rep #1–#4 . . . . 9.95

SPARTAN: WARRIOR SPIRIT

1 thru 4 . . . . @2.95

SPAWN
Image/TMP May 1992

1 TM,I:Spawn,w/GP,DK pinups . 22.00
2 TM,V:The Violator 18.00
3 TM,V:The Violator 16.00
4 TM,V:The Violator,+coupon #2 18.00
4a w/o coupon 3.50
5 TM,O:Billy Kincaid 14.00
6 TM,I:Overt-Kill 8.00
7 TM,V:Overt-Kill 8.00
8 TM,AMo(s),F:Billy Kincaid 8.00

Spawn #10 © Rob Liefeld

9 NGa(s),TM,I:Angela 13.00
10 DS(s),TM,A:Cerebus 7.00
11 FM(s),TM 6.00
12 TM,Chapel killed Spawn 6.00
13 TM,A:Youngblood 5.00
14 TM,A:The Violator 5.00
15 TM 5.00
16 GCa,I:Anti-Spawn 5.00
17 GCa,V:Anti-Spawn 8.00
18 GCa,ATi,D:Anti-Spawn 15.00
19 & 20 see after #25

21 TM,The Hunt,pt.1 . . . . 15.00
22 TM,The Hunt,pt.2 . . . . 5.50
23 TM,The Hunt,pt.3 . . . . 5.50
24 TM,The Hunt,pt.4 . . . . 5.50
25 Image X Book,MS,BTn 9.00
19 I:Houdini 6.00
20 J:Houdini 6.00
26 TM 5.50
27 I:The Curse 5.50
28 Faces Wanda 5.50
29 Returns From Angela 5.50
30 A:KKK 5.50
31 R:Redeemer 5.00
32 TM,GCa,New Costume 6.00
33 R:Violator 4.50
34 V:Violator 4.50
35 F:Sam & Twitch 4.50
36 Talks to Wanda 4.50
37 I:The Freak 4.50
38 & 39 . . . . @4.50
40 & 41 V:Curse . . . . @4.50
42 thru 49 . . . . @4.00
50 48pgs 6.00
51 and 52 . . . . @4.00
53 A:Malebolgia 3.00
54 return to New York, alliance with
Terry Fitzgerald 3.00
55 plans to defeat Jason Wynn . . 3.00
56 efforts to defeat Jason Wynn . 4.00
57 . . . . 3.00
58 sequel to Spawn #29 . . . . . . 3.00
59 . . . . 3.00
60 battle between Spawn and Clown
cont. 3.00
61 battle with Clown concl. 3.00
62 Spawn is Al Simmons for 1 day 2.50
63 Operation: Wynn fall, pt.1 . . . 2.50
64 Wynn falls, bagged with toy
catalog 2.50
65 recap issue 2.50
66 TM,GCa,lives of alley bums . . 2.50
67 TM,GCa,Sam and Twitch 2.50
68 TM,GCa,R:Freak 2.50
69 TM,GCa,F:Freak 2.50
70 TM,GCa 2.50
71 TM,GCa,Cold Blooded Truth . . 2.50
72 TM,GCa,Haunting of the Heap . 2.25
73 TM,GCa,R:The Heap 2.25
74 TM,GCa,pathway to misery . . 2.25
75 TM,GCa,Deadly Revelations . . 2.25
76 TM,GCa,Granny Blake 2.25
77 TM,GCa,confronts 2.25
TPB Capital Collection rep.#1-3
limited to 1,200 copies 300.00
TPB TM,rep.#1–#5 . . . . 9.95
TPB Spawn III rep. #12–#15 . . . 9.95
TPB Spawn IV rep. #16–#20 . . . 9.95
TPB Spawn V rep.#21–#25 . . . . 9.95
TPB Spawn VI, rep.#26–#30 . . . 9.95
GN Spawn Movie adapt. 5.00

SPAWN/BATMAN
Image/DC

1 FM(s),TM, ... 5.00

SPAWN BLOOD FEUD

1 V:Vampires 4.00
2 . . . . 4.00
3 Hunted as a Vampire 4.00
4 V:Heartless John 4.00

SPAWN BIBLE
Image/TMP

1 TM,GCa 2.00

IMAGE

SPAWN THE IMPALER
Image/TMP
Mini-series
1 (of 3) MGr, fully painted 5.00
2 and 3 MGr . . . . @4.00

SPAWN: BLOODFEUD
1 thru 4 reoffered 4.00

SPAWN/WILDC.A.T.S
1 thru 4 mini-series 3.50

SPIRIT OF THE TAO
Image/Top Cow May 1998
1 BTn,F:Lance & Jasmine 2.50
2 BTn,mission to destroy base . . 2.50
3 BTn,V:Jaikap Clan 2.50
4 BTn,F:Jasmine & Lance 2.50

SPLITTING IMAGE
1 DsM,A:Marginal Seven 2.25
2 DsM,A:Marginal Seven 2.25

STAR
1 F:Star from Savage Dragon . . . 2.50
2 Buried Alive 2.50
3 A:Savage Dragon,Rapture 2.50
4 A:Savage Dragon,Rapture 2.50

STARCHILD: MYTHOPOLIS
Image (B&W) 1997
0 JOn, "Prologue" 2.95
1 JOn, "Pinehead" 2.95
2 JOn, "Pinehead," pt.2 . . . . 2.95
3 JOn, "Pinehead," pt.3 . . . . 2.95
4 JOn, "Fisher King," pt.1 . . . . . . 2.95
5 JOn, "Fisher King," pt.2 . . . . . . 2.95

StormWatch #3 © Jim Lee

STORMWATCH
Image/Wildstorm 1993
0 JSc(c),O:StormWatch,
 V:Terrorists,w/card 2.50
1 JLe(c&s),ScC,TvS(i),
 I:StormWatch 2.25

1a Gold Ed. 4.00
2 JLe(c&s),ScC,TvS(i),I:Cannon,
 Winter,Fahrenheit,Regent 2.25
3 JLe(c&s),ScC,TvS(i),V:Regent,
 I:Backlash 4.00
4 V:Daemonites 2.50
5 SRf(s),BBh,V:Daemonites 2.25
6 BCi,ScC,TC,A:Mercs 2.25
7 BCi,ScC,TC,A:Mercs 2.25
8 BCi,ScC,TC,A:Mercs 2.25
9 BCi,I:Defile 2.25
25 BCi,A:Spartan 2.50
10 V:Talos 2.00
10a variant (c) 3.00
11 the end? 2.00
12 V:Hellstrike 2.00
13 V:M.A.D.-1 . . . . 2.00
14 Despot 2.00
15 Batallion, Flashpoint 2.00
16 V:Defile 2.00
17 D:Batallion 2.00
18 R:Argos 2.50
19 R:M.A.D.-1,L:Winter 2.50
20 F:Cannon,Winter,Bendix 2.50
21 V:Wildcats 2.50
22 RMz,BWS(c),WildStorm
 Rising,pt.9,w/2 cards 2.50
22a Newsstand ed. 1.95
23 R:Despot,Warguard 2.50
24 V:Despot 2.50
25 BCi,A:Spartan 2.75
26 V:Despot 2.50
27 Rebuilding 2.50
28 New Adventures 2.50
29 Reorganization 2.50
30 . . . . 2.50
31 V:Middle Eastern Terrorists . . . 2.50
32 thru 34 . . . . @2.50
35 Fire From Heaven,pt.5 . . . . . . 2.50
36 Fire From Heaven 2.50
37 Double size 3.50
38 . . . . 2.50
39 . . . . 2.50
40 virus 2.50
41 . . . . 2.50
42 Weatherman discovers a
 conspiracy 2.50
43 . . . . 2.50
44 history of Jenny Sparks 2.50
45 Battalion visits his family 2.50
46 secrets and more secrets,
 prologue 2.50
47 WEI(s), JLe, SW, dangerous
 experiment gone awry 2.50
48 "Change or Die" pt.1 . . . . 2.50
49 "Change or Die" pt.2 . . . . 2.50
50 "Change or Die" concl.large size 4.50
Sourcebok JLe(s),DT 2.75
Spec.#1 RMz(s),DT 4.25
Spec.#2 F:Fleshpoint 2.50
Ashcan 1 . . . . 3.00
TPB Change the World 9.95

STORMWATCH
Image/Wildstorm Oct. 1997
1 WEI,bacterial horror 2.50
1a Variant cover 2.50
1b Voyager bagged pack 3.50
2 WEI,Stormwatch Black team . . . 2.50
3 WEI,Black team,concl. 2.50
4 WEI,A Finer World, pt.1 . . . . . . 2.50
5 WEI,A Finer World, pt.2 . . . . . . 2.50
6 WEI,A Finer World, pt.3 . . . . . . 2.50
7 WEI,Bleed, pt.1 . . . . 2.50
8 WEI,Bleed, pt.2 . . . . 2.50

9 WEI,Bleed, pt.3 . . . . 2.50
10 WEI,call it quits? 2.50

STRANGERS IN PARADISE VOL. 3
Homage Comics (B&W) 1996
1 TMr 6.00
2 TMr 4.00
Image/Homage Comics
3 TMr,David & Katchoo fight 2.75
4 TMr,Katchoo makes startling
 discovery 2.75
5 TMr,Francine's college days . . 2.75
6 TMr,Katchoo searches for David 2.75
7 TMr, ... 2.75
8 TMr,demons of the past 2.75

STRIKEBACK!
1 thru 4 . . . . @2.50

SUPER-PATRIOT
1 N:Super-Patriot 2.25
2 KN(i),O:Super-Patriot 2.25
3 A:Youngblood 2.25
4 . . . . 1.95

SUPER-PATRIOT: LIBERTY AND JUSTICE
1 R:Covenant 2.50
2 Tokyo 2.50
3 Tokyo gets Trashed 2.50
4 Final issue 2.50

SUPREME
Image/Supreme 1992
0 O:Supreme 2.50
1 B:RLd(s&i),BrM, V:Youngblood 3.00
1a Gold Ed. 5.00
2 BrM,I:Heavy Mettle 2.50
3 thru 4 BrM 2.50
5 BrM(a&s),Clv(i),I:Thor,V:Chrome 2.50
6 BrM,Clv(i),I:Starguard,
 A:Thor,V:Chrome 2.50
7 Rip,ErS(s),SwM,A:Starguard,
 A:Thor, ... 2.50
8 Rip(s),SwM,V:Thor, ... 2.50
9 Rip&KtH(s),BrM,Clv(i), V:Thor . 2.50
10 KrH(s),BrM,JRu(i), BU:I:Black &
 White 2.50
11 I:Newmen 2.50
12 SPa(c),RLd(s),SwM, ... 4.00
25 SPa(c),RLd(s),SwM,V:Simple
 Simon,Images of Tomorrow . . . 6.00
13 B:Supreme Madness 2.50
14 Supreme Madness, pt.2 . . . . . 2.50
15 RLd(s)A:Spawn 2.50
16 V:StormWatch 2.50
17 Supreme Madness, pt.5 . . . . . 2.50
18 E:Supreme Madness 2.50
19 V:The Underworld 2.50
20 V:The Unterworld 2.50
21 God Wars 2.50
22 RLd,CNn,God Wars, V:Thor . . 2.50
23 ExtremeSacrifice x-over,pt.1 . . 2.50
24 Identity Questions 2.50
#25, see above, after #12
26 F:Kid Supreme 2.50
27 Rising Son,I:Cortex 2.50
28 Supreme Apocalypse:Prelude . 2.50
29 Supreme Apocalypse,pt.1 . . . . 2.50
30 . . . . 2.50
31 V:Equinox 2.50
32 V:Cortex 2.50

Supreme #23 © Image Comics

33 Extreme Babewatch	2.50
34 She-Supreme	2.50
35 thru 38	@2.50
39 AMo	2.50
40 AMo	2.50
41 AMo	5.00
42 AMo,"Secret Origins"	5.00
43 AMo,"Secrets of the Citadel	
Supreme"	2.50
44 See Color Comics section	
Ann.#1 TMB,CAd,KG,I:Vergessen	2.95
Ashcan #1	3.00
Ashcan #2	2.00

SUPREME: GLORY DAYS
1 Supreme in WWI 2.95
2 (of 2) BNa&KIA(s),DdW,GyM,
   A:Superpatriot 2.95

SWORD OF DAMOCLES
1 prelude to Fire From Heaven x-
over 2.50

TALES OF THE DARKNESS
Image/Top Cow
1 WPo,F:Jackie Estacado 2.95
2 WPo,concl. first story 2.95
3 Dungeon, Fire, and Sword,pt.1 2.95

TALES OF THE WITCHBLADE
Image/Top Cow 1996
1 TnD,F:Anne Bonney 8.00
1a TnD, variant cover (1:4) 12.00
2 TnD,F:Annabella 5.00
3 WEI,BTn,future 4.00
4 WEI,BTn,future, pt.2 .... 4.00
5 RiB,past 2.95
6 RGr, time of Celts 2.95
Coll.Ed.#1, rep. #1–#2 .... 4.95

TEAM 1: STORMWATCH
1 I:First StormWatch Team 2.50
2 V:Helspont,D:Think Tank 2.50

TEAM 1: WILDCATS
1 I:First Wildcats Team 2.50
2 B:Cabal 2.50

TEAM 7
Image/Wildstorm 1994–95
1 New team 4.00
2 New powers 2.50
3 Members go insane 2.50
4 final issue,V:A Nuke 2.50
Ashcan 2.00
TPB 9.95

TEAM 7 OBJECTIVE: HELL
1 CDi,CW,BWS(c),WildStorm
   Rising,Prologue,w/2 cards .. 2.50
1a Newsstand ed. 1.95
2 Cambodia 2.50

TEAM 7 III: DEAD REACONING
1 thru 4 .... @2.50

TEAM YOUNGBLOOD
Image/Extreme 1993
1 B:ErS(s),ATi(c),CYp,NRD(i),
   I:Masada,Dutch,V:Giger 2.50
2 ATi(c),CYp,NRd(i),V:Giger 2.25
3 RLd(s),CYp,NRd(i),C:Spawn,
   V:Giger 2.25
4 ErS(s), ... 2.25
5 ErS(s),CNn,V:Lynx 2.25
6 ErS(s),N:Psi-Fire,
   BU:Black&White 2.25
7 ErS(s),CYp,ATh,Extreme
   Prejudice#1,I:Quantum, BU:Black
   & White 2.25
8 ErS(s),CYp,ATh,Extreme Prejudice #5, V:Quantum, BU:B&W 2.25
9 RLd 2.50
10 ErS(s),CYp,ATh, ... 2.50
11 RLd,ErS,Cyp 2.00
12 RLd,ErS,Cyp 2.50
13 ErS,Cyp 2.50
14 RLd,ErS,Cya 2.50
15 New Blood 2.50
16 RLd,ErS,TNu,I:New Sentinel,
   A:Bloodpool 2.50
17 ExtremeSacrifice x-over,pt.5 . 2.50
18 MS, membership drive 2.50
19 R:Brahma 2.50
20 Contact,pt.1 1000 yr Badrock . 2.50
21 Contact,pt.2 .... 2.50
22 Shadowhunt x-over,pt.4 ..... 2.50

TEENAGE MUTANT NINJA TURTLES
Image/Highbrow (B&W)
1 thru 3 .... @2.00
4 Donatello resurrected 2.00
5 FFo,Warlord Komodo uses
   Splinter as guinea pig 2.50
6 FFo 2.50
7 FFo,Raphael joins Foot Clan? . 2.50
8 FFo,Michelangelo tries to rescue
   Casey Jones' daughter 2.95
9 Enter: the Knight Watchman .. 2.95
10 "Enter: The Dragon" 2.95
11 V:DeathWatch,A:Vanguard ... 2.95
12 F:Raph, Foot Gang warfare . 2.95
13 Shredder is back! 2.95

14 Shredder vs. Splinter	2.95
15 F:Donatello	2.95
16 reunited with Splinter	2.95
17 F:Leonardo	2.95
18 UFO Sightings	2.95
TPB A New Beginning	9.95

TENTH, THE
Image Comics
1 BSt,TnD,Last stand against Hell
   on Earth 7.00
2 BSt,TnD,invasion of Darklon
   Corp. begins 4.00
3 BSt,TnD,Tenth & Espy team-up 3.00
4 BSt,TmD.confrontation with
   possible Armageddon 2.50
TPB rep.#1–#4 .... 10.95
Regular Series
1 TnD,BSt,V:Blackspell 4.00
2 TnD,BSt,V:Blackspell 3.50
3 TnD,BSt,Gozza,Eve 3.00
4 TnD,BSt,teleported to Japan .. 2.50
5 TnD,BSt 2.50
6 TnD,BSt,CollateralDamage,pt.1 2.50
7 TnD,BSt,CollateralDamage,pt.2 2.50
8 TnD,BSt,Darkk Wind At Your
   Back 2.50
9 TnD,BSt,F:Adrenalynn 2.50
10 TnD,pt.1 (of 3) 2.50
10a variant TnD(c) 2.50
11 TnD,Victor retains Tenth 2.50
11a variant cover 2.50
12 TnD,Black reign begins 2.50
Coll.Ed.Vol.1 rep. #1–#2 ..... 4.95
Spec.Configuration#1, sourcebook 2.50

TOP COW/BALLISTIC
Swimsuit Spec.#1 MS(c) (1995) . 4.00

TOP COW SECRETS
Winter Lingerie Spec. (1996) ... 3.00

A TOUCH OF SILVER
Image (B&W) Jan. 1997
1 JV,"Birthday" 2.95
2 JV,"Dance" 2.95
3 JV,"Bullies" 2.95
4 JV,"Separation" 2.95
5 JV,inc. Tomorrow Syndicate vs.
   Round Table of America, 12pg.
   color section 2.95
6 JV "Choices" Aug. 1963 ..... 2.95
TPB A Sociopath in Training .. 12.95

TRENCHER
1 KG,I:Trencher 2.25
2 KG, ... 2.25
3 KG,V:Supreme 2.25
4 KG,V:Elvis 2.25

TRIBE
1 TJn(s),LSn,I:The Tribe 2.50
1a Ivory(White) Editon 3.00
2 .... 2.25
Ashcan 1 .... 3.00

TROLL
Image/Extreme Dec. 1993
1 RLd(s),JMs,I:Evangeliste,
   V:Katellan Command, ... 2.50
2 .... 2.50
Halloween Spec.#1 .... 2.50
X-Mas Stocking Stuffer #1 .... 2.95

IMAGE

Troll Once a Hero #1 © Image Comics

TROLL: ONCE A HERO
1 Troll in WWII 2.50

TROUBLEMAN
Image/Motown June 1996
1 and 2 Charles Drost . . . . . . @2.50

TUG & BUSTER
Image (B&W) June 1998
1 MaH, humor, F:Stinkfinger 2.95

"21"
Image/Top Cow
1 thru 3 LWn,MDa, ... @2.50
4 LWn,MDa,"Time Bomb" pt.1 . . 2.50
5 LWn,MDa,"Time Bomb" pt.2 . . 2.50
6 LWn,MDa,"Time Bomb" pt.3
"Detonation" 2.50

UNBOUND
Image (B&W) Jan. 1998
1 by Joe Pruett & Michael Peters 2.95
2 . . . . 2.95
3 F:Marta & Erik 2.95

UNION
Image/Wildstorm
0 O:Union 2.50
0a WPo(c), ... 3.00
1 MT,I:Union,A:StormWatch 2.75
2 MT 2.75
3 MT 2.75
4 MT,Good Intentions 2.75
Regular Series 1995
1 R:Union, Crusade 2.50
2 V:Crusade & Mnemo 2.50
3 A:Savage Dragon 2.50
4 JRo,BWS(c), WildStorm
Rising,pt.3,w/2 cards 2.50
4a Newsstand ed. 1.95
5 V:Necros 2.50
6 V:Necros 2.50
7 Jill's Surprise 2.50
8 Regal Vengeance,pt.1 . . . . . . 2.50
9 Regal Vengeance,pt.2 . . . . . . 2.50
10 Regal Vengeance,pt.3 . . . . . 2.50

1-shot Final Vengeance, MHs,
V:Regent (1997) 2.50

UNION
Image/Wildstorm 1996
1 MHs,RBn 2.50
2 MHs,RBn 2.50
3 MHs,RBn 1.75

VANGUARD
Image/Highbrow 1993–94
1 EL(s),BU:I:Vanguard 2.25
2 EL(s),Roxann, ... 2.25
3 AMe, ... 2.25
4 AMe, ... 2.25
5 AMe,V:Aliens 2.25
6 V:Bank Robber 1.95

VANGUARD: STRANGE VISITORS
1 (of 4) SEa,BAn,A:Amok 2.95
2 SEa,BAn, ... 2.95
3 SEa,BAn, ... 2.95
4 SEa,BAn,finale 2.95

VELOCITY
1 V:Morphing Opponent 2.50
2 V:Charnel 2.50
3 & 4 conclusion . . . . @2.50

VIOLATOR
1 AMo(s),BS,I:Admonisher 2.25
2 AMo(s),BS 1.95
3 AMo(s),BS,last issue 1.95

VIOLATOR/BADROCK
1 AMo(s),A:Celestine 2.50
2 V:Celestine 2.50
3 F:Dr. McAllister 2.50
4 Final issue 2.50
TPB Rep. 9.95

VISITATIONS
Image (B&W) 1997
GN by C. Stott Morse 6.95

VOGUE
1 F:Vogue,I:Redbloods 2.50
2 & 3 conclusion 2.50

VOODOO
Image/Wildstorm Nov. 1997
1 AMo(s),WildStorm universe . . 2.50
2 AMo(s),in old New Orleans . . . 2.50
3 AMo(s), ... 2.50
4 AMo(s), Christian Charles . . . 2.50

WARBLADE: ENDANGERED SPECIES
1 I:Pillar 2.95
2 V:Ripclaw 2.50
3 I:Skinner 2.50
4 final issue 2.50

WAY OF THE CODA: THE COLLECTED WILDC.A.T.S
TPB VOL.II 12.95

WEAPON ZERO
Image/Top Cow
T-Minus-4 WS 4.50
T-Minus-3 Alien Invasion 4.00
T-Minus-2 Formation of a Team . . 4.00
T-Minus-1 Alien Invasion 4.00
0 Whole Team Together 4.00
1 . . . . 3.50
2 . . . . 3.50
3 . . . . 3.50
4 WS,JBz 3.00
5 WS,JBz 3.00
6 WS,JBz 3.00
7 WS,JBz 3.00
8 WS,JBz 3.00
9 WS,JBz 3.00
10 WS,ScL,"Devil's Reign" tie-in . 3.00
11 WS,JBz,Weapon Zero & Lilith
return to T'srii moonbase . . . 3.00
12 WS,JBz, What's wrong with
Jamie 3.00
13 WS,JBz,problems with Jamie . 3.00
14 JBz,T'Srrii have returned 3.00
15 JBz,T'Srrii,concl.,48pg 3.50

WETWORKS
Image/Wildstorm 1994
1 WPo 4.00
2 WPo,BCi 3.00
3 WPo,BCi,V:Vampire 3.00
4 WPo,BCi,Dozer 2.50
5 WPo,BCi,Pilgrim's Turn 2.50
6 WPo,BCi,Civil War 2.50
7 WPo,BCi,F:Pilgrim 2.50
8 WPo,SW,BWS(c), Wildstorm
Rising,pt.7,w/2 cards 2.50
8a Newsstand ed. 2.25
9 F:Jester,Pilgrim Dozer 2.50
10 R:Dozer to Action 2.50
11 Blood Queen Vs. Dane 2.50
12 V:Vampire Nation 2.50
13 Fire From Heaven,pt.1 . . . . . 2.50
14 Fire From Heaven,pt.2 . . . . . 2.50
15 Fire From Heaven,pt.3 . . . . . 2.50
16 Fire From Heaven,pt.4 . . . . . 2.50
17 FTa, ... 2.50
18 FTa, ... 2.50
19 FTa, ... 2.50
20 FTa, ... 2.50
21 FTa, ... 2.50
22 FTa,Dave vs.Bloodqueen concl. 2.50
23 FTa,Flattop & Crossbones,
V:Lady Feign 2.50
24 FTa, ... 2.50
25 FTa,Can Pilgrim withstand the
beast that lurks within her,
double size 3.00
26 team parts ways with Armand
Waering 2.50
27 V:Craven, no rest for the weary 2.50
28 Vampire tracked in Pacific
Northwest,A:Johnny Savoy . . . 2.50
29 V:Soulbender 2.50
30 "Secret of the Symbiotes" . . . 2.50
31 "Time of the Blood War" 2.50
32 StG,PtL,V:Drakkar 2.50
32a Voyager pack, bagged with
Phantom Guard preview 3.50
33 StG,PtL,Sacraments, pt.2 . . . 2.50
34 StG,PtL,Sacraments, pt.3 . . . 2.50
35 StG,PtL,Sacraments, pt.4 . . . 2.50
36 StG 2.50
37 StG,V:St.Crispin 2.50
38 StG,on West Coast 2.50

IMAGE

39 StG,in South America 2.50
40 StG,in the crosshairs 2.50
41 StG,V:Stormwatch 2.50
42 StG,Mother One missing 2.50
43 StG,Mother One concl. 2.50
Sourcebook 2.50
TPB Rebirth 9.95

WETWORKS/VAMPIRELLA
Image/Wildstorm
1 JMi & GK, x-over 2.95

WILDC.A.T.S.
Image/Wildstorm 1992
1 B:BCi(s),JLe, SW(i), I:Wild-
C.A.T.S. 5.00
1a Gold Ed. 5.00
1b Gold and Signed 10.00
2 JLe,SW(i),V:Master Gnome,
I:Wetworks, Prism foil(c),
w/coupon#5 . . . . 4.00
2a w/o coupon 2.00
3 RLd(c),JLe,SW(i), V:Youngblood 3.00
4 E:BCi(s),JLe,LSn,SW(i),w/card,
A:Youngblood,BU:Tribe 3.00
4a w/red card 4.00
5 BCi(s),JLe,SW 3.00
6 BCi(s),JLe,SW,Killer Instinct,
A:Misery,C:Ripclaw 3.00
7 BCi(s),JLe,SW, A:Cyberforce . 3.00
8 BCi(s),JLe,SW, ... 3.00
9 BCi(s),JLe,SW, ... 3.00
10 CCi(s),JLe,SW,I:Huntsman . . 2.50
11 CCi(s),JLe,SW,V:Triad,
A:Huntsman 2.50
11a WPo(c) 4.00
12 JLe,CCi,A:Huntsman 3.00
13 JLe,CCi,A:Huntsman 2.50
14 X book 2.50
15 F:Black Razors 2.50
16 Black Razors 2.50
17 A:StormWatch 2.50
18 R:Hightower 2.50
19 V:Hightower 2.50
20 TC,JeR,BWS(c),WildStorm
Rising,pt.2,w/2 cards 2.50
20a Newsstand ed. 2.00
21 Into Space Back Home 2.50
22 Space Adventures 2.50
23 F:Mr. Majestic's Team 2.50
24 O:Maul 2.50
25 double sized 5.00
26 . . . . 2.50
27 . . . . 2.50
28 . . . . 2.50
29 Fire From Heaven,pt.7 . . . . . 2.50
30 BKs 2.50
31 BKs 2.50
32 BKs 2.50
33 BKs,gang war rages on 2.50
34 AMo,MtB,New York seconds
away from nuclear disaster . . . 2.50
35 AMo,MtB,BKs,V:Crusade . . . 2.50
36 AMo,MtB,BKs,V:Crusade,
A:Union, pt.2 . . . . 2.50
37 BCi,JPe,MtB,WildC.A.T.s team
divided 2.50
38 BCi,JPe,MtB,Puritans debut . . 2.50
39 BCi,JPe,MtB,"C.A.T. Fight" . . . 2.50
40 BCi,JPe,MtB,MtB(c) 2.50
40a variant cover by TC 2.50
41 BCi,JPe,MtB,backwards in time 2.50
42 BCi,JPe,MTb,in WWI 2.50
43 BCi,JPe,MTb,in ancient China . 2.50

44 BCi,JPe,MTb,Renaissance . . . 2.50
45 BCi,JPe,MTb 2.50
46 BCi,JPe,MTb,escape from
Rome 2.50
47 BCi,JPe,MTb,time trip concl. . . 2.50
47a variant JMd(c) 2.50
48 BCi,JPe,trapped in mothership 2.50
49 BCi,JPe,return to present . . . 2.50
50 BCi,JPe,AMo,new
costumes,40pg 3.50
TPB A Gathering of Eagles 9.95
Spec.#1 SrG(s),TC,SW,I:Destine,
Pin-ups 3.50
Spec.#2 . . . . 2.50
3-D #1 rep. #1, with glasses 4.95
3-Da variant cover, glasses 4.95
TPB rep. #1-4,w/0 . . . . 11.00
TPB Homecoming rep.#21–#27 . 19.95
Ann.#1 JRo,LSn (1998) 2.95
TPB WildC.A.T.S/Cyberforce
Killer Instinct 16.95

WILDC.A.T.S ADVENTURES
Image/Wildstorm 1994
1 From animated TV series 2.50
2 Helspont,Troika 2.00
3 Caught in war 2.00
4 V:The President 2.50
5 I:Lonely 2.50
6 I:Majestics 2.50
7 . . . . 2.50
8 Betrayed 2.50
9 V:Black Razors 2.50
10 F:Voodoo 2.50
Sourcebook (JS(c)) 2.95

WILDC.A.T.S/ALIENS
Image/Wildstorm 1998
1-shot WEI,CSp,KN 4.95
1-shota, variant GK&KN(c)(1:4) . . 4.95

WildCats Trilogy #2 © Jim Lee

WILDC.A.T.S. TRILOGY
1 BCi(s),JaL,V:Artemis 2.50
2 BCi(s),JaL,V:Artemis 2.25
3 BCi(s),JaL,V:Artemis 2.25

WILDC.A.T.S/X-MEN
Image/Wildstorm Feb. 1997
1 (of 4) SLo,TC, giant Marvel/Image
crossover 4.50
1a alternate cover by JLe 4.50
2 & 4 see Marvel

WILDC.A.T.S/X-MEN
Image/Wildstorm June 1997
Golden Age #1 . . . . 4.95
Golden Age #1a variant JLe(c) . . 4.95
3-D Golden Age #1, with glasses . 4.95
3-D Golden Age #1, variant cover 4.95
Silver Age #1 SLo, JLe & SW, cross
over 4.50
Silver Age #1a signed 19.95
Silver Age #1b signed, deluxe . 29.95
3-D Silver Age #1, with glasses . 6.50
3-D Silver Age #1, NA(c) variant . 6.50
Modern Age #1, JRo,AHu,MFm . 4.50
Modern Age #1a variant cover . . 4.50
3-D Modern Age #1, with glasses 4.95
3-D Modern Age #1, variant cover 4.95

WILDCORE
Image/Wildstorm Nov. 1997
1 BBh,SRf,BBh(c), V:Drahn 2.50
1a variant TC(c) 2.50
1b Voyager bagged pack 3.00
2 BBh,SRf,Brawl joins 2.50
3 BBh,SRf,V:D'rahn 2.50
4 BBh,SRf,A:Majestic 2.50
5 BBh,SRf,Tapestry 2.50
6 BBh,SRf,Zealot missing 2.50
7 BBh,SRf,caught in fantasy world 2.50

WILDSTAR
1 JOy,AG,I:WildStar 2.25
1a Gold Ed. 3.00
2 JOy,AG 2.25
3 JOy,AG,V:Savage Dragon,
D:WildStar 2.25
4 JOy,AG,Last Issue,Pin-ups . . 2.25
TPB 12.95
[Regular Series]
1 R:WildStar 2.00
2 V:Mighty Man 2.50
3 . . . . 2.50
Ashcan 1.00
TPB WildStar Sky Zero 12.95

WILDSTORM!
Image/Wildstorm
1 F:Spartan,Black Razors 2.50
2 F:Deathblow 2.50
3 F:Taboo,Spartan 2.50
4 . . . . 2.50
Winter Wonderfest Spec.#1 . . . . 3.50
Spec. #1 Chamber of Horrors . . . 3.50
Spec. Swimsuit Special '97 . . . . 2.50
Spec. Ultimate Sports Official
Program 2.50
Sketchbook 2.95
Spec. Halloween '97 . . . . 2.50

WILDSTORM ARCHIVES GENESIS
Image/Wildstorm June 1998
1 The #1 Collection, 238 pg 7.00

IMAGE

WILDSTORM RISING
Image/Wildstorm
1 JeR,BWS(c&a) WildStorm Rising, pt.1:Tricked by Defile, w/2 cards	2.50
1a Newsstand ed.	1.95
2 RMz,BBo,BWS(c) WildStorm Rising,pt.10,w/2 cards	2.50
2a Newsstand ed.	1.95
Wildstorm Sourcebook #1	2.50
TPB Rep. Mini-series	16.95

WILDSTORM SPOTLIGHT
Image/Wildstorm Feb. 1997
1 AMo,F:Majestic, at the end of time	2.50
2 StG,RMr,Loner returns	2.50
3 StG,RMr,Secret past of original Loner	2.50
4 F:Hellstrike	2.50

WILDSTORM UNIVERSE '97
Image/Wildstorm Nov. 1997
Sourcebook #1 thru #3	@2.50

WITCHBLADE
Image/Top Cow 1995–96
1 I:Witchblade	40.00
1A Special retailer edition	40.00
1B Wizard Ace edition,acetate(c)	45.00
2	35.00
2 encore edition	7.00
3	25.00
4	23.00
5	16.00
6	13.00
7	10.00
8	10.00

Top Cow 1996
9	9.00
9A variant cover	11.00
10 I:Darkness (Jackie Estacado)	5.00
10a variant Darkness cover (1:4)	15.00
11	6.00
12 Connection between Lisa, Microwave Murderer and Kenneth Irons	4.00

Image/Top Cow 1997
13 Dannette Boucher's secret past	3.00
14 Sara searches for Microwave Murderer	3.00
15 "There is a war brewing..."	3.00
16 "Will Witchblade come between Sarah and Jake?"	3.00
17 New York City in shambles	3.00
18 Family Ties, pt.1,x-over	3.00
18a variant (c)	7.00
19 Family Ties, pt.4,x-over	3.00
20 Chief Siry, Ian Nottingham	2.50
21 another big surprise	2.50
22 F:Sara	2.50
23 F:Ian Nottingham	2.50
24 JPn,Sara learns truth	2.50
25 Save Jake's Life, 32 pg	2.95
Coll.Ed.Vol.#1	4.95
Coll.Ed.Vol.#2	4.95
Coll.Ed.Vol.#3	4.95
Coll.Ed.Vol.#4, rep. #7 & #8	4.95
Coll.Ed.Vol.#5, rep. #9 & #10	4.95
Coll.Ed.Vol.#6, rep. #11 & #12	4.95
Coll.Ed.Vol.#7, rep. #13 & #14	4.95
Coll.Ed.Vol.#8, rep. #15–#17	6.95
Delux Coll.Ed. rep.1–#8	24.95

WIZARDS TALE, THE
Image/Homage Comics 1997
TPB KBk,DWe	19.95
TPB 2nd printing	19.95
HC	29.95
HC, signed, limited	39.95

WOLVERINE/ WITCHBLADE
Image/Top Cow Jan. 1997
one-shot "Devil's Reign" pt.5 (of 8)	4.00

WYNONNA EARP
Image/Wildstorm
1 BSt,	2.50
2 BSt,The Law comes to San Diablo	2.50
3 BSt,desperate to stop Hemo from going nationwide	2.50
4 BSt,goes to New York, V:ancient evil	2.50
5 BSt,battle with Raduk—Eater of the Dead concl.	2.50

Youngblood #8 © Rob Liefeld

YOUNGBLOOD
Image/Extreme
0 RLd,O:Youngblood,w/coupon#7	3.00
0a without coupon	1.50
0b gold coupon	9.00
1 RLd,I:Youngblood(flipbook)	5.00
1a 2nd print.,gold border	2.50
1b RLD,Silent Edition	12.95
2 RLd,I:ShadowHawk	5.00
3 RLd,I:Supreme	3.00
4 RLd,DK,A:Prophet,BU:Pitt	3.00
5 RLd,Flip book,w/Brigade #4	2.50
6 RLd(a&s),J:Troll,Knight Sabre, 2nd Die Hard, Proposal to Girl friend	3.50
7 Badrock, V:Overtkill	2.50
8 Chapel, V:Spawn	2.50
9	2.50
9a variant cover	5.00
10 Bravo, Badrock, Troll	2.50
Yr.Bk.#1 CYp,I:Tyrax	2.75
Ashcan #1	8.00
Ashcan #2	4.00

TPB rep. #1-#5	16.95

[Volume 2] 1995
1 New Roster	2.50
2 The Program Continues	2.50
3 Extreme Babewatch	2.50
4 thru 6	@2.50
7 Shadowhunt x-over,pt.3	2.50
8 thru 10, ErS,RCz	@2.50
TPB Baptism of Fire, F:Spawn	
See Color Pub. section	

YOUNGBLOOD BATTLEZONE
1 BrM	2.25
2	2.95

YOUNGBLOOD STRIKEFILE
Image/Extreme 1993
1 JaL,RLd,I:Allies,A:Al Simmons (Spawn)	3.00
1a Gold Ed.	4.00
2 JaL,RLd,V:Super Patriot, Giger	2.50
2a Gold Ed.	3.50
3 RLd,JaL,DaM(i), A:Super Partiot	2.50
4 I:Overtkill	2.25
5	3.00
6 flip book	3.00
7 flip book	3.00
8 Shaft	3.00
9 Knight Sabre	3.00
10 RLd,TNu,I:Bloodpool,Task, Psilence,Wylder,Rubble	3.50
11 O:Link Crypt	2.50
TPB rep.#1-#3,sketchbook	12.95
Ashcan	3.00

YOUNGBLOOD/X-FORCE
Image/Extreme/Marvel 1996
1-shot Mojo visits Image x-over	5.00
1-shot RLd variant cover	5.00

YOUNGBLOOD YEARBOOK
1 CYp,I:Tyrax	2.75

YOUNGBLOOD: YEAR ONE
1 KBk(s),RLd, the early years	2.50
2 KBk(s),RLd,V:Giger,Cybernet	2.50

ZEALOT
Image/Wildstorm 1995
1 O:Zealot	2.50
2 In Japan	2.50
3 V:Prometheus	2.50

ZORRO
Image (B&W) 1998
TPB #1 rep. classic Alex Toth	15.95
TPB #2 rep. classic Alex Toth	15.95

IMAGE

MALIBU

Airman #1 © Malibu Comics

AIRMAN
1 I:Thresher 1.95

ALL NEW EXILES
Ultraverse 1995–96
Infinity F:Juggernaut, Blaze 2.50
1 TKa,KeL,Beginning the Quest . 1.50
1a Computer painted cover (1:6) . 2.50
1b signed edition 4.00
2 I:Hellblade, Phoenix flip issue . 1.50
3 TKa,KeL,Phoenix Resurrection 1.50
4 . . . . 1.50
5 . . . . 1.50
6 I:Moloch 1.50
7 . . . . 1.50
8 I:Maxis 1.50
9 . . . . 1.50
10 "Aladdin Attacks" 1.50
11 V:Maxis,A:Ripfire 1.50

ANGEL OF DESTRUCTION
Oct. 1996
1 . . . . 2.50

ARROW
1 V:Dr.Sheldon,A:Man O'War . . . 1.95

BATTLETECH
Feb. 1995
0 . . . . 2.95

BATTLETECH: FALLOUT
Dec. 1994–Mar. 1995
1 3 tales, Based on FASA game . 2.95
1a gold foil limited edition 3.50
1b limited holographic editon . . . 5.00
2 V:Clan Jade Falcon 2.95
3 R:Lea 2.95
4 Conclusion 2.95

BLACK SEPTEMBER
Ultraverse 1995
Infinity End of Black September . . 2.95

BRAVURA
1995
0 Preview book, mail-in 5.00

BREAK-THRU
Ultraverse 1993–94
1 GJ(s),GP,AV(i),A:All Ultraverse
Heroes 2.75
1a Foil Edition 7.50
2 GJ(s),GP,AV(i),A:All Ultraverse
Heroes 2.75

'BREED
Bravura
[Limited Series] 1994
1 JSn(a&s),Black (c),I:Stoner . . . 3.00
2 JSn(a&s),I:Rachel 2.75
3 JSn(a&s),V:Rachel 2.75
4 JSn(a&s),I:Stoner's Mom 2.75
5 JSn(a&s),V:Rachel 2.75
6 JSn(a&s),final issue 2.50
TPB Book of Genesis, rep.#1-#6 12.95

'BREED II
Bravura
[Limited Series] 1994–95
1 JSn,The Book of Revelation . . 2.95
1a gold foil edition 4.00
2 JSn,A:Rachel 2.95
3 JSn,V:Actual Demon 2.95
4 JSn,Language of Demons 2.95
5 JSn,R:Rachael 2.95
6 JSn,final issue 2.95

BRUCE LEE
1994
1 MBn(s), Stories of B.Lee 2.95
2 MBn(s) 2.95
3 MBn(s) 2.95
4 thru 6 . . . . @2.95

CODENAME: FIREARM
Ultraverse 1995
0 I:New Firearm 2.95
1 F:Alec Swan 2.95
2 Dual Identity 2.95
3 F:Hitch and Lopez 2.95
4 F:Hitch and Lopez 2.95
5 Working Together 2.95

CURSE OF RUNE
Ultraverse 1995
1A CU,Rune/Silver Surfer tie-in . . 2.50
1B CU, alternate cover 2.50
2 COntrol of the Soul Gem 2.50
3 F:Marvel's Adam Warlock 2.50
4 N:Adam Warlock 2.50

DEAD CLOWN
1 I:Force America 2.50
2 I:Sadistic Six 2.50
3 TMs(s),last issue 2.50

DINOSAURS FOR HIRE
1 3-D rep. B&W 3.00
[2nd Series] 1993–94
1 B:TMs(s),A:Reese,Archie,
Lorenzo 3.00
2 BU:Dinosaurs 2099 . . . . 2.50
3 A:Ex-Mutants 2.50
4 V:Poacher,Revenue 2.50
5 . . . . 2.50
6 V:Samantha 2.50
7 V:Turret 2.50
8 Genesis #2, with Skycap 2.50
9 Genesis #5 . . . . 2.50
10 Flip(c) 2.50
11 V:Tiny Lorenzo 2.50
12 I:Manhatten Bob 2.50
13 I:Lil' Billy Frankenstein 2.50
14 final issue 2.50

DREADSTAR
Bravura 1994–95
1 JSn(c),PDd(s),EC,I:New
Dreadstar (Kalla),w/stamp 2.75
2 JSn(c),PDd(s),EC,w/stamp . . . 2.50
3 JSn(c),PDd(s),EC,w/stamp . . . 2.75
4 PDd,EC,Kalla's origin,w/stamp . 2.50
5 PDd,F:Vanth,w/stamp 2.50
6 PDd,w/stamp 2.50

EDGE
Bravura 1994–95
1 GK,I:Edge 2.50
2 GK,STg,Gold Stamp 2.50
3 GK,The Ultimates 2.50
4 GK,V:Mr. Ultimate 2.50

ELIMINATOR
Ultraverse 1995
0 Man,DJa,MZ,Zothros tries to re-
open passage to the Godwheel 2.95
1 MZ,Man,DRo, The Search for the
Missing Infinity Gems,I:Siren . . 2.95
1a Black Cover ed. 3.95
2 MZ 2.50
3 MZ, Infinity Gem tie-in,finale . . 2.50

ELVEN
Ultraverse 1994
0 Rep.,A:Prime, double size 2.95
Mini-Series 1994–95
1 A:Prime, Primevil 2.50
2 AaL,R:Maxi-Man 2.50
3 AaL,V:Duey, Primevil 2.50
4 AaL,F:Primevil 2.50

ETERNITY TRIPLE ACTION
B&W
1 F:Gazonga 1.95
2 F:Gigantor 2.50

EXILES
Ultraverse 1993
1 TMs(s),PaP,I:Exiles 4.00
1a w/out card 2.25
1b Gold hologram ed. 10.00

1c Ultra-limited	12.00
2 V:Kort	3.00
3 BWS,Mastodon,BU:Rune	4.00
4 V:Kort	3.00

EX-MUTANTS
Nov. 1992–Apr. 1994
1 I&O:Ex-Mutants	2.25
2 V:El Motho,Beafcake,Brickhouse	2.25
3 A:Sliggo,Zygote	2.25
4	2.25
5 Piper Kidnapped	1.95
6 A:Dr.Kildare	1.95
7 V:Dr.Kildare	1.95
8 O:Gelson	1.95
9 F:Dillion	1.95
10 F:Sluggtown	1.95
11 Man(s),Genesis#1,w/card	2.25
12 R0M(s),Genesis#4	2.25
13 J:Gravestone,Arc	2.25
14 C:Eye	2.25
15 A:Arrow	2.50
16 A:Arrow,I:KillCorp	2.50
17 A:Arrow,V:KillCorp	2.50
18 A:Arrow,V:KillCorp	2.50

FERRET
1 (From Protectors),DZ,V:Purple Dragon Tong,A:Iron Skull	2.25

[Regular Series] 1992–93
1 thru 3	2.50
4 V:Toxin	2.50
4a Newstand Ed.	2.25
5 SEr,Genesis	2.25
6 SEr,Genesis crossover	2.25
7 V:Airman	2.25
8 I:Posse	2.25
9 DZ,R:Iron Skull,I:Deathsong	2.25
10 DZ	2.25
11	2.25

FIREARM
Ultraverse 1993–95
0 w/video,I:Duet	4.00
1 I:Firearm,Alec Swan	2.50
1 silver foil, limited edition	4.00
2 BWS,A:Hardcase,BU:Rune	2.75
3 V:Sportsmen	2.25
4 HC,Break-Thru x-over	2.25
5 O:Prime,I:Ellen	2.25
6 A:Prime	2.25
7 V:Killer	2.25
8 DIB(c)	2.25
9 at the Rose Bowl	1.95
10 The Lodge	2.25
11 Ultraverse Premier #5,BU:Prime	3.50
12 Rafferty Saga,pt.1	1.95
13 Rafferty Saga,pt.2	1.95
14 Swan	1.95
15 Rafferty Saga,pt.3	1.95
16 Rafferty Saga,pt.4	1.95
17 Rafferty Saga,pt.5	1.95
18 JeR,HC(c),Rafferty Saga,finale	2.50

FLOOD RELIEF
Ultraverse 1994
TPB Ultraverse Heroes	5.00

FOXFIRE
Ultraverse 1996
1 From Phoenix Resurrection	1.50
2 Fate of Mastodon revealed	1.50
3 & 4	@1.50

FRANKENSTEIN
1 thru 3 movie promo	@2.50

Freex #4 © Malibu Comics

FREEX
Ultraverse 1993–95
1 I:Freex w/Ultraverse card	3.00
1a Ultra-Limited	4.00
1b Full Hologram (c)	5.00
2 L:Valerie,I:Rush	3.00
3 A:Rush	3.00
4 GJ(s),DdW,BWS,BU:Rune	2.75
5 GJ(s),V:Master of the Hunt	2.50
6 GJ(s),BH,Break Thru x-over, A:Night Man	2.25
7 BHr,MZ,O:Hardcase	2.25
8 BHr,V:Lost Angel	2.25
9 BHr,A:Old Man	2.25
10 BHr,V:Ms. Contrary	2.25
11 BHr,E:Origins	2.25
12 GJ,Ultraforce	1.95
13 New look	1.95
14 R:Boomboy	1.95
15 Death of Teamate	3.50
16 Prelude to Godwheel	1.95
17 A:Rune	2.50
18 GJ,A:Contray, Cayman, Juice	2.50
Giant Size#1 A:Prime	2.50

GENESIS
0 GP,w/Pog,F:Widowmaker, A:Arrow	3.50
0a Gold Ed.	5.00

GODWHEEL
Ultraverse 1995
0 R:Argus to Godwheel	2.50
1 I:Primevil	2.50
2 Hardcase new costume	2.50
3 F:Lord Pumpkin	2.50
TPB Wheel of Thunder,rep.#0–#3	9.95

GRAVESTONE
July 1993–Feb. 1994
1 D:Gravestone,V:Wisecrack	2.25
1a Newstand Ed.	1.95
2 A:Eternal Man, V:Night Plague	2.25
2a Newstand Ed.	1.95

3 Genesis Tie in,w/skycap	2.25
4 Genesis	2.25
5 V:Scythe	2.25
6 V:Jug	1.95
7 R:Bogg	2.25
8 & 9	@2.25

HARDCASE
Ultraverse 1993–95
1 I:Hardcase,D:The Squad	3.00
1a Ultra-Limited, silver foil	4.00
1b Full Hologram (c)	5.00
1c Platinum edition	3.50
2 w/Ultraverse card	3.00
3 Hard decisions	2.75
4 A:Strangers	2.75
5 BWS,V:Hardwire,BU:Rune	2.75
6 V:Hardwire	2.50
7 ScB,Break-Thru x-over, I:Nanotech,A:Solution	2.25
8 GP,O:Solitare	2.25
9 B:O:Choice,I:Turf	2.25
10 O:Choice	2.25
11 ScB,V:Aladdin	2.25
12 AV,A:Choice	1.95
13 A:Choice	2.25
14 A:Choice	2.25
15 Hardwires, NIM-E	1.95
16 NIM-E	3.50
17 Prime,NIM-E	1.95
18 V:Nim-E, Battle Royale	1.95
19 Prelude to Godwheel	1.95
20 R:Rex Mindi	2.50
21 Mundiquest prelude	2.50
22 Mundiquest.	2.50
23 A:Loki	2.50
24 Mundiquest,pt.3	2.50
25 Mundiquest,concl.	2.95
26 Time Gem Disaster	2.95

HOSTILE TAKEOVER
1 ashcan Ultraverse x-over	.75

LITA FORD
Rock-It Comix
1 JBa	3.95

LORD PUMPKIN
Oct. 1994
0 Sludge	2.50

MAN CALLED A-X
Bravura 1994–95
[Limited Series]
0 1st Puzzle piece	2.95
1 MWn,SwM	2.95
1a Gold foil Edition	4.00
2 MWn,SwM,VLElectobot	2.95
3 MWn,SwM,Mercy Island	2.95
4 MWn,SwM,One Who Came Before	2.95
5 MWn,SwM,Climax	2.95

MAN OF WAR
1993–94
1 thru 3 V:Lift	2.50
1a thru 5a Newstand Ed.	1.95
4 w/poster	2.50
5 V:Killinger	2.50
6 KM,Genesis Crossover	2.50
7 DJu,Genesis Crossover	2.50
8 TMs(s),A:Rocket Ranger	2.25
9 thru 12	@2.25

MANTRA
Ultraverse 1993–95
1 AV,I:Mantra,w/Ultraverse card . 3.00
1a Full Hologram (c) 12.00
1b Silver foil (c) 5.00
2 AV,V:Warstrike 2.50
3 AV,V:Kismet Deadly 2.50
4 BWS,Mantra's marriage, BU:Rune
    story 2.50
5 MiB(s),AV(i),V:Wiley Wolf 2.00
6 MiB(s),AV(i),Break Thru x-over 2.00
7 DJu,TA,A:Prime, O:Prototype . . 2.00
8 B:MiB(s),A:Warstrike 2.00
9 V:Iron Knight,Puppeteer 2.00
10 NBy(c),DaR,B:Archmage Quest,
    Flip/UltraversePremiere #2 . 3.00
11 MiB(s),V:Boneyard 2.00
12 MiB(s),A:Strangers 2.00
13 Topaz, Boneyard 2.00
14 Tradesmen, Boneyard 2.00
15 A:Prime,Doc Gross 2.00
16 A:Prime 2.00
17 A:Necromantra 2.00
18 Pregnancy 2.25
19 MiB,Pregnancy 2.25
20 Aftermath of Godwheel 2.25
21 TyD,MiB,Mantra goes bad ... 2.25
22 A:Marvel's Loki 2.25
23 I:Tremblor, A:Prime 2.25
24 V:Topaz 2.25
Giant Sized#1 GP(c),I:Topaz . . 2.25
Ashcan #1 .... 2.00

MANTRA
Ultraverse 1995–96
Infinity N:Mantra 2.50
1 Mantra in all Female Body 1.50
1a Computer Painted Cover 1.50
2 Phoenix flip issue 1.50
3 Phoenix Resurrection 1.50
4 .... 1.50
5 .... 1.50
6 TMs,I:Tattoo,A:Rush 1.50
7 .... 1.50

MANTRA: SPEAR OF DESTINY
Ultraverse 1995
1 Search for Artifact 2.50
2 MiB,Eden vs. Aladdin 2.50

MARVEL/ULTRAVERSE BATTLEZONES
Ultraverse 1996
1 DPs(c),The Battle of the Heroes 3.95

MEGADETH
Rock-it Comix
1 .... 4.25

METALLICA
Rock-it Comix
1 .... 4.25

METAPHYSIQUE
Bravura 1995
1 NBy,I:Metaphysique 2.95
1a Gold foil edition 4.00
2 NBy,Mandelbrot malfunctions . . 2.95
3 I:Harridas 2.95
4 D:Maj.Character,B:Superious . . 2.95

5 V:Astral Kid 2.95
6 Apocalyptic Armageddon, finale 2.95
Ashcan NBy,B&W 1.00

The Mighty Magnor #2 © Malibu Comics

MIGHTY MAGNOR, THE
1 thru 6 SA .... @1.95

MONSTER POSSE
B&W
1 I:Monster Posse 2.50
2 I:P.O.N.E,Wack Mack Dwac's
    sister,D-Vicious 2.50

MORTAL KOMBAT
1994
0 Four stories 2.95
1 Based on the Video Game . . 2.95
1a Foil Ed 4.00
1b with new material 2.95
2 .... 2.95
3 .... 2.95
4 .... 2.95
5 I:Mortal Kombat II 2.95
6 Climax 2.95
Spec. #1 Tournament edition 3.95
Spec. #2 Tournament edition II . . 3.95
TPB rep. #1–#6 .... 14.95

MORTAL KOMBAT: BARAKA
1 V:Scorpion 2.95

MORTAL KOMBAT: BATTLEWAVE
1 New series 2.95
2 Action, Action, Action 2.95
3 The Gathering 2.95
4 F:Goro 2.95
5 F:Scorpion 2.95
6 final issue 2.95

MORTAL KOMBAT: GORO, PRINCE OF PAIN
1 Goro 2.95
1a Platinum Edition 6.25
2 Goro, V:Kombatant 2.95

3 Goro, V:God of Pain 2.95

MORTAL KOMBAT: KITANA & MILEENA
1 Secrets of Outworld 2.95

MORTAL KOMBAT: KUNG LAO
1 one-shot Battlewave tie-in 2.95

MORTAL KOMBAT: RAYDEN AND KANO
1 J:Rayden Kano 2.95
1a Deluxe Edition 4.95
2 A:Reptile 2.95
3 Kano, conclusion 2.95

MORTAL KOMBAT: U.S. SPECIAL FORCES
1 V:Black Dragon 3.50
2 V:Black Dragon 2.95

NECROMANTRA/ LORD PUMPKIN
Ultraverse 1995
1 A:Loki (from Marvel) 2.95
2 MiB,V:Godwheel, flipbook 2.95
3 O:Lord Pumpkin 2.95
4 Infinity Gem tie-in 2.95
4a variant cover 3.50

NECROSCOPE
1 Novel adapt., holo(c) 3.25
1a 2nd printing 2.95
2 thru 4 Adapt. cont. .... @2.95
Book II
1 thru 5 .... 2.95

NIGHT MAN, THE
Ultraverse 1993–95
1 I:Night Man,Deathmask 2.75
1a Silver foil (c) 4.00
2 GeH,V:Mangle 2.25
3 SEt,GeH,A:Freex,Mangle 2.25
4 HC,I:Scrapyard,O:Firearm 2.25
5 SEt(s) 2.25
6 V:TNTNT 2.25
7 V:Nick 2.25
8 V:Werewolf 1.95
9 V:Werewolf 2.25
10 .... 1.95
11 .... 1.95
12 .... 1.95
13 .... 1.95
14 V:Rafferty 1.95
15 I:Rigoletto 1.95
16 I:Bloodfly 3.50
17 D:Playland 2.50
18 DZ,SEt,V:Bloodfly 2.50
19 DZ,SEt,V:Deathmask 2.50
20 DZ,V:Bloody fly 2.50
21 Identity Revealed 2.50
22 Infinity Gem tie-in,A:Loki 2.50
23 R:Rhianon 2.50
Ann.#1 V:Pilgrim, 64pg. 3.95

NIGHT MAN, THE
Ultraverse 1995
Infinity Night Man vs. Night Man . 2.50
1 Discovers New powers 1.50
1a Computer Painted Cover ... 1.50

MALIBU

2 phoenix flip issue 1.50
3 Phoenix Resurrection 1.50
4 final issue 1.50

NIGHT MAN/GAMBIT
1996
1 thru 3 . . . . @2.50

NOCTURNALS
Bravura 1995
1 DIB,I:Nocturnals 2.95
1a Glow-in-the-Dark 4.00
2 DIB,I:Komodo, Mister Fane . . 2.95
3 DIB,F:Raccoon 2.95
4 DIB,I:The Old Wolf 2.95
5 Discovered by Police 2.95
6 DIB, ... 2.95

ORIGINS
Ultraverse
1 O:Ultraverse Heroes 1.25

OZZY OSBORNE
Rock-It Comix
1 w/guitar pick 3.95

PANTERA
Rock-it Comix
1 . . . . 3.95
1a Gold Ed. 19.95

PHOENIX RESURRECTION
Ultraverse 1995–96
0 Intro to Phoenix Resurrection . . 1.95
Genesis, A:X-Men 3.95
Revelations, A:X-Men 3.95
Aftermath, A:X-Men 3.95

PLAN 9 FROM OUTER SPACE
GNv Movie Adapt. 4.95

POWER & GLORY
Bravura 1994
1A HC(a&s),I:American
 Powerhouse 3.00
1B alternate cover 3.00
1c Blue Foil (c) 5.00
1d w/seirgraph 5.00
1e Newsstand 3.00
2 HC(a&s), O:American
 Powerhouse 2.75
3 HC(a&s) 2.50
4 HC(a&s) 2.50
Winter Special 2.95
TPB Series reprint, w/stamp . . . 12.95

POWER OF PRIME
Ultraverse 1995
1 O:Prime Powers,Godwheel tie-in 2.50
2 V:Doc Gross, Godwheel tie-in . 2.50
3 F:Prime Phade 2.50
4 F:Elven,Turbocharge 2.50

PRIME
Ultraverse 1993–95
1 B:GJ(s),I:Prime 4.00
1a Ultra-Limited 5.00
1b Full Hologram (c) 5.00
2 V:Organism 8, with Ultraverse
 card 3.00

3 NBy,I:Prototype 3.00
4 NBy,V:Prototype 3.00
5 NBy,BWS,I:Maxi-Man, BU:Rune 3.00
6 NBy,A:Pres. Clinton 2.75
7 NBy,Break-Thru x-over 2.25
8 NBy,A:Mantra 2.25
9 NBy,Atomic Lies 2.25
10 NBy,A:Firearm,N:Prime 2.25
11 NBy 2.25

Prime #12 © Malibu Comics

12 NBy,(Ultraverse Premiere#3)
 I:Planet Class 3.50
13 NBy,V:Kutt,Planet Class 2.95
14 DaR,I:Voodoo Master 2.25
15 abused kids 1.95
16 I:Turbo 1.95
17 Atalon 1.95
18 Prime's new partner 1.95
19 Prime accused 1.95
20 GJ,LeS,A:Rafferty 2.50
21 GJ,LeS,World without Prime . 2.50
22 GJ,LeS,F:Primevil 2.50
23 F:Prime's Mother 2.50
24 F:Prime's Mother 2.50
25 A:Chelsea Clinton 2.50
26 True Powers 2.50
Ashcan (first) 7.00
Ashcan #1 BV(c),B&W 75
Ann.#1 R:Doc Gross 3.95
TPB Rep. #1-#4 . . . . 9.95

PRIME
Ultraverse 1995–96
Infinty I:Spider-Prime 3.00
1 Spider-Prime vs. Lizard 1.50
1a Computer painted cover 2.00
2 Phoenix flip issue 1.50
3 Phoenix Resurrection 1.50
4 . . . . 1.50
5 . . . . 1.50
6 Prime on Drugs,pt.1,F:Solitaire 1.50
7 F:Solitaire, pt.2 . . . . 1.50
8 F:Solitaire, pt.3 . . . . 1.50
9 and 10 . . . . @1.50
11 "Absolute Power Corrupts?
 Absolutely!" 1.50
12 HuR,KG, pt.3 (of 3) 1.50
13 KG,Prime exposed, V:Colonel

Rinaldo 1.50
14 KG, Return of Lord Pumpkin . . 1.50
15 Return of Lord Pumpkin 1.50

PRIME/CAPTAIN AMERICA
Ultraverse 1996
1 GJ,NBy 3.95

PRIME VS. HULK
0 . . . . 10.00
0a signed premium edition 20.00

PROJECT A-KO
1 thru 4 Based on anime movie @2.95

Protectors #12 © Malibu Comics

PROTECTORS
1992–94
1 I:Protectors, inc. JBi poster
 (direct) 3.00
1a thru 12a Newsstand . . . . . @1.95
2 V:Mr.Monday,w/poster 2.50
3 V:Steel Army,w/poster 2.50
4 V:Steel Army 2.50
5 Die Cut(c),V:Mr.Monday 2.50
6 V:Mr.Monday 2.50
7 A:Thresher 2.50
8 V:Wisecrack 1.95
9 V:Wisecrack 2.50
10 I:Mantoka 2.50
11 A:Ms.Fury,V:Black Fury 2.50
12 A:Arrow 2.50
13 RAJ(s),Genesis#3 . . . . 2.25
14 RB(c),RAJ(s),Genesis#6 . . . . 2.25
15 RAJ(s),J:Chalice 2.25
16 So Help Me God 2.25
17 L:Ferret 2.25
18 V:Regulators,BU:Mantako, R:Mr.
 Monday 2.25
19 A:Gravestone,Arc 2.50
20 V:Nowhere Man 2.50
Protectors Handbook 2.50

PROTOTYPE
Ultraverse 1993–95
1 V:Ultra-Tech,w/card 2.50
1a Ultra-lim. silver foil(c) 5.00
1b Hologram 6.00

2 I:Backstabber 2.50
3 LeS(s),DvA,JmP,BWS, V:Ultra-
   Tech,BU:Rune 2.50
4 TMs(s),V:Wrath 2.25
5 TMs(s),A:Strangers,Break-Thru
   x-over 2.25
6 TMs(s),Origins Month C:Arena . 2.25
7 TMs(s),V:Arena 2.25
8 TMs(s),V:Arena 2.25
9 Prototype Unplugged 2.25
10 TMs(s),V:Prototype 1.95
11 TMs(s),R:Glare 2.25
12 V:Ultratech 1.95
13 Ultraverse Premiere #6 . . . . . 3.50
14 Jimmy Ruiz, new boss 1.95
15 Techuza, Donovan 1.95
16 New CEO for Terrordy 1.95
17 Ranger Vs. Engine 1.95
18 Turf War 2.50
G-Size, Hostile Takeover 2.50
Spec.#0 LeS,JQ/JP(c) 2.50

PROTOTYPE: TURF WAR
Ultraverse
1 LeS,V:Techuza 2.50
2 LeS,F:Ranger,Arena 2.50
3 . . . . 2.50

RAFFERTY
1 Ashcan 1.00

Raver #3 © Malibu Comics

RAVER
1 Prism cover 3.00
1a Newsstand 2.25
2 . . . . 1.95
3 Walter Koenig(s) 1.95
4 and 5 . . . . @1.95

RIPFIRE
0 Prequel to Ripfire Series 2.50

RUNE
Ultraverse 1994–95
0 BWS(a&s) 4.00
1 BWS(a&s),from Ultraverse 2.50
1a Foil cover 4.00

2 CU(s),BWS,V:Aladdin 2.25
3 DaR,BWS,(Ultraverse Premiere
   #1), Flip book 3.75
4 BWS,V:Twins 2.25
5 BWS 1.95
6 BWS 1.95
7 CU,JS 1.95
8 Rise of Gods,pt.2 . . . . 1.95
9 Prelude to Godwheel 1.95
G-Size #1 . . . . 2.50
TPB BWS(c&a),CU,The Awakening,
   rep.#1—#5 . . . . 12.95

RUNE
Ultraverse 1995–96
Infinity V:Annihilus 2.50
1 A:Adam Warlock 1.50
1a Computer painted cover 1.50
2 Phoenix flip issue,A:Adam
   Warlock 1.50
3 Phoenix Resurrection 1.50
4 . . . . 1.50
5 . . . . 1.50
6 LKa,A:Warlock 1.50

RUNE:
HEARTS OF DARKNESS
Ultraverse 1996
1 DgM(s),KHt,TBd, flip book 1.50
2 DgM,KHt,TBd, flip book 1.50
3 DgM,KHt,TBd, flip book 1.50

RUNE/SILVER SURFER
Ultravrse 1995
1 BWS(c),A:Adam Warlock 5.95
1a Lim. edition (5,000 made) . . . 8.00
1b Standard ed.newsprint 2.95

RUNE VS. VENOM
Ultraverse 1996
1 one-shot x-over 1.95

RUST
1 O:Rust 2.95
2 V:Marion Labs 2.95
3 I:Ashe Sapphire,5th Anniv. . . . 2.95
4 I:Rustmobile 2.95

SANTANA
Rock-it Comix
1 TT(c&s),TY 3.95

SIREN
Ultraverse 1995
Infinity V:War Machine 2.50
1 V:War Machine 1.50
1a Computer painted cover 1.50
2 Phoenix flip issue 1.50
3 Phoenix Resurrection 1.50
Spec. #1 O:Siren 1.95

SLUDGE
Ultraverse 1993–94
1 BWS,I:Sludge,BU:I:Rune 2.75
1a Ultra-Limited 5.00
2 AaL,I:Bloodstorm 2.25
3 AaL,V:River Men 2.50
4 AaL,Origins Month, V:Alligator . 2.25
5 AaL,V:Garret Whale 2.25
6 AaL,A:Dragon Fang,Lord
   Pumpkin 2.25

Sludge #5 © Malibu Comics

7 V:Frank Hoag 2.25
8 AaL,V:Monsters 2.25
9 AaL,O:Sludge 2.25
10 AaL,O:Sludge 1.95
11 AaL,V:Bash Brothers 1.95
12 AaL,V:Prime, w/flip book
   w/Ultraverse Premiere #8 . . . . 3.50
13 . . . . 1.95
Red X-Mas 2.50

SOLITAIRE
Ultraverse 1993–94
1 black baged edition with playing
   card: Ace of Clubs, Diamonds,
   Hearts or Spades 2.75
1d Newsstand edition,no card . . . 2.25
2 GJ(s),JJ,Break-Thru x-over,
   V:Moon Man 2.25
3 Origins Month, I:Monkey-Woman 2.25
4 O:Solitaire 2.25
5 JJ,V:Djinn 2.25
6 JJ,V:Lone 1.95
7 JJ,I:Double Edge 2.25
8 GJ,I:Degenerate 1.95
9 GJ,Degenerate Rafferty 1.95
10 Hostile Takeover #2 . . . . 1.95
11 V:Djinn 1.95
12 V:Anton Lowe 1.95

SOLUTION
Ultraverse 1993–95
0 DaR,O:Solution 4.00
1 DaR,I:Solution 2.50
1a foil cover 4.00
2 DaR,BWS,V:Rex Mundi,Quatro,
   BU:Rune 2.50
3 DaR,A:Hardcase,Choice 2.50
4 DaR,Break-Thru x-over,
   A:Hardcase,Choice 2.50
5 F:Dropkick 2.25
6 B:O:Solution 2.25
7 KM,O:Solution 2.25
8 KM(c),E:O:Solution 2.25
9 F:Shadowmage 2.25
10 V:Vyr 2.25
11 V:Vorlexx 2.25
12 JHi 1.95

13 Hostile Takeover pt.3	1.95
14 old foes	1.95
15 V:Casino	1.95
16 Flip/UltraverePremiere#10	3.50
17 F:Casino, Dragons Claws	2.50

SQUAD, THE
0-A Hardcase's old team	2.50
0-B	2.50
0-C L.A.Riots	2.50

STAR SLAMMERS
Bravura 1994
1 WS(a&s)	2.75
2 WS(a&s),F:Meredith	2.75
3 WS(a&s)	2.50
4 WS(a&s)	2.50
5 WS,Rojas Choice	2.50

STAR TREK: DEEP SPACE NINE
1 Direct ed.	3.25
1a Photo(c).	3.00
1b Gold foil	5.00
2 w/skycap	3.50
3 Murder on DS9	2.75
4 MiB(s),F:Bashir,Dax	2.75
5 MiB(s),V:Slaves	2.75
6 MiB(s),Three Stories	2.75
7 F:Kira	2.75
8 B:Requiem	2.75
9 E:Requiem	2.75
10 Descendants	2.50

Star Trek: Deep Space Nine #16
© Malibu Comics

11 A Short Fuse	2.75
12 Baby on Board	2.50
13 Problems with Odo	2.75
14 on Bejor	2.75
15 mythologic dilemma	2.75
16 Shangheid	2.50
17 Voyager preview	2.50
18 V:Gwyn	2.50
19 Wormhole Mystery	2.50
20 Sisko Injured	2.50
21 Smugglers attack DS9	2.50
22 Commander Quark	2.50

23 Secret of the Lost Orb,pt.1	2.50
24 Secret of the Lost Orb,pt.2	2.50
25 Secret of the Lost Orb,pt.3	2.50
26 Mudd's Pets, pt.1	2.50
27 Mudd's Pets, pt.2	2.50
28 F:Ensign Ro	2.50
29 F:Thomas Riker,Tuvok	2.50
30 F:Thomas Riker	2.50
31 thru 32	@2.50
Ann.#1 Looking Glass	3.95

STAR TREK: DEEP SPACE NINE CELEBRITY SERIES: BLOOD AND HONOR
1 Mark Lenard(s)	2.95
2 Rules of Diplomacy	2.95

STAR TREK: DEEP SPACE NINE: LIGHTSTORM
1 Direct ed.	3.50
1a Silver foil	8.00

STAR TREK: DEEP SPACE NINE: HEARTS AND MINDS
[Limited Series]
1	3.00
2	2.50
3 Into the Abyss,X-over preview	2.50
4 final issue	2.50

STAR TREK: DEEP SPACE NINE: THE MAQUIS
[Limited Series]
1 Federation Renegades	2.50
1a Newsstand, photo(c)	2.50
2 Garack	2.50
3 F:Quark, Bashir	2.50

STAR TREK: DEEP SPACE NINE/ THE NEXT GENERATION
1 Prophet & Losses, pt.2	2.50
2 Prophet & Losses, pt.4	2.50

STAR TREK: DEEP SPACE NINE: TEROK NOR
0 Fully painted by Goring	2.95

STAR TREK: DEEP SPACE NINE SPECIAL
1 Collision COurse	3.50

STAR TREK: VOYAGER
A V:Maquis	2.75
Aa Newsstand, photo(c)	2.50
B conclusion	2.75
Ba Newsstand, photo(c)	2.50

STRANGERS, THE
Ultraverse 1993–95
1 I:Strangers	3.00
1a Ultra-Limited	4.00
1b Full Hologram (c)	5.00
2 A:J.D.Hunt,w/Ultraverse card	3.00
3 I:TNTNT	2.50
4 A:Hardcase	2.50
5 BWS,BU:Rune	2.50

6 J:Yrial,I:Deathwish	2.25
7 Break-Thru x-over	2.25
8 RHo,ANi,O:Solution	2.25
9 AV(i),I:Ulta Pirates	2.25

The Strangers #9 © Malibu Comics

10 AV(i),V:Bastinado	2.25
11 in Alderson Disk	2.25
12 O:Yrial	2.25
13 (Ultraverse Premiere#4)	3.50
14	2.25
15 Zip-Zap, Yrail	1.95
16 Ultras, Teknight	1.95
17 Rafferty	1.95
18 Ultra Pirates	1.95
19 V:Pilgrim	1.95
20 Stranger Destroyed	1.95
21 A:Rex Mundi	2.50
22 SEt,V:Guy Hunt	2.50
23 SEt,RHo,V:Tabboo	2.50
24 RHo,SEt,V:Taboo	2.50
25 V:Godwheel Aliens	2.50
26 RHo,SEt,V:Aladdin	2.50
Ann.#1 Death	3.95
TPB rep. #1-#4	9.95
Ashcan 1 (signed)	8.00
Ashcan 1 (unsigned)	8.00

STREET FIGHTER
1 thru 3 Based on Video Game	@3.00

STRIKEBACK
Bravura 1994–95
1	2.95
2	2.95
3 V:Doberman	2.95
4 V:Dragonryder Island	2.95
Spec.#1 KM,JRu,V:Dragon	3.50

TARZAN: THE BECKONING
1 TY,I:The Spider Man	2.75
2 TY,Going back to Africa	2.50
3 thru 6	2.50

TARZAN THE WARRIOR
1 SBs(c),O:Tarzan	3.50
2	2.75

MALIBU

3 .... 2.75	
4 Wom'cha's Ship 2.75	
5 .... 2.75	

TARZAN: LOVE, LIES, AND THE LOST CITY
1 MWg&WS(s),Short Stories ... 3.95
2 The lost city of Opar 2.50
3 Final issue 2.50

TERMINATOR 2: CYBERNETIC DAWN
1995–96
1 thru 4 .... @2.50
0 flip-book/T2 Nuclear Twilight .. 2.50

TERMINATOR 2: NUCLEAR TWILIGHT
1995–96
1 thru 4 .... @2.50
0 flip-book, see above

ULTRAFORCE
Ultraverse 1994–95
1 Prime, Prototype 2.50
2 .... 1.95
3 .... 1.95
4 .... 1.95
5 V:Atalon 1.95
6 V:Atalon 2.50
7 CU,GP(c),F:Ghoul 2.50
8 MWn,CV,GP,F:Black Knight ... 2.50
9 A:Marvel's Black Knight 2.50
10 .... 2.50
Spec.#0 .... 2.50

UltraForce #3 © Malibu Comics

ULTRAFORCE
Ultraverse 1995–96
Infinity Fant. Ultraforce Four 2.50
1 George Perez cover 1.50
1a Computer painted cover 1.50
2 Phoenix flip issue,I:Lament .. 1.50
3 .... 1.50
4 .... 1.50
5 .... 1.50

6 Smoke and Bone,pt.2 ...... 1.50	
7 .... 1.50	
8 .... 1.50	
9 .... 1.50	
10 A:Sersi,Eliminator 1.50	
11 .... 1.50	

12 MD2,LWn, cont. from All-New
   Exiles #12 .... 1.50
13 LWn,MD2,new UltraForce lineup 1.50
14 LWn,MD2,Hardcase returns .. 1.50
15 LWn,MD2,Hardcase returns .. 1.50

ULTRAFORCE/AVENGERS
Ultraverse Aug. 1995
1 GP 3.95

ULTRAFORCE/ SPIDER-MAN
Ultraverse 1996
1 .... 3.95

ULTRAVERSE DOUBLE FEATURE
Ultraverse
1 F:Prime, Solitaire 3.95

ULTRAVERSE FUTURE SHOCK
Ultraverse 1996
1 one-shot,MPc,alternate futures . 2.50

ULTRAVERSE ORIGINS
Ultraverse
1 O:Ultraverse Heroes 1.25
1a Silver foil cover 12.50

ULTRAVERSE UNLIMITED
Ultraverse 1996
1 F:Warlock 1.50
2 LWn,KWe, A:All-New Exiles,V:Max 1.50

ULTRAVERSE: YEAR ZERO: THE DEATH OF THE SQUAD
Ultraverse 1995
0-A hardace's old team 2.50
0-B 2.50
0-C L.A. Riots 2.50
1 JHI,A:Squad, Mantra 2.95
2 JHI,DaR(c) prequel to Prime#1 2.95
3 Cont. Year Zero Story 2.95
4 I:NM-E 2.95

ULTRAVERSE: YEAR ONE
Ultraverse 1995
1 Handbook, double size 4.95
2 Prime 1.95

ULTRAVERSE: YEAR TWO
Ultraverse 1996
1 Marvel/Ultraverse/Info 4.95

VIRTUA FIGHTER
1 New Video Game Comic 2.95

WARSTRIKE
Ultraverse 1994–95
1 HNg,TA,in South America 1.95
2 HNg,TA,Gatefold(c) 1.95

3 in Brazil 1.95
4 HNg,TA,V:Blind Faith 1.95
5 .... 1.95
6 Rafferty 1.95
7 Origin 1.95

WARSTRIKE: PRELUDE TO GODWHEEL
Ultraverse 1994
1 Blind Faith/Lord Pumpkin 1.95

WORLD DOMINATION
1 .... 3.95
1a 3.95

Wrath #1 © Malibu Comics

WRATH
Ultraverse 1994–95
1 B:MiB(s),DvA,JmP,C:Mantra .. 2.25
1a Silver foil 3.00
2 DvA,JmP,V:Hellion 2.25
3 DvA,JmP,V:Radicals, I:Slayer . 2.25
4 DvA,JmP,V:Freex 2.25
5 DvA,JmP,V:Freex 1.95
6 DvA,JmP 2.25
7 DvA,JmP,I:Pierce,Ogre, Doc
   Virtual 1.95
8 .... 1.95
9 A:Prime 2.25
G-Size #1 .... 2.50

COLOR COMICS

ABBOTT AND COSTELLO
Charlton Comics 1968–71
1 . . . . 50.00
2 thru 9 . . . . @30.00
10 thru 21 . . . . @20.00
22 . . . . 18.00

ACCIDENT MAN: THE DEATH TOUCH
Apocalypse
One Shot rep.Toxic #10-#16 . . . . 3.95

ACME NOVELTY LIBRARY
Fantagraphics 1994–98
1 thru 5 . . . . @4.50
6 thru 11 Jimmy Corrigan Meets
His Dad, pt. 1 – pt. 6 (of 8) . @4.50
1 thru 7, 2nd printings . . . . . . @3.95

A.D.A.M.
Toyman 1998
1 . . . . 2.50
2 . . . . 2.50

ADAM-12
Gold Key 1973–76
1 Photo(c), From TV show 50.00
2 thru 9 . . . . @25.00
10 . . . . 22.00

ADAPTERS, THE
1 and 2 . . . . @2.00

ADDAMS FAMILY
Gold Key 1974–75
1 TV cartoon adapt. 100.00
2 . . . . 50.00
3 . . . . 35.00

ADLAI STEVENSON
Dell Publishing Co. Dec., 1966
1 Political Life Story 25.00

ADVENTURES OF BARON MUNCHAUSEN
Now Comics 1989
1 thru 4 movie adapt. series . . @1.75

ADVENTURES OF CHRISSIE CLAUS, THE
Hero Graphics
1 Trouble in Toyland 2.95

ADVENTURES OF FELIX THE CAT
Harvey 1992
1 Short Stories 1.25

ADVENTURES OF KUNG FU PIG NINJA FLOUNDER AND 4-D MONKEY
1 thru 6 . . . . @1.80

7 thru 10 . . . . @2.00

ADVENTURES OF ROBIN HOOD
Gold Key 1974–75
1 From Disney cartoon 6.00
2 thru 7 . . . . @3.50

ADVENTURES OF ROGER WILCO
Adventure
1 Based on Space-Quest Computer
games 2.95

Adventures of the Fly #14
© Archie Publications

ADVENTURES OF THE FLY
Archie Publications/ Radio Comics 1959–65
1 JSm/JK,O:Fly,I:SpiderSpry
A:Lancelot Strong/Shield . . . 550.00
2 JSm/JK,DAy,AW 300.00
3 Jack Davis Art, O:Fly 250.00
4 V:Dazzler NA panel 125.00
5 A:Spider Spry 75.00
6 V:Moon Men 75.00
7 A:Black Hood 75.00
8 A:Lancelot Strong/Shield 75.00
9 A:Lancelot Strong/Shield I:Cat
Girl 75.00
10 A:Spider Spry 75.00
11 V:Rock Men 50.00
12 V:Brute Invaders 50.00
13 I:Kim Brand 55.00
14 I:Fly-Girl(Kim Brand) 75.00
15 A:Spider 50.00
16 A:Fly-Girl 50.00
17 A:Fly-Girl 50.00
18 A:Fly-Girl 50.00
19 A:Fly-Girl 50.00
20 O:Fly-Girl 55.00

21 A:Fly-Girl 40.00
22 A:Fly-Girl 40.00
23 A:Fly-Girl,Jaguar 40.00
24 A:Fly-Girl 40.00
25 A:Fly-Girl 40.00
26 A:Fly-Girl,Black Hood 40.00
27 A:Fly-Girl,Black Hood 40.00
28 A:Black Hood 40.00
29 A:Fly-Girl,Black Hood 40.00
30 A:Fly-Girl,R:Comet 50.00
31 A:Black Hood, Shield, Comet 55.00
Becomes: Flyman

ADVENTURES OF THE JAGUAR
Archie Publications/ Radio Comics 1961–63
1 I:Ralph Hardy/Jaguar 150.00
2 10 cent cover 65.00
3 Last 10 cent cover 60.00
4 A:Cat-Girl 45.00
5 A:Cat-Girl 45.00
6 A:Cat-Girl 38.00
7 . . . . 30.00
8 . . . . 30.00
9 . . . . 30.00
10 . . . . 30.00
11 . . . . 30.00
12 A:Black Hood 30.00
13 A:Cat-Girl,A:Black Hood 30.00
14 A:Black Hood 30.00
15 V:Human Octopus,last issue . 25.00

ADVENTURES OF YOUNG DR. MASTERS
Archie Comics 1964
1 . . . . 15.00
2 . . . . 10.00

ADVENTUROUS UNCLE SCROOGE McDUCK
Gladstone Oct. 1997
1 . . . . 1.95
2 Don Rosa, A Little Something
Special 1.95
3 The Black Widow 1.95

AETERNUS
Brick Comics
1 thru 3 . . . . @2.95

AGAINST BLACKSHARD
Sirius Comics Aug., 1986
1 3-D 2.25

AGENT: AMERICA
Awesome Entertainment 1997
1 RLe 2.50
2 RLe,JSb,JLb,F:Supreme,V:Smash 2.50

AIR FIGHTERS, SGT. STRIKE SPECIAL
Eclipse 1988
1 A:Airboy,Valkyrie 1.95

All comics prices listed are for *Near Mint* condition.

AIR WAR STORIES
Dell Publishing Co. 1964

1	40.00
2	30.00
3 thru 8	@20.00

AIRBOY
Eclipse 1986–89

1 TT/TY,D:Golden Age Airboy O:New Airboy	3.25
2 TT/TY,I:Marisa,R:SkyWolf	2.25
3 A:The Heap	2.50
4 A:Misery	2.50
5 DSt(c),R:Valkyrie	4.00
6 R:Iron Ace,I:Marlene	3.00
7 PG(c),	2.50
8 FH/TT(c)	2.50
9 R:Flying Fool, Riot, O'Hara Cocky, Judge & Turtle	1.75
10 I:Manic,D:Cocky, Judge & Turtle	1.50
11 O:Birdie	1.50
12 R:Flying Fool	1.50
13 I:New Bald Eagle	1.50
14 A:Sky Wolf, Iron Ace	1.50
15 A:Ku Klux Klan	1.50
16 D:Manic,A:Ku Klux Klan	1.50
17 A:HarryS.Truman,Misery	1.75
18 A:Gold.Age Black Angel	1.75
19 A:Gold.Age Rats	1.75
20 Rat storyline	1.75
21 I:Lester Mansfield (rel. of Gold.Age Rackman), Artic Deathzone #1	1.75
22 DSp,Artic Deathzone #2	1.75
23 A:Gold.Age Black Angle, Artic Deathzone #3	1.75
24 A: Heap	1.75
25 TY,I:Manure Man,A:Heap	1.50
26 R:Flying Dutchman	1.50
27 A:Iron Ace, Heap	1.50
28 A:Heap	1.50
29	1.50
30 A:Iron Ace; Sky Wolf story	1.50
31 A:Valkyrie; Sky Wolf story	1.75
32 Hostage Virus,	1.75
33 DSp,SkyWolf sty,A:Sgt.Strike	1.75
34 DSp,A:La Lupina	1.75
35 DSp,A:La Lupina, Sky Wolf	1.75
36	1.75
37 DSp	1.75
38 CI, Heap story	1.75
39 CI, Heap story	1.75
40 CI, Heap story	1.75
41 V:Steel Fox, Golden Age rep. O:Valkyrie	1.75
42 A:Rackman	1.95
43 Sky Wolf sty, A:Flying Fool	1.95
44 A:Rackman	1.95
45	1.95
46 EC,Airboy Diary #1	1.95
47 EC,Airboy Diary #2	1.95
48 EC,Airboy Diary #3	1.95
49 EC,Airboy Diary #4	1.95
50 AKu/NKu,double-size	3.95
Spec. Meets the Prowler	1.95
Spec. Mr. Monster	1.75
Spec. Vs Airmaidens	1.95

AIRMAIDENS SPECIAL
Eclipse Comics 1987

1 A:Valkyrie	1.75

AKEMI
Brainstorm Comics 1997

1	2.95

ALADDIN
Walt Disney
Prestige. Movie Adapt. 4.95

ALARMING ADVENTURES
Harvey Publications 1962–63

1 AW,RC,JSe	55.00
2 AW,BP,RC,JSe	35.00
3 JSe	35.00

ALARMING TALES
Harvey Publications 1957–58

1 JK,JK(c)	125.00
2 JK,JK(c)	100.00
3 JK	65.00
4 JK,BP	60.00
5 JK,AW	75.00
6 JK	50.00

ALBEDO, VOL. 3
Antartic Press 1994–95
Vol. 1 and II, See B&W

1 thru 4 Various Artists	@2.95

ALIAS
Now Comics 1990

1	2.00
2 thru 5	@1.75

ALIAS: STORMFRONT
Now Comics

1	1.75
2	1.75

ALIEN ENCOUNTERS
Eclipse Comics 1985–87

1	3.50
2	3.00
3 "I Shot the Last Martian"	3.00
4 JBo(c)	2.00
5 RCo,"Night of the Monkey"	2.00
6 "Now You See It,""Freefall"	2.00
7	2.00
8 TY,"Take One Capsule Every Million Years,M.Monroe(c)	2.75
9 The Conquered	2.00
10	2.00
11 TT,"Old Soldiers"	2.00
12 "What A Relief,""Eyes of the Sibyl"	2.00
13 GN,"The Light at the End"	2.00
14 JRy,GN,TL,RT,"Still born"	2.00

ALIEN TERROR
Eclipse 1986
3-D #1 "Standard Procedure" 2.00

ALIEN WORLDS
Pacific 1982

1 AW,VM,NR	4.00
2 DSt	3.50
3	3.00
4 DSt(i)	3.00
5	3.00
6	3.00
7	3.00
3-D #1 AAd,DSt	5.50

Alien Worlds #2 © Pacific Comics
Eclipse 1985

8 AW	2.50
9	2.50

[CAPTAIN JOHNER AND] ALIENS, THE
Gold Key 1967
1 Rep. Magnus Robot Fighter . . 12.50

ALISTER THE SLAYER
Midnight Press 1995

1 I:Alister The Slayer	2.50
2 V:Lady Hate	2.50
3 JQ&JP(c) V:Subterranean Vampire Bikers	2.50

ALL AMERICAN SPORTS
Charlton 1967

1	10.00

ALL HALLOWS EVE
Innovation 1991

1	4.95

ALLEY OOP
Dell Publishing Co. 1962–63

1	50.00
2	45.00

ALLEY OOP ADVENTURES
Antarctic Press 1998

1	2.95

ALPHA KORPS
Diversity Comics 1996

1 I:Alpha Korps	3.00
1 signed	4.95
2 "The Price of Freedom," pt.2	2.50
2 signed	4.95
3 "The Price of Freedom," pt.3	2.50
3 signed	4.95
4 "The Price of Freedom," pt.4 (of 4)	2.50

COLOR PUB.

ALPHA WAVE
Darkline 1987
1 .... 1.75

ALTER EGO
First 1986
1 RTs, Ron Harris 1.75
2 .... 1.50
3 .... 1.50
4 .... 1.25

ALVIN
(& THE CHIPMUNKS)
Dell Publishing Co. 1962–73
1 .... 100.00
2 .... 65.00
3 .... 50.00
4 thru 10 .... @45.00
11 thru 20 .... @35.00
21 thru 28 .... @30.00
1 Alvin for President & his pals in
Merry Christmas with Clyde
Crashcup & Leonardo 25.00

AMAZING CHAN &
THE CHAN CLAN
Gold Key 1973
1 .... 22.00
2 .... 10.00
3 and 4 .... @9.00

AMAZING HEROES
SWIMSUIT ANNUALS
Fantagraphics 1990–93
1990 Spec. A:Dawn 25.00
1990 2nd printing 15.00
1991 A: Dawn 20.00
1992 A: Dawn 20.00
1993 A: Dawn 20.00

AMAZON, THE
Comico 1989
1 .... 1.95
2 .... 1.95
3 end mini-series 1.95

AMERICAN FLAGG
First 1983–88
1 HC,I:American Flagg, Hard
Times, pt.1 .... 3.50
2 HC,Hard Times,pt.2 ...... 2.75
3 HC,Hard Times,pt.3 ...... 2.75
4 HC,Southern Comfort,pt.1 .. 2.75
5 HC,Southern Comfort,pt.2 .... 2.75
6 HC,Southern Comfort,pt.3 ... 2.75
7 HC,State of the Union,pt.1 ... 2.50
8 HC,State of the Union,pt.2 ... 2.50
9 HC,State of the Union,pt.3 ... 2.50
10 HC,Solidarity-For Now,pt.1
I:Luther Ironheart 2.50
11 HC,Solidarity-For Now,pt.2 .. 2.50
12 HC,Solidarity-For Now,pt.3 .. 2.50
13 HC 2.25
14 PB 2.25
15 HC,American Flagg A Complete
story,pt.1 .... 2.25
16 HC,Complete Story,pt.2 .... 2.00
17 HC,Complete Story,pt.3 .... 2.00
18 HC,Complete Story,pt.4 .... 2.00
19 HC,Bullets & Ballots, pt.1 .... 2.00
20 HC,LSn,Bullets & Ballots,pt.2 . 2.00

American Flagg #25 © First Comics

21 AMo,HC,LSn,Bull&Ballots,pt.3 2.00
22 AMo,HC,LSn,Bull&Ballots,pt.4 . 2.00
23 AMo,HC,LSn,England Swings,
pt.1 .... 2.00
24 AMo,HC,England Swings,pt.2 . 2.00
25 AMo,HC,England Swings,pt.3 . 2.00
26 AMO,HC,England Swings,pt.4 . 2.00
27 AMo with Raul the Cat 2.00
28 BWg 1.50
29 JSon 1.50
30 JSon 1.50
31 JSon,O:Bob Violence 1.50
32 JSon,A:Bob Violence 1.50
33 A:Bob Violence 1.50
34 A:Bob Violence 1.50
35 A:Bob Violence 1.50
36 A:Bob Violence 1.50
37 A:Bob Violence 1.50
38 New Direction 1.50
39 JSon,A:Bob Violence 1.50
40 A:Bob Violence 1.50
41 .... 1.50
42 F:Luther Ironheart 1.50
43 .... 1.50
44 .... 1.50
45 .... 1.50
46 PS 1.75
47 PS 1.75
48 PS 1.75
49 .... 1.75
50 HC,last issue 1.75
Special #1 HC,I:Time² 2.50
See Also: Howard Chaykin's
American Flagg

AMERICOMICS
AC Comics 1983
1 GP(c),O:Shade 3.00
2 .... 2.00
3 Blue Beetle 2.00
4 O:Dragonfly 2.00
5 and 6 .... @1.75
Spec.#1 Capt.Atom,BlueBeetle .. 1.50

AMERICAN WOMAN
Antarctic Press 1998
1 by Richard Stockton & Brian
Denham 2.95

2 .... 2.95
2a deluxe 5.95

ANDROMEDA
Andromeda
1 I:Andromeda 2.50
2 Andromeda vs. Elite Force .. 2.50

ANGEL FIRE
Crusade Comics 1997
1 BiT, from Shi #12, BiT(c) 2.95
1a with Roberto Flores cover ... 2.95
1b with photo cover 2.95
2 F:Shi 2.95
3 F:Shi, concl. 2.95

ANIMAL MYSTIC:
WATER WARS
Sirius 1996
1 (of 6) DOe 4.00
2 thru 5 DOe .... @3.00

ANNE McCAFFREY'S
THE UNICORN GIRL
Big Entertainment 1997
GN F:Acorna 22.00

ANYTHING GOES
Fantagraphics 1986
1 GK,FlamingCarot,Savage 3.50
2 S:AnM,JK,JSt,SK 3.50
3 DS,NA(c),A:Cerebus 3.00
4 .... 2.50
5 A:TMNTurtles 5.00
6 .... 2.00

APE NATION
Adventure Comics 1991
1 Aliens land on Planet of the
Apes 3.00
2 General Ollo 3.00
3 V:Gen.Ollo,Danada 2.50
4 D:Danada 2.50

APOLLO SMILE
Eagle Wing 1998
1 When the Levee Breaks 2.95

ARACHNAPHOBIA
Walt Disney 1990
1 Movie Adapt 5.95
1a Newsstand 2.95

ARAKNIS
Mushroom Comics 1995–96
1 I:Araknis, Shades of Evil pt.1 . 3.50
2 Shades of Evil pt.2 .... 3.50
3 with pin-ups 2.50
4 .... 2.50

ARAKNIS
Mushroom Comics April 1996
0 Michael & Mario Ortiz 3.00
0 signed 4.00
1 .... 2.50
1 special edition 10.00
Mystic Comics
2 thru 6 .... @2.50

COLOR PUB.

ARAKNIS: RETRIBUTION
Morning Star Productions 1997
1 (of 4) by Michael & Mario Ortiz 2.50
1 signed 10.00
2 thru 4 . . . . @2.50

ARAKNIS: SHADES OF EVIL
Morning Star Productions
1 thru 4 . . . . @2.50

ARCHANGELS: THE SAGA
Eternal Studios
1 I:Cameron 2.50
2 V:Demons 2.50
3 . . . . 2.75
4 . . . . 2.75
5 . . . . 2.50

ARCHIE
Archie Publications
1 thru 300 see Golden Age Section
301 thru 400 . . . . @2.00
401 thru 449 . . . . @2.00
450 thru 467 . . . . @2.00
468 thru 477 . . . . @1.75
Archie's Christmas Stocking #4 . . 2.00
Archie's Christmas Stocking #5 . . 2.00
Archie's Spring Break Spec.1 . . 2.00
Archie's Spring Break Spec.2 . . 2.00
Archie's Spring Break Spec.3 . . 2.25
Archie's Vacation Spec.#4 . . . . . 2.00
Archie's Vacation Spec.#5 . . . . . 2.00
Archie's Vacation Spec.#6 . . . . . 2.25

ARCHIE AMERICANA SERIES
Archie Comics
TPB Best of the Forties 10.95
TPB Best of the Forties,2nd print 10.95
TPB Best of the Fifties 8.95
TPB Best of the Fifties,2nd print . 8.95
TPB Best of the Sixties 9.95
TPB Best of the Seventies 9.95

ARCHIE AND FRIENDS
Archie Publications 1992—95
1 thru 10 . . . . @1.50
11 thru 20 . . . . @1.50
20 thru 26 . . . . @1.50
27 thru 31 . . . . @1.75

ARCHIE AND ME
Archie Publications 1964—87
1 . . . . 135.00
2 . . . . 65.00
3 . . . . 30.00
4 . . . . 25.00
5 . . . . 25.00
6 thru 10 . . . . @20.00
11 thru 20 . . . . @7.00
21 thru 100 . . . . @5.00
101 thru 162 . . . . @2.00

ARCHIE AS PUREHEART THE POWERFUL
Archie Publications 1966—67
1 superhero parody 60.00
2 . . . . 35.00
3 thru 6 Captain Pureheart . . @25.00

ARCHIE AT RIVERDALE HIGH
Archie Publications 1972
1 . . . . 50.00
2 . . . . 20.00
3 . . . . 10.00
4 . . . . 8.00
5 . . . . 7.00
6 thru 10 . . . . @3.00
11 thru 114 . . . . @2.00

ARCHIE COMICS DIGEST
Archie Comics Digest 1973
1 . . . . 35.00
2 . . . . 20.00
3 . . . . 9.00
4 . . . . 6.00
5 thru 10 . . . . @2.00
11 thru 88 . . . . @1.00

ARCHIE MEETS THE PUNISHER
Archie/Marvel 1994
one-shot crossover, same contents as
Punisher meets Archie 3.00

ARCHIE'S MADHOUSE
Archie Publications 1959—69
1 . . . . 200.00
2 . . . . 100.00
3 thru 5 . . . . @75.00
6 thru 10 . . . . @40.00
11 thru 16 . . . . @30.00
17 thru 21 . . . . @15.00
22 . . . . 40.00
23 thru 30 . . . . @12.00
31 thru 40 . . . . @5.00
41 thru 66 . . . . @2.00

ARCHIE'S PAL JUGHEAD
SEE: JUGHEAD

ARCHIE'S SUPERHERO MAGAZINE
Archie Publications
1 JSm/SK,Rept.Double of

Archie 3000 #12 © Archie Publications

Capt.Strong #1,FLy,Black Hood 1.20
2 GM,NA/DG,AMc,I:'70's Black
Hood, Superhero rept. 2.00

ARCHIE'S TV LAUGH-OUT
Archie Publications 1969–86
1 . . . . 40.00
2 . . . . 15.00
3 . . . . 7.00
4 . . . . 7.00
5 . . . . 7.00
6 thru 10 . . . . @3.00
11 thru 106 . . . . @2.00

ARCHIE 3000
Archie Publications
May, 1989–July, 1991
1 thru 16 . . . . 1.00

ARENA, THE
Alchemy
1 . . . . 1.00
2 . . . . 1.00

ARIANE & BLUEBEARD
Eclipse 1988
Spec. CR 3.95

ARISTOKITTENS, THE
Gold Key 1971–75
1 Disney 25.00
2 thru 9 . . . . @15.00

ARMAGEDDON FACTOR
AC Comics
1 Sentinels of Justice 1.95
2 . . . . 1.95

ARMOR
Continuity 1985
1 TGr,NA,A:Silver Streak, Silver
logo 5.00
1a 2nd printing,red logo 2.50
2 TGr,NA(c) 2.50
3 TGr,NA(c) 2.50
4 TGr,NA(c) 2.50
5 BS,NA(c) 2.50
6 TVE,NA(c) 2.50
7 NA(c) 2.50
8 FS,NA(c) 2.50
9 FS,NA&KN(c) 2.50
10 FS,NA&KN(c) 2.50
11 SDr(i),KN(c) 2.50
12 KN(c) 2.50
13 NA(c),direct sales 2.50
14 KN(c), newsstand 2.50
[2nd Series]
1 V:Hellbender,Trading Card . . . 2.50
[3rd Series, Deathwatch 2000]
1 Deathwatch 2000 pt.3,w/card . . 4.00
2 Deathwatch 2000 pt.9,w/card . . 2.50
3 Deathwatch 2000 pt.15,w/card . . 2.50
4 . . . . 2.50
5 Rise of Magic 2.50
6 Rise of Magic 2.50

ARMORED TROOPER VOTOMS
CPM Comics
1 TEI 2.95
2 TEI 2.95

All comics prices listed are for *Near Mint* condition.

3 TEI	2.95
4 TEI	2.95
GN Supreme Survivor	16.95

ARMY ATTACK
Charlton 1964
1 SG	35.00
2 SG	15.00
3 SG	10.00
4 thru 47	@10.00

ARMY WAR HEROES
Charlton 1963–70
1	35.00
2	15.00
3 thru 21	@15.00
22 GS,O&I:Iron Corporal	20.00
23 thru 38	@10.00

ART OF ZEN INTER-GALACTIC NINJA
Entity Comics 1994
1 Various artists	2.95

ASH
Event Comics
1 JQ,JP,Fire and Crossfire,pt.1	12.00
1a David Finch/Batt(c)	2.95
2 JQ,JP,Fire and Crossfire,pt.2	8.00
2a David Finch/Batt (c)	2.95
3 JQ,JP,Secret of Origin	4.50
4 I:Actor	3.00
5 I:New Character	3.00
6 V:Gabriel	3.00
0 Red Laser ed., Current Ash (c)	25.00
0 Red Laser ed., Future Ash (c)	25.00
TPB rep. #1–#5	14.95
TPB Vol. 1, JQ,JP,sgn. lim.	34.95

ASH: CINDER AND SMOKE
Event Comics 1997
1 MWa,BAu,HuR,JP	2.95
1a autographed virgin JQ cover	19.95
1b signed limited edition	29.95
2 HuR(c)	2.95
2 JQ(c)	2.95
3 (of 6) JQ&JP(c)	2.95
3 variant JP&HuR(c)	2.95
4 (of 6) JQ&JP(c)	2.95
4 variant JP&HuR(c)	2.95
5 (of 6) JQ&JP(c)	2.95
5 variant JP&HuR(c)	2.95
6 (of 6) JQ&JP(c)	2.95
6 variant JP&HuR(c)	2.95

ASH FILES, THE
Event Comics 1997
1 JQ,JP	2.95
1 signed, limited	19.95

ASH: THE FIRE WITHIN
Event Comics
2 JQ,JP	2.95
3 JQ,JP, Ash Rooftop cover	2.95
3a JQ,JP, Ash Firefighter cover	2.95

ASH/22 BRIDES
Event Comics 1996
1 FaN,HuR,JP	2.95

ASSASSIN, INC.
Solson
1 thru 4	@1.95

ASTER
Entity Comics 1995
0 O:Aster the Celestial Knight	4.50
1 I:Celestial Knight	5.00
1b 2nd printing	3.00
2	3.50
3 V:Tolmek	3.25
3a Variant cover	7.00
4 Final Issue	3.00
TPB Rep.#1–#4 + pin-up gallery	12.95

ASTER THE LAST CELESTIAL KNIGHT
Entity Comics 1995
1 R:Aster Chromium Cover	2.50
1a Clear Chromium Edition	4.00
1b Holo Chrome Edition	5.00
2 World Defender	2.50

ASTRO BOY
Gold Key Aug., 1965
1 I:Astro Boy	300.00

ASTRO BOY Now
Prev.	Original Astro Boy	
18	1.75
19	1.75
20	1.75

ASYLUM
Pendragon 1995
1	2.95
2	2.95
3 three stories	2.95

ASYLUM
Maximum Press Dec. 1995
1 Warchild, Beanworld, Avengelyne, Battlestar Galactica	3.00
2 I:Deathkiss	3.00
3	3.00
4 RLd,A:Cybrid	3.00
5 I:Black Seed	3.00
6 R:Steve Austin & Jaime Sommers	3.00
7 RLe,F:Bloodwulf	3.00
8 RLd	3.00
9 RLd	3.00
10	3.00
11	3.00
12 MMy,F:Blindside	3.00
13	3.00

ATOM ANT
Gold Key Jan., 1966
1	75.00

ATOM-AGE COMBAT
Fago Magazines 1958–59
1	165.00
2	140.00
3	120.00

ATOMIK ANGELS
Crusade Entertainment 1996
1 BiT	2.95

1 variant cover (1:25)	5.00
2 BiT	2.95
3 BiT	2.95
4 BiT, conclusion	2.95

ATOMIC RABBIT
Charlton Comics 1955–58
1	150.00
2	50.00
3 thru 10	@30.00
11	50.00
Becomes:	

ATOMIC BUNNY
12	75.00
13 thru 18	@35.00
19 Dec., 1959	35.00

AVENGEBLADE
Maximum Press 1996
1 RLe	3.00
2 RLe	3.00

Avengelyne #2 © Maximum Press

AVENGELYNE
Maximum Press 1995
1 RLd,I:Avengelyne Dir ed.	4.00
1a Newstand Edition	4.00
1b Holochrome Edition	5.00
1 gold edition	6.00
2 V:B'Lial	4.00
3 I:Magogi	3.00
3 variant cover, pin-up	4.00
TPB rep. #1–#3	9.95
Regular Series April 1996	
0 RLd,O:Avengelyne	3.00
1 RLd,BNa,F:Devlin	2.95
1 variant photo cover	2.95
2 I:Darkchylde	2.95
2a variant photo cover	2.95
3	2.95
4 A:Cybrid	2.95
5 A:Cybrid	3.00
6 RLd,F:Divinity	3.00
7 RLd,F:Divinity	3.00
8 RLd	3.00
9 RLd	3.00
10 BNa,"The Possession," pt.1	3.00
11 BNa,"The Possession," pt.2	3.00

12 BNa,"The Possession," pt.3 . . 3.00
13 BNa,"The Possession," pt.4 . . 3.00
14 A:Bloodwulf 3.00
15 A:Glory, Prophet 3.00
Swimsuit Edition 3.50
Swimsuit book, American
  Entertainment exclusive 7.50

AVENGELYNE: ARMAGEDDON
Maximum Press 1996–97
1 (of 3) RLd 3.00
2 RLd, ... 3.00
3 BNa,ScC, finale 3.00

AVENGELYNE BIBLE: REVELATIONS
Maximum Press
one-shot RLd, ... 3.50

AVENGELYNE: DEADLY SINS
Maximum Press 1996
1 RLd (c) 3.00
1 photo (c) 3.00
2 RLd(c) 3.00

AVENGELYNE/GLORY
Maximum Press 1995
1 V:B'Lial 3.95
1a variant cover 5.00
Swimsuit Spec. #1 . . . . 2.95

AVENGELYNE/GLORY: THE GODYSSEY
Maximum Press 1996
1 RLd,BNa 3.00
2 thru 5 RLd . . . . @3.00

AVENGELYNE/POWER
Maximum Press 1995–96
1 RLd,V:Hollywood 3.00
1 variant cover 3.50
2 RLd(c) 2.95

Avengelyne/Prophet #1
© Maximum Press

3 . . . . 2.95
3a photo (c) 2.95

AVENGELYNE/PROPHET
Maximum Press April 1996
1 RLd,BNa,MD2 . . . . 2.95

AVENGELYNE/ WARRIOR NUN AREALA
Maximum Press 1997
Spec. 3.00

AVENGELYNE/ WARRIOR NUN AREALA II THE NAZARENE AFFAIR
Awesome Entertainment 1997
one-shot? 3.00

AVENGERS, THE
Gold Key Nov., 1968
1 . . . . 250.00

AWESOME HOLIDAY SPECIAL
Awesome Entertainment 1997
Spec. #1 . . . . 2.50

AXA
Eclipse 1987
1 "Axa the Adopted" 1.75
2 . . . . 1.75

AXEL PRESSBUTTON
Eclipse 1984
1 BB(c),Origin 1.75
2 . . . . 1.75
3 thru 4 . . . . @1.75
Becomes:
PRESSBUTTON

AXION
Icon Creations
1 I:Obsidion 2.50

AXIS ALPHA
Axis Comics
1 LSn,I:BEASTIES,Dethgrip,
  Shelter,W 2.75

AZ
Comico
1 . . . . 3.00
2 . . . . 2.25

AZTEC ACE
Eclipse 1984
1 NR(i),I:AztecAce 3.50
2 NR(i) 3.50
3 NR(i) 3.00
4 NR(i) 3.00
5 NR(i) 3.00
6 NR(i) 3.00
7 NR(i) 3.00
8 NR(i) 3.00
9 NR(i) 3.00
10 NR(i) 2.00
11 . . . . 3.50
12 . . . . 2.50
13 . . . . 2.50

14 . . . . 2.50
15 F:Bridget 2.50

BABES OF BROADWAY
Broadway 1996
1 . . . . 2.95

BABY HUEY, THE BABY GIANT
Harvey Publications 1956–80
1 . . . . 300.00
2 . . . . 150.00
3 . . . . 100.00
4 . . . . 75.00
5 . . . . 75.00
6 thru 10 . . . . @35.00
11 thru 20 . . . . @25.00
21 thru 40 . . . . @20.00
41 thru 60 . . . . @10.00
61 thru 79 . . . . @8.00
80 . . . . 8.00
81 thru 95 . . . . @4.00
96 Giant size 5.00
97 Giant size 5.00
98 . . . . 2.50
99 . . . . 2.50

BABY HUEY AND PAPA
Harvey Publications 1962–68
1 . . . . 125.00
2 . . . . 50.00
3 . . . . 35.00
4 . . . . 35.00
5 . . . . 35.00
6 . . . . 15.00
7 . . . . 15.00
8 . . . . 15.00
9 . . . . 15.00
10 . . . . 15.00
11 thru 20 . . . . @5.00
21 thru 33 . . . . @3.50

BABY HUEY DUCKLAND
Harvey Publications 1962–66
1 . . . . 90.00
2 . . . . 50.00
3 . . . . 50.00
4 . . . . 50.00
5 . . . . 50.00
6 thru 14 . . . . @15.00
15 . . . . 15.00

BACHELOR FATHER
Dell Publishing Co. 1962
1 . . . . 75.00
2 . . . . 60.00

BACK TO THE FUTURE
Harvey 1991
1 Chicago 1927 . . . . 1.25
2 Cretaceous Period 1.25
3 World War I 1.25
4 Doc Retires 1.25

BAD BOY
Oni Press 1997
GN Frank Miller & Simon Bisley . . 4.95

BAD COMPANY
Quality 1988
1 thru 19 . . . . @1.50

BADGER
Capital 1983

1 JBt,I:Badger,Ham,Daisy Yak,Yeti	3.00
2 JBt,I:Riley,A:YakYeti	3.00
3 JBt,O:Badger,Ham	3.00
4 JBt,A'Ham	3.00

First 1984–91

5 BR,DruidTree Pt1	2.50
6 BR,DruidTree Pt2	2.50
7 BR,I:Wonktendonk,Lord Weterlackus	2.50
8 BR,V:Demon	2.50
9 BR,I:Connie,WOatesCbra	2.50
10 BR,A:Wonktendonk, I:Hodag Meldrum	2.50
11 BR,V:Hodag,L.W'lackus	2.50
12 BR,V:Hodag,L.W'lackus	2.50
13 BR,A:L.W'lakus,Clonezone, Judah	2.50
14 BR,I:HerbNg	2.50
15 BR,I:Wombat,JMoranIbob	2.50
16 BR,A:Yak,Yeti	2.50
17 JBt,I:Lamont	3.00

Badger #22 © Capital Comics

18 BR,I:SpudsGroganA:Cbra	2.50
19 BR,I:Senator1,CIZone	2.50
20 BR,Billionaire'sPicnic	2.50
21 BR,I&O:Phantom	2.50
22 BR,I:Dr.Buick Riviera	2.50
23 I:BobDobb,A:Yeti	2.50
24 BR,A:Riley	2.50
25 BR,I:Killdozer	2.50
26 BR,I:RoachWranger	2.50
27 BR,O:RoachWranger	2.50
28 BR,A:Yeti	2.50
29 A:Clonezone,C:GrimJack	2.50
30 BR,I:Dorgan	2.00
31 BR,I:HopLingSung	2.00
32 BR,D:Dorgan,HopLingSng	2.00
33 RLm/AN,I:KidKang	3.00
34 RLm,I:Count Kohler	3.00
35 RLm,I:Count Kohler	3.00
36 RLm,V:Dire Wolf	3.00
37 AMe,A:Lamont	2.50
38 Animal Band	2.00
39 I:Buddy McBride	2.00
40 RLm,I:Sister Twyster	3.50
41 RLm,D:Sister Twyster	3.50
42 RLm,A:Paul Bunyan	3.50
43 RLm,V:Vampires	3.50

44 RLm,V:Vampires	3.50
45 RLm,V:Dr.Buick Riviera	3.50
46 RLm,V:Lort Weterlackus	3.50
47 RLm,Hmds.Sacr.BloodI	3.50
48 RLm,Hmds.Sacr.BloodII	3.50
49 RLm,TRoof off SuckerI	3.50
50 RLm,TRoof off SuckerII	5.00
51 RLm,V:Demon	3.00
52 TV,Tinku	4.00
53 TV,I:Shaza,Badass	4.00
54 TV,D:Shaza	4.00
55 I:Morris Myer	2.00
56 I:Dominance	2.00
57 A:KKang,V:L.W'lackus	2.00
58 A:Lamont,W'bat,V:SpudsJack	2.00
59 Bad Art Issue	2.00
60 I:ChisumBros	2.25
61 V:ChismBros	2.00
62 I:Shanks	2.00
63 V:Shanks	2.00
64 A:Mavis Sykes	2.25
65 A:BruceLee	2.25
66 I:Joe Nappleseed	2.25
67 Babysitting	2.25
68 V:GiantFoot	2.25
69 O:Mavis	2.25
70 BR:Klaus(last monthly)	2.25
Graphic Nov.BR,I:Mazis Sykes,D:Hodag	10.00
Badger Bedlam	4.95

BADGER GOES BERSERK
First 1989

1 I:Larry,Jessie	4.00
2 MZ,V:Larry,Jessie	3.50
3 JBt/MZ,V:Larry,Jessie	3.00
4 JBt/MZ,V:Larry,Jessie	3.00

BAD GIRLS OF BLACKOUT
Blackout Comics 1995

0	3.50
1 I:Ms. Cyanide, Ice	3.50
Ann.#1 Hari Kari, Lady Vampre	3.50
Ann.#1 Commemorative ed.	9.95

BADROCK/WOLVERINE
Awesome Entertainment 1997

Spec. #1 JV,CYp,V:Sauron,48pg . 4.95

BAKER STREET

1	3.00
2	2.50

BALLAD OF HALO JONES
Quality 1987

1 IG Alan Moore story	2.00
1a IG rep.	2.00
2 thru 12	@1.25

BAMM BAMM & PEBBLES FLINTSTONE
Gold Key Oct., 1964

1	50.00

BARBARIANS, THE
Atlas June, 1975

1 O:Andrax,F:Iron Jaw 1.75

BARBIE & KEN
Dell Publishing Co.
May-July, 1962

1	350.00
2	250.00
3	250.00
4	250.00
5	275.00

THE BARBIE TWINS ADVENTURES
Topps 1995

1 I:Shane, Sia 2.50

BARNEY AND BETTY RUBBLE
Charlton Comics 1973–76

1	35.00
2	15.00
3	15.00
4	15.00
5	15.00
6 thru 10	@10.00
11 thru 23	@8.00

BARRY M. GOLDWATER
Dell Publishing Co. March, 1965

1 . . . . 30.00

BART-MAN
Bongo 1993

1 Foil(c),I:Bart-Man	4.00
2 I:Penalizer	2.25
3 When Bongos Collide,pt.3, with card	2.25
4 Crime-Time,pt.1	2.25
5 Bad Guys Strike Back	2.25

BART SIMPSONS TREEHOUSE OF HORROR
Bongo Comics 1995

1 Bart People	2.95
2 thru 3	@2.95

BART SIMPSON'S TREEHOUSE OF TERROR
Bongo Comics 1995

One-shot 2.50

BASEBALL
Kitchen Sink 1991

1 WE (c) reprint of 1949 orig.	3.95
2 Ray Gotto (c), w/4 BB cards	2.95

BAT, THE
Adventure

1 R:The Bat,inspiration for Batman says Bob Kane 2.50

BATTLE FORCE
Blackthorne 1987

1 and 2	@1.50
3	1.75

BATTLE OF THE PLANETS
Gold Key June, 1979

1 TV Cartoon	15.00
2	10.00

COLOR PUB

3	10.00
4	10.00
5	

Whitman

6	7.00
7 thru 10	7.00

BATTLESTAR GALACTICA
Maximum Press 1995

1 Finds Earth	2.50
2 Council of Twelve	2.50
3 R:Adama	2.50
4 Pyramid Secrets	2.50
TPB series rep.	12.95
Spec. Ed. Painted Book (1997)	3.00
Battlestar Galactica: The Compendium #1 rep. from Asylum	3.00

BATTLESTAR GALACTICA
Realm Press 1997

1 by Chris Scalf	3.00
1a variant cover	3.00
2 Law of Volhad	3.00
3 Prison of Souls, pt.1	3.00
3a alternate cover	3.00
4 Prison of Souls, pt.2	3.00
5	3.00
6 A Path of Darkness, pt.1	3.00
7 A Path of Darkness, pt.2	3.00
7a photo (c)	3.00
7b signed and numbered	6.00
8 Centurion Prime	3.00
TPB New Beginnings, rep. #1–#4	14.00

BATTLESTAR GLACTICA: APOLLO'S JOURNEY
Maximum Press April 1996

1 story by Richard Hatch	2.95
2	2.50
3	2.50

BATTLESTAR GLACTICA: THE ENEMY WITHIN
Maximum Press Feb. 1996

1	3.00
2	2.50
3	2.50

BATTLESTAR GLACTICA: JOURNEY'S END
Maximum Press 1996

1 (of 4) RLd	3.00
2 RLd	3.00
3 RLd, the end of Galactica?	3.00
4 RLd, conclusion	3.00

BATTLESTAR GLACTICA: STARBUCK
Maximum Press 1997

1 (of 3) RLd	2.50
2 RLd	2.95
3 RLd, the end of Galactica?	2.95

BATTLETECH
Blackthorne 1987

1	1.50
2	1.50
3	1.50
4	1.75
5	1.75
6	1.75

(Changed to Black & White)

1 3-D	2.50
2 3-D	2.50

BEAGLE BOYS, THE
Gold Key 1964–79

1	40.00
2 thru 5	@30.00
6 thru 10	@20.00
11 thru 20	@15.00
21 thru 46	@10.00
47	10.00

BEANIE THE MEANIE
Fargo Publications 1958

1 thru 3	@30.00

B.E.A.S.T.I.E.S.
Axis Comics

1 JS(a&s),I:Beasties	2.25

THE BEATLES, LIFE STORY
Dell Publishing Co. 1964

1	500.00

BEAUTY AND THE BEAST
Innovation

1 From TV series	2.50
1a Deluxe	3.95
2	2.50
3	2.50
4 Siege	2.50
5 Siege	2.50
6 Halloween	2.50
7	2.50

BEAUTY AND THE BEAST PORTRAIT OF LOVE
First 1989–90

1 WP,TV tie in	12.00
2	8.00
Book II:Night of Beauty	5.95

BEAUTY AND THE BEAST
Walt Disney 1992

Movie adapt.(Prestige)	4.95
Movie adapt.(newsstand)	2.50

mini-series

1 Bewitched	1.50
2 Elsewhere	1.50
3 A:Catherine	2.50

BEDLAM!
Eclipse 1985

1 SBi,RV,reprint horror	1.75
2 SBi,RV,reprint horror	1.75

BEETLE BAILEY
Harvey 1992

1 F:Mort Walker's B.Bailey	1.95
2 Beetle builds a bridge	1.25
3 thru 12	1.25

BEETLEJUICE
Harvey 1991

1 EC,"This is your lice"	2.00
Holiday Special #1	1.25

BEN CASEY
Dell Publishing Co.
June-July, 1962

1 Ph(c)	45.00
2 Ph(c)	30.00
3 Ph(c)	30.00
4 Drug, Ph(c)	35.00
5 Ph(c)	30.00
6 thru 10 Ph(c)	@30.00

Berni Wrightson Master of the Macabre #5 © Eclipse

BERNI WRIGHTSON MASTER OF THE MACABRE
Pacific

1 BWr	5.25
2 BWr	3.75
3 BWr	3.50
4 BWr	3.50

Eclipse 1984

5 BWr	3.50

BEST FROM BOY'S LIFE
Gilberton Company Oct., 1957

1	80.00
2	50.00
3	40.00
4 LbC	60.00
5	40.00

BEST OF DONALD DUCK & UNCLE SCROOGE
Gold Key 1964–67

1	75.00
2	70.00

BEST OF DONALD DUCK
Gold Key Nov., 1965

1	75.00

BEST OF BUGS BUNNY
Gold Key 1966–68

1 Both Giants	35.00
2	25.00

COLOR PUB.

BEST OF DENNIS THE MENACE, THE
Hallden/Fawcett Publ.
Summer, 1959
1 . . . . 35.00
2 thru 5 Spring, 1961 . . . . . . 20.00

BETTA: TIME WARRIOR
Immortal Comics 1997
1 (of 3)Beginnings's End,pt.1 . . . 2.95
2 The Beginnings's End,pt.2 . . . . 2.95

BETTY
Archie Publications 1992
1 thru 39 . . . . @1.50
40 thru 57 . . . . @1.50
58 thru 67 . . . . @1.75

BETTY AND ME
Archie Publications 1965–92
1 . . . . 100.00
2 . . . . 50.00
3 . . . . 30.00
4 . . . . 30.00
5 . . . . 30.00
6 thru 10 . . . . @15.00
11 thru 30 . . . . @8.00
31 thru 50 . . . . @4.00
51 thru 55 . . . . @3.00
56 thru 199 . . . . @2.00
200 . . . . 2.00

Betty and Veronica #62
© Archie Comics

BETTY AND VERONICA
Archie Publications June, 1987
1 thru 100 . . . . @1.50
101 thru 104 . . . . @1.50
105 "The Ugly Truth" 1.50
106 "Hearing Aided" 1.50
107 two stories 1.50
108 "Visions of a Sugarplum" 1.50
109 . . . . 1.50
110 "The Trophy" 1.50
111 "Now Weight A Minute" 1.50
112 "Archie's Choice" 1.50
113 "Attitudes" 1.50

114 "Heard the Word" 1.50
115 "Moving Line" 1.50
116 "Model Muddle" 1.50
117 "Friends Til the Bitter End" . . 1.50
118 "Make Note of This" 1.50
119 "The New Girl in Town" 1.50
120 "Tis The Season to be Jolly" . 1.75
121 "Winter Blues" 1.75
122 . . . . 1.75
123 "Empress Veronica The First (and Last)" 1.75
124 . . . . 1.75
125 . . . . 1.75
126 "Star Wars" 1.75
127 . . . . 1.75
128 "The Epidemic" 1.75
129 "Express Yourself" 1.75
Summer Fun Special #5 . . . . . . 2.25

BETTY & VERONICA SPECTACULAR
1 thru 22 . . . . @1.50
23 "Scent Of Humor" 1.50
24 "Life's No Picnic" 1.50
25 "Warrior Princess of Riverdale" 1.50
26 "Grand Entrance" 1.50
27 "Blame That Tune" 1.50
28 "That's Of Snow Account" 1.75
29 "Just Desserts" 1.75
30 "Prom Here to Eternity" 1.75
31 "Lost at Sea" 1.75
32 "Made For Each Other" 1.75

BETTY BOOP'S SUNDAY BEST
Kitchen Sink 1998
TPB Complete Color Comics, 1934–36, new printing 19.95
HC Complete Color Comics, 1934–36, new printing 34.95

BEVERLY HILLBILLYS
Dell Publishing Co.
April-June, 1963
1 Ph(c) 150.00
2 Ph(c) 80.00
3 Ph(c) 50.00
4 . . . . 30.00
5 . . . . 50.00
6 . . . . 50.00
7 . . . . 50.00
8 Ph(c) 50.00
9 Ph(c) 50.00
10 Ph(c) 50.00
11 Ph(c) 50.00
12 Ph(c) 50.00
13 Ph(c) 50.00
14 Ph(c) 50.00
15 . . . . 30.00
16 . . . . 30.00
17 Ph(c) 30.00
18 Ph(c) 30.00
19 Ph(c) 30.00
20 Ph(c) 30.00
21 Ph(c) 30.00

BEWITCHED
Dell Publishing Co.
April-June, 1965
1 . . . . 135.00
2 . . . . 75.00
3 Ph(c) 50.00
4 Ph(c) 50.00

5 Ph(c) 50.00
6 Ph(c) 50.00
7 Ph(c) 50.00
8 Ph(c) 50.00
9 Ph(c) 50.00
10 Ph(c) 50.00
11 Ph(c) 50.00
12 Ph(c) 50.00
13 Ph(c) 50.00
14 . . . . 30.00

BEYOND THE GRAVE
Charlton Comics 1975–84
1 SD,TS(c),P(c) 20.00
2 thru 5 . . . . @15.00
6 thru 17 . . . . @10.00

BIG BANG
Caliber Press
0 Whole Timeline inc. 2.95
1 . . . . 1.95
2 . . . . 1.95
3 . . . . 1.95
4 25 years after #3 . . . . 1.95

BIG VALLEY, THE
Dell Publishing Co. June, 1966
1 Ph(c) 45.00
2 . . . . 20.00
3 . . . . 20.00
4 . . . . 20.00
5 . . . . 20.00
6 . . . . 20.00

BILL BLACK'S FUN COMICS
AC Comics
1 Cpt.Paragon,B&W 2.50
2 and 3 B&W . . . . @2.25
4 Color 2.25

BILL THE GALACTIC HERO
Topps
1 thru 3 Harry Harrison adapt. . @4.95

BILLY NGUYEN
Caliber
1 . . . . 2.50

BILLY THE KID
Charlton Publ. Co. 1957–83
9 . . . . 50.00
10 . . . . 30.00
11 . . . . 25.00
12 . . . . 20.00
13 AW,AT 30.00
14 . . . . 20.00
15 AW,O:Billy the Kid 30.00
16 AW 30.00
17 . . . . 20.00
18 . . . . 20.00
19 . . . . 20.00
20 . . . . 30.00
21 . . . . 30.00
22 . . . . 30.00
23 . . . . 10.00
24 . . . . 30.00
25 JSe 30.00
26 JSe 30.00
27 . . . . 10.00

Billy the Kid #62 © Charlton Publications

BLACK ENCHANTRESS
Heroic Publishing
1 and 2 Date Rape issues ... @1.95

BLACK FLAG
Maximum Press
1 Dan Fraga	3.00
2 I:New Character	2.50
3 V:Network, I:Glitz	2.50
4 V:Glitz, Network	2.50
5 I:Jammers	2.50
6 I:Alphabots	2.50

BLACK FURY
Charlton Comics May, 1955
1	45.00
2	20.00
3 thru 15	@8.00
16 SD	35.00
17 SD	35.00
18 SD	35.00
19 and 20	@5.00
21 thru 30	@3.00
31 thru 56	@3.00
57 March-April, 1966	3.00

BLACK HOLE, THE
Whitman 1980
1 & 2 movie adaptation	@1.50
3 & 4 new stories	@1.50

BLACK HOOD
Archie Publications
1 ATh,GM,DW	1.00
2 ATh,DSp,A:Fox	1.00
3 ATh,GM	1.00

BLACK JACK
Charlton Comics 1957–59
20	55.00
21	20.00
22	30.00
23 AW,AT	35.00
24 SD	30.00
25 SD	30.00
26 SD	30.00
27	15.00
28 SD	30.00
29	12.00
30	12.00

BLACKJACK: BLOOD & HONOR
Dark Angel 1997
1 by Alex Simmons,JoB, 1930s Adventure, Hildebrandts(c)	2.95
2 KeL	2.95
3 Tim Cheng disappears	2.95
4	2.95

BLACK PHANTOM
AC Comics
1 F:Red Mask	2.50
2 F:Red Mask	2.50

BLACK RAVEN
Mad Monkey Press 1996
1 Blueprints pt.1	2.95
2 Blueprints pt.2	2.95
3 V:Temple Assassins	2.95
4 Blueprints pt.4	2.95

GN#1 Blueprints	6.95
GN#2 Blueprints	4.95

BLACK TERROR
Eclipse 1989–90
1	3.95
2	3.95
3	4.95

BLACK WEB
Inks Comics
1 thru 3 V:Seeker .... @2.50

BLACKBALL COMICS
Blackball Comics
1 KG,A:Trencher 3.25

BLAST-OFF
Harvey Publications Oct., 1965
1 JK,AW 45.00

BLAZING COMBAT
Warren Publishing Co. 1965–66
1 FF(c)	90.00
2 FF(c)	20.00
3 and 4 FF(c)	@15.00

BLAZING SIX-GUNS
Skywald Comics 1971
1 F: Red Mask, Sundance Kid	15.00
2 Jesse James	10.00

BLONDIE
See Golden Age Section

BLOOD & ROSES
Sky Comics
1 I:Blood,Rose 2.75

BLOOD SWORD
Jademan 1988
1	3.00
2	2.50
3 thru 5	@2.00
6 thru 9	@1.75
10 thru 21	@2.50
22 LW	1.95
23 LW,D:Poisonkiller	1.95
24 LW,A:Hero	1.95
25	1.95
26	1.95
27	1.95
28 V:DevilHeart	1.95
29	1.95
30 A:Purgatory	1.95
31	1.95
32 V:Mummy	1.95
33 V:Mummy	1.95
34	1.95
35	1.95
36 A:King Rat	1.95
37	1.95
38 Kim Hung in Danger	1.95
39 Masked Men to the Rescue	1.95
40	1.95
41	1.95
42	1.95
43 A:Russell School Pack	1.95
44 FirefoxV:Tyrant of Venom	1.95
45 A:Yuen Mo	1.95
46 V:Cannibal	2.50

28	10.00
29	10.00
30	10.00
31 thru 40	@8.00
41 thru 60	@6.00
61 thru 80	@3.00
81 thru 153	@2.00

BIONEERS
Mirage/Next
1 New Heroes	2.75
2	2.75
3 All-out War	2.75

BIONIC WOMAN, THE
Charlton
1 ... Oct, 1977, TV show adapt.	2.00
2	1.50
3	1.50
4	1.50
5	1.50

BIONIX
Maximum Press 1996
1 (of 3) RLd,F:Steve Austin & Jaime Sommers	3.00
2 RLd,	3.00

BIZARRE 3-D ZONE
Blackthorne
1 .... 2.50

[ORIGINAL] BLACK CAT
1 Reprints	2.00
2 MA(c) rep.	2.00
3 rep.	2.00

BLACK DIAMOND
AC Comics
1 Colt B..U. story	3.00
2 PG(c)	2.00
3 PG(c)	2.00
4 PG(c)	2.00
5 PG(c)	2.00

47 .... 1.95
48 A:Clairvoyant Assassin 1.95
49 Prophecy of Hero's fate 1.95
50 D:Poison Entity 1.95
51 .... 1.95
52 Hero vs.Cannibal 1.95
53 Hero vs.Cannibal 1.95

BLOOD SWORD DYNASTY
Jademan 1989
1 .... 2.25
2 thru 6 .... @1.50
7 thru 14 MB .... @1.95
15 thru 18 MB .... @1.25
19 Kim & Zeo Escape the Crips .. 1.25
20 Skeleton Executioners 1.25
21 Kim,Seeto 1.25
22 Infinite Wounded 1.25
23 Kim vs. Ask me not 1.25
24 .... 1.25
25 .... 1.25
26 V:Fiery Bird 1.25
27 A:Hero, Shou, Fiery Bird 1.25
28 Hero vs. Fiery Bird 1.25
29 .... 1.25
30 .... 1.25
31 V:Devil Child 1.25
32 .... 1.25
33 .... 1.25
34 .... 1.25
35 Hero's ancestry 1.25
36 Hero & son in danger 1.25
37 A:Hell Clan,D:North Pole ... 1.25
38 Fiery Hawk Vs.Inf.Seeto 1.25
39 Hero vs.Infinite seeto 1.25
40 Kim Hung vs.Inf.Seeto 1.25

BLOODBATH
Samson Comics
1 I:Alien,V:Starguile 2.50

BLOODCHILDE
Millenium
0 O:Bloodchilde 2.95
1 Neil Gaiman, Vampires 2.95
1 signed (lim. to 500) 4.95
2 Neil Gaiman, Vampires 2.95
3 Neil Gaiman, Vampires 2.95
4 .... 2.95
5 Talk Show Host 2.95

BLOODFIRE
Lightning Comics
0 O:Bloodfire 3.00
1 JZy(s),JJn, red foil 5.00
1a Platinum foil Ed. 5.00
1b B&W Promo Ed. Silver ink ... 4.00
1c B&W Promo Ed. Gold ink 6.00
2 JZy(s),JJn,O:Bloodfire 4.00
3 JZy(s),JJn,I:Dreadwolf,
   Judgement Day,Overthrow ... 3.00
4 JZy(s),JJn,A:Dreadwolf, ... 3.00
5 JZy(s),JJn,I:Bloodstorm, w/card 3.00
6 SZ(s),TLw,V:Storman 3.00
7 SZ(s),TLw,A:Pres.Clinton 3.00
8 SZ(s),TLw,O:Prodigal 3.00
9 SZ(s),TLw,I:Prodigal (in
   Costume) 3.00
10 SZ(s),TLw,B:Rampage,I:Thorpe 3.00
11 .... 2.95
12 .... 2.95

BLOODFIRE/HELLINA
Lightning Comics
1 V:Slaughterhouse 3.00
1a Nude Version 9.95

BLOODLORE
Brave New Worlds
1 Dreamweavers 1.95
2 A Blow to the Crown 1.95

BLOODSCENT
Comico
1 GC 2.00

"HOT WAR IN THE ARCTIC"
Blue Beetle N# © Charlton Comics

BLUE BEETLE
Charlton Comics June, 1964
{1st S.A. Series}
1 O:Dan Garrett/BlueBeetle .. 75.00
2 .... 50.00
3 V:Mr.Thunderbolt 55.00
4 V:Praying Mantis Man 40.00
5 V:Red Knight 40.00
{2nd S.A. Series} July 1965
Previously: UNUSUAL TALES
50 V:Scorpion 50.00
51 V:Mentor 50.00
52 V:Magno 50.00
53 V:Praying Mantis Man ... 50.00
54 V:Eye of Horus 50.00
Becomes: GHOSTLY TALES
{3rd S.A. Series} 1967
1 SD,I:Question 75.00
2 SD,O:TedKord,D:DanGarrett . 35.00
3 SD,I:Madmen,A:Question .. 25.00
4 SD,A:Question 25.00
5 SD,VicSage(Question) app. in
   Blue Beetle Story 25.00

BLUE BULLETEER
AC Comics
1 .... 2.25

BLUE PHANTOM, THE
Dell Publishing Co.
June-Aug., 1962
1 .... 50.00

BLUE RIBBON
Archie Publications
1 JK,AV,O:Fly rep. 1.50
2 TVe,Mr.Justice 1.50
3 EB/TD,O:Steel Sterling 1.50
4 .... 1.00
5 S&K,Shield rep. 1.00
6 DAy/TD,Fox 1.00
7 TD,Fox 1.00
8 NA,GM,Blackhood 1.00
9 thru 11 .... @1.00
12 SD,ThunderAgents 1.00
13 Thunderbunny 1.00
14 Web & Jaguar 1.00

BOLD ADVENTURE
Pacific
1 .... 2.00
2 .... 1.50
3 JSe 1.50

BOLT & STARFORCE
AC Comics
1 .... 1.75
Bolt Special #1 .... 1.50

BOMBAST
Topps
1 V:Savage Dragon,Trading Card 3.25

BONANZA
Dell Publishing Co.
June-Aug., 1960
1 .... 200.00
2 .... 100.00
3 thru 10 .... @75.00
11 thru 20 .... @50.00
21 thru 37 .... @40.00

BORIS KARLOFF
TALES OF MYSTERY
Gold Key 1963–80
1 (Thriller) 85.00
2 (Thriller) 60.00
3 thru 8 .... @30.00
9 WW 40.00
10 .... 25.00
11 AW,JO 35.00
12 AT,AMc,JO 30.00
13 & 14 .... @25.00
15 RC,GE 25.00
16 thru 20 .... @25.00
21 JJ,Screaming Skull 40.00
22 thru 50 .... @20.00
51 thru 74 .... @15.00
75 thru 97 .... @10.00

BOZO
Innovation
1 1950's reprint stories 6.95

BOZO THE CLOWN
Blackthorne
1 3-D 2.50
2 3-D 2.50

BRADY BUNCH, THE
Dell Publishing Co. Feb., 1970
1 .... 45.00
2 .... 40.00

BRAIN BOY
Dell Publishing Co.
April-June, 1962

1	100.00
2	60.00
3	50.00
4	50.00
5	50.00
6	50.00

BREEDING GROUND
Samson Comics

1 I:Mazit, Zero 2.50

BRENDA LEE STORY, THE
Dell Publishing Co. Sept., 1962

1 .... 65.00

BRENDA STARR REPORTER
Dell Publishing Co. Oct., 1963

1 .... 150.00

BRIAN BOLLAND'S BLACK BOOK
Eclipse 1985

1 BB 2.50

BRAM STOKER'S BURIAL OF THE RATS
Roger Corman's Comics 1995

1 thru 3 film adaptation ..... @2.50

BRIDES IN LOVE
Charlton Comics 1956–65

1	35.00
2	15.00
3 thru 10	@10.00
11 thru 30	@5.00
31 thru 44	@3.00
45	3.00

BRUTE, THE
Atlas Feb.–July 1975

1 thru 3 .... @12.00

BUCK ROGERS
Gold Key 1964

1 P(c)	55.00
2 AMc,FBe,P(c),movie adapt	15.00
3 AMc,FBe,P(c),movie adapt	15.00
4 FBe,P(c)	15.00
5 AMc,P(c)	10.00
6 AMc,P(c)	10.00

Whitman

7 thru 9 AMc,P(c)	@8.00
10 and 11 AMc,P(c)	@4.00
12 and 13 P(c)	3.00
14 thru 16	3.00

BUCK ROGERS
TSR 1990–91

1 thru 3 O:Buck Rogers	@2.95
4 thru 6 Black Barney	@2.95
7 thru 10 The Martian Wars	@2.95

BUCKY O'HARE
Continuity

1 MGo 2.75

2 & 3 .... @2.00

BUFFALO BILL JR.
Dell Publishing Co. 1956

1	50.00
2	30.00
3	30.00
4	30.00
5	30.00
6	25.00
7	25.00
8	25.00
9	25.00
10	25.00
11 thru 13	@25.00

BUGGED-OUT ADVENTURES OF RALFY ROACH
Bugged Out Comics

1 I: Ralfy Roach 2.95

BULLWINKLE
Gold Key 1962

1 Bullwinkle & Rocky	200.00
2	125.00
3 thru 5	@60.00
6 and 7, rep.	@50.00
8 thru 11	60.00
12 rep.	35.00
13 and 14	@40.00
15 thru 19	@35.00
20 thru 24, rep.	@15.00
25	25.00

Bullwinkle and Rocky #2
© Charlton Comics

BULLWINKLE
Charlton Comics July, 1970

1 .... 35.00

Becomes:

BULLWINKLE AND ROCKY
Charlton Comics 1970–71

2 thru 7 .... @25.00

BULLWINKLE & ROCKY
Eclipse

3-D 15.00

BULLWINKLE FOR PRESIDENT
Blackthorne

1 3-D Special 2.50

BURKE'S LAW
Dell Publishing Co. 1964

1 from TV Show	45.00
2	30.00
3	30.00

BUTCH CASSIDY
Skywald Comics 1971

1	12.00
2 & 3	10.00

CABBOT: BLOODHUNTER
Maximum Press 1997

1 thru 4 RV .... @2.50

CADILLACS & DINOSAURS
Kitchen Sink

1 Rep. from Xenozoic Tales in 3-D 6.00

Topps

BLOOD & BONES

1 thru 3 rep. Xenozoic Tales, all
covers .... @2.50

MAN-EATER

1 thru 3, all covers 2.50

THE WILD ONES

1 thru 3, all covers 2.50

CAGES
Tundra

1 DMc	14.00
2 DMc	11.00
3 DMc	7.50
4 DMc	7.50
5 thru 7 DMc	5.00

CAIN
Harris

1 B:DQ(s),I:Cain,Frenzy	5.00
2 BSz(c),HBk,V:Mortatira	3.25

CAIN'S HUNDRED
Dell Publishing Co.
May-July, 1962

1	20.00
2	15.00

CALIFORNIA RAISINS
Blackthorne

1 thru 4 3-D	@2.50
5 3-D,O:Calif.Raisins	2.50
6 thru 8 3-D	@2.50

CALVIN & THE COLONEL
Dell Publishing Co.
April-June, 1962

1	75.00
2	50.00

COLOR PUB.

CAP'N QUICK & FOOZLE
Eclipse 1984–85
1	2.00
2 and 3	@2.50

CAPT. ELECTRON
Brick Computers Inc.
1	2.00
2	2.25

CAPTAIN ATOM
See STRANGE SUSPENSE STORIES

CAPTAIN CANUCK
Comely Comix 1975–81
1 I:Blue Fox	12.00
2 I:Red Coat	10.00
3 I:Heather	10.00
4 thru 14	7.00
Summer Spec. #1	7.00

CAPTAIN GLORY
Topps
1 A:Bombast,Night Glider, Trading Card	3.25

CAPTAIN HARLOCK: FALL OF THE EMPIRE
Eternity
1 R:Captain Harlock	2.50
2 V:Tadashi	2.50
3 Bomb on the Arcadia	2.50
4 Final issue	2.50

CAPTAIN MARVEL
M. F. Enterprises April, 1966
1	25.00
2	20.00
3 Fights The Bat	15.00
4	15.00
5 Captain Marvel Presents the Terrible Five	12.00

CAPTAIN NAUTICUS
Entity 1994
1 V:Fathom	2.95
2 V:Fathom's Henchman	2.95
3 Surf's Up	1.95

CAPTAIN NICE
Gold Key Nov., 1967
1 Ph(c)	50.00

CAPTAIN PARAGON
Americomics
1 thru 4	@2.00

CAPTAIN POWER
Continuity
1a NA,TVtie-in(direct sale)	2.00
1b NA,TVtie-in(newsstand)	2.00
2 NA	2.00

CAPTAIN STERN
Kitchen Sink Press
1 BWr,R:Captain Stern	5.25
2 BWr,Running Out of Time	4.95

Captain Thunder and Blue Bolt #1
© Hero Graphics

CAPTAIN THUNDER AND BLUE BOLT
Hero Graphics
1 I:Capt.Thunder & Paul Fremont	1.95
2 Paul becomes Blue Bolt	1.95
3 O:Capt.Thunder	1.95
4 V:Iguana Boys	1.95
5 V:Ian Shriver, in Scotland	1.95
6 V:Krakatoa	1.95
7 V:Krakatoa	1.95
8 A:Sparkplug (from League of Champions)	1.95
9 A:Sparkplug	1.95
10 A:Sparkplug	1.95

CAPTAIN VENTURE & THE LAND BENEATH THE SEA
Gold Key Oct., 1968
1	50.00
2	40.00

CAPTAIN VICTORY AND THE GALACTIC RANGERS
Pacific 1982
1 JK	2.00
2 JK	1.50
3 JK,BU:NA,I:Ms.Mystic	1.75
4 JK	1.00
5 JK	1.00
6 JK,SD	1.00
7 thru 13 JK	@1.00
Spec.#1 JK	1.50

CAR 54, WHERE ARE YOU?
Dell Publishing Co.
March-May, 1962
1 Ph(c)	70.00
2 thru 7 Ph(c)	@40.00

CARCA JOU RENAISSANCE
1 and 2	@1.50

CARNOSAUR CARNAGE
Atomeka
TPB	4.95

CAROLINE KENNEDY
Charlton Comics 1961
1	50.00

CASEY JONES & RAPHAEL
Mirage
1 Family War	2.75
2 Johnny Woo Woo	2.75
3 V:Johnny Woo Woo	2.75
4 9mm Raphael	2.75

CASPER ENCHANTED TALES
Harvey
1 short stories	1.25

CASPER
Harvey
1 thru 7	@1.00
8 thru 14	@1.25
15 thru 28	@1.50

CASPER THE FRIENDLY GHOST
Blackthorne
1 3-D	2.50

CASPER & FRIENDS
Harvey
1 thru 4	@1.00
5 short stories, cont	1.25

CASPER GHOSTLAND
Harvey
1 short stories	1.25

CASPER'S GHOSTLAND
Harvey Publications
Winter, 1958-59
1	125.00
2	50.00
3 thru 10	@30.00
11 thru 20	@20.00
21 thru 40	@10.00
41 thru 61	@8.00
62 thru 77	@5.00
78 thru 97	@3.00
98 Dec., 1979	3.00

CASPER THE FRIENDLY GHOST
Harvey 1990–91
Prev: The Friendly Ghost Casper
254 thru 260	@1.00

[Second Series] 1991–94
1 thru 14	@1.25
15 thru 28	@1.50

CAT TALES
Eternity
1 3-D	1.95

CAULDRON
Real Comics 1995
1 Movie Style Comic 2.95
1a Variat cover 2.95

CAVE GIRL
AC Comics
1 . . . . 2.95

CAVE KIDS
Gold Key 1963
1 . . . . 25.00
2 . . . . 15.00
3 . . . . 15.00
4 . . . . 15.00
5 . . . . 15.00
6 . . . . 10.00
7 A:Pebbles & Bamm Bamm . 15.00
8 thru 10 . . . . 8.00
11 thru 16 . . . . 8.00

CHAINS OF CHAOS
Harris
1 Vampirella, Rook 5.00
2 V:Chaoschild 3.25
3 Final issue 3.25

Champions #2 © Eclipse

CHAMPIONS
Eclipse 1986–87
1 I:Flare,League of Champions
    Foxbat, Dr.Arcane 15.00
2 I:Dark Malice 15.00
3 I:Lady Arcane 10.00
4 O:Dark Malice 15.00
5 O:Flare 8.00
6 D:Giant Demonmaster 8.00
[New Series]
Hero Graphics
1 EL,I:Madame Synn,Galloping
    Galooper 5.00
2 I:Fat Man, Black Enchantress . 2.25
3 I:Sparkplug&Icicle,O:Flare . . 2.25
4 I:Exo-Skeleton Man 2.25
5 A:Foxbat 2.25
6 I:Mechanon, C:Foxbat 1.95
7 A:Mechanon,J:Sparkplug,Icicle . 1.95
8 O:Foxbat 1.95

9 Flare #0 (Flare preview) . . . 1.95
10 Olympus Saga #1 . . . . 1.95
11 Olympus Saga #2 . . . . 1.95
12 Olympus Saga #3 . . . . 1.95
Ann.#1 O:Giant & DarkMalice . . 2.75
Ann.#2 . . . . 3.95

CHAMPIONS CLASSIC
Hero Graphics
1 GP(c),Rep.1st champions series 1.00

CHAOS BIBLE
Chaos! Comics
1 Character Profiles 3.50

CHAOS! GALLERY
Chaos! Comics 1997
1 . . . . 2.95

CHAOS! NIGHTMARE THEATER
Chaos! Comics 1997
1 (of 4) BWr(c) 2.50
2 BWr(c) 2.50
3 BWr(c) 2.50
4 BWr(c) 2.50

CHAOS QUARTERLY
Harris Comics 1995
1 F:Lady Death 4.95
1a Premium Edition 10.95
1b Signed,limited edition 20.00

CHAPEL
Awesome Entertainment 1997
1 BNa, from Spawn,Youngblood . 2.95

CHARLEMAGNE
Defiant
1 JiS(s),From Hero 2.00
2 JiS(s),I:Charles Smith 2.75
3 JiS(s),A:War Dancer 2.75
4 DGC(s),V:Dark Powers 2.75
5 Schism prequel 2.75
6 V:Wardancer 2.75
7 R:To Vietnam 2.75

CHARLIE CHAN
Dell Publ. Co.Oct.-Dec., 1965
1 . . . . 30.00
2 . . . . 20.00

CHARLTON BULLSEYE
Spec. #1 . . . . 2.00

CHARLTON SPORT LIBRARY
Charlton 1970
1 Professional Football 15.00

CHASSIS
Millenium/Expand 1995
1 I:Chassis McBain, Aero Run . . 2.95
1 2nd printing 2.95
1 chrome cover 9.95
2 . . . . 2.95
2a with racing card 4.95
2b Amanda Conner cover 2.95
2c Amanda Conner cover, signed 9.95
2d foil cover, signed 7.95

[Vol. 2]
Hurricane Comics 1998
1 . . . . 2.95
2 . . . . 2.95
3 . . . . 2.95

CHASTITY: THEATRE OF PAIN
Chaos! Comics 1997
1 (of 3) BnP, ... 2.95
2 . . . . 2.95
3 . . . . 2.95
TPB rep.#1–#3, Sketchbook . . . 9.95

CHEAP SHODDY ROBOT TOYS
Eclipse
1 A:Ronald Reagan 1.75

CHECKMATE
Gold Key Oct., 1962
1 Ph(c) 40.00
2 Ph(c) 30.00

CHEMICAL MAN
1 . . . . 1.75

CHERYL BLOSSOM
Archie Comics April 1996
1 "Love Showdown" 1.50
2 "Inn Big Trouble" 1.50
3 "Home Um-Improvement" . . . 1.50
4 "Radio Daze" 1.50
5 "Cheryl in the Morning" 1.50
6 "What a Disaster" 1.50
7 "Educating Cheryl" 1.50
8 "Masquerade Madness" 1.50
9 "Tis the Season" 1.75
10 "Who's That Girl", pt.1 . . . . 1.75
11 "Who's That Girl", pt.2 . . . . 1.75
12 "Stop the Presses" 1.75
13 . . . . 1.75
14 "Cheers to You" 1.75
15 "Cheryl's Beach Bash, pt.1" . . 1.75
16 "Lights, Camera, Action," pt.2 . 1.75
17 "Cheryl-Mania" 1.75

CHERYL BLOSSOM GOES HOLLYWOOD
Archie Comics 1996
1 (of 3) by Dan Parent & Bill
    Golliher 1.50
2 and 3 . . . . @1.50

CHEYENNE
Dell Publishing Co. Oct., 1956
1 Ph(c) all 150.00
2 . . . . 75.00
3 . . . . 50.00
4 thru 12 . . . . @40.00
13 thru 25 . . . . @35.00

CHEYENNE KID
(see WILD FRONTIER)

CHI-CHIAN
Sirius 1997
1 (of 6) by Voltaire 2.95
2 thru 6 . . . . @2.95

COLOR PUB.

CHILD'S PLAY 2
Innovation
1 Movie Adapt Pt 1	2.50
2 Adapt Pt 2	2.50
3 Adapt Pt 3	2.50

CHILD'S PLAY 3
Innovation
1 Movie Adapt Pt 1	2.50
2 Movie Adapt Pt.2	2.50

CHILD'S PLAY: THE SERIES
Innovation
1 Chucky's Back	2.50
2 Straight Jacket Blues	2.50
3 M.A.R.K.E.D.	2.50
4 Chucky in Toys 4 You	2.50
5 Chucky in Hollywood	2.50

CHILDREN OF FIRE
Fantagor
1 thru 3 RCo	@2.00

CHILLING ADVENTURES IN SORCERY AS TOLD BY SABRINA
Archie 1972–74
1	12.00
2	10.00
3 thru 5	@8.00

CHIP 'N DALE
Dell Publishing 1955–66
4	50.00
5 thru 10	@45.00
11 thru 30	@35.00

Gold Key 1967
1 reprints	20.00
2 thru 10	@10.00
11 thru 20	@5.00
21 thru 83	@2.50

CHIP 'N DALE RESCUE RANGERS
Walt Disney 1990
1 Rescue Rangers to the Rescue, pt.1	3.50
2 Rescue Rangers to the Rescue, pt.2	3.00
3 thru 7	@2.50
8 Coast to Coast Pt 1	2.00
9 Coast to Coast Pt 2	2.00
10 Coast to Coast Pt 3	2.00
11 Coast to Coast Pt 4	2.00
12 "Showdown at Hoedown"	1.75
13 Raining Cats & Dogs	1.75
14 "Cobra Kadabra"	1.75
15 I:Techno-Rats,WaspPatrol Fearless Rescue Pt.1	1.75
16 A:Techno-Rats,WaspPatrol, Fearless Rescue Pt.2	1.75
17 "For the Love of Cheese"	1.75
18 "Ghastly Goat of Quiver Moore, Pt.1	1.50

CHOO CHOO CHARLIE
Gold Key Dec., 1969
1	50.00

CHOPPER: EARTH, WIND, AND FIRE
Fleetway
1 F:Chopper	2.95

CHOSEN, THE
Click Comics 1995
1 I:The Chosen	2.50
2 I:Herman Cortez	2.50

CHRISTIAN
Maximum Press 1996
1 and 2 (of 3) RLd	@2.95

CHRISTMAS PARADE
Gladstone
1 GiantEdition	4.00
2	3.50

CHRISTMAS SPIRIT, THE
Kitchen Sink
TPB Will Eisner art	15.00

CHROMA-TICK SPECIAL EDITION
New England Press
1 Rep.Tick#1,new stories	3.95
2 Rep.Tick#2,new stories	3.95
3 thru 8 Reps.& new stories	@3.50

CHROME
Hot Comics
1 Machine Man	3.50
2 thru 4	@2.00

CHROME WARRIORS IN A '59 CHEVY
Black Out Comics 1998
0	2.95
0a Nude cover	9.95
0b deluxe nude edition	14.95
1 Rob Roman & Tommy Castillo	2.95
1a nude cover	9.95
1b deluxe nude edition	14.95

CHROMIUM MAN, THE
Triumphant Comics
0 Blue Logo	6.00
0 Regular	2.50
1 I:Chromium Man,Mr.Death	3.50
2 I:Prince Vandal	3.00
3 I:Candi,Breaker,Coil	2.50
4 JnR(s),AdP,Unleashed	2.50
5 JnR(s),AdP,Unleashed	2.50
6 JnR(s),Courier,pt.1	2.50
7 JnR(s),Courier,pt.2	2.50
8 JnR(s),Chromium finds peace	2.50
9 V:Tarsak	2.50
10	2.50
11 Prince Vandal #8	2.50
12 Prince Vandal #9	2.50
13 V:Realm	2.50
14 A:Light	2.50
15	2.50

CHROMIUM MAN: VIOLENT PAST
Triumphant Comics
1 thru 4 JnR(s)	@2.50

Chronicles of Corum #1 © First

CHRONICLES OF CORUM
First 1987–88
1 Michael Moorcock adapt.	2.25
2 thru 12	@2.00

CICERO'S CAT
Dell Publishing Co. July-Aug., 1959
1	25.00
2	20.00

CIMMARON STRIP
Dell Publishing Co. Jan., 1968
1	45.00

CITY PERILOUS
Broadway Comics
1 GI,"I Remember the Future," part #1	2.95
2 GI,"I Remember the Future," part #2	2.95

Becomes:
KNIGHTS ON BROADWAY
3 GI,"I Remember the Future," part #3	2.95
4 GI,"I Remember the Future," part #4	2.95
5 GI,"I Remember the Future," part #5	2.95

CLASSICS ILLUSTRATED
See Also:
CLASSICS ILLUSTRATED SECTION

CLASSICS ILLUSTRATED
First
1 GW,The Raven	3.75
2 RG,Great Expectations	3.75
3 KB,Thru the Looking Glass	3.75
4 BSz,Moby Dick	3.75
5 SG,TM,KE, Hamlet	3.75
6 PCr,JT, Scarlet Letter	3.75
7 DSp,Count of Monte Cristo	3.75
8 Dr.Jekyll & Mr.Hyde	3.75
9 MP,Tom Sawyer	3.75

     All comics prices listed are for *Near Mint* condition.

10 Call of the Wild	3.75
11 Rip Van Winkle	3.75
12 Dr. Moreau	3.75
13 Wuthering Heights	3.75
14 Fall of House of Usher	3.75
15 Gift of the Magi	3.75
16 A: Christmas Carol	3.75
17 Treasure Island	3.75
18 The Devils Dictionary	3.95
19 The Secret Agent	3.95
20 The Invisible Man	3.95
21 Cyrano de Bergerac	3.95
22 The Jungle Book	3.95
23 Swiss Family Robinson	3.95
24 Rime of Ancient Mariner	3.95
25 Ivanhoe	3.95
26 Aesop's Fables	3.95
27 The Jungle	3.95

CLAUS
Draco 1997
1 by John Kennedy Bowden & Corinne Y. Guichardon	2.95
2	3.25
3	3.25
4	3.25

CLIVE BARKER'S DREAD
Eclipse
Graphic Album	7.95

CLIVE BARKER'S TAPPING THE VEIN
Eclipse
1	13.00
2	8.50
3	8.50
4	8.50
5 inc."How Spoilers Breed"	8.50

CLYDE CRASHCUP
Dell Publishing Co.
Aug.-Oct., 1963
1	65.00
2	50.00
3 thru 5	@50.00

COBALT 60
Innovation
1 reprints	4.95

COBALT BLUE
Innovation
Spec.#1	1.95
Spec.#2	1.95
1 and 2	@1.95

CODENAME: DANGER
Lodestone
1 RB/BMc,I:Makor	2.50
2 KB,I:Capt.Energy	2.00
3 PS/RB	1.50
4 PG	1.50

CODE NAME: DOUBLE IMPACT
High Impact 1997
1 RCl	3.00
1 variant cover	10.00
1 signed holofoil cover	14.95

CODENAME: STRIKEFORCE
Spectrum
1	1.00

COLLECTOR'S DRACULA
Millennium
1	4.25

COLOSSAL SHOW, THE
Gold Key Oct., 1969
1	35.00

COLOUR OF MAGIC
Innovation
1 Terry Pratchet novel adapt	3.00
2 "The Sending of Eight"	2.50
3 "Lure of the Worm"	2.50
4 final issue	2.50

COLT .45
Dell Publishing Co. 1958
1 Ph(c) all	85.00
2	50.00
3	50.00
4	50.00
5	65.00
6 ATh	50.00
7	50.00
8	50.00
9	50.00

COLT SPECIAL
AC Comics
1	1.75
2	1.75
3	1.75

COMBAT
Dell Publishing Co. 1961
1 SG	40.00
2 SG	20.00
3 SG	20.00
4 JFK cover, Story 2-D	25.00
5 SG	20.00

Comet #1 © Red Circle

6 SG	15.00
7 SG	15.00
8 SG	15.00
9 SG	15.00
10 SG	15.00
11 thru 27 SG	@10.00
28 thru 40 SG	@7.00

COMET
Red Circle/Archie Publications
1 CI,O:Comet	1.00
2 CI,D:Hangman	1.00

COMET, THE
Red Circle 1983
1 Alex Nino	1.50

COMIC ALBUM
Dell Publishing Co. 1958
March-May, 1958
1 Donald Duck	75.00
2 Bugs Bunny	30.00
3 Donald Duck	50.00
4 Tom & Jerry	30.00
5 Woody Woodpecker	30.00
6 Bugs Bunny	30.00
7 Popeye	35.00
8 Tom & Jerry	30.00
9 Woody Woodpecker	30.00
10 Bugs Bunny	30.00
11 Popeye	35.00
12 Tom & Jerry	25.00
13 Woody Woodpecker	25.00
14 Bugs Bunny	25.00
15 Popeye	35.00
16 Flintstones	60.00
17 Space Mouse	30.00
18 3 Stooges,Ph(c)	75.00

COMICO X-MAS SPECIAL
Comico
1 SR/AW/DSt(c)	1.50

COMIX INTERNATIONAL
Warren Magazines July, 1974
1	35.00
2 WW,BW	20.00
3	10.00
4 RC	10.00
5 Spring, 1977	5.00

COMMANDER BATTLE AND HIS ATOMIC SUB
#20 3-D	2.50

COMMANDOSAURS
1	3.50

CONSTRUCT
Mirage
1 I:Constructs	2.75
2 F:Sect.Eight, Armor	2.75
3 O:Constructs	2.75
4 Fist-O-God	2.75

CORBEN SPECIAL
Pacific
1 RCo	1.75

COLOR PUB.

COLOR PUB.

CORUM: THE BULL & THE SPEAR
First
1 thru 4 Michael Moorcock adapt@1.95

COSMONEERS SPECIAL
1 . . . . 1.95

COUGAR, THE
Atlas Apr.–July 1975
1 & 2 . . . . @10.00

COURTSHIP OF EDDIE'S FATHER
Dell Publishing Co. 1970
1 Ph(c) 30.00
2 Ph(c) 20.00

COVEN
Awesome Entertainment 1997
1 IaC,JLb,JSb,V:The Pentad . . . 10.00
1a variant covers 10.00
2 IaC,JLb,Who is Spellcaster? . . 6.00
3 IaC,JLb,V:The Pentad 4.00
4 IaC,JLb,Pentad, concl. 2.50
5 IaC,JLb, ... 2.50
6 IaC,JLb,Mardi Gras madness . . 2.50
7 IaC,JLb,V:Babylon 2.50
8 IaC,JLb,F:Thor, the God of Thunder 2.50
9 IaC,JLb, ... 2.50
Coll.Ed. #1, rep. #1–#2, new IaC(c) 4.95
Fan Appreciation #1, rep. #1, new cover 2.50

COVEN 13
No Mercy Comics 1997
1 by Rikki Rockett & Matt Busch . 2.50
2 . . . . 2.50
3 . . . . 2.50
4 . . . . 2.50

COVER GIRL
1 . . . . 1.95

COWBOY IN AFRICA
Gold Key March, 1968
1 Chuck Conners,Ph(c) 25.00

CRACKED
Major Magazines Feb.-Mar. 1958
1 AW 125.00
2 . . . . 50.00
3 thru 6 . . . . @30.00
7 thru 10 . . . . @20.00
11 thru 20 . . . . @15.00
21 thru 30 . . . . @10.00
31 thru 60 . . . . @4.00
61 thru 252 . . . . @3.00

[THE INCREDIBLE] CRASH DUMMIES
Harvey 1993
1 thru 3, from the toy series . . @1.50

CRAZYMAN
Continuity
[1st Series]
1 Embossed(c),NA/RT(i), O:Crazyman 6.00

---

2 NA/BB(c) 2.50
3 DBa,V:Terrorists 2.50
[2nd Series]
1 Die Cut(c) 2.50
2 thru 3 . . . . 2.50
4 In Demon World 2.50

CREATURE
Antarctic Press Oct. 1997
1 (of 2) by Don Walker & Jason Maranto 2.95
2 concl. 2.95

CREED/TEENAGE MUTANT NINJA TURTLES
Lightning Comics April 1996
1 . . . . 3.00
1 variant cover 3.00
1 platinum edition B&W . . . 9.95

CREED: CRANIAL DISORDER
Lightning Comics
1 (of 3) 3.00
1a variant cover, *Previews* exclusive 3.00
1b Platinum edition 9.00
1c Platinum edition, autographed 16.00
2 . . . . 3.00
2a variant cover 3.00

CRIME MACHINE
Skywald Publications Feb., 1971
1 . . . . 20.00
2 . . . . 15.00

CRIME SUSPENSE STORIES
Russ Cochran
1 Rep. C.S.S. #1 (1950) 1.75
2 Rep. C.S.S. 1.75
3 Rep. C.S.S. 1.75
4 thru 6 Rep. C.S.S 2.00
7 Rep. C.S.S 2.00
8 thru 15 Rep. 2.00
16 thru 24 EC comics reprint . . @2.50
Ann.#1, rep. #1–#5 . . . . 8.95
Ann.#2, rep. #6–#10 . . . . 8.95
Ann.#3, rep. #11–#15 . . . . 9.95
Ann.#4, rep. #16–#19 . . . . 10.50
Ann.#5, rep. #20–#23 . . . . 10.95

CRIMSON NUN
Antarctic Press 1997
1 (of 4) 2.95
2 . . . . 2.95
3 . . . . 2.95
4 concl 2.95

CRIMSON PLAGUE
Event Comics
1 GP,F:DiNA: Simmons 2.95
2 GP, ... 2.95

CROSSFIRE
Eclipse 1984–86
1 DSp 3.00
2 DSp 2.50
3 DSp 1.50

Crossfire #1 © Eclipse Comics

4 DSp 1.50
5 DSp 1.50
6 DSp 1.50
7 DSp 2.50
8 DSp 2.50
9 DSp 1.75
10 DSp 1.75
11 DSp 1.75
12 DSp,DSt(c),M.Monroe cover & story 2.50
13 DSp 1.75
14 DSp 1.75
15 DSp,O:Crossfire 1.75
16 DSp,"The Comedy Place" . . . 1.75
17 DSp,"Comedy Place" Pt.2 . . . 1.75

CROSSFIRE & RAINBOW
Eclipse 1986
1 DSp,V:Marx Brothers 1.75
2 DSp,PG(c),V:Marx Brothers . . . 1.50
3 DSp,HC(c),A:Witness 1.50
4 DSp,DSt(c),"This Isn't Elvis" . . . 3.50

CROSSROADS
First
1 Sable,Whisper 4.00
2 Sable,Badger 4.00
3 JSon,JAI,Badger/Luther Ironheart 4.00
4 Grimjack/Judah Macabee 4.00
5 LM,Grimjack/Dreadstar/Nexus . 4.00

CROW, THE: CITY OF ANGELS
Kitchen Sink
1 thru 3 movie adaptation . . . . @2.95
1 thru 3 movie adaptation, photo covers . . . . @2.95
TPB The Crow, The Movie, new printing 18.95

CRYING FREEMAN III
Viz
1 A:Dark Eyes,Oshu 6.00
2 A:Dark Eyes, V:Oshu 5.25
3 Freeman vs. Oshu 5.25
4 Freeman Defeated 5.25

All comics prices listed are for *Near Mint* condition.

5 Freeman clones, A:Nitta 5.25
6 V:Nitta 5.25
7 .... 4.95
8 .... 4.95
9 .... 4.95

CRYING FREEMAN IV
Viz
1 B:The Pomegranate 4.95
2 .... 2.75
3 .... 2.75
4 .... 2.75
5 thru 7 .... @2.75
8 E:The Pomegranate 2.75
[2nd Series]
1 The Festival 2.50

CRYPT OF DAWN
Sirius 1996
1 JLi 2.95

CRYPTIC WRITINGS
OF MEGADETH
Chaos! Comics 1997
1 BnP 2.95
1a Tour Edition, leather 25.00
1b Tour Edition, deluxe 50.00
2 BnP 2.95
3 BnP 2.95
4 BnP 2.95

CYBER CITY: PART ONE
CPM Comics 1995
1 I:Oedo City 2.95
2 Sengoku 2.95

CYBER CITY: PART TWO
CPM Comics 1995
1 Based on Animated Movie 2.95

CYBERCRUSH:
ROBOTS IN REVOLT
Fleetway/Quality
1 inc.Robo-Hunter, Ro-Busters .. 1.95
2 and 3 .... @1.95
4 and 5 V:Terraneks .... @1.95

CYBERFROG
Harris 1995
0 O:Cyberfrog 2.95
0 AAd(c), signed 19.95
0 Alternate AAd(c) 9.95
1 .... 2.00
1a Signed,numbered 24.95
1b Ultra Violent Cover 49.95
2 .... 2.95
3 .... 2.95
4 .... 2.95
4a alternate cover, signed &
   numbered (#300) 29.95

CYBERFROG:
RESERVOIR FROG
Harris
1 Preview Ashcan, signed &
   numbered 24.95
1 EL(c),V:the Swarm, Mr.
   Skorpeone 2.95
1 Signed & numbered (#250) .. 19.95
2 .... 2.95

1 & 2 Signed & numbered, in
   binder (#250) 39.95

CYBERHOOD
Entity Comics 1995
1 R:Cyberhood 2.50
1a with PC Game 6.95

CYBERPUNK
Innovation
1 .... 1.95
2 .... 1.95
Book 2,#1 .... 2.25
Book 2,#2 .... 2.25

CYBERPUNK:
THE SERAPHIM FILES
Innovation 1990
1 .... 2.50
2 .... 2.50

CYBERPUNX
Maximum Press 1997
1 MHw, ... 2.50

CYBERRAD
Continuity
1 NA layouts,I:Cyberran 3.00
2 NA I/o 2.50
3 NA I/o 2.50
4 NA I/o 2.50
5 NA I/o Glow in the Dark cov . 5.00
6 NA I/o,Pullout poster 2.50
7 NA I/o,See-thru(c) 2.50
[2nd Series]
1 Hologram cover 2.00
2 NA(c),"The Disassembled Man" 2.00
[3rd Series]
1 Holo.(c),just say no 3.50
[4th Series, Deathwatch 2000]
1 Deathwatch 2000 pt.8,w/card . 2.50
2 Deathwatch 2000 pt. w/card .. 2.50

CYBRID
Maximum Press 1995
1 F:Cybrid, I:The Clan 2.95

CYBRID
Maximum Press 1997
0 RLd, 48pg 3.50
1 MsM,BNa 3.00
2 MsM,BNa 3.00

CYNDER
Immortelle Studios
1 thru 3: see B&W
Ann. #1 .... 2.95
Series II 1997
1 A:Nira X 2.95

CYNDER/NIRA X
Immortelle Studios 1996
1 x-over 2.95
1 variant cover 3.00
1 gold edition 10.00

DAEMONSTORM
Caliber 1997
1 TM(c),JMt 3.95
1 signed 3.95

1 gold edition 19.95

DAEMONSTORM:
DEADWORLD
Caliber
one-shot 3.95

DAEMONSTORM: OZ
Caliber 1997
1 .... 3.95

DAGAR THE INVINCIBLE
Gold Key 1972–82
1 O:Daggar,I:Villians Olstellon &
   Scorpio 15.00
2 .... 12.00
3 I:Graylon 8.00
4 .... 8.00
5 .... 8.00
6 1st Dark Gods story 5.00
7 .... 5.00
8 .... 5.00
9 .... 5.00
10 .... 5.00
11 thru 19 .... @3.00

Dai Kamikaze #10 © Now Comics

DAI KAMIKAZE
Now 1987–88
1 Speed Racer 7.00
1a 2nd printing 1.50
2 .... 2.00
3 .... 1.50
4 .... 1.50
5 .... 1.50
6 thru 12 .... @1.75

DAKTARI
Dell Publishing Co. July, 1967
1 .... 20.00
2 .... 15.00
3 .... 15.00
4 .... 15.00

DALGODA
Fantagraphics
1 .... 3.50

COLOR PUB.

2 KN,I:Grinwood'Daughter 3.00
3 KN 2.50
4 thru 8 . . . . @2.25

DALKIEL: THE PROPHECY
Verotik 1998
1-shot, prequel to Satanika 3.95

DANGER
Charlton Comics June, 1955
12 . . . . 50.00
13 . . . . 35.00
14 . . . . 35.00
Becomes:
JIM BOWIE
15 . . . . 25.00
16 . . . . 12.00
17 . . . . 12.00
18 . . . . 12.00
19 April, 1957 . . . . 12.00

DANGER RANGER
Checker Comics 1998
1 I:Kirby Jackson, BSz(c) 1.95

DANIEL BOONE
Gold Key 1965–69
1 . . . . 75.00
2 thru 5 . . . . @30.00
6 thru 14 . . . . @20.00
15 . . . . 15.00

DANNY BLAZE
Charlton Comics Aug., 1955
1 . . . . 40.00
2 . . . . 35.00
Becomes:
NATURE BOY
3 JB,O:Blue Beetle 125.00
4 . . . . 100.00
5 Feb., 1957 . . . . 85.00

DARE
Fantagraphics
1 F:Dan Dare 2.75
2 F:Dan Dare 2.75
3 F:Dan Dare 2.50
4 F:Dan Dare 2.50

DARE THE IMPOSSIBLE
Fleetway/Quality
1 DGb,rep.Dan Dare from 2000AD 1.95
2 DGb, Dare on Waterworld . . . 1.95
3 DGb 1.95
4 DGb 1.95
5 DGb,"The Garden of Eden" . . 1.95
6 DGb 1.95
7 DGb,V:Deadly Primitives 1.95
8 DGb,The Doomsday Machine . 1.95
9 thru 14 DGb . . . . @1.95

DARK, THE
Continüm 1992
1 LSn(c),MBr,V:Futura 4.00
2 LSn,Shot by Futura 3.00
3 MBr,Dark has amnesia 3.00
4 GT(c),MBr,O:The Dark 3.00
Convention Book 1992 MBr,GP,
 MFm,MMi,VS,LSn,TV 5.00
Convention Book 1993 MBr,PC,
 ECh,BS,BWi,GP(c),Foil(c), . . . 4.00

Aug. House
1 BS(c),Red Foil(c), ... 3.00
1a BS(c),newstand ed. 3.00
1b BS(c),Blue foil 3.00
2 . . . . 3.00
3 BS(c),Foil(c), ... 3.00
4 GP(c),Foil(c),w/cards 3.00
5 thru 9 . . . . @2.50
[2nd Series]
1 Dark Regains Memory 3.00
1a Signed, Foil Cover 2.75
2 War on Crime 2.75
3 Geoffery Stockton 2.50
4 I:First Monster 2.50

DARK ADVENTURES
1 thru 3 . . . . @1.75

DARK CHYLDE
Maximum Press June 1996
1 RQu 18.00
1 American Entertainment edition 15.00
1 variant cover 15.00
2 RQu 13.00
2 variant cover 15.00
3 RQu 11.00
3 variant cover 12.00
4 RQu 5.00
5 RQu,"No One Here Gets Out
Alive" 12.00

DARK CHYLDE/ AVENGELYNE
Maximum Press
Spec. RLd,RQu,I:Witch Tower . . . 3.00

DARK CHYLDE/GLORY
Maximum Press
Spec. RQu, ... 3.00

Dark Dominion #3 © Defiant Comics

DARK DOMINION
Defiant
1 SD,I:Michael Alexander 3.25
2 LWn(s),SLi(i), ... 2.75
3 LWn(s),SLi(i), ... 2.75
4 LWn(s),B:Hoxhunt 3.00

5 LWn(s),I:Puritan,Judah 2.75
6 LWn(s),I:Lurk 2.75
7 LWn(s),V:Glimmer 2.75
8 LWn(s),V:Glimmer 2.50
9 LWn(s)V:Puritan 2.50
10 LWn(s),Schism Prequel 2.50
11 LWn(s), X-Over 2.50
12 LWn(s), V:Chasm 2.50

DARK ONE'S THIRD EYE
Sirius April 1996
one-shot DOe 4.95

DARK SHADOWS
Gold Key March, 1969
1 W/Poster,Ph(c) 250.00
2 Ph(c) 100.00
3 W/Poster,Ph(c) 125.00
4 thru 7,Ph(c) . . . . @75.00
8 thru 10 . . . . @60.00
11 thru 20 . . . . @50.00
21 thru 35 . . . . @40.00

DARK SHADOWS
Innovation
1 Based on 1990's TV series . . 3.50
2 O:Victoria Winters 2.50
3 Barnabus Imprisoned 2.50
4 V: Redmond Swann 2.75
[2nd Series]
1 A:Nathan 2.75
2 thru 4 . . . . 2.75
Dark Shadows:Resurrected 15.95

DARK SIDE
Maximum Press 1997
1 RLd,RQu 3.00

DARK TOWN
Mad Monkey Press
1 (of 13) 3.95
2 thru 7 . . . . @3.95

DARKLON THE MYSTIC
Pacific
1 JSn 1.50

DARKWING DUCK
Walt Disney
1 I:Darkwing Duck 1.75
2 V:Taurus Bulba 1.75
3 "Fowl Play" 1.75
4 "End o/t beginning,"final issue . 1.75

DARKWOOD
Aircel
1 thru 5 . . . . @2.00

DAUGHTERS OF TIME
3-D
1 I:Kris,Cori,Lhana 3.95

FRONTIER FIGHTER
Charlton Comics Aug., 1955
1 . . . . 50.00
2 . . . . 25.00
Becomes:
DAVY CROCKETT
3 thru 7 . . . . @20.00
8 Jan., 1957 . . . . 15.00

COLOR PUB.

Becomes:

KID MONTANA
```
9 ............................ 20.00
10 ........................... 9.00
11 ........................... 6.00
12 ........................... 6.00
13 ........................... 14.00
14 thru 20 ............. @6.00
21 thru 35 ............. @3.50
36 thru 49 ............. @2.00
50 March, 1965 ......... 2.00
```

DAWN
Sirius 1995–97
```
½ ............................ 15.00
½ variant ................. 25.00
1 JLi,R:Dawn ......... 12.00
1a white trash edition .. 40.00
1b black light edition .. 35.00
1c look sharp edition .. 45.00
2 JLi, Trip to Hell ..... 8.00
2 variant cover ......... 36.00
3 JLi ....................... 9.00
3 limited edition ....... 40.00
4 JLi,"The Gauntlet" .. 5.00
4a variant cover ....... 30.00
5 JLi,"Everybody Dies" .. 4.00
5a variant cover ....... 20.00
6 (of 6) JLi ............... 3.50
6a variant cover ....... 15.00
TPB Lucifer's Halo .... 20.00
TPB Tears of Dawn .... 18.00
```

DAZEY'S DIARY
Dell Publishing Co.
June-Aug., 1962
```
1 ............................ 30.00
```

DEAD BOYS:
DEATH'S EMBRACE
London Night 1996
```
1 EHr ....................... 3.00
1 platinum edition ...... 6.00
```

DEAD KING
Chaos! Comics 1997
```
1 (of 4) Burnt, pt.1, F:Homicide .. 2.95
2 Burnt, pt.2 ............. 2.95
3 Burnt, pt.3 ............. 2.95
4 Burnt, pt.4, concl. .. 2.95
```

DEAMON DREAMS
Pacific
```
1 ............................ 1.50
2 ............................ 1.50
```

DEAR NANCY PARKER
Gold Key 1963
```
1 P(c) ..................... 18.00
2 P(c) ..................... 15.00
```

DEATHDEALER
Verotika 1995
```
1 FF(c), I:Deathdealer .. 12.00
2 thru 4 FF(c) .......... @8.00
```

DEATH OF HARI KARI
Blackout Comics 1997
```
0 ............................ 2.95
0 super Sexy Kari Cover .. 9.95
0 3-D super Sexy Kari Cover .. 14.95
```

DEATHRACE 2020
Roger Corman Cosmic Comics
```
1 Pat Mills, Tony Skinner ..... 2.50
2 V:Spyda, Sawmill Jones ... 2.50
3 O:Frankenstein ............. 2.50
4 Deathrace cont. ............ 2.50
5 F:Death Racers, D:Alchoholic . 2.50
6 V:Indestructiman ........... 2.50
7 Smallville Mall ............. 2.50
```

DEATH OF LADY VAMPRE
Blackout Comics 1995
```
1 V:Baraclaw ............. 2.95
1 Commemorative Issue ...... 9.95
```

DEATH RATTLE
Kitchen Sink 1985–88
```
1 thru 7 ................. @2.00
8 I:Xenozoic Tales ...... 5.00
9 thru 18 ............... @2.00
```

DEFENDERS, THE
Dell Publishing Co.
Sept.-Nov., 1962
```
1 ............................ 45.00
2 ............................ 30.00
```

DEFIANT:
ORIGIN OF A UNIVERSE
Defiant
```
1 Giveaway ............... 1.50
```

DEITY
Hyperwerks Sept. 1997
```
0 ............................ 2.95
1 KIA ...................... 2.95
1a Director's Cut ........ 2.95
2 thru 6 KIA ............ @2.95
TPB rep. #1–#3 ......... 7.95
TPB rep. #4–#6 ......... 7.95
```

DELIVERER
Zion Comics
```
1 thru 3 ................. 1.95
4 F:Gabriel ............... 1.95
5 V:Division ............. 1.95
```

DEMONIC TOYS
Eternity
```
1 Based on 1992 movie ...... 2.50
2 thru 4 ................. 2.50
```

DEMONIQUE
London Night 1996
```
0 Manga ................... 3.00
0a nude cover variant ...... 10.00
0a nude cover variant, signed .. 8.00
1 EHr ....................... 3.00
1a nude cover ............ 6.00
1a nude cover, signed .. 8.00
2 (of 2) ................... 3.00
2a nude cover ............ 6.00
```

DEN
Fantagor
```
1 thru 10 RCo .......... @2.00
```

DEN SAGA
Tundra/Fantagor
```
1 RCo,O:Den begins ......... 4.95
```

DENNIS THE MENACE
Fawcett 1960-61
```
Fun Book #1 ............. 50.00
And his Pal Joey #1 ... 30.00
And his Dog Ruff #1 ... 30.00
Television Special #1 .. 40.00
Triple Feature #1 ...... 40.00
Television Special #2 .. 25.00
```

DENNIS THE MENACE
AND HIS FRIENDS
[VARIOUS SUBTITLES]
Fawcett 1969–1980
```
1 thru 10 rep. .......... @10.00
11 thru 20 rep. ......... @8.00
21 thru 46 rep. ......... @4.00
```

DENNIS THE MENACE
GIANTS
[VARIOUS SUBTITLES]
Fawcett 1955–69
```
N# Vacation Special ... 100.00
N# Christmas ............ 100.00
2 thru 10 ................ 75.00
11 thru 20 ............... 50.00
21 thru 30 ............... 25.00
31 thru 40 ............... 15.00
41 thru 75 ............... 10.00
```
Becomes:

DENNIS THE MENACE
BONUS MAGAZINE
[VARIOUS SUBTITLES]
Fawcett 1970–79
```
76 thru 100 ............. @4.00
101 thru 120 ............ @3.00
121 thru 185 ............ @2.00
186 thru 196 Big Bonus Series @2.00
```
Becomes:

DENNIS THE MENACE
Fawcett 1979–80
```
#16 Fun Fest ............ 2.00
#17 Fun Fest ............ 2.00
#10 Big Bonus Series ... 2.00
#11 Big Bonus Series ... 2.00
```

Dennis the Menace Fun Fest #17
© Fawcett Comics

COLOR PUB.

DEPUTY DAWG
Gold Key Aug., 1965
1 . . . . 100.00

DER VANDALE
Innervision 1998
1 (of 3) 2.50
2 (of 3) 2.50
3 (of 3) 2.50
3 variant cover 2.50

DESTROYER DUCK
Eclipse 1982–84
1 JK,AA,SA,I:Groo 12.00
2 JK,AA,Starling 1.50
3 thru 5 JK . . . . @1.50
6 thru 7 JK . . . . @2.00

DESTRUCTOR, THE
Atlas Feb.–Aug. 1975
1 thru 4 . . . . @12.00

DETECTIVES, INC.
Eclipse 1985
1 MR,rep.GraphicNovel 3.00
2 MR 2.25
[2nd Series]
1 GC,"A Terror of Dying Dreams" 2.50
2 GC 2.25
3 GC,"Cut to the Bone" 1.50

DETONATOR
Chaos! Comics 1994–95
1 I:Detonator 2.95
2 V:Messiah & Mindbender 2.75

DEVIL KIDS
STARRING HOT STUFF
Harvey Publications 1962–81
1 . . . . 80.00
2 . . . . 40.00
3 thru 10 . . . . @20.00
11 thru 20 . . . . @15.00
21 thru 30 . . . . @10.00
31 thru 40 . . . . @7.00
41 thru 50 68 pgs. . . . . @7.00
51 thru 55 62 pgs. . . . . @5.00
56 thru 70 . . . . @3.00
71 thru 100 . . . . @2.00
101 thru 106 . . . . @1.00
107 . . . . 1.00

DEVILMAN
Verotika 1995
1 Go Nagi 2.95
1a San Diego Con Gatefold edition 4.95
2 F:Devilman 2.95
3 Through History 2.95
4 French Revolution 2.95
5 Custer's Last Stand 2.95

DEVLIN
Maximum Press 1996
1 A:Avengelyne,3-part mini-series 2.50
2 (of 3) RLd,BNa,A:Avengelyne . 2.50

DICK TRACY
1 3-D 2.50

DICK TRACY:
BIG CITY BLUES
1 Mini Series 3.95
2 Mini Series 5.95
3 Mini Series 5.95

DINO ISLAND
Mirage
1 thru 2 . . . . 2.75

DINOSAUR REX
Upshot/Fantagraphics 1987
1 thru 3 by Jan Strand & Henry
Mayo . . . . @2.00

DINOSAURS
Walt Disney
1 Citizen Robbie(From TV) 2.95

DINOSAURS ATTACK
Eclipse
1 HT,Based on Topps cards 3.50
2 and 3 HT,Based on cards . . @3.50

DISNEY ADVENTURES
Walt Disney
1 . . . . 2.75
2 . . . . 2.50
3 thru 6 . . . . @2.25
7 Joe Montana 2.25
8 Bronson Pinchot 2.25
9 Hulk Hogan 2.25
10 Mayim Bialik 2.25
11 . . . . 2.25
12 Monsters 2.25
13 A:Darkwing Duck (inc. work by
DW) 2.25
14 inc. "Big Top, Big Shot" 1.95
15 . . . . 1.95
16 inc."Turnabout is Fowl Play" . 1.95
17 inc."Kitty Kat Kaper" 1.95
18 Kitty Kat Kaper 1.95
19 The Voice of Wisdom 1.95
20 thru 28 . . . . @1.95

DISNEY COLOSSAL
COMICS COLLECTION
Walt Disney
1 inc.DuckTales, Chip'n'Dale . . 2.25
2 inc.Tailspin,Duck Tales 1.95
3 inc.Duck Tales 1.95
4 O:Darkwing Duck 1.95
5 Tailspin,Duck Tales 1.95
6 Darkwing Duck,Goofy 1.95
7 inc.Darkwing Duck.Goofy 1.95
8 inc.Little Mermaid 1.95
9 inc.Duck Tales 1.95

DISNEY COMICS IN 3-D
Walt Disney
1 . . . . 2.95

DISNEY COMICS SPEC:
DONALD & SCROOGE
1 inc."Return to Xanadu" 8.95

DISNEYLAND BIRTHDAY
PARTY
Gladstone
1 . . . . 6.00

DIVER DAN
Dell Publishing Co.
Feb.-April, 1962
1 . . . . 45.00
2 . . . . 30.00

DIVINE MADNESS
Dark Moon
1 Human Flesh Artist 2.50
2 . . . . 2.50
3 Ancient Cult 2.50

DNAgents #20 © Eclipse Comics

DNAGENTS
Eclipse 1983–85
1 O:DNAgents 4.00
2 . . . . 3.00
3 . . . . 2.50
4 . . . . 2.50
5 . . . . 2.50
6 . . . . 2.50
7 . . . . 2.50
8 . . . . 2.50
9 DSp 2.50
10 . . . . 2.00
11 . . . . 2.00
12 . . . . 2.50
13 . . . . 2.00
14 . . . . 2.00
15 . . . . 2.50
16 . . . . 2.50
17 thru 21 . . . . @2.00
22 . . . . 1.75
23 . . . . 1.75
24 DSt(c) 1.75
25 . . . . 1.75
See also: NEW DNAGENTS

DO YOU BELIEVE
IN NIGHTMARES?
St. John Publishing Co. 1957–58
1 SD 250.00
2 DAy 160.00

DOBER-MAN
1 . . . . 2.50

DOC SAVAGE
Millenium
1 V:Russians 2.50

DOC SAVAGE,
THE MAN OF BRONZE
Millenium
1 Monarch of Armageddon,pt.1 . . 3.00
2 Monarch of Armageddon,pt.2 . . 2.75
3 Monarch of Armageddon,pt.3 . . 2.75
4 Monarch of Armageddon,pt.4 . . 2.75

DOC SAVAGE:
THE DEVIL'S THOUGHTS
Millenium
1 V:Hanoi Shan 2.50
2 V:Hanoi Shan 2.50
3 Final issue 2.50

DOC SAVAGE:
DOOM DYNASTY
Millenium
1 and 2 . . . . @2.50

DOC SAVAGE:
MANUAL OF BRONZE
Millenium
1 Fact File 2.50

DOC SAVAGE: REPEL
Innovation
1 DvD(c) 2.50

DOCTOR BOOGIE
Media Arts
1 and 2 . . . . @1.75

DOCTOR CHAOS
Triumphant Comics 1993
1 JnR(s),I:Doctor Chaos 2.50
2 JnR(s), ... 2.50
3 JnR(s),The Coming of the
  Cry,pt.1,I:Cry 2.50
4 JnR(s),The Coming of the
  Cry,pt.2,b:Ky'Li 2.50
5 JnR(s),E:Coming of the
  Cry,pt.3,V:Cry 2.50
6 Recovery 2.50
7 w/coupon 2.50
8 w/coupon 2.50
9 V:Mirth 2.50
10 Co. X #3 . . . . 2.50
11 Co. X #4 . . . . 2.50
12 A:Charlotte 2.50

DOCTOR SOLAR
MAN OF THE ATOM
Gold Key
1 BF,I:Dr. Solar 300.00
2 BF,I:Prof.Harbinger 110.00
3 BF,The Hidden Hands 75.00
4 BF,The Deadly Sea 75.00
5 BF,I:Dr.Solar in costume 75.00
6 FBe,I:Nuro 50.00
7 FBe,Vanishing Oceans 50.00
8 FBe,Thought Controller 50.00
9 FBe,Transivac The Energy
  Consuming Computer 50.00
10 FBe,The Sun Giant 50.00
11 FBe,V:Nuro 35.00

12 FBe,The Mystery of the
  Vanishing Silver 35.00
13 FBe,The Meteor from 100 Million
  BC 35.00
14 FBe,Solar's Midas Touch . . . 35.00
15 FBe O:Dr.Solar 45.00
16 FBe,V:Nuro 35.00
17 FBe,The Fatal Foe 35.00
18 FBe,The Mind Master 35.00
19 FBe,SolarV:Solar 35.00
20 AMc,Atomic Nightmares 35.00
21 AMc,Challenge from Outer
  Space 25.00
22 AMc,Nuro,I:King Cybernoid . . 25.00
23 AMc,A:King Cybernoid 25.00
24 EC,The Deadly Trio 25.00
25 EC,The Lost Dimension 25.00
26 EC,When Dimensions Collide 25.00
27 (1969) The Ladder to Mars . 25.00
28 (1981),1 pg AMc,The Dome of
  Mystery 12.00
29 DSp,FBe,Magnus 12.00
30 DSp,FBe,Magnus 12.00

DOGHEAD
Tundra
1 Al Columbia,"Poster Child" . . 4.95

DOGS OF WAR
Defiant
1 F:Shooter,Ironhead 2.75
2 . . . . 2.50
3 Mouse Deserts 2.50
4 Schism Prequel 2.50
5 X-over 2.50
6 Aftermath 2.50

DOLLMAN
Eternity
1 Movie adapt. sequel 2.50
2 V:Sprug & Braindead Gang . . . 2.50
3 Toni Costa Kidnapped 2.50
4 . . . . 2.50

DONALD DUCK
Dell/Gold Key Dec. 1962
85 thru 97 . . . . 35.00

Donald Duck #203 © Gold Key

98 rep. #46 CB 35.00
99 . . . . 25.00
100 . . . . 22.00
101 . . . . 20.00
102 A:Super Goog 20.00
103 thru 111 . . . . @20.00
112 I:Moby Duck 20.00
113 thru 133 . . . . @20.00
134 CB rep. 20.00
135 CB rep. 20.00
136 thru 156 . . . . @18.00
157 CB rep. 15.00
158 thru 163 . . . . @12.00
164 CB rep. 12.00
165 thru 216 . . . . @5.00

Whitman
217 . . . . 5.00
218 . . . . 5.00
219 CB rep. 5.00
220 thru 245 . . . . @5.00

Gladstone
246 CB,Gilded Man 15.00
247 CB 10.00
248 CB,Forbidden Valley 10.00
249 CB 10.00
250 CB,Pirate Gold 15.00
251 CB,Donald's Best Xmas 4.00
252 CB,Trail o/t Unicorn 4.00
253 CB 3.50
254 CB, in old Calif 7.00
255 CB 3.50
256 CB,Volcano Valley 3.50
257 CB,Forest Fire 4.00
258 thru 260 CB . . . . @3.00
261 thru 266 CB . . . . @2.50
267 thru 277 CB . . . . @2.00
278 CB 4.00
279 CB 4.00
280 thru 298 CB rep. . . . . @1.50
299 "Life Guard Daze" 1.50
300 "Donald's 300th Triumph" 48pg 2.25
301 "The Gold Finder" 1.95
302 "Monkey Business" 1.95
303 "The Cantankerous Cat" 1.95
304 "Donald Duck Rants about
  Ants" 1.95
305 "Mockingbird Ridge" 1.95
306 "Worst Class Mail" 1.95
307 "Going to Sea" 1.95
308 "Worst Class Mail" 1.95

DONALD DUCK
ADVENTURES
Gladstone
1 CB,Jungle Hi-Jinks 5.00
2 CB,Dangerous Disquise 4.00
3 CB,Lost in the Andes 5.00
4 CB,Frozen Gold 4.00
5 Rosa Art 3.50
6 . . . . 2.50
7 . . . . 2.50
8 Rosa 3.50
9 . . . . 2.50
10 . . . . 2.50
11 . . . . 2.50
12 Giant size,Rosa 3.50
13 Rosa(c) 2.50
14 . . . . 3.00
15 CB 2.00
16 . . . . 2.00
17 . . . . 2.00
18 . . . . 2.00
19 . . . . 4.00
20 Giant size 4.00

COLOR PUB.

21 thru 30 . . . . @2.95
31 thru 40 . . . . @1.50
41 "Bruce McDuck" 1.50
42 "The Saga of Sourdough Sam" 1.50
43 "The Lost Charts of Columbus" 1.50
44 "The Kitchy-Kaw Diamond" . . . 1.95
45 "The Red Duck" 1.95
46 . . . . 1.95
47 "Trick or Treat" 1.95
48 "The Saphead Factor" 1.95

DONALD DUCK ADVENTURES
Walt Disney 1990

1 Don Rosa, "The Money Pit" . . 5.00
2 . . . . 3.00
3 . . . . 2.50
4 . . . . 2.50
5 . . . . 2.50
6 . . . . 2.50
7 . . . . 2.00
8 . . . . 2.00
9 . . . . 2.00
10 "Run-Down Runner" 2.00
11 "Whats for Lunch-Supper" . . . 2.00
12 "Head of Rama Putra" 2.00
13 "JustAHumble,BumblingDuck" . 2.00
14 "DayGladstonesLuckRanOut" . 1.75
15 "A Tuft Luck Tale" 1.75
16 "Magica's Missin'Magic" 1.75
17 "Secret of Atlantis" 1.75
18 "Crocodile Donald" 1.75
19 "Not So Silent Service" 1.75
20 "Ghost of Kamikaze Ridge" . . . 1.50
21 "The Golden Christmas Tree" . 1.50
22 "The Master Landscapist" . . . 1.50
23 "The Lost Peg Leg Mine" 1.50
24 "On Stolen Time" 1.50
25 Sense of Humor 1.50
26 Race to the South Seas 1.50
27 Nap in Nature 1.50
28 Olympic Tryout 1.50
29 rep.March of Comics#20 . . . . 1.50
30 A:The Vikings 1.50
31 The Sobbing Serpent of Loch
   McDuck 1.50
32 It Was No Occident 1.50
33 Crazy Christmas on Bear
   Mountain 1.50
34 Sup.Snooper Strikes Again . . . 1.50
35 CB rep. 1.50
36 CB rep. 1.50
37 CB rep. 1.50

DONALD DUCK ALBUM
Dell Publishing Co.
May-July, 1959

1 CB(c) 50.00
2 . . . . 30.00

DONATELLO
Mirage

1 . . . . 10.00

DONNA MIA
Dark Fantasy Prod. 1995

1 I:Donna Mia 4.00
1a Deluxe Edition 5.00
1 signed & numbered (100 copies)8.95
2 . . . . 3.00

DOOMSDAY + 1
Charlton July, 1975

1 JBy,JBy(c),P(c) 15.00
2 . . . . 10.00
3 JBy,JBy(c),P(c) 7.00
4 JBy,JBy(c),P(c),I:Lok 7.00
5 and 6 JBy,JBy(c),P(c) . . . . . @7.00
7 thru 12 JBy,JBy(c),P(c),rep . . 3.00

Doomsday Squad #7 Fantagraphics

DOOMSDAY SQUAD
Fantagraphics

1 rep. JBy 2.00
2 rep. JBy 2.00
3 rep. SS,A:Usagi Yojimbo 4.00
4 thru 7, rep. JBy . . . . @2.00

DOUBLE DARE ADVENTURES
Harvey Publications

1 I:B-man,Glowing Gladiator,
  Magicmaster 22.00
2 AW/RC rep. A:B-Man,Glowing
  Gladiator, Magicmaster 17.00

DOUBLE IMPACT
High Impact Studios 1995–96

1 RCI,I:China & Jazz, chrome(c) . 7.00
1 holographic rainbow (c) with
  certificate 15.00
1 rainbow (c), no certificate . . . 10.00
1 chromium variant (c) 8.00
2 RCI,V:Castillo 3.00
2a signed, with certificate 4.00
2b nude cover 8.00
2c China Exposed edition 8.00
2d signed by China 10.00
3 China on cover 5.00
3a Jazzler on cover 3.00
3b Nikki on cover 3.00
3c "Blondage" 6.00
4 F:Mordred, The Rattler 2.95
4a "Phoenix" variant (c) 6.00
5 RCI 3.00
5a nude cover 6.00
6 "Buttshots" 4.00
6a Jazz (c) 3.00
6a signed 6.00

7 I:Nikki Blade 3.00
8 . . . . 3.00
8a variant (c) 4.00
Gold edition, Lingerie special . . 3.00
Volume 2 1996–97
0 RCI 3.00
0a nude cover 8.00
1 RCI 3.00
1a deluxe edition 4.00
1b prism foil (c) 5.00
1cgold foil (c) 5.00
2 RCI 3.00
2a Swedish Erotica cover 5.00
2b Swedish Erotica cover, signed 12.00
3 . . . . 2.95
3a special edition RCI(c) 8.00
3b Photo nude cover 12.00

DOUBLE IMPACT/ HELLINA
High Impact 1996

1-shot RCI 3.00
1a nude cover 9.95
1b Gold edition, nude cover 9.95
1c Spec. nude cover, signed . . 14.95

DOUBLE IMPACT/ LETHAL STRYKE: DOUBLE STRIKE
High Impact/London Night 1996

1-shot RCI 3.00
1a nude cover 9.95

DOUBLE IMPACT SUICIDE RUN
High Impact

1 RCI 3.00
1 gold edition 10.00
1 platinum edition 20.00
2 . . . . 3.00
2a Suicide Cover 10.00
2b Photo Nude cover 14.95

DOUBLE LIFE OF PRIVATE STRONG
Archie Publications

1 JSm/JK,I:Lancelot Strong/Shield
  The Fly 450.00
2 JSm/JK,GT A:Fly 300.00

DR. KILDARE
Dell Publishing Co.
April-June, 1962

1 . . . . 50.00
2 . . . . 40.00
3 . . . . 40.00
4 . . . . 40.00
5 . . . . 40.00
6 . . . . 40.00
7 . . . . 40.00
8 . . . . 40.00
9 . . . . 40.00

DRACULA
Dell Publishing Co. Nov., 1966

2 O:Dracula 25.00
3 . . . . 15.00
4 . . . . 15.00
6 . . . . 12.00
7 . . . . 10.00
8 . . . . 10.00

DRACULA
Topps
1 MMi,Movie adaptation (trading
   cards in each issue) 5.00
1a Red Foil Logo 12.00
1b 2nd Print 2.95
2 MMi,Movie adapt.contd. 4.00
3 MMi,Movie adapt.contd. 4.00
4 MMi,Movie adapt.concludes . . . 4.00
TPB Collected Album 13.95

DRACULA CHRONICLES
Topps
1 True Story of Dracula 2.50
2 RTs,rep. Vlad #2 . . . . 2.50
3 RTs,rep. Vlad #3 . . . . 2.50

DRACULA VS. ZORRO
Topps
1 DMg(s),TY,Black(c), ... 3.25
2 DMg(s),TY,w/Zorro #0 . . . . . . 2.95
TPB 5.95

DRACULA: VLAD THE IMPALER
Topps
1 EM,I:Vlad Dracua, w/cards . . . 3.25
1a Red Foil 10.00
2 EM, w/cards 3.25

DRAGONCHIANG
Eclipse
1 TT 2.95

DRAGONFLIGHT
Eclipse 1991
1 Anne McCaffrey adapt. 4.95
2 novel adapt 4.95
3 novel adapt 4.95

DRAGONFLY
AC Comics
1 . . . . 3.50
2 and 3 . . . . @2.00
4 thru 8 . . . . @1.75

DRAGONFORCE
Aircel
1 DK 7.50
2 thru 7 DK . . . . @5.00
8 thru 12 . . . . @5.00
13 . . . . 2.00

DRAGONRING
Aircel 1987–88
Vol. 2
1 . . . . 3.50
2 O:Dragonring 2.50
3 thru 15 . . . . @2.00
See also: B&W

DRAKKON WARS, THE
Realm Press
0 by Richard Hatch & Chris Scalf 3.00
1 . . . . 3.00

DREADSTAR
First
27 JSn,from Epic,traitor 2.50
28 JSn 2.25

Dreadstar #64 © First

29 JSn,V:Lord Papal 2.25
30 JSn,D:Lord Papal 2.25
31 JSn,I:The Power 2.25
32 JSn 2.25
33 . . . . 2.25
34 LM/VM,A:Malchek 2.25
35 LM/VM 2.25
36 LM/VM 2.25
37 LM/VM,A:Last Laugh 2.25
38 LM/VM 2.25
39 AMc,Crossroads tie-in 2.25
40 LM/VM 2.25
41 AMe 2.25
42 JSn,AMe,B.U.Pawns begins . 2.25
43 JSn,AMe,Pawns,pt.2 . . . . . . 2.25
44 JSn,AMe,Pawns,pt.3 . . . . . . 2.25
45 JSn,AMe,Pawns,pt.4 . . . . . . 2.25
46 JSn,AMe,Pawns,pt.5 . . . . . . 2.25
47 JSn,AMe,Pawns,pt.6 . . . . . . 2.25
48 JSn,AMe,Pawns,pt.7 . . . . . . 2.25
49 JSn,AMe,Pawns,pt.8 . . . . . . 2.25
50 JSn,AMe,Pawns,pt.9 prestige
   format 4.25
51 PDd,Woj,Pawns,pt.10, Paladox
   epic begins 2.25
52 AMe 2.25
53 AMe,"Messing with Peoples
   Minds" 2.25
54 JSn,AMe,Pawns ends 2.25
55 AMe,I:Iron Angel 2.25
56 AME,A:Iron Angel 2.25
57 A:Iron Angel 2.25
58 A:Iron Angel 2.25
59 A:Iron Angel 2.25
60 AMe,Paladox epic ends 2.25
61 AME,A:Iron Angel 2.25
62 O:Dreadstar,I:Youngscuz . . . 2.25
63 AMe,A:Youngscuz 2.25
64 AMe,A:Youngscuz 2.25

DREDD RULES
Fleetway/Quality
1 SBs(c),JBy,Prev.unpubl. in USA 5.00
2 inc."Eldster Ninja Mud Wrestling
   Vigilantes" 3.50
3 inc."That Sweet Stuff" 3.50
4 Our Man in Hondo City 3.50
5 . . . . 3.25
6 BKi,DBw 3.25

7 "Banana City" 3.25
8 "Over the Top" 3.25
9 "Shooting Match" 3.25
10 SBs,inc.Mega-City primer . . . 3.25
11 SBs,Legend/Johnny Biker . . . 3.25
12 SBs,Rock on Tommy Who . . . 3.25
13 BMy,The Ballad of Toad
   McFarlane 3.25
14 thru 15 . . . . @3.25
16 A:Russians 3.25
17 F:Young Giant 3.25
18 F:Jonny Cool 2.95
19 V:Hunter's Club 2.95

DRIFT MARLO
Dell Publishing Co.
May-July, 1962
1 . . . . 25.00
2 . . . . 20.00

DRUG WARS
Pioneer
1 . . . . 1.95
2 . . . . 1.95
3 . . . . 1.95

DRUNKEN FIST
Jademan
1 . . . . 3.25
2 . . . . 2.50
3 . . . . 2.00
4 . . . . 1.75
5 . . . . 1.75
6 thru 9 . . . . @1.75
10 thru 27 . . . . @1.95
28 D:Mack 1.95
29 . . . . 1.95
30 . . . . 1.95
31 . . . . 1.95
32 Wong Mo-Gei vs.Swordsman . 1.95
33 Mo-Gei commits suicide 1.95
34 . . . . 1.95
35 . . . . 1.95
36 D:Fire Oak 1.95
37 Iron Law Kills Elephant-Man . 1.95
38 A:Wayne Chan 1.95
39 D:Wayne Chan 1.95
40 D:Toro Yamamoto 1.95
41 Lord Algol vs. Ghing Mob . . . 1.95
42 . . . . 1.95
43 D:Yamamoto,Swordsman in USA .95
44 "Cool Hand Wong" 1.95
45 "Black Cult Rising" 1.95
46 . . . . 1.95
47 . . . . 1.95
48 Evil Child 1.95
49 I:Hurricane Child 1.95
50 Lord Algol vs.Diabol.Ent. . . . 1.95
51 F:Flying Thunder 1.95
52 Madcap vs.Yama 1.95
53 Swordsman vs.Catman 1.95

DUCKMAN
Topps
1 USA Cartoon 2.50
2 XXX Files 2.50
3 I:King Chicken 2.50
4 V:Toys 2.50
5 F:Cornfed 2.50
6 Star Trek Parody 2.50
7 rep. 1990 B&W 1st app., now in
   color 2.50

DUCKMAN: THE MOB FROG SAGA
Topps
1 I:Mob Frog 2.50
2 D:Mob Frog 2.50
3 In the Name of the Duck 2.50

DUCK TALES
Gladstone
1 CB(r)I:LaunchpadMcQuck 6.00
2 CB(r) 4.00
3 .... 4.00
4 CB(r) 4.00
5 thru 11 .... @4.00
12 .... 5.00
13 .... 5.00

DUCK TALES
Walt Disney
1 .... 4.00
2 .... 2.50
3 .... 2.25
4 .... 2.25
5 Scrooges'Quest 2.25
6 Scrooges'Quest 2.00
7 Return to Duckburg 2.00
8 .... 2.00
9 7 Sojourns of Scrooge 2.00
10 Moon of Gold 2.00
11 Once & Future Warlock 2.00
12 Lost Beyond the MilkyWay ... 2.00
13 The Doomed of Sarras 2.00
14 Planet Blues 2.00
15 The Odyssey Ends 2.00
16 The Great Chase 2.00
17 Duck in Time Pt.1 .... 2.00
18 Duck in Time Pt.2 .... 2.00
19 Bail Out 2.00

DUDLEY DO-RIGHT
Charlton Comics 1970–71
1 .... 45.00
2 thru 7 .... @30.00

DUNC & LOO
Dell Publishing Co.
Oct.–Dec., 1961
1 .... 65.00
2 .... 50.00
3 thru 8 .... @30.00

DWIGHT D. EISENHOWER
Dell Publishing Co. Dec., 1969
1 .... 30.00

DYNAMO
Tower Comics Aug., 1966
1 WW,MSy,RC,SD,I:Andor ... 40.00
2 WW,DA,GT,MSy,Weed solo story
A:Iron Maiden 30.00
3 WW,GT,Weed solo story, A:Iron
Maiden 30.00
4 WW,DA,A:Iron Maiden, June,
1967 .... 30.00

DYNAMO JOE
First 1986–87
1 .... 3.00
2 .... 2.00
3 thru 14 .... @1.50
Spec.#1 .... 1.25

EARLY DAYS OF SOUTHERN KNIGHTS
Vol. 2 Graphic Novel 5.00

EARTH 4
Continuity
[1st Series, Deathwatch 2000]
1 Deathwatch 2000 Pt.6,w/card . 2.50
2 Deathwatch 2000 Pt.11,w/card . 2.50
3 V:Hellbenders, w/card 2.50
[2nd Series]
1 WMc, ... 2.50
2 .... 2.50
3 .... 2.50

EAST MEETS WEST
Innovation
1 .... 2.50
2 .... 2.50
3 .... 2.50

EBONY WARRIOR
Africa Rising
1 I:Ebony Warrior 1.95

ECHO OF FUTUREPAST
Continuity
1 NA,MGo,I:Bucky O'Hare,
Frankenstein 4.00
2 NA,MGo,A:Bucky O'Hare,
Dracula, Werewolf 3.50
3 NA,MGo,A:Bucky 3.50
4 NA,MGo,A:Bucky 3.50
5 NA,MGo,A:Drawla&Bucky ... 3.50
6 Ath,B:Torpedo 3.50
7 Ath 3.50
8 Ath, ... 3.25
9 Ath,Last issue 3.25

ECLIPSE GRAPHIC NOVELS
Eclipse
1 Axa 7.00
2 MR,I Am Coyote 7.00
3 DSt,Rocketeer 10.00
3a hard cover 40.00
4 Silver Heels 9.00
4a hard cover 40.00
5 Sisterhood of Steel 10.00
6 Zorro in Old Calif. 8.00

ECLIPSE MONTHLY
Eclipse
1 SD,DW,I:Static&Rio 2.00
2 GC,DW 2.00
3 thru 8 DW .... @1.50
9 DW 1.75
10 DW 1.75

EDGE OF CHAOS
Pacific
1 GM 2.00
2 GM 2.00
3 GM 2.00

87th PRECINCT
Dell Publishing Co.
April–June, 1962
1 BK 75.00
2 .... 60.00

Elementals #13 © Comico

ELEMENTALS
Comico 1984–88
1 BWg,I:Destroyers 5.00
2 BWg 3.00
3 BWg 3.00
4 BWg 2.50
5 BWg 2.50
6 BWg 2.00
7 BWg 2.00
8 BWg 2.00
9 BWg 2.00
10 BWg 2.00
11 BWg 1.50
12 BWg 1.50
13 thru 22 .... @1.50
23 thru 29 .... @1.75
Spec.#1 .... 1.75
Spec.#2 .... 1.95
[Second Series] 1989–94
1 .... 2.25
2 thru 4 .... @1.95
5 thru 28 .... @2.50
Spec.#1 Lingerie special 2.95
GN The Natural Order, rep. 9.95
GN Death & Resurrection 12.95
[Third Series] 1995
1 R:Elementals, polybagged with
Chrysalis promo card 2.50
2 R:Original Monolith, polybagged
with Chrysalis promo card 2.50
3A Destroy the Shadowspear ... 2.50
3B variant cover 2.50
4 Memoirs,pt.1 .... 2.95
5 Memoirs,pt.2 .... 2.95
GN Ghost of a Chance 5.95
Spec. "Babes," photo multimedia
bikini special 3.95
Spec. Hot Bikini Valentine 3.95
Spec. All New Summer Special .. 4.95
Spec.#1 Lingerie Metalite 3.95

ELEMENTALS: HOW THE WAR WAS ONE
Comico 1996
1 thru 4 .... @2.95

ELEMENTALS: THE VAMPIRE'S REVENGE
Comico 1996–97
1 thru 4 . . . . @2.95

ELEMENTALS VS. THE CHARNEL PRIESTS
Comico 1996
Spec. 1 (of 2) 2.95
2 . . . . 2.95

ELEVEN OR ONE
Sirius 1995
1 JLi 5.00

ELFLORD
Aircel 1986–88
Volume 1: *See B&W*
Volume II
1 . . . . 3.50
2 . . . . 2.50
3 thru 20 . . . . @2.00
21 double size 4.95
22 thru 24 . . . . @2.00
Spec.#1 . . . . 2.00
25 thru 32, see B&W

ELFQUEST
Warp Graphics 1998
TPB 20th Anniv. Special 8.95
HC Bedtime Stories,RPi, 128pg. 19.95
TPB Scores, WPi, best of Elfquest
stories 19.95

ELFQUEST: BLOOD OF TEN CHIEFS
Warp Graphics 1993–95
1 WP 2.50
2 WP 2.25
3 WP,B:Swift Spear pt. 1 . . . . . . 2.25
4 WP,B:Swift Spear pt. 2 . . . . . . 2.25
5 V:Dinosaurs 2.25
6 Snowbeast 2.25
7 . . . . 2.25
8 Spirit Quest 2.25
9 Shadow Shifter 2.25
10 Spheres pt. 1 . . . . 2.25
11 Spheres pt. 2 . . . . 2.25
12 . . . . 2.25
13 Forest 2.25
14 F:Mantricker 2.25
15 F:Bearclaw 2.25
16 Scar Vs. Bearclaw 2.50
17 F:Eldolil,"Howl for Eldolil" . . . 2.50
18 F:Finder 2.50
19 F:Cutter & Skywise 2.50
20 final issue 2.50

ELFQUEST: HIDDEN YEARS
Warp Graphics
1 WP 3.00
2 WP, w/coupon promo. 2.75
3 WP, w/coupon promo.Cont.sty.
previewed in Harbinger#11 . . . 3.25
4 WP,w/coupon 2.50
5 WP,O:Skywise 2.50
6 WP,F:Timmain 2.50
7 F:Timmain 2.50
8 Daughter's Day 2.50
9 WP(s),Enemy Face 2.50

Elfquest: Hidden Years #9½
© *Warp Graphics*

9 1/2 WP,JBy,Holiday Spec. . . . 3.50
10 thru 14 WP . . . . @2.50
15 WP Wolfrider Tribe Splits 3.50
16 thru 18 WP 2.25
19 Mousehunt 2.25
20 F:Recognition 2.25
21 F:Teir, Messenger 2.50
22 F:Embu, Making a Point 2.50
23 Not Wolf And Teir 2.50
24 Magic Menace 2.50
25 B&W Wolfrider's Death 2.25
26 thru 29 B&W finale . . . . @2.25

ELFQUEST: JINK
Warp Graphics 1994–96
1 Future 3.00
2 Future 2.25
3 Neverending Story 2.25
4 Neverending Story 2.25
5 V:True Sons, Hide and Seek . . 2.50
6 V:Truth Holder, Should Auld
Acquaintance 2.50
7 F:Black Snakes 2.50
8 B&W V:Black Snakes 2.25
9 thru 12 . . . . 2.50

ELFQUEST: NEW BLOOD
Warp Graphics 1992–96
1 JBy,artists try Elfquest 5.00
2 Barry Blair story 3.50
3 thru 5 . . . . @2.50
6 thru 24 . . . . @2.25
25 Forevergreen pt. 13 . . . . 2.25
26 V:Humans 2.25
27 V:Door 2.25
28 I:Windkin, Triompe and Defeat 2.50
29 F:Windkin 2.50
30 V:Door 2.50
31 F:The Wanderer 2.50
32 B&W Sorrow's End 2.25
33 thru 35 B&W 2.25
Summer Spec.1993 . . . . 4.25

ELFQUEST: THE REBELS
Warp Graphics 1994–96
1 Aliens, set several hundred years
in future 2.75
2 Escape 2.50
3 He That Goes 2.25
4 Reasons 2.25
5 V:Skyward 2.50
6 F:Shimmer, The Edge 2.50
7 . . . . 2.50
8 Squatters & Defenders 2.50
9 B&W Brother vs. Brother 2.25
10 thru 12 . . . . @2.50

ELFQUEST: SHARDS
Warp Graphics 1994–96
1 Division 2.25
2 thru 5 . . . . @2.25
6 F:Two-Edge 2.25
7 F:Shuma 2.25
8 WP,Turnabout,pt.1 . . . . 2.25
9 WP,Turnabout,pt.2,V:Djun . . . 2.50
10 Revelations,pt.1 . . . . 2.50
11 V:Humans 2.50
12 B&W F:High One Timmain . . 2.25
13 thru 16 B&W finale . . . . @2.25

ELFQUEST: WAVE DANCERS
Warp Graphics 1993–96
1 Foil enhanced 3.25
2 thru 6 . . . . @2.25
Spec. #1 . . . . 3.00

ELIMINATOR COLOR SPECIAL
Eternity 1991
1 DDo(c) set in the future 2.95

ELRIC
Pacific 1983–84
1 CR 4.00
2 CR 3.00
3 thru 6 CR . . . . @2.50

ELRIC
Topps April 1996
0 NGa,CPR, "One Life," based on
Michael Moorcock character . . 2.95

ELRIC, BANE OF THE BLACK SWORD
First 1988–89
1 Michael Moorcock adapt. 1.75
2 . . . . 1.75
3 thru 5 . . . . @1.95

ELRIC, SAILOR ON THE SEAS OF FATE
First 1985–86
1 Michael Moorcock adapt. 4.00
2 . . . . 3.00
3 thru 7 . . . . @2.00

ELRIC–VANISHING TOWER
First 1987–88
1 Michael Moorcock adapt. 2.50
2 thru 6 . . . . @2.00

All comics prices listed are for *Near Mint* condition.

ELRIC, WEIRD OF THE WHITE WOLF
First 1986–87
1 Michael Moorcock adapt. 3.00
2 thru 5 . . . . @2.00
Graphic Novel CR 7.00

E-MAN
Charlton Comics 1973–75
1 JSon,O:E-Man 20.00
2 SD 8.00
3 . . . . 8.00
4 SD 8.00
5 SD,Miss Liberty Belle 6.00
6 JBy,Rog 2000 . . . . 8.00
7 JBy,Rog 2000 . . . . 8.00
8 J:Nova 10.00
9 JBy,Rog 2000 . . . . 8.00
10 JBy,Rog 2000 . . . . 8.00

E-MAN
First
1 JSon,O:E-Man & Nova, A:Rog
  2000, 1 pg. JBy 1.75
2 JSon,I:F-Men (X-Men satire) 1
  page Mike Mist 1.25
3 JSon, V:F-Men 1.25
4 JSon,Michael Mauser solo 1.25
5 JSon,I:Psychobabbler,A:Omaha,
  The Cat Dancer 1.25
6 JSon,O:E-Man,V:Feeder 1.25
7 JSon,V:Feeder 1.25
8 JSon,V:HotWax,A:CuteyBunny . 1.25
9 JSon,I:Tyger Lili 1.25
10 JSon,O:Nova Kane pt.1 . . . . . 1.25
11 JSon,O:Nova Kane pt.2 . . . . . 1.25
12 JSon,A:Tyger Lili 1.25
13 JSon,V:Warp'sPrinceChaos . . . 1.25
14 JSon,V:Randarr 1.25
15 JSon,V:Samuel Boar 1.25
16 JSon,V:Samuel Boar 1.25
17 JSon,"Smeltquest" satire 1.25
18 JSon,"Rosemary..& Time" 1.25
19 JSon, "Hoodoo Blues" 1.25
20 JSon,A:Donald Duke 1.25
21 JSon,A:B-Team,(satire) 1.25
22 JSon,A:Teddy Q 1.25
23 JSon,A:TygerLili,B-Team 1.25
24 JSon,O:Michael Mauser 1.25
25 JSon,last issue 1.25
Spec. #1 . . . . 2.75

E-MAN
Comico 1990
1 JSon 2.75
2 and 3 JSon . . . . @2.50

E-MAN
Alpha Productions 1993
1 JSon 2.75

EMERGENCY
Charlton Comics 1976
1 JSon(c),JBy 18.00
2 JSon 12.00
3 Thru 4 . . . . 10.00

ENCHANTED: THE AWAKENING
Sirius 1998
1 by Robert Chang 2.95

ENGIN
Samson Comics
1 I:The Mesh 2.50

ENSIGN O'TOOLE
Dell Publishing Co.
Aug.-Oct., 1962
1 . . . . 30.00
2 . . . . 20.00

EPSILON WAVE
Independent
1 . . . . 3.00
2 . . . . 2.50
3 . . . . 2.25
4 . . . . 2.00
Elite Comics
5 thru 10 . . . . @2.00

ESC.<ESCAPE>
Comico 1996
1 SPr 2.95
2 SPr 2.95
3 SPr 2.95
4 SPr 2.95
TPB SPr Rep. #1–#4 . . . . 14.95

ESC: NO EXIT
Comico 1997
1 . . . . 2.95
1 medallion edition 9.95
2 . . . . 2.95

ESPERS
Eclipse
1 I:ESPers 2.00
2 JBo(c),V:Terrorists 1.50
3 V:Terrorists 1.50
4 Beirut 1.75
5 "The Liquidators" 1.75
6 V:Benito Giovanetti 1.75

ESPIONAGE
Dell Publishing Co.
May-July, 1964
1 . . . . 25.00
2 . . . . 20.00

ETERNITY SMITH
Hero
1 . . . . 1.50
2 . . . . 1.50
3 . . . . 1.50
4 Knightshade solo 1.50
5 Knightshade solo 1.50
6 . . . . 1.50
7 . . . . 1.95
8 I:Indigo 1.95
9 A:Walter Koenig 1.95
10 . . . . 1.95
Heroic Publishing
1 Man Vs. Machine 1.95
2 Man Vs. Machine 1.95

EVA THE IMP
Red Top Comic/Decker 1957
1 . . . . 20.00
2 . . . . 15.00

EVANGELINE
Comico 1984
1 Guns of Mars 4.00
2 . . . . 3.00
Lodestone
1 . . . . 2.50
2 . . . . 2.50

Evangeline #10 © First Comics
First
1 . . . . 3.00
2 thru 9 . . . . @1.75
10 . . . . 1.95
11 . . . . 1.95
12 . . . . 1.95

EVERYTHING'S ARCHIE
Archie Publications May, 1969
1 . . . . 55.00
2 . . . . 25.00
3 thru 5 . . . . @15.00
6 thru 10 . . . . @10.00
11 thru 20 . . . . @5.00
21 thru 40 . . . . @3.00
41 thru 134 . . . . @3.00

EVIL ERNIE
Eternity 1991–92
See: B&W

EVIL ERNIE (THE SERIES)
Chaos! Comics 1998
1 V:Purgatori 2.95
2 Search for Chastity, A:Savior . . 2.95
3 V:Purgatori 2.95

EVIL ERNIE: DESTROYER
Chaos! Comics 1997
Prev.#1 . . . . 2.95
1 (of 9) BnP 2.95
2 BnP 2.95
3 to Atlanta 2.95
4 siege of Atlanta 2.95
5 . . . . 2.95
6 Nuclear launch codes 2.95
7 Nuclear attack 2.95
8 Nuclear attack continues 2.95
9 New forms of living dead, concl. 2.95

All comics prices listed are for *Near Mint* condition.

EVIL ERNIE: REVENGE
Chaos! Comics 1994–95
1 SHu,BnP,A:LadyDeath,glow(c)	10.00
1a limited, glow-in-the-dark (c)	25.00
1a Commemorative edition	20.00
2 SHu,BnP,Loses Smiley	8.00
3 SHu,BnP,V:Dr. Price	7.00
4 SHu,BnP,Final Issue	7.00
TPB Rep. #1-#4	12.95

EVIL ERNIE: STRAIGHT TO HELL
Chaos! Comics 1995–96
1 Rampage in Hell, coffin(c)	5.00
1 limited, chromium edition	25.00
2 Cremator	4.00
3	4.00
3a Chastity (c)	22.00
4 and 5	@4.00
Ashcan	1.50
Spec.	25.00

EVIL ERNIE: THE RESURRECTION
Chaos! Comics 1993–94
1 R:Evil Ernie	20.00
1a gold edition	50.00
2 Enhanced Cover	14.00
3 "Massive Mayhem" Lady Death poster	14.00
4 final issue, extra pages	14.00
TPB Rep. #1-#4	14.95

EVIL ERNIE VS. THE MOVIE MONSTERS
Chaos! Comics
1 one-shot	3.00
1 omega edition	5.00

EVIL ERNIE VS. THE SUPER-HEROES
Chaos! Comics 1995
1 one-shot	3.50
1a foil (c)	30.00
1b limited	20.00
Spec. #2 by Hart Fisher & Steve Butler	2.95

EVIL ERNIE'S BADDEST BATTLES
Chaos! Comics 1996
1-shot, imaginary battles	2.00

EXECUTIONER
Innovation 1993
1 Don Pendleton(s),F:Mack Bolan	3.95
1a Collector's Gold Ed.	2.95
1b Tyvek cover	3.95
2 War against Mafia	2.75
3 War against Mafia,pt.3	2.75

EXEMPLARS
1 and 2	@1.95

EXODUS, THE
Conquest Comics
1 V:Aliens	2.50

EXO-SQUAD
Topps 1994
[Mini-Series]
0	1.00
1 From Animated Series	2.50
2 F:Nara Burns	2.50
3 V:Neo-Sapiens	2.50

EXPLORERS
Explorer Press 1995
1 I:Explorers	2.95
2 The Cellar	2.95

EXTREME VIOLET
Blackout Comics
0 I:Violet	2.95
1 V:Drug Lords	2.95

Becomes:

EXTREMES OF VIOLET
2 A:Matt Chaney	2.95
Commemorative Issue, 5000c	9.95

EXTINCTIONERS
Vision Comics 1998
1 by Shawntae Howard & Malcolm Earle	3.95
2	3.95

EYE OF THE STORM
Rival Productions
1 I:Killian, Recon, Finesse, Stray	2.95
2 Conspiracy	2.95
3 3-D Comic Background	2.95
4 F:Recon	2.95
5 Sinclair & Rott	2.95

FALCON, THE
Aircel
Spec. #1	2.00

FAMILY AFFAIR
Gold Key Feb., 1970
1 W/Poster,Ph(c)	30.00
2	20.00
3 Ph(c)	20.00
4 Ph(c)	20.00

FAMILY MATTER
Kitchen Sink 1998
GN by Will Eisner	15.95

FAMOUS INDIAN TRIBES
Dell Publishing Co.
July-Sept., 1962
1	18.00
2	10.00

FANG
Sirius
1 V:Vampires, I:Fang	4.00
2	3.25
3 V:The Master	2.95

FANTASTIC VOYAGES OF SINBAD, THE
Gold Key Oct., 1965
1 Ph(c)	30.00
2 June, 1967	20.00

FANTASY FEATURES
AC
1	1.75
2	1.75

FASHION IN ACTION
Eclipse
Summer Special #1	1.75
Winter Special #1	2.00

FAT ALBERT
Gold Key 1974–79
1	15.00
2	10.00
3 thru 10	@10.00
11 thru 29	@8.00

FATALE
Broadway 1995
1 thru 6 JJo, "Inherit the Earth," pt.5	@2.95
7 Fatale now Queen of the World	2.95
8 "Crown of Thorns," pt.2	2.95
9 "Crown of Thorns," pt.3	2.95
TPB Inherit the Earth	14.95
HC Inherit the Earth	75.00

FATE'S FIVE
Innervision 1998
1 (of 4)	2.50
1 variant cover	2.50
2 (of 4)	2.50
3 (of 4)	2.50

Fathom #2 © Comico

FATHOM
Comico 1987
1 thru 3 From Elementals	@2.50

FATMAN, THE HUMAN FLYING SAUCER
Lightning Comics April, 1967
1 CCB,O:Fatman & Tin Man	45.00
2 CCB	30.00
3 CCB,(Scarce)	45.00

COLOR PUB.

FAZE ONE
AC Comics
1 .... 1.75

FAZE ONE FAZERS
AC Comics
1 .... 5.00
2 .... 3.00
3 .... 2.00
4 thru 6 .... @1.75

FEARBOOK
Eclipse
1 SBi,RV,"A Dead Ringer" 1.75

FELIX THE CAT
Harvey
1 thru 4 .... 1.25
5 thru 7 .... 1.50

FELIX THE CAT: THE MOVIE
Felix Comics 1998
1-shot, issued a mere 10 years after movie 3.95

FELIX'S NEPHEWS INKY & DINKY
Harvey Publications Sept., 1957
1 .... 45.00
2 thru 7 .... @20.00

FEM 5
Entity 1995
1 thru 4 five-part series ...... @2.95
1 signed & numbered 12.95

FEMFORCE
AC Comics
1 O:Femforce 5.00
2 A:Captain Paragon 3.50
3 "Skin Game" 3.00
4 "Skin Game" 3.00
5 Back in the Past 3.00
6 EL,Back in the Past 3.00
7 HB,O:Captain Paragon 3.00
8 V:Shade 3.00
9 V:Dr.Rivits 3.00
10 V:Dr.Rivits 3.00
11 D:Haunted Horsemen 3.00
12 V:Dr.Rivits 3.00
13 V:She-Cat 3.00
14 V:Alizarin Crimson 3.00
15 V:Alizarin Crimson 3.00
16 thru 56 See Black & White Pub.
57 V:Goat God 2.75
58 I:New Sentinels 2.75
59 I:Paragon 2.75
60 V:Sentinels 2.75
61 F:Tara 2.75
62 V:Valkyra 2.75
63 I:Rayda 2.75
64 thru 67 .... @2.75
68 "Spellbound" 2.75
69 "She-Cat Possessed" 2.75
70 "Island Out of Time" 2.75
71 .... 2.75
72 w/Sentinels of Justice 4.00
72a no extras 3.00
73 w/Compact Comic 4.00
73a Regular edition 3.00

74 Daughter of Darkness 4.00
74a Regular edition 3.00
75 Gorby Poster 5.00
75a Regular edition 3.00
76 Daughters pt. 3, polybagged with Compact Comic 4.00
76a no bag or comic 3.00
77 V:Sea Monster 3.00
78 V:Gorgana, bagged with comic 5.00
78a no bag or comic 3.00
79 V:Iron Jaw, polybagged with Index 5.00
79a no bag or index 3.00
80 polybagged with Index 6.00
80a F:Mr. Brimstone, Rad 3.00
81 polybagged with Index 6.00
81a Valentines Day Spec. 3.00
82 polybagged with Index 6.00
82a F:Ms. Victory 3.00
83 F:Paragon 3.00
84 The Death of Joan Wayne polybagged with index #4B . 6.00
84a no bag or index 3.00
85 Synn vs. Narett, polybagged with card 5.00
85a no bag or card 3.00
86 polybagged with index #5 .. 5.00
86a unbagged, no suplements ... 3.00
87 Pandemonium in Paradise, polybagged with plate 10.00
87a unbagged, no plate 3.00
88 F:Garganta, polybagged with index #6 .... 6.00
88a unbagged, no index 3.00
89 polybagged with index 6.00
89a unbagged, no index 3.00
90 polybagged with index 6.00
90a unbagged, no index 3.00
91 polybagged with index 6.00
91a unbagged, no index 3.00
92 polybagged with index 6.00
92a unbagged, no index 3.00
Spec.#1 .... 1.50
Untold Origin Spec #1 .... 4.95

FEMFORCE: UP CLOSE
AC Comics
1 F:Stardust 2.75
2 F:Stardust 2.75

Femforce: Up Close #6 © AC Comics

3 .... 2.75
4 .... 2.75
5 with Sticker 3.95
5a Regular Edition 2.95
6 with Sticker 3.95
6a Regular Edition 2.95
7 with Sticker 3.95
7a Regular Edition 2.95
8 with Sticker 3.95
8a Regular Edition 2.95
9 thru 11 .... @2.95

FENRY
Raven Publications
1 .... 6.95
1a Platinum Ed. 15.00

FIGHT THE ENEMY
Tower Comics Aug., 1966
1 BV,Lucky 7 .... 30.00
2 AMc 20.00
3 WW,AMc 20.00

FIGHTING AMERICAN
Harvey
1 SK,Rep Fighting American from 1950's 17.50

FIGHTING AMERICAN
Awesome Entertainment
1 .... 4.00
1a variant (c) 4.00
1b Platinum (c) 15.00
2 .... 3.00
Coll.Ed.#1 rep.#1–#2 .... 4.95

FIGHTING AMERICAN: COLD WAR
Awesome Entertainment 1998
1 RLe,JLb 2.50

FIGHTING AMERICAN: RULES OF THE GAME
Awesome Entertainment 1997
1 JLb 3.00
2 JLb 2.50
3 JLb, Baby Buzz Bomber 2.50

FIRST ADVENTURES
First
1 thru 5 .... @1.25

FIRST GRAPHIC NOVELS
First
1 JBi,Beowolf 8.00
1a 2nd Printing 7.00
2 TT,Time Beavers 6.00
3 HC,American Flag Hard Times 12.00
4 Nexus,SR 8.00
5 Elric,CR 15.00
6 Enchanted Apples of Oz 6.00
7 Secret Island of Oz 8.00
8 HC,Time 2 .... 28.00
9 TMNT 20.00
10 TMNT II 18.00
11 Sailor on the Sea 15.00
12 HC,American Flagg 12.00
13 Ice Ring 8.00
14 TMNT III 14.00
15 Hex Breaker 8.00

16 Forgotten Forest	9.00
17 Mazinger	9.00
18 TMNT IV	13.00
19 O;Nexus	8.00
20 American Flagg	12.00

1st FOLIO
Pacific
1 Joe Kubert School	1.50

FISH POLICE
Comico
Vol 2 #6 thru #15 rep.	@2.50
Vol 2 #16 rep.	3.00
Vol 2 #17 rep.,AuA	3.00
1 Color Special (July 1987)	3.50

FITCH IN TIME
1 and 2	@1.50

FLARE
Hero Graphics
1 I:Darkon&Prof.Pomegranite	4.00
2 Blonde Bombshell,A:Galooper	3.00
3 I:Sky Marshall	3.00
Ann.#1	4.50

[2nd Series]
1 A:Galloping Galooper	3.00
2 A:Lady Arcane	3.00
3 I:Britannia	3.00
4 A:Indigo	2.50
5 R:Eternity Smith,O:Die Kriegerin	3.95
6 I:Tigress	3.50
7 V:The Enemies	3.95
8 Morrigan Wars#4,A:Icicle Dragon	3.50
9 Morrigan Wars Pt.7 (B&W)	3.50

FLARE ADVENTURES
Hero Graphics
1 rep.	2.95
2 flipbook w/Champions Classics	2.95
3 flipbook w/Champions Classics	2.95
Becomes B&W	

FLASH GORDON
Gold Key June, 1965
1	15.00

FLASH GORDON
King 1966–69
1 AW,DH,A:Mandrake	35.00
1a Comp. Army giveaway	50.00
2 FBe,A:Mandrake,R:Ming	25.00
3 RE,"Lost in the Land of The Lizardmen"	30.00
4 AW,B:Secret Agent X-9	32.00
5 AW	32.00
6 RC,On the Lost Continent of Mongo	30.00
7 MR, rep. "In the Human Forest"	30.00
8 RC,JAp	30.00
9 AR,rep	35.00
10 AR,rep	35.00
11 RC	25.00

Charlton 1969–70
12 RC	25.00
13 JJ	20.00
14	20.00
15	20.00
16	20.00
17 Brick Bradford story	20.00
18 MK,"Attack of the Locust Men"	20.00

Flash Gordon #7 © King Comics
Gold Key Oct.-Nov 1975
19 Flash returns to Mongo	6.00
20 thru 30	@5.00
31 thru 37 AW movie adapt	@3.00

FLATLINE COMICS
Flatline Comics
1 Three stories River Prarie	2.50

FLAXEN: ALTER EGO
Caliber
1 V:Dark Flaxen	2.95

FLESH AND BONES
Fantagraphics
1 Moore	2.50
2 thru 4 Moore	@2.00

FLINTSTONES
Harvey
1	1.25
2 Romeo and Juliet	1.25

FLINTSTONES
Archie 1995
1 thru 10	@1.50
11 thru 14	@1.50
15 "Frankenstone's Monster"	1.50
20 "An Heir-Raising Tale"	1.50
21 "King Fred The Last"	1.50
22 "Something Gruesome This Way Comes"	1.50

FLINTSTONES, THE
Dell Publishing Co.
Nov.-Dec., 1961
#1 see Dell Giant	
2	100.00
3	75.00
4	75.00
5 and 6	@60.00

Gold Key
7	60.00
8 A:Mr.& Mrs J. Evil Scientists	50.00
9 A:Mr.& Mrs.J. Evil Scientists	50.00
10 A:Mr.& Mrs.J. Evil Scientists	50.00

11 I:Pebbles	60.00
12 "The Too-Old Cowhand"	40.00
13 thru 15	@40.00
16 I:Bamm-Bamm	50.00
17 thru 20	@40.00
21 thru 23	@25.00
24 I:Gruesomes	28.00
25 thru 29	@22.00
30 "Dude Ranch Roundup"	22.00
31 Christmas(c)	22.00
32	20.00
33 A:Dracula & Frankenstein	22.00
34 I:The Great Gazoo	30.00
35	20.00
36 "The Man Called Flintstone"	20.00
37 thru 40	@20.00
41 thru 60	@16.00

FLINTSTONES, THE
Charlton Comics 1970
1	40.00
2	22.00
3 thru 7	@15.00
8	18.00
9	15.00
10	15.00
11 thru 20	@12.00
21 thru 50	@10.00

FLINTSTONES IN 3-D
Blackthorne
1 thru 5	@2.50

FLIPPER
Gold Key April, 1966
1 Ph(c) from TV series	40.00
2 and 3 Ph(c)	@25.00

FLY IN MY EYE EXPOSED
Eclipse
1 JJo(c),"Our Visitor"	4.95

FLY, THE
Archie Publications
1 JSn,A:Mr.Justice	1.25
2 thru 9 RB,SD	@1.00

FLYING SAUCERS
Dell April, 1967
1	22.00
2 thru 5	15.00

FLYMAN
Archie Publications
{Prev: Adventures of the Fly}
31 I:Shield (Bill Higgins), A:Comet, Black Hood	35.00
32 I:Mighty Crusaders	30.00
33 A:Mighty Crusaders, R:Hangman Wizard	30.00
34 MSy,A:Black Hood,Comet Shield back-up story begins	20.00
35 O:Black Hood	20.00
36 O:Web,A:Hangman in Shield strip	20.00
37 A:Shield	20.00
38 A:Web	18.00
39 A:Steel Sterling	17.00

COLOR PUB.

FOES
Ram Comics
1 TheMaster's Game	1.95
2 TheMaster's Game #2	1.95

FOODANG
Aug. House
1 I:Foodang	1.95
1a Signed, Foil cover	2.50
2 I:Maude	2.50
3 V:Undead Clown Man	2.50
4 V:Executioner	2.50

FOOTSOLDIERS
Maximum Press 1996
1 KJo,PhH,	2.75

FORBIDDEN PLANET
Innovation 1992
1 Movie Adapt	2.50
2 Movie adapt.contd.	2.50
3 Movie adapt.contd.	2.50
4 Movie adapt.concl.	2.50
GN rep.#1–#4 (1997)	8.95

FORCE OF THE BUDDHA'S PALM
Jademan
1	3.00
2	2.25
3 thru 10	@1.75
11 thru 24	@1.95
25 V:Maskman	1.95
26 V:Maskman	1.95
27 A:SmilingDemon	1.95
28 Maskman v 10 Demons	1.95
29 Giant Bat	1.95
30	1.95
31	1.95
32 "White Crane Villa"	1.95
33 Devilito defeats White Crane & Giant Bat	1.95
34 Samsun vs. Devilito	1.95
35 Samsun vs. Devilito	1.95
36 Samsun vs. Devilito	1.95
37 D:Galacial Moon	1.95
38 Persian Elders, Iron Boy	1.95
39 V:Mad Gen.,White Crane, Iron Boy	1.95
40 D:Heaven & Earth Elders	1.95
41 thru 43	@1.95
44 D:White Crane	1.95
45 V:Iron Boy	1.95
46 thru 48	@1.95
49 Iron Boy vs Sainted Jade	1.95
50 Iron Boy & The Holy Blaze	1.95
51 D:Aquarius	1.95
52 V:Son o/t Gemini Lord	1.95
53 Nine Continent's return to full powers	1.95

4-D MONKEY
1 thru 3	@1.80

FOREVER WAR, THE
NBM
GN Vol. 1 Joe Haldeman adapt.	8.95
GN Vol. 2 Joe Haldeman adapt.	8.95
GN Vol. 3 Joe Haldeman adapt.	8.95

FRANK
Nemesis
1 thru 4 DGc(s),GgP	2.50

FRANK FRAZETTA FANTASY ILLUSTRATED
Frank Frazetta 1998
1	6.00
1a variant cover	6.00
3	6.00
3 Neil Gaiman signed & numbered	24.95
3 Daniel signed & numbered	19.95

FRANK FRAZETTA DEATH DEALER
Verotik 1997
1 thru 4 by Glenn Danzig	@6.95

FRANK IN THE RIVER
Tundra
1 Avery/Jones style cartoons	2.95

FRANK MERRIWELL AT YALE
Charlton Comics 1955–56
1	30.00
2 thru 4	@20.00

FRANKENSTEIN
Dell Publishing Co. 1964
1	30.00
2	20.00
3 and 4	@15.00

FRANKENSTEIN
Caliber
Novel Adaptation	2.95

FRANKENSTEIN DRACULA WAR
Topps
1 Frank Vs. Drac	2.50
2 F:Saint Germaine	2.50
3 Frank Vs. Drac	2.50

FREDDY
Dell Publishing Co. 1963
1	15.00
2 and 3	@10.00

FREDDY'S DEAD
3-D	2.50
1 GN, Movie Adapt	6.95

FREDDY'S DEAD: THE FINAL NIGHTMARE
Innovation
1 Movie adaption, Pt.1	2.50
2 Movie adaption, Pt.2	2.50

FRIDAY FOSTER
Dell Publishing Co. Oct., 1972
1	22.00

FRIENDLY GHOST CASPER, THE
Harvey Publications 1958
1	200.00

The Friendly Ghost Casper #146
© Harvey Comics

2	100.00
3 thru 10	@50.00
11 thru 20	@35.00
21 thru 30	@25.00
31 thru 50	@20.00
51 thru 100	@10.00
101 thru 159	@5.00
160 thru 163 52 pgs.	@4.00
164 thru 253	@3.00

Becomes:
CASPER THE FRIENDLY GHOST

FRIGHT NIGHT
Now
1 thru 22	@1.75

FRIGHT NIGHT
Now
1 Dracula,w/3-D Glasses	2.95

FRIGHT NIGHT II
Now
Movie Adaptation	3.95

FRISKY ANIMALS ON PARADE
Ajax-Farrell Publ. Sept., 1957
1 LbC(c)	60.00
2	20.00
3 LbC(c)	40.00

FROGMEN, THE
Dell Publishing Co. 1962
1 GE,Ph(c)	65.00
2 GE,FF	50.00
3 GE,FF	50.00
4	25.00
5 ATh	30.00
6 thru 11	@20.00

FROM HERE TO INSANITY
Charlton Comics Feb., 1955
8	100.00
9	75.00
10 SD(c)	125.00

11 JK	150.00
12 JK	150.00
3-1	250.00

FRONTLINE COMBAT
EC Comics 1995
1 thru 4 rep.	@2.00

Gemstone
5 thru 13 rep.	@2.50

"Annuals"
TPB Vol. 1 rebinding of #1–#5	10.95
TPB Vol. 2 rebinding of #6–#10	12.95

F-TROOP
Dell Publishing Co. 1966
1 Ph(c)	75.00
2 thru 7 Ph(c)	@40.00

FUN-IN
Gold Key 1970–74
1	25.00
2 thru 6	@15.00
7 thru 10	@10.00
11 thru 15	@8.00

FUNKY PHANTOM
Gold Key 1972–75
1	35.00
2 thru 5	@15.00
6 thru 13	@12.00

FUTURIANS
Lodestone
1 DC,I:Dr.Zeus	1.00
2 DC,I:MsMercury	1.00
3 DC	1.00
Eternity Graphic Novel, DC, Rep. +new material	9.95

GALL FORCE: ETERNAL STORY
CPM
1 F:Solnoids	2.95
2 V:Paranoid	2.95
3	2.95
4 Implant Secrets	2.95

GALLANT MEN, THE
Gold Key Oct., 1963
1 RsM	20.00

GALLEGHER BOY REPORTER
Gold Key May, 1965
1	22.00

GARRISON
Zion Comics
1 I:Wage, Garrison	2.50

GARRISON'S GORRILLAS
Dell Publishing Co. Jan., 1968
1 Ph(c)	30.00
2 thru 5 Ph(c)	@20.00

GASP!
American Comics Group
March, 1967
1	25.00

---

2 thru 4, Aug. 1967	@15.00

G-8 & BATTLE ACES
1 based on '40's pulp characters	3.00

GENE RODDENBERRY'S LOST UNIVERSE
Teckno-Comics 1994
0 I:Sensua	2.50
1 Gene Roddenberry's	2.50
2 Grange Discovered	2.25
3 Secrets Revealed	1.95
4 F:Penultra	1.95
5 I:New Alien Race	1.95
6 Two Doctor Granges	1.95
7 F:Alaa Chi Tskare	1.95

GENE RODDENBERRY'S XANDER IN LOST UNIVERSE
Teckno-Comics 1995
1 V:Black Ghost	2.25
2 V:Walker	2.25
3 V:Lady Sensua	2.25
4 thru 7	@2.25
8 F:Lady Sensua	2.25

[Mini-Series]
Teckno-Comics 1995
1 RoR,F:L.Nimoy's Primortals	2.25

GENSAGA: ANCIENT WARRIOR
Entity Comics 1995
1 I:Gensaga	2.50
1a with Computer Games	2.50
2 V:Dinosaurs	2.50
3 V:Lord Abyss	2.50

GENTLE BEN
Dell Publishing Co. Feb., 1968
1 Ph(c)	30.00
2	20.00
3 thru 5	@18.00

GEORGE OF THE JUNGLE
Gold Key Feb., 1969
1 From animated TV show	50.00
2	40.00

GE ROUGE
Verotik 1997
1 by Glenn Danzig & Calvin Irving	2.95
2 and 3	@2.95

GET SMART
Dell Publishing Co. June, 1966
1 Ph(c) all	80.00
2 SD	50.00
3 SD	45.00
4 thru 8	@40.00

[FILMATION'S] GHOSTBUSTERS
First 1987
1 thru 4	@1.50

GHOST BUSTERS II
Now
1 thru 3 Mini-series	@1.95

GHOST STORIES
Dell Publishing Co.
Sept.-Nov., 1962
1	40.00
2	20.00
3 thru 10	@15.00
11	12.00
12 thru 19	@10.00
20	12.00
21 thru 33	@10.00
34 rep	10.00
35 rep	12.00
36 rep	10.00
37 rep	10.00

GHOSTLY TALES
Charlton 1966
Previously: Blue Beetle
55 I&O Dr. Graves	12.00
56 thru 70	@8.00
71 thru 169	@6.00

GIANT COMICS
Charlton Comics Summer, 1957
1 A:Atomic Mouse,Hoppy	120.00
2 A:Atomic Mouse	80.00
3	80.00

GIDGET
Dell Publishing Co. April, 1966
1 Ph(c),Sally Field	75.00
2 Ph(c),Sally Field	60.00

GIFT, THE
First
Holiday Special	6.00

G.I. JOE 3-D
Blackthorne
1	3.00
2 thru 5	@2.50
Ann. #1	2.50

GIL THORPE
Dell Publishing Co. 1963
1	35.00

GINGER FOX
Comico
1 thru 4	@1.75

GIN-RYU
Believe In Yourself
1 F:Japanese Sword	2.75
2 Identity Revealed	2.75
3	2.75
4 Manhunt For Gin-Ryu	2.75
Ash Can	.75

G.I. R.A.M.B.O.T.
Wonder Color 1987
1 thru 3	@2.00

G.I. ROBOT
Eternity
1	1.80

GIRL FROM U.N.C.L.E.
Gold Key Jan., 1967
1 "The Fatal Accidents Affair"	75.00

All comics prices listed are for *Near Mint* condition.

2 "The Kid Commandos Caper"   40.00
3 "The Captain Kidd Affair" 40.00
4 "One-Way Tourist Affair" 40.00
5 "The harem-Scarem Affair" .. 40.00

GLOBAL FORCE
Silverline
1 thru 4 .... @1.95

GLORY
Maximum Press 1996
1–15 see Image
16 JDy 2.50
17 JDy 2.50
18 JDy 2.50
19 JDy,A:Demeter, Silverfall 2.50
20 JDy,A:Silverfall 2.50
21 JDy 2.50
22 JDy 2.50
23 A:Prophet 2.50
TPB Vol. 2, rep. 16.95
TPB Glory/Angela RLd,JDy 16.95

GLORY/CELESTINE: DARK ANGEL
Maximum Press 1996
1 & 2 *See: Image*
3 (of 3) JDy 2.50

G-MAN
Conquest Comics
1 I:Richard Glenn 2.50

GOBLIN LORD, THE
Goblin Studios 1996
1 (of 6) sci-fi/fantasy 2.50
2 signed & numbered 9.95
3 .... 2.50
3a signed & numbered 9.95
4 thru 6 .... @2.50

GO-GO
Charlton Comics June, 1966
1 Miss Bikini Luv 40.00
2 Beatles 50.00
3 Blooperman 20.00
4 .... 20.00
5 .... 15.00
6 JAp 20.00
7 .... 20.00
8 JAp 20.00
9 Ph(c),Oct., 1965 .... 20.00

GODS FOR HIRE
Hot Comics
1 thru 7 .... @1.75

GOLDEN COMICS DIGEST
Gold Key 1969–76
1 Tom & Jerry,Woody Woodpecker, Bugs Bunny 20.00
2 Hanna-Barbera, TV Fun Favorites 25.00
3 Tom & Jerry, Woody Woodpecker 10.00
4 Tarzan 20.00
5 Tom & Jerry, Woody Woodpecker, Bugs Bunny ... 10.00
6 Bugs Bunny 10.00
7 Hanna-Barbera, TV Fun

Favorites 12.00
8 Tom & Jerry, Woody Woodpecker, Bugs Bunny 8.00
9 Tarzan 15.00
10 Bugs Bunny 8.00
11 Hanna-Barbera, TV Fun Favorites 8.00
12 Tom & Jerry,Bugs Bunny 8.00
13 Tom & Jerry 8.00
14 Bugs Bunny, Fun Packed Funnies 8.00
15 Tom & Jerry, Woody Woodpecker, Bugs Bunny ... 8.00
16 Woody Woodpecker 8.00
17 Bugs Bunny 8.00
18 Tom & Jerry, ... 8.00
19 Little Lulu 15.00
20 Woody Woodpecker 8.00
21 Bugs Bunny Showtime 8.00
22 Tom & Jerry Winter Wingding . 8.00
23 Little Lulu & Tubby Fun Fling . 14.00
24 Woody Woodpecker Fun Festival 8.00
25 Tom & Jerry 8.00
26 Bugs Bunny Halloween Hulla-Boo-Loo,Dr. Spektor article ... 8.00
27 Little Lulu & Tubby in Hawaii . 12.00
28 Tom & Jerry 8.00
29 Little Lulu & Tubby 12.00
30 Bugs Bunny Vacation Funni .. 8.00
31 Turk, Son of Stone 15.00
32 Woody Woodpecker Summer Fun 8.00
33 Little Lulu & Tubby Halloween Fun 12.00
34 Bugs Bunny Winter Funnies .. 8.00
35 Tom & Jerry Snowtime Funtime 8.00
36 Little Lulu & Her Friends 14.00
37 WoodyWoodpecker County Fair 8.00
38 The Pink Panter 8.00
39 Bugs Bunny Summer Fun 8.00
40 Little Lulu 15.00
41 Tom & Jerry Winter Carnival .. 8.00
42 Bugs Bunny 8.00
43 Little Lulu in Paris 14.00
44 Woody Woodpecker Family Fun Festival 8.00
45 The Pink Panther 8.00
46 Little Lulu & Tubby 12.00
47 Bugs Bunny 8.00
48 The Lone Ranger 8.00

GOLD DIGGER BETA
Antarctic Press 1998
Spec. 0 by Ben Dunn, Special Origin Issue, 24pg 1.95
1A bu Fred Perry, John Pound (c) 2.95
1B Jeff Henderson (c) 2.95
2 and 3 .... @2.95

GOLDEN PICTURE STORY BOOK
Racine Press (Western) Dec., 1961
1 Huckleberry Hound 150.00
2 Yogi Bear 150.00
3 Babes In Toy Land 225.00
4 Walt Disney 150.00

GOLDEN WARRIOR
Industrial Design
1 by Eric Bansen & RB 2.95
2 and 3 .... @2.95

GOMER PYLE
Gold Key July, 1966
1 Ph(c) from TV show 60.00
2 and 3 .... @50.00

GOOD GUYS
Defiant
1 JiS(s),I:Good Guys 3.75
2 JiS(s),V:Mulchmorg 3.25
3 V:Chasm 2.75
4 Seduction of the Innocent ... 3.25
5 I:Truc 2.75
6 A:Charlemagne 2.75
7 JiS(s),V:Scourge 2.50
8 thru 11 .... @2.50

GOOFY ADVENTURES
Walt Disney 1990
1 "Balboa de Goofy" 2.50
2 .... 2.00
3 thru 9 .... @1.75
10 Samurai 1.75
11 Goofis Khan 1.75
12 "Arizona Goof" Pt. 1 .... 1.75
13 "Arizona Goof" Pt. 2 .... 1.75
14 "Goofylution" 1.75
15 "Super Goof Vs.Cold Ray" ... 1.75
16 "Sheerluck Holmes" 1.50
17 GC,TP,"Tomb of Goofula" ... 1.50

GORGO
Charlton Comics 1961–65
1 SD 150.00
2 SD,SD(c) 75.00
3 SD,SD(c) 55.00
4 SD(c) 45.00
5 thru 10 .... @45.00
11 .... 22.00
12 .... 15.00
13 thru 15 .... @22.00
16 SD 22.00
17 thru 23 .... @15.00

GORGO'S REVENGE
Charlton Comics 1962
1 .... 35.00
Becomes:
THE RETURN OF GORGO
2 .... 25.00
3 .... 25.00

G.O.T.H.
Verotik 1995
1 thru 3 mini-series .... @2.95
TPB SBi, rep. of series 9.95

THE GOTHIC SCROLLS, DRAYVEN
Davdez Arts 1997
1 16pg. 1.50
1a limited edition, new cover ... 2.95
2 and 3 .... @2.50
4 V:Lucifer 2.50
GN 12.95

GRATEFUL DEAD COMIX
Kitchen Sink
1 TT,inc.DireWolf(large format) .. 5.50
2 TT,inc.Jack Straw 4.95

3 TT,inc. Sugaree	4.95
4 TT,inc. Sugaree	4.95
5 TT,Uncle John's Band	4.95
6 TT,Eagle Mall #1	4.95

GREASE MONKEY
Kitchen Sink 1997

1 by Tim Elred	3.50
2 by Tim Elred	3.50

GREAT AMERICAN WESTERN
AC Comics

1	1.75
2	2.95
3	2.95
4	3.50

GREAT EXPLOITS
Decker Publ./Red Top
Oct., 1957

91 BK	65.00

GREEN HORNET, THE
Gold Key Feb., 1967

1 Bruce Lee,Ph(c)	175.00
2 Ph(c)	125.00
3 Ph(c)	125.00

GREEN HORNET
Now

1 O:40's Green Hornet	10.00
1a 2nd Printing	4.00
2 O:60's Green Hornet	6.00
3 thru 5	@4.00
6	3.00
7 BSz(c),I:New Kato	3.00
8 thru 12	@3.50
13 V:Ecoterrorists	3.50
14 V:Ecoterrorists	3.50
Spec.#1	2.50
Spec.#2	2.25
[2nd Series]	
1 V:Johnny Dollar Pt.1	2.25
2 V:Johnny Dollar Pt.2	2.25
3 V:Johnny Dollar Pt.3	2.25
4 V:Ex-Con/Politician	1.95
5 V:Ex-Con/Politician	1.95
6 Arkansas Vigilante	1.95
7 thru 9 The Beast	@1.95
10 Green Hornet-prey	1.95
11 F:Crimson Wasp	1.95
12 Crimson Wasp/Johnny Dollar Pt.1,polybagged w/Button	2.50
13 TD(i),Wasp/Dollar Pt.2	2.50
14 TD(i),Wasp/Dollar Pt.3	2.50
15 TD(i),Secondsight	1.95
16 A:Commissioner Hamiliton	1.95
17 V:Gunslinger	1.95
18 V:Sister-Hood	1.95
19 V:Jewel Thief	1.95
20 F:Paul's Friend	1.95
21 V:Brick Arcade	1.95
22 V:Animal Testers, with Hologravure card	2.95
23 with Hologravure card	1.95
24 thru 25 Karate Wars	@1.95
26 B:City under Siege	1.95
27 with Hologravure card	1.95
28 V:Gangs	1.95
29 V:Gangs	1.95
30 thru 37	@1.95

Green Hornet #20 © Now Comics

38 R:Mei Li	2.50
39 Crimson Wasp	2.50
40	2.50
41	2.50
42 Baby Killer	2.50
43 Wedding Disasters	2.50
44 F:Amy Hamilton	2.50
45 Plane Hijacking	2.50
46 Airport Terrorists	2.50
Ann.#1 The Blue & the Green	2.50
1993 Ann	2.95

Bonus Books

TPB rep. Now comics #1–#12, 296pg.	10.00
TPB deluxe rep. Now comics #1–#12, 296pg.	19.95

GREEN HORNET: DARK TOMORROW
Now

1 thru 3 Hornet Vs Kato	@2.50

GREEN HORNET: SOLITARY SENTINAL
Now

1 Strike Force	2.50
2 thru 3	2.50

GREENHAVEN
Aircel

1	3.00
2	2.50
3	2.00

GRENDEL
Comico 1986–91

1	8.00
1a 2nd printing	2.00
2	5.00
3 thru 6	@4.00
7 MW	4.00
8 thru 12	@4.00
13 KSy(c)	3.00
14 KSy(c)	3.00
15 KSy(c)	3.00
16 Mage	5.00
17 thru 19	@4.00

20 thru 32	@3.00
33	3.50
34 thru 36	@3.00
37	5.00
38	9.00
39	8.00
40	15.00

GREYLORE
Sirius 1985–86

1 thru 5	@2.00

GRIMJACK
First 1984–91

1 TT Teenage suicide story	3.00
2 TT A:Munden's Bar	2.50
3 TT A:Munden's Bar	2.00
4 TT A:Munden's Bar	2.00
5 TT,JSon,A:Munden's Bar	2.00
6 TT,SR,A:Munden's Bar	2.00
7 TT,A:Munden's Bar	2.00
8 TT,A:Munden's Bar	2.00
9 TT "My Sins Remembered"	2.00
10 TT,JOy,A:Munden's Bar	2.00
11 TT,A:Munden'sBar	1.75
12 TT,A:Munden'sBar	1.75
13 TT,A:Munden's Bar	1.75
14 TT,A:Munden's Bar	1.75
15 TT,A:Munden'sBar	1.75
16 TT,A:Munden'sBar	1.75
17 TT,A:Munden'sBar	1.75
18 TT,A:Munden's Bar	1.75
19 TT,A:Munden'sBar	1.75
20 TT,A:Munden'sBar	1.75
21 TS,A:Munden's Bar	1.75
22 A:Munden's Bar	1.75
23 TS,A:Munden's Bar	1.75
24 PS,TT,rep.Starslayer10-11	1.75
25 TS,A:Munden's Bar	1.75
26 1st color TMNTurtles	10.00
27 TS,A:Munden's Bar	1.50
28 TS,A:Munden's Bar	1.50
29 A:Munden's Bar	1.50
30 A:Munden's Bar	1.50
31 A:Munden's Bar	1.50
32 A:Spook	1.50
33 JSon,Munden'sBarChristmas Tale	1.50
34 V:Spook	1.50
35 A:Munden's Bar	1.50
36 3rd Anniv.IssueD:Grimjack	2.50
37 A:Munden's Bar	1.50
38 A:Munden's Bar	1.50
39 R.Grimjack	1.50
40	1.75
41 "Weeping Bride"	1.75
42 "Hardball"	1.75
43 "Beneath the Surface"	1.75
44 Shadow Wars	1.75
45 Shadow Wars	1.75
46 Shadow Wars	1.75
47 Shadow Wars,A:EddyCurrent	1.75
48 Shadow Wars	1.75
49 Shadow Wars	1.75
50 V:Dancer,ShadowWars ends	1.75
51 Crossroads tie-in,A:Judah Macabee	2.00
52	2.00
53 Time Story	2.00
54	2.50
55 FH	2.00
56 FH	2.00
57 FH	2.00
58 FH	2.00

59 FH	2.00
60 FH,Reunion Pt.1	2.00
61 FH,Reunion Pt.2	2.00
62 FH,Reunion Pt.3	2.00
63 FH,A:Justice Drok	2.00
64 FH,O:Multiverse	2.00
65 FH	2.00
66 FH(c),Demon Wars Pt.1	2.00
67 FH(c),Demon Wars Pt.2	2.00
68 Demon Wars Pt.3	2.00
69 Demon Wars Pt.4	2.00
70 FH,I:Youngblood	2.00
71 FH,A:Youngblood	2.00
72	2.00
73 FH(c)	2.00
74 FH(c)	2.00
75 FH,TS,V:The Major	2.00
76 FH,A:Youngblood	2.00
77 FH,A:Youngblood	2.25
78	2.25
79 FH,Family Business #1	2.25
80 FH,Family Business #2	2.25
81 FH,Family Business #3	2.25

GRIMJACK CASEFILE
First 1990

1 thru 5 rep. @1.95

GRIMM'S GHOST STORIES
Gold Key/Whitman 1972–82

1	25.00
2	10.00
3	10.00
4	10.00
5 AW	12.00
6	8.00
7	8.00
8 AW	12.00
9	8.00
10	8.00
11 thru 16	@7.00
17 RC	10.00
18 thru 60	@7.00

GROO
Pacific

1 SA,I:Sage,Taranto 22.00

Groo #6 © Pacific Comics

2 SA,A:Sage	12.00
3 SA,C:Taranto	10.00
4 SA,C:Sage	9.00
5 SA,I:Ahax	9.00
6 SA,I:Gratic	9.00
7 SA,I:Chakaal	9.00
8 SA,A:Chakaal	9.00

Eclipse

Spec.#1 SA,O:Groo,rep Destroyer
Duck #1 23.00

GROUND ZERO

1 1.35

GROUP LARUE
Innovation

1	1.95
2	1.95
3	1.95

GUILLOTIN
ABC 1997

1 JQ(c)	3.00
1a RCI(c)	6.00
1b gold cover, polybagged with trading card	10.00
2	3.00
2a Serpent (c)	6.00
2b Cold Series (c)	6.00

GULLIVER'S TRAVELS
Dell Publishing Co.
Sept.-Nov., 1965

1	40.00
2 and 3	@30.00

GUMBY
Comico

1 AAd,Summer Fun Special	5.00
2 AAd,Winter Fun Special	3.50

GUMBY IN 3-D

Spec.#1	4.00
2 thru 7	@2.50

GUNSMOKE
Dell Publishing Co. Feb., 1956

1 J.Arness Ph(c) all	135.00
2	65.00
3	65.00
4	65.00
5	65.00
6	50.00
7	50.00
8	60.00
9	60.00
10 AW,RC	65.00
11	60.00
12 AW	65.00
13 thru 27	@50.00

GUY WITH A GUN: A ZOMBIE NIGHTMARE
Alpha Productions

1 V:Gracel, Zombies 2.75

HALL OF FAME
J.C. Productions

1 WW,GK,ThunderAgents	1.00
2 WW,GK,ThunderAgents	1.00
3 WW,Thunder Agents	1.00

HALLOWEEN HORROR
Eclipse 1987

1 1.75

HALO: AN ANGEL'S STORY
Sirius April 1996

1 thru 3 by Chris Knowles	@2.95
TPB rep. #1–#3	12.95

HAMMER OF GOD
First

1 thru 4	@1.95
Deluxe #1"Sword of Justice Bk#1"	4.95
Deluxe #2"Sword of Justice Bk#2"	4.95

HAMSTER VICE

10	2.00
3-D #1	2.50

HAND OF FATE
Eclipse

1 I:Artemus Fate	1.75
2 F:Artemis & Alexis	2.00
3 Mystery & Suspense	2.00

HANDS OF THE DRAGON
Atlas June 1975

1 15.00

HANNA-BARBERA ALL-STARS
Archie 1995

1 thru 5 1.50

HANNA-BARBERA BAND WAGON
Gold Key 1962–63

1	70.00
2	50.00
3	45.00

HANNA-BARBERA PARADE
Charlton Comics 1971–72

1	60.00
2 thru 10	@30.00

HANNA-BARBERA PRESENTS
Archie 1995

1 thru 15 @1.50

HANNA-BARBERA SUPER TV HEROES
Gold Key April, 1968

1 B:Birdman,Herculiods,Moby Dick, Young Samson & Goliath	100.00
2	85.00
3 thru 7 Oct. 1969	@75.00

HARDY BOYS, THE
Gold Key April, 1970

1	20.00
2 thru 4	@12.00

All comics prices listed are for *Near Mint* condition.

HARI KARI
Blackout Comics 1995
0 I:Hari Kari	2.95
1	2.95
1a commemorative, variant(c)	10.00

Specials & 1-shots
1 The Beginning, O:Kari (1996)	2.95
1a The Beginning, commemorative, signed	9.95
1 Bloodshed (1996)	3.00
1a Bloodshed, deluxe, variant(c)	10.00
1 Live & Untamed! (1996)	2.95
1 Rebirth (1996)	2.95
0 The Silence of Evil (1996)	2.95
0 The Silence of Evil, limited, foil stamped	12.95
½ The Diary of Kari Sun (1997)	2.95
½ The Diary of Kari Sun, deluxe	9.95
0 Life or Death (1997)	2.95
0a Life or Death, super sexy parody edition	12.95
1 Passion & Death (1997)	2.95
1 Passion & Death, photo(c)	9.95
1 Possessed by Evil (1997)	2.95
1 Resurrection (1997)	2.95
1 Resurrection, nude(c) edition	9.95

HARLEM GLOBTROTTERS
Gold Key April, 1972
1	25.00
2 thru 12, Jan. 1975	@15.00

HARLEY RIDER
1 GM,FS	2.00

HARRIERS
Entity 1995
1 I:Macedon Arsenal, Cardinal	2.95
1a with Video Game	6.95
2	2.50
3 V:Kr'llyn	2.50

HARSH REALM
Harris
1 thru 6 JHi(s),	@2.95

HARVEY HITS
Harvey Publications 1957–67
1 The Phantom	250.00
2 Rags Rabbit	20.00
3 Richie Rich	750.00
4 Little Dot's Uncles	100.00
5 Stevie Mazie's Boy Friend	15.00
6 JK(c),BP,The Phantom	150.00
7 Wendy the Witch	150.00
8 Sad Sack's Army Life	20.00
9 Richie Rich's Golden Deeds	350.00
10 Little Lotta	75.00
11 Little Audrey Summer Fun	50.00
12 The Phantom	125.00
13 Little Dot's Uncles	50.00
14 Herman & Katnip	20.00
15 The Phantom	125.00
16 Wendy the Witch	60.00
17 Sad Sack's Army Life	30.00
18 Buzzy & the Crow	20.00
19 Little Audrey	30.00
20 Casper & Spooky	40.00
21 Wendy the Witch	30.00
22 Sad Sack's Army Life	22.00
23 Wendy the Witch	30.00
24 Little Dot's Uncles	45.00
25 Herman & Katnip	15.00

26 The Phantom	100.00
27 Wendy the Good Little Witch	25.00
28 Sad Sack's Army Life	15.00
29 Harvey-Toon	20.00
30 Wendy the Witch	20.00
31 Herman & Katnip	10.00
32 Sad Sack's Army Life	15.00
33 Wendy the Witch	25.00
34 Harvey-Toon	15.00
35 Funday Funnies	10.00
36 The Phantom	100.00
37 Casper & Nightmare	14.00
38 Harvey-Toon	12.00
39 Sad Sack's Army Life	10.00
40 Funday Funnies	10.00
41 Herman & Katnip	10.00
42 Harvey-Toon	10.00
43 Sad Sack's Army Life	10.00
44 The Phantom	75.00
45 Casper & Nightmare	12.00
46 Harvey-Toon	10.00
47 Sad Sack's Army Life	10.00
48 The Phantom	75.00
49 Stumbo the Giant	50.00
50 Harvey-Toon	10.00
51 Sad Sack's Army Life	10.00
52 Casper & Nightmare	15.00
53 Harvey-Toons	10.00
54 Stumbo the Giant	25.00
55 Sad Sack's Army Life	10.00
56 Casper & Nightmare	12.00
57 Stumbo the Giant	25.00
58 Sad Sack's Army Life	10.00
59 Casper & Nightmare	12.00
60 Stumbo the Giant	25.00
61 Sad Sack's Army Life	10.00
62 Casper & Nightmare	12.00
63 Stumbo the Giant	22.00
64 Sad Sack's Army Life	10.00
65 Casper & Nightmare	10.00
66 Stumbo the Giant	22.00
67 Sad Sack's Army Life	10.00
68 Casper & Nightmare	10.00
69 Stumbo the Giant	22.00
70 Sad Sack's Army Life	10.00
71 Casper & Nightmare	10.00
72 Stumbo the Giant	22.00
73 Little Sad Sack	10.00
74 Sad Sack's Muttsy	10.00
75 Casper & Nightmare	10.00
76 Little Sad Sack	10.00
77 Sad Sack's Muttsy	10.00
78 Stumbo the Giant	20.00
79 Little Sad Sack	10.00
80 Sad Sack's Muttsy	10.00
81 Little Sad Sack	10.00
82 Sad Sack's Muttsy	10.00
83 Little Sad Sack	10.00
84 Sad Sack's Muttsy	10.00
85 Gabby Gob	10.00
86 G.I. Juniors	10.00
87 Sad Sack's Muttsy	10.00
88 Stumbo the Giant	20.00
89 Sad Sack's Muttsy	8.00
90 Gabby Goo	8.00
91 G.I. Juniors	8.00
92 Sad Sack's Muttsy	8.00
93 Sadie Sack	8.00
94 Gabby Goo	8.00
95 G.I. Juniors	8.00
96 Sad Sack's Muttsy	8.00
97 Gabby Goo	8.00
98 G.I. Juniors	8.00
99 Sad Sack's Muttsy	8.00
100 Gabby Goo	8.00

101 G.I. Juniors	6.00
102 Sad Sack's Muttsy	6.00
103 Gabby Goo	6.00
104 G.I. Juniors	6.00
105 Sad Sack's Muttsy	6.00
106 Gabby Goo	6.00
107 G.I. Juniors	6.00
108 Sad Sack's Muttsy	6.00
109 Gabby Goo	6.00
110 G.I. Juniors	6.00
111 Sad Sack's Muttsy	6.00
112 G.I. Juniors	6.00
113 Sad Sack's Muttsy	6.00
114 G.I. Juniors	6.00
115 Sad Sack's Muttsy	6.00
116 G.I. Juniors	6.00
117 Sad Sack's Muttsy	6.00
118 G.I. Juniors	6.00
119 Sad Sack's Muttsy	6.00
120 G.I. Juniors	6.00
121 Sad Sack's Muttsy	6.00
122 G.I. Juniors	6.00

HATE
Fantagraphics
1 thru 15, see B&W	
16 thru 29	@2.95
30 48pg.	3.95
TPB Hey, Buddy, rep. #1–#5	12.95
TPB Buddy the Dreamer, rep. #6–#10	12.95
TPB Fun with Buddy and Lisa	12.95
TPB Buddy Go Home	16.95

Haunted #12 © Charlton Comics

HAUNTED
Charlton 1971–75
1	20.00
2	10.00
3 thru 5	@10.00
6 thru 10	@7.00
11 thru 20	@7.00

HAUNT OF FEAR
Gladstone
1 EC Rep. H of F #17,WS#28	3.00
2 EC Rep. H of F #5,WS #29	2.50

HAUNT OF FEAR
Russ Cochran 1991
1 EC Rep. H of F #15 . . . . . 1.50
2 thru 5 EC Rep. H of F . . . . . @1.50
Second Series 1992
1 EC Rep. H of F #14,WS#13 . . 2.25
2 EC Rep. H of F #18,WF#14 . . . 2.00
3 EC Rep. H of F #19,WF#18 . . . 2.00
4 EC Rep. H of F #16,WF#15 . . . 2.00
5 EC Rep. H of F #5,WF#22 . . . 2.00
6 EC Rep. H of F 2.00
7 EC Rep. H of F 2.00
8 thru 15 Rep. . . . . @2.00
Gemstone
16 thru 24 EC comics reprint . . @2.50
"Annuals"
TPB Vol. 1 rebinding of #1–#5 . . . 8.95
TPB Vol. 2 rebinding of #6–#10 . . 8.95
TPB Vol. 3 rebinding of #11–#15 . 8.95
TPB Vol. 4 rebinding of #16–#20 12.95

HAVE GUN, WILL TRAVEL
Dell Publishing Co. Aug., 1958
1 Richard Boone Ph(c) all . . . 150.00
2 . . . . 100.00
3 . . . . 100.00
4 thru 14 . . . . @75.00

HAWKMOON, COUNT BRASS
First
1 Michael Moorcock adapt. 1.95
2 . . . . 1.95
3 . . . . 1.95
4 . . . . 1.95

HAWKMOON JEWEL IN THE SKULL
First
1 Michael Moorcock adapt. 3.00
2 . . . . 2.50
3 . . . . 2.00
4 . . . . 2.00

HAWKMOON, MAD GOD'S AMULET
First
1 Michael Moorcock adapt. 2.00
2 . . . . 1.75
3 . . . . 1.75
4 . . . . 1.75

HAWKMOON, SWORD OF THE DAWN
First
1 Michael Moorcock adapt. 2.00
2 thru 4 . . . . @1.75

HAWKMOON, THE RUNESTAFF
First
1 Michael Moorcock adapt. 2.00
2 . . . . 2.00
3 . . . . 1.95
4 . . . . 1.95

HEADMAN
Innovation
1 . . . . 2.50
2 . . . . 2.50

HEARTSTOPPER
Millenium
1 V:Demons 2.95
2 V:Demons 2.95
3 F:Hellfire 2.95

HEAVY METAL MONSTERS
3-D-Zone
1 w/3-D glasses 3.95

HECTOR HEATHCOTE
Gold Key March, 1964
1 . . . . 40.00

HELLINA
See Also B&W

HELLINA/ DOUBLE IMPACT
Lightning 1996
1-shot JCy(c) 3.00
1-shot variant (c) 3.00
1-shot nude cover 9.95
1-shot platinum edition, nude cover9.95
1-shot spec. nude cover, signed 12.00

HELLINA: HEART OF THORNS
Lightning Comics 1996
1 . . . . 3.00
1 nude cover editions 10.00
1 autographed edition 10.00
2 . . . . 3.00
2 variant cover 3.00
2 platinum edition 5.95
2 nude cover editions 10.00

HELLINA: HELLBORN
Lightning 1997
1 . . . . 2.95
1 autographed edition 9.95

HELLINA/NIRA X: ANGEL OF DEATH
Lightning 1996
1A cover A 3.00
1B cover B 3.00
1C Platinum cover 9.00
1D signed 9.00

HELLINA/NIRA X: CYBERANGEL
Lightning
1 autographed edition 9.95

HERBIE
American Comics Group April-May, 1964
1 . . . . 125.00
2 . . . . 65.00
3 . . . . 60.00
4 . . . . 60.00
5 A:Beatles,Dean Martin, Frank Sinatra 80.00
6 . . . . 50.00
7 . . . . 50.00
8 O:Fat Fury 60.00
9 . . . . 50.00

10 . . . . 50.00
11 . . . . 30.00
12 . . . . 30.00
13 . . . . 30.00
14 A:Nemesis,Magic Man 30.00
15 thru 22 . . . . @30.00
23 Feb., 1967 . . . . 30.00

HERCULES
Charlton Comics Oct., 1967
1 . . . . 20.00
2 thru 7 . . . . @10.00
8 scarce 25.00
9 thru 13 Sept. 1969 . . . . 10.00

HERCULES: THE LEGENDARY JOURNEYS
Topps 1996
1 & 2 . . . . @3.00
3 RTs,JBt,SeM,The Shaper,pt.1 . 5.00
3a Xena Ph(c) 15.00
4 RTs,JBt,SeM,The Shaper,pt.2 . 5.00
5 RTs,JBt,SeM,The Shaper,pt.3 . 5.00

HERE COMES THE BIG PEOPLE
Event Comics 1997
1 ACo&JP(c) 2.95
1b JfD(c) 2.95
1c JQ&JP alternate (c) 9.95
1d JQ&JP alternate (c) signed . 29.95

Hero Alliance #14 © Innovation

HERO ALLIANCE
Wonder Color Comics 1987
1 . . . . 2.00
Innovation 1989–91
1 RLm,BS(c),R:HeroAlliance . . . 6.00
2 RLm,BS(c),Victor vs.Rage 5.00
3 RLm,A:Stargrazers 4.00
4 . . . . 3.00
5 RLm(c) 2.50
6 BS(c),RLm pin-up 3.25
7 V:Magnetron 2.50
8 I:Vector 2.50
9 BS(c),V:Apostate 2.50
10 A:Sentry 2.25
11 . . . . 2.25

12 I:Bombshell	2.25
13 V:Bombshell	2.25
14 Kris Solo Story	2.25
15 JLA Parody Issue	2.25
16 V:Sepulchre	2.25
17 O:Victor,I&D:Misty	2.25
Annual #1 PS,BS,RLm	3.00

HERO ALLIANCE: THE END OF THE GOLDEN AGE
Pied Piper 1986

1 Bart Sears/Ron Lim	20.00
1a signed	25.00
1b 2nd printing	2.50
2	12.00
3	3.00
Graphic Novel	10.00

Innovation 1989

1 RLm	5.00
1A 2nd printing	2.50
2 RLm	4.00
3 RLm	3.00

HERO ALLIANCE & JUSTICE MACHINE: IDENTITY CRISES
Innovation

1	2.50

HERO ALLIANCE QUARTERLY
Innovation

1 Hero Alliance stories	2.75
2 inc."Girl Happy"	2.75
3 inc."Child Engagement"	2.75
4	2.75

HERO ALLIANCE SPECIAL
Innovation

1 Hero Alliance update	2.50

HI-SCHOOL ROMANCE DATE BOOK
Harvey Publications Nov., 1962

1 BP	18.00
2	8.00
3 March, 1963	8.00

HIGH CHAPPARAL
Gold Key Aug., 1968

1	40.00

HIGH SCHOOL CONFIDENTIAL DIARY
Charlton Comics June, 1960

1	20.00
2 thru 11	@10.00

Becomes:
CONFIDENTIAL DIARY

12	10.00
13 thru 17 March, 1963	@8.00

HIGH VOLTAGE
Blackout 1996

O	2.95

HILLBILLY COMICS
Charlton Comics Aug., 1955

1	25.00
2 thru 4 July 1956	@12.00

HIS NAME IS ROG... ROG 2000
A Plus Comics

1	1.75

HOBBIT, THE
Eclipse

1	8.00
1a 2ndPrinting	6.00
2	7.00
2a 2ndPrinting	5.00
3	6.00

HOGAN'S HEROES
Dell Publishing Co. June, 1966

1 Ph(c)	60.00
2 Ph(c)	35.00
3 JD,Ph(c)	35.00
4 thru 8 Ph(c)	@25.00
8 and 9	@25.00

HONEY WEST
Gold Key Sept., 1966

1	100.00

HONEYMOONERS
Lodestone

1	4.00
5 Mag.	2.50

Triad
[2nd Series]

1 "They Know What They Like"	3.00
2 "The Life You Save"	2.50
3 X-mas special,inc.Art Carney interview	3.50
4 "In the Pink"	3.00
5 "Bang, Zoom, To the Moon"	2.00
6 "Everyone Needs a Hero" inc. Will Eisner interview	2.00
7	2.00
8	2.00
9 Jack Davis(c)	4.50
10 thru 13	@2.00

HONG KONG
Blackout Comics 1996

0 A:Hari Kari	2.95
0 limited commemorative edition	9.95

HOT COMICS PREMIERE
Hot Comics

1 F:Thunderkill, Jacknife	1.95

HOT ROD RACERS
Charlton Comics Dec., 1964

1	50.00
2 thru 5	@40.00
6 thru 15 July 1967	@25.00

HOT STUFF, THE LITTLE DEVIL
Harvey Publications Oct., 1967

1	175.00
2 1st Stumbo the Giant	100.00
3 thru 5	@75.00

Hot Stuff, The Little Devil #66
© Harvey Publications

6 thru 10	@50.00
11 thru 20	@30.00
21 thru 40	@20.00
41 thru 60	@10.00
61 thru 100	@5.00
101 thru 105	@4.00
106 thru 112 52 pg Giants	@5.00
113 thru 172	@2.00

HOT STUFF SIZZLERS
Harvey Publications July, 1960

1 B:68 pgs	90.00
2 thru 5	@50.00
6 thru 10	@30.00
11 thru 20	@25.00
21 thru 30	@20.00
31 thru 44	@10.00
45 E:68 pgs	8.00
46 thru 50	@6.00
51 thru 59	@5.00

HOTSHOTS

1 thru 4	@1.95

HOTSPUR
Eclipse

1 RT(i),I:Josef Quist	1.75
2 RT(i),Amulet of Kothique Stolen	1.75
3 RT(i),Curse of the SexGoddess	1.75

HOWARD CHAYKIN'S AMERICAN FLAGG!
First

1 thru 9	@1.75
10 thru 12	@1.95

H.P.LOVECRAFT'S CTHULHU
Millenium

1 I:Miskatonic Project,V:Mi-Go	2.50
2 Arkham, trading cards	2.50

HUCK & YOGI JAMBOREE
Dell Publishing Co. March, 1961

1	75.00

HUCKLEBERRY HOUND
Charlton Nov., 1970
1 .... 25.00
2 thru 7 .... @15.00
3 Jan., 1972 .... 16.00

HUCKLEBERRY HOUND
Dell Publishing Co.
May-July, 1959
1 .... 100.00
2 .... 75.00
3 thru 7 .... @60.00
8 thru 10 .... @50.00
11 thru 17 .... @35.00
Gold Key
18 Chuckleberry Tales 60.00
19 Chuckleberry Tales 50.00
20 Chuckleberry Tales 40.00
21 thru 30 .... @20.00
31 thru 43 .... @10.00

HUEY, DEWEY & LOUIE JUNIOR WOODCHUCKS
Gold Key Aug., 1966
1 .... 50.00
2 thru 5 .... @30.00
6 thru 17 .... @25.00
18 .... 15.00
19 thru 25 .... @18.00
26 thru 30 .... @15.00
31 thru 57 .... @15.00
58 .... 12.00
59 .... 12.00
60 thru 80 .... @8.00
81 1984 .... 8.00

HYBRIDS
Continuity
1 .... 2.50

HYBRIDS
Continuity
0 Deathwatch 2000 prologue ... 5.00
1 Deathwatch 2000 pt.4,w/card .. 2.50
2 Deathwatch 2000 pt.13,w/card . 2.50
3 Deathwatch 2000 w/card 2.50
4 A:Valeria 2.50
5 O:Valeria 2.50

HYBRIDS: ORIGIN
Continuity
1 thru 5 .... 2.50

HYDE-25
Harris
1 New Drug 2.95

I DREAM OF JEANNIE
Dell Publishing Co. April, 1965
1 Ph(c),B.Eden 60.00
2 Ph(c),B.Eden 55.00

I SPY
Gold Key Aug., 1966
1 Bill Cosby Ph(c) 250.00
2 Ph(c) 150.00
3 thru 4 AMc,Ph(c) .... @125.00
5 thru 6 Ph(c) Sept.1968 .. @125.00

I'M DICKENS – HE'S FENSTER
Dell Publishing Co.
May-July, 1963
1 Ph(c) 35.00
2 Ph(c) 35.00

I•BOTS
Big Comics 1996
1 F:Lady Justice 2.25
2 thru 4 .... @2.25
5 StG(s),PB 2.25
6 StG(s),PB 2.25
7 PB,"Rebirth," pt.1, triptych (c) .. 2.25
8 PB,"Rebirth," pt.2, triptych (c) .. 2.25
9 PB,"Rebirth," pt.3, Original I•Bots
  return, triptych (c) 2.25

ICICLE
Hero Graphics
1 A:Flare,Lady Arcane,
  V:Eraserhead 4.95

IMP
1 .... 2.25

INMATES: PRISONERS OF SOCIETY
Delta Comics 1997
1 (of 4) 2.95
2 and 3 .... @2.95

INNER CIRCLE
Mushroom Comics 1995
1.1 I:Point Blank 2.50
1.2 V:Deathcom 2.50
1.3 V:Deathcom 2.50
1.4 V:Deathcom 2.50

INNOCENTS
Radical Comics 1995
1 I:Innocent 2.50

INNOVATORS
Dark Moon
1 I:Innovator, LeoShan 2.50
2 O:Mr. Void 2.50
3 I:Quill 2.50

INTERVIEW WITH A VAMPIRE
Innovation
1 based on novel,preq.to Vampire
  Chronicles 3.50
2 .... 3.00
3 Death & Betrayal 3.00
4 .... 3.00
5 D:Lestat 2.50
6 Transylvania Revelation 2.50
7 Louis & Claudia in Paris 2.50
8 thru 10 .... @2.50
11 .... 2.50

INTERVIEW WITH A VAMPIRE
Innovation
1 based on novel, preq. to Vampire
  Chronicles 3.50
2 .... 3.00
3 Death & Betrayal 3.00

4 .... 3.00
5 D:Lestat 2.50
6 Transylvania Revelation 2.50
7 Louis & Claudia in Paris 2.50

INTIMATE
Charlton Comics Dec., 1957
1 thru 3 .... @15.00
Becomes:
TEEN-AGE LOVE
4 .... 10.00
5 thru 9 .... @8.00
10 thru 35 .... @6.00
36 thru 96 .... @5.00

INTRUDER
TSR 1990–91
1 thru 4 .... @2.95
5 thru 8 The Next Dimension . @2.95

Invaders From Home #4
© Piranha Press

INVADERS FROM HOME
Piranha Press 1990
1 thru 6 .... @2.50

INVADERS, THE
Gold Key Oct., 1967
1 Ph(c),DSp 100.00
2 Ph(c),DSp 75.00
3 Ph(c),DSp 75.00
4 Ph(c),DSp 75.00

INVINCIBLE FOUR OF KUNG FU & NINJA
Victory
1 .... 2.75
2 and 3 .... @2.50
4 .... 1.80
5 thru 11 .... @2.00

IO
Invictus Studios
1 I:IO 2.25
2 .... 2.25
3 V:Major Damage 2.25

COLOR PUB

IRON HORSE
Dell Publishing Co. March, 1967
1	25.00
2	25.00

IRONJAW
Atlas Jan.–July , 1975
1 NA(c),MSy	10.00
2 NA(c)	8.00
3	8.00
4 O:IronJaw	8.00

IRON MARSHAL
Jademan
1	2.00
2	1.75
3	1.75
4	1.75
5	1.75
6 V:Bloody Duke	1.75
7	1.75
8	1.75
9 The Unicorn Sword	1.75
10 The Great Thor	1.75
11 A:Exterminator	1.75
12 Bloddy Duke vs. Exterminator	1.75
13 Secret of Unicorn Supreme	1.75
14 A:The Great Thor	1.75
15 A:The Great Thor	1.75
16 V:Tienway Champ	1.75
17 thru 20	1.75
21 Bloody Duke wounded	1.75
22 A:Great Thor	1.75
23	1.75
24	1.75
25	1.75
26 Iron Marshal Betrayed	1.75
27 thru 30	@1.75

IRREGULARS, THE: BATTLETECH Miniseries
Blackthorne
1	1.75
2	1.75
3 B&W	1.75

IRUKASHI
1	1.75

ISAAC ASIMOV'S I-BOTS
Tekno-Comix 1995
1 I:I-Bots	1.95
2 O:I-Bots	1.95
3 V:Black OP	2.25

IT! TERROR FROM BEYOND SPACE
Millenium
1	2.50
2	2.50

IT'S ABOUT TIME
Gold Key Jan., 1967
1 Ph(c)	35.00

ITCHY & SCRATCHY
Bongo Comics
1 DaC(s),	2.25
2 DaC(s),	2.25

IVANHOE
Dell Publishing Co.
July–Sept., 1963
1	30.00

JACK
Med Systems Company
1 Anubis in the 90's	2.95
2 Modern Society	2.95

JACK HUNTER
Blackthorne
1	1.25
2	1.25
3	1.25

JACKIE CHAN'S SPARTAN X
Topps 1997
1 "The Armor of Heaven," pt.1	2.95
2 "The Armor of Heaven," pt.2	2.95
3 (of 6)	2.95

JADEMAN COLLECTION
1	4.50
2	3.00
3	2.50
4	2.50
5	2.50

JADEMAN KUNG FU SPECIAL
1 I:Oriental Heroes, Blood Sword, Drunken Fist	5.00

JAGUAR GOD
Verotika 1995
1 Frazetta, I:Jaguar God	2.95
2 V:Yi-Cha	2.95
3 V:Yi-Cha	2.95
4 V:Yi-Cha	2.95
5 AOI	2.95
6 LSh,AOI	2.95
7 LSh,AOI	2.95
8 AOI	2.95

JAGUAR GOD: RETURN TO X'IBALBA
Verotik
1 by Glenn Danzig & RCo	4.95

JAKE TRASH
Aircel
1 thru 3	@2.00

JAMES BOND 007
Eclipse
1 MGr,PerfectBound	5.50
2 MGr	5.00
3 MGr,end series	5.00
GN Licence to Kill, MGr I/o	8.00

JAMES BOND: GOLDENEYE
Topps 1995
1 Movie adaptation	2.95
2 thru 3 Movie adaptation	@2.95

JAM SPECIAL
Comico
1	2.50

JASON GOES TO HELL
Topps
1 Movie adapt.,w/3 cards	3.25
2 Movie adapt.,w/3 cards	3.25
3 Movie adapt.,w/3 cards	3.25

JASON VS. LEATHERFACE
Topps 1995
1 Jason Meets Leatherface	2.95
2 SBi(c) Leatherface's family	2.95
3 SBi(c),conclusion	2.95

JAVERTZ
Firstlight
1 New Series	2.95
2 thru 5 Pieces of an Icon	2.95

JET DREAM
Gold Key June, 1968
1	35.00

JETSONS, THE
Gold Key Jan., 1963
1	200.00
2	125.00
3 thru 10	@100.00
11 thru 20	@65.00
21 thru 36 Oct. 1970	@50.00

JETSONS, THE
Charlton Comics Nov., 1970
1 from Hanna-Barbera TV show	65.00
2	40.00
3 thru 10	@25.00
11 thru 20 Dec. 1973	@20.00

The Jetsons #2 © Harvey Comics

JETSONS, THE
Harvey Comics 1991–92
1 thru 5	@1.95

JETSONS, THE
Archie 1995
1 thru 17 .... @1.50

JEZEBEL JADE
Comico
1 AKu,A:Race Bannon 2.00
2 AKu 2.00
3 AKu 2.00

JIGSAW
Harvey Publications Sept., 1966
1 .... 6.00
2 .... 3.50

JIMBO
Bongo Comics
1 R:Jimbo 2.95
2 thru 4 .... @2.95

JIMMY CORRIGAN
Fantagraphics
1 Chris Ware 3.95

J. N. WILLIAMSON'S MASQUES
Innovation
1 TV,From horror anthology 4.95
2 Olivia(c) inc.Better Than One .. 4.95

JOHN BOLTON, HALLS OF HORROR
Eclipse
1 JBo 1.75
2 JBo 1.75

JOHN F. KENNEDY LIFE STORY
(WITH 2 REPRINTS)
Dell Publishing Co.
Aug.-Oct., 1964
1 .... 40.00
2 .... 25.00
3 .... 25.00

JOHN JAKES MULLKON EMPIRE
Tekno Comix 1995
1 I:Mulkons 2.25
2 O:Mulkons 1.95
3 D:Company Man 1.95
4 Disposal Problems 1.95
5 F:Granny 1.95
6 Where's Karma 2.25

JOHN LAW
Eclipse 1983
1 WE 2.00

JOHNNY GAMBIT
1 .... 1.75

JOHNNY JASON TEEN REPORTER
Dell Publishing Co. 1962
1 .... 20.00
2 .... 20.00

JOHNNY NEMO
Eclipse 1985–86
1 I:Johnny Nemo 2.00
2 .... 2.00
3 F:Sindy Shade 2.50

JOHN STEELE SECRET AGENT
Gold Key Dec., 1964
1 .... 70.00

JONNY QUEST
Gold Key Dec., 1964
1 TV show 150.00

JONNY QUEST
Comico June, 1986
1 DW,SR,A:Dr.Zin 4.50
2 WP/JSon,O:RaceBannon 3.50
3 DSt(c) 3.00
4 TY/AW,DSt(i) 2.50
5 DSt(c)A:JezebelJade 2.50
6 AKu 2.00
7 .... 2.00
8 KSy 2.00
9 MA 2.00
10 King Richard III 2.00
11 JSon,BSz(c) 1.50
12 DSp 1.50
12 DSp 1.50
13 CI 1.50
14 .... 1.50
15 thru 31 .... @1.75
Spec.#1 .... 1.75
Spec.#2 .... 1.75

JONNY QUEST CLASSICS
Comico
1 DW 2.00
2 DW,O:Hadji 2.00
3 DW 2.00

JON SABLE
First
1 MGr,A:President 4.50
2 MGr,Alcohol Issue 3.50
3 MGr,O:Jon Sable 3.00
4 MGr,O:Jon Sable 3.00
5 MGr,O:Jon Sable 3.00
6 MGr,O:Jon Sable 3.00
7 MGr,The Target 2.50
8 MGr,Nuclear Energy 2.50
9 MGr,Nuclear Energy 2.50
10 MGr,Tripitych 2.50
11 MGr,I:Maggie 2.50
12 MGr,Vietnam 2.50
13 MGr,Vietnam 2.50
14 MGr,East Germany 2.50
15 MGr,Nicaragua 2.50
16 MGr,A:Maggie 2.50
17 MGr,1984 Olympics 2.50
18 MGr,1984 Olympics 2.50
19 MGr,,The Widow 2.50
20 MGr,The Rookie 2.50
21 MGr,Africa 2.25
22 MGr,V:Sparrow 2.25
23 MGr,V:Sparrow 2.25
24 MGr,V:Sparrow 2.25
25 MGr,Shatter 3.00
26 MGr,Shatter 3.00
27 MGr,Shatter 3.00

Jon Sable #30 © First Comics

28 MGr,Shatter 3.00
29 MGr,Shatter 3.00
30 MGr,Shatter 2.25
31 MGr,Nicaragua 2.00
32 MGr,Nicaragua 2.00
33 MGr,SA,Leprechauns 2.25
34 MGr,Indians 2.00
35 MGr,Indians 2.00
36 MGr,Africa 2.00
37 MGr,Africa 2.00
38 MGr,Africa 2.00
39 MGr,Africa 2.00
40 MGr,1st Case 2.00
41 MGr,1st Case 2.00
42 MGr,V:Sparrow 2.00
43 MGr,V:Sparrow 2.00
44 Hard Way 2.00
45 Hard Way II 2.00
46 MM,The Tower pt.1 .... 2.00
47 MM,The Tower pt.2 .... 2.00
48 MM,Prince Charles 2.00
49 MM,Prince Charles 2.00
50 A:Maggie the Cat 2.00
51 Jon Sable,babysitter pt.1 .... 2.00
52 Jon Sable,babysitter pt.2 .... 2.00
53 MGr. 2.00
54 Jacklight pt.1 .... 2.00
55 Jacklight pt.2 .... 2.00
56 Jacklight pt.3 .... 2.00

JOSIE
Archie Publications Feb., 1963
1 .... 100.00
2 .... 50.00
3 .... 25.00
4 .... 20.00
5 .... 25.00
6 thru 10 .... @15.00
11 thru 20 .... @12.00
21 thru 30 .... @7.00
31 thru 40 .... @5.00
41 thru 54 .... @4.00
55 thru 74 .... @2.00
75 thru 105 .... @1.00
106 Oct., 1962 .... 1.00

COLOR PUB.

JUDGE COLT
Gold Key Oct., 1969
1	15.00
2	10.00
3	10.00
4 Sept., 1980	10.00

JUDGE DREDD
Eagle 1983
1 BB,I:Judge Death(in USA)	15.00
2 BB(c&a),The Oxygen Board	12.00
3 BB(c),Judge Dredd Lives	10.00
4 BB(c),V:Perps	10.00
5 BB(c),V:Perps	8.00
6 BB(c),V:Perps	8.00
7 BB(c),V:Perps	8.00
8 BB(c),V:Perps	8.00
9 BB(c),V:Perps	8.00
10 BB(c),V:Perps	8.00
11 BB(c)	5.00
12 BB(c)	5.00
13 BB(c), The Day the Law Died, pt.5	5.00
14 BB(c),Dredd vs. Dredd	5.00
15 BB(c)	5.00
16 BB(c)	5.00
17 BB(c)	5.00
18 BB(c)	5.00
19 BB(c)	5.00
20 BB(c)	5.00
21 BB(c)	5.00
22 BB(c),V:Perps	4.00
23 BB(c),V:Perps	4.00
24 BB(c),V:Perps	4.00
25 BB(c),V:Perps	4.00
26 BB(c),V:Perps	4.00
27 BB(c),V:Perps	4.00
28 A:Judge Anderson,V:Megaman	5.00
29 A:Monty, the guinea pig	4.00
30 V:Perps	4.00
31 Destiny's Angel, Pt. 1	4.00
32 Destiny's Angel, Pt. 2	4.00
33 V:League of Fatties	4.00
34 V:Executioner	4.00

JUDGE DREDD
Quality
1 Cry of the Werewolf Pt.1	7.00
2 Cry of the Werewolf Pt.2	5.00
3 Anti-smoking	4.00
4 Wreckers	4.00
5 Highwayman	4.00
6	3.00
7	3.00
8	3.00
9	3.00
10	3.00
11	3.00
12 Starborn Thing, Pt.1	3.00
13 Starborn Thing, Pt.2	3.00
14 BB, V:50 foot woman	3.00
15 City of the Damned Pt.1	3.00
16 City of the Damned Pt.2	3.00
17 City of the Damned conc.	3.00
18 V:Mean Machine Angel	3.00
19 Dredd Angel	3.00
20 V:Perps	3.00
21 V:Perps	3.00
22/23 Booby Trap	3.00
24 Junk food fiasco	3.00
25/26 V:Perps	3.00
27 V:Perps	3.00
28 Dredd Syndrome	3.00
29 V:Perps	3.00
30 V:Perps	3.00
31 Hunt Pudge Dempsey's killer	3.00
32 V:Mutated Sewer Alligator	3.00
33 V:Perps	3.00
34 V:Executioner	3.00
35 V:Shojan	3.00
36 V:Shojan	3.00
37 V:Perps	3.00
38 V:Perps	3.00
39 V:Perps	3.00
40 V:Perps	3.00
41 V:Perps	3.00
42 V:Perps	3.00
43 V:Perps	3.00
44 V:Perps	3.00
45 V:DNA Man	2.50
46 Genie lamp sty	2.50
47 V:Perps	2.50
48 Murder in Mega-City One	2.50
49 V:Perps	2.50
50 V:Perps	2.50
51 V:Perps	2.50
52 V:Perps	2.50
53 V:Perps	2.50
54 V:Perps	2.50
55 V:Perps	2.50
56 inc.JudgeDredd Postcards	2.50
57 V:Perps	2.50
58 V:370lb Maniac	2.50
59 V:Perps	2.50
60 Social Misfit	2.50
61 V:Perps	2.50

Becomes:
JUDGE DREDD CLASSICS
62	2.50
63 Mutants from the Radlands	2.50
64	2.50
65	2.50
66 Wit and wisdom of Dredd	2.50
67 V:Otto Sump	2.50
68 V:Otto Sump	2.50
69	2.50
70 Dinosaurs in Mega City 1	2.50
71	2.50
72 Pirates o/t Black Atlantic	2.50
73	2.50
74	2.50
75	2.50
76 Diary of a Mad Citizen	3.00
TPB:Democracy Now	10.95
TPB:Rapture	12.95
Judge Dredd Special #1	2.50
GN Bad Science	7.95
GN Hall of Justice	7.95

JUDGE DREDD: AMERICA
Fleetway
1 I:America	3.50

JUDGE DREDD: JUDGE CHILD QUEST
Eagle
1 thru 3	@3.00
4 BB(c)	3.00
5	3.00

JUDGE DREDD'S CRIME FILE
Eagle 1984
1 Ron Smith, "The Perp Runners"	2.50
2 thru 6	@2.50

Judge Dredd's Crime File #2
© Eagle Comics

Quality
(Prestige format)
1 A:Rogue Trooper	6.50
2 IG,V:Fatties, Energy Vampires & Super Fleas	5.95
3 Battles foes from dead A:Judge Anderson	5.95

JUDGE DREDD'S EARLY CASES
Eagle
1 Robot Wars, Pt.1	4.00
2 Robot Wars, Pt.2	3.00
3 V:Perps	3.00
4 IG, Judge Giant	3.00
5 V:Perps	3.00
6 V:Judge killing car Elvis	3.00

JUDGE DREDD'S HARDCASE PAPERS
Fleetway/Quality
1 V:The Tarantula	7.50
2 Junkies & Psychos	6.50
3 Crime Call Vid. Show	6.50
4 "Real Coffee",A:Johnny Alpha	6.50

JUDGE DREDD: THE MEGAZINE
Fleetway/Quality 1991
1 Midnite's Children Pt.1 A:Chopper, Young Death	5.25
2 Midnite's Children Pt.2	4.95
3	4.95
23 thru 34	@3.95
35 thru 43	@5.25
44 thru 45	@6.95

JUDGE PARKER
Argo Feb., 1956
1	25.00
2	15.00

JUDGMENT DAY
Lightning Comics
1 B:JZy(s),KIK,V:Razorr, Rift,

Nightmare, red prism(c) 5.00
1a Gold Prism(c) 5.00
1b Purple Prism(c) 7.00
1c Misprint,Red Prism(c), Bloodfire
Credits inside 8.00
1d Misprint,Gold Prism(c), Bloodfire
Credits inside 8.00
1e Misprint,Green Prism(c),
Bloodfire Credits inside 8.00
1f B&W promo ed. Gold ink 5.00
1g B&W promo ed. platinum ed. . 7.00
2 TLw,I:War Party,BU:Perg, w/Perg
card 4.00
3 ErP,O:X-Treme 3.25
4 ErP,In Hell 3.25
5 TLw,In Hell 3.25
6 TLw,I:Red Front,O:Salurio . . . 3.25
7 O:Safeguard 3.25
8 . . . . 2.95
9 . . . . 2.95
10 . . . . 2.95

JUDGMENT DAY
Maximum Press 1997
Alpha AMo(s) 2.50
Alpha variant cover 2.50
Omega AMo(s) 2.50
Omega variant cover 2.50
Final Judgment AMo(s) 2.50
Final Judgment variant cover . . . 2.50

JUDOMASTER
Charlton Comics
(Special War Series #4) I:Judomaster.00
89 FMc,War stories begin 7.00
89 (90) FMc,A:Thunderbolt 6.00
91 FMc,DG,A:Sarge Steel 6.00
92 FMc,DG,A:Sarge Steel 6.00
93 FMc,DG,I:Tiger 6.00
94 FMc,DG,A:Sarge Steel 6.00
95 FMc,DG,A:Sarge Steel 5.00
96 FMc,DG,A:Sarge Steel 5.00
97 FMc,A:Sarge Steel 4.00
98 FMc,A:Sarge Steel 4.00

JUGHEAD
Archie Publications
Dec., 1965–June, 1987
127 thru 130 . . . . @12.00
131 thru 150 . . . . @10.00
151 thru 160 . . . . @8.00
161 thru 352 . . . . 1.50

JUGHEAD
Archie Publications
[2nd Series] Aug., 1987
1 thru 45 . . . . @1.25
Becomes:
ARCHIE'S PAL JUGHEAD
June, 1993
46 thru 50 . . . . @1.25
51 thru 70 . . . . @1.50
71 thru 99 . . . . @1.50
100 A Storm Over Uniforms, x-over
(Betty #57, Archie #467) 1.50
101 thru 110 . . . . 1.75

JUGHEAD AS
CAPTAIN HERO
Archie Publications Oct., 1966
1 . . . . 35.00
2 . . . . 20.00

3 thru 7 . . . . @15.00

JUGHEAD'S FANTASY
Archie Publications Aug., 1960
1 . . . . 80.00
2 . . . . 60.00
3 . . . . 45.00

JUGHEAD'S JOKES
Archie Publications Aug., 1967
1 . . . . 26.00
2 . . . . 14.00
3 thru 5 . . . . @7.00
6 thru 10 . . . . @5.00
11 thru 30 . . . . @2.00
31 thru 77 . . . . @1.00
78 Sept., 1982 . . . . 1.00

JUGHEAD WITH
ARCHIE DIGEST
Archie Publications March, 1974
1 . . . . 15.00
2 . . . . 8.00
3 thru 10 . . . . @5.00
11 thru 91 . . . . 3.00
130 thru 138 . . . . @3.00
139 thru 144 . . . . 3.00

JUNGLE ADVENTURES
Skywald March–June 1971
1 F:Zangar,Jo-Jo,Blue Gorilla . 20.00
2 F:Sheena, Jo-Jo,Zangar 15.00
3 F:Zangar,Jo-Jo,White Princess 10.00

JUNGLE BOOK, THE
NBM 1997
TPB by P. Craig Russell, Kipling
adapt. 16.95

JUNGLE COMICS
Blackthorne
1 DSt(c) 2.00
2 . . . . 2.00
3 . . . . 2.00

JUNGLE TALES
OF TARZAN
Charlton Comics Dec., 1964
1 . . . . 30.00
2 . . . . 25.00
3 . . . . 25.00
4 July, 1965 . . . . 25.00

JUNGLE WAR STORIES
Dell Publishing Co.
July-Sept., 1962
1 P(c) all 25.00
2 . . . . 10.00
3 . . . . 10.00
4 . . . . 10.00
5 . . . . 10.00
6 . . . . 10.00
7 . . . . 10.00
8 . . . . 10.00
9 . . . . 10.00
10 . . . . 10.00
11 . . . . 10.00
Becomes:
GUERRILLA WAR
12 thru 14 . . . . @10.00

JUNIOR WOODCHUCKS
Walt Disney
1 CB,"Bubbleweight Champ" 2.00
2 CB,"Swamp of no Return" 2.00
3 "Rescue Run-Around" 2.00
4 "Cave Caper" 2.00

JURASSIC PARK
Topps
1 Movie Adapt.,w/card 5.00
1a Newsstand Ed. 4.00
2 Movie Adapt.,w/card 3.25
2a Newsstand Ed. 2.75
3 Movie Adapt.,w/card 3.25
3a Newsstand Ed. 2.75
4 Movie Adapt.,w/card 3.25
4a Newsstand Ed. 2.75
Ann.#1 Death Lizards 3.95

JURASSIC PARK:
ADVENTURES
Topps
1 thru 10 reprints titles . . . . . @1.95

JURASSIC PARK:
RAPTOR
Topps
1 SE w/Zorro #0 ashcan & cards . 3.25
2 w/3 cards 2.95

JURASSIC PARK:
RAPTORS ATTACK
Topps
1 SEt(s), ... 2.75
2 SEt(s), ... 2.75
3 SEt(s), ... 2.75
4 SEt(s), ... 2.75

JURASSIC PARK:
RAPTOR HIJACK
Topps
1 SEt(s), ... 2.50
2 SEt(s), ... 2.50
3 SEt(s), ... 2.50

Jurassic Park: The Lost World #2
© Topps Comics

COLOR PUB.

4 SEt(s), ... 2.50

[JURASSIC PARK:]
THE LOST WORLD
Topps 1997
1 (of 4) movie adapt 2.95
2 thru 4 . . . . @2.95

JUSTICE MACHINE
Noble Comics 1981–85
1 JBy(c) Mag size,B&W 30.00
2 MGu,Mag size,B&W 16.00
3 MGu,Mag size,B&W 10.00
4 MGu,Bluecobalt 8.00
5 MGu 7.00
Texas Comics
Ann.#1:BWG,I:Elementals, A:
Thunder Agents 5.00

JUSTICE MACHINE
[Featuring the Elementals]
Comico 1986
1 thru 4 . . . . @2.50

Justice Machine #2 © Comico

JUSTICE MACHINE
Comico 1987–89
1 MGu 2.50
2 MGu 2.00
3 thru 14 MGu . . . . @1.50
15 thru 27 MGu . . . . @1.75
28 MGu 1.95
29 MGu,IW 1.95
Ann.#1 . . . . 2.50
SummerSpectacular 1 . . . . 2.75
MINI SERIES 1990
1 thru 4 F:Elementals . . . . . . @1.95
Innovation 1990
1 . . . . 1.95
2 thru 4 The Ragnarok Portfilio @1.95
5 thru 7 Demon trilogy . . . . . @1.95

JUSTICE MACHINE:
CHIMERA CONSPIRACY
Millenium
1 AH,R&N:Justice Machine,
wraparound cover 2.50

JUST MARRIED
Charlton Comics Jan., 1958
1 . . . . 35.00
2 . . . . 20.00
3 thru 10 . . . . @15.00
11 thru 30 . . . . @10.00
31 thru 113 . . . . @8.00
114 Dec., 1976 . . . . 8.00

KABOOM
Awesome Entertainment 1997
1 JLb,JMs, ... 4.00
1a variant (c)s 3.00
2 JLb,JMs, ... 3.00
3 JLb,JMs, ... 3.00
4 JLb,JMs,Kaboom the
Barbarian,pt.1 (of 3) 2.50
5 JLb,JMs,Barbarian,pt.2 . . . . 2.50
6 JLb,JMs,Barbarian,pt.3 . . . . 2.50

KABUKI
Caliber Press
1 Color Gallery,32 paintings . . . 3.00
1-shot Color Special, inc. pin-up
gallery 3.00
1-shot Fear the Reaper (1994) . . 7.00

KABUKI: SKIN DEEP
Caliber
1 DMk 2.95
2 DMk(c) 2.95
2 AxR(c) 2.95
3 Origin issue 2.95
4 . . . . 2.95

KATO OF THE
GREEN HORNET
Now
1 BA,1st Kato solo story 2.50
2 BA,Kato in China contd. 2.50
3 Kato in China contd 2.50
4 Final Issue 2.50

KATO II
Now
1 VM,JSh,A:Karthage 2.50
2 VM,JSh,V:Karthage 2.50
3 VM,JSh,V:Karthage 2.50

KATY KEENE FASHION
BOOK MAGAZINE
Archie Publications
1955
1 . . . . 350.00
2 . . . . 200.00
3 thru 10 not published
11 thru 18 . . . . @150.00
19 . . . . 125.00
20 . . . . 125.00
21 . . . . 125.00
22 . . . . 125.00
23 Winter 1958-59 . . . . 125.00

KATY KEENE
PINUP PARADE
Archie Publications
1955
1 . . . . 350.00
2 . . . . 200.00
3 . . . . 175.00
4 . . . . 175.00

5 . . . . 175.00
6 . . . . 150.00
7 . . . . 150.00
8 . . . . 150.00
9 . . . . 150.00
10 . . . . 150.00
11 Story on comics 200.00
12 . . . . 150.00
13 . . . . 150.00
14 . . . . 150.00
15 Sept., 1961 . . . . 300.00

KELLY GREEN
Eclipse
1 SDr,O:Kelly Green 2.50
2 SDr,"One,Two,Three" 2.00
3 SDr,"Million Dollar Hit" 2.00
4 SDr,Rare 4.00

KELVIN MACE
Vortex
1 . . . . 6.50
1a 2nd printing 1.75
2 . . . . 4.00

KID DEATH & FLUFFY
Event Comics 1997
Spec.#1 Halloween Spec. John
Cebollero(c) 2.95
Spec.#1a Halloween Spec. JQ(c) . 2.95

KILLER TALES
Eclipse 1985
1 Tim Truman 1.75

KING COMICS PRESENTS
King Comics
1 I:Rick Dees, Angel Lopez 1.95

KING LEONARDO AND
HIS SHORT SUBJECTS
Dell Publishing Co.
Nov.-Jan., 1961-62
1 . . . . 100.00
2 . . . . 75.00
3 . . . . 75.00
4 . . . . 75.00

KING LOUIE & MOWGLI
Gold Key May, 1968
1 . . . . 30.00

KING OF DIAMONDS
Dell Publishing Co.
July-Sept., 1962
1 Ph(c) 40.00

KIT KARTER
Dell Publishing Co.
May-July, 1962
1 . . . . 25.00

KNIGHTS OF THE
ROUND TABLE
Dell Publishing Co.
Nov.-Jan., 1963-4
1 P(c) 35.00

KNUCKLES
Archie Comics
4 Lost Paradise	1.50
5	1.50
6 "Lost Paradise"	1.50
7 "Dark Vengeance"	1.50
8 "The Gauntlet"	1.50
9 x-over Sonic #56	1.75
10 "The Forgotten Tribe"	1.75
11 Sonic x-over	1.75
12 Sonic x-over	1.75
13 The Chaotix	1.75
14 "A Tenuous Grip on Reality"	1.75
15 "The Chaotix Caper" concl.	1.75
16 "Reunions"	1.75
17 "The Guardian Who Failed"	1.75
18 "Debt of Honor"	1.75

KNUCKLES: THE DARK LEGION
Archie Comics 1997
1	1.50
2	1.50
3 (of 3)	1.50

KOL MANIQUE RENAISSANCE
1	1.50
2	1.50

KOMAH
Anubis Press
1 Urban Decay Title	2.75

KOMBAT
Random Comics
1 (of 2) by Marcu Marshall & Pablo Villalobos	2.95
2 concl	2.95

KONA
Dell Publishing Co.
Feb.-April, 1962
1 P(c) all,SG	45.00
2 SG	20.00
3 SG	20.00
4 SG,B:Anak	20.00
5 SG	20.00
6 SG	20.00
7 SG	20.00
8 SG	20.00
9 SG	20.00
10 SG	20.00
11 SG	15.00
12 SG	15.00
13 SG	15.00
14 SG	15.00
15 SG	15.00
16 SG	15.00
17 SG	15.00
18 SG	15.00
19 SG	15.00
20 SG	15.00
21 SG	15.00

KONGA
Charlton Comics 1960–65
1 SD,DG(c), movie adapt.	200.00
2 DG(c)	100.00
3 SD	75.00
4 SD	75.00
5 SD	75.00
6 thru 15 SD	@55.00
16 thru 23	@30.00

KONGA'S REVENGE
Charlton Comics
2 Summer, 1962	30.00
3 SD,Fall, 1964	40.00
1 Dec., 1968	17.00

KOOKIE
Dell Publishing Co.
Feb.-April, 1962
1	60.00
2	50.00

KORAK, SON OF TARZAN
Gold Key Jan., 1964
1	50.00
2 thru 11	@30.00
12 thru 21	@20.00
22 thru 30	@10.00
31 thru 40	@8.00
41 thru 44	@5.00
45 Jan., 1972	5.00

Continued by DC

KRUSTY COMICS
Bongo Comics
1 Rise and Fall of Krustyland	2.25
2 Rise and Fall of Krustyland	2.25
3 Rise and Fall of Krustyland	2.25

KULL IN 3-D
Blackthorne
1	2.50
2	2.50
3	2.50

KUNG FU & NINJA
1	1.80
2	1.80
3	1.80
4	1.80

LAD: A DOG
Dell Publishing Co. 1961
1	30.00
2	25.00

LADY ARCANE
Hero Graphics
1 A: Flare,BU:O:Giant	4.95
2 thru 3	2.95

LADY DEATH
Chaos! Comics
1 BnP, A:Evil Ernie	50.00
1a signed gold foil	75.00
2 BnP	30.00
3 BnP	15.00
HC Foil Stamped Rep. #1-#3	24.95
TPB Rep. #1-#3	6.95
TPB The Reckoning	12.95
TPB The Reckoning, revised, BnP,Shu	12.95

Specials & 1-shots
1 Swimsuit Edition	12.00
1a Velvet Edition	30.00
1 reprint with 8-page pin-up gallery	2.95
1 Lady Death in Lingerie,various	
artists	5.00
1 Lady Death & the Women of Chaos! Gallery, pin-ups (1996)	2.25
1-shot Dragon Wars (1998)	2.95
1-shot Retribution (1998)	2.95
1-shot Retribution (1998) variant cover	2.95

LADY DEATH
Chaos! Comics 1998
½ signed, limited	30.00
1	2.95
2 R:Lady Demon	2.95
3 V:Levithia	2.95
4 V:Pagan	2.95
5 The Harrowing, pt.1	2.95
6 V:Uriel	2.95
7 V:Moloch	2.95
8 time to sieze Hell	2.95

LADY DEATH: BETWEEN HEAVEN & HELL
Chaos! Comics
1 V:Purgatori	6.00
1a Limited Edition 5,000c	30.00
2 Lives As Hope	4.00
3 V:Purgatori	4.00
4 final issue	4.00
TPB	12.95

LADY DEATH: THE CRUCIBLE
Chaos! Comics 1996
1 (of 6) BnP,SHu,	3.50
1 leather limited edition	18.00
2 BnP,SHu,	3.50
3 BnP,SHu,	3.50
4 BnP,SHu,	3.50
5 BnP,SHu,	3.50
6 BnP,SHu,V:Genocide,concl.	2.95

LADY DEATH: DEATH BECOMES HER
Chaos! Comics 1997
0 follows the *Crucible*, leads to *Wicked Ways*	2.95

LADY DEATH: THE ODYSSEY
Chaos! Comics 1996
Sneak Peek Preview	1.50
1 embossed cover	8.00
1 SHu(c) premium edition	22.00
2	4.00
3	4.00
4	4.00
4a variant cover	20.00
TPB	9.95

LADY PENDRAGON
Maximum Press 1996
1 mini-series	2.50
2	2.50
3 (of 3) MD2	2.50

LADY RAWHIDE
Topps 1995
1 All New Solo series	5.00
2 It Can't Happen Here,pt.2	3.50
3	3.00
4	3.00

5 conclusion 3.00
Spec.#1 Rep. Zorro #2-#3 . . . . . 6.50

LADY RAWHIDE
Topps
Mini-Series
1 DMG 4.00
1a DMG,signed, numbered 9.95
2 DMG 2.95
3 DMG 2.95
4 DMG, EM, "Intimate Wounds" . 2.95
5 DMG, EM 2.95
6 DMG 2.95
7 DMG 2.95
TPB 10.95

LADY RAWHIDE:
OTHER PEOPLE'S BLOOD
Topps 1996
Mini-Series
1 DMG,EM,"A Slice of Breast" . . 2.95

LADY VAMPRE
Blackout 1995
0 B&W 3.50
1 . . . . 3.00

LANCELOT STRONG,
THE SHIELD
Red Circle 1983
1 A:Steel Sterling 3.50
2 A:Steel Sterling 2.00
3 AN/EB,D:Lancelot Strong 2.00

LAND BEFORE TIME, THE
Kitchen Sink 1998
1-shot 3-D Adventure 3.95

LARS OF MARS
Eclipse 1987
1 3-D MA 2.50

LASER ERASER &
PRESSBUTTON
Eclipse 1985–87
1 GL,R:Laser Eraser 1.75
2 GL 1.75
3 GL,CK,"Tsultrine" 1.75
4 MC,"Death" 1.75
5 MC,JRy,"Gates of Hell" 95
6 "Corsairs of Illunium" 95
3-D#1 MC,GL(c),"Triple Cross" . . 1.50

LASH LARUE WESTERN
AC Comics
1 . . . . 3.50
Annual 2.95

LAST OF THE
VIKING HEROES
Genesis West
1 JK 4.00
2 JK 3.50
3 . . . . 3.00
4 . . . . 2.50
5A sexy cover 3.00
5B mild cover 2.50
6 . . . . 2.50
7 AA(c) 3.50
8 . . . . 2.25

9 Great Battle of Nidhogger 2.50
10 "Death Among the Heroes" . . . 2.50
Summer Spec.#1 FF,JK 3.50
Summer Spec.#2 . . . . 3.00
Summer Spec.#3,A:TMNT 2.50

LAUGH
Archie 1987–91
1 thru 29 . . . . @1.00

LAUREL AND HARDY
Dell Publishing Co. Oct., 1962
1 . . . . 55.00
2 . . . . 40.00
3 . . . . 40.00
4 . . . . 40.00

LAUREL & HARDY
Gold Key Jan., 1967
1 . . . . 50.00
2 Oct., 1967 . . . . 35.00

LAWMAN
Dell Publishing Co. Feb., 1959
1 Ph(c) all 100.00
2 . . . . 65.00
3 ATh 70.00
4 . . . . 40.00
5 . . . . 40.00
6 . . . . 40.00
7 . . . . 40.00
8 thru 11 . . . . @40.00

LAW AND ORDER
Maximum Press 1995
1 MMy,D:Law,I:New Law, Order . 2.50
2 V:Max Spur 2.50
3 V:Law's Murderer 2.50

LAW OF DREDD
Quality
1 V:Perps 5.00
2 BB,Lunar Olympics 4.00
3 BB,V:Judge Death 3.00
4 V:Father Earth 3.00
5 Cursed Earth 3.00
6 V:Perps 3.00
7 V:Perps 3.00
Fleetway
8 Blockmania 3.00
9 BB,DGi,Framed for murders . . 3.00
10 BB,Day the Law Died Pt.1 . . . 2.50
11 BB,Day the Law Died Pt.2 . . . 2.50
12 BB,V:Judge Cal 2.50
13 V:Judge Caligula 2.50
14 BB, V:Perps 2.50
15 Under investigation 2.50
16 V:Alien Mercenary 2.50
17 thru 24 . . . . @2.50
25 Ugly Clinic 2.50
26 Judge Dredd & Gavel? 2.50
27 Cycles,Lunatics & Graffiti
   Guerillas 2.50
28 Cadet Training Mission 2.50
29 "Guinea Pig that changed the
   world 2.50
30 Meka-City,V:Robot 2.50
31 Iso-Block 666 . . . . 2.50
32 Missing Game Show Hosts . . . 2.50
33 League of Fatties,final issue . . 3.00

LAZARUS
CHURCHYARD
Tundra
1 From UK Blast anthology 4.50
2 Goodnight Ladies 4.50

LEAGUE OF
CHAMPIONS
Hero Graphics
{Cont. from Champions #12}
1 Olympus Saga #4 . . . . 2.95
2 Olympus Saga #5,O:Malice . . . 2.95
3 Olympus Saga ends 2.95

LEATHERFACE
North Star
1 thru 3 . . . . @2.75

Legacy #2 © Majestic

LEGACY
Majestic
0 platinum 12.50
1 I:Legacy 2.25
2 . . . . 2.25

LEGEND OF CUSTER, THE
Dell Publishing Co. Jan., 1968
1 Ph(c) 25.00

LEGEND OF
SLEEPY HOLLOW
Tundra
One shot.BHa,W.Irving adapt. . . . 6.95

LEGEND OF
THE ELFLORD
Davdez Arts 1998
1 by Barry Blair & Colin Chan . . . 2.95
2 . . . . 2.50

LEGENDS OF
JESSE JAMES, THE
Gold Key Feb., 1966
1 . . . . 30.00

LEGENDS OF LUXURA
Comic Cavalcade 1998
Commemorative #1 by Kirk Lindo 5.95
Commemorative #1a deluxe ... 14.95

LEGENDS OF NASCAR
Vortex
1 HT,Bill Eliott ($1.50 cover Price)
  15,000 copies .... ±25.00
1a ($2.00 cover price) 45,000
  copies .... ±8.00
1b 3rd pr., 80,000 copies 5.00
2 Richard Petty 5.00
3 Ken Schroder 3.50
4 Bob Alison 3.00
5 Bill Elliott 2.50
6 Jr. Johnson 2.50
7 Sterling Marlin 2.25
8 Benny Parsons 2.00
9 Rusty Wallace 2.00

LEGENDS OF THE STARGRAZERS
Innovation
1 thru 5 .... @1.95

LEJENTIA
1 .... 1.95
2 .... 2.25

LEMONADE KID
AC Comics
1 .... 2.50

Leonard Nimoy's Primortals #13
© Teckno-Comics

LEONARD NIMOY'S PRIMORTALS
Teckno-Comics 1994
1 I:Primortals 5.50
2 Zeerus Reveals Himself 4.00
3 Contact 2.50
4 Message Deciphered 2.25
5 Place & Time Announced 2.25
6 Zeerus Arrives on Earth 2.25
7 Zeerus Recieved 2.25
8 Hyperspace Escape 2.25

9 Pristar Lands on Earth 1.95
10 V:U.S. Army 1.95
11 V:U.S. Army 1.95
12 V:Zeerus 2.25
13 thru 15 .... @2.25
Big Entertainment April 1996
0 SEa,MKb 2.25
1 .... 2.25
2 KWo,ANi 2.25
3 KWo,ANi 2.25
4 KWo,ANi 2.25
5 KWo,ANi 2.25
6 KWo,"Scorched Earth," concl. . 2.25
7 PB,KWo&ANi(c),Zeerus & Narab
  together again 2.25

LEONARDO
Mirage
1 TMNT Character 5.00

LEOPARD
Millenium
1 I:Leopard 2.95
1a Gold Cover 3.95
2 O:Leopard,V:Razor's Edge .. 2.95

LETHAL STRYKE
London Night Studios 1995
1 F:Stryke 3.00
2 O:Stryke 3.00
Ann. #1 EHr 3.00
Ann. #1 platinum edition 10.00

LETHAL STRIKE/ DOUBLE IMPACT: LETHAL IMPACT
London Night April 1996
1 by Jude Millien 3.00
1 limited 5.00
1 nude edition 6.00

LIBERTY PROJECT, THE
Eclipse 1987–88
1 I:Liberty Project 2.50
2 .... 1.75
3 V:Silver City Wranglers 1.75
4 .... 1.75
5 .... 1.75
6 F:Cimarron,"Misery and Gin" . 1.75
7 I:Menace 1.75
8 V:Savage 1.75

LIDSVILLE
Gold Key Oct., 1972
1 .... 20.00
2 .... 10.00
3 and 4 .... @10.00
5 Oct., 1973 .... 10.00

LIEUTENANT, THE
Dell Publishing Co.
April-June, 1962
1 Ph(c) 35.00

LIFE & ADVENTURES OF SANTA CLAUS
Tundra
GN MP,L.Frank Baum adapt. ... 24.95

LIFE IN HELL
Blackthorne
1 3-D 2.50

LIFE WITH ARCHIE
Archie Publications Sept., 1958
1 .... 225.00
2 .... 100.00
3 .... 60.00
4 .... 60.00
5 .... 60.00
6 .... 30.00
7 .... 30.00
8 .... 30.00
9 .... 30.00
10 .... 30.00
11 thru 20 .... @20.00
21 thru 30 .... @15.00
31 thru 40 .... @10.00
41 .... 7.00
42 B:Pureheart 5.00
43 .... 5.00
44 .... 5.00
45 .... 5.00
46 O:Pureheart 15.00
47 thru 59 .... @3.50
60 thru 100 .... @2.50
101 thru 285 .... @1.00

LIGHT FANTASTIC, THE
Innovation
1 Terry Pratchett adapt. 2.50
2 Adaptation continues 2.50
3 Adaptation continues 2.50
4 Adapt.conclusion 2.50

LIGHTNING COMICS PRESENTS
Lightning Comics
1 B&W Promo Ed. 3.50
1a B&W Promo Ed. Platinum .. 3.50
1b B&W Promo Ed. Gold 3.50

LILLITH: DEMON PRINCESS
Antarctic Press 1996
1 (of 3) from Warrior Nun Areala . 2.95
2 and 3 .... @2.95

LINCOLN-16
Skarwood Productions
1 GI 2.95
2 GI 2.95
3 GI 2.95

LINDA LARK
Dell Publishing Co.
Oct.-Dec., 1961
1 .... 25.00
2 .... 15.00
3 .... 15.00
4 .... 15.00
5 .... 15.00
6 .... 15.00
7 .... 15.00
8 .... 15.00

LINUS, THE LIONHEARTED
Gold Key Sept., 1965
1 .... 65.00

All comics prices listed are for *Near Mint* condition.

COLOR PUB.

LIPPY THE LION AND HARDY HAR HAR
Gold Key March, 1963
1 .... 60.00

LISA COMICS
Bongo Comics
1 F:Lisa Simpson 2.25

LITTLE AMBROSE
Archie Publications Sept., 1958
1 .... 75.00

Little Archie #137 © Archie Publications

LITTLE ARCHIE
Archie Publications
1956
1 .... 300.00
2 .... 150.00
3 .... 100.00
4 .... 100.00
5 .... 100.00
6 thru 10 .... @75.00
11 thru 20 .... @40.00
21 thru 30 .... @25.00
31 thru 40 .... @15.00
41 thru 60 .... @10.00
61 thru 80 .... @5.00
81 thru 100 .... @3.00
101 thru 180 .... @2.00

LITTLE ARCHIE MYSTERY
Archie Publications May, 1963
1 .... 75.00
2 Oct., 1963 .... 40.00

LITTLE AUDREY & MELVIN
Harvey Publications May, 1962
1 .... 50.00
2 thru 5 .... @20.00
6 thru 10 .... @15.00
11 thru 20 .... @10.00
21 thru 40 .... @7.00
41 thru 50 .... @5.00

51 thru 53 52 pgs Giant size .. @5.00
54 thru 60 .... @8.00
61 Dec., 1973 .... 6.00

LITTLE AUDREY TV FUNTIME
Harvey Publications Sept., 1962
1 A:Richie Rich 35.00
2 same 20.00
3 same 15.00
4 .... 15.00
5 .... 15.00
6 thru 10 .... @6.00
11 thru 20 .... @5.00
21 thru 32 .... @3.50
33 Oct., 1971 .... 3.50

LITTLE DOT DOTLAND
Harvey Publications July, 1962
1 .... 50.00
2 .... 25.00
3 .... 22.00
4 .... 18.00
5 .... 18.00
6 thru 10 .... @10.00
11 thru 20 .... @7.00
21 thru 50 .... @3.50
51 thru 60 .... @2.50
61 Dec., 1973 .... 2.50

LITTLE DOT'S UNCLES & AUNTS
Harvey Enterprises Oct., 1961
1 .... 55.00
2 .... 30.00
3 .... 25.00
4 .... 15.00
5 .... 15.00
6 thru 10 .... @12.00
11 thru 20 .... @10.00
21 thru 40 .... @7.00
41 thru 51 .... @5.00
52 April, 1974 .... 5.00

LITTLE LOTTA
Harvey Publications Nov., 1955
1 B:Richie Rich and Little Lotta 225.00
2 .... 125.00
3 .... 100.00
4 .... 60.00
5 .... 60.00
6 .... 45.00
7 .... 45.00
8 .... 45.00
9 .... 45.00
10 .... 45.00
11 thru 20 .... @30.00
21 thru 40 .... @20.00
41 thru 60 .... @15.00
61 thru 80 .... @7.00
81 thru 99 .... @5.00
100 thru 103 52 pgs .... @3.00
104 thru 120 .... @2.00
121 May, 1976 .... 2.00

LITTLE LOTTA FOODLAND
Harvey Publications Sept., 1963
1 68 pgs 75.00
2 .... 40.00
3 .... 25.00
4 .... 14.00

5 .... 14.00
6 thru 10 .... @10.00
11 thru 20 .... @7.00
21 thru 26 .... @5.50
27 .... 4.50
28 .... 4.50
29 Oct., 1972 .... 3.50

LITTLE MERMAID
Walt Disney
1 based on movie 1.75
2 "Serpent Teen" 1.50
3 "Guppy Love" 1.50
4 .... 1.50

LITTLE MONSTERS, THE
Gold Key Nov., 1964
1 .... 45.00
2 .... 25.00
3 thru 10 .... @15.00
11 thru 20 .... @10.00
21 thru 43 .... @10.00
44 Feb., 1978 .... 10.00

LITTLE MONSTERS
Now
1 thru 6 .... @1.75

LITTLE REDBIRDS
1 .... 2.50
2 .... 2.50
3 .... 2.50
4 .... 2.50

LITTLE SAD SACK
Harvey Publications Oct., 1964
1 Richie Rich(c) 30.00
2 .... 10.00
3 .... 10.00
4 .... 10.00
5 .... 10.00
6 thru 19 Nov. 1967 ...... @10.00

LITTLE STOOGES, THE
Gold Key Sept., 1972
1 .... 25.00
2 .... 12.00
3 .... 12.00
4 .... 12.00
5 .... 12.00
6 and 7 March, 1974 ...... @12.00

LLOYD LLEWELLYN
1 .... 2.00

LOBO
Dell Publishing Co.
Dec., 1965
1 .... 10.00
2 .... 8.00

LOCKE
Blackthorne
1 PO.Jones 1.75
2 TD 2.25
3 .... 1.25
4 .... 1.25
5 .... 1.25

LONE RANGER, THE
Gold Key Sept., 1964
1	50.00
2	25.00
3	20.00
4	20.00
5	20.00
6 thru 10	@15.00
11 thru 18	@15.00
18 thru 27	@12.00
28 March, 1977	12.00

Lone Ranger and Tonto #4 © Topps

LONE RANGER AND TONTO, THE
Topps 1994
1 JLd,TT,RM,The Last Battle	2.50
2 JLd,TT,RM	2.50
3 JLd,TT,RM, O:Lone Ranger	2.50
4 JLd,TT,RM, It Crawls	2.50
TPB rep. #1–#4	9.95

LOOKERS
Avatar
Combo Spec. 16pg.	3.00
Combo Spec. nude cover, 16pg.	5.00

LOST HEROES
Davdez Arts 1998
0 by Rob Prior, lost SF heroes	2.95
1 thru 5	@2.50

LOST IN SPACE
Innovation
{based on TV series}
1 O:Jupiter II Project	3.00
2 "Cavern of IdyllicSummersLost"	2.75
2a Special Edition	2.50
3 Do Not Go Gently into that Good Night',Bill Mumy script	2.50
4 "People are Strange"	2.50
5 The Perils of Penelope	2.50
6 Time Warp	2.50
7 thru 9	@2.50
10 inc.Afterthought	2.50
11 F:Judy Robinson	2.50
12	2.95
Project Krell	2.50

Ann.#1 (1991)	2.95
Ann.#2 (1992)	2.95
Spec.#1 & #2 rep. Seduction of the Innocent	@2.50
GN Strangers among Strangers	6.00
1-shot Project Robinson, follows story in issue #12 (1993)	2.50

Becomes

LOST IN SPACE: VOYAGE TO THE BOTTOM OF THE SOUL
Innovation 1993–94
13	2.95
14 thru 18	@2.50

LOST PLANET
Eclipse 1987–88
1 BHa,I:Tyler FLynn	2.00
2 BHa,R:Amelia Earhart	1.75
3 BHa	1.25
4 BHa,"Devil's Eye"	1.25
5 BHa,A:Amelia Earhart	2.00
6	2.00

LOVECRAFT
Adventure Comics
1 "The Lurking Fear" adapt.	2.95
2 Beyond the Wall of Sleep	2.95
3	2.95
4	2.95

LOVE DIARY
Charlton Comics July, 1958
1	30.00
2	15.00
3	10.00
4	10.00
5	7.00
6	10.00
7 thru 10	@7.00
11 thru 15	@3.00
16 thru 20	@3.00
21 thru 40	@1.50
41 thru 101	@1.00
102 Dec., 1976	1.00

LOVE SHOWDOWN COLLECTION
Archie Comics 1997
TPB x-over rep. Archie #429 (pt.1), Betty #19 (pt.2), Betty & Veronica #82, (pt.3), Veronica #39 (pt.4) Return of Cheryl Blossom	4.95

LUCIFER'S HAMMER
Innovation 1993–94
1 thru 6 Larry Niven & Jerry Pournelle novel adaptation	@2.50

LUCY SHOW, THE
Gold Key June, 1963
1 Ph(c)	120.00
2 Ph(c)	75.00
3 thru 5	@60.00

LUDWIG VON DRAKE
Dell Publishing Co. Nov.-Dec., 1961
1	65.00
2 thru 4	@35.00

LUFTWAFFE 1946
Antarctic Press 1998
1 color special, by Ted Namura	2.95

LUGER
Eclipse 1986–87
1 TY,I:Luger,mini-series	2.00
2 TY	1.75
3 TY,BHa,V:Sharks	1.75

LUNATIC
1 and 2	@1.75

LUNATIC FRINGE
Innovation
1	1.95
2	1.75

LUNATIC FRINGE
Innovation
1	1.75

LUXURA
Comic Cavalcade 1998
Commemorative #1 by Kirk Lindo	5.95
Commemorative #1a deluxe	14.95

LUXURA COLLECTION
Brainstorm
Commemorative edition, red foil cover, 48pg.	10.00

LYNCH MOB
Chaos! Comics
1 GCa(c), I:Mother Mayhem	3.00
2 Lynch Mob Loses	2.50
3 1994 Time Trip	2.50
3a Gold cover	3.00
4 Mother Mayhem at UN	2.50

LYNDON B. JOHNSON
Dell Publishing Co. March, 1965
1 Ph(c)	25.00

M
Eclipse 1990–91
1 thru 4 JMu	4.95

MACROSS
Comico
1	12.00

Becomes:
Robotech, The Macross Saga

MAD FOLLIES
E.C. Comics
1963
(N#)	275.00
2 1964	200.00
3 1965	150.00
4 1966	165.00
5 1967	125.00
6 & 7 1968 and 1969	@100.00

MAD HOUSE
Red Circle 1974–82
95 thru 97 Horror stories	@10.00
98 thru 130 Humor stories	@5.00
Annual #8 thru #11	@6.00

MADMAN
Tundra 1992
1	15.00
2	12.00
3	10.00

MADMAN ADVENTURES
Tundra 1992
1 R & N:Madman	10.00
2	8.00
3	5.00

MADRAVEN HALLOWEEN SPECIAL
Hamilton Comics 1995
1 Song of the Silkies	2.95

MAD SPECIAL
E.C. Publications, Inc.
Fall, 1970
1	75.00
2	50.00
3	35.00
4 thru 8	@35.00
9 thru 13	@30.00
14	20.00
15	25.00
16	20.00
17	20.00
18	22.00
19 thru 21	@22.00
22 thru 31	@10.00
32	12.00
33 thru 58	@8.00

MAGE
Comico
1 MWg,I:Kevin Matchstick	20.00
2 MWg,I:Edsel	10.00
3 MWg,V:Umbra Sprite	8.00
4 MWg,V:Umbra Sprite	8.00
5 MWg,I:Sean (Spook)	8.00
6 MWg,Grendel begins	22.00
7 MWg,Grendel	10.00
8 MWg,Grendel	6.00
9 MWg,Grendel	6.00
10 MWg,Grendel,Styx	6.00
11 MWg,Grendel,Styx	6.00
12 MWg,D:Sean,Grendel	6.00
13 MWg,D:Edsel,Grendel	6.00
14 MWg,Grendel,O:Kevin	6.00
15 MWg,D:Umbra Sprite	12.00

MAGEBOOK
Comico
1 rep. Mage #1-4	8.95
2 rep. Mage #5-8	8.95

MAGIC FLUTE
Eclipse 1989
1 CR	4.95

MAGILLA GORILLA
Gold Key May, 1964
1	40.00
2 thru 10 Dec. 1968	@30.00

MAGILLA GORILLA
Charlton Comics Nov., 1970
1	65.00
2 thru 5	@35.00

MAGNUS: ROBOT FIGHTER
Gold Key Feb., 1963
1 RM,I:Magnus,Teeja,A-1, I&B:Capt.Johner&aliens	250.00
2 RM,I:Sen.Zeremiah Clane	125.00
3 RM,I:Xyrkol	125.00
4 RM,I:Mekamn,Elzy	75.00
5 RM,The Immortal One	75.00
6 RM,I:Talpa	70.00
7 RM,I:Malev-6,ViXyrkol	85.00
8 RM,I:Outsiders(Chet, Horio, Toun, Malf)	70.00
9 RM, I:Madmot	70.00
10 RM,Mysterious Octo-Rob	70.00
11 RM,I:Danae,Neo-Animals	50.00
12 RM,The Volcano Makers	50.00
13 RM,I:Dr Lazlo Noel	55.00
14 RM,The Monster Robs	50.00
15 RM,I:Mogul Radur	50.00
16 RM,I:Gophs	50.00
17 RM,I:Zypex	50.00
18 RM,I:V'ril Trent	50.00
19 RM,Fear Unlimited	50.00
20 RM,I:Bunda the Great	50.00
21 RM, Space Spectre	50.00
22 Rep. #1	35.00
23 DSp,Mission Disaster	35.00
24 Pied Piper of North Am	35.00
25 The Micro Giants	35.00
26 The Venomous Vaper	35.00
27 Panic in Pacifica	35.00
28 Threats from the Depths	35.00
29 Rep. #7	16.00
30 Rep. #15	16.00
31 Rep. #14	16.00
32 Rep. #2	16.00
33 Rep. #21	16.00
34 Rep. #13	16.00
35 Rep. #6	16.00
36 Rep. #8	16.00
37 Rep. #11	16.00
38 Rep. #12	16.00
39 Rep. #16	16.00
40 Rep. #17	16.00
41 Rep. #18	16.00
42 Rep. #19	16.00
43 Rep. #20	16.00
44 Rep. #23	16.00
45 Rep. #24	16.00
46 Rep. #25	16.00

MAJOR DAMAGE
Invictus Studios
1 I:Major Damage	2.25
2 V:Godkin	2.25
3 First Contact Conclusion	2.25

MAKABRE
Apocalypse
1 Gangsters	3.95

MALICE
Heroic Publishing
1 I:Queen of the Dead	1.95

MANDRAKE THE MAGICIAN
King Comics 1966
1	50.00
2	30.00
3	30.00

Mandrake the Magician #5
© King Comics

4 A:Girl Phantom	30.00
5 Cape Cod Caper	30.00
6	30.00
7 O:Lothar	30.00
8	35.00
9 A:Brick Bradford	30.00
10 A:Rip Kirby	35.00

MAN FROM PLANET X
Planet X Prod.
1	3.00

MAN FROM U.N.C.L.E.
Gold Key Feb., 1965
1 "The Explosive Affair"	150.00
2 "The Forthur Cookie Affair"	75.00
3 "The Deadly Devices Affair"	50.00
4 "The Rip Van Solo Affair"	50.00
5 "Ten Little Uncles Affair"	50.00
6 "The Three Blind Mice Affair"	50.00
7 "The Pixilated Puzzle Affair" I:Jet Dream (back-up begins)	55.00
8 "The Floating People Affair"	50.00
9 "Spirit of St.Louis Affair"	50.00
10 "The Trojan Horse Affair"	50.00
11 "Three-Story Giant Affair"	40.00
12 "Dead Man's Diary Affair"	40.00
13 "The Flying Clowns Affair"	40.00
14 "Great Brain Drain Affair"	40.00
15 "The Animal Agents Affair"	40.00
16 "Instant Disaster Affair"	40.00
17 "The Deadly Visions Affair"	40.00
18 "The Alien Affair"	40.00
19 "Knight in Shining Armor Affair"	40.00
20 "Deep Freeze Affair"	40.00
21 rep. #10	35.00
22 rep. #7	35.00

MAN FROM U.N.C.L.E.
Entertainment
1 thru 11	1.50

MAN FROM U.N.C.L.E.
Millennium
1 The Birds of Prey Affair,pt.1	2.95
2 The Birds of Prey Affair,pt.2	2.95

COLOR PUB.

MANGA SHI 2000
Crusade Entertainment 1997
1 (of 3) BiT, "Final Jihad" flip-book
Shi: Heaven and Earth 2.95
2 BiT, flip-book Tomoe:
Unforgettable Fire preview . . . 2.95
3 BiT, conclusion 2.95

MANGLE TANGLE TALES
Innovation
1 . . . . 2.95

MANIFEST DESTINY
1 . . . . 1.95

MAN IN BLACK
Harvey Publications Sept., 1957
1 . . . . 75.00
2 . . . . 45.00
3 . . . . 45.00
4 March, 1958 . . . . 45.00

MANIK
Millenium/Expand (1995)
1 I:Macedon, Arsenal,Cardinal . . 2.95

MAN OF WAR
Eclipse 1987–88
1 thru 3 . . . . @1.75

MARK RAND'S SKY TECHNOLOGIES INC.
Red Mercenary 1995
1 I:Jae,Elliot,Firnn 2.95

MARKSMAN, THE
Hero Graphics
1 O:Marksman, Pt.#1 . . . . 1.95
2 O:Marksman, Pt.#2 . . . . 1.95
3 O:Marksman ends.I:Basilisk . . . 1.95
4 A:Flare 1.95
5 I:Radar,Sonar 1.95
Ann. #1, A:Champions 1.95

MARRIED... WITH CHILDREN
Now
1 . . . . 6.00
1a 2nd printing 2.00
2 . . . . 4.00
3 . . . . 3.00
4 . . . . 2.50
5 . . . . 2.50
6 . . . . 2.00
7 . . . . 2.50
[2nd Series]
1 Peg-Host of Radio Show 2.25
2 The Bundy Invention 1.95
3 Psychodad,(photo cover) 1.95
4 Mother-In-Law,(photo cover) . . 1.95
5 Bundy the Crusader 1.95
6 Bundy J: The Order of the Mighty
Warthog 1.95
7 Kelly the VJ 1.95
Spec. 1.95
3-D Spec. 2.50

MARRIED WITH CHILDREN: DYSFUNCTIONAL FAMILY
Now
1 I:The Bundies 2.50
2 TV Appearance 2.50
3 Morally Pure Bundys 2.50

MARRIED WITH CHILDREN: FLASHBACK SPECIAL
Now
1 Peg and Al's first date 1.95
2 and 3 . . . . @1.95

MARRIED WITH CHILDREN: KELLY BUNDY SPECIAL
Now
1 with poster 1.95
2 and 3 with poster . . . . @1.95

MARRIED... WITH CHILDREN: QUANTUM QUARTET
Now
1 thru 4 Fantastic Four parody @1.95
Fall 1994 Spec., flip book 1.95

MARRIED WITH CHILDREN 2099
Mirage
1 thru 3 Cable Parody . . . . @2.50

MARS
First
1 thru 12 . . . . @1.25

Mars Attacks #2 © Topps

MARS ATTACKS
Topps
1 KG(s) 6.00
2 . . . . 4.00
3 thru 6 KG(s) 4.00

[Series 2] 1995
1 Counterstrike 3.50
2 Counterstrike,pt.2 . . . . 2.95
3 Counterstrike,pt.3 . . . . 2.95
4 Counterstrike,pt.4 Convictions . 2.95
5 Counterstrike concl. 2.95
6 "The Rescue of Janice Brown,"
pt. 1 . . . . 2.95
7 "The Rescue of Janice Brown,"
pt. 2 . . . . 2.95
8 . . . . 2.95
Spec. Baseball 3.00

MARS ATTACKS HIGH SCHOOL
Topps 1997
Spec. #1 (of 2) BSz(c) 2.95
Spec. #2 . . . . 2.95

MARS ATTACKS THE SAVAGE DRAGON
Topps
1 . . . . 3.00
2 . . . . 3.00
3 . . . . 3.00
4 (of 4) 3.00

MARSHALL LAW: HATEFUL DEAD
Apocalypse
1 "Rise of the Zombies" 5.95

MARTIANS!!! IN 3-D
1 . . . . 2.00

MARY WORTH
ARGO March, 1956
1 . . . . 45.00

MASKED MAN
Eclipse 1985–88
1 . . . . 3.00
2 . . . . 2.00
3 . . . . 2.00
4 . . . . 2.00
5 . . . . 2.00
6 V:Roxie Lamada 2.00
7 . . . . 2.00
8 "Roxy" 1.75
9 W:Dick and Maggie 1.75
10 . . . . 2.00

MASTERWORK SERIES
Seagate DC
1 FFrep.DC,ShiningKnight 1.50
2 FFrep.DC,ShiningKnight 1.50
3 BWr,Horror DC rep. 1.50

MAVERICK
Dell Publishing Co. April, 1958
1 Ph(c) all 275.00
2 Ph(c) 125.00
3 Ph(c) 125.00
4 Ph(c) 125.00
5 Ph(c) 125.00
6 thru 15 Ph(c) . . . . @85.00

MAVERICK MARSHALL
Charlton Comics Nov., 1958
1 . . . . 30.00

2	20.00
3	20.00
4	20.00
5	20.00
6	20.00
7 May, 1960	20.00

MAVERICKS
Dagger
1 PuD,RkL, I:Mavericks	2.50
2 PuD,RkL	2.50

MAXIMORTAL
King Hell/Tundra
1 RV,A:True-Man	4.50
2 Crack in the New World	4.25
3 RV,Secret of the Manhattan Project revealed	4.25
4	4.25
5 A:True Man	3.25
6 A:El Guano	3.25
Kitchen Sink 1997
HC Book 1: Cheek, Chin, Knuckle or Knee	35.00

MAYA
Gold Key March, 1968
1	25.00

MAZE AGENCY
Comico
1 O:Maze Agency	3.00
2 thru 6	@2.50
7	2.75
8 thru 11	@1.95
12	2.50
13 thru 15	@1.95
16 thru 23	@2.50
Spec. #1	2.75

McHALE'S NAVY
Dell Publishing Co.
May-July, 1963
1 Ph(c) from TV show	55.00
2 Ph(c)	35.00
3 Ph(c)	35.00

McKEEVER & THE COLONEL
Dell Publishing Co.
Feb.-April, 1963
1 Ph(c)	45.00
2 Ph(c)	30.00
3 Ph(c)	30.00

M.D. GEIST
CPM
1 Cartoon Adaptation	2.95
2 J:Army	2.95
3 V:Final Terminator	2.95

MECHANICS
Fantagraphics
1 HB,rep.Love & Rockets	3.00
2 HB,rep.Love & Rockets	2.50
3 HB,rep.Love & Rockets	2.50

MEDIA STARR
Innovation
1 thru 3	@1.95

MEGALITH
Continuity
1 MT	6.00
2 MT	4.00
3 MT, Painted issue	2.50
4 NA,TVE	2.50
5 NA,TVE	2.50
6 MN	2.50
7 MN	2.50
8	2.50
9 SDr(i)	2.50
10	2.50
[2nd Series, Deathwatch 2000]
0 Deathwatch 2000 prologue	5.00
1 Deathwatch 2000 Pt.5,w/card	2.50
2 Deathwatch 2000 Pt.10,w/card	2.50
3 pt.16,Indestructible(c),w/card	2.50
4 and 5 Rise of Magic	@2.50
6 and 7	2.50

MEGATON
1	1.50
Entity Comics
Holiday Spec. w/card	2.95

MEGATON EXPLOSION
1 RLd,AMe,I:Youngblood preview	25.00

MEGATON MAN
Kitchen Sink
1 Don Simpson art, I:Megaton Man	6.00
1a rep. B&W	2.00
2	4.00
3 and 4	@3.00
5	2.50
6 Border Worlds	2.50
7 Border Worlds	2.50
8 Border Worlds	2.50
9 Border Worlds	2.50
10 final issue, 1986	2.50

MELTING POT
Kitchen Sink
1	4.00
2 and 3	@2.95
4	3.50
TPB KEa,SBs, rep.	19.95

Memories #1 © Epic

HC signed, numbered	50.00

MELVIN MONSTER
Dell Publishing Co.
April-June, 1965
1	125.00
2 thru 10	@75.00

[Katshuiro Otomo's] MEMORIES
Epic 1992
1	2.50

MEN FROM EARTH
Future Fun
1 based on Matt Mason toy	6.50

MENACE
Awesome Entertainment 1998
1 by Jada Pinkett & Don Fraga	2.50
2	2.50
3	2.50

MERCENARY
NBM
The Voyage	10.95
The Black Globe	9.95
The Fortress	9.95

MERCHANTS OF DEATH
Eclipse 1988
1 King's Castle, The Hero	3.50
2 King's Castle,Soldiers of Fortune	3.50
3 Ransom, Soldier of Fortune	3.50
4 ATh(c),Ransom, Men o/t Legion	3.50
5 Ransom,New York City Blues	3.50

MERLIN REALM
Blackthorne
1 3-D	2.50

META 4
First 1990
1 IG	3.95
2 IG	2.25
3 IG/JSon,final monthly	2.25

METAL MILITIA
Entity Comics 1995
1 I:Metal Militia	2.50
1a with Video Game	6.95
2 ICO	2.50
3 F:Detective Calahan	2.50
Ashcan	2.50

MICHAELANGELO
Mirage
1 TMNT Character	15.00

MICKEY & DONALD
Gladstone
1 1449 Firestone	8.00
2	4.00
3 Man of Tomorrow	3.00
4 thru 15	@2.50
16 giant-size	2.50
17	3.00
18	4.00
Becomes:	

DONALD AND MICKEY
19 thru 26 . . . . @1.50

MICKEY MANTLE COMICS
Magnum
1 JSt,Rise to Big Leagues 1.75

MICKEY MOUSE
Gladstone
219 FG,Seven Ghosts 6.00
220 FG,Seven Ghosts 7.00
221 FG,Seven Ghosts 7.00
222 FG,Editor in Grief 5.00
223 FG,Editor in Grief 4.00
224 FG,Crazy Crime Wave 3.00
225 FG,Crazy Crime Wave 3.00
226 FG,Captive Castaways 3.00
227 FG,Captive Castaways 3.00
228 FG,Captive Castaways 3.00
229 FG,Bat Bandit 3.00
230 FG,Bat Bandit 2.50
231 FG,Bobo the Elephant . . . 2.50
232 FG,Bobo the Elephant . . . 2.50
233 FG,Pirate Submarine 2.50
234 FG,Pirate Submarine 2.50
235 FG,Photo Racer 2.50
236 FG,Photo Racer 2.50
237 FG,Race for Riches 2.50
238 FG,Race for Riches 2.50
239 FG,Race for Riches 2.50
240 FG,March of Comics 2.50
241 FG 4.00
242 FG 2.50
243 FG 2.50
244 FG,60th Anniv 5.00
245 FG 2.25
245 FG 2.25
246 FG 2.25
247 FG 2.25
248 FG 2.25
249 FG 5.00
250 FG 2.25
251 FG 2.25
252 FG 2.25
253 FG 2.25
254 FG 2.25
255 FG 4.00
256 FG 4.00

MICKEY MOUSE
Walt Disney 1990
1 "The Phantom Gondolier" . . . 3.50
2 . . . . 3.00
3 . . . . 2.50
4 . . . . 2.50
5 . . . . 2.50
6 . . . . 2.00
7 Phantom Blot 2.00
8 Phantom Blot 2.00
9 . . . . 2.00
10 Sky Adventure 2.00
11 When Mouston Freezes Over . 2.00
12 Hail & Farewell 2.00
13 "What's Shakin'" 2.00
14 Mouseton,Eagle-Landing 2.00
15 "Lost Palace of Kashi" 2.00
16 "Scoundrels in Space" 2.00
17 "Sound of Blunder" Pt.1 . . . 1.75
18 "Sound of Blunder" Pt.2 . . . 1.75
19 50th Ann. Fantasia Celebration
  Sorcerer's Apprentice adapt . . 1.50

MICKEY SPILLANE'S MIKE DANGER
Tekno Comix 1995
1 I:Mike Danger 2.25
2 Underside of the City 1.95
3 Judicial System 1.95
4 Mike's First Job 1.95
5 Old New York 1.95
6 Sin Syndicate Leader 2.25
7 thru 11 . . . . @2.25
Big Entertainment 1996
1 . . . . 2.25
2 . . . . 2.25
3 MCn,PGr,TBe,EB 2.25
4 . . . . 2.25
5 "Time Heels" 2.25
6 TBe,"Paradox Rule" 2.25
7 TBe,"Red Menace," pt.1 . . . . 2.25
8 TBe,"Red Menace," pt.2 . . . . 2.25
9 TBe,"Red Menace," pt.3. . . . . 2.25
10 TBe,"Red Menace," concl. . . 2.25

MICROBOTS, THE
Gold Key Dec., 1971
1 . . . . 10.00

MIDNIGHT EYE: GOKU PRIVATE INVESTIGATOR
Viz
1 A.D. 2014: Tokyo city 5.25
2 V:Hakuryu,A:Yoko 4.95
3 A:Ryoko,Search for Ryu 4.95
4 Goku vs. Ryu 4.95
5 Leilah Abducted 4.95
6 Lisa's I.D. discovered 4.95

MIGHTY COMICS
{Prev: Flyman}
40 A:Web 12.00
41 A:Shield, Black Hood 10.00
42 A:Black Hood 10.00
43 A:Shield, Black Hood,Web . . 9.00
44 A:Black Hood, Steel Sterling
  Shield 9.00
45 Shield-Black Hood team-up
  O:Web 9.00
46 A:Steel Sterling, Black Hood,
  Web 9.00
47 A:Black Hood & Mr.Justice . . 9.00
48 A:Shield & Hangman 9.00
49 Steel Sterling-Black Hood team
  up, A:Fox 9.00

[ALL NEW ADVENTURES OF] THE MIGHTY CRUSADERS
Red Circle
[1st Series] 1983
1 O:Shield (Joe Higgins & Bill
  Higgins) 25.00
2 MSy,O:Comet 20.00
3 O:Fly-Man 15.00
4 A:Fireball,Jaguar,Web,Fox,
  Blackjack Hangman & more
  Golden Age Archie Heroes . 18.00
5 I:Ultra-Men&TerrificThree . . . 15.00
Archie Publications
6 V:Maestro,A:Steel Sterling . . 12.00
7 O:Fly-Girl,A:Steel Sterling . . 12.00
[2nd Series]
1 RB,R:Joe Higgins & Lancelot
  Strong as the SHIELD, Mighty
  Crusaders, A:Mr.Midnight 1.50

2 RB,V:Brain Emperor & Eterno . 1.50
3 RB,I:Darkling 1.50
4 DAy,TD 1.50
5 . . . . 1.00
6 DAy,TD,Shield 1.00
7 . . . . 1.00
8 . . . . 1.00
9 Trial of the Shield 1.00
10 . . . . 1.00
11 DAy,D:Gold Age Black Hood, I:
  Riot Squad, series based on toy
  lines 1.00
12 DAy,I:She-Fox 1.00
13 Last issue 1.00

MIGHTY HERCULES, THE
Gold Key July, 1963
1 . . . . 75.00
2 . . . . 60.00

Mighty Morphin Power Rangers #2
© Hamilton

MIGHTY MORPHIN POWER RANGERS
Hamilton 1994–95
1 From TV Series 2.75
2 Switcheroo 2.50
3 . . . . 2.25
4 F:White Ranger 1.95
5 F:Pink Ranger 1.95
6 V:Garganturon 1.95
TPB Re. #1-#6 photo (c) 9.95
[Series 2] 1995
1 Unstoppable Force 1.95
2 V:Mechanical Octopus 1.95
3 . . . . 1.95
4 Lost Ranger 1.95
[Series 3] 1995
1 O:Green Ranger 1.95
2 O:Green Ranger 1.95
3 I:New Megazords 1.95

MIGHTY MOUSE
Spotlight 1987
1 FMc,PC(c) 1.50
2 FMc,CS(c) 1.50
1 Holiday Special 1.75

MIGHTY MUTANIMALS
Archie Publications
[Mini-Series]

1 Cont.from TMNT Adventures#19, A:Raphael, Man Ray, Leatherhead, Mondo Gecko,Deadman, Wingnut & Screwloose	1.25
2 V:Mr.Null,Malinga,Soul and Bean and the Malignoid Army	1.25
3 Alien Invasion help off, Raphael returns to Earth	1.25
4 "Days of Future Past"	1.25
5 "Into the Sun"	1.25
6 V:Null & 4 Horsemen Pt#2	1.25
7 Jaws of Doom	1.50
Spec.#1 rep. all #1-3 +SBi pin-ups	2.95

MIGHTY MUTANIMALS
Archie

1 Quest for Jagwar's Mother	1.25
2 V:Snake Eyes	1.25
3	1.25
4 "Days of Future Past"	1.25
5 "Into the Sun"	1.25
6 V:Null & 4 Horsemen Pt#2	1.25
7 Jaws of Doom	1.50

MIGHTY SAMSON
Gold Key 1964–82

1 O:Mighty Samson	50.00
2	20.00
3	20.00
4	20.00
5	20.00
6 thru 10	@15.00
11 thru 20	@12.00
21 thru 32	@10.00

MIKE GRELL'S SABLE
First

1 thru 8 rep.	@1.75
9	1.75
10 Triptych	1.75

MIKE SHAYNE PRIVATE EYE
Dell Publishing Co.
Nov.–Jan., 1961-62

1	35.00
2	20.00
3	20.00

MILLENNIUM INDEX
Independent Comics 1988

1	2.00
2	2.00

MILTON THE MONSTER & FEARLESS FLY
Gold Key May, 1966

1	55.00

MIRACLEMAN
Eclipse 1985–94

1 R:Miracleman	5.00
2 AD,Moore,V:Kid Miracleman	4.00
3 AD,Moore,V:Big Ben	4.00
4 AD,Moore,R:Dr.Garganza	4.00
5 AD,Moore,O:Miracleman	4.00
6 Moore,V:Miracledog, D:Evelyn	

Miracleman #4 © Eclipse

Cream	4.00
7 Moore,D:Dr.Garganza	4.00
8 Moore	4.00
9 RV,Moore,Birth of Miraclebaby	4.50
10 JRy,RV,Moore	4.00
11 JTo,Moore,Book III, I:Miraclewoman	5.00
12 thru 14 Moore	5.00
15 Moore	12.00
16 thru 23	@4.00
24 BWS(c),NGa(s),	5.00
25 thru 28	@2.95
3-D Special #1	2.75
Graphic Albums	
HC Book 1 A Dream of Flying	29.95
TPB Book 1 A Dream of Flying	9.95
HC Book 2 The Red Kings Syndrome	30.95
TPB Book 2 The Red Kings Syndrome	9.95
HC Book 3 Olympus	30.95
TPB Book 3 Olympus	12.00

MIRACLEMAN APOCRYPHA
Eclipse 1991–92

1 inc."Rascal Prince"	2.50
2 Miracleman, Family Stories	2.50
3	2.50

MIRACLEMAN FAMILY
Eclipse 1988

1 British Rep.,A:Kid Miracleman	1.95
2 Alan Moore (s)	1.95

MIRACLE SQUAD, THE
Upshot/Fantagraphics 1986

1 Hollywood 30's	2.00
2 thru 4	@2.00

MISS FURY
Adventure Comics

1 O:Cat Suit	2.50
2 Miss Fury impersonator	2.50
3 A:Three Miss Fury's	2.50
4 conclusion	2.50

MISSION IMPOSSIBLE
Dell Publishing Co. May, 1967

1 Ph(c)	100.00
2 Ph(c)	60.00
3 Ph(c)	50.00
4 Ph(c)	50.00
5 Ph(c)	50.00

MISSIONS IN TIBET
Dimension Comics 1995

1 I:New Series	2.50
2 F:Orlando,Ting,Alex	2.50
3 Two Worlds Collide	2.50
4 V:Sada	2.50

MISS PEACH
(& SPECIAL ISSUES)
Dell Publishing Co. 1963

1	50.00

MR. AND MRS. J. EVIL SCIENTIST
Gold Key Nov., 1963

1	60.00
2	40.00
3	40.00
4	40.00

MR. JIGSAW

Spec. #1	1.75

MR. MONSTER
Eclipse 1985–87

1 I:Mr. Monster	9.00
2 DSt(c)	5.00
3 V:Dr. NoZone	3.50
4 "Trapped in Dimension X"	3.00
5 V:Flesh-eating Amoebo	3.00
6 KG,SD,reprints	3.00
7	3.00
8 V:Monster in the Atomic Telling Machine	3.00
9 V:Giant Clams	3.00
10 R:Dr.No Zone, 3-D	2.00

MR. MONSTER ATTACKS
Tundra

1 DGb,SK,short stories	4.25
2 SK,short stories cont.	4.25
3 DGb,last issue	4.25

MR. MONSTER SUPERDUPER SPECIAL
Eclipse 1986–87

1	2.50
2	2.00
3	2.00
4	2.00
5	2.00
6	2.00
Hi-Voltage Super Science	2.00
3-D Spec. Hi-Octane Horror,JKu, "Touch of Death" reprint	1.75
Triple Treat	3.95

MR. MONSTER TRUE CRIME
Eclipse

1	1.75

2 . . . . 1.75
3-D Spec. #1 . . . . 2.00

MR. MUSCLES
Charlton Comics 1956
22 . . . . 40.00
23 . . . . 35.00

MR. MYSTIC
Eclipse
1 . . . . 2.00
2 . . . . 2.00
3 . . . . 2.00

MR. T AND THE T FORCE
Now
1 NA,R:Mr.T,V:Street Gangs 2.50
1a Gold Ed. 10.00
2 NA,V:Demons 2.25
3 NBy,w/card 2.25
4 NBy,In Urban America 2.25
5 thru 10, with card . . . . @2.25

MISTER X
Vortex
1 HB 8.00
2 HB 5.00
3 HB 3.50
4 HB 3.00
5 . . . . 3.00
6 thru 10 . . . . @2.50
11 thru 13 . . . . @2.00
14 . . . . 2.25

The Mod Squad #1 © Dell Publishing

MOD SQUAD
Dell Publishing Co. 1969–71
1 . . . . 55.00
2 . . . . 30.00
3 . . . . 30.00
4 thru 8 . . . . @30.00

MOD WHEELS
Gold Key 1971–76
1 . . . . 20.00
2 thru 18 . . . . @10.00
19 . . . . 8.00

MONKEE'S, THE
Dell Publishing Co. 1967
1 Ph(c) 80.00
2 Ph(c) 40.00
3 Ph(c) 40.00
4 Ph(c) 40.00
5 . . . . 30.00
6 Ph(c) 40.00
7 Ph(c) 40.00
8 and 9 . . . . @30.00
10 Ph(c) 40.00
11 thru 17 . . . . 30.00

MONOLITH
Comico
1 From Elementals 2.50
2 "Seven Levels of Hell" 2.50
3 "Fugue and Variation" 2.50
4 "Fugue and Variation" 2.50

MONROE'S, THE
Dell Publishing Co. April, 1967
1 Ph(c) 25.00

MONSTER MASSACRE
Atomeka
1 SBs, DBr,DGb 8.50
1a Black Edition 35.00

MOONWALKER IN 3-D
Blackthorne
1 thru 3 . . . . @2.50

MORBID ANGEL
London Night
½ Angel's Tear, signed 10.00

MORBID ANGEL: PENANCE
London Night
Revised Color Spec., double size . 4.00

MORE THAN MORTAL
Liar Comics 1997
1 . . . . 2.95
1a 2nd printing 2.95
2 Derdre vs. the Host 2.95
2a variant painted cover 5.95
3 MS(c) 2.95
4 concl. 2.95
TPB rep. #1–#4 . . . . 14.95

MORE THAN MORTAL: SAGAS
Liar Comics 1998
1 by Sharon Scott & Romano
Molenaar 2.95
1a variant Tim Vigil(c) 2.95

MORE THAN MORTAL: TRUTHS AND LEGENDS
Liar Comics 1998
1 by Sharon Scott, Steve Firchow,
Mark Prudeaux, O:Witchfinder . 2.95
2 . . . . 2.95

MORLOCK 2001
Atlas Feb.–July 1975
1 thru 3 F:Midnight Men . . . . @10.00

MORNINGSTAR
Spec. #1 . . . . 2.50

MORRIGAN
Sirius 1997
1 by Lorenzo Bartoli & Saverio
Tenuta 2.95
2 and 3 . . . . @2.95
GN rep. #1–#3 . . . . 9.95

MOTORBIKE PUPPIES
Dark Zulu Lies
1 I:Motorbike Puppies 2.50

MOVIE COMICS
Gold Key/Whitman Oct., 1962
Alice in Wonderland 30.00
Aristocats 75.00
Bambi 1 . . . . 30.00
Bambi 2 . . . . 25.00
Beneath the Planet of the Apes . 40.00
Big Red 25.00
Blackbeard's Ghost 25.00
Buck Rogers Giant Movie Edition 22.00
Bullwhip Griffin 35.00
Captain Sinbad 50.00
Chitty, Chitty Bang Bang 45.00
Cinderella 25.00
Darby O'Gill & the Little People . 45.00
Dumbo 25.00
Emil & the Detectives 30.00
Escapade in Florence 75.00
Fall of the Roman Empire 30.00
Fantastic Voyage 45.00
55 Days at Peking 30.00
Fighting Prince of Donegal 25.00
First Men of the Moon 30.00
Gay Purr-ee 30.00
Gnome Mobile 25.00
Goodbye, Mr. Chips 30.00
Happiest Millionaire 25.00
Hey There, It's Yogi Bear 40.00
Horse Without a Head 20.00
How the West Was Won 35.00
In Search of the Castaways 60.00
Jungle Book, The 35.00
Kidnapped 25.00
King Kong 30.00
King Kong N# 10.00
Lady and the Tramp 30.00
Lady and the Tramp 1 . . . . 45.00
Lady and the Tramp 2 . . . . 20.00
Legend of Lobo, The 25.00
Lt. Robin Crusoe 20.00
Lion, The 25.00
Lord Jim 25.00
Love Bug, The 25.00
Mary Poppins 45.00
Mary Poppins 1 . . . . 65.00
McLintock 100.00
Merlin Jones as the Monkey's
Uncle 45.00
Miracle of the White Stallions . . 25.00
Misadventures of Merlin Jones . . 45.00
Moon-Spinners, The 60.00
Mutiny on the Bounty 30.00
Nikki, Wild Dog of the North . . . 20.00
Old Yeller 25.00
One Hundred & One Dalmations 25.00
Peter Pan 1 . . . . 30.00
Peter Pan 2 . . . . 25.00
P.T. 109 . . . . 45.00
Rio Conchos 40.00

Robin Hood	25.00
Shaggy Dog & the Absent-Minded	
Professor	45.00
Snow White & the Seven Dwarfs	25.00
Son of Flubber	25.00
Summer Magic	55.00
Swiss Family Robinson	25.00
Sword in the Stone	25.00
That Darn Cat	50.00
Those Magnificent Men in Their	
Flying Machines	30.00
Three Stooges in Orbt	90.00
Tiger Walks, A	40.00
Toby Tyler	25.00
Treasure Island	25.00
20,000 Leagues Under the Sea	25.00
Wonderful Adventures of	
Pinocchio	25.00
X, the Man with the X-Ray Eyes	70.00
Yellow Submarine	225.00

MS. MYSTIC
Pacific
1 NA,Origin		8.00
2 NA,Origin,I:Urth 4		6.00

Continuity
1 NA,Origin rep.	2.00
2 NA,Origin,I:Urth 4 rep	2.00
3 NA,New material	2.00
4 TSh	2.00
5 DT	2.00
6	2.00
7	2.00
8 CH/Sdr,B:Love Story	2.00
9 DB	2.00
9a Newsstand(c)	2.00

[3rd Series]
1 O:Ms.Mystic	2.50
2 A:Hybrid	2.50
3	2.50
4	2.50

[4th Series, Deathwatch 2000]
1 Deathwatch 2000 pt.8,w/card	2.50
2 Deathwatch 2000 w/card	2.50
3 Indestructible cover, w/card	2.50

MS. TREE'S THRILLING DETECTIVE ADVENTURES
Eclipse 1983
1 Miller pin up	4.00
2	2.50
3	2.00

Becomes:
MS. TREE 1984–89
4 thru 6	@2.00
7	2.50
8	8.00
9	2.00

Aardvark–Vanaheim
10	2.00

Renegade
1 3-D	2.00

MS. VICTORY GOLDEN ANNIVERSARY
AC Comics
1 Ms.Victory celebration	5.00

MS. VICTORY SPECIAL
AC Comics
1	1.75

The Mummy, or Ramses the Damned #11 © Millennium

MUMMY, OR RAMSES THE DAMNED, THE
Millenium 1992
1 Anne Rice Adapt.	5.00
2 JM,"Mummy in Mayfair"	3.75
3 JM	3.25
4 JM, To Egypt	3.00
5 JM"The Mummy's Hand"	2.50
6 JM 20th Century Egypt	2.50
7 JM,More Ramses Past Revealed	2.50
8 JM,Hunt for Cleopatra	2.50
9 JM,Cleopatra's Wrath contd.	2.50
10 JM,Subterranian World	2.50
11 JM	2.50

MUMMY ARCHIVES
Millenium
1 JM,Features,articles	2.50

MUNDEN'S BAR ANNUAL
First
1 BB,JOy,JSn,SR	2.95

MUNSTERS, THE
Gold Key 1965–68
1	200.00
2	100.00
3 thru 5	@75.00
6 thru 16	@70.00

MUPPET BABIES
Harvey
1 Return of Muppet Babies	1.25

MUTANTS & MISFITS
Silverline
1 thru 4	@1.95

MY FAVORITE MARTIAN
Gold Key 1964–66
1	150.00
2	75.00
3 thru 9	@60.00

MY LITTLE MARGIE
Charlton Comics 1954–65
1 Ph(c)	175.00
2 Ph(c)	100.00
3	50.00
4	50.00
5	50.00
6	50.00
7	50.00
8	50.00
9	45.00
10	30.00
11	15.00
12	15.00
13	30.00
14 thru 19	@25.00
20	50.00
21 thru 35	@15.00
36 thru 53	@10.00
54 Beatles (c)	100.00

MYSTERIES OF UNEXPLORED WORLDS/ SON OF VULCAN
Charlton Comics 1956
1	200.00
2	75.00
3	125.00
4 SD	135.00
5 SD,SD(c)	150.00
6 SD	150.00
7	155.00
8 SD	150.00
9 SD	150.00
10 SD,SD(c)	155.00
11 SD,SD(c)	155.00
12	100.00
13 thru 18	@30.00
19 SD(c)	80.00
20	30.00
21 thru 24 SD	@90.00
25	20.00
26 SD	90.00
27 thru 30	@20.00
31 thru 45	@15.00
46 I:Son ofVulcan,Dr.Kong(1965)	20.00
47 V:King Midas	12.00
48 V:Captain Tuska	12.00

Becomes:
SON OF VULCAN
49 DC redesigns costume	6.00
50 V:Dr.Kong	5.00

MYSTERIOUS SUSPENSE
Charlton 1968
1 SD,F:Question	55.00

MYSTERY COMICS DIGEST
Gold Key March, 1972–75
1 WW	30.00
2 WW	25.00
3	15.00
4 Ripleys Believe It or Not	10.00
5 Boris Karloff	10.00
6 Twilight Zone	10.00
7 thru 20	@10.00
21 thru 26	@8.00

MYSTIC ISLE
1	1.95

NANCY & SLUGGO
Dell Publishing Co. 1957
146 B:Peanuts	40.00
147	25.00
148	25.00
149	25.00
150 thru 161	25.00
162 thru 165	35.00
166 thru 176 A:OONA	40.00
177 thru 180	35.00
181 thru 187	20.00

NATIONAL VELVET
Dell Publishing Co.
May-July, 1961
1 Ph(c)	45.00
2 Ph(c)	40.00

NEAT STUFF
Fantagraphics
1	4.50
2	3.00
3 thru 5	@2.50
6	2.25
7	2.25

NECROPOLIS
Fleetway
1 SBs(c),CE,A:Dark Judges/ Sisters Of Death	2.95
2	2.95
3 thru 9	@2.95

NEIL GAIMAN'S LADY JUSTICE
Tekno Comix (1995)
1 I:Lady Justice	2.50
1a	6.00
2 V:Blood Pirate	1.95
3 V:Blood Pirate	1.95
4 New Story Arc	1.95
5 Street Gang War	1.95
6 Street Gang War	2.25
7 thru 11	@2.25
Big Entertainment April 1996	
1 thru 4	@2.25
5 DIB(s)	2.25
6 DIB(s),"Woman About Town," pt.1	2.25
7 DIB(s),"Woman About Town," pt.2	2.25
8 DIB(s),"Woman About Town," pt.3	2.25

NEIL GAIMAN'S MR. HERO THE NEWMATIC MAN
Tekno-Comics 1994
1 I:Mr. Hero, Tecknophage	2.50
2 A:Tecknophage	2.25
3 I:Adam Kaine	1.95
4 I:New Body	1.95
5 Earthquake	1.95
6 I:New Character	1.95
7 I:Deadbolt, Bloodboil	1.95
8 V:Avatar	1.95
9 in London	1.95
10 V:Demon	1.95
11 V:Monster	1.95
12 The Great Goward	2.25
13 thru 17	@2.25

NEIL GAIMAN'S PHAGE
Tekno-Comics 1996
1	2.25

NEIL GAIMAN'S PHAGE: SHADOW DEATH
Big Entertainment
1 thru 4	@2.25
5 O:Orlando Holmes,A:Lady Messalina	2.25
6 conclusion	2.25

NEIL GAIMAN'S TECKNOPHAGE
Teckno-Comics 1995
1 I:Kalighoul, Tom Vietch	1.95
1a Steel Edition	3.95
2 F:Mayor of New Yorick	1.95
3 Phange Building	1.95
4 Horde eevils	1.95
5 Middle Management	1.95
6 Escape from Phange	1.95
7 Mecca	2.25

NEIL GAIMAN'S WHEEL OF WORLDS
Teckno-Comics 1995
0 Deluxe Edition w/Posters	2.95
0a I:Lady Justice	1.95
1	3.25

NEMESIS THE WARLOCK
Eagle
1	2.00
2 thru 8	@1.50

NEW ADVENTURES OF FELIX THE CAT
Felix Comics,Inc
1 New stories	2.25
2 "The Magic Paint Brush"	2.25

NEW ADVENTURES OF PINNOCCIO
Dell Publishing Co. 1962
1	75.00
2 and 3	@60.00

NEW ADVENTURES OF SPEED RACER
Now
0 Premiere, 3-D cover	1.95
1 thru 11	@1.95

NEW AMERICA
Eclipse 1987–88
1 A:Scout	1.75
2 A:Scout	1.75
3 A:Roman Catholic Pope	1.75
4 A:Scout	1.75

NEW BREED
Pied Piper
1	2.75
2	2.25

NEW CHAMPIONS
1 and 2	@2.95

New DNAgents #6 © Eclipse

NEW DNAGENTS, THE
Eclipse 1985–87
1 R:DNAgents	1.50
2 F:Tank	1.00
3 Repopulating the World	1.00
4 Major Catastrophe for Earth	1.00
5 "Last Place on Earth"	1.00
6 JOy(c),"Postscript"	1.00
7 V:Venimus	1.00
8 DSp,V:Venimus	1.00
9 V:Venimus,I:New Wave	1.00
10 I:New Airboy	1.00
11 Summer Fun Issue	1.25
12 V:Worm	1.25
13 EL,F:Tank	1.25
14 EL,Nudity,"Grounded"	1.25
15 thru 17	@1.25
3-D #1	2.50

NEW JUSTICE MACHINE
Innovation
1 and 2	@1.95
2	1.95

NEWMEN
Maximum Press
1–22 see Image
23 ErS,CSp,AG,"Anthem," pt.3	2.50
24 ErS,CSp,AG,"Anthem," pt.4	2.50
25 ErS,CSp,AG,"Anthem," pt.5	2.50

NEW ORLEANS SAINTS
1 Playoff season(football team)	6.00

NEW STATESMEN
Fleetway
1	4.50
2 thru 5	@3.95

NEWSTRALIA
Innovation
1 and 2	@1.75
3	1.95

New Terrytoons #44 © Gold Key

NEW TERRYTOONS
Dell Publishing Co. 1960–61
1	45.00
2 thru 8	@30.00

Gold Key 1962
1 F:Heckle & Jeckle	60.00
2	50.00
3 thru 10	@18.00
11 thru 20	@8.00
21 thru 30	@5.00
31 thru 40	@4.00
41 thru 54	@3.00

NEW WAVE, THE
Eclipse 1986–87
1 Error Pages	2.00
1a Correction	1.50
2	1.00
3 "Space Station Called Hell"	1.00
4 Birth of Megabyte	1.00
5 PG(c),O:Avalon	1.50
6 O:Megabyte	1.50
7 Avalon disappears	1.00
8 V:Heap,V:Druids	1.00
9	1.00
10 V:Heap Team	1.00
11	1.50
12	1.50
13 V:Volunteers	1.50
14 1/3 issue	2.00

NEW WAVE vs. THE VOLUNTEERS
Eclipse
1 3-D,V:Volunteers	2.50
2 3-D,V:Volunteers	2.50

NEXT MAN
Comico 1985
1 I&O:Next Man	2.50
2	1.75
3	1.75
4	1.50
5	1.50

NEXT NEXUS
First
1 SR	1.95
2 SR	1.95
3 SR	1.95
4 SR	1.95

NEXUS
Capital
1 SR,I:Judah Maccabee	9.00
2 SR,Origin,V:Bellows	5.50
3 SR,Sundra Captive	5.00
4 SR,V:Ziggurat	5.00
5 SR,"I'm Bored!"	5.00
6 SR,A:Badger,TrialogueTrilogy#1	4.00

First
7 SR,A:Badger,TrialogueTrilogy#2	5.00
8 SR,A:Badger,TrialogueTrilogy#3	4.00
9 SR,Teen Angel	2.50
10 SR,BWg,Talking Heads	2.00
11 SR,V:Clausius	2.00
12 SR,V:The Old General	2.00
13 SR,Sundra Peale solo	2.00
14 SR,A:Clonezone,Hilariator	2.00
15 SR,A:Clonezone	2.00
16 SR,A:Clonezone	2.00
17 Judah vs. Jacque,the Anvil	2.00
18 SR,A:Clonezone	2.00
19 SR,A:Clonezone	2.00
20 SR,A:Clonezone	2.00
21 SR,A:Clonezone	2.00
22 KG,A:Badger	2.00
23 SR,A:Clonezone	2.00
24 SR,A:Clonezone	2.00
25 SR,A:Clonezone	2.00
26 SR,A:Clonezone	2.00
27 SR,A:Clonezone	2.00
28 MMi	2.00
29 A:Kreed & Sinclair	2.00
30 JL,C:Badger	2.50
31 Judah solo story	2.00
32 JG,Judah solo story	2.00
33 SR,A:Kreed & Sinclair	2.00
34 SR,Judah solo story	2.00
35 SR,Judah solo story	2.00
36 SR	2.00
37 PS	2.00
38	2.00
39 SR, The Boom Search	2.00
40 SR	2.00
41 SR	2.00
42 SR,Bowl-Shaped world	2.00
43 PS	2.00
44 PS	2.00
45 SR,A:Badger Pt.1	2.00
46 SR,A:Badger Pt.2	2.00
47 SR,A:Badger Pt.3	2.00
48 SR,A:Badger Pt.4	2.00
49 PS,A:Badger Pt.5	2.00
50 SF,double size,A:Badger Pt.6 Crossroads tie-in	3.50
51 PS	2.00
52 PS	2.00
53 PS	2.00
54 PS	2.00
55 PS	2.00
56	2.00
57 AH	2.00
58 Sr,I:Stanislaus Korivitsky as Nexus	2.00
59 SR	2.00
60 SR	2.00
61	2.00
62	2.00

63 V:Elvonic Order	2.00
64 V:Elvonic Order	2.00
65 V:Elvonic Order	2.00
66 V:Elvonic Order	2.00
67 V:Elvonic Order	2.00
68 LM	2.00
69	2.00
70	2.00
71 V:Bad Brains	2.00
72 V:Renegade heads	2.00
73 Horatio returns to Ylum	2.00
74 Horatio vs. Stan	2.00
75 Horatio vs. Stan	2.00
76	2.25
77	2.25
78 O:Nexus,Nexus Files Pt#1	2.25
79 Nexus Files Pt#2	2.25
80 Nexus.Files Pt#3,last iss.	2.25

NEXUS LEGENDS
First
1 thru 13 rep.Nexus	@1.50
14 rep.Nexus	1.75
15 rep.Nexus	1.75
16 rep.Nexus	1.75
17 rep.Nexus	1.75
18 rep.Nexus	1.95
19 rep.Nexus	1.95
20 SR,Sanctuary	1.95
21 thru 23 SR	@1.95

NICK HOLIDAY
Argo May, 1956
1 Strip reprints	40.00

NICKI SHADOW
Relentless Comics
1 by Eric Burnham & Ted Naifeh	2.50
2 Killing Zone, pt.2	2.50
3 Killing Zone, pt.3	2.50
4 Killing Zone, concl.	2.50

NIGHT GLIDER
Topps
1 V:Bombast,C:Captain Glory, Trading Card	3.25

NIGHTMARE
Innovation
1	2.50

NIGHTMARE AND CASPER
Harvey Publications 1963
1	50.00
2	30.00
3	30.00
4	30.00
5	30.00

Becomes:

CASPER AND NIGHTMARE
6 B:68 pgs	15.00
7	7.00
8	7.00
9	7.00
10	7.00
11 thru 20	@3.50
21 thru 30	@2.50
31	2.50
32 E:68 pgs	2.50

33 thru 45 . . . . @2.00
46 Aug., 1974 . . . . 2.00

NIGHTMARE ON ELM STREET
Blackthorne
1 3-D 2.50
2 3-D 2.50
3 3-D 2.50

NIGHTMARES ON ELM STREET
Innovation
1 Yours Truly, Freddy Krueger Pt.1 3.00
2 Yours Truly ,Freddy Krueger Pt.2 2.50
3 Loose Ends Pt.1,Return to
  Springwood 2.50
4 Loose Ends Pt 2 . . . . 2.50
5 . . . . 2.50
6 . . . . 2.50

NIGHTMARES
Eclipse 1985
1 . . . . 2.50
2 . . . . 2.00

NIGHT MUSIC
Eclipse 1984–88
1 . . . . 2.50
2 . . . . 2.50
3 CR, Jungle Bear 3.00
4 Pelias & Melisande 2.00
5 Pelias 2.00
6 same as Salome #1
7 same as Red Dog #1
Graphic Novel 8.00

NIGHTS INTO DREAMS
Archie Comics 1997
1 based on Sega game 1.75
2 thru 6 . . . . 1.75

NIGHTSHADE
No Mercy Comics 1997
1 by Mark Williams 2.50
2 and 3 . . . . @2.50

NIGHTVEIL
AC Comics
1 . . . . 3.50
2 . . . . 2.50
3 . . . . 2.25
4 . . . . 2.25
5 . . . . 2.25
6 . . . . 1.75
7 . . . . 1.75
Spec.#1 . . . . 1.95

NIGHT WALKER
Fleetway
1 thru 2 . . . . 2.95

NIGHTWOLF
1 . . . . 1.75
2 . . . . 1.75

9 LIVES OF FELIX
Harvey
1 thru 4 . . . . @1.25

NINE LIVES TO LIVE
Fantagraphics
HC 9"x12" Felix the Cat strips, by
  Otto Messmer 40.00

NINJA HIGH SCHOOL
Eternity
1 Reps.orig.N.H.S.in color 1.95
2 thru 13 reprints . . . . @1.95

Ninja High School Featuring Speed Racer #2B © Eternity

NINJA HIGH SCHOOL FEATURING SPEED RACER
Eternity 1993
1B 2.95
2B 2.95

NINJA STAR
1 . . . . 1.95

NIRA X: ANIMÉ
Entity Comics 1997
1 BMs 2.95
1a deluxe, foil cover 3.50
2 BMs 2.95
2a deluxe, foil cover 3.50
Swimsuit #0 . . . . 2.75
Swimsuit #0 Manga (c) 2.75

NIRA X: CYBERANGEL
Entity 1994
1 From pages of Zen 2.95
1a 2nd printing 2.75
2 V:Parradox 2.50
3 In Hydro-Dams 2.50
4 final issue 2.50
4a with computer game 6.95
Ashcan 2.50
TPB Birth of an Angel 12.95
[Series 2] 1995
1 R:Nira X 3.75
1a Clear Chromium Edition 8.00
1b Holo-Chrome edition 10.00

2 Alien Invasion 2.50
3 Mecha New York 2.50
4 Final Issue 2.50
[Series 3] 1996
0 . . . . 2.75
0a signed & numbered 8.00
1 . . . . 2.50
1a gold edition, signed & numb. . 5.00
2 . . . . 2.50
3 . . . . 3.00

NIRA X/CYNDER: ENDANGERED SPECIES
Entity Comics 1996
1 . . . . 3.00
1a gold ink enhanced, bagged . 13.00

NOID IN 3-D
Blackthorne
1 thru 3 . . . . @2.50

NOMAN
Tower Comics 1966
1 GK,OW 45.00
2 OW,A:Dynamo 30.00

NOOGIE KOOTCH: SECRET AGENT MAN
Hobo Comics
1 I:Noogie Kootch 2.75
2 F:Celutron City 2.75

NOSFERATU: PLAGUE OF TERROR
Millenium
1 I:Orlock 2.50
2 19th Century India,A:Sir W.
  Longsword 2.50
3 WWI/WWII to Viet Nam 2.50
4 O:Orlock,V:Longsword,conc. . . 2.50

NO TIME FOR SERGEANTS
Dell Publishing Co. July, 1958
1 Ph(c) 50.00
2 Ph(c) 35.00
3 Ph(c) 35.00

NOVA HUNTER
Ryal Comics
1 thru 3 . . . . @2.50
4 Climax 2.50
5 Death and Betrayal 2.50

NUBIAN KNIGHT
Samson Comics
1 I:Shandai 2.50

NURSES, THE
Gold Key April, 1963
1 . . . . 30.00
2 . . . . 20.00
3 . . . . 20.00

NYOKA, JUNGLE GIRL
Charlton Comics 1955–57
14 . . . . 40.00
15 . . . . 25.00
16 . . . . 25.00

17	25.00
18	25.00
19	25.00
20	25.00
21	25.00
22	25.00

NYOKA, THE JUNGLE GIRL
AC Comics

1 and 2	@1.95

OBLIVION
Comico 1995

1 R:The Elementals	2.50
2 I:Thunderboy, Lilith	2.50
3 I:Fen, Ferril	2.50
4 War	2.95
5 The Unholy Trilogy	2.95

OCCULT FILES OF DR. SPEKTOR
Gold Key April, 1973

1 I:Lakot	25.00
2 thru 5	12.00
6 thru 10	10.00
11 I:Spertor as Werewolf	10.00
12 and 13	8.00
14 A:Dr. Solar	25.00
15 thru 24	8.00

Whitman

25 rep	2.00

O.G. WHIZ
Gold Key 1971–79

1	60.00
2	35.00
3	25.00
4	25.00
5	25.00
6	25.00
7	8.00
8	8.00
9	8.00
10	8.00
11	8.00

OINK: BLOOD AND CIRCUS
Kitchen Sink 1997

1 (of 4) by John Mueller	4.95
2	4.95
3	4.95
4 conclusion	4.95

O'MALLEY AND THE ALLEY CATS
Gold Key 1971–74

1	25.00
2 thru 9	@20.00

OMEGA 7
Omega 7

1 V:Exterminator X	3.95
½ by Alonzo L. Washington	3.95

OMEGA ELITE
Blackthorne

1	1.50
2	1.50

OMEGA SAGA, THE
Southpaw Publishing 1998

0 by Mike Gerardo & Chris Navetta	3.00
1 Episode One, pt.1	3.00
2 Episode One, pt.2	3.00

Axess Comics

3 by Mike Gerardo, Heroes (c)	3.00
3b Villains (c)	3.00

OMEN, THE
Chaos! Comics

Preview Book, BnP	1.50
1 by Phil Nutman & Justiniano	2.95
2	2.95
3	2.95
4	2.95
5 concl.	2.95

OMNI MEN
Blackthorne

1	1.25
2	1.25

ON A PALE HORSE
Innovation

1 Piers Anthony adapt	4.95
2 "Magician",I:Kronos	4.95
3	4.95
4 VV,	4.95
5	4.95
6	4.95

ONE-ARM SWORDSMAN

1	2.95
2	2.95
3	2.75
4	1.80
5	1.80
6	1.80
7	1.80
8	1.80
9	2.00
10	2.00
11	2.00

ORBIT
Eclipse 1990

1 DSt(c)	3.95
2	3.95
3	4.95

ORIENTAL HEROES
Jademan

1	2.50
2	2.00
3 thru 13	@1.50
14 thru 27	@1.95
28 V:Skeleton Secretary	1.95
29 Barbarian vs.Lone Kwoon	1.95
30 Barbarian vs.Lone Kwoon	1.95
31 SkeletonSecretaryUprisng	1.95
32 Uprising Continues	1.95
33 Jupiter Kills His Brother	1.95
34 Skeleton Sec. Suicide	1.95
35 Red Sect Vs. Global Cult	1.95
36 A:Tiger	1.95
37 Old Supreme	1.95
38 Tiger vs. 4 Hitmen	1.95
39 D:Infinite White, V:Red Sect.	1.95
40 The Golden Buddhha Temple	1.95
41 thru 43	1.95
44 SilverChime rescue	1.95

45 Global Cult Battle	1.95
46 thru 48	@1.95
49 F:GoldDragon/SilverChime	1.95
50 Return to Global Cult	1.95
51 Gang Of Three Vs.White Beau & Lone Kwoon-Tin	1.95
52 Global Cult vs Red Sect	1.95
53 Global Cult vs.Red Sect	1.95

Original Astro Boy #1 © Now Comics

ORIGINAL ASTRO BOY
Now

1 KSy	3.00
2 thru 5 KSy	@2.00
6 thru 17 KSy	@1.75

ORIGINAL DICK TRACY
Gladestone

1 rep.V:Mrs.Pruneface	1.95
2 rep.V:Influence	1.95
3 rep.V:TheMole	1.95
4 rep.V:ItchyOliver	1.95
5 rep.V:Shoulders	2.00

ORIGINAL E-MAN
First
{rep. Charlton stories}

1 JSon,O:E-Man & Nova	1.75
2 JSon,V:Battery,SamuelBoar	1.75
3 JSon,"City in the Sand"	1.75
4 JSon,A:Brain from Sirius	1.75
5 JSon,V:T.V. Man	1.75
6 JSon,I:Teddy Q	1.75
7 JSon,Vamfire	1.75

ORIGINAL SHIELD
ABC

1 DAy/TD,O:Shield	1.00
2 DAy,O:Dusty	.75
3 DAy	.75
4 DAy	.75

ORIGIN OF THE DEFIANT UNIVERSE
Defiant

1 O:Defiant Characters	1.50

COLOR PUB.

OUTBREED 999
Blackout Comics
1 thru 4 . . . . @2.95
5 Search For Daige 2.95

OUTCASTS
1 . . . . 1.25

OUTER LIMITS, THE
Dell Publishing Co.
Jan.-March, 1964
1 P(c) 75.00
2 P(c) 50.00
3 P(c) 35.00
4 P(c) 35.00
5 P(c) 35.00
6 P(c) 35.00
7 P(c) 35.00
8 P(c) 35.00
9 P(c) 35.00
10 P(c) 35.00
11 thru 18 P(c) 30.00

OUTLAWS OF THE WEST
Charlton Comics 1956–80
11 . . . . 40.00
12 . . . . 20.00
13 . . . . 20.00
14 Giant 25.00
15 . . . . 20.00
16 . . . . 20.00
17 . . . . 20.00
18 SD 50.00
19 . . . . 15.00
20 . . . . 15.00
21 thru 30 . . . . @10.00
31 thru 50 . . . . @6.00
51 thru 70 . . . . @4.00
71 thru 88 . . . . @3.00

OUT OF THIS WORLD
Charlton Comics 1956–59
1 . . . . 150.00
2 . . . . 75.00
3 SD 175.00
4 SD 175.00
5 SD 175.00
6 SD 175.00
7 SD,SD(c) 175.00
8 SD 150.00
9 SD 150.00
10 SD 150.00
11 SD 150.00
12 SD 150.00
13 thru 15 . . . . @50.00
16 . . . . 135.00

OUTPOSTS
Blackthorne
1 thru 6 . . . . @1.25

OWL, THE
Gold Key April, 1967
1 . . . . 30.00
2 April, 1968 . . . . 20.00

PACIFIC PRESENTS
Pacific 1992
1 DSt,Rocketeer,(3rd App.) 16.00
2 DSt,Rocketeer,(4th App.) 14.00

---

3 SD,I:Vanity 2.50
4 and 5 . . . . @2.00

P.A.C.
Artifacts Inc
1 I:P.A.C. 1.95

PAINKILLER JANE
Event Comics 1997
1 JQ(c) 2.95
1 RL(c) 2.95
1 Red foil logo, signed 24.95
2 JQ&JP(c) 2.95
2 JP&RL(c) 2.95
3 JQ&JP(c) 2.95
3a JP&RL(c) 2.95
4 JQ&JP(c) A Too Bright Place For Dying 2.95
4a RL&JP(c) 2.95
5 JQ&JP(c) Purgatory Station—Next Stop Hell 2.95
5a RL&JP(c) 2.95
6 RL&JP(c) Blood Harvest 2.95
6a BSz&JP(c) 2.95
7 Jane in the Jungle, pt.1,BiT&JP(c) 2.95
7a RL&JP(c) 2.95
Spec. Painkiller Jane/Hellboy Ancient Laughter (1998) 2.95
Spec. Painkiller Jane/The Darkness, signed, limited edition, JQ(c) . 29.95

PAINKILLER JANE VS. THE DARKNESS: STRIPPER
Event Comics 1997
1 GEn,JP,x-over, Amanda Connor cover 2.95
1a Greg & Tim Hildebrandt 2.95
1b MS(c) 2.95
1c JQ(c) 2.95

PALADIN ALPHA
Firstlight
1 I:Paladin Alpha 2.95
2 V:Hellfire Triger 2.95

PANDEMONIUM: DELIVERANCE
Chaos! Comics 1998
1-shot by Jesse Leon McCann & Jack Jadson 2.95

PANIC
Gemstone 1997
1 thru 7 EC Comics reprint . . . @2.50
"Annuals"
TPB Vol. 1 rebinding #1–#4 . . . . 10.50

PANTHA
Harris Comics 1997
1 (of 2) MT 3.50

PARADAX
Eclipes
1 . . . . 2.25

PARADIGM
Gauntlet
1 A:Predator 2.95

Paragon Dark Apocalypse #1
© AC Comics

PARAGON DARK APOCALYPSE
AC 1993
1 thru 4, Fem Force crossover . . 2.95

PARANOIA
Adventure Comics
1 (based on video game)"Clone1" 3.25
2 King-R-Thr-2 . . . . 2.95
3 R:Happy Jack,V:N3F 2.95
4 V:The Computer 2.95
5 V:The Computer 2.95
6 V:Lance-R-Lot,last issue 2.95

PARTRIDGE FAMILY, THE
Charlton Comics 1971–73
1 . . . . 35.00
2 thru 4 . . . . @20.00
5 Summer Special 25.00
6 thru 21 . . . . @20.00

PASSOVER
Maximum Press
1 (of 2) BNa 3.00
2 BNa,A:Avengelyne 3.00

PATHWAYS TO FANTASY
Pacific
1 BS,JJ art 3.00

PAT SAVAGE: WOMAN OF BRONZE
Millenium
1 F:Doc Savage's cousin 2.50

PEACEMAKER
Charlton
1 A:Fightin' 5 . . . . 5.00
2 A:Fightin' 5 . . . . 3.00
3 A:Fightin' 5 . . . . 3.00
4 O:Peacemaker,A:Fightin' 5 . . . 4.00
5 A:Fightin' 5 . . . . 2.50

PEANUTS
Dell Publishing Co. 1958
1	100.00
2	75.00
3	75.00
4	50.00
5	35.00
6	35.00
7	35.00
8	35.00
9	35.00
10	35.00
11	35.00
12	35.00
13	35.00

PEANUTS
Gold Key May, 1963
1	50.00
2 thru 4	30.00

PEBBLES & BAMM BAMM
Charlton Comics 1972–76
1	40.00
2 thru 10	@20.00
11 thru 36	@15.00

PEBBLES FLINTSTONE
Gold Key Sept., 1963
1 "A Chip off the old block" 70.00

PELLESTAR
1 .... 1.75

PERG
Lightning Comics
1 Glow in the dark(c),JS(c),
B:JZy(s),KIK,I:Perg 3.75
1a Platinum Ed. 5.00
1b Gold Ed. 7.00
1 gold edition, glow-in-the-dark flip
cover 30.00
2 KIK,O:Perg 3.25
2a Platinum Ed. 5.00
3 Flip Book (c), ... 3.25
3a Platinum Ed. 5.00
4 TLw,I:Hellina 9.00
4a Platinum Ed 5.00
5 A:Hellina 3.25
6 PIA,A:Hellina 9.00
6 nude cover 3.00
7 .... 3.00
8 V:Police 3.00

PERRY MASON MYSTERY MAGAZINE
Dell Publishing Co. 1964
1	40.00
2 Ray Burr Ph(c)	30.00

PETER PAN: RETURN TO NEVERNEVER LAND
1 Peter in Mass. 2.50
2 V:Tiger Lily 2.50

PETER POTAMUS
Gold Key Jan., 1965
1 .... 50.00

PETTICOAT JUNCTION
Dell Publishing Co. 1964
1 Ph(c)	60.00
2 Ph(c)	45.00
3 Ph(c)	45.00
4	45.00
5 Ph(c)	45.00

PHANTOM, THE
Gold Key 1962
1 RsM	125.00
2 B:King, Queen & Jack	75.00
3	50.00
4	50.00
5	50.00
6	50.00
7 "The Super Apes"	50.00
8	50.00
9	50.00
10 "The Sleeping Giant"	50.00
11 E:King,Queen and Jack	40.00
12 B:Track Hunter	40.00
13	40.00
14 "The Historian"	40.00
15	40.00
16	40.00
17 "Samaris"	40.00

Phantom #22 © King Comics

King Comics Sept. 1966
18 "The Treasure of the Skull Cave;"BU:Flash Gordon	50.00
19 "The Astronaut & the Pirates"	30.00
20 A:GirlPhantom,E:FlashGordon	30.00
21 BU:Mandrake	30.00
22 "Secret of Magic Mountain"	30.00
23	30.00
24 A:Girl Phantom	30.00
25	30.00
26	30.00
27	30.00
28	30.00
29	30.00

Charlton Comics 1969–77
30	20.00
31 JAp,"Phantom of Shang-Ri-La"	20.00
32 JAp,"The Pharaoh Phantom"	20.00
33	20.00
34	20.00
35	20.00
36	20.00
37	20.00
38	20.00
39	20.00
40 "The Ritual"	20.00
41	15.00
42	15.00
43	15.00
44 "To Right A Wrong"	15.00
45	15.00
46 I:Piranha	20.00
47 "The False Skull Cave"	15.00
48	15.00
49	15.00
51 "A Broken Vow"	15.00
52	15.00
53	15.00
54	15.00
55	15.00
56	15.00
57 NightmareMedicine in Bengali	15.00
58	15.00
59	15.00
60	15.00
61 "A Dead Man's Promise"	15.00
62	15.00
63	15.00
64 "Duel With Death"	15.00
65	15.00
66 "Goldbeard the Pirate"	15.00
67 "Triumph of Evil"	15.00
68	15.00
69	15.00
70	15.00
71	10.00
72 "Man in the Shadows"	10.00
73	10.00
74	10.00

PHANTOM
Wolf Publishing 1992
1 Drug Runners	2.25
2 Mystery Child of the Sea	2.25
3 inc.feature pages on Phantom/Merchandise	2.25
4 TV Jungle Crime Buster	2.25
5 Castle Vacula-Transylvania	2.25
6 The Old West	2.25
7 Sercet of Colussus	2.75
8 Temple of the Sun God	2.75

PHANTOM BOLT, THE
Gold Key 1964–66
1	50.00
2	30.00
3	20.00
4	20.00
5	20.00
6	20.00
7	20.00

PHANTOM FORCE
Genesis West 1994
Previously: Image
0 JK/JLe(c) 2.75
3 thru 10 .... @2.50

PHAZE
Eclipse 1988
1 BSz(c),Takes place in future .. 2.25
2 PG(c),V:The Pentagon 1.95
3 Schwieger Vs. Mammoth 1.95

COLOR PUB.

PHOENIX
Atlas 1975
1 thru 4 . . . . @5.00

PINK PANTHER, THE
Gold Key April, 1971
1 . . . . 45.00
2 thru 10 . . . . @25.00
11 thru 30 . . . . @15.00
31 thru 60 . . . . @10.00
61 thru 10.00

PINOCCHIO
1 . . . . 1.50

PIRACY
Gemstone 1998
1 EC comics reprint 2.50
2 EC comics reprint 2.50
3 EC comics reprint 2.50
4 EC comics reprint 2.50
5 EC comics reprint 2.50
6 EC comics reprint 2.50
7 EC comics reprint 2.50
"Annuals"
TPB Vol. 1 rebinding #1–#4 . . . . 10.50

PIRATE CORP.
Eternity
1 thru 5 . . . . @1.95

P.I.'S, THE
First
1 JSon,Ms.Tree,M Mauser 1.50
2 JSon,Ms.Tree,M Mauser 1.25
3 JSon,Ms.Tree,M Mauser 1.25

PITT
Full Bleed Studios
1 thru 9, see Image
10 thru 14 DK . . . . @2.50
14a variant cover 8.00
15 DK 2.50
16 DK, Ugly Americans, pt.1 . . . 2.50
17 DK, Ugly Americans, pt.2 . . . 2.50
18 DK, Ugly Americans, pt.3, concl.2.50

PITT CREW
Full Bleed Studios 1998
1 Monster 2.50

PLANET COMICS
Blackthorne
1 DSt(c) 2.00
2 thru 4 . . . . @2.00

PLANET OF VAMPIRES
Atlas Feb.–July 1975
1 thru 3 . . . . @5.00

POGZ N SLAMMER
Blackout Comics 1995
1 I:Pogz N Slammer 1.95
2 Contact Other Schools 1.95

POIZON
London Night Studios 1995
0 . . . . 3.00
0 signed gothchik edition 15.00
1/2 O:Poizon 3.00

---

1 . . . . 3.00
1a Necro-Nude edition 5.95
1b Photo Nude Edition signed . 15.00
1c signed 10.00
2 EHr 3.00

POIZON: CADILLACS AND GREEN TOMATOES
London Night 1997
2 . . . . 3.00
2a deluxe nude cover 6.00
3 . . . . 3.00
6 deluxe 6.00

POIZON: DEMON HUNTER
London Night 1998
1 . . . . 3.00
1 Green Death edition 14.95

POIZON: LOST CHILD
London Night Studios 1996
0 . . . . 3.00
1 mini series 3.00
1a Necro-Nude variant cover . . . 5.95
1 signed 10.00
1 Green Death edition 14.95
2 thru 3 . . . . @3.00

POPEYE
Gold Key 1962
1-65 See Golden Age Section
66 . . . . 75.00
67 . . . . 50.00
68 thru 80 . . . . @20.00
King Comics 1966
81 thru 92 . . . . @15.00
Charlton 1969
94 thru 99 . . . . @12.50
100 . . . . 15.00
101 thru 138 . . . . @12.50
Gold Key 1978
139 thru 143 . . . . @6.00
144 50th Aniv. Spec. 7.50
155 . . . . @6.00
Whitman
156 thru 159 . . . . @4.00
162 thru 171 . . . . @4.00

Popeye #146 © Gold Key Comics

POPEYE
Harvey Comics 1993–94
1 thru 7 . . . . @1.50
Summer Spec.#1 . . . . 2.25

POPEYE SPECIAL
Ocean 1987–88
1 . . . . 1.75
2 . . . . 2.00

POWER FACTOR
Wonder Color Comics 1986
1 . . . . 4.00
2 . . . . 3.00
3 . . . . 3.00

POWER FACTOR
Innovation
1 thru 4 . . . . @2.25

POWERKNIGHTS
Amara 1995
P I:Powerknights 1.50

POWER RANGERS ZEO/YOUNGBLOOD
Maximum Press 1997
1 TNu,NRd 3.00

POWERS THAT BE
Broadway Comics
Preview Editions Sept. 1995
1 thru 3 B&W . . . . @2.50
Regular Series Nov. 1995
1 JiS,I:Fatale, Star Seed 3.00
2 thru 4 . . . . @2.95
5 "It's the End of the World As We
   Know It" pt.1 . . . . 2.95
6 "It's the End of the World As We
   Know It" pt.2 . . . . 2.95
Becomes:
STAR SEED
7 "It's the End of the World As We
   Know It" pt.3 . . . . 2.95
8 "It's the End of the World As We
   Know It" pt.4 . . . . 2.95
9 "It's the End of the World As We
   Know It" pt.5 . . . . 2.95
10 JiS(s),JRs,"It's the End of the
   World As We Know It" pt6. . . . 2.95
11 JiS(s),JRs,"It's the End of the
   World As We Know It" pt7. . . . 2.95

PRESSBUTTON
Eclipse
(see Axel Pressbutton)
5 and 6 . . . . @1.75

PRIEST
Maximum Press 1996
1 RLd, F:Michael O'Bannon 3.00
2 RLd,BNa, ... 3.00
3 RLd 3.00

PRIMAL RAGE
Sirius 1996
1 TAr,from video game 2.95
1 foil cover, limited edition 2.95
2 TAr,DOe(c) 2.95

COLOR PUB.

Primer Vol. 2 #1 © Comico

PRIMER
Comico 1982–84
1	10.00
2 I:Grendel	85.00
3	5.00
4 C:Maxx	7.00
5 I:Maxx	30.00
6 I:Evangelyne	14.00
[Volume 2] 1996	
1 F:Lady Bathory	2.95

PRIMUS
Charlton Comics 1972
1	10.00
2 thru 5	@10.00
6 thru 7	@8.00

PRINCESS SALLY
Archie Comics
1 thru 3 Sonic tie-in . . . . @

PRINCE VANDAL
Triumphant
1 JnR(s),	2.50
2 JnR(s),	2.50
3 JnR(s),ShG,I:Claire,V:Nicket, Vandal goes to Boviden	2.50
4 JnR(s),ShG,Game's End	2.50
5 JnR(s),ShG,The Sickness, the rat appears	2.50
6 JnR(s),ShG,B:Gothic	2.50

PRIORITY: WHITE HEAT
AC Comics 1986
1 thru 2 miniseries . . . . @1.75

PRISON SHIP
1	1.75

PRIVATEERS
Vanguard Graphics
1	1.50
2	1.50

PROFESSIONAL: GOGOL 13
Viz
1	4.95
2 and 3	@4.95

PROFESSOR OM
Innovation
1 I:Rock Warrior	2.50
2 Samurai Drama	2.50

PROJECT A-KO 0
Antarctic Press 1994
0 digest size 5.00
Continued by Malibu

PROJECT A-KO 2
CPM 1995
Previously Malibu
1 Space Saga	2.95
2 Space Saga	2.95
3 Queen Margarita	2.95

PROJECT A-KO: VERSUS THE UNIVERSE
CPM 1995
1 Based on Animation	2.95
2 strange magician	3.00
3	3.00
4 (of 5) TEI	2.95

PROPHECY
Immortelle Studios 1998
1 by Hawk, Lovalle, & Wong,F:Cynder & War Dragon	2.95
2	2.95

PROPHET/CABLE
Maximum 1997
1 (of 2) RLd x-over	3.50
2 RLd x-over,A:Domino, Kirby, Blaquesmith	3.50

PROWLER
Eclipse 1987
1 I:Prowler	1.75
2 GN,A:Original Prowler	1.75
3 GN	1.75
4 GN	1.75
5 GN, adaption of "Vampire Bat"	1.75
6 w/flexi-disk record	1.75

PROWLER IN "WHITE ZOMBIE", THE
Eclipse 1988
1	1.75

PRUDENCE AND CAUTION
Defiant
1 CCl(s),	3.25
1a Spanish Version	3.25
2 CCl(s),	2.50
2a Spanish Version	2.50
3 CCl(s),	2.50
3a Spanish Version	2.50
4 CCl(s),	2.50
4a Spanish Version	2.50
5 CCl(s),	2.50
5a Spanish Version	2.50

PSYCHO
Innovation
1 Hitchcock movie adapt	2.50
2 continued	2.50
3 continued	2.50

PSYCHOBLAST
First
1 thru 9 . . . . @1.75

PUBLIC DEFENDER IN ACTION
Charlton Comics 1957
7	50.00
8 and 9	@40.00
10 thru 12,	@40.00

PUDGE PIG
Charlton Comics Sept., 1958
1	16.00
2	15.00

PUPPET MASTER
Eternity
1 Movie Adapt.Andre Toulon	2.50
2 Puppets Protecting Diary	2.50
3 R:Andre Toulon	2.50
4	2.50

PUPPET MASTER: CHILDREN OF THE PUPPET MASTER
Eternity
1 Killer Puppets on the loose	2.50
2 concl.	2.50

PURGATORI
Chaos! Comics
1-shot prelude	3.00
1-shot signed, limited + print	25.00

PURGATORI: THE DRACULA GAMBIT
Chaos! Comics 1997
1 DQ & Brian LeBlanc	3.00
1a signed	20.00

PURGATORI: THE VAMPIRES MYTH
Chaos! Comics
1 (of 3)	4.00
1-shot limited chromium edition	19.95
2 BnP,JBa	3.00
3 BnP,JBa, final issue	3.00
TPB rep.	9.95
TPB with CD	30.00

QUANTUM LEAP
Innovation
{based on TV series}
1 1968 Memphis	3.50
1a Special Edition	2.50
2 Ohio 1962,"Freedom of the Press"	3.00
3 1958 "The $50,000 Quest"	3.00
4 "Small Miracles"	2.50
5	2.50

6 . . . . 2.50
7 Golf Pro,School Bus Driver . . . 2.50
8 1958,Bank Robber 2.50
9 NY 1969,Gay Rights 2.50
10 1960s' Stand-up Comic 2.50
11 1959,Dr.(LSD experiments) . . . 2.50
12 . . . . 2.50

QUEEN OF THE DAMNED
Innovation
1 Anne Rice Adapt."On the Road to
  the Vampire Lestat" 3.50
2 Adapt. continued 2.50
3 The Devils Minion 2.50
4 Adapt.continued 2.50
5 Adapt.continued 2.50
6 Adapt.continued 2.50
7 Adapt.continued 2.50
8 Adapt.continued 2.50

Quick Draw McGraw #4 © Charlton

QUICK-DRAW McGRAW
Charlton Comics 1970–72
1 TV Animated Cartoon 45.00
2 . . . . 30.00
3 . . . . 30.00
4 thru 8 . . . . @30.00

Q-UNIT
Harris
1 I:Q-Unit,w/card 3.25

RACE FOR THE MOON
Harvey Publications 1958
1 BP 100.00
2 JK,AW,JK/AW(c) 175.00
3 JK,AW,JK/AW(c) 175.00

RACER-X
Now
Premire Special 5.00
1 thru 3 . . . . @2.50
4 thru 11 . . . . @1.75
[2nd Series]
1 thru 10 . . . . @1.75

RACK & PAIN
Chaos! Comics
3 (of 4) BnP,LJi, ... 2.95
4 BnP,LJi, final issue 2.95

RACK & PAIN: KILLERS
Chaos! Comics
1 (of 4) JaL(c) 2.95
2 BnP,LJi,JaL(c) 2.95

RADICAL DREAMER
Blackball
0 . . . . 2.00
1 thru 5 V:Jorge Futran . . . . . @2.50

RADIOACTIVE MAN
Bongo
1 I:Radioactive Man 4.00
1 80pg offered again 3.25
88 V:Lava Man 2.00
212 V:Hypno Head 2.00
412 V:Dr. Crab 2.25
679 with card 2.25
1000 Final issue 2.25

RAEL
Eclipse
Vol 1 . . . . 6.95

RAGAMUFFINS
Eclipse 1985
1 . . . . 3.00

RALPH SNART ADVENTURES
Now
[Volumes 1 & 2]
see B&W
9 and 10, color 2.50
[Volume 3]
1 . . . . 4.00
2 thru 10 . . . . @3.00
11 thru 21 . . . . @2.00
22 thru 26 . . . . @1.75
TPB 9.95
[Volume 4]
1 thru 3, with 1 of 2 trading cards 2.50
[Volume 5]
1 thru 5, with 1 of 2 trading cards 2.50
3-D Spec.#1 with 3-D glasses and
  12 trading cards 3.50

RAMAR OF THE JUNGLE
Toby Press 1954
1 Ph(c), John Hall 125.00
Charlton
2 . . . . 85.00
3 . . . . 85.00
4 . . . . 85.00
5 Sept., 1956 . . . . 85.00

RAMPANT
Manifest Destiny Comics
1/2 Various Artists 2.50

RANDOM 5
Amara Inc. 1995
1 I:Random 5 . . . . 1.50

RANGO
Dell Publishing Co. Aug., 1967
1 Tim Conway Ph(c) 35.00

RANMA 1/2
Viz 1992
1 I:Ranma 50.00
2 I:Upperclassmen Kuno 17.00
3 F:Upperclassmen Kuno 15.00
4 Confusion 5.00
5 A:Ryoga 5.00
6 Ryoga plots revenge 9.00
7 Conclusion 5.00
[Part 2]
1 . . . . 10.00
2 . . . . 5.00
3 thru 7 . . . . @4.00
8 . . . . 5.00
9 . . . . 7.00
10 and 11 . . . . 3.00
continued, see Other Pub. B&W

RAPHAEL
Mirage
1 TMNTurtle characters 15.00

RARE BREED
Dark Moon Productions 1995
1 V:Anarchy 2.50
2 V:Anarchy 2.50

RAT BASTARD
Crucial Comics 1997
1 by The Huja Brothers 1.95
2 . . . . 1.95
3 . . . . 1.95
4 (of 4) 1.95
5 . . . . 1.95

RAT PATROL, THE
Dell Publishing Co. March, 1967
1 Ph(c) 60.00
2 . . . . 40.00
3 thru 6 Ph(c) . . . . @30.00

RAVEN
Renaissance Comics
1 I:Raven 2.50
2 V:Macallister 2.50
3 thru 5 . . . . @2.50
6 V:Nightmare Creatures 2.75

RAVENING
Avatar 1998
1/2 Busch (c) F:Ravyn & Glyph . 3.00
1/2a Meadows(c) 3.00
1/2b nude cover 6.00
1/2b nude leather cover 30.00

RAVENS AND RAINBOWS
Pacific
1 . . . . 1.50

RAY BRADBURY CHRONICLES
Byron Press
1 short stories 10.00
2 short stories 10.00
3 short stories 10.00

COLOR PUB.

RAY BRADBURY COMICS
Topps 1993–94
1 thru 5 w/Trading Card 3.25
Spec.#1 The Illustrated Man 3.00
Spec. Trilogy of Terror 2.50
Spec. The Martian Chronicles . . . 3.00

R.A.Z.E.
Firstlight
1 I:R.A.Z.E., Secret Weapon 2.95
2 V:Exterminators 2.95

RAZOR
London Night Studios
0 . . . . 15.00
0a second printing 3.00
1 I:Razor 15.00
1a second printing 3.00
2 . . . . 10.00
2a limited ed., red & blue 20.00
2b platinum ed. 25.00
3 . . . . 9.00
3a with poster 18.00
4 . . . . 4.00
4a with poster 15.00
5 . . . . 9.00
5a platinum ed. 22.00
6 . . . . 7.00
7 . . . . 5.00
8 . . . . 3.00
9 . . . . 3.00
10 . . . . 3.00
11 & 12 B&W . . . . @3.00
Ann.#1 I:Shi 25.00
Ann.#2 O:Razor B&W 35.00
Becomes
RAZOR UNCUT
see B&W
Volume 2 1996
1 DQ, ... 3.00
1 holochrome edition 8.00
2 DQ 3.00
2 holochrome edition 5.00
3 . . . . 3.00
4 . . . . 3.00
5 . . . . 3.00
6 . . . . 3.00
7 . . . . 3.00

RAZOR AND SHI SPECIAL
London Night Studios 1994
1 Rep. Razor Ann.#1 + new art . 5.00
1a platinum version 12.00

RAZOR ARCHIVES
London Night
1 & 2 see B&W
3 rep. Razor #10–12 . . . . 7.00

RAZOR BURN
London Night Studios 1994
1 V:Styke 3.00
1a signed 5.00
2 Searching for Styke 3.00
2a Platinum 8.00
3 Stryke's War 3.00
4 D:Razor, bagged 3.00
5 Epilogue 3.00

RAZOR: CRY NO MORE
London Night Studios 1995
1-shot 3.00

1a variant 4.00

RAZOR/MORBID ANGEL: SOUL SEARCH
London Night
1 (of 3) 3.00
1 platinum edition 5.00
1 Chromium edition 8.00
2 . . . . 3.00
3 . . . . 3.00

RAZOR: THE SUFFERING
London Night Studios 1994
1 . . . . 4.00
1a Director's cut 3.00
1b signed, limited 12.00
2 . . . . 3.00
2a Director's cut 2.50
3 final chapter 3.00

Razor: Torture #6
© Pacific Comics

RAZOR: TORTURE
London Night Studios 1995
0 Razor back from dead 4.00
0a signed edition 8.00
1 . . . . 3.00
2 . . . . 3.00
3 EHr 3.00
4 . . . . 3.00
5 alt. cover, signed 4.00
6 alt. cover, signed 4.00
7 . . . . 3.00

RAZOR SWIMSUIT SPECIAL
London Night Studios 1995
1 pin-ups 3.00
1a platinum version 8.00
1b commemorative edition 4.00

RAZOR/ WARRIOR NUN AREALA: FAITH
London Night
1 by Jude Millien 3.00

1a variant cover 4.00

REAL GHOSTBUSTERS
Now
1 KSy(c) 4.50
2 thru 7 . . . . @2.50
8 thru 24 . . . . @1.75
[2nd Series]
1 Halloween Special 1.75
Ann. 3-D w/glasses & pinups . . . 2.95

REALITY CHECK
Sirius 1996
1 by Tavicat 2.95
2 thru 8 . . . . @2.95
9 Nonesuch Nonsense, pt.1 . . . . 2.95
10 Nonesuch Nonsense, pt.2 . . . 2.95
11 Nonesuch Nonsense, pt.3 . . . 2.95
TPB Vol. 1 . . . . 17.95

REAL WAR STORIES
Eclipse 1987–91
1 BB 3.00
1a 2nd printing 1.50
2 . . . . 4.95

RE-ANIMATOR
Adventure Comics
1 movie adaption 2.95
2 movie adaption 2.95

RE-ANIMATOR
Adventure
1 Prequel to Orig movie 2.50

RE-ANIMATOR: DAWN OF THE RE-ANIMATOR
Adventure
1 Prequel to movie 2.50
2 . . . . 2.50
3 . . . . 2.50
4 V:Erich Metler 2.50

RE-ANIMATOR: TALES OF HERBERT WEST
Adventure Comics
1 H.P.Lovecraft stories 4.95

RED DOG
Eclipse 1988
1 CR,Mowgli "Jungle Book" story   2.00

RED DRAGON
Comico 1995
1 SBs,I:Red Dragon 2.50
2 How Soon is Nau? 2.95

REDEEMERS
Antarctic Press 1997
1 (of 5) by Herb Mallette & Patrick
   Blain 2.95
2 . . . . 2.95

RED HEAT
1 3-D 2.50

RED SONJA in 3-D
Blackthorne
1 thru 3 . . . . @2.50

All comics prices listed are for *Near Mint* condition.   CVA Page 561

REESE'S PIECES
Eclipse 1985
1 reprint from Web of Horror ... 1.50
2 reprint from Web of Horror ... 1.50

RE: GEX
Awesome Entertainment 1998
1 RLe,JLb 2.50
2 RLe,JLb 2.50

REGGIE
Archie Publications 1963–65
15 . . . . 40.00
16 . . . . 35.00
17 . . . . 35.00
18 . . . . 35.00
Becomes:

REGGIE AND ME
Archie Publications 1966–80
19 . . . . 15.00
20 thru 23 . . . . @7.00
24 thru 40 . . . . @2.50
41 thru 126 . . . . @1.00

REGGIE'S WISE GUY JOKES
Archie Publications April, 1968
1 . . . . 25.00
2 . . . . 12.00
3 . . . . 12.00
4 . . . . 12.00
5 . . . . 5.00
6 . . . . 5.00
7 . . . . 5.00
8 . . . . 5.00
9 . . . . 5.00
10 . . . . 5.00
11 thru 60, Jan. 1982 . . . . . . @3.00

REIVERS
Enigma
1 thru 3 Rock 'n' Roll 2.95

REPTILICUS
Charlton Comics Aug., 1961
1 . . . . 100.00
2 . . . . 60.00
Becomes:

REPTISAURUS
3 . . . . 40.00
4 . . . . 35.00
5 . . . . 35.00
6 . . . . 35.00
7 . . . . 35.00
8 Summer, 1963 . . . . 35.00

RETURN OF KONGA, THE
Charlton Comics 1962
N# 40.00

RETURN OF MEGATON MAN
Kitchen Sink
1 Don Simpson art (1988) 2.00
2 Don Simpson art 2.00
3 Don Simpson art 2.00

RETURN TO JURASSIC PARK
Topps 1995
1 R:Jurassic Park 2.50
2 V:Blosyn Team, Army 2.50
3 The Hunted 2.50
4 Army 2.50
5 Heirs to the Thunder,pt.1 . . . . 2.95
6 Heirs to the Thunder,pt.2 . . . . 2.95
7 Inquiring Minds,pt.1 . . . . 2.95
8 Photo Finish, concl. 2.95
9 Jurassic Jam issue 2.95

REVENGE OF THE PROWLER
Eclipse 1988
1 GN,R:Prowler 1.75
2 GN,A:Fighting Devil Dogs with
   Flexi-Disk 2.50
3 GN,A:Devil Dogs 1.75
4 GN,V:Pirahna 1.75

REVENGERS
Continuity
1 NA,O:Megalith,I:Crazyman 5.50
2 NA,Megalith meets Armor &
   Silver Streak,Origin Revengers#1 2.50
3 NA/NR,Origin Revengers #2 . . 2.50
4 NA,Origin Revengers #3 . . . . 2.50
5 NA,Origin Revengers #4 . . . . 2.50
6 I:Hybrids 3.00
Spec. #1 F:Hybrids 4.95

RIBIT
Comico
1 FT,Mini-series 1.95
2 FT,Mini-series 1.95
3 FT,Mini-series 1.95
4 FT,Mini-series 1.95

Richie Rich #107 © Harvey Publications

RICHIE RICH
Harvey Publications 1960–91
1 . . . . 1,200.00
2 . . . . 400.00
3 . . . . 250.00
4 . . . . 250.00

5 . . . . 250.00
6 . . . . 150.00
7 . . . . 150.00
8 . . . . 150.00
9 . . . . 150.00
10 . . . . 150.00
11 thru 20 . . . . @100.00
21 thru 40 . . . . @75.00
41 thru 60 . . . . @50.00
61 thru 80 . . . . @20.00
81 thru 99 . . . . @10.00
100 . . . . 15.00
101 thru 111 . . . . @7.00
112 thru 116 52 pg Giants . . . . @8.00
117 thru 120 . . . . @6.00
121 thru 140 . . . . @4.00
141 thru 160 . . . . @3.00
161 thru 180 . . . . @2.00
181 thru 254 . . . . @1.00

RICHIE RICH
Harvey 1991
1 thru 15 . . . . @1.25
16 thru 28 . . . . @1.50

RICHIE RICH BANK BOOKS
Harvey 1972–82
1 . . . . 25.00
2 thru 5 . . . . @15.00
6 thru 10 . . . . @7.50
11 thru 20 . . . . @5.00
21 thru 30 . . . . @4.00
31 thru 40 . . . . @3.00
41 thru 59 . . . . @3.00

RICHIE RICH BILLIONS
Harvey 1974–82
1 . . . . 12.50
2 thru 5 . . . . @7.50
6 thru 10 . . . . @5.00
11 thru 20 . . . . @4.00
21 thru 30 . . . . @2.00
31 thru 48 . . . . @1.50

RICHIE RICH DIAMONDS
Harvey 1972–82
1 . . . . 32.00
2 thru 5 . . . . @15.00
6 thru 10 . . . . @7.00
11 thru 20 . . . . @5.00
21 thru 30 . . . . @2.00
31 thru 59 . . . . @1.50

RICHIE RICH DOLLARS & CENTS
Harvey Publications 1963–82
1 . . . . 135.00
2 . . . . 50.00
3 thru 5 . . . . @25.00
6 thru 10 . . . . @15.00
11 thru 20 . . . . @10.00
21 thru 30 . . . . @7.00
31 thru 43 . . . . @5.00
44 thru 60 . . . . @4.00
61 thru 70 . . . . @3.00
71 thru 109 . . . . @3.00

RICHIE RICH FORTUNES
Harvey 1971–82

1	30.00
2 thru 5	@15.00
6 thru 10	@7.00
11 thru 20	@4.00
21 thru 30	@2.00
31 thru 63	@2.00

RICHIE RICH GEMS
Harvey 1974–82

1	15.00
2 thru 5	@6.00
6 thru 10	@4.00
11 thru 20	@3.00
21 thru 30	@2.00
31 thru 43	@2.00

RICHIE RICH JACKPOTS
Harvey 1974–82

1	25.00
2 thru 5	@7.00
6 thru 10	@5.00
11 thru 20	@3.00
21 thru 30	@2.00
31 thru 58	@2.00

RICHIE RICH MILLIONS
Harvey Publications 1961–82

1	150.00
2	75.00
3 thru 10	@60.00
11 thru 20	@40.00
21 thru 30	@20.00
31 thru 48	@8.00
49 thru 60	@6.00
61 thru 64	@4.00
65 thru 74	@3.00
75 thru 94	@2.50
95 thru 113	@2.00

Richie Rich Profits #14
© Harvey Publications

RICHIE RICH MONEY WORLD
Harvey 1972–82

1	25.00
2 thru 5	@7.00
6 thru 10	@5.00
11 thru 20	@3.00
21 thru 30	@2.00
31 thru 59	@2.00

RICHIE RICH PROFITS
Harvey 1974–82

1	15.00
2 thru 5	@7.00
6 thru 10	@5.00
11 thru 20	@3.00
21 thru 30	@2.00
31 thru 47	@2.00

RICHIE RICH RICHES
Harvey 1972–82

1	15.00
2 thru 5	@7.00
6 thru 10	@5.00
11 thru 20	@3.00
21 thru 30	@2.00
31 thru 59	@2.00

RICHIE RICH SUCCESS STORIES
Harvey Publications 1964–82

1	100.00
2 thru 5	@50.00
6 thru 10	@25.00
11 thru 30	@15.00
31 thru 38	@10.00
39 thru 55	@5.00
56 thru 66	@3.00
67 thru 105	@2.00

RICHIE RICH VAULT OF MYSTERY
Harvey 1974–82

1	10.00
2 thru 5	@5.00
6 thru 10	@4.00
11 thru 20	@3.00
21 thru 30	@2.00
31 thru 47	@2.00

RICHIE RICH ZILLIONS
Harvey 1976–82

1	10.00
2 thru 5	@5.00
6 thru 10	@4.00
11 thru 20	@2.00
21 thru 33	@2.00

RIFLEMAN, THE
Dell Publishing Co. 1959

1 Chuck Connors Ph(c) all	250.00
2	125.00
3 ATh	100.00
4	85.00
5	85.00
6 ATh	110.00
7	85.00

8	85.00
9	85.00
10	85.00
11	75.00
12	75.00
13	75.00
14	75.00
15	75.00
16	75.00
17	75.00
18	75.00
19	75.00
20	75.00

RIOT GEAR
Triumphant

1 JnR(s),I:Riot Gear	2.50
2 JnR(s),I:Rabin	2.50
3 JnR(s),I:Surzar	2.50
4 JnR(s),D:Captain Tich	2.50
5 JnR(s),reactions	2.50
6 JnR(s),Tich avenged	2.50
7 JnR(s),Information Age	2.50
8 JnR(s),	2.50

RIOT GEAR: VIOLENT PAST
Triumphant

1 and 2	@2.50

R.I.P.
TSR 1990–91

1 thru 4	@2.95
5 thru 8 Brasher, Avenger of the Dead	@2.95

RIPLEY'S BELIEVE IT OR NOT!
Gold Key 1967–80

4 Ph(c),AMc	40.00
5 GE,JJ	25.00
6 AMc	25.00
7	15.00
8	25.00
9	15.00
10 GE	25.00
11	10.00
12	10.00
13	10.00
14	10.00
15 GE	12.00
16	10.00
17	10.00
18	10.00
19	10.00
20	10.00
21 thru 30	@8.00
31 thru 38	@5.00
39 RC	6.00
40 thru 50	@5.00
51 thru 94	@4.00

RISK
Maximum Press 1995

1 V:Furious	2.50

ROBIN HOOD
Eclipse 1991

1 TT,Historically accurate series	2.75
2 and 3 TT	@2.75

ROBO HUNTER
Eagle
1 .... 1.50
2 thru 5 .... @1.00

ROBOTECH
Antarctic Press 1997
1 by Fred Perry & BDn 2.95
2 .... 2.95
3 .... 2.95
4 Rolling Thunder, pt.1 .... 2.95
5 Rolling Thunder, pt.2 .... 2.95
6 Rolling Thunder, pt.3 .... 2.95
7 Rolling Thunder, pt.4 .... 2.95
8 Variants, pt.1 .... 2.95
9 Variants, pt.2 .... 2.95
TPB Megastorm by Fred Perry & Ben Dunn 7.95

ROBOTECH: GENESIS
The Legend of Zor
Eternity
1 O:Robotech w/cards 2.95
1a Limited Edition,extra pages with cards #1 & #2 .... 5.95
2 thru 6, each with cards .... @2.50

ROBOTECH IN 3-D
Comico
1 .... 2.50

Robotech, The Macross Saga #4
© Comico

ROBOTECH,
THE MACROSS SAGA
Comico 1985–89
(formerly Macross)
2 .... 5.00
3 .... 4.00
4 .... 3.00
5 .... 2.50
6 J:Rick Hunter 2.50
7 V:Zentraedi 2.00
8 A:Rick Hunter 2.00
9 V:Zentraedi 2.00
10 "Blind Game" 2.00
11 V:Zentraedi 2.00

12 V:Zentraedi 2.00
13 V:Zentraedi 2.00
14 "Gloval's Reports" 2.00
15 V:Zentraedi 2.00
16 V:Zentraedi 2.00
17 V:Zentraedi 2.00
18 D:Roy Fokker 2.00
19 V:Khyron 2.00
20 V:Zentraedi 2.00
21 "A New Dawn" 2.00
22 V:Zentraedi 2.00
23 "Reckless" 2.00
24 HB,V:Zentraedi 2.00
25 "Wedding Bells" 2.00
26 "The Messenger" 2.00
27 "Force of Arms" 2.00
28 "Reconstruction Blues" ... 2.00
29 "Robotech Masters" 2.00
30 "Viva Miriya" 2.00
31 "Khyron's Revenge" 2.00
32 "Broken Heart" 2.00
33 "A Rainy Night" 2.00
34 "Private Time" 2.00
35 "Season's Greetings" 2.00
36 last issue 2.00
Graphic Novel #1 .... 6.00

ROBOTECH MASTERS
Comico 1985–88
1 .... 4.00
2 .... 3.00
3 Space Station Liberty 3.00
4 V:Bioroids 2.50
5 V:Flagship 2.50
6 "Prelude to Battle" 2.50
7 "The Trap" 2.50
8 F:Dana Sterling 2.50
9 "Star Dust" 2.50
10 V:Zor 2.50
11 A:De Ja Vu 2.00
12 2OR 2.00
13 .... 2.00
14 "Clone Chamber,"V:Zor ... 2.00
15 "Love Song" 2.00
16 V:General Emerson 2.00
17 "Mind Games" 2.00
18 "Dana in Wonderland" ... 2.00
19 .... 2.00
20 A:Zor,Musica 2.00
21 "Final Nightmare" 2.00
22 "The Invid Connection" .. 2.00
23 "Catastrophe," final issue .. 2.00

ROBOTECH:
THE NEW GENERATION
Comico 1985–88
1 .... 4.00
2 "The Lost City" 3.00
3 V:Yellow Dancer 3.00
4 A:Yellow Dancer 3.00
5 SK(i),A:Yellow Dancer 2.50
6 F:Rook Bartley 2.50
7 "Paper Hero" 2.00
8 .... 2.00
9 KSy,"The Genesis Pit" 2.00
10 V:The Invid 2.00
11 F:Scott Bernard 2.00
12 V:The Invid 2.00
13 V:The Invid 2.00
14 "Annie"s Wedding" 2.00
15 "Seperate Ways" 2.00
16 "Metamorphosis" 2.00
17 "Midnight Sun" 2.00
18 .... 2.00

19 .... 2.00
20 "Birthday Blues" 2.00
21 "Hired Gun" 2.00
22 "The Big Apple" 2.00
23 Robotech Wars 2.00
24 Robotech Wars 2.00
25 V:Invid, last issue 2.00

ROBOTECH SPECIAL
DANA"S STORY
Eclipse
1 .... 5.00

ROBOTECH II:
THE SENTINELS
Eternity
Swimsuit Spec.#1 .... 2.95

ROCK & ROLL
Revolutionary
Prev: Black & White
15 Poison 3.50
16 Van Halen 1.95
17 Madonna 2.50
18 AliceCooper 1.95
19 Public Enemy, 2 Live Crew ... 2.50
20 Queensryche 1.95
21 Prince 1.95
22 AC/DC 1.95
23 Living Color 1.95
24 Anthrax 1.95
25 Z.Z.Top 2.50
26 Doors 2.50
27 Doors 2.50
28 Ozzy Osbourne 2.50
29 The Cure 2.50
30 .... 2.50
31 Vanilla Ice 2.50
32 Frank Zappa 2.50
33 Guns n" Roses 2.50
34 The Black Crowes 2.50
35 R.E.M. 2.50
36 Michael Jackson 2.50
37 Ice T 2.50
38 Rod Stewart 2.50
39 .... 2.50
40 N.W.A./Ice Cube 2.50
41 Paula Abdul 2.50
42 Metallica II 2.50
43 Guns "N" Roses 2.50
44 Scorpions 2.50
45 Greatful Dead 3.00
46 Grateful Dead 3.00
47 Grateful Dead 3.00
48 (now b/w),Queen 2.50
49 Rush 2.50
50 Bob Dylan Pt.1 .... 2.50
51 Bob Dylan Pt.2 .... 2.50
52 Bob Dylan Pt.3 .... 2.50
53 Bruce Springsteen 2.50
54 U2 Pt.1 .... 2.50
55 U2 Pt.2 .... 2.50
56 thru 72 .... @2.50

ROCK 'N' ROLL
HIGH SCHOOL
Cosmic Comics 1995
1 Sequel to the movie 2.50

ROCKETEER
Walt Disney
1 DSt(c)RH,MovieAdaptation ... 7.00

All comics prices listed are for *Near Mint* condition.

SAVAGE COMBAT TALES
Atlas Feb.–July, 1975
1 F:Sgt Strykers Death Squad	10.00
2 ATh,A:Warhawk	8.00
3 final issue	8.00

SAVAGE DRAGON/ TEENAGE MUTANT NINJA TURLES CROSSOVER
Mirage
1 EL(s).	2.75

SAVED BY THE BELL
Harvey
1 based on TV series	1.25

SCARLET CRUSH
Awesome Entertainment 1998
1 by John Stinsman	2.50
2	2.50
3 Icaria's decision	2.50
4 Nirasawa arrives	2.50

SCARY TALES
Charlton 1975
1	15.00
2 thru 11	@10.00
12 thru 46	@5.00

SCAVENGERS
Quality 1988–89
1 thru 7	@1.25
8 thru 14	@1.50

SCAVENGERS
Triumphant Comics 1993–94
0 Fso(c),JnR(s),	2.50
0a "Free Copy"	2.50
0b Red Logo	2.50
1 JnR(s),I:Scavengers,Ximos, C:Doctor Chaos	2.50
1a 2nd Printing	2.50
2 JnR(s),	2.50
3 JnR(s),I:Lurok	2.50
4 JnR(s),	2.50
5 Fso(c),JnR(s),D:Jack Hanal	2.50
6 JnR(s),	2.50
7 JnR(s),I:Zion	2.50
8 JnR(s),Nativity	2.50
9 JnR(s),The Challenge	2.50
10 JnR(s),Snowblind	2.50

SCHISM
Defiant
1 thru 4 Defiant's x-over	3.25

SCIENCE COMIC BOOK
Nature Publishing House 1997
TPB Earth Adventures by James Laurie	8.95
TPB Car Adventure by James Laurie	8.95
TPB Volcano Adventures by Stu Duval	8.95
TPB World of Dinosaurs, by Paul Xu and James Passmore	8.95
TPB Beyond the Star, by James Passmore	8.95
TPB Weather Genie, by James	

Laurie	8.95

SCION
1 and 2	@2.00

15¢

Scooby Doo #5 © Charlton

SCOOBY DOO
Gold Key 1970–75
1	45.00
2	30.00
3	20.00
4	20.00
5	20.00
6	15.00
7	15.00
8	15.00
9	15.00
10	15.00
11 thru 20	@10.00
21 thru 30	@8.00

SCOOBY DOO
Charlton Comics 1975–76
1	18.00
2	8.00
3	8.00
4	8.00
5	8.00
6	6.00
7	6.00
8	6.00
9	6.00
10	6.00
11	6.00

SCOOBY DOO
Archie 1995
1 thru 10	@1.50
11 thru 13	@1.50
14 "The Balloon Busters"	1.50
15 "On the Boardwalk in Atlantic City"	1.50
16 "The Ghost of Central Park"	1.50
19 "Electric Monster"	1.50
20 "The Legend of Spooky Doo"	1.50
21 "Monster Park After Dark"	1.50

SCORCHED EARTH
Tundra 1991
1 Earth 2025,I:Dr.EliotGodwin	3.50
2 Hunt for Eliot	2.95
3 Mystical Transformation	2.95

SCORPION, THE
Atlas 1975
1 HC, bondage cover	5.00
2 HC,BWi,MK	4.00
3	3.00

SCORPION CORP.
Dagger 1993
1 PuD,JRI,CH,	2.75
2 PuD,JRI,CH,V:Victor Kyner	2.75
3 PuD,BIH,V:Victor Kyner	2.75

SCORPIO ROSE
Eclipse 1983
1 MR/TP,I:Dr.Orient	2.00
2 MR/TP	2.00

SCOUT
Eclipse 1985–87
1 TT,I:Scout,Fash.In Action	6.00
2 TT,V:Buffalo Monster	3.00
3 TT,V:President Grail	2.50
4 TT,V:President Grail	2.50
5 TT,"Killin' Floor"	2.50
6 TT,V:President Grail	2.50
7 TT,TY,Rosanna's Diary	2.50
8 TT,TY	2.50
9 TT,TY,A:Airboy	2.50
10 TT,TY,I:Proj.Mountain Fire	2.00
11 TT,FH,V:Rangers	2.00
12 TT,FH,"Me and the Devil"	2.00
13 TT,FH,Monday:Eliminator	2.00
14 TT,FH,Monday:Eliminator	2.00
15 TT,FH,Monday:Eliminator	2.00
16 TT,3-D issue,F:Santana	2.00
17 TT,A:Beanworld	2.00
18 TT,FH,V:Lex Lucifer	2.00
19 TT,w/Record,V:Lex Lucifer	3.00
20 TT,A:Monday:Eliminator	2.00
21 TT,A:Monday:Eliminator	1.75
22 TT,A:Swords of Texas	1.75
23 TT,A:Swords of Texas	1.75
24 TT,last Issue	1.75

SCOUT: WAR SHAMAN
Eclipse 1988–89
1 TT,R:Scout (now a father)	2.25
2 TT,I:Redwire	1.95
3 TT,V:Atuma Yuma	1.95
4 TT,"Rollin' on the River"	1.95
5 TT,Hopi Katchina dieties	1.95
6 TT,Scout vs. Rosa Winter	1.95
7 TT,R:Redwire	1.95
8 TT,R:Beau LaDuke	1.95
9 TT,V:Doodyists	1.95
10 TT,TY,V:Redwire	1.95
11 TT,V:Redwire	1.95
12 TT,V:Snow Leopards	1.95
13 TT,F:Beau LaDuke	1.95
14 TT,V:Redwire	1.95
15 TT,V:Redwire	1.95
16 TT,"Wall of Death,"last issue	1.95

SEADRAGON
Elite 1986–87
1	3.00

1a 2nd printing 1.75
2 . . . . 2.00
3 . . . . 2.00
4 . . . . 2.00
5 thru 8 . . . . @1.75

SEA HUNT
Dell Publishing Co. 1958
1 L.BridgesPh(c) all 125.00
2 . . . . 100.00
3 ATh 110.00
4 RsM 100.00
5 RsM 100.00
6 RsM 100.00
7 . . . . 90.00
8 RsM 100.00
9 RsM 100.00
10 RsM 100.00
11 RsM 100.00
12 . . . . 100.00
13 RsM 100.00

SEAQUEST
Nemesis 1994
1 HC(c),DGC,KP,AA,Based on TV
Show 2.50

SEBASTIAN
Walt Disney
1 From Little Mermaid 1.50
2 "While da Crab's Away" 1.50

SECRET AGENT
Gold Key Nov., 1966
1 . . . . 120.00
2 . . . . 75.00

Secret City Saga #3 © Topps Comics

SECRET CITY SAGA
Topps 1993
0 JK 3.25
0 Gold Ed. 15.00
0 Red 10.00
1 w/3 cards 3.25
2 w/3 cards 3.25
3 w/3 cards 3.25
4 w/3 cards 3.25

SECRET SQUIRREL
Gold Key Oct., 1966
1 . . . . 50.00

SEDUCTION OF THE INNOCENT
Eclipse 1985–86
1 ATh,"Hanged by the Neck" reps. 2.50
2 . . . . 2.25
3 ATh,"The Crushed Gardenia" . . 2.00
4 ATh,NC,"World's Apart" 2.00
5 ATh,"The Phantom Ship" 2.00
6 ATh,RA,"Hands of Don Jose" . . 2.00
3-D #1 DSt(c) 2.25
3-D #2 ATh,MB,BWr,"Man Who Was
Always on Time" 2.00

SEEKER
Sky Comics 1995
1 JMt(s),I:Seeker 2.50

SENSEI
First
1 Mini-Series 2.75
2 . . . . 2.75
3 . . . . 2.75
4 . . . . 2.75

SENTINELS OF JUSTICE
AC Comics
1 Capt.Paragon 1.75
2 . . . . 1.75
3 . . . . 1.75
4 . . . . 1.75
5 . . . . 1.75
6 . . . . 1.75
7 . . . . 1.75

SENTRY: SPECIAL
Innovation 1991
1 . . . . 2.75

SERAPHIM
Innovation 1990
1 and 2 . . . . @2.50

SERINA
Antarctic 1996
1 . . . . 2.95

SERPENTINA
Lightning 1997
1 . . . . 3.00
1a variant cover 3.00

SEVEN SISTERS
Zephyr Comics 1997
1 by Curley, Cruickshank & Garcia 2.95
2 . . . . 2.95
3 . . . . 2.95
4 . . . . 2.95

77 SUNSET STRIP
Dell Publishing Co.
Jan.-March, 1960
1 Ph(c) 75.00
2 Ph(c),RsM 80.00

SHADE SPECIAL
AC Comics
1 . . . . 1.50

SHADOW, THE
Archie Comics 1964–65
1 . . . . 50.00
2 . . . . 35.00
3 . . . . 35.00
4 . . . . 35.00
5 . . . . 35.00
6 and 8 . . . . @30.00

SHADOW COMICS
1 Guardians of Justice & The
O-Force 1.50

SHADOW OF THE TORTURER, THE
Innovation 1991
1 thru 6 Gene Wolfe adapt. . . @1.95

SHADOW RAVEN
Poc-It Comics
1 I:Shadow Raven 2.95

SHADOW STATE
Preview Editions
1 and 2 B&W 2.50
Broadway 1995
1 thru 4 F:BloodS.C.R.E.A.M. . @2.50
5 JiS, "Image Isn't Everything,"
concl. 2.50
6 "Anger of Lovers" pt.1 . . . . . 2.50
7 "Anger of Lovers" pt.2 . . . . . 2.95

SHAFT
Maximum Press 1997
1 RLd 2.50

SHAIANA
Entity 1995
1 R:Shaiana from Aster 3.75
1a clear chromium 8.00
1b Holochrome 10.00
2 Guardians of Earth 2.50

SHANGHAI BREEZE
1 . . . . 1.75

SHAOLIN
Black Tiger Press
1 I:Tiger 2.95
2 I:Crane 2.95

SHATTER
First 1985–88
1 . . . . 3.00
2 . . . . 2.50
3 . . . . 2.50
4 and 5 . . . . @2.00
6 thru 14 . . . . @1.75
Spec. #1 Computer Comic 5.00
#1a 2nd Printing 2.00

SHE-DEVILS ON WHEELS
Aircel
1 V:Man-Eaters 2.95

2 V:Man-Eaters 2.95
3 V:Man-Eaters 2.95

SHEENA: QUEEN OF THE JUNGLE
London Night
0 by Gabriel Cain & Wilson 3.00
0a Zebra Edition 5.00
0b Leopard Edition 5.00
0c Alligator Edition 5.00

SHEENA: QUEEN OF THE JUNGLE: BOUND
London Night
1 (of 4) by Everette Hartsoe & Art
Wetherell 3.00
1 ministry ed. 5.00
1 Leather retro edition 15.00

SHERIFF OF TOMBSTONE
Charlton Comics 1958–61
1 AW,JSe 50.00
2 . . . . 30.00
3 thru 10 . . . . @20.00
11 thru 17 . . . . @20.00

Shi #4 © Crusade Comics

SHI
Crusade Comics
1 BiT,HMo,I:Shi 40.00
2 BiT 20.00
2 BiT, reissue, new cover 2.95
3 BiT 15.00
4 BiT 8.00
5 V:Arashi 6.00
5a variant cover 15.00
6 V:Tomoe 6.00
7 V:Nara Warriors 5.00
8 New costume 4.00
9 thru 11 . . . . @4.00
12 "Way of the Warrior" concl, flip-
book Angel Fire. 3.00
TPB Shi:Way of the Warrior 12.95
Shi/Cyblade Spec.#1 Battle of the
Independents 4.00
Spec.#1a variant cover 6.00

TPB Vol. 1 revised rep.JuB(c) . . 14.95
TPB Vol. II, rep. #5–#8 . . . . 14.95
TPB rep. Shi #9–#12 & Shi vs. Tomoe 17.95

SHI: THE SERIES
Crusade Entertainment 1997
1 sequel to *Shi: Heaven and Earth*,
F:Tomoe 2.95
2 Unforgettable Fire, concl. 2.95
3 A Rock and a Hard Place, pt.1 2.95
4 A Rock and a Hard Place, pt.2 2.95
5 A Rock and a Hard Place, pt.3 2.95
6 . . . . 2.95
7 Photographer's lucky picture . 2.95
8 V:Gemini Dawn twins 2.95
9 Bad Blood, pt.1 . . . . 2.95
9a variant BTi(c) 2.95
9b variant Ahn (c) 2.95
9c variant Kevin Lau (c) 2.95
10 Bad Blood, pt.2 . . . . 2.95
10a variant BTi(c) 2.95
10b variant Ahn (c) 2.95
10c variant Kevin Lau (c) 2.95
11 Bad Blood, pt.3 . . . . 2.95
12 The Dark Crusade, pt.1 (of 8) . 2.95
13 The Dark Crusade, pt.2 (of 8) . 2.95
14 The Dark Crusade, pt.3 (of 8) . 2.95
15 The Dark Crusade, pt.4 (of 8) . 2.95
16 The Dark Crusade, pt.5 (of 8) . 2.95
1-shot The Essential Dark Crusade 2.95

SHI: ART OF WAR TOUR BOOK
Crusade Entertainment
Wizard Chicago Con (c) 5.95

SHI: BLACK WHITE & RED
Crusade Entertainment
1 Night of the Rat, pt.1 . . . . 2.95
2 Night of the Rat, pt.2 . . . . 2.95
Coll. Ed. rep. #1–#2 . . . . 6.95

SHI/CYBLADE
Crusade
Spec.#1 The Battle for
Independents...Endgame 2.95

SHI: EAST WIND RAIN
Crusade Entertainment 1997
1 BiT,MSo, fully painted 3.50
2 BiT, concl. 3.50

SHI: HEAVEN AND EARTH
Crusade Entertainment 1997
1 (of 3) BiT 2.95
1 variant cover 2.95
2 BiT 2.95
3 BiT 2.95
4 BiT 2.95
TPB rep. #1–#4 . . . . 15.95

SHI: MASQUERADE
Crusade Entertainment 1997
1 by Christopher Golden 3.50

SHI: NIGHTSTALKERS
Crusade Entertainment 1997
1-shot by Christopher Golden &
VMk,F:T.C.B. 3.50

SHI: REKISHI
Crusade Entertainment 1997
1 (of 2) BiT 2.95
2 BiT, conclusion 2.95
Coll.Ed. Shi:Reshiki, sourcebook,
MS(c) 4.95

SHI/VAMPIRELLA
Crusade 1997
1 WEI, ... 2.95

SHI VS. TOMOE
Crusade April 1996
Spec. #1 BiT, double size 3.95

SHI-SENRYAKU
Crusade 1995
1 BiT,R:Shi 3.00
1a variant cover 8.00
1 (of 3) 2nd edition 2.50
2 BiT,Arts of Warfare 3.00
2 2nd edition 2.50
3 BiT 3.00
3 2nd edition 2.50
HC Rep.#1-#2 . . . . 24.95
TPB Rep.#1-#2 . . . . 12.95

SHOCK SUSPENSE STORIES
Russ Cochran Press 1992
1 reps.horror stories 1.50
2 inc.Kickback 1.50
3 thru 4 . . . . @2.00
5 thru 7 reps.horror stories 2.00
8 reps.horror stories 2.00

Gemstone
18 EC comics reprint 2.50
TPB Vol. 1 rebinding of #1–#5 . . 8.95
TPB Vol. 2 rebinding of #5–#10 . 9.95
TPB Vol. 3 rebinding of #11–#15 . 8.95
TPB Vol. 4 rebinding of #16–#20 . 9.95

SHOCK THE MONKEY
Millenium/Expand 1995
1 Shock therapy 2.95

SHOGUNAUT
Firstlight
1 I:Shogunaut 2.95
2 V:Teckno Terror 2.95

SHOOTING STARS
1 . . . . 2.50

SHOTGUN MARY
Antarctic Press 1995
1 I:Shotgun Mary 2.95
1a with CD Soundtrack 8.95
1b Red Foil cover 8.00
2 . . . . 2.95
Shooting Gallery 2.95
Deviltown 2.95

SHOTGUN MARY
Antarctic Press
1 by Herb Mallette & Kelsey
Shannon 2.95
2 Early Days, pt.2 . . . . 2.95
3 Early Days, pt.3 . . . . 2.95

(margin) **COLOR PUB.**

SHOTGUN MARY: BLOOD LORE
Antarctic Press 1997
1 (of 4) by Herb Mallette & Neil
  Googe 2.95
2 .... 2.95
3 .... 2.95
4 concl. 2.95

SHOTGUN MARY: SON OF THE BEAST, DAUGHTER OF LIGHT
Antarctic Press 1997
1 by Miljenko Horvatic & Esad T.
  Ribic 2.95

SIEGEL & SHUSTER
Eclipse 1984–85
1 .... 1.50
2 .... 1.75

SILENT MOBIUS
Viz 1991–92
1 Katsumi 5.75
2 Katsumi vs. Spirit 5.25
3 Katsumi trapped within entity . 4.95
4 Nami vs. Dragon 4.95
5 Kiddy vs. Wire 4.95
6 Search for Wire 4.95
GN 14.95

SILENT MOBIUS II
Viz
1 AMP Officers vs. Entities cont . 4.95
2 Entities in Amp H.Q. 4.95
3 V:Entity 4.95
4 The Esper Weapon 4.95
5 Last issue 4.95

SILENT MOBIUS III
Viz
1 F:Lebia/computer network ... 2.75
2 Lebia/computer link cont. 2.75
3 Lebia in danger 2.75
4 Return to Consciousness 2.75
5 Conclusion 2.75

SILVERBACK
Comico 1989–90
1 thru 3 .... @2.50

SILVER CROSS
Antarctic Press 1997
1 (of 3) by Ben Dunn 2.95
2 .... 2.95

SILVERHEELS
Pacific 1983–84
1 .... 2.00
2 and 3 .... @1.50

SILVER STAR
Pacific 1983–84
1 JK 1.00
2 JK 1.00
3 JK 1.00
4 JK 1.00
5 JK 1.00
6 JK 1.00

SILVER STAR
Topps
1 w/Cards 2.95

SILVER STORM
1 .... 2.25
2 .... 1.95
3 .... 1.95
4 .... 1.95

SIMPSONS COMICS
Bongo Comics 1993
1 Colossal Horner 3.00
2 A:Sideshow Bob 2.00
3 F:Bart 2.00
4 F:Bart 2.25
5 A:Itchy & Scratchy 2.25
6 F:Lisa 2.25
7 Circus in Town 2.25
8 Mr. Burns Voyage 2.25
9 Autobiographies 2.25
10 Tales of the Kwik-E-Mart .. 2.25
11 Ned Flanders Public Enemy .. 2.25
12 In the Blodome 2.25
13 F:Bart & Millhouse 2.25
14 Homer owns beer company . 2.25
15 Waltons parody 2.25
16 thru 18 .... @2.25
19 thru 23 .... @2.25
24 .... 2.25
25 .... 2.25
26 Bart: action hero! 2.25
27 .... 2.25
28 Krusty the Clown, tax protest . 2.25
29 Captain Slamtastic 2.25
30 Montgomery Burns clones
  Smithers 2.25
31 Radioactive Homer 2.25
32 F:Lisa and her sax 2.95
33 Reality on the blink 2.25
34 C. Montgomery Burns
  International Games 2.25
35 20 kids 2.25
36 Three geeks computer company 2.25
37 Grampa Abe Simpson 2.25
38 chemically-engineered donuts . 2.25
TPB Rep.#1-#4 .... 10.00
TPB Wing Ding, 120pg 11.95
TPB Simpsons Comics on Parade
  (1998) 11.95
Comic Spectacular,Vol.1 Rep. .. 10.00
Comic Spectacular,Vol.2 Rep. .. 10.00

SIMPSONS COMICS & STORIES
Welsh Publishing 1993
1 with poster 4.00
1a without poster 2.50
Bongo Comics 1998
1 F:Bartman, Itchy & Scratchy .. 2.95

SINTHIA
Lightning 1997
1A by Joseph Adam, Daughter of
  Lucifer 3.00
1B 3.00
1c Platinum Edition 9.95
1d Autographed Edition 9.95
2 Sisters of Darkness 2.95
2a variant cover 2.95
3 Wagner(c) 2.95
3a variant Abrams cover 2.95
3b deluxe variant cover 9.95

4 Wagner(c) 2.95
3a variant John Cleary cover ... 2.95

SISTERS OF MERCY
No Mercy Comics
TPB rep. #1–#5 .... 14.95
Vol 2
1 by Mark Williams & Rikki Rockett 2.50
2 .... 2.50
3 .... 2.50

Six Million Dollar Man #1
© Charlton Comics Group

SIX MILLION DOLLAR MAN, THE
Charlton June 1976
1 JSon,Lee Majors Ph(c) 15.00
2 NA(c),JSon,Ph(c) 12.00
3 Ph(c) 8.00
4 Ph(c) 8.00
5 Ph(c) 8.00
6 Ph(c) 8.00
7 Ph(c) 8.00
8 Ph(c) 8.00
9 Ph(c) 8.00

666: MARK OF THE BEAST
Fleetway/Quality
1 I:Fludd, BU:Wolfie Smith 1.95
2 thru 18. .... @1.95

SKATEMAN
Pacific 1983
1 NA 1.50

SKY WOLF
Eclipse 1988
1 V:Baron Von Tundra 1.75
2 TL,V:Baron Von Tundra 1.75
3 TL,cont. in Airboy #41 ...... 1.75

SLAINE THE BERSERKER
Quality 1987–89
1 thru 14 .... @1.25

15/16	1.50
17	1.50
18/19	1.50
20 thru 28	@1.50

Becomes:

SLAINE THE KING
26	1.50

SLAINE
Fleetway
1 thru 4 SBs,From 2000 AD	@4.95

SLAINE
THE HORNED GOD
Egmont Fleetway 1998
1 (of 3) Pat Millagan & SBs, 68pg.	7.00
2 (of 3) Pat Millagan & SBs, 68pg.	7.00

SLIMER
Now 1989
1	2.50
2 thru 15	@1.75

Becomes:

SLIMER &
REAL GHOSTBUSTERS
16 thru 18	@1.75

SMILEY
Chaos! Comics 1998
1 the Psychotic Button	2.95

SNAGGLEPUSS
Gold Key 1962–63
1	50.00
2	35.00
3	35.00
4	35.00

SNOOPER AND
BLABBER DETECTIVES
Gold Key 1962–63
1	50.00
2	35.00
3	35.00

SNOW WHITE &
SEVEN DWARVES
GOLDEN ANNIVERSARY
Gladstone
1 w/poster & stickers	24.00

SO DARK THE ROSE
CFD 1995
1 Fully Painted	2.95

SOLDIERS OF
FREEDOM
Americomics 1987
1	1.75
2	1.95

SOLOMON KANE
Blackthorne
1 3-D Special	2.50
2 3-D Special	2.50
1 thru 4	@2.50

SOMERSET HOLMES
Pacific 1983–84
1 BA,AW,I:Cliff Hanger & Somerset Holmes	2.50
2 thru 4 BA,AW	@2.00
Eclipse 1984
5 BA,AW	2.00
6 BA	2.00

SONG OF THE CID
Calibre/Tome
1 Story of El Cid	2.95
2 Story of El Cid concl.	2.95

SONIC THE HEDGEHOG
Archie Publications 1993
1 A:Mobius,V:Robotnik	1.50
2 thru 36	@1.50
40 thru 54	1.50
55	1.75
56 x-over with Knuckles #9	1.75
57	1.75
58 x-over with Knuckles #11	1.75
59 R:Horizont-Al and Verti-Cal	1.75
60 Arsenal of the Iron King	1.75
61 Downunda	1.75
62 in Sand Dalvador	1.75
63	1.75
64 "The Naugus Trilogy" pt.1	1.75
GN Sonic Firsts, rep.#0, #1/4 ashcan,#3,#4,#13	4.95
Sonic Live Spec.#1	2.00

SONIC QUEST:
THE DEATH EGG SAGA
Archie Comics
1 (of 3) by Mike Gallagher & MaG, cont. from Sonic the Hedgehog #41	1.50
2 and 3	@1.50

SONIC THE HEDGEHOG
PRESENTS
KNUCKLES CHASTIC
Archie Comics 1995
1 I:New Heroes	2.00
Sonic Versus Knuckles Battle Royal Spec.#1	2.00

SONIC THE HEDGEHOG
PRESENTS TAILS
Archie Comics 1995
1 F:Tails	1.50
2 F:Tails	1.50

SONIC'S FRIENDLY
NEMESIS: KNUCKLES
Archie 1996
1	1.50

SONIC SUPER SPECIAL
Archie Comics 1997
1 Brave New World	2.00
3 Sonic Firsts	2.00
4 The Return of the King	2.25
5 Sonic Kids	2.25
6 Expanded Sonic #50, 48pg	2.25

SON OF MUTANT WORLD
Fantagor 1990
1 BA	2.00
2	2.00

SOUJOURN
Dreamer Comics
1 by Jim Somerville, Stranger & Stranger, pt.1	2.95
2 Stranger & Stranger, pt.2	2.95
3 Malice in Wonderland	2.95
4 A Game of Conscience, pt.1	2.95

SOULQUEST
Innovation 1989
1 BA	3.95

SOUPY SALES
COMIC BOOK
Archie Publications 1965
1	75.00

Space Adventures #5 © Charlton

SPACE ADVENTURES
Charlton 1967–79
Volume 3
1 (#60) O&I:Paul Mann & The Saucers From the Future	35.00
2 thru 8 (1968–69)	@20.00
9 thru 13 (1978–79)	@10.00

SPACE:
ABOVE AND BEYOND
Topps 1995
1 thru 3 TV pilot adaptation	@2.95

SPACE:
ABOVE AND BEYOND—
THE GAUNTLET
Topps 1996
1	2.95
2 (of 2)	2.95

SPACE ARK
AC Comics 1985–87
1	3.00
2	2.00

SPACE FAMILY ROBINSON
Gold Key Dec., 1962–69
1 DSp	250.00
2	125.00
3	75.00
4	75.00
5	75.00
6 B:Captain Venture	75.00
7	75.00
8	75.00
9	75.00
10	75.00
11 thru 20	@50.00
21 thru 36	@25.00

SPACE GHOST
Gold Key March, 1967
1	150.00

SPACE GHOST
Comico 1987
1 SR,V:Robot Master	6.00

SPACE GIANTS, THE
Pyramid Comics 1997
0	1.00
0a deluxe	2.25
1	1.00
3 by Jeff Newman	1.00

SPACE MAN
Dell Publishing Co. 1962–72
1	75.00
2	40.00
3	40.00
4	30.00
5	30.00
6	30.00
7	30.00
8	30.00
9	30.00
10	30.00

SPACE: 1999
Charlton 1975–76
1	10.00
2 JSon,"Survival"	8.00
3 JBy,"Bring Them Back Alive"	7.00
4 JBy	7.00
5 JBy	7.00
6 JBy	7.00
7	7.00
8 B&W	7.00

SPACE: 1999
A Plus Comics
1 GM,JBy	2.50

SPACE USAGI
Mirage 1993
1 thru 3 From TMNT	@2.75

SPACE WAR
Charlton Comics Oct., 1959
1	125.00
2	65.00
3	60.00
4 SD,SD(c)	125.00
5 SD,SD(c)	125.00
6 SD	125.00
7	30.00
8 SD,SD(c)	125.00
9	35.00
10 SD,SD(c)	125.00
11	35.00
12	35.00
13 thru 15	@35.00
16 thru 27	@30.00

Becomes:
FIGHTIN' FIVE
28 SD,SD(c)	35.00
29 SD,SD(c)	35.00
30 SD,SD(c)	40.00
31 SD,SD(c)	40.00
32	5.00
33 SD,SD(c)	40.00
34 Sd,SD(c)	40.00

SPECTRUM COMICS PRESENTS
Spectrum
1 I:Survivors	3.50

Speed Racer #6 © Now Comics

SPEED RACER
Now 1987–90
1	3.50
1a 2nd printing	1.50
2 thru 33	@2.00
34 thru 38	@1.75
Spec. #1	2.50
#1 2nd printing	1.75
Spec. #2	3.50
Classics, Vol #2	3.95
Classics, Vol #3	3.95
[2nd Series]	
1 R:Speed Racer	1.95
2	1.95
3 V:Giant Crab	1.95
4	1.95

5 Racer-X	1.95
6	1.95
7	1.95

SPELLBINDERS
Quality 1986–88
1 Nemesis the Warlock	1.25
2 Nemesis the Warlock	1.25
3 Nemesis the Warlock	1.25
4 Nemesis the Warlock	1.25
5 Nemesis the Warlock	1.25
6 Nemesis the Warlock	1.25
7 Nemesis the Warlock	1.25
8 Nemesis the Warlock	1.25
9 Nemesis the Warlock	1.25
1O Nemesis the Warlock	1.25
11 Nemesis the Warlock	1.25

S.P.I.C.E.
Awesome Entertainment 1998
1 RLe,JLb,F:Kaboom	2.50

SPIDER
Eclipse 1991
1 TT,"Blood Dance"	7.00
2 TT,"Blood Mark"	6.00
3 TT,The Spider Unmasked	5.50

SPIDER: REIGN OF THE VAMPIRE KING
Eclipse 1992
1 TT,I:Legion of Vermin	5.25
2 thru 4 TT	@2.50

SPIDERFEMME
Personality
1 Rep. parody	2.50

SPIDER-MAN/BADROCK
Maximum Press
1 (of 2) DJu,MMy x-over	3.00
2 DJu,DaF x-over	3.00

SPIRAL PATH
Eclipse 1986
1 V:Tairngir	1.75
2 V:King Artuk	1.75

SPIRIT
Harvey 1966
1 WE,O:Spirit	60.00
2 WE,O:The Octopus	50.00

SPIRIT, THE
Kitchen Sink 1983–92
1 WE(c) (1983)	5.25
2 WE(c)	4.25
3 WE(c) (1984)	4.00
4 WE(c)	4.00
5 WE(c)	3.00
6 WE(c)	3.00
7 WE(c)	3.00
8 thru 11 WE(c) (1985) color	3.00
See: B&W section	

SPIRIT, THE: THE NEW ADVENTURES
Kitchen Sink 1997
1 AMo,DGb	3.95
2 Eisner/Stout cover	3.50

2a Eisner/Schultz cover 3.50
3 AMo,Last Night I Dreamed of Dr.
    Cobra 3.50
4 Dr. Broca von Bitelbaum 3.50
5 Cursed Beauty 3.50

SPOOKY HAUNTED HOUSE
Harvey Publications 1972–75
1 . . . . 20.00
2 . . . . 10.00
3 thru 5 . . . . @10.00
6 thru 10 . . . . @5.00
11 thru 15 . . . . @3.00

Spooky Spooktown #53
© Harvey Publications

SPOOKY SPOOKTOWN
Harvey Publications 1966–76
1 B:Casper,Spooky,68 pgs 85.00
2 . . . . 50.00
3 . . . . 35.00
4 . . . . 35.00
5 . . . . 35.00
6 thru 10 . . . . @20.00
11 thru 20 . . . . @15.00
21 thru 30 . . . . @15.00
31 thru 39 E:68 pgs . . . . @4.50
40 thru 45 . . . . @3.00
46 thru 66 . . . . @3.00

SPYMAN
1 GT,JSo,1st prof work,I:Spyman 15.00
2 DAy,JSo,V:Cyclops 10.00
3 . . . . 8.00

SQUALOR
First 1989
1 . . . . 2.75
2 . . . . 2.75
3 . . . . 2.75

STAINLESS STEEL RAT
Eagle 1986
1 Harry Harrison adapt. 2.25
2 thru 6 . . . . @1.50

STAR BLAZERS
Comico 1989
1 . . . . 3.00
2 . . . . 1.75
3 . . . . 1.75
4 . . . . 1.75
[2nd Series]
1 . . . . 1.95
2 . . . . 1.95
3 thru 5 . . . . @2.50

STARBLAZERS
Argo Press 1995
0 Battleship Yamato 2.95
1 F:Dereck Wildstar 2.95
2 After the Comet War 2.95
3 . . . . 2.95
4 TEI 2.95
5 . . . . 2.95
6 . . . . 2.95
7 Icarus, pt.2 . . . . 2.95
8 . . . . 2.95
9 . . . . 2.95
10 . . . . 2.95
11 . . . . 2.95
12 Nova captured 2.95

STARFORCE SIX SPECIAL
AC Comics
1 . . . . 1.50

STARGATE
Entity Comics 1996
1 . . . . 2.95
2 . . . . 2.95
3 . . . . 2.95
4 (of 4) 2.95
4a deluxe limited edition 3.50

STARGATE: DOOMSDAY WORLD
Entity Comics 1996
1 new crew explores 2nd StarGate 2.95
1 prism-foil edition 3.50
2 . . . . 2.95
3 . . . . 2.95
3 deluxe 3.50

STARGODS
Antarctic Press 1998
1 by Zachary, Clark & Beaty 2.95
1a deluxe 5.95

STARLIGHT
1 . . . . 1.95

STAR MASTERS
AC Comics
1 . . . . 1.50

STAR REACH CLASSICS
Eclipse 1984
1 JSn,NA(r) 2.00
2 AN 2.00
3 HC 2.00
4 FB(r) 2.00
5 . . . . 2.00
6 . . . . 2.00

STAR SEED
See: POWERS THAT BE

STARSLAYER
Pacific 1982–83
1 MGr,O:Starslayer 3.00
2 MGr,DSt,I:Rocketeer 12.00
3 DSt,MGr,A:Rocketeer(2ndApp.) 8.00
4 MGr,Baraka Kuhr 2.00
5 MGr,SA,A:Groo 10.00
6 MGr.conclusion story 2.00
First
7 MGr layouts 2.00
8 MGr layouts, MG 1.50
9 MGr layouts, MG 2.25
10 TT,MG,I:Grimjack 4.00
11 TT,MG,A:Grimjack 2.00
12 TT,MG,A:Grimjack 2.00
13 TT,MG,A:Grimjack 2.00
14 TT,A:Grimjack 2.00
15 TT,A:Grimjack 2.00
16 TT,A:Grimjack 2.00
17 TT,A:Grimjack 2.00
18 TT,Grimjack x-over 2.00
19 TT,TS,A:Black Flame 1.25
20 TT,TS,A:Black Flame 1.25
21 TT,TS,A:Black Flame 1.25
22 TT,TS,A:Black Flame 1.25
23 TT,TS,A:Black Flame 1.25
24 TT,TS,A:Black Flame 1.25
25 TS,A:Black Flame 1.25
26 TS,Black Flame full story 1.25
27 A:Black Flame 1.25
28 A:Black Flame 1.25
29 TS,A:Black Flame 1.25
30 TS,A:Black Flame 1.25
31 2nd Anniversary Issue 1.25
32 TS,A:Black Flame 1.25
33 TS,A:Black Flame 1.25
34 last issue 1.25
Graphic Novel 9.95

STAR TREK
Gold Key 1967–79
1 Planet of No Return 500.00
2 Devil's Isle of Space 300.00
3 Invasion of City Builders . . . 200.00
4 Peril of Planet Quick Change 200.00
5 Ghost Planet 200.00
6 When Planets Collide 165.00
7 Voodoo Planet 175.00
8 Youth Trap 150.00
9 Legacy of Lazarus 150.00
10 Sceptre of the Sun 100.00
11 Brain Shockers 100.00
12 Flight of the Buccaneer 90.00
13 Dark Traveler 80.00
14 Enterprise Mutiny 80.00
15 Museum a/t End of Time . . . 80.00
16 Day of the Inquisitors 80.00
17 Cosmic Cavemen 80.00
18 The Hijacked Planet 80.00
19 The Haunted Asteroid 80.00
20 A World Gone Mad 80.00
21 The Mummies of Heitus VII . . 65.00
22 Siege in Superspace 65.00
23 Child's Play 65.00
24 The Trial of Capt. Kirk 65.00
25 Dwarf Planet 65.00
26 The Perfect Dream 65.00
27 Ice Journey 65.00
28 The Mimicking Menace 65.00
29 rep. Star Trek #1 . . . . 65.00
30 Death of a Star 50.00

---

31 "The Final Truth". 50.00
32 "The Animal People" 50.00
33 "The Choice" 50.00
34 "The Psychocrystals" 50.00
35 rep. Star Trek #4 . . . . 50.00
36 "A Bomb in Time" 50.00
37 rep. Star Trek #5 . . . . 35.00
38 "One of our Captains is Missing"35.00
39 "Prophet of Peace" 35.00
40 AMc,Furlough to Fury, A:
  Barbara McCoy 35.00
41 AMc,The Evictors 35.00
42 "World Against Time" 35.00
43 "World Beneath the Waves" . 35.00
44 "Prince Traitor" 35.00
45 rep. Star Trek #7 . . . . 35.00
46 "Mr. Oracle" 35.00
47 "This Tree Bears Bitter
  Fruit" 35.00
48 AMc,Murder on Enterprise . . 35.00
49 AMc,"A Warp in Space" 35.00
50 AMc,"The Planet of No Life" . 35.00
51 AMc,DestinationAnnihilation6 30.00
52 AMc,"And A Child Shall Lead
  Them" 30.00
53 AMc,"What Fools..Mortals Be" 30.00
54 AMc,"Sport of Knaves" 30.00
55 AMc,A World Against Itself . . 30.00
56 AMc,No Time Like The Past,
  A:Guardian of Forever 30.00
57 AMc,"Spore of the Devil" . . . 30.00
58 AMc,"Brain Damaged Planet" 30.00
59 AMc,"To Err is Vulcan" 30.00
60 AMc,"The Empire Man" 30.00
61 AMc,"Operation Con Game" . 30.00

STAR WARS IN 3-D
Blackthorne
1 thru 7 . . . . @2.50

STARWOLVES:
JUPITER RUN
1 . . . . 1.95

S.T.A.T.
Majestic 1993
1 FdS(s),PhH,I:S.T.A.T. 2.50

STEALTH SQUAD
Petra Comics 1993
1 I:Stealth Squad 2.50

STEED & MRS PEEL
Eclipse 1990
1 IG,The Golden Game 4.95
2 IG,The Golden Game 4.95
3 IG,The Golden Game 4.95

STEEL CLAW
Quality
1 H:Ken Bulmer 1.25
2 . . . . 1.00
3 . . . . 1.00
4 . . . . 1.00

STEEL STERLING
Archie Publications 1984
(formerly LANCELOT STRONG)
4 EB 1.00
5 EB 1.00
6 EB 1.00
7 EB 1.00

STEVE CANYON 3-D
Kitchen Sink 1986
Milton Caniff & Peter Poplaski(c),
w/glasses (1985) 2.00

STEVE ZODIAC
& THE FIREBALL XL-5
Gold Key Jan., 1964
1 . . . . 50.00

STING OF THE
GREEN HORNET
Now 1992
1 Polybagged w/trading card . . 2.75
2 inc.Full color poster 2.75
3 inc.Full color poster 2.75

STINGER
1 . . . . 1.75

STITCH
Samsons Comics
1 I:Stitch 2.50

STORMQUEST
Caliber 1994
1 I:Stormquest 1.95
2 Time Stone 1.95
3 BU:Seeker 1.95
4 F:Shalimar 1.95
5 Reunion 1.95
6 V:Samuroids 1.95

STRANGE DAYS
Eclipse 1984–85
1 . . . . 3.50
2 . . . . 2.50
3 . . . . 1.50

STRANGE SUSPENSE
STORIES/
CAPTAIN ATOM
Charlton Comics
75 SD,O:CaptainAtom,1960Rep. 125.00
76 SD, Capt.Atom,1960Rep. . . . 75.00

Captain Atom #89 © Charlton Comics

77 SD, Capt.Atom,1960Rep. . . . 75.00
Becomes:

CAPTAIN ATOM
Charlton Comics 1965–67
78 SD, new stories begin 100.00
79 SD,I:Dr.Spectro 65.00
80 SD 65.00
81 SD,V:Dr.Spectro 65.00
82 SD,I:Nightshade,Ghost 65.00
83 SD,I:Ted Kord/Blue Beetle . . 45.00
84 SD,N:Captain Atom 40.00
85 SD,A:Blue Beetle,I:Punch &
  Jewelee 40.00
86 SD,A:Ghost, Blue Beetle . . . 40.00
87 SD,JAp,A:Nightshade 40.00
88 SD/FMc,JAp,A:Nightshade . . 40.00
89 SD/FMc,JAp,A:Nightshade,
  Ghost, last issue Dec.1967 . . 40.00

STRAW MEN
Innovation
1 & 2 . . . . @1.95

STREET FIGHTER
Ocean 1986–87
1 thru 3 . . . . @1.75

STREET SHARKS
Archie Comics 1995
1 & 2 Based on Cartoons . . . . @1.50

STRIKE!
Eclipse 1988
1 TL,RT,I&O:New Strike 1.75
2 TL,RT 1.25
3 TL,RT 1.25
4 TL,RT,V:Renegade CIA Agents 1.25
5 TL,RT,V:Alien Bugs 1.25
6 TL,RT,"Legacy of the Lost" . . 1.75
Spec. #1 Strike vs. Sgt. Strike
  TL,RT,"The Man" 1.95

STRIKER
Viz
1 thru 2 . . . . 2.75

STRIKEFORCE AMERICA
Comico 1995
1 ScC,SK(c),I:StrikeforceAmerica 2.50
2 V:Superior-prisoner 2.95
3 Breakout, pt.2 . . . . 2.95
[Volume 2] 1995
1 ScC,polybagged with Chrysalis
  promo card 2.95

STRONG MAN
AC Comics
1 . . . . 2.95

STRONTIUM DOG
Eagle 1985
1 . . . . 1.50
2 . . . . 1.25
3 . . . . 1.25
4 . . . . 1.25
5 . . . . 1.25
6 . . . . 1.25
Quality
7 . . . . 1.25
8 . . . . 1.25
9 . . . . 1.25

10	1.25
11	1.25
12	1.25
13	1.25
14	1.25
15/16	1.50
17	1.50
18/19	1.50
20 thru 29	@1.50

[2nd Series]

1	1.25

Quality

Spec.#1	1.50

STRYKE
London Night Studios 1995

0 I:Stryke	5.00
1	4.00

STUMBO THE GIANT
Blackthorne

1 3-D	2.50

STUMBO TINYTOWN
Harvey Publications 1963–66

1	110.00
2	60.00
3	40.00
4	40.00
5	40.00
6 thru 13	@25.00

STUPID HEROES
Next

1 PeL(s),w/ 2 card-strip	2.75
2	2.75
3 F:Cinder	2.75

STURM THE TROOPER

1	1.95
2	1.95
3	1.95

SUBSPECIES
Eternity 1991

1 Movie Adaptation	3.00
2 Movie Adaptation	2.50
3 Movie Adaptation	2.50
4 Movie Adaptation	2.50

SUN GLASSES AFTER DARK
Verotik 1995

1	2.95
2 and 3	@2.95
4 thru 6	@3.95
½ prequel, San Diego Con ed.	2.95

SUN-RUNNERS
Pacific 1984

1	2.50
2	2.00
3	2.00

Eclipse 1984–86

4	2.00
5	2.00
6 "Sins of the Father"	1.75
7 "Dark Side of Mark Dancer"	1.75
Summer Special #1	1.75

SUNSET CARSON
AC Comics

1 Based on Cowboy Star	5.00

SUPERBABES: FEMFORCE
AC Comics

1 Various Artists	5.00

SUPER CAR
Gold Key 1962–63

1	150.00
2	75.00
3	75.00
4	100.00

Super Cops #1 © Red Circle

SUPERCOPS
Now 1990

1 thru 4	@1.75

SUPER COPS, THE
Red Circle 1974

1	1.00

SUPER GOOF
Gold Key 1965–82

1	25.00
2 thru 10	@15.00
11 thru 20	@10.00
21 thru 30	@8.00
31 thru 74	@5.00

SUPER HEROES VERSUS SUPERVILLIANS
Archie Publications July, 1966

1 A:Flyman,Black Hood,The Web, The Shield	50.00

SUPERHUMAN SAMURAI SYBER SQUAD
Hamilton Comics 1995

0 Based on TV Show	2.95

SUPERNAUT
Anarchy 1997

1 (of 3)	3.00
1 gold logo	6.00
2 by Rob Hand, Hand of Doom	3.00
2a gold logo	6.00

SUPREME
Maximum Press

#1–#43 see Image

44 AMo, JoB, A:Glory	2.50
45 AMo, JoB, A:Glory	2.50
46 AMo,Suprema	2.50
47 AMo	2.50
48 AMo	2.50
49 AMo	2.50
50 double size	3.95
51	3.50
52A AMo, Book 1	3.50
52B AMo, Book 2, continuation	3.50
53 AMo,CSp,AG,V:Omniman	3.00
54 AMo,CSp,AG,Ballad of Judy Jordan	3.00
55 AMo,CSp,AG,Silence At Gettysburg	3.00
56 AMo,CSp,AG,Reflections,pt.1	3.00
57 AMo,CSp,AG,Reflections,pt.2	3.00
58 AMo,CSp,AG,A World of His Own	3.00
59 AMo,CSp,AG,Professor Night of the Prism World	3.00
60 AMo,CSp,AG,F:Radar in Puppy Love	3.00
61 AMo,CSp,AG,Meet Mr. Meteor	3.00
Coll.Ed.#1, rep.#1–#2	4.95
Coll.Ed.#2, rep.	4.95
Coll.Ed.#3 rep. #45–#46, AMo	4.95
TPB Supreme Madness	14.95
TPB rep. #41–#46, AMo	14.95

SURGE
Eclipse 1984

1 A:DNAgents	3.00
2 A:DNAgents	2.00
3 A:DNAgents	3.00
4 A:DNAgents	3.00

SURROGATE SAVIOR
Hot Brazer Comic Pub.

1 I:Ralph	2.50
2 Baggage	2.50

SURVIVORS
Spectrum

1 Mag. size	5.00
2	3.50
3 The Old One	2.50
4	2.50

SURVIVORS
Fantagraphics

1 thru 3	@2.50

SUSPIRA: THE GREAT WORKING
Chaos! Comics 1997

1 (of 4) PNa	2.95
2 PNa	2.95
3 PNa	2.95
4 PNa	2.95
HC signed, limited	20.00

All comics prices listed are for *Near Mint* condition.

SWORDS OF TEXAS
Eclipse 1987
1 FH,New America 2.00
2 FH,V:Baja Badlands 1.75
3 FH,TY(c),V:Dogs of Danger . 1.75
4 FH,V:Samurai Master 1.75

SYMBOLS OF JUSTICE
High Impact Studios
1 I:Granger,Justice,Rayven 2.95
2 V:Devil's Brigade 2.95

SYPHONS
Now 1994
1 .... 1.50
2 thru 7 .... @1.50

SYPHONS: COUNTDOWN
Now
1 F:Brigade 2.95
2 Led By Cross 2.95
3 Blown Cover 2.95
1995 Ann. Doomsday Device 2.95

SYPHONS: THE STARGATE STRATAGEM
Now
1 thru 3 .... @2.95

TALES CALCULATED TO DRIVE YOU BATS
Archie Publications 1961–62
1 .... 75.00
2 .... 50.00
3 thru 6 .... @35.00

TALES FROM THE CRYPT
Gladstone 1990–91
1 E.C.rep.AW/FF,GS 5.00
2 rep. 4.00
3 rep. 3.50
4 rep. 3.00
5 rep.TFTC #45 .... 3.00
6 rep.TFTC #42 .... 3.00

TALES FROM THE CRYPT
Russ Cochran Publ 1992
1 rep. TFTC #31,CSS#12 ...... 2.75
2 rep. TFTC #34,CSS#15 ..... 2.50
3 rep. TFTC, CSS 2.50
4 rep. TFTC #43,CSS#18 ..... 2.50
5 rep. TFTC,CSS#23 .... 2.00
[2nd Series]
1 rep.horror stories 2.00
2 inc.The Maestro's Hand 2.00
3 thru 6 .... @2.00
7 thru 8 .... @2.00
Gemstone
16 thru 25 EC comics reprint . @2.50
"Annuals"
TPB Vol. 1 rebinding of #1–#5 ... 8.95
TPB Vol. 2 rebinding of #5–#10 .. 8.95
TPB Vol. 3 rebinding of #11–#15 . 8.95
TPB Vol. 4 rebinding of #16–#20 12.95

TALES OF EVIL
Atlas Comics 1975
1 .... 5.00

TALES OF TERROR
Eclipse 1985–87
1 .... 3.00
2 "Claustrophobia" 2.00
3 GM,"Eyes in the Darkness" ... 2.00
4 TT,TY,JBo(c),"The Slasher" ... 2.00
5 "Back Forty,""Shoe Button Eyes" 2.00
6 "Good Neighbors" 2.00
7 SBi,JBo,SK(i),"Video" 2.00
8 HB,"Revenant,""Food for Thought" 2.00
9 .... 2.00
10 .... 2.00
11 TT,JBo(c),"Black Cullen" ... 2.00
12 JBo,FH,"Last of the Vampires" 2.00
13 .... 2.00

TALES OF THE GREEN BERET
Dell Publishing Co. Jan., 1967
1 SG 30.00
2 thru 4 .... @20.00
5 .... 15.00

TALES OF THE GREEN HORNET
Now 1990
1 NA(c),O:Green Hornet Pt.1 ... 3.00
2 O:Green Hornet Pt.2 .... 2.50
3 Gun Metal Green 2.50
4 Targets 1.95

TALES OF THE MYSTERIOUS TRAVELER
Charlton Comics Aug., 1956
1 DG 275.00
2 SD 250.00
3 SD,SD(c) 250.00
4 SD,SD(c) 275.00
5 SD,SD(c) 275.00
6 SD,SD(c) 275.00
7 SD 225.00
8 SD 225.00
9 SD 225.00
10 SD,SD(c) 250.00
11 SD,SD(c) 250.00
12 .... 100.00
13 .... 100.00
14 (1985) 3.00
15 (1985) 3.00

TALES OF THE SUN RUNNERS
Sirius Comics 1986
1 .... 1.50
2 and 3 .... @2.00

TALESPIN
**Walt Disney 1991
(Reg.-Series)**
1 "Sky-Raker" Pt.1 .... 2.50
2 "Sky-Raker" Pt.2 .... 2.00
3 "Idiots Abroad" 1.75
4 "Contractual Desperation" .. 1.75
5 "The Oldman & the Sea Duck" . 1.75
6 "F'reeze a Jolly Good Fellow" . 1.75

TALESPIN
**Walt Disney 1991
[Mini-Series]**
1 Take-off Pt.1 .... 3.00

2 Take-off Pt 2 .... 3.00
3 Take-off Pt 3,Khan Job ... 2.00
4 Take-off pt 4 .... 2.00

TARGET AIRBOY
Eclipse 1988
1 SK,A:Clint 1.95

TARGITT
Atlas March–July 1975
1 thru 3 .... @5.00

Tarzan of the Apes #192 © ERB, Inc.

TARZAN OF THE APES
Gold Key 1962–72
prev. Dell (see Golden Age)
132 .... 25.00
133 .... 20.00
134 .... 20.00
135 .... 20.00
136 .... 20.00
137 .... 20.00
138 .... 20.00
139 I:Korak 22.00
140 .... 20.00
141 .... 20.00
142 .... 20.00
143 .... 20.00
144 .... 20.00
145 .... 20.00
146 .... 20.00
147 .... 20.00
148 .... 20.00
149 .... 20.00
150 .... 20.00
151 .... 20.00
152 .... 20.00
153 .... 20.00
154 .... 20.00
155 O:Tarzan 25.00
156 .... 15.00
157 Banlu, Dog o/t Arande, Pt.1 15.00
158 Banlu, Dog o/t Arande, Pt.2 15.00
159 Banlu, Dog o/t Arande, Pt.3 15.00
160 .... 15.00
161 .... 15.00
162 TV photo (c) 18.00
163 .... 15.00
164 .... 15.00

All comics prices listed are for *Near Mint* condition.

165 TV photo (c)	20.00
166	15.00
167	15.00
168 TV photo (c)	20.00
169 A:Leopard Girl	15.00
170	15.00
171 TV photo (c)	20.00
172	10.00
173	10.00
174	10.00
175	10.00
176	10.00
177	10.00
178 O:Tarzan, rep. #155	10.00
179 A:Leopard Girl	10.00
180	10.00
181	10.00
182	10.00
183 Down Trails of Terror	10.00
184	10.00
185	10.00
186	10.00
187	10.00
188	10.00
189	10.00
190	10.00
191	10.00
192 Tarzan and the Foreign Legion adaptation	10.00
193 "Escape From Sumatra"	10.00
194 thru 199	@10.00
200	15.00
201 thru 205	@10.00
206 last issue	10.00

Continued by DC; see also Marvel

TARZAN IN COLOR
NBM 1997
TPB Vol. 1, 1931–1933, by Hal Foster	21.95
TPB Vol. 2, 1933–1935, by Hal Foster	24.95
TPB Vol. 3, 1935–1937, by Hal Foster	24.95

TASK FORCE ALPHA
Alpha Productions
1 Forged in Fire	3.50

TASMANIAN DEVIL & HIS TASTY FRIENDS
Gold Key Nov., 1962
1	100.00

TASTEE-FREEZ COMICS
Harvey Comics 1957
1 Little Dot	40.00
2 Rags Rabbit	20.00
3 Casper	30.00
4 Sad Sack	20.00
5 Mazie	20.00
6 Dick Tracy	35.00

TEAM ANARCHY
Anarchy 1993
1 I:Team Anarchy	2.75
2 thru 3	2.75
4 PuD,MaS,I:Primal	2.75

TEAM YANKEE
First 1989
1 Harold Coyle novel adapt.	1.95
2 thru 6	@1.95

Trade Paperback	12.95

T.E.C.H. BOYZ HYPERACTIVE
Dynasty Comics
1 I:T.E.C.H. Boyz	2.95
2 Man vs. Nature	2.95

TEEN-AGE CONFIDENTIAL CONFESSIONS
Charlton Comics 1960–64
1	20.00
2 thru 5	@15.00
6 thru 10	@10.00
11 thru 22	@5.00

TEENAGE HOTRODDERS
Charlton Comics April, 1963
1	30.00
2 thru 5	@25.00
6 thru 10	@15.00
11 thru 23	@10.00
24	8.00

Becomes:
TOP ELIMINATOR
25 thru 29	@5.00

Becomes:
DRAG 'N' WHEELS
30	6.00
31 thru 58	@4.00
59 May, 1973	4.00

TEENAGE MUTANT NINJA TURTLES
First
1	6.00
2	4.50
Graphic Novel	17.00

TEENAGE MUTANT NINJA TURTLES
Archie
(From T.V. Series)
1 O:TMNT,April O'Neil,Shredder Krang	6.00
2 V:Shredder,O:Bebop & Rocksteady	4.00
3 V:Shredder & Krang	3.00

TEENAGE MUTANT NINJA TURTLES
Mirage 1993
1 A:Casey Jones	3.00
2 JmL(a&s)	3.00
3 thru 8	@2.75
9 V:Baxter Bot	2.75
10 Mr. Braunze	2.75
11 V:Raphael	2.75
12 V:Darpa	2.75
13 J:Triceraton	2.75

TEENAGE MUTANT NINJA TURTLES ADVENTURES
Archie 1988
[2nd Series]
1 Shredder,Bebop,Rocksteady return to earth	5.00
2 I:Baxter Stockman	3.00
3 "Three Fragments" #1	3.00

4 "Three Fragments" #2	2.50
5 Original adventures begin, I:Man Ray	2.50
6 I:Leatherhead,Mary Bones	2.50
7 I:Cuddley the Cowlick; Inter-Galactic wrestling issue	2.50
8 I:Wingnut & Screwloose	2.00
9 I:Chameleon	2.00
10 I:Scumbug, Wyrm	2.00
11 I:Rat King & Sons of Silence; Krang returns to earth	2.00
12 Final Conflict #1, A:Leatherhead Wingnut, Screwloose,Trap, I:Malinga	2.00
13 Final Conflict #2	2.00
14 Turtles go to Brazil;I:Jagwar Dreadman	2.00
15 I:Mr. Null	1.50
16 I&D:Bubbla,the Glubbab	1.50
17 Cap'n Mossback	1.25
18 'Man Who Sold World'	1.25
19 I: Mighty Mutanimals	1.25
20 V:Supersoldier,War.Dragon	1.25
21 V:Vid Vicious	1.25
22 GC,Donatello captured	1.50
23 V:Krang,I:Slash, Belly Bomb	1.50
24 V:Krang	1.50
25	1.50
26 I:T'Pau & Keeper	1.50
27 I:Nevermore,Nocturno&Hallocat	1.50
28 Turtle go to Spain, I:Nindar & Chein Klan	1.50
29 Warrior Dragon captured	1.50
30 TMNT/Fox Mutant Ninjara team-up	1.25
31 TMNT/Ninjara team-up cont	1.25
32 A:Sumo Wrestler Tatoo	1.25
33 The Karma of Katmandu	1.25
34 Search For Charlie Llama	1.25
35	1.25
36 V:Shredder	1.25
37 V:Shredder	1.25
38 V:Null & 4 Horsemen Pt.1	1.25
39 V:Null & 4 Horseman Pt.3	1.25
40 1492,A:The Other	1.25
41 And Deliver us from Evil	1.25
42 Time Tripping Trilogy #1	1.25
43 thru 51	@1.25
52 thru 54	@1.50
55 thru 57 Terracide	@1.50
58 thru 70	@1.50
1990 Movie adapt(direct)	5.50
1990 Movie adapt(newsstand)	2.50
1991 TMNT meet Archie	2.50
1991 Movie Adapt II	2.50
Spec.#2 Ghost of 13 Mile Island	2.50
Spec.#3 Night of the Monsterex	2.50
TMNT Mutant Universe Sourcebook	1.95

TEENAGE MUTANT NINJA TURTLES/ FLAMING CARROT
Mirage/Dark Horse
1 JmL	3.00
2 thru 3 JmL	3.00
4 JmL	3.00

TMNT PRESENTS: APRIL O'NEIL
Archie
1 A:Chien Khan,Vid Vicious	1.25
2 V:White Ninja,A:V.Vicious	1.25
3 V:Vhien Khan,concl.	1.25

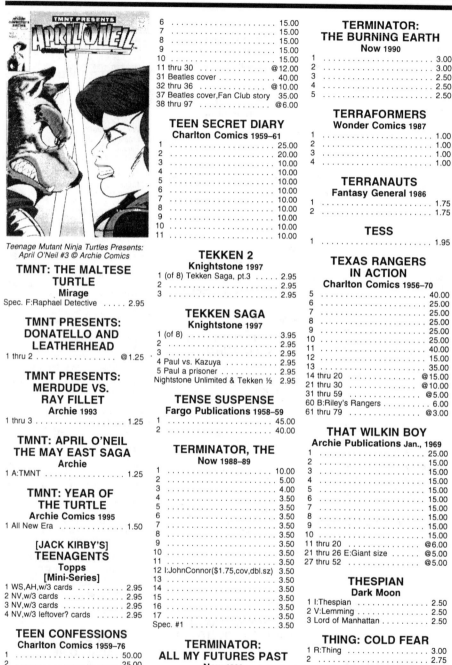

Teenage Mutant Ninja Turtles Presents:
April O'Neil #3 © Archie Comics

TMNT: THE MALTESE TURTLE
Mirage
Spec. F:Raphael Detective 2.95

TMNT PRESENTS: DONATELLO AND LEATHERHEAD
1 thru 2 . . . . @1.25

TMNT PRESENTS: MERDUDE VS. RAY FILLET
Archie 1993
1 thru 3 . . . . 1.25

TMNT: APRIL O'NEIL THE MAY EAST SAGA
Archie
1 A:TMNT 1.25

TMNT: YEAR OF THE TURTLE
Archie Comics 1995
1 All New Era 1.50

[JACK KIRBY'S] TEENAGENTS
Topps
[Mini-Series]
1 WS,AH,w/3 cards 2.95
2 NV,w/3 cards 2.95
3 NV,w/3 cards 2.95
4 NV,w/3 leftover? cards 2.95

TEEN CONFESSIONS
Charlton Comics 1959–76
1 . . . . 50.00
2 . . . . 25.00
3 . . . . 15.00
4 . . . . 15.00
5 . . . . 15.00

6 . . . . 15.00
7 . . . . 15.00
8 . . . . 15.00
9 . . . . 15.00
10 . . . . 15.00
11 thru 30 . . . . @12.00
31 Beatles cover 40.00
32 thru 36 . . . . @10.00
37 Beatles cover,Fan Club story 35.00
38 thru 97 . . . . @6.00

TEEN SECRET DIARY
Charlton Comics 1959–61
1 . . . . 25.00
2 . . . . 20.00
3 . . . . 10.00
4 . . . . 10.00
5 . . . . 10.00
6 . . . . 10.00
7 . . . . 10.00
8 . . . . 10.00
9 . . . . 10.00
10 . . . . 10.00
11 . . . . 10.00

TEKKEN 2
Knightstone 1997
1 (of 8) Tekken Saga, pt.3 . . . . . 2.95
2 . . . . 2.95
3 . . . . 2.95

TEKKEN SAGA
Knightstone 1997
1 (of 8) 3.95
2 . . . . 2.95
3 . . . . 2.95
4 Paul vs. Kazuya 2.95
5 Paul a prisoner 2.95
Nightstone Unlimited & Tekken ½ 2.95

TENSE SUSPENSE
Fargo Publications 1958–59
1 . . . . 45.00
2 . . . . 40.00

TERMINATOR, THE
Now 1988–89
1 . . . . 10.00
2 . . . . 5.00
3 . . . . 4.00
4 . . . . 3.50
5 . . . . 3.50
6 . . . . 3.50
7 . . . . 3.50
8 . . . . 3.50
9 . . . . 3.50
10 . . . . 3.50
11 . . . . 3.50
12 I:JohnConnor($1.75,cov,dbl.sz) 3.50
13 . . . . 3.50
14 . . . . 3.50
15 . . . . 3.50
16 . . . . 3.50
17 . . . . 3.50
Spec. #1 . . . . 3.50

TERMINATOR: ALL MY FUTURES PAST
Now 1990
1 Painted Art 3.00
2 Painted Art 3.00

TERMINATOR: THE BURNING EARTH
Now 1990
1 . . . . 3.00
2 . . . . 3.00
3 . . . . 2.50
4 . . . . 2.50
5 . . . . 2.50

TERRAFORMERS
Wonder Comics 1987
1 . . . . 1.00
2 . . . . 1.00
3 . . . . 1.00
4 . . . . 1.00

TERRANAUTS
Fantasy General 1986
1 . . . . 1.75
2 . . . . 1.75

TESS
1 . . . . 1.95

TEXAS RANGERS IN ACTION
Charlton Comics 1956–70
5 . . . . 40.00
6 . . . . 25.00
7 . . . . 25.00
8 . . . . 25.00
9 . . . . 25.00
10 . . . . 25.00
11 . . . . 40.00
12 . . . . 15.00
13 . . . . 35.00
14 thru 20 . . . . @15.00
21 thru 30 . . . . @10.00
31 thru 59 . . . . @5.00
60 B:Riley's Rangers 6.00
61 thru 79 . . . . @3.00

THAT WILKIN BOY
Archie Publications Jan., 1969
1 . . . . 25.00
2 . . . . 15.00
3 . . . . 15.00
4 . . . . 15.00
5 . . . . 15.00
6 . . . . 15.00
7 . . . . 15.00
8 . . . . 15.00
9 . . . . 15.00
10 . . . . 15.00
11 thru 20 . . . . @6.00
21 thru 26 E:Giant size . . . . . . @5.00
27 thru 52 . . . . @5.00

THESPIAN
Dark Moon
1 I:Thespian 2.50
2 V:Lemming 2.50
3 Lord of Manhattan 2.50

THING: COLD FEAR
1 R:Thing 3.00
2 . . . . 2.75

THIRD WORLD WAR
Fleetway 1990–91
1 HamburgerLady 2.50

COLOR PUB.

2	2.50
3 The Killing Yields	2.50
4	2.50
5	2.50
6	2.50

13: ASSASSIN
TSR 1990–91

1 thru 4 from game	@2.95
5 thru 8 The Search for Maggie Darr	@2.95

THOSE ANNOYING POST BROTHERS
Vortex

1	1.75
2	1.75
3	1.75
4	1.75
5	1.75
6	1.75

3-D ZONE PRESENTS
Renegade 1987–89

1 L.B.Cole(c)	2.00
2	2.00
3	2.00
4	2.00
5	2.00
12 3-D Presidents	2.50
13 Flash Gordon	2.50
14 Tyranostar	2.50
15 Tyranostar	2.50
16 SpaceVixen	2.50

3-D ZONE - 3 DEMENTIA

15	2.50

THREE FACES OF GNATMAN

1	1.75

THREE STOOGES
Dell Publishing Co.
Oct.-Dec., 1959

6 Ph(c),B:Prof. Putter	100.00
7 Ph(c)	100.00
8 Ph(c)	100.00
9 Ph(c)	100.00

Gold Key 1962

10 Ph(c)	100.00
11 Ph(c)	75.00
12 Ph(c)	75.00
13 Ph(c)	75.00
14 Ph(c)	75.00
15 Ph(c)	90.00
16 Ph(c),E:Prof. Putter	75.00
17 Ph(c),B:Little Monsters	75.00
18 Ph(c)	75.00
19 Ph(c)	75.00
20 Ph(c)	75.00
21 Ph(c)	75.00
22 Ph(c),Movie Scenes	75.00
23 Ph(c)	60.00
24 Ph(c)	60.00
25 Ph(c)	60.00
26 Ph(c)	60.00
27 Ph(c)	60.00
28 Ph(c)	60.00
29 Ph(c)	60.00
30 Ph(c)	60.00
31 Ph(c)	50.00

Three Stooges #28 © Gold Key

32 Ph(c)	50.00
33 Ph(c)	50.00
34 Ph(c)	50.00
35 Ph(c)	50.00
36 Ph(c)	50.00
37 Ph(c)	50.00
38 Ph(c)	50.00
39 Ph(c)	50.00
40 Ph(c)	50.00
41 Ph(c)	50.00
42 Ph(c)	50.00
43 Ph(c)	50.00
44 Ph(c)	50.00
45 Ph(c)	50.00
46 Ph(c)	50.00
47 Ph(c)	50.00
48 Ph(c)	50.00
49 Ph(c)	50.00
50 Ph(c)	50.00
51	40.00
52 Ph(c)	50.00
53 Ph(c)	50.00
54 Ph(c)	50.00
55 Ph(c)	50.00

THREE STOOGES 3-D
Eclipse 1991

1 thru 3 reprints from 1953	@2.50
4 reprints from 1953	3.50

THRILLING SCIENCE TALES
AC Comics 1989

1	3.50

THRILLOGY
Pacific 1984

1	1.50

THRILL-O-RAMA
Harvey Publications 1965–66

1 A:Man in Black(Fate),DW,AW	30.00
2 AW,A:Pirana,I:Clawfang, The Barbarian	25.00
3 A:Pirana, Fate	20.00

THUNDER AGENTS
Tower 1965–69

1 WW,RC,GK,MSy,GT,I:Thunder Agents,IronMaiden,Warlord	125.00
2 WW,MSy,D:Egghead	75.00
3 WW,DA,MSy,V:Warlords	50.00
4 WW,MSy,RC,I:Lightning	20.00
5 WW,RC,GK,MSy	50.00
6 WW,SD,MSy,I:Warp Wizard	40.00
7 WW,MSy,SD,D:Menthor	40.00
8 WW,MSy,GT,DA,I:Raven	40.00
9 OW,WW,MSy,A:Andor	40.00
10 WW,MSy,OW,A:Andor	40.00
11 WW,DA,MSy	25.00
12 SD,WW,MSy	25.00
13 WW,OW,A:Undersea Agent	25.00
14 SD,WW,GK,N:Raven,A:Andor	25.00
15 WW,OW,GT,A:Andor	20.00
16 SD,GK,A:Andor	20.00
17 WW,OW,GT	20.00
18 SD,OW,RC	20.00
19 GT,I:Ghost	20.00
20 WW,RC,MSy,all reprints	10.00

T.H.U.N.D.E.R. AGENTS
J.C. Productions 1983

1 MA,Centerfold	2.00
2 I:Vulcan	2.00

T.H.U.N.D.E.R. AGENTS
Maximum 1995

1 and 2	@2.95

THUNDERBOLT
Charlton Comics 1966–67

1 PAM,O:Thuderbolt	20.00
Prev: Son of Vulcan	
51 PAM,V:Evila	10.00
52 PAM,V:Gore the Monster	4.00
53 PAM,V:The Tong	5.00
54 PAM,I:Sentinels	5.00
55 PAM,V:Sentinels	4.00
56 PAM,A:Sentinels	4.00
57 A:Sentinels	4.00
58 PAM,A:Sentinels	4.00
59 PAM,A:Sentinels	4.00
60 PAM,JAp,I:Prankster	5.00

TIGER GIRL
Gold Key Sept., 1968

1	35.00

TIGER-MAN
Atlas April–Sept. 1975

1 thru 3	@6.00

TIME TUNNEL, THE
Gold Key Feb., 1967

1 from TV show	55.00
2	45.00

TIME TWISTERS
Quality 1987–89

1 Alan Moore ser.	1.25
2 Alan Moore ser.	1.25
3 Alan Moore ser.	1.25
4 Alan Moore ser.	1.25
5	1.25
6 Alan Moore ser.	1.25
7 Alan Moore ser.	1.25
8	1.25

COLOR PUB.

9 . . . . 1.25
10 . . . . 1.25
11 . . . . 1.25
12 . . . . 1.25
13 thru 21 . . . . @1.50

TIME 2
1 Graphic Novel 8.00

TIPPY'S FRIENDS GO-GO & ANIMAL
Tower Comics 1966–69
1 . . . . 15.00
2 . . . . 8.00
3 . . . . 8.00
4 . . . . 8.00
5 . . . . 8.00
6 . . . . 8.00
7 . . . . 8.00
8 Beatles on cover & back 30.00
9 thru 15 . . . . @8.00

TIPPY TEEN
Tower Comics Nov., 1965–70
1 . . . . 15.00
2 thru 27 . . . . @10.00

TO DIE FOR
1 3-D 2.50

TOM MIX WESTERN
AC Comics 1988
1 . . . . 2.95

TOMMY & THE MONSTERS
1 . . . . 2.00

TOM TERRIFIC!
Pines Comics
Summer, 1957
1 . . . . 150.00
2 . . . . 100.00
3 . . . . 100.00
4 . . . . 100.00
5 . . . . 100.00
6 Fall, 1958 . . . . 100.00

TOMMI-GUNN
London Night 1997
0 . . . . 3.00
0 nude cover 6.00
½ 3.00
½a photo nude edition 10.00
1 signed 15.00
1a, chromium, elite edition 19.95
2 . . . . 3.00
2 photo nude edition 6.00
3 . . . . 3.00
3 photo nude edition 6.00

TOMMI-GUNN: KILLER'S LUST
London Night 1997
1 . . . . 3.00
1 Japanese Chromium edition . 12.00
2 . . . . 3.00
2 photo nude edition 6.00
2 photo nude edition, signed . . . 15.00

TOMOE
Crusade Entertainment 1996
0 BiT, ... 3.00
1 BiT,Fan Appreciation Edition . . 3.00
2 . . . . 3.00
TPB rep. 13.95

TOMOE/WITCHBLADE: FIRE SERMON
Crusade Entertainment 1996
1 . . . . 5.00
1a Gold foil 10.00

TOMOE: UNFORGETTABLE FIRE
Crusade Entertainment 1997
1 (of 3) 2.95

TOOL AND DIE
Samson Comics
1 Autographed 4.95
1a Blue Edition 9.95

Top Cat #20 © Charlton Comics

TOP CAT
Charlton Comics 1970–73
1 . . . . 30.00
2 thru 10 . . . . @20.00
11 thru 20 . . . . @15.00

TOR IN 3-D
Eclipse 1986
1 JKu 3.00
1a B&W limited 100 sign 5.00
2 JKu 3.00

TORI-SHI-KITA
Relative Burn
1 Hunter Prey 2.50

TORMENTRESS: MISTRESS OF HELL
Blackout Comics 1977
0 . . . . 2.95
0a nude variant 9.95

TOTAL ECLIPSE
Eclipse 1988–89
1 BHa,BSz(c),A:Airboy,Skywolf . . 3.95
2 BHa,BSz(c),A:New Wave, Liberty
Project 3.95
3 BHa,BSz(c),A:Scout,Ms.Tree . . 3.95
4 BHa,BSz(c),A:Miracleman,
Prowler 3.95
5 BHa,BSz(c),A:Miracleman, Aztec
Ace 3.95

TOTAL ECLIPSE, THE SERAPHIM OBJECTIVE
Eclipse 1988
1 tie-in Total Eclipse #2 . . . . . . 1.95

TOTAL WAR
Gold Key July, 1965
1 . . . . 50.00
2 . . . . 50.00
Becomes:

M.A.R.S. PATROL
3 WW 50.00
4 . . . . 25.00
5 . . . . 25.00
6 . . . . 25.00
7 . . . . 25.00
8 . . . . 25.00
9 . . . . 25.00
10 . . . . 25.00

TOY BOY
Continuity 1986–91
1 NA.I&O:Toy Boy,A:Megalith . . . 2.00
2 TVE 2.00
3 TVE 2.00
4 TVE 2.00
5 TVE 2.00
6 TVE 2.00
7 MG 2.00

TRANCERS: THE ADVEN-TURES OF JACK DETH
Eternity
1 I:Jack Deth 2.50
2 A:Whistler, final issue 2.50

TRANSFORMERS
1 Robotics 1.50
2 . . . . 2.00
3 . . . . 2.50

TRANSFORMERS in 3-D
Blackthorne
1 thru 5 . . . . @2.50

TRAVEL OF JAMIE McPHEETERS, THE
Gold Key Dec., 1963
1 Kurt Russell 30.00

TRAVELLER
Maximum Press 1996
1 (of 3) RLd,MHw, ... 3.00

TRIBE
Axis Comics 1993–94
1 see Image Comics section
2 TJn(s),LSn,V:Alex 2.25

3 TJn(s),LSn,	1.95

Good Comics 1996

0 TJn,LSn	2.95
1 TJn,LSn,Choice and Responsibility	2.95
2 TJn,LSn,Choice and Responsibility	2.95

TROLL LORDS
Comico 1989–90

Spec. #1	1.75
1	1.75
2 and 3	@1.75
4	2.50

TROUBLE WITH GIRLS
Comico 1987–88

1	3.00
2	2.50
3	2.50
4	1.95

TRUE LOVE
Eclipse 1986

| 1 ATh,NC,DSt(c),reprints | 2.00 |
| 2 ATh,NC,BA(c),reprints | 1.50 |

TRUE ROMANCE
Pyramid Comics 1997

1	1.00
1a deluxe	2.25
2	1.00
3	1.00
4	1.00

TUFF GHOSTS STARRING SPOOKY
Harvey Publications 1962–72

1	50.00
2	30.00
3	30.00
4	30.00
5	30.00
6	20.00
7	20.00
8	20.00
9	20.00
10	20.00
11 thru 20	@10.00
21 thru 30	@7.00
31 thru 39	@5.00
40 thru 42 52 pg. Giants	@5.00
43	5.00

TUROK: SON OF STONE
1 thru 29 see Golden Age
Gold Key 1962

30	55.00
31 thru 40	@40.00
41 thru 50	@30.00
51 thru 60	@25.00
61 thru 75	@20.00
76 thru 91	@15.00

Whitman

| 92 thru 130 | @7.00 |
| Giant #1 | 75.00 |

TURTLE SOUP
Millenium 1991

| 1 Book 1, short stories | 2.50 |
| 2 thru 4 | 2.50 |

TV CASPER & COMPANY
Harvey Publications 1963–74

1 B:68 pg. Giants	60.00
2	30.00
3	30.00
4	30.00
5	30.00
6	25.00
7	25.00
8	25.00
9	25.00
10	25.00
11 thru 20	@10.00
21 thru 31 E:68 pg. Giants	@8.00
32 thru 46	@5.00

TWEETY AND SYLVESTER
Gold Key 1963–84

1	35.00
2 thru 10	@15.00
11 thru 30	@10.00
31 thru 121	@6.00

22 BRIDES
Event 1996

1	3.00
2	3.00
2a variant (c)	4.00
3	3.00
3a variant (c)	4.00
4	3.00

TWILIGHT AVENGER
Elite 1986

| 1 thru 4 | @1.75 |

TWILIGHT MAN
First 1989

1 Mini-Series	2.75
2 Mini-Series	2.75
3 Mini-Series	2.75
4 Mini-Series	2.75

TWILIGHT ZONE, THE
Gold Key
March–May, 1961

1 RC,FF,GE,P(c) all	100.00
2	75.00
3 ATh,MSy	55.00
4 ATh	55.00
5	50.00
6	50.00
7	50.00
8	50.00
9 ATh	60.00
10	50.00
11	50.00
12 AW	50.00
13 AW,RC,FBe,AMc	40.00
14 RC,JO,RC,AT	40.00
15 RC,JO	40.00
16	25.00
17	25.00
18	25.00
19 JO	25.00
20	20.00
21 RC	25.00
22 JO	25.00
23 JO	25.00
24	20.00

The Twilight Zone #78
© Gold Key Comics

25 GE,RC,ATh	20.00
26 RC,GE	20.00
27 GE	20.00
28	15.00
29	15.00
30	15.00
31	15.00
32 GE	20.00
33	15.00
34	15.00
35	15.00
36	15.00
37	15.00
38	15.00
39 WMc	15.00
40	12.00
41	12.00
42	12.00
43 RC	15.00
44	12.00
45	12.00
46	12.00
47	12.00
48	12.00
49	12.00
50 FBe,WS	12.00
51 AW	15.00
52	12.00
53	12.00
54	12.00
55	12.00
56	12.00
57 FBe	12.00
58	12.00
59 FBe,AMc	15.00
60	10.00
61	10.00
62	10.00
63	10.00
64	10.00
65	10.00
66	10.00
67	10.00
68	10.00
69	10.00
70	10.00
71 rep	8.00
72	10.00

COLOR PUB.

73 rep	8.00
74	10.00
75	10.00
76	10.00
77 FBe	12.00
78 FBe,AMc,The Missing Mirage	12.00
79 rep	8.00
80 FBe,AMc	12.00
81	10.00
82 AMc	12.00
83 FBe,WS	12.00
84 FBe,AMc	12.00
85	10.00
86 rep	8.00
87 thru 91	@10.00

TWILIGHT ZONE
Now 1990

1 NA,BSz(c)	8.00
1a 2nd printing Prestige +Harlan Ellison sty	6.00

[Volume 2]

#1 "The Big Dry" (direct)	2.50
#1a Newsstand	1.95
2 "Blind Alley"	1.95
3 Extraterrestrial	1.95
4 The Mysterious Biker	1.95
5 Queen of the Void	1.95
6 Insecticide	1.95
7 The Outcasts,Ghost Horse	1.95
8 Colonists on Alcor	1.95
9 Dirty Lyle's House of Fun (3-D Holo)	2.95
10 Stairway to Heaven,Key to Paradise	1.95
11 TD(i),Partial Recall	1.95
3-D Spec.	2.50
Ann. #1	2.75

[Volume 3]

1 thru 2	2.50

TWISTED TALES
Pacific 1982–84

1 RCo. "Infected"	3.50
2	2.00
3	2.00
4	2.00
5	2.00
6	2.00
7	2.00
8	2.00

Eclipse

9	2.00
10 GM,BWr	2.00

TWISTED TALES OF BRUCE JONES
Eclipse 1982–84

1	2.00
2	2.00
3	2.00
4	2.00

TWISTER
Harris

1 inc.Special newspaper/poster, and trading cards	2.95

TWO FISTED TALES
Russ Cochran 1992

1 JSe,HK,WW,JCr,reps	1.50
2 Reps inc.War Story	1.50

3 rep.	1.50
4 thru 6 rep.	2.00
7 thru 8 rep.	2.00

Gemstone

17 thru 24 EC comics reprints	@2.50

"Annuals"

TPB Vol.#4 reprint #16–#20	12.95
TPB Vol. 2 rebinding of #5–#10	9.95
TPB Vol. 3 rebinding of #11–#15	10.95
TPB Vol. 4 rebinding	10.95
TPB Vol. 5 rebinding	10.95

2000 A.D. Monthly #1 © Eagle Comics

2000 A.D. MONTHLY
Eagle 1985

1 A:JudgeDredd	4.00
2 A:JudgeDredd	30.00
3 A:JudgeDredd	1.25
4 A:JudgeDredd	1.25
5	1.25
6	1.25

[2nd Series]

1	1.25
2	1.25
3	1.25
4	1.25

Quality

5	1.25
6	1.25
7 thru 27	@1.25
28/29	1.50
30	1.50
31/32	1.50
33	1.50
34	1.50
35	1.50
36	1.50
37	1.50

Becomes:

2000 A.D. SHOWCASE

38	1.50
39	1.50
40	1.50
41	1.50
42	1.95
43	1.95
44	1.95
45	1.95
46	1.50

47	1.75
48 thru 54	@1.75
TPB:Killing Time	12.95

TZU THE REAPER
Murim Studios 1997

1 by Gary Cohn & C.S. Chun	2.95
2	2.95
3	2.95
4	2.95
5	2.95

TZU: SPIRITS OF DEATH
Murim Studios 1997

1	2.95

UFO FLYING SAUCERS
Gold Key Oct. 1968

1	25.00
2	20.00
3 thru 13	@10.00

Becomes:

UFO & OUTER SPACE
Gold Key June 1978

14 thru 25	@5.00

ULTRAMAN
Nemesis 1994

1 EC,O:Ultraman	2.25
2	2.50
3	2.50
4 V:Blue Ultraman	2.50

ULTRAMAN
Harvey/Ultracomics 1993

1 with 1 of 3 cards	2.50
2 with 1 of 3 cards & virgin cover	2.50
3 with 1 of 3 cards & virgin cover	2.50

UNCLE SCROOGE
Dell/Gold Key Dec. 1962

40	125.00
41	100.00
42	100.00
43	100.00
44	100.00
45	100.00
46 Lost Beneath the Sea	100.00
47	100.00
48	100.00
49 Loony Lunar Gold Rush	100.00
50 Rug Riders in the Sky	100.00
51 How Green Was my Lettuce	90.00
52 Great Wig Mystery	90.00
53 Interplanetary Postman	90.00
54 Billion-Dollar Safari!	90.00
55 McDuck of Arabia	90.00
56 Mystery of the Ghost Town Railroad	90.00
57 Swamp of No Return	90.00
58 Giant Robot Robbers	90.00
59 North of the Yukon	90.00
60 Phantom of Notre Duck	90.00
61 So Far and No Safari	75.00
62 Queen of the Wild Dog Pack	75.00
63 House of Haunts!	75.00
64 Treasure of Marco Polo!	75.00
65 Micro-Ducks from OuterSpace	75.00
66 Heedless Horseman	75.00
67 CB rep.	75.00
68 Hall of the Mermaid Queen!	75.00
69 Cattle King!	75.00

Uncle Scrooge #258 © Walt Disney

70 CB,The Doom Diamond!	75.00
71	60.00
72 CB rep.	75.00
73 CB rep.	75.00
74 thru 110	@50.00
111 thru 148	@30.00
149	20.00
150 thru 168	@15.00
169 thru 173	@10.00

Whitman

174 thru 182	@8.00
183 thru 200	@6.00
201 thru 209	@5.00

Gladstone

210 CB	15.00
211 CB,Prize of Pizzaro	15.00
212 CB,city-golden roofs	15.00
213 CB,city-golden roofs	15.00
214 CB	15.00
215 CB, a cold bargain	15.00
216 CB	15.00
217 CB,7 cities of Cibola	15.00
218 CB	15.00
219 Don Rosa,Son of Sun	25.00
220 CB,Don Rosa	5.00
221 CB,A:BeagleBoys	3.00
222 CB,Mysterious Island	3.00
223 CB	3.00
224 CB,Rosa,Cash Flow	6.00
225 CB	3.00
226 CB,Rosa	4.00
227 CB,Rosa	4.00
228 CB	3.00
229 CB	3.00
230 CB	5.00
231 CB,Rosa(c)	3.00
232 CB	3.00
233 CB	3.00
234 CB	3.00
235 Rosa	3.50
236 CB	3.00
237 CB	3.00
238 CB	3.00
239 CB	3.00
240 CB	3.00
241 CB,giant	5.00
242 CB,giant	4.00

Walt Disney 1990

243 CB,"Pie in the Sky"	3.50
244	2.50
245	2.50
246	2.50
247	2.50
248	2.50
249	2.50
250 CB	3.50
251	2.50
252 "No Room For Human Error"	2.50
253 "Fab.Philosophers Stone	2.50
254 The Filling Station	2.50
255 The Flying Dutchman	2.50
256 CB,"Status Seeker"	2.50
257 "Coffee,Louie or Me"	2.50
258 CB,"Swamp of no return"	2.50
259 "The only way to Go"	2.50
260 The Waves Above, The Gold Below	2.50
261 Rosa,"Return to Zanadu" Pt.1	2.50
262 Rosa,"Return to Zanadu" Pt.2	2.50
263 Rosa,"Treasure Under Glass"	2.50
264 Snobs Club	2.25
265 CB,Ten Cent Valentine	2.25
266 The Money Ocean,Pt.1	2.25
267 The Money Ocean,Pt 2	2.25
268 CB,Rosa,Island in the Sky	2.00
269 The Flowers	2.25
270 V:Magica DeSpell	2.25
271 The Secret o/t Stone	2.25
272 Canute The Brute's Battle Axe	2.25
273 CB,Uncle Scrooge-Ghost	2.00
274 CB,Hall of the Mermaid Queen	2.00
275 CB,Rosa,Christmas Cheers,inc. D.Rosa centerspread	2.50
276 Rosa, thru 277	@2.25
278 thru 280	@2.25

Gladstone

281 Rosa	5.00
282 thru 284	2.50
285 Rosa, Life & Times	10.00
286 thru 293 Rosa, Life & Times	@5.00
294 thru 299	@1.50
300 Rosa & Barks	3.00
301 "Statuesque Spendthrifts"	1.50
302	1.50
303 "Rocks to Riches"	1.50
304 "My Private Eye"	1.95
305 "The Vigilante of Pizen Bluff"	1.95
306	1.95
307 "Temper Temper"	1.95
308 "Revenge of the Witch"	1.95

Prestige format, 64pg.

309 "Whadalottajargon"	6.95
310 "The Sign of the Triple Distelfink"	6.95
311 "The Last Lord of Eldorado"	6.95
312 "The Hands of Zeus"	6.95
313 "The Fantastic River Race"	6.95
314	6.95

UNCLE SCROOGE ADVENTURES
Gladstone

1 CB,McDuck of Arabia	9.00
2 translated from Danish	5.00
3 translated from Danish	5.00
4 CB	5.00
5 Rosa	5.00
6 CB	3.50
7 CB	3.00
8 CB	3.00
9 Rosa	3.50
10 CB	3.00
11 CB	3.00
12 CB	3.00
13 CB	3.00
14 Rosa	3.50
15 CB	3.00
16 CB	3.00
17 CB	3.00
18 CB	3.00
19 CB,Rosa(c)	3.50
20 CB,giant	4.00
21 CB,giant	4.00
22 Rosa(c)	5.00
23 CB,giant	4.00
24 thru 26	@2.00
27 Rosa,O:Jr. Woodchuck	4.00
28 giant	3.00
29	1.50
30 giant	4.00
31 thru 32	@3.00
33 Barks	4.00
34 thru 40	@3.00
41	2.00
42 "The Dragon's Amulet"	2.00
43 "Queen of the Wild Dog Pack"	2.00
44	2.00
45 "The Secret of the Duckburg Triangle"	2.00
46 "The Tides Turn"	2.25
47 "The Menehune Mystery"	2.25
48 "The Tenth Avatar"	2.25
49 "Dead-Eye Duck"	2.25
50 CB,"The Secret of Atlantis"	2.50
51	1.95
52 The Black Diamond	1.95
53 Secret of the Incas	1.95
54 Secret of the Incas, pt.2	1.95

UNCLE SCROOGE ADVENTURES
Gladstone 1997–98
Don Rosa Specials

Spec.#1 (of 4)	10.95
Spec.#2 thru #4	@9.95

Van Horn Specials

Spec.#1	9.95
Spec.#2	9.95
Spec.#3	9.95
Spec.#4	9.95

UNCLE SCROOGE ADVENTURES IN COLOR
Gladstone
Carl Barks reprints

1 thru 32	@8.95
33 thru 35.	@9.95
36 32pg.	8.95
37 thru 53	@9.95

UNCLE SCROOGE & DONALD DUCK
Gold Key

1 rep.	75.00

UNCLE SCROOGE AND DONALD DUCK
Gladstone Oct. 1997

1	1.95
2 Christmas stories	1.95
3 Back to Long Ago	1.95
TPB Vol. 1	9.95
TPB Vol. 2	9.95
TPB Vol. 3	9.95
TPB Vol. 4	9.95

COLOR PUB.

UNCLE SCROOGE GOES TO DISNEYLAND
Gladstone 1985
1 CB,etc. 100pp 11.00

UNDERDOG
Spotlight 1987
1 FMc,PC(c),The Eredicator 1.50
2 FMc,CS(c), Prisoner of Love/ The
  Return of Fearo 1.50

UNDERDOG
Charlton July, 1970
1 Planet Zot 70.00
2 Simon Sez/The Molemen . . . 40.00
3 Whisler's Father 40.00
4 The Witch of Pycoon 40.00
5 The Snowmen 40.00
6 The Big Shrink 40.00
7 The Marbleheads 40.00
8 The Phoney Booths 40.00
9 Tin Man Alley 40.00
10 Be My Valentine (Jan. 1972) . 40.00

UNDERDOG
Gold Key March, 1975
1 The Big Boom 40.00
2 The Sock Singer Caper 20.00
3 The Ice Cream Scream 20.00
4 . . . . 20.00
5 . . . . 20.00
6 Head in a Cloud 20.00
7 The Cosmic Canine 20.00
8 . . . . 20.00
9 . . . . 20.00
10 Bouble Trouble Gum 20.00
11 The Private Life of Shoeshine
  Boy 15.00
12 The Deadly Fist of Fingers . . 15.00
13 . . . . 15.00
14 Shrink Shrank Shrunk 15.00
15 Polluter Palooka 15.00
16 The Soda Jerk 15.00
17 Flee For Your Life 15.00
18 Rain Rain Go Away...Okay . . 15.00
19 Journey To the Center of the
  Earth 15.00
20 The Six Million Dollar Dog . . 15.00
21 Smell of Success 15.00
22 Antlers Away 15.00
23 Wedding Bells In Outer Space
  (Feb.,1979) 15.00

UNDERDOG IN 3-D
Blackthorne
1 Wanted Dead or Alive 2.50

UNDERSEA AGENT
Tower 1966–97
1 F:Davy Jones,UndeseaAgent 50.00
2 thru 4 . . . . @35.00
5 O&I:Merman 40.00
6 GK,WW(c) 40.00

UNEARTHLY SPECTACULARS
1 DW,AT,I:Tiger Boy 20.00
2 WW,AW,GK,I:Earthman,Miracles,I
  nc. A:Clawfang,TigerBoy . . . 35.00
3 RC,AW,JO,A:Miracles,Inc. . . . 30.00

U.N. FORCE
Gauntlet Comics
0 BDC(s) 2.95
1 B:BDC(s),I:U.N.Force 2.95
2 O:Indigo 2.95
3 . . . . 2.95
4 A:Predator 2.95
5 B:Critial Mass 2.95

U.N. FORCE FILES
Gauntlet Comics
1 KP(c),F:Hunter Seeker, Lotus . 2.95

UNIVERSAL SOLDIER
Now 1992
1 Based on Movie,Holo.(c) 2.75
2 Luc & Ronnie on the run from
  UniSols 2.50
2a Photo cover 1.95
3 Photo(c) 1.95

UNKNOWN WORLDS OF FRANK BRUNNER
Eclipse 1985
1 and 2 FB . . . . @2.50

UNLEASHED!
Triumphant
0 JnR(s),I:Skyfire 2.50
1 JnR(s), ... 2.50

UNLV
1 Championship season (basketball
  based on college team) 3.00

UNTAMED LOVE
1 FF 2.00

UNUSUAL TALES
Charlton Comics 1955–65
1 . . . . 150.00
2 . . . . 75.00
3 thru 5 . . . . @50.00
6 SD,SD(c) 125.00
7 SD,SD(c) 125.00
8 SD,SD(c) 125.00
9 SD,SD(c) 150.00
10 SD,SD(c) 135.00
11 SD 135.00
12 SD 100.00
13 . . . . 40.00
14 SD 100.00
15 SD,SD(c) 110.00
16 thru 20 . . . . @40.00
21 . . . . 25.00
22 SD 75.00
23 . . . . 25.00
24 . . . . 25.00
25 SD 75.00
26 SD 75.00
27 SD 75.00
28 . . . . 25.00
29 SD 75.00
30 thru 49 . . . . @25.00

URI-ON
1 and 2 . . . . @1.50

URTH 4
Continuity 1990
1 TVE,NA(c) 2.00

2 TVE,NA 2.00
3 TVE,NA 2.00
4 NA,Last issue 2.00

USAGI YOJIMBO
Mirage 1993
1 A:TMNT 3.00
2 . . . . 3.00
3 . . . . 3.00
4 thru 16 . . . . @3.00
17 . . . . 8.00

VALERIA THE SHE BAT
Continuity 1993
1 NA,I:Valeria 20.00
2 thru 4   **[NOT RELEASED]**
5 Rise of Magic 2.50

VALKYRIE
Eclipse 1988
1 PG,I:Steelfox,C:Airboy, Sky Wolf 3.00
2 PG,O:New Black Angel 2.50
3 PG 2.50
[2nd Series]
1 BA,V:Eurasian Slavers 2.00
2 BA,V:Cowgirl 2.00
3 BA,V:Cowgirl 2.00

Valley of the Dinosaurs #1
© Charlton Comics

VALLEY OF THE DINOSAURS
Charlton 1975
1 Hanna-Barbera TV adapt. 3.00
2 thru 11 . . . . @2.00

VALOR
Gemstone 1998
1 EC comics reprint 2.50

VAMPEROTICA
Brainstorm
1–16 see B&W
17 . . . . 3.00
17a signed 5.00
17 Holochrome cover 65.00
18 Blood of the Damned (color) . . 3.00

18a Blood of the Damned, nude
  cover 4.00
18b signed 5.00
18c nude cover, signed 10.00
19 "Hunter's Blood" 3.00
19a deluxe 3.00
20 "Vampire Quest" 3.00
20a nude edition 4.00
21 hunting & feeding 3.00
21a nude edition 4.00
21b nude luxury edition 10.00
21c nude deluxe luxury edition . . 15.00
22 . . . . 3.00
22a nude edition 4.00
TPB Red Reign, rep. 12.95

VAMPEROTICA LINGERIE
Comic Cavalcade 1998
Commemorative #1 by Kirk Lindo   5.95
Commemorative #1a deluxe . . 14.95

VAMPIRE LESTAT
Innovation 1990–91
1 Anne Rice Adapt. 26.00
1a 2nd printing 4.00
1b 3rd printing 2.50
2 . . . . 13.00
2a 2nd printing 4.00
2b 3rd printing 2.50
3 . . . . 10.00
3a 2nd printing 2.50
4 . . . . 8.00
4a 2nd printing 2.50
5 . . . . 7.00
6 . . . . 5.00
7 . . . . 5.00
8 . . . . 5.00
9 scarce 8.00
9a 2nd Printing 3.00
10 . . . . 5.00
11 "Those Who Must Be Kept" . . . 4.00
12 conclusion 4.00
Vampire Companion #1 . . . . 4.00
Vampire Companion #2 (preview
  "Interview With The Vampire"   . 3.00
Vampire Companion #3 . . . . 3.00
GN rep.#1-#12 (Innovation) 24.95
GN rep.#1-#12 (Ballantine) 25.00

VAMPIRELLA
Warren Publishing Co. 1969–83
1 NA,FF(c),I:Vampirella 350.00
2 B:Amazonia 100.00
3 Very scarce 250.00
4 . . . . 75.00
5 FF(c) 75.00
6 . . . . 75.00
7 FF(c) 100.00
8 B:horror 75.00
9 BWS,BV(c),WW 85.00
10 No Vampirella,WW 50.00
11 TS,FF(c)O&I Pendragon. . . . 50.00
12 WW 50.00
13 . . . . 40.00
14 . . . . 40.00
15 . . . . 40.00
16 . . . . 40.00
17 B:Tomb of the Gods 40.00
18 . . . . 40.00
19 WW,1973 Annual 50.00
20 thru 25 . . . . @40.00
26 . . . . 35.00
27 1974 Annual 40.00
28 thru 30 . . . . @35.00

31 FF(c) 40.00
32 thru 36 . . . . @30.00
37 1975 Annual 40.00
38 . . . . 30.00
39 . . . . 30.00
40 . . . . 30.00
41 thru 45 . . . . @25.00
46 O:Vampirella 30.00
47 thru 99 . . . . @25.00
100 Double Size 35.00
101 thru 110 . . . . @20.00
111 Giant Edition 30.00
112 . . . . 25.00

VAMPIRELLA
Harris 1992
0 Dracula Wars 5.00
0a Blue version 50.00
1 V:Forces of Chaos, w/coupon for
  DSt poster 40.00
1a 2nd printing 15.00
2 AH(c) 40.00
3 A:Dracula 15.00
4 A:Dracula 10.00
5 . . . . 8.00
TPB The Dracula War signed &
  numbered 39.95
Harris Comics 1996
0 gold foil signed & numbered   100.00
1 Commemorative Edition 3.00
1 Commemorative Edition, sgn &
  num. 17.00
25th Anniv. Spec., FF(c) 5.95
25th Anniv. Spec., lim. 6.95
25th Anniv. Spec., lim., signed, . 49.95
Spec. Death of Vampirella,
  memorial, chromium cover . . . . .
Spec. Death of Vampirella,
  memorial, chromium cover,
  signed 29.95

VAMPIRELLA
Harris Comics 1997
1 (of 3) Ascending Evil, pt.1 . . 2.95
1 ultra-violent cover 2.95
1 JaL(c) 9.95
1 signed & numbered 19.95
2 Ascending Evil, pt.2 . . . . 2.95
2a JaL(c) 9.95
3 Ascending Evil, pt.3 . . . . 2.95
3a JaL(c) 9.95
4 Holy War, pt.1 . . . . 2.95
4a Crimson edition, Joe Linsner (c)2.95
5 Holy War, pt.2 . . . . 2.95
6 Holy War, pt.3 . . . . 2.95
7 Queen's Gambit, pt.1 . . . . . . 2.95
7a variant cover, signed 29.95
8 Queen's Gambit, pt.2 . . . . . . 2.95
9 Queen's Gambit, pt.3, concl. . . 2.95
Ashcan, Ascending Evil, b&w, 16pg.1.50
Ashcan, Ascending Evil, b&w,
  signed, limited 24.95
Ashcan, Queen's Gambit, 16 pg.
  b&w 6.00
Ashcan, Queen's Gambit, 16 pg.
  b&w, signed & numbered . . . 24.95
TPB Ascending Evil 7.50

VAMPIRELLA/CAIN
Harris 1996
1 flipbook 6.95

VAMPIRELLA/DRACULA:
THE CENTENNIAL
Harris 1997
1-shot Vampirella/Dracula & Pantha
  Showcase, 16pg 1.50
1 48pg 4.95

VAMPIRELLA/
PAINKILLER JANE
Harris 1998
1 foil JQ(c) 3.50
1a signed & numbered 39.95
1b alternate RL&JP(c) 9.95
1c alternate RL&JP(c) signed &
  numbered 29.95
Ashcan Preview, signed &
  numbered 29.95

VAMPIRELLA/
SHADOWHAWK:
CREATURES OF
THE NIGHT
Harris/Image 1995
1 Book One 5.50

VAMPIRELLA/SHI
Harris
Ash-Can #1, limited, 16pg 5.00
1 . . . . 2.95
1a Chromium Edition 10.00
1b signed & numbered 19.95
1c penciled cover 9.95
1c penciled cover, signed and
  numbered 29.95

VAMPIRELLA/WETWORKS
Harris 1997
1 StG,SSh,image x-over 2.95
1 signed & numbered 17.95
1b Sean Shaw & Kevin Nowlan (c)9.95

VAMPIRELLA:
BLOOD LUST
Harris 1997

Vampirella: Death and Destruction #1
© Harris Comics

All comics prices listed are for *Near Mint* condition.

1 (of 2) JeR & JJu 3.95
2 JJu(c) 3.95
Book 1, JJu(c) Virgin edition . . . 10.95
Book 2, JJu(c) Virgin edition . . . 10.95

VAMPIRELLA CLASSIC
Harris Comics 1995
1 Dark Angel 3.50
2 V:Demogorgon 3.25
3 V:Were Beast 3.25
4 R:Papa Voodoo 3.25
5 . . . . 3.00

VAMPIRELLA: CROSSOVER GALLERY
Harris 1997
1 art gallery 2.95
1a signed and numbered 19.95
1b chromium edition 10.00
1c Painkiller Jane JQ(c),signed . 29.95
1d Holochrome cover 20.00

VAMPIRELLA: DEATH AND DESTRUCTION
Harris
1 limited preview ash can 5.00
1a limited preview ash can, signed
& numbered 35.00
1b "The Dying of the Light" 3.00
1c signed & numbered 3.00
1d satin edition 30.00
1e satin edition, signed & numb. 60.00
1f Limited Edition, Mark Beachum
(c) 9.95
2 "The Nature of the Beast" 3.00
3 (of 3) TSg,ACo,JP,JJu(c),Mistress
Nyx kills Vampi 2.95
TPB 14.95

VAMPIRELLA LIVES
Harris
1 Linen Edition 15.00
1a Censored Photo cover edition 10.00
2 Vengeance edition 3.00
2 Model photo edition 3.00
2 alternate edition, AH(c) 10.00
2 alternate edition, AH(c) signed 30.00
3 WEI(s),ACo,JP,Graveyard edition,
JSC(c) 3.00
3 WEI(s),ACo,JP,Model photo
edition 3.00

VAMPIRELLA OF DRAKULON
Harris Comics 1996
1 V:assassin 3.00
1a alternate MiB(c) 9.95
2 Dracula returns 3.00
2a signed & numbered 20.00
3 thru 5 . . . . @3.00

VAMPIRELLA PINUP SPECIAL
Harris Comics 1995
1 Various Artists 3.50

VAMPIRELLA: SAD WINGS OF DESTIMY
Harris
1 DQ(s),JJu(c) 4.00

1 signed & numbered (#1,500) . . 5.00
Gold Emblem Seal Edition 4.00
Gold Emblem Seal Edition, signed 25.00

VAMPIRELLA STRIKES
Harris Comics 1995
1 The Prize,pt.1 . . . . 3.00
1a limited, signed & numbered . 30.00
1b full moon background 3.50
2 V:Dante Corp.,A:Passion 3.00
3 V:subway stalker 3.00
4 IEd,RN "Soul Food" 3.00
5 DQ,RN,F:Eudaemon 3.00
5 signed & numbered, (200) . . . 20.00
6 . . . . 3.00
6 signed, alternate cover 25.00
6 signed & numbered 40.00
7 silver special flip book 3.00
Ann. #1 new cover 10.00
Ann. #1 new cover, signed &
numbered 25.00

VAMPIRELLA VS. EUDAEMON
Harris 1996
1 . . . . 10.00
1 signed & numbered 25.00

VAMPIRELLA VS. HEMORRHAGE
Harris 1997
1 IEd,MIB 3.50
1 signed & numbered 24.95
1 Linen edition, signed & numb. 39.95
1 MIB alternate cover 9.95
2 IEd,MIB 3.50
3 (of 3) IEd,MIB 3.50

VAMPIRELLA VS. PANTHA
Harris 1997
Showcase #1 preview 2.00
1 MMr,MT, MT(c) Vampirella vs.
Pantha 3.50
1 MMr,MT, MT(c) Pantha vs.
Vampirella 3.50
1 MT(c) Vampirella vs. Pantha,
signed 19.95
1 MT(c) Pantha vs. Vampirella,
signed 19.95
1a MMr,MT, MT(c) 9.95
1a MMr,MT, MT(c) signed &
numbered 29.95

VAMPRESS LUXURA, THE
Brainstorm 1996
1 . . . . 3.00
1a gold edition 10.00
2 . . . . 2.95
2a gold foil 10.00

VANGUARD
1 . . . . 1.50

VANGUARD ILLUSTRATED
Pacific 1983
1 . . . . 1.50
2 DSt(c) 1.50
3 thru 5 SR . . . . @1.50
6 GI 1.50
7 GE,I:Mr.Monster 6.00

Vanguard Illustrated #4
© Pacific Comics

VANITY
Pacific 1984
1 and 2 . . . . @1.50

VAULT OF HORROR
Gladstone 1990–91
1 Rep.GS,WW 5.00
2 Rep.VoH #27 & HoF #18 . . . . 3.00
3 Rep.VoH #13 & HoF #22 . . . . 3.00
4 Rep.VoH #23 & HoF #13 . . . . 2.50
5 Rep.VoH #19 & HoF #5 . . . . . 2.50
6 Rep.VoH #32 & WF #6 . . . . . 2.50
7 Rep.VoH #26 & WS #7 . . . . . 2.50

VAULT OF HORROR
Russ Cochran Publ. 1991–92
1 Rep.VoH #28 & WS #18 . . . . 2.25
2 Rep.VoH #33 & WS #20 . . . . 2.25
3 Rep.VoH #26 & WS #7 . . . . . 2.25
4 Rep.VoH #35 & WS #15 . . . . 2.00
4 Rep.VoH #18 & WS #11 . . . . 2.00
5 Rep.VoH #18 & WS #11 . . . . 2.00
2nd Series
1 thru 7 Rep.VoH . . . . @1.50
8 . . . . 2.00
Gemstone
17 thru 25 EC comics reprints . @2.50
"Annuals"
TPB Vol. 1 rebinding of #1–#5 . . . 8.95
TPB Vol. 2 rebinding of #6–#10 . . 8.95
TPB Vol. 3 rebinding of #11–#15 10.95
TPB Vol. 4 rebinding of #16–#20 12.95

VECTOR
Now 1986
1 . . . . 2.50
2 thru 5 . . . . @1.75

VEGAS KNIGHTS
Pioneer 1989
1 . . . . 1.95
2 . . . . 1.95
3 . . . . 1.95

VENGEANCE OF VAMPIRELLA
Harris 1994

1 Hemmorage	30.00
1a Gold Edition	28.00
1 gold edition, signed, numbered	99.95
2 Dervish	17.00
3 On the Hunt	11.00
4 Teenage Vampries	8.00
5 Teenage Vampries	6.00
6	6.00
7	6.00
8 bagged w/card	6.00
9	6.00
10 Bad Jack Rising	5.00
11 Pits of Hell, w/card	5.00
12 V:Passion	4.00
13 V:Passion	4.00
14 Prelude to the Walk,pt.2	4.00
14a Buzz	20.00
15 The Mystery Walk,pt.1	3.25
15a Buzz	20.00
16 The Mystery Walk,pt.2	3.25
16a Buzz	20.00
17 The Mystery Walk,pt.3	3.25
17a Buzz	20.00
18 The Mystery Walk,pt.4	3.00
18a Buzz	20.00
19 The Mystery Walk,pt.5	3.00
19a Buzz	20.00
20 Mystery Walk epilog	3.00
21 thru 24	@3.00
25 "The End"	3.00
25 variant cover, signed & numbered	30.00
25 signed & numbered (2,500)	40.00
25 gold edition, signed & numb.	100.00
25 alternate cover, signed by Jae Lee & numbered (#1,500)	29.95
Mini-comic gold foil, signed	39.95
TPB 1-3 Bloodshed	6.95

VENTURE
AC Comics 1986

1	2.00
2 thru 4	@1.75

VERONICA
Archie Publications April, 1989

1 thru 50	@1.50
51 thru 71	@1.50
72 thru 81	@1.75

VEROTIKA
Verotika 1995

1 thru 3 Jae Lee, Frazetta	@2.95
4 thru 9	@2.95

VEROTIK ILLUSTRATED
Verotik 1997

1 48pg	6.95
2	6.95
3	6.95
3a alternate cover	6.95

VEROTIK ROGUES GALLERY OF VILLAINS
Verotik 1998

1-shot	3.95

VESPERS
Mars Media Group

1 Tony Caputo	2.50
2 I:Dark Side	2.50

VIC FLINT
Argo Publ. Feb., 1956

1	40.00
2	30.00

Vicki #1 © Atlas

VICKI
Atlas Feb.–Aug. 1975

1 Rep.	8.00
2 thru 4	@5.00

VILLAINS & VIGILANTES
Eclipse 1986–87

1 A:Crusaders,Shadowman	2.00
2 A:Condor	2.00
3 V:Crushers	2.00
4 V:Crushers	2.00

VIOLENT CASES
Tundra

1 20's Chicago	11.00

VIRGINIAN, THE
Gold Key June, 1963

1	50.00

VOLTRON
Solson 1985

1 TV tie-in	2.00
2	1.50
3	1.50

VORTEX
Vortex 1982–88

1 Peter Hsu art	22.00
2 Mister X on cover	9.00
3	5.00
4	4.00
5	3.00
6 thru 8	@3.00
9 thru 13	@1.75

VORTEX
Comico 1991

1 SBt,from Elementals	2.50
2 SBt,	2.50

VORTEX: THE SECOND COMING
Entity 1996

1 (of 6)	2.95
1a variant cover	2.95
2	2.95

VOYAGE TO THE DEEP
Dell Publishing Co. Sept.-Nov., 1962

1 P(c)	45.00
2 P(c)	30.00
3 P(c)	30.00
4 P(c)	30.00

WACKY ADVENTURES OF CRACKY
Gold Key 1972–75

1	12.00
2 thru 11	@8.00
12	5.00

WACKY WITCH
Gold Key 1971–75

1	20.00
2	10.00
3 thru 20	@6.00
21	4.00

WAGON TRAIN
Gold Key Jan.–Oct., 1964

1	50.00
2	35.00
3	35.00
4	35.00

WALLY
Gold Key 1962–63

1	25.00
2	20.00
3	20.00
4	20.00

WALLY WOOD'S THUNDER AGENTS
Delux 1984–86

1 GP,KG,DC,SD,I:New Menth	3.00
2 GP,KG,DC,SD,"The Raven"	2.50
3 KG,DC,SD	2.00
4 GP,KG,RB,DA	2.00
5 JOy,KG,A:CodenamDangr	2.00

WALT DISNEY ANNUALS

Walt Disney's Autumn Adventure	4.00
Walt Disney's Holiday Parade #1	3.50
Walt Disney's Spring Fever	3.25
Walt Disney's Summer Fun	3.25
Walt Disney's Holiday Parade #2	3.25

WALT DISNEY'S AUTUMN ADVENTURE

1 Rep. CB	4.00

WALT DISNEY'S COMICS AND STORIES
Dell/ Gold Key 1962

264 CB;Von Drake & Gearloose	30.00
265 CB; Von Drake & Gearloose	30.00
266 CB; Von Drake & Gearloose	30.00
267 CB; Von Drake & Gearloose	30.00
268 CB; Von Drake & Gearloose	30.00
269 CB; Von Drake & Gearloose	30.00
270 CB; Von Drake & Gearloose	30.00
271 CB; Von Drake & Gearloose	30.00
272 CB; Von Drake & Gearloose	30.00
273 CB; Von Drake & Gearloose	30.00
274 CB; Von Drake & Gearloose	30.00
275 CB	25.00
276 CB	25.00
277 CB	25.00
278 CB	25.00
279 CB	25.00
280 CB	25.00
281 CB	25.00
282 CB	25.00
283 CB	25.00
284	15.00
285	15.00
286 CB	25.00
287	15.00
288 CB	20.00
289 CB	20.00
290	15.00
291 CB	20.00
292 CB	20.00
293 CB; Grandma Duck's Farm Friends	20.00
294 CB	20.00
295	15.00
296	15.00
297 CB; Gyro Gearloose	20.00
298 CB; Daisy Duck's Dairy	20.00
299 CB rep.	20.00
300 CB rep.	20.00
301 CB rep.	20.00
302 CB rep.	20.00
303 CB rep.	20.00
304 CB rep.	20.00
305 CB rep. Gyro Gearloose	20.00
306 CB rep.	20.00
307 CB rep.	20.00
308 CB	20.00
309 CB	20.00
310 CB	20.00
311 CB	20.00
312 CB	20.00
313 thru 327	@15.00
328 CB rep.	20.00
329	12.00
330	12.00
331	12.00
332	12.00
333	12.00
334	12.00
335 CB rep.	15.00
336	12.00
337	12.00
338	12.00
339	12.00
340	12.00
341	12.00
342 CB rep.	15.00
343 CB rep.	15.00
344 CB rep.	15.00
345 CB rep.	15.00
346 CB rep.	15.00
347 CB rep.	15.00

348 CB rep.	15.00
349 CB rep.	15.00
350 CB rep.	15.00
351 CB rep. with poster	20.00
351a CB rep. without poster	15.00
352 CB rep. with poster12	20.00
352a CB rep. without poster	15.00
353 CB rep. with poster	20.00
353a CB rep. without poster	15.00
354 CB rep. with poster	20.00
354a CB rep. without poster	15.00
355 CB rep. with poster	20.00
355a CB rep. without poster	15.00
356 CB rep. with poster	20.00
356a CB rep. without poster	15.00
357 CB rep. with poster	20.00
357a CB rep. without poster	15.00
358 CB rep. with poster	20.00
358a CB rep. without poster	15.00
359 CB rep. with poster	20.00
359a CB rep. without poster	15.00
360 CB rep. with poster	20.00
360a CB rep. without poster	15.00
361 thru 400 CB rep.	@15.00
401 thru 409 CB rep.	@12.00
410 CB rep. Annette Funichello	12.00

Walt Disney's Comics and Stories #446
© Walt Disney

411 thru 429 CB rep.	@12.00
430	8.00
431 CB rep.	10.00
432 CB rep.	10.00
433	8.00
434 CB rep.	10.00
435 CB rep.	10.00
436 CB rep.	10.00
437	5.00
438	5.00
439 CB rep.	8.00
440 CB rep.	8.00
441	5.00
442 CB rep.	8.00
443 CB rep.	8.00
444	5.00
445	5.00
446 thru 465 CB rep.	@8.00
466	8.00
467 thru 473 CB rep.	@8.00

Whitman

474 thru 493 CB rep.	@6.00

494 CB rep.Uncle Scrooge	7.00
495 thru 505 CB rep.	@6.00
506	5.00
507 CB rep.	6.00
508 CB rep.	6.00
509 CB rep.	6.00
510 CB rep.	6.00

Gladstone

511 translation of Dutch	22.00
512 translation of Dutch	15.00
513 translation of Dutch	15.00
514 translation of Dutch	8.00
515 translation of Dutch	8.00
516 translation of Dutch	8.00
517 translation of Dutch	3.50
518 translation of Dutch	3.50
519 CB,Donald Duck	3.50
520 translation of Dutch, Rosa	7.00
521 Walt Kelly	3.00
522 CB,WK,nephews	3.00
523 Rosa,Donald Duck	7.00
524 Rosa,Donald Duck	7.00
525 translation of Dutch	3.00
526 Rosa,Donald Duck	7.00
527 CB	3.00
528 Rosa,Donald Duck	5.00
529 CB	3.00
530 Rosa,Donald Duck	5.00
531 WK(c),Rosa,CB	5.00
532 CB	2.50
533 CB	2.50
534 CB	2.50
535 CB	2.50
536 CB	2.50
537 CB	2.50
538 CB	2.50
539 CB	2.50
540 CB new art	3.50
541 double-size,WK(c)	3.00
542 CB	5.00
543 CB,WK(c)	2.50
544 CB,WK(c)	2.50
545 CB	2.50
546 CB,WK,giant	4.00
547 CB,WK,Rosa,giant	4.50

Walt Disney 1990

548 CB,WK,"Home is the Hero"	3.00
549 CB,	2.50
550 CB,prev.unpub.story!	3.50
551	2.25
552	2.25
553	2.25
554	2.25
555	2.25
556	2.25
557	2.25
558 "Donald's Fix-it Shop"	2.25
559 "Bugs"	2.25
560 CB,April Fools Story	2.00
561 CB,Donald the "Flipist"	2.00
562 CB,"3DirtyLittleDucks"	2.00
563 CB,"Donald Camping"	2.00
564 CB,"Dirk the Dinosaur"	2.00
565 CB,DonaldDuck,TruantOfficer	2.00
566 CB,"Will O' the Wisp"	2.00
567 CB,"Turkey Shoot"	2.00
568 CB,"AChristmas Eve Story"	2.00
569 CB, New Years Resolutions	2.00
570 CB,Donald the Mailman +Poster	2.00
571 CB,"Atom Bomb"	4.50
572 CB, April Fools	2.00
573 TV Quiz Show	2.00
574 Pinnochio,64pgs	3.50
575 Olympic Torch Bearer, Li'l Bad Wolf,64 pgs.	3.50

576 giant	3.50
577 A:Truant Officers,64 pgs.	3.50
578 CB,Old Quacky Manor	2.00
579 CB,Turkey Hunt	2.00
580 CB,The Wise Little Red Hen, 64 page-Sunday page format	3.50
581 CB,Duck Lake	2.00
582 giant	3.50
583 giant	3.50
584	1.75
585 CB, giant	3.00

Gladstone

586	2.00
587 thru 600	@2.00
601 thru 605 prestige format	@5.95
606 "Winging It"	6.95
607 "Number 401"	6.95
608 "Sleepless in Duckburg"	6.95
609	6.95
610 "Treasures Untold"	6.95
611 "Romance at a Glance"	6.95
612 "The Sod Couple"	6.95
613 "Another Fine Mess"	6.95
614 "Airheads"	6.95
615 "Backyard Battlers"	6.95
616	6.95
617 "Tree's A Crowd"	6.95
618 "A Dolt from the Blue"	6.95
619 "Queen of the Ant Farm"	6.95
620 "Caught in the Cold Rush"	6.95
621 "Room and Bored"	6.95
622 ""	6.95
623 "All Quacked Up"	6.95
624 "Their Loaded Forebear"	6.95
625 "Mummery's the Word"	6.95
626 "A Real Gone Guy"	6.95
627 "To Bee or Not to Bee"	6.95
628 "Officer for a Day"	6.95
629 "The Ghost Train"	6.95

WALT DISNEY COMICS DIGEST
Gold Key 1968–76
[All done by Carl Barks]

1 Rep,Uncle Scrooge	40.00
2	25.00
3	25.00
4	25.00
5	45.00
6	20.00
7	20.00
8	20.00
9	20.00
10	20.00
11	20.00
12	20.00
13	20.00
14	10.00
15	10.00
16 rep.Donald Duck #26	20.00
17	15.00
18	15.00
19	15.00
20	15.00
21	18.00
22	18.00
23	18.00
24	18.00
25	18.00
26	18.00
27	18.00
28	18.00
29	18.00
30	18.00

31	18.00
32	8.00
33	18.00
34 rep.Four Color #318	15.00
35	15.00
36	15.00
37	15.00
38 rep.Disneyland#1	15.00
39	15.00
40	10.00
41	8.00
42	8.00
43	8.00
44 Rep. Four Color #29 & others	25.00
45	6.00
46 CB	8.00
47	6.00
48	6.00
49	6.00
50 CB	8.00
51 rep.Four Color #71	12.00
52 CB	8.00
53	6.00
54	6.00
55	6.00
56 CB,rep. Uncle Scrooge #32	10.00
57 CB	8.00

WALT DISNEY SHOWCASE
Gold Key 1970–80

1 Boatniks (photo cover)	20.00
2 Moby Duck	10.00
3 Bongo & Lumpjaw	8.00
4 Pluto	10.00
5 $1,000,000 Duck (photo cover)	15.00
6 Bedknobs & Broomsticks	12.00
7 Pluto	10.00
8 Daisy & Donald	10.00
9 101 Dalmatians rep.	14.00
10 Napoleon & Samantha	12.00
11 Moby Duck rep.	7.00
12 Dumbo rep.	8.00
13 Pluto rep.	8.00
14 World's Greatest Athlete	12.00
15 3 Little Pigs rep.	12.00
16 Aristocats rep.	12.00
17 Mary Poppins rep.	12.00
18 Gyro Gearloose rep.	12.00
19 That Darn Cat rep.	12.00
20 Pluto rep.	10.00
21 Li'l Bad Wolf & 3 Little Pigs	7.00
22 Unbirthday Party rep.	10.00
23 Pluto rep.	10.00
24 Herbie Rides Again rep.	8.00
25 Old Yeller rep.	8.00
26 Lt. Robin Crusoe USN rep.	7.00
27 Island at the Top of the World	7.00
28 Brer Rabbit, Bucky Bug rep.	10.00
29 Escape to Witch Mountain	8.00
30 Magica De Spell rep.	15.00
31 Bambi rep.	12.00
32 Spin & Marty rep.	10.00
33 Pluto rep.	10.00
34 Paul Revere's Ride rep.	7.00
35 Goofy rep.	7.00
36 Peter Pan rep.	7.00
37 Tinker Bell & Jiminy Cricket rep.	7.00
38 Mickey & the Sleuth, Pt. 1	8.00
39 Mickey & the Sleuth, Pt. 2	8.00
40 The Rescuers	8.00
41 Herbie Goes to Monte Carlo	10.00
42 Mickey & the Sleuth	7.00
43 Pete's Dragon	10.00

44 Return From Witch Mountain & In Search of the Castaways	12.00
45 The Jungle Book rep.	12.00
46 The Cat From Outer Space	7.00
47 Mickey Mouse Surprise Party	8.00
48 The Wonderful Adventures of Pinocchio	7.00
49 North Avenue Irregulars; Zorro	7.00
50 Bedknobs & Broomsticks rep.	6.00
51 101 Dalmatians	6.00
52 Unidentified Flying Oddball	6.00
53 The Scarecrow	6.00
54 The Black Hole	6.00

WALT DISNEY COMICS IN COLOR
Gladstone 1998

TPB Vol. 1	9.95
TPB Vol. 2	9.95
TPB Vol. 3	9.95
TPB Vol. 4	9.95

WALT KELLY'S CHRISTMAS CLASSICS
Eclipse 1987

1	2.00

WALT KELLY'S SPRINGTIME TALES
Eclipse 1988

1	2.50

WARCAT SPECIAL
Entity Press 1995

1 I:Warcat	2.95

WARCHILD
Maximum Press 1995

1 I:Sword, Stone	3.50
2 I:Morganna Lefay	3.00
3 V: The Black Knight	2.50
4 Rescue Merlyn	2.50
[2nd Series]	
1	2.50

WAR DANCER
Defiant 1994

1 B:JiS(s),I:Ahrq Tsolmec	2.75
2 I:Massakur	2.75
3 V:Massakur	2.75
4 JiS(s),A:Nudge	3.25

WARHAWKS
TSR 1990–91

1 thru 6 from game	@2.95
7 thru 10 The Battle of Britain	@2.95

WARHAWKS 2050
TSR

1 Pt.1	2.95

WAR HEROES
Charlton Comics 1963–67

1	12.00
2 thru 10	@6.00
11 thru 27	@5.00

WARLASH
CFD

1 Project Hardfire	2.95

COLOR PUB.

WARMASTER
1 and 2 . . . . @3.95

WARP
First March, 1983
1 FB,JSon,I:Lord Cumulus & Prince
Chaos, play adapt pt.1 . . . . . . 2.00
2 FB,SD,play adapt pt.2 . . . . . . 1.50
3 FB,SD,play adapt pt.3 . . . . . . 1.50
4 FB,SD,I:Xander,play pt.4 . . . . 1.50
5 FB, play adapt pt.5 . . . . 1.50
6 FB/MG, play adapt pt.6 . . . . . 1.50
7 FB/MG, play adapt pt.7 . . . . . 1.50
8 FB/MG,BWg,play adapt pt.8 . . 1.25
9 FB/MG,BWg,play adapt conc. . . 1.25
10 JBi/MG,BWg, Second Saga,
I:Outrider 1.25
11 JBi/MG,A:Outrider 1.25
12 JBi/MG,A:Outrider 1.25
13 JBi/MG,A:Outrider 1.25
14 JBi/MG,A:Outrider 1.25
15 JBi/MG/BWg 1.25
16 BWg/MG,A:Outrider 1.25
17 JBi/MG,A:Outrider 1.25
18 JBi/MG,A:Outrider&Sargon . . 1.25
19 MG,last issue 1.25
Spec. #1 HC,O:Chaos 1.50
Spec. #2 MS/MG,V:Ylem 1.50
Spec. #3 . . . . 1.50

Warrior Nun Areala Vs. Razor #1
© Antarctic

WARRIOR NUN AREALA
Antartic Press 1995
1 V:Lilith 4.00
1a limited edition 7.00
2 V:Lilith 3.00
3 V:Hellmaster 3.00
3 silver edition 12.00
TPB Rep.#1–#3 . . . . 9.95
BOOK II: RITUALS 1996
1 Land of Rising Sun 2.95
1 Red edition 12.00
1 signed 9.95
2 I:Cheetah 2.95
3 Iraq, 1989 . . . . 2.95
4 . . . . 2.95
5 Rituals,pt.5 . . . . 2.95
6 . . . . 2.95

Spec. Warrior Nun Portraits 3.95
TPB Rituals 15.95
BOOK III 1997
1 The Hammer & the Holocaust . 2.95
2 Hammer & the Holocaust,pt.2 . 2.95
3 Hammer & the Holocaust,pt.3 . 2.95
4 Holy Man, Holy Terror,pt.1 . . . 2.95
5 Holy Man, Holy Terror,pt.2 . . . 2.95
6 by Barry Lyga & Ben Dunn . . . 2.95
TPB Vol. 1 . . . . 9.95
TPB Vol. 1 reprint 9.95
HC Vol. 2, lim. to 1,000 copies . 29.95
Spec. Warrior Nun Areala/Glory by
Ben Dunn 2.95
Spec. poster edition 5.95
Spec. Warrior Nun Areala vs. Razor,
BDn,JWf x-over 3.95

WARRIOR NUN AREALA: SCORPIO ROSE
Antartic Press 1996
1 SEt & BDn 2.95
2 thru 4 (of 4) . . . . @2.95

WARRIOR NUN DEI: AFTERTIME
Antarctic Press 1997
1 (of 3) by Patrick Thornton . . . 2.95
2 . . . . 2.95

WARRIOR NUN: FRENZY
Antarctic Press 1998
1 (of 2) by Miki Horvatic & Esad T.
Ribic 2.95
2 . . . . 2.95

WARRIORS OF PLASM
Defiant 1993–95
1 JiS(s),DL,A:Lorca 3.25
2 JiS(s),DL,Sedition Agenda . . . 3.25
3 JiS(s),DL,Sedition Agenda . . . 3.25
4 JiS(s),DL,Sedition Agenda . . . 3.25
5 JiS(s),B:The Demons of
Darkedge 2.75
6 JiS(s),The Demons of
Darkedge,pt.2 . . . . 2.75
7 JiS(s),DL, ... 2.75
8 JiS(s),DL,40pages 3.00
9 JiS(s),LWn(s),DL,40pages . . . 3.00
10 DL 2.50
GN Home for the Holidays 5.95

WART AND THE WIZARD
Gold Key Feb., 1964
1 . . . . 14.00

WAVE WARRIORS
1 . . . . 2.00
2 . . . . 2.00

WAXWORK in 3-D
Blackthorne
1 . . . . 2.50

WAYFARERS
Eternity
1 . . . . 1.80
2 . . . . 1.80

WEAPON ZERO
See: Image

WEASEL GUY WITCHBLADE
Hyperwerks 1998
1-shot by Steve Succellato 2.95
1a variant Jeff Matsuda(c) 2.95
1b variant Karl Altstoeter(c) . . . 2.95

WEB-MAN
Argosy
1 flip book with Time Warrior . . . 2.50

WEB OF HORROR
Major Magazines Dec., 1969
1 JJ(c),Ph(c),BWr 85.00
2 JJ(c),Ph(c),BWr 60.00
3 BWr,April, 1970 . . . . 60.00

WEIRD FANTASY
Russ Cochran 1992
1 Reps 2.00
2 Reps.inc.The Black Arts 2.00
3 thru 4 rep. . . . . @2.00
5 thru 7 rep. 2.50
8 . . . . 2.50
Gemstone
9 thru 22 EC comics reprint . . @2.50
"Annuals"
TPB Vol. #1 rebinding of #1–#5 . 8.95
TPB Vol. #2 rebinding of #6–#10 . 9.95
TPB Vol. #3 rebinding of #11–#14 8.95
TPB Vol. #4 rebinding of #15–#18 9.95
TPB Vol. #5 rebinding of #19–#22 10.50

WEIRD SCIENCE
Gladstone 1990–91
1 Rep. #22 + Fantasy #1 . . . . . . 4.00
2 Rep. #16 + Fantasy #17 . . . . . 3.50
3 Rep. #9 + Fantasy #14 . . . . . . 3.50
4 Rep. #27 + Fantasy #11 . . . . . 2.00
Russ Cochran/Gemstone 1992
1 thru 21 EC comics reprint . . @2.50
"Annuals"
TPB Vol. #1 rebinding of #1–#5 . 8.95
TPB Vol. #2 rebinding of #6–#10 . 9.95
TPB Vol. #3 rebinding of #11–#15 8.95
TPB Vol. #4 rebinding of #16–#18 9.95
TPB Vol. #5 rebinding of #19–#22 10.50

WEIRD SCIENCE-FANTASY
Russ Cochran/Gemstone 1992
1 Rep. W.S.F. #23 (1954) 2.00
2 Rep. Flying Saucer Invasion . . 2.00
3 Rep. 2.00
4 thru 6 Rep. 2.00
7 rep #29 . . . . 2.00
8 . . . . 2.00
Gemstone
"Annuals"
TPB Vol. #1 rebinding of #1–#5 . . 8.95
TPB Vol. #2 rebinding of #6–#10 12.95

WEIRD SUSPENSE
Atlas Feb.–July 1975
1 thru 3 F:Tarantula . . . . @12.00

WEIRD TALES ILLUSTRATED
Millenium 1992
1 KJo,JBo,PCr,short stories 4.95

WENDY
Blackthorne
1 3-D 2.50

WENDY, THE GOOD LITTLE WITCH
Harvey Publications 1960–76
1	125.00
2	50.00
3	30.00
4	30.00
5	30.00
6	25.00
7	25.00
8	25.00
9	25.00
10	25.00
11 thru 20	@15.00
21 thru 30	@8.00
31 thru 50	@5.00
51 thru 69	@4.00
70 thru 74 52 pg Giants	@4.00
75 thru 93	@2.00

WENDY WITCH WORLD
Harvey Publications 1961–74
1	75.00
2	30.00
3	30.00
4	30.00
5	30.00
6	15.00
7	15.00
8	15.00
9	15.00
10	15.00
11 thru 20	@9.00
21 thru 30	@5.00
31 thru 39	@3.00
40 thru 50	@2.00
51 thru 53	@2.00

WEREWOLF
Blackthorne
1 3-D 3.50

WESTERN ACTION
Atlas Feb. 1975
1 F:Kid Cody,Comanche Kid 1.00

WESTWYND
Westwynd 1995
1 I:Sable,Shiva,Outcast,Tojo .. 2.50

WHAM
1 .... 1.75

WHISPER
Capital 1983–84
1 MG(c) 10.00
2 .... 8.00
First
1 .... 2.50
2 .... 2.00
3 .... 2.00

4	1.50
5	1.50
6 thru 12	@1.25
13 thru 19	@1.75
20 O:Whisper	1.95
21 thru 26	@1.95
27 Ghost Dance #2	1.95
28 Ghost Dance #3	1.95
29 thru 37	@1.95
Spec. #1	4.00

WHITE FANG
Walt Disney 1990
1 Movie Adapt. 5.95

WHITE TRASH
Tundra
1 I:Elvis & Dean 3.95
2 Trip to Las Vegas contd. 3.95
3 V:Purple Heart Brigade 3.95

WHODUNNIT
Eclipse 1986–87
1 DSp,A:Jay Endicott 2.00
2 DSp,"Who Slew Kangaroo?" .. 2.00
3 DSp,"Who Offed Henry Croft" . 2.00

WIDOW MADE IN BRITAIN
N Studio
1 I:Widow 2.60
2 F:Widow 2.60
3 Rampage 2.60
4 In Jail 2.60

WIDOW METAL GYPSIES
London Night Studios 1995
1 I:Emma Drew 3.00
2 Father Love 3.00
3 Final issue 3.00

WILD ANIMALS
Pacific 1982
1 .... 1.50

WILD BILL PECOS
AC Comics 1989
1 .... 3.50

WILDFIRE
Zion Comics
1 thru 3 V:Mr. Reeves ..... @1.95
4 Lord D'Rune 1.95

WILD FRONTIER
Charlton Comics Oct., 1955
1 Davy Crockett	50.00
2 same	30.00
3 same	30.00
4 same	30.00
5 same	30.00
6 same	30.00
7 O:Cheyenne Kid	30.00

Becomes:
CHEYENNE KID
8	25.00
9	15.00
10	45.00
11	45.00
12	45.00
13	30.00
14	30.00

15	15.00
16	15.00
17	15.00
18	30.00
19	15.00
20	18.00
21	18.00
22	18.00
23	8.00
24	8.00
25	15.00
26	10.00
27	8.00
28	8.00
29	8.00
30	10.00
31 thru 59	@3.00
60 thru 98	@2.00
99 Nov., 1973	2.00

WILD WEST C.O.W.-BOYS OF MOO MESA
Archie 1992–93
1 Based on TV cartoon 1.25
2 Cody kidnapped 1.25
3 Law of the Year Parade, last issue 1.25
(Regular series)
1 Valley o/t Thunder Lizard 1.25
2 Plains, Trains & Dirty Deals ... 1.25

Wild Western Action #2 © Skywald

WILD WESTERN ACTION
Skywald 1971
1 thru 3 .... @8.00

WILD WILD WEST
Gold Key 1966–69
1 TV show tie-in	125.00
2	100.00
3	75.00
4	75.00
5	75.00
6	75.00
7	75.00

WILD WILD WEST
Millenium 1990–91
1 .... 2.95
2 thru 4 .... @2.95

WILL EISNER'S 3-D CLASSICS
Kitchen Sink
WE art, w/glasses (1985) 2.00

WIN A PRIZE COMICS
Charlton Comics Feb., 1955
1 S&K,Edgar Allen adapt. 200.00
2 S&K 150.00
Becomes:

TIMMY THE TIMID GHOST
3 .... 30.00
4 .... 20.00
5 .... 20.00
6 .... 10.00
7 .... 10.00
8 .... 10.00
9 .... 10.00
10 .... 10.00
11 .... 20.00
12 .... 20.00
13 thru 20 .... @5.00
21 thru 44 .... @4.00
45 1966 .... 2.00

WINDRAGE
1 and 2 .... @1.25

WINTERWORLD
Eclipse 1987–88
1 JZ,I:Scully, Wynn 1.75
2 JZ,V:Slave Farmers 1.75
3 JZ,V:Slave Farmers 1.75

WIREHEADS
Fleetway
1 .... 2.95

WITCHBLADE
See Image

WITCHING HOUR, THE
Millenium/Comico
1 Anne Rice adaptation 2.50
2 thru 5 .... 2.50

WOODY WOODPECKER
Harvey 1991–93
1 thru 5 .... 1.25

WORLD OF ARCHIE
Archie 1994
1 thru 21 .... @1.50

WORLD OF WOOD
Eclipse 1986–87
1 WW 1.75
2 WW,DSt(i) 1.75
3 WW 1.75
4 WW 1.75

Wulf the Barbarian #2
© Atlas Comics

WULF THE BARBARIAN
Atlas Feb.–Sept., 1975
1 O:Wulf 10.00
2 NA,I:Berithe The Swordsman . 8.00
3 & 4 .... @5.00

WYATT EARP
Dell Publishing Co. Nov., 1957
1 .... 123.00
2 .... 75.00
3 .... 60.00
4 .... 50.00
5 .... 50.00
6 .... 50.00
7 .... 50.00
8 .... 50.00
9 .... 50.00
10 .... 50.00
11 .... 40.00
12 .... 40.00
13 .... 40.00

XANADU
Eclipse 1988
1 .... 2.00

XENYA
Sanctuary Press 1994
1 Hildebrandt Brothers 4.00
2 .... 3.25
3 .... 3.25
4 conclusion, Homecoming 2.95

XENA: WARRIOR PRINCESS
Topps 1997
1 RTs,Revenge of the Gorgons,
pt.1 .... 3.00
1a photo (c) 8.00
2 (of 2) rescue of Gabrielle 3.00
TPB 9.95
[VOL 2]
0 AaL Temple of the Dragon God 3.00
1 (of 3) Joxer, Warrior Prince, pt.1 4.00
1a deluxe 8.00

2 Joxer, Warrior Prince, pt.2 .... 5.00
2a photo (c) 4.50
TPB rep. #0–#2 .... 9.95

XENA: WARRIOR PRINCESS: BLOOD LINES
Topps 1997
1 (of 3) ALo 3.00
1a photo (c) 5.00
2 (of 3) ALo 2.95
2a photo (c) 2.95

XENA: WARRIOR PRINCESS: CALLISTO
Topps 1997
1 (of 3) RTs, ... 3.00
1a photo (c) 5.00
2 (of 3) RTs, ... 2.95
2a photo (c) 2.95
3 (of 3) RTs, ... 2.95
3a photo (c) 2.95

XENA: WARRIOR PRINCESS: ORPHEUS
Topps 1998
1 (of 3) 3.00
1a photo (c) 2.95
2 (of 3) 2.95
2a photo (c) 2.95
3 (of 3) 2.95
3a photo (c) 2.95

XENA: WARRIOR PRINCESS: THE ORIGINAL OLYMPICS
Topps 1998
1 (of 3) 2.95
1a photo cover 2.95
2 F:Hercules 2.95
2a photo cover 2.95
3 .... 2.95
3a photo cover 2.95

XENA: WARRIOR PRINCESS: THE WEDDING OF XENA & HERCULES
Topps 1998
1-shot 2.95
1-shot photo (c) 2.95

XENA: WARRIOR PRINCESS: XENA AND THE DRAGON'S TEETH
Topps 1997
1 (of 3) RTs, ... 3.00
1a photo (c) 4.00
2 (of 3) RTs, ... 4.00
2a photo (c) 4.00
3 (of 3) RTs, ... 3.00
3a photo (c) 4.00

XENO MAN
1 .... 1.75

COLOR PUB.

XENOTECH
Mirage 1993–94
1 I:Xenotech	2.75
2	2.75
3 w/2 card strip	2.75

X-Files #20 © Topps Comics

X-FILES
Topps 1994–97
1 From Fox TV Series	50.00
1a Newstand	40.00
2 Aliens Killing Witnesses	30.00
3 The Return	20.00
4 Firebird,pt.1	15.00
5 Firebird,pt.2	10.00
6 Firebird,pt.3	8.00
7 Trepanning Opera	7.00
8 Silent Cities of the Mind,pt.1	6.00
9 Silent Cities of the Mind,pt.2	5.00
10 Feeling of Unreality,pt.1	5.00
11 Feeling of Unreality,pt.2	5.00
12 Feeling of Unreality,pt.3	5.00
13 A Boy and His Saucer	5.00
14	4.00
15 Home of the Brave	4.00
16 Home of the Brave,pt.2	3.50
17 DgM,CAd	3.50
18 thru 21	@3.50
22 JRz,CAd,"The Kanishibari"	3.00
23 JRz,CAd,"Donor"	3.00
24 JRz,"Silver Lining"	3.00
25 JRz,CAd,"Remote Control", pt.1 (of 3)	3.00
26 JRz,CAd,"Remote Control", pt.2	3.00
27 JRz,CAd,"Remote Control", pt.3	3.00
28 JRz,"Be Prepared," pt.1,V:Windigo	3.00
29 JRz,"Be Prepared", pt.2	3.00
30 JRz,"Surrounded," pt.1	3.00
31 JRz,"Surrounded," pt.2 (of 2)	3.00
32	3.00
33 widows on San Francisco	2.95
33 variant photo (c)	2.95
34 Project HAARP	2.95
35 Near Death Experience	2.95
36 Near Death Experience, pt.2	2.95
37 JRz,The Face of Extinction	2.95
38 JRz,	2.95
39 JRz, Widow's Peak	2.95

40 Devil's Advocate	2.95
40a photo cover	2.95
Ann.#1 Hollow Eve	5.00
Ann.#2 E.L.F.S.	4.50
Spec.#1 Rep. #1-#3	6.00
Spec.#2 Rep. #4-#6 Firebird	5.00
Spec.#3 Rep. #7-#9	5.00
Spec.#4 Rep.	5.00
TPB Vol. 2	19.95
GN Afterflight	5.95
GN Official Movie Adapt. (1998)	5.95

X-FILES DIGEST
Topps 1995
1 All New Series, 96pg.	3.50
2 and 3	3.50

X-FILES, THE: GROUND ZERO
Topps 1997
1 (of 4) based on novel	2.95
2	2.95
3	2.95
4	2.95

X-FILES, THE: SEASON ONE
Topps
1 RTs,JVF(c) "Deep Throat"	4.95
Deep Throat, variant (c)	7.50
2 RTs,JVF(c) "Squeeze"	3.95
Squeeze, RTs, JVF(c)	4.95
3 RTs,SSc,"Conduit"	3.95
Conduit, RTs	4.95
4 RTs,"The Jersey Devil"	3.95
5 RTs,"Shadows"	3.95
Shadows JVF(c)	4.95
6 "Fire"	3.95
Fire	4.95
7 RTs,JVF,"Ice"	3.95
Ice	4.95
8 RTs,"Space"	3.95
Space JVF(c)	4.95
Spec. Pilot Episode RTs,JVF new JVF(c)	4.95
Beyond the Sea JVF(c)	4.95

XIMOS: VIOLENT PAST
Triumphant 1994
1 JnR(s)	2.50
2 JnR(s)	2.50

XL
1	1.25

XXXENA: WARRIOR PORNSTAR VS. BUSTY THE VAMPIRE MURDERER
Blatant Comics 1998
1 parody	2.95
2 nude cover	9.95

YAKKY DOODLE & CHOPPER
Gold Key Dec., 1962
1	35.00

YIN FEI
Leung's Publications 1988–90
5	1.80
6 thru 11	@2.00

YOGI BEAR
Dell Feb.-March, 1962
#1 thru #6, See Dell Four Color
7 thru 9	50.00

Gold Key
10	50.00
11 Jellystone Follies	50.00
12	35.00
13 Surprise Party	50.00
14 thru 19	@35.00
20 thru 29	@20.00
30 thru 42	@15.00

YOGI BEAR
Charlton Comics 1970–76
1	25.00
2 thru 10	@15.00
11 thru 35	10.00

YOGI BEAR
Archie Comics 1997
1	1.50

YOSEMITE SAM
Gold Key/Whitman 1970–84
1	20.00
2 thru 10	@12.00
11 thru 40	@6.00
41 thru 81	@4.00

YOUNGBLOOD
Maximum Press/Extreme
Volume 2 1996
Vol. 1 and Vol. 2 #1–#10, see Image
11 RLd,RCz,	2.50
12 Rle, V:Lord Dredd,A:New Man,double size	3.50
13 RLd,RCz,F:Die-Hard	2.50
14 RLd,RCz,	2.50
Super Spec.#1 ErS,CSp,AG	3.00
TPB Youngblood, rep. orig. Youngblood #1–#5	16.95
TPB Baptism of Fire rep. Youngblood #6–#8, #10 & Team Youngblood #9–#11	16.95

YOUNGBLOOD
Awesome Entertainment 1998
1 AMo,SSr	2.50
1a variant covers, 7 different	2.50
2 AMo,SSr,Baptism of Fire	2.50
3 AMo,SSr,V:Professor Night	2.50
4 AMo,SSr,Young Guns	2.50
5 AMo,SSr,Young Guns	2.50

YOUNGBLOOD CLASSICS
Image/Extreme Sept. 1996
1 RLd,ErS,rewritten & redrawn, new cover	2.25
2 RLd,ErS,rewritten & redrawn, new cover	2.25
3 RLd,ErS,rewritten & redrawn, new cover	2.25

COLOR PUB.

YOUNGBLOOD/X-FORCE
Awesome Entertainment 1998
1-shot, 48pg. 4.95

ZAANAN
Mainstream Comics
1 The Collectio,I:Zaanan 2.50

Zen Intergalactic Ninja #3
© Archie Comics

ZEN INTERGALACTIC NINJA
Archie 1992
1 Rumble in the Rain Forest
prequel,inc.poster 1.25
2 Rumble in Rain Forest #1 . . . . 1.25
3 Rumble in Rain Forest #2 . . . . 1.25
Entity Comics 1994
0 Chromium (c),JaL(c) 4.00
1 Joe Orbeta 2.50
1a Platinum Edition 20.00
2 Deluxe Edition w/card 4.95
3 V:Rawhead 3.00
4 thru 7 . . . . 3.25
GN A Fire Upon The Earth 12.95
[2nd Series]
1 Joe Orbeta 4.95
2 . . . . 4.95
3 thru 5 . . . . @2.50
Zen Comics 1998
Commemorative Ed. #1 . . . . 5.95

ZEN/NIRA X: HELLSPACE
Zen Comics
1 . . . . 2.95

ZEN: NOVELLA
Eternity Comics
1 thru 8 . . . . 2.95

ZEN SPECIALS
Eternity
Spring#1 V:Lord Contaminous . . . 2.50
April Fools#1 parody issue 2.50
Color Spec.#0 . . . . 3.50

ZEN: WARRIOR
Eternity Comics 1994
1 vicious video game 3.00

ZENITH PHASE II
Fleetway
1 thru 2 . . . . 1.95

ZERO PATROL
Continuity 1984–90
1 EM,NA,O&I:Megalith 2.50
2 EM,NA 1.95
3 EM,NA,I:Shaman 1.95
4 EM,NA 1.95
5 EM 1.95
6 thru 8 EM . . . . @2.00

ZERO TOLERANCE
First 1990–91
1 TV 3.50
2 TV 3.00
3 TV 2.25
4 TV 2.25

ZOONIVERSE
Eclipse 1986–87
1 I:Kren Patrol,wrap-around(c) . . 1.25
2 . . . . 1.25
3 . . . . 1.25
4 V:Wedge City 1.25
5 Spak vs. Agent Ty-rote 1.25
6 last issue 1.25

ZORRO
Dell Publ. Co. 1959–61
1 thru 8, see Dell 4-Color
8 . . . . 100.00
9 . . . . 85.00
10 . . . . 85.00
11 . . . . 85.00
12 ATh 100.00
13 . . . . 75.00
14 . . . . 75.00
15 . . . . 75.00

ZORRO
Gold Key 1966–68
1 Rep. 75.00
2 Rep. 50.00
3 Rep. 50.00
4 Rep. 50.00
5 Rep. 50.00
6 Rep. 50.00
7 Rep. 50.00
8 Rep. 50.00
9 Rep. 50.00

ZORRO
Topps Nov., 1993
0 BSf(c),DMG(s), came bagged
with Jurassic Park Raptor #1 and
Teenagents #4 . . . . 4.00
1 DMG(s),V:Machete 3.00
2 DMG(s) 5.00
3 DMG(s) I:Lady Rawhide 15.00
4 MGr(c),DMG(s),V:Moonstalker . 2.50
5 MGr,DMG(s),V:Moonstalker . . . 2.50
6 A:Lady Rawhide 8.00
7 A:Lady Rawhide 7.00
8 MGr(c),DMG(s) 3.00
9 A:Lady Rawhide 4.00
10 A:Lady Rawhide 4.50

11 A:Lady Rawhide 8.00

Zot! #1 © Eclipse Comics

ZOT!
Eclipse 1984–85
1 by Scott McCloud 7.00
2 . . . . 3.00
3 . . . . 3.00
4 . . . . 3.00
5 . . . . 3.00
6 . . . . 2.00
7 . . . . 2.50
8 . . . . 2.00
9 . . . . 2.50
10 . . . . 2.00
10a B&W 6.00
10b 2nd printing 2.50
Original Zot! Book 1 . . . . 9.95
Book One TPB 24.95
(Changed to B & W)

ZOT!
Kitchen Sink
Book One TPB 24.95
Book One HC signed & numbered 55.00

B & W PUBLISHERS

A1
Atomeka Press 1989–92
1 BWs,A:Flaming Carrot,Mr.X.	10.00
2 BWs	9.75
3	9.75
4	5.95
5	6.95
6a	4.95

AARDWOLF
Aardwolf 1994
1 DC,GM(c)	2.95
1a Certificate ed. signed	12.00
2 World Toughest Milkman	2.95
3 R.Block(s),O:Aardwolf	2.95

A.B.C. WARRIORS
Fleetway/Quality
1 thru 8	@1.95

ABSOLUTE ZERO
Antarctic Press 1995
1	2.95
2 Rooftop,Athena	2.95
3 Stan Sakai	3.50
4 3-D Man and Kirby	2.95
5 & 6 Super Powers	@2.95

AC ANNUAL
Aircel 1990
1	3.95
2 Based on 1940's heroes	5.00
3 F:GoldenAge Heroes	3.50
4 F:Sentinels of Justice	3.95

ACE COMICS PRESENTS
Ace 1987
1 thru 7	@1.75

ACES
Eclipse 1988
1 thru 5, mag. size	@2.95

ACHILLES STORM
Brainstorm 1997
1 by Sandra Chang	2.95
1a nude cover	2.95

ACHILLES STORM: DARK SECRET
Brainstorm 1997
1 by Sandra Chang	2.95
1 nude cover edition	3.95
2	2.95
2a nude cover edition	2.95
2 luxury edition	5.00

ACME
Fandom House
1 thru 9	@1.95

ACOLYTE CHRONICLES
Azure Press 1995
1 I:Korath	2.95
2 V:Korath	2.95

ACTION FORCE
Lightning 1987
1	1.75

ACTION GIRL COMICS
Slave Labor Graphics 1994
1 thru 7	@2.75
1 thru 7, later printings	@2.75
8 thru 12	@2.95
13 Halloween issue	2.95
14 F:Elizabeth Lavin	2.95
15	2.95

ADAM AND EVE A.D.
Bam
1	3.00
2 thru 10	@1.50

ADDAM OMEGA
Antarctic Press 1997
1 (of 4) by Bill Hughes	2.95
2	2.95
3	2.95
4 concl.	2.95

Adolescent Radioactive Blackbelt Hamsters #3 © Eclipse

ADOLESCENT RADIOACTIVE BLACK-BELT HAMSTERS
Eclipse
1 I:Bruce,Chuck,Jackie,Clint	2.50
1a 2nd printing	2.00
2 A parody of a parody	2.00
3 I:Bad Gerbil	2.00
4 A:Heap (3-D),Abusement Park	1.50
5 Abusement Park #2	1.50
6 SK,Abusement Park #3	2.00
7 SK,V:Toe-Jam Monsters	2.00
8 SK	2.00
9 All-Jam last issue	2.00
[2nd Series]

Parody Press
1	2.50
2 Hamsters Go Hollywood	2.50

ADVENTURES INTO THE UNKNOWN
A Plus Comics 1990
1 AW,WW, rep. classic horror	2.95
2 AW	2.95
3 AW	2.95
Halloween Spec. reps. Charlton & American Comics GroupHorror	2.50
ACG Comics 1997
1 FF,AW, Charlton comics reprint	2.95

ADVENTURERS
Aircel/Adventure Publ.
0 Origin Issue	2.50
1 with Skeleton	5.00
1a Revised cover	3.00
1b 2nd printing	2.00
2 Peter Hsu (c)	2.50
3 Peter Hsu (c)	2.50
4 Peter Hsu (c)	2.00
5 Peter Hsu (c)	2.00
6 Peter Hsu (c)	2.00
7 thru 9	@2.00

ADVENTURERS BOOK II
Adventure Publ.
0 O:Man Gods	1.95
1	1.95
2 thru 9	@1.95

ADVENTURERS BOOK III
1A Lim.(c)Ian McCaig	2.25
1B Reg.(c)Mitch Foust	2.25
2 thru 6	@2.25

ADVENTURES OF CHRISSY CLAWS, THE
Heroic 1991
1 thru 2	@3.25

ADVENTURES OF CHUK THE BARBARIC
White Wolf
1 & 2	@1.25

ADVENTURES OF LUTHER ARKWRIGHT
Valkyrie Press 1987–89
1 thru 9	@2.25
See Also: Dark Horse section

ADVENTURES OF MR. PYRIDINE
Fantagraphics
1	2.25

ADVENTURES OF THE AEROBIC DUO
Lost Cause Productions
1 thru 3	@2.25

All comics prices listed are for *Near Mint* condition.

4 Gopher Quest 2.25
5 V:Stupid Guy 2.25

ADVENTURES OF
THEOWN
Pyramid 1986
1 thru 3, Limited series . . . . . @1.75

AESOP'S FABLES
Fantagraphics
1 Selection of Fables 2.25
2 Selection of Fables 2.25
3 inc. Boy who cried wolf 2.25

AETOS
Hall of Heroes Jan. 1997
1 by Dan Parsons 2.50
1 variant cover 4.00
2 . . . . 2.50

AETOS 2: CHILDREN OF
THE GRAVES
Orpahn Underground 1995
1 A:Nightmare 2.50

AGENT UNKNOWN
Renegade
1 thru 3 . . . . @2.00

AGE OF HEROES, THE
Halloween Comics 1996
1 JHI 2.95
1A signed 2.95
2 JHI 2.95
2A signed 2.95

AGONY ACRES
AA² Entertainment
1 thru 3 . . . . @2.50
4 and 5 . . . . @2.95

AIRCEL
1 Graphic Novel year 1 . . . . . . 6.95

AIRFIGHTERS CLASSICS
Eclipse
1 O:Airboy,rep.Air Fighters#2 . . . 3.00
2 rep.Old Airboy appearances . . 3.00
3 thru 6 . . . . @3.95

AIRMEN
Mansion Comics
1 I:Airmen 2.50

AIRWAVES
Caliber 1990
1 Radio Security 2.50
2 A:Paisley,Ganja 2.50
3 Formation of Rebel Alliance . . . 2.50
4 Big Annie,Pt. 1 . . . . 2.50
5 Big Annie, Pt 2 . . . . 2.50

AKIKO
Sirius 1996
1 MCi 3.50
2 MCi 3.00
3 thru 17 MCi . . . . @2.50
18 Alia Rellapor, concl. 2.50
19 new story, pt.1 . . . . 2.50

20 F:Mr. Beeba 2.50
21 On the Road 2.50
22 . . . . 2.50
23 space station Fognon-6 . . . . . 2.50
24 escape spaceship 2.50
25 Done in One, 32pg. 2.95
26 reunited on planet Smoo 2.50
27 MCi,Bornstone's Elixir, pt.2 . . . 2.50
TPB Vol. 1 rep. #1–#6 . . . . . . 14.95
HC Vol. 1 . . . . 20.00
TPB Vol. 2 rep. #8–#13 . . . . . 11.95
Spec. Akiko on the Planet Smoo . 3.50

ALBEDO
Thoughts & Images
0 white cover, yellow drawing table
    Blade Runner 50.00
0a white(c) 30.00
0b blue(c),1st ptg 25.00
0c blue(c),2nd ptg 20.00
0d blue(c),3rd ptg 5.00
0e Photo(c),4th ptg.,inc. extra
    pages 3.00
1 SS,I:Nilson Groundthumper, dull
    red cover 15.00
1a bright red cover 12.00
2 SS,I:Usagi Yojimbo 10.00
3 SS,Erma, Usagi 4.00
4 SS,Usagi 6.00
5 Nelson Groundthumper 5.00
6 Erma, High Orbit 4.00
7 . . . . 2.00
8 Erna Feldna 2.00
9 High Orbit,Harvest Venture . . . 2.00
10 thru 14 . . . . @2.00

ALBEDO VOL. II
Antartic Press 1991–93
1 New Erma Story 2.50
2 E.D.F. HQ 2.50
3 Birth of Erma's Child 2.50
4 Non action issue 2.50
5 The Outworlds 2.50
6 War preparations 2.50
7 Ekosiak in Anarchy 2.50
8 EDF High Command 2.50
Spec. Color 3.00

VOL. III
1 . . . . 3.50

ALIEN ENCOUNTERS
Fantagor
1 . . . . 1.25

ALIEN FIRE
Kitchen Sink Press 1987
1 Eric Vincent art 3.50
2 Eric Vincent art 2.50
3 Eric Vincent art 2.00

ALIEN NATION:
A BREED APART
Adventure Comics 1990
1 Friar Kaddish 3.00
2 . . . . 2.50
3 The 'Vampires' Busted 2.50
4 Final Issue 2.50

ALIEN NATION:
THE FIRSTCOMERS
Adventure Comics 1991
1 New Mini-series 2.50

Alien Fire #1 © Kitchen Sink

2 Assassin 2.50
3 Search for Saucer 2.50
4 Final Issue 2.50

ALIEN NATION:
THE PUBLIC ENEMY
Adventure Comics 1991
1 'Before the Fall' 2.50
2 Earth & Wehlnistrata 2.50
3 Killer on the Loose 2.50

ALIEN NATION:
THE SKIN TRADE
Adventure Comics 1991
1 'Case of the Missing Milksop' . . 2.50
2 'To Live And Die in L.A' 2.50
3 A:Dr. Jekyll 2.50
4 D.Methoraphan Exposed 2.50

ALIEN NATION:
THE SPARTANS
Adventure Comics
1 JT/DPo,Yellow wrap 4.00
1a JT/DPo,Green wrap 4.00
1b JT/DPo,Pink wrap 4.00
1c JT/DPo,blue wrap 4.00
1d LTD collectors edition 7.00
2 JT,A:Ruth Lawrence 2.50
3 JT/SM,Spartians 2.50
4 JT/SM,conclusion 2.50

ALIEN4 STRIKE FORCE
1 . . . . 1.95

ALL-PRO SPORTS
All Pro Sports
1 Unauthorized Bio-Bo Jackson . 2.50
2 Unauthorized Bio-Joe Montana 2.50

ALLURA AND
THE CYBERANGELS
Avatar Press 1998
Spec.#1 by Bill Maus 3.95
Spec.#1 nude cover 6.00

All comics prices listed are for *Near Mint* condition.

ALLY
Ally Winsor Productions 1995
1 I&O: Ally 2.95
2 and 3 . . . . @2.95

ALTERNATE HEROES
Prelude Graphics
1 and 2 . . . . @1.95

AMAZING COMICS
PREMIERES
1 thru 9 . . . . @1.95

AMAZING CYNICALMAN
Eclipse
1 . . . . 1.50

AMAZON WOMAN
Fantaco
Christmas Spec. 4.95
Beach Party 5.95
Amazing Colossal Amazon Woman
#1 . . . . 7.95
Amazing Colossal Amazon Album 12.95
Jungle Annual #1 . . . . 5.95
Jungle Album 9.95
TPB Amazon Woman: The Art of
Tom Simonton 9.95
TPB Amazon Woman: The Art of
Tom Simonton, deluxe 19.95
Spec. Invaders of Terror by Tom
Simonton 5.95
TPB Book One by Tom Simonton 14.95
TPB Book Two The Curse of the
Amazon 14.95
HC, limited 50.00
HC, limited, signed, numbered . . 75.00
1-shot Attack of the Amazon Girls,
by Tom Simonton, contains
nudity 4.95

AMAZONS GONZANGAS: BAD GIRLS OF THE JUNGLE
Academy Comics 1995
0 Rites of passage(Jason Waltrip) 3.50

AMERICAN ANNIHILATOR
Night Realm Publishing
0 V:Synthetic Assassin 1.85

AMERICAN SPLENDOR
Harvey Bekar 1976–90
1 thru 15 . . . . @3.25
Tundra 1991
16 . . . . 3.95

AMERICAN WOMAN
Antarctic Press 1998
1 by Brian Denham & Richard
Stockton 2.95

AMUSING STORIES
Blackthorne
1 thru 3 . . . . @2.00

ANATOMIC BOMBS
Brainstorm 1998
1 Angelissa, by Mike James 2.95

1a Angelissa, nude cover edition 3.95
1 Bad Tabitha, by Mike James . . 2.95
1a Bad Tabitha, photo cover edition 3.95

ANGEL GIRL
Angel Entertainment 1997
0 by David Campiti & Al Rio 2.95
1 by David Campiti & Richard
Fraga 2.95
1 deluxe 5.95
1 Virgin nude cover 5.00
1 Nude Manga cover 5.00
1 Nude Platinum cover 5.00
Spec. #1 Angels Illustrated Swimsuit
Special 5.00
Spec. #1 Swimsuit Special, Nude
Oily Angels (c) 5.00
1-shot Against All Evil 2.95
1-shot Against All Evil, nude cover 2.95
1-shot Before the Wings 2.95
1-shot Before the Wings, nude cover
A 2.95
1-shot Before the Wings, nude cover
B 2.95
1-shot Demonworld, by Ellis Bell &
Mark Kuettner 2.95
1-shot Doomsday, by Ellis Bell &
Mark Kuettner 3.00

ANGEL GIRL: HEAVEN SENT
Angel Entertainment 1997
0 by David Campiti & Al Rio 2.95
0 Virgin nude 5.00
0 nude platinum cover 12.00
1 . . . . 3.00
1 nude Michelle in Hell cover . . 4.00

ANGEL OF DEATH
Innovation
1 thru 4 . . . . @2.25

ANIMAL MYSTIC
Cry For Dawn/Sirus 1993–95
1 DOe 55.00
1a variant, signed 85.00
1b 2nd printing, new (c) 15.00
2 I:Klor 55.00
2a 2nd printing, new (c) 12.00
3 . . . . 25.00
3a 2nd printing 7.00
4 last issue 10.00
4a special 15.00
TPB DOe 14.95

ANIMERICA
Viz Comics
1 F:Bubble Gum Crisis 2.95
2 F:Bubble Gum Crisis 2.95
3 F:Bubble Gum Crisis 2.95

ANTARES CIRCLE
Antarctic Press
1 . . . . 1.75
2 . . . . 1.75

ANUBIS
Unicorn Books
1 I:Anubis 2.50
2 F:Anubis 2.50
3 . . . . 2.50

Didactic Chocolate Press
3 by Scott Berwanger 2.75
4 thru 6 . . . . @2.75
Adventure Comics
7 "Sandy's Plight" 2.75
8 . . . . 2.95

A-OK #3 © Antarctic Press

A-OK
Antarctic Press
1 Ninja H.S. spin-off series 2.50
2 F:Paul,Moniko,James 2.50
3 Confrontation 2.50
4 . . . . 2.50

APATHY KAT
Entity 1995
1 . . . . 2.75
1 signed, numbered 9.95
1 2nd printing 2.75
2 . . . . 2.75
2 2nd printing 2.75
3 & 4 . . . . 2.75
TPB Kollection #1 . . . . 7.95

APE CITY
Adventure Comics
1 Monkey Business 3.00
2 thru 4 . . . . @2.50

APPARITION, THE
Caliber
1 thru 4 . . . . @2.95
5 "Black Clouds" 2.95

APPLESEED
Eclipse
1 MSh,rep. Japanese comic . . . 12.00
2 MSh,arrival in Olympus City . . . 6.00
3 MSh,Olympus City politics 5.00
4 MSh,V:Director 5.00
5 MSh,Deunan vs. Chiffon 5.00
Book Two
1 MSh,AAd(c),Olympus City 4.00
2 MSh,AAd(c),Hitomi vs.EswatUnit 3.50
3 MSh,AAd(c),Deunan vs.Gaia . . 3.50
4 MSh,AAd(c),V:Robot Spiders . . 3.50
5 MSh,AAd(c),Hitome vs.Gaia . . 3.50

Book Three
1 MSh,Brigreos vs.Biodroid 5.00
2 MSh,V:Cuban Navy 3.50
3 MSh,'Benandanti' 3.50
4 MSh,V:Renegade biodroid 3.50
5 MSh 3.50
Book Four 1990
1 MSh,V:Munma Terrorists 3.50
2 MSh,V:Drug-crazed Munma ... 3.50
3 Msh,V:Munma Drug Addicts .. 3.50
4 MSh,Deunan vs. Pani 3.50

ARAMIS WEEKLY
1 mini-series 1.95
2 .... 1.95
3 .... 1.95

AREA 88
Eclipse
1 I:Shin Kazama 3.00
1a 2nd printing 1.50
2 Dangerous Mission 2.00
2a 2nd printing 1.50
3 O:Shin,Paris '78 .... 2.00
4 thru 8 .... @2.00
9 thru 39 .... @1.50
40 .... 1.75
41 .... 1.75
42 .... 2.00

ARGONAUTS
Eternity
1 thru 5 .... @1.95

ARGOSY
Caliber
1 'Walker' vs. Myth Beasts 2.50

ARIK KHAN
A Plus Comics
1 I:Arik Khan 2.50
2 .... 2.50
ACG Comics 1998
1 by Frank Reyes, heroic fantasy 2.95

ARISTOCRATIC EXTRA-TERRESTRIAL TIME-TRAVELING THIEVES
Fictioneer Books
1 V:IRS 3.00
2 V:Realty 1.75
3 V:MDM 1.75
4 thru 12 .... @1.75

ARIZONA: A SIMPLE HORROR
London Night/ EH Productions 1998
1 (of 3) by Joe Kennedy & Jerry
   Beck 3.00
1a nude cover 6.00
2 double sized 3.00
2a nude cover 6.00
3 .... 3.00
3a nude cover 6.00
1-shot Wild at Heart, signed
   alternate cover 10.00

A.R.M.
Adventure Comics 1990
1 Larry Niven adapt. Death by
   Ecstasy,pt.1 .... 2.50
2 Death by Ecstasy,pt.2 ...... 2.50
3 Death by Ecstasy,pt.3 ...... 2.50

ARTHUR: KING OF BRITAIN
Tome Press
1 Saga of King Arthur Chronicled
   by Geoffrey of Monmouth ... 2.95

ASHEN VICTOR
Viz Communications 1998
1 (of 4) by Yukito Kishiro 2.95
2 thru 4 concl. .... @2.95

ASHES
Caliber 1990–91
1 thru 6 .... @2.50

ASHLEY DUST
Knight Press 1995
1 thru 3 .... @2.50
4 V:Allister Crowley 2.50
5 Metaphysical Adventure 2.50

ASRIAL VS. CHEETAH
Antarctic Press 1995–96
1 & 2 Ninja High School Gold
   Digger x-over .... @2.95

ASSASSINETTE
Pocket Change Comics
1 thru 3 .... @2.50
4 Psychic Realm 2.50
5 V:Nemesis 2.50
6 The Second Coming,pt.2 ..... 2.50
7 The Second Coming,pt.3 ..... 2.50
8 V:Crazy Actor 2.50
9 .... 2.50
10 final issue. 2.50
Spec. Assassinette Returns 2.50
Spec. Assassinette Violated 2.50
Deluxe Assassinette Violated 4.25

A.R.M. #1 © Adventure Comics

ASSASSINETTE: HARDCORE
Pocket Change Comics
1 By Shadow Slasher Team 2.50
2 V:Bolero 2.50

ATHENA
A.M. Works
7 thru 14 by Dean Hsieh .... @2.95
TPB Vol. 1 .... 14.95
TPB Vol. 2 .... 15.95

ATOMIC COMICS
1 .... 1.50
Becomes: MARK I

ATOMIC MAN
1 .... 3.00
2 .... 2.00
3 .... 1.75

ATOMIC MOUSE
A Plus Comics 1990
1 A:Atomic Bunny 2.50

ATOMIC OVERDRIVE
Caliber
1 by Dave Darrigo & PGr 2.95
2 1950s Sci-Fi,Horror,Humor ... 2.95
3 .... 2.95

A TRAVELLER'S TALE
Antarctic Press
1 I:Goshin the Traveller 2.50
2 .... 2.50

ATOMIC CITY TALES
Kitchen Sink
1 thru 4 by Jay Stephens .... @3.50
TPB Vol. 1 Go Power 12.95
TPB Vol. 1 signed & numbered . 20.95

ATTACK OF THE MUTANT MONSTERS
A Plus Comics
1 SD,rep.Gorgo(Kegor) 2.50

AURORA
Dreamer Comics
1 I:Canadian Heroes   2.35

AUTUMN
Caliber Press 1995
1 I:James Turell 2.95
GN 7"x10" 12.95

AVALON
Harrier
1 thru 3 .... 1.50

AVANT GUARD
Day 1 Comics
1 thru 4 F:Feedback 2.50

AV IN 3D
Aardvark–Vanaheim
1 Color,A:FlamingCarot 6.00

AVENUE X
Innovation
1 Based on NY radio drama 2.50
Purple Spiral
3 signed & numbered 3.00

AWESOME COMICS
1 thru 3 .... @2.00

AWESOME
Awesome Entertainment
1 anthology, partial color 2.95

AXED FILES, THE
Entity Comics
1 X-Files Parody 2.50
1 3rd printing, parody 2.75

B-MOVIE PRESENTS
B-Movie Comics
1 .... 1.70
2 .... 1.70
3 Tasma, Queen of the Jungle .. 1.70
4 .... 1.70

BABES OF AREA 51
Blatant Comics 1997
1 .... 2.95
1a Nude Alien Autopsy cover .. 9.95
1b Nude Roswell Crash cover .. 9.95

BABY ANGEL X
Brainstorm 1996
1 .... 2.95
2 .... 2.95
3 gold edition 5.00
3a signed edition 10.00

BABY ANGEL X:
SCORCHED EARTH
Brainstorm 1997
1 by Scott Harrison 2.95
1a nude cover 2.95
2 .... 2.95
2a nude cover 2.95

BABYLON CRUSH
Boneyard Press
1 I:Babylon Crush 2.95
2 V:A Gang 2.95
3 V:Mafiaso Brothers 2.95
4 & 5 .... @2.95
CFD
6 & 7 .... @3.95
Boneyard 1998
1-shot Buddha, F:Lesbian dominatrix
   vigilante 4.95
Spec. Babylon Bondage Christmas 2.95
Spec. Bondage nude cover 3.95
Spec. Girlfriends 2.95
Spec. Girlfriends, nude cover 3.95

BAD APPLES
High Impact Jan. 1997
1 .... 2.95
1 Bad Candies cover 9.95
2 .... 2.95
2 deluxe 15.00
3 by Billy Patton 2.95
3 deluxe adult cover 10.00

BAKER STREET
(Prev. color)
Caliber
3 .... 3.25
4 .... 1.95
5 Children of the Night Pt.1 .... 1.95
6 Children of the Night Pt.2 .... 1.95
7 thru 10 Children of the Night
   pt.3–pt.6 .... @2.50

BAKER ST.: GRAPHITTI
Caliber
1 'Elemenary, My Dear' 2.50

BALANCE OF POWER
MU Press 1990–91
1 thru 4 .... @2.50

BANDY MAN, THE
Caliber 1996
1 SPr,CAd 2.95
2 SPr,CAd,JIT 2.95
3 SPr,CAd,JIT, conclusion 2.95
HC 96pg 19.95
HC Deluxe 39.95

Baoh #5 ©Viz Comics

BAOH
Viz 1990
1 thru 8 .... @2.95
GN V:Juda Laboratory 14.95

BARABBAS
Slave Labor
1 .... 4.50
2 thru 4 .... @1.50

BARBARIC TALES
Pyramid
1 .... 3.00
2 and 3 .... @1.70

BARBARIANS
ACG Comics
1 by Jeff Jones, Mike Kaluta,
   Wayne Howard 2.95

2 WW 2.95

BASEBALL SUPERSTARS
Revolutionary
1 Nolan Ryan 2.50

BATTLE ANGEL ALITA
Viz 1992
1 I:Daisuka,Alita 9.00
2 Alita becomes warrior 5.00
3 A:Daiuke,V:Cyborg 4.00
4 Alita/Cyborg,A:Makaku 4.00
5 The Bounty Hunters Bar 4.00
6 Confrontation 4.00
7 Underground Sewers,A:Fang .. 2.75
8 & 9 .... @2.75
Part II 1993
1 V:Zapan 2.95
2 V:Zapan 2.95
3 F:Ido 2.75
4 thru 7 V:Zapan .... @2.75
TPB Killing Angel 15.95
Part Three 1993
1 thru 5 .... @2.75
6 .... 5.00
7 thru 13 .... @2.75
Part Four 1994
1 thru 7 .... @2.75
Part Five 1995
1 thru 6 .... @2.75
7 .... 2.95
Part Six
1 thru 8 YuK .... @2.95
TPB Angel of Chaos 15.95
Part Seven Oct. 1996
1 thru 8 YuK .... @2.95
Part Eight 1997
1 thru 9 YuK .... @2.95
TPB Vol. 2 Tears of an Agnel .. 15.95
TPB Vol. 4 Angel of Victory ... 15.95
TPB Vol. 5 .... 15.95
TPB Vol. 6 Angel of Death ... 15.95
TPB Vol. 7 Angel of Chaos ... 15.95
TPB Vol. 8 Fallen Angel 15.95
TPB Vol. 9 Angel's Ascension .. 16.95

BATTLE ARMOR
Eternity
1 thru 4 .... @1.95

BATTLE BEASTS
Blackthorne
1 thru 4 .... @1.50

BATTLEGROUND EARTH
Best Comics 1996
1 .... 2.50
2 .... 2.50
3 "Destiny Quest: The Vengeance"
   concl. 2.50
4 V:Conjura 2.50
5 "The Pit of Black Death" 2.50

BATTLE GROUP PEIPER
Caliber
1 Bio S.S.Lt.Col Peiper 2.95

BATTLETECH
(Prev. Color)
7 thru 12 .... @1.75
Ann.#1 .... 4.50

All comics prices listed are for *Near Mint* condition.

BATTRON
NEC
1 WWII story 2.75
2 WWII contd. 2.75

BEAST WARRIOR
OF SHAOLIN
1 thru 5 . . . . @1.95

THE BEATLES
EXPERIENCE
Revolutionary
1 Beatles 1960's 3.00
2 Beatles 1964-1966 . . . . 2.50
3 . . . . 2.50
4 Abbey Road, Let it be 2.50
5 The Solo Years 2.50
6 Paul McCartney & Wings 2.50
7 The Murder of John Lennon . . 2.50
8 To 1992, final issue 2.50

BECK AND CAUL
Gauntlet
1 I:Beck and Caul 2.95
2 thru 6 . . . . @2.95
Ann.#1 A Single Step 3.50

BERZERKER
Gauntlet (Caliber)
1 thru 6 . . . . @2.95

BESET BY DEMONS
Tundra
1 Short stories by M.McLester . . 3.50

BEST CELLARS
Out of the Cellar 1995
1 New Anthology Comic 2.50

BEST OF THE WEST
AC Comics 1998
1 F:Durango Kid 4.95
2 F:The Haunted Horseman 4.95

BETHANY THE VAMPFIRE
Brainstorm Dec. 1997
0 O:Bethany 2.95
0a nude cover 3.95
1 by Holly Galightly 2.95
1 luxury edition 5.00
2 . . . . 2.95
2a nude cover 3.95
3 . . . . 2.95
3a nude cover 3.95
3b Photo cover 3.95

BEYOND HUMAN
Battlezone Comics
0 . . . . 3.50

BEYOND MARS
Blackthorne
1 thru 5 . . . . @2.00

BIG BLACK KISS
Vortex
3 HC some color 3.75

BIG NUMBERS
1 BSz 6.00
2 BSz 5.50

BIG PRIZE
Eternity
1 . . . . 1.95

BILL AND MELVIN
Newcomers Publishing
1 O:Bill & Melvin 2.95

BILL THE BULL
Boneyard Press
1 I:Bill the Bull 2.95
2 & 3 For Hire . . . . @2.95

BILLY DOGMA
Millennium April 1997
1 by Dean Haspiel 2.95
1 signed print edition 4.95
2 . . . . 2.95
3 . . . . 2.95
4 They Found A Sawed-Off in My
Afro 2.95

BILLY NGUYEN
PRIVATE EYE
Caliber 1990
1 . . . . 2.00
1a 2nd Printing 2.00
2 thru 6 . . . . @2.00

BioBooster Armor Guyver #3
© Viz Comics

BIO-BOOSTER
ARMOR GUYVER
Viz
Part II
1 thru 3 F:Sho . . . . @2.75
4 V:Enzyme II 2.75
5 Sho VS Enzyme II 2.75
6 Final Issue 2.75
Part III
1 Sho Unconscious 2.75
2 V:Zoanoids 2.75

3 F:Murahani 2.75
4 . . . . 2.75
5 . . . . 2.75
6 V:Commando Guyver 2.75
7 Sho to the rescue 2.75
TPB Revenge of Chronos 15.95
TPB Vol. 4 Escape From Chronos 15.95
Part Four
1 thru 7 . . . . @2.95
Part Five
1 thru 7 . . . . @2.95
Part Six Dec. 1996
1 thru 6 by Yoshiki Takaya . . . @2.95
Vol. 1 . . . . 15.95
Vol. 2 Revenge of Chronos . . . 15.95
Vol. 4 Escape From Chronos . . . 15.95
Vol. 5 Guyver Reborn 15.95
Vol. 6 Heart of Chronos 15.95
Vol. 7 Armageddon 15.95

BIZARRE HEROES
Kitchen Sink
1 DonSimpson art,parody (1990) . 2.50

BIZARRE HEROES
Fiasco Comics
1 DSs, reprint 2.95

[Original] BLACK CAT
4 rep.. . . . . 2.00
5 A:Ted Parrish 2.00
6 50th Anniv. Issue 2.00
7 rep. 2.00

BLACKENED
Enigma
1 V:Killing Machine 2.95
2 V:Killing Machine 2.95
3 Flaming Altar 2.95

BLACK KISS
Vortex
1 HC,Adult 7.00
1a 2nd printing 4.00
1b 3rd printing 1.25
2 HC 6.00
2a 2nd printing 3.00
3 HC 5.00
4 HC 4.00
5 & 6 HC . . . . @2.00
7 thru 12 HC 1.50

BLACKMASK
Eastern Comics
1 thru 6 . . . . @1.75

BLACK MIST
Caliber Core 1998
1 by James Pruett & Mike Perkins,
Blood of Kali, pt.1 . . . . 2.95
1a variant MV(c) 2.95
1b variant Jordan Raskin(c) 2.95
1c variant GyD(c) 2.95
1d premium edition, signed 9.95
2 thru 4 Blood of Kali,pt.2–pt.4 @2.95

BLACK SCORPION
Special Studio 1991
1 Knight of Justice 2.75
2 A Game for Old Men 2.75
3 Blackmailer's Auction 2.75

B & W PUB

BLACKTHORNE 3 in 1
1 and 2 . . . . @2.00

BLACK ZEPPLIN
Renegade
1 . . . . 2.50
2 thru 6 . . . . @2.00

Blade of Shuriken #1 © Eternity

BLADE OF SHURIKEN
Eternity
1 thru 8 . . . . @1.95

BLANDMAN
Eclipse
1 Sandman parody 2.50

BLAZING WESTERN
1 rep. 2.50

BLIND FEAR
Eternity
1 thru 4 . . . . @1.95

BLOOD & ROSES ADVENTURES
Knight Press
1 F:Time Agents 2.95
2 F:Time Agents 2.95
3 Search for Time Agents 2.95
4 Time Adventures 2.95

BLOOD 'N' GUTS
Aircel 1990
1 thru 3 . . . . @2.50

BLOODBROTHERS
Eternity
1 thru 4 . . . . @1.95

BLOOD IS THE HARVEST
Eclipse 1992
1 I:Nikita,Milo 4.50
2 V:M'Raud D:Nikita? 2.50
3 Milo captured 2.50
4 F:Nikita/Milo 2.50

BLOOD JUNKIES
Eternity
1 Vampires on Capitol Hill 2.50
2 final issue 2.50

BLOODLETTING
Fantaco
1 A Shilling for a Redcoat 2.95
2 . . . . 2.95
3 Flee 2.95
4 thru 10 (of 11) by Chynna
  Clugston. . . . . @3.95

BLOOD MASTERS
Night Realm Publishing
1 I:Blood Masters 1.80

BLOOD OF DRACULA
Apple 1987–90
1 thru 7 . . . . @1.75
8 thru 14 . . . . @1.95
15 +Record&Mask 3.50
16 . . . . 1.95
17 thru 20 . . . . @2.25

BLOOD OF INNOCENT
Warp Graphics
1 thru 4 . . . . @2.50

BLOODSHED
Damage
1 Little Brother 2.95
1a Commemorative issue 4.00
1 Encore edition, gold foil(c) 3.50
2 Little Brother 2.95
3 O:Bloodshed 2.95
3 "The Wastelands," cont. 3.50
4 The City 3.50
5 the end is near 3.50
6 . . . . 3.50
7 Lies, concl. 3.50
"M" 3.50
"M" deluxe 5.00
Spec. Lunatics Fringe 3.50
Spec. Lies Epilogue, final issue . . 3.50
Spec. Chris Mass #1 . . . . 3.50
Spec. Requiem 3.50

BLOODWING
Eternity
1 thru 5 . . . . @1.95

BLUDGEON
Aardwolf 1997
1 by JPi & David Chylsetk 2.95
2 "Alise in Wonderland" 2.95
3 "Seeing Red" 2.95

BOB POWELL'S TIMELESS TALES
Eclipse
1 . . . . 2.00

BOGIE MAN: CHINATOON
Atomeka
1 I:Francis Claine 2.95
2 F:Bogie Man 2.95
3 thr 4 F:Bogie Man 2.95

BOGIE MAN: MANHATTEN PROJECT
Apocalypse
One Shot. D.Quale Assassination Pl. 2.95

BONAFIDE
Bonafide Productions
1 F:Doxie 'th Mutt 3.50
2 F:Doxie 'th Mutt 3.50
3 F:Doxie 'th Mutt 3.50

BONE
Cartoon Books 1991
1 I:Bone 150.00
1a 2nd printing 20.00
1b 3rd Printing 10.00
1c 4th printing 5.00
1d thru 1f 5th-7th printing . . . . @4.00
2 . . . . 85.00
2a 2nd printing 10.00
2b thru 2e 3rd-6th printing . . . @3.00
3 . . . . 60.00
3a 2nd printing 8.00
3b thru 3d 3rd-5th printing . . . @3.00
4 . . . . 50.00
4a thru 4c 2nd-4th printing . . . @3.00
5 . . . . 40.00
5a thru 5c 2nd-4th printing . . . @3.00
6 . . . . 40.00
6a thru 6c 2nd-4th printing . . . @3.00
7 . . . . 30.00
7a,7b 2nd,3rd printing . . . . . . @3.00
8 . . . . 25.00
8a,8b 2nd,3rd printing . . . . . . @4.00
9 . . . . 10.00
9a 2nd printing 4.00
10 . . . . 7.00
11 . . . . 6.00
12 . . . . 6.00
13 . . . . 10.00
14 thru 17 . . . . @3.25
18 V:Bar owner 3.25
19 F:Phoney Bone 3.25
20 Dragonslayer Phoney Bone . . 3.25
21 thru 27, see Image
21 thru 27 reprints . . . . @2.95
28 "Rockjaw: Master of the Eastern
   Border" 3.00
29 . . . . 3.00
30 . . . . 2.95
31 . . . . 2.95
32 Bartleby the Rat Creature Cub
   saga, concl. 2.95
33 Phoney's fate 2.95
TPB rep.#1-4 . . . . 14.00
TPB Vol. 1 Rep.1-#6 . . . . 12.95
TPB Vol. 2 Rep.#7-#12 . . . . . 12.95
TPB Vol. 3 Eyes of the Storm . . 16.95
HC Vol. 3 . . . . 24.95
TPB Vol.4 Dragonslayer 16.95
HC Vol. 4 . . . . 24.95
TPB Vol. 5 Rock Jaw: Master of the
   Eastern Border 14.95
HC Vol. 5 . . . . 22.95
TPB Bone Reader 9.95

BONESHAKER
Caliber Press
1 Suicidal Wrestler 3.50

BOOK OF BALLADS AND SAGAS
Green Man Press
1 False Knight in the Road 2.95
2 thru 5 . . . . 3.00
5 . . . . 3.50

BOOK OF THE TAROT
Caliber Tome Press 1998
1 History/Development o/t Tarot . 3.95
1 64pg 4.95
1 signed 4.95

BOONDOGGLE
Knight Press 1995
1 Waffle War 2.95
2 Waffle War 2.95
3 Waffle War 2.95

BOONDOGGLE
Caliber Tapestry 1997
Spec. 2.95
Spec., signed 2.95
1 thru 3 . . . . @2.95
4 At Wo's 2.95

BORDER WORLDS
Kitchen Sink
1 adult 2.00
2 thru 7 . . . . @2.00

BORDER WORLDS: MAROONED
1 . . . . 2.00

BORIS' ADVENTURE MAGAZINE
Nicotat
1 and 2 . . . . @2.00
3 thru 6 . . . . @2.95

BORIS THE BEAR
Nikotat
1–12: See Dark Horse section
13 thru 29 . . . . @2.00
30 thru 34 . . . . @2.50

BORN TO BE WILD
Eclipse
one shot. Benefit P.E.T.A. 10.95

BORN TO KILL
Aircel 1991
1 thru 3 . . . . @2.50

BOSTON BOMBERS
Caliber
1 . . . . 1.95
2 . . . . 2.50
Spec.#1 . . . . 3.95
Note: other issues are flipbooks with:
Oz #17; The Searchers #5; Raven
Chronicles #12; & LegendLore #6

BOUNTY
Caliber 1991
1 'Bounty,"Navarro' Pt.1 . . . . . 2.50
2 'Bounty,"Navarro' Pt.2 . . . . . 2.50
3 'Bounty,"Navarro' Pt.3 . . . . . 2.50

BOX OFFICE POISON
Antarctic Press 1996
1 by Alex Robinson 3.50
2 thru 10 . . . . @2.95
Big Super Spec.#1 . . . . 4.95

BRAT PACK
King Hell Publications
1 . . . . 6.00
1a 2nd printing 3.00
2 thru 4 . . . . @4.00
5 . . . . 4.00
Brat Pack Collection 13.00

BRATPACK/MAXIMORTAL
King Hell
Super Spec.#1 RV 3.00
Super Spec.#2 RV 3.00

BREAKNECK BLVD
Slave Labor Graphics 1995–96
1 thru 3 Jhonen Vasques art . @2.95
4 by Timothy Markin 2.95
5 . . . . 2.95
6 . . . . 2.95

BRENDA STAR PIN UPS
ACG Comics 1998
1 rep. from 40s and 50s 2.95

BRENDA STARR, ACE REPORTER
ACG Comics 1998
1 by Dale Messick, Charlton reprint 3.00
2 . . . . 2.95

BRILLIANT BOY
Circus Comics 1997
1 . . . . 2.95
2 Drake, pt.1 (of 5) 2.95
3 Drake, pt.2 . . . . 2.50
4 Drake, pt.3 . . . . 2.50
5 Drake, pt.4 . . . . 2.50
6 Drake, pt.5 . . . . 2.50
7 The Great Thunder, pt. 1 (of 6) 2.50
8 The Great Thunder, pt. 2 . . . 2.50

Broid #2 © Eternity

BRINGERS
Blackthorne
1 . . . . 3.50

BROID
Eternity
1 thru 4 . . . . @2.25

BROKEN HEROES
Sirius 1998
1 by Fillbach Bros 2.50
2 The Neon Graveyard 2.50
3 Rocket Man 2.50
4 . . . . 2.50
5 . . . . 2.50
6 . . . . 2.50

BRONX
Eternity 1991
1 A.Saichann Short Stories 2.50
2 to 3 . . . . @2.50

BRONX
Aircel
Reprint 2.95

BROTHER MAN
New City Comics
1 . . . . 5.00
1a 2.00
2 thru 7 . . . . @2.00

BRUCE JONES: OUTER EDGE
Innovation
1 All reprints 2.00

BRUCE JONES: RAZORS EDGE
Innovation
1 All reprints 2.50
2 D:Grimm, Gritty 2.50

BRU-HEAD
Schism Comics
1 Blockhead 2.95
1a 2nd printing 2.75
2 Blockhead 2.95
Vol 1 Bru-Hed's Bunnies, Baddies &
  Buddies (1998) 2.50
Vol 1 Bru-Hed's Guide to Gettin'
  Girls Now 2.50

BRYMWYCK THE IMP
Planet X Productions
1 . . . . 1.50

BUCE-N-GAR
RAK
1 . . . . 1.75
2 . . . . 1.75
3 . . . . 1.75

BUCK GODOT
Palliard Press
1 I:Buck Godot 2.95

BUCK GODOT:
ZAP GUN FOR HIRE
Studio Foglio
1 thru 7 . . . . @2.95
7 by Phil Foglio & Barb Kaalberg 2.95
8 finale 3.50

BUFFALO WINGS
Antarctic Press
1 and 2 . . . . @2.50

BUG
Planet X Productions
1 . . . . 1.50
2 . . . . 1.50

BULLET CROW
Eclipse
1 & 2 . . . . @2.00

BULWARK
Millenium 1995
1 I:Bulwark 2.95
2 O:Bulwark 2.95

BURNING KISS
1 with poster 4.95

BUSHIDO
Eternity
1 thru 6 . . . . @1.95

BUZZ
Kitchen Sink
1 Mark Landman (c) (1990) 2.95
2 Mark Landman (c) 2.95
3 Mark Landman (c) (1991) 2.95

CABLE TV
Parody Press
1 Cable Satire 2.50

CADILLACS
AND DINOSAURS
Kitchen Sink
3-D comic 3.95

CALIBER CORE
Caliber 1998
0 48pg 2.95
1 gestalt cover 2.95
1a Rain People cover 2.95
1b Spiral cover 2.95

CALIBER PRESENTS
(Prev. High Caliber)
1 TV,I:Crow 100.00
2 Deadworld 15.00
3 Realm 3.00
4 Baker Street 3.00
5 TV,Heart of Darkness,
  Fugitive 2.50
6 TV,Heart of Darkness,
  Fugitive 2.50
7 TV,Heart of Darkness,
  Dragonfeast 2.50
8 TV,Cuda,Fugitive 2.50
9 Baker Street,Sting Inc. 2.00
10 Fugitive, The Edge 2.50

11 Ashes,Random Thoughts 2.50
12 Fugitive,Random Thoughts . . . 2.50
13 Random Thoughts,Synergist . . 2.50
14 Random Thoughts,Fugitive . . . 2.50
15 Fringe, F:The Crow 25.00
16 Fugitive, The Verdict 3.50
17 Deadworld, The Verdict 3.50
18 Orlak,The Verdict 3.50
19 Taken Under,Go-Man 3.50
20 The Verdict,Go-Man 3.50
21 The Verdict,Go-Man 3.50
22 The Verdict,Go-Man 3.50
23 Go-Man,Heat Seeker 3.50
24 Heat Seeker,MacktheKnife . . . 3.50
Christmas Spec A:Crow,Deadworld
  Realm,Baker Street 25.00
Summer Spec. inc. the Silencers,
  Swords of Shar-Pei (preludes) . 3.95
1-Shot 2.50
1-shot Hybrid 2.50

CALIBER SPOTLIGHT
Caliber
1 F:Kabuki,Oz 2.95

CALIBRATIONS
Caliber
1 WEI,MCy,"Atmospherics," pt.1 . 2.95
2 WEI,MCy,"Atmospherics," pt.2 . 2.95
3 WEI,MCy,"Atmospherics," pt.3 . 2.95
4 WEI,MCy,"Atmospherics," pt.4 . 2.95
5 WEI,MCy,"Atmospherics," concl. 2.95

CALIFORNIA GIRLS
Eclipse
1 thru 8 . . . . @2.00

CALIGARI 2050
1 Gothic Horror 2.25
2 Gothic Horror 2.25

CAMELOT ETERNAL
Caliber 1990
1 . . . . 3.00
2 . . . . 2.50
3 . . . . 2.50
4 Launcelot & Guineuere 2.50
5 Mordred Escapes 2.50
6 MorganLeFay returns from dead 2.50
7 Revenge of Morgan 2.50
8 Launcelot flees Camelot 2.50

CANCER, THE
Humanity
1 V:Catharsis 2.50

CAPTAIN CANUCK
REBORN
Semple Comics 1995–96
1 thru 3 by Richard Comely . . @2.50

CAPT. CONFEDERACY
Steel Dragon 1985–88
1 adult 7.00
2 . . . . 2.50
3 . . . . 2.00
4 . . . . 1.50
4a . . . . @2.00
5 thru 8 . . . . @2.00
9 thru 11 . . . . @1.75
12 . . . . 1.95

CAPT. ELECTRON
Brick Computers Inc.
1 . . . . 2.00
2 . . . . 2.25

CAPTAIN HARLOCK
Eternity
1 . . . . 3.00
1a 2nd printing 2.50
2 . . . . 2.50
3 . . . . 2.50
4 thru 13 . . . . @1.95
Christmas special 2.50

CAPTAIN HARLOCK
DEATHSHADOW RISING
Eternity 1991
1 . . . . 2.75
2 . . . . 2.50
3 . . . . 2.25
4 Harlock/Nevich Truce 2.25
5 Reunited with Arcadia Crew . . . 2.25
6 . . . . 2.95

CAPTAIN HARLOCK:
THE MACHINE PEOPLE
Eternity
1 O:Captain Harlock 2.50

[ADVENTURES OF]
CAPTAIN JACK
Fantagraphics
1 . . . . 4.00
2 & 3 . . . . @2.50
4 thru 12 . . . . @2.00

CAPTAIN KOALA
Koala Comics 1997
1 . . . . 2.95
2 thru 7 . . . . @2.50

CAPTAIN PHIL
Steel Dragon
1 . . . . 1.50

CAPTAIN STERNN:
RUNNING OUT OF TIME
Kitchen Sink
1 BWr(c) (1993) 4.95
2 BWr(c) 4.95
3 BWr(c) (1994) 4.95
4 BWr(c) 4.95

CAPTAIN THUNDER
AND BLUE BOLT
Hero Graphics
1 New stories 3.50
2 Hard Targets 3.50

CARTOON HISTORY OF
THE UNIVERSE
Rip Off Press
1 Gonick art 2.50
2 Sticks & Stones 2.50
3 River Realms 2.50
4 Old Testament 2.50
5 Brains & Bronze 2.50
6 These Athenians 2.50
7 All about Athens 2.50

B & W PUB

CARTUNE LAND
Magic Carpet Comics
1 . . . . 1.50

CASES OF SHERLOCK HOLMES
Renegade
1 thru 18 . . . . @2.00
19 . . . . 2.25

CASTLE WAITING
Olio 1997
1 by Linda Medley 2.95
2 . . . . 2.95
1a 2nd printing 2.95
2a 2nd printing 2.95
3 Labors of Love 2.95
4 birth of Lady Jain's baby 2.95
5 . . . . 2.95
6 City Mouse, Country Mouse, pt.1 2.95
7 City Mouse, Country Mouse, pt.2 2.95
Spec. The Curse of Brambly Hedge
  (1996) 2.95

Cat & Mouse #7 © Aircel

CAT & MOUSE
Aircel 1989–92
1 . . . . 4.00
2 . . . . 3.00
3 thru 8 . . . . @2.25
9 Cat Reveals Identity 2.25
10 Tooth & Nail 2.25
11 Tooth & Nail 2.25
12 Tooth & Nail, Demon 2.25
13 'Good Times, Bad Times' 2.25
14 Mouse Alone 2.25
15 Champion ID revealed 2.25
16 Jerry Critically Ill 2.25
17 Kunoichi vs. Tooth 2.25
18 Search for Organ Donor 2.25
Graphic Novel 9.95

CAT CLAW
Eternity 1990
1 O:Cat Claw 2.75
1a 2nd printing 2.50
2 thru 9 . . . . @2.50

CATFIGHT
Lightning Comics
1 V:Prince Nightmare 4.00
1a Gold Edition 6.00
Spec.#1 Dream Warrior, V:The
  Slasher 2.75
Spec.#1 Dream intoAction,A:Creed 3.00
Spec.#1a signed and numbered . . 8.00
Spec.#1b nude cover edition 8.00
Spec.#1 Escape From Limbo 2.75
Spec.#1a variant cover (1996) . . . 2.75
Spec.#1b platinum cover 5.95
Spec.#1c nude cover 8.00
Spec.#1d variant nude cover 8.00
Spec.#1 Sweet Revenge (1997) . . 2.95
Spec.#1a variant cover 2.95
Spec.#1b nude cover 8.00
Spec.#1c nude variant cover 8.00

CAT-MAN RETRO COMIC
AC Comics
0 by Bill Black & Mark Heike . . . 5.95
1 thru 3 . . . . @5.95
Ashcan #1 I:Catman & Kitten . . . 5.95

CAVEWOMAN
Bacement/Caliber 1994–95
1 . . . . 70.00
1 by Budd Root 2nd printing 4.00
1 3rd printing, new cover 3.00
2 . . . . 40.00
2a 2nd printing 3.00
2 3rd printing, new cover 3.00
3 . . . . 35.00
4 . . . . 35.00
5 Cavewoman vs. Klyde, Round
  Two 25.00
6 . . . . 25.00

CAVEWOMAN: RAIN
Caliber 1996
1 by Budd Root 7.00
1a 2nd printing 3.00
2 . . . . 5.00
2a 2nd printing 3.00
3 . . . . 4.00
3a 2nd edition, new cover 3.00
4 . . . . 4.00
4a 2nd edition, new cover 3.00
5 . . . . 3.50
5 2nd edition, new cover 3.00
6 thru 8 . . . . @3.00

CAVEWOMAN: MISSING LINK
Basement Comics 1997
1 (of 4) 2.95
2 thru 4 . . . . @2.95

CECIL KUNKLE
Darkline Comics 1987
1 . . . . 1.50

CELESTIAL MECHANICS
Innovation
1 thru 3 . . . . @2.25

CEMENT SHOOZ
Horse Feathers 1991
1 with color pin-up 2.50

CENOTAPH: CYBER GODDESS
Northstar
1 I:Cenotaph 3.95

CEREBUS
Aardvark–Vanaheim
0 . . . . 3.00
0a Gold Ed. 10.00
1 B:DS(s&a),I:Cerebus 300.00
1a Counterfeit 50.00
2 DS,V:Succubus 100.00
3 DS,I:Red Sophia 100.00
4 DS,I:Elrod 70.00
5 DS,A:The Pigs 60.00
6 DS,I:Jaka 60.00
7 DS,R:Elrod 50.00
8 DS,A:Conniptins 35.00
9 DS,I&V:K'cor 35.00
10 DS,R:Red Sophia 35.00
11 DS,I:The Cockroach 35.00
12 DS,R:Elrod 35.00
13 DS,I:Necross 30.00
14 DS,V:Shadow Crawler 30.00
15 DS,V: Shadow Crawler 30.00
16 DS, at the Masque 25.00
17 DS,"Champion" 25.00
18 DS,Fluroc 25.00
19 DS,I:Perce & Greet-a 25.00
20 DS,Mind Game 25.00
21 DS,A:CaptCockroach,rare . . . 50.00
22 DS,D:Elrod 20.00
23 DS,DuFort's school 10.00
24 DS,IR:Prof.Clarmont 10.00
25 DS,A:Woman-thing 10.00
26 DS,High Society 10.00
27 DS,Kidnapping of an Avrdvark 10.00
28 DS,Mind Game!! 10.00
29 DS,Reprocussions 10.00
30 DS,Debts 8.00
31 DS,Chasing Cootie 8.00
32 DS 8.00
33 DS,DS,Friction 5.00
34 DS,Three Days Before 5.00
35 thru 50 DS . . . . @5.00
51 DS,(scarce) 17.00
52 DS 5.00
53 DS,C:Wolveroach 7.00
54 DS,I:Wolveroach 9.00
55 DS,A:Wolveroach 8.00
56 DS,A:Wolveroach 8.00
57 DS 5.00
58 DS 5.00
59 DS,Memories Pt.V 5.00
60 DS,more vignettes 5.00
61 DS,A:Flaming Carrot 6.00
62 DS,A:Flaming Carrot 6.00
63 DS,Mind Game VI 5.00
64 DS,Never Pray for Change . . . 5.00
65 DS,Papal Speech 5.00
66 DS,Thrill of Agony 5.00
67 thru 70 DS . . . . @5.00
71 thru 74 DS . . . . @4.00
75 DS,Terrible Analogies 4.00
76 DS,D:Weisshaupt 4.00
77 DS,Surreal daydream 4.00
78 DS,Surreal daydream 4.00
79 DS,Spinning Straw 4.00
80 DS,V:Stone Tarim 4.00
81 DS,A:Sacred Wars Roach . . . 4.00
82 DS,A:Tarim 3.50
83 DS,A:Michele 3.50
84 DS,Weisshaupt's Letter 3.50
85 DS,A:Mick Jagger 3.50

86 DS,A:Mick Jagger 3.50
87 DS,Tower Climb 3.50
88 DS,D:Stone Tarim 3.50
89 DS,A:Cute Elf 3.50
90 DS,Anti-Apartheid(c) 3.50
91 DS 3.50
92 DS,A:Bill & Seth 3.50
93 DS,Astoria in Prison 3.50
94 DS,Rape of Astoria 3.50
95 DS,Sophia-Astoria Dream 3.50
96 DS,Astoria in Prison 3.50
97 DS,Escape Planned 3.50
98 DS,Astoria's Trial 3.50
99 DS,Sorcery in Court 3.50
100 DS,A:Cirin 3.50
101 DS,The Gold Sphere 3.00
102 DS,The Final Ascension 3.00
103 DS,On the Tower 3.00
104 DS,A:Flaming Carrot 3.00
105 DS,V:Fred & Ethel 3.00
106 DS,D:Fred & Ethel 3.00
107 DS,Judge on the Moon 3.00
108 DS,All History 3.00
109 DS,O:Universe 3.00
110 DS,More Universe 3.00
111 DS,Cerebus' Fate 3.00
112 DS,Memories 3.00
113 DS,Memories 3.00
114 DS,I:Rick nash 3.00
115 DS,I:Pud Withers 3.00
116 DS,Rick Meets Cerebus 3.00
117 DS,Young Jaka Injured 3.00
118 DS,Cerebus Apologizes 3.00
119 DS,Jaka Opens Door 3.00
120 DS,I:Oscar 3.00
121 DS,Women Explained 3.00
122 DS,lest History 3.00
123 DS,Each One's Dream 3.00
124 DS 3.00
125 DS,C:Lord Julius 3.00
126 DS,R:Old Vet'ran 2.50
127 DS,Jaka Dances 2.50
128 DS,L:Cerebus as Fred 2.50
129 DS,Jaka's Story 2.50
130 DS,D:Pud Withers 2.50
131 DS,Jaka Imprisoned 4.00
132 DS,A:Nurse 4.00
133 DS,I:Mrs. Thatcher 4.00
134 DS,Dancing Debate 4.00
135 DS,Jaka Signs 4.00
136 DS,L:Rick 4.00
137 DS,Like-a-Looks 4.00
138 DS,Maids'Gossip 4.00
139 A:Misogynist-roach 4.00
140 I:Old Oscar 4.00
141 A:Cerebus 4.00
142 C:Mick Jagger 4.00
143 DS,Oscars Forboding 4.00
144 DS,I:Doris 4.00
145 thru 146 DS . . . . @4.00
147 Neil Gaiman, DS 11.00
148 thru 150 DS 3.00
151 DS,B:Mothers & Daughters,
    Book 1: Flight pt.1 . . . . 4.00
151a 2nd printing 2.50
152 DS,Flight pt.2 . . . . 4.00
152a 2nd printing 2.50
153 DS,Flight pt.3 . . . . 4.00
153a 2nd printing 2.50
154 DS,Flight pt.4 . . . . 4.00
155 DS,Flight pt.5 . . . . 4.00
156 DS,Flight pt.6 . . . . 3.00
157 DS,Flight pt.7 . . . . 3.00
158 DS,Flight pt.8 . . . . 3.00
159 DS,Flight pt.9 . . . . 3.00

Cerebus #47 © Aardvark-Vanaheim

160 DS,Flight pt.10 . . . . 3.00
161 DS,Flight pt.11, Bone story . 11.00
162 DS,E:M&D,Bk.1:Flight pt.12 . 3.00
163 DS,B:Mothers & Daughters
    Book 2: Women pt.1 . . . . 2.75
164 DS,Women pt.2,inc. Tour
    Momentos 2.50
165 thru 174 Women pt.3–12 . @2.50
175 DS,B:Mothers & Daughters,
    Book 3: Reads pt.1 . . . . 2.50
175 thru 186 Reads pt.1–12 . . @2.50
187 DS,B:Mothers & Daughters,
    Book 4:Minds pt.1 . . . . 2.50
188 thru 199 Minds pt.5–13 . . @2.25
200 . . . . 2.50
201 thru 219 Guys pt.1 to pt.19 @2.25
220 thru 231 Rick's Story, pt.1 to
    pt.12 . . . . @2.25
232 pt. 1 (of 34) 2.25
233 . . . . 2.25
Spec.#1 Cerebus Companion . . 3.95
TPBs
Vol.1 Cerebus, rep.#1–#25 . . . . 25.00
Vol.2 High Society, rep.#26–#50 25.00
Vol.3 Church & State I,
    rep.#52–#85 . . . . 30.00
Vol.4 Church & State II,
    rep.#86–#111 . . . . 30.00
Vol.5 Jaka'sStory,rep.#114–#136 25.00
Vol.6 Melmoth, rep.#139–#150 . 17.00
Vol.7, Flight, rep.#151–#162 . . . 17.00
Vol.8 Women, rep.#163–#174 . . 17.00
Vol.9 Reads, rep.#175–#186 . . . 17.00
Vol.9 Reads, 2nd printing 15.00
Vol.9 Reads, signed & numb. . . 28.00
Vol.10 Minds, rep.#187–#199 . . 16.00
Vol.11 Guys rep.#201–#219 . . . 30.00
Vol.11, 2nd printing 20.00

CEREBUS
CHURCH & STATE
Aardvark–Vanaheim
1 DS rep #51 . . . . 2.25
2 thru 30 DS rep #52-#80 . . . @2.00

CEREBUS HIGH SOCIETY
Aardvark–Vanaheim
1 thru 14 DS (biweekly) . . . . . @1.70
15 thru 24 DS rep. . . . . @2.00
25 DS rep. #50, final 2.00

CEREBUSJAM
Aardvark–Vanaheim
1 MA,BHa,TA,WE,A:Spirit 15.00

CEREBUS REPRINTS
Aardvark–Vanaheim
1A thru 28A DS rep . . . . @1.25
See also: Church & State
See also: Swords of Cerebus

CHAINSAW VIGILANTE
New England Press
1 Tick Spinoff 3.25

CHAMPION, THE
Special Studio 1991
1 . . . . 2.50

CHAMPION OF KITARA:
DUM DUM & DRAGONS
MU Press
1 Dragons Secret 2.95
2 Dragons Secret 2.95
3 Dragons Secret 2.95

CHARLIE CHAN
Eternity
1 thru 4 . . . . @1.95
5 and 6 . . . . @2.25

CHASER PLATOON
Aircel 1990–91
1 Interstellar War 2.25
2 Ambush 2.25
3 New Weapon 2.25
4 Saringer Battle Robot 2.25
5 Behind Enemy Lines 2.25
6 Operation Youthtest 2.25

CHESTY SANCHEZ
Antarctic Press 1995
1 & 2 . . . . @2.95

CHINA & JAZZ
CODE NAME
DOUBLE IMPACT
High Impact Oct. 1996
1 . . . . 3.00
1a nude cover 9.95
2 . . . . 2.95
2a nude RCI(c) cover 9.95

CHINA & JAZZ:
TRIGGER HAPPY
ABC Comics 1998
1 (of 4) by Clayton Henry 3.00
1a Jazz Bikini cover 3.95
1b China Bikini cover 3.95
1c gold variant cover 5.95
2 . . . . 3.00
2a Playtoy edition 5.95
2b Mercenary edition 5.95
2c Gold edition 5.95

CHIRALITY
CPM Manga Comics 1997
6 by Satoshi Urushihara, SS(c) . . 2.95
7 final battle for Shiori's life 2.95
8 . . . . 2.95
9 Adam transformed into duplicate
 Carol 2.95
10 . . . . 2.95
11 . . . . 2.95
12 V:Adam 2.95
13 toward Alaska 2.95
14 reach Gaia 2.95
15 Carol and Shiori 2.95
16 . . . . 2.95
17 descend into Gaia 2.95
18 final issue 2.95
Spec. Gallery, pin-up book 3.95
GN Book One rep. #1–#4 . . . . . 9.95
GN Book Two rep. #4–#8 . . . . . 9.95

CHIRALITY:
TO THE PROMISED LAND
CPM Comics 1997
1 by Satoshi Urushihara 2.95
2 thru 4 . . . . @2.95

CHIRON
Annurel Studio Graphics
1 . . . . 2.50
1a 2nd printing 2.50
2 Transported to Doran 2.50
3 Transported to Doran 2.50
3a Gold Edition 4.00

CHRONOS CARNIVAL
Fleetway
1 reps. 200 AD stories 7.95

CHUCK CHICKEN
AND BRUIN BEAR
Jabberwocky
1 . . . . 3.00

CIRCLE WEAVE, THE
Indigo Bean Productions 1995
1 Apprentice to a God 2.00
2 Apprentice to a God,pt.2 . . . . . 2.00
3 Apprentice to a God,pt.3 . . . . . 2.00
4 Apprentice to a God,pt.4 . . . . . 2.00
5 Apprentice to a God,pt.5 . . . . . 2.50

CLANDE, INC.
Domain Publishing
1 I:Sam Davidson, Jeremy Clande 2.95
2 V:Dias 2.95

CLERKS:
THE COMIC BOOK
Oni Press 1998
1 by Kevin Smith & Jim Mahfood 2.95

CLIFFHANGER COMICS
AC Comics
1 rep. 2.50
2 rep. 2.50

CLINT THE HAMSTER
Eclipse
1 . . . . 2.50
2 . . . . 1.50

COBRA
Viz 1990–91
1 thru 6 . . . . @2.95
7 . . . . 3.25
8 V:SnowHawks 3.25
9 Zados 3.25
10 thru 12 . . . . @3.25

COLD BLOODED
CHAMELEON
COMMANDOS
Blackthorne 1986
1 . . . . 2.00
2 . . . . 1.50
3 . . . . 1.50
4 . . . . 1.75
5 . . . . 1.75
6 . . . . 2.00
7 . . . . 2.00

COLD EDEN
Legacy 1995
1 Last City on Earth 2.35
2 V:Mutant Hunting Pack 2.35
3 D6 Tower 2.35

COLE BLACK
1 Vol.I 15.00
2 Vol.I 10.00
3 Vol.I 10.00
4 Vol.I 10.00
5 Vol.I 12.00
1 Vol.II 3.50
2 Vol.II 2.00
3 Vol.II 1.50

COLONEL KILGORE
Special Studios
1 WWII stories 2.50
2 Command Performance 2.50

COLT
K-Z Comics
1 . . . . 4.00
2 pin-up by Laird 6.00
2 pin-up by Henbeck 2.00
3 thru 5 . . . . @1.00

COMICS EXPRESS
1 thru 4 . . . . @2.95
5 thru 11 . . . . @3.95

COMING OF APHRODITE
Hero Graphics
1 Aphrodite/modern day 3.95

COMMAND REVIEW
Thoughts & Images
1 rep. Albedo #1-4 . . . . 6.00
2 rep. Albedo #5-8 . . . . 4.00
3 rep. Albedo #9-13 . . . . 4.00

CONDOM-MAN
Aaaahh!! Comics
1 I:Condom Man 3.50
2 F:Condom Man 3.50
3 V:Alien Army 3.50
4 Brother bought back to life 3.50
5 O:Condom-Man (Chris Swafford) 3.50

Conqueror #6 © Harrier

CONQUEROR
Harrier 1984–86
1 . . . . 3.50
2 thru 4 . . . . @2.00
5 thru 9 . . . . @1.75

CONQUEROR UNIVERSE
Harrier
1 . . . . 2.75

CONSPIRACY COMICS
Revolutionary
1 Marilyn Monroe 2.50
2 Who Killed JFK 2.50
3 Who Killed RFK 2.50

CONSTELLATION
GRAPHICS
STG
1 thru 4 . . . . @1.50

CONSTRUCT
Caliber "New Worlds"
1 (of 6) PJe,LDu, sci-fi,48pg . . . 3.95
2 PJe,LDu 2.95
3 PJe,LDu 2.95
4 PJe,LDu 2.95
5 PJe,LDu 2.95
6 PJe,LDu, conclusion 2.95

CONTRACTORS
Eclipse
1 . . . . 2.25

CORMAC MAC ART
1 thru 4 R.E.Howard adapt. . . @1.95

CORTO MALTESE:
BALLAD OF
THE SALT SEA
NBM 1997
1 by Hugo Pratt 2.95
1 a 2nd printing 2.95
2 by Hugo Pratt 2.95
3 Escondida 2.95

B & W PUB.

4	2.95
5	2.95
6	2.95
7 final issue	2.95
TPB by Hugo Pratt, "In Siberia"	10.95
TPB "Fable of Venice"	10.95
TPB "Banana Conga"	8.95
TPB "Voodoo for the President"	8.95
TPB "Midwinter's Morning"	8.95
TPB "In Africa"	8.95

COSMIC HEROES
Eternity
1 Buck Rogers rep.	1.95
2 thru 6 Buck Rogers rep.	@1.95
7 thru 9 Buck Rogers rep.	@2.25
10	3.50
11	3.95

COUNTER PARTS
Tundra
1 thru 3	@2.95

COVENTRY
Fantagraphics Oct. 1996
1 BWg, "The Frogs of God"	3.95
2 BWg, "Thirteen Dead Guys Named Bob"	3.95
3 BWg	3.95
4	3.95

Cray Baby Adventures #4 © TV Comics

CRAY BABY ADVENTURES, THE
Electric Milk 1997
1 by Art Baltazar	2.95

TV Comics 1997
1 2nd printing	2.95
2	2.95
4 Captain Camel	2.95
5	2.95
Adventure Spec. San Diego Con lim. ed.	4.95
TPB Vol. 1 rep. #1–#5	14.95

CRAY BABY ADVENTURES: WRATH OF THE PEDDIDLERS
TV Comics 1998
1 (of 3) by Art Baltazar	2.95
2	2.95
3 concl.	2.95

CREED
Hall of Heroes 1994
1 TKn,I:Mark Farley	30.00
1A Wizard Ace edition rep.	20.00
2 TKn,Camping	35.00

CREED
Lightning Comics 1995
1-shot TKn retelling of #1&#2	2.75

See also: *Color*

CREED THE VOID
TPB Collected edition	5.95
TPB Deluxe	9.95

CREED/TEENAGE MUTANT NINJA TURTLES
Lightning Comics 1996
1 TKn(c)	3.00
2 TKn(c)	3.00
1 Gold Collector's Edition	5.95
1 Platinum Edition	9.95

CREED: CRANIAL DISORDER
Lightning Comics
1	3.00
1A Previews variant cover	3.00
1B Platinum Edition	6.00
1C signed platinum edition	8.00
2	3.00
2b variant cover	2.95
3	2.95
3b variant cover	2.95
3c limited edition	9.95

CREED: THE GOOD SHIP & THE NEW JOURNEY HOME
Lightning Comics
1	2.95
1a variant cover	2.95
1b limited edition	9.95

CREED: USE YOUR DELUSION
Avatar Press 1998
1 (of 2) by Trent Kaniuga	3.00
1 white leather	30.00
2	3.00
2 deluxe	4.95

CRIME BUSTER
AC Comics
0 from FemForce	2.95
1 Rep. From Boys Illustrated	3.95

CRIME CLASSICS
Eternity
1 thru 11 rep Shadow comicstrip	@1.95
12	2.25

CRIME SMASHERS
Special Edition
1	1.80

CRIMSON DREAMS
Crimson
1 thru 11	@2.00

CRIMSON NUN
Antarctic Press 1997
1 (of 4)	2.95

CRITTERS
Fantagraphics Books 1986–90
1 SS,Usagi Yojimbo,Cutey	5.00
2 Captain Jack,Birthright	4.00
3 SS,Usagi Yojimbo,Gnuff	4.00
4 Gnuff,Birthright	3.00
5 Birthright	3.00
6 SS,Usagi Yojimbo,Birthright	3.00
7 SS,Usagi Yojimbo,Jack Bunny	3.00
8 SK,Animal Graffiti,Lizards	2.50
9 Animal Graffiti	2.50
10 SS,Usagi Yojimbo	3.00
11 SS,Usagi Yojimbo,	3.00
12 Birthright II	2.00
13 Birthright II,Gnuff	2.00
14 SS,Usagi Yojimbo,BirthrightII	2.50
15 Birthright II,CareBears	2.00
16 SS,Groundthumper,Gnuff	2.00
17 Birthright II,Lionheart	2.00
18 Dragon's	2.00
19 Gnuff,Dragon's	2.00
20 Gnuff	2.00
21 Gnuff	2.00
22 Watchdogs,Gnuff	2.00
23 Flexi-Disc,X-Mas Issue	4.00
24 Angst,Lizards,Gnuff	2.00
25 Lionheart,SBi,Gnuff	2.00
26 Angst,Gnuff	2.00
27 SS,Ground Thumper	2.00
28 Blue Beagle,Lionheart	2.00
29 Lionheart,Gnuff	2.00
30 Radical Dog,Gnuff	2.00
31 SBi,Gnuffs,Lizards	2.00
32 Lizards,Big Sneeze	2.00
33 Gnuff,Angst,Big Sneeze	2.00
34 Blue Beagle vs. Robohop	2.00
35 Lionheart,Fission Chicken	2.00
36 Blue Beagle,Fission Chicken	2.00
37 Fission Chicken	2.00
38 SS,double size,Usagi Yojimbo	2.75
39 Fission Chicken	2.00
40 Gnuff	2.00
41 Duck'Bill Platypus	2.00
42 Glass Onion	2.00
43 Lionheart	2.00
44 Watchdogs	2.00
45 Ambrose the Frog	2.00
46 Lionheart	2.00
47 Birthright	2.00
48 Birthright	2.00
49 Birthright	2.00
50 SS,Neil the Horse, UsagiYojimbo	5.00
Spec.1 Albedo,rep+new 10pgStory	2.00

CROSSFIRE
Eclipse
18 thru 26 DSp	@2.00

CROW, THE
Caliber
1	30.00
1a 2nd Printing	4.00
1b 3rd Printing	3.00
2	25.00
2a 2nd Printing	4.00
2b 3rd Printing	3.00
3	20.00
3a 2nd Printing	3.00
4	20.00

Tundra
1 reps. Crow #1, #2	20.00
2	8.00
3	10.00
TPB	20.00

CROW, THE
Kitchen Sink
TPB Flesh & Blood Collection	10.95
TPB The Crow Collection, 7th printing 224pg	15.95

CROW, THE: DEAD TIME
Kitchen Sink
1	5.00
2	4.00
3	3.00
TPB Collection rep.	10.95

CROW, THE: DEMON IN DISGUISE
Kitchen Sink 1997
1 (of 4) by John J. Miller & Dean Ormston	2.95
2	2.95
3	2.95

CROW, THE: FLESH AND BLOOD
Kitchen Sink 1996
1 thru 3	@2.95
TPB rep.	10.95

CROW, THE: WAKING NIGHTMARES
Kitchen Sink Jan. 1997
1 PhH	2.95
2 thru 4 PhH	@2.95

CROW, THE: WILD JUSTICE
Kitchen Sink
1 thru 3	@2.95

CROW/RAZOR: KILL THE PAIN
London Night 1998
1 (of 3) JOb,EHr	3.00
1b EHr & Jerry Beck, Director's Cut, 40pg	5.00
1c black leather, signed & numbered	29.95
1d Ministry of Night (c)	5.00
2	3.00
2a Ministry of Night (c)	5.00
3	3.00
3a Ministry of Night (c)	5.00
1-shotA Tour Book, cover A	5.00
1-shotB Tour Book, cover B	5.00

1-shotC Tour Book, cover C	5.00
1-shot Tour Book, ministry edition	5.00
1-shot Tour Book, limited black leather	15.00

CROW OF THE BEAR CLAN
Blackthorne
1	2.25
2 thru 6	@1.75

CRUSADERS
Guild
1 Southern Knights	10.00

CRY FOR DAWN
Cry For Dawn 1989–90
1	140.00
1a 2nd Printing	65.00
1b 3rd Printing	50.00
2	80.00
2a 2nd Printing	25.00
3	60.00
4	35.00
5	30.00
6	30.00
7 Corporate Ladder,Rock A Bye Baby	25.00
8 Decay,This is the Enemy	25.00
9	25.00
1-shot Subtle Violents,F:Ryder	3.00

CRYING FREEMAN
Viz 1989
1	4.00
2	3.50
3 thru 5	@3.50
6 thru 8	@3.00

CRYING FREEMAN II
Viz 1990–91
1	4.00
2	3.00
3	3.00
4 thru 6	@3.00
7 V:Bugnug	3.00
8 Emu & The Samurai Sword	3.00
9 Final Issue	3.00

CRYING FREEMAN III
Viz 1991
1 thru 10	@3.00

CRYING FREEMAN IV
Viz 1992
1 thru 3	@3.00
4 thru 8	@2.75

CRY FREEMAN V
Viz 1993
1 Return to Japan	4.00
2 A:Tateoka-assassin	4.00
3	4.00
4 A:Bagwana	4.00
5 V:Tsunaike	4.00
6 V:Aido Family	4.00
7 V:Tsunaike	4.00
GN:Taste of Revenge	14.95

CRYPT OF DAWN
Sirius 1996
1 JLi(c)	6.00
1 variant cover	15.00
2 JLi(c)	3.50
3	3.00
4 JLi(c)	3.00

CRYSTAL BREEZE
High Impact 1996
1 thru 3	@2.95
1 thru 3a nude covers	@10.00
Spec.#1 Crystal Breeze Unleashed	3.00
Spec.#1a nude cover	14.95
Spec.#1 Crystal Breeze Revenge	2.95
Spec.#1a adult photo cover	10.00
Spec.#1b gold edition cover	10.00

CUDA
Rebel Studios
1 I:Cuda,Zora,V:Shanga Bai	2.00

CULTURAL JET LAG
Fantagraphics
1	2.50

CUTEY BUNNY
1	8.00
2 thru 4	@4.00
Eclipse
5	3.00

CUTIE HONEY
Ironcat 1997
1 crime fighting android	2.95
2	2.95
3 Wonderful Mask	2.95
4 thru 6	@2.95
VOL 2 CUTIE HONEY '90 1998
1 Sorayama cover	2.95
2 thru 6	@2.95

CYBER 7
Eclipse
1	2.50
2 thru 5	@2.00

Cyber 7 #6 © Rockland

     All comics prices listed are for *Near Mint* condition.

Book 2   Rockland 1990
1 thru 7 . . . . @2.00
8 thru 10 . . . . @2.50

CYBERFROG
Hall of Heroes
1 I:Cyberfrog 5.00
1a 2nd printing 2.50
2 V:Ben Riley 4.00
2a 2nd printing 2.50

CYBERFROG
Harris Jan. 1997
1 3rd Anniv. Special 3.00
1a Walt Simonson(c) 6.00
1b signed & numbered 10.00
2 . . . . 3.50
2a variant cover 4.00
3 . . . . 3.50
4 . . . . 3.50
4a signed 10.00

CYBERFROG VS CREED
Harris 1997
1 . . . . 3.50
1 Creed vs. Cyberfrog, alternate
   edition 9.95

CYBERZONE
Jet Black Graphics
1 thru 5 Never-never Land 2.50

CYCLOPS
Blackthorne
1 Mini-series 1.95
2 . . . . 1.95
3 . . . . 1.95

CYGNUS X-1
Twisted Pearl Press
1 V:Yag'Nost 2.50
2 F:Rex and Bounty Hunters . . . 2.50

CYNDER
Immortelle Studios
1 I:Cynder 5.00
2 . . . . 3.00
3 conclusion 2.50
Second Series
1 thru 3 . . . . 3.00

CYNDER/HELLINA
Immortelle Studios
Spec. 1 x-over 3.00

DAFFY QADDAFI
Comics Unlimited Ltd.
1 . . . . 2.00

DAIKAZU
1 . . . . 5.00
1a 2nd Printing 1.50
2 . . . . 3.00
2a 2nd Printing 1.50
3 . . . . 3.00
3a 2nd Printing 1.50
4 thru 7 . . . . @1.50
8 . . . . 1.75

DA'KOTA
Millennium Jan. 1997
1 by Pavlet & Petersen 2.95
1 signed 4.95
1 foil edition 9.95
2 . . . . 2.95
2 foil edition 4.95
3 foil deluxe edition 6.95
3 . . . . 2.95
3a variant cover 2.95
Spec.#1 Orig.Art Edition 9.95

DAMONSTREIK
Imperial Comics
1 I:Damonstreik 1.95
2 V:Sonix 1.95
3 V:Sonix 1.95
4 J:Ohm 1.95
5 V:Drakkus 1.95

DANGEROUS TIMES
1 MK 2.50
2 MA(c) 2.00
2a 2nd printing 1.75
3 MR(c) 1.95
3a 2nd printing 1.95
4 GP(c) 1.95

DAN TURNER
HOLLYWOOD DETECTIVE
Eternity 1991
1 'Darkstar of Death' 2.50
Spec.#1 Dan Turner, Homicide
   Hunch, Dan Turner Framed . . 2.50
Spec.#1 Dan Turner, The Star
   Chamber, Death of Folly
   Hempstead 2.50

DARK ANGEL
Boneyard 1997
1 by Hart Fisher & James
   Helkowski 1.95
2 . . . . 1.95
3 by Hart Fisher & John Cassaday 1.95
4 The Quiet Demon 1.95
Spec.#1 Dark Angel/Bill the Bull, 48
   pg. (1998) 4.95

DARK ASSASSIN
1 thru 3 . . . . @1.50
Vol. 2
1 thru 5 . . . . @2.00

DARK CITY ANGEL
Freak Pit Productions
1 I:Lt.Michelle Constello 3.50
2 . . . . 3.50
3 Sex Doll is Prime Suspect . . . 3.50

DARK FANTASIES
Dark Fantasy 1994–97
0 Donna Mia foil (c) 8.00
0 Destiny Angel foil (c) 7.50
0 photo or nude (c)s . . . . @6.00
1 Jli (c) 9.00
1a test print Jli (c) 12.00
1 2nd printing 3.95
1 signed & numbered 7.95
2 Kevin J. Taylor Girl (c) 3.50
2a foil stamped 3.50
3 JOb Crow (c) 4.00
3a foil stamped 3.50

4 . . . . 2.95
4a foil stamped 3.50
5 . . . . 2.95
5a foil stamped 3.50
6 Angel Destiny 2.95
6a foil stamped 3.50
7 . . . . 2.95
7a foil stamped 3.50
8 . . . . 2.95
8 Blue cover 3.50
8 Red cover 3.50
8 deluxe foil-enhanced 3.95
9 Destiny Angel (c) 3.50
9a Destiny Angel, red foil (c) . . . 3.95
9b Horror (c) 3.50
9c Horror, red foil (c) 3.95
10 . . . . 3.50
10a red foil (c) 3.95
Spec.#1 Summers Eve Pin-up . . . 2.95
Spec.#1 foil-stamped 3.50

DARK FORCE
Omega 7
1 A:Dark Force 2.00

DARK FRINGE
Brainstorm 1996
1 . . . . 2.95

DARK FRINGE:
SPIRITS OF THE DEAD
Brainstorm 1997
1 by Eman Torre & John Kisse . . 2.95
2 concl. 2.95

DARK ISLAND
Davdez Arts 1998
1 by Barry Blair & Colin Chan . . . 2.50
2 thru 4 . . . . @2.50

DARK JUSTICE
IMP Press
1 I:Dark Justice 2.50

DARK LORD
RAK
1 thru 3 . . . . @1.75

DARK MANGA
London Night
1 Featuring Demonique 4.95
1 nude cover 6.00

DARK MUSE
Dark Muse Productions
1 with mini-comic 3.50
1a with mini-comic 5.00
2 . . . . 3.95
3 F:Coffin Joe 3.95

DARK REGIONS
1 . . . . 2.50
2 . . . . 2.50
3 Scarce 3.00
4 and 5 . . . . @1.50

DARK STAR
1 I:Ran 2.25
2 thru 3 . . . . @2.25

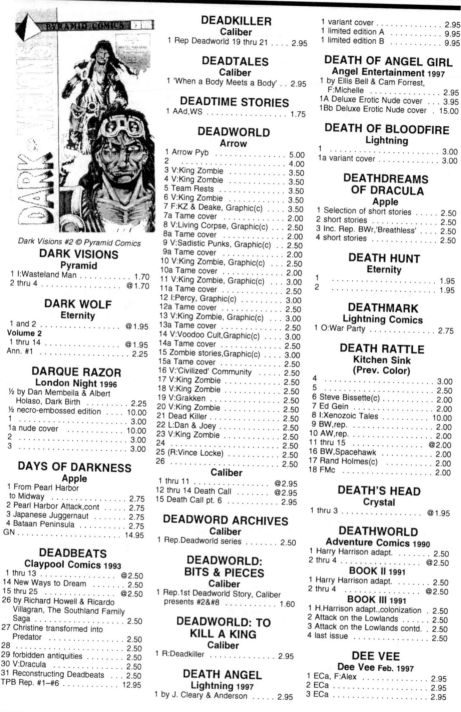

Dark Visions #2 © Pyramid Comics

DARK VISIONS
Pyramid
1 I:Wasteland Man 1.70
2 thru 4 . . . . @1.70

DARK WOLF
Eternity
1 and 2 . . . . @1.95
Volume 2
1 thru 14 . . . . @1.95
Ann. #1 . . . . 2.25

DARQUE RAZOR
London Night 1996
½ by Dan Membeila & Albert
  Holaso, Dark Birth 2.25
½ necro-embossed edition 10.00
1 . . . . 3.00
1a nude cover 10.00
2 . . . . 3.00
3 . . . . 3.00

DAYS OF DARKNESS
Apple
1 From Pearl Harbor
  to Midway 2.75
2 Pearl Harbor Attack,cont 2.75
3 Japanese Juggernaut 2.75
4 Bataan Peninsula 2.75
GN 14.95

DEADBEATS
Claypool Comics 1993
1 thru 13 . . . . @2.50
14 New Ways to Dream 2.50
15 thru 25 . . . . @2.50
26 by Richard Howell & Ricardo
  Villagran, The Southland Family
  Saga 2.50
27 Christine transformed into
  Predator 2.50
28 . . . . 2.50
29 forbidden antiquities 2.50
30 V:Dracula 2.50
31 Reconstructing Deadbeats . . 2.50
TPB Rep. #1–#6 . . . . 12.95

DEADKILLER
Caliber
1 Rep Deadworld 19 thru 21 . . . . 2.95

DEADTALES
Caliber
1 'When a Body Meets a Body' . . 2.95

DEADTIME STORIES
1 AAd,WS 1.75

DEADWORLD
Arrow
1 Arrow Pyb 5.00
2 . . . . 4.00
3 V:King Zombie 3.50
4 V:King Zombie 3.50
5 Team Rests 3.50
6 V:King Zombie 3.50
7 F:KZ & Deake, Graphic(c) 3.50
7a Tame cover 2.00
8 V:Living Corpse, Graphic(c) . . 2.50
8a Tame cover 2.00
9 V:Sadistic Punks, Graphic(c) . . 2.50
9a Tame cover 2.00
10 V:King Zombie, Graphic(c) . . . 2.50
10a Tame cover 2.00
11 V:King Zombie, Graphic(c) . . . 3.00
11a Tame cover 2.50
12 I:Percy, Graphic(c) 3.00
12a Tame cover 2.50
13 V:King Zombie, Graphic(c) . . . 3.00
13a Tame cover 2.50
14 V:Voodoo Cult,Graphic(c) . . . 3.00
14a Tame cover 2.50
15 Zombie stories,Graphic(c) . . . 3.00
15a Tame cover 2.50
16 V:'Civilized' Community 2.50
17 V:King Zombie 2.50
18 V:King Zombie 2.50
19 V:Grakken 2.50
20 V:King Zombie 2.50
21 Dead Killer 2.50
22 L:Dan & Joey 2.50
23 V:King Zombie 2.50
24 . . . . 2.50
25 (R:Vince Locke) 2.50
26 . . . . 2.50
Caliber
1 thru 11 . . . . @2.95
12 thru 14 Death Call . . . . . . @2.95
15 Death Call pt. 6 . . . . 2.95

DEADWORD ARCHIVES
Caliber
1 Rep.Deadworld series 2.50

DEADWORLD:
BITS & PIECES
Caliber
1 Rep.1st Deadworld Story, Caliber
  presents #2&#8 . . . . 1.60

DEADWORLD: TO
KILL A KING
Caliber
1 R:Deadkiller 2.95

DEATH ANGEL
Lightning 1997
1 by J. Cleary & Anderson 2.95

1 variant cover 2.95
1 limited edition A 9.95
1 limited edition B 9.95

DEATH OF ANGEL GIRL
Angel Entertainment 1997
1 by Ellis Bell & Cam Forrest,
  F:Michelle 2.95
1A Deluxe Erotic Nude cover . . . 3.95
1Bb Deluxe Erotic Nude cover . 15.00

DEATH OF BLOODFIRE
Lightning
1 . . . . 3.00
1a variant cover 3.00

DEATHDREAMS
OF DRACULA
Apple
1 Selection of short stories 2.50
2 short stories 2.50
3 Inc. Rep. BWr,'Breathless' . . . 2.50
4 short stories 2.50

DEATH HUNT
Eternity
1 . . . . 1.95
2 . . . . 1.95

DEATHMARK
Lightning Comics
1 O:War Party 2.75

DEATH RATTLE
Kitchen Sink
(Prev. Color)
4 . . . . 3.00
5 . . . . 2.50
6 Steve Bissette(c) 2.00
7 Ed Gein 2.00
8 I:Xenozoic Tales 10.00
9 BW,rep. 2.00
10 AW,rep. 2.00
11 thru 15 . . . . @2.00
16 BW,Spacehawk 2.00
17 Rand Holmes(c) 2.00
18 FMc 2.00

DEATH'S HEAD
Crystal
1 thru 3 . . . . @1.95

DEATHWORLD
Adventure Comics 1990
1 Harry Harrison adapt. 2.50
2 thru 4 . . . . @2.50
BOOK II 1991
1 Harry Harrison adapt. 2.50
2 thru 4 . . . . @2.50
BOOK III 1991
1 H.Harrison adapt.,colonization . 2.50
2 Attack on the Lowlands 2.50
3 Attack on the Lowlands contd. . 2.50
4 last issue 2.50

DEE VEE
Dee Vee Feb. 1997
1 ECa, F:Alex 2.95
2 ECa 2.95
3 ECa 2.95

4 thru 8 . . . . @2.95
Spec. #1 Life is Cheap 2.95

Defenseless Dead #3
© *Adventure Comics*

DEFENSELESS DEAD
Adventure Comics 1991
1 Larry Niven adapt. A:Gil 2.50
2 A:Organlegger 2.50
3 A:Organlegger 2.50

DELTA TENN
1 thru 11 . . . . @1.50

DEMON BABY
SQP/666 Comics Jan. 1997
1 by Rich Larson, seq. to Hell on
Heels 2.95
1a deluxe 9.95
2 . . . . 2.95
2a deluxe 9.95
3 . . . . 2.95
3a deluxe 9.95

DEMON BITCH
Forbidden 1997–98
1-shot 2.95
Nude cover 2.95
Spec.#1 DemonBitch vs.AngelGirl 2.95
Nude cover 4.00
Spec.#1 Demon Bitch: Devilspawn,
by Angela Benoit & Nirut
Chaswan 3.00
Nude cover 3.00
Spec.#1 Demon Bitch: Hellslave,
Free on Earth cover 3.00
Nude Hellslave cover 3.00
Spec.#1 Demon Bitch: Tales of the
Damned 2.95
Nude cover 4.00

DEMONGATE
Sirius 1996–97
1 thru 12 by Bao Lin Hum & Colin
Chan . . . . @2.50

DEMON GUN
Crusade Entertainment
1 thru 3 GCh,KtH . . . . @2.95

DEMON HUNTER
Aircel
1 thru 4 . . . . @1.95

DEMONIQUE
London Night 1997
½ by SKy Owens, A:Anvil 3.00
½a nude cover 6.00
1 by Membeila & Owens 3.00
1a nude cover variant 8.00
2 F:Viper 3.00
3 Mayhem 3.00
4 Final issue 3.00

DEMONIQUE: ANGEL OF NIGHT
London Night 1997
1 (of 3) by Skylar Owens 3.00
1a nude cover variant 6.00
2 . . . . 3.00
2a nude cover variant 6.00
3 final issue 3.00
3a nude cover variant 6.00

DEMON'S TAILS
Adventure
1 . . . . 2.50
2 A:Champion 2.50
3 V:Champion 2.50
4 V:Champion 2.50

DEMON WARRIOR
1 thru 12 . . . . @1.50
13 and 14 . . . . @1.75

DENIZENS OF DEEP CITY
Jabberwocky
1 thru 8 . . . . @2.00

DEPRESSOR
Humanity
1 I:Depressor 2.50

DERRECK WAYNE'S STRAPPED
Gothic Images
1 Confrontation Factor 2.25
2 Confrontation Factor 2.25

DESCENDING ANGELS
Millenium 1995
1 I:3 Angels 2.00
2 F:Jim Johnson 2.95
3 F:Jim Johnson 2.95

DESERT PEACH
Thoughts & Images
1 thru 4 . . . . @2.00

DESTINY ANGEL
Dark Fantasy Productions 1996
1 (of 3) 3.95
1 2nd printing 3.95
1a deluxe 4.50

2 "Sunless Garden" 3.50
2a foil cover 3.95
2b photo cover 3.95

DESTROY
Eclipse
1 Large Size 4.95
2 Small Size,3-D 4.95

DEVIL JACK
Doom Theatre 1995
1 I:Devil Jack 2.95
1a Directors Cut 2.95
2 V:Belegosi 2.95
3 . . . . 3.00

DEVIL'S WORKSHOP
Blue Comet Press 1995
1 Iron Cupcakes 2.95

DIATOM
Photographics
1 Dan Duto Photographic 4.95

DICK TRACY MAGAZINE
1 V:Little Face Finnyo 3.95

DICK TRACY MONTHLY
Blackthorne
1 thru 25 . . . . @2.00

DICK TRACY: THE EARLY YEARS
5 and 6 . . . . @2.95
7 and 8 . . . . @3.50

DICK TRACY WEEKLY
26 thru 108 . . . . @2.00
Unprinted Stories #3 . . . . 2.95
1 3-D Special 3.00
Spec. #1 . . . . 2.95
Spec. #2 . . . . 2.95
Spec. #3 . . . . 2.95

DIGGERS, THE
C&T
3 . . . . 1.75

DILLINGER
Rip Off Press
1 Outlaw Dillinger 2.50

DINOSAURS
Caliber
1 History of Dinosaurs 3.00

DINOSAURS FOR HIRE
Eternity
1 . . . . 3.00
1a Rep. 1.95
2 thru 9 . . . . @1.95
Fall Classic #1 . . . . 2.25
Malibu
#1 3-D special 3.50

DIRECTORY TO A NON-EXISTENT UNIVERSE
Eclipse
1 . . . . 1.95

B & W PUB.

DIRTY PAIR
1	10.00
2	8.00
3	7.00
4 end mini-series	7.00

Eclipse
reprint 1-3	6.00
Vol 2 #1 thru 5	@6.00

DIRTY PAIR: PLAGUE OF ANGELS
Eclipse 1990
1 thru 5	@5.00

DIRTY PAIR: SIM EARTH
Eclipse
1 thru 4	3.50

A DISTANT SOIL
Warp Graphics
1 A:Panda Khan	17.00
2	9.00
3	8.00
4	6.00
5	6.00
6 thru 9	@6.00

Aria Press
1 F:Seasons of Spring	5.00
1a-2nd to 4th printing	2.50
2	3.50
3	3.00
4	3.00
5 thru 8	2.00
9 thru 11 Knights of the Angel	@2.50
12 thru 14	@3.00
GN Knights of the Angel, deluxe	15.95
GN Immigrant Song rep.#1–#3	6.95

DITKOS WORLD: STATIC
Renegade
1 thru 3 SD	@1.70

DR. GORPON
Eternity 1991
1 I:Dr.Gorpon,V:Demon	2.25
2 A:Doofus,V:ChocolateBunny	2.50
3 D:Dr.Gorpon	2.50

DR. RADIUM
Silverline
1	3.00
2	2.00
3 and 4	@1.50

DR. RADIUM: MAN OF SCIENCE
Slave Labor
1 And Baby makes 2, BU: Dr. Radiums' Grim Future	2.50

DOC WEIRD'S THRILL BOOK
1 AW	1.75
2	1.75
3	1.75

DOCTOR WEIRD
Caliber Press
1 V:Charnogg	2.50
2 V:Charnogg	2.50

DODEKAIN
Antartic Press
1 and 2 by Masayuki Fujihara	@2.95
3 Rampage Vs. Zogerians	2.95
4 V:Zogerians	2.95
5 F:Takuma	2.95
6 Dan vs. Takuma	2.75
7 V:Okizon	2.75
8 V:Okizon	2.95

DOGAROO
Blackthorne 1988
1	2.00

DOGS O'WAR, THE
Crusade Entertainment 1996–97
1 thru 3 (of 3)	@2.95

DOLLS
Sirius
1-shot science fiction	2.95

DOMETRIUS KUIR
Newcomers Publishing
1 Walt Bayless	2.95

DOMINION
Eclipse
1	3.00
2 thru 6	@2.00

DOMINO CHANCE
Chance
1 1,000 printed	10.00
1a 2nd printing	3.50
2 thru 6	@3.00
7 I:Gizmo	7.00
8 A:Gizmo	11.00
9	2.50

[2nd Series]
1	3.00
2 and 3	@1.95

DONATELLO
Mirage
1 A: Turtles	12.00

Donatello #1 © Mirage

DONNA MIA
Avatar Press 1997
0 by Tevlin Utz	3.00
0 nude cover	4.95
0 leather cover	25.00
0 signed	10.00
1	3.95
1 signed	10.00
2	3.95
2a deluxe	4.50
3 (of 3)	3.00
3 deluxe	10.00
Giant Size #1	3.00
Giant Size #1 nude	4.95
Giant Size #1 leather cover	25.00
Giant Size #1 signed	10.00
Giant Size #2	3.95
Giant Size #2 Deluxe	10.00
TPB rep. #0–#3 & Giant Size #1–#2	5.95
HC rep. #0–#3 & Giant Size #1–#2 deluxe	39.95
HC rep. #0–#3 & Giant Size #1–#2 with original sketch	150.00
Spec. Infinity	3.00
Spec. Infinity, nude cover	4.95
Spec. Infinity, Leather cover	25.00
Spec.#1 Pin-up (1997)	3.00
Spec.#1a nude cover	4.95

DON SIMPSON'S BIZARRE HEROES
Fiasco Comics
0 thru 7	2.95
8 V:Darkcease	2.95
9 R:Yan Man	2.95
10 F:Mainstreamers	2.95
11 Search for Megaton Man	2.95
12	2.95
13 House of Megaton Man	2.95
14 Cec Vs. Dark Cease	2.95
TPB Apocalypse Affiliation	12.95

DOUBLE EDGE DOUBLE
Double Edge
1 thru 3	3.50
4 Heroes Inc. Rep.#1–#2	2.95

DOUBLE IMPACT
High Impact Studios 1995–96
1 I: China & Jazz	5.00
1a Chromium (c) variant, signed	6.00
1b Rainbow (c) w/certificate	15.00
1c Rainbow (c) w/o certificate	15.00
2 Castilo's Crime	3.00
2a nude cover variant	10.00
2b silver version	10.00
2c signed, w/certificate	5.00
3	5.00
3a Bondage (c)	15.00
4	5.00
4a Phoenix (c)	15.00
5	5.00
5a nude cover	15.00
6 China cover	3.00
6a Jazz cover	3.00
6b signed China or Jazz(c)	15.00
6c bondage(c)	10.00
7 & 8	@3.00
8a variant (c)	8.00

2nd Series 1996–97
0	3.00
0a nude (c)	10.00
1	3.00

All comics prices listed are for *Near Mint* condition.

1a chromium (c) 4.00
1b Chromium variant edition . . . 14.95
1c Christmas (c) 10.00
2 . . . . 3.00
2a Sweedish Erotica(c) 10.00
Spec.#1 Double Impact/Lethal
  Strike: Double Strike, x-over . . 3.00
  Nude RCI(c) cover 9.95
Spec.#1 Double Impact/Nikki Blade:
  Hard Core x-over (1997) . . 2.95
  Platinum variant RCI(c) 3.00
  Gold Metal variant RCI(c) . . . 20.00

ABC Comics 1998
1 encore 3.00
1a encore, Chicago cover 6.00
1b encore, San Diego nude cover 6.00
Spec. Double Impact/Luxura (1998)3.00
Spec. nude collectors edition . . 5.95
Spec. Vampeurotica edition. . . . 5.95

**DOUBLE IMPACT:
ASSASSINS FOR HIRE**
High Impact April 1997
1 RCI,RkB 3.00
1 nude art cover 10.00
1 nude photo cover 15.00
2 . . . . 3.00
2 gold nude cover 10.00
2 signed nude cover 15.00
ABC Comics 1998
1 . . . . 3.00
1a gold nude RCI cover 10.00
1b gold nude RCI cover, signed 15.00

**DOUBLE IMPACT:
FROM THE ASHES**
ABC Comics 1998
1 (of 2) RCI 3.00
1B variant Swedish Erotika cover B5.95
1C variant Swedish Erotika cover C5.95
2 RCI 3.00
2A variant cover A 5.95
2B variant cover B 5.95

DOUBLE IMPACT RAW
ABC Comics 1997
1 (of 3) RCI, adult 3.00
1a adult variant (c) 10.00
1b Star photo (c) 15.00
1A Wraparound cover A 5.95
1B Wraparound cover B 5.95
2 . . . . 2.95
2a nude cover 5.95
3 concl. 2.95
3A Variant cover A 5.95
3B Variant live model nude cover B5.95

**DOUBLE IMPACT
SUICIDE RUN**
ABC Comics 1998
1 (of 2) RCI 3.00
1a nude variant (c) 6.00
1b Nude live model (c) 8.00
1b Leather cover 30.00

**DOUBLE IMPACT:
RAISING HELL**
High Impact 1997
1 RCI,RkB 2.95
1 nude art cover 10.00
1 nude photo cover 15.00

DRACULA
1 . . . . 3.75
1a 2nd printing 2.50
2 thru 4 . . . . @2.50

DRACULA IN HELL
Apple
1 O:Dracula 2.50
2 O:Dracula contd. 2.50

DRACULA: SUICIDE CLUB
Adventure
1 I:Suicide Club in UK 2.50
2 Dracula/Suicide Club cont. . . . 2.50
3 Club raid,A:Insp.Harrison 2.50
4 Vision of Miss Fortune 2.50

DRACULA: THE LADY
IN THE TOMB
Eternity
1 . . . . 2.50

DRACULA'S
COZY COFFIN
Draculina Publishing 1995
1 thru 4 Halloween issue 2.95

DRAGONBALL
Viz Communications March 1998
1 (of 12) by Akira Toriyama . . 2.95
2 thru 5 . . . . @2.95

DRAGONBALL Z
Viz Communications March 1998
1 (of 9) by Akira Toriyama 2.95
2 thru 6 . . . . @2.95

DRAGONFORCE
Aircel
(Prev. Color)
8 thru 13 DK . . . . @2.50

DRAGONFORCE
CHRONICLES
Aircel
Vol. 1 thru Vol. 5 rep. . . . . . . @2.95

DRAGONMIST
Raised Brow Publications
1 I:Dragonmist 2.75
2 F:Assassin 2.75

DRAGON OF THE VALKYR
1 . . . . 1.75
2 thru 4 . . . . @2.00

DRAGON QUEST
1 TV 15.00
2 TV 7.50
3 TV 6.50

DRAGONRING
[1st Series]
1 B.Blair,rare 110.00
Aircel
1 . . . . 3.50
2 . . . . 2.00
3 thru 6 . . . . @1.75

DRAGON WARS
Ironcat 1998
1 by Ryukihei 2.95
2 thru 5 . . . . @2.95

DRAGON WEEKLY
1 Southern Knights 1.75
2 and 3 . . . . @1.75

DREAD OF NIGHT
Hamilton
1 Horror story collection 3.95
2 Json, inc.'Genocide' 3.95

DREAM ANGEL
AND ANGEL GIRL
Angel Entertainment 1998
1 . . . . 2.95
1a nude delicious Dream Angel (c)4.00
1b nude anxious Angel Girl (c) . . 4.00

DREAM ANGEL:
THE QUANTUM DREAMER
Angel Entertainment 1997
0 Nude Manga cover 5.00
1 by Mort Castle & Adriana Melo 2.95
1 Virgin nude cover 5.00
1 Nude Platinum cover 15.00
2 . . . . 2.95
2 Virgin nude cover 5.00
2 Nude Platinum cover 15.00

DREAM ANGEL:
WORLD WITHOUT END
Angel Entertainment 1998
1 Dream world cover 3.00
1 nude nightmare cover 3.00

DREAMGIRL
Angel Entertainment 1996
0 by David Campitti & Al Rio . . . 2.95
0 Virgin Nude cover 5.00
0 Lost in Heaven nude cover . . . 7.00
0 platinum edition, nude cover . . 8.00
1 . . . . 2.95
1 deluxe 5.95
1 Manga cover 5.00
1 Nude Manga cover 5.00

DREAMERY
Eclipse
1 thru 13 . . . . @2.00

DREAMLANDS
Caliber "New Worlds" 1996
1 . . . . 2.95
2 flip book with Boston Bombers #32.95

DREAMTIME
Blind Rat
1 Young Deserter 2.95
2 Gypsy Trouble 2.50

DREAMWALKER
Caliber Tapestry 1997
1 . . . . 2.95
2 . . . . 2.95

3 . . . . 2.95
4 . . . . 2.95
5 by Jenni Gregory, 2nd story arc. 2.95
6 2nd story arc, concl. 2.95

DREAMWOLVES
Dramenon Studios
1 . . . . 3.00
2 . . . . 3.00
3 F:Desiree 3.00
4 V:Venefica 3.00
5 V:Venefica 3.00
6 R:Carnifax 3.00
7 . . . . 3.00
8 F:Wendy Bascum 3.00

DRIFTERS
Infinity Graphics 1986
1 . . . . 1.75

DRYWALL AND OSWALD SHOW, THE
Fireman Press 1998
1 by Mandy Carter,Trent Kaniuga 2.95

DUNGEONEERS
1 thru 8 . . . . @1.50

Eagle #2 © Crystal

EAGLE
Crystal
1 . . . . 3.00
1a signed & limited 5.00
2 thru 5 . . . . @2.75
6 thru 11 . . . . @2.25
12 . . . . 2.50
13 thru 17 . . . . @2.00
Apple
18 thru 26 . . . . @1.95

EAGLE: DARK MIRROR
Comic Zone
1 A:Eagle, inc reps 2.75
2 In Japan, V:Lord Kagami 2.75
3 . . . . 2.95
4 . . . . 2.95

EAGLES DARE
Aager Comics
1 thru 4 . . . . 1.95
5 V:Dragon 1.95

EARTH LORE: LEGEND OF BEK LARSON
Eternity
1 . . . . 1.80

EARTH LORE: REIGN OF DRAGON LORD
1 . . . . 1.80
2 . . . . 1.75

EARTH WAR
Newcomers Publishing 1995
1 and 2 from Newcomers Illus. . . 2.95

EARTH: YEAR ZERO
Eclipse
1 thru 4 . . . . @2.00

EAT-MAN
Viz Communications 1997
1 (of 6) by Akihito Yoshitami 2.95
2 thru 6 . . . . @2.95
Vol. 1 Full Course Meal, rep. Part
One 15.95
PART TWO Feb. 1998
1 (of 5) by Akihito Yoshitami 2.95
2 (of 5) 3.50
3 thru 5 . . . . @3.25

EB'NN THE RAVEN
Now
1 . . . . 5.00
2 . . . . 3.00
3 . . . . 2.50
4 . . . . 2.00
5 thru 9 . . . . @1.50

EBONIX-FILES, THE
Blatant Comics 1998
1A TV parody, cover A 3.95
1B TV parody, cover B 3.95
1c Nude Agent Sculky cover 9.95
1d Nude Agents in Bed cover . . . 9.95

EDDIE CAMPELL'S BACCHUS
Eddie Campell Comics 1995
1 V:Telchines 2.95
1 2nd printing 2.95
2 thru 10 V:Telchines 2.95
11 thru 26 ECa . . . . @2.95
27 thru 37 ECa . . . . @2.95
GN Collected Bacchus, Vol. 1 . . . 9.95
GN Collected Bacchus, Vol. 2 . . . 9.95
GN Collected Bacchus, Vol. 3,
Doing the Islands 17.95
GN Collected Bacchus, Vol. 4, One
Man Show 8.50
GN Collected Bacchus, Vol. 9, King
Bacchus 12.95

EDDY CURRENT
1 thru 12 . . . . @2.00

EDGAR ALLAN POE
Tell Tale Heart 1.95
Pit & Pendulum 1.95
Masque of the Red Death 1.95
Murder in the Rue Morgue 1.95

EDGE
1 . . . . 3.00
Vol 2 #1 thru #3 . . . . @3.00
Vol 2 #4 thru #6 . . . . @2.00

EIGHTBALL
Fantagraphics
1 . . . . 10.00
1a 2nd to 6th printing 3.00
2 . . . . 7.00
2a 2nd to 5th printing 3.00
3 . . . . 6.00
3a 2nd to 4th printing 3.00
4 . . . . 5.00
4a 2nd to 4th printing 3.00
5 . . . . 5.00
5 3rd printing 3.50
6 thru 10 . . . . @4.00
11 A:Ghost World 3.50
12 F:Ghost World 3.25
13 thru 17 . . . . @3.00
18 . . . . 4.00
19 . . . . 3.95
TPB Orgy Bound, rep. from #7–#14 4.95
TPB Lout Rampage 14.95
TPB Pussey 8.95

ELECTRIC BALLET
Caliber
1 Revisionist History of Industrial
Revolution 2.50

ELFLORD
[1st Series]
1 all rare 50.00
2 . . . . 35.00
3 . . . . 30.00
4 . . . . 25.00
5 . . . . 25.00
6 . . . . 40.00
7 . . . . 30.00
8 . . . . 40.00
9 thru 15 . . . . @30.00

ELFLORD
Aircel 1986
1 I:Hawk 5.00
1a 2nd printing 3.50
2 . . . . 3.00
2a 2nd printing 2.00
3 V:Doran 3.00
4 V:Doran 3.00
5 V:Doran 2.00
6 V:Nendo 2.00
Compilation Book 4.95
(Vol 2, #1 to #24, see Color)
25 thru 31 . . . . @1.95
32 . . . . 2.50

ELFLORD
Warp Graphics Jan. 1997
1 (of 4) by Barry Blair & Colin Chan 2.95
2 . . . . 2.95
3 . . . . 2.95
4 . . . . 2.95

All comics prices listed are for *Near Mint* condition.

B & W PUB.

ELFLORD: ALL THE LONELY PLACES
Warp Graphics Aug. 1997
1 (of 4)Barry Blair & Colin Chan . 2.95
becomes:

HAWK AND WINDBLADE: ALL THE LONELY PLACES
2 (of 2) 2.95

ELFLORD CHRONICLES
Aircel 1990
1 (of 12) thru 8 rep B.Blair . . . @2.50

ELFLORD CUTS LOOSE
Warp Graphics Sept. 1997
1 by Barry Blair and Colin Chan . 2.95
2 F:Hawk Erik-san 2.95
3 . . . . 2.95
4 all out attack 2.95
5 north to safety 2.95
6 homward 2.95
7 back to Greenhaven 2.95
8 Greenhaven Siege 2.95
9 Felines, Nothing More Than
  Felines 2.95

ELFLORD: HAWK
China Winds 1998
1-shot by Barry Blair and Colin
  Chan 3.50

ELFLORE: THE HIGH SEAS
Raw Comics
4 by Barry Blair (500 copies) . . . 4.95

ELFQUEST
Warp Graphics 1979–85
1 WP 40.00
1a WP,2nd printing 12.00
1b WP,3rd printing 5.00
1c WP,4th printing (1989) 4.00
2 WP 20.00
2a WP,2nd printing 4.00
2b WP,3rd printing 3.00
2c WP,4th printing (1989) 2.50
3 WP 15.00
3a WP,2nd printing 4.00
3b WP,3rd printing 3.00
3c WP,4th printing (1989) 2.50
4 WP 15.00
4a WP,2nd printing 4.00
4b WP,3rd printing 3.00
4c WP,4th printing (1989) 2.50
5 WP 15.00
5a WP,2nd printing 4.00
5b WP,3rd printing 3.00
6 WP 15.00
6a WP,2nd printing 4.00
6b WP,3rd printing 3.00
7 WP 12.00
7a WP,2nd printing 3.00
8 WP 12.00
8a WP,2nd printing 3.00
9 WP 12.00
9a WP,2nd printing 3.00
10 thru 15 . . . . @8.00
16 WP,I:DistantSoil 8.00
17 thru 21 WP . . . . @8.00
TPB Gatherum 19.95

ELFQUEST
Warp Graphics
4 thru 14 ed. RPi 4.95
15 . . . . 4.95
16 What if Cutter never became
  chief 4.95
17 F:Fire-Eye 4.95
18 Dreamtime, concl. 4.95
19 Wolfrider begins 4.95
20 . . . . 4.95
21 20th anniv. 4.95
22 F:Wolfrider 4.95
23 F:WaveDancers 4.95
24 F:Wolfrider 4.95
25 F:Wolfrider 4.95
26 Wild Hunt 4.95
27 . . . . 4.95
HC Book 1 Fire & Flight 19.95
HC Book 2 Forbidden Grove . . . 19.95
HC Book 3 Captives of Blue
  Mountain 19.95
HC Book 4 Quest's End 19.95
HC Book 6 The Secret of Two-Edge 9.95
HC Book 7 The Cry From Beyond 19.95
GN Shards 13.95
GN Legacy (Hidden Years #16–#22) 1.95
GN A Gift of Her Own 16.95
HC Wolfrider's Guide to the World of
  Elfquest 19.95
HC New Blood 19.95

ELFQUEST: KAHVI
Warp Graphics 1995
1 thru 6 I:Kahvi . . . . @2.25

ELFQUEST: KINGS OF THE BROKEN WHEEL
Warp Graphics 1990–92
1 WP 2.25
2 thru 9 WP . . . . @2.25

ELFQUEST: METAMORPHOSIS
Warp Graphics April 1996
Spec.#1 WP,RPi 2.95

Elfquest: Seige at Blue Mountain #1
© Warp Graphics

ELFQUEST: SEIGE AT BLUE MOUNTAIN
Warp Graphics/Apple Comics
1987–88
1 WP,JSo 11.00
1a 2nd printing 3.00
2 WP 6.00
2a 2nd printing 3.00
3 WP 5.00
3a 2nd printing 2.00
4 thru 8 WP . . . . @5.00

ELFQUEST: TWO SPEAR
Warp Graphics 1995
1 thru 3 (of 5) Two-Spears past @2.25

ELFQUEST: WOLFRIDER
Warp Graphics
Spec.#1 . . . . 2.95

ELFQUEST: WORLDPOOL
Warp Graphics
Spec.#1 (of 2) 2.95
Spec.#2 (of 2) 2.95

ELFTHING
Eclipse
1 . . . . 3.00

ELFTREK
Dimension
1 Elfquest's Star Trek parody . . . 2.00
2 . . . . 1.75

ELF WARRIOR
1 . . . . 3.00
2 . . . . 2.50
3 thru 5 . . . . @1.95

ELIMINATOR
Eternity
1 'Drugs in the Future' 2.50
2 . . . . 2.50

ELVIRA, MISTRESS OF THE DARK
Claypool Comics
1 thru 35 . . . . @2.50
36 thru 64 photo covers . . . . . @2.50
TPB Elvira, Mistress of the Dark 12.95

ELVIRA
Eclipse
1 Rosalind Wyck 2.50

ELVIS: UNDERCOVER
1 . . . . 2.00

EMBRACE
London Night
1 NC17 edition, EHr, signed . . . 10.00

EMBRACE: HUNGER OF THE FLESH
London Night 1997
1 DQ,last of the original vampire
  race 3.00
1a DQ,deluxe 6.00
1b signed by Kevin West 15.00

---

2 DQ 3.00
2a DQ,deluxe 6.00
3 by Dan Membiela & Kevin West,
concl. 3.00
3a nude cover edition 6.00

EMERALDAS
Eternity 1990
1 thru 4 . . . . @2.25

EMMA DAVENPORT
Lohamn Hill Press
1 I:Emma Davenport 2.75
2 . . . . 2.75
3 O:Hammerin Jim 2.75
4 Cookie Woofer War 2.75

EMPIRE
Eternity
1 thru 4 . . . . @1.95

EMPIRE LANES
Comico
1 . . . . 2.95

ENCHANTED
Sirius 1997
1 (of 3) by Robert Chang 2.95
2 . . . . 2.95
3 concl. 2.95

ENCHANTED VALLEY
Blackthorne
1 . . . . 1.75
2 . . . . 1.75

ENCHANTER
Eclipse
1 thru 3 . . . . @2.00

ENCHANTER: APOCALYPSE WIND NOVELLA
Entity
1 Foil Enhanced Cover 2.95

ENFORCERS
Dark Visions Publishing 1995
0 From Anthology Title 2.50

ENTITY
Avatar
½ Nira X cover 5.95
½ Snowman cover 10.95
½ Nira X silver cover 10.95
½ Snowman silver cover 15.95

ENTROPY TALES
1 . . . . 2.00
2 Domino Chance 1.50
3 thru 5 . . . . @1.50

EPSILON WAVE
Elite
1 . . . . 3.00
2 . . . . 2.00
3 thru 5 . . . . @1.60

EQUINE THE UNCIVILIZED
Graphspress
1 . . . . 4.00
2 . . . . 2.50
3 thru 6 . . . . @2.00

EQUINOX CHRONICLES
Innovation
1 I:Team Equinox, Black Avatar . 2.25
2 Black Avatar Plans US conquest 2.25

EQUIS MORTIS
Crimson Studios
1 I:Carl Ragland (Equis Mortis) . . 2.50

ERADICATORS
Greater Mercury 1990–91
1 RLm (1st Work) 5.00
1a 2nd printing 1.50
2 . . . . 2.50
3 Vigil 2.00
4 thru 8 . . . . @1.50

ERIC PRESTON IS THE FLAME
B-Movie Comics
1 Son of G.A.Flame 95

ESCAPE TO THE STARS
Visionary
1 thru 7 . . . . @1.25
[2nd Series]
1 . . . . 1.25
2 . . . . 1.25

Escape Velocity #1
© Escape Velocity Press

ESCAPE VELOCITY
Escape Velocity Press
1 and 2 . . . . @1.50

ESMERALDAS
Eternity
1 thru 4 . . . . 2.25

ESPERS
Halloween Comics April 1996
1 JHI, R:ESPers 2.95
1 JHI,signed 2.95
2 JHI,signed 2.95
3 JHI, ... 2.95
3 JHI,signed 2.95
4 thru 6 JHI, conclusion . . . . @2.95
Volume 2
1 "Undertow" 2.95
2 . . . . 2.95

EVENT PRESENTS THE ASH UNIVERSE
Event Comics 1998
1-shot JQ,JP, 48pg 2.95

EVIL ERNIE
Eternity 1991–92
1 SHu,BnP,I&O:Evil Ernie, Lady
Death 100.00
1a Spec. 1992 reprint, 16 extra
pages 60.00
2 Death & Revival of Ernie, A:Lady
Death, 1st (c) 75.00
3 Psycho Plague, A:Lady Death 70.00
4 A:Lady Death 60.00
5 A:Lady Death 60.00
TPB rep #1-5 . . . . 10.95

EVIL ERNIE
Chaos! Comics
1 thru 5 reprints . . . . @2.50
Spec. Youth Gone Wild, die-cut
cover, Director's cut 5.00
TPB Youth Gone Wild 9.95

EVIL ERNIE
Chaos! Comics 1996
1 encore presentation 2.50
2 thru 5 encore presentation . . . 1.95

EXIT
Caliber 1995
1 I:New series 2.95
2 thru 4 "The Traitors," pt.2–pt.4 . 2.95
Epilogue 2.95
GN rep. 320 pages 19.95
GN rep. 160 pages 14.95

EX-MUTANTS
Amazing Comics 1986
1 AC/RLm 5.00
1a 2nd printing 2.00
2 and 3 . . . . @3.00
EC
4 and 5 . . . . @2.00
6 PP 1.95
7 . . . . 1.95
8 . . . . 1.95
Ann. #1 . . . . 1.95
Pin-Up Spec. #1 . . . . 1.95

EX-MUTANTS: THE SHATTERED EARTH CHRONICLES
Eternity
1 thru 3 . . . . @1.95
4 RLd(c) 2.75
5 RLd(c) 2.75

All comics prices listed are for *Near Mint* condition.

6 thru 14 . . . . @1.95
Winter Special #1 . . . . 1.95

EXPLORERS
Caliber Tapestry 1997
1 . . . . 2.95
2 . . . . 2.95
3 "Nahuatl" 2.95
4 "The Sky is Falling" 2.95

EXTINCT
NEC
1 Rep Golden age stories 3.50

EXTREMELY SILLY
Antarctic Press
1 . . . . 4.00
1 Vol. II 1.25
2 Vol. II 1.25

EYE OF MONGOMBO
Fantagraphics Books 1990–91
1 . . . . 3.00
2 thru 7 . . . . @2.00

FAERIE KING
Moordam Comics
1 In View of Man 2.50

FAITH
Lightning Comics 1997
1 (of 2) 2.95
1a variant cover 2.95
1b Limited, cover A 9.95
1c Limited, cover B 9.95
1d signed & numbered 9.95
1 encore edition 2.95
1a encore, cover B 2.95
1b deluxe encore edition, cover A 9.95
1c deluxe encore edition, cover B 9.95

FANG: TESTAMENT
Sirius 1997
1 by Kevin J. Taylor 2.50
2 . . . . 2.50
3 . . . . 2.50
4 (of 4) 2.50

FANGS OF THE WIDOW
Ground Zero
1 I:Emma 2.50
London Night Studios 1995
1 O:The Widow 3.00
1a platinum edition 5.00
2 Body Count 3.00
3 Emma Revealed 3.00
Ground Zero
7 thru 9 "Metal Gypsies," pt.#1–#3 3.00
10 thru 13 rep. Widow: Bound by
    Blood #1–#4 + additional material 3.50
14 "Search and Destroy" pt.1 . . . 3.00
15 "Search and Destroy" pt.2 . . . 3.00
Ann. #1 Search and Destroy 5.95

FANTASCI
Warp Graphics-Apple
1 . . . . 2.50
2 and 3 . . . . @2.00
4 . . . . 4.00
5 thru 8 . . . . @1.75
9 'Apple Turnover' 1.75

FANTASTIC ADVENTURES
1 thru 5 . . . . @1.75

FANTASTIC FABLES
Silver Wolf
1 and 2 . . . . @1.50

FANTASTIC PANIC
Antarctic 1993–94
1 thru 8 Ganbear . . . . @2.75
[Volume 2]
1 thru 4 . . . . @2.75
4 thru 9 . . . . @2.95
10 concl. 3.50

FANTASTIC WORLDS
Flashback Comics
1 Space Opera 2.95
2 F:Attu, Captain Courage 2.95

FANTASY QUARTERLY
1 1978 1st Elfquest 65.00

FART WARS: SPECIAL EDITION
Entity Comics 1997
1 Star Wars trilogy parody,A:Nira X 2.75
1a Empire Attacks Back cover . 2.75
1b Return of the One-Eye cover . 2.75

FASTLANE ILLUSTRATED
Fastlane Studios
1 Super Powers & Hot Rods 2.50

FAT NINJA
Silver Wolf Comics 1985–86
1 . . . . 2.50
2 Vigil 2.50
3 thru 8 . . . . @1.50

FAUST
North Star
1 Vigil 42.00
1a Vigil,2nd Printing 5.00
1b Vigil,3rd Printing 2.00
1c Tour Edition 30.00
2 Vigil 32.00
2a Vigil,2nd Printing 3.00
2b Vigil,3rd Printing 2.50
3 Vigil 18.00
3a Vigil,2nd Printing 2.50
4 Vigil 15.00
5 Vigil 9.00
6 Vigil 9.00
Rebel Studios
7 Vigil 5.00
8 TV 3.50
9 TV,Love of the Damned 3.50
10 E:DQ(s),TV,Love o/t Damned . 3.50

FAUST VOL. II
REBEL
1 TV,Love of the Damned 2.50

FAUST PREMIERE
North Star
1 Vigil 45.00

FELIX THE CAT B&W
Felix Comics 1997
1 inc. Felix's Cafe 1.95
2 Crusin' for a Brusin' 1.95
3 Ah Choo 1.95
4 inc. Spaced Out 1.95

FEM FANTASTIQUE
AC Comics
1 . . . . 1.95

FEM FORCE
AC Comics
1 thru 15 See Color
16 I:Thunder Fox 3.00
17 F:She-Cat,Ms.Victory, giant . 3.00
18 double size 3.00
19 . . . . 3.00
20 V:RipJaw, Black Commando . 3.00
21 V:Dr.Pretorius 3.00
22 V:Dr.Pretorius 3.00
23 V:Rad 3.00
24 A:Teen Femforce 3.00
25 V:Madame Boa 3.00
26 V:Black Shroud 3.00
27 V:Black Shroud 3.00
28 A:Arsenio Hall 3.00
29 V:Black Shroud 3.00
30 V:Garganta 3.00
31 I:Kronon Captain Paragon . . 3.00
32 V:Garganta 3.00
33 Personal Lives of team 3.00
34 V:Black Shroud 2.75
35 V:Black Shroud 2.75
36 giant,V:Dragonfly,Shade . . . 2.75
37 A:Blue Bulleteer,She-Cat . . . 2.75
38 V:Lady Luger 2.75
39 F:She-Cat 2.75
40 V:Sehkmet 2.75
41 V:Captain Paragon 2.75
42 V:Alizarin Crimson 2.75
43 V:Glamazons of Galaxy G . . 2.75
44 V:Lady Luger,F:Garganta . . . 2.75
45 Nightveil Rescued 2.75
46 V:Lady Luger 2.75
47 V:Alizarin Crimson 2.75
48 . . . . 2.75
49 I:New Msw.Victory 2.75
50 Ms.Victory Vs.Rad,flexi-disc . 2.95
51 . . . . 2.75
52 V:Claw & Clawites 2.75
53 I:Bulldog Deni,V:(Dick
    Briefer's)Frightenstein 2.75
54 The Orb of Bliss 2.75
55 R:Nightveil 2.75
56 V:Alizarin Crimson 2.75
57 thru 92 See Color
93 "Shattered Memories," pt.2 . . 3.00
93a deluxe 5.90
94 "Shattered Memories," pt.3 . . 3.00
94a deluxe 5.90
95 . . . . 3.00
95a deluxe 5.90
96 . . . . 3.00
96a deluxe 5.90
97 . . . . 3.00
98 deluxe 5.90
98 . . . . 3.00
98 deluxe 5.90
99 . . . . 3.00
99 deluxe 5.90
100 Anniv. issue, with poster . .6.90
100A signed, with poster 12.00
100B no poster, not signed 4.00

THE YESTERDAY SYNDROME
101 Pt.1 . . . . 4.95
102 Pt.2 . . . . 4.95
103 Pt.3 . . . . 4.95
RETURN FROM THE ASHES
104 pt.1 Firebeam, 44pg 4.95
105 pt. 2 . . . . 4.95
106 pt. 3 concl. 4.95
DARKGODS: RAMPAGE
107 Darkgods: Rampage, pt.1 . 4.95
108 Darkgods: Rampage, pt.2 . 4.95
109 Darkgods: Rampage, pt.3 . 5.95
Spec.#1 FemForce Timelines,
O:Femforce (1995) 2.95
Spec.#1 FemForce:Frightbook,
Horror tales by Briefer,Ayers,
Powell 2.95
Untold Origin of FemForce 4.95
GN The Capricorn Chronicles . . 12.50
GN FemForce: Timestorm 9.95
GN, FemForce: Timestorm, deluxe14.95
TPB Origins 12.95
TPB Origins, signed 13.95
Secret Files of Femforce, deluxe . 4.95

FEVER, THE
Dark Vision Publishing
1 O:The Fever 2.50
2 Fever's Father 2.50

FIFTIES TERROR
Eternity
1 thru 6 . . . . @1.95

FINAL CYCLE
Sirius
Graphic Novel 4.00
1 thru 4 . . . . @1.50

FINDER
Lightspeed Comics Nov. 1996
1 thru 5 by Carla Speed McNeil @2.95
6 thru 11 . . . . @2.95

FIRE TEAM
Aircel 1990
1 thru 3 by Don Lomax . . . . . @2.50

Fish Police #2 © Fishwrap Productions

4 V:Vietnamese Gangs 2.50
5 Cam in Vietnam 2.50
6 . . . . 2.50

FISH POLICE
Fishwrap Productions
December 1985
1 1st printing 7.00
1a 2nd printing 3.00
2 . . . . 5.00
3 thru 5 . . . . @4.00
Comico Publ.
6 thru 12 . . . . @3.50
13 thru 17 **see Color Issues**
Apple Publ.
18 thru 24 . . . . @2.50

FISH SHTICKS
Apple
1 and 2 . . . . @2.75
3 and 4 . . . . @2.50

FIST OF GOD
Eternity
1 thru 4 . . . . @1.95

FIST OF THE NORTH STAR
Viz Select
1 thru 3 . . . . @3.25
4 . . . . 1.95
5 . . . . 3.25
6 . . . . 2.95
7 . . . . 2.95
TPB Vol. 2 Night of the Jackal, rep16.95
Part Three
1 thru 5 by Buronson & Tetsuo
Hara . . . . @2.95
Part Four Dec. 1996
1 thru 7 . . . . @2.95
TPB Volume 2: Southern Cross . 16.95

FITCH IN TIME
Renegade
1 . . . . 1.50

FLAG FIGHTERS
Ironcat 1997
1 by Masaomi Kanzaki 2.95
2 Student Flagger, pt.1 . . . . . . 2.95
3 Student Flagger, pt.2 . . . . . . 2.95
4 Student Flagger, pt.3 . . . . . . 2.95
5 . . . . 2.95
6 Death Window 2.95
7 F:Murasame 2.95

FLAMING CARROT
Aardvark–Vanaheim
1 1981 Killian Barracks 65.00
1a 1984 . . . . 35.00
2 . . . . 30.00
3 . . . . 30.00
4 thru 6 . . . . @25.00
Renegade
7 . . . . 18.00
8 . . . . 12.00
9 . . . . 10.00
10 . . . . 10.00
11 . . . . 6.00
12 . . . . 6.00
13 thru 15 . . . . @5.00

15a variant without cover price . 10.00
16 and 17 . . . . @5.00
See: Dark Horse

FLARE
Hero Graphics
1 thru 8 . . . . @3.95
9 F:Sparkplug 3.95
10 thru 12 . . . . 2.95

FLARE ADVENTURES
Hero Graphics
1 Rep 1st issue Flare 1.00
Becomes:
FLARE ADVENTURES/ CHAMPIONS CLASSICS
2 thru 15 . . . . @3.95

FLARE VS. TIGRESS
Hero Graphics
1 and 2 . . . . @3.50

FLASH MARKS
Fantagraphics
1 . . . . 2.95

FLOYD FARLAND
Eclipse
1 . . . . 2.95

FORBIDDEN KINGDOM
1 thru 11 . . . . @1.95

FORBIDDEN VAMPIRE TALES
Forbidden 1997
0 . . . . 2.95
0A Erotic nude cover 3.95
0b Erotic nude cover 3.95
1 sexy vampire 2.95
1a nude cover 3.95
1b photo nude cover 3.95
2 . . . . 2.95
2A Dulexe erotic nude cover A . 3.95
2b Deluxe erotic nude cover B . . 3.95
3 . . . . 2.95
3a nude cover 2.95
4 . . . . 2.95
4a erotic nude cover 2.95
5 . . . . 2.95
5a erotic nude cover 2.95
6 . . . . 3.00
6a Forbidden Embrace nude cover4.00
7 Bloodlust and Bust cover 3.00
6a Nude Kissing the Countess
cover 3.00

FORBIDDEN VAMPIRE TALES: VAULT OF INNOCENTS
Forbidden 1998
1 . . . . 2.95
1 nude cover 4.00

FORBIDDEN WORLDS
ACG 1996
1 SD,JAp,rep. 2.50

FORCE 10
Crow Comics
0 Ash Can Preview 75
1 I:Force 10 . . . . 2.50
2 Children of the Revolution,pt#2 2.50
3 Against all Odds 2.50

FOREVER WARRIORS
Aardwolf 1996
1 (of 3) RTs,RB 2.95
2 RTs,RB 2.95
3 RTs,RB, concl. 2.95

FOREVER WARRIORS
CFD 1997
1 RB,RTs 2.95
2 RB,RTs,KN 2.95
3 RB,RTs, finale 2.95

FOX COMICS
1 Spec. 2.95
25 . . . . 2.95
26 . . . . 3.50

FRANKENSTEIN
Eternity
1 . . . . 1.95
2 . . . . 1.95
3 . . . . 1.95

FRANKIES FRIGHTMARES
1 Celebrates Frank 60th ann . . . 1.95

FRANK THE UNICORN
Fish Warp
1 thru 7 . . . . @2.00

FREAK-OUT ON
INFANT EARTHS
1 Don Chin 1.75
2 Don Chin 1.75

FREAKS
Monster Comics
1 Movie adapt 2.50
2 Movie adapt.cont. 2.50
3 thru 4 Movie adapt. 2.50

FRENCH ICE
Renegade Press
1 thru 15 . . . . @2.00

FRIENDS
1 thru 5 . . . . @2.00

FRIGHT
Eternity
1 thru 13 . . . . @1.95

FRINGE
Caliber
1 thru 7 . . . . @2.50

FROM BEYOND
Studio Insidio
1 Short stories-horror 2.25
2 inc.Clara Mutilares 2.50
3 inc.The Experiment 2.50
4 inc.Positive Feedback 2.50

FROM HELL
Tundra
1 . . . . 18.00
1a 2nd printing 8.00
2 . . . . 10.00
Kitchen Sink
Volume Three
1 AMo,ECa 9.00
2 AMo,ECa 5.00
2a 2nd printing 6.00
3 . . . . 5.00
3a 2nd printing 6.00
4 . . . . 6.00
4 new printing 5.00
5 . . . . 6.00
5 new printing 5.00
6 . . . . 5.00
7 . . . . 5.00
8 . . . . 5.00
8 AMo,ECa,new printing 5.00
9 AMo,ECa 5.00
9 new printing 5.00
10 AMo,ECa 5.00
10 new printing 5.00

FROM THE DARKNESS
Adventure Comics 1990
1 JBa 30.00
2 . . . . 35.00
3 and 4 . . . . @15.00

FROM THE DARKNESS II
BLOODVOWS
Cry For Dawn
1 R:Ray Thorn,Desnoires 15.00
2 V:Desnoires 10.00
3 . . . . 10.00

FROM THE VOID
1 1st B.Blair,1982 . . . . 75.00

FROST
1 Heart of Darkness 1.95

FROST:
THE DYING BREED
Caliber
1 thru 3 Vietnam Flashbacks . @2.95

F–III BANDIT
Antartic Press
1 F:Akira, Yoohoo 2.95
2 F:Yukio 2.95
3 F:Were-Women 2.95
4 . . . . 2.95
5 Romeo & Juliet story 2.95
6 thru 8 . . . . @2.95

FUGITOID
Mirage
1 TMNT Tie-in 12.00

FULL METAL FICTION
London Night Feb. 1997
1 EHr 4.00
1a Nun with a Gun edition 10.00
1b dark room edition cover 4.00
2 . . . . 4.00
2a signed 10.00
3 "Hellborne" concl. 4.00

4 . . . . 4.00
5 EHr 4.00
6 . . . . 4.00
7 . . . . 4.00
8 . . . . 4.00

FURRLOUGH
Antarctic Press 1991
1 Funny Animal Military stories . . 3.00
2 thru 10 . . . . @2.50
11 thru 20 . . . . @2.75
21 thru 33 . . . . @2.75
34 . . . . 2.95
35 48pg 4.00
36 thru 40 . . . . @2.95
41 thru 51 . . . . @2.95
Best of Furlough, Vol.1 . . . . . . 4.95
Best of Furlough, Vol.2 . . . . . . 4.95
Radio Comix
52 "Ninjara", pt.4 . . . . 2.95
53 "Bronze Age" 2.95
54 "Heebas" 2.95
55 "Star Run" cont. 2.95
56 "Tobias Wah: Vampire Hunter". 2.95
57 "Star Run" 2.95
58 F:Heebas 2.95
59 Sixth anniv., 48pg 3.95
60 F:Tobias Wah: Vampire Hunter" 2.95
61 "" 2.95
62 F:Tobias Wah 2.95
63 F:Full Knight Gear 2.95
64 F:The Wild 2.95
65 F:Full Knight Gear 2.95
66 F:Tobias Wah: Vampire Hunter 2.95
67 F:Full Knight Gear 2.95
68 inc. "Misty the Mouse" 2.95

FURY
Aircel
1 thru 3 . . . . @1.70

FURY OF HELLINA, THE
Lightning Comics 1995
1 V:Luciver 3.50
1a limited & signed 10.00
1b platinum 10.00

FUSION
Eclipse
1 . . . . 2.50
2 thru 17 . . . . @2.00

FUTURAMA
Slave Labor
1 thru 4 . . . . @1.75

FUTURETECH
Mushroom Comics
1 Automotive Hi-Tech 3.50
2 Cyber Trucks 3.50

FUTURIANS
Aardwolf 1995
0 DC R:Futurians, sequal to
   Lodestone color series 2.95
0 second printing, DC 2.95

GAIJIN
Caliber 1990
1-shot, 64pg. 3.50
1 thru 3 . . . . @1.95

GALAXION
Helikon 1997
1 by Tara Jenkins, science fiction 2.75
2 .... 2.75
3 .... 2.75
4 Choices 2.75
5 .... 2.75
6 Communication 2.75
Spec. #1, 16pg. 1.00

GATEKEEPER
GK Publishing
1 .... 2.50
2 and 3 .... @2.95

GATES OF THE NIGHT
Jademan
1 thru 4 .... @3.50

GATEWAY TO HORROR
1 BW 1.75

GEMS OF THE SAMURAI
Newcomers Publishing
1 I:Master Samurai 2.95

GENOCYBER
Viz
1 I:Genocyber 2.75
2 .... 2.75
3 ToT 2.75
4 ToT 2.75
5 ToT 2.75

GERIATRIC GANGRENE JUJITSU GERBILS
Planet X Productions
1 .... 2.50
2 .... 1.50

GHOSTS OF DRACULA
Eternity
1 A:Dracula & Houdini 2.50
2 A:Sherlock Holmes 2.50
3 A:Houdini 2.50
4 Count Dracula's Castle 2.50
5 Houdini, Van Helsing, Dracula
team-up 2.50

GIANT SIZE MINI COMICS
Eclipse
1 thru 4 .... @1.50

GI GOVERNMENT ISSUED
Paranoid Press
1 thru 7 F:Mac, Jack .... @2.00

GIDEON HAWK
Big Shot Comics
1 I:Gideon Hawk, Max 9471 .... 2.00
2 The Jewel of Shamboli,pt.2 ... 2.00
3 The Jewel of Shamboli,pt.3 ... 2.00
2 The Jewel of Shamboli,pt.4 ... 2.50
3 The Jewel of Shamboli,pt.5 ... 2.50

GIFT, THE
First
1 .... 5.95

GIZMO
Chance
1 .... 7.50
Mirage
1 .... 5.50
2 .... 2.50
3 .... 2.00
4 thru 7 .... @1.50

GIZMO & THE FUGITOID
1 and 2 .... @1.75

GNATRAT
Prelude
1 .... 5.00
2 Early Years 2.00

GNATRAT: THE MOVIE
1 .... 2.25

GOBBLEDYGOOK
Mirage
1 1st series, Rare 275.00
2 1st series, Rare 275.00
1 TMNT series reprint 12.00

GOJIN
Antarctic Press 1995
1 F:Terran Defense Force 2.95
2 F:Terran Defense Force 2.95
3 V:Alien Monster 2.95
4 Aliens Bone 2.95
5 thru 8 .... @2.95

GOLD DIGGER
Antarctic Press
[Limited Series]
1 Geena & Cheetah in Peru 8.00
2 Adventures contd. 6.00
3 Adventures contd 6.00
4 Adventures contd 5.00
GN Rep. #1–#4 + new material . 9.95
[Volume 2]
1 by Fred Perry .... @12.00
2 and 3 Fred Perry .... @9.00
4 Fred Perry 7.00
5 misnumbered as #0 .... 6.00
6 thru 8 by Fred Perry ..... @4.00
9 and 10 by Fred Perry ..... @3.50
11 thru 27 by Fred Perry .... @3.00
28 and 29 by Fred Perry .... @2.75
30 .... 3.00
31 .... 3.00
32 Time Warp Part One 3.00
33 .... 3.00
34 .... 3.00
35 Time Warp Part Seven 3.00
36 .... 3.00
37 .... 2.95
38 V:Dynasty of Evil 2.95
39 .... 2.95
40 Wedding day 2.95
41 Gold Digger Beta 2.95
42 .... 2.95
43 Beta Phase phenomenon 2.95
Ann.1995, 48pg 3.95
Ann.1996 .... 3.95
Ann. 1997 .... 3.95
Collected Gold Digger,Vol.1 ... 9.95
Coll. Vol. 1, 4th printing 9.95
Collected Gold Digger,Vol.2 .... 9.95
Coll. Vol. 2, 3rd printing 9.95
Collected Gold Digger,Vol.3 .... 9.95
Coll. Vol. 3, 2nd printing 9.95
Collected Gold Digger,Vol. 4 ... 9.95
Collected Gold Digger,Vol. 5 ... 9.95
Collected Gold Digger,Vol. 6 .. 10.95
Coll. Vol. 7 .... 10.95

GOLDEN AGE GREATS
AC Comics 1995
Vol.#1 thru #6 40s and 50s ... @9.95
Vol. 7 Best of the West 9.95
Vol. 8 F:Phantom Lady, Miss Victory 9.95
Vol. 11 Roy Rogers & The Silver
Screen Cowboys 11.95
Vol. 9 Fabulous Femmes of Fiction
House 9.95
Vol. 12 Thrilling Science Fiction .. 9.95

GOLDEN WARRIOR ICZER ONE
Antartic 1994
1 thru 5 .... @2.95

GOLDWYN 3-D
Blackthorne
1 .... 2.00

GO-MAN
1 thru 4 .... @1.50
Graphic Novel 'N' 9.95

Good Girls #1 © Fantagraphics

GOOD GIRL COMICS
AC
1 F:Tara Fremont 3.95

GOOD GIRLS
Fantagraphics
1 adult 2.00
2 thru 4 .... @2.00

GORE SHRIEK
Fantagor
1 .... 2.50
2 and 3 .... @1.50
4 +Mars Attacks 2.95
5 .... 2.95

6 . . . . 3.50
Vol 2 #1 . . . . 2.50

GOTHESS: DARK ECSTASY
SCC Entertainment 1997
1 (of 3) 2.95
2 . . . . 2.95
2a nude Kristen edition 9.95
2b nude Gothess edition 9.95
3 . . . . 2.95
3a nude vampire slayer edition . . 9.95
3b nude halloween edition 9.95

GRAPHIC STORY MONTHLY
1 thru 5 . . . . @2.95

GRAPHIQUE MUSIQUE
Slave Labor 1989–90
1 . . . . 45.00
2 . . . . 40.00
3 . . . . 35.00

GRAVE TALES
Hamilton
1 JSon,GM, mag. size 3.95
2 JSon,GM, short stories 3.95
3 JSon,GM, inc.'Stake Out' 3.95

GREMLIN TROUBLE
Anti-Ballistic Pixelation
1 & 2 Airstrike on Gremlin Home @2.95
1 new printing 2.95
3 thru 5 . . . . @2.95
6 "Fun with Electricity" 2.95
7 "Cypher in Fairyland" 2.95
8 . . . . 2.95
9 F:Candy Tsai 2.95
10 The Tuberians are coming . . . 2.95
11 V:X-the-Unmentionable 2.95
12 preemptive strike on Site X . . . 2.95
13 Gremlin-Goblin war 2.95
14 . . . . 2.95
TPB Vol.1 . . . . 14.95

GRENDEL
Comico
1 MW,Rare 75.00
2 MW,Rare 60.00
3 MW,Rare 55.00

GREY
Viz Select
Book 1 . . . . 5.00
Book 2 scarce 5.50
Book 3 . . . . 3.00
Book 4 . . . . 3.00
Book 5 . . . . 3.00
Book 6 thru Book 9 . . . . @2.50

GREYMATTER
Alaffinity Studios
1 thru 14 by Marcus Harwell . @2.95

GRIFFIN, THE
Slave Labor
1 . . . . 1.75
1a 2nd printing 1.75
2 thru 4 . . . . @1.75
5 . . . . 1.95

GRIPS
Silver Wolf
1 Vigil 20.00
2 Vigil 16.00
3 Vigil 11.00
4 Vigil 9.00
Vol 1 #1 rep 2.50
Volume 2
1 . . . . 2.50
2 . . . . 2.50
3 thru 6 . . . . @2.00
7 . . . . 2.25
8 . . . . 2.25
9 thru 12 . . . . @2.50

GROUND POUND
1 John Pound art 2.00

GROUND ZERO
Eternity
1 Science Fiction mini-series . . . 2.50
2 Alien Invasion Aftermath 2.50

GUERRILA GROUNDHOG
Eclipse
1 . . . . 1.50
2 . . . . 1.50

GUILLOTINE
Silver Wolf
1 and 2 . . . . @1.50

GUN CRISIS
Ironcat 1998
1 (of 3) by Masoami Kanzaki . . . 2.95
2 . . . . 2.95
3 . . . . 2.95

GUN FURY
Aircel
1 thru 10 . . . . @1.95

GUN FURY RETURNS
Aircel
1 . . . . 2.95
2 . . . . 2.95
3 V:The Yes Men 2.25
4 . . . . 2.25

GUNS OF SHAR-PEI
Caliber
1 The Good,the Bad & the Deadly 2.95

HADES
Domain Publishing 1995
1 F:Civil War Officer 3.00

HALL OF HEROES
Hall of Heroes 1993
1 I:Dead Bolt 16.00
2 and 3 . . . . @4.50
Halloween Horror Special 2.50

HALL OF HEROES PRESENTS
Hall of Heroes 1996–97
0 by Doug Brammer & Matt Roach,
  "Slingers" by Matt Martin 2.50
1 . . . . 2.50
1a signed & numbered 4.00

2 "The Last Days" 2.50
3 "The Power of the Golem" . . . 2.50
4 F:Turaxx the Trobbit 2.50
5 . . . . 2.50

HALLOWEEN TERROR
Eternity
1 . . . . 2.50

HALLOWIENERS
Mirage
1 . . . . 1.50
2 . . . . 1.50

HALO BROTHERS
Fantagraphics
Special #1 . . . . 2.25

HAMMER GIRL
Brainstorm April 1996
1 dinosaur, sci-fi adventure 2.95
2 . . . . 2.95
2a deluxe 5.00

HAMSTER VICE
Blackthorne
1 . . . . 3.50
2 . . . . 2.50
3 thru 11 . . . . @2.00
New Series
Eternity
1 and 2 . . . . @1.95

HARD ROCK COMICS
Revolutionary
1 Metallica-The Early Years 2.50

HARI KARI
Blackout 1995
1 . . . . 3.00
1a platinum 10.00
1-shot Possessed by Evil(1997) . . 2.95
1-shot Hari Kari Goes Hollywood
  (1997) 2.95
  Nude edition 9.95
  Deluxe 14.95
Spec #1 Sexy Summer Rampage,
  gallery issue (1997) 2.95
  Deluxe, super sexy cover 9.95
1-shot Cry of Darkness (1998) . . 2.95
  Variant photo ultra sexy ed. . . 9.95
1-shot The Last Stand (1998) . . . 2.95
  Ultra sexy edition 9.95
  Deluxe 14.95

HARI KARI MANGA
Blackout Comics 1998
Spec. 0 Sex, Thugs & Rock 'n' Roll 2.95
  Nude cover 9.95
1-shot Manga Adventures (1997) 2.95
1-shot Deadly Exposure, by Rob
  Roman & Nigel Tully 2.95
  Nude cover 9.95
  Deluxe 14.95
1-shot Deadtime Stories, by Rob
  Roman & Nigel Tully 2.95
  Nude cover 9.95
  Deluxe edition 14.95

B & W PUB.

HARTE OF HARKNESS
Eternity
1 I:Dennis Harte,Vampire private-
eye 2.50
2 V:Satan's Blitz St.Gang 2.50
3 Jack Grissom/Vampire 2.50
4 V:Jack Grissom, conc. 2.50

HARVY FLIP BOOK
Blackthorne
1 . . . . 2.00
2 . . . . 2.00
3 . . . . 2.00

HATE
Fantagraphics
1 . . . . 20.00
2 . . . . 15.00
3 . . . . 10.00
4 . . . . 10.00
5 . . . . 9.00
6 . . . . 6.00
7 . . . . 7.00
8 thru 10 . . . . 5.00
11 and 12 . . . . 4.00
1a to 12a reprints . . . . @2.50
13 thru 15 . . . . 3.00

HEAD, THE
1 Old Airboy (1966) 2.00

HEARTBREAK COMICS
Eclipse
1 . . . . 1.50

HEAVY METAL MONSTERS
Revolutionary
1 'Up in Flames' 2.25

HE IS JUST A RAT
Exclaim Bound Comics
1 & 2 V:Jimmy and Billy Bob . . . 2.75

HELLGIRL
Knight Press
1 I:Jazzmine Grayce 2.95
1-shot Demonseed II, Bob Hickey &
Bill Nichols (1997) 2.95
1-shot Demonsong, Bob Hickey &
Bill Nichols (1997) 2.95
1-shot Purgatory (1997) 2.95

HELLINA
Lightning Comics 1994
1-shot I&O:Hellina 5.00
Commemorative 10.00
Nude cover 8.00
1996 rep. gold 5.00
1996 rep nude (c) 8.00
Spec. Hellina: Genesis with poster
(1996) 3.00
Platinum edition 4.00
Nude cover 5.00
Platinum nude edition 8.00
Spec. Hellina: In the Flesh (1997)
two diff. mild covers . . . . . @3.00
Nude covers, 2 diff. . . . . . @5.00
Spec. Hellina: Naked Desire (1997) 2.95
Cover B 2.95
Signed, ... 2.95

Nude cover A 5.00
Nude cover B 5.00
Spec. Hellina: Taking Back the Night
(1995) V:Michael Naynar 3.00
Nude cover 5.00
Spec. Hellina: Wicket Ways (1995)
A:Perg 2.75
Nude cover 5.00
Encore editions 3.00
Encore variant (c) 3.00
Encore, nude cover 5.00
Encore, nude variant (c) 5.00
Spec. Hellina: X-Mas in Hell (1996)
two different covers 3.00
Platinum edition 5.00
Nude cover 5.00
Nude variant cover 5.00
Nude platinum edition 15.00
Spec. Hellina: The Relic 3.00
Variant cover 3.00
Nude cover 5.00
Variant nude cover 5.00
Spec. 1997 Pin-up 3.50
1997 Pin-up, cover B 3.50
1997 Pin-up, cover A, nude . . 5.00
1997 Pin-up, cover B, nude . . 5.00
X-Over Hellina/Catfight (1995)
V:Prince of Sommia 2.75
Gold 4.00
Nude cover 4.00
Encore edition, mild covers, 2
different 2.95
Encore, nude covers, 2 diff. . . 5.00
X-Over Hellina/Cynder (1997) cover
A 2.95
Cover B 2.95
Nude cover A 5.00
Nude cover B 5.00
Spec Hellina #1 Skybolt Toyz lim.
ed. (1997) 1.50
TPB rep. Hellina appearances . . . 8.95
TPB rep. one-shots 12.95

HELLINA: HEART OF THORNS
Lightning Comics
1 (of 2) 3.00
1a nude cover 5.00
1b autographed 5.00
2 . . . . 2.75
2a variant cover 2.75
2b platinum edition 5.95
2c nude cover 5.00
2d variant nude cover 5.00
2e platinum nude edition 12.00

HELLINA: HELL'S ANGEL
Lightning Comics Oct. 1996
1 . . . . 2.75
1a platinum edition 8.00
1a platinum edition, signed . . . 10.00
1b nude cover 5.00
1c nude platinum edition 15.00
2 . . . . 2.75
2a platinum edition 8.00
2b nude cover 5.00
2c nude platinum edition 15.00
1 encore edition, cover A 2.95
1a encore edition, cover B 2.95
1b deluxe encore edition, cover A 5.00
1c deluxe encore edition, cover B 5.00

HELLINA: KISS OF DEATH
Lightning Comics 1995
1-shot A:Perg 4.00
1-shot nude cover 5.00
1-shot gold edition 10.00
1-shot Encore editions 3.00
1-shot Encore, nude cover . . . 5.00
Lightning Feb. 1997
1A 2.95
1B variant cover 2.95
1A nude cover 5.00
1B nude cover 5.00
1 encore, signed & numbered . . . 5.00

HELSING
Caliber Core March 1998
1W by Gary Reed & Low,
Wozniak(c) 2.95
1L Loudon (c) 2.95
1 variant cover 8.95
1 premium, signed 9.95
2 . . . . 2.95
3 . . . . 2.95

HELTER SKELTER
Antarctic Press 1997
0 by Mike Harris & Duc Tran . . 2.95
1 (of 4) 2.95
2 thru 4 . . . . @2.95
5 . . . . 2.95
6 . . . . 2.95

HEPCATS
Double Diamond
1 . . . . 35.00
2 . . . . 25.00
3 Snow Blind 15.00
4 thru 9 . . . . @10.00
10 thru 13 . . . . @3.50
14 Chapter 12 . . . . 3.00
15 Snowblind Chp. 13 . . . . 2.75
Antarctic Press
1 by Martin Wagner 3.00
2 "Trial by Intimacy" 3.00
3 Snowblind, pt.1 . . . . 3.00
4 Snowblind, pt.2 . . . . 3.00
5 Snowblind, pt.3 . . . . 3.00
6 Snowblind, pt.4 . . . . 3.00
7 Snowblind, pt.5 Intrusion . . 2.95
8 Snowblind, pt.6 Super Heroes . 2.95
9 Snowblind, pt.7 Kevin and
Kathryn 2.95
10 Snowblind, pt.8 Exorcism,
Prelude 2.95
11 Snowblind, pt.10 Exorcism(a) . 2.95
12 Snowblind, pt.10 Exorcism(b) . 2.95
13 Snowbling, pt.11 It's a Garden of
Eden... . . . . 3.50
TPB Collected Hepcats 14.95

HERCULES
A Plus Comics
1 Hercules Saga 2.50

HERCULES PROJECT
Monster Comics 1991
1 Origin issue,V:Mutants 1.95

HEROES
Blackbird
1 . . . . 6.00
2 . . . . 3.00

All comics prices listed are for *Near Mint* condition.

3	2.25
4 comic size	2.00
5 thru 7	@2.00

HEROES FROM WORDSMITH
Special Studios
1 WWI,F:Hunter Hawke ... 2.50

HEROES INCORPORATED
Double Edge Publishing
1 I:Heroes, Inc. ... 2.95
2 Betrayal ... 2.95

HEROIC TALES
Lone Star Press 1997
1 by Robb Phipps & Bill Williams 2.50
2 Steel of a Soldier's Heart, pt.2 2.50
3 Steel of a Soldier's Heart, pt.3 2.50
4 ... 2.50
5 ... 2.50
6 The Belles of Freedom, prequel 2.50
7 The Children of Atlas, pt.1 ... 2.50
8 by Bill Williams & Jeff Parker, I:Atlas ... 2.50

HEROINES, INC.
1 thru 5 ... @1.75

Hero Sandwitch #1 © Slave Labor
HERO SANDWICH
Slave Labor
1 thru 4 ... @1.50
5 thru 8 ... @1.75
9 ... 1.95
Graphic Novel ... 7.95

HIGH CALIBER
1 ... 4.00
2 ... 3.00
3 and 4 ... @2.50
Becomes:Caliber Presents

HIGH CALIBER
Caliber 1997
1 64pg ... 4.00
1 signed edition ... 4.00

2 64pg	4.00
3 48pg	4.00
4	4.00

HIGH SCHOOL AGENT
Sun Comics
1 I:Kohsuke Kanamori ... 2.50
2 Treasure Hunt at North Pole . 2.50
3 and 4 ... @2.50

HIGH SHINING BRASS
Apple
1 thru 4 ... @2.75

HIGH SOCIETY
Aardvark–Vanaheim
1 DS,Cerebus ... 25.00

HILLY ROSE'S SPACE ADVENTURES
Astro Comics 1995
1 confronts Steeltrap ... 8.00
1 2nd & 3rd pr. by B.C. Boyer . 3.00
2 ... 5.00
2 2nd & 3rd printing ... 3.00
3 ... 3.50
3 2nd printing ... 3.00
4 thru 9 ... @3.00
TPB Vol.1 Rocket Reporter ... 12.95

HIT THE BEACH
Antarctic 1993
1 ... 2.95
1a deluxe edition ... 5.00
2 & 3 ... @2.95

HITOMI AND HER GIRL COMMANDOS
Antarctic Press 1992
1 Shadowhunter,from Ninja HS .. 2.50
2 Synaptic Transducer ... 2.50
3 Shadowhunter in S.America ... 2.50
4 V:Mr.Akuma,last issue ... 2.50
[Series II]
1 thru 10 ... @2.75

HOLO BROTHERS, THE
Monster Comics
1 thru 10 ... @1.95
Fantagraphics
Spec.#1 ... 2.25
TPB The Curse of the Bloated Toad4.95

HOLY KNIGHT
Pocket Change Comics
1 thru 3 ... @2.50
4 V:His Past ... 2.50
5 V:Souljoiner ... 2.50
6 V:Demon Priest ... 2.50
7 Silent Scream,pt.2 ... 2.50
8 "Dragon Quest," pt.1 ... 2.50
9 "Dragon Quest," pt.2 ... 2.50
10 "Dragon Quest," pt.3 ... 2.50
11 "Dragon Quest," pt.4 ... 2.50

HONK
Fantagraphics
1 Don Martin ... 2.75
2 ... 2.75
3 ... 2.75

HONOR AMONG THIEVES
Gateway Grapnics
1 and 2 ... @1.50

HOON
Eenieweenie Comics
1 I:Hoon ... 2.50
2 Calazone Disaster ... 2.50
3 Reality Check ... 2.50
4 thru 8 ... @2.50

HOON, THE
Caliber Tapestry 1996
1 ... 2.95
2 ... 2.95
3 ... 2.95

HORNET SPECIAL
1 ... 2.00

HOROBI
Viz
1 ... 4.00
2 thru 8 ... @3.75
Book 2 1990–91
1 by Yoshihisa Tagami ... 3.50
2 D:Okado,Shoko Kidnapped . 4.25
3 Madoka Attacks Zen ... 4.25
4 D:Abbess Mitsuko ... 4.25
5 Catharsis! ... 4.25
6 Shuichi Vs. Zen ... 4.25
7 Shuichi vs. Zen, conc. ... 4.25

HORROR IN THE DARK
Fantagor
1 RCo,Inc.Blood Birth ... 2.00
2 RCo,Inc.Bath of Blood ... 2.00
3 RCo ... 2.00
4 RCo,Inc.Tales o/tBlackDiamond 2.00

HORROR SHOW
Caliber
1 GD,1977-80 reprint horror ... 3.50

HOUSE OF FRIGHTENSTEIN
AC Comics
1 ... 2.95

HOUSE OF HORROR
AC Comics
1 ... 2.50

HOWL
Eternity
1 & 2 ... @2.25

HOW TO DRAW TEENAGE MUTANT NINJA TURTLES
Solson
1 Lighter cover ... 15.00
1a Dark cover ... 5.00

H.P. LOVECRAFT'S THE DREAM-QUEST OF UNKNOWN KADATH
Mock Man Press 1997
1 (of 5) by Jason Thompson ... 2.95

B & W PUB.

1 2nd printing	2.95
2	2.95
3	2.95
4 (of 5)	2.95

HUGO
Fantagraphics

1	4.00
2	2.00
3	2.00
4	2.00

HUMAN GARGOYLES
Eternity

Book one	1.95
Book two	1.95
Book three	1.95
Book four	1.95

HUMAN HEAD
Caliber

1 Alice in Flames	2.50

HUNT AND THE HUNTED, THE
Newcomers Publishing

1 I:Aramis Thiron	2.95
2 V:Werewolves	2.95
3 Rio De Janero	2.95
4 F:Aramis Thiron	2.95

HURRICANE GIRLS
Antarctic Press 1995

1 & 2 Tale of Dinon	@3.50
3 thru 7 seven part series	@2.95

HURRICANE LEROUX
Inferno Studios

1 I:Deja Vu Jones	2.50

HUZZAH
1 I:Albedo'sErmaFelna	60.00

HY-BREED
Division Publishing

1 thru 3 F:Cen Intel	@2.25
4 thru 9	@2.50

I.F.S. ZONE
1 thru 6	@1.25

I AM LEGEND
Eclipse

1 Novel Adaptation	5.95
2 Novel Adaptation cont'd	5.95
3 Novel Adaptation cont'd	5.95

ICARUS
1 thru 9	@1.70

ICON DEVIL
1	2.00
2	2.00
2nd Series	
1 thru 5	@1.85

IDIOTLAND
Fantagraphic

1	2.95

ILIAD
Amaze Ink 1997

1 by Darren Brady & Alex Ogle	2.95
2	2.95
3	2.95
4	2.95
5	2.95
6	2.95
7	2.95

ILIAD II
1	3.00
1a 2nd cover variation	3.00
2	2.00
3	2.00
4	1.70

ILLUMINATUS
1	2.00
2	2.50
3	2.50

INFERNO
Caliber Press

1 I:City of Inferno	2.95
2 Search for Identity	2.95
3 V:Malateste	2.95
4 by MCy and Michael Gaydos	2.95
5	2.95

INFINITE LINE COMICS PRESENTS
Infinite Line Comics

1 Arcone	1.00

INTERZONE
Brainstorm Comics

1 w/4 cards	2.50
2 w/4 cards	2.50

INU YASHA
Viz Communications Jan. 1997

1 thru 5 (of 10) by Rumiko Takahashi	@2.95
PART TWO: A FEUDAL FAIRY TALE	
1 (of 9) by Rumiko Takahashi	2.95
2 (of 9)	2.95
6	2.95
7	2.95
8	3.25
11 thru 15 (of 15)	@3.25
TPB	15.95
TPB Vol. 2	15.95

INVADERS FROM MARS
Eternity

1	2.50
2	2.50
3	2.50
BOOK II 1991	
1 Sequel to '50's SF classic	2.50
2 Pact of Tsukus/Humans	2.50
3 Last issue	2.50

INVASION '55
Apple

1	2.25
2	2.25
3	2.25

INVISIBLE PEOPLE
Kitchen Sink

1 WE,I:Peacus Pleatnik	2.95
2 WE,The Power	2.95
3 WE,Final issue	2.95

ISMET
1 Cartoon Dog	12.00
2	5.00
3 Rare	5.00
4	5.00

IT'S SCIENCE WITH DR. RADIUM
1 thru 7	@1.50
8	1.75
9	1.95
Spec #1	2.95

Jackaroo #1 © Eternity

JACKAROO
Eternity

1 GCh	2.25
2 GCh	2.25
3 GCh	2.25

JACK HUNTER
Blackthorne

1	3.50
2	3.50
3	3.50

JACK OF NINES
1	1.25
2 thru 4	@1.50
5	2.00

JACK THE RIPPER
1 thru 4	@2.25

JAM, THE
Slave Labor

1	2.00
2	2.00
3 thru 5	@2.25
Dark Horse	
6 thru 8	2.50

    All comics prices listed are for *Near Mint* condition.

Caliber
9	2.95
9 signed edition	2.95
10 It's a Kafka Thing	2.95
11 thru 14	@2.95
15 "The Kinetic," pt.3	2.95

JAM SPECIAL, THE
Matrix
1	2.50

JASON AND THE ARGONAUTS
Caliber
1 thru 5	@2.50

JAY & SILENT BOB
Oni Press 1998
1 (of 4) by Kevin Smith & Duncan Fregedo	2.95
2	2.95
3	2.95

JAZZ
High Impact
1 Gold variant edition RCI(c)	9.95

JAZZ: SOLITAIRE
ABC Comics 1998
1 (of 4) by Jose Varese	3.00
1a photo cover	5.95
1b nude variant (c)	5.95
2	3.00
2a Variant Exotika (c)	5.95
2b Variant Naughty (c)	5.95
3	3.00
3a Variant Kaspar nude (c)	5.95
3b Variant Jazz nude (c)	5.95

JAZZ: SUPERSTAR
ABC Comics 1998
1 (of 3) by Jose Varese	3.00
1a JQ cover	6.00
1b Jazz nude variant (c)	10.00

JAZZ AGE CHRONICLES
1 thru 6	@1.50
7	2.50

JCP FEATURES
1 1st MT;S&K,NA/DG rep. A:T.H.U.N.D.E.R.Agents,TheFly, Black Hood Mag.Size	4.50

JEREMIAH: BIRDS OF PREY
Adventure Comics
1 I: Jeremiah,A:Kurdy	2.50
2 conclusion	2.50

JEREMIAH: FIST FULL OF SAND
Adventure Comics
1 A:Captain Kenney	2.50
2 conclusion	2.50

JEREMIAH: THE HEIRS
Adventure Comics 1991
1 Nathanial Bancroft estate	2.50

2 conclusion	2.50

JERRY IGERS FAMOUS FEATURES
Blackthorne
1	3.00
2 thru 4	@2.00

Pacific
5 thru 8	@2.00

JIM
Fantagraphics 1987–90
1	20.00
2	15.00
3 and 4	@10.00

Second Series 1994
1	4.00
1a 2nd printing	3.00
2	3.50
2a 2nd printing	3.00
3 thru 5	@3.00

JOE PSYCHO & MOO FROG
Goblin Studios
1 Fanatics Edition	2.50
1 Fanatics signed and numbered Edition	9.95
2	2.50
2 signed & numbered	9.95
3	2.50
4	2.50
4B San Diego con cover	4.95
5	2.50
Spec. Psychosis Abnormalis	2.50

JOE SINN
Caliber
1 I:Joe Sinn,Nikki	2.95
2	2.95

JOHNNY ATOMIC
Eternity
1 I:Johnny A.Tornick	2.50
2 Project X-contingency plan	2.50
3	2.50

JOHNNY DARK
Double Edge
1 V:Biker Gang	2.95

JOHNNY THE HOMICIDAL MANIAC
Slave Labor 1996
1 by Jhonen Vasquez	45.00
1 3rd printing	4.00
1 signed, limited	9.00
2	20.00
2 3rd printing	3.00
3	12.00
3 3rd printing	3.00
4	5.00
4 2nd & 3rd printing	3.00
5	4.00
5 2nd printing	3.00
6	3.00
7	3.00
TPB	19.95
HC	29.95
TPB Director's Cut	19.95

JOURNEY
Aardvark–Vanaheim
1	13.00
2	9.00
3	8.00
4	5.00
5 thru 7	@3.00
8 thru 14	@2.50

Fantagraphics
15	2.50
16 thru 28	@2.00

JR. JACKALOPE
1 orange cover,1981	8.00
1a Yellow cover,1981	15.00
2	8.00

JUNGLE COMICS
Blackthorne
4 thru 6	@2.00

JUNGLE GIRLS
AC Comics
1 incGold.Age reps.	1.95
2	1.95
3 Greed,A:Tara	2.75
4 CaveGirl	2.75
5 Camilla	2.75
6 TigerGirl	2.75
7 CaveGirl	2.75
8 Sheena Queen o/t Jungle	2.95
9 Wild Girl,Tiger Girl,Sheena	2.95
10 F:Tara,Cave Girl,Nyoka	2.95
11 F:Sheena,Tiger Girl,Nyoka	2.95
12 F:Sheena,Camilla,Tig.Girl	2.95
13 F:Tara, Tiger Girl	2.95

JUNGLE COMICS
A List Comics
1 thru 5 reprint of golden age	@2.95
TPB Book of Jungle Comics Covers, 1940–54	7.95

JURASSIC JANE
London Night 1997
1 by Sky Owens, F:Tira, elf princess of Atlantis	3.00
1 deluxe nude edition	6.00
1 deluxe nude edition, signed	10.00
2	3.00
2 deluxe	6.00
3	3.00
3 deluxe	6.00
4 EHr, Sky Owens	3.00
4 nude cover edition	6.00
5 by Preston Owens	3.00
5 nude cover edition	6.00
6 by Sky Owens	3.00
6 nude cover edition	6.00
7 by Sky Owens	3.00
7 nude cover edition	6.00
Coll. Ed.	5.00
Coll. Ed. nude EHr(c)	7.00

JUSTICE
Newcomers Publishing 1995
1 I:Judiciary Urban Strike Team	2.95

JUSTY
1 thru 9	@1.75

KABUKI: CIRCLE OF BLOOD
Caliber Press
1 R:Kabuki 7.00
2 Kabuki Goes Rogue 5.00
3 V:Noh Agents 5.00
4 V:Noh Agents 3.50
5 V:Kai 3.00
6 . . . . 3.00
TPB Rep.#1-#6 . . . . 16.95
TPB 2nd printing 16.95
HC DAv,rep.#1–#6 272pg. . . 100.00
TPB deluxe, signed, etc. 24.95
TPB Compilation 7.95

KABUKI: DANCE OF DEATH
London Night Studios
1 1st Full series 5.00

KABUKI: MASKS OF THE NOH
Caliber April 1996
1A JQ(c) 3.00
1B Mays/Mack(c) 3.00
1C Buzz(c) 3.00
2 . . . . 3.00
3 DMk 3.00
4 epilog 3.00

KAFKA
1 thru 5 . . . . @2.00
The Execution Spec. 2.25

KAMUI
Eclipse
1 Sanpei Shirato Art 4.00
1a 2nd printing 2.50
2 Mystery of Hanbie 1.50
2a 2nd printing 1.50
3 V:Ichijiro 2.00
3a 2nd printing 1.50
4 thru 15 . . . . @1.50
16 thru 19 . . . . @1.95
20 thru 37 . . . . @1.50

KAOS MOON
Caliber 1996
1 by DdB 3.50
1a 2nd edition 3.00
2 . . . . 3.00
2a 2nd edition, new cover 3.00
3 . . . . 3.00
4 Anubian Nights, Chapter 2 . . 3.00
GN Full Circle, rep #1–#2 . . . . . 5.95

KAPTAIN KEEN
1 thru 3 . . . . @1.75
4 and 5 . . . . @1.50
6 and 7 . . . . @1.75

KATMANDU
Antarctic Press
1 thru 3 . . . . @2.75
4 & 5 Woman of Honor 2.75
6 F:Laska 2.75
Med Systems
7 and 8 . . . . @1.95
Vision Comics
9 "When Warriors Die," pt.3(of 3) 1.95
10 "The Curse of the Blood," pt.1 . 2.50

11 "The Curse of the Blood," pt.2 . 2.50
12 "The Curse of the Blood," concl 2.95
13 "The Search For Magic," pt.1 . 2.95
14 "The Search For Magic," pt.2 . 2.95
15 "The Search For Magic," pt.3 . 2.95
16 "Ceremonies," pt.1 (of 3) 2.95

KEIF LLAMA
1 thru 6 . . . . @2.00

KELLEY BELLE, POLICE DETECTIVE
Newcomers Publishing
1 Debut issue 2.95
2 Case of the Jeweled Scarab . . 2.95
3 Case o/t Jeweled Scarab,pt.2 . . 2.95
TPB #1 . . . . 8.95

KELLEY BELLE: PERIL ON THE HIGH SEAS
Atlantis Comics 1996
1 (of 6) 2.95

KELLY BELLE: SEARCH FOR THE GOLDEN MONKEY
Atlantis 1996
1 (of 2) by James Watson & Rob Ewing 2.95

KID CANNIBAL
Eternity
1 I:Kid Cannibal 2.50
2 Hunt for Kid Cannibal 2.50
3 A:Janice 2.50
4 final issue 2.50

KI-GORR THE KILLER
AC
1 I:Ki-Gorr, Rae 2.95

KIKU SAN
Aircel
1 thru 6 . . . . @1.95

KILLING STROKE
Eternity 1991
1 British horror tales 2.50
2 inc.'Blood calls to Blood' 2.50
3 and 4 . . . . @2.50

KILROY
Caliber Core 1998
1C by Joe Pruett & Feliciano Zecchin, John Cassaday(c) . . . 2.95
1P JoP (c) 2.95
1a premium edition 9.95
2 . . . . 2.95
3 . . . . 2.95

KILROY IS HERE
Caliber Press 1995
1 Kilroy Rescues Infant 2.95
2 Reflections,pt.2 . . . . 2.95
3 Reflections,pt.3 . . . . 2.95
4 Lincoln Memorial 2.95
5 thru 8 . . . . @2.95
9 and 10 . . . . @2.95

11 WEI,RPc,"Screen" 2.95
12 Khymer Rouge 2.95

KILROY: DAEMONSTORM
Caliber 1997
1 one-shot 2.95

KIMBER, PRINCE OF FELONS
Antarctic Press
1 I:Kimber 2.50
2 V:Lord Tyrex 2.50

KINGDOM OF THE WICKED
Caliber 1996
1 IEd 2.95
2 IEd 2.95
3 IEd 2.95
4 IEd 2.95
HC rep. #1–#4 . . . . 49.95
TPB rep. #1–#4 . . . . 12.95

King Kong #1 © Monster Comics
KING KONG
Monster Comics 1991
1 thru 6 . . . . @2.50

KINGS IN DISGUISE
1 thru 5 . . . . @2.00
6 end Mini-series 2.00

KIRBY KING OF THE SERIALS
Blackthorne
1 . . . . 2.00
2 . . . . 2.00
3 . . . . 2.00
4 . . . . 2.00

KITZ 'N' KATZ
1 . . . . 3.50
Eclipse
2 . . . . 2.00
3 . . . . 1.50
4 and 5 . . . . @2.00

All comics prices listed are for *Near Mint* condition.

KLOWN SHOCK
North Star
1 Horror Stories 2.75

KNIGHTMARE
Antartic Press
1 . . . . 2.75
2 . . . . 2.75
3 Wedding Knight pt.1 . . . . 2.75
4 Wedding Knight pt.2 . . . . 2.75
5 F:Dream Shadow 2.75
6 V:Razorblast 2.75

KNIGHT MASTERS
1 thru 7 . . . . @1.50

KNIGHTS OF THE DINNER TABLE
Kenzer & Company
4 Have Dice Will Travel 2.95
5 Master of the Game 2.95
6 on the high seas 2.95
7 Lord of Steam 2.95
8 A:magic cow 2.95
9 To Dice for Sister Sara 2.95
16 thru 18 . . . . 2.95
19 Heroes of the Hack League . . 2.95
20 Hack in Space 2.95
21 Home is Where You Hang Yer
   Dice Bag 2.95
22 Opportunity Knocks 2.95
TPB Vol. 1 Bundle of Trouble . . 9.95
TPB Tales From the Vault 9.95

KNIGHT WATCHMAN
Caliber Press
1 Graveyard pt. 1 . . . . 2.95
2 Graveyard pt. 1 . . . . 2.95

KOMODO & THE DEFIANTS
1 thru 6 . . . . @1.50

KUNG FU WARRIORS
(Prev. ROBOWARRIORS)
CFW
12 . . . . 1.95
13 thru 19 . . . . @2.25

KUNOICHI
Lightning Comics 1996
1 2 diff. mild covers 3.00
1 platinum edition 5.95
1 autographed edition 9.95

KYRA
Elsewhere 1989
1 thru 5 by Robin Ator . . . . . . @1.75
TPB rep #1–#5 + pin-ups 6.95

L.A. RAPTOR
Morbid Graphics
1 Velocaraptor loose 2.95

LABOR FORCE
Blackthorne
1 thru 4 . . . . @1.50
5 thru 8 . . . . @1.75

LA COSA NOSTROID
Fireman Press 1997
1 by Don Harmon & Rob Schrab   2.95
2 by Don Harmon & Edvis 2.95
3 . . . .'. . 2.95
4 . . . . 2.95
5 . . . . 2.95
6 x-over madness 2.95
7 . . . . 2.95
8 . . . . 2.95
9 . . . . 2.95
10 final issue of Volume 1 . . . . . 2.95

LACUNAE
CFD Producitons 1995
1 thru 4 F:Monkey Boys 2.50
5 thru 10 . . . . @2.50
11 HMo 2.50

LADIES OF LONDON NIGHT
London Night 1997
Fall Special 5.00
Nude Heather Parkhurst (c) . . 7.00
Nude Gloria Gilbert (c) 7.00
Winter Special 5.00
   Winter Wonderland Edition . . 7.00
Spring 98 Special 5.00
   Nude Gloria Ann (c) 7.00
   Nude Wendy Leigh (c) 7.00
Spotlight: Devon Michaels 3.95
   Devon Michaels nude (c) 6.00

LADY ARCANE
Heroic Publishing
1 thru 3 . . . . @3.50

LADY CRIME
AC Comics
1 Bob Powell reprints 2.75

LADY VAMPRÉ
Blackout Comics 1996
0 (1995) 2.75
1 flip-book 2.95

LADY VAMPRÉ: IN THE FLESH
Blackout Comics 1996
1 . . . . 2.95
1 photo sexy cover 9.95

LADY VAMPRÉ RETURNS
Blackout Comics 1998
1 by Rob Roman & Kirk Manley . 2.95
1a nude cover 9.95
1b Deluxe edition 14.95

LAFFIN GAS
Blackthorne
1 . . . . 2.50
2 thru 12 . . . . @2.00

LANCE STANTON WAYWARD WARRIOR
1 and 2 . . . . @1.50

LANDER
Mermaid Producions
1 Power of the Dollar,pt.1 . . . . . 2.25
2 Power of the Dollar,pt.2 . . . . . 2.25
3 Power of the Dollar,pt.3 . . . . . 2.25
Vol. 2
1 "By Whose Authority," pt.1 . . 2.75
2 "By Whose Authority," pt.2 . . . 2.75

LANDRA
Polyventura Entertainment Group
1 . . . . 2.50

LAST DITCH
Edge Press
1 CCa(s),THa, ... 2.50

LAST GENERATION
Black Tie Studios
1 . . . . 6.00
2 . . . . 4.00
3 . . . . 2.25
4 . . . . 2.25
5 . . . . 2.25
Book One Rep. 6.95

LAST KISS, THE
Eclipse
Spec. 3.95

LATIGO KID WESTERN
AC Comics
1 . . . . 1.95

LAUREL & HARDY
1 3-D 2.50

LEAGUE OF CHAMPIONS
Hero Comics
(cont. from Innovation L.of C. #3)
1 GP,F:Sparkplug,Icestar 3.50
2 GP(i),F:Marksman,Flare,Icicle . 3.50
3 . . . . 3.50
4 F:Sparkplug,League 3.50
5 Morrigan Wars Pt.#1 . . . . 3.50
6 Morrigan Wars Pt.#3 . . . . 3.50
7 Morrigan Wars Pt.#6 . . . . 3.50
8 Morrigan Wars Conclusion . . . 3.50
9 A:Gargoyle 3.50
10 A:Rose 3.50
11 thru 12 . . . . 3.95
13 V:Malice 3.95
14 V:Olympians 3.95
15 V:Olympians 2.95

LE FEMME VAMPRIQUE
Brainstorm 1997
1 . . . . 3.50
1a nude edition 5.00

LEGEND LORE
1 and 2 . . . . @2.00
combined rep. 8.95

LEGENDLORE
Caliber "New Worlds"
1 JMt signed 2.95
3 JMt 2.95
4 JMt 2.95

5 JMt 2.95
6 flip book with Boston Bombers #4
. . . . 2.95
7 JMt 2.95
8 JMt 2.95
TPB Tainted Soul, rep. #1–#4 . . 12.95
TPB In Misery's Shadow, Rep.
   #5–#7 . . . . 9.95

LEGENDLORE: REALM WARS
Caliber "New Worlds"
1 by Joe Martin & Philip Xavier,
   Fawn cover by Xavier 2.95
1 Falla cover by Boller 2.95
1a signed 2.95
2 . . . . 2.95
3 . . . . 2.95
4 concl. 2.95

LEGENDLORE: SLAVE OF FATE
Caliber Fantasy 1998
1-shot by JMt & Philip Xavier . . . 2.95

LEGENDLORE: WRATH OF THE DRAGON
Caliber Fantasy 1998
1 by JMt & Philip Xavier 2.95
1 variant Philip Xavier(c) 2.95
2 . . . . 2.95
3 . . . . 2.95
4 . . . . 2.95

LEGEND OF LEMNEAR
CPM Manga 1997
1 . . . . 2.95
2 . . . . 2.95
3 . . . . 2.95
4 . . . . 2.95
5 . . . . 2.95
6 . . . . 2.95
7 . . . . 2.95
8 . . . . 2.95

LEGENDS OF LUXURA
Brainstorm 1996
1 platinum edition 5.00
2 gold edition 5.00
3 . . . . 2.95
TPB #1 . . . . 12.95

LEGION OF LUDICROUS HEROES
1 . . . . 2.00

LEGION X-I
1 McKinney 5.00
2 McKinney, rare 15.00
Volume 2
1 thru 4 . . . . @2.00

LEGION X-2
Vol 2 #1 . . . . 2.00
Vol 2 #2 . . . . 2.00
Vol 2 #3 . . . . 2.00
Vol 2 #4 . . . . 2.00

LENSMAN
Eternity 1990
1 E.E.'Doc' Smith adapt. 2.25
2 . . . . 2.25
3 . . . . 2.25
4 . . . . 2.25
5 On Radelix 2.25
6 . . . . 2.25
Collectors Spec #1, 56 pgs. 3.95
TPB Birth of a Lensman, rep. . . . 5.95
TPB Secret of the Lens, rep. 5.95

LENSMAN: GALACTIC PATROL
Eternity 1990
1 thru 7 E.E. 'Doc' Smith adapt. @2.25

Lensman: War of the Galaxies #5
© Eternity Comics

LENSMAN: WAR OF THE GALAXIES
Eternity 1990
1 thru 7 . . . . @2.25

LEONARDO
1 TMNT 13.00

LETHAL LADIES OF BRAINSTORM
Brainstorm 1997
1 F:Luxura, Vampfire, etc. 2.95
1 nude cover edition 3.95
1 luxury edition 5.00

LETHAL STRIKE
London Night 1998
TPB 12.95

LETHAL STRIKE ARCHIVES
London Night 1997
1 rep. Razor #7, #10 & Uncut
   #19–#21 . . . . 3.00
1 nude cover edition 10.00

LETHAL STRIKE: SHADOW VIPER
London Night 1998
1 (of 2) from Razor: Torture #4 . . 3.00
1 nude cover 6.00
1 leather 15.00

LEVEL X
Caliber 1997
1 . . . . 2.95
2 32pg 2.95
3 48pg 3.95

LEVEL X: THE NEXT REALITY
Caliber 1997
1 (of 2) by Dan Harbison & Randy
   Buccini, 64pg 3.95
2 48pg 3.95

LIBBY ELLIS
1 . . . . 1.95
2 . . . . 1.95
Eternity
1 thru 4 . . . . @1.95

LIBERATOR
Eternity
1 thru 6 . . . . @1.95

L.I.F.E. BRIGADE
Blue Comet
1 A:Dr. Death 1.50
1a 2nd printing 1.50
2 . . . . 1.50

LIVINGSTONE MOUNTAIN
Adventure Comics 1991
1 I:Scat,Dragon Rax 2.50
2 Scat & Rax Create Monsters . . 2.50
3 Rax rescue attempt 2.50
4 Final issue 2.50

LLOYD LLEWELLYN
Fantagraphics
1 Mag Size 4.00
2 Mag Size 2.25
3 Mag Size 2.25
4 Mag Size 2.25
5 Mag Size 2.25
6 Mag Size 2.25
7 Regular Size 2.25

LOCO VS. PULVERINE
Eclipse
1 Parody 2.50

LOGAN'S RUN
Adventure Comics 1990
1 thru 6 Novel adapt. . . . . . . @2.50

LOGAN'S WORLD
Adventure Comics 1991
1 Seq. to Logan's Run 2.50
2 thru 6 . . . . @2.50

LONER
Fleetway
1 Pt. 1 of 7 . . . . 1.95

B & W PUB.

2 Pt. 2	1.95
3 Pt. 3	1.95
4 Pt. 4	1.95
5 Pt. 5	1.95
6 Pt. 6	1.95

LONE WOLF & CUB
First

1 FM(c)	7.00
1a 2nd printing	2.50
1b 3rd printing	1.50
2	4.00
2a 2nd printing	2.00
3	3.50
4 thru 10	@3.00
11 thru 17	@2.75
18 thru 25	@2.50
26 thru 36	@2.95
37 and 38	@3.25
39 120 Page	5.95
40	3.25
41 MP(c), 60 page	3.95
42 MP(c)	3.25
43 MP(c)	3.25
44 MP(c)	3.25
45 MP(c)	3.25

LORD OF THE DEAD
Conquest

1 R.E.Howard adapt.	2.95

LOST, THE
Caliber

1	3.00
1a special ed.	7.00
1b signed	3.00
2 thru 4	@3.00

LOST ANGEL
Caliber

1	3.50

LOST CONTINENT
Eclipse 1990

1 thru 5, Manga	@3.50

LOST WORLD, THE
Millennium 1996

1 & 2 Arthur Conan Doyle adapt	@2.95

LOTHAR
Powerhouse Graphics

1 I:Lothar,Galactic Bounty Hunter	2.50
2 I:Nightcap	2.50

LOVE AND ROCKETS
Fantagraphics Books 1982–96

1 HB,B&W cover, adult	60.00
1a HB,Color cover	35.00
1b 2nd printing	4.00
2 HB	25.00
3 HB	15.00
4 HB	15.00
5 HB	15.00
6 HB	7.00
7 HB	9.00
8 HB	9.00
9 HB	7.00
10 HB	8.00
11 HB	5.00
12 HB	5.00
13 HB	5.00
14 HB	5.00
15 HB	5.00
16 thru 21 HB	@3.00
22 thru 39 HB	@3.00
40 thru 50	@3.00
Bonanza rep.	3.00
TPB Vol 9 Flies on the Ceiling, 2nd printing	16.95
HC Vol 10 Love & Rockets X	35.00
HC Vol 10 deluxe	39.95
TPB Vol 10	11.95
HC Vol 11 Wigwam Bam	35.00
HC Vol 11 deluxe	39.95
TPB Vol 11	14.95
HC Vol 12 Poison River	35.00
HC Vol 12 deluxe	39.95
TPB Vol 12	16.95
HC Vol 13 Chester Square	34.95
TPB Vol 14 Luba Conquers the World	14.95
HC Vol 14 Luba Conquers the World	34.95
HC Vol 14 , signed	39.95
TPB Vol 15	14.95
HC Vol 15	34.95
HC Vol 15 , signed	39.95

LUFTWAFFE 1946
Antarctic Press

1 (of 4) by Ted Namura & BDn	2.95
2 Luftsturm, pt.2 thru 4	@2.95
3	2.95
4	2.95
5 new weapons	2.95
6 Projekt Saucer, pt.1	2.95
7 Projekt Saucer, pt.2	2.95
8 Projekt Saucer, pt.3	2.95
9 Projekt Saucer, pt.4	2.95
10 Projekt Saucer, pt.5	2.95
11 Projekt Saucer, epilogue	2.95
12 Richthofen's Flying Circus, pt.1	2.95
13 Richthofen's Flying Circus, pt.2	2.95
Tech Manual Vol. 1	3.95
Spec. #1 Triebflugel	2.95
Ann. #1 prototype artwork	2.95
TPB Vol.1, rep.mini-series #1–#4	10.95
TPB Vol.2, rep. #1–#5	10.95

LUM*URUSEI YATSURA

1 Art by Rumiko Takahashi	2.95
2	2.95
3	2.95
4	2.95
5	3.25
6 thru 8	@2.95

LUXURA
Brainstorm 1996

Convention Book 2	2.95

LUXURA & VAMPFIRE
Brainstorm 1997

1 by Fauve	2.95
1a nude cover	3.95

LUXURA ANNUAL
Brainstorm 1998

1 48pg	3.95
1a nude cover	3.95

LUXURA/BABY ANGEL X
Brainstorm 1996

Spec. x-over	2.95

Spec. deluxe	5.00
Luxury edition	10.00
Deluxe luxury edition	15.00

LUXURA LEATHER
Brainstorm

Platinum edition	5.00
Signed edition	10.00

LUXURA/WIDOW: BLOOD LUST
Brainstorm

Omega x-over pt.2 concl.	2.95
Omega Fusion cover	5.00
Luxury edition	10.00
Deluxe luxury edition	15.00
See: Widow/Luxura for pt.1	

MACH 1
Fleetway

1 I:John Probe-Secret Agent	1.95

MACKENZIE QUEEN

1 thru 5	@3.75

MACROSS II
Viz

1 Macross Saga sequel	2.75
2 A:Ishtar	2.75
3 F:Reporter Hibiki, Ishtar	2.75
4 V:Feff,The Marduk	2.75
5	2.75
6	2.75
7 Sylvie Confesses	2.75
8 F:Ishtar	2.75
9 V:Marduk Fleet	2.75
10	2.75

MACROSS II: THE MICRON CONSPIRACY
Viz 1994

1 Manga	2.75

MAD DOGS
Eclipse 1992

1 I:Mad Dogs(Cops)	2.50

Mad Dogs #1 © Eclipse

2 V:Chinatown Hood 2.50
3 . . . . 2.50

MAD RACCOONS
MU Press 1991
1 thru 7 by Cathy Hill, Angst of an
Artist . . . . @2.95

Maelstrom #1 © Aircel

MAELSTROM
Aircel
1 thru 5 . . . . @1.70
6 thru 13 . . . . @1.50

MAGGOTS
1 JSon, mag size 3.95
2 JSon, mag size 3.95
3 GM/JSon,inc.'Some Kinda
Beautiful' 3.95

MAGICAL MATES
Antarctic Press 1995
1 & 2 Manga, by Mio Odagi . . @2.95
3 thru 8 (of 8) . . . . @2.95

MAGUS
Caliber Core May 1998
1L by Gary Reed & Craig Brasfield,
VcL(c) 2.95
1D GyD(c) 2.95
1 premium edition, signed 9.95
2 Magus secrets 2.95

MAI, THE PSYCHIC GIRL
Eclipse
1 I:Mai,Alliance of 13 Sages 3.75
1a 2nd printing 2.00
2 V:Wisdom Alliance 2.00
2a 2nd printing 1.50
3 V:Kaieda,I:Ojii-San 2.00
4 . . . . 2.00
5 thru 19 . . . . @1.75
20 thru 28 . . . . @1.50

MAISON IKKOKU
Viz
1 thru 7 . . . . 2.95

[Part Two]
1 thru 6 . . . . 2.95
[Part Three]
1 thru 6 . . . . 2.95
[Part Four]
1 thru 6 F:Kyoko 2.95
7 thru 9 Plum Wine 2.95
10 Hickey on Yusaku 2.95
[Part Six] Aug. 1996
1 thru 11 by Rumiko Takahashi @3.50
TPB Vol. 4 Good Housekeeping 15.95
TPB Vol. 5 Empty Nest 15.95
TPB Vol. 6 Bedside Manners . . . 15.95
TPB Vol. 7 Intensive Care 15.95
[Part Seven] July 1997
1 thru 8 by Rumiko Takahashi @3.25
9 thru 13 . . . . @3.50
[Part Eight] Aug. 1998
1 (of 8) 3.25
TPB Vol 8 Domestic Dispute . . 16.95
TPB Dogged Pursuit 17.95

MAN EATING COW
1 Spin-off from the Tick 3.25
2 O:Mr.Krinkles,A:Lt.Valentine . . 2.75
3 Final issue 2.75
Bonanza #1, 128pg 4.95
Bonanza #2, 100pg. 4.95

MAN-ELF
3 A:Jerry Cornelius 2.25

MANDRAKE
1 . . . . 3.95
2 . . . . 3.95
3 . . . . 3.95
Ultimate Mandrake 14.95

MANDRAKE MONTHLY
1 . . . . 3.95
2 . . . . 3.95
3 . . . . 4.95
4 . . . . 4.95
5 . . . . 4.95
6 . . . . 6.95
Special #1 . . . . 6.95

MAN FROM U.N.C.L.E.
Entertainment Publ.
1 'Number One with a Bullet Affair 2.50
2 'Number One with a Bullet Affair 2.00
3 'The E-I-E-I-O Affair' 1.50
4 'The E-I-E-I-O Affair,' concl. . . . 1.50
5 'The Wasp Affair' 1.50
6 'Lost City of THRUSH Affair' . . 1.50
7 'The Wildwater Affair' 1.50
8 'The Wilder West Affair' 1.50
9 'The Cahadian Lightning Affair' 1.75
10 'The Turncoat Affair' 1.75
11 'Craters of the Moon Affair' . . 1.75

MANGA MONTHLY
0 . . . . 3.00

MANGA VIZION
Viz
1 thru 8 Ogre Slayer 4.95

MANGAZINE
Antartic Press
1 newsprint cover 7.00

1a reprint 3.00
2 . . . . 5.00
3 . . . . 4.00
4 . . . . 2.00
5 . . . . 1.50
New Series
1 . . . . 3.00
2 . . . . 3.00
3 . . . . 1.75
4 . . . . 1.75
5 thru 7 . . . . @1.95
8 thru 13 . . . . @2.25
14 New Format 2.95
15 . . . . 2.95
16 . . . . 2.95
17 . . . . 2.95

MANIMAL
1 EC,rep. 1.70

MAN OF RUST
Blackthorne 1986
1 Cover A 1.50
1 Cover B 1.50

MANSLAUGHTER
Brainstorm 1996
1 . . . . 2.95
1a gold foil edition 5.00

MANTUS FILES
Eternity
1 Sidney Williams novel adapt . . 2.50
2 Vampiric Figures 2.50
3 Secarus' Mansion 2.50
4 A:Secarus 2.50

MARCANE
Eclipse
1 Book 1,JMu 5.95

MARK I
(Prev.: Atomic Comics)
2 . . . . 1.50

MARQUIS, THE
Caliber 1997
1 GyD 3.00
1 spec. double gatefold cover . . . 7.00
2 Marquis cover by Vincent Locke 3.00
2a Marquis view of world GyD(c) 3.00
3 . . . . 3.00

MARQUIS, THE:
GALLERY OF HELL
Caliber
1-shot GyD 3.95

MARQUIS, THE:
LES PRELUDES
Caliber 1996
1 GyD, prelude edition 2.95
1 signed, prelude editon GyD . . . 2.95

MASKED MAN
Eclipse
12 . . . . 2.00

    All comics prices listed are for *Near Mint* condition.

MASKED WARRIOR X
Antarctic Press April 1996
1 (of 6) by Masayuki Fujihara . . . 3.50
2 . . . . 2.95
3 The Girls of Olympus," pt.2 . . . 2.95
4 "Protect the Silver Fortress" . . . 2.95

MASQUERADE
Eclipse
1 . . . . 1.50
2 . . . . 1.95
3 . . . . 1.95

MATAAK
K-Blamm 1995
1 I:Mataak 2.50
2 Spirit of Peace 2.50

MATT CHAMPION
1 EC 2.00
2 EC 2.00

MAX OF REGULATORS
1 . . . . 5.00
2 . . . . 3.50
3 . . . . 3.50
4 . . . . 3.50

MAXWELL MOUSE FOLLIES
1 Large format (1981) 5.00
1a Comic Size(1986) 3.00
2 thru 6 . . . . @2.00

MAYHEM
1 thru 6 . . . . @2.50

MAZE AGENCY
Caliber 1997
1 "The Death of Justice Girl" reprint
series 2.95
1a signed 2.95
2 stranded in a monastery, Gene
Gonzales(c) 2.95
2a Adam Hughes (c) 2.95
3G The Two Wrong Rhoades,
Gonzales(c) 2.95
3H Adam Hughes(c) 2.95

MECHANOIDS
Caliber 1991
1 . . . . 2.50
2 thru 5 . . . . @3.50

MECHARIDER: THE REGULAR SERIES
Castle
1 thru 3 F:Winter 2.95
Spec.#1 Limited Edition 2.95

MEGATON
Megaton
1 JG(c),EL(1stProWork),GD,MG,
A:Ultragirl,Vanguard 8.00
2 EL,JG(pin-up),A:Vanguard 5.00
3 MG,AMe,JG, EL, I:Savage
Dragon 16.00
4 AMe,EL,2nd A:Savage Dragon
(inc.EL profile) 12.00
5 AMe,RLd(inside front cover) . . 3.00

6 AMe,JG(inside back cover),
EL(Back cover) 3.00
7 AMe 3.00
8 RLd,I:Youngblood(Preview) . . 18.00

MEGATON MAN
1 . . . . 2.00

MEGATON MAN MEETS THE UNCATEGORIZABLE X-THEMS
Jabberwocky
1 . . . . 2.00

MEGATON MAN VS. FORBIDDEN FRANKENSTEIN
Fiasco Comics April 1996
1 by Don Simpson & Anton Drek   2.95

MELISSA MOORE: BODYGUARD
Draculina Publishing 1995
1 thru 3 V:Machine Gun Eddie   @2.95

MEN IN BLACK
Aircel 1991
1 by Lowell Cunningham & Sandy
Carruthers, basis of Movie . . 80.00
2 . . . . 60.00
3 F:Jay, Arbiter Doran 60.00
(Book II) 1991
1 . . . . 20.00
2 thru 3 . . . . @10.00

MEN IN BLACK: THE ROBORG INCIDENT
Castle
1 thru 3 . . . . @2.95

MEMORY MAN
Emergency Stop Press 1995
1 thru 2 Some of the Space Man   2.95

MERCHANTS OF DEATH
Eclipse
1 thru 5 . . . . @1.95

MERCY
Avatar Press Dec. 1997
0 O:Mercy 3.00
0a nude cover 6.00
0b leather cover 30.00
1 (of 2) by Bill Maus 3.00
1 nude cover 4.95
1 leather cover 25.00
1 signed 10.00

MERLIN
Adventure Comics Dec. 1990
1 BMC,Merlin's Visions 2.50
2 V:Warlord Carados 2.50
3 . . . . 2.50
4 Ninevah 2.50
5 D:Hagus 2.50
6 Final Issue 2.50
[2nd Series]
1 Journey of Rhiannon & Tryon . 2.50
2 Conclusion 2.50

MERMAID'S GAZE
Viz
1 thru 3 V:Shingo 2.75
4 final issue 2.75
TPB 15.95

Metacops #2 © Monster Comics

METACOPS
Monster Comics
1 and 2 . . . . @1.95

METAL GUARDIAN FAUST
Viz Communications March 1997
1 thru 5 (of 8) by Tetsuo Ueyama @2.95
6 thru 8 . . . . @2.95
TPV Vol. 1 . . . . 16.95

MOBILE POLICE PATLABOR
Viz Communications
1 (of 12) by Masami Yuki 2.95
PART TWO
1 by Masami Yuki 2.95
2 thru 6 . . . . @2.95
TPB Vol. 1 . . . . 15.95

METAPHYSIQUE
Eclipse
1 NB,Short Stories 2.50
2 NB,Short Stories 2.50

MIAMI MICE
Rip Off Press
1 1st printing 3.00
1a 2nd printing 2.00
3 . . . . 2.00
4 Record,A:TMNT 3.00

MICHELANGELO
Mirage
1 TMNT 17.00
1a 2nd Printing 4.50

MICRA
Fictioneer
1 . . . . 4.00

2	3.00
3	3.00
4	2.00
5 thru 7	@1.75
8	2.25

MIDNIGHT
Blackthorne
1 thru 4 . . . . @1.75

MIDNIGHT PANTHER
CPM Comics 1997
1 Manga, translated 2.95
2 . . . . 2.95
3 . . . . 2.95
4 . . . . 2.95
5 . . . . 2.95
6 Den of Scoundrels 2.95
7 The Sleeping Town 2.95
8 to Reincarnation City 2.95
9 O:Midnight Panthers 2.95
10 . . . . 2.95
11 . . . . 2.95
12 . . . . 2.95
TPB Sex, Death and Rock 'n' Roll.
rep #1–#6 . . . . 15.95

MIDNIGHT PANTHER: SCHOOL DAZE
CPM Comics 1998
1 (of 5) by Yu Asagiri 2.95
2 . . . . 2.95
3 . . . . 2.95
4 . . . . 2.95
5 final issue 2.95

MIDNITE SKULKER
1 thru 7 . . . . @1.75

MIGHTY GUY
C&T
1 thru 6 . . . . @1.50
Summer Fun Spec #1 . . . . 2.50

MIGHTY MITES
Continüm
1 I:X-Mites 1.95
2 . . . . 1.95

MIGHTY MOUSE ADVENTURE MAGAZINE
1 . . . . 2.00

MIGHTY TINY
1 thru 4 . . . . @1.75
5 . . . . 2.50
Mouse Marines Collection rep. . . . 7.50

MIKE MIST MINUTE MYSTERIES
Eclipse
1 . . . . 3.00

MILK & CHEESE
Slave Labor 1991–97
1 EDo, Milk Products gone bad 100.00
1a 2nd thru 7th printing 3.50
2 . . . . 50.00
2a 2nd thru 4th printing 10.00
3 . . . . 30.00

3a 2nd thru 4th printing	10.00
4	20.00
4a 2nd & 3rd printing	3.00
5	20.00
5a 2nd & 3rd printing	3.00
6	15.00
6a 2nd printing	2.75
Other #1	2.75
Third #1	2.75
Fourth #1	2.75
First #2	2.75
Six Six Six #1	2.75
Six Six Six 2nd printing, EDo	2.75
Latest Thing	2.95
TPB Fun with Milk & Cheese, rep.	
1st 4 issues	11.95

MINDLESS MADCAP MIS-ADVENTURES OF THE MANIAC MUTANT MACHO MALLARD
Pocket Change Comics 1995
1 V:Toilet Paper Thieves 2.50

MIRACLE SQUAD BLOOD & DUST
Apple
1 thru 3 . . . . @1.95

MISTER X
Vortex
Vol 2
1 thru 11 . . . . @2.00

MITES
1 . . . . 2.50
1a 1.90
2B 1.80
3 and 4 . . . . @1.80

MODERN PULP
Special Studio
1 Rep.from January Midnight . . . 2.75

MOEBIUS COMICS
Caliber 1996
1 Moe 2.95
2 Moe 2.95
3 Moe 2.95
4 Moe,MP 2.95
5 Moe,SL 2.95
6 Moe 2.95

MOGOBI DESERT RATS
Midnight Comics
1 I&O:Desert Rats 'Waste of the World' 2.25

MONNGA
Daikaiyu Enterprises 1995
1 & 2 Titanic Omega 3.95

MONSTER BOY
Monster Comics
1 A:Monster Boy 2.25

MONSTER FRAT HOUSE
Eternity
1 . . . . 2.25

Monster Posse #3 © Adventure Comics

MONSTER POSSE
Adventure
1 thru 3 . . . . 2.50

MONSTERS ATTACK
1 GM,JSe 2.00
2 GC 1.75
3 ATh,GC 1.50

MONSTERS FROM OUTER SPACE
Adventure 1992
1 thru 3 . . . . @2.50

MORBID ANGEL: DESPERATE ANGELS
London Night 1998
0 EHr, & Jude Millien 3.00
0A Powell(c) 5.00
0B Powell(c) 5.00

MORBID ANGEL: PENANCE
London Night Studios 1995
1 I:Brandon Watts 4.00

MORBID ANGEL: TO HELL AND BACK
London Night Oct. 1996
1 (of 3) EHr, ... 4.00
2 and 3 . . . . @3.00

MORTAL COIL
Mermaid
1 thru 3 . . . . @2.25
4 F:Red-Line,Gift 2.25
5 Pin-Up Issue 2.25

MORTAR MAN
Marshall Comics
1 I:Mortar Man 1.95
2 thru 3 . . . . @1.95

All comics prices listed are for _Near Mint_ condition.

MOSAIC
Oktober Black Press
1 F:Halo,Daeva	2.25
2 "Gun Metal Gray"	2.50
3	2.50
4 Elf(c)	2.50
5 Wisps	2.50

MOUNTAIN WORLD
Newcomers Press 1995
1 I:Jeremiah Rainshadow	2.95

MR. FIXITT
Apple
1 and 2	@1.95

MR. MYSTIC
Eclipse
1 Will Eisner	2.50

MR. NIGHTMARE'S WONDERFUL WORLD
Moonstone 1995
1 thru 3 Dreams So Real, pt.1–pt.3	@2.95

MS. CHRIST
Draculina Publishing 1995
1 I:Ms. Christ	2.95

MS. TREE
Aardvark–Vanaheim
1-10 see Other Pub. (color)
11 thru 18	@2.00

Renegade
19 thru 49	@2.00
50	4.50
1 3-D Classic	2.95

MUMMY, THE
Monster Comics
1 A:Dr.Clarke,Prof.Belmore	1.95
2 Mummy's Curse	1.95
3 A:Carloph	1.95
4 V:Carloph, conc.	1.95

The Munsters #2 © TV Comics

MUMMY'S CURSE
Aircel 1990
1 thru 4 B.Blair	@2.25

MUNSTERS, THE
TV Comics 1998
1 photo (c)	2.95
1a variant (c)	7.95
2 Beverly Owen(c)	2.95
2 Pat Priest (c)	2.95
2 Pat Priest (c) signed	19.95
3	2.95
3a Celebrity autograph edition	22.95
4	2.95
4a variant photo (c)	2.95
4b variant (c) celebrity autograph edition	22.95
5 Herman photo (c)	2.95
5 Grandpa photo (c)	2.95
Spec. Comic Con edition	9.95
Celebrity Autograph Edition: Butch Patrick	22.95
TPB Vol 1, rep. #1–#4	10.95

MUNSTERS CLASSICS
TV Comics
0 The Fregosi Emerald	2.95

MURCIELAGA: SHE-BAT
Hero Graphics
1 Daerick Gross reps.	1.50
2 Reps. contd	2.95

MURDER
Renegade 1986
1 SD	1.70
2 CI(c)	1.70
3 SD	1.70

MURDER (2nd series)
1	2.00

MUTANT ZONE
Aircel
1 Future story	2.50
2 F.B.I. Drone Exterminators	2.50
3 conclusion	2.50

MYSTERY MAN
Slave Labor
1 thru 5	@1.75

MYTH ADVENTURES
Warp Graphics
1 Mag size	1.50
2 thru 4	@1.50
5 Comic size	1.50
6 thru 11	@1.50
12	1.75

MYTH CONCEPTIONS
Apple
1	1.75
2	1.75
3 thru 8	@1.95

MYTHOGRAPHY
Bardic Press 1966
1 F:Poison Elves	3.95
2 fantasy stories	3.95

3 fantasy stories, inc. Elfquest	3.95
4	4.25
5 72pg.	4.25
6 F:Anubis Squadron 72pg.	3.95
7 80 pg.	4.25
8 72 pg.	4.25

MYTHOS
Wonder Comix
1 and 2	@1.50

NATURE OF THE BEAST
Caliber
1 thru 3 'The Beast'	@2.95

NAUSICAÄ OF THE VALLEY OF WIND
Viz Select
Book One	4.50
Book Two	5.50
Book Three	4.00
Book Four	3.00
Book Five	2.50
Book Six	2.95
Book Seven	2.95

[Part 2]
#1 thru #4	@2.95

[Part 3]
#1 thru #3	@2.95
TPB Vol. 4	17.95

NAZRAT
Imperial 1986
1	2.50
2 thru 6	@2.00

NECROSCOPE
Caliber 1997
1 Brian Lumley adapt.	2.95
1 signed	2.95
2	2.95
3	2.95
4	2.95

NEGATIVE BURN
Caliber
1 I:Matrix 7, Flaming Carrot	5.00
2	3.50
3 Bone preview	15.00
4 thru 12 various stories	@3.25
13 Strangers in Paradise	17.00
14 thru 18 various stories	@3.50
19 Flaming Carrot	5.00
20 In the Park	3.25
21 Trollords	3.00
22 Father the Dryad	3.00
23 I:The Creep	3.00
24 The Factor	3.00
25 The Factor	4.00
26 Very Vicki	3.00
27 Nancy Kate	4.00
28 Favorite Song	4.00
29 thru 33	4.00
34 Kaos Moon	8.00
35 thru 38	@4.00
39 "Iron Empires," pt. 4	4.00
40 "Suzi Romaine"	4.00
41 "Iron Empires," cont.	4.00
42	4.00
43 "Iron Empires," concl.	4.00
44 "Skeleton Key"	4.00
45 "Divine Winds"	4.00

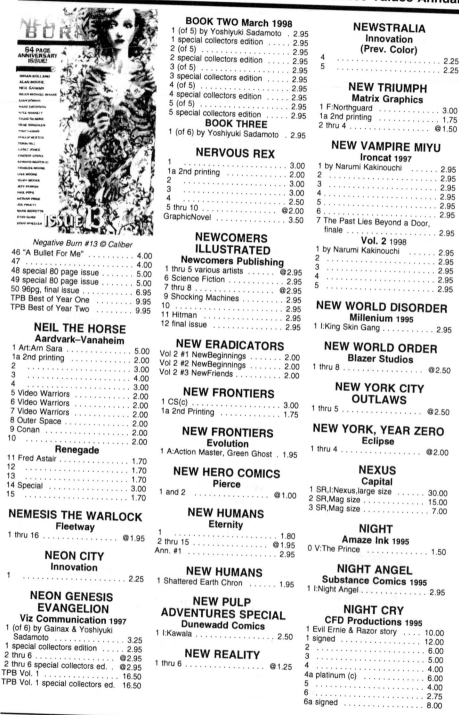

Negative Burn #13 © Caliber

46 "A Bullet For Me" 4.00
47 . . . . 4.00
48 special 80 page issue 5.00
49 special 80 page issue 5.00
50 96pg, final issue 6.95
TPB Best of Year One 9.95
TPB Best of Year Two 9.95

NEIL THE HORSE
Aardvark–Vanaheim
1 Art:Arn Sara 5.00
1a 2nd printing 2.00
2 . . . . 3.00
3 . . . . 4.00
4 . . . . 3.00
5 Video Warriors 2.00
6 Video Warriors 2.00
7 Video Warriors 2.00
8 Outer Space 2.00
9 Conan 2.00
10 . . . . 2.00
Renegade
11 Fred Astair 1.70
12 . . . . 1.70
13 . . . . 1.70
14 Special 3.00
15 . . . . 1.70

NEMESIS THE WARLOCK
Fleetway
1 thru 16 . . . . @1.95

NEON CITY
Innovation
1 . . . . 2.25

NEON GENESIS EVANGELION
Viz Communication 1997
1 (of 6) by Gainax & Yoshiyuki
Sadamoto 3.25
1 special collectors edition 2.95
2 thru 6 . . . . @2.95
2 thru 6 special collectors ed. . @2.95
TPB Vol. 1 . . . . 16.50
TPB Vol. 1 special collectors ed. 16.50

BOOK TWO March 1998
1 (of 5) by Yoshiyuki Sadamoto . 2.95
1 special collectors edition 2.95
2 (of 5) 2.95
2 special collectors edition 2.95
3 (of 5) 2.95
3 special collectors edition 2.95
4 (of 5) 2.95
4 special collectors edition 2.95
5 (of 5) 2.95
5 special collectors edition 2.95
BOOK THREE
1 (of 6) by Yoshiyuki Sadamoto . 2.95

NERVOUS REX
1 . . . . 3.00
1a 2nd printing 2.00
2 . . . . 3.00
3 . . . . 3.00
4 . . . . 2.50
5 thru 10 . . . . @2.00
GraphicNovel 3.50

NEWCOMERS ILLUSTRATED
Newcomers Publishing
1 thru 5 various artists . . . . . @2.95
6 Science Fiction 2.95
7 thru 8 . . . . @2.95
9 Shocking Machines 2.95
10 . . . . 2.95
11 Hitman 2.95
12 final issue 2.95

NEW ERADICATORS
Vol 2 #1 NewBeginnings 2.00
Vol 2 #2 NewBeginnings 2.00
Vol 2 #3 NewFriends 2.00

NEW FRONTIERS
1 CS(c) 3.00
1a 2nd Printing 1.75

NEW FRONTIERS
Evolution
1 A:Action Master, Green Ghost . 1.95

NEW HERO COMICS
Pierce
1 and 2 . . . . @1.00

NEW HUMANS
Eternity
1 . . . . 1.80
2 thru 15 . . . . @1.95
Ann. #1 . . . . 2.95

NEW HUMANS
1 Shattered Earth Chron 1.95

NEW PULP ADVENTURES SPECIAL
Dunewadd Comics
1 I:Kawala 2.50

NEW REALITY
1 thru 6 . . . . @1.25

NEWSTRALIA
Innovation
(Prev. Color)
4 . . . . 2.25
5 . . . . 2.25

NEW TRIUMPH
Matrix Graphics
1 F:Northguard 3.00
1a 2nd printing 1.75
2 thru 4 . . . . @1.50

NEW VAMPIRE MIYU
Ironcat 1997
1 by Narumi Kakinouchi 2.95
2 . . . . 2.95
3 . . . . 2.95
4 . . . . 2.95
5 . . . . 2.95
6 . . . . 2.95
7 The Past Lies Beyond a Door,
finale 2.95
Vol. 2 1998
1 by Narumi Kakinouchi 2.95
2 . . . . 2.95
3 . . . . 2.95
4 . . . . 2.95
5 . . . . 2.95

NEW WORLD DISORDER
Millenium 1995
1 I:King Skin Gang 2.95

NEW WORLD ORDER
Blazer Studios
1 thru 8 . . . . @2.50

NEW YORK CITY OUTLAWS
1 thru 5 . . . . @2.50

NEW YORK, YEAR ZERO
Eclipse
1 thru 4 . . . . @2.00

NEXUS
Capital
1 SR,I:Nexus,large size 30.00
2 SR,Mag size 15.00
3 SR,Mag size 7.00

NIGHT
Amaze Ink 1995
0 V:The Prince 1.50

NIGHT ANGEL
Substance Comics 1995
1 I:Night Angel 2.95

NIGHT CRY
CFD Productions 1995
1 Evil Ernie & Razor story 10.00
1 signed 12.00
2 . . . . 6.00
3 . . . . 5.00
4 . . . . 4.00
4a platinum (c) 6.00
5 . . . . 4.00
6 . . . . 2.75
6a signed 8.00

NIGHT LIFE
Caliber
1 thru 7 . . . . @1.50

NIGHT MASTER
1 Vigil 5.50
2 Vigil 2.50
3 . . . . 1.50

NIGHT OF THE LIVING DEAD
Fantaco
0 prelude 1.75
1 based on cult classic movie . . . 4.95
2 Movie adapt,continued 4.95
3 Movie adapt,conclusion 4.95
5 . . . . 5.95
TPB Official Complete story, rep. 24.95
TPB London, Clive Barker's story 14.95

NIGHT'S CHILDREN
Fantaco
1 . . . . 3.50
2 . . . . 3.50
3 . . . . 3.50

NIGHT'S CHILDREN
Millenium 1995
1 The Ripper, Klaus Wulfe 3.95
Spec. High Noon (1996) 2.95
Spec. The Churchyard (1997) . . 3.25

NIGHT'S CHILDREN: THE VAMPIRE
Millenium 1995
1 F:Klaus Wulfe 2.95
2 F:Klaus Wulfe 2.95

NIGHT STREETS
Arrow
1 . . . . 2.50
2 thru 4 . . . . @1.50

NIGHTVISION
London Night Nov. 1996
1 DQ,KHt, All About Eve 3.00
1 signed 12.95
1a erotica edition 10.00

NIGHT ZERO
Fleetway
1 thru 4 . . . . @1.95

NIKKI BLADE
High Impact 1997
0 . . . . 2.95
0a deluxe adult cover 10.00
0b gold edition variant cover . . . 14.95
Spec.#0 Nikki Blade: Forever Nikki
  (1997) MIB(c) 2.95
  Deluxe RCI(c) 10.00
ABC Comics 1998
Spec. Nikki Blade: Blades of Death
  (1998) by RCI & Clayton Henry 3.00
  Puzzle variant A cover 5.95
  Puzzle variant B cover 5.95
  Puzzle variant C cover 5.95
Spec. Nikki Blade: Revenge . . . 3.00
  RCI nude cover 5.95
  Clayton Henry nude variant (c) 5.95

NINGA-BOTS
Prelude
1 . . . . 2.00

NINJA
Eternity
1 . . . . 3.00
2 thru 6 . . . . @1.80
7 thru 13 . . . . @1.95

NINJA ELITE
1 thru 5 . . . . @1.50
6 thru 8 . . . . @1.95

NINJA FUNNIES
Eternity
1 and 2 . . . . @1.80
3 thru 5 . . . . @1.95

NINJA HIGH SCHOOL
Eternity
1 . . . . 1.75
2 thru 4 . . . . @1.50
5 thru 22 . . . . @1.95
23 Zardon Assassin 2.25
24 . . . . 2.25
25 Return of the Zetramen 2.25
26 Stanley the Demon 2.25
27 Return of the Zetramen 2.25
28 Threat of the super computer . 2.25
29 V:Super Computer 2.25
30 I:Akaru 2.25
31 Jeremy V:Akaru 2.25
32 thru 34 V:Giant Monsters Pt.1
  thru Pt. 3 . . . . @2.50
35 thru 43 . . . . @2.50
44 Combat Cheerleaders 2.75
45 Cheerleader Competition 2.75
46 Monsters From Space 2.75
47 . . . . 2.75
48 F:Jeremy Feeple 2.95
49 thru 51 . . . . @2.95
52 thru 57 Time Warp, pt.4–pt.8 @2.95
58 Zardon ambassador, BU:BDn . 2.95
59 Akaru overwhelmed 2.95
60 to the Himalayas 2.95
61 ancient Himalayan temple . . . 2.95
62 Hillbilly girl 2.95
63 F:Tetsuo Rivalsan 2.95
64 Jeremy Feeple: Saboteur? . . . 2.95
Special #1 . . . . 2.95
Special #2 . . . . 2.95
Special #3 . . . . 2.95
Special #3 1/2 . . . . 2.25
Ann. 1989 . . . . 2.95
Ann.#3 . . . . 3.95
TPB Vol. 1 rep. #1–3 . . . . 12.00
TPB Vol. 1, new edition 14.95
TPB Vol. 2 rep. #4–7 . . . . 12.00
TPB Vol. 3 rep. #8–11 . . . . 9.00
TPB Vol. 3, rep. #8–#11 . . . . . 10.95
TPB Vol. 4 rep. #12–15 . . . . . . 8.00
TPB Vol. 4, rep. #12–#15 . . . . 10.95
TPB Vol. 5 rep. #16–18 . . . . . . 7.95
TPB Vol. 6 rep. #19–21 . . . . . . 7.95
TPB Vol. 7 rep. #22–24 . . . . . . 7.95
TPB Vol. 7, rep. #22–#24 The Ides
  of May 10.95
TPB Vol. 8 rep. #25–27 . . . . . . 7.95
TPB Vol. 9 rep. #28–31 . . . . . 10.95
TPB Vol. 9, rep. #28–#31 Long
  Distance Bottle 10.95
TPB Vol. 10 rep. #32–35 . . . . 10.95

TPB Vol. 11 rep. #36–39 . . . . . 10.95
TPB Vol. 11, rep. #36–#39 Shades
  of Grey 10.95
TPB Vol. 15 three stories 7.95
Yearbook 1994 . . . . 4.00
Yearbook 1995 . . . . 3.95
Yearbook 1996 . . . . 3.95
Yearbook 1997, cover A 3.95
Yearbook 1997, cover B 3.95
Spec. Girls of Ninja High School
  (1997) 3.95
Spec. Girls of Ninja High School
  1998 cover A 2.95
  1998 cover B 2.95

NINJA HIGH SCHOOL GIRLS
Antarctic Press
0 . . . . 2.75
1 and 2 rep. . . . . @2.75
3 thru 5 rep. 3.95
Yearbook 3.95

NINJA HIGH SCHOOL PERFECT MEMORY
Antarctic Press
1 thru 2, 96pg . . . . @4.95

NINJA HIGH SCHOOL SMALL BODIES
Antarctic Press
1 "Monopolize" 2.50
2 Omegadon Cannon 2.75
3 Omegadon Cannon 2.75
3a deluxe 4.50
4 Omegadon Cannon 2.75
5 Wrong Order 2.75
6 Chicken Rage 2.95
7 . . . . 2.95

NIRA X: CYBERANGEL
Entity Comics April 1996
1 . . . . 5.00
1a deluxe 8.00
2 BMs 4.00
3 and 4 BMs . . . . @3.00
4a with PC Game 8.00
Ann.#1 BMs flip-cover 2.75
2nd Mini Series 1995
1 . . . . 4.00
1a 2nd printing 2.50
2 thru 4 . . . . @2.50
3rd Mini Series 1995–96
1 . . . . 2.50
1a Gold(c) 5.00
2 . . . . 2.50
3 . . . . 3.00
Regular Series
1 . . . . 2.75
1a with game 7.00
2 thru 4 . . . . @2.75
4a with game 7.00
Spec. Nira X:Headwave, encore
  special toy edition 2.50
Encore special toy edition, signed
  & numbered 12.95
Spec. Nira X:Memoirs (1997) BMs 2.75
  Deluxe 3.50

NIRA X/HELLINA: HEAVEN & HELL
Entity Comics
1 San Diego Con edition, BMs . . . 5.00
1a foil 3.00

NIRA X: EXODUS
Avatar 1997
0 (of 2) BMs 3.00
0a Nude cover 4.95
0b Leather cover 25.00
0 signed 10.00
1 (of 2) 3.00
1a nude cover 4.95
1b leather cover 25.00
1 signed 10.00
2 . . . . 3.00
2 nude cover 4.95
Spec. Shoot First 3.00
Spec. Shoot First, nude cover . . . 4.95

NIRA X: SOUL SKURGE
Entity Oct. 1996
1 (of 3) BMs, A:Vortex 2.75
2 BMs, ... 2.75
3 . . . . 2.75

NO GUTS, NO GLORY
Fantaco
1 One Shot, K.Eastman's 1st solo
work since TMNT 2.95

NOMADS OF ANTIQUITY
1 thru 6 . . . . @1.50

NO NEED FOR TENCHI
Viz Comics
Part One
1 thru 7 (of 7) . . . . @2.95
Part Two Nov. 1996
1 thru 7 by Hitoshi Okuda . . . . @2.95
TPB Sword Play 15.95
Part Three 1997
1 (of 6) by Hitoshi Okuda 2.95
2 . . . . 2.95
3 thru 6 . . . . @2.95
TPB Magical Girl Pretty Sammy . 15.95
PART FOUR Dec. 1997
1 (of 6) by Hitoshi Okuda 2.95
2 thru 6 . . . . @2.95
PART FIVE 1998
1 (of 6) 2.95
2 (of 6) 2.95
3 (of 6) 2.95

NORMAL MAN
Aardvark–Vanaheim
1 . . . . 4.00
2 thru 9 . . . . @2.50
Renegade
10 thru 19 . . . . @1.70

NOVA GIRLS
MN Design 1998
1 The Immortality Quest,pt.1 . . . 1.95
1a JJu (c) 2.95
1b photo (c) 3.95
1 variant Starship Discover #0
cover 3.95
1 variant Phazer #0 cover 3.95

2 The Immortality Quest, pt.2 . . . 1.95
2a deluxe 2.95
3 The Immortality Quest, pt.3 . . . 1.95
3a deluxe 2.95
Space 34–24–34 Gold Seal 10th
Anniv. Edition 74.95

NOWHERESVILLE
Caliber March 1996
1 thru 3 by MRc . . . . @2.95
Spec. The History of Cool 2.95

NYOKA THE JUNGLE GIRL
AC Comics
3 . . . . 2.25
4 . . . . 2.25
5 . . . . 2.50

OCTOBERFEST
Now & Then
1 (1976) Dave Sim 15.00

OFFERINGS
Cry For Dawn
1 Sword & Sorcery stories 7.00
2 and 3 . . . . @6.00

OFFICIAL BUZ SAWYER
1 . . . . 2.00
2 . . . . 2.00
3 . . . . 2.00
4 . . . . 1.50
5 . . . . 2.00
6 . . . . 2.00

OFFICIAL HOW TO DRAW G.I. JOE
Blackthorne
1 thru 5 . . . . @2.00

OFFICIAL HOW TO DRAW ROBOTECH
Blackthorne
1 thru 11 . . . . @2.00
12 . . . . 2.95
13 thru 16 . . . . @2.00

OFFICIAL HOW TO DRAW TRANSFORMERS
Blackthorne
1 thru 7 . . . . @2.00

OFFICIAL JOHNNY HAZARD
1 thru 3 . . . . @2.00
4 . . . . 1.50
5 . . . . 2.00

OFFICIAL JUNGLE JIM
1 thru 5 AR,rep. . . . . @2.00
6 AR,rep. 1.50
7 thru 10 AR,rep. . . . . @2.00
11 thru 20 AR,rep. . . . . @2.50
Ann.#1 . . . . 2.00
Giant Size 3.95

OFFICIAL MANDRAKE
1 thru 5 . . . . @2.00

6 . . . . 1.50
7 thru 10 . . . . @2.00
11 . . . . 2.50
12 . . . . 2.00
13 thru 17 . . . . @2.50
Ann. #1 . . . . 3.95
King Size #1 . . . . 3.95
Giant Size #1 . . . . 3.95

OFFICIAL MODESTY BLAISE
Pioneer 1988
1 thru 4 . . . . @2.00
5 . . . . 1.50
6 thru 14 . . . . @2.00
Ann. #1 . . . . 3.95
King Size #1 . . . . 3.95

OFFICIAL PRINCE VALIANT
1 Hal Foster,rep. 2.00
2 Hal Foster,rep. 2.00
3 Hal Foster,rep. 2.00
4 Hal Foster,rep. 2.00
5 Hal Foster,rep. 2.00
6 Hal Foster,rep. 2.00
7 . . . . 1.50
8 thru 14 . . . . @2.00
15 thru 24 . . . . @2.50
Ann. #1 . . . . 3.95
King Size #1 . . . . 3.95

OFFICIAL RIP KIRBY
1 thru 3 AR . . . . @2.00
4 AR 1.50
5 and 6 AR . . . . @2.00

Official Secret Agent #4 © Pioneer

OFFICIAL SECRET AGENT
Pioneer
1 thru 5 AW rep . . . . @2.00
6 AW 1.50
7 thru 9 AW . . . . @2.00

OH..
B Publications
1 Tomboy Meets Agents street . . 2.95

All comics prices listed are for *Near Mint* condition.

OHM'S LAW
Imperial Comics
1 thru 2	@1.95
3 V:Men in Black	1.95
4 A:Damonstriek	1.95
5 F:Tryst	1.95

OKTOBERFEST
Now & Then
1 (1976) Dave Sim	20.00

OMEGA
North Star
1 1st pr by Rebel,rare	80.00
1a Vigil(Yellow Cov.)	27.00
2	2.00

OMEN
North Star
1	8.00
1a 2nd printing	2.00
2 thru 4	@3.50

OMICRON
1 and 2	@2.25
3	2.50

ONE SHOT WESTERN
Calibur
One Shot F:Savage Sisters, Tornpath Outlaw	2.50

ONI DOUBLE FEATURE
Oni Press 1997
1 F:Secret Broadcast	2.95
2 F:Car Crash on the 405	2.95
3 F:Troy Nixey	2.95
4 F:A River in Egypt	2.95
5 F:Fan Girl From Hell	2.95
6 inc. NGa Only the End of the World, pt.1	2.95
7 inc. NGa Only the End of the World, pt.2	2.95
8 inc. NGa Only the End of the World, pt.3	2.95

OPEN SEASON
Renegade
1 thru 7	@2.00

OPERATIVE SCORPIO
Blackthorne
1	3.50

OPTIC NERVE
Adrian Tomine 1990
1 thru 5, mini-comic	18.00
6	7.00
7	5.00

OPTIC NERVE
Drawn & Quarterly 1995
1 Summer Job	7.00
1a 2nd printing	3.00
2	5.00
3 and 4	@3.00
5	2.95
HC Sleepwalk and Other Stories, limited	29.95

ORACLE PRESENTS
1 thru 4	@1.50

ORBIT
Eclipse
1 and 2	@3.95
3	4.95

Original Tom Corbet #2 © Eternity

ORIGINAL TOM CORBET
Eternity 1990
1 thru 10 rep. newspaper strips	@2.95

ORLAK: FLESH & STEEL
Caliber
1 '1991 A.D.'	2.50

ORLAK REDUX
Caliber 1991
1 rep. Caliber Presents,64pg.	3.95

OTHERS, THE
Cormac Publishing
1	1.50

OUTLANDER
1	4.50
2	3.00
3 thru 5	@2.50
6 and 7	@1.95
8	2.25

OUTLAW OVERDRIVE
Blue Comet Press
1 Red Edition I:Deathrow	2.95
1a Black Edition	2.95
1b Blue Edition	2.95

OVERLOAD
Eclipse
1	1.50

OZ
Imperial Comics
1 Land of Oz Gone Mad	12.00
2 Land of Oz Gone Mad	10.00
3 Land of Oz Gone Mad	6.00
4 Tin Woodsmen	6.00
5 F:Pumkinhead	6.00
6 Emerald City	6.00
7 V:Bane Wolves	4.00
8 V:Nome Hordes	4.00
9 Freedom Fighters Vs. Heroes	4.00
10 thru 15	@4.00
16	3.50
Spec.#1	6.00
Spec. Scarecrow #1	3.00
Spec. Lion #1	3.00
Spec. Tin Man #1	3.00
Spec. Freedom Fighters #1	3.00
TPB Rep. #1-#4	14.95

Caliber "New Worlds"
17 by Ralph Griffith, Stuart Kerr & Tim Holtrop	3.50
18	3.00
19	3.00
20	3.00
21 "Witches War" pt.1 (of 5)	3.00
22	2.95
GN Heroes of Oz	14.95

OZ: ROMANCE IN RAGS
Caliber 1996
1 thru 3 Bill Bryan	@2.95

OZ SQUAD
Patchwork Press
1 thru 6	@2.95
7 Time Train Destroyed	2.95
8 Old West	2.75

OZ: STRAW AND SORCERY
Caliber "New Worlds" 1997
1 thru 3	@2.95

PAKKINS' LAND
Caliber Tapestry 1996
1	6.00
1a signed edition	3.00
1a second edition, new cover	3.00
2	4.00
2a second edition, new cover	3.00
3	3.00
3 2nd edition, new cover	3.00
4 thru 6	@3.00
GN Book One: Paul's Adventure	9.95

PAKKINS' LAND: FORGOTTEN DREAMS
Caliber March 1998
1 by Gary & Rhoda Shipman	2.95
2	2.95
3	2.95

PAKKINS' LAND: QUEST FOR KINGS
Caliber 1997
1G by Gary & Rhoda Shipman, Shipman(c)	2.95
1J by Gary & Rhoda Shipman, JSi(c)	2.95
2	2.95
3 Rahsha's city	2.95
4	2.95
5	2.95

PALANTINE
Gryphon Rampant 1995
1 thru 5 V:Master of Basilisk 2.50

PANDA KHAN
1 thru 4 . . . . @2.00

PANDORA
Brainstorm 1996
1 (of 2) 3.00
1a nude cover 5.00

PANDORA
Avatar Press 1997
0 . . . . 3.00
0 nude cover 4.95
1 signed 15.00
2 (of 2 . . . . 3.00
2 deluxe 10.00
X-over Pandora/Rancor: Devil Inside
  (1998) signed 15.00
  Rick Lyon nude (c) 6.00
  Haley (c) 5.00
X-Over Pandora/Shotgun Mary:
  Demon Nation (1998) 3.00
  Deluxe 4.95
  Leather 30.00
X-over Pandora/Widow (1997) . . . 3.95
  Nude cover 4.95
  Leather cover 25.00
Spec. Pandor Special (1997) 3.00
  Nude cover 4.95
  Leather cover 25.00
  Avatar convention cover edition 15.00
Spec. Pandor Pin-up (1997) 3.00
  Nude cover 4.95
  Signed 20.00
Spec. Nudes (1997) 3.50
  Nude Lyon cover 6.00
  Nude Meadows cover 6.00

PANDORA:
DEMONOGRAPHY
Avatar Press 1997
1 . . . . 3.00
1 nude cover 5.00
2 (of 3) 3.00
2 nude cover 4.95
3 (of 3) 3.00
3 nude cover 4.95

PANDORA:
PANDEMONIUM
Avatar Press 1997
1 Pandora goes to Hell 3.00
1 nude cover 4.95
1 leather cover 25.00
1 signed 10.00
2 (of 3) 3.00
2 nude cover 4.95

PAPER CUTS
1 E Starzer-1982 . . . . 17.50
2 and 3 . . . . @2.50

PARTICLE DREAMS
Fantagraphics
1 . . . . 3.00
2 thru 6 . . . . @2.25

PARTNERS IN
PANDEMONIUM
Caliber
1 'Hell on Earth' 2.50
2 Sheldon&Murphy become mortal 2.50
3 A:Abra Cadaver 2.50

PARTS OF A HOLE
Caliber 1991
1 Short Stories 2.50

PARTS UNKNOWN
Eclipse
1 I:Spurr,V:Aliens 2.50
2 Aliens on Earth cont. 2.50

PARTS UNKNOWN:
DARK INTENTIONS
Knight Press
0 . . . . 2.95
1 I:Prelude to limited Series 2.95
2 V:Luggnar 2.95
3 V:Luggnar 2.95
4 . . . . 2.95
1-shot, Handbook, The Roswell
  Agenda 2.95
Super-Ann. #1 . . . . 3.95

PAUL THE SAMURAI
New England Comics 1991
1 thru 3 . . . . @2.75
Bonanza #2 100pg. 4.95
GN Collected 8.95

PENDULUM
Adventure
1 Big Hand,Little Hand 2.50
2 The Immortality Formula 2.50
3 . . . . 2.50

PENTACLE: SIGN OF 5
Eternity
1 . . . . 2.25
2 Det.Sandler,H.Smitts 2.25
3 Det.Sandler => New Warlock . . 2.25
4 5 warlocks Vs. Kaji 2.50

FEAR CITY BEGINS HERE!

Phantom of Fear City #1 © Claypool

PHANTOM
1 thru 3 . . . . @5.95
4 and 5 . . . . @6.95

PHANTOM OF FEAR CITY
Claypool 1994–95
1 thru 12 . . . . 2.50

PHANTOM OF
THE OPERA
Eternity
1 . . . . 1.95

PHASE ONE
Victory
1 . . . . 3.00
2 . . . . 2.00
3 thru 5 . . . . @1.50

PHIGMENTS
Eternity
1 . . . . 5.00
2 . . . . 2.00
3 . . . . 1.95

PHONEY PAGES
Renegade
1 and 2 . . . . @1.70

PIED PIPER OF HAMELIN
Tome
1 . . . . 2.95

PINEAPPLE ARMY
1 thru 10 . . . . @1.75

PINK FLOYD EXPERIENCE
Revolutionary
1 based on rock group 2.50
2 Dark Side of the Moon 2.50
3 Dark Side of the Moon, Wish you
  were here 2.50
4 The Wall 2.50
5 A Momentary lapse of reason . 2.50

PIRATE CORPS!
Eternity
6 and 7 . . . . @1.95
Spec. #1 . . . . 1.95

PIRANHA! IS LOOSE
Special Studio
1 Drug Runners,F:Piranha 2.95
2 Expedition into Terror 2.95

PIXI JUNKET
Viz
1 thru 6 . . . . @2.75

P.J. WARLOCK
Eclipse
1 thru 3 . . . . @2.00

PLANET COMICS
Blackthorne
(Prev. Color)
4 and 5 . . . . @2.00

PLANET OF TERROR
1 BW 1.75

PLANET OF THE APES
Adventure Comics 1990
1 WD,collect.ed. 7.00
1 2 covers 5.00
1a 2nd printing 2.50
1b 3rd printing 2.25
2 . . . . 3.00
3 . . . . 2.75
4 . . . . 2.75
5 D:Alexander? 2.75
6 Welcome to Ape City 2.75
7 . . . . 2.75
8 Christmas Story 2.50
9 Swamp Ape Village 2.50
10 Swamp Apes in Forbidden City 2.50
11 Ape War continues 2.50
12 W.Alexander/Coure 2.50
13 Planet of Apes/Alien Nation/ Ape
   City x-over 2.50
14 Countdown to Zero Pt.1 . . . . 2.50
15 Countdown to Zero Pt.2 . . . . 2.50
16 Countdown to Zero Pt.3 . . . . 2.50
17 Countdown to Zero Pt.4 . . . . 2.50
18 Ape City (after Ape Nation mini-
   series 2.50
19 1991 'Conquest..' tie-in 2.50
20 Return of the Ape Riders 2.50
21 The Terror Beneath,Pt.1 . . . . 2.50
22 The Terror Beneath,Pt.2 . . . . 2.50
23 The Terror Beneath,Pt.3 . . . . 2.50
Ann #1,'Day on Planet o/t Apes' . 3.50
Lim.Ed. #1 . . . . 5.00

PLANET OF THE APES: BLOOD OF THE APES
Adventure Comics
1 A:Tonus the Butcher 3.00
2 Valia/Taylorite Connection 2.50
3 Ape Army in Phis 2.50
4 . . . . 2.50

PLANET OF THE APES: FORBIDDEN ZONE
Adventure
1 Battle for the Planet o/t Apes &
   Planet o/t Apes tie-in 2.50
2 A:Juilus 2.50

PLANET OF THE APES: SINS OF THE FATHER
Adventure Comics
1 Conquest Tie in 2.50

PLANET OF THE APES URCHAKS' FOLLY
Adventure Comics
1 . . . . 3.00
2 . . . . 2.50
3 'The Taylorites' 2.50
4 Conclusion 2.50

PLANET 29
Caliber
1 A Future Snarl Tale 2.50
2 A:Biff,Squakman 2.50

PLANET-X
Eternity 1991
1 three horror stories 2.50

PLAN 9 FROM OUTER SPACE
Eternity
1 . . . . 2.50
2 and 3 . . . . @2.25

PLASMA BABY
Caliber
1 'Strange New World' 2.50

PLASTIC LITTLE
CPM Comics 1997
1 (of 5) Manga, by Satoshi
   Urushihara R:Captain Tita 2.95
2 F:Joshua Balboa 2.95
3 . . . . 2.95
4 . . . . 2.95
5 concl. 2.95
TPB Captain's Log, rep. #1–#5 . 15.95

PLASTRON CAFE
Mirage
1 RV,inc.North by Downeast 2.25

PLAYGROUND 1826
Caliber
1 . . . . 2.50

POE
Cheese Comics
1 by Jason Asala, reoffer 2.00
2 . . . . 2.00
3 "The System of Doctor Tarr and
   Professor Fether" 2.00
4 thru 7 . . . . @2.00
Sirius/Dog Star
10 by Jason Asala, Small Town, pt.2 2.50
TPB Vol. 1 . . . . 14.95
VOL 2
1 by Jason Asala 2.50
2 House of Usher, pt.1 (of 4) . . . 2.50
3 House of Usher, pt.2 . . . . 2.50
4 House of Usher, pt.3 . . . . 2.50
5 House of Usher, pt.4 . . . . 2.50
6 . . . . 2.50
7 . . . . 2.50
8 Small Town 2.50
9 Small Town, pt.2 . . . . 2.50

POINT BLANK
Eclipse
1 thru 5 . . . . @2.95

POISON ELVES
Mulehide Graphics 1993–95
Prev: I, Lusipher
8 DHa(c&a) 35.00
9 DHa 30.00
10 DHa 30.00
11 DHa, comic size 32.00
12 DHa 25.00
13 DHa 35.00
14 and 15 DHa . . . . @25.00
15a 2nd printing 10.00
16 and 17 DHa . . . . @20.00
17a 2nd printing 8.00
18 DHa 20.00

19 DHa 22.00
20 DHa 20.00
2nd Series, Sirius 1995–97
1 F:Lusipher 10.00
2 V:Assassins Guild 5.00
3 Sanctuary, pt.3 . . . . 5.00
4 Sanctuary, pt.4 . . . . 6.00
5 Sanctuary, pt.5 . . . . 5.00
6 I:Lester Gran 5.00
7 thru 24 . . . . @4.00
25 DHa 3.00
26 DHa 2.50
27 DHa, ... 2.50
28 DHa,F:Lusiphur 2.50
29 DHa, ... 2.50
30 DHa,F:Vido 2.50
31 DHa 2.50
32 DHa, Cassandra is dead 2.50
33 DHa, temporary truce 2.50
34 DHa, Lusiphur's feminine side . 2.50
35 DHa, Purple Marauder reappears 2.50
36 DHa, Lusiphur tracked down . . 2.50
37 DHa, questionable hlep 2.50
38 DHa 2.50
TPB Vol. 1 Requiem for an Elf . . 14.95
TPB Vol. 2 Traumatic Dogs 14.95
TPB Vol. 3 Desert of the Third Sin 14.95
TPB Vol. 4 Patrons, 48pg 4.95

POIZON: DEMON HUNTER
London Night 1998
1 . . . . 3.00
1a nude cover edition 6.00
2 . . . . 3.00
2a deluxe 6.00
3 . . . . 3.00
3a nude cover edition 6.00
4 double sized finale 3.00
4a nude cover edition 6.00

POLIS
Brave New World
1 I:Polis 2.50

POPCORN
Discovery 1993
1 . . . . 3.95

PORK KNIGHT
Silver Snail
1 . . . . 1.75

PORT
Silver Wolf
1 . . . . 1.50
2 . . . . 1.50

PORTIA PRINZ
Eclipse
1 thru 5 . . . . @2.00

POST BROTHERS
Rip Off Press
15 thru 18 . . . . @2.00
19 and 20 . . . . @2.50

POWER COMICS
1 Smart-Early Ardvaark 25.00
1a 2nd printing 8.00
2 I:Cobalt Blue 10.00
3 and 4 . . . . @3.00
5 . . . . 4.00

B & W PUB

POWER COMICS
Eclipse
1 BB,DGb,Powerbolt	2.00
2 BB,DGb	2.00
3 BB,DGb	2.00

PRACTICE IN PAIN
Dramemon Studios
1 I:Queen of the Dead	3.00

PREMIERE
Diversity Comics 1995
1 F:Kolmec The Savage	2.75

PRETEEN DIRTY GENE KUNG FU KANGAROOS
Blackthorne 1986
1 and 2	@1.50

PRETTY CITY ROXX
Mars Press
1 I:Roxx	3.50

PREY
Monster Comics
1 I:Prey,A:Andrina	2.25
2 V:Andrina	2.25
3 conclusion	2.25

PRICE, THE
1 Dreadstar mag. size	20.00

PRIMITIVES
Spartive Studios 1995
1 thru 3 On the Moon	@2.50

PRIME CUTS
Fantagraphics
1 adult	3.50
2 thru 6	@3.50
7 thru 12	@3.95

PRIMER
Comico
1	10.00
2 MW,I:Grendel	100.00
3	5.00
4	8.00
5 SK(1st work),I:Maxx	32.00
6 IN,Evangeline	16.00

PRIME SLIME TALES
Mirage
1	5.00
2	2.50
3 thru 6	@1.50

PRINCE VALIANT
1 thru 4	@4.95
Spec #1	6.95

PRINCE VALIANT MONTHLY
1 thru 6	@3.95
6	4.95
7	4.95
8	4.95
9	6.95

PRIVATE EYES
Eternity
1 Saint rep.	1.95
2	1.95
3	1.95
4	1.95
5	1.95

PSI–JUDGE ANDERSON
1 thru 15	@1.95

PSYCHOMAN
Revolutionary
1 I:Psychoman	2.50

PUMA BLUES
Aardvark–Vanaheim
1 10,000 printed	4.50
1a 2nd printing	2.00
2	3.00
3	2.00
4 thru 19	@1.70
20 Special	2.25

Mirage
21 thru 24	@1.70
25	2.50
26 thru 28	@1.75

QUACK
Star Reach
1	2.00
2	2.00
3	2.00
4 Dave Sim	3.00
5 Dave Sim	3.00
6	2.00

QUEST PRESENTS
Quest
1 JD	1.75
2 JD	1.75
3 JD	1.75

RABID MONKEY
D.B.I. Comics Jan. 1997
1 thru 4 by Joel Steudler	@2.25
5 thru 7	@2.25
8 thru 13	@2.50
#1–#5 Autographed pack	12.00

RADICAL DREAMER
Mark's Giant Economy Sized Comics
1 thru 3 F:Max Wrighter	3.00
4 is Max the Devil?	3.00

VOL 2 1998
1 (of 6) by Mark Wheatley, sci-fi	2.95

RADIO BOY
Eclipse
1	2.00

RAGNAROK
Sun Comics
1 I:Ragnarok Guy,Honey	2.50
2 The Melder Foundation	2.50
3 Guy/Honey mission contd.	2.50
4 I:Big Gossage	2.50

RAIKA
Sun Comics
1 thru 12	@2.50

RAISING HELL
ABC Comics 1997
1	2.95
1a gold series, 2 extra pages	3.00
1b nude Jazz gold series	10.00
2 RCI,F:China & Jazz	2.95
2 live nude model cover	14.95
3 conclusion, A:Wild Things	2.95
3 Baby Cheeks edition	10.00
3 Baby Cheeks Gold Edition	14.95

Ralph Snart #1 © Now Comics

RALPH SNART
Now
1	5.00
2	4.00
3	4.00

[Volume 2]
1	3.00
2 thru 8	@1.50
Trade Paperback	2.95

RAMBO
Blackthorne
1 thru 5	@2.00

RAMBO III
Blackthorne
1	2.00

RAMM
Megaton Comics 1987
1 and 2	@1.50

RANMA 1/2
Viz 1993
Parts 1 & 2, see color
[Part 3] 1993–94
1 thru 13	3.00

[Part 4] 1995
1 thru 11	3.00

[Part 5] 1996

1 thru 9	3.00
10 thru 12	@3.00

[Part Six] Dec. 1996

1 thru 8 (of 14)	@3.00
9 thru 14	@3.00
TPB Vol. 6	15.95
TPB Vol. 7	15.95
TPB Vol. 8	15.95
TPB Vol. 9	15.95
TPB Vol. 11 rep. Part Six, 2nd half	15.95
TPB Vol. 19 rep. Part Six, 1st half	15.95

[Part Seven] Feb. 1998

1 thru 7 (of 14)	@2.95

RAPHAEL

1 TMNT	17.50
1a 2nd printing	7.50

RAPTUS
High Impact

1	3.00
1 2nd printing, new cover	3.00
2	3.00
3	3.00

RAPTUS: DEAD OF NIGHT
High Impact

1	2.95
2	2.95
3	3.00

RAT FINK
World of Fandom

1	2.50
2	2.50

RAVEN CHRONICLES
Caliber Press

1	2.95
1a Special Edition	5.95
2 Landing Zone	2.95
3 The Rain People	2.95
4 The Healer	2.95
5 thru 9	@2.95

Caliber "New Worlds"

10 by Scott Andrews, Laurence Campbell & Tim Perkins	2.95
11 "The Ghost of Alanzo Mann"	2.95
12 "The Compensators" flip book with Boston Bombers #1	2.95
13 48pg, bagged with back issue	3.95
14	2.95
15	2.95
16 inc. Black Mist	2.95
HC	19.95
GN 192pg rep.	16.95

RAVEN CHRONICLES: HEART OF THE DRAGON
Caliber "New Worlds"

1	2.95

RAVENING, THE
Avatar Press 1997

0 Trevlin Utz (c)	3.95
0 Matt Martin (c)	3.95
0 Matt Haley (c)	3.95
0 nude cover	6.00
0 leather cover	25.00
0 signed	15.00

1	3.00
1 nude cover	4.95
1 leather cover	25.00
1 Avatar con cover edition	15.00
2 (of 2)	3.00
2 nude cover	4.95

RAW CITY
Dramenon Studios

1 I:Dya,Gino	3.00
2 V:Crucifier	3.00
3 The Siren's Past	3.00

RAW MEDIA MAGS.
Reb

1 TV,SK,short stories	5.00

RAZOR
London Night

VOL 1

6 signed	25.00
10 signed	15.00
TPB The Suffering, rep. #1–#3	12.95
GN Let Us Prey, rep. of Razor/Wild Child, 80pg.	5.00
X-over Razor/Embrace: The Spawning (1997)	3.00
Carmen Electra photo (c)	3.00
Carmen Electra photo embossed (c), signed	19.00
Spec. Razor: Switchblade Symphony, Tour Book, limited black leather	15.00

RAZOR: ARCHIVES
London Night 1997

1 EHr, rep #1–#4	5.00
1a signed	15.00
2 EHr, rep #5–#8	5.00
3 EHr, rep #9–#15	5.00
4 EHr, rep #16–#17	5.00

RAZOR/DARK ANGEL: THE FINAL NAIL
Boneyard/London Night

1 X-over (Boneyard Press)	4.00
2 X-over concl.(London Night)	3.00

RAZOR: GOTHIC
London Night 1998

1 (of 4) by EHr and Scott Wilson	3.00
1 nude photo cover	6.00
1 leather	15.00

RAZOR: TORTURE
London Night

0 chromium signed	12.00
1 platinum signed	12.00

RAZOR UNCUT
London Night Studios
Prev. RAZOR (Ind. Color)

13	3.00
14 V:Child Killer	3.00
15 Questions About Father	3.00
16 Nicole's Life,pt.1	3.00
17 Nicole's Life,pt.2	3.00
18	3.00
19 & 20 Kiss from a Rose	@3.00
21 "Kiss From a Rose," pt.3	3.00
22 thru 24	@3.00

25 mild cover I:Knyfe	3.00
25a nude photo cover	4.00
25b signed	12.95
26	3.00
27 A:Sade, pt.1	3.00
28 A:Sade, pt.2	3.00
29	3.00
30	3.00
31 "Strength by Numbers"	3.00
32 double sized	3.50
32a signed nude edition	6.00
33 "Let Us Prey," pt.2	3.00
34 "Let Us Prey," pt.4 (of 4)	3.00
35 Let the battle begin	3.00
36 all-out war for Queen City	3.00
37 "After the Fall" pt.1	3.00
38 "After the Fall," pt.2	3.00
39 "Money For Hire"	3.00
40 "Father's Bane," pt.1	3.00
40 nude cover	5.00
41 "Father's Bane," pt.2	3.00
42 "Father's Bane," pt.3	3.00
43 "Father's Bane," pt.4	3.00
44 Razor finds abandoned child	3.00
45 An American Tragedy, pt.1 (of 5)	3.00
45a commemmorative edition, EHr	5.00
46 An American Tragedy, pt.2	3.00
47 An American Tragedy, pt.3	3.00
48 An American Tragedy, pt.4	3.00
49 An American Tragedy, pt.5	3.00
50 back in Asylum, Tony Daniel (c)	3.00
50a Michael Bair (c)	5.00
50b Stephen Sandoval (c)	5.00
50c Blood Red Velvet EHr (c)	25.00
Spec. Deep Cuts (1997) 5th Anniv. rep. #6,#13–#15, 80 pg	5.00
Nude cover	10.00

Razorguts #4 © Monster Comics

RAZORGUTS
Monster Comics 1992

1 thru 4	2.25

REACTOMAN
B-Movie Comics

1	1.50
1a signed,numbered	2.75
2 thru 4	@1.50
collection	4.95

REAGAN'S RAIDERS
1 thru 6 . . . . @2.50

REALM
Arrow
1 Fantasy 7.50
2 . . . . 4.00
3 . . . . 3.00
4 TV,Deadworld 21.00
5 I:L.Kazan 2.00
6 thru 13 . . . . @1.50
14 thru 18 . . . . @1.95
19 . . . . 2.50

REAL STUFF
Fantagraphic
1 thru 12 . . . . 2.50

REAPER
Newcomers Publishing
1 V:The Chinde 2.95
2 . . . . 2.95
3 conclusion 2.95

REBELLION
Daikaiyu Enterprises 1995
1 I:Rebellion 2.50

RED FOX
Harrier
1 scarce 6.00
1a 2nd printing 2.50
2 rare 5.00
3 . . . . 3.00
4 I:White Fox 3.00
5 I:Red Snail 3.00
6 . . . . 1.75
7 Wbolton 1.75
8 . . . . 1.75
9 Demosblurth 1.75

RED & STUMPY
Parody Press
1 Ren & Stimpy parody 2.95

RED HEAT
Blackthorne
1 . . . . 2.00

REDLAW
Caliber
1 Preview Killer of Crows 2.50

RED SHETLAND
Blackthorne
1 . . . . 2.00

REID FLEMING
Blackbird-Eclipse
1 David Boswell,I:Reid Fleming . 10.00
1a 2nd printing 5.50
1b 3rd–5th printing . . . . @2.50
Volume 2
#1 Rogues to Riches Pt.1 . . . . . 6.00
#2 Rogues to Riches Pt.2 . . . . . 4.00
#2a Later printings 2.50
#3 Rogues to Riches Pt.3 . . . . . 3.00
#3a Later printings 2.50
#4 Rogues to Riches Pt.4 . . . . . 3.00
#5 Rogues to Riches Pt.5 . . . . . 2.50

REID FLEMING, WORLD'S TOUGHEST MILKMAN
Deep-Sea Comics
3 "Rogue to Riches," pt.2,4th pr . 2.95
4 "Rogue to Riches," pt.3,3rd pr . 2.95
5 "Rogue to Riches," pt.4,2nd pr . 2.95
6 "Rogue to Riches," pt.5,2nd pr . 2.95
7 "Another Dawn,"Pt.1 . . . . 2.95
8 "Another Dawn,"Pt.2 . . . . 2.95
9 "Another Dawn,"Pt.3 . . . . 2.95
TPB Rogue to Riches rep. 13.95

REIVERS
Enigma
1 thru 2 Ch'tocc in Space 2.95

RENEGADE
Rip Off Press
1 . . . . 2.50

RENEGADES OF JUSTICE
Blue Masque
1 I:Monarch,Bloodshadow 2.50
2 Madfire 2.50
3 Television Chronicles 2.50
4 R:Karen Styles 2.50

RENFIELD
Caliber
GN Conclusion of series 8.95
HC by Gary Reed & Galen
    Showman 19.95
HC Deluxe 39.95

REPENTANCE
Advantage Graphics 1995
1 I:Repentance 1.95

REPLACEMENT GOD
Amaze Ink 1995
1 Child in The Land of Man 6.00
1a 2nd & 3rd printing 3.00
2 Eye of Knute 4.00
3 & 4 "Bravery" . . . . @3.50
5 thru 7 . . . . @3.00
8 Fairie, book one, concl. 2.95
TPB rep. #1–#8 . . . . 19.95

REPLACEMENT GOD & OTHER STORIES
Handicraft Guild
Previously published by Image
6 by Zander Cannon, 80pg 6.95

RETALIATOR
Eclipse
1 I&O:Retaliator 2.50
2 O:Retaliator cont. 2.50

RETIEF
Adventure 1990
1 thru 6 Keith Laumer adapt. . @2.00
[New Series]
1 thru 6 . . . . @2.25
Spec.#1 Retief:Garbage Invasion 2.50
Spec.#1 Retief:The Giant Killer,
    V:Giant Dinosaur 2.50
Spec.#1 Grime & Punishment,
    Planet Slunch 2.50

RETIEF OF THE CDT
1 Keith Laumer Novel Adapt. . . . 2.00
2 . . . . 2.00

RETIEF AND THE WARLORDS
Adventure Comics
1 Keith Laumer Novel Adapt. . . . 2.50
2 Haterakans 2.50
3 Retief Arrested for Treason . . . 2.50
4 Final Battle (last issue) 2.50

RETIEF: DIPLOMATIC IMMUNITY
Adventure Comics
1 Groaci Invasion. 2.50
2 Groaci story cont. 2.50

RETRO-DEAD
Blazer Unlimited
1 Dimensional Rift 2.95
2 by Dan Reed 2.95

RETROGRADE
Eternity
1 thru 4 . . . . @1.95

RETURN OF HAPPY THE CLOWN
Caliber Press
1 & 2 V:Oni 2.95

Return of Skyman #1 © Ace Comics

RETURN OF THE SKYMAN
Ace Comics
1 SD 1.75

REVOLVER
Renegade
1 SD 1.70
2 thru 6 . . . . @1.70
Ann. #1 . . . . 2.00

REVOLVING DOORS
Blackthorne
1	1.75
2	1.75
3	1.75
Graphic Novel	3.95

RHUDIPRRT PRINCE OF FUR
MU Press 1990–91
1 thru 6	@2.00

RICK RAYGUN
1	2.00
2 thru 8	@1.75

RIO KID
Eternity
1 I:Rio Kid	2.50
2 V:Blow Torch Killer	2.50
3	2.50

RION 2990
Rion
1	2.75
2	1.50

RIOT
Viz 1995
1 F:Riot,Axel	2.75
2 & 3	2.75
4 final issue	2.75
TPB Rep.	15.95

RIOT ACT TWO
Viz Comics
1 thru 7	@2.95
TPB rep.	15.95

RIP IN TIME
Fantagor
1 RCo,Limited series	3.00
2 RCo	2.00
3 RCo	2.00
4 RCo	2.00
5 RCo,Last	2.00

RIPLASH: SWEET VENGEANCE
Pocket Change Comics
1 O:Riplash	2.95

ROACHMILL
1	5.50
2	3.00
3	3.00
4	3.00
See: Dark Horse	

ROBIN HOOD
1 thru 4	@2.25

ROBO DEFENSE TEAM MECHA RIDER
Castle Comics
1 I:RDT Mecha Rider	2.95
2 Identity of Outlaw	2.95

R.O.B.O.T. BATTALION 2050
Eclipse
1	2.00

ROBO WARRIORS
CFW
1 thru 11	@1.95
Becomes:	

KUNG FU WARRIORS

Robotech: Return to Macross #20
© Academy

ROBOTECH
Eternity
1-shot Untold Stories	2.50

Academy Comics 1995–96
0 Robotech Information	2.50
Spec. #1 & #2 Robotech The Movie, Benny R. Powell & Chi	@2.95
1-shot Robotech Romance	2.95
GN The Threadbard Heart	9.95

Antarctic Press 1998
Ann. #1	2.95

ROBOTECH: ACADEMY BLUES
Academy Comics
0 Classroom Blues	3.50
1 F:Lisa	2.95
2 Bomb at the Academy	2.95
3 Roy's Drinking Buddy	2.95

ROBOTECH: AFTERMATH
Academy Comics
1 thru 10 R:Bruce Lewis	@2.95
11 Zentradi Traitor	2.95
12 and 13	@2.95

ROBOTECH: CLONE
Academy Comics
1 Dialect of Duality	2.95
2 V:Monte Yarrow	2.95
3 Ressurection	2.95
4 Ressurection	2.95
5 F:Bibi Ava	2.95

ROBOTECH: COVERT OPS
Antarctic Press 1998
1 (of 2) by Greg Lane	2.95

ROBOTECH: ESCAPE
Antarctic Press 1998
1	2.95

ROBOTECH: INVID WAR
Eternity 1993
1 No Man's Land	2.50
2 V:Defoliators	2.50
3 V:The Invid,Reflex Point	2.50
4 V:The Invid	2.50
5 Moonbase Aluce II	2.50
6 Moonbase-Zentraedi plot	2.50
7 Zentraedi plot contd.	2.50
8 A:Lancer	2.50
9 A:Johnathan Wolfe	2.50
10	2.50
11 F:Rand	2.50
12 thru 15	2.50

ROBOTECH: INVID WAR AFTERMATH
Eternity
1 thru 6 F:Rand	2.75

ROBOTECH: MACROSS TEMPEST
Academy Comics 1995
1 F:Roy Fokker, Tempest	2.95

ROBOTECH: MECH ANGEL
Academy Comics 1995
0 I:Mech Angel	2.95

ROBOTECH: MORDECAI
Academy Comics
1	2.95
2 Annie meets her clone	2.95

ROBOTECH: RETURN TO MACROSS
Eternity 1993
1 thru 5	2.50

Academy Comics
1 thru 17 Roy Fokker	2.75
18 F:The Faithful	2.75
19 F:Lisa	2.75
20 F:Lisa	2.75
21 V:Killer Robot	2.95
22 War of the Believers	2.95
23 War of the Believers,pt.2	2.95
24 War of the Believers,pt.3	2.95
25 War of the Believers,pt.4	2.95
26 thru 30	@2.95
31 What is the Federalist Plan?	2.95
32 thru 34	@2.95
35 Typhoon threatens Macross Island	2.95
36	2.95
37 round up of Federalist Agents	2.95

ROBOTECH: SENTINELS: RUBICON
Antarctic Press 1998
1 (of 7) 2.95
2 Shadows of the Past 2.95

ROBOTECH: SENTINELS STAR RUNNERS: CARPENTER'S JOURNEY
Academy Comics 1996
1 . . . . 2.95

ROBOTECH: THE MISFITS
Academy Comics
1 Misfits from Sothern Cross
transferred to Africa 2.95

ROBOTECH II THE SENTINELS
Eternity
1 . . . . 3.50
1a 2nd printing 1.95
2 . . . . 3.00
2a 2nd printing 1.95
3 . . . . 2.00
3a 2nd printing 1.95
4 thru 16 . . . . @1.95
Book 2
1 thru 12 . . . . @2.25
13 thru 20 . . . . @2.25
Wedding Special #1 . . . . 1.95
Wedding Special #2 . . . . 1.95
Robotech II Handbook 2.50
Book Three
1 thru 8 V:Invid 2.50
Book Four
Academy Comics Dec. 1995
1 by Jason Waltrip 2.95
2 thru 4 F:Tesla . . . . @2.75
5 JWp,JWt,interior of Haydon IV . 2.95
6 thru 8 . . . . @2.95
9 JWp,JWt,Breetai, Wolf & Vince
return to Tirol 2.95
10 JWp,JWt,*Ark Angel* attacked by
The Black Death Destroyers . . 2.95
11 JWp,JWt,Tirol, Wolff, Vince &
Breetai on trial for treason 2.95
12 JWp,JWt,Dr. Lang exposes
General Edwards' evil designs 2.95
13 F:Tesla 2.75
14 V:Invid 2.75
15 . . . . 2.75
16 . . . . 2.75
17 V:Invid Mechas 2.75
18 F:"HIN" 2.95
19 V:Invid 2.95
20 Final Aplp. Invid Regiss 2.95
21 Predator and Prey 2.95
22 A Clockwork Planet 2.95
Halloween Special JWp,JWt, ... 2.95

ROBOTECH II: THE SENTINELS: CYBERPIRATES
Eternity 1991
1 The Hard Wired Coffin 2.25
2 thru 4 . . . . @2.25

*Robotech II: The Sentinels:
The Malcontent Uprising #10 © Eternity*

ROBOTECH II: THE SENTINELS: THE MALCONTENT UPRISING
Eternity
1 thru 12 . . . . @1.95

ROBOTECH: VERMILION
Antarctic Press 1997
1 (of 4) by Duc Tran 2.95
2 Why did Hiro die? 2.95
3 . . . . 2.95
4 . . . . 2.95

ROBOTECH: WARRIORS
Academy Comics
1 F:Breetai 2.95
2 F:Mirya 2.95
3 F:Mirya 2.95
GN The Terror Maker 9.95

ROBOTECH: WINGS OF GIBRALTAR
Antarctic Press 1998
1 (of 2) by Lee Duhig 2.95

ROCK & ROLL COMICS
Revolutionary
1 Guns & Roses 6.00
1a 2nd printing 3.50
1b 3rd printing 2.00
1c 4th-7th printing 2.00
2 Metalica 5.00
2a 2nd printing 3.00
2b 3rd-5th printing 2.00
3 Bon Jovi 3.50
4 Motley Crue 4.00
5 Def Leppard 2.50
6 RollingStones 5.00
6a 2nd-4th printing 2.00
7 The Who 3.50
7a 2nd-3rd printing 2.00
9 Kiss 6.00
9a 2nd-3rd Printing 2.00

10 Warrant/Whitesnake 2.50
10a 2nd Printing 2.00
11 Aerosmith 2.00
12 New Kids on Block 4.00
12a 2nd Printing 2.00
13 LedZeppelin 3.00
14 Sex Pistols 2.00
See Independent Color

ROCKET RANGERS
Adventure
1 . . . . 2.95
2 . . . . 2.95
3 . . . . 2.95

ROCKIN ROLLIN MINER ANTS
Fate Comics
1 As seen in TMNT #40 . . . . . . 2.25
1a Gold Variant copy 7.50
2 Elephant Hunting, A:Scorn,Blister2.25
3 V:Scorn, Inc.,K.Eastman Ant pin-
up 2.25
4 Animal Experiments,V:Loboto . 2.25

ROLLING STONES: THE SIXTIES
Personality
1 Regular Version 2.95
1a Deluxe Version,w/cards 6.95

ROSE
Hero Graphics
1 From The Champions 3.50
2 A:Huntsman 3.50
3 thru 5 . . . . @2.95

ROSE AND GUNN
London Night
1 . . . . 3.00
1a nude cover 6.00
1b signed 10.00
2 . . . . 3.00
3 . . . . 3.00

ROSE AND GUNN: RECKONING
London Night
1 (of 2) 3.00

ROSE 'N GUNN
Bishop Pres 1995
1 Deadly Duo 5.00
2 V:Marilyn Monroe 3.00
3 Presidential Affairs 3.00
4 Without Each Other 3.00
5 V:Red 3.00
6 & 7 . . . . @3.00
Creator's Choice Rep. #1 . . . . . 2.95
Creator's Choice Rep. #2 . . . . . 2.95
Creator's Choice Rep. #3 . . . . . 2.95

ROVERS
Eternity
1 thru 7 . . . . @1.95

RUBES REVIVED
Fish Warp
1 . . . . 2.00
2 and 3 . . . . @2.00

RUK BUD WEBSTER
Fish Warp
1 thru 3 . . . . @1.70

SADE
Bishop Press
0 B:Adventures of Sade	3.00
1	3.00
1a variant	6.00
2	3.00

SADE
London Night
1	3.00
1a nude cover	7.00
2 thru 5	@3.00

SADE SPECIAL
Bishop Press
1 V:Razor	5.00
1a signed	7.00

SADE/ROSE AND GUNN
London Night Nov. 1996
1 Confederate Mist 3.00

SADE: TESTAMENTS OF PAIN
London Night Jan. 1997
1 (of 2) 3.00

SAGA OF THE MAN-ELF
1 thru 5 . . . . @2.25

SAGE
Fantaco 1995
1 O:Sage 4.95

SAINT
Kick Ass Comics
1 & 2 V:Cerran 2.50

SAINT GERMAINE
Caliber "Core" 1997
0 O:St. Germaine	3.95
1 VcL, two immortals, St. Germain cover	2.95
1 Lilith cover	2.95
2 VcL	2.95
3 VcL	2.95
3a signed	2.95
4 VcL	2.95
5 The Kilroy Mandate, VcL(c) . .	2.95
5a Meyer (c)	2.95
6 Kilroy Mandate	2.95
8 Ghost Dance	2.95
8 The Man in the Iron Mask . .	2.95
10 The Tragedy of Falstaff	2.95
11 by Gary Reed & James Lyle . .	2.95
GN Shadows Fall, rep. #1–#4 . .	14.95
Spec. Restoration, VcL	3.95

SALIMBA
Blackthorne
1 . . . . 3.50

SAMURAI (1st series)
1	60.00
2	30.00
3	30.00

4	30.00
5	30.00

SAMURAI
Aircel
1 rare	6.00
1a 2nd printing	3.00
1b 3rd printing	2.00
2	5.00
2a 2nd printing	2.50
3	3.00
4	3.00
5 thru 12	@2.00
13 DK (1st art)	4.00
14 thru 16 DK	@4.00
17 thru 22	@2.00

[3rd series]
#1 thru 3	@1.70
#4 thru 7	@1.95
Compilation Book	4.95

SAMURAI
Warp Graphics 1997
1 by Barry Blair & Colin Chan . . .	2.95
2	2.95
3	2.95
4	2.95

SAMURAI FUNNIES
Solson
1 thru 3 . . . . @2.00

SAMURAI PENGUIN
Solson
1	3.00
2 I:Dr.Radium	2.00
3	2.00
4	1.50
5 FC	1.50
6 color	2.25
7	2.25
8	1.75
9	1.75

SAMURAI 7
Gauntlet Comics
1 I: Samurai 7 . . . . 2.50

SAMURAI, SON OF DEATH
Eclipse
1	3.95
1a 2nd printing	3.95

SANCTUARY
Viz
1 World of Yakuza	4.95
2 thru 4	@4.95
5 thru 9	@4.95

[Part Five] 1996
7 thru 13 by Sho Fumimura & Ryoichi Ikegami	@3.50
GN rep. ½ of part 4 & ½ part 5 .	16.95
GN Vol. 5	17.95
GN Vol. 6	17.95
GN Vol. 9	16.95

SANTA CLAWS
Eternity
1 'Deck the Mall with Blood and Corpses' 2.95

SAVAGE HENRY
Vortex
1 thru 13 . . . . @1.75
Rip Off Press
14 thru 15	@2.00
16 thru 24	@2.50

SCARAMOUCH
Innovation
1 . . . . 2.50

SCARLET IN GASLIGHT
1 A:SherlockHolmes	4.00
2	3.00
3 & 4	@2.50

SCARLET SCORPION/ DARKSIDE
AC Comics
1 & 2 Flipbooks 3.50

SCARLET THUNDER
Amaze Ink
1 thru 3 . . . . @2.50

SCIMIDAR
Eternity
1	4.25
1a 2nd Printing	2.50
2 and 3	@3.00
4 HotCover	3.50
4A MildCover	3.00

SCORN
SCC Entertainment 1996
Lingerie Spec.	2.95
Lingerie Spec. deluxe	9.95
Super Spec.#1 rep. Deadly Rebellion, Headwave, Fabric of the Mind	4.95
X-over Scorn/Ardy: Alien Influence (1997) by Rob Potchak & Timothy Johnson	3.95
Bill Maus (c)	3.95
Deluxe gold	9.95
X-over Scorn/Dracula: The Vampire's Blood (1997)	3.95
Dracula cover	3.95
Scorn cover	3.95
Nude cover	9.95
Spec.#1A Scorn; Dead or Alive (1997) Mike Morales(c)	3.95
Andrea Seri(c)	3.95
Spec.# Scorn:Deadly Rebellion . .	3.95
Birthday Suit cover	9.95
Celebrity photo cover	9.95
Spec.#1 Scorb: Fractured (1997) Fear cover	3.95
Rage cover	3.95
Nude cover	9.95
Spec: Scorn: Heatwave (1997) by Chris Crosby & Mike Morales .	3.95
Nude cover	9.95
Spec. Scorn: Hostage	3.95
Nude cover	9.95
Spec. Scorn: Naked Truth (1997) .	3.95
Nude cover	9.95

SCOUT HANDBOOK
Eclipse
1 . . . . 1.75

SCRATCH
Outside
1	3.00
2	2.00
3	1.75
4	1.75

SCRIMIDAR
CFD Productions 1995
1 I:Bloody Mary	2.75

SCUD:
DISPOSABLE ASSASSIN
Fireman Press
1 I:Scud	15.00
1a 3rd printing	3.50
2	12.00
3	10.00
4 thru 6 F:Scud	@7.00
7 Lupine Thoughts	5.00
8 Scud Looks for His Arm	5.00
9 Scud Looks for His Arm	5.00
10 thru 16 by Rob Schrab	@4.00
17	4.00
18	4.00
19	4.00
20 Horse series, concl.	4.00
TPB Rep.#1–#4	12.95
TPB Programmed for Damage, rep.#5–#9	14.95
TPB Solid Gold Bomb	17.95

SCUD: TALES FROM
THE VENDING MACHINE
Fireman Press 1998
1	2.50
2	2.50
3	2.50
4	2.50

SEARCHERS
Caliber "New Worlds"
1A Red cover, signed	3.00
1B Blue cover, signed	3.00
3	3.00
4	3.00
5 flip book with Boston Bombers	3.00

SEARCHERS:
APOSTLE OF MERCY
Caliber 1997
1 (of 2)	3.95
2	3.95
Vol 2?	
1 (of 4)	2.95
2	2.95
3 (of 3) 48pg	3.95

SECRET FILES
Angel Entertainment 1996
0 gold edition	8.00
0 nude cover	10.00
0 commemorative edition	2.95
0 nude commemorative edition	5.00
1	2.95
1 spooky silver foil edition	5.95
1 nude signed	10.00
2	2.95
2 deluxe	5.95
2 nude cover A	10.00
2 nude cover B	10.00

Spec. Secret Files vs. Vampire Girls: The Vampire Effece (1997)	2.95
Erotic nude cover	2.95
Pin-up Book Secret Files: Erotic Experiments (1997)	2.95
Erotic nude cover A	2.95
Erotic nude cover B	2.95
Spec.#1 Secret Files: F.B.I. Conspiracy (1997)F:Sabrina & Susanna Sorenson	2.95
Nude cover	2.95

SECRET FILES:
THE STRANGE CASE
Angel Entertainment 1996
0 by David Campitti & Al Rio	2.95
0 Virgin nude cover	5.00
0 Slimy Wet Twins nude cover	7.00
0 nude manga cover	5.00
0 nude platinum cover	15.00
1 by David Campitti & Al Rio	2.95
1 Virgin nude cover	5.00
1 nude manga cover	5.00
1 nude platinum cover	15.00

SECTION 8
Noir Press 1995
1 Anthology series	2.50
2 thru 6	@2.50
7 "Retribution," pt.1	2.50
8 "Retribution," pt.2	2.50
9	2.50
10 "Chance"	2.50

SEEKER
Caliber "Core" 1998
1M by Gary Reed & Chris Massarotto, Meadows(c)	2.95
1W David Williams(c)	2.95
1a variant Greg Louden (c)	2.95
1 premium, signed	9.95
2	2.95
3	2.95

SENTINEL
1	1.95
2 thru 4	@1.95

SERAPHIN
Newcomers Press 1995
1 I:Roy Torres	2.95

SHADES OF GRAY
COMICS AND STORIES
Caliber Tapestry 1996
1	2.95
2	2.95
3	2.95
4	2.95
Super Summer Spec. rep.	3.95

SHADOW CROSS
Darkside Comics 1995
1 I:Shadow Cross	4.95
2 thru 7	@2.50

SHADOWALKER
Aircel
1 thru 4	@1.70

SHADOW SLASHER
Pocket Change Comics
1 I:Shadow Slasher	2.50
2 V:Riplash	2.50
3 F:Matt Baker	2.50
4 Evolution	2.50
5 F:Riplash	2.50
6 Next Victim	2.50
7 What Can Kill Him	2.50
8	2.50
9 final issue	2.50

SHANDA [THE PANDA]
Antarctic Press
1 thru 11	@2.75
12 thru 14	@2.95
Med Systems	
15 and 16	@1.95
Vision Comics	
17 by Mike Curtis & Michelle Light	1.95
18 "Rocky Horror Picture Show"	1.95
19 "Shine on Me, Cajun Moon"	2.50
20 falling in love	2.50
22 Bright Eyes	2.95
23 Sweet Young Things	2.95
24 graduation night	2.95

SHANGHAIED
Eternity
1 & 2	@1.80
3 & 4	@1.95

SHARDS
Acension Comics
1 I:Silver, Raptor, RIpple	2.50
2 F:Anomoly	2.50

SHATTERED EARTH
Eternity 1988–89
1 thru 9	@1.95

SHATTERPOINT
Eternity 1990
1 thru 4 Broid miniseries	@2.25

SHE-CAT
AC Comics
1 thru 4	@2.50

SHE-DEVILS ON WHEELS
Aircel
1 thru 3	2.95

SHERLOCK HOLMES
Eternity
1 thru 22	@1.95

SHERLOCK HOLMES
Caliber/Tome Press 1997
1-shot Return of the Devil	3.95
1-shot Return of the Devil, signed	3.95
GN Adventure of the Opera Ghost	6.95
TPB Case of Blind Fear	12.95
TPB Scarlet in Gaslight	12.95
TPB Sussex Vampire	12.95

SHERLOCK HOLMES
CASEBOOK
Eternity
1 and 2	@2.25

SHERLOCK HOLMES: CHRONICLES OF CRIME AND MYSTERY
Northstar
1 'The Speckled Band' 2.25

SHERLOCK HOLMES: DR. JEKYLL AND MR. HOLMES
Caliber/Tome Press 1998
1 by Steve Jones & Seppo Makinen2.95

SHERLOCK HOLMES: HOUND OF THE BASKERVILLES
Caliber/Tome Press Dec. 1997
1 (of 3) by Martin Powell & PO . . 2.95

SHERLOCK HOLMES: MARK OF THE BEAST
Caliber/Tome Press 1997
1 (of 3) by Martin Powell & Seppo
Makinen 2.95
2 . . . . 2.95
GN 12.95

SHERLOCK HOLMES MYSTERIES
Moonstone 1997
1-shot by Joe Gentile & Richard
Gulick 2.95

SHERLOCK HOLMES OF THE '30's
Eternity
1 thru 7 . . . . @2.95

SHERLOCK HOLMES: RETURN OF THE DEVIL
Adventure
1 V:Moriarty 2.50
2 V:Moriarty 2.50

SHERLOCK JUNIOR
Eternity
1 Rep.NewspaperStrips 1.95
2 Rep.NewspaperStrips 1.95
3 Rep.NewspaperStrips 1.95

SHI: BLACK, WHITE, AND RED
Crusade Entertainment 1998
1 by Tom Sniegoski & J.G. Jones 2.95

SHI: KAIDAN
Crusade Entertainment
1 macabre 2.95

SHIELA TRENT VAMPIRE HUNTER
Draculina Publishing
1 O:Sheild Trent 2.50

SHIP OF FOOLS
Caliber 1996
1 signed edition 3.00

2 "Dante's Compass" 3.00
3 The Great Escape begins 3.00
4 MiA 3.00
5 MiA 3.00
Spec. #1, Bon Voyage, Go to Hell,
Mama Hades 3.95
continued: See Image Comics

SHOCK THE MONKEY
Millenium
1 & 2 Entering the Psychotic Mind 3.95

SHOCKWAVES
Knight Press
1 . . . . 2.95

SHRED
CFW
1 thru 10 . . . . @2.25

SHRIEK
1 . . . . 4.95
2 . . . . 4.95
3 . . . . 7.95

SHURIKEN
Victory 1986
1 Reggi Byers 6.00
1a 2nd printing 1.50
2 . . . . 3.00
3 . . . . 2.00
4 . . . . 1.75
5 thru 13 . . . . @1.50
Graphic Nov. Reggie Byers 8.00

Shuriken #6 © Eternity Comics

SHURIKEN
Eternity 1991
1 Shuriken vs. Slate 2.50
2 Neutralizer, Meguomo 2.50
3 R:Slate 2.50
4 Morgan's Bodyguard Serrate . . 2.50
5 Slate as Shuriken & Megumo . 2.50
6 Hunt for Bionauts, final issue . . 2.50

SHURIKEN: COLD STEEL
1 . . . . 1.95

2 . . . . 1.95
3 thru 6 . . . . @1.95

SHURIKEN TEAM-UP
1 thru 3 . . . . @1.95

SIEGEL & SHUSTER
2 . . . . 1.70

SILBUSTER
Antarctic Press
1 thru 10 . . . . 3.50
11 I:Kizuki Sister 3.50
12 thru 14 . . . . @3.50
15 . . . . 3.95
16 thru 19 . . . . @3.50
TPB Rep. #1-#4 . . . . 10.95
TPB Vol.2 . . . . 10.95

SILENT INVASION
Renegade
1 . . . . 4.00
2 thru 12, final issue . . . . @3.00

SILENT INVASION
Caliber
4 Red Shadows, pt.1 . . . . 3.00
5 Red Shadows, pt.2 . . . . 3.00

SILENT INVASION: ABDUCTIONS
Caliber 1998
1 by Larry Hancock & Michael
Cherkos 2.95

SILVER STORM
Aircel 1990
1 thru 4 . . . . 2.25

SIMON/KIRBY READER
1 . . . . 1.75

SINBAD
1 . . . . 2.25
2 . . . . 2.25
3 . . . . 2.25
4 . . . . 2.25

SINBAD: HOUSE OF GOD
Adventure Comics
1 Caliph's Wife Kidnapped 2.50
2 Magical Genie 2.50
3 Escape From Madhi 2.50
4 A:Genie 2.50

SINNAMON
Catfish Comics 1995
1 remastered 2.75
1a remastered deluxe 3.75
6 thru 8 . . . . @2.75
Mythic Comics
9 "Ashes to Ashes—The Pyre-Anna
Saga," pt.2 . . . . 2.75
10 "Twas Beauty Bashed The
Beast" 2.75
11 . . . . 2.75
12 M.G.Delaney (c) 2.75
12 Poliwko (c) 2.75
Archives #1 . . . . 2.75

SISTER ARMAGEDDON
Dramenon Studios
1 & 2 Nun with a Gun 2.50
3 Mother Superior 2.50
4 V:Apoligon 2.95

SKELETON KEY
Amaze Ink 1995
1 1 I:Skeleton Key 1.50
. 1 2nd printing 1.75
2 F:Tansin 1.50
3 V:Japanese Burglar 1.50
4 V:Closet Monster 1.50
5 thru 10 . . . . @1.75
11 . . . . 1.75
12 . . . . 1.75
14 by Andi Watson 1.75
15 "The Celestial Calendar" . . . 1.75
16 thru 29 . . . . @1.75
Spec. 4.95
TPB Vol. 1, Threshold rep.#1–#6 11.95
TPB Vol. 3, rep. #19–#24 . . . . 12.95
TPB Vol. 4, Cats & Dogs, rep.
  #25–#30 . . . . 12.95

SKIN 13
Entity/Parody 1995
1/2a Grungie/Spider-Man 2.50
1/2b Heavy Metal 2.50
1/2c Gen-Et Jackson 2.50

SKUNK, THE
Entity Comics April 1997
#Uno 2.75
5 BMs 2.75
6 BMs 2.75
Collection #1 rep. #1–#3 . . . . . 4.95
Collection #1a signed & numbered 9.95
Collection #2 rep. #4–#6 . . . . . 4.95

SKUNK/FOODANG
FOODANG/SKUNK
Entity Comics
Spec. 1 BMs, BMs(c) 2.75
Spec. 1a BMs, Mike Duggan(c) . . 2.75

SKYNN & BONES:
DEADLY ANGELS
Brainstorm April 1996
1 . . . . 2.95

SKYNN & BONES:
FLESH FOR FANTASY
Brainstorm 1997
1 erotic missions 2.95
1a nude cover 2.95
2 erotic missions 2.95
2a nude cover 2.95
Spec. #1 Dare to Bare 3.00
Spec. #1 Dare to Bare, nude cover 4.00

SLACK
Legacy Comics
1 Slacker Anthology 2.50
2 Loser 2.50

SLAUGHTERHOUSE
Caliber
1 Bizarre medical Operations . . . 2.95
2 House of Death 2.95

3 House of Death 2.95
4 Dead Killer vs. Mosaic 2.95

SMALL PRESS
SWIMSUIT SPECTACULAR
Allied Press
1 Supports Am. Cancer Assn. . . 2.95

SNAKE, THE
Special Studio 1991
1 . . . . 3.50

SNARF
Kitchen Sink
1 thru 10 . . . . @2.00
10 (c)BE 2.00
11 thru 13 . . . . @2.00

SNOWMAN
Hall of Heroes 1996
1 . . . . 20.00
1a variant (c) 25.00
1 3rd printing 2.75
1 San Diego Con. ed. 5.00
2 . . . . 10.00
2a 2nd printing 2.75
2b variant (c) 12.00
3 . . . . 6.00
3a variant (c) 9.00

SNOWMAN
Avatar Press 1997
0 by Matt Martin, O:Snowman . . 3.00
0a Frozen Fear extra-bloody . . . 4.95
0b Leather cover 25.00
0c signed 10.00
Spec.#1 Snowman 1944 . . . . . . 3.95
Spec.#1 Snowman 1944, deluxe . 4.95
Spec.#1 Snowman 1944, signed 10.00

SNOWMAN:
DEAD & DYING
Avatar Press 1997
1 (of 3) by Matt Martin 3.00
1 deluxe 4.95
1 signed 10.00
2 . . . . 3.00
2 deluxe 4.95
3 by Matt Martin 3.00
3 Frozen Fear 4.95
3 White Velvet 25.00

SNOWMAN:
HORROR SHOW
Avatar Press 1998
1 by Matt Martin 3.00
1a Frozen Fear (c) 4.95
1b Leather cover 30.00
1 deluxe 4.95

SNOWMAN: 1994
Entity Oct. 1996
1 flip cover #0, by Matt Martin,
  O:Snowman 3.00
1 signed, numbered 8.00
3 . . . . 2.75
3 deluxe, variant, foil cover 3.50
4 . . . . 2.75
4 deluxe, variant, foil cover 3.50

SNOWMAN²
Avatar Press 1997
1 (of 2) Snowman vs. Snowman . 3.00
1a Face-off cover 4.95
1b Leather cover 30.00
1c Royal Blue edition 75.00
2 concl. 3.00
2a Sudden Death variant cover . . 4.95

SOB: SPECIAL
OPERATIONS BRANCH
Promethean Studios 1994
1 I:SOB 2.50

SOCKETEER
Kardia
Rocketeer parody 2.25

SOLD OUT
Fantagor
1 & 2 . . . . @1.75

SOLO EX-MUTANTS
Eternity
1 thru 6 . . . . @1.95

SOLSON PREVIEW
Solson
1 . . . . 2.00

SONG OF THE SIRENS
Millennium
Earth 2.95
Earth, signed print edition 6.95
Fire 2.95
Fire, signed print edition 9.95
Wind 2.95
Wind collectors edition 4.95
Wind with trading card 4.95
Secrets, Lies, & Videotape Pin-Up
  Special 2.95
Secrets, Lies, & Videotape Pin-Up
  Special, foil logo 5.95
Secrets, Lies, & Videotape Pin-Up
  Special, deluxe 9.95

SOUL
Samson Comics
1 thru 3 F:Sabbeth . . . . @2.50

SOULFIRE
Aircel
1 mini-series 1.70
2 . . . . 1.70
3 . . . . 1.70

SOULSEARCHERS
AND CO.
Claypool 1993–98
1 thru 10 Peter David(s) . . . . . @3.00
11 thru 20 . . . . @2.50
21 thru 24 . . . . @2.50
25 ACo&SL(c) 2.50
26 O:Soulsearchers, pt.1 . . . . . 2.50
27 O:Soulsearchers, pt.2 . . . . . 2.50
28 O:Soulsearchers, pt.3 . . . . . 2.50
29 O:Soulsearchers, pt.4 . . . . . 2.50
30 . . . . 2.50
31 The Mystery of the Lighthouse
  Pirate Treasure 2.50

TPB 12.95

SOUTHERN KNIGHTS
1 See Crusaders
2 . . . . 8.00
3 and 4 . . . . @5.00
5 thru 7 . . . . @4.00
Fictioneer
8 thru 11 . . . . @2.50
12 thru 33 . . . . @2.00
34 . . . . 2.25
35 The Morrigan Wars Pt.#2 . . . 3.50
36 Morrigan Wars Pt.#5 . . . . . . 3.50
Ann. #1 . . . . 2.50
DreadHalloweenSpec #1 . . . . . . 2.25
Primer #1 . . . . 2.25

Southern Squadron Freedom of Information Act #1 © Eternity

SOUTHERN SQUADRON
Aircel
1 thru 4 . . . . @2.25
Eternity
1 I:SQUAD 2.50
2 . . . . 2.25
3 . . . . 2.25
4 . . . . 2.25

SOUTHERN SQUADRON FREEDOM OF INFO. ACT.
Eternity
1 F.F.#1 Parody/Tribute cov. . . . 2.50
2 A:Waitangi Rangers 2.50
3 . . . . 2.50

SPACE ARK
Apple
1 . . . . 2.75
2 . . . . 2.50
3 . . . . 1.75
4 . . . . 1.75
5 . . . . 1.75

SPACE BEAVER
Ten-Buck Comics
1 . . . . 2.50
2 . . . . 1.50

---

3 O&I:Stinger 1.50
4 A:Stinger 1.50
5 . . . . 1.50
6 O:Rodent 1.50
7 thru 12 . . . . @1.50

SPACED
1 I:Zip; 800 printed 40.00
2 . . . . 25.00
3 I:Dark Teddy 15.00
4 . . . . 15.00
5 and 6 . . . . @5.00
7 and 8 . . . . @2.00
Eclipse
9 . . . . 1.75
10 . . . . 1.75
11 thru 13 . . . . @1.50

SPACE PATROL
Adventure
1 thru 3 . . . . 2.50

SPACE 34-24-34
1 . . . . 4.50

SPACE USAGI
Mirage Studios
1 Stan Sakai,Future Usagi 2.00
2 Stan Sakai,Future Usagi 2.00
3 Stan Sakai,Future Usagi 2.00

SPACE WOLF
Antarctic Press
1 From Albedo,by Dan Flahive . . 2.50

SPANDEX TIGHTS
Lost Cause Prod. Jan. 1997
Vol.2
1 . . . . 2.50
2 prelude to Space Opera 2.95
6 . . . . 2.95
Spec. Vs. Mighty Awful Sour
  Rangers, signed 2.95

SPANDEX TIGHTS PRESENTS: SPACE OPERA
Lost Cause Productions 1997
Part 1 by Bryan J.L. Glass & Bob
  Dix, parody 2.95
Part 1, signed, Star Wars parody . 2.95
Part 2 "Star Bored," pt.2 . . . . . . 2.95
Part 3 . . . . 2.95

THE GIRLS OF '95
1 The Good, Bad and Deadly,
  signed (1997) 3.95

WIN A DREAM DATE WITH SPANDEX-GIRL
1 (of 3) (1998) 2.95
2 . . . . 2.95
3 . . . . 2.95

SPANDEX TIGHTS: THE LOST ISSUES
Lost Cause Productions
1 (of 4) 2.95
2 . . . . 2.95
3 . . . . 2.95
4 concl. 2.95

SPARKPLUG
Hero Graphics
1 From League of Champions . . 2.95

SPARKPLUG SPECIAL
Heroic Publishing
1 V:Overman 2.50

SPARROW
Millenium
1 I:Sparrow 2.95
2 . . . . 2.95
3 Valley of Fire 2.50

SPEED RACER
1 . . . . 3.00
1a 2nd Printing 1.50

SPENCER SPOOK
A.C.E. Comics
1 and 2 . . . . @.95
3 thru 8 . . . . @1.75

SPICY TALES
1 thru 13 . . . . @1.95
14 thru 20 . . . . @2.25
Special #2 . . . . 2.25

SPIDER KISS
1 Harlan Ellison 3.95

SPINELESS MAN
Parody Press
1 Spider-Man 2099 spoof 2.50

SPIRIT, THE
Kitchen Sink
Note: #1 to #11 are in color
12 thru 86 WE,rep (1986–92) . @2.00
GN The Spirit Casebook 16.95
GN The Spirit Jam, 50 artists in
  48pg (1998) 5.95

SPIRIT, THE: THE ORIGIN YEARS
Kitchen Sink 1997
1 F:The Origin of the Spirit 3.00
2 F:The Black Queen's Army . . . 3.00
3 F:Palyachi,The Killer Clown . . . 3.00
4 F:The Return of the Orang . . . 3.00
5 WE 3.00
6 WE,Kiss of Death 3.00
7 F:The Kidnapping of Ebony . . . 3.00
8 F:Christmas Spirit of 1940 . . . . 3.00
9 WE 3.00
10 F:The Substitute Spirits 3.00

SPIRIT OF THE DRAGON
Double Edge
0 Dragon Scheme 75

SPIRITS
Mindwalker 1995
1 thru 3 Silver City 2.95
4 Caleb Escapes Zeus 2.95

SPITTING IMAGE
Eclipse
1 Marvel & Image parody 2.50

SQUEE
Slave Labor 1997
1 by Jhonen Vasquez	2.95
1a 2nd printing	2.95
2	2.95
3	2.95
4	2.95
TPB	15.95

STAINLESS STEEL ARMIDILLO
Antarctic Press
1 I:Saisni, Tania Badan	2.95
2 V:Mirage	2.95
3 V:Mirage	2.95
4 Spirit of Gaia	2.95
5 V:Giant	2.95
6 finale	2.95

STAR BLEECH THE GENERATION GAP
Parody Press
1 Parody	3.95

STARCHILD
Taliesin Press 1992–97
0	35.00
1	50.00
1a 2nd printing	4.00
2	50.00
2a 2nd printing	4.00
3	15.00
4	7.00
5	5.00
6	5.00
7	5.00
8	5.00
9	5.00
10 thru 13	5.00
14	3.00

Coppervale
TPB Coll. Ed. Awakenings, rep. #1–#12	20.00
HC	35.00

STARCHILD: CROSSROADS
Coppervale
1 thru 4, reoffer, by James Owen	@2.95
TPB Coll. Ed.112 pg.	12.00
HC Coll.Ed.	20.00
Conoisseurs Edition	100.00

STARCHILD MYTHOPOLIS
Coppervale 1997
6 (of 14) Fisher King, concl.	2.95

STARGATE: THE NEW ADVENTURES COLLECTION
Entity 1997
1 rep. Underworld; One Nation Under Ra	5.95
1a photo cover	4.95

STARGATE: ONE NATION UNDER RA
Entity March 1997
1	2.75
1a deluxe	3.50

STARGATE: REBELLION
Entity 1997
1 (of 3) from novel, sequel to movie	2.75
1 deluxe	3.50
2	2.75
2 deluxe	3.50
3 (of 3)	2.75
3 foil cover	3.50
GN rep. 80 pg.	7.95
GN photo (c)	7.95

STARGATE: UNDERWORLD
Entity April 1997
1	2.75
1a deluxe	3.50

STAR JAM COMICS
Revolutionary
1 F:Hammer	2.50

STARK FUTURE
Aircel
1	2.50
2 thru 7	@1.75
8	2.00
9 thru 14	@1.70

STAR RANGERS
1 thru 3	@3.00
4	1.95

BOOK II
1	1.95
2	1.95

STAR REACH
Taliesin Press
1 HC,I:CodyStarbuck	8.00
2 DG,JSn	2.00
3 FB	2.00
4 HC	2.00
5 JSon	2.00
6 GD,Elric	2.00
7 DS	2.00
8 CR,KSy	2.00
9 KSy	2.00
10 KSy	2.00
11 GD	2.00
12 MN,SL	2.00
13 SL,KSy	2.00
14	2.00
15	2.00
16	2.00
17	2.00
18	2.00

STARLIGHT AGENCY
Antarctic Press
1 I:Starlight Agency	1.95
2 Anderson Kidnapped	1.95
3	1.50

STARLIGHT SQUADRON
Blackthorne
1	2.00

STATIC
1 SD	1.50
2 SD	1.50
3 SD	1.50

STEALTH FORCE
1 thru 8	@.95

STEALTH SQUAD
Petra Comics
0 O:Stealth Squad	2.50
1 I:Stealth Squad	2.50
2 I:New Member	2.50
Volume II	
1 F:Solar Blade	2.50
2 American Ranger Vs.Jericho	2.50

STEEL DRAGON STORIES
Steel Dragon
1	1.50

STEELE DESTINES
Nightscapes
1 & 2 I:One Eyed Stranger	2.95
3 Kidnapped by Aliens	2.95

STERN WHEELER
Spotlight
1 JA	1.75

STEVE CANYON
Kitchen Sink
1 thru 14	@5.00
3-D Spec. #1	6.00

STEVEN
Kitchen Sink
1	4.00
1a 2ndPrinting	2.95
2	4.00
3	2.95
4 and 5	@3.50
TPB The Best of Steven by Doug Allen (1998)	12.95

STICKBOY
Revolutionary
1	2.00
2 thru 5	@2.50

STIG'S INFERNO
Vortex
1	6.00
2	3.50
3	3.00
4	3.00
5	2.00
Eclipse	
6	1.75
7	1.75

STING
Artline
1	2.50

STINZ
Fantagraphics
1	4.00
2	4.00
3	4.00
4	4.00
[2nd series]	
Brave New Words	
1 thru 3	2.50

STORMBRINGER
Taliesin Press
1 thru 3 . . . . @2.00

STORMWATCHER
Eclipse
1 thru 4 . . . . @2.00

STRAND, THE
Trident
1 . . . . 2.50

STRANGE BEHAVIOR
Twilite Tone Press
1 LSn,MBr,Short Stories 2.95

STRANGE BREW
Aardvark–Vanaheim
1 . . . . 5.00

STRANGEHAVEN
Abiogenesis Press
1 Surrealistic Comic 2.95
2 Secret Brotherhood 2.95
3 thru 10 by Gary S. Millidge . @2.95
TPB Arcadia, rep. #1–#6 . . . . . . 14.95

Strange Sports Stories #1
© Adventure

STRANGE SPORTS STORIES
Adventure 1992
1 w/2 card strip 2.50
2 The Pick-Up Game,w/cards . . . 2.50
3 Spinning Wheels,w/cards 2.50
4 thru 6 w/cards . . . . @2.50

STRANGE WORLDS
1 . . . . 3.95
2 thru 4 . . . . @3.95

STRANGES IN PARADISE
Antarctic Press 1993–94
1 by Terry Moore, I:Katchoo . . . 75.00
1a 2nd printing 20.00
2 . . . . 50.00

3 . . . . 38.00

Abstract Studio
1 TMr, Gold Logo edition 25.00
1a 2nd printing 5.00
2 and 3, Gold Logo edition . . @12.00
4 . . . . 7.00
5 R:Mrs. Parker 7.00
6 . . . . 6.00
7 Darcey Uses Francine 6.00
8 thru 13 TMr . . . . @4.00
HC Complete Strangers In Paradise,
   Book One 29.95
VOL. 2
1 TMr, Gold Logo edition, I Dream
   of You . . . , ... 2.75
2 thru 13 gold logo . . . . @2.75
TPB I Dream of You 16.95
VOL III
1 thru 8 See Image
9 TMr,Detective Walsh returns . . 2.75
10 . . . . 2.75
11 . . . . 2.75
12 . . . . 2.75
13 High School, pt.1 (of 3) 2.75
14 High School, pt.2 . . . . 2.75
15 High School, pt.3 . . . . 2.75
16A Francine/Katchoo Princess
   Warrior (c) 2.75
16B Tambi Princess Warrior (c) . . 2.75
17 . . . . 2.75
TPB Vol.4 Love Me Tender 12.95
TPB Vol.5 Immortal Enemies, rep.
   #6–#12 . . . . 12.95

STRANGELOVE
Entity Comics 1995
1 I:Strangelove 2.50
2 V:Hyper Bullies 2.50
3 I:Bogie 2.50

STRATA
Renegade 1986
1 . . . . 3.00
2 . . . . 2.50
3 . . . . 1.70
4 . . . . 1.70
5 . . . . 1.70
6 . . . . 2.00

STRAW MEN
1 thru 5 . . . . @1.95
6 thru 8 . . . . @2.25

STRAY BULLETS
El Capitan
1 . . . . 25.00
1a 2nd & 3rd printing 4.00
2 . . . . 20.00
2a 2nd printing 3.50
3 . . . . 16.00
4 . . . . 15.00
5 Dysfunctional Family 5.00
6 F:Amy Racecar 4.50
7 Virginias Freedom 4.50
8 DL,"Lucky to Have Her" 3.00
9 DL,"26 Guys Named Nick" . . . 3.00
10 DL,"Here Comes the Circus" . . 3.00
11 DL,"How to Cheer Up Your Best
   Friend" 3.00
12 DL, People Will be Hurt 3.00
13 DL "Selling Candy" 2.95
14 DL,The Killers arrive,48pg . . . 3.50
15 Sex and Violence 2.95

16 . . . . 2.95
TPB Vol. 1 . . . . 11.95

STREET FIGHTER
Ocean Comics
1 thru 4 limited series . . . . @1.75

STREET HEROES 2005
Eternity
1 thru 3 . . . . @1.95

STREET MUSIC
Fantagraphics
1 . . . . 2.75
2 . . . . 2.75
3 . . . . 2.95
4 . . . . 2.95
5 . . . . 2.50
6 . . . . 3.95

STREET POET RAY
Fantagraphics
1 . . . . 2.50
2 . . . . 2.00
3 . . . . 2.95
4 . . . . 2.95

STREET WOLF
1 limited series 2.00
2 and 3 . . . . @2.00
Graphic Novel 6.95

STRIKER: SECRET OF THE BERSERKER
Viz
1 & 2 V:The Berserker 2.75
3 F:Yu and Maia 2.75

STRIKER: THE ARMORED WARRIOR
Viz
1 Overture 2.75
2 V:Child Esper 2.75
3 Professor taken hostage 2.75
GN Vol.1 The Armored Warrior . 16.95
GN Vol.2 Forest of No Return . . 15.95

STYGMATA YEARBOOK
Entity
1 V:The Rodent 2.95
TPB Dragon Prophet 6.95

SUBTLE VIOLENTS
CFD Productions 1991
1 Linsner (c&a) 42.00
1a San Diego Con 100.00

SUGAR RAY FINHEAD
Wolf Press
1 I&O Sugar Ray Finhead 2.50
2 I:Bessie & Big-Foot Benny the Pit
   Bull Man 2.95
3 thru 7 Mardi Gras . . . . @2.95
9 & 10 . . . . @2.95

SULTRY TEENAGE SUPER-FOXES
Solson
1 thru 4 RB,Woj . . . . @2.00

SUPERSWINE
Caliber
1 Parody, I:Superswine 2.50

SURF NEMO
Star Tiger 1995
1 Clone Wars 2.95

SURVIVALIST CHRONICLES
Survival Art
1 . . . . 6.50
2 . . . . 6.50
3 I:Bessie & Big Foot Benny 1.95

SWAN
Little Idylls
1 thru 3 Ghost of Lord Kaaren . . 2.95
4 V:Slake 2.95

SWEET CHILDE BATTLE BOOK
Advantage Graphics 1995
1 I:Tasha Radcliffe 2.50

SWEET CHILDE: LOST CONFESSIONS
Anarchy Bridgeworks 1997
1 F:Tasha Radcliffe 2.95

SWEET LUCY
Brainstorm Comics
1 w/4 cards 2.50
2 . . . . 2.50

SWERVE
Amaze Ink Dec. 1995
1 thru 3 by Kyle Hunter . . . . . @1.75

SWIFTSURE
Harrier Comics
1 . . . . 2.00
2 . . . . 2.00
3 thru 8 . . . . @1.75
9 . . . . 9.00
9a 2nd printing 1.75
10 . . . . 1.75
11 . . . . 1.95

SWORD OF VALOR
A Plus Comics
1 JAp,rep.Thane of Bagarth 2.50
2 JAp/MK rep 2.50

SWORDS AND SCIENCE
Pyramid
1 thru 3 . . . . @1.70

SWORDS OF CEREBUS
Aardvark–Vanaheim
1 rep. Cerebus 1-4 . . . . 18.00
1a reprint editions 10.00
2 rep. Cerebus 5-8 . . . . 12.00
2a reprint editions 8.00
3 rep. Cerebus 9-12 . . . . 12.00
3a reprint editions 8.00
4 rep. Cerebus 13-16 . . . . 12.00
4a reprint editions 8.00
5 rep. Cerebus 17-20 . . . . 12.00

5a reprint editions 8.00
6 rep. Cerebus 21-25 . . . . 12.00
6a reprint editions 8.00

SWORDS OF SHAR-PAI
Caliber 1991
1 Mutant Ninja Dog 2.50
2 Shar-Pei 2.50
3 Final issue 2.50

SWORDS OF VALORS: ROBIN HOOD
A Plus Comics
1 rep. of Charlton comics 2.50

System 7 #2 © Arrow

SYSTEM SEVEN
Arrow
1 thru 4 . . . . @1.50

TAKEN UNDER COMPENDIUM
Caliber
1 rep. Cal Presents #19-#22 . . . 2.95

TALES FROM DIMENSION X
Edge Publishing 1995
1 Dinosaur Mansion 3.95

TALES FROM THE ANIVERSE
Arrow
1 7,400 printed 10.00
2 . . . . 4.00
3 10,000 printed 2.50
4 . . . . 2.50

[2nd series]
Massive Comics Group
1 thru 3 . . . . 1.50

TALES FROM THE EDGE
Vanguard
5 . . . . 2.95
5 signed 5.95

6 . . . . 2.95
7 . . . . 2.95
7 signed 5.95
8 . . . . 2.95
8 signed 5.95
9 . . . . 2.95
10 . . . . 2.95
10 signed 5.95
11 F:Sacred Monkeys 2.95
12 spec.F:Steranko 4.00
12 signed, limited 15.00
13 F:Steranko 2.95
Spec. Nightstand Chillers Benefit
   Edition 4.95

TALES FROM THE HEART
1 thru 5 . . . . @1.75
6 . . . . 1.95
7 . . . . 1.95

TALES OF BEANWORLD
Eclipse
1 . . . . 10.00
2 . . . . 4.00
3 . . . . 2.50
4 I:Beanish 1.50
5 thru 20 . . . . @2.00

TALE OF MYA ROM
Aircel
1 . . . . 1.70

TALES OF TEENAGE MUTANT NINJA TURTLES
1 . . . . 13.00
1B 2nd printing 3.00
2 . . . . 8.00
3 . . . . 5.00
4 . . . . 5.00
5 . . . . 5.00
6 thru 9 . . . . @4.00

TALES OF THE FEHNRIK
Antarctic Press
1 I:Lady Zeista 2.95

TALES OF THE JACKALOPE
BF
1 . . . . 5.00
2 . . . . 3.00
3 and 4 . . . . @2.50
5 thru 9 . . . . @2.00

TALES OF THE NINJA WARRIORS
CFW
1 thru 14 . . . . @1.95
15 thru 19 . . . . @2.25

TALES OF THE PLAGUE
Eclipse
1 RCo 4.00

TALES TOO TERRIBLE TO TELL
1 thru 6 Pre-code horror stories @3.50

TANTALIZING STORIES
Tundra
1 F:Frank & Montgomery Wart .. 2.25
2 Frank & Mont.stories cont. 2.25

TAOLAND
Sunitek
1 V:The Crocodile Warlord 1.50
2 & 3 I:New Enemy 3.25

TASK FORCE ALPHA
Academy Comics
1 I:Task Force Alpha 3.50

TATTOOMAN SPECIAL
Fantagraphics
1 .... 2.75

TEAM NIPPON
Aircel
1 thru 7 .... @1.95

TECHNOPHILIA
Brainstorm Comics
1 w/4 cards 2.50

TEENAGE MUTANT NINJA TURTLES*
Mirage Studios
Counterfeits Exist - Beware
1 I:Turtles 350.00
1a 2nd printing 50.00
1b 3rd printing 25.00
1c 4th printing 15.00
1d 5th printing 4.00
2 .... 80.00
2a 2nd printing 18.00
2b 3rd printing 4.00
3 .... 25.00
3a 2nd printing 3.50
3b Special printing,rare 75.00
4 .... 10.00
4a 2nd printing 3.50
5 A:Fugitoid 8.00
5a 2nd printing 3.50
6 A:Fugitoid 7.00
6a 2nd printing 2.50
7 A:Fugitoid 8.00
7a 2nd printing 2.50
8 A:Cerebus 10.00
9 .... 7.00
10 V:Shredder 7.00
11 A:Casey Jones 6.00
12 thru 18 .... @6.00
19 Return to NY 4.00
20 Return to NY 4.00
21 Return to NY,D:Shredder 4.00
22 thru 32 .... @4.00
33 color, Corben 3.50
34 Toytle Anxiety 3.50
35 Souls Withering 3.50
36 Souls Wake 3.50
37 Twilight of the Rings 3.50
38 Spaced Out Pt.1, A:President
Bush 3.50
39 Spaced Out Pt.2 .... 3.50
40 Spaced Out concl.,I:Rockin'
Rollin' Miner Ants (B.U. story) . 2.00
41 Turtle Dreams issue 2.00
42 Juliets Revenge 2.00
43 Halls of Lost Legends 2.00
44 V:Ninjas 2.00

Teenage Mutant Ninja Turtles #38
© Mirage Studios

45 A:Leatherhead 2.00
46 V:Samurai Dinosaur 2.00
47 Space Usagi 2.00
48 Shades of Grey Part 1 ..... 2.00
49 Shades of Grey Part 2 ..... 2.00
50 Eastman/Laird,new direction,
inc.TM,EL,WS pin-ups 2.00
51 City at War #2 .... 2.00
52 City at War #3 .... 2.25
53 City at War #4 .... 2.25
54 City at War #5 .... 2.25
55 thru 65 .... @2.25
1990 Movie adaptation 6.50
Spec. The Haunted Pizza 2.25
Volume 2
1 thru 8 .... 2.75
9 V:Baxter Bot 2.75
10 Mr. Braunze 2.75
11 F:Raphael 2.75
12 V:DARPA 2.75
13 J:Triceraton 2.75

TMNT TRAINING MANUAL
1 .... 5.00
2 thru 5 .... @3.00

TEKQ
Caliber
1 .... 2.95

TELL-TALE HEART & OTHER STORIES
1 .... 2.50

TEMPEST COMICS PRESENTS
Academy Comics
1 I:Steeple, Nemesis 2.50

TERROR ON THE PLANET OF THE APES
Adventure Comics 1991
1 MP,collectors edition 2.50
2 MP, the Forbidden Zone 2.50
3 .... 2.50

TERROR TALES
Eternity
1 Short stories 2.50

TERRY AND THE PIRATES
ACG Comics 1998
1 by Georges Wunder, Charlton
reprint 3.00
2 .... 2.95
3 .... 2.95

TEX BENSON
Metro Comics
1 thru 3 .... @2.00

39 SCREAMS
1 thru 6 .... @2.00

THEY WERE 11
Viz
1 Galactic University 2.75
2 The Accident 2.75
3 Virus 2.75
4 V:Virus 2.75

THIEVES AND KINGS
I Box 1994–97
1 F:Ruebel The Intrepid 9.00
1a 2nd printing 2.50
2 .... 6.00
2a 2nd printing 2.50
3 .... 5.00
3a 2nd printing 2.50
4 .... 4.00
5 .... 4.00
6 V:Shadow Lady 4.00
7 V:Shadow Lady 2.50
8 thru 18 by Mark Oakley .... @2.50
19 thru 23 .... @2.35
TPB Vol. 1: The Red Book,
rep.#1–#6 .... 12.00
TPB Vol. 1: 2nd printing 13.50
TPB Vol. 2: The Green Book ... 14.00
TPB Vol. 2: 2nd printing 16.50

THIS MAGAZINE IS HAUNTED
A Plus Comics
1 .... 1.95

THISTLE
Fat Jar 1995
1 Three Policemen & Monk 2.00

THORR SUERD OR SWORD OF THOR
1 .... 3.00
1a 2nd printing 2.00
2 .... 1.75
3 .... 1.50

THREAT
1 .... 5.00
2 .... 3.00
3 and 4 .... @2.00
5 thru 10 .... @2.25

3 X 3 EYES
Innovation
1 Labyrinth o/t DemonsEyePt.1 .. 2.25

2 Labyrinth o/t DemonsEyePt.2 . . 2.25	
3 Labyrinth o/t DemonsEyePt.3 . . 2.25	
4 Labyrinth o/t DemonsEyePt.4 . . 2.25	
5 Labyrinth o/t DemonsEye conc. 2.25	

THREE MUSKETEERS

1	1.95
2	1.95
3	1.95

THREE ROCKETEERS
Eclipse

1 JK,AW,rep.	2.00
2 JK,AW,rep.	2.00

THRESHOLD
Avatar Press 1998

1 Snowman cover	4.50
1a Tales of the Cyberangels cover	4.50
1b Tales of the Cyberangels, nude cover	6.00
1c Furies cover	4.50
1d Furies, nude cover	6.00
1e Fuzzie Dice cover	4.50
2 Snowman cover	4.95
2a Tales of the Cyberangels cover	4.95
2b Tales of the Cyberangels, nude cover	6.00
2c Furies cover	4.95
2d Furies, nude cover	6.00
2e Pandora cover	4.95
3 Ravening (c)	4.95
3a Ravening Nude (c)	6.00
3b Tales of the Cyberangels (c)	4.95
3c Calico (c)	4.95
3d Pandora (c)	4.95
3e Pandora nude (c)	6.00
4 Donna Mia (c)	4.95
4a Dona Mia nude (c)	6.00
4b Lookers (c)	4.95
4c Lookers nude (c)	6.00
4d Black Reign (c)	4.95
4e Journeymen (c)	4.95
5 Black Reign (c)	4.95
5a Journeymen (c)	4.95
5b Midnight Doyle (c)	4.95
5c Midnight Doyle nude (c)	6.00
5d Widow (c)	4.95
5e Widow nude (c)	6.00
6 Luna cover	4.95
6a Pandora (c)	4.95
6b Onyx (c)	4.95
6c Onyx nude (c)	6.00
7 Darkness in Collision, Cavewoman(c)	4.95
7a Ravening (c)	4.95
7b 777 Wrath (c)	4.95
7c 777 Wrath nude (c)	6.00

THRESHOLD OF REALTY

1 5,000 printed	2.50
2 thru 4	@2.00

THRILLKILL
Caliber

1 rep. Cal.Presents #1-#4	2.50

THUNDERBIRD
Newcomers Publishing

1 & 2 2 Stories	@2.95
3	2.95
4 I:Mercer	2.95
5 R:Raven	2.95

6 & 7	2.95
8 final issue	3.50
Ann.#1 The Great Escape	3.50

THUNDER BUNNY

1 O:Thunder Bunny	2.50
2 VO:Dr.Fog	2.00
3 I:GoldenMan	1.75
4 V:Keeper	1.75
5 I:Moon Mess	1.75
6 V:Mr.Endall	1.75
7 VI:Dr.Fog	1.75
8	1.75
9 VS:Gen. Agents	1.75
10 thru 12	@1.75

THUNDER MACE

1 Proto type-blue & red very rare:1,000 printed	15.00
1a four color cover	3.00
2 thru 5	@1.75
6	2.00
7	2.00
Graphic Novel, rep.1-4	5.00

Tick #7 © New England Comics

TICK
New England Comics

1 BEd	65.00
1a 2nd printing	35.00
1b 3rd printing	6.00
1c 4th printing	2.50
2 BEd	50.00
2a 2nd printing	25.00
2b 3rd printing	4.00
2c 4th printing	2.50
3 BEd	25.00
3a 2nd printing	2.50
4 BEd	15.00
4a 2nd printing	2.50
5 BEd	15.00
6 BEd	11.00
7 BEd,A:Chairface Chippendale	11.00
8 BEd	11.00
8a Spec.No Logo edition	20.00
9 BEd,A:Chainsaw Vigilante, Red Eye	5.00
10 BEd	5.00
11 thru 12 BEd	4.00

9 thru 12, new printings	2.95
Spec. Ed. #1, I:Tick	45.00
Spec. Ed. #2, 2nd App. Tick	40.00
Spec. #1 Reprise edition	5.95
TPB Omnibus #1 rep. #1–#6	17.95
TPB Omnibus #2 BEd,fifth printing	14.95
TPB Omnibus #3 BEd	10.95
TPB Omnibus #4 BEd	10.95
The Tick Big Yule Log Special 1998	3.50
Big Giant Summer Special #1, The Sidekicks are Revolting	3.50

TICK, THE:
BIG BLUE DESTINY
New England Comics 1997

1 by Eli Stone, Keen edition	2.95
1 Wicked Keen edition	4.95
2A cover A	2.95
2B cover B	2.95
3	3.50
4	3.50
5 The Chrysalis Crisis	3.50

TICK: GIANT CIRCUS OF THE MIGHTY
New England Press

1 A-O	3.00
2 P-Z	3.00
3	3.00

TICK: KARMA TORNADO
New England Press

1	4.00
1 2nd printing	3.00
2	3.50
2 2nd printing	3.00
3 thru 9	3.50
3 thru 9 2nd printings	3.00
TPB #1 second edition	13.95

TICK, THE: LUNY BIN
New England Comics 1998

1 (of 3) by Eli Stone, Back to the Luny Bin	3.50
Preview Special, 32pg	1.50

TICK OMNIBUS
New England Press

1 1 to 6 Rep.	14.95

TICK'S BACK, THE
New England Comics

0 by Eli Stone, V:Toy DeForce	3.00

TIGERS OF TERRA
Mind-Visions

1 6,000 printed	4.50
1a Signed & Num.	14.00
2	2.00
2a Signed & Num.	11.00
5 thru 7	@3.50
8 thru 10	@3.75
Antarctic	
11 and 12	@3.95
[Vol. 2]	
0 thru 14	@2.75
15 Totenkopf Police,pt.2	2.75
16 Battleship Arizona,pt.3	2.75
17 thru 22	@2.95
23 "Trouble with Tigers" pt.3	2.95
24 48pg 10th Anniv.	3.95

25 "Battle for Terra" pt.1 . . . . 2.95
TPB Book Two 9.95
TPB Book Three 9.95
TPB Book Four 9.95

TIGRESS
Hero Graphics
3 A:Lady Arcane 2.95
4 inc. B.U. Mudpie 2.95

TIGER-X
Eternity
Special #1 . . . . 2.50
Spec. #1a 2nd printing 2.25
1 thru 3 . . . . @1.95
Book II
1 thru 4 . . . . @1.95

TIME DRIFTERS
Innovation
1 . . . . 2.25
2 . . . . 2.25
3 . . . . 2.25

TIME GATES
Double Edge
1 SF series,The Egg #1 . . . . 1.95
2 The Egg #2 . . . . 1.95
3 Spirit of the Dragon #1 . . . . . . 1.95
4 Spirit of the Dragon #2 . . . . . . 1.95
4a Var.cover 1.95

TIME JUMP WAR
Apple
1 thru 3 . . . . @1.95

TIME MACHINE
1 thru 3 . . . . @2.50

TIME WARRIORS
Fantasy General
1 rep.Alpha Track #1 . . . . 1.50
1a Bi-Weekly 75
2 .75
3 .75

TITANESS
Draculina Publishing 1995
1 I:Titaness,Tomboy 2.95

TO BE ANNOUNCED
1 thru 6 . . . . @1.50

TO DIE FOR
Blackthorne
1 . . . . 2.00

TOM CORBETT
SPACE CADET
Eternity
1 . . . . 2.00
2 . . . . 2.00
3 . . . . 2.25
4 . . . . 2.25

TOM CORBETT II
1 . . . . 2.25
2 . . . . 2.25
3 . . . . 2.25
4 . . . . 2.25

TOM MIX
HOLIDAY ALBUM
Amazing Comics
1 . . . . 3.50

TOM MIX WESTERN
AC Comics
1 . . . . 2.50
2 . . . . 2.50

TOMMI GUNN:
KILLERS LUST
London Night Jan. 1997
1 . . . . 3.00
1a nude cover 6.00
1 photo cover 6.00
3 nude cover, signed 12.00
Ann. #1 . . . . 3.00
Ann. #1a nude cover edition 3.00

TOMMY &
THE MONSTERS
1 thru 3 . . . . @1.95

TOMORROW MAN
Antarctic
1 R:Tommorrow Man 2.95
Spec.#1 48 pages 3.95

TOO MUCH COFFEE MAN
Adhesive Comics 1995
1 F:Too Much Coffee Man 20.00
1a 2nd printing 5.00
2 Wheeler (s&a) 12.00
3 Wheeler (s&a) 6.00
4 In love 5.00
5 thru 7 . . . . @4.00
8 . . . . 3.00

TORG
Adventure
1 Based on Role Playing Game . 2.50
2 thru 3 Based on Game . . . . @2.50

TOR JOHNSON:
HOLLYWOOD STAR
Monster Comics
1 Biographical story 2.50

TORRID AFFAIRS
1 . . . . 2.25
2 . . . . 2.25
3 thru 5, 60 pages . . . . @2.95

TOTALLY ALIEN
1 . . . . 17.00
2 . . . . 12.00
3 . . . . 8.00

TOUGH GUYS AND
WILD WOMEN
Eternity
1 . . . . 2.25
2 . . . . 2.25

TRACKER
Blackthorne
1 . . . . 2.00
2 . . . . 1.75

3 . . . . 2.00
4 . . . . 2.00

TRANSIT
1 . . . . 2.00
2 thru 6 . . . . @1.75

TRIAD
Blackthorne
1 . . . . 1.75

TRIARCH
Caliber
1 . . . . 2.00

TRICKSTER
KING MONKEY
1 thru 5 . . . . @1.75

TRIDENT
1 thru 7 . . . . @3.50
8 . . . . 4.50

TRIMUVERATE
Mermaid Productions
1 I:Trimverate 2.25
2 & 3 Team captured 2.25
4 V:Ord,Ael 2.25

TROLLORDS
Tru Studios 1986
1 1st printing 6.00
1a 2nd printing 2.00
2 . . . . 3.00
3 . . . . 2.00
4 thru 15 . . . . @1.50
#1 special 1.75

TROLLORDS
Apple Comics 1989–90
1 thru 6 . . . . @2.50

TROLLORDS
Caliber Tapestry 1996
1 and 2 . . . . @2.95

TROLLORDS:
DEATH & KISSES
1 . . . . 1.95
2 thru 5 . . . . @2.25

TROUBLE SHOOTERS
Nightwolf
1 I:Trouble Shooters 2.50
2 V:Ifrit,Djin,Ghul 2.50
3 V:Morgath 2.50

TROUBLE WITH GIRLS
Eternity 1989–91
1 . . . . 3.00
2 . . . . 2.50
3 thru 14 . . . . @1.95
15 thru 21 . . . . @2.25
22 Lester's Origin 2.25
Ann. #1 . . . . 2.95
Graphic Novel 7.95
Graphic Novel #2 . . . . 7.95
Xmas special 'World of Girls' 2.95
NEW SERIES
1 thru 4 see color

The Trouble With Girls #10 © Eternity
5 thru 11 . . . . @1.95

TROUBLE WITH TIGERS
Antartic Press
1 NinjaHighSchool/Tigers x-over . 2.00
2 . . . . 2.00

TRUE CRIME
Eclipse
1 thru 2 . . . . 2.95

TRUFAN ADVENTURES THEATRE
1 . . . . 8.00
2 3-D issue 5.00

TRYPTO THE ACID DOG
Renegade
1 . . . . 2.00

TURTLE SOUP
1 A:TMNT 6.00

TURTLES TEACH KARATE
Solson
1 . . . . 4.00
2 . . . . 3.50

TWILIGHT AVENGER
Eternity
1 thru 18 . . . . @1.95
Miracle Studios
Spec. Twilight Avenger Super
   Summer Special 2.75

TWILIGHT X QUARTERLY
Antarctic Press
1 thru 3 by Joseph Wright . . . @2.95
4 Celebration 2.95

TWIST
Kitchen Sink
1 . . . . 1.95
2 and 3 . . . . @2.00

TWISTED TANTRUMS OF THE PURPLE SNIT
Blackthorne 1986
1 . . . . 2.50
2 . . . . 2.00

2001 NIGHTS
Viz 1990–91
1 by Yukinobu Hoshino 5.00
2 . . . . 4.00
3 thru 5 . . . . @3.75
6 thru 10 . . . . @4.25

TYLOR
Double Edge
0 The Egg 2.95

TYRANNY REX
Fleetway
GN reps. from 2000A.D. 7.95

ULTIMATE STRIKE
London Night 1996
1 . . . . 2.00
1 holochrome edition 15.00
1a nude commemorative edition . 5.00
2 . . . . 2.00
3 . . . . 2.00
4 . . . . 2.00
4 Photo nude cover 5.00
5 . . . . 2.00
5 Photo nude cover 5.00
6 sequel to Strike #0 . . . . 2.00
6 limited nude cover 5.00
7 by Kevin Hill, "Stryke: Year One"
   concl. 2.00
7 limited nude cover 5.00
8 Year One, ... 2.00
8a nude cover 5.00
9 Year One, cont. 2.00
9a Nude cover. 5.00
10 . . . . 2.00
10a Nude cover. 5.00
11 . . . . 2.00
11a Nude cover. 5.00
12 . . . . 2.00
12a Nude cover. 5.00

ULTRA KLUTZ
Onward Comics
1 . . . . 2.50
2 thru 18 . . . . @1.50
19 thru 24 . . . . @1.75
25 thru 30 . . . . @2.00
Bad Habit
TBP Book One, rep. #1–#23 . . 29.95

UNCANNY MAN-FROG
Mad Dog
1 and 2 . . . . @1.75

UNCENSORED MOUSE
Eternity
1 Mickey Mouse 10.00
2 Mickey Mouse 11.00

UNFORGIVEN, THE
Trinity Comics Ministries
Mission of Tranquility
1 thru 6 V:Dormian Grath 1.95

7 I:Faith 1.95

UNICORN ISLE
Genesis West
1 . . . . 2.50
2 . . . . 1.50
3 . . . . 1.50
Apple
4 thru 6 . . . . @1.75

UNLEASHED
Caliber Press
1 F:Carson Davis 2.95
2 V:North Harbor Crime 2.95

UNSUPERVISED EXISTENCE
1 . . . . 2.00
2 and 3 . . . . @2.50

UNTOLD ORIGIN OF MS. VICTORY
1 . . . . 2.50

UNTOUCHABLES
1 thru 20 . . . . @.75

UNTOUCHABLES
Caliber 1997
1K by Joe Pruett & John Kissee,
   MK(c) 2.95
1S by Joe Pruett & John Kissee,
   Showman (c) 2.95
2 . . . . 2.95
3 MK (c) 2.95
4 MK (c) 2.95
HC New Beginning 19.95

UNTOUCHABLES: THE HIGH SOCIETY KILLER
Caliber 1998
1 . . . . 3.95

USAGI YOJIMBO
Fantagraphics 1987
1 SS 10.00
1a 2nd printing 5.00
2 SS,Samurai 8.00
3 SS,Samurai,A:Croakers 6.00
4 SS 5.00
5 thru 7 SS . . . . @5.00
8 SS,A Mother's Love 5.00
8a 2nd printing 3.00
9 SS 4.00
10 SS,A:Turtles 5.00
10a 2nd printing 3.00
11 thru 18 SS . . . . @4.00
19 SS,Frost & Fire,A:Nelson
   Groundthumper 3.50
20 thru 21 SS . . . . @3.50
22 SS,A:Panda Khan 3.50
23 SS,V:Ninja Bats 3.50
24 SS 3.50
25 SS,A:Lionheart 3.50
26 SS,Gambling 3.50
27 SS 3.50
28 thru 31 SS,Circles pt.1–4 . . @3.50
32 . . . . 3.50
33 SS,Ritual Murder 3.50
34 thru 37 . . . . @3.50

Spec.#1 SS,SummerSpec, C:Groo		45.00
TPB Vol 4, rep.		16.95
TPB Vol 6, rep., new printing		12.95

Radio Comix

Vol. 1 The Art of Usagi Yojimbo . . 3.95

VALENTINO
Renegade

1	1.70
2 and 3	@2.00

VALOR THUNDERSTAR
1 and 2 . . . . @1.75

VAMPEROTICA
Brainstorm Comics

1 I:Luxura	10.00
1a 2nd & 3rd printing	3.00
2	8.00
2 2nd printing	3.00
3	4.00
4 I:Blood Hunterq	4.00
5 Deadshot	4.00
6 Deadshot	4.00
7 Baptism	4.00
8 Pains,Peepers	4.00
9 thru 11	@4.00
12 thru 16	@3.00
17 thru 22 see: color	
20 signed	5.00
20 nude cover, signed	5.00
21 nude cover, signed	5.00
23	3.00
23a nude edition	3.00
23 encore edition	2.95
23a encore edition, nude cover . .	3.95
24	3.00
24a nude cover	3.00
25	3.00
25a deluxe, nude cover	3.00
26	3.00
26a nude cover	3.00
26a nude cover	3.95
27	3.00
27 Nude Luxury edition	5.00
28 A:China & Jazz	3.00
28a nude cover	3.00
28 Nude Luxury edition	5.00
28 Nude Luxury edition, signed . .	5.00
29 mild cover	3.00
30 Legends of Luxura x-over, concl	2.95
30a nude cover	3.95
31 V:Red Militia	2.95
31a nude cover	3.95
32	2.95
32a nude cover	3.95
33 by Kirk Lindo	2.95
33a nude cover	3.95
34 V:Pontius Vanthor	2.95
34a nude cover edition	5.00
34b luxury edition	5.00
35	2.95
35a nude cover	5.00
36 I:Countess Vladimira	2.95
36a nude cover edition	3.95
36a photo cover edition	3.95
37	2.95
37 nude cover	2.95
37 statue cover	2.95
38	2.95
38 nude cover	3.95
38 nude luxury edition	5.00
39 Death From Above, pt.1	2.95
39a nude cover	3.95

39b nude embrace cover		3.95
40 Death From Above, pt.2		2.95
40a nude cover		3.95
40a nude embrace cover		3.95
41		3.00
41a nude cover		4.00
42 Hostile Seduction		3.00
42a nude cover		4.00
43 Harvest		3.00
43a nude cover		4.00
Commemorative Edition		2.95
Lingerie Special #1		2.95
Spec. Lingerie, encore edition . .		2.95
Spec. Lingerie, deluxe		3.95
Spec. Swimsuit, encore edition . .		2.95
Spec. Swimsuit, deluxe nude cover		3.95
Bondage Spec. #1		2.95
Bondage Spec. #1, nude cover . .		3.95
Bondage Spec. #1, manga		3.95
Ann. #1 Encore		3.00
Ann. #1 Encore, nude cover		4.00
Spec. #2 Dare to Bare		3.00
Spec. #2 Dare to Bare, nude cover		4.00
Spec. #4 Encore Edition, new(c) .		2.95
Spec. #4a Encore Edition, nude(c)		2.95
Spec. #5 Encore Edition		2.95
Spec. #5a Encore Edition, nude(c)		3.95
Spec.#1 Vamperotica Presents:		
Countess Vladimira (1998) . . .		3.00
Nude cover edition		4.00

VAMPEROTICA MANGA
Brainstorm 1998

1	2.95
1a nude cover	3.95
1b nude embrace cover	3.95
2	3.00
2a nude cover	4.00

VAMPEROTICA TALES
Brainstorm 1998

1	2.95
1a nude cover edition	3.95
1 nude luxury edition	5.00
2	2.95
2a nude cover	3.95
2b nude embrace cover	3.95
3	3.00
3a nude cover	4.00
4 Veiled Threat	3.00
4a nude cover	4.00
5 A Night of Wine and Roses . . .	3.00
5a nude cover	4.00

VAMPFIRE
Brainstorm 1996

1	2.95
1a nude cover	3.95
1 commemorative photo cover .	10.00
2	2.95
2a nude cover	5.00
2 signed	5.00
2 nude, signed	5.00
Pin-Up Spec.	2.95
Pin-Up Spec. deluxe	3.95
Tour Book #1	2.95
Tour Book #1 nude cover	2.95

VAMPFIRE: EROTIC ECHO
Brainstorm 1997

1 by Fauve	2.95
1a nude cover	2.95
1b photo cover	3.00

2	2.95
2a nude cover	2.95
2b photo cover	2.95

VAMPFIRE: NECROMANTIQUE
Brainstorm 1997

1 by Holly Golightly	2.95
1a nude edition	3.95
1b luxury edition, virgin cover . . .	5.00
1c luxury edition, signed	15.00
1d regular, signed	8.00
1e nude cover, signed	10.00
2 by Fauve	2.95
2a nude edition	3.95

VAMPIRE BITES
Brainstorm

2	2.95
2a nude cover	2.95

VAMPIRE CONFESSIONS
Brainstorm 1998

1	3.00
1a nude cover	4.00

VAMPIRE GIRLS: CALIFORNIA 1969
Angel Entertainment 1996

0 nude cover, signed	10.00
1 blood red foil deluxe edition . . .	5.95
2	2.95
2 deluxe	5.95
2 nude cover A	10.00
2 nude cover B	10.00
TPB	5.00

VAMPIRE GIRLS: NEW YORK 1979
Angel Entertainment 1996

0	2.95
0 virgin nude cover	5.00
0 nude platinum cover	15.00
0 gold edition	8.00
1	2.95
1 virgin nude cover	5.00
1 nude platinum cover	15.00

VAMPIRE GIRLS EROTIQUE
Angel Entertainment 1996

1	2.95
1 nude cover	2.95
2	2.95
2 erotic nude cover A	2.95
2 deluxe nude cover B	2.95
3	2.95
3 nude cover	2.95
4	2.95
4 erotic nude cover	2.95
5	2.95
5 erotic nude kissing Candaze	
cover	4.00
6	2.95
6 nude cover	2.95
7 Bloodsucker cover	3.00
7 nude gettin lunch cover	3.00
Spec. Gravedigger (1996) by	
Alexandra Scott & Bill Wylie . .	3.00
Nude Alexandra cover	3.00
Nude Candice and Simone cover	3.00

B & W PUB.

Spec. Paris 1968 (1997) by
  Alexandra Scott & Dean Burnett 2.95
  Nude cover 4.00
Spec. Titanic 1912 (1998) by
  Alexandra Scott & Dean Burnett 2.95
  Nude cover 4.00

VAMPIRE GIRLS: BUBBLEGUM & BLOOD
Angel Entertainment 1996
1. . . . . 2.95
1 deluxe edition 5.95
1 nude cover 10.00
2. . . . . 2.95
2 deluxe edition 5.95
2 nude cover 10.00

VAMPIRE GIRLS VS. ANGEL GIRL
Angel Entertainment 1997
1. . . . . 2.95
1a erotic nude cover 3.95
1b deluxe nude cover 3.95

VAMPIRELLA
Harris
1 DC,SL,Summer Nights,48page   3.95

VAMPIRELLA
Silver Anniversary Collection
Harris 1996
0 Vampirella of Darkulon, EM . . . 3.00
1 good girl edition 2.50
1a bad girl edition 2.50
2 good girl edition 2.50
2a bad girl edition 2.50
3 good girl edition 2.50
3a bad girl edition. 2.50
4 Silkie(c) 2.50
4a MBc(c) 2.50

Vampirella: Morning in America, Book 3
© Harris/Dark Horse

VAMPIRELLA: MORNING IN AMERICA
Harris/Dark Horse 1991–92
Book 1 thru 4 . . . . 7.00

Book 2 thru 4 . . . . @5.00
TPB 25.00

VAMPIRELLA/ PAINKILLER JANE
Harris 1998
Ashcan, preview 6.00

VAMPIRELLA RETRO
Harris 1998
1 (of 3) rep. Warren stories 2.50
2 (of 3) rep. Warren stories 2.50
3 (of 3) rep. Warren stories 2.50

VAMPIRELLA VS. HEMORRHAGE
Harris
1 Limited Preview Ashcan 5.00

VAMPIRE MIYU
Antarctica Press
1 I:Vampire Princess Miyu 2.95
2 thru 5 . . . . @3.95
6 48pg 4.95

VAMPIRE'S TATTOO
London Night 1997
1 (of 2) by Art Wetherell 3.00
1 deluxe edition, nude cover 6.00
2 . . . . 3.00
2 deluxe edition, nude cover 6.00
1b nude cover edition, signed . . 10.00
3 . . . . 3.00
3a nude cover 6.00

VAMPIRE ZONE, THE
Brainstorm 1998
1 . . . . 2.95
1a nude cover 3.95

VAMPORNRELLA
Forbidden 1997
1 parody 2.95
1 erotic nude cover A 2.95
1 erotic nude cover B 2.95

VAMPYRES
Eternity
1 thru 4 . . . . @2.25

VANGUARD: OUTPOST EARTH
1 and 2 . . . . @2.00

VAULT OF DOOMNATION
B-Movie Comics
1 . . . . 1.70

VENGEANCE OF DREADWOLF
Lightning Comics
1 O:Dreadwolf 2.75

VERDICT
Eternity
1 thru 4 . . . . @1.95

VEROTIKA
Verotika 1995–97
1 Magical Times 15.00
2 . . . . 8.00
3 . . . . 5.00
4 thru 6 . . . . @4.00
7 thru 15 . . . . @3.00

VERY VICKY
Meet Danny Ocean
1 . . . . 3.50
1a 2nd printing 3.00

VERY VICKY: CALLING ALL HILLBILLIES
Meet Danny Ocean 1995
1 Pea Pickin Patty 2.50

VIC & BLOOD
Renegade
1 and 2 RCo,Ellison . . . . @2.00

VICKY VALENTINE
Renegade
1 thru 4 . . . . @1.70

VICTIMS
Silver Wolf
1 & 2 . . . . @1.50

VICTIMS
Eternity
1 thru 5 . . . . @1.95

VIDEO CLASSICS
1 Mighty Mouse 3.50
2 Mighty Mouse 3.50

VIETNAM JOURNAL
Apple Comics
1 . . . . 5.00
1a 2nd printing 3.00
2 . . . . 3.00
3 thru 5 . . . . @2.50
6 thru 13 . . . . @2.00
14 thru 16 . . . . @2.25

VIGIL: DESERT FOXES
Millenium
1 & 2 F:Grace Kimble 3.95

VIGIL: FALL FROM GRACE
Innovation
1 'State of Grace' 2.75
2 The Graceland Hunt 2.50

VINSON WATSON'S RAGE
Trinity Visuals
1 I:Rena Helen 3.00

VINSON WATSON'S SWEET CHILDE
Advantage Graphics Vol. 2
1 F:Spyder 1.95

B & W PUB

VIRGIN: SLUMBER
Entity 1997
1 BMs 2.75
1 deluxe 3.50

VIRGIN: SURROUNDED
Entity 1997
1 BMs 2.75
1 deluxe 3.50

VIRGIN: TILL DEATH DO US PART
Entity April 1997
1 BMs 2.75
1 deluxe 3.50

VISIONS
Vision Publication 1979–83
1 I:Flaming Carrot 125.00
2 Flaming Carrot 30.00
3 Flaming Carrot 20.00
4 Flaming Carrot 30.00

VISUAL ASSAULT OMNIBUS
Visual Assault Comics 1995
1 thru 4 O:Dimensioner 3.00

VIXEN
Meteor Comics
1 & 2 Battle of the Vixens 2.95

VORTEX
Hall of Heroes
1 . . . . 20.00
1a commemorative 5.00
2 . . . . 12.00
3 thru 5 . . . . @3.50
6 V:The Reverend 3.00

VORTEX SPECIAL: CYBERSIN
Avatar Press 1997
1 by Matt Martin & Bil Maus 3.00
1 nude cover 4.95
1 velvet cover 25.00
1 signed 10.00

VORTEX: DR. KILBOURN
Entity March 1997
1 by Matt Martin 2.75
1a deluxe 3.50

VORTEX: INTO THE DARK
Entity 1997
1 . . . . 2.75
1 deluxe 3.50

VOX
Apple
1 JBy(c) 1.95
2 and 3 . . . . @1.95
4 and 5 . . . . @2.25

WABBIT WAMPAGE
Amazing Comics 1987
1 . . . . 2.00

Wabbit Wampage #1
© Amazing Comics

WACKY SQUIRREL
1 thru 4 . . . . @1.75
Summer Fun Special #1 . . . . . . 2.00
Christmas Special #1 . . . . 1.75

WALKING DEAD
Aircel
1 thru 4 . . . . @2.25
Zombie Spec. 1 . . . . 2.25

WALK THROUGH OCTOBER
Caliber
1 I:Mr. Balloon 2.95
2 . . . . 2.95
3 All Hallow's Eve 2.95

WALT THE WILDCAT
Motion Comics 1995
1 I:Walt the Wildcat 2.50

WANDERING STAR
Pen & Ink
1 I:Casandra Andrews 32.00
1a 2nd & 3rd printing 3.00
2 . . . . 10.00
3 thru 7 . . . . 3.00
8 and 9 F:Casandra Andrews . . . 2.75
10 R:Mekron 2.75
11 . . . . 2.75
Sirius 1995–97
12 thru 20 TWo . . . . @2.50
21 TWo, final issue 2.50
TPB Vol. 1 rep. #1–#7 . . . . 14.95

WAR
A Plus Comics
1 . . . . 2.50

WARCAT
Alliance Comics
1 thru 7 A:Ebonia 2.50

WARD: A BULLET SERIES
Liar Comics
1 Foresight,pt.1 . . . . 2.50
2 Foresight,pt.2 . . . . 2.50
3 Foresight,pt.3 . . . . 2.50

WARLACE
K-Blamm 1995
1 I:Warlace 2.95

WARLOCK 5
Aircel
1 . . . . 6.00
2 . . . . 5.00
3 . . . . 6.00
4 . . . . 5.00
5 . . . . 5.00
6 thru 11 . . . . @4.00
12 . . . . 3.50
13 . . . . 3.50
14 thru 16 . . . . @2.00
17 . . . . 1.70
18 . . . . 1.75
19 thru 22 . . . . @1.95
Book 2 #1 thru #7 . . . . @2.00

WARLOCK 5
Sirius 1997
1 (of 4) by Barry Blair & Colin Chan 2.50
2 . . . . 2.50
3 . . . . 2.50
4 finale 2.50

WARLOCKS
Aircel
1 thru 3 . . . . @1.70
4 thru 12 . . . . @1.95
Spec #1 Rep. 2.25

WAR OF THE WORLDS
Eternity
1 TV tie-in 1.95
2 thru 6 . . . . @1.95

WAR OF THE WORLDS, THE
Caliber "New Worlds" 1996
1 from H.G. Wells 2.95
1a signed 2.95
2 war for Kansas City 2.95
3 Haven & The Hellweed 2.95
4 . . . . 2.95
5 . . . . 2.95
TPB rep. #1–#5 . . . . 14.95

WAR OF THE WORLDS: THE MEMPHIS FRONT
Arrow Comics 1998
1 (of 5) by Randy Zimmerman & Richard Gulick 2.95
2 . . . . 2.95
3 . . . . 2.95

WAR PARTY VS. DEATHMARK
Lightning Comics
1 War Party vs. Deathmark 2.75

WARP WALKING
Caliber
1 'Quick and the Dead' 2.50

WARRIOR NUN: BLACK AND WHITE
Antarctic Press 1997
1 . . . . 3.00
2 . . . . 3.00
3 . . . . 3.00
4 Winter Jade, pt.1 F:Ninja Nun . 3.00
5 Winter Jade, pt.2 . . . . 3.00
6 Winter Jade, pt.3 . . . . 3.00
7 . . . . 3.00
8 . . . . 3.00
9 Return of the Redeemers 3.00
10 Return of Lillith 3.00
11 The Redeemers, cont. 3.00
12 The Redeemers, cont. 3.00

WARRIORS
1 . . . . 2.50
2 thru 7 . . . . @1.95

WARZONE
Entity
1 I:Bella & Supra 2.95
2 F:Bladeback, Alloy, Granite . . . 2.95
3 F:Bladeback 2.95

WATCHDOG
Hammerhead Comics
1 I:Watchdog 2.95

WEASEL PATROL
Eclipse
Spec. #1 . . . . 2.00

WEBWITCH
Avatar Press 1997
0 by Raff Ienco 3.00
0 nude cover 5.00
1 (of 2) signed 10.00
1 (of 2) 3.00
1 nude cover 5.00
2 (of 2) 3.00
2 nude cover 4.95
Boxed Set, all rare editions 35.00

WEBWITCH: PRELUDE TO WAR
Avatar Press 1998
1 by Raff Jenco 3.00
1a nude cover 6.00
1b Leather cover 30.00

WEBWITCH: WAR
Avatar Press 1998
1 (of 2) by Bill Maus 3.00
1a nude cover 6.00
1b Leather cover 30.00
2 conclusion 3.00
2a nude cover 6.00

WEIRDFALL
Antarctic Press 1995
1 I:Weirdfall 2.75
2 O:Weirdfall 2.75
3 . . . . 2.75

WEIRD ROMANCE
Eclipse
1 . . . . 2.00

WEIRDSVILLE
Blindwolf Studios 1997
1 . . . . 2.95
1 2nd printing 2.95
2 . . . . 2.95
2 2nd printing 2.95
3 . . . . 2.95
3 2nd printing 2.95
4 . . . . 2.95
5 . . . . 2.95
6 The Usual Weirdoes, concl. . . . 2.95
7 . . . . 2.95
8 An American Werewolf in
  Weirdsville, pt.1 (of 2) 2.95
9 An American Werewolf in
  Weirdsville, pt.2 . . . . 2.95

WEREWOLF
Blackthorne 1988–89
1 TV tie-in 2.00
2 thru 7 . . . . @2.00

WHAT IS THE FACE?
A.C.E. Comics
1 SD/FMc,I:New Face 1.95
2 SD/FMc 1.95
3 SD 1.75

WHISPERS & SHADOWS
1 8 1/2 x 11 . . . . 2.00
1a Regular size 1.50
2 8 1/2 x 11 . . . . 1.50
3 8 1/2 x 11 . . . . 1.50
4 thru 9 . . . . @1.50

White Devil #6 © Eternity

WHITE DEVIL
Eternity
1 thru 6 adult 2.50

WHITEOUT
Oni Press 1998
1 (of 4) by Greg Rucka & Steve

Leiber 2.95
2 . . . . 2.95

WHITE RAVEN
Visionary Publications
1 Government Intrigue 2.95
2 . . . . 2.95
3 Mystery Man Gets Wheels 2.95
4 Facility 2.95
5 V:Douglas 2.95
6 . . . . 2.95
7 . . . . 2.95

WHITLEY STRIEBER'S BEYOND COMMUNION
Caliber Sept. 1997
1 UFO Odyssey 2.95
1 signed 2.95
1 special edition, signed by Strieber
  . . . . 6.95
1a 2nd printing 2.95
2 . . . . 2.95
3 . . . . 2.95
4 . . . . 2.95

WICKED
Millenium
1 thru 4 . . . . 2.50

WICKED: THE RECKONING
Millenium
1 R:Wicked 2.95
2 F:Rachel Blackstone 2.95

WIDOW
Ground Zero 1996
Cinegraphic Spec.#1: Daughter of
  Darkness 4.00

WIDOW/LUXURA: BLOOD LUST
Ground Zero 1996
Alpha x-over, pt.1 . . . . 3.50
see Luxura/Widow for pt. 2

WIDOW: BOUND BY BLOOD
Ground Zero 1996
1 thru 5 by Mike Wolfer . . . . . @3.50

WIDOW: PROGENY
Ground Zero April 1997
1 by Mike Wolfer & Karl Moline . . 3.00
2 (of 3) 3.00
3 concl. 3.00

WIDOW: THE COMPLETE WORKS
Ground Zero 1996
Vol.1 Flesh and Blood 10.95
Vol.1 deluxe 16.95
Vol.2 Kill Me Again 10.95
Vol.2 deluxe 16.95
Vol.3 Metal Gypsies 10.95
Vol.3 deluxe 16.95

WIDOW
Avatar Press 1997
0 by Mike Wolfer	3.95
0a nude cover	6.00
0b Black leather cover	25.00
0 signed	10.00

WIDOW: THE ORIGIN
Avatar Press 1997
1 (of 3) by Mike Wolfer	3.95
1a nude cover	6.00
1a leather cover	25.00
2 (of 3)	3.00
2 nude cover	4.95

WILD, THE
1 and 2	@1.50
3 thru 7	@1.75

WILD KNIGHTS
Eternity
1 thru 10	@1.95
Shattered Earth Chron. #1	1.95

WILDMAN
1 and 2	@1.50
3 thru 6	@1.85

WILD THINGZ
ABC Comics 1998
0 RCI & Armando Huerta	3.00
0a painted cover	6.00
0b Fan edition	5.95
0c Summer edition	5.95
0d Leather cover, original art	55.00
1 (of 2) RCI	3.00
1a nude gold (c)	8.00
1b Leather cover	30.00
1c virgin cover	3.00
1d gold cover	5.95
1e Platinum cover	5.95

WILLOW
Angel Entertainment 1996
0 commemorative edition	2.95
0 nude edition	5.00
1	2.95
1 black magic foil edition	5.95
1 nude signed	10.00
2	2.95
2 gold edition	8.00
2 Virgin nude cover	5.00
2 Virgin Sacrifice nude cover	7.00
2 nude manga cover	5.00
2 nude platinum cover	15.00

WIND BLADE
1 Elford 1st Blair	60.00

WINDRAVEN
Hero Graphics/Blue comet
1 The Healing,(see Rough Raiders)	2.95

WINDRAVEN
Heroic
1	2.95

WISHMASTER
Pocket Change Comics
1 I:Hell Bore	2.50

WITCH
Eternity
1	1.95

WIZARD OF TIME
David House
1	1.50
1a 2nd printing(blue)	1.50
2 and 3	@1.50

WOLFF & BYRD, COUNSELORS OF THE MACABRE
Exhibit A
12 thru 16 BLs	@2.50
17	2.50
18	2.50
19	2.50
20	2.50
TPB Casefiles Vol. I rep. #1–#4, 3rd printing	9.95
TPB Casefiles Vol. 2 rep. #5–#8	9.95
TPB Casefiles Vol. III rep. #9–#12	10.95
TPB Casefiles Vol. IV rep. #13–#16	10.95
TPB Supernatural Law	7.95
TPB Supernatural Law rep.	7.95
TPB Fright Court rep.	9.95
Spec.#1 Greatest Writs (1997) BLs	2.95

WOLF H
Blackthorne
1 and 2	@1.75

WORDSMITH
Renegade
1	3.00
2 thru 6	@1.70
7 thru 12	@2.00

WORLD HARDBALL LEAGUE
Titus Press
1 F:Big Bat	2.95
2 F:Big Bat	2.95
3 Mount Evrest	2.95
4 Juan Hernandez	2.95

WORLD OF ROBOTECH
Academy Comics 1995
GN Tales of Planets	12.95

WORLD OF WOOD
Eclipse
5 Flying Saucers	2.00

WORLDS OF FANTASY
Newcomers Publishing 1995
1 The Jenn Chronicles	2.95

WORLDS OF H.P. LOVECRAFT
Caliber Tome Press 1997
1-shot The Alchemist	2.95
1-shot The Tomb	2.95
1-shot The Lurking Fear	2.95

WRAITH
Outlander
1 'Resurrected & the Damned'	1.75

WRETCH, THE
Caliber 1996
1 PhH	2.95
2 PhH	2.95

Amaze Ink 1997
3 PhH	2.95
4 PhH	2.95
5 PhH & Jim Woodyard	2.95
6 PhH & Bruce McCorkindale	2.95
7 PhH	2.95

WU WEI
Animus
1 "Debaser"	2.50
2 Blind Whisper	2.50
3	2.50
4	2.50
5 "Testament" pt.5	2.50
6 by Oscar Stern	2.50
7 Explicador	2.95

XANADU
Thoughts & Images
1 thru 5	@2.00

XENA
Brown Study Comics
1 I:Xena	2.95

XENON
Eclipse
1	3.00
2 thru 23	@1.50

Xenozoic Tales #3 © Kitchen Sink

XENOZOIC TALES
Kitchen Sink 1986
1 by Mark Schultz	14.00
1aRep.	2.00
2	10.00
2a Rep.	2.00
3	8.00
4	6.00
5 thru 7	@4.00
8 thru 13	@3.00
14 MSh	2.95

X-BABES VS. JUSTICE BABES
Personality
1 Spoof/parody 2.95

X-CONS
Parody Press
1 X-Men satire,flip cover 2.50

X-FARCE
Eclipse
One-Shot X-Force parody 3.00

X-FLIES BUG HUNT
Twist and Shout 1997
1 Vampires 2.95
2 Monsters 2.95
3 Aliens 2.95
4 The Truth 2.95
Conspiracy 2.95
Spec. #1 Flies in Black 2.95

XIOLA
Zion Comics
1 thru 3 F:Kantasia . . . . @1.95
4 Visitor 1.95

XMEN
1 Parody 1.50

X-1999
Viz
1 I:Kamir Shiro 2.75
2 thru 5 F:Princess Hitane 2.75
6 Battle for X-1999 . . . . 2.75

X-THIEVES
1 . . . . 3.00
2 . . . . 1.75
3 . . . . 1.75

YAHOO
Fantagraphics
1 thru 4 . . . . @2.00

YAKUZA
Eternity
1 thru 5 . . . . @1.95

YAWN
Parody Press
1 Spawn parody 2.50
Enigma
1 Spawn parody rep.? 2.75

YOUNG MASTERS
1 thru 10 . . . . @1.75

Z
Keystone Graphics
1 . . . . 2.75
2 House of Windsor-YakonaraI . . 2.75
3 House of Windsor-YakonaraII . 2.75

ZELL THE SWORDDANCER
1 Steve Gallacci 5.50
2 and 3 . . . . @2.00

ZEN ILLUSTRATED NOVELLA
Entity
1 thru 4 R:Bruce Lewis . . . . . . @2.95
5 Immortal Combat 2.95
6 Bubble Economy 2.95
7 Zen City 2.95
8 V:Assassins 2.95

ZEN, INTER-GALACTIC NINJA
Entity
1 . . . . 4.00
2 . . . . 3.00
3 thru 9 . . . . @3.00
X-mas Spec #1,V:Black Hole Bob 2.95
[2nd Series]
1 'Down to Earth' 2.50
2 RA, A:Jeremy Baker 2.50
2a polybagged, limited 5.00
3 thru 5 . . . . @2.50
[3rd Series]
0 . . . . 2.95
1 thru 3 A:Niro . . . . @2.95
Sourcebook #1 . . . . 3.50

ZEN INTERGALACTIC NINJA: STARQUEST
Entity
1 thru 6 V:Nolan the Destroyer @2.95
7 V:Dimensional 2.95
8 thru 9 I:New Team . . . . @2.95
10 In Deep Space 2.95
11 Dimensional Terrorists 2.95
TPB Rep. #1-#4 . . . . @6.95

ZEN INTERGALACTIC NINJA VS. MICHEAL JACK-ZEN
Entity
1 Cameos Galore 2.95

ZENISMS WIT AND WISDOMS
Entity
1 R:Bruce Lewis 2.95

ZEN: MISTRESS OF CHAOS
1 . . . . 2.95

ZENITH: PHASE II
Fleetway
1 GMo(s),SY,Rep.2000 AD 1.95

ZETRAMAN
Antarctic
1 thru 3 . . . . @1.95
[Vol. 2]
1 and 2 . . . . @2.75

ZETRAMAN: REVIVAL
Antarctic Press
1 thru 3 . . . . @2.75

ZILLION
Eternity
1 thru 4 . . . . @2.50

Zillion #2 © Eternity

ZOLASTRAYA AND THE BARD
1 thru 5 . . . . @1.70

ZOMBIE WAR: EARTH MUST BE DESTROYED
Fantaco 1993
1 thru 3 Kevin Eastman 3.95

ZONE CONTINUUM
Caliber
1 Master of the Waves 2.95
2 . . . . 2.95

ZOT!
Eclipse
(#1-#10 See: Color)
11 New Series 3.00
12 thru 15 . . . . @3.00
16 A:De-Evolutionaries 3.00
17 thru 36 . . . . @3.00
Kitchen Sink
Book Two TPB rep. #11-#15,
  #17-#18 . . . . 19.95
Book Two TPB signed and
  numbered 34.95
Book Three TPB rep. #16, #21-#27 9.95

ZOOT!
Fantagraphics
1 thru 5 . . . . @2.50

Issued As Classic Comics
001-THE THREE MUSKETEERS
By Alexandre Dumas

10/41 **(---)** MKd,MKd(c),
Original,10¢ (c) Price 4,500.00
05/43 **(10)** MKd,MKd(c),
No(c)Price; rep 250.00
11/43 **(15)** MKd,MKd(c),Long
Island Independent Ed; 175.00
6/44 **(18/20)** MKd,MKd(c),
Sunrise Times Edition;rep 125.00
7/44 **(21)** MKd,MKd(c),Richmond
Courrier Edition;rep 110.00
6/46 **(28)** MKd,MKd(c);rep 90.00
4/47 **(36)** MKd,MKd(c),
New CILogo;rep 40.00
6/49 **(60)** MKd,MKd(c),Cl Logo;rep 25.00
10/49 **(64)** MKd,MK(c),Cl Logo;rep 25.00
12/50 **(78)** MKd,MKd(c),15¢(c)
Price; Cl Logo;rep 18.00
03/52 **(93)** MKd,MKd(c),
Cl Logo;rep 16.00
11/53 **(114)** Cl Logo;rep 12.00
09/56 **(134)** MKd,MKd(c),New
P(c),Cl Logo,64 pgs;rep 12.00
03/58 **(143)** MKd,MKd(c),P(c),
Cl Logo,64 pgs;rep 11.00
05/59 **(150)** GE&RC New Art,
P(c),ClLogo;rep 11.00
03/61 **(149)** GE&RC,P(c),
Cl Logo;rep 7.00
62-63 **(167)** GE&RC,P(c),
Cl Logo;rep 7.00
04/64 **(167)** GE&RC,P(c),
Cl Logo;rep 7.00
01/65 **(167)** GE&RC,P(c),
Cl Logo;rep 7.00
03/66 **(167)** GE&RC,P(c),
Cl Logo;rep 7.00
11/67 **(166)** GE&RC,P(c),
Cl Logo;rep 7.00
Sp/69 **(166)** GE&RC,P(c),25¢(c)
Price,ClLogo, Rigid(c);rep . 7.00
Sp/71 **(169)** GE&RC,P(c),
Cl Logo,Rigid(c);rep 7.00

002-IVANHOE
By Sir Walter Scott

1941 **(---)** EA,MKd(c),Original . 1,800.00
05/43 **(1)** EA,MKd(c),word "Presents"
Removed From(c);rep 225.00
11/43 **(15)** EA,MKd(c),Long Island
Independent Edition;rep 150.00
06/44 **(18/20)** EA,MKd(c),Sunrise
Times Edition;rep 125.00
07/44 **(21)** EA,MKd(c),Richmond
Courrier Edition;rep 110.00
06/46 **(28)** EA,MKd(c),rep 90.00
07/47 **(36)** EA,MKd(c),New
Cl Logo; rep 50.00
06/49 **(60)** EA,MKd(c),Cl Logo;rep 30.00
10/49 **(64)** EA,MKd(c),Cl Logo;rep 25.00
12/50 **(78)** EA,MKd(c),15¢(c)
Price; Cl Logo;rep 18.00
11/51 **(89)** EA,MKd(c),Cl Logo;rep 16.00
04/53 **(106)** EA,MKd(c),Cl
Logo;rep 14.00
07/54 **(121)** EA,MKd(c),Cl
Logo;rep 12.00
01/57 **(136)** NN New Art,New
P(c),Cl Logo;rep 14.00
01/58 **(142)** NN,P(c),Cl Logo;rep .. 6.00
11/59 **(153)** NN,P(c),Cl Logo;rep .. 6.00
03/61 **(149)** NN,P(c),Cl Logo;rep .. 6.00

62/63 **(167)** NN,P(c),Cl Logo;rep . 5.00
05/64 **(167)** NN,P(c),Cl Logo;rep .. 6.00
01/65 **(167)** NN,P(c),Cl Logo;rep .. 6.00
03/66 **(167)** NN,P(c),Cl Logo;rep .. 6.00
09/67 **(166)** NN,P(c),Cl Logo;rep .. 6.00
1968 **(166)** NN,P(c),Cl Logo;rep .. 6.00
Wr/69 **(169)** NN,P(c),Cl
Logo Rigid(c);rep 6.00
Wr/71 **(169)** NN,P(c),Cl
Logo,Rigid(c);rep 6.00

Cl #4 Last of the Mohicans,
© Gilberton Publications

003-THE COUNT OF MONTE CRISTO
By Alexandre Dumas

03/42 **(---)** ASm,ASm(c),Original 1,200.00
05/43 **(10)** ASm,ASm(c);rep ... 200.00
11/43 **(15)** ASm,ASm(c),Long Island
Independent Edition;rep 150.00
06/44 **(18/20)** ASm, ASm(c),
Sunrise Times Edition;rep .. 135.00
06/44 **(20)** ASm,ASm(c),Sunrise
Times Edition;rep 125.00
07/44 **(21)** ASm,ASm(c),Richmond
Courrier Edition;rep 110.00
06/46 **(28)** ASm,ASm(c);rep ... 100.00
04/47 **(36)** ASm,ASm(c),New
Cl Logo; rep 50.00
06/49 **(60)** ASm,ASm(c),Cl
Logo;rep 35.00
08/49 **(62)** ASm,ASm(c),Cl
Logo;rep 45.00
05/50 **(71)** ASm,ASm(c),Cl
Logo;rep 25.00
09/51 **(87)** ASm,ASm(c),15¢(c)
Price, Cl Logo;rep 18.00
11/53 **(113)** ASm,ASm(c),
Cl Logo; rep 15.00
11/56 **(---)** LC New Art,New
P(c), Cl Logo;rep 15.00
03/58 **(135)** LC,P(c),Cl Logo;rep .. 6.00
11/59 **(153)** LC,P(c),Cl Logo;rep .. 6.00
03/61 **(161)** LC,P(c),Cl Logo;rep .. 6.00
62/63 **(167)** LC,P(c),Cl Logo;rep .. 6.00
07/64 **(167)** LC,P(c),Cl Logo;rep .. 6.00
07/65 **(167)** LC,P(c),Cl Logo;rep .. 6.00
07/66 **(167)** LC,P(c),Cl Logo;rep .. 6.00
1968 **(166)** LC,P(c),25¢(c)
Price, Cl Logo;rep 6.00
Wn/69 **(169)** LC,P(c),Cl Logo,
Rigid(c);rep 6.00

004-THE LAST OF THE MOHICANS
By James Fenimore Cooper

08/42 **(---)** RR,RR(c),Original .. 1,000.00
06/43 **(12)** RR,RR(c),Price
Balloon Deleted;rep 200.00
11/43 **(15)** RR,RR(c),Long Island
Independent Edition;rep 175.00
06/44 **(20)** RR,RR(c),Long Island
Independent Edition;rep 150.00
07/44 **(21)** RR,RR(c),Queens
Home News Edition;rep 125.00
06/46 **(28)** RR,RR(c);rep 100.00
04/47 **(36)** RR,RR(c),New
Cl Logo; rep 50.00
06/49 **(60)** RR,RR(c),Cl Logo;rep . 35.00
10/49 **(64)** RR,RR(c),Cl Logo;rep . 25.00
12/50 **(78)** RR,RR(c),15¢(c)
Price,Cl Logo rep 20.00
11/51 **(89)** RR,RR(c),Cl Logo;rep . 18.00
03/54 **(117)** RR,RR(c),Cl Logo;rep 15.00
11/56 **(135)** RR,New P(c),
Cl Logo; rep 15.00
11/57 **(141)** RR,P(c),Cl Logo;rep . 16.00
05/59 **(150)** JSe&StA New Art;
P(c), Cl Logo;rep 15.00
03/61 **(161)** JSe&StA,P(c),Cl
Logo; rep 6.00
62/63 **(167)** JSe&StA,P(c),Cl
Logo; rep 6.00
06/64 **(167)** JSe&StA,P(c),Cl
Logo; rep 6.00
08/65 **(167)** JSe&StA,P(c),Cl
Logo; rep 6.00
08/66 **(167)** JSe&StA,P(c),Cl
Logo; rep 6.00
1967 **(166)** JSe&StA,P(c),25¢(c)
Price, Cl Logo;rep 6.00
Sp/69 **(169)** JSe&StA,P(c),Cl
Logo, Rigid(c);rep 6.00

005-MOBY DICK
By Herman Melville

09/42 **(---)** LZ,LZ(c),Original ... 1,300.00
05/43 **(10)** LZ,LZ(c),Conray Products
Edition, No(c)Price;rep 225.00
11/43 **(15)** LZ,LZ(c),Long Island
Independent Edition;rep 175.00
06/44 **(18/20)** LZ,LZ(c),Sunrise
Times Edition;rep 150.00
07/44 **(20)** LZ,LZ(c),Sunrise
Times Edition;rep 135.00
07/44 **(21)** LZ,LZ(c),Sunrise
Times Edition;rep 125.00
06/46 **(28)** LZ,LZ(c);rep 100.00
04/47 **(36)** LZ,LZ(c),NewCILogo;rep 60.00
06/49 **(60)** LZ,LZ(c),Cl Logo;rep . 35.00
08/49 **(62)** LZ,LZ(c),Cl Logo;rep . 40.00
05/50 **(71)** LZ,LZ(c),Cl Logo;rep . 25.00
09/51 **(87)** LZ,LZ(c),15¢(c)
Price, Cl Logo;rep 20.00
04/54 **(118)** LZ,LZ(c),Cl Logo;rep . 15.00
03/56 **(131)** NN New Art,New
P(c), Cl Logo;rep 15.00
05/57 **(138)** NN,P(c),Cl Logo;rep .. 6.00
01/59 **(148)** NN,P(c),Cl Logo;rep .. 6.00
09/60 **(158)** NN,P(c),Cl Logo;rep .. 6.00
62/63 **(167)** NN,P(c),Cl Logo;rep .. 6.00
06/64 **(167)** NN,P(c),Cl Logo;rep .. 6.00
07/65 **(167)** NN,P(c),Cl Logo;rep .. 6.00
03/66 **(167)** NN,P(c),Cl Logo;rep .. 6.00
09/67 **(166)** NN,P(c),Cl Logo;rep .. 6.00
Wn/69 **(166)** NN,P(c),25¢(c) Price,
Cl Logo, Rigid(c);rep 12.00
Wn/71 **(169)** NN,P(c),Cl Logo;rep 12.00

006-A TALE OF TWO CITIES
By Charles Dickens
11/42 **(---)** StM,StM(c),Original . 1,000.00
09/43 **(14)** StM,StM(c),No(c)
Price; rep 200.00
03/44 **(18)** StM,StM(c),Long Island
Independent Edition;rep 150.00
06/44 **(20)** StM,StM(c),Sunrise
Times Edition;rep 135.00
06/46 **(28)** StM,StM(c);rep 90.00
09/48 **(51)** StM,StM(c),New CI
Logo; rep 50.00
10/49 **(64)** StM,StM(c),CI
Logo;rep 30.00
12/50 **(78)** StM,StM(c),15¢(c)
Price, CI Logo;rep 20.00
11/51 **(89)** StM,StM(c),CI Logo;rep 18.00
03/54 **(117)** StM,StM(c),CI
Logo;rep 15.00
05/56 **(132)** JO New Art,New
P(c), CI Logo;rep 18.00
09/57 **(140)** JO,P(c),CI Logo;rep . . 6.00
11/57 **(147)** JO,P(c),CI Logo;rep . . 6.00
09/59 **(152)** JO,P(c),CI Logo;rep 125.00
11/59 **(153)** JO,P(c),CI Logo;rep . . 6.00
03/61 **(149)** JO,P(c),CI Logo;rep . . 6.00
62/63 **(167)** JO,P(c),CI Logo;rep . . 6.00
06/64 **(167)** JO,P(c),CI Logo;rep . . 6.00
08/65 **(167)** JO,P(c),CI Logo;rep . . 6.00
05/67 **(166)** JO,P(c),CI Logo;rep . . 6.00
Fl/68 **(166)** JO,NN New P(c),
25¢(c)Price,CI Logo;rep 15.00
Sr/70 **(169)** JO,NN P(c),CI
Logo, Rigid(c);rep 15.00

007-ROBIN HOOD
By Howard Pyle
12/42 **(---)** LZ,LZ(c),Original 800.00
06/43 **(12)** LZ,LZ(c),P.D.C.
on(c) Deleted;rep 200.00
03/44 **(18)** LZ,LZ(c),Long Island
Independent Edition;rep 150.00
06/44 **(20)** LZ,LZ(c),Nassau
Bulletin Edition;rep 135.00
10/44 **(22)** LZ,LZ(c),Queens
City Times Edition;rep 125.00
06/46 **(28)** LZ,LZ(c);rep 90.00
09/48 **(51)** LZ,LZ(c),New CI
Logo;rep 45.00
06/49 **(60)** LZ,LZ(c),CI Logo;rep . 25.00
10/49 **(64)** LZ,LZ(c),CI Logo;rep . 20.00
12/50 **(78)** LZ,LZ(c),CI Logo;rep . 20.00
07/52 **(97)** LZ,LZ(c),CI Logo;rep . 18.00
03/53 **(106)** LZ,LZ(c),CI Logo;rep . 15.00
07/54 **(121)** LZ,LZ(c),CI Logo;rep . 15.00
11/55 **(129)** LZ,New P(c),
CI Logo;rep 15.00
01/57 **(136)** JkS New Art,P(c);rep . . 6.00
03/58 **(143)** JkS,P(c),CI Logo;rep . . 6.00
11/59 **(153)** JkS,P(c),CI Logo;rep . . 6.00
10/61 **(164)** JkS,P(c),CI Logo;rep . . 6.00
62/63 **(167)** JkS,P(c),CI Logo;rep . . 6.00
06/64 **(167)** JkS,P(c),CI Logo;rep . . 7.00
05/65 **(167)** JkS,P(c),CI Logo;rep . . 6.00
07/66 **(167)** JkS,P(c),CI Logo;rep . . 6.00
12/67 **(168)** JkS,P(c),CI Logo;rep . . 7.00
Sr/69 **(169)** JkS,P(c),CI
Logo, Rigid(c);rep 6.00

008-ARABIAN KNIGHTS
By Antoine Galland
03/43 **(---)** LCh,LCh(c),Original 1,400.00
09/43 **(14)** LCh,LCh(c);rep 500.00
01/44 **(17)** LCh,LCh(c),Long Island

Independent Edition;rep 550.00
06/44 **(20)** LCh,LCh(c),Nassau
Bulletin Edition,64 pgs;rep . . . 400.00
06/46 **(28)** LCh,LCh(c);rep 250.00
09/48 **(51)** LCh,LCh(c),New CI
Logo; rep 250.00
10/49 **(64)** LCh,LCh(c),CI
Logo;rep 200.00
12/50 **(78)** LCh,LCh(c),CI
Logo;rep 160.00
10/61 **(164)** ChB New Art,P(c),
CI Logo;rep 135.00

CI #7 Robin Hood,
© Gilberton Publications

009-LES MISERABLES
By Victor Hugo
03/43 **(---)** RLv,RLv(c),Original . . 750.00
09/43 **(14)** RLv,RLv(c);rep 200.00
03/44 **(18)** RLv,RLv(c),Nassau
Bulletin Edition;rep 160.00
06/44 **(20)** RLv,RLv(c),Richmond
Courier Edition;rep 150.00
06/46 **(28)** RLv,RLv(c);rep 125.00
09/48 **(51)** RLv,RLv(c),New CI
Logo; rep 50.00
05/50 **(71)** RLv,RLv(c),CI
Logo;rep 40.00
09/51 **(87)** RLv,RLv(c),CI Logo,
15¢(c)Price;rep 35.00
03/61 **(161)** NN New Art,GMc
New P(c), CI Logo;rep 30.00
09/63 **(167)** NN,GMc P(c),CI
Logo; rep 25.00
12/65 **(167)** NN,GMc P(c),CI
Logo; rep 25.00
1968 **(166)** NN,GMc P(c),25¢(c)
Price, CI Logo;rep 25.00

010-ROBINSON CRUSOE
By Daniel Defoe
04/43 **(---)** StM,StM(c),Original . . 650.00
09/43 **(14)** StM,StM(c);rep 225.00
03/44 **(18)** StM,StM(c),Nassau Bulletin
Ed.,'Bill of Rights'Pge.64;rep . 175.00
06/44 **(20)** StM,StM(c),Queens
Home News Edition;rep 150.00
??/45 **(23)** StM,StM(c);rep 100.00
06/46 **(28)** StM,StM(c);rep 100.00
09/48 **(51)** StM,StM(c),New CI
Logo; rep 45.00
10/49 **(64)** StM,StM(c),CI Logo;rep 30.00
12/50 **(78)** StM,StM(c),15¢(c)
Price, CI Logo;rep 25.00

07/52 **(97)** StM,StM(c),CI Logo;rep 20.00
12/53 **(114)** StM,StM(c),CI
Logo;rep 20.00
01/56 **(130)** StM,New P(c),CI
Logo; rep 20.00
09/57 **(140)** SmC New Art,P(c),
CI Logo; rep 15.00
11/59 **(153)** SmC,P(c),CI Logo;rep . 6.00
10/61 **(164)** SmC,P(c),CI Logo;rep . 6.00
62/63 **(167)** SmC,P(c),CI Logo;rep . 9.00
07/64 **(167)** SmC,P(c),CI Logo;rep 10.00
05/65 **(167)** SmC,P(c),CI Logo;rep . 6.00
06/66 **(167)** SmC,P(c),CI Logo;rep . 9.00
Fl/68 **(166)** SmC,P(c),CI Logo,
25¢(c)Price;rep 8.00
1968 **(166)** SmC,P(c),CI Logo,No
Twin Circle Ad;rep 7.00
Sr/70 **(169)** SmC,P(c),CI Logo,
Rigid(c);rep 7.00

011-DON QUIXOTE
By Miguel de Cervantes Saavedra
05/43 **(---)** LZ,LZ(c),Original 700.00
03/44 **(18)** LZ,LZ(c),Nassau
Bulletin Edition;rep 200.00
07/44 **(21)** LZ,LZ(c),Queens
Home News Edition;rep 150.00
06/46 **(28)** LZ,LZ(c);rep 100.00
08/53 **(110)** LZ,TO New P(c),New
CI Logo;rep 25.00
05/60 **(156)** LZ,TO P(c),Pages
Reduced to 48,CI Logo;rep . . . 15.00
1962 **(165)** LZ,TO P(c),CI Logo;rep 8.00
01/64 **(167)** LZ,TO P(c),CI
Logo;rep 8.00
11/65 **(167)** LZ,TO P(c),CI
Logo;rep 8.00
1968 **(166)** LZ,TO P(c),CI Logo,
25¢(c)Price;rep 20.00

012-RIP VAN WINKLE & THE HEADLESS HORSEMAN
By Washington Irving
06/43 **(---)** RLv,RLv(c),Original . 675.00
11/43 **(15)** RLv,RLv(c),Long Island
Independent Edition;rep 180.00
06/44 **(20)** RLv,RLv(c),Long Island
Independent Edition;rep 150.00
10/44 **(22)** RLv,RLv(c),Queens
City Times Edition;rep 135.00
06/46 **(28)** RLv,RLv(c);rep 100.00
06/49 **(60)** RLv,RLv(c),New CI
Logo;rep 40.00
08/49 **(62)** RLv,RLv(c),CI
Logo;rep 30.00
05/50 **(71)** RLv,RLv(c),CI
Logo;rep 25.00
11/51 **(89)** RLv,RLv(c),15¢(c)
Price, CI Logo;rep 15.00
04/54 **(118)** RLv,RLv(c),CI
Logo;rep 15.00
05/56 **(132)** RLv,New P(c),
CI Logo; rep 18.00
05/59 **(150)** NN New Art;P(c),
Logo; rep 18.00
09/60 **(158)** NN,P(c),CI Logo;rep . . 6.00
62/63 **(167)** NN,P(c),CI Logo;rep . . 6.00
12/63 **(167)** NN,P(c),CI Logo;rep . . 6.00
04/65 **(167)** NN,P(c),CI Logo;rep . . 7.00
04/66 **(167)** NN,P(c),CI Logo;rep . . 6.00
1969 **(166)** NN,P(c),CI Logo,
25¢(c)Price,Rigid(c);rep 12.00
Sr/70 **(169)** NN,P(c),CI Logo,
Rigid(c);rep 12.00

013-DR. JEKYLL AND MR.HYDE
By Robert Louis Stevenson
08/43 (---) AdH,AdH(c),Original . 950.00
11/43 (15) AdH,AdH(c),Long Island
Independent Edition;rep 250.00
06/44 (20) AdH,AdH(c),Long Island
Independent Edition;rep 175.00
06/46 (28) AdH,AdH(c),No(c)
Price; rep 125.00
06/49 (60) AdH,HcK New(c),New CI
Logo,Pgs.reduced to 48;rep ... 40.00
08/49 (62) AdH,HcK(c),CI
Logo;rep 35.00
05/50 (71) AdH,HcK(c),CI
Logo;rep 25.00
09/51 (87) AdH,HcK(c),Erroneous Return
of Original Date,CI Logo;rep ... 20.00
10/53 (112) LC New Art,New
P(c), CI Logo;rep 20.00
11/59 (153) LC,P(c),CI Logo;rep .. 7.00
03/61 (161) LC,P(c),CI Logo;rep .. 7.00
62/63 (167) LC,P(c),CI Logo;rep .. 7.00
08/64 (167) LC,P(c),CI Logo;rep .. 7.00
11/65 (167) LC,P(c),CI Logo;rep .. 7.00
1968 (166) LC,P(c),CI Logo,
25¢(c)Price;rep 8.00
Wr/69 (169) LC,P(c),CI Logo,
Rigid(c);rep 7.00

014-WESTWARD HO!
By Charles Kingsley
09/43 (---) ASm,ASm(c),Original 1,500.00
11/43 (15) ASm,ASm(c),Long Island
Independent Edition;rep 550.00
07/44 (21) ASm,ASm(c);rep ... 400.00
06/46 (28) ASm,ASm(c),No(c)
Price; rep 300.00
11/48 (53) ASm,ASm(c),Pages reduced
to 48, New CI Logo;rep 275.00

015-UNCLE TOM'S CABIN
By Harriet Beecher Stowe
11/43 (---) RLv,RLv(c),Original .. 550.00
11/43 (15) RLv,RLv(c),Blank
Price Circle, Long Island
Independent Ed.;rep 200.00
07/44 (21) RLv,RLv(c),Nassau
Bulliten Edition;rep 150.00
06/46 (28) RLv,RLv(c),No(c)
Price; rep 100.00
11/48 (53) RLv,RLv(c),Pages Reduced
to 48, New CI Logo;rep 40.00
05/50 (71) RLv,RLv(c),CI Logo;rep 30.00
11/51 (89) RLv,RLv(c),15¢(c)
Price, CI Logo;rep 30.00
03/54 (117) RLv,New P(c),CI
Logo, Lettering Changes;rep .. 15.00
09/55 (128) RLv,P(c),"Picture
Progress"Promotion,CI Logo;rep 12.00
03/57 (137) RLv,P(c),CI Logo;rep . 6.00
09/58 (146) RLv,P(c),CI Logo;rep . 6.00
01/60 (154) RLv,P(c),CI Logo;rep . 6.00
03/61 (161) RLv,P(c),CI Logo;rep . 6.00
62/63 (167) RLv,P(c),CI Logo;rep . 6.00
06/64 (167) RLv,P(c),CI Logo;rep . 6.00
05/65 (167) RLv,P(c),CI Logo;rep . 6.00
05/67 (166) RLv,P(c),CI Logo;rep . 6.00
Wr/69 (166) RLv,P(c),CI
Logo, Rigid(c);rep 12.00
Sr/70 (169) RLv,P(c),CI
Logo, Rigid(c);rep 12.00

016-GULLIVER'S TRAVELS
By Johnathan Swift

12/43 (----) LCh,LCh(c),Original . 550.00
06/44 (18/20) LCh,LCh(c),Queen's Home
News Edition,No(c)Price;rep .. 175.00
10/44 (22) LCh,LCh(c),Queen's
Home News Editon;rep 135.00
06/46 (28) LCh,LCh(c);rep 100.00
06/49 (60) LCh,LCh(c),Pgs. Reduced
To 48, New CI Logo;rep 40.00
08/49 (62) LCh,LCh(c),CI Logo;rep 25.00
10/49 (64) LCh,LCh(c),CI Logo;rep 25.00
12/50 (78) LCh,LCh(c),15¢(c)
Price, CI Logo;rep 15.00
11/51 (89) LCh,LCh(c),CI Logo;rep 15.00
03/60 (155) LCh,New P(c),CI
Logo; rep 6.00
1962 (165) LCh,P(c),CI Logo;rep . 6.00
05/64 (167) LCh,P(c),CI Logo;rep . 6.00
11/65 (167) LCh,P(c),CI Logo;rep . 6.00
1968 (166) LCh,P(c),CI Logo,
25¢(c)Price;rep 6.00
Wr/69 (169) LCh,P(c),CI
Logo, Rigid(c);rep 6.00

CI #11 Don Quixote
© Gilberton Publications

017-THE DEERSLAYER
By James Fenimore Cooper
01/44 (----) LZ,LZ(c),Original ... 500.00
03/44 (18) LZ,LZ(c),No(c)Price;rep 175.00
10/44 (22) LZ,LZ(c),Queen's
City Times Edition;rep 150.00
06/46 (28) LZ,LZ(c);rep 100.00
06/49 (60) LZ,LZ(c),Pgs. Reduced
to 48,New CI Logo;rep 40.00
10/49 (64) LZ,LZ(c),CI Logo;rep . 25.00
07/51 (85) LZ,LZ(c),15¢(c)
Price, CI Logo;rep 20.00
04/54 (118) LZ,LZ(c),CI Logo;rep . 18.00
05/56 (132) LZ,LZ(c),CI Logo;rep . 15.00
11/66 (167) LZ,LZ(c),CI Logo;rep . 15.00
1968 (166) LZ,StA New P(c),CI
Logo, 25¢(c)Price;rep 20.00
Sg/71 (169) LZ,StA P(c),CI Logo,
Rigid(c), Letters From Parents
and Educators;rep 15.00

018-THE HUNCHBACK OF NOTRE DAME
By Victor Hugo
03/44 (---) ASm,ASm(c),Original
Gilberton Edition 700.00
03/44 (---) ASm,ASm(c),Original
Island Publications Edition ... 600.00
06/44 (18/20) ASm,ASm(c),Queens

Home News Edition;rep 200.00
10/44 (22) ASm,ASm(c),Queens
City Times Edition;rep 150.00
06/46 (28) ASm,ASm(c);rep 125.00
06/49 (60) ASm,HcK New(c)8 Pgs.
Deleted, New CI Logo;rep 40.00
08/49 (62) ASm,HcK(c),CI
Logo;rep 25.00
12/50 (78) ASm,HcK(c),15¢(c)
Price; CI Logo;rep 20.00
11/51 (89) ASm,HcK(c),CI
Logo;rep 15.00
04/54 (118) ASm,HcK(c),CI
Logo;rep 25.00
09/57 (140) ASm,New P(c),CI
Logo; rep 20.00
09/58 (146) ASm,P(c),CI Logo;rep 20.00
09/60 (158) GE&RC New Art,GMc
New P(c),CI Logo;rep 7.00
1962 (165) GE&RC,GMc P(c),CI
Logo; rep 7.00
09/63 (167) GE&RC,GMc P(c),CI
Logo; rep 7.00
10/64 (167) GE&RC,GMc P(c),CI
Logo; rep 6.00
04/66 (167) GE&RC,GMc P(c),CI
Logo; rep 6.00
1968 (166) GE&RC,GMc P(c),CI
Logo, 25¢(c)Price;rep 6.00
Sr/70 (169) GE&RC,GMc P(c),CI
Logo, Rigid(c);rep 6.00

019-HUCKLEBERRY FINN
By Mark Twain
04/44 (---) LZ,LZ(c),Original
Gilberton Edition 400.00
04/44 (---) LZ,LZ(c),Original Island
Publications Company Edition 450.00
03/44 (18) LZ,LZ(c),Nassau
Bulliten Editon;rep 200.00
10/44 (22) LZ,LZ(c),Queens City
Times Edition;rep 150.00
06/46 (28) LZ,LZ(c);rep 100.00
06/49 (60) LZ,LZ(c),New CI Logo,
Pgs.Reduced to 48;rep 35.00
08/49 (62) LZ,LZ(c),CI Logo;rep . 25.00
12/50 (78) LZ,LZ(c),CI Logo;rep . 20.00
11/51 (89) LZ,LZ(c),CI Logo;rep . 18.00
03/54 (117) LZ,LZ(c),CI Logo;rep . 18.00
03/56 (131) FrG New Art,New
P(c), CI Logo; rep6.00
09/57 (140) FrG,P(c),CI Logo;rep . 6.00
05/59 (150) FrG,P(c),CI Logo;rep . 6.00
09/60 (158) FrG,P(c),CI Logo;rep . 6.00
1962 (165) FrG,P(c),CI Logo;rep . 6.00
62/63 (167) FrG,P(c),CI Logo;rep . 6.00
06/64 (167) FrG,P(c),CI Logo;rep . 6.00
10/65 (167) FrG,P(c),CI Logo;rep . 6.00
09/67 (166) FrG,P(c),CI Logo;rep . 6.00
Wr/69 (166) FrG,P(c),CI Logo,
25¢(c)Price, Rigid(c);rep 6.00
Sr/70 (169) FrG,P(c),CI Logo,
Rigid(c);rep 6.00

020-THE CORSICAN BROTHERS
By Alexandre Dumas
06/44 (---) ASm,ASm(c),Original
Gilberton Edition 425.00
06/44 (---) ASm,ASm(c),Original
Courier Edition 400.00
06/44 (---) ASm,ASm(c),Original Long
Island Independent Edition ... 400.00
10/44 (22) ASm,ASm(c),Queens

City Times Edition;rep 175.00
06/46 **(28)** ASm,ASm(c);rep . . . 150.00
06/49 **(60)** ASm,ASm(c),No(c)Price,
New CI Logo,Pgs. Reduced
to 48;rep 125.00
08/49 **(62)** ASm,ASm(c),CI
Logo;rep 115.00
12/50 **(78)** ASm,ASm(c),15¢(c)
Price, CI Logo;rep 100.00
07/52 **(97)** ASm,ASm(c),CI
Logo;rep 90.00

CI #17 The Deerslayer
© Gilberton Publications

021-FAMOUS MYSTERIES
By Sir Arthur Conan Doyle
Guy de Maupassant
& Edgar Allan Poe
07/44 **(---)** ASm,AdH,LZ,ASm(c),
Original Gilberton Edition 750.00
07/44 **(---)** ASm,AdH,LZ,ASm(c),
Original Island Publications
Edition; No Date or Indicia . . 775.00
07/44 **(---)** ASm,AdH,LZ,ASm(c),Original
Richmond Courier Edition 700.00
10/44 **(22)** ASm,AdH,LZ,ASm(c),
Nassau Bulliten Edition;rep . . . 275.00
09/46 **(30)** ASm,AdH,LZ,ASm(c);
rep 225.00
08/49 **(62)** ASm,AdH,LZ,ASm(c),
New CI Logo;rep 185.00
04/50 **(70)** ASm,AdH,LZ,ASm(c),
CI Logo;rep 175.00
07/51 **(85)** ASm,AdH,LZ,ASm(c),
15¢(c) Price,CI Logo;rep 150.00
12/53 **(114)** ASm,AdH,LZ,New
P(c), CI Logo;rep 150.00

022-THE PATHFINDER
By James Fenimore Cooper
10/44 **(---)** LZ,LZ(c),Original
Gilberton Edition 350.00
10/44 **(---)** LZ,LZ(c),Original
Island Publications Edition; . . . 300.00
10/44 **(---)** LZ,LZ(c),Original
Queens County Times Edition 300.00
09/46 **(30)** LZ,LZ(c),No(c)
Price;rep 100.00
06/49 **(60)** LZ,LZ(c),New CI Logo,
Pgs.Reduced To 48;rep 35.00
08/49 **(62)** LZ,LZ(c),CI Logo;rep . 28.00
04/50 **(70)** LZ,LZ(c),CI Logo;rep . 25.00
07/51 **(85)** LZ,LZ(c),15¢(c)

Price, CI Logo;rep 20.00
04/54 **(118)** LZ,LZ(c),CI Logo;rep . 15.00
05/56 **(132)** LZ,LZ(c),CI Logo;rep . 15.00
09/58 **(146)** LZ,LZ(c),CI Logo;rep . 25.00
11/63 **(167)** LZ,NN New P(c),CI
Logo; rep 20.00
12/65 **(167)** LZ,NN P(c),CI
Logo;rep 20.00
08/67 **(166)** LZ,NN P(c),CI
Logo;rep 20.00

023-OLIVER TWIST
By Charles Dickens
(First Classic produced by
the Iger shop)
07/45 **(---)** AdH,AdH(c),Original . 350.00
09/46 **(30)** AdH,AdH(c),Price
Circle is Blank;rep 250.00
06/49 **(60)** AdH,AdH(c),Pgs. Reduced
To 48, New CI Logo;rep 35.00
08/49 **(62)** AdH,AdH(c),CI
Logo;rep 25.00
05/50 **(71)** AdH,AdH(c),CI
Logo;rep 25.00
07/51 **(85)** AdH,AdH(c),15¢(c)
Price CI Logo;rep 20.00
04/52 **(94)** AdH,AdH(c),CI
Logo;rep 20.00
04/54 **(118)** AdH,AdH(c),CI
Logo;rep 15.00
01/57 **(136)** AdH,New P(c),CI
Logo;rep 15.00
05/59 **(150)** AdH,P(c),CI Logo;rep 12.00
1961 **(164)** AdH,P(c),CI Logo;rep . 12.00
10/61 **(164)** GE&RC New Art,P(c),
CI Logo;rep 20.00
62/63 **(167)** GE&RC,P(c),CI
Logo; rep 6.00
08/64 **(167)** GE&RC,P(c),CI
Logo; rep 6.00
12/65 **(167)** GE&RC,P(c),
CI Logo;rep 6.00
1968 **(166)** GE&RC,P(c),CI
Logo, 25¢(c)Price;rep 6.00
Wr/69 **(169)** GE&RC,P(c),CI
Logo, Rigid(c);rep 6.00

024-A CONNECTICUT
YANKEE IN KING
ARTHUR'S COURT
By Mark Twain
09/45 **(---)** JH,JH(c),Original . . . 300.00
09/46 **(30)** JH,JH(c),Price Circle
Blank;rep 100.00
06/49 **(60)** JH,JH(c),8 Pages
Deleted,New CI Logo;rep 30.00
08/49 **(62)** JH,JH(c),CI Logo;rep . 28.00
05/50 **(71)** JH,JH(c),CI Logo;rep . 20.00
09/51 **(87)** JH,JH(c),15¢(c) Price
CI Logo;rep 18.00
07/54 **(121)** JH,JH(c),CI Logo;rep 15.00
09/57 **(140)** JkS New Art,New
P(c),CI Logo; rep 15.00
11/59 **(153)** JkS,P(c),CI Logo;rep . 6.00
1961 **(164)** JkS,P(c),CI Logo;rep . . 6.00
62/63 **(167)** JkS,P(c),CI Logo;rep . . 6.00
07/64 **(167)** JkS,P(c),CI Logo;rep . . 6.00
06/66 **(167)** JkS,P(c),CI Logo;rep . . 6.00
1968 **(166)** JkS,P(c),CI logo,
25¢(c)Price;rep 6.00
Sg/71 **(169)** JkS,P(c),CI Logo,
Rigid(c);rep 6.00

025-TWO YEARS
BEFORE THE MAST
By Richard Henry Dana Jr.
10/45 **(---)** RWb,DvH,Original; . . 300.00
09/46 **(30)** RWb,DvH,Price Circle
Blank;rep 100.00
06/49 **(60)** RWb,DvH,8 Pages
Deleted,New CI Logo;rep 35.00
08/49 **(62)** RWb,DvH,CI Logo;rep 30.00
05/50 **(71)** RWb,DvH,CI Logo;rep 20.00
07/51 **(85)** RWb,DvH,15¢(c) Price
CI Logo;rep 15.00
12/53 **(114)** RWb,DvH,CI Logo;rep 15.00
05/60 **(156)** RWb,New P(c),CI Logo,
3 Pgs. Replaced By Fillers;rep . 15.00
12/63 **(167)** RWb,DvH,P(c),CI
Logo; rep 6.00
12/65 **(167)** RWb,DvH,P(c),CI
Logo; rep 6.00
09/67 **(166)** RWb,DvH,P(c),CI
Logo; rep 6.00
Wr/69 **(169)** RWb,DvH,P(c),25¢(c)
Price, CI Logo,Rigid(c);rep 6.00

026-FRANKENSTEIN
By Mary Wollstonecraft Shelley
12/45 **(---)** RWb&ABr,RWb
& ABr(c), Original 750.00
09/46 **(30)** RWb&ABr,RWb &ABr(c),
Price Circle Blank;rep 225.00
06/49 **(60)** RWb&ABr,RWb&ABr(c),
New CI Logo;rep 65.00
08/49 **(62)** RWb&ABr,RWb
& ABr(c), CI Logo;rep 100.00
05/50 **(71)** RWb&ABr,RWb
& ABr(c), CI Logo;rep 45.00
04/51 **(82)** RWb&ABr,RWb &ABr(c),
15¢(c) Price,CI Logo;rep 30.00
03/54 **(117)** RWb&ABr,RWb
& ABr(c),CI Logo;rep 20.00
09/58 **(146)** RWb&ABr,NS
New P(c), CI Logo; rep 20.00
11/59 **(153)** RWb&ABr,NS
P(c),CI Logo; rep 35.00
01/61 **(160)** RWb&ABr,NS
P(c),CI Logo; rep 6.00
165 **(1962)** RWb&ABr,NS P(c),
CI Logo; rep 6.00
62/63 **(167)** RWb&ABr,NS P(c),
CI Logo; rep 6.00
06/64 **(167)** RWb&ABr,NS P(c),
CI logo; rep 6.00
06/65 **(167)** RWb&ABr,NS P(c),
CI Logo; rep 6.00
10/65 **(167)** RWb&ABr,NS P(c),
CI Logo; rep 6.00
09/67 **(166)** RWb&ABr,NS P(c),
CI Logo; rep 6.00
Fl/69 **(169)** RWb&ABr,NS P(c),25¢(c)
Price,CI Logo,Rigid(c);rep 6.00
Sg/71 **(169)** RWb&ABr,NS P(c),
CI Logo, Rigid(c);rep 6.00

027-THE ADVENTURES
MARCO POLO
By Marco Polo & Donn Byrne
04/46 **(----)** HFI,HFI(c);Original . . 300.00
09/46 **(30)** HFI,HFI(c);rep 85.00
04/50 **(70)** HFI,HFI(c),8 Pages Deleted,
No(c) Price,New CI Logo;rep . . 25.00
09/51 **(87)** HFI,HFI(c),15¢(c)
Price, CI Logo;rep 20.00
03/54 **(117)** HFI,HFI(c),CILogo;rep 15.00
01/60 **(154)** HFI,New P(c),CI
Logo;rep 15.00

1962 **(165)** HFI,P(c),CI Logo;rep . . 6.00
04/64 **(167)** HFI,P(c),CI Logo;rep . . 6.00
06/66 **(167)** HFI,P(c),CI Logo;rep . . 6.00
Sg/69 **(169)** HFI,P(c),CI Logo,
  25¢(c)Price,Rigid(c);rep 6.00

028-MICHAEL STROGOFF
By Jules Verne
06/46 **(---)** AdH,AdH(c),Original . 325.00
09/48 **(51)** AdH,AdH(c),8 Pages
  Deleted,New CI Logo;rep 100.00
01/54 **(115)** AdH,New P(c),CI
  Logo; rep 25.00
03/60 **(155)** AdH,P(c),CI Logo;rep 10.00
11/63 **(167)** AdH,P(c),CI Logo;rep 10.00
07/66 **(167)** AdH,P(c),CI Logo;rep 10.00
Sr/69 **(169)**AdH,NN,NewP(c),25¢(c)
  Price, CI Logo,Rigid(c);rep 15.00

*CI #24 A Connecticut Yankee in King
Arthur's Court © Gilberton Publications*

029-THE PRINCE
AND THE PAUPER
By Mark Twain
07/46 **(---)** AdH,AdH(c),Original . 500.00
06/49 **(60)** AdH,New HcK(c),New CI
  Logo,8 Pages Deleted;rep 35.00
08/49 **(62)** AdH,HcK(c),CILogo;rep 30.00
05/50 **(71)** AdH,HcK(c),CILogo;rep 25.00
03/52 **(93)** AdH,HcK(c),CILogo;rep 20.00
12/53 **(114)** AdH,HcK(c),CI
  Logo;rep 15.00
09/55 **(128)** AdH,New P(c),CI
  Logo; rep 15.00
05/57 **(138)** AdH,P(c),CI Logo;rep . 6.00
05/59 **(150)** AdH,P(c),CI Logo;rep . 6.00
1961 **(164)** AdH,P(c),CI Logo;rep . 6.00
62/63 **(167)** AdH,P(c),CI Logo;rep . 6.00
07/64 **(167)** AdH,P(c),CI Logo;rep . 6.00
11/65 **(167)** AdH,P(c),CI Logo;rep . 6.00
1968 **(166)** AdH,P(c),CI Logo,
  25¢(c)Price;rep 6.00
Sr/70 **(169)** AdH,P(c),CI Logo,
  Rigid(c);rep 6.00

030-THE MOONSTONE
By William Wilkie Collins
09/46 **(---)** DRi,DRi(c),Original . . 300.00
06/49 **(60)** DRi,DRi(c),8 Pages
  Deleted,New CI Logo;rep 40.00
04/50 **(70)** DRi,DRi(c),CI Logo;rep 35.00
03/60 **(155)** DRi,LbC New P(c),
  CI Logo;rep 45.00

1962 **(165)** DRi,LbC P(c),CI Logo;
  rep 20.00
01/64 **(167)** DRi,LbC P(c),CI Logo;
  rep 18.00
09/65 **(167)** DRi,LbC P(c),CI Logo;
  rep 10.00
1968 **(166)** DRi,LbC P(c),CI Logo,
  25¢(c)Price;rep 8.00

031-THE BLACK ARROW
By Robert Louis Stevenson
10/46 **(---)** AdH,AdH(c),Original . 275.00
09/48 **(51)** AdH,AdH(c),8 Pages
  Deleted,New CI Logo;rep 35.00
10/49 **(64)** AdH,AdH(c),CI
  Logo;rep 20.00
09/51 **(87)** AdH,AdH(c),15¢(c)
  Price;CI Logo;rep 17.00
06/53 **(108)** AdH,AdH(c),CI
  Logo;rep 15.00
03/55 **(125)** AdH,AdH(c),CI
  Logo;rep 14.00
03/56 **(131)** AdH,New P(c),CI
  Logo; rep 12.00
09/57 **(140)** AdH,P(c),CI Logo;rep . 6.00
01/59 **(148)** AdH,P(c),CI Logo;rep . 6.00
03/61 **(161)** AdH,P(c),CI Logo;rep . 6.00
62/63 **(167)** AdH,P(c),CI Logo;rep . 6.00
07/64 **(167)** AdH,P(c),CI logo;rep . 6.00
11/65 **(167)** AdH,P(c),CI Logo;rep . 6.00
1968 **(166)** AdH,P(c),CI Logo,
  25¢(c)Price;rep 6.00

032-LORNA DOONE
By Richard Doddridge Blackmore
12/46 **(---)** MB,MB(c),Original . . . 300.00
10/49 **(53/64)** MB,MB(c),8 Pages
  Deleted,New CI Logo;rep 40.00
07/51 **(85)** MB,MB(c),15¢(c)
  Price, CI Logo;rep 30.00
04/54 **(118)** MB,MB(c),CI Logo;rep 20.00
05/57 **(138)** MB,New P(c); Old(c)
  Becomes New Splash Pge.,CI
  Logo;rep 20.00
05/59 **(150)** MB,P(c),CI Logo;rep . 6.00
1962 **(165)** MB,P(c),CI Logo;rep . 6.00
01/64 **(167)** MB,P(c),CI Logo;rep . 6.00
11/65 **(167)** MB,P(c),CI Logo;rep . 6.00
1968 **(166)** MB,New P(c),CI Logo;
  rep 18.00

033-THE ADVENTURES
OF SHERLOCK HOLMES
By Sir Arthur Conan Doyle
01/47 **(---)** LZ,HcK(c),Original . 1,000.00
11/48 **(53)** LZ,HcK(c),"A Study in Scarlet"
  Deleted,New CI Logo;rep 350.00
05/50 **(71)** LZ,HcK(c),CI Logo;rep 275.00
11/51 **(89)** LZ,HcK(c),15¢(c)
  Price,CI Logo;rep 225.00

034-MYSTERIOUS ISLAND
By Jules Verne
Last Classic Comic
02/47 **(---)** RWb&DvH,Original . . 325.00
06/49 **(60)** RWb&DvH,8 Pages
  Deleted,New CI Logo;rep 35.00
08/49 **(62)** RWb&DvH,CI Logo;rep 25.00
05/50 **(71)** RWb&DvH,CI Logo;rep 40.00
12/50 **(78)** RWb&DvH,15¢(c) Price,
  CI Logo;rep 20.00
02/52 **(92)** RWb&DvH,CI Logo;rep 20.00
03/54 **(117)** RWb&DvH,CI Logo;rep 20.00
09/57 **(140)** RWb&DvH,New P(c),CI
  Logo;rep 20.00

05/60 **(156)** RWb&DvH,P(c),CI
  Logo;rep 6.00
10/63 **(167)** RWb&DvH,P(c),CI
  Logo;rep 6.00
05/64 **(167)** RWb&DvH,P(c),CI
  Logo;rep 6.00
06/66 **(167)** RWb&DvH,P(c),CI
  logo;rep 6.00
1968 **(166)** RWb&DvH,P(c),CI Logo,
  25¢(c)Price;rep 6.00

035-LAST DAYS
OF POMPEII
By Lord Edward Bulwer Lytton
First Classics Illustrated
03/47 **(---)** HcK,HcK(c),Original . 325.00
03/61 **(161)** JK,New P(c),
  15¢(c)Price;rep 30.00
01/64 **(167)** JK,P(c);rep 15.00
07/66 **(167)** JK,P(c);rep 15.00
Sg/70 **(169)** JK,P(c),25¢(c)
  Price, Rigid(c);rep 16.00

036-TYPEE
By Herman Melville
04/47 **(---)** EzW,EzW(c),Original . 175.00
10/49 **(64)** EzW,EzW(c),No(c)price,
  8 pages deleted;rep 40.00
03/60 **(155)** EzW,GMc New
  P(c);rep 15.00
09/63 **(167)** EzW,GMc P(c);rep . . 10.00
07/65 **(167)** EzW,GMc P(c);rep . . 10.00
Sr/69 **(169)** EzW,GMc P(c),25¢(c)
  Price, Rigid(c);rep 10.00

037-THE PIONEERS
By James Fenimore Cooper
05/47 **(37)** RP,RP(c),Original . . . 135.00
08/49 **(62)** RP,RP(c),8 Pages
  Deleted;rep 30.00
04/50 **(70)** RP,RP(c);rep 25.00
02/52 **(92)** RP,RP(c),15¢(c)price;rep25.00
04/54 **(118)** RP,RP(c);rep 20.00
03/56 **(131)** RP,RP(c);rep 20.00
05/56 **(132)** RP,RP(c);rep 20.00
11/59 **(153)** RP,RP(c);rep 15.00
05/64 **(167)** RP,RP(c);rep 15.00
06/66 **(167)** RP,RP(c);rep 15.00
1968 **(166)** RP,TO New P(c),
  25¢(c)Price;rep 25.00

038-ADVENTURES
OF CELLINI
By Benvenuto Cellini
06/47 **(---)** AgF,AgF(c),Original . 225.00
1961 **(164)** NN New Art,New P(c);
  rep 20.00
12/63 **(167)** NN,P(c);rep 10.00
07/66 **(167)** NN,P(c);rep 10.00
Sg/70 **(169)** NN,P(c),25¢(c)
  Price, Rigid(c);rep 12.00

039-JANE EYRE
By Charlotte Bronte
07/47 **(---)** HyG,HyG(c),Original . 225.00
06/49 **(60)** HyG,HyG(c),No(c)Price,
  8 pages deleted;rep 35.00
08/49 **(62)** HyG,HyG(c);rep 30.00
05/50 **(71)** HyG,HyG(c);rep 25.00
02/52 **(92)** HyG,HyG(c),15¢(c)
  Price; rep 20.00
04/54 **(118)** HyG,HyG(c);rep 20.00
01/58 **(142)** HyG,New P(c);rep . . 20.00
01/60 **(154)** HyG,P(c);rep 20.00

1962 **(165)** HjK New Art,P(c);rep	20.00
12/63 **(167)** HjK,P(c);rep	20.00
04/65 **(167)** HjK,P(c);rep	20.00
08/66 **(167)** HjK,P(c);rep	20.00
1968 **(166)** HjK,NN New P(c);rep	40.00

040-MYSTERIES
**(The Pit & the Pendulum,
The Adventures of Hans Pfall,
Fall of the House of Usher)**
By Edgar Allan Poe
08/47 **(---)** HcK,AgF,HyG,HcK(c), Original	525.00
08/49 **(62)** HcK,AgF,HyG,HcK(c), 8 Pages deleted;rep	225.00
09/50 **(75)** HcK,AgF,HyG, HcK(c);rep	200.00
02/52 **(92)** HcK,AgF,HyG,HcK(c) 15¢(c) Price;rep	150.00

041-TWENTY YEARS AFTER
By Alexandre Dumas
09/47 **(---)** RBu,RBu(c),Original	400.00
08/49 **(62)** RBu,HcK New(c),No(c) Price, 8 Pages Deleted;rep	35.00
12/50 **(78)** RBu,HcK(c),15¢(c) Price; rep	25.00
05/60 **(156)** RBu,DgR New P(c);rep	20.00
12/63 **(167)** RBu,DgR P(c);rep	10.00
11/66 **(167)** RBu,DgR P(c);rep	10.00
Sg/70 **(169)** RBu,DgR P(c);rep Price,Rigid(c);rep	10.00

042-SWISS FAMILY ROBINSON
By Johann Wyss
10/47 **(42)** HcK,HcK(c),Original	150.00
08/49 **(62)** HcK,HcK(c),No(c)price, 8 Pages Deleted,Not Every Issue Has 'Gift Box' Ad;rep	35.00
09/50 **(75)** HcK,HcK(c);rep	25.00
03/52 **(93)** HcK,HcK(c);rep	20.00
03/54 **(117)** HcK,HcK(c);rep	15.00
03/56 **(131)** HcK,New P(c);rep	15.00
03/57 **(137)** HcK,P(c);rep	15.00
11/57 **(141)** HcK,P(c);rep	15.00
09/59 **(152)** NN New art,P(c);rep	15.00
09/60 **(158)** NN,P(c);rep	8.00
12/63 **(165)** NN,P(c);rep	15.00
12/63 **(167)** NN,P(c);rep	7.00
04/65 **(167)** NN,P(c);rep	7.00
05/66 **(167)** NN,P(c);rep	7.00
11/67 **(166)** NN,P(c);rep	6.00
Sg/69 **(169)** NN,P(c);rep	6.00

043-GREAT EXPECTATIONS
By Charles Dickens
11/47 **(---)** HcK,HcK(c),Original	700.00
08/49 **(62)** HcK,HcK(c),No(c)price; 8 pages deleted;rep	400.00

044-MYSTERIES OF PARIS
By Eugene Sue
12/47 **(44)** HcK,HcK(c),Original	550.00
08/47 **(62)** HcK,HcK(c),No(c)Price, 8 Pages Deleted,Not Every Issue Has'Gift Box'Ad;rep	225.00
12/50 **(78)** HcK,HcK(c),15¢(c) Price; rep	200.00

045-TOM BROWN'S SCHOOL DAYS
By Thomas Hughes
01/48 **(44)** HFI,HFI(c),Original, 1st 48 Pge. Issue	125.00
10/49 **(64)** HFI,HFI(c),No(c) Price;rep	40.00
03/61 **(161)** JTg New Art,GMc New P(c);rep	15.00
02/64 **(167)** JTg,GMc P(c);rep	12.00
08/66 **(167)** JTg,GMc P(c);rep	12.00
1968 **(166)** JTg,GMc P(c), 25¢(c)Price;rep	12.00

046-KIDNAPPED
By Robert Louis Stevenson
04/48 **(47)** RWb,RWb(c),Original	100.00
08/49 **(62)** RWb,RWb(c),Red Circle Either Blank or With 10¢;rep	62.00
12/50 **(78)** RWb,RWb(c),15¢(c) Price; rep	25.00
09/51 **(87)** RWb,RWb(c);rep	20.00
04/54 **(118)** RWb,RWb(c);rep	15.00
03/56 **(131)** RWb,New P(c);rep	15.00
09/57 **(140)** RWb,P(c);rep	6.00
05/59 **(150)** RWb,P(c);rep	6.00
05/60 **(156)** RWb,P(c);rep	6.00
1961 **(164)** RWb,P(c),Reduced Pge. Wdth;rep	6.00
62/63 **(167)** RWb,P(c);rep	6.00
03/64 **(167)** RWb,P(c);rep	6.00
06/65 **(167)** RWb,P(c);rep	6.00
12/65 **(167)** RWb,P(c);rep	6.00
09/67 **(167)** RWb,P(c);rep	6.00
Wr/69 **(166)** RWb,P(c),25¢(c) Price, Rigid(c);rep	6.00
Sr/70 **(169)** RWb,P(c),Rigid(c);rep	6.00

047-TWENTY THOUSAND LEAGUES UNDER THE SEA
By Jules Verne
05/58 **(47)** HcK,HcK(c),Original	100.00
10/49 **(64)** HcK,HcK(c),No(c) Price; rep	30.00
12/50 **(78)** HcK,HcK(c),15¢(c) Price; rep	25.00
04/52 **(94)** HcK,HcK(c);rep	25.00
04/54 **(118)** HcK,HcK(c);rep	20.00
09/55 **(128)** HcK,New P(c);rep	15.00
07/56 **(133)** HcK,P(c);rep	15.00
09/57 **(140)** HcK,P(c);rep	6.00
01/59 **(148)** HcK,P(c);rep	6.00
05/60 **(156)** HcK,P(c);rep	6.00
62/63 **(165)** HcK,P(c);rep	6.00
05/48 **(167)** HcK,P(c);rep	6.00
03/64 **(167)** HcK,P(c);rep	6.00
08/65 **(167)** HcK,P(c);rep	6.00
10/66 **(167)** HcK,P(c);rep	6.00
1968 **(166)** HcK,NN New P(c), 25¢(c)Price;rep	12.00
Sg/70 **(169)** HcK,NN P(c), Rigid(c);rep	12.00

048-DAVID COPPERFIELD
By Charles Dickens
06/48 **(47)** HcK,HcK(c),Original	100.00
10/49 **(64)** HcK,HcK(c),Price Circle Replaced By Image of Boy Reading;rep	30.00
09/51 **(87)** HcK,HcK(c),15¢(c) Price; rep	25.00
07/54 **(121)** HcK,New P(c);rep	15.00

10/56 **(130)** HcK,P(c);rep	7.00
09/57 **(140)** HcK,P(c);rep	7.00
01/59 **(148)** HcK,P(c);rep	7.00
05/60 **(156)** HcK,P(c);rep	7.00
62/63 **(167)** HcK,P(c);rep	6.00
04/64 **(167)** HcK,P(c);rep	6.00
06/65 **(167)** HcK,P(c);rep	6.00
05/67 **(166)** HcK,P(c);rep	6.00
R/67 **(166)** HcK,P(c);rep	11.00
Sg/69 **(166)** HcK,P(c),25¢(c) Price, Rigid(c);rep	6.00
Wr/69 **(169)** HcK,P(c),Rigid(c);rep	6.00

CI #31 The Black Arrow
© Gilberton Publications

049-ALICE IN WONDERLAND
By Lewis Carroll
07/48 **(47)** AB,AB(c),Original	135.00
10/49 **(64)** AB,AB(c),No(c)Price;rep	40.00
07/51 **(85)** AB,AB(c),15¢(c)Price;rep	30.00
03/60 **(155)** NN New P(c);rep	30.00
1962 **(165)** AB,P(c);rep	25.00
03/64 **(167)** AB,P(c);rep	20.00
06/66 **(167)** AB,P(c);rep	20.00
Fl/68 **(166)** AB,TO New P(c),25¢(c) Price, New Soft(c);rep	30.00
Fl/68 **(166)** AB,P(c),Both Soft & Rigid(c)s;rep	50.00

050-ADVENTURES OF TOM SAWYER
By Mark Twain
08/48 **(51)** ARu,ARu(c),Original	125.00
09/48 **(51)** ARu,ARu(c),Original	130.00
10/49 **(64)** ARu,ARu(c),No(c) Price; rep	25.00
12/50 **(78)** ARu,ARu(c),15¢(c) Price; rep	20.00
04/52 **(94)** ARu,ARu(c);rep	20.00
12/53 **(114)** ARu,ARu(c);rep	15.00
03/54 **(117)** ARu,ARu(c);rep	15.00
05/56 **(132)** ARu,ARu(c);rep	15.00
09/57 **(140)** ARu,New P(c);rep	10.00
05/59 **(150)** ARu,P(c);rep	15.00
10/61 **(164)** New Art,P(c);rep	6.00
62/63 **(167)** P(c);rep	6.00
01/65 **(167)** P(c);rep	6.00
05/67 **(166)** P(c);rep	6.00
12/67 **(166)** P(c);rep	6.00
Fl/69 **(169)** P(c),25¢(c) Price, Rigid(c);rep	6.00
Wr/71 **(169)** P(c);rep	6.00

All comics prices listed are for *Near Mint* condition.

051-THE SPY
By James Fenimore Cooper
09/48 **(51)** AdH,AdH(c),Original,
  Maroon(c) 100.00
09/48 **(51)** AdH,AdH(c),Original,
  Violet(c) 100.00
11/51 **(89)** AdH,AdH(c),15¢(c)
  Price; rep 25.00
07/54 **(121)** AdH,AdH(c);rep 20.00
07/57 **(139)** AdH,New P(c);rep . . . 15.00
05/60 **(156)** AdH,P(c);rep 6.00
11/63 **(167)** AdH,P(c);rep 6.00
07/66 **(167)** AdH,P(c);rep 6.00
Wr/69 **(166)** AdH,P(c),25¢(c)Price,
  Both Soft & Rigid(c)s;rep 20.00

052-THE HOUSE OF SEVEN GABLES
By Nathaniel Hawthorne
10/48 **(53)** HyG,HyG(c),Original . 100.00
11/51 **(89)** HyG,HyG(c),15¢(c)
  Price; rep 25.00
07/54 **(121)** HyG,HyG(c);rep 20.00
01/58 **(142)** GWb New Art,New
  P(c); rep 15.00
05/60 **(156)** GWb,P(c);rep 6.00
1962 **(165)** GWb,P(c);rep 6.00
05/64 **(167)** GWb,P(c);rep 6.00
03/66 **(167)** GWb,P(c);rep 6.00
1968 **(166)** GWb,P(c),25¢(c)
  Price; rep 6.00
Sg/70 **(169)** GWb,P(c),Rigid(c);rep . 6.00

053-A CHRISTMAS CAROL
By Charles Dickens
11/48 **(53)** HcK,HcK(c),Original . 125.00

054-MAN IN THE IRON MASK
By Alexandre Dumas
12/48 **(55)** AgF,HcK(c),Original . 100.00
03/52 **(93)** AgF,HcK(c),15¢(c)
  Price; rep 25.00
09/53 **(111)** AgF,HcK(c);rep 35.00
01/58 **(142)** KBa New Art,New
  P(c); rep 15.00
01/60 **(154)** KBa,P(c);rep 6.00
1962 **(165)** KBa,P(c);rep 6.00
05/64 **(167)** KBa,P(c);rep 6.00
04/66 **(167)** KBa,P(c);rep 6.00
Wr/69 **(166)** KBa,P(c),25¢(c)
  Price, Rigid(c);rep 6.00

055-SILAS MARINER
By George Eliot
01/49 **(55)** AdH,HcK(c),Original . 100.00
09/50 **(75)** AdH,HcK(c),Price Circle
  Blank,'Coming next'Ad(not
  usually in reps.);rep 30.00
07/52 **(97)** AdH,HcK(c);rep 20.00
07/54 **(121)** AdH,New P(c);rep . . . 15.00
01/56 **(130)** AdH,P(c);rep 6.00
09/57 **(140)** AdH,P(c);rep 6.00
01/60 **(154)** AdH,P(c);rep 6.00
1962 **(165)** AdH,P(c);rep 6.00
05/64 **(167)** AdH,P(c);rep 6.00
06/65 **(167)** AdH,P(c);rep 6.00
05/67 **(166)** AdH,P(c);rep 6.00
Wr/69 **(166)** AdH,P(c),25¢(c) Price,
  Rigid(c);rep,Soft & Stiff 16.00

056-THE TOILERS OF THE SEA
By Victor Hugo
02/49 **(55)** AgF,AgF(c),Original . 175.00
01/62 **(165)** AT New Art,New
  P(c); rep. 30.00
03/64 **(167)** AT,P(c);rep. 20.00
10/66 **(167)** AT,P(c);rep. 20.00

057-THE SONG OF HIAWATHA
By Henry Wadsworth Longfellow
03/49 **(55)** AB,AB(c),Original . . . 100.00
09/50 **(75)** AB,AB(c),No(c)price,'
  Coming Next'Ad(not usually
  found in reps.);rep 30.00
04/52 **(94)** AB,AB(c),15¢(c)
  Price;rep 20.00
04/54 **(118)** AB,AB(c);rep 20.00
09/56 **(134)** AB,New P(c);rep . . . 15.00
07/57 **(139)** AB,P(c);rep 6.00
01/60 **(154)** AB,P(c);rep 6.00
62/63 **(167)** AB,P(c),Erroneosly
  Has Original Date;rep 6.00
09/64 **(167)** AB,P(c);rep 6.00
10/65 **(167)** AB,P(c);rep 6.00
Fl/68 **(166)** AB,P(c),25¢(c) Price;rep 6.00

Cl #58 The Prairie
© Gilberton Publications

058-THE PRAIRIE
By James Fenimore Cooper
04/49 **(60)** RP,RP(c),Original . . . 100.00
08/49 **(62)** RP,RP(c);rep 45.00
12/50 **(78)** RP,RP(c),15¢(c) Price
  In Double Circle;rep 25.00
12/53 **(114)** RP,RP(c);rep 20.00
03/56 **(131)** RP,RP(c);rep 15.00
05/56 **(132)** RP,RP(c);rep 15.00
09/58 **(146)** RP,New P(c);rep . . . 15.00
03/60 **(155)** RP,P(c);rep 6.00
05/64 **(167)** RP,P(c);rep 6.00
04/66 **(167)** RP,P(c);rep 6.00
Sr/69 **(169)** RP,P(c),25¢(c)
  Price; Rigid(c);rep 6.00

059-WUTHERING HEIGHTS
By Emily Bronte
05/49 **(60)** HcK,HcK(c),Original . 110.00
07/51 **(85)** HcK,HcK(c),15¢(c)
  Price; rep 35.00
05/60 **(156)** HcK,GB New P(c);rep 20.00
01/64 **(167)** HcK,GB P(c);rep 8.00
10/66 **(167)** HcK,GB P(c);rep 8.00
Sr/69 **(169)** HcK,GBP(c),25¢(c)
  Price, Rigid(c);rep 7.00

060-BLACK BEAUTY
By Anna Sewell
06/49 **(62)** AgF,AgF(c),Original . 100.00
08/49 **(62)** AgF,AgF(c);rep 125.00
07/51 **(85)** AgF,AgF(c),15¢(c) Price;
  rep 25.00
09/60 **(158)** LbC&NN&StA New
  Art, LbC New P(c);rep 25.00
02/64 **(167)** LbC&NN&StA,LbC
  P(c); rep 20.00
03/66 **(167)** LbC&NN&StA,LbC
  P(c);rep 20.00
03/66 **(167)** LbC&NN&StA,LbC
  P(c), 'Open Book'Blank;rep . . . 50.00
1968 **(166)** LbC&NN&StA,AlM New
  P(c) 25¢(c) Price;rep 35.00

061-THE WOMAN IN WHITE
By William Wilke Collins
07/49 **(62)** AB,AB(c),Original,
  Maroon & Violet(c)s 110.00
05/60 **(156)** AB,DgR New P(c);rep 25.00
01/64 **(167)** AB,DgR P(c);rep 20.00
1968 **(166)** AB,DgR P(c),
  25¢(c)Price;rep 20.00

062-WESTERN STORIES
(The Luck of Roaring Camp & The Outcasts of Poker Flat)
By Bret Harte
08/49 **(62)** HcK,HcK(c),Original . . 90.00
11/51 **(89)** HcK,HcK(c),15¢(c)
  Price; rep 25.00
07/54 **(121)** HcK,HcK(c);rep 20.00
03/57 **(137)** HcK,New P(c);rep . . . 15.00
09/59 **(152)** HcK,P(c);rep 7.00
10/63 **(167)** HcK,P(c);rep 7.00
06/64 **(167)** HcK,P(c);rep 6.00
11/66 **(167)** HcK,P(c);rep 6.00
1968 **(166)** HcK,TO New P(c),
  25¢ Price;rep 20.00

063-THE MAN WITHOUT A COUNTRY
By Edward Everett Hale
09/49 **(62)** HcK,HcK(c),Original . 100.00
12/50 **(78)** HcK,HcK(c),15¢(c)Price
  In Double Circles;rep 25.00
05/60 **(156)** HcK,GMc New P(c);rep 22.00
01/62 **(165)** AT New Art,GMc P(c),
  Added Text Pages;rep 12.00
03/64 **(167)** AT,GMc P(c);rep 6.00
08/66 **(167)** AT,GMc P(c);rep 6.00
Sr/69 **(169)** AT,GMc P(c),25¢(c)
  Price, Rigid(c);rep 6.00

064-TREASURE ISLAND
By Robert Louis Stevenson
10/49 **(62)** AB,AB(c),Original 90.00
04/51 **(82)** AB,AB(c),15¢(c)
  Price;rep 25.00
03/54 **(117)** AB,AB(c);rep 17.00
03/56 **(131)** AB,New P(c);rep 14.00
05/57 **(138)** AB,P(c);rep 6.00
09/58 **(146)** AB,P(c);rep 6.00
09/60 **(158)** AB,P(c);rep 6.00
1962 **(165)** AB,P(c);rep 6.00

All comics prices listed are for *Near Mint* condition.

CLASSICS ILLUSTRATED

62/63 **(167)** AB,P(c);rep 6.00
06/64 **(167)** AB,P(c);rep 6.00
12/65 **(167)** AB,P(c);rep 6.00
10/67 **(166)** AB,P(c);rep 11.00
10/67 **(166)** AB,P(c),GRIT Ad
Stapled In Book;rep 64.00
Sg/69 **(169)** AB,P(c),25¢(c)
Price, Rigid(c);rep 6.00

065-BENJAMIN FRANKLIN
By Benjamin Franklin
11/49 **(64)** AB,RtH,GS(Iger Shop),
HcK(c),Original 100.00
03/56 **(131)** AB,RtH,GS(Iger Shop),
New P(c) ;rep 20.00
01/60 **(154)** AB,RtH,GS(Iger Shop),
P(c);rep 7.00
02/64 **(167)** AB,RtH,GS(Iger Shop),
P(c);rep 7.00
04/66 **(167)** AB,RtH,GS(Iger Shop),
P(c);rep 7.00
Fl/69 **(169)** AB,RtH,GS(Iger Shop),
P(c), 25¢(c)Price,Rigid(c);rep . . . 9.00

066-THE CLOISTER AND THE HEARTH
By Charles Reade
12/49 **(67)** HcK,HcK(c),Original . 200.00

067-THE SCOTTISH CHIEFS
By Jane Porter
01/50 **(67)** AB,AB(c),Original 90.00
07/51 **(85)** AB,AB(c),15¢(c)
Price;rep 25.00
04/54 **(118)** AB,AB(c);rep 20.00
01/57 **(136)** AB,New P(c);rep 15.00
01/60 **(154)** AB,P(c);rep 10.00
11/63 **(167)** AB,P(c);rep 10.00
08/65 **(167)** AB,P(c);rep 10.00

CI #68 Julius Caesar,
© Gilberton Publications

068-JULIUS CEASAR
By William Shakespeare
02/50 **(70)** HcK,HcK(c),Original . . 90.00
07/51 **(85)** HcK,HcK(c),15¢(c)
Price; rep 25.00
06/53 **(108)** HcK,HcK(c);rep 20.00
05/60 **(156)** HcK,LbC New P(c);rep 25.00
1962 **(165)** GE&RC New Art,
LbC P(c);rep 25.00
02/64 **(167)** GE&RC,LbC P(c);rep . 6.00

10/65 **(167)** GE&RC,LbC P(c),Tarzan
Books Inside(c);rep 6.00
1967 **(166)** GE&RC,LbC P(c);rep . . 6.00
Wr/69 **(169)** GE&RC,LbC P(c),
Rigid(c);rep 6.00

069-AROUND THE WORLD IN 80 DAYS
By Jules Verne
03/50 **(70)** HcK,HcK(c),Original . . 90.00
09/51 **(87)** HcK,HcK(c),15¢(c)
Price; rep 25.00
03/55 **(125)** HcK,HcK(c);rep 20.00
01/57 **(136)** HcK,New P(c);rep . . . 15.00
09/58 **(146)** HcK,P(c);rep 6.00
09/59 **(152)** HcK,P(c);rep 6.00
1961 **(164)** HcK,P(c);rep 6.00
62/63 **(167)** HcK,P(c);rep 6.00
07/64 **(167)** HcK,P(c);rep 6.00
11/65 **(167)** HcK,P(c);rep 6.00
07/67 **(166)** HcK,P(c);rep 6.00
Sg/69 **(169)** HcK,P(c),25¢(c)
Price, Rigid(c);rep 6.00

070-THE PILOT
By James Fenimore Cooper
04/50 **(71)** AB,AB(c),Original 75.00
10/50 **(75)** AB,AB(c),15¢(c)
Price;rep 25.00
02/52 **(92)** AB,AB(c);rep 20.00
03/55 **(125)** AB,AB(c);rep 20.00
05/60 **(156)** AB,GMc New P(c);rep 15.00
02/64 **(167)** AB,GMc P(c);rep 15.00
05/66 **(167)** AB,GMc P(c);rep 10.00

071-THE MAN WHO LAUGHS
By Victor Hugo
05/50 **(71)** AB,AB(c),Original . . . 125.00
01/62 **(165)** NN,NN New P(c);rep . 70.00
04/64 **(167)** NN,NN P(c);rep 65.00

072-THE OREGON TRAIL
By Francis Parkman
06/50 **(73)** HcK,HcK (c),Original . . 75.00
11/51 **(89)** HcK,HcK (c),15¢(c)
Price; rep 25.00
07/54 **(121)** HcK,HcK (c);rep 20.00
03/56 **(131)** HcK,New P(c);rep . . . 15.00
09/57 **(140)** HcK,P(c);rep 7.00
05/59 **(150)** HcK,P(c);rep 6.00
01/61 **(164)** HcK,P(c);rep 6.00
62/63 **(167)** HcK,P(c);rep 6.00
08/64 **(167)** HcK,P(c);rep 6.00
10/65 **(167)** HcK,P(c);rep 6.00
1968 **(166)** HcK,P(c),25¢(c)Price;rep 6.00

073-THE BLACK TULIP
By Alexandre Dumas
07/50 **(75)** AB,AB(c),Original . . . 225.00

074-MR. MIDSHIPMAN EASY
By Captain Frederick Marryat
08/50 **(75)** BbL,Original 225.00

075-THE LADY OF THE LAKE
By Sir Walter Scott
09/50 **(75)** HcK,HcK(c),Original . . 70.00
07/51 **(85)** HcK,HcK(c),15¢(c)
Price; rep 25.00
04/54 **(118)** HcK,HcK(c);rep 20.00

07/57 **(139)** HcK,New P(c);rep . . . 15.00
01/60 **(154)** HcK,P(c);rep 6.00
1962 **(165)** HcK,P(c);rep 6.00
04/64 **(167)** HcK,P(c);rep 6.00
05/66 **(167)** HcK,P(c);rep 6.00
Sg/69 **(169)** HcK,P(c),25¢(c)
Price, Rigid(c);rep 6.00

076-THE PRISONER OF ZENDA
By Anthony Hope Hawkins
10/50 **(75)** HcK,HcK(c),Original . . 65.00
07/51 **(85)** HcK,HcK(c),15¢(c) Price;
rep 25.00
09/53 **(111)** HcK,HcK(c),rep 20.00
09/55 **(128)** HcK,New P(c);rep . . . 15.00
09/59 **(152)** HcK,P(c);rep 6.00
1962 **(165)** HcK,P(c);rep 6.00
04/64 **(167)** HcK,P(c);rep 6.00
09/66 **(167)** HcK,P(c);rep 6.00
Fl/69 **(169)** HcK,P(c),25¢(c) Price,
Rigid(c);rep 6.00

077-THE ILLIAD
By Homer
11/50 **(78)** AB,AB(c),Original 70.00
09/51 **(87)** AB,AB(c),15¢(c)
Price;rep 25.00
07/54 **(121)** AB,AB(c);rep 20.00
07/57 **(139)** AB,New P(c);rep 15.00
05/59 **(150)** AB,P(c);rep 6.00
1962 **(165)** AB,P(c);rep 6.00
10/63 **(167)** AB,P(c);rep 6.00
07/64 **(167)** AB,P(c);rep 6.00
05/66 **(167)** AB,P(c);rep 6.00
1968 **(166)** AB,P(c),25¢(c)Price;rep 6.00

078-JOAN OF ARC
By Frederick Shiller
12/50 **(78)** HcK,HcK(c),Original . . 70.00
09/51 **(87)** HcK,HcK(c),15¢(c)
Price; rep 25.00
11/53 **(113)** HcK,HcK(c);rep 20.00
09/55 **(128)** HcK,New P(c);rep . . . 15.00
09/57 **(140)** HcK,P(c);rep 6.00
05/59 **(150)** HcK,P(c);rep 6.00
11/60 **(159)** HcK,P(c);rep 6.00
62/63 **(167)** HcK,P(c);rep 6.00
12/63 **(167)** HcK,P(c);rep 6.00
06/65 **(167)** HcK,P(c);rep 6.00
06/67 **(166)** HcK,P(c);rep 6.00
Wr/69 **(166)** HcK,TO New P(c),
25¢(c)Price, Rigid(c);rep 20.00

079-CYRANO DE BERGERAC
By Edmond Rostand
01/51 **(78)** AB,AB(c),Original,Movie
Promo Inside Front(c) 70.00
07/51 **(85)** AB,AB(c),15¢(c)
Price;rep 25.00
04/54 **(118)** AB,AB(c);rep 20.00
07/56 **(133)** AB,New P(c);rep 20.00
05/60 **(156)** AB,P(c);rep 15.00
08/64 **(167)** AB,P(c);rep 15.00

080-WHITE FANG
By Jack London
(Last Line Drawn (c)
02/51 **(79)** AB,AB(c),Original 70.00
09/51 **(87)** AB,AB(c);rep 25.00
03/55 **(125)** AB,AB(c);rep 20.00
05/56 **(132)** AB,New P(c);rep 20.00
09/57 **(140)** AB,P(c);rep 6.00

All comics prices listed are for *Near Mint* condition.

11/59 **(153)** AB,P(c);rep 6.00
62/63 **(167)** AB,P(c);rep 6.00
09/64 **(167)** AB,P(c);rep 6.00
07/65 **(167)** AB,P(c);rep 6.00
06/67 **(166)** AB,P(c);rep 6.00
Fl/69 **(169)** AB,P(c),25¢(c)
　Price, Rigid(c);rep 6.00

081-THE ODYSSEY
By Homer
(P(c)s From Now on)
03/51 **(82)** HyG,AB P(c),Original . 65.00
08/64 **(167)** HyG,AB P(c);rep 15.00
10/66 **(167)** HyG,AB P(c);rep 15.00
Sg/69 **(169)** HyG,TyT New P(c),
　Rigid(c);rep 15.00

082-THE MASTER OF BALLANTRAE
By Robert Louis Stevenson
04/51 **(82)** LDr,AB P(c),Original . . 50.00
08/64 **(167)** LDr,AB P(c);rep 18.00
Fl/68 **(166)** LDr,Syk New P(c),
　Rigid(c);rep 18.00

083-THE JUNGLE BOOK
By Rudyard Kipling
05/51 **(85)** WmB&AB,AB P(c),
　Original 40.00
08/53 **(110)** WmB&AB,AB P(c);rep . 7.00
03/55 **(125)** WmB&AB,AB P(c);rep . 6.00
05/56 **(134)** WmB&AB,AB P(c);rep . 6.00
01/58 **(142)** WmB&AB,AB P(c);rep . 6.00
05/59 **(150)** WmB&AB,AB P(c);rep . 6.00
11/60 **(159)** WmB&AB,AB P(c);rep . 6.00
62/63 **(167)** WmB&AB,AB P(c);rep . 6.00
03/65 **(167)** WmB&AB,AB P(c);rep . 6.00
11/65 **(167)** WmB&AB,AB P(c);rep . 6.00
05/66 **(167)** WmB&AB,AB P(c);rep . 6.00
1968 **(166)** NN Art,NN New P(c),
　Rigid(c);rep 18.00

084-THE GOLD BUG & OTHER STORIES
(The Gold Bug-The Telltale HeartThe Cask of Amontillado)
By Edgar Allan Poe
06/51 **(85)** AB,RP,JLv,AB P(c),
　Original 90.00
07/64 **(167)** AB,RP,JLv,AB P(c);rep 65.00

085-THE SEA WOLF
By Jack London
08/51 **(87)** AB,AB P(c);rep . . 30.00
07/54 **(121)** AB,AB P(c);rep 5.00
05/56 **(132)** AB,AB P(c);rep 5.00
11/57 **(141)** AB,AB P(c);rep 5.00
03/61 **(161)** AB,AB P(c);rep 5.00
02/64 **(167)** AB,AB P(c);rep 5.00
11/65 **(167)** AB,AB P(c);rep 5.00
Fl/69 **(169)** AB,AB P(c),25¢(c)
　Price, Rigid(c);rep 5.00

086-UNDER TWO FLAGS
By Oluda
08/51 **(87)** MDb,AB P(c),Original . 30.00
03/54 **(117)** MDb,AB P(c);rep 6.00
07/57 **(139)** MDb,AB P(c);rep 6.00
09/60 **(158)** MDb,AB P(c);rep 6.00
02/64 **(167)** MDb,AB P(c);rep 6.00
08/66 **(167)** MDb,AB P(c);rep 6.00
Sr/69 **(169)** MDb,AB P(c),25¢(c)
　Price, Rigid(c);rep 6.00

Cl #80 White Fang
© Gilberton Publications

087-A MIDSUMMER NIGHTS DREAM
By William Shakespeare
09/51 **(87)** AB,AB P(c),Original . . 30.00
03/61 **(161)** AB,AB P(c);rep 6.00
04/64 **(167)** AB,AB P(c);rep 5.00
05/66 **(167)** AB,AB P(c);rep 5.00
Sr/69 **(169)** AB,AB P(c),25¢(c)
　Price; rep 5.00

088-MEN OF IRON
By Howard Pyle
10/51 **(89)** HD,LDr,GS,Original . . 35.00
01/60 **(154)** HD,LDr,GS,P(c);rep . . 6.00
01/64 **(167)** HD,LDr,GS,P(c);rep . . 6.00
1968 **(166)** HD,LDr,GS,P(c),
　25¢(c)Price;rep 6.00

089-CRIME AND PUNISHMENT
By Fedor Dostoevsky
11/51 **(89)** RP,AB P(c),Original . . 35.00
09/59 **(152)** RP,AB P(c);rep 6.00
04/64 **(167)** RP,AB P(c);rep 6.00
05/66 **(167)** RP,AB P(c);rep 6.00
Fl/69 **(169)** RP,AB P(c),25¢(c)
　Price, Rigid(c);rep 6.00

090-GREEN MANSIONS
By William Henry Hudson
12/51 **(89)** AB,AB P(c),Original . . 35.00
01/59 **(148)** AB,New LbC P(c);rep . 15.00
1962 **(165)** AB,LbC P(c);rep 5.00
04/64 **(167)** AB,LbC P(c);rep 5.00
09/66 **(167)** AB,LbC P(c);rep 5.00
Sr/69 **(169)** AB,LbC P(c),25¢(c)
　Price, Rigid(c);rep 5.00

091-THE CALL OF THE WILD
By Jack London
01/52 **(92)** MDb,P(c),Original 30.00
10/53 **(112)** MDb,P(c);rep 6.00
03/55 **(125)** MDb,P(c),'PictureProgress'
　Onn. Back(c);rep 5.00
09/56 **(134)** MDb,P(c);rep 5.00
03/58 **(143)** MDb,P(c);rep 5.00
1962 **(165)** MDb,P(c);rep 5.00
1962 **(167)** MDb,P(c);rep 5.00
04/65 **(167)** MDb,P(c);rep 5.00

03/66 **(167)** MDb,P(c);rep 5.00
03/66 **(167)** MDb,P(c),Record
　Edition;rep 5.00
11/67 **(166)** MDb,P(c);rep 5.00
Sg/70 **(169)** MDb,P(c),25¢(c)
　Price, Rigid(c);rep 5.00

092-THE COURTSHIP OF MILES STANDISH
By Henry Wadsworth Longfellow
02/52 **(92)** AB,AB P(c),Original . . 30.00
1962 **(165)** AB,AB P(c);rep 5.00
03/64 **(167)** AB,AB P(c);rep 5.00
05/67 **(166)** AB,AB P(c);rep 5.00
Wr/69 **(169)** AB,AB P(c),25¢(c)
　Price, Rigid(c);rep 5.00

093-PUDD'NHEAD WILSON
By Mark Twain
03/52 **(94)** HcK,GMc P(c),Original 32.00
1962 **(165)** HcK,GMc New P(c);rep 10.00
03/64 **(167)** HcK,GMc P(c);rep . . . 8.00
1968 **(166)** HcK,GMc P(c),25¢(c)
　Price, Soft(c);rep 9.00

094-DAVID BALFOUR
By Robert Louis Stevenson
04/52 **(94)** RP,P(c),Original 32.00
05/64 **(167)** RP,P(c);rep 12.00
1968 **(166)** RP,P(c),25¢(c)Price;rep 12.00

095-ALL QUIET ON THE WESTERN FRONT
By Erich Maria Remarque
05/52 **(96)** MDb,P(c),Original 80.00
05/52 **(99)** MDb,P(c),Original 60.00
10/64 **(167)** MDb,P(c);rep 18.00
11/66 **(167)** MDb,P(c);rep 18.00

096-DANIEL BOONE
By John Bakeless
06/52 **(97)** AB,P(c),Original 30.00
03/54 **(117)** AB,P(c);rep 5.00
09/55 **(128)** AB,P(c);rep 5.00
05/56 **(132)** AB,P(c);rep 5.00
----- **(134)** AB,P(c),'Story of
　Jesus'on Back(c);rep 5.00
09/60 **(158)** AB,P(c);rep 5.00
01/64 **(167)** AB,P(c);rep 5.00
05/65 **(167)** AB,P(c);rep 5.00
11/66 **(167)** AB,P(c);rep 5.00
Wr/69 **(166)** AB,P(c),25¢(c)
　Price, Rigid(c);rep 12.00

097-KING SOLOMON'S MINES
By H. Rider Haggard
07/52 **(96)** HcK,P(c),Original 30.00
04/54 **(118)** HcK,P(c);rep 8.00
03/56 **(131)** HcK,P(c);rep 5.00
09/51 **(141)** HcK,P(c);rep 5.00
09/60 **(158)** HcK,P(c);rep 5.00
02/64 **(167)** HcK,P(c);rep 5.00
09/65 **(167)** HcK,P(c);rep 5.00
Sr/69 **(169)** HcK,P(c),25¢(c)
　Price; Rigid(c);rep 6.00

098-THE RED BADGE OF COURAGE
By Stephen Crane
08/52 **(98)** MDb,GS,P(c),Original . 30.00
04/54 **(118)** MDb,GS,P(c);rep 5.00

All comics prices listed are for *Near Mint* condition.   CVA Page 671

05/56 **(132)** MDb,GS,P(c);rep 5.00
01/58 **(142)** MDb,GS,P(c);rep 5.00
09/59 **(152)** MDb,GS,P(c);rep 5.00
03/61 **(161)** MDb,GS,P(c);rep 5.00
62/63 **(167)** MDb,GS,P(c);Erronously
Has Original Date;rep 5.00
09/64 **(167)** MDb,GS,P(c);rep 5.00
10/65 **(167)** MDb,GS,P(c);rep 5.00
1968 **(166)** MDb,GS,P(c),25¢(c)
Price, Rigid(c);rep 15.00

099-HAMLET
By William Shakespeare
09/52 **(98)** AB,P(c),Original 32.00
07/54 **(121)** AB,P(c);rep 5.00
11/57 **(141)** AB,P(c);rep 5.00
09/60 **(158)** AB,P(c);rep 5.00
62/63 **(167)** AB,P(c),Erronously
Has Original Date;rep 5.00
07/65 **(167)** AB,P(c);rep 5.00
04/67 **(166)** AB,P(c);rep 5.00
Sg/69 **(169)** AB,EdM New P(c),
25¢(c)Price, Rigid(c);rep 15.00

100-MUTINY ON THE BOUNTY
By Charrles Nordhoff
10/52 **(100)** MsW,HcK P(c),Original 28.00
03/54 **(117)** MsW,HcK P(c);rep ... 5.00
05/56 **(132)** MsW,HcK P(c);rep ... 5.00
01/58 **(142)** MsW,HcK P(c);rep ... 5.00
03/60 **(155)** MsW,HcK P(c);rep ... 5.00
62/63 **(167)** MsW,HcK P(c);Erronously
Has Original Date;rep 5.00
05/64 **(167)** MsW,HcK P(c);rep ... 5.00
03/66 **(167)** MsW,HcK P(c),N#
or Price;rep 10.00
Sg/70 **(169)** MsW,HcK P(c),
Rigid(c); rep 4.00

101-WILLIAM TELL
By Frederick Schiller
11/52 **(101)** MDb,HcK P(c),Original 28.00
04/54 **(118)** MDb,HcK P(c);rep ... 5.00
11/57 **(141)** MDb,HcK P(c);rep ... 5.00
09/60 **(158)** MDb,HcK P(c);rep ... 5.00
62/63 **(167)** MDb,HcK P(c),Erronously
Has Original Date;rep 5.00
11/64 **(167)** MDb,HcK P(c);rep ... 5.00
04/67 **(166)** MDb,HcK P(c);rep ... 5.00
Wr/69 **(169)** MDb,HcK P(c)25¢(c)
Price, Rigid(c);rep 5.00

102-THE WHITE COMPANY
By Sir Arthur Conan Doyle
12/52 **(101)** AB,P(c),Original 65.00
1962 **(165)** AB,P(c);rep 25.00
04/64 **(167)** AB,P(c);rep 25.00

103-MEN AGAINST THE SEA
By Charles Nordhoff
01/53 **(104)** RP,HcK P(c),Original 32.00
12/53 **(114)** RP,HcK P(c);rep ... 20.00
03/56 **(131)** RP,New P(c);rep ... 15.00
03/59 **(149)** RP,P(c);rep 15.00
09/60 **(158)** RP,P(c);rep 25.00
03/64 **(167)** RP,P(c);rep 15.00

104-BRING 'EM BACK ALIVE
By Frank Buck & Edward Anthony

02/53 **(105)** HcK,HcK P(c)Original 27.00
04/54 **(118)** HcK,HcK P(c);rep 5.00
07/56 **(133)** HcK,HcK P(c);rep 5.00
05/59 **(150)** HcK,HcK P(c);rep 5.00
09/60 **(158)** HcK,HcK P(c);rep 5.00
10/63 **(167)** HcK,HcK P(c);rep 5.00
09/65 **(167)** HcK,HcK P(c);rep 5.00
Wr/69 **(169)** HcK,HcK P(c),25¢(c)
Price, Rigid(c);rep 5.00

105-FROM THE EARTH TO THE MOON
By Jules Verne
03/53 **(106)** AB,P(c),Original 28.00
04/54 **(118)** AB,P(c);rep 5.00
03/56 **(132)** AB,P(c);rep 5.00
11/57 **(141)** AB,P(c);rep 5.00
09/58 **(146)** AB,P(c);rep 5.00
05/60 **(156)** AB,P(c);rep 5.00
62/63 **(167)** AB,P(c),Erronously
Has Original Date;rep 5.00
05/64 **(167)** AB,P(c);rep 5.00
05/65 **(167)** AB,P(c);rep 5.00
10/67 **(166)** AB,P(c);rep 5.00
Sr/69 **(169)** AB,P(c),25¢(c)
Price, Rigid(c);rep 5.00
Sg/71 **(169)** AB,P(c);rep 5.00

CI #105 From the Earth to the Moon
© Gilberton Publications

106-BUFFALO BILL
By William F. Cody
04/53 **(107)** MDb,P(c),Original ... 28.00
04/54 **(118)** MDb,P(c);rep 5.00
03/56 **(132)** MDb,P(c);rep 5.00
01/58 **(142)** MDb,P(c);rep 5.00
03/61 **(161)** MDb,P(c);rep 5.00
03/64 **(167)** MDb,P(c);rep 5.00
07/67 **(166)** MDb,P(c);rep 5.00
Fl/69 **(169)** MDb,P(c),Rigid(c);rep . 5.00

107-KING OF THE KHYBER RIFLES
By Talbot Mundy
05/53 **(108)** SMz,P(c),Original ... 30.00
04/54 **(118)** SMz,P(c);rep 5.00
09/58 **(146)** SMz,P(c);rep 5.00
09/60 **(158)** SMz,P(c);rep 5.00
62/63 **(167)** SMz,P(c);Erronously
Has Original Date;rep 5.00
62/63 **(167)** SMz,P(c);rep 5.00
10/66 **(167)** SMz,P(c);rep 5.00

108-KNIGHTS OF THE ROUND TABLE
By Howard Pyle?
06/53 **(108)** AB,P(c),Original 30.00
06/53 **(109)** AB,P(c),Original 36.00
03/54 **(117)** AB,P(c);rep 5.00
11/59 **(153)** AB,P(c);rep 5.00
1962 **(165)** AB,P(c);rep 5.00
04/64 **(167)** AB,P(c);rep 5.00
04/67 **(166)** AB,P(c);rep 5.00

109-PITCAIRN'S ISLAND
By Charles Nordhoff
07/53 **(110)** RP,P(c),Original 32.00
1962 **(165)** RP,P(c);rep 9.00
03/64 **(167)** RP,P(c);rep 9.00
06/67 **(166)** RP,P(c);rep 9.00

110-A STUDY IN SCARLET
By Sir Arthur Conan Doyle
08/53 **(111)** SMz,P(c),Original ... 100.00
1962 **(165)** SMz,P(c);rep 60.00

111-THE TALISMAN
By Sir Walter Scott
09/53 **(112)** HcK,HcK P(c),Original 40.00
1962 **(165)** HcK,HcK P(c);rep 6.00
05/64 **(167)** HcK,HcK P(c);rep 6.00
Fl/68 **(166)** HcK,HcK P(c),
25¢(c)Price;rep 6.00

112-ADVENTURES OF KIT CARSON
By John S. C. Abbott
10/53 **(113)** RP,P(c),Original 40.00
11/55 **(129)** RP,P(c);rep 6.00
11/57 **(141)** RP,P(c);rep 6.00
09/59 **(152)** RP,P(c);rep 6.00
03/61 **(161)** RP,P(c);rep 6.00
62/63 **(167)** RP,P(c);rep 6.00
02/65 **(167)** RP,P(c);rep 6.00
05/66 **(167)** RP,P(c);rep 6.00
Wr/69 **(166)** RP,EdM New P(c),
25¢(c)Price, Rigid(c);rep 12.00

113-THE FORTY-FIVE GUARDSMEN
By Alexandre Dumas
11/53 **(114)** MDb,P(c),Original ... 60.00
07/67 **(166)** MDb,P(c);rep 25.00

114-THE RED ROVER
By James Fenimore Cooper
12/53 **(115)** PrC,JP P(c),Original . 60.00
07/67 **(166)** PrC,JP P(c);rep 25.00

115-HOW I FOUND LIVINGSTONE
By Sir Henry Stanley
01/54 **(116)** SF&ST,P(c),Original . 65.00
01/67 **(167)** SF&ST,P(c);rep 30.00

116-THE BOTTLE IMP
By Robert Louis Stevenson
02/54 **(117)** LC,P(c),Original 70.00
01/67 **(167)** LC,P(c);rep 35.00

117-CAPTAINS COURAGEOUS
By Rudyard Kipling

All comics prices listed are for *Near Mint* condition.

03/54 **(118)** PrC,P(c),Original ... 55.00
02/67 **(167)** PrC,P(c);rep 20.00
Fl/69 **(169)** PrC,P(c),25¢(c)
　Price, Rigid(c);rep 18.00

118-ROB ROY
By Sir Walter Scott
04/54 **(119)** RP,WIP,P(c),Original . 70.00
02/67 **(167)** RP,WIP,P(c);rep 35.00

119-SOLDERS OF FORTUNE
By Richard Harding Davis
05/54 **(120)** KS,P(c),Original 50.00
03/67 **(166)** KS,P(c);rep 20.00
Sg/70 **(169)** KS,P(c),25¢(c)
　Price, Rigid(c);rep 18.00

120-THE HURRICANE
By Charles Nordhoff
1954 **(121)** LC,LC P(c),Original .. 50.00
03/67 **(166)** LC,LC P(c);rep 30.00

121-WILD BILL HICKOCK
Author Unknown
07/54 **(122)** MI,ST,P(c),Original .. 25.00
05/56 **(132)** MI,ST,P(c);rep 6.00
11/57 **(141)** MI,ST,P(c);rep 6.00
01/60 **(154)** MI,ST,P(c);rep 6.00
62/63 **(167)** MI,ST,P(c);rep 6.00
08/64 **(167)** MI,ST,P(c);rep 6.00
04/67 **(166)** MI,ST,P(c);rep 6.00
Wr/69 **(169)** MI,ST,P(c),Rigid(c);rep 6.00

122-THE MUTINEERS
By Charles Boardman Hawes
09/54 **(123)** PrC,P(c),Original ... 30.00
01/57 **(136)** PrC,P(c);rep 6.00
09/58 **(146)** PrC,P(c);rep 6.00
09/60 **(158)** PrC,P(c);rep 6.00
11/63 **(167)** PrC,P(c);rep 6.00
03/65 **(167)** PrC,P(c);rep 6.00
08/67 **(166)** PrC,P(c);rep 6.00

123-FANG AND CLAW
By Frank Buck
11/54 **(124)** LnS,P(c),Original ... 30.00
07/56 **(133)** LnS,P(c);rep 6.00
03/58 **(143)** LnS,P(c);rep 6.00
01/60 **(154)** LnS,P(c);rep 6.00
62/63 **(167)** LnS,P(c),Erroneously
　Has Original Date;rep 6.00
09/65 **(167)** LnS,P(c);rep 6.00

124-THE WAR OF THE WORLDS
By H. G. Wells
01/55 **(125)** LC,LC P(c),Original .. 50.00
03/56 **(131)** LC,LC P(c);rep 8.00
11/57 **(141)** LC,LC P(c);rep 8.00
01/59 **(148)** LC,LC P(c);rep 8.00
05/60 **(156)** LC,LC P(c);rep 10.00
1962 **(165)** LC,LC P(c);rep 8.00
62/63 **(167)** LC,LC P(c);rep 8.00
11/64 **(167)** LC,LC P(c);rep 8.00
11/65 **(167)** LC,LC P(c);rep 8.00
1968 **(166)** LC,LC P(c),25¢(c)
　Price; rep 8.00
Sr/70 **(169)** LC,LC P(c),Rigid(c);rep 8.00

125-THE OX BOW INCIDENT
By Walter Van Tilberg Clark
03/55 **(---)** NN,P(c),Original 25.00
03/58 **(143)** NN,P(c);rep 6.00
09/59 **(152)** NN,P(c);rep 6.00
03/61 **(149)** NN,P(c);rep 6.00
62/63 **(167)** NN,P(c);rep 6.00
11/64 **(167)** NN,P(c);rep 6.00
04/67 **(166)** NN,P(c);rep 6.00
Wr/69 **(169)** NN,P(c),25¢(c)
　Price, Rigid(c);rep 6.00

126-THE DOWNFALL
By Emile Zola
05/55 **(---)** LC,LC P(c),Original,'Picture
Progress'Replaces Reorder List 30.00
08/64 **(167)** LC,LC P(c);rep 10.00
　Price;rep 10.00

127-THE KING OF THE MOUNTAINS
By Edmond About
07/55 **(128)** NN,P(c),Original 30.00
06/64 **(167)** NN,P(c);rep 10.00
Fl/68 **(166)** NN,P(c),25¢(c)Price;rep 10.00

128-MACBETH
By William Shakespeare
09/55 **(128)** AB,P(c),Original 32.00
03/58 **(143)** AB,P(c);rep 6.00
09/60 **(158)** AB,P(c);rep 6.00
62/63 **(167)** AB,P(c);rep 6.00
06/64 **(167)** AB,P(c);rep 6.00
04/67 **(166)** AB,P(c);rep 6.00
1968 **(166)** AB,P(c),25¢(c)Price;rep 6.00
Sg/70 **(169)** AB,P(c),Rigid(c);rep .. 6.00

CI #133 The Time Machine
© Gilberton Publications

129-DAVY CROCKETT
Author Unknown
11/55 **(129)** LC,P(c),Original 75.00
09/66 **(167)** LC,P(c);rep 60.00

130-CAESAR'S CONQUESTS
By Julius Caesar
01/56 **(130)** JO,P(c),Original 40.00
01/58 **(142)** JO,P(c);rep 6.00
09/59 **(152)** JO,P(c);rep 6.00

03/61 **(149)** JO,P(c);rep 6.00
62/63 **(167)** JO,P(c);rep 6.00
10/64 **(167)** JO,P(c);rep 6.00
04/66 **(167)** JO,P(c);rep 6.00

131-THE COVERED WAGON
By Emerson Hough
03/56 **(131)** NN,P(c),Original 25.00
03/58 **(143)** NN,P(c);rep 6.00
09/59 **(152)** NN,P(c);rep 6.00
09/60 **(158)** NN,P(c);rep 6.00
62/63 **(167)** NN,P(c);rep 6.00
11/64 **(167)** NN,P(c);rep 6.00
Wr/69 **(169)** NN,P(c),25¢(c)
　Price, Rigid(c);rep 6.00

132-THE DARK FRIGATE
By Charles Boardman Hawes
05/56 **(132)** EW&RWb,P(c),Original 30.00
05/59 **(150)** EW&RWb,P(c);rep ... 9.00
01/64 **(167)** EW&RWb,P(c);rep ... 9.00
05/67 **(166)** EW&RWb,P(c);rep ... 9.00

133-THE TIME MACHINE
By H. G. Wells
07/56 **(132)** LC,P(c),Original 45.00
01/58 **(142)** LC,P(c);rep 8.00
09/59 **(152)** LC,P(c);rep 8.00
09/60 **(158)** LC,P(c);rep 8.00
62/63 **(167)** LC,P(c);rep 8.00
06/64 **(167)** LC,P(c);rep 10.00
03/66 **(167)** LC,P(c);rep 8.00
03/66 **(167)** LC,P(c),N# Or Price;rep 8.00
12/67 **(166)** LC,P(c);rep 8.00
Wr/71 **(169)** LC,P(c),25¢(c)
　Price, Rigid(c);rep 8.00

134-ROMEO AND JULIET
By William Shakespeare
09/56 **(134)** GE,P(c),Original 30.00
03/61 **(161)** GE,P(c);rep 6.00
09/63 **(167)** GE,P(c);rep 6.00
05/65 **(167)** GE,P(c);rep 6.00
06/67 **(166)** GE,P(c);rep 6.00
Wr/69 **(166)** GE,EdM New P(c),
　25¢(c)Price, Rigid(c);rep 21.00

135-WATERLOO
By Emile Erckmann & Alexandre Chatrian
11/56 **(135)** Grl,AB P(c),Original . 30.00
11/59 **(153)** Grl,AB P(c);rep 5.00
62/63 **(167)** Grl,AB P(c);rep 5.00
09/64 **(167)** Grl,AB P(c);rep 5.00
1968 **(166)** Grl,AB P(c),25¢(c)
　Price; rep 5.00

136-LORD JIM
By Joseph Conrad
01/57 **(136)** GE,P(c),Original 30.00
62/63 **(165)** GE,P(c);rep 5.00
03/64 **(167)** GE,P(c);rep 5.00
09/66 **(167)** GE,P(c);rep 5.00
Sr/69 **(169)** GE,P(c),25¢(c)
　Price, Rigid(c);rep 5.00

137-THE LITTLE SAVAGE
By Captain Frederick Marryat
03/57 **(136)** GE,P(c),Original 30.00
01/59 **(148)** GE,P(c);rep 5.00

All comics prices listed are for *Near Mint* condition.

05/60 **(156)** GE,P(c);rep 5.00
62/63 **(167)** GE,P(c);rep 5.00
10/64 **(167)** GE,P(c);rep 5.00
08/67 **(166)** GE,P(c);rep 5.00
Sg/70 **(169)** GE,P(c),25¢(c)
Price, Rigid(c);rep 5.00

138-A JOURNEY TO THE CENTER OF THE EARTH
By Jules Verne
05/57 **(136)** NN,P(c),Original 45.00
09/58 **(146)** NN,P(c);rep 5.00
05/60 **(156)** NN,P(c);rep 5.00
09/60 **(158)** NN,P(c);rep 5.00
62/63 **(167)** NN,P(c);rep 5.00
06/64 **(167)** NN,P(c);rep 8.00
04/66 **(167)** NN,P(c);rep 8.00
1968 **(166)** NN,P(c),25¢(c)Price;rep 5.00

139-IN THE REIGN OF TERROR
By George Alfred Henty
07/57 **(139)** GE,P(c),Original 25.00
01/60 **(154)** GE,P(c);rep 5.00
62/63 **(167)** GE,P(c),Erroneusly
Has Original Date;rep 5.00
07/64 **(167)** GE,P(c);rep 7.00
1968 **(166)** GE,P(c),25¢(c)Price;rep 5.00

140-ON JUNGLE TRAILS
By Frank Buck
09/57 **(140)** NN,P(c),Original 25.00
05/59 **(150)** NN,P(c);rep 5.00
01/61 **(160)** NN,P(c);rep 5.00
09/63 **(167)** NN,P(c);rep 5.00
09/65 **(167)** NN,P(c);rep 5.00

141-CASTLE DANGEROUS
By Sir Walter Scott
11/57 **(141)** StC,P(c),Original 25.00
09/59 **(152)** STC,P(c);rep 7.00
62/63 **(167)** StC,P(c);rep 7.00
07/67 **(166)** StC,P(c);rep 7.00

142-ABRAHAM LINCOLN
By Benjamin Thomas
01/58 **(142)** NN,P(c),Original 35.00
01/60 **(154)** NN,P(c);rep 5.00
09/60 **(158)** NN,P(c);rep 5.00
10/63 **(167)** NN,P(c);rep 5.00
07/65 **(167)** NN,P(c);rep 5.00
11/67 **(166)** NN,P(c);rep 5.00
Fl/69 **(169)** NN,P(c),25¢(c) Price,
Rigid(c);rep 5.00

143-KIM
By Rudyard Kipling
03/58 **(143)** JO,P(c)Original 30.00
62/63 **(165)** JO,P(c);rep 6.00
11/63 **(167)** JO,P(c);rep 6.00
08/65 **(167)** JO,P(c);rep 6.00
Wr/69 **(169)** JO,P(c),25¢(c) Price,
Rigid(c);rep 6.00

144-THE FIRST MEN IN THE MOON
By H. G. Wells
05/58 **(143)** GWb,AW,AT,RKr,GMC
P(c), Original 32.00
11/59 **(153)** GWb,AW,AT,RKr,GMC
P(c); rep 6.00
03/61 **(161)** GWb,AW,AT,RKr,GMC

P(c); rep 6.00
62/63 **(167)** GWb,AW,AT,RKr,GMC
P(c); rep 6.00
12/65 **(167)** GWb,AW,AT,RKr,GMC
P(c); rep 6.00
Fl/68 **(166)** GWb,AW,AT,RKr,GMC P(c),
25¢(c) Price,Rigid(c);rep 6.00
Wr/69 **(169)** GWb,AW,AT,RKr,GMC
P(c), Rigid(c);rep 15.00

145-THE CRISIS
by Winston Churchill
07/58 **(143)** GE,P(c),Original 30.00
05/60 **(156)** GE,P(c);rep 6.00
10/63 **(167)** GE,P(c);rep 6.00
03/65 **(167)** GE,P(c);rep 6.00
1968 **(166)** GE,P(c),25¢(c)Price;rep 6.00

146-WITH FIRE AND SWORD
By Henryk Sienkiewicz
09/58 **(143)** GWb,P(c),Original ... 35.00
05/60 **(156)** GWb,P(c);rep 9.00
11/63 **(167)** GWb,P(c);rep 9.00
03/65 **(167)** GWb,P(c);rep 9.00

147-BEN-HUR
By Lew Wallace
11/58 **(147)** JO,P(c),Original 30.00
11/59 **(153)** JO,P(c);rep 35.00
09/60 **(158)** JO,P(c);rep 6.00
62/63 **(167)** JO,P(c),Has the
Original Date;rep 6.00
----- **(167)** JO,P(c);rep 6.00
02/65 **(167)** JO,P(c);rep 6.00
09/66 **(167)** JO,P(c);rep 6.00
Fl/68 **(166)** JO,P(c),25¢(c)Price,
Both Rigid & Soft (c)s;rep 30.00

148-THE BUCKANEER
By Lyle Saxon
01/59 **(148)** GE&RJ,NS P(c),orig. 30.00
----- **(568)** GE&RJ,NS P(c),Juniors
List Only;rep 10.00
62/63 **(167)** GE&RJ,NS P(c);rep .. 6.00
09/65 **(167)** GE&RJ,NS P(c);rep .. 6.00
Sr/69 **(169)** GE&RJ,NS P(c),25¢(c)
Price, Rigid(c);rep 6.00

149-OFF ON A COMET
By Jules Verne
03/59 **(149)** GMc,P(c),Original ... 25.00

CI #144 Off on a Comet
© Gilberton Publications

03/60 **(155)** GMc,P(c);rep 6.00
03/61 **(149)** GMc,P(c);rep 6.00
12/63 **(167)** GMc,P(c);rep 6.00
02/65 **(167)** GMc,P(c);rep 6.00
10/66 **(167)** GMc,P(c);rep 6.00
Fl/68 **(166)** GMc,EdM New P(c),
25¢(c)Price;rep 20.00

150-THE VIRGINIAN
By Owen Winster
05/59 **(150)** NN,P(c),Original 40.00
1961 **(164)** NN,DrG P(c);rep 15.00
62/63 **(167)** NN,DrG P(c);rep 20.00
12/63 **(167)** NN,DrG P(c);rep 15.00

151-WON BY THE SWORD
By George Alfred Henty
07/59 **(150)** JTg,P(c),Original 40.00
1961 **(164)** JTg,P(c);rep 15.00
10/63 **(167)** JTg,P(c);rep 15.00
1963 **(167)** JTg,P(c);rep 15.00
07/67 **(166)** JTg,P(c);rep 15.00

152-WILD ANIMALS I HAVE KNOWN
By Ernest Thompson Seton
09/59 **(152)** LbC,LbC P(c),Original 40.00
03/61 **(149)** LbC,LbC P(c),P(c);rep . 6.00
09/63 **(167)** LbC,LbC P(c);rep 5.00
08/65 **(167)** LbC,LbC P(c);rep 5.00
fl/69 **(169)** LbC,LbC P(c),25¢(c)
Price, Rigid(c);rep 5.00

153-THE INVISIBLE MAN
By H. G. Wells
11/59 **(153)** NN,GB P(c),Original . 45.00
03/61 **(149)** NN,GB P(c);rep 8.00
62/63 **(167)** NN,GB P(c);rep 6.00
02/65 **(167)** NN,GB P(c);rep 6.00
09/66 **(167)** NN,GB P(c);rep 6.00
Wr/69 **(166)** NN,GB P(c),25¢(c)
Price, Rigid(c);rep 6.00
Sg/71 **(169)** NN,GB P(c),Rigid(c),
Words Spelling'Invisible Man'
Are' Solid'Not'Invisible';rep 6.00

154-THE CONSPIRACY OF PONTIAC
By Francis Parkman
01/60 **(154)** GMc,GMc P(c),Original 40.00
11/63 **(167)** GMc,GMc P(c);rep .. 15.00
07/64 **(167)** GMc,GMc P(c);rep .. 15.00
12/67 **(166)** GMc,GMc P(c);rep .. 15.00

155-THE LION OF THE NORTH
By George Alfred Henty
03/60 **(154)** NN,GMc P(c),Original 42.00
01/64 **(167)** NN,GMc P(c);rep ... 15.00
1967 **(166)** NN,GMc P(c),25¢(c)
Price; rep 12.00

156-THE CONQUEST OF MEXICO
By Bernal Diaz Del Castillo
05/60 **(156)** BPr,BPr P(c),Original 35.00
01/64 **(167)** BPr,BPr P(c);rep 10.00
08/67 **(166)** BPr,BPr P(c);rep 10.00
Sg/70 **(169)** BPr,BPr P(c),25¢(c)
Price; Rigid(c);rep 9.00

157-LIVES OF THE HUNTED
By Ernest Thompson Seton
07/60 **(156)** NN,LbC P(c),Original   40.00
02/64 **(167)** NN,LbC P(c);rep   15.00
10/67 **(166)** NN,LbC P(c);rep 15.00

158-THE CONSPIRATORS
By Alexandre Dumas
09/60 **(156)** GMc,GMc P(c),Original 40.00
07/64 **(167)** GMc,GMc P(c);rep .. 15.00
10/67 **(166)** GMc,GMc P(c);rep .. 15.00

159-THE OCTOPUS
By Frank Norris
11/60 **(159)** GM&GE,LbC P(c),
Original 40.00
02/64 **(167)** GM&GE,LbC P(c);rep 15.00
166 **(1967)** GM&GE,LbC P(c),25¢(c)
Price;rep 15.00

160-THE FOOD OF THE GODS
By H.G. Wells
01/61 **(159)** TyT,GMc P(c),Original 40.00
01/61 **(160)** TyT,GMc P(c),Original;
Same Except For the HRN# ... 35.00
01/64 **(167)** TyT,GMc P(c);rep ... 15.00
06/67 **(166)** TyT,GMc P(c);rep ... 15.00

161-CLEOPATRA
By H. Rider Haggard
03/61 **(161)** NN,Pch P(c),Original . 45.00
01/64 **(167)** NN,Pch P(c);rep 20.00
08/67 **(166)** NN,Pch P(c);rep 20.00

162-ROBUR THE CONQUEROR
By Jules Verne
05/61 **(162)** GM&DPn,CJ P(c),
Original 40.00
07/64 **(167)** GM&DPn,CJ P(c);rep 15.00
08/67 **(166)** GM&DPn,CJ P(c);rep 15.00

163-MASTER OF THE WORLD
By Jules Verne
07/61 **(163)** GM,P(c),Original 40.00
01/65 **(167)** GM,P(c);rep 15.00
1968 **(166)** GM,P(c),25¢(c)
Price;rep 15.00

164-THE COSSACK CHIEF
By Nicolai Gogol
1961 **(164)** SyM,P(c),Original ... 35.00
04/65 **(167)** SyM,P(c);rep 15.00
Fl/68 **(166)** SyM,P(c),25¢(c)
Price;rep 15.00

165-THE QUEEN'S NECKLACE
by Alexandre Dumas
01/62 **(164)** GM,P(c),Original ... 35.00
04/65 **(167)** GM,P(c);rep 15.00
Fl/68 **(166)** GM,P(c),25¢(c)
Price;rep 15.00

166-TIGERS AND TRAITORS
By Jules Verne
05/62 **(165)** NN,P(c),Original 65.00
02/64 **(167)** NN,P(c);rep 20.00
11/66 **(167)** NN,P(c);rep 20.00

167-FAUST
By Johann Wolfgang von Goethe
08/62 **(165)** NN,NN P(c),Original . 100.00
02/64 **(167)** NN,NN P(c);rep 50.00
06/67 **(166)** NN,NN P(c);rep 50.00

168-IN FREEDOM'S CAUSE
By George Alfred Henty
Wr/69 **(169)** GE&RC,P(c),
Original, Rigid (c) 100.00

169-NEGRO AMERICANS THE EARLY YEARS
AUTHOR UNKNOWN
Sg/69 **(166)** NN,NN P(c),
Original, Rigid(c) 90.00
Sg/69 **(169)** NN,NN P(c),
Rigid; rep 60.00

See Also:
Independent Color Listings

CLASSICS ILLUSTRATED GIANTS

An Illustrated Library of Great
Adventure Stories
 -(reps. of Issues 6,7,8,10) .. 1,100.00
An Illustrated Library of Exciting
Mystery Stories
 -(reps. of Issues 30,21,40,13) 1,200.00
An Illustrated Library of Great
Indian Stories
 -(reps. of Issues 4,17,22,37) . 1,100.00

CLASSICS ILLUSTRATED JUNIOR
501-Snow White and the
  Seven Dwarves 70.00
502-The Ugly Duckling 40.00
503-Cinderella 25.00
504-The Pied Piper 20.00
505-The Sleeping Beauty 20.00
506-The Three Little Pigs 20.00
507-Jack and the Beanstalk ... 20.00
508-Goldilocks and the Three
  Bears 20.00
509-Beauty and the Beast 20.00
510-Little Red Riding Hood 20.00
511-Puss-N-Boots 20.00
512-Rumpelstilskin 20.00
513-Pinnochio 35.00
514-The Steadfast Tin Soldier ... 40.00
515-Johnny Appleseed 20.00
516-Alladin and His Lamp 25.00
517-The Emperor's New Clothes . 20.00
518-The Golden Goose 20.00
519-Paul Bunyan 20.00
520-Thumbelina 28.00
521-King of the golden River 20.00
522-The Nightingale 15.00
523-The Gallant Tailor 20.00
524-The Wild Swans 15.00
525-The Little Mermaid 20.00
526-The Frog Prince 18.00
527-The Golden-Haired Giant ... 15.00
528-The Penny Prince 15.00
529-The Magic Servants 15.00
530-The Golden Bird 15.00
531-Rapunzel 18.00
532-The Dancing Princesses ... 15.00
533-The Magic Fountain 15.00
534-The Golden Touch 15.00
535-The Wizard of Oz 35.00
536-The Chimney Sweep 15.00
537-The Three Faires 15.00
538-Silly Hans 15.00
539-The Enchanted Fish 30.00
540-The Tinder-Box 30.00
541-Snow White and Rose Red .. 20.00
542-The Donkey's Tail 20.00
543-The House in the Woods ... 15.00
544-The Golden Fleece 35.00
545-The Glass Mountain 20.00
546-The Elves and the Shoemaker 18.00
547-The Wishing Table 15.00
548-The Magic Pitcher 15.00
549-Simple Kate 15.00
550-The Singing Donkey 15.00
551-The Queen Bee 15.00
552-The Three Little Dwarves ... 20.00
553-King Thrushbeard 15.00
554-The Enchanted Deer 15.00
555-The Three Golden Apples .. 15.00
556-The Elf Mound 15.00
557-Silly Willy 30.00
558-The Magic Dish 30.00
559-The Japanese Lantern 30.00
560-The Doll Princess 30.00
561-Hans Humdrum 15.00
562-The Enchanted Pony 30.00
563-The Wishing Well 15.00
564-The Salt Mountain 15.00
565-The Silly Princess 15.00
566-Clumsy Hans 15.00
567-The Bearskin Soldier 15.00
568-The Happy Hedgehog 15.00
569-The Three Giants 15.00
570-The Pearl Princess 12.00
571-How Fire Came to the Indians 15.00
572-The Drummer Boy 18.00
573-The Crystal Ball 18.00
574-Brightboots 18.00
575-The Fearless Prince 20.00
576-The Princess Who Saw
  Everything 30.00
577-The Runaway Dumpling 35.00

CLASSICS ILLLUSTRATED SPECIAL ISSUE
N# United Nations 250.00
129-The Story of Jesus 65.00
132A-The Story of America 45.00
135A-The Ten Commandments . 50.00
138A-Adventures in Science ... 40.00
141A-The Rough Rider 40.00
144A-Blazing the Trails 40.00
147A-Crossing the Rockies 50.00
150A-Royal Canadian Police ... 45.00
153A-Men, Guns, and Cattle 45.00
156A-The Atomic Age 45.00
159A-Rockets, Jets and Missles . 45.00
162A-War Between the States .. 100.00
165A-To the Stars 50.00
166A-World War II 75.00
167A-Prehistoric World 80.00

AMAZING DOPE TALES
Greg Shaw
1 Untrimmed black and white pages,
   out of order;artist unknown . 110.00
2 Trimmed and proper pages . . . 95.00

AMERICAN SPLENDOR
Harvey Pekar May, 1976
1 B:Harvey Pekar Stories,
   HP,RCr,GDu,GBu 20.00
2 HP,RCr,GDu,GBu 10.00
3 HP,RCr,GDu,GBu 10.00
4 HP,RCr,GDu,GBu 8.00
5 HP,RCr,GDu,GBu 8.00
6 HP,RCr,GDu,GBu,GSh 7.00
7 HP,GSh,GDu,GBu 5.00
8 HP,GSh,GDu,GBu 3.00
9 and 10 HP,GSh,GDu,GBu . . @3.00
11 . . . . 3.00
12 . . . . 4.50
13 thru 19 . . . . @3.50
20 E:Harvey Pekar Stories 4.00

ANTHOLOGY OF SLOW DEATH
Wingnut Press/Last Gasp
1 140 pgs, RCr,RCo, GiS, DSh,
   Harlan Ellison VB,RTu 37.00

APEX TREASURY OF UNDERGROUND COMICS, THE
Links Books Inc. Oct.,1974
1 . . . . 40.00

APEX TREASURY OF UNDERGROUND COMICS –BEST OF BIJOU FUNNIES
Quick Fox 1981
1 Paperback,comix,various artists 21.00

ARCADE THE COMICS REVUE
Print Mint Inc. Spring, 1975
1 ASp,BG,RCr,SRo,SCW 16.50
2 ASp,BG,RCr,SRo 12.00
3 ASp,BG,RCr,RW,SCW 8.50
4 ASp,BG,RCr,WBu,SCW . . 8.50
5 thru 7 ASp,BG,SRo,RW,SCW @7.50

BABYFAT
Comix World/Clay Geerdes 1978
1 B:8pg news parodies, one page
   comix by various artists 4.50
2 thru 9 same . . . . @3.00
10 thru 26 same . . . . @2.00

BATTLE OF THE TITANS
University of Illinois SF Society 1972
1 Sci-Fi;VB,JGa 50.00

BEST BUY COMICS
Last Gasp Eco-Funnies
1 Rep Whole Earth Review;RCr . 3.50

BEST OF BIJOU FUNNIES, THE
Links Books Inc. 1975
1 164 pgs,paperback 235.00

BEST OF RIP-OFF PRESS
Rip Off Press Inc. 1973
1 132 pgs paperback,SCW,
   RCr,SRo,RW 25.00
2 100 pgs,GS,FT 27.50
3 100 pgs,FS 10.75
4 132 pgs,GiS,DSh 13.00

BIG ASS
Rip Off Press 1969–71
1 28 pgs,RCr 80.00
2 RCr 50.00

BIJOU FUNNIES
Bijou Publishing Empire 1968
1 B:JLy,editor;RCr,GS SW . . . 285.00
2 RCr,GS,SW 110.00
3 RCr,SWi,JsG 60.00
4 SWi,JsG 30.00
5 SWi,JsG 33.50
6 E:JLy,editor,SWi,RCr,JsG . . . 27.00
7 and 8 . . . . @26.00

BINKY BROWN MEETS THE HOLY VIRGIN MARY
Last Gasp Eco-Funnies March, 1972
N# Autobiography about Growing up
   w/a Catholic Neurosis,JsG . 22.50
2nd Printing:only text in
   bottom left panel 12.00

BIZARRE SEX
Kitchen Sink Komix May, 1972
1 B:DKi,editor,various
   artists 27.00
2 . . . . 22.00
3 . . . . 16.00
4 thru 6 . . . . @11.00
7 . . . . 4.00

Bizarre Sex #8
© Kitchen Sink

8 . . . . 3.50
9 Omaha the Cat Dancer,RW . . 16.50

BLACK LAUGHTER
Black Laughter Pub. Co, Nov. 1972
1 James Dixon art 64.00

BLOOD FROM A STONE (GUIDE TO TAX REFORM)
New York Public Interest Research Group Inc. 1977
1 Tax reform proposals 8.50

BOBBY LONDON RETROSPECTIVE AND ART PORTFOLIO
Cartoonist Representatives
1 . . . . 19.50

BOBMAN AND TEDDY
Parrallax Comic Books Inc 1966
1 RFK & Ted Kennedy's struggle to
   control Democratic party 35.50

BODE'S CARTOON CONCERT
Dell Sept., 1973
1 132 pgs; VB 27.50

BOGEYMAN COMICS
San Fransisco Comic Book Co., 1969
1 Horror,RHa 55.00
2 Horror,RHa 42.00
The Company & Sons
3 . . . . 31.00

BUFFALO RAG/THE DEAD CONCERT COMIX
Kenny Laramey Dec. 1973
1 Alice in Wonderland parody . . 55.00

CAPTAIN GUTS
The Print Mint 1969
1 Super patriotV:Counter
   culture 26.50
2 V:Black Panthers 19.00
3 V:Dope Smugglers 19.00

CAPTAIN STICKY
Captain Sticky 1974–75
1 Super lawyer V:SocialInjustice 17.50

CARTOON HISTORY OF THE UNIVERSE
Rip Off Press Sept., 1978
1 Evolution of Everything;
   B:Larry Gonick 6.50
2 Sticks and Stones 6.50
3 River Realms-Sumer & Egypt . 6.50
4 Part of the Old Testament . . . 4.50
5 Brains and Bronze 4.50
6 Who are these Athenians 3.75

CASCADE COMIX MONTHLY
Everyman Studios March, 1978
1 Interviews,articles about
   comix & comix artists 6.50

2 and 3 same . . . . @6.50
4 thru 11 . . . . @3.00
12 thru 23 . . . . @2.25

CHECKERED DEMON
Last Gasp July, 1977
1 SCW 13.00
2 SCW 8.50
3 SCW 6.50

CHEECH WIZARD
Office of Student Publications,
Syracuse U 1967
n/n VB 120.00

CHICAGO MIRROR
Jay Lynch/Mirror
Publishing Empire Autumn, 1967
1 B:Bijou Funnies 45.00
2 same 35.00
3 same 115.00

COLLECTED CHEECH WIZARD, THE
Company & Sons 1972
n/n VB 55.00

COLLECTED TRASHMAN #1, THE
Fat City & The Red Mountain
Tribe Productions
n/n SRo 32.50

COMICS & COMIX
October, 1975
1 . . . . 12.00

COMIX BOOK
Magazine Management Co.
Oct., 1974
1 Compilation for newsstand
distribution 14.50
2 and 3 . . . . @9.00
Kitchen Sink Enterprises
4 . . . . 14.50
5 . . . . 8.50

Comix Book #3
© Magazine Management Co.

COMIX COLLECTOR, THE
Archival Press Inc. Dec., 1979
1 Fanzine 5.00
2 & 3 Fanzine . . . . @4.00

COMMIES FROM MARS
Kitchen Sink March, 1973
1 TB 32.50
Last Gasp
2 thru 5 TB . . . . @9.50

COMPLETE FRITZ THE CAT
Belier Press 1978
n/n RCr,SRo,DSh 55.00

CONSPIRACY CAPERS
The Conspiracy 1969
1 Benefit Legal Defense of the
Chicago-8 . . . . 79.00

DAN O'NEIL'S COMICS & STORIES
VOL.1
Company & Sons
1 B:Dan O'Neill 45.00
2 & 3 . . . . @30.00
1971 VOL.2
1 . . . . 6.50
2 and E:Dan O'Neill . . . . @4.50

DAS KAMPF
Vaughn Bode May, 1963
N# 100 Loose pgs. 750.00
2nd Printing 52pgs.-produced by
Walter Bachner&Bagginer,1977 9.50

DEADBONE EROTICA
Bantam Books Inc. April, 1971
n/n 132 pgs VB 45.00

DEADCENTER CLEAVAGE
April, 1971
1 14 pgs 40.00

DEATH RATTLE
Kitchen Sink June, 1972
1 RCo,TB 25.00
2 TB 20.00
3 TB 16.00

DESPAIR
The Print Mint 1969
1 RCr 33.00

DIRTY DUCK BOOK, THE
Company & Sons March, 1972
1 Bobby London 25.00

DISNEY RAPES THE 1st AMENDMENT
Dan O'Neil 1974
1 Benefit Air Pirates V:Disney
Law suit; Dan O'Neill 8.50

DOPE COMIX
Kitchen Sink Feb., 1978
1 Drugs comix;various artists . . . 7.50

2 same 5.75
3 & 4 LSD issue . . . . @4.00

DOPIN DAN
Last Gasp Eco-Funnies April, 1972
1 TR 12.00
2 and 3 TR . . . . @8.50
4 Todays Army,TR 7.50

DR. ATOMIC
Last Gasp Eco-Funnies Sept., 1972
1 B:Larry S. Todd 12.00
2 and 3 . . . . @10.00
4 . . . . 7.50
5 E:Larry S. Todd 4.75

DR. ATOMIC'S MARIJUANA MULTIPLIER
Kistone Press 1974
1 How to grow great pot 7.50

DRAWINGS BY S. CLAY WILSON
San Francisco Graphics
1 28 pgs 185.00

DYING DOLPHIN
The Print Mint 1970
n/n 14.50

EBON
San Francisco Comic Book Company
1 Comix version; RCr 25.00
1 Tabloid version 18.00

EL PERFECTO COMICS
The Print Mint 1973
N# Benefit Timothy Leary 27.00
2nd Printing-1975 . . . . 4.00

ETERNAL TRUTH
Sunday Funnies Comic Corp
1 Christian Comix 19.50

EVERMUCH WAVE
Atlantis Distributors
1 Nunzio the Narc; Adventures
of God 60.00

FABULOUS FURRY FREAK BROTHERS, THE
COLLECTED ADVENTURES OF
Rip Off Press #1 Feb., 1971
1 GiS 75.00

FURTHER ADVENTURES OF
Rip Off Press #2
1 GiS,DSh 47.50

A YEAR PASSES LIKE NOTHING WITH
Rip Off Press #3
1 GiS 17.00

BROTHER CAN YOU SPARE $.75 FOR
Rip Off Press #4
1 GiS,DSh 12.00

FABULOUS FURRY FREAK BROTHERS, THE
Rip Off Press #5
1 GiS,DSh 9.50

SIX SNAPPY SOCKERS FROM THE ARCHIVES OF
Rip Off Press #6
1 GiS 5.25

FANTAGOR
1970
1 (Corben), fanzine 100.00
1a (Last Gasp) 22.00
2 & 3 .... @20.00
4 .... 30.00

THE ADVENTURES OF FAT FREDDY'S CAT,
Rip Off Press Feb., 1977
1 .... 14.00
2 .... 4.50
3 .... 6.00
4 .... 5.00
5 & 6 .... @2.50

FEDS 'N' HEADS
Gilbert Shelton/Print Mint 1968
N# I:Fabulous Furry Freak Bros.;
Has no 'Print Mint' Address
24 pgs. 350.00
2nd printing, 28 pgs. 55.00
3rd printing, May, 1969 ..... 45.00
4th printing, Says 'Forth
Printing' 17.50
5th-12th printings .... @8.00
13th printing 6.50
14th printing 4.75

FELCH
Keith Green
1 RW,SCW,RCr 40.00

FEVER PITCH
Kitchen Sink Enterprises July, 1976
1 RCo 20.00
Jabberwocky Graphix
2 250 signed & numbered 14.50
3 400 signed & numbered 13.50
4 .... 8.50

50'S FUNNIES
Kitchen Sink Enterprises 1980
1 Larry Shell, editor,various
artists 5.00

FLAMING CARROT
Kilian Barracks Free Press 1981
1 Bob Budden,various artists .. 10.00

FLASH THEATRE
Oogle Productions 1970
1 44 pgs 37.50

FLESHAPOIDS FROM EARTH
Popular Culture Dec., 1974
1 36 pgs 33.00

THE COMPLETE FOO!
Bijou Publishing Sept., 1980
1 RCr, Charles Crumb, r:Crumb
brothers fanzines 40.00

FRITZ BUGS OUT
Ballentine Books 1972
n/n RCr 60.50

FRITZ THE CAT
Ballentine Books 1969
n/n RCr 120.00

FRITZ THE NO-GOOD
Ballentine Books 1972
n/n RCr 50.00

FRITZ: SECRET AGENT FOR THE CIA
Ballentine Books 1972
n/n RCr 45.00

FUNNY AMINALS
Apex Novelties/Don Donahue 1972
1 RCr 60.00

GAY COMIX
Kitchen Sink Sept., 1981
1 36 pgs 7.50
2 36 pgs 5.00

GEN OF HIROSHIMA
Educomics/Leonard Rifas Jan., 1980
1 Antiwar comix by Hiroshima
survivor Keiji Nakawaza 9.50
2 same 6.50

GHOST MOTHER COMICS
John "Mad" Peck 1969
1 SCw,JsG 47.50

GIMMEABREAK COMIX
Rhuta Press Feb., 1971
2 48 pgs, #0 & #1 were advertised,but
may not have been printed .. 95.00

GIRLS & BOYS
Lynda J. Barry 1980
1 B:12 pgs with every other page
blank, all Barry art 8.00
2 thru 10 same .... @6.50
11 thru 20 same .... @4.50
20 thru 25 same .... @3.50

GOD NOSE
Jack Jackson/
Rip Off Press 1964
N# 42 pgs. 995.00
2nd printing,Pinkish(c);44p ... 60.00
3rd printing,Blue Border(c) ... 30.00
4th printing,Red Border(c) ... 15.00

GOTHIC BLIMP WORKS LTD.
East Village Other/
Peter Leggieri 1969
1 VB,Editor,various artists ... 185.00
2 same 145.00
3 KDe,editor 135.00

4 KDe,editor 130.00
5 thru 7 KDe,editor ...... @125.00
8 various artists 185.00

GREASER COMICS
Half-Ass Press Sept. 1971
1 28 pgs, George DiCaprio 17.50
Rip Off Press July 1972
2 George DiCaprio 10.00

GRIM WIT
Last Gasp 1972
1 RCo 35.00
2 RCo 25.00

HAROLD HEAD, THE COLLECTED ADVENTURES OF
Georgia Straight 1972
1 .... 45.00
2 .... 10.00

HARRY CHESS THAT MAN FROM A.U.N.T.I.E.
The Uncensored Adventures
Trojan Book Service 1966
N# 1st Comix By & For Gay
Community 100.00

HEAR THE SOUND OF MY FEET WALKING....
Glide Urban Center 1969
1 Dan O'Neill, 128 pgs 65.00

HISTORY OF UNDERGROUND COMIX
Straight Arrow Books 1974
1 Book by Mark James Estren about
Underground Comix 30.00

HOMEGROWN FUNNIES
Kitchen Sink 1971
1 RCr 45.00

HONKYTONK SUE, THE QUEEN OF COUNTRY SWING
Bob Boze Bell Feb., 1979
1 BBB 7.00
2 & 3 BBB .... @5.00

IKE LIVES
Warm Neck Funnies 1973
1 20 pgs,Mark Fisher 10.00

INSECT FEAR
Last Gasp 1970
1 SRo,GiS,RHa,JsG 75.00
Print Mint 1970–72
2 .... 30.00
3 .... 20.00

IT AIN'T ME BABE
Last Gasp Eco-Funnies July. 1970
n/n First all women comix
Womens Liberation theme .. 32.50

JAPANESE MONSTER
Carol Lay July, 1979
1 8pgs, Carol Lay 5.00

JESUS LOVES YOU
Zondervan Books/Craig Yoe 1972
1 Christian, RCr 29.50

THE NEW ADVENTURES OF JESUS
Rip Off Press Nov., 1971
1 44 pgs, FSt 50.00

JIZ
Apex Novelty 1969
1 36 pgs; RCr, SRo, VMo, SCW; hand trimmed and unevenly stapled 45.00

JUNKWAFFEL
The Print Mint 1971
1 VB 30.00
2 and 3 VB . . . . @25.00
4 VB,JJ 18.00

KANNED KORN KOMIX
Canned Heat Fan Club 1969
1 20pgs 8.00

KAPTAIN AMERIKA KOMIX
Brief Candle Comix March 1970
1 anti U.S. involvement in Laos . 27.50

KING BEE
Apex/Don Donahue & Kerry Clark 1969
1 RCr,SCW 120.00

KURTZMAN COMIX
Kitchen Sink Sept., 1976
1 HK,RCr,GiS,DKi,WE 20.00

LAUGH IN THE DARK
Last Gasp
n/n KDe,RHa,SRo,SCW 14.00

LENNY OF LAVEDO
Sunbury Productions/Print Mint 1965
N# Green(c);1st Joel Beck-a . . 545.00
2nd printing, Orange(c) 390.00
3rd printing, White(c) 195.00

THE MACHINES
Office of Student Publications Syracuse University 1967
1 VB 125.00

THE MAN
Office of Student Publications Syracuse University 1966
1 VB 155.00

MAGGOTZINE
Charles Schneider May, 1981
1 Various Artists,conceptual maggot stuff 3.50

MANTICORE
Joe Kubert School of Cartooning & Graphic Arts Inc. Autumn, 1976
1 Fanzine,various artists 7.50

MEAN BITCH THRILLS
The Print Mint 1971
1 SRO 7.00

MICKEY RAT
Los Angeles Comic Book Co. May, 1972
1 Robert Armstrong 32.50
2 same 29.00
3 same 9.50

MOM'S HOMEMADE COMICS
Kitchen Sink June 1969
1 DKi, RCr 125.00
The Print Mint
2 DKi 35.00
Kitchen Sink Enterprises
3 DKi,RCr 17.00

MONDAY FUNNIES, THE
Monday Funnies 1977
1 8pgs,various artists 6.50
2 16pgs,various artists 9.00
3 16pgs,various artists 6.50
4 16pgs,various artists 5.50

MONDAY FUNNIES, THE
Passtime Publ. July–Aug., 1980
1 thru 8 Marc L.Reed . . . . . . @4.00

MOUSE LIBERATION FRONT
COMMUNIQUE #2 August, 1979
1 SRo, SCW, VMo,DKi; Disney's sues Dan O'Neil's Air Pirates 9.50

MOONCHILD COMICS
Nicola Cuti 1968
0 Nicola Cuti 27.00
2 Nicola Cuti 27.00
3 Nicola Cuti 75.00

MOONDOG
The Print Mint March, 1970
1 All George Metzer 11.00
2 same 6.50
3 and 4 same . . . . @3.75

MORE ADVENTURES OF FAT FREDDY'S CAT
Rip Off Press Jan., 1981
1 GiS 14.00

MOTOR CITY COMICS
Rip Off Press April, 1969
1 RCr 165.00
2 RCr 125.00

MR. NATURAL
San Fransisco Comic Book Co. August, 1970
1 RCr 100.00
2 RCr 50.00

Mr. Natural #3 © Robert Crumb
Kitchen Sink
3 RCr, (B&W) 20.00

NARD 'N' PAT, JAYZEY LYNCH'S
Cartoonists Cooperative Press March, 1974
1 Jay Lynch 7.00
2 Jay Lynch 4.50
Kitchen Sink Press 1972
3 . . . . 10.00

NEVERWHERE
Ariel Inc. Feb., 1978
1 RCo 17.50

NICKEL LIBRARY
Gary Arlington
1 1 pg heavy stock colored paper, Reed Crandall 5.00
2 Kim Deitch 1.50
3 Harrison Cady 1.50
4 Frank Frazetta 4.00
5 Will Eisner 4.00
6 Justin Green 1.50
7 C.C. Beck 4.00
8 Wally Wood 4.00
9 Winsor McCay 1.50
10 Jim Osborne 1.50
11 Don Towlley 1.50
12 Frank Frazetta 4.00
13 Will Eisner 4.00
14 Bill Griffith 1.50
15 George Herriman 1.50
16 Cliff Sterrett 1.50
17 George Herriman 1.50
18 Rory Hayes & Simon Deitch . . 1.50
19 Disney Studios 2.00
20 Alex Toth 2.00
21 Will Eisner 2.00
22 Jack Davis 3.00
23 Alex Toth 2.00
24 Michele Brand 1.50
25 Roger Brand 1.50
26 Arnold Roth 1.50
27 Murphy Anderson 2.00
28 Wally Wood 3.00
29 Jack Kirby 4.00

30 Harvey Kurtzman	3.00
31 Jay Kinney	1.50
32 Bill Plimpton	1.50
33	1.50
34 Charles Dallas	1.50
35 thru 39	@1.50
40 Bill Edwards	1.50
41 Larry S. Todd	1.50
42 Charles Dallas	1.50
43 Jim Osborne	1.50
43 1/2 Larry S. Todd	1.50
44 Jack Jackson	1.50
45 Rick Griffin	1.50
46 Justin Green	1.50
47 and 48 Larry S. Todd	@1.50
49 Charles Dallas	1.50
50 Robert Crumb	3.00
51 Wally Wood	3.00
52 Charles Dallas	3.00
53 and 54 Larry S. Todd	@1.50
55 Charles Dallas	1.50
56 Jim Chase	1.50
57 Charles Dallas	1.50
58 Larry S. Todd	1.50
59 Dave Geiser	1.50
60 Charles Dallas	1.50

ODD WORLD OF RICHARD CORBEN
Warren Publishing 1977
1 84pgs paperback 20.00

O.K. COMICS
Kitchen Sink June, 1972
1 and 2 Bruce Walthers .... @7.00

O.K. COMICS
O.K. Comic Company 1972
1 Tabloid with comix, articles, reviews, nudie cuties photos . 27.50
2 thru 18 .... @18.75

ORACLE COMIX
Thru Black Holes
Comix Productions Oct., 1980
1 and 2 Michael Roden ..... @2.50

PENGUINS IN BONDAGE
Sorcerer Studio/
Wayne Gibson July, 1981
1 8pgs,Wayne Gibson 2.75

PHANTOM LADY
Randy Crawford June, 1978
1 Sex funnies 4.50

PHUCKED UP FUNNIES
Suny Binghamton 1969
1 ASp;insert bound in yearbook 400.00

PINK FLOYD, THE
October, 1974
1 sold at concerts 27.50

PLASTIC MAN
Randy Crawford May, 1977
1 Sex funnies,RandyCrawford ... 4.00

PORK
Co-op Press May, 1974
1 SCW 11.00

PORTFOLIO OF UNDERGROUND ART
Schanes & Schanes 1980
1 SRo,SCW,VMo,RW and many others 13 loose sheets in folder, 32pg book, 1200 signed & numb. . 75.00

POWERMAN AND POWER MOWER SAFETY
Frank Burgmeir, Co.
Outdoor Power Equipment
1 VB; educational comic about power mower safety 185.00

PROMETHIAN ENTERPRISES
Promethian Enterprises
Memorial Day, 1969
1 B:Jim Vadeboncuor editor .. 72.00
2 same 60.00
3 thru 5 .... @25.00

PURE ART QUARTERLY
John A. Adams July, 1976
1 16pgs, All John A.Adams 8.50
2 thru 5 same .... @8.50
6 thru 10 same .... @5.00
11 thru 14 same .... @3.50

QUAGMIRE COMICS
Kitchen Sink Summer, 1970
1 DKi,Peter Poplaski 11.00

RAW
Raw Books 1980
1 36pgs,10pgs insert 310.00
2 36pgs,20pgs insert 185.00
3 52pgs,16pgs insert 155.00
4 44pgs,32pgs insert,Flexi disk record 125.00

R. CRUMB'S COMICS AND STORIES
Rip Off Press 1969
1 RCr 90.00

RAWARARAWAR
Rip Off Press 1969
1 GSh 55.00

RED SONJA & CONAN "HOT AND DRY"
Randy Crawford May, 1977
1 Sex funnies,Randy Crawford .. 3.50

REID FLEMING WORLD'S TOUGHEST MILKMAN
David E. Boswell Dec., 1980
1 .... 6.00

RIP OFF COMIX
Rip Off Press April, 1977
1 GiS,FSt,JsG,DSh 17.50

2 thru 5 GiS,FSt	@6.00
6 thru 10	@4.25

ROWLF
Rip Off Press July, 1971
1 RCo 55.00

RUBBER DUCK TALES
The Print Mint March, 1971
1 Michael J Becker 12.00
2 Michael J Becker 11.00

S. CLAY WILSON TWENTY DRAWINGS
Abington Book Shop Inc. 1967
N# (a),Cowboy(c) 460.00
(b),Pirate(c) 460.00
(c),Motorcyclist(c) 460.00
(d),Demon(c) 460.00
(e),Deluxe with all 4 variations on same(c) with Gold Embossed Lettering 675.00

SAN FRANCISCO COMIC BOOK
San Francisco Comic Book Co.
Jan.-Feb., 1970

1	120.00
2	20.00
3	17.50
4 thru 6	@12.00

SAVAGE HUMOR
The Print Mint 1973
1 .... 4.00

SAY WHAT?
Loring Park Shelter
Community Cartooning Workshop
April, 1979
1 B:Charles T. Smith,editor, various artists 7.00
2 thru 6 same .... @6.50

SCHIZOPHRENIA, CHEECH WIZARD
Last Gasp Eco-Funnies Jan., 1974
1 VB 30.00

SEX AND AFFECTION
C.P. Family Publishers 1974
1 Sex Education for Children ... 5.50

SHORT ORDER COMIX
Head Press/Family Fun 1973
1 50 cents,36pgs. 8.50
2 75 cents,44pgs 2.25

SKULL COMICS
Last Gasp March, 1970
1 Horror,RHa 47.00
2 GiS,DSh,RCo 25.50
3 SRo,DSh,RCo 14.00
4 DSh,Lovecraft issue 14.00
5 SRo,RCo,Lovecraft issue ... 14.00
6 RCo,Herman Hesse 14.00

SLOW DEATH FUNNIES
Last Gasp April 1970
1 Ecological Awarness & Red
Border on (c) 47.00
2nd-4th Printings White
Border(c) 10.00
2 Silver(c);1st edition' 34 pgs . . 85.00
2b Non Silver(c);Says 1st
Edition, 34 pgs 20.00
2nd Amorphia Ad on pg 34 . . . . 6.75
3rd Yellow Skull on (c) 5.00
4th 'Mind Candy For the Masses'
Ad on pg. 34 . . . . 5.00
5th $1.00(c) price 3.50
3 thru 5 . . . . @12.00
6 thru 10 . . . . @4.50

SMILE
Kitchen Sink Summer, 1970
1 Jim Mitchell 13.50
2 Jim Mitchell 12.00
3 Jim Mitchell 11.00

SNARF
Kitchen Sink Feb., 1972
1 DKi,editor,various artists 24.50
2 thru 5 same . . . . @15.00
6 thru 9 same . . . . @6.50

SNATCH COMICS
Apex Novelties 1968
1 RCr,SCW 295.00
2 RCr,SCW 150.00
3 RCr,SCW,RW 75.00

SNATCH SAMPLER
Keith Green 1979
n/n RCr,SCw,RW,RHa 32.00

SPACE INVADERS COMICS, DON CHIN'S
Comix World/Clay Geerdes April, 1972
1 8pgs 4.00

SPASM!
Last Gasp Eco-Funnies April, 1973
1 JJ 15.00

STONED PICTURE PARADE
San Francisco Comic Book Co., 1975
1 RCr,SRo,SCW,WE 20.00

SUBVERT COMICS
Rip Off Press Nov., 1970
1 SRo 25.00
2 SRo 20.00
3 SRo 12.00

TALES OF SEX & DEATH
Print Mint 1971
1 JsG,KDe.RHa,SRo 32.50
2 JsG,KDe.RHa,SRo 19.50

THRILLING MURDER COMICS
San Francisco Comic Book Co., 1971
1 SCW,KDe,RCr,SRo,Jim

Arlington,editor 24.50

2 (TWO)
Keith Green Feb., 1975
1 SCW 7.00

VAMPIRELLA
Randy Crawford June, 1978
1 Sex Funnies 3.50

VAUGHN BODE THE PORTFOLIO
Northern Comfort Com. 1976
1 VB,16pgs 125.00

VAUGHN BODE PORTFOLIO #1
Vaughn Bode Productions 1978
1 VB,10 pgs 35.00

VAUGHN BODE'S CHEECH WIZARD, THE COLLECTED ADVENTURES OF THE CARTOON MESSIAH
Northern Comfort Com. 1976
1 VB,88pgs 55.00

VAUGHN BODE'S DEADBONE, THE FIRST TESTAMENT OF CHEECH WIZARD
Northern Comfort Com. 1975
1 VB 65.00

VIETNAM
N# 20pgs. Role of Blacks in
the War,TG Lewis 125.00

WEIRDO
Last Gasp Eco-Funnies March, 1981
1 thru 3 RCr . . . . @10.00

WEIRDO, THE
Rodney Schroeter Oct., 1977
1 B:Rodney Schroezer,1pg 4.50
2 88pgs 4.50
3 44pgs 4.50

WIMMEN'S COMIX
Last Gasp Eco-Funnies Nov., 1972
1 All women artists&comix 10.75
2 thru 3 same . . . . @10.00
4 thru 7 same . . . . @6.75

WONDER WART-HOG AND THE NURDS OF NOVEMBER
Rip Off Press Sept., 1980
1 GiS 15.00

WONDER WART-HOG, CAPTAIN CRUD & OTHER SUPER STUFF
Fawcett Publications 1967
1 GiS,VB 22.00

YELLOW DOG
The Print Mint May, 1968
1 4pgs,RCr 30.00
2 and 3 8pgs,RCr . . . . @25.00
4 8pgs,RCr,SCW 25.00
5 8pgs,RCr,SCW,KDe 25.00
6 thru 12 . . . . @25.00
13/14 52pgs RCr,Jay Lynch 12.00
15 Don Scheneker,editor 59.00
16 . . . . 55.00
17 thru 24 . . . . @15.00

YOUNG AND LUSTLESS
San Francisco Comic Book Co., 1972
1 BG 15.50

YOUNG LUST
Company & Sons Oct., 1970
1 BG,ASp 27.00
2 BG 15.00
3 BG,JsG,RCr,ASp 12.00
4 KDe,BG,SRo 10.50
5 BG,SRo 7.50
6 SRo,KDe 5.50

YOW
Last Gasp April, 1978
1 BG 5.75
2 BG 4.75
Becomes:

ZIPPY
3 BG 6.50

Zap Comix #0 © Apex Novelties

ZAP COMIX
Apex Novelties Oct., 1967
0 RCr 335.00
1 RCr 325.00
2 RCr,SCW 100.00
3 RCr,SCW,VMo,SRo 55.00
4 VMo,RW,RCr,SCW.SRo,GiS . . 55.00
5 RW,GiS,RCr,SCW,SRo 50.00
6 RW,GiS,RCr,SCW,SRo 25.00
7 RW,GiS,RCr,SCW,SRo 18.50
8 RW,GiS,RCr,SCW,SRo 10.00
9 RW,GiS,RCr,SCW,SRo 12.00

All comics prices listed are for *Near Mint* condition.